Murray

AN AMERICAN TEXT-BOOK OF PHYSIOLOGY

edited by William H. Howell, Ph.D., M.D.
W. B. Saunders and Company
1896

A TEXT-BOOK OF PHYSIOLOGY
FOR MEDICAL STUDENTS AND PHYSICIANS

written by William H. Howell, Ph.D., M.D., LL.D.
W. B. Saunders and Company
1905

HOWELL'S TEXTBOOK OF PHYSIOLOGY
15th Edition

edited by John F. Fulton, M.D.
W. B. Saunders Company
1946

A TEXTBOOK OF PHYSIOLOGY
16th and 17th Editions

edited by John F. Fulton, M.D.
W. B. Saunders Company
1949 and 1955

MEDICAL
PHYSIOLOGY
AND BIOPHYSICS

Edited by

THEODORE C. RUCH, Ph.D.

PROFESSOR AND EXECUTIVE OFFICER

DEPARTMENT OF PHYSIOLOGY AND BIOPHYSICS

UNIVERSITY OF WASHINGTON SCHOOL OF MEDICINE

and

JOHN F. FULTON, M.D.

LATE STERLING PROFESSOR OF THE HISTORY OF MEDICINE

YALE UNIVERSITY SCHOOL OF MEDICINE

Eighteenth Edition

OF

HOWELL'S TEXTBOOK OF PHYSIOLOGY

W. B. SAUNDERS COMPANY

Philadelphia and London

Contributors

DONALD H. BARRON, Ph.D.

Professor of Physiology, Yale University School of Medicine

ROSEMARY BIGGS, B.Sc., Ph.D., M.D.

Scientific Officer, Medical Research Council, Blood Coagulation Research Unit, Churchill Hospital, Oxford, England

JOHN R. BROBECK, Ph.D., M.D.

Professor of Physiology, University of Pennsylvania School of Medicine

ALAN C. BURTON, Ph.D.

Professor of Biophysics, University of Western Ontario Faculty of Medicine

LOREN D. CARLSON, Ph.D.

Chairman, Department of Physiology, University of Kentucky College of Medicine

PAUL F. FENTON, Ph.D.

Professor of Biology, Brown University

THOMAS R. FORBES, A.B., Ph.D.

Associate Professor of Anatomy and Associate Dean, Yale University School of Medicine

RAÚL HERNÁNDEZ-PEÓN, M.D.

Director, Unit for Brain Research, Medical Center, Mexico City

DAVID I. HITCHCOCK, Ph.D.

Associate Professor of Physiology, Yale University School of Medicine

CHARLES W. HOOKER, Ph.D.

Professor of Anatomy, University of North Carolina

ALAN KOCH, Ph.D.

Research Instructor in Physiology and Biophysics, University of Washington School of Medicine

ROBERT B. LIVINGSTON, M.D.

Director of Basic Research, National Institute of Mental Health and National Institute of Neurological Diseases and Blindness, United States Public Health Service, Bethesda, Maryland; Lecturer in Anatomy and Physiology (Professor), University of California at Los Angeles Medical Center

JOHN L. PATTERSON, JR., M.S., M.D.

Research Professor of Medicine, Medical College of Virginia

HARRY D. PATTON, Ph.D., M.D.

Professor of Physiology and Biophysics, University of Washington School of Medicine

THEODORE C. RUCH, Ph.D.

Professor and Executive Officer, Department of Physiology and Biophysics, University of Washington School of Medicine

ROBERT F. RUSHMER, M.D.

Professor of Physiology and Biophysics, University of Washington School of Medicine; Senior Consultant, Madigan General Hospital, Fort Lewis, Washington

JANE A. RUSSELL, Ph.D.

Associate Professor of Biochemistry, Emory University

ALLEN M. SCHER, B.A., Ph.D.

Associate Professor of Physiology, University of Washington School of Medicine

ARNOLD L. TOWE, B.A., Ph.D.

Assistant Professor of Physiology and Biophysics, University of Washington School of Medicine

FRANK W. WEYMOUTH, Ph.D.

Professor of Physiology, Emeritus, Stanford University; Professor of Physiological Optics, Los Angeles College of Optometry

WALTER WOODBURY, Ph.D.

Associate Professor of Physiology and Biophysics, University of Washington School of Medicine

HELEN M. PAYLING WRIGHT, B.Sc., Ph.D., L.M.S.S.A.

Research Assistant, University College Hospital, London

ALLAN C. YOUNG, Ph.D.

Associate Professor of Physiology and Biophysics, University of Washington School of Medicine

Preface to the Eighteenth Edition

THIS BOOK, which has been a significant force in medical education for nearly three quarters of a century, has received a new title for this edition. The new title was chosen to represent the editors' conviction that physiology should be developed and taught "in depth." Such depth is attained by ranging from fundamental approaches derived directly from the university disciplines, especially physics, through classic physiology to clinical physiology. The first of these orientations is conveyed, somewhat inadequately, by adding the word "biophysics" to the title—inadequately because psychology as well as physics, physical chemistry and mathematics is becoming increasingly important to physiology.

No incompatibility is seen between emphasizing fundamental approaches and the inclusion of more clinical physiology. This has not been done by adding paragraphs of dilute clinical medicine at the end of each chapter. Instead, whether it be a sentence, a paragraph or a chapter devoted to pathologic physiology, the criterion has been: does physiology illuminate the pathologic state or, conversely, does the abnormal function point up the normal physiology? The emphasis on the clinical applications of physiology has been considerably increased in this edition, but space limitations prevent a complete and systematic presentation. Whole textbooks are devoted to pathologic physiology and some believe, with reason, that the first course cannot adequately cover both normal and pathologic physiology. Even so, such a course gains by the inclusion of some clinical physiology, and the student and the physician gain by having both side by side rather than separated in time and space.

In the 18th edition we have sought to maintain an important feature of previous editions, the authority which comes with drawing authors from various laboratories. At the same time we have attempted to gain a uniformity of level, point of view and style by having many excellent chapters of the 17th edition rewritten or revised by a geographically related group of authors and by editing for content and expression considerably more than is usual for textbooks with many authors. Thanks are therefore due to past as well as present contributors for taking time from busy lives in the interest of producing an authoritative book suitable for medical students. I would like also to acknowledge my debt to Professor John F. Fulton, not only for the fine heritage of scholarship represented by the 17th edition but also for his good counsel and active participation in the planning and execution of this edition.

Many chapters are completely or extensively rewritten. In this category are nearly all of the chapters on nerve, muscle, reflexes and motor systems of the brain; the chapters on blood, hemodynamics, the cardiac cycle, the electrocardiogram and the control of cardiac output; and all but one of the chapters on respiration. In addition, renal physiology has been freshly described, using the terminology and concepts of physical chemistry and emphasizing the concepts of active transport. The chapters on the endocrines and reproductive physiology have been thoroughly revised in the light of recent advances in these fields. All chapters, whether newly written or revised, have been carefully edited by Maryeva W. Terry and many of the figures have been drawn or redrawn by Helen N. Halsey; to them the authors and editors owe a great debt.

Three excellent chapters have been dropped from this edition on the grounds that their subject matter has largely passed into the realm of biochemistry and are adequately handled in textbooks of that field. On the other hand, two chapters have been added, one on the biophysics of the cell membrane and the other on the neurophysiology of emotion. These two new chapters—standing at the opposite ends of the physiologic spectrum, subcellular analysis and physiologic integration—indicate that physiology is indeed rapidly growing in depth and breadth, and owes much of its recent advance to a solid base in the university disciplines.

T. C. RUCH

Preface to the First Edition

IN THE PREPARATION of this book the author has endeavored to keep in mind two guiding principles: first, the importance of simplicity and lucidity in the presentation of facts and theories; and, second, the need of a judicious limitation of the material selected. In regard to the second point every specialist is aware of the bewildering number of researches that have been and are being published in physiology and the closely related sciences, and the difficulty of justly estimating the value of conflicting results. He who seeks for the truth in any matter under discussion is oftentimes forced to be satisfied with a suspension of judgment, and the writer who attempts to formulate our present knowledge upon almost any part of the subject is in many instances obliged to present the literature as it exists and let the reader make his own deductions. This latter method is doubtless the most satisfactory and the most suitable for large treatises prepared for the use of the specialist or advanced student, but for beginners it is absolutely necessary to follow a different plan. The amount of material and the discussion of details of controversies must be brought within reasonable limits. The author must assume the responsibility of sifting the evidence and emphasizing those conclusions that seem to be most justified by experiment and observation. As far as material is concerned, it is evident that the selection of what to give and what to omit is a matter of judgment and experience upon the part of the writer, but the present author is convinced that the necessary reduction in material should be made by a process of elimination rather than by condensation. The latter method is suitable for the specialist with his background of knowledge and experience, but it is entirely unfitted for the elementary student. For the latter, brief comprehensive statements are oftentimes misleading, or fail at least to make a clear impression. Those subjects that are presented to him must be given with a certain degree of fullness if he is expected to obtain a serviceable conception of the facts, and it follows that a treatment of the wide subject of physiology is possible, when undertaken with this intention, only by the adoption of a system of selection and elimination.

The fundamental facts of physiology, its principles and modes of reasoning, are not difficult to understand. The obstacle that is most frequently encountered by the student lies in the complexity of the subject—the large number of more or less disconnected facts and theories which must be considered in a discussion of the structure, physics, and chemistry of such an intricate organism as the human body. But once a selection has been made of those facts and principles which it is most desirable that the student should know, there is no intrinsic difficulty to prevent them from being stated so clearly that they may be comprehended by anyone who possesses an elementary knowledge of anatomy, physics, and chemistry. It is doubtless the art of presentation that makes a textbook successful or unsuccessful. It must be admitted, however, that certain parts of physiology, at this particular period in its development, offer peculiar difficulties to the writers of textbooks. During recent years chemical work in the fields of digestion and nutrition has been very full, and as a result theories hitherto generally accepted have been subjected to criticism and alteration, particularly as the important advances in theoretical chemistry and physics have greatly modified the attitude and point of view of the investigators in physiology. Some former views have been unsettled and much information has been collected which at present it is difficult to formulate and apply to the explanation of the normal processes of the animal body. It would seem that in some of the fundamental problems of metabolism physiological investigation has pushed its experimental results to a point at which, for further progress, a deeper knowledge of the chemistry of the body is especially needed. Certainly the amount of work of a chemical character that bears directly or indirectly on the problems of physiology has shown a remarkable increase within the last decade. Amid the conflicting results of this literature it is difficult or impossible to follow always the true trend of development. The best that the textbook can hope to accomplish in such cases is to give as clear a picture as possible of the tendencies of the time.

Some critics have contended that only those facts or conclusions about which there is no difference of opinion should be presented to medical students. Those who are acquainted with the subject, however, understand that books written from this standpoint contain much that represents the uncertain compromises of past generations, and that the need of revision is felt as frequently for such books as for those constcruted on more liberal principles. There does not seem to be any sound reason why a textbook for medical students should aim to present only those conclusions that have crystallized out of the controversies of other times, and ignore entirely the live issues of the day which are of so much interest and importance not only to physiology, but to all branches of medicine. With this idea in mind the author has endeavored to make the student realize that physiology is a growing subject, continually widening its knowledge and readjusting its theories. It is important that the student should grasp this conception, because, in the first place, it is true; and, in the second place, it may save him later from disappointment and distrust in science if he recognizes that many of our conclusions are not the final truth, but provisional only, representing the best that can be done with the knowledge at our command. To emphasize this fact as well as to add somewhat to the interest of the reader short historical *résumés* have been introduced from time to time, although the question of space alone has prevented any extensive use of such material. It is a feature, however, that a teacher might develop with profit. Some knowledge of the gradual evolution of our present beliefs is useful in demonstrating the enduring value of experimental work as compared with mere theorizing, and also in engendering a certain appreciation and respect for knowledge that has been gained so slowly by the exertions of successive generations of able investigators.

A word may be said regarding the references to literature inserted in the book. It is perfectly obvious that a complete or approximately complete bibliography is neither appropriate nor useful, however agreeable it may be to give every worker full recognition of the results of his labors. But for the sake of those who may for any reason wish to follow any particular subject more in detail some references have been given, and these have been selected usually with the idea of citing those works which themselves contain a more or less extensive discussion and literature. Occasionally also references have been made to works of historical importance or to separate papers that contain the experimental evidence for some special view.

W. H. HOWELL

Contents

Section III.   MOTOR FUNCTIONS OF THE NERVOUS SYSTEM

Chapter 5

Chapter 6

Chapter 7

Chapter 8

Chapter 9

Chapter 10

Section V. CEREBRAL CORTEX IN GENERAL;
NEUROPHYSIOLOGY OF BEHAVIOR

Section VII.   CIRCULATION OF BLOOD AND LYMPH

Section VIII. RESPIRATION

Section IX. KIDNEY FUNCTION AND BODY FLUIDS

Section X.   DIGESTIVE AND URINARY SYSTEMS

Chapter 42

By *Paul F. Fenton*

Chapter 43

By *Paul F. Fenton*

Chapter 44

By *Paul F. Fenton*

Chapter 45

By *Paul F. Fenton*

Section XIII.   REPRODUCTION

Chapter 58

By *Charles W. Hooker*

SECTION I

Biophysics of the Cell Membrane

CHAPTER 1

The Cell Membrane:
Ionic and Potential Gradients and Active Transport

By J. WALTER WOODBURY

ANY ANIMAL TISSUE such as muscle or brain is composed of a group of cells and the solution bathing them, the *interstitial* fluid. The cell plasm or *intracellular* fluid and the interstitial fluid are similar; both consist largely of water and both fluids have roughly equal numbers of particles per unit volume dissolved in them. The boundary between the intracellular and interstitial fluids is, for the purposes of this section, considered to be a thin (100 Ångstroms) nonaqueous layer, which is called the *electrical membrane* here because its nature has been deduced largely from electrical measurements. The differences between the intracellular and interstitial fluids are more striking than their similarities. This chapter deals with two of these differences. (i) The concentrations of ions are markedly different. The concentrations of sodium (Na^+) and chloride (Cl^-) are much higher in the interstitial fluid than in the intracellular fluid. The situation is just reversed for potassium (K^+); its concentration is much higher in intracellular than in interstitial fluid (see Table 1). (ii) There is an electric potential difference between the intracellular and interstitial fluids. In skeletal muscle cells, the cell plasm is about 90 mV. (.09 V.) negative to the interstitial fluid.

Since these large differences in concentration and potential appear across the thin electrical membrane of the cell, it is reasonable to suppose that this membrane plays an important role in the maintenance of these differences. Two aspects of the cell membrane are largely responsible for the observed concentration and potential differences. (i) Ions diffuse through the membrane at a minute fraction of the rate at which they diffuse through water. This barrier to diffusion is probably a result of the membrane structure, which consists of alternating thin layers of lipid and protein. In most cell membranes, the rate of diffusion of Na^+ is much slower than is the diffusion rate of K^+ and Cl^-. (ii) Energy derived from metabolism is used by cells to transport Na^+ out of the cell and K^+ into the cell. These ionic movements just balance, on the average, the diffusion of Na^+ into and K^+ out of the cell. This *active transport* of Na^+ and K^+ maintains the intracellular Na^+ concentration at low values and the intracellular K^+ at high values.

More generally, the role of the electrical membrane in cellular function is to regulate the interchange of materials between a cell and its environment. The nature of the membrane is such that nutrients enter and waste products leave the cell relatively easily, while those substances necessary to cellular function, whether inside or outside the cell, cross only with difficulty. Because of the crucial functions of the cell electrical membrane in regulating interchange of ions and other substances, a description of its properties is a useful starting point for a study of physiology. The transfer of nonionized * substances is not treated here. The permeation and active transport of ions through the membrane and the consequences of these ion movements are the subject matter of this chapter. These concepts as they will be developed here are necessary for an understanding of a wide range of physiologic phenomena: (i) the electrical activity of nerve and muscle cells and the processes of synaptic transmission (Chaps. 2, 3, 4 and 5); (ii) the distribution of ions and water between the various body fluid compartments (Chap. 40) and the regulation of interstitial and intracellular pH (Chap. 24); (iii) the role of active ion transport in the secretive and absorptive processes of the gastrointestinal tract and in the formation of urine by the kidney (Chap. 39).

In this chapter the main ideas concerning the origins of transmembrane concentration and potential differences will first be sketched. Then the step-by-step development of present concepts of the origins of these potential and concentration differences will be described, and, where necessary, the underlying physical and chemical principles will be briefly reviewed. Lastly, two less obvious and more speculative, but nevertheless important, aspects of ion movements through cell membranes—regulation of cell volume and intracellular pH—will be discussed. Most of the concepts presented in this chapter were developed during the past 15 years, largely through the efforts of A. L. Hodgkin and his coworkers at Cambridge.[8, 9] In addition, there are numerous reviews[2, 3, 5, 6, 17] and symposia[15, 18] on various aspects of this subject.

ELECTRIC POTENTIALS AND ION CONCENTRATIONS IN MUSCLE

As stated above, there are two striking characteristics of cells to be considered in this chapter: the large difference in ion concentrations and the large difference in electric potential between the inside of the cell and the interstitial fluid. These facts have been

* Substances lacking an electric charge are often termed "un-ionized"—a word which becomes ambiguous when the hyphen is dropped, as it frequently is.

known for several decades. However, there have been many recent advances in our understanding of these phenomena through improvements in electrophysiologic techniques and the introduction of radioactive tracer methods. Measurements sufficiently accurate and delicate to test quantitatively the various ideas in respect to he mechanism have been made. One of these techniques, transmembrane potential measurements, is described briefly here in order to give a more concrete picture of the phenomena under discussion. Radioactive tracer methods will be described on page 18.

Intracellular Recording.   Figure 1 is a schematic diagram showing how the difference in electric potential between the inside and the outside of a cell can be measured directly and quite accurately. The technique for this was perfected by Ling and Gerard.[14] An ultramicroelectrode* is made by drawing a piece of glass tubing down to a small tip and then filling the tubing with a concentrated solution of KCl. If the elec-

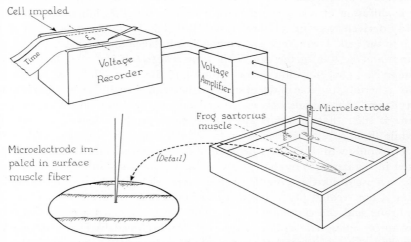

FIG. 1.   Intracellular recording. Schematic diagram of experimental arrangement for measuring transmembrane electric potential differences. A frog sartorius muscle is dissected free and pinned to a wax-bottomed chamber (right) filled with a physiologic (Ringer's) solution. A capillary microelectrode is held in position over muscle with a micromanipulator (not shown). Electrical connection is made to microelectrode and chamber by means of spirals of chlorided silver wires. Potential difference between tip of microelectrode and bathing medium is amplified and displayed as a function of time by recorder. When electrode penetrates the cell membrane (arrow on record at left), pen is suddenly deflected, thus indicating a transmembrane potential ($\mathcal{E}_s$). Center drawing is enlarged view of electrode inserted through membrane of a single cell to show that tip of electrode (0.5μ) is much smaller than diameter of muscle fiber (100 μ).

trode tip is no larger than about 1 μ, it can be inserted transversely through the cell membrane of a muscle fiber without detectable damage to the membrane. Any electrode larger than this at the tip appreciably damages the membrane and lowers the measured potential. The potential of the microelectrode tip when it is in the solution bathing the muscle is taken as zero. When the microelectrode is advanced toward the surface of the muscle, the potential of the electrode does not change until the tip penetrates a cell membrane. At this time (*arrow* in Fig. 1), the potential drops abruptly to −90 mV. (inside negative) and remains at this value as long as the electrode is in the cell. This transmembrane potential is commonly called the *resting potential* but will be referred to here as the *steady* potential ($\mathcal{E}_s$), the $\mathcal{E}$ being derived from electromotive force. Measured transmembrane steady potentials in different tissues vary from about −20 mV. to

* This designation is in conformity with the histologists' conventions—the tip size being just below visibility by light microscopy.

−100 mV., but their generation, active Na^+ transport, is probably the same in all tissues.

Ion Concentration in Muscle. The term "extracellular fluid" refers to all fluids not inside cells. Blood, lymph, cerebrospinal fluid, etc., are in this category. "Interstitial fluid" is the fluid in direct contact with the tissue cells, and, therefore, knowledge of the concentrations of ions in this fluid is necessary in the study of membrane phenomena. The concentrations of ions in the interstitial fluid are slightly different from those in blood plasma, because plasma contains an appreciable concentration of ionized protein. However, ion concentrations in interstitial fluid can be calculated from measured concentrations in the blood if the concentrations of plasma proteins and their charges are known.

The left hand columns in Table 1 give the approximate concentrations of the more important ions in the interstitial fluid of mammals. Intracellular concentrations are estimated from chemical analysis of a known weight of tissue and a measurement of the fraction of the tissue water which is in the interstitial space. The total amount of any ion in the interstitial fluid is then obtained by the product of the interstitial concentra-

TABLE 1.   *APPROXIMATE STEADY STATE ION CONCENTRATIONS AND POTENTIALS IN MAMMALIAN MUSCLE CELLS AND INTERSTITIAL FLUID**

INTERSTITIAL FLUID		INTRACELLULAR FLUID			
	$[Ion]$ $\mu M.$ per cm^3		$[Ion]$ $\mu M.$ per cm^3	$\dfrac{[Ion]_o}{[Ion]_i}$	$\varepsilon_{ion} = \dfrac{60}{Z}\log\dfrac{[Ion]_o}{[Ion]_i}(mV.)$
Cations		Cations			
Na^+	145	Na^+	12	12.1	65
K^+	4	K^+	155	1/39	−95
H^+	3.8×10^{-5}	H^+	13×10^{-5}	1/3.4	−32
pH	7.43	pH	6.9		
others	5				
Anions		Anions			
Cl^-	120	Cl^-	3.8 †	31.6	−90
HCO_3^-	27	HCO_3^-	8	3.4	−32
others	7	A^-	155		
Potential	0		−90 mV.	31.6 †	−90

* Vertical double line represents membrane
† Calculated from membrane potential using the Nernst Equation

tion and the fractional volume. This amount is subtracted from the total amount of ion in the tissue sample to give the amount of ion in the intracellular water. Intracellular concentration is the ratio of the amount of ion to the amount of water in the cells. The middle columns in Table 1 show the concentration of the more important ions in the intracellular water of mammalian skeletal muscle. Although intracellular concentrations vary considerably from tissue to tissue, the electrolyte pattern of muscle is fairly representative. To summarize Table 1, interstitial fluid has high concentrations of Na^+ and Cl^- ions; the intracellular fluid has high concentrations of K^+ ions and the largely unknown organic anions (A^-). The right hand columns are explained on p. 17.

Factors Affecting Ion Diffusion Through Membranes. PASSIVE FACTORS. Because of their random motion, the individual molecules of a substance in solution are continually intermixing (diffusing). If the concentration of the dissolved substance is higher in one region than in an adjacent one, molecules will move both ways, but there is a net tendency for the substance to diffuse from the region of higher to the region of lower concentration. Thus Na^+ and Cl^- tend to diffuse into cells and K^+ and A^- tend to diffuse out of cells. The rate of diffusion of these substances through the membrane depends not only on the concentration difference but also on the ease with which they pass through the membrane. In fact, the cell membrane severely limits the rate at which substances diffuse through it.

If the substance is ionized, the transmembrane potential also affects the rate of diffusion of the substance through the membrane. This effect is exerted because a transmembrane potential difference means that electric charges are separated by the cell membrane. This follows from the usual definition of the potential difference between two points as the work done against electric forces in carrying a unit positive charge from one point to the other. No electric work is done in carrying a charge through the membrane unless charges are separated by the membrane. These separated charges (inside negative) exert a force on any ions in the membrane. This force tends to drive cations $(+)$ into the cell and anions $(-)$ out of the cell; i.e., any cations which enter the membrane are attracted by the negative charges on the inside of the membrane.

K^+ ions tend to diffuse out of the cell because of their high internal concentration, but they tend to diffuse into the cell because of the electric charges separated by the membrane. These two tendencies nearly, but not quite, cancel each other, so that there is a slight tendency for K^+ to diffuse out of the cell. A similar argument holds for Cl^-, but in this instance the tendency for Cl^- to diffuse into the cell due to its high interstitial concentration is exactly balanced by the tendency of the electric forces to keep the negatively charged I^- from entering the cell. Since there is no net diffusion of Cl^- through the membrane, the inside and outside concentrations of Cl^- are in equilibrium.

ACTIVE TRANSPORT. The situation is quite different for Na^+ and A^-, both the concentration and potential difference acting in the same direction. There is a strong tendency for A^- to diffuse out of the cell and for Na^+ to diffuse into it. However, the membrane is believed to be nearly impermeable to A^- and is much less permeable to Na^+ than to K^+. Nevertheless, there is an appreciable steady leakage of Na^+ into cells. Despite this leakage, the internal concentration of Na^+ remains at low values in living cells. Therefore, some mechanism present in the cell must carry Na^+ out of the cell as fast as it enters, on the average. Since work must be done to carry a Na^+ ion from a region of lower to a region of higher concentration and from a lower to a higher electric potential, it must be concluded that energy derived from cellular metabolism is used to carry Na^+ out of the cell.

Little is known of how metabolic energy is used to extrude Na^+ from the cell. It is known that the extrusion of a Na^+ is usually accompanied by the uptake of a K^+. This process is often referred to as active Na^+ transport, as the *Na^+–K^+ pump*, or more simply as the *Na^+ pump*. The word "pump" denotes that metabolic energy is required by the process. *Active transport* is another term used to describe the process. The linkage of K^+ uptake to Na^+ extrusion accounts for the slight unbalance in the distribution of K^+; the net outward diffusion of K^+ is balanced by the inward pumping of K^+. The transmembrane potential arises because the membrane is much more permeable to K^+ than it is to Na^+ and because the Na^+–K^+ pump maintains the internal Na^+ concentration at a low value. K^+ ions would diffuse out of the cell faster than Na^+ ions would diffuse into it if there were no membrane potential; K^+ ions diffusing out leave A^- ions behind and thus charge the membrane.

SUMMARY. The factors which affect the movements of ions through the membrane, considered dimensionally, have the form of force per mol of ions. It is difficult to conceive of a difference in concentration as exerting a force on the solute molecules, but it is relatively easy to think of the transmembrane potential as exerting a force on charged molecules in the membrane. Four forces which govern the flow of ions through the membrane have now been mentioned: (i) transmembrane concentration differences,

(ii) the cell membrane structure as a frictional retarding force, (iii) transmembrane potential differences, and (iv) active Na^+–K^+ transport. The remainder of this chapter is devoted to a discussion of these forces, their interrelationships, and their role in the functioning of the cell.

PASSIVE FORCES AFFECTING ION MOVEMENTS

Concentration Gradient. DIFFUSION. All the molecules in a solution, both solute and solvent, move in random directions between collisions with other molecules. The average kinetic energy of the molecules attributable to random motion is directly proportional to the absolute temperature. The random motion of the molecules is such that the rate at which molecules diffuse out of a small volume is proportional to the concentration [mols (M.) per liter or millimols (mM.) per cm.^{3}] of the substance in the small volume. Even in a solution in which the concentration of a substance is everywhere constant, a molecule found in one region at one time may be found in any region at a later time. This process of intermixing of solute (and solvent) particles is called *diffusion*.

GRADIENT AND FLUX. In a solution where the concentration of a substance varies from one region to another, there will be a net movement (flux; **M**) of solute particles from regions of higher to regions of lower concentration, because more molecules per second leave than enter the region of higher concentration. The net diffusion of a substance from regions of higher to lower concentrations is quite analogous to the flow of water in a river. The rate of flow is proportional to the steepness of the stream bed: the steeper the grade, the faster the flow. Water flows directly downhill, i.e., in the direction of steepest slope; a substance diffuses "downhill" in the direction of "steepest slope." The magnitude of the steepest slope or rate of change of concentration and the direction of this steepest slope constitute a vector. This vector is called the *concentration gradient*, abbreviated "grad [S]." Square brackets are used to denote concentration of the substance included in them; thus, [S] denotes the concentration of the substance S (usually given as μM. per cm.^{3}).

Any quantity that varies with distance has a gradient which can be calculated at any point. If concentration increases with increasing distance, then grad [S] is positive. However, net flux is in the opposite direction, so the net flux of S ($\mathbf{M}_S$) is proportional to −grad [S] (Fig. 2a). For a given concentration gradient, $\mathbf{M}_S$ depends on the ease with which the molecules of S move through the solvent; the greater the ease of movement (the less the frictional resistance to flow), the greater the flux. The measure of the ease of motion is called the *diffusion constant* (D). Therefore, $\mathbf{M}_S = -D_S$ grad [S]. In words, the net flux of S (M. per cm.^{2}-sec.) is given by the product of the diffusion constant of that substance (D_S; in cm.^{2} per sec.) and the concentration gradients of S (in M. per cm.^{3}-cm. or M. per cm.^{4}).

The presence of a cell membrane in a system greatly simplifies the description of the diffusion of a substance because all dissolved substances diffuse through the membrane so much more slowly than they diffuse through water that the diffusion time in water usually can be neglected (Fig. 2b). In other words, the concentrations of a substance in the interstitial fluid and in the intracellular fluid are nearly constant, even when there is a net flux of the substance through the system. More precisely, the rate of diffusion of a substance through the membrane is so slow that a negligibly small concentration gradient in the aqueous media suffices to bring the substance up to the membrane as rapidly as it diffuses through the membrane. Therefore, the rate of penetration of a substance depends on the properties of the membrane and on the concentration gradient of the substance in the membrane. Since the membrane is a thin, fixed structure and the concentration gradient in the solution is negligible, the average concentration gradient through the membrane is obtained, to a good approximation, by dividing the difference in concentration between the interstitial and intracellular fluids by the thickness of the membrane (δ). Thus, in the membrane, grad $[S]_m = ([S]_o - [S]_i)/\delta$. The subscript "m" is used to denote the value of a quantity in the *membrane*; the subscript "o" (for *outside* the cell), the value in the interstitial fluid; and the subscript "i" (for *inside* the cell), the value in the intracellular fluid. Thus, $[S]_o$ means the concentration of S in the interstitial fluid.

Cell Membrane.   The concentration gradient of a substance can be thought of as a force tending to move the substance. However, the rate of movement of S is determined not only by grad $[S]$ but also by the frictional resistance to flow. Resistance is the second of the forces listed above as affecting the movement of a substance. In a tissue, most resistance to flow of materials is in the cell membrane and its immediate vicinity. Therefore, the membrane structure and the various mechanisms whereby a substance may cross the membrane are important.

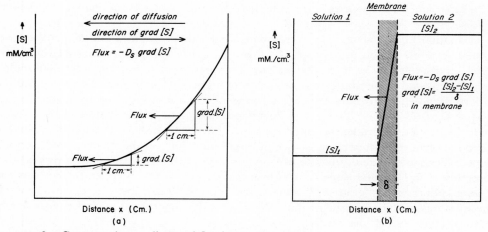

FIG. 2.   Concentration gradient and flux in one dimension.

a, Graph of concentration of a substance ($[S]$) against distance in a one compartment aqueous system. $[S]$ increases from left to right; consequently, net diffusion of S is from right to left. Rate of diffusion is proportional to concentration gradient, grad $[S]$, i.e., flux $= -D_s$ grad $[S]$, where D_s is the diffusion constant. Grad $[S]$ is defined, in one dimension, as the slope of the $[S]$, x curve as shown.

b, A thin membrane divides the system into two compartments. S is assumed to diffuse much more slowly through the membrane than through the aqueous media on both sides. Therefore, grad $[S]$ in the water is nearly zero, and grad $[S]$ across the membrane is large. The average gradient of S in the membrane is difference in $[S]$ across the membrane ($[S]_2 - [S]_1$), divided by the membrane thickness, δ. Grad $[S]$ is large if δ is thin, but flux is small because D_s is so small in the membrane.

PERMEABILITY.   The net influx (M_S) through the membrane is quite simply calculated from the following equation (see Fig. 2*b*):

$$M_S = -D_S \text{ grad } [S]_m = -(D_S/\delta)([S]_i - [S]_o) = P_S([S]_o - [S]_i) \qquad (1)$$

The ratio D_S/δ is called the *permeability* of the membrane to the substance S (P_S). D_S is the diffusion constant of S in the membrane. P_S depends only on the properties of the membrane and of the substance. Permeability is thus a measure of the ease with which a substance can penetrate the membrane; i.e., the greater the permeability, the less the frictional drag force exerted by the membrane on the substance. In words, equation 1 states that the net flux of a substance (number of mols entering the cell each second through 1 cm.² of membrane minus the number of mols per cm.²-sec. leaving the cell) is equal to the permeability constant times the difference between the external and internal concentrations of the substance. In amphibian skeletal muscle the permeability of the cell membrane to K^+ ions (P_K) is about 10^{-6} cm. per second, whereas P_{Na} is about 2×10^{-8} cm. per second. The permeability to K^+ of a layer of water of the same thickness as the membrane (100 Ångstroms) is about 10 cm. per second, or ten million times greater than the P_K of the cell membrane. This ratio indicates the extreme effectiveness of the cell membrane in limiting the flow of ions.

MEMBRANE STRUCTURE.[4, 5, 6, 16, 17] The cell electrical membrane probably consists of a few alternating layers of lipids and proteins. In the lipid layer, the long, thin lipid molecules are closely packed, with their long axes parallel and oriented perpendicular to the membrane. The lipid layer is two molecules thick; the nonpolar ends of the lipid molecules are opposed. The unit layer of membrane structure quite possibly consists of a bimolecular layer of lipid sandwiched between two monomolecular layers of protein. The protein layers are bonded to the lipids at their polar ends. The membrane is probably only one (85 Ångstroms) or two (170 Ångstroms) lipid-protein unit layers thick.[4, 16] Lipids are hydrophobic, and it seems unlikely that water and water-soluble substances can penetrate the membrane in a region where the lipid layer is closely packed.

In view of this probable membrane structure, the problem becomes not one of accounting for the low permeability of the membrane to water-soluble substances but of explaining the occurrence of any penetration at all. Lipid-soluble substances presumably penetrate by dissolving in the membrane substance. The available data suggest that ions and some other substances traverse the membrane by one or both of the following means:

(i) The membrane is perforate, containing small-diameter (about 3 Ångstroms), water-filled pores. Ions could diffuse through these pores quite rapidly. The limitation of fluxes is attributed to the comparatively small number of pores per unit area of membrane and to restrictive effects of the pores. The membrane is roughly 100 times more permeable to K^+ than it is to Na^+. This difference is one reason for assuming that the pore diameter is 3 Ångstroms,[17] intermediate between the hydrated diameters of K^+ (2.2 Ångstroms) and Na^+ (3.4 Ångstroms).

(ii) There is a special lipid-soluble *carrier* molecule (possibly a phosphatide), limited to the membrane, which combines highly preferentially with particular ions. An ion from the interstitial fluid could combine with this carrier molecule at the outer surface of the membrane; the ion-carrier complex might then diffuse through the membrane to the inner surface. The ion might there dissociate from the carrier and enter the intracellular fluid. It has become increasingly necessary to evoke a carrier to explain both passive (diffusion) and active transport of ions and other substances. The exact manner in which ions cross the membrane is not known, but for passive movements it does not matter. When transport is passive, the net flux is approximately proportional to the concentration gradient of the ion across the cell membrane; the concept of permeability still applies.

Voltage Gradient. Electric forces also affect the rate at which ions move through a membrane or solution. For an uncharged (nonionized) substance in a nonflowing solution, the only passive force tending to cause a net movement of the solute is the concentration gradient. However, if particles in solution are electrically charged, their diffusion may also be influenced by electric forces; and, conversely, their diffusion may generate a voltage. More precisely, voltage gradients as well as concentration gradients exert forces on charged particles in solution. The mechanism whereby voltage gradients can affect the diffusion of ions is most easily understood in terms of the forces acting on an ion moving through a relatively impermeable membrane.

Figure 3 is a diagram of a portion of a simplified membrane bathed by interstitial and intracellular fluid. This hypothetical membrane has been drawn with holes or pores piercing it at intervals. The diagram should be used only as an aid to thinking, not as a portrayal of a real membrane, for the scheme is far too simple. Nevertheless, it is useful in describing voltage gradients generated by the diffusion of ions.

The pores in the membrane are assumed to be just large enough to permit easy passage of K^+ and Cl^- ions but small enough that the slightly larger Na^+ ions can penetrate only with difficulty, i.e., P_K and P_{Cl} are much greater than P_{Na}. (Although Na has a lower atomic weight than K, Na^+ ions are larger than K^+ and Cl^- ions in solution because Na^+ ions bind more water molecules; i.e., they are more hydrated.) The large A^- ions are presumed too large to penetrate; i.e., $P_A = 0$. The concentration of each ionic species in the interstitial and intracellular fluid is shown qualitatively in Figure 3

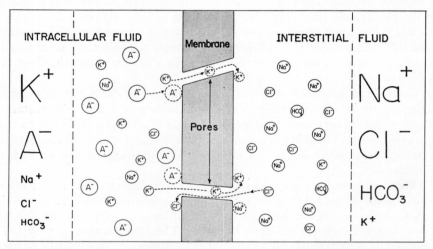

FIG. 3.   Development of transmembrane voltage by an ion concentration gradient. Diagram of an intracellular fluid–membrane–interstitial fluid system. Membrane shown has some, but not all, properties of a real cell membrane. Hypothetical membrane is pierced by pores of such size that K^+ and Cl^- ions can move through them easily, Na^+ ions with difficulty, and A^- not at all. Sizes of symbols in left- and right- hand columns indicate relative concentrations of ions in fluids bathing the membrane. Dashed arrows and circles show paths taken by K^+, A^-, Na^+ and Cl^- ions as a K^+ or Cl^- travels through a pore. Penetration of the pore by a K^+ or Cl^- follows a collision between the K^+ or Cl^- and water molecules (not shown), giving the K^+ or Cl^- the necessary kinetic energy and proper direction. An A^- or Na^+ unable to cross the membrane is left behind when a K^+ or Cl^-, respectively, diffuses through a pore. Because K^+ is more concentrated on left than on right, more K^+ diffuses from left to right than from right to left, and conversely for Cl^-. Therefore, right-hand border of membrane becomes positively charged (K^+, Na^+) and left-hand negatively charged (Cl^-, A^-). Fluids away from the membrane are electrically neutral because of attraction between + and − charges. Charges separated by membrane stay near it because of their attraction.

by the size of its symbol at the left and right edges. Even if it is supposed that there is no potential difference (no charges are separated) across the membrane at some instant, a voltage will be generated immediately thereafter by the diffusion of K^+ and Cl^- ions along their concentration gradients. This potential arises because K^+ ions, which permeate the membrane easily, diffuse out of the cell through the pores and Cl^- ions diffuse inward. Hereafter, the behavior of K^+ ions only will be described, but it must be kept in mind that Cl^- ions give rise to the same effects. Wherever the outward diffusion of K^+ is mentioned, the inward diffusion of Cl^- would produce nearly the same effect.

Consider the sequence of events as each K^+ ion diffuses out of the cell. Although K^+ ions are charged particles, their outward movement cannot be accompanied by a corresponding movement of A^-, nor can an equal number of Na^+ move inward in exchange for outflowing K^+ ions. Thus, K^+ ions reach the outside of the membrane alone and are not replaced within the cell by Na^+ ions. Consequently, the outside acquires a net positive charge and the inside a net negative charge. Since electric charges of opposite sign attract each other, the excess K^+ ions on the outside are attracted to the excess A^- ions left inside the cell. Therefore, the excess charges stay in the immediate vicinity of the membrane, as shown in Figure 3. Note that, despite the electrical attraction between the K^+ and A^- ions, movement of the K^+ ions back toward the inside of the cell is counteracted by the concentration gradient of K^+ ions, which exerts an outward force on them. The outward diffusion of K^+ due to the concentration gradient separates positive and negative charges and thus generates an electric field. This electric field retards further outward diffusion of K^+ ions (or any cation) and speeds their inward diffusion. Any positively charged ion in the membrane (Fig. 3) is acted upon by the charges the membrane separates. The positive charges on its outer surface exert an *inward* repulsive force on a positive ion in the membrane; the negative charges on the inner surface exert an additive inward attractive force.

Since the diffusion of a single ionic species through the membrane generates its own retarding force, the electric field, the process is self-limiting, and eventually a state will be reached (equilibrium) in which the outflux equals influx (net outflux is zero). At equilibrium, the tendency for K^+ ions to diffuse out, resulting from the high value of $[K^+]_i$, is exactly balanced by the tendency for them to diffuse inward that results from the electric field in the membrane. Because K^+ ions inside the cell are more concentrated, they will enter pores in the membrane as a result of their random motion much more frequently than will the K^+ ions outside. However, a cation entering a pore from the inside must have much kinetic energy to move through the membrane against the retarding electric field. Conversely, because of the low $[K^+]_o$ few K^+ ions enter the pores from the outside, but nearly all those that do will continue on through the membrane, aided by the electric field. Since much of present knowledge of cell membrane function has come from measurements of the electrical characteristics of the membrane, knowledge of some principles of electricity is necessary for an understanding of membrane function.

ELECTROSTATICS

Charge.   Electric charge, like mass, is a fundamental property of matter. There are two kinds of charge, arbitrarily designated as positive $(+)$ (protons) and negative $(-)$ (electrons). Like electric charges repel and unlike charges attract each other. Since each atom contains one or more electrons and an equal number of protons, the total number of charges in a macroscopic object is extremely large, but there is little or no net charge. The strong mutual attraction of unlike charges is sufficient to insure electroneutrality in any object unless other forces (e.g., mechanical or chemical) act to separate the charges and keep them separated. The common unit of electric charge is the *coulomb*. A coulomb is the charge of 6.25×10^{18} electrons. The charge on an electron is thus 1.6×10^{-19} coulombs. The force between charges is most easily considered in a system in which all the charges are held in a fixed position in vacuum (or air). Nonelectrical forces are required to keep the charges separated and static.

Electric Field Intensity.   The force (F) of attraction or repulsion between two point charges (q_1 and q_2) is given by Coulomb's law:

$$F = K(q_1q_2/r^2)$$

where K is a constant determined by the units chosen and r is the distance between them. If q is in coulombs, r is in meters, and F in newtons (1 kg.-m. per sec.^{2}), then $K = 9 \times 10^9$ joule-meter per coulomb^2. The force is in the direction of the line joining the two charges. Repulsion is defined as a positive force, and attraction as a negative force.

The *electric field intensity* (E) at a point is defined as the electric force that would be exerted on a unit positive charge placed at that point (Fig. 4). In other words, the electric field is the electric force per unit charge. The existence of an unchanging electric field at any point in space means that electric charges of opposite sign have been separated. Thus, the only way to generate an electric field is to separate positive and negative charges by applying a nonelectrical force. These separated charges attract each other and also either attract or repel any other charge brought into the neighborhood. The electric field at any point is a convenient way of specifying the electric forces acting in a region. However, E is a vector, i.e., has magnitude and direction. A more convenient way to describe the field is to calculate the electric potential, a scalar quantity—i.e., one having magnitude only.

Electric Potential or Voltage. Because of the force of attraction between + and − charges, work must be done to separate them. Work is defined as a force multiplied

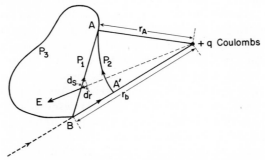

FIG. 4.   Voltage and voltage difference in neighborhood of a fixed charge of +q coulombs. E is the force, due to charge +q, on a charge of +1 coulomb at any point. E is directed radially outward, and $E = K(q/r^2)$; distance from +q to any point is r; dr is a small movement in a radial direction away from +q. S is distance traveled by exploratory +1 charge along any path between B and A (P_1, P_2, P_3); dS is a small movement along any path. Voltage at point B ($\mathcal{E}_B$) is work required to bring +1 charge from a large distance up to point B; $\mathcal{E}_B = Kq/r_B$. Voltage difference ($\mathcal{E}_{AB}$) between A and B is work required to carry +1 charge from B to A; $\mathcal{E}_{AB} = \mathcal{E}_A - \mathcal{E}_B$. Since work is done only when the +1 moves in a radial direction, the work to go from B to A is the same no matter what path (P_1, P_2, P_3, etc.) is taken. Along path P_2 (BA′A) all the work is done along BA′ (radial); no work is done along A′A. So $\mathcal{E}_{AB}$ depends only on r_A and r_B.

by the distance in the direction of the force through which the force has acted. Since the work done depends only on the size of the force and the distance moved, work is scalar quantity. The *electric potential* or *voltage* ($\mathcal{E}$) *at a point is the amount of work done against electric forces that is required to carry a unit + charge (1 coulomb) to the point from a large distance away.* That is, voltage or potential is the potential energy per unit charge. The potential difference between the two points A and B in Figure 4 is $\mathcal{E}_{AB} = \mathcal{E}_A - \mathcal{E}_B$ and is the work required to move a +1 charge from B to A. If the distance r_A is less than the distance r_B, work must be done to move a charge from B to A, and the potential is positive. If work is done by the charge (this would happen if +q were replaced by a negative charge), the potential is negative. Since work is force multiplied by the distance moved in the direction of the force, the work done (the potential change) during movement of the +1 charge from B to A along path P_2 (BA′A) is all done in moving from B to A′. Since A′A is an arc of a circle centered at +q, the force is always perpendicular to the direction of movement, and no work is required in the movement from A′ to A. Thus, work involved in movement of the +1 charge along any path, such as P_2 in Figure 4, is the same as that required for movement along any other path, e.g., P_1 and P_3. Only movement in the radial direction requires work, so the voltage depends only on the distances r_A and r_B. It is for this reason—work done on a charge is independent of path—that the concept of potential is useful.

In the example of Figure 4, the potential between A and B ($\mathcal{E}_{AB}$) is most easily calculated along BA'A. The force (E) on a unit + charge at any distance (r) from q is $E = K(q/r^2)$. The work done ($d\mathcal{E}$) to move the unit + charge a radial distance (dr) is $d\mathcal{E} = -Edr$. The negative sign is used because r is measured outward from q and because work is done by the charge when it moves in a +r direction. The result is a fall in voltage. The total work done on the charge as it moves from B to A is

$$\mathcal{E}_{AB} = \int_{r_B}^{r_A} -Edr = \int_{r_B}^{r_A} -K\frac{q}{r^2}dr = Kq\left(\frac{1}{r_A} - \frac{1}{r_B}\right)$$

The potential of point A is obtained by taking $r_B = \infty$. Since $1/\infty = 0$, $\mathcal{E}_A = Kq/r_A$; for example, $K = 9 \times 10^9$ joule-meter per coulomb^2, and if $q = 10^{-12}$ coulombs (1 micromicrocoulomb), $r_A = 0.1$ m., and $r_B = 1$ m., then $\mathcal{E}_A = (9 \times 10^9 \times 10^{-12})/0.1 = 0.09$ joules per coulomb $= 0.09$ V. and $\mathcal{E}_{AB} = 9 \times 10^9 \times 10^{-12} [(1/0.1) - (1/1)] = 9 \times 10^{-3}(10 - 1) = 0.081$ V. In words, 0.09 joules of work must be done on a +1 coulomb charge to carry it from a large distance to 0.1 m. away from a charge of 10^{-12} coulombs.

VOLTAGE GRADIENT. The electric field is often referred to as the (negative) voltage gradient (grad $\mathcal{E}$)—the rate at which voltage changes with distance in the direction in which the voltage is changing most rapidly. This reverse definition of electric field in terms of voltage follows from the definition of voltage as the potential energy per unit charge and the definition of a gradient. This potential energy is derived from the work done on the charge in order to move it against the electric field. Thus, the rate of change of work (energy) with distance is the force, and the rate of change of voltage with distance is the electric field.

By definition, $d\mathcal{E} = -E \cdot dr$, where dr is in the direction of the electric field. Therefore, $E = -(d\mathcal{E}/dr) = -\text{grad } \mathcal{E}$. Because of this relation, the electric field is referred to as the negative of the voltage gradient and is the electric force on a unit change, just as $-\text{grad } [S]$ is the diffusional force per mol.

Cell Membrane Capacitor. CONDUCTORS. A *conductor* is a substance in which charges are free to move. Metals are good conductors because their outer shell electrons are loosely bound to the nuclei. Salt solutions are also good conductors, because their solute particles are charged (ionized) and can move freely in the solvent. Because charges can move freely in a conductor, no electric field can exist inside it when charges are not moving. If the conductor contained a field, it would exert a force on the free charges, and some of them would move into such position on the surface of the conductor that the field would be reduced to zero. Since the field must be zero in a conductor, all points in and on it must be at the same potential, for no electric work is required to move a charge through a region where E is zero.

The potential of an isolated conductor is not necessarily zero. For example, if some excess charges, all positive or all negative, are put on an isolated conductor, they will exert a force on any charge outside the conductor, and work will be required to bring a +1 charge from infinity. The excess charges must be on the surface of the conductor in order to cancel E everywhere in the interior. More simply, the excess charges repel each other and so distribute themselves as widely as possible on the surface.

INSULATORS. An *insulator* is any region in which there are no free charges, e.g., a vacuum. In an insulating material called a *dielectric*, all the charges are tightly bound and cannot migrate under the influence of an external electric field. The charges in a dielectric are not rigidly fixed, so they separate slightly in an external field. This charge separation in the dielectric is proportional to E and is such as to reduce E. However, the force on an exploring charge in a dielectric varies in the same way as the force on a charge *in vacuo*, but the forces in a dielectric are reduced by a factor $1/\kappa$. The denominator κ is the *dielectric constant*. Its value depends on the nature of the material; for example, κ is about 5 for most oils. The cell membrane is a dielectric. Its dielectric constant is unknown, but since the membrane contains a high proportion of lipids κ may be about 5.

CAPACITY. In a static situation, the existence of a potential difference between two points (A and B) means that $+$ and $-$ charges have been separated. This condition follows from the definition of $\mathcal{E}_{AB}$ as the work done against *electric* forces in carrying a $+1$ charge from B to A and because there are no electric forces in a region unless charges are separated there. The greater the amount of charge separated, the greater the electric field and the greater is $\mathcal{E}_{AB}$. In particular, if $+$ charges are put on an insulated fixed conductor (A) and an equal number of $-$ charges are put on a second fixed conductor (B), the potential difference between the two conductors is directly proportional to the amount of charge on either conductor. Any arrangement of two conductors separated by an insulator is called a *capacitor* or *condenser*. The proportionality constant relating charge to voltage is called the *capacity* or *capacitance* (C) of a capacitor and is given by the equation $C = q/\mathcal{E}_{AB}$, where q is the total amount of charge on either conductor.

The capacity of a capacitor depends on the geometry of the conductors (i.e., on their spatial extent and separation) and on the dielectric constant of the insulating material. These dependencies arise because the force between two conductors is determined by the distance separating them and because the relative distribution of the charges on the surface of an insulated conductor is the same no matter how much charge there is on the conductor. The less the work per unit charge required to charge a capacitor, the higher its capacity. Hence, the closer two conductors are together, the higher the capacity between them, for less work is required to move a unit charge through the shorter distance. It follows, then, that the capacity between two closely spaced parallel sheets or plates of metal separated by an insulator is high. Since the electric field in the region between the plates depends mostly on the nearest charges, increasing the area of the plates permits the addition of charges to the plates without an increase in the electric field between them. Therefore, the greater the surface area of the plates, the greater the capacity between them. The opposite charges on the plates of a capacitor attract each other, and so they must be on the surface of the conductors. The charges on the surfaces of the two conductors lie as close to each other as they can, their closeness being limited by the insulator. If the insulation is not perfect—if some charge can move through the insulator—charges placed on the conductors will slowly leak off.

CELL MEMBRANE CAPACITY. An animal cell and its surrounding fluids form a capacitor: the two conductors are the interstitial and intracellular fluids, and the insulator separating them is the cell membrane. Since ions can penetrate the membrane to a limited extent, the cell is not a perfect capacitor. Charges separated across the membrane will eventually leak off unless there are some means of restoring the charge as fast as it leaks off. Membrane capacity is relatively high because the membrane is extremely thin (100 Ångstroms). The cell may be regarded as a parallel plate capacitor, because the distance between the conductors is small compared to the diameter of a cell. It is natural to give membrane capacities in terms of capacity per unit area, because the capacity of a parallel plate capacitor is proportional to its surface area.

The unit of capacity is the *farad* (f.). A capacitor has a capacity of 1 f. if 1 coulomb of charge taken from one plate and placed on the other produces a potential difference of 1 V. between the plates. In terms of physical size, a 1 f. capacitor is large, and the capacitors commonly encountered have capacities of the order of 1 microfarad (1 μf. $= 10^{-6}$). The nerve fibers of the squid, which have been studied extensively because they are large, have membrane capacities of about 1 μf. per cm.^{2}. The capacities of frog skeletal muscle fibers are nearly 10 μf. per cm.^{2}. The amount of charge (q) separated by 1 cm.^{2} of muscle cell membrane is the product of the steady potential difference ($\mathcal{E}_s$) across the cell membrane and the capacity (C_m) $q = C_m\mathcal{E}_s$. $\mathcal{E}_s$ for a frog muscle fiber is -90 mV., so $q = 10 \times 10^{-6}$ f. per cm.$^2 \times 0.09$ V. $= 9 \times 10^{-7}$ coulombs per cm.^{2}.

Since the charges separated by the membrane are ions, the amount of charge can be given more meaning by expressing it in mols per square centimeter rather than in coulombs per square centimeter. There are 6.023×10^{23} molecules in 1 M. of any substance, and a monovalent ion has a charge of ± 1 electronic charge; therefore, since one electron has a charge of 1.6×10^{-19} coulombs, the charge of 1 M. of monovalent ions is $(6.023 \times 10^{23}$ monovalent ions per 1 M.$) \times (1.6 \times 10^{-19}$ coulombs per monovalent ion$) = 96,500$ coulombs per 1 M. of monovalent ions. It follows that a charge of 9×10^{-7} coulombs per cm.^{2} on a muscle fiber membrane means that there are only 9.5×10^{-12} M. of ions separated by 1 cm.^{2} of cell membrane. By comparison, 1 cm.^{3} of interstitial or intracellular fluid contains 1.5×10^{-6} M. of cations (or anions). In other words, a layer of interstitial fluid only 6×10^{-8} cm. (6 Ångstroms) thick is sufficient to supply the ions necessary to charge the cell membrane capacity to 90 mV.

CHARGE NEUTRALITY. The charging of the membrane by the outward movement of K^+ produces a readily measurable voltage across the membrane. However, the change in $[K^+]_i$ necessary to charge the membrane is not detectable by chemical measurements. Despite the extremely small changes in ion concentration required to charge the membrane capacity, it is worth emphasizing that the law of macroscopic electroneutrality does not apply to macroscopic parts of the intracellular fluid–membrane–interstitial fluid system. The whole system is electrically neutral, but the intracellular fluid contains a slight excess of anions and the interstitial fluid an equal excess of cations. These excess charges are, of course, attracted to each other, and thus distribute themselves with uniform density over the surfaces of the membrane.

CHARGING MEMBRANE CAPACITY. The process whereby the diffusion of an ionic species down its concentration gradient can generate a counteracting voltage gradient can now be further discussed (Fig. 3). When a K^+ ion traverses a pore (dashed lines, Fig. 3) and leaves the cell, this cation leaves behind a nonpermeating A^- ion. The outside fluid thus acquires a positive charge and the inside a negative charge. In other words the membrane capacity is slightly charged, and a voltage difference is built up between the conductors. More simply, the separation of charge means that there is an electric field in the membrane and that work must be done on a unit $+$ charge to carry it out of the cell. The electric field in the membrane is uniform because the separated charges must distribute themselves uniformly over its surfaces in order to make the electric field zero everywhere in the inside and outside conducting fluids. This is true even in the case of penetration of the membrane by a single ion; the excess cation on one side and the excess anion on the other move the charges in the conducting media. This movement has the effect of distributing the single charge over the cell membrane surface. Since the electric field in the membrane is constant, the voltage across the membrane is simply the product of the electric field and the membrane thickness (δ), $\mathcal{E}_s = E\delta$.

IONIC EQUILIBRIUM

If a membrane is permeable only to K^+ ions, for example, and if there is a concentration gradient of K^+ across the membrane, the diffusion of K^+ through the membrane is self-limiting. The first K^+ ions to penetrate the membrane generate an electric field which retards the diffusion of other K^+ ions. As long as there is a net outflux of K^+, $+$ and $-$ charges are being separated and the electric field is increasing, so that eventually E must attain a strength to permit influx to equal outflux. Outflowing K^+ ions are driven by the high $[K^+]_i$ and retarded by E; inflowing ions are accelerated by E, but the low $[K^+]_o$ means that K^+ ions enter the membrane at a slower rate. If no work is needed to carry a small amount of a substance across the membrane, that substance is said to be distributed at *equilibrium*. An alternative statement of the equilibrium condition is that influxes and effluxes are equal. This statement is true because there can be no net flux of the substance unless there is a force acting on it, and the existence of a force acting on ions means that a potential energy difference also exists.

The equilibrium condition for uncharged molecules is simply that the internal and external concentrations are equal, for this is the condition at zero net flux. The equilibrium condition for ions is more complicated: both the concentration and the voltage difference across the membrane must be known in order to calculate the potential energy difference between the inside and outside and thus the equilibrium condition. Any inside concentration of an ionic species may be brought into equilibrium with any outside concentration by applying the appropriate transmembrane voltage. Experimentally, this situation may be achieved by separating two ionic solutions with a membrane permeable only to the ionic species for which the equilibrium is desired. The charging process illustrated in Figure 3 then generates a potential difference which equalizes influxes and effluxes. The transmembrane potential which equalizes fluxes for a particular ion is called the *equilibrium potential* for that ion. Its value depends on the ratio of the internal and external concentrations of the ion.

Electrochemical Potential.   The relationship between the external and internal concentrations of an ion and the transmembrane potential at equilibrium is obtained by setting to zero the expression for the total transmembrane potential energy difference for that ion. This total potential energy difference per mol of ion is called the *electrochemical potential difference* ($\Delta\mu$) and is the sum of the electrical and concentration energy difference across the membrane for that ion. An expression for the electrochemical difference for K^+ ions will be developed here, but the same considerations hold for any ion present in a tissue.

The *electric potential energy difference* of 1 M. of K^+ ions is the work that must be done solely against electric forces to carry 1 M. of K^+ across the membrane, from outside to inside, with the transmembrane potential held at its original value. This work (W_E) is simply the product of $\mathcal{E}_m$, the transmembrane voltage (joules per coulomb), F, the Faraday (number of coulombs per mole of charge) and Z_K, the valence of the K^+ ion: $W_E = Z_K F \mathcal{E}_m$. The *concentration potential energy difference* W_C is the work to carry 1 M. of K^+ ions from outside to inside solely against the concentration gradient, with the external and internal K^+ concentrations held at their original values. W_C is not easily calculable, but it can be shown that W_C is proportional to the difference between the logarithms of the internal and external concentrations rather than directly proportional to their difference. Thus $W_C = RT(\log_e[K^+]_i - \log_e[K^+]_o)$, where R is the universal gas constant, T is the absolute temperature, and e is 2.718 (the base of natural logarithms); RT has the unit of energy per mol. The electrochemical potential difference for K^+ is, then, $\Delta\mu_K = W_E + W_C$, so

$$\Delta\mu_K = Z_K F \mathcal{E}_m + RT \log_e \frac{[K^+]_i}{[K^+]_o} \tag{2}$$

If $\mathcal{E}_m$, $[K^+]_o$ and $[K^+]_i$ are such that $\Delta\mu_K = 0$, then K^+ ions are equilibrated across the membrane. If $\Delta\mu_K$ is not zero, it is a measure of the net tendency of K^+ ions to diffuse through the membrane. The larger $\Delta\mu_K$, the greater the net flux of K^+.

Nernst Equation.   The condition for ionic equilibrium is that the electrochemical potential of an ion is zero. Setting $\Delta\mu_K = 0$ in Equation 2, replacing $\mathcal{E}_m$ by $\mathcal{E}_K$, and solving for $\mathcal{E}_K$ gives

$$\mathcal{E}_K = \frac{RT}{FZ_K} \log_e \frac{[K^+]_o}{[K^+]_i} \tag{3}$$

This is the Nernst equation. The term $\mathcal{E}_K$ indicates that this equation determines the value that $\mathcal{E}_m$ must have if K^+ ions are to be in equilibrium. $\mathcal{E}_K$ is called the *potassium equilibrium potential*. If we substitute the values R = 8.2 joules per mol-degree abs., T = 310 degrees abs. (37° C.), F = 96,500 coulombs per mol, and $Z_K = +1$, and then convert to logarithms to the base 10 and express $\mathcal{E}_K$ in millivolts, a useful form of the Nernst equation is obtained:

$$\mathcal{E}_K = 60 \log_{10} \frac{[K^+]_o}{[K^+]_i} \tag{4}$$

Note that if $\mathcal{E}_K = 0$, the equilibrium condition for ions reduces to that for neutral substances, i.e., $[K^+]_o = [K^+]_i$. The Nernst equation can be written for every ion present in the system.

With the equilibrium conditions for ion concentrations quantitatively stated by the Nernst equation, it is possible to determine which ions in a cell's environment are distributed in equilibrium with the transmembrane potential. The requisite numbers for the most important ions in mammalian skeletal muscle are given in Table 1. The external and internal concentrations, their ratio, and the equilibrium potentials are given in the main body of the Table. The steady transmembrane potential $\mathcal{E}_s$, as measured with an intracellular microelectrode, is given at the bottom of the Table to facilitate comparison with calculated ionic equilibrium potentials. $\mathcal{E}_s$ is defined as the potential of the inside solution minus the potential of the outside solution. Since the cell interior is negatively charged, $\mathcal{E}_s$ is a negative number. K^+, Cl^- and Na^+ ions will be discussed here and H^+ and HCO_3^- ions on page 28.

POTASSIUM IONS. From Table 1, $[K^+]_o = 4$ μM. per cm.[3] and $[K^+]_i = 155$ μM. per cm.[3]; therefore, $\mathcal{E}_K = 60 \log_{10} (4/155) = -95$ mV. This value is close to the measured $\mathcal{E}_s$, -90 mV. This calculation accords with qualitative arguments given above that the concentration gradient for K^+ is largely counteracted by the membrane voltage gradient; i.e., little energy is needed to carry 1 M. of K^+ across the membrane. $\mathcal{E}_K$ and $\mathcal{E}_s$ are not significantly different in this case, but there is good evidence, nevertheless, that K^+ are not quite at equilibrium in tissues (p. 22).

CHLORIDE IONS. The extracellular concentration of chloride is high, and its intracellular concentration is low. $[Cl^-]_i$ is difficult to estimate from analyses of the chloride content of the tissues, since these determinations include both extracellular and intracellular fluids, and most of the Cl^- is in the interstitial fluid. Since there is no strong evidence to the contrary, it is assumed here that the distribution of Cl^- ions is in equilibrium with the membrane voltage. Cl^- ions have a negative charge, so the electric field in the membrane drives Cl^- ions out of the cell and maintains a low internal concentration. Nernst's equation indicates this, since Z = -1 for Cl^- ions. The equilibrium voltage for these ions ($\mathcal{E}_{Cl}$) is given by the calculation $\mathcal{E}_{Cl} = [60/(-1)]$ log (120/3.8) = -90 mV. Actually, the value $[Cl^-]_i = 3.8$ μM. per cm.[3] was obtained by setting $\mathcal{E}_{Cl} = \mathcal{E}_s$ and solving for $[Cl^-]_i$.

SODIUM IONS. To a first approximation, K^+ and Cl^- ions are distributed across the membrane in equilibrium with the membrane voltage ($\mathcal{E}_{Cl} \simeq \mathcal{E}_s \simeq \mathcal{E}_K$). Two interpretations of this finding are possible: (i) the membrane voltage is generated by the existing concentration gradients of K^+ and Cl^- ions in the manner described above (p. 10), the mechanism whereby these concentration gradients are maintained not being specified, or (ii) the membrane voltage is maintained by unspecified means and the K^+ and Cl^- ions distribute themselves in equilibrium with the voltage. Even though these two possibilities cannot be differentiated at present, they highlight the question of how the resting potential and/or the concentration gradients are generated and maintained by the cell. The key to this question lies in the behavior of Na^+ ions. The high external Na^+ and low internal Na^+ concentrations are far out of equilibrium with the membrane voltage. Both the concentration gradient and the voltage gradient act to drive Na^+ into the cell. The Na^+ equilibrium potential $\mathcal{E}_{Na}$ is given by Nernst's equation: $\mathcal{E}_{Na} = (60/1) \log (145/12) = +65$ mV. This means that the membrane potential would have to be $+65$ mV. (inside positive) in order to counteract the inward concentration force on Na^+ ions, whereas $\mathcal{E}_m$ is actually -90 mV. (inside negative).

ACTIVE SODIUM TRANSPORT

Sodium Influx. Na^+ is distributed so far from equilibrium—i.e., $\Delta\mu_{Na}$ is so high—as to pose forcefully the question of how this disequilibrium is maintained in living cells. There are at least two possibilities. If Na^+ ions are unable to penetrate the membrane, the disequilibrium is only apparent and would persist indefinitely. If Na^+ can penetrate the membrane, some other energy term must be included in the calculation of the expected Na^+ distribution. The first possibility is simple and, therefore, attractive. However, it must be rejected, since studies with radioactive Na^+ have shown that these ions penetrate the membrane, although not so readily as K^+ and Cl^-. Therefore, the second possibility must be explored.

SODIUM TRACER EXPERIMENTS.[10, 11] The penetration of Na^+ through the membrane is demonstrated experimentally by placing a small muscle or a single large nerve cell into a solution with an ionic composition the same as that of the interstitial fluid, a radioactive isotope of Na^+ constituting part of the Na^+ ions. If Na^+ ions can penetrate the membrane, part of the nonradioactive Na^+ ions in the intracellular fluid will, in time, exchange positions with radioactive Na^+ ions in the bathing medium. The amount of radiosodium taken up by the muscle after a period of soaking is measured by counting the number of disintegrations per minute occurring in the tissue. The total entry during soaking can be ascertained by comparing the number of counts per minute from the muscle with the number of counts per minute from a known volume and the Na^+ concentration of the radioactive bathing medium. The result must, of course, be corrected for the amount of radiosodium in the interstitial fluid in the muscle and for the interstitial concentration of sodium. If the total surface area of all fibers in the muscle is known, the influx of Na^+ ions (mols per cm.^{2}-sec.) can be calculated.

Measured Na^+ ion influx in frog sartorius muscle is of the order of 10^{-11} M. per cm.^{2}-second.[11] If this influx were not matched by an equal outflux,* the internal Na^+ concentration in a muscle fiber 100 μ in diameter would increase at the rate of about 14 μM. per cm.^{3}-hour. Since Na^+_i is about 12 μM. per cm.^{3}, $[Na^+]_i$ would about double in the first hour.

Sodium Efflux. To return to the second possibility mentioned above, namely that another term is needed to balance influx and efflux of Na^+, there are three apparently contradictory facts about the behavior of Na^+ in tissues which must be considered. (i) The distribution of Na^+ in tissues is far from equilibrium. (ii) Na^+ ions can penetrate the cell membrane. (iii) This disequilibrium is maintained by living cells; $[Na^+]_i$ remains low and $\Delta\mu_{Na}$ remains high despite an appreciable influx of Na^+. Therefore, for some reason, Na^+ efflux must equal Na^+ influx; i.e., it is necessary to postulate that some force other than voltage and concentration gradients is expelling Na^+ from the cell at an average rate equal to the rate of passive entry.

Since Na^+ enters cells spontaneously, work must be done to carry Na^+ out of the cell. Further, Na^+ is entering all the time, so work must be continuously expended to eject the entering Na^+ and maintain a low $[Na^+]_i$. The power (time rate of supplying energy or of doing work) to eject Na^+ continually comes ultimately from the oxidation of glucose or other metabolites by the cell. *The process whereby the cell continuously uses metabolic energy to maintain an efflux of Na^+ is called active Na^+ transport* or, colloquially, *the Na^+ pump.*

The term "active transport" implies that the transport process requires a continuous

---

* The expected passive efflux is negligible, less than 1 per cent of influx.

supply of energy. By contrast, the diffusion of a substance down its electrochemical gradient is called "passive transport." The detailed mechanism involved in active Na^+ transport is not known. Nevertheless, in addition to the reasons given above for supposing there must be an active Na^+ transport, there is considerable direct experimental evidence that such a mechanism exists in many types of cells, e.g., giant nerve fibers of the squid,[10] human red blood cells[5, 6, 7] and frog skin (from outside to inside).[13, 15, 18] In addition, active Na^+ transport almost certainly occurs in all nervous tissue and all skeletal,[12] cardiac and smooth muscle. Active Na^+ reabsorption is probably the major energy-consuming process in the kidney. Na^+ pumping is also importantly involved in the formation of saliva and other ion-containing gastrointestinal secretions. Many substances besides Na^+ are actively transported by cells. The kidney is specialized for the active secretion or reabsorption of many inorganic and organic substances.

ENERGY REQUIREMENTS FOR ACTIVE SODIUM TRANSPORT. The postulate that the disequilibrium of Na^+ between cells and bathing medium is maintained through the expenditure of metabolic energy is subject to a stringent yet simple experimental test. The minimum power required to transport Na^+ out of a cell at the observed rate must be less than the rate of energy production of the cell. The rate of energy production can be calculated from the oxygen consumption of the cell. The minimum transport power is the product of the transport work per mol of Na^+ and the number of mols of Na^+ transported per second, i.e., the product of the negative of the electrochemical potential of Na^+ and the Na^+ efflux (M_{Na}^{out}). Thus, the Na^+ transport power ($\dot{W}_{Na}$)* is $\dot{W}_{Na} = - \Delta\mu_{Na} M_{Na}^{out}$. The negative sign is used in front of $\Delta\mu_{Na}$ because it is defined as the electrical and concentration work to carry 1 M. of Na^+ into the cell through the membrane; this work is, of course, the negative of the work to carry the Na^+ out. $\Delta\mu_{Na}$ is of the same form as $\Delta\mu_K$, given in equation 2, so

$$\dot{W}_{Na} = - \left(Z_{Na} F \mathcal{E}_m + RT \log_e \frac{[Na^+]_i}{[Na^+]_o} \right) M_{Na}^{out} \qquad (5)$$

Keynes and Maisel[12] have made the necessary measurements on frog skeletal muscle to test whether the Na^+ transport power requirement is less than the energy production rate of a cell. In one experiment, they obtained the following data:

$\mathcal{E}_m = - 88$ mV., $[Na^+]_o = 115$ μM. per cm.^{3}, $[Na^+]_i = 20$ μM. per cm.^{3}, $M_{Na}^{out} = 8.7$ μM.

per hour and per gram of muscle.† Energy production, calculated from oxygen consumption, was 0.17 calorie per hour and per gram of muscle. Substituting these values in equation 5 gives the value $\dot{W}_{Na} = 0.027$ calorie per hour and per gram of muscle as the power requirement for Na^+ transport, assuming 100 per cent efficiency for the process. In other words, a minimum of 15 per cent of the oxygen consumption of a noncontracting muscle is used to pump Na^+. Keynes and Maisel obtained values of about 10 per cent in most of their experiments. It should be borne in mind that the pumping efficiency is unlikely to be greater than about 50 per cent, so that at least 20 per cent of resting oxygen consumption, probably more, goes for Na^+ transportation. In any event, the energy demands of the Na^+ pump are not excessive, and the postulate of active Na^+ transport is possible energetically.

Active Sodium-Potassium Exchange. Although the detailed mechanism for utilization of metabolic energy to carry Na^+ out of the cell is not yet known, the process

---

* A dot over a symbol for a quantity means the time rate of change of the quantity; orally, such a symbol is referred to as "W-dot." Thus W_{Na} is work done on or energy of 1 M. of Na^+; $\dot{W}_{Na}$ is the time rate of doing work, or power.

† Strictly speaking this is not efflux, but it is the desired figure, since oxygen consumption is given in cubic millimeters per hour and per gram of tissue.

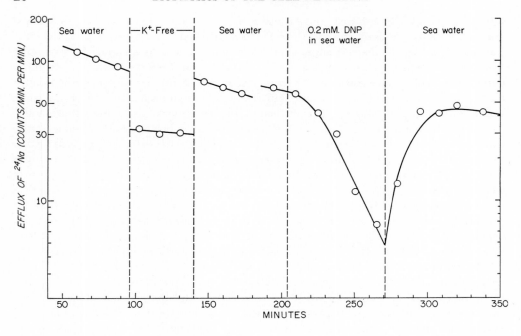

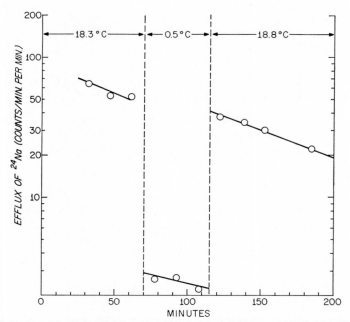

FIG. 5. Na$^+$ efflux in giant axon of *Sepia* (cuttlefish). Ordinates are efflux of radioactive Na$^+$ from cell; total (radioactive + normal) Na$^+$ of efflux is proportional to radioactive efflux except for gradual dilution of radioactive Na$^+$ by normal Na$^+$ as these ions exchange (the gradual fall shown under sea water).

Upper, Effects of various bathing media. Second column from left shows that reducing [K$^+$]$_o$ from 10 μM. per cm.^{3} to zero immediately reduces Na$^+$ efflux to about one-third that in artificial sea water; this effect is immediately reversed when the axon is returned to artificial sea water (middle column). Next, adding the metabolic inhibitor DNP reduces Na$^+$ efflux to values near zero within one to two hours; this effect is slowly reversible (right column).

Lower, The effects of temperature on another axon. Reduction of temperature from 18° to 0.5° C. immediately reduces Na$^+$ efflux to near zero; raising the temperature immediately restores efflux. (From Hodgkin and Keynes. *J. Physiol.,* 1955, *128:*28–60.)

has been intensively studied in many tissues and some of the broad characteristics of Na^+ pumping have been defined. These characteristics seem to be much the same in all the tissues studied. Hodgkin and Keynes[10] carefully investigated Na^+ and K^+ movements in giant axons (150 to 300 μ in diameter) of *Sepia* (cuttlefish). These findings form a compact summary of the present state of knowledge. (i) Na^+ efflux is roughly proportional to $[Na^+]_i$. (ii) Na^+ efflux is decreased to values near zero by the addition, at appropriate concentrations, of a metabolic inhibitor to the bathing medium (Fig. 5). Metabolic inhibitors are substances which block the metabolic cycle at some point. Such an inhibitor would be expected to stop Na^+ extrusion by depriving the pump of its source of energy. (iii) K^+ influx is greatly reduced by metabolic inhibitors. These inhibitors produce about equal decreases in K^+ influx and Na^+ efflux. (iv) Na^+ influx and K^+ efflux are not greatly affected by metabolic inhibitors. (v) Na^+ efflux is greatly reduced, but not abolished, by removal of K^+ from the external bathing medium (Fig. 5) and increases when $[K^+]_o$ is increased. (vi) Na^+ influx (Fig. 5) and K^+ efflux are highly temperature-dependent; a reduction in temperature markedly decreases the fluxes (Q_{10} of 3 to 4, i.e., a temperature reduction of $10°$ C. reduces these fluxes to 1/3 to 1/4 of their original values). On the other hand, Na^+ influx and K^+ efflux are relatively insensitive to temperature changes (Q_{10} from 1.1 to 1.4).

Figure 5 shows the effects of a K^+-free solution, of the metabolic inhibitor 2,4 dinitrophenol (DNP), and of low temperature on the Na^+ efflux of a *Sepia* axon. The ordinate, which indicates the number of disintegrations of radiosodium atoms per minute that occur among radiosodium ions that have left the cell in one minute, is nearly proportional to Na^+ efflux.* It can be seen that removal of K^+ from the bathing medium immediately reduces the Na^+ efflux to about 0.3 of its previous value. In contrast, the addition of DNP (0.2 μM. per cm.^{3}) reduces the efflux over a period of about one hour. The slow onset of the effect of DNP is attributed to the time required for the axon to consume the energy stores on hand when metabolism is inhibited.

These findings are strong evidence for the existence of an active Na^+ transport process in cells. Further, the findings suggest that there is also an active uptake of K^+ and that this uptake is coupled with Na^+ extrusion. A reduction in the amount of available energy, either by metabolic inhibitors or by temperature reduction, has parallel effects in reducing Na^+ efflux and K^+ influx. A coupled Na^+-K^+ exchange mechanism is also suggested by the reduction in Na^+ efflux when all the K^+ is removed from the bathing medium and the increase in Na^+ exit when $[K^+]_o$ is increased. However, since Na^+ efflux is 30 per cent of normal when $[K^+]_o = 0$, the linkage between Na^+ and K^+ is not rigid. The dependence of $[K^+]_o$ on Na^+ extrusion has been observed in a number of other tissues and the existence of such a relationship is presumptive evidence of a one-for-one Na^+-K^+ exchange. It will be assumed hereafter that all Na^+ pumping is coupled with an uptake of K^+. This assumption, although not strictly true, simplifies, without invalidating, deductions on the consequences of active Na^+ for K^+ transport. The effects of active inward K^+ transport on the distribution of K^+ will be discussed on page 23.

HYPOTHETICAL SCHEME OF SODIUM-POTASSIUM EXCHANGE. How does the cell use metabolic energy to extrude Na^+? The answer is not known, but it is worthwhile, for the sake of concreteness, to describe a specific model of Na^+-K^+ transport (Fig. 6). However, there are numerous other possible mechanisms, and there are insufficient

---

* The number of radioactive sodium ions in a sample is proportional to the number of counts per minute. After correction is made for the gradual dilution of the radioactive ions by inactive ones, the total number of Na^+ present is proportional to the number of radioactive Na^+ present. Counts per minute appearing in the external medium in one minute are thus of the form of mols per minute. Dividing by the surface area of the axon involved gives the flux in mols per cm.^{2}-minute.

experimental data at present to distinguish between the various possibilities. The most probable method of pumping Na^+ is to "disguise" or "smuggle" it, i.e., to let Na^+ diffuse through the membrane down a concentration gradient of an organo-Na^+ compound that is continuously produced inside the cell and destroyed outside the cell. Another way of saying this is that the "force other than the concentration and potential gradients" that was invoked on page 18 to explain the efflux of Na^+ is simply a concentration gradient, maintained by metabolism, of an organo-Na^+ compound.

Figure 6 is a scheme of a hypothetical Na^+-K^+ exchange mechanism that accounts for many of the known facts. Na^+ is carried out of the cell combined with a substance (Y) which has a high affinity for Na^+; that is, the reaction $Na^+ + Y = Na^+Y$ is far to the right. Y may or may not be ionized. Once outside the cell, or at the outer surface of the cell membrane, some of the Na^+Y dissociates into $Na^+ + Y$. Y is immediately converted into a K^+-specific carrier substance (X), the rate of the spontaneous reaction being increased by an enzyme on the outer surface of the cell membrane. X combines with K^+ and the K^+X diffuses into the cell under its own concentration gradient. The

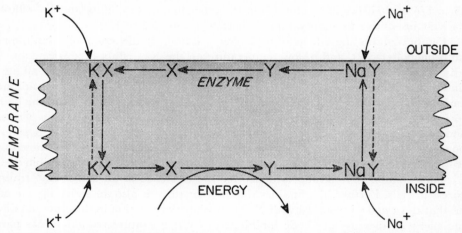

FIG. 6.   Hypothetical scheme of a Na^+-K^+ exchange pump. The substances X and Y are assumed to be confined to the membrane. X has a high affinity for K^+; Y has a high affinity for Na^+. X and Y move through the membrane only when in combination with an ion. (Modified from Shaw by Glynn. *Progr. Biophys.*, 1957, 8:241–307.)

X formed when K^+X dissociates inside the cell is converted to Y by an energy-requiring reaction, thus completing the transport cycle.

This scheme does not require a rigid Na^+-K^+ coupling. For instance, the maintenance of some Na^+ efflux when $[K^+]_o = 0$ may be explained by assuming that Na^+ has a slight affinity for the X substance. A carrier-mediated one-for-one exchange of Na^+ between inside and outside, called *exchange diffusion*, has also been advanced as a explanation of residual Na^+ efflux when $[K^+]_o = 0$ and of other phenomena (see Ussing[15, 18]).

GENERATION AND MAINTENANCE OF ION AND POTENTIAL DIFFERENCES

The more important factors affecting the movements of ions have been analyzed in the previous section. It should now be possible to explain the observed transmembrane concentration and voltage differences of cells solely in terms of these factors. In this section it will be shown (i) that the Na^+-K^+ exchange pump is sufficient to maintain voltages and concentrations at their observed values and (ii) how, starting with interstitial fluid on both sides of the membrane, a neutral Na^+-K^+ pump can establish the observed voltage and intracellular ion concentrations.

Although the picture presented here accounts in a highly satisfactory way for a large amount of our knowledge of these matters, it should be remembered that it is simplified and incomplete, for all membrane phenomena are not taken into account. The first part of this section describes the maintenance of the steady state; the second part describes the transient state—the changes occurring in potentials and concentrations during the build-up to the steady state. The terms "steady state" and "transient state" are defined at the appropriate places below.

Maintenance of Ionic Distributions by a Sodium-Potassium Pump. STEADY STATE. In this discussion of a cell system, the term *steady state* indicates that the concentrations and voltages are unvarying in time but that the system is not in equilibrium. Energy must be continuously expended to maintain the steady state. There is a steady flow of oxygen and glucose into the cell and a steady flow of carbon dioxide out of the cell. Substance Y is constantly made from X and flows out of the cell; X is made from Y and flows into the cell (Fig. 6). "Unchanging ionic concentrations" means that the net flux of each ion is zero. Thus the steady state condition occurs when the influx and efflux of a substance are equal if the substance is neither manufactured nor destroyed in the cell; otherwise net efflux is equal to the rate of production of the substance in the cell, or the net influx equals the rate of destruction in the cell. At equilibrium the influx and efflux of a substance are equal and passive; in the steady state the influx equals the efflux, although the fluxes may have both active and passive components.

POTASSIUM ION DISTRIBUTION. The one-way flux of an ion equals the sum of the passive and active fluxes. The influx of K^+ consists of a passive component, K^+ ions driven inward by the voltage gradient, and an active component, the inward leg of the Na^+-K^+ exchange pump. K^+ efflux is passive. If the steady state membrane potential ($\mathcal{E}_s$) were just equal to the K^+ equilibrium potential ($\mathcal{E}_K$), the passive fluxes would be equal; the active influx would thus be unbalanced, and $[K^+]_i$ would be increasing. Therefore, in the steady state, $\mathcal{E}_s$ cannot be as large a number as $\mathcal{E}_K$. In other words, $[K^+]_i$ must be larger than predicted from the Nernst equation in order to make the passive outflux equal to the summed passive and active influxes. The steady state values given in Table 1 show that $\mathcal{E}_K$ (-95 mV.) has a slightly larger negative value than $\mathcal{E}_s$ (-90 mV.). The difference need be no greater than this in the steady state, because of the relatively high permeability of the membrane to K^+ ions. A small increase in $[K^+]_i$ suffices to increase K^+ efflux enough to match the active influx. In view of the possible errors in the measurement of $[K^+]_i$ and $\mathcal{E}_s$, the difference between $\mathcal{E}_K$ and $\mathcal{E}_s$ is not significant. However, significant differences have been consistently found in other tissues; e.g., in frog muscle the difference is about 20 mV., which means that $[K^+]_i$ in these cells is about twice what it would be if $\mathcal{E}_K = \mathcal{E}_s$. In human red blood cells $\mathcal{E}_K$ is about -90 mV., whereas $\mathcal{E}_s$ is about -10 mV.

SODIUM ION DISTRIBUTION. Qualitatively, Na^+ distribution across the membrane is a mirror image of K^+ distribution: Na^+ low inside, K^+ low outside; Na^+ pumped out, K^+ pumped in; Na^+ high outside, K^+ high inside. The arguments concerning K^+ fluxes given in the preceding paragraph apply equally well to Na^+ fluxes simply by interchanging the words "influx" and "outflux" wherever they occur. Here, however, the symmetry ends. The membrane is about 50 times more permeable to K^+ than to Na^+. $[K^+]_i$ need be only slightly higher than at equilibrium to balance the active influx. However, because P_{Na} is low, $[Na^+]_i$ will fall to values much lower than the equilibrium value before the net inward driving force is large enough to make the passive influx equal active outflux. These arguments indicate that the steady state transmembrane potential is near $\mathcal{E}_K$, because P_K is much greater than P_{Na}, but they do not reveal what processes lead to the separation of charge across the membrane that generates $\mathcal{E}_s$.

Figure 7 is a schematic diagram which compactly summarizes the fluxes of Na^+

and K^+ ions in the steady state. Although the diagram is largely self-explanatory, it should be emphasized that the ordinate is the difference between the transmembrane potential and the equilibrium potential for either Na^+ or K^+ ions, i.e., an indication of the driving force on the ion. Cl^- and A^- ions are not discussed here nor included in the diagram, because Cl^- ions are probably distributed in equilibrium with $\mathcal{E}_s$ and because the membrane is assumed to be impermeable to A^- ions.

Generation of Membrane Potential by a Sodium-Potassium Pump. TRANSIENT STATE. If a system is not in a steady state—if some quantities are changing in time—then the system is in a *transient* or *changing state*. The transient state in a cell with respect to changes in ionic concentrations and membrane potential can be classified according to the rate at which these quantities change. For example, if in a steady state system,

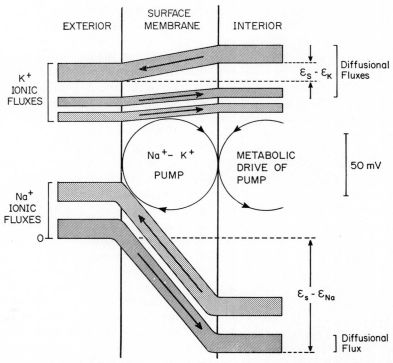

FIG. 7.   Active and passive Na^+ and K^+ fluxes through the membrane in the steady state. Ordinate is electrochemical potential of ion ($\mathcal{E}_s - \mathcal{E}_K$ for K^+, $\mathcal{E}_s - \mathcal{E}_{Na}$ for Na^+); abscissa is distance in vicinity of membrane. Width of band indicates size of that particular one way flux. Passive (downhill) and active (uphill) fluxes are distinguished by the shading of the bands. Passive efflux of Na^+ is negligible and is not shown. (After Eccles. *The physiology of nerve cells.* Baltimore, Johns Hopkins Press, 1957.)

$[K^+]_o$ is suddenly increased and $[Na^+]_o$ is decreased the same amount, the transient state preceding the establishment of a new steady state is characterized by two distinct transients: (i) a fast transient lasting a few milliseconds during which there is a net penetration of charge; i.e., some of the added K^+ ions cross the membrane and reduce the potential. However, the reduction in $\mathcal{E}_m$ increases K^+ efflux and Cl^- influx, and a new $\mathcal{E}_m$ in which concentrations and voltage change much more slowly is soon established. (ii) This slow transient lasts minutes or hours. During this time, the internal concentrations are changing toward their new steady state values. Some aspects of the slow transient are described here. Other aspects of it and the fast transient are discussed in Chapter 2.

SLOW TRANSIENT IN CELLS.   The existence of a steady potential difference between two points always means that electric charges have been separated. If the extrusion of a Na^+ ion is always accompanied by the uptake of a K^+ ion, how does this electrically neutral pump give rise to the transmembrane potential? This question can be conveniently answered by considering the sequence of changes that occurs when a Na^+-K^+ pump is started up in a hypothetical cell whose membrane potential is zero and whose intracellular fluid has nearly the same composition as the interstitial fluid. In this way, the processes which lead to the separation of charges across the membrane and to the establishment of ionic concentration differences will become evident.

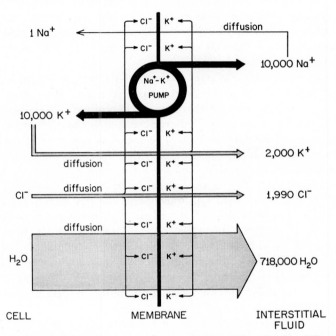

CELL   MEMBRANE   INTERSTITIAL
                                FLUID

FIG. 8. Simplified scheme of ion and water movements during the first jiffy of operation of a Na^+-K^+ pump in a hypothetical cell. Cell membrane is assumed to contain a one-for-one Na^+-K^+ exchange pump and to be 50 times more permeable to K^+ and Cl^- than to Na^+. Cell is assumed to have a large initial volume, and ionic compositions of interstitial and intracellular fluid are assumed to be the same except that the latter also contains K^+A^- at a low concentration. Width of arrow indicates size of flux. As shown, exchange of 10,000 Na^+ and 10,000 K^+ ions results in net movement of 8000 K^+ into cell and 9999 Na^+, 1990 Cl^- and 718,000 H_2O out of cell. Nine K^+ and Cl^- have separated, charging the membrane capacity (fine line branches from K^+ and Cl^- efflux lines). Operation of pump gradually reduces cell volume and increases ε_m; $[Cl^-]_i$ decreases and $[A^-]_i$ increases. In steady state, all net fluxes are zero and cell volume has decreased until $[A^-]_i$ is approximately equal to $[Cl^-]_o$. Na^+-K^+ pumping rate and membrane permeabilities in real cells are such that hours would be required to achieve steady state condition.

It is not possible to build up the observed steady state from an intracellular fluid having a composition identical to the interstitial fluid, because the cell finally has a high concentration of anions (A^-), absent from the bathing medium, which are unable to penetrate the membrane. This difficulty can be avoided by supposing that the hypothetical cell has an initial volume large compared to its final volume and that the cell fluid consists of interstitial fluid containing K^+A^- at a low concentration. The membrane is assumed to be perfectly elastic, to contain a Na^+-K^+ pump, and to have the same ion permeabilities as a real cell membrane. As will be shown below, operation of the pump gradually reduces cell volume until in the steady state the A^- ions have been concentrated to their observed high value (Table 1).

Figure 8 illustrates the changes that occur initially when the Na^+-K^+ pump is suddenly started at a fixed rate at some instant, $t = 0$. Suppose that in a jiffy* 10,000 Na^+ are extruded and that simultaneously 10,000 K^+ are taken into the cell through 0.1 mm.² of the membrane. This exchange slightly reduces $[Na^+]_i$ and increases $[K^+]_i$. Extracellular volume is assumed to be infinite, so the external concentrations are not altered by the exchange. Although the concentration gradients set up by this exchange are small, some of the pumped Na^+ will diffuse back into the cell and some of the K^+ will diffuse out of it. P_K is about 50 times as large as P_{Na}, so that, if the concentration gradients of Na^+ and K^+ were equal, the net flux of K^+ initially would be 50 times as great as the net flux of Na^+. However, $[K^+]_o$ is about 1/40 of $[Na^+]_o$ (Table 1). Since $[K^+]_i = [K^+]_o$ at the outset, an equal exchange of Na^+ and K^+ produces a change in $[K^+]_i$ 50 times greater than that in $[Na^+]_i$. The result of these two effects is that after 1 jiffy K^+ is diffusing out of the cell at about $50 \times 40 = 2000$ times the rate at which Na^+ is diffusing into the cell.

In the first jiffy following the start of the Na^+-K^+ pump, 10,000 ions each of Na^+ and K^+ are exchanged. Suppose that in this same jiffy 2000 K^+ diffuse out of the cell and only 1 Na^+ diffuses into the cell; therefore, 1999 positive charges have left the cell in the first jiffy (Fig. 8). These cations will charge the membrane capacity to some potential unless they are accompanied by anions. The membrane is highly permeable to Cl^- ions, which are present in high concentration; therefore, Cl^- will accompany most of the K^+ as they diffuse to the outside (i.e., the membrane voltage attracts anions to the positive side).

As a result of this concurrent Cl^- movement, the net membrane charge is quite small. For instance, suppose 1990 Cl^- moved through the membrane in the first jiffy. This leaves 9 K^+ in excess just outside the cell membrane and 9 Cl^- in excess just inside the membrane. The Cl^- will not completely neutralize the excess K^+, because the only force acting to move Cl^- out of the cell is the voltage gradient; therefore, the outside must be slightly positive to maintain the now slightly lower $[Cl^-]_i$. In other words, the concentration gradients of K^+ and Cl^- both act to maintain a transmembrane potential which is inside negative.

The net ionic movements at the end of 1 jiffy of operation of the Na^+-K^+ pump are as follows: Na^+, 10,000 ions out via the pump -1 ion diffusing in $=$ net of 9999 ions out; K^+, 10,000 ions in via the pump -2000 ions out by diffusion $=$ net of 8000 ions in; Cl^-, 1990 ions out by diffusion in company with K^+; net membrane charge, $+9$ (K^+ ions) outside and -9 (Cl^- ions) inside; $\mathcal{E} = q/C = 1.4 \times 10^{-10}$ V. The generation of a membrane voltage by a neutral Na^+-K^+ pump results largely, then, from the difference in membrane permeability to Na^+ and K^+.

In addition to the ion movements, water will also move out of the cell during the first jiffy. The cell has lost a net of 1999 cations (9999 Na^+ out $-$ 8000 K^+ in) and 1990 Cl^- ions. Thus, 3989 particles dissolved in water have left the cell. This exit increases the concentration of water in the cell, so that a slight gradient develops across the membrane. Since the membrane is highly permeable to water, this gradient forces water out of the cell. Each liter (55.5 M.) of water in extracellular fluid contains 0.31 M. of particles. For every particle that leaves the cell, $55.5/0.31 = 180$ molecules of water must also leave. Therefore, $180 \times 3989 = 718,000$ water molecules leave the cell in the first jiffy. One jiffy's operation of the Na^+-K^+ pump results, then, in a net loss of Na^+, Cl^- and water and a net gain of K^+ by the cell and an increase in $[A^-]_i$.

In the second and each succeeding jiffy following the start of the Na^+-K^+ pump, 10,000 more Na^+ and 10,000 more K^+ ions are pumped across the membrane. There is now a small potential difference across the membrane which hinders the back diffusion

* A "jiffy" is a short length of time—in this case about 1 millionth of a second if the cell has a surface area of 0.1 mm.².

of K^+ and helps the back diffusion of Na^+. However, $[K^+]_i$ increases and $[Na^+]_i$ decreases. The resulting concentration gradients have opposite and larger effects on the movements of K^+ and Na^+ than does membrane voltage, since $\mathcal{E}_m$ originates from them. For example, some time later when the potential is 18 mV. ($= 60 \log_{10}2$), $[K^+]_i$ is about three times $[K^+]_o$, and 1000 K^+ ions will diffuse out and 2 Na^+ into the cell in a jiffy. The voltage increases slightly during each jiffy, causing more Cl^- to move out, and water accompanies the Na^+ and Cl^-. The changes in concentration, voltage and volume are smaller in each succeeding jiffy. The net extrusion of Na^+, Cl^- and water reduces the cell volume and, therefore, increases $[A^-]_i$. In other words, as $[Cl^-]_i$ decreases, $[A^-]_i$ increases equally. Eventually, a steady state is reached in which the net fluxes of Na^+, K^+, Cl^- and water are zero, the membrane potential is constant, and $[A^-]_i$ is about equal to $[Cl^-]_o$.

Factors determining steady state potential. The steady state value of the transmembrane potential depends on the ratio of P_{Na} to P_K. Suppose that, in a cell in the steady state, P_{Na} were suddenly decreased or P_K increased. Immediately and transiently, outflow of K^+ would exceed inflow of Na^+; thus more charges would be separated across the membrane, and $\mathcal{E}_s$ would increase. In the new steady state, $\mathcal{E}_s$ is increased and $[Na^+]_i$ is decreased. The second factor that determines $\mathcal{E}_s$ is the rate of Na^+ pumping. In the absence of a Na^+-K^+ pump, the steady state membrane voltage is near zero—so, conversely, the higher the pumping rate, the higher the $\mathcal{E}_s$.

Factors determining cell volume. The volume of a cell depends directly on the number of particles dissolved in the cell water. Since the membrane is highly permeable to water, there can be no concentration gradient of water across the membrane in the steady state, provided, of course, that water is not actively transported. As a result, the concentration of water in the cell equals the concentration in the bathing fluid. The greater the number of dissolved particles per unit volume of solution, the lower the concentration of water; so an equivalent statement of the equality of water concentrations is that total solute concentrations are equal.

A large fraction of the substances dissolved in interstitial and intracellular water is ionized. In the cell, A^- constitute about half of the dissolved particles. Because A^- ions cannot penetrate the membrane, and because they do not exist in appreciable quantities outside the cell, cell volume would be very large in the absence of Na^+ pumping. Operation of the Na^+ pump reduces $[Na^+]_i$, and the consequent development of a membrane potential reduces $[Cl^-]_i$. A net exit of NaCl reduces the cell volume correspondingly. Since the total amount of A^- in a cell is relatively fixed, cell volume changes reflect changes in $[Cl^-]_i$, which in turn depends on $\mathcal{E}_s$. However, if $\mathcal{E}_s$ is 60 mV. or greater, $[Cl^-]_i = 0.1\ [Cl^-]_o$. A rather large reduction in $\mathcal{E}_s$ is therefore required to increase cell volume appreciably; e.g., at $\mathcal{E}_s = 18$ mV. cell volume would be increased about 50 per cent. On the basis of the simple picture of ion transport developed here, it is seen that the Na^+-K^+ pump not only maintains the transmembrane differences in ion concentration and potential, but also prevents swelling and bursting of the cells.

Red blood cells.[5, 6, 7] Human red cells have an interesting pattern of intracellular electrolyte concentrations: $[Na^+]_i = 20\ \mu M.$ per cm.³, $[K^+]_i = 140\ \mu M.$ per cm.³ and $[Cl^-]_i = 80\ \mu M.$ per cm.³. The intracellular concentrations of Na^+ and K^+ are about the same as those in muscle, but $[Cl^-]_i$ is much higher than it is in muscle. Also, the red cell membrane is several thousand times more permeable to Cl^- and HCO_3^- than it is to K^+ or Na^+. The high anion permeability is important for the carrying of carbon dioxide by the blood (Chap. 24). The ionic distribution of red cells is easily explained by supposing that the cell membrane has a Na^+-K^+ exchange pump and that the membrane is nearly as permeable to Na^+ as to K^+. If it is assumed that Cl^- and HCO_3^- are passively distributed, then the transmembrane potential is: $\mathcal{E}_s = \mathcal{E}_{Cl} = 60 \log_{10}80/120$

$= -10$ mV. As pointed out above, $\mathcal{E}_s$ depends on the ratio of P_{Na} to P_K; the higher P_{Na}/P_K, the lower $\mathcal{E}_s$.

There is considerable evidence for the existence of a Na^+-K^+ exchange pump in red cells. Indeed, some of the earliest evidence of this type of pumping process was found in red cells.[7] Flux measurements indicate that ion movements are more complex than expected from this simple explanation, but there seems little doubt that it is generally correct. Because of the high $[Cl^-]_i$ and high P_{Cl}, the cell is quite liable to rather large, rapid changes in volume.[6] However, these cells can swell considerably without bursting, owing to their shape, biconcave discs.

CALCULATION OF STEADY STATE POTENTIAL. The dependence of $\mathcal{E}_s$ and cell volume (V_c) on P_{Na}/P_K and the Na^+ pumping rate can be calculated approximately by making certain assumptions: (i) Total cellular A^- content is known. (ii) P_{Na} and P_K are known. (iii) All Na^+ extrusion is by means of a one-to-one Na^+ and K^+ exchange. (iv) The rate of active Na^+ extrusion (M_{Na}^{out}) is directly proportional to $[Na^+]_i$; $M_{Na}^{out} = j_{Na}[Na^+]_i$, where j_{Na} is the specific active transport rate of Na^+; j_{Na} has the unit of permeability. This assumption, although approximately correct at near normal $[Na^+]_i$,[10] must be incorrect for high $[Na^+]_i$ because the energy requirements are excessive. Since excitable cells need to maintain a low $[Na^+]_i$ (Chap. 2), it seems reasonable that an increase in $[Na^+]_i$ should increase the active efflux of Na^+ at least proportionately. (v) The quantitative effects of membrane voltage on ionic fluxes are known. Equations based on these assumptions give $\mathcal{E}_s$ and V_c in terms of external ion concentrations, the total amount of intracellular A^- and its valence (Z_A), and the ratios j/P_{Na} and P_{Na}/P_K. However, in most cells (but not in red cells) Z_A is about 1 and j/P_{Na} is so large that $\mathcal{E}_s$ and V_c do not depend on the exact value of j/P_{Na}. In this case, the steady state transmembrane potential and the cell volume are given by the following equations.

$$\mathcal{E}_s = -\frac{RT}{F} \log_e \frac{[Na^+]_o + [K^+]_o}{[K^+]_o + \frac{P_{Na}}{P_K}[Na^+]_o} \tag{6}$$

$$V_c = \frac{A^-}{[Na^+]_o \left(1 - \frac{P_{Na}}{P_K}\right)} \tag{7}$$

These equations are somewhat more complicated if Z is not equal to 1, or if j_{Na}/P_{Na} is less than about 100. The term $(P_{Na}/P_K)[Na^+]_o$ can be considered an effective external Na^+ concentration. From the values in Table 1, $P_{Na}/P_K = 1/650$ for mammalian skeletal muscle. The equation for cell volume shows that V_c is quite constant for values of P_{Na}/P_K much less than 1. If $P_{Na}/P_K = 1$, cell volume is infinite, as expected. These equations are only approximately correct, but they clearly indicate the important factors in the determination of $\mathcal{E}_s$ and V_c.

Intracellular pH.[1, 2] The concentrations of hydrogen (H^+) and bicarbonate (HCO_3^-) ions in the interior of the cell are not those that would be expected from the external concentrations and the membrane potential; i.e., these ions are not at equilibrium with $\mathcal{E}_s$. With glass electrodes, Caldwell[1] measured directly the intracellular pH in crab muscle fibers. The intracellular pH (pH_i) is normally about 7.0, as compared with the $pH_o = 7.4$ of the blood plasma. (By definition, $pH = -\log_{10}[H^+]$, so $[H^+]_i = 10^{-7}$ M. per liter or mM. per cm.[3].) This value agrees well with indirect measurements in other tissues. If H^+ were distributed in accordance with membrane voltage, $[H^+]_i$ would be about 30 times $[H^+]_o$, or pH_i would be $-\log (30\ H_o) = pH_o - \log 30 = 5.9$.

H^+ and HCO_3^- combine to form carbonic acid: $H^+ + HCO_3^- = H_2CO_3$. H_2CO_3 in turn decomposes into water and carbon dioxide: $H_2CO_3 = H_2O + CO_2$. CO_2 is constantly produced in cellular metabolism, and the cellular concentration of CO_2 is approximately constant. In effect, there is an unlimited supply of CO_2 and, thus, of H_2CO_3. $[H_2CO_3]_i$ depends on the metabolic rate and rate of conversion to CO_2 and is constant. From the law of mass action, $[H^+]_i[HCO_3^-]_i = K[H_2CO_3]_i$, where K is the dissociation constant of carbonic acid. Therefore, the product $[H^+]_i[HCO_3^-]_i$ is a constant, so a decrease in the concentration of one causes an increase in the concentration of the other. Since $[H^+]_i$ is about ten times lower than expected from $[H^+]_o$ and $\mathcal{E}_s$, $[HCO_3^-]_i$ is about ten times greater than expected. (Measurement of tissue CO_2 content is one basis for indirect estimates of pH_i.)

ACTIVE H^+ TRANSPORT.[2] If either or both H^+ and HCO_3^- can penetrate the membrane, the disequilibrium between the external and internal concentrations of H^+ and HCO_3^- leads to the assumption that one or both ions are actively transported—H^+ out of the cell or HCO_3^- into the cell. This assumption is made more necessary because the production of CO_2 inside the cell should tend to increase $[H^+]_i$ above equilibrium values. Nothing is known of the mechanism for active transport of H^+ or HCO_3^-, but it seems more probable that H^+ is transported out of the cell than that HCO_3^- is moved into it. A simple hypothesis to explain H^+ transport is to assume that H^+ has some affinity for the Na^+ carrier substance Y (Fig. 6): $H^+ + Y = H^+Y$. It is supposed that H^+Y can penetrate the membrane as readily as Na^+Y can.

If H^+ is transported by the Na^+-K^+ pump, what are the relative rates of transport for Na^+ and H^+? An upper limit on transport of H^+ can be estimated from the data of Keynes and Maisel,[12] who measured Na^+ efflux and O_2 consumption of frog muscle. If it is assumed that one CO_2 molecule is produced for every O_2 molecule consumed, then about four Na^+ ions are ejected from the cell for every CO_2 molecule produced. Even if all the CO_2 produced in the cell were to leave it as H^+ (in the pump) and HCO_3^-, only about 20 per cent of the Na^+-K^+ pump would have to be devoted to extrusion of H^+.

The number of H^+ that must be ejected each second (flux) is not known, but it is much less than the total production of CO_2, because membrane permeability to CO_2 is much greater than membrane permeability to the ion. Most of the CO_2 will leave the cell as rapidly as it is produced, and $[CO_2]_i$ need be only slightly larger than $[CO_2]_o$ to make net CO_2 efflux equal to the rate at which CO_2 is produced.

The same considerations apply to H^+ as to Na^+ as far as internal concentrations are concerned. The smaller the membrane permeability to H^+ (P_H) and to HCO_3^- (P_{HCO_3}) the smaller is the active H^+ efflux needed to maintain constant $[H^+]_i$. P_H is difficult to measure experimentally because of the dissociation of water. A lower limit on the H^+ pumping rate can be obtained by assuming $P_{HCO_3} = 0$.* If P_H is about the same as P_{Na}, then only one H^+ need be pumped for every four million Na^+. Because of the small radius of hydrated H^+ (H_3O^+), the permeability of the membrane to these ions is probably at least as great as P_K. In most tissues P_K is about 100 times P_{Na}. If $P_H = P_K$, then one H^+ must be transported out of the cell for every 40,000 Na^+—still a negligible quantity. However, the affinity of H^+ for the Na^+ carrier Y must be rather high, about equal to its affinity for Na^+.

INTERNAL pH AND CELL VOLUME. Cell volume (V_c) depends, critically, on both $(Cl^-)_i$ and $[H^+]_i$. $[Cl^-]_i$ is determined by $\mathcal{E}_s$, which depends on Na^+ transport, and $[H^+]_i$ depends on H^+ transport. Since V_c is directly proportional to the total number of solute particles within the cell, any change that increases the total number of these particles increases V_c. A reduction of $\mathcal{E}_m$ increases V_c because Cl^- enter. An increase in pH$_i$ also increases the total number of solute particles within the cell because the internal anion A^- is a weak acid.† A exists as the anion A^- and as HA, the two forms being in equilibrium, $HA = H^+ + A^-$. The concentration of each form depends on $[H^+]_i$; if pH$_i$ were lowered by the addition of a strong acid (most easily accomplished by raising the $[CO_2]_o$ since H_2CO_3 is nearly all dissociated at normal pH$_i$), the above reaction would be forced to the left. Addition of acid decreases the average valence (Z_A) of A^-. The complete reaction is:

$$H_2CO_3$$
$$\downarrow$$
$$H^+ + HCO_3^- + K^+ + A^- = HA + \underbrace{K^+ + HCO_3^-}_{\text{may diffuse out of cell}}$$

* The assumption of a zero P_{HCO_3} is not realistic because $[HCO_3^-]_i$ is 100,000 times $[H^+]_i$, and even a small P_{HCO_3} could allow large numbers of HCO_3^- to leave the cell by diffusion compared to the number of H^+ diffusing in. Thus active H^+ efflux or HCO_3^- influx would have to be much larger.

† A^- is not one substance. In the giant axon of the squid, A^- consists largely of isethionate; aspartate, glutamate, succinate and fumarate are also present. It seems likely that amino acids, amino acid derivatives and phosphates are the principal anions in other tissues as well.

The result is an eventual relative decrease in the number of solute particles in the cell. Some of the A^- have combined with H^+ to form HA; the K^+ which matched the A^- now have HCO_3^- for counter ions. The K^+ and HCO_3^- may diffuse slowly out of the cell, taking water with them (but see Harris[6]). The result would be a slow decrease in the total number of solute particles in the cell and a corresponding decrease in the cell volume.

The expected effects on a cell of an increase in $[CO_2]_o$ are an immediate fall in pH_i[2] and an immediate small increase or decrease in V_c. These immediate effects cause a slow fall in V_c. On the other hand, the addition of HCl to the interstitial fluid with $[CO_2]_o$ kept constant causes at most a slow fall in pH_i and a correspondingly slow fall in V_c, because the passive influx of H^+ (or efflux of HCO_3^-) is small and may be counteracted by increased H^+ pumping.

Animal cells and their surrounding connective tissue supportive structures do not have sufficient tensile strength to oppose changes in cell volume by developing a counter-balancing hydrostatic pressure across the cell membrane. It must be supposed, then, that the animal cell has rather elaborate mechanisms for preventing rupture of the cell membrane as a result of swelling. Partial failure of the Na^+-K^+ pump tends to increase V_c because of the increase in $[Cl^-]_i$, especially in cells with a low $\mathcal{E}_m$; but a concomitant failure of a linked H^+ extrusion has a counteracting effect, because a falling pH_i may eventually decrease V_c. It is also likely that the cell can change its total A^- content over a long period. Much of the discussion in this section is speculative. However, it has been included because the regulation of pH_i and V_c is important to an understanding of some aspects of the normal and pathologic physiology of cells.

REFERENCES

1. CALDWELL, P. C. *J. Physiol.*, 1954, *126*:169–180.

2. CALDWELL, P. C. *Int. Rev. Cytol.*, 1956, *5*:229–277.

3. ECCLES, J. C. *The physiology of nerve cells.* Baltimore, Johns Hopkins Press, 1957, xi, 270 pp.

4. FINEAN, J. B. *Exp. Cell Res.*, 1958, Suppl. *5*:18–32.

5. GLYNN, I. M. *Progr. Biophys.*, 1957, *8*:241–307.

6. HARRIS, E. J. *Transport and accumulation in biological systems.* New York, Academic Press, 1956, ix, 291 pp.

7. HARRIS, E. J. and MAIZELS, M. *J. Physiol.*, 1951, *113*:506–524.

8. HODGKIN, A. L. *Biol. Rev.*, 1951, *26*:339–409.

9. HODGKIN, A. L. *Proc. roy. Soc.*, 1957, *B148*:1–37, pl. 1.

10. HODGKIN, A. L. and KEYNES, R. D. *J. Physiol.*, 1955, *128*:28–60.

11. KEYNES, R. D. *Proc. roy. Soc.*, 1954, *B142*:359–382.

12. KEYNES, R. D. and MAISEL, G. W. *Proc. roy. Soc.*, 1954, *B142*:383–392.

13. KOEFOED-JOHNSEN, V. and USSING, H. H. *Acta physiol. scand.*, 1958, *42*:298–308.

14. LING, G. and GERARD, R. W. *J. cell. comp. Physiol.*, 1949, *34*:383–396.

15. MURPHY, Q. R., ed. *Metabolic aspects of transport across cell membranes.* Madison, University of Wisconsin Press, 1957, xxiv, 379 pp.

16. SCHMITT, F. O. *Exp. Cell Res.*, 1958, Suppl. *5*:33–57.

17. SHANES, A. M. *Pharmacol. Rev.*, 1958, *10*:59–164.

18. *Symp. Soc. exp. Biol.*, 1954, *8*:vii, 516 pp.

SECTION II

Nerve and Muscle

CHAPTER 2

Action Potential; Cable and Excitable Properties of the Cell Membrane

By J. WALTER WOODBURY *and* HARRY D. PATTON

THE initiation and propagation of the nerve impulse is a subject which has been greatly illuminated in recent years by fundamental physiologic discoveries, the invention of ingenious recording techniques and the application of physics and mathematics. It is a phase of physiology which has become quantitative. Unfortunately, the physical explanations of subcellular neural functions are not easily comprehended. For this reason the present chapter is divided into two sections. In the first the important facts and phenomena of nerve impulse initiation and propagation are presented descriptively with some indication of the direction in which the explanations and proofs lie. The second section covers much the same territory, presenting the physical explanations necessary for a basic understanding of the phenomena described in the first half of the chapter.

In Chapter 1 it was emphasized that the ability to separate charged ions is a property common to the membranes of all living cells. Because of this property steady transmembrane potentials are developed and maintained. In addition the membranes of some cells possess the highly distinctive additional property of excitability. In excitable cells, an environmental change (called a *stimulus*) may bring about a transient change in the ionic permeability of the membrane. In turn, this transient alteration of permeability brings about a transient change in the transmembrane potential. Nerve cells (neurons), muscle cells and gland cells are the three major types of excitable cells.

In elongated excitable cells, such as those of nerve and muscle tissue, the change initiated by the stimulus is not confined to the site of the stimulus. Once aroused, the change is propagated rapidly from the stimulus site to adjacent regions of the membrane and thus is spread as a wave over the membrane of the entire cell. This property is known as *conductivity* or *self-propagation*. The propagated disturbance is known as an *impulse;* its electrical manifestation is called the *action potential*. Nerve and muscle cells, because of their excitable and conductive properties, are thus adapted to the transmission of messages (impulses) from one part of the body to another, and these messages constitute the basis of adaptive behavior to environmental changes or stimuli.

A simple, concrete example may serve to illustrate how the nervous system detects changes in the environment and transmits messages to the muscles which, by contraction, initiate appropriate movement. If the hand touches a hot object, the muscles of the arm contract so that the hand is withdrawn and tissue damage is either avoided or limited. Although this adaptive response occupies only a fraction of a second, it can be shown that the following sequence of events, illustrated diagrammatically in Figure 9, takes

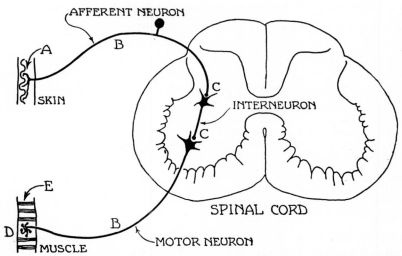

FIG. 9. Diagram of simple reflex arc. Excitation of afferent neurons occurs at point *A*. Conduction of impulses takes place in nerve fibers, *B*. Impulses are conducted toward central nervous system in the afferent fibers and away from central nervous system in motoneurons. Synaptic transmission between neurons occurs at *C*. Neuromuscular transmission occurs at *D*. Contraction occurs in muscle fiber, *E*.

place. The stimulus (heat and tissue damage) initiates impulses in nerve endings in the skin (*A*). Once initiated, these impulses are propagated over the *afferent nerve fibers* which traverse the dorsal root to reach the spinal cord, where they make connections with a second nerve cell, an *interneuron*. The impulse in the intraspinal afferent endings constitutes a stimulus to the interneuron, and the resulting impulse is propagated to a third neuron, the *motor* or *efferent neuron*, in which an impulse is generated. The latter impulse is propagated over the ventral root to the muscle, where it constitutes the stimulus giving rise to a muscle impulse which then spreads rapidly over the membrane of the muscle cell. Coincidentally with the spread of the impulse over the muscle membrane the contractile elements are activated and movement occurs. The entire system including the afferent neuron, the interneuron, the motor neuron and the muscle is a simple *reflex arc.* In more complex reflex systems many interneurons may be interposed. More-over, the final effector organ need not be the skeletal muscle (*somatic reflex arc*), as in the illustrative example, but may be smooth muscle, heart muscle or gland tissue (*autonomic reflex arc*).

The somatic reflex arc is the physiologic mechanism by which the organism reacts adaptively to its external environment. Autonomic reflex arcs are responsible for auto-matic adjustments of visceral structures (e.g., the heart and blood vessels)—adjustments which adapt the organism not only to external environmental changes (e.g., tempera-ture) but also to internal environmental changes occasioned by somatic behavior (e.g., exercise). The principle of the reflex arc thus permeates all phases of physiology and is therefore treated in some detail in the initial chapters of this book.

For this purpose it is convenient to break the reflex arc up into its component parts. In this and the next chapter the nature of the message, i.e., the impulse and the way in which it is initiated, is considered. In Chapter 4 the transfer of the message from nerve to muscle, the muscle membrane, and the contractile mechanism of muscle are described (*D* and *E* in Fig. 9). Chapter 5 deals with the mechanism of excitation of nerve cell by nerve cell (*C* in Fig. 9), and Chapters 6, 9 and 10 describe synthetically the functional organization of somatic and autonomic reflex regulatory systems.

ELECTRICAL PHENOMENA AT REST AND IN ACTION[5,7]

It has been recognized for more than a century that the nerve impulse is an elec-trical phenomenon. A clear picture of the mechanism of the action potential was not developed, however, until critical experiments were made possible by intracellular recording techniques, which were introduced independently in 1939–1940 by Cole and Curtis in the United States and by Hodgkin and Huxley in England.

Direct measurement of transmembrane potentials was delayed until this late date because most mammalian nerve and muscle fibers are exceedingly small (usually less than 100 μ in diameter) and hence difficult to penetrate with a recording electrode. In 1936, J. Z. Young discovered in the squid and cuttlefish giant nerve fibers or axons as large as 1 mm. in diameter. With such large nerve fibers it is relatively easy to introduce an internal electrode longitudinally down the axon and measure its potential with respect to an externally located electrode. Also, sufficient quantities of axoplasm can be extracted from the giant axon to permit chemical analysis. The first studies of transmembrane potentials of "resting" and "excited" nerve fibers were made on such giant fibers. Subsequently, with the development of ultramicroelectrodes (see Chap. 1), it became possible to confirm in mammalian nerve and muscle fibers many of the observations made on giant axons.

The Resting or Steady Potential.   Like other cells, nerve and muscle fibers main-tain a steady potential (inside negative) across their membranes. This steady potential is usually referred to as the *resting potential* to distinguish it from the action potential. In Chapter 1 it was shown that the size of the resting potential generated by the sodium-potassium pump depends largely on the relative permeability of the membrane to sodium and potassium ions; the greater the ratio of the permeability to potassium to the permeability to sodium, the greater the potential. In nerve and muscle this ratio is quite high, about 50 to 1, and the resting potential is -70 to -90 mV. In the steady state chloride anions are distributed in equilibrium with the resting potential, while the in-ternal sodium concentration is much lower and the internal potassium concentration higher than expected from the membrane potential.

Since the membrane is relatively highly permeable to potassium, the resting po-tential may be greatly altered by changing the concentration of potassium in the medium bathing an excised nerve or muscle. An increase in the external concentration of potas-sium ions momentarily increases their influx and thus reduces the membrane charge and potentials. Thus in response to changes in the external potassium concentration the cell behaves much as though it were permeable only to potassium, i.e., like a potassium electrode. This is particularly true at higher external concentrations of potassium and, to a fair approximation, the resting potential equals the equilibrium potential of potassium. In 1902, Bernstein advanced the view that the resting potential arises from the potassium concentration gradient. He based his hypothesis on the finding that the injury potential (which is proportional to the resting potential) is directly proportional to the absolute temperature. However, the variation of the membrane potential with the external potassium concentration constitutes the strongest evidence for Bernstein's view. Although this view is incomplete in the light of present knowledge, it has had to be modified only in the past few years.[21] The effects of external potassium concentration on the resting potential of excised skeletal muscle are shown in Figure 10. Since $\mathcal{E}_K = 58$ $\log_{10}[K^+]_o/[K^+]_i$, a plot of the resting potential against the logarithm of the external potassium concentration will give a straight line with a slope of 58 mV. per tenfold change in external potassium concentration if the transmembrane potential is really a potassium equilibrium potential.

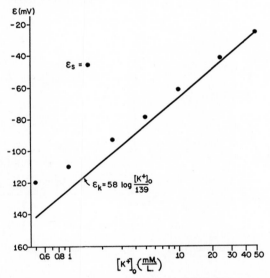

FIG. 10. Immediate changes in steady transmembrane potential ($\mathcal{E}_s$) of frog sartorius muscle fibers produced by alterations in external potassium concentration, $[K^+]_o$. *Abscissa*, $[K^+]_o$ on a logarithmic scale; *ordinate*, $\mathcal{E}_s$, potential of intracellular fluid minus potential of extracellular fluid. Points are experimental results. Straight line is plot of equilibrium potential for potassium, $\mathcal{E}_K$. Note that at high values of $[K^+]_o$, $\mathcal{E}_s$ changes with $\mathcal{E}_K$ and that at K^+ concentrations in normal range, $\mathcal{E}_s$ changes less rapidly than $\mathcal{E}_K$. (After Adrian. *J. Physiol.*, 1956, *133*:631–658.)

The solid points show the measured membrane potential for different values of $[K^+]_o$, the latter being plotted on a logarithmic scale; the solid line shows the relation between $\mathcal{E}_K$ and $[K^+]_o$ calculated from the Nernst equation. In accordance with the hypothesis, the membrane potential diminishes as $[K^+]_o$ increases, and when $[K^+]_o = [K^+]_i$ the membrane potential is zero. Moreover, through a considerable range, the membrane potential varies linearly with $\log [K^+]_o$, as predicted from the Nernst equation. However, at low values of $[K^+]_o$ (near the normal values for extracellular fluid) the curve deviates from linearity, and increments of $[K^+]_o$ cause less than the expected change in the potential. This deviation of observed from calculated values reflects the action of the Na^+-K^+ pump. With normal and near normal values of $[K^+]_o$, a significant part of the K^+ influx is propelled by the pump. At higher values of $[K^+]_o$ the *proportion* of the total K^+ influx due to the steady action of the pump is diminished, and the membrane potential approaches $\mathcal{E}_K$, as predicted from the Nernst equation.

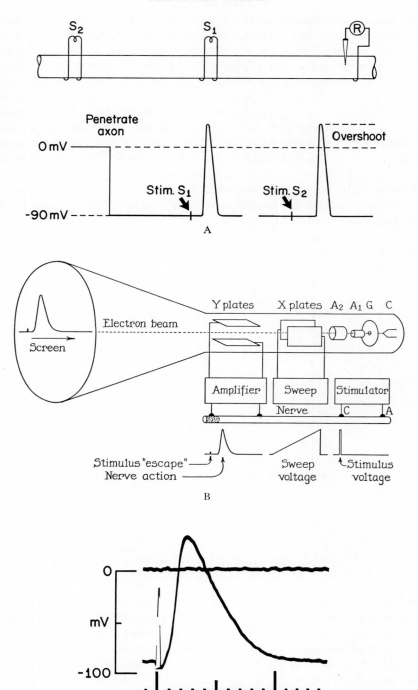

FIG. 11. *See facing page for legend.*

Recording the Action Potential. When a brief electric current* is passed outward through the membrane of an axon or a muscle cell, the membrane potential undergoes a sequence of changes which is peculiar and unique to excitable cells. This sequence constitutes the *action potential*.

Figure 11 shows diagrammatically the experimental arrangement for eliciting and recording an action potential in a nerve fiber and introduces the symbols for a stimulator with its electrodes and the recording device with its leads. The fiber is supplied with two pairs of stimulating electrodes (S_1 and S_2) placed at different distances from the recording site (R). When the microelectrode penetrates the axon, the steady or resting potential is registered. When a brief electric shock (signaled by the shock artefact) is applied to the nerve through S_1, the membrane potential decreases rapidly toward zero but *overshoots, so that for a brief period the membrane potential is reversed*, i.e., the inside becomes positive to the outside. Thereafter the potential reverts somewhat more slowly to the resting level. The action potential of a cat dorsal root fiber is shown in Figure 11. For such large myelinated fibers the duration of the action potential is 0.5 to 0.6 millisecond, and the total amplitude is often 120 mV. the overshoot accounting for 30 mV. When the shock is applied at the more distant electrode S_2 rather than at S_1, the sequence of events is exactly the same, except that the *latency* (time interval between shock artefact and the beginning of the action potential) is longer. Systematic investigation reveals that this latency is directly related to the distance between the stimulating and recording electrodes. The action potential is thus revealed as a brief potential reversal of the membrane, beginning at the stimulating electrodes and sweeping at a constant speed as a wave along the axon.

* Excitable tissues may also be stimulated by mechanical or chemical means; but in experimental work electrical stimuli are almost exclusively used, because the intensity can be easily and quantitatively varied and because mild electrical stimuli, even when repeated many times, do not damage the tissue.

FIG. 11. *A, upper,* Schematic diagram illustrating a method for studying electrical activity of nerve fibers. Two pairs of stimulating electrodes, S_1 and S_2, are applied to a dissected nerve trunk at different distances from recording microelectrode (*far right*). Microelectrode may be inserted into any fiber in trunk. *Lower,* Diagram of sequence of potential changes recorded by microelectrode inserted into a fiber when nerve trunk is stimulated by short shocks applied first at S_1 and then at S_2. *Abscissa,* Time of order of a few milliseconds; *ordinate,* transmembrane potential in millivolts. When microelectrode is inserted into a nerve fiber, recorded potential changes abruptly from 0 to about -70 to -90 mV. Following stimulation at S_1 (indicated in recording by stimulus "escape"), an action potential (AP) is recorded after a short but definite delay. An AP rises rapidly to a peak (depolarization) and then recovers somewhat more slowly to the steady value (repolarization). At peak of AP transmembrane potential has reversed in sign, the inside being positive to the outside. Depolarization and repolarization processes occupy about 0.5 millisecond. After a pause, indicated by break in line, nerve is stimulated at S_2. An identical AP is recorded, but delay is longer.

B, Diagram of apparatus for stimulating nervous tissue and for obtaining records of its response. Recording instrument is a cathode ray oscillograph. Records are obtained by photographing screen while spot formed by electron beam striking fluorescent material of screen traces electrical changes impressed upon X and Y deflecting plates. Within tube itself, cathode (C) serves as source of electrons, grid (G) controls intensity of electron beam and so brightness of spot, first anode (A_1) compresses flow of electrons into narrow beam (in effect "focuses" the beam) and second anode (A_2) or "Gun," being highly positive, accelerates beam of electrons. Stimulator applies a brief (or any chosen) voltage "pip" to nerve stimulating electrodes, one of which is cathode (C), the other anode (A). Potential changes in nerve, nerve action, are led to amplifier by means of recording electrodes and thence to Y plates of cathode ray oscillograph to cause vertical displacement of spot. At instant of stimulation a stimulus "escape" causes deflection in amplifier. Time between this and beginning of action measures latency, which in this example would be due to conduction time. Sweep generates a "saw-tooth" sweep voltage that moves beam from left to right at a constant speed. Sweep is repeated many times each second. Stimulus is given at a fixed time after beginning of each sweep so that nerve activity is traced as a function of time, as indicated on screen in diagram. (After Erlanger and Gasser, *Electrical signs of nervous activity,* Philadelphia, University of Pennsylvania Press, 1937.)

C, Tracing of action potential recorded from cat dorsal root fiber. Conduction distance about 1 cm. Photograph was a double exposure, consisting of one sweep when microelectrode was in fiber and one sweep after electrode was withdrawn from fiber.

Threshold and the "All-or-Nothing" Law.   An essential step in the generation of an action potential by any means is that the membrane potential be lowered to some critical value, called the *threshold*. Once this has been accomplished the action potential develops explosively and is thereafter entirely independent of the stimulus. *The energy for the action potential is contained in the axon; the stimulus, by lowering the membrane potential, serves merely to trigger the axon into activity.* Thus, once the stimulus reaches an intensity sufficient to lower the membrane potential to the critical threshold value, any additional increase in stimulus intensity has no effect on the amplitude of the action potential. For a given stimulus the axon either responds with a full-sized action potential or it does not; its behavior is thus "all-or-nothing."* It should not be inferred that the action potentials of an axon always have the same amplitude; many factors can alter the energy stores of the axon and hence alter the amplitude of the action potential. For any given state, however, the axon always responds maximally to a threshold stimulus. For further discussion of the all-or-nothing law, see Chapter 4.

Excitation of Nerve; Cable Properties.   In the experiment illustrated in Figure 11 the membrane voltage was brought to the threshold value by passing an electric current through two electrodes placed in contact with the fiber. Much of this current (Fig. 12) flows from the anode to the cathode in the low-resistance external fluid surrounding the fiber and only indirectly affects the membrane potential. Some current, however, flows in through the membrane under and adjacent to the anode, flows through the axoplasm, and then flows out through the membrane at and near the cathode. The density of inward and outward current flow is greatest directly under the anode and the cathode respectively. Current flow *through* the membrane has a pronounced effect on the membrane potential because the membrane has resistance. When current flows through resistors, there is a potential drop across the resistor. At the cathode, where current flows *out through the membrane*, the potential drop (positive inside, negative outside) is opposite in sign to the resting membrane potential (negative inside, positive outside) and hence diminishes it; the membrane is said to be *hypopolarized* or *depolarized*. At the anode, the current flows *inward* across the membrane and the membrane voltage is increased; the membrane is *hyperpolarized*. The action potential begins at the cathode if the transmembrane current flow is sufficient to reduce the membrane potential to the threshold value. Conversely at the anode, where inward current flow across the membrane resistance hyperpolarizes the membrane, excitability (i.e., ease of eliciting an action potential) is decreased.

Although considering the membrane as a simple resistance circuit is a useful device for visualizing the changes in membrane potential associated with transmembrane current flow, an accurate picture of the effect of such current flows must include the fact that the high resistance membrane separating the highly conductive external and internal fluids constitutes a capacitor. Although capacitive properties of the membrane do not alter the direction of a voltage change induced by transmembrane current flow, they do markedly affect the time course and spatial distribution of the voltage change.

Since voltage is proportional to charge on a capacitor, a current flowing out through the membrane at the cathode must neutralize some of the charges on the membrane in order to reduce the voltage. Current consists of the flow of electric charges, and time is required to change the charge on the membrane; consequently, the membrane capacitor acts to slow the changes in membrane voltage induced by transmembrane current flow at any point on the fiber.

Because nerve and muscle fibers are many thousands of times greater in length than in diameter, the resistance of the axoplasm to current flow is quite high, so that voltage

---

* Note that these statements apply to single axons. A nerve will grade its response to graded electrical stimuli because the axons making up the nerve have different thresholds. The phrase "all-or-none" is sometimes used instead of "all-or-nothing."

differences can exist between points in the axoplasm. As soon as the membrane voltage is altered in one region, current starts to flow into it from adjacent regions of membrane. Charges on normally polarized adjacent membrane flow through the interstitial fluid to the depolarized region, through the membrane, and back through the axoplasm to a point just opposite their starting point, thus reducing the charge and voltage there. Since these charges encounter resistance to their flow through the axoplasm, the change in the potential in the adjacent regions is smaller and slower than the change in the potential at the cathode. This behavior, described in more detail below, can be summarized by the statement that the changes in membrane potential produced by current applied at a point are greatest at the electrode and progressively diminish as the distance from the electrode increases. Further, the changes in potential follow an exponential curve, falling at first very rapidly and then progressively more slowly as the distance

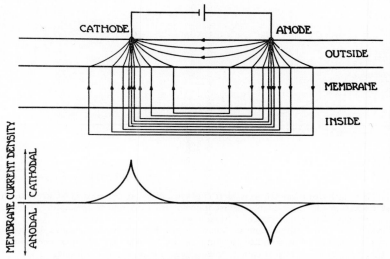

FIG. 12. Diagram of current distribution in nerve fiber during passage of constant current from external source. Only a segment of fiber is shown. *Above,* Lines with directional marks indicate approximate paths of flow of current. Closely spaced lines indicate high current density. Current spreads from electrodes in all available directions and passes through membrane over wide area. Note that current spreads laterally into extrapolar regions. Lateral spread of penetrating current lines is illustrated below by plot of density of current lines (membrane current) against distance along nerve. Current falls off exponentially with distance from electrode. As electrodes are brought closer together, cathodal and anodal effects interfere in interpolar region. Transmembrane potential at a point is altered proportionately to current density at that point.

increases. Figure 15 illustrates these *cable* properties of nerve and muscle fibers as demonstrated by the intracellular microelectrode method.

Equivalent circuit.   Considerations such as these have led to visualizing the axon in terms of an *equivalent circuit,* as in Figure 17. This circuit includes capacitors because of the insulating sheath and resistors because both the membrane and the axoplasm have resistance. A scheme of this sort accounts for the spatial and temporal aspects of the potential under the cathode. The quantitative aspects of the equivalent circuit are given later. At this point it is sufficient to think of a capacitor as a reservoir and the resistor as a partially clogged pipe to visualize how, for example, the potential change builds up at the cathode.

Strength-Duration Curve.   The strength of an abruptly applied and terminated current (square wave) required to initiate an impulse in an axon depends on the length of the time during which the current flows. For an impulse to be initiated, the membrane must be depolarized to threshold at some point. If a current applied at a point on an axon flows for a long time, the membrane capacities will become charged, and the change in membrane potential will be maixmal for that current. Therefore, the threshold strength for a prolonged stimulus is less than that for a stimulus which does not last long enough to charge membrane capacity completely. A curve relating the strength of a threshold stimulus to its duration is called a *strength-duration* curve (Fig. 13). The strength-duration curve is determined experimentally by applying external stimulating electrodes

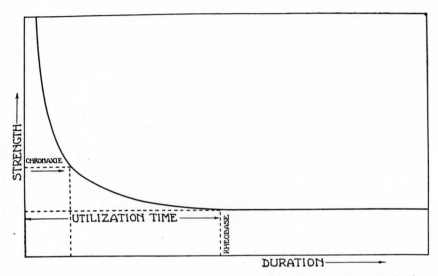

FIG. 13.   Strength-duration curve, which expresses relation between least strength of an applied current and least time during which it must flow in order to reach threshold. There is a minimal current density below which excitation does not occur, but strength-duration curves do not express subliminal events. Since utilization time is difficult to measure accurately, Lucas, Lapicque and others have taken as a measure of excitability the time during which current twice rheobase must flow in order to excite. This time interval is called *chronaxy* (chronaxie) or *excitation time*.

to a whole nerve or muscle and measuring for each pulse duration the minimum current which will excite the nerve or muscle. The shape of the strength-duration curve is about the same for all tissues, although the time and current scales vary. The shape of the curve is accounted for mathematically on page 63. Chronaxy is simply one point on the strength-duration curve, i.e., the length of time a current twice rheobase strength must flow in order to excite a cell. Chronaxy is greater for muscle than for nerve.

Effect of Subthreshold Current Flow upon Excitability.   Although current flow through the membrane must be sufficient to drop the membrane potential to a certain critical level before an action potential is elicited, lesser currents produce detectable changes in excitability. In order to measure the change in excitability produced by a subthreshold shock it is necessary to probe or test the excitability at varying time intervals by using a second shock of an intensity which can be varied. It is possible to determine the time course of an excitability change caused by the first shock. This procedure, known as the *conditioning-testing technique*, is widely used in neurophysiology; the shock used to induce the change is called the "conditioning" shock, and that used to measure or test the change is called the "test" shock.

When a brief subthreshold conditioning shock is applied to a nerve, the strength of test shock required to generate an action potential decreases; i.e., the excitability increases. The heightened excitability persists beyond the duration of the conditioning shock. This persistence is a consequence of the cable property of nerve, for the slowly waning voltage change induced by the conditioning shock persists beyond the shock and can sum with the voltage changes induced by the test shock. Moreover, as one might expect from cable properties, the heightened excitability is not spatially confined to the site of the conditioning cathode but extends on either side, decreasing exponentially to the resting threshold level.

The same procedure can be used to test the effect of prolonged rather than brief subliminal conditioning shocks. In this instance excitability increases at the cathode with the onset of current flow, but, even though current flow continues at a constant level, excitability then drops to a steady intermediate value. This decline from peak excitability during constant current flow is called *accommodation*. Following cessation of current flow excitability at the cathode declines below the resting level and recovers only slowly. This is known as *postcathodal depression*. Discussion of the mechanisms of accommodation and postcathodal depression will be deferred until a later section.

Refractory Period; Recovery Following Excitation. The conditioning-testing procedure can be used to study the changes in excitability which follow the generation of an action potential. In this instance the conditioning shock is suprathreshold, and the intensity of test shock required to elicit a second action potential at varying conditioning-testing intervals is determined. For a brief period following the action potential it is impossible to elicit a second action potential, no matter how intense the test shock. This interval is known as the *absolutely refractory period*. Thereafter a second action potential (usually of less than normal amplitude) can be elicited, but only if the test shock is considerably above the resting threshold value. Excitability then returns to the resting threshold along an approximately exponential time course. The interval between absolute refractoriness and complete recovery to resting excitability is known as the *relatively refractory period*. Refractoriness limits the frequency of impulse discharge in nerve fibers; for example, an axon with an absolutely refractory period of 1 millisecond can be driven at rates not exceeding 1000 impulses per second—and then only if the stimulus is considerably more intense than that required to initiate a single action potential in the axon at rest.

Ionic Permeability Changes Associated with the Action Potential. In the foregoing sections it has been established that an imposed reduction of the membrane potential to a critical, threshold value brings about a sudden, transient, active change in membrane properties and that this change underlies the membrane potential alteration during the action potential. This change in membrane properties can now be examined in more detail.

Prior to the introduction of intracellular recording techniques no accurate measures of transmembrane potential changes during the action potential were available. In 1902, Bernstein suggested that the action potential was due to a transient increase in membrane permeability to all ions, so that for a brief period ionic flow was unrestricted and consequently the membrane potential dropped to zero. With the introduction of intracellular recording, however, it became obvious that such a simple view was invalid, because during the action potential the membrane potential does not simply drop to zero but rather reverses, so that the inside of the membrane becomes positive to the outside (overshoot). Reference to Table 1 (Chap. 1) reveals that the only biologically occurring ion which has a positive equilibrium potential is sodium. Consequently, Hodgkin[14] first suggested that the underlying mechanism of the action potential is a brief and highly specific change in permeability of the membrane to Na^+; this change permits Na^+ to flow into the cell so that the membrane potential approaches the sodium equilibrium potential. More specifically, when the membrane permeability to Na^+

suddenly increases and becomes much greater than the permeability to K^+, there results a sudden net influx of Na^+ ions. The membrane potential (negative inside) and concentrations of Na^+ (high outside, low inside) combine to drive the Na^+ into the cell.

There is ample evidence that the rising phase of the action potential is the result of a large (500-fold) increase in permeability to sodium. But how does a threshold stimulus act to produce this dramatic increase? The answer is that a rapid reduction in membrane voltage causes a large increase in permeability to sodium. Moreover, once threshold voltage is reached, the increased influx of sodium ions occasioned by the increased permeability to them produces further depolarization, which in turn further increases permeability to sodium, and so forth.

The membrane in the resting state can be thought of as a "potassium membrane," the membrane being permeable only to K^+ and the potential tending to be near the potassium equilibrium potential. Similarly, the active membrane is a "sodium membrane," the membrane being permeable only to Na^+ and the potential tending toward sodium equilibrium potential. On this basis, then, an action potential consists roughly of a sudden change from a K^+ to a Na^+ membrane, followed by an almost equally rapid reversion to a K^+ membrane (Fig. 11C). A threshold stimulus alters the membrane's characteristics from those of a K^+ membrane to those of a Na^+ membrane, so that the membrane potential changes from the K^+ to the Na^+ equilibrium potential.

But what causes the rapid recovery to a K^+ membrane? The answer is quite simple. The increased permeability to Na^+ during activity is transient, so that the permeability to Na^+ falls to near resting values in a matter of a millisecond or so. Additionally, when the membrane potential is near zero or positive inside, the permeability to K^+ commences to increase comparatively slowly. Both the increase in permeability to K^+ and the decrease in permeability to Na^+ make the potential fall rapidly toward the resting level. Following the return of the membrane potential to the resting level, permeability to K^+ falls to its normal value. Both these events limit the duration of the action potential and lead to repolarization.

Effects of external sodium concentration on the action potential.   Hodgkin and Katz[14] supported their explanation of overshoot by studying the effects of changes in $[Na^+]_o$ on the amplitude of the action potential in the squid giant axon. They found that replacing some of the Na^+ in the bathing medium with $Choline^+$ reduced the amplitude of the action potential (eliminating the overshoot) by about the amount that would be expected from the Nernst equation for Na^+: $\mathcal{E}_{Na} = 58 \log_{10} [Na^+]_o/[Na^+]_i$. For example, there should be no overshoot unless the concentration of Na^+ is greater outside than inside the fiber. If the two concentrations are equal, the equilibrium potential is zero.

A dependence of the action potential on $[Na^+]_o$ is found in nearly all types of excitable tissues. Figure 14 shows the changes in amplitude of the action potential of excised frog skeletal muscle as $[Na^+]_o$ is varied. For comparison, the value of Na^+ equilibrium potential as calculated from the Nernst equation for $[Na^+]_i = 17$ μM. per cm.[3] is also shown. It can be seen that the membrane reversal during activity is rather less than the Na^+ equilibrium potential but varies with $[Na^+]_o$ as rapidly as does this potential. Hodgkin and Katz interpreted the failure of the action potential to reach the Na^+ equilibrium potential as evidence that the contributions of other ions are not negligible, i.e., that the permeability to K^+ and Cl^- ions is an appreciable but not large fraction of the permeability to Na^+ at the peak of the action potential.

A second way of gaining insight into the action potential is the so-called "voltage clamp" technique. The method, reasoning, and calculations involved in voltage clamp experiments are beyond the scope of this section but are discussed in detail later in the chapter.

Propagation of the Action Potential.[3] The sequence of events in the *propagation* of a nerve impulse can now be described. Once an action potential has been initiated, the membrane potential at the active region is near the Na^+ equilibrium potential. The potential of the adjacent inactive membrane is near the K^+ equilibrium potential. Consequently, charges on the outside of the membrane in the inactive region flow through the interstitial fluid to the active region. There, they flow in through the membrane, to return through the intracellular fluid and flow out through the inactive membranes. This *local circuit current* reduces the membrane charge and voltage in the inactive region. When threshold is reached, permeability to Na^+ increases, the inactive region becomes active, and the membrane potential approaches the Na^+ potential here also. In this manner, the impulse propagates away from the stimulating cathode in both

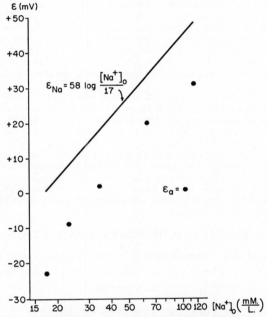

FIG. 14. Changes in overshoot of action potential of frog sartorius muscle fibers produced by changes in external Na^+ concentration. NaCl in bathing solution was replaced by choline chloride. *Abscissa*, $[Na^+]_o$ on logarithmic scale; *ordinate*, potential of intracellular fluid minus potential of extracellular fluid at peak of action potential. Points are experimental results; straight line is plot of equilibrium potential for Na^+ (ε_{Na}). Note that peak of action potential is considerably lower than ε_{Na}, but that both change at about same rate with changes in $[Na^+]_o$. (After Nastuk and Hodgkin, *J. cell. comp. Physiol.*, 1950, *35*:39–74.)

directions at a constant speed. After a few tenths of a millisecond, Na^+ permeability has decreased, and the permeability to K^+ has increased sufficiently so that K^+ efflux exceeds Na^+ influx. The membrane potential stops rising toward the Na^+ equilibrium potential and starts falling back rapidly toward that of K^+. This process is repeated successively at each point of the membrane, and the action potential is propagated at a constant velocity and duration determined by the excitable and cable properties of the fiber.

Saltatory conduction. The foregoing description explains adequately the mechanism of conduction in unmyelinated axons. Conduction in sheathed axons involves a slightly different application of the same principles. Medullated fibers, found only in vertebrates, have a thick covering of a fatty material called "myelin." This *myelin sheath*, which is an effective insulator, is interrupted at intervals of up to 2 mm. along the length of the fiber by the nodes of Ranvier. The extreme distance between these nodes in comparison with fiber diameter can be visualized from their ratio, 100 to 1. The electrical membrane is presumed to be in effective contact with the interstitial fluid only at these nodes. Evidence indicates that local circuit flow is from one node of Ranvier to the next. Consequently the impulse hops along the fiber from node to node. This is referred to as *saltatory conduction* (from the Latin *saltare*—to dance). A consequence of saltatory conduction is an increase in conduction speed, because only restricted patches of the membrane need be depolarized for propagation to occur. It is estimated that conduction speed is about 20 times greater in myelinated than in unmyelinated fibers of the same diameter and temperature.

Role of organic ions. Nachmansohn[20] has forcefully advanced the hypothesis that the liberation and destruction of acetylcholine (ACh) are essential steps in the generation of the action potential in nerve as well as at the neuromuscular junction. He has marshaled an impressive array of evidence to support this view. For example, the enzyme acetylcholinesterase (AChE), which is highly specific for ACh, is localized and highly concentrated in the membrane of the squid giant axon. Further, means for synthesizing ACh, the choline-acetylase system, are available in adequate amounts in nerve.

The postulated role of ACh in nerve conduction is as follows: (i) Depolarization liberates ACh from a bound, inactive form already present in the membrane. (ii) The ACh acts to increase membrane permeability to Na^+ by combining with a "receptor" protein. (iii) The ACh is in equilibrium with the receptor protein, so that some of the ACh is in free form, susceptible to rapid hydrolysis (inactivation) by the high concentration of AChE present. (iv) Destruction of the acetylcholine permits repolarization of the membrane.

This hypothesis has much to recommend it. It is a simple explanation of the role of ACh in nerve function. The universal distribution of AChE in nervous tissue and its high concentration leave little doubt that ACh has an important role in nerve activity. However, Hebb[2] cites much evidence that ACh is not synthesized in appreciable quantities in a few nerves, notably the optic tract, and is therefore not universal. If no ACh is synthesized in a particular nerve, it is difficult to argue that the production and destruction of ACh are essential steps in impulse conduction in other nerves. This evidence is controversial, but if it is true the hypothesis loses its unifying simplicity. Another argument against the hypothesis is that, if ACh causes the specific increase in permeability to Na^+ during activity, inhibition of the AChE in the nerve should allow ACh to accumulate in the membrane and keep it in a permanently depolarized condition. Although anticholinesterase drugs block conduction, they do not do so by depolarizing the membrane.

BIOPHYSICS OF NERVE CONDUCTION

In this section the same phenomena of nerve excitation and conduction described in the previous section will be discussed from a more physical point of view. The discussion will assume a knowledge of these phenomena.

CABLE PROPERTIES OF NERVE

The effects of electric currents on membrane potentials of cells are particularly prominent in nerve and muscle fibers because these fibers are cylindrical and have lengths many times their diameters. With this geometry, the cell plasm is highly resistant to current flow, and different potentials exist at different parts of the cell plasm and membrane during current flow. As described briefly above, the combination of cell plasm resistance and membrane resistance and capacitance found in nerve fibers acts in a typical manner to attenuate in distance and slow in time the effects of current flow on membrane potentials. This behavior of a nerve cell is denoted by the term "cable properties." This term is used because an underseas telephone cable has very similar electrical characteristics. *

Measurement of Cable Properties. Figure 15*A* shows an experimental arrangement for measuring the effects of current flow on the potentials of a giant axon or a skeletal muscle fiber. Two microelectrodes are inserted into a cell; an abruptly applied current is passed through one electrode, and the other is used to record the resulting

* The words "electronus," "electrotonic potential" and "polarization potential" have frequently been used in the physiologic literature to denote the cable properties of nerve. For reasons given by Hodgkin and Rushton[16] these terms are misleading and hence undesirable.

changes in the transmembrane potential ($\Delta \mathcal{E}_m$).* Current flows out of the electrode into the axoplasm and then out through the membrane by the lowest resistance path available. $\Delta \mathcal{E}_m$ as a function of time is recorded at one position of the recording electrode. This electrode is then removed from the cell and reinserted at another distance from the current-applying electrode. In this way, $\Delta \mathcal{E}_m$'s at several distances are recorded. The results of such an experiment, conducted on frog sartorius muscle fibers, are shown in Figure 15B. These results are typical of those obtained for all long, thin cells—myelinated and unmyelinated nerve and skeletal, cardiac and smooth muscle cells. In response to an abruptly applied constant current (internal electrode positive) $\Delta \mathcal{E}_m$ is relatively rapid

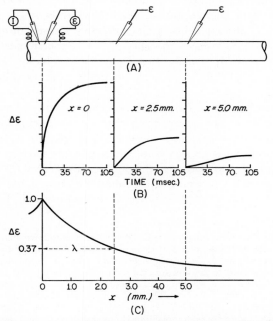

FIG. 15. Cable properties of nerve fibers. A, Experimental arrangement. Abruptly applied current flows from source (I) at extreme left, out through microelectrode and membrane, and back to source through electrode in external solution. Changes in transmembrane potential ($\Delta \mathcal{E}$) at different points along fiber are measured with another intracellular electrode system, $\mathcal{E}$. B, Changes in transmembrane potential as function of time recorded with electrode inserted in fiber at distances from current electrode indicated by dashed extension of vertical ordinate lines. Note that as distance is increased potential rises progressively more slowly and reaches lower final values. C, Plot of final value of $\Delta \mathcal{E}$ as a function of distance along fiber, λ, called space constant of fiber, is measure of rate at which final potential falls off with distance, in either direction.

and large near the current source (Fig. 15B, x = 0), but rises progressively more slowly and becomes smaller as the recording electrode is moved farther from the current electrode in either direction (Fig. 15B, x = 2.5 or x = 5.0 mm.).

Figure 15C shows the way the final, maximum voltage change across the membrane varies with distance from the current-applying electrode. As described briefly above, the slowing of the changes in potential is a consequence of membrane capacitance (charge storage); the diminution of the change with distance is a consequence of membrane and axoplasmic resistance to current flow. Further explanation of these cable properties depends on a more detailed description of the behavior of circuits containing resistances and capacitances. In fact, the behavior illustrated in Figure 15 is attributable

* A capital delta (Δ) is placed before a symbol to indicate a change in the value of the quantity represented by the symbol. Here $\Delta \mathcal{E}_m$ refers to a change in $\mathcal{E}_m$ from its steady value; $\Delta \mathcal{E}_m = \mathcal{E}_m - \mathcal{E}_s$. $\mathcal{E}_m$ symbolizes the transmembrane voltage at any time and place.

solely to the membrane resistance and capacitance and to axoplasmic resistance. A circuit containing resistances and capacitances can be constructed that will have the same response to an applied current as a nerve or muscle fiber does.

Current flow in resistors. The amount of electric current flowing in a resistance is analogous to the amount of charge on a capacitor, both amounts being proportional to the potential difference between the terminals. In a static system of charges (e.g., an isolated capacitor), all parts of a conductor are at the same potential. The simplest case of a nonstatic system, i.e., a system in which the potential of a conductor is not constant, is one in which charges are flowing steadily (constant current). In this case, charges move through the conductor under the influence of a constant electric field which is maintained by a constant voltage source. The free charges in any material conductor flow at a constant rate, although they are acted on by a constant acceleration, because they lose energy (heat is produced) in collisions with other molecules of the material. This flow of charges occurs uniformly throughout the conductor, so there is a constant flow of + charges (current) from the + terminal of the constant voltage source (battery) into the − terminal.

For a fixed potential, the amount of current depends on the amount of energy lost in the conductor. This loss determines the resistance of the conductor. An increase in voltage across the conductor increases the velocity of change flow, and thus the current is reduced proportionately. Ohm's law states that the current (I) flowing through a segment of conductor is proportional to the potential difference ($\mathcal{E}$) across that segment; $I = G\mathcal{E}$. The proportionality constant (G) is called the "conductance" of the conductor. Usually, Ohm's law is written $I = \mathcal{E}/R$, where $R = 1/G$ is called the "resistance" of the conductor.

A more detailed description and derivation of Ohm's law is as follows. Figure 16 is a diagrammatic representation of an electrolytic conductor and some of the factors governing the flow of the ions in the solution. The fixed potential sets up an electric field in the medium proportional to the voltage. The metal plates at the opposite ends of the box are charged by the battery to $\mathcal{E}_B$, and these charges exert a downward force ($E = \mathcal{E}_B/\kappa L$) on a + charge anywhere in the box, where κ is the dielectric constant of the medium and L the length of the box. The Na^+ ions in the solution are acted upon by a downward electric force (Ee) and the Cl^- ions by an upward force ($-Ee$), e being the charge of a cation in coulombs. Gravitational forces are negligible. The direction of the force is determined by the valence (Z), so force equals EeZ.

In the absence of opposing forces, the ions would accelerate in the electric field. However, an ion moving through a solution encounters "frictional" resistance to flow. The ion frequently collides with H_2O molecules; between collisions the ion accelerates under the influence of the applied force, but some kinetic energy is lost in each collision. The ion soon reaches a velocity at which, on the average, the energy lost in each collision just equals the kinetic energy gained from acceleration between collisions; i.e., there is a net movement of the ion at a constant velocity in the direction of the applied force superimposed on its random motion. A macroscopic situation analogous to an ion moving through water is that of a steel ball falling with a constant velocity in a jug of molasses. The greater the applied force, the greater the average velocity ($\bar{v}$)* of the ions; that is, $\bar{v}$ is proportional to E; $\bar{v} = \eta EeZ$, $\bar{v}_{Na} = \eta_{Na}Ee$, $\bar{v}_{Cl} = -\eta_{Cl}Ee$. The constant η is a measure of the mobility of the ion, the ease with which it can move through the solution. The mobility constant and the diffusion constant are closely related properties of an ion in solution.

Ohm's law. The current I (in amperes) flowing through the box in Figure 16 is defined as the total amount of charge (in coulombs) flowing through any cross section in 1 second. By definition, current flows in the direction in which the positive charges move, which is the direction of E. In an electrolyte, the total current is the sum of the currents carried by each ionic species; anions flowing upward and cations flowing downward both constitute a downward current. The current flowing through the box can be calculated from the average velocity of the ions. For example, suppose that the Na^+ are moving downward with an average velocity of 0.3 cm. per second, that the concentration of Na^+ is 10 μM. per cm.^{3}, and that the cross-sectional area (A) is 10 cm.^{2}; then the Na^+ current passing through 1 cm.^{2} (current density) is 10 μM. per cm.^{3} $\times$ 0.3 cm. per second = 3 μM. per cm.^{2}-second, and the total Na^+ current (I_{Na}) is 30 μM. per second. To convert this current to amperes, multiply

---

* A dash above a symbol is a common convention for indicating an average or mean quantity.

by F = 0.0965 coulombs per μM.; I_{Na} = 2.9 coulombs per second = 2.9 amperes. In algebraic form,

$$I_{Na} = Z_{Na}\bar{v}_{Na}[Na^+]FA, \text{ and } I_{Cl} = Z_{Cl}\bar{v}_{Cl}[Cl^-]FA$$

For Cl^- both Z and $\bar{v}_{Cl}$ are negative, so the current is positive.

In words, current density is proportional to the velocity and the concentration of the ions. Ion velocity is proportional to the electric field, and the field is proportional to the applied voltage. Thus current flow is proportional to the applied voltage. This is *Ohm's law*.

The proportionality between I and $\mathcal{E}$ can be obtained by combining the equations relating $\mathcal{E}_B$ and E, $\bar{v}$ and E, and I and $\bar{v}$. The relationship obtained is:

$$I = \frac{AFe}{L\kappa}(Z^2_{Na}[Na^+]\eta_{Na} + Z^2_{Cl}[Cl^-]\eta_{Cl})\mathcal{E}_B = \frac{A}{L\rho}\mathcal{E}_B$$

All terms in the middle equation except A, L and $\mathcal{E}_B$ have been combined into the constant ρ, called the specific resistivity of the substance. From the equation it can be seen that resistivity depends inversely on ionic concentrations and mobility. Concentrated solutions containing ions of high mobility and valence have a low resistance. The numerical value of ρ (in ohm-cm.) is the resistance between the faces of 1 cm. cube. In mammalian extracellular fluid ρ approximately equals ($\simeq$) 60 ohm-cm.

The resistance of a block of conductor depends on the properties of the material (e.g., number of free charges, energy loss per collision) and on the dimensions of the block. Consider the box containing a solution of NaCl illustrated in Figure 16. The

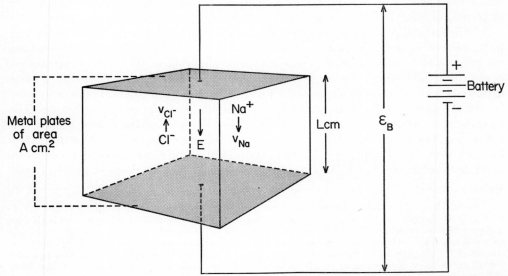

FIG. 16.   Illustration of Ohm's law. A box L cm. long with a cross-sectional area of A is filled with solution of NaCl in water. A battery of voltage $\mathcal{E}_B$ is connected to metal plates at each end of box. E is electric field set up in medium by applied voltage; v_{Na} and v_{Cl} are average drift velocities of Na^+ and Cl^- ions, respectively, and are proportional to E.

greater the cross-sectional area of the box (perpendicular to the direction of current flow), the lower the resistance, because more ions are available to carry current; the greater the length of the block (parallel to flow), the higher the resistance. In longer blocks, ions move at a slower velocity because the force on each ion is reduced. Thus, the resistance of a block of conducting material (a resistor) depends on the properties of the material (*specific resistivity*), is directly proportional to the length of the block, and is inversely proportional to its cross-sectional area.

Longitudinal Resistance of an Axon.   Since the axoplasm is a rather dilute (0.3 M. per liter) solution of ionized substances, it has a comparatively high specific resistivity ($\rho \simeq$ 200 ohm-cm.). The resistance to axial current flow in the axoplasm of a nerve fiber is high because of the high specific resistivity and the small cross-sectional area. For instance, in a myelinated nerve fiber 20 μ in diameter, the axoplasm is only 10 μ in diameter, and the *longitudinal resistance* (r_i) of a segment 1 cm. long is 260 million ohms. The larger the diameter, the less r_i is. Thus, in a muscle fiber 100 μ in diameter, r_i = 2.6 million ohms per cm. Current inside the cell must flow within the volume surrounded by the cell membrane. The interstitial medium, on the other hand, is large; hence current can spread widely as it flows. Therefore, although the specific resistivity of the extracellular fluid is half as large as for intracellular fluid, the total resistance (r_0) of the interstitial fluid is negligible in comparison with r_i.

This statement is true in experimental arrangements where an isolated cell or tissue is immersed in a relatively large fluid bath, but it is much less true of tissues *in situ*. Electron micrographs indicate that the true interstitial space is extremely small in most tissues. Inactive cells surrounding an active one do, to a certain extent, provide a path for current flow, but there is a relatively high resistance because the cell membrane is a good insulator.

Membrane Conductance and Permeability. Since, to a limited extent, ions can penetrate the membrane, it has the properties of a resistor; at small current flows Ohm's law is obeyed. The permeability of a membrane to a substance is a measure of the ease with which that substance, when driven by the difference in concentration across the membrane, can penetrate it. The membrane conductance of an ion, the reciprocal of its electrical resistance in the membrane, is determined by the ease with which the ion can penetrate the membrane when driven by a potential difference across it. (Conductance is determined by Ohm's law.) As long as the driving force is constant, the rate at which an ion penetrates depends upon membrane structure. Thus, membrane permeability and membrane conductance to an ion are different measures of the same membrane property. For example, the ease with which K^+ can penetrate the membrane can be referred to as P_K or as g_K, the conductance to K^+ of 1 cm.^{2} of membrane. The total membrane conductance* (g_m) is the sum of all the ionic conductances; $g_m = g_K + g_{Na} + g_{Cl}$. The total membrane resistance (r_m) is $1/g_m$. The resistance of 1 cm.^{2} of inactive membrane is quite variable from cell to cell in the same tissues and even more variable from tissue to tissue. Measured values usually fall in the range of 1000 to 10,000 ohms.

Since ions moving through the membrane are driven by both concentration and potential differences, the movements can be treated as though $\mathcal{E}_m$ modified the concentrations of the ions on both sides of the membrane, or as though the concentrations modified $\mathcal{E}_m$. In this sense, the effective voltage driving an ion across the membrane is simply $\mathcal{E}_m$ minus the equilibrium potential of the ion. For example, the current of K^+ through the membrane (I_K) is given by the equation $I_K = g_K(\mathcal{E}_m - \mathcal{E}_K)$. This equation defines g_K. If $\mathcal{E}_m = \mathcal{E}_K$, then $I_K = 0$. The latter statement is precisely what is meant by $\mathcal{E}_K$: the value of $\mathcal{E}_m$ at which the net flux (current) is zero.

Equivalent Circuit of an Axon. The membrane has capacity because of its insulating, charge-separating properties and has high resistance because ions are able to penetrate it at a limited rate. The axoplasm and interstitial fluids, being solutions of ions, are resistors. If an axon is marked off into short segments, an approximately equivalent circuit consisting of resistors and capacitors can be drawn for each segment. When connected, the circuit equivalents of adjacent segments will constitute an equivalent circuit for the whole axon. This equivalent circuit has the same response to an applied current as has the nerve fiber it represents.

Figure 17 illustrates how the equivalent circuit is obtained. The electrical equivalent of a segment of axoplasm is simply a resistor (r_i) whose resistance is that of the segment (segments *a* and *b* in Figure 17*A* and the correspondingly marked resistors in Figure

---

* The total membrane conductance of a cell is directly proportional to its surface area; it is better, for purposes of comparison, to calculate or measure the conductance of 1 cm.^{2} of membrane. This number is the specific membrane conductance, although the word "specific" is frequently omitted.

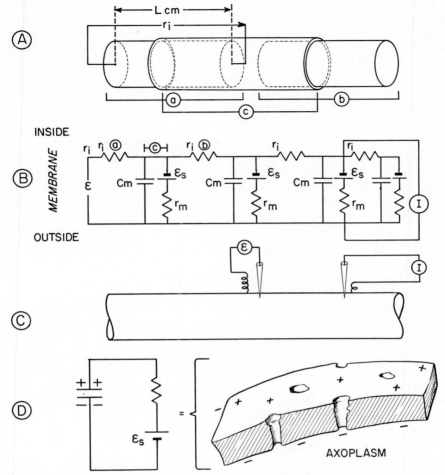

FIG. 17. Derivation of approximate equivalent electrical circuit of a long, thin, cylindrical axon. In an electrical circuit diagram, a straight line (————) represents an ideal conductor (zero resistance), a zigzag line (—\/\/\/—) represents an ideal resistance (no capacitance between its terminals), and ——|⊢—— represents an ideal capacitor (infinite resistance between its terminals). In A, the axoplasm and membrane are each marked off into halfway overlapping segments L cm. long (accurate representation of the nerve requires that L be no more than about 0.05 cm.). Any segment of axoplasm has a resistance (r_i) which is in series with the adjoining segments. Thus the upper line in B consists of a series of resistors, each of which is the electrical equivalent of the correspondingly labeled segment of axoplasm in A. Extracellular fluid is large and is assumed to have no resistance; this is represented by lower horizontal line in B. Equivalent circuit of a segment of membrane (c) must be connected between intracellular and extracellular fluid equivalents at the junction of two r_i's. For example, segment c is connected between the axoplasmic segments a and b.

C, Experimental arrangement for measuring cable properties. Compare with B, where a current source is shown applied across the membrane at one point; the "transmembrane potential" of the equivalent circuit can be measured at any other point. If B is an accurate electrical representation of the nerve fiber, then curves of the type shown in Figure 15 should be obtained in the equivalent experiment.

D, Derivation of equivalent circuit of a membrane segment. Equivalent consists of a capacitor (c_m) representing the insulating, ion-impermeable regions of membrane in parallel with a resistor (r_m) representing the ion-permeable regions of membrane. (For convenience, ion-permeable region is indicated by pores penetrating the membrane.) A battery of potential $\mathcal{E}_s$ is connected in series with r_m to signify the existence of a steady transmembrane potential.

17B). The equivalent circuit of a segment of membrane is more complicated, consisting of three components derived as shown in Figure 17D: (i) a capacity (c_m) representing the insulating charge-storing aspect of the membrane, (ii) a resistance (r_m) representing the limited ability of ions to penetrate the membrane, and (iii) a battery of voltage $\mathcal{E}_s$, the steady potential. The battery and the resistance are drawn in series because the membrane capacity is charged by ions (principally K^+ and Cl^-) driven through the membrane resistance by concentration gradients. In Figure 17A, the segment of membrane (c) is placed halfway between the two segments of axoplasm (a and b) to illustrate how the circuits representing the axoplasmic and membrane segments must be connected: the r_i's in series and the membrane portions connected between the junction of two r_i's and the line (representing a zero resistance conductor) that is equivalent to r_o, the extracellular resistance (Fig. 17B). An axon has cable properties because it has the particular electrical circuit properties shown in Figure 17B. In turn, these circuit properties are a consequence of the axon's structure.

Figure 17C is a duplicate of Figure 15A that illustrates how cable properties are observed experimentally. Current is applied through an intracellularly placed electrode (I electrode), and the changes in membrane potential some distance away are recorded with the other ($\mathcal{E}$) electrode. The same type of experiment on the equivalent circuit is shown in Figure 17B, right; current is applied across a segment of membrane and the potential is recorded across a membrane segment one r_i away.

The advantage of drawing an equivalent circuit for an axon is that the behavior of this type of circuit is amenable to mathematical analysis. Such an analysis shows that the circuit always behaves in the manner described above and that the cable properties are completely characterized by two numbers: (i) the *time constant* (τ), which is a measure of the slowness of voltage changes in time, and (ii) the *space constant* (λ), a measure of the rate at which the voltage falls off with distance.

Membrane Time Constant. If a constant current* is abruptly applied to a resistance, the voltage across it appears equally abruptly. However, if a capacitor (c_m) is connected in parallel with the resistor (r_m), a condition equivalent to one segment of membrane, the voltage ($\Delta\mathcal{E}_m$) across this combination rises slowly in response to the abruptly applied current (Fig. 18A). The reason is that time is required for the flow of charges (current) to alter the amount of charge on the capacitor and thus the voltage across it. At the instant the switch is closed all the charge supplied by the current source goes to charging the capacitor; there is no current through the resistor because the potential across it and the capacitor is zero. As time passes, the charge on the capacitor increases; $\Delta\mathcal{E}_m$ increases, and some current is diverted to the resistor, the rate of charging the capacitor being correspondingly decreased. This process continues—more and more current flowing through the resistor and less and less through the capacitor—until, finally, all the current is flowing through the resistor.

The time course of these potential changes is shown in Figure 18A, right. Also shown is $\Delta\mathcal{E}_m$ as a function of time after the switch is opened. In this case, the charge on c_m leaks off through r_m, rapidly at first and then progressively more slowly. The time constant (τ) of this circuit is defined as the product of the resistance (r_m) and the capacitance (c_m): $\tau = r_m c_m$. If r_m is in ohms and c_m is in farads, τ is in seconds. A means of measuring the time constant is also shown in Figure 18A, right. The shape and time course of $\Delta\mathcal{E}_m$ are the same no matter what values r_m and c_m have individually, as long as their product is a constant.

* The term "constant current" means that the total current flow in the circuit does not depend on its resistance. A simple way to obtain a source of constant current is to connect a battery, with the voltage $\mathcal{E}_B$, to the circuit through a resistor (r_s) which has a resistance much higher than the resistance of the circuit. The current flow is then $I = \mathcal{E}_B/(r_s + r_c)$, where r_c is the total circuit resistance; however, $r_s + r_c \simeq r_s$, so $I \simeq \mathcal{E}_B/r_s$.

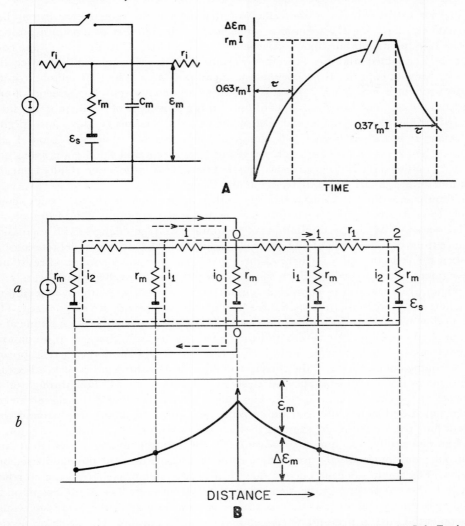

FIG. 18. *A*, Time constant; properties of a resistance-capacitance (RC) circuit. *Left*, Equivalent circuit of a segment of membrane and means for switching on or off an external current source (I). *Right*, Time course of voltage changes ($\Delta\varepsilon_m = \varepsilon_m - \varepsilon_s$) across the capacity when the switch is closed and then, after a long time, opened. A method for measuring the time constant ($\tau = r_m c_m$) of the membrane is shown.

B, Space constant. *a*, Approximate equivalent circuit of an axon with the membrane capacity removed. Current flow in a circuit with capacitors is the same, after a long time, as the current flow in this circuit at any time. Arrows show various paths of flow of applied current, *I*. The longer the current flow path, the greater the resistance and hence the smaller the proportion of current flowing in that branch. *b*, Graph of membrane voltage as a function of distance from point of current application.

The time constant of the membrane segment in Figure 18*A* ($r_m c_m$) is also the time constant for any other length of segment, so this time constant characterizes the time behavior of the voltage changes across the membrane. It should be borne in mind, however, that the membrane voltage changes in a whole fiber are much more complex than those in a single resistance-capacitance circuit, although both are determined by τ. The equality of the time constants of any two segments of different length can be seen by calculating τ for segments 1 and 2 mm. long. The membrane resistance of the 2 mm. segment is half that of the 1 mm. segment, because, with respect to current flow from the interior to the exterior of the cell, two adjacent 1 mm. segments are in parallel. Alternatively, doubling the membrane area doubles the number of ions in a position to penetrate the membrane under a particular driving force. Thus the membrane conductance is doubled and the resistance halved. The double segment has twice the capacity because capacity is proportional to membrane area. The time constant of the double segment is $2 c_m \times r_m/2 = r_m c_m$. The same arguments apply to segments of any length, so the number $\tau = r_m c_m$ depends only on the properties of the membrane, since it is independent of the shape and size of the cell. In carcinus (crab) axons specific membrane resistance is about 7500 ohms-cm.^{2}, and specific capacity is about 1 μF. per cm.^{2}; hence $\tau = 7.5$ milliseconds. τ is about 1 millisecond in squid giant axons and about 35 milliseconds in frog sartorius muscle fibers. This large value results from the high membrane capacity of muscle, about 10 μF. per cm.^{2}.

Membrane Space Constant. The other factor necessary to specify completely the cable properties of a nerve fiber is the space constant, a measure of the spatial decay of $\Delta\mathcal{E}_m$. The diminution of membrane voltage changes with increasing distance from the current-applying electrode results from the series-parallel relationship between the resistance of a segment of membrane (r_m) and the longitudinal resistance of a segment of axoplasm (r_i). Each successive segment reduces the voltage.

Figure 18*B* shows the equivalent circuit of a nerve fiber with the membrane capacitors removed so that the spatial features of cable properties are emphasized. The current flow in the resistors is the same as would occur in a nerve fiber a long time after the application of the current when all the capacitors are fully charged. If a constant current is applied to the resistor network (Fig. 18*B, top*) at O, some of the current spreads into adjoining regions. Most of the current will flow directly through branch O. Because the axoplasm has a high resistance, successively lesser amounts will flow through other branches of the circuit (1, 2, 3, etc.). The longer the current flow path, the greater is its resistance and hence the less the current, because the voltage drop around any current flow path must be the same as that across branch O; $\Delta\mathcal{E}_o = r_m i_o$.

Experimentally, the quantity measured is the transmembrane potential at any point. Internal longitudinal current flow causes a voltage drop in the axoplasm, but changes in $\mathcal{E}_m$ result *only* from current flow through the membrane. However, to reach the point where it penetrates the membrane, this current must flow in the axoplasm as well and is thus attenuated. If the internal resistance were zero, the axoplasm would be isopotential, and all membrane elements would be in parallel. The cable properties would then consist merely of simple resistance—capacitance charge and discharge curves; i.e., there would be no spatial component. This situation obtains, approximately, in nearly spherical cells such as the nerve cell body. In such a case, the applied current produces nearly equal $\Delta\mathcal{E}_m$'s at every point.

The decay of potential with distance has the same shape as the decay of potential with time in a resistance-capacitance circuit, i.e., exponential. Figure 18*B*, bottom, shows a plot of $\Delta\mathcal{E}_m$ as a function of distance from the point of application of the current. The size of the space constant (λ) depends directly on membrane resistance and inversely on axoplasmic resistance. More precisely $\lambda = \sqrt{r_m/r_i}$, where r_m is the membrane resistance and r_i is the axoplasmic resistance of a 1 cm. length of fiber. Since both r_m and r_i depend on fiber diameter as well as on fiber properties, λ also depends on diameter: the larger the diameter, the larger the space constant. In frog skeletal muscle fibers 100 μ in diameter, λ is about 2.5 mm. Similar or smaller values are found in nerve fibers. Thus if a fiber were depolarized to zero at one end by a current, changes in membrane potential would be undetectable 1 cm. away. This fact shows how rapidly a fiber attenuates an applied "signal." It also shows that some method is needed to boost the signal at each point if information is to be transmitted over the distances found in the body.

Summary. The spatial and temporal aspects of potential changes in cables can now be combined. At $t = 0$ a constant current is suddenly applied to an axon at $x = 0$ (Figs. 15, 17). At first, all the current flows directly through the membrane because $\mathcal{E}_m$ cannot change until the charge on c_m at that point is changed. Since $I = \mathcal{E}/R$, no current will flow laterally through r_i or directly through r_m until $\Delta\mathcal{E}_0$ at $x = 0$ is not zero. Immediately after the current is applied, then, it is confined to the immediate region of application. As time passes, $\Delta\mathcal{E}_0$ gradually increases, and some current is diverted to r_{m0} and to capacitors at adjacent regions. However, it takes even longer to charge membrane capacity at adjacent regions. At $x = 0$, an abruptly applied current produces, initially, a linear rise in voltage; applied to adjacent RC membrane segments through r_i, this voltage produces delayed, concave, upward changes in $\mathcal{E}_m$. As the charge and $\mathcal{E}_m$ rise in immediately adjacent regions, the current spreads to still greater distances. Finally, after a long time, all the c_m's are fully charged and all the current is flowing through the r_m and r_i (Fig. 18B).

Initially, current flow is limited to a narrow region around $x = 0$, and is all devoted to charging capacitors; finally, the current is widespread and is entirely in resistors. The transition between these two states is shown in the curves giving potential as a function of time at different distances (Fig. 15). Hodgkin and Ruston[4, 16] have analyzed mathematically the passive cable properties of an unmyelinated nerve and have developed methods for measuring r_m, c_m and r_i (see also Lorente de Nó[18]).

PROPERTIES OF THE EXCITABLE MEMBRANE [7, 8, 9, 10, 11, 12, 13]

Active Na^+–K^+ transport and cable properties are attributes of all animal cell membranes. The membrane of an excitable cell has certain unique properties in addition. These properties were precisely described by Hodgkin and Huxley in their classic studies on the behavior of the squid giant axon when its membrane potential was held constant by artificial means (voltage clamping). The defining property of excitable cells is that rapid depolarization (reduction of transmembrane voltage) increases the membrane permeability to Na^+ (P_{Na}). Within limits, the greater the depolarization, the greater the increase in P_{Na}. An ancillary property is that the increase in P_{Na} induced by depolarization is transient. Even if the membrane voltage is maintained near $\mathcal{E}_{Na}$ by other means (e.g., external current), P_{Na} falls to its resting value in a matter of a few milliseconds. This fall in permeability to Na^+ is called *inactivation*. The properties of the excitable membrane are described in terms of changes in membrane permeability or conductance, because no information is yet available regarding the membrane mechanisms which give rise to the large and specific changes in the ionic permeability of the membrane.

There are three principal methods of studying the changes in ionic permeability during activity: (i) observing the effects of changes in external ion concentrations on the action potential, (ii) studying by means of radioisotopes the net and one way ionic fluxes during activity, and (iii) voltage-clamping, measuring membrane current as a function of time while $\mathcal{E}_m$ is fixed. The first two methods yield only a rough estimate of peak or mean ion permeabilities during activity. Voltage clamping,[13] however, makes possible a detailed quantitative analysis of the time and voltage dependencies of Na^+ and K^+ conductances.

Events Near Threshold Voltage. Accurate description of the sequence of ionic permeability changes during an action potential requires a knowledge of the voltage-clamping studies of the squid giant axon. The voltage-clamping technique is different from ordinary techniques, and the results obtained with it are difficult to comprehend.

Therefore, the ion permeabilities and fluxes at membrane voltages near threshold are described first, so that some idea of the functional characteristics of the active membrane can be obtained.

Experimentally, an action potential may be initiated in a nerve or muscle fiber by sufficiently depolarizing the membrane with an outward current applied through an intracellular microelectrode. Another microelectrode, for measuring membrane potential, may be inserted near the stimulating electrode (Fig. 19A). The changes in $\mathcal{E}_m$ associated with the initiation of an impulse are shown diagrammatically in Figure 19B. Hyperpolarizing currents (curve 1) of any size and small depolarizing currents (curve 2) change $\mathcal{E}_m$ in the manner expected from the cable properties of the fiber (compare with x = 0, Fig. 15B). When the depolarizing current applied to skeletal muscle fibers

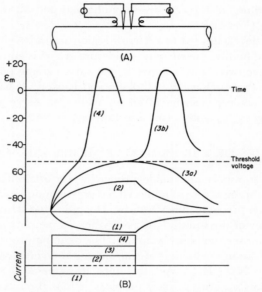

FIG. 19.   Threshold. A, Schematic diagram of experimental arrangement showing intracellular stimulating (I) and recording (ε) electrodes. B, Changes in $\mathcal{E}_m$ (upper records) produced by suddenly applied and terminated constant currents (lower records). Curve 1 in current records produced voltage changes shown by Curve 1 in ε records, and so forth for Curves 2 to 6. Hyperpolarizing and subthreshold depolarizing currents of any strength produce the $\mathcal{E}_m$ changes expected from electrotonic considerations (Curves 1 and 2). Current of just threshold strength will produce one of two responses: Either membrane potential returns to steady value after a delay (3a), or an action potential is generated with its typical rapid rise and fall (3b). Any stronger stimulus (4) also generates an action potential, but progressively shorter times are required to depolarize membrane to threshold.

is just strong enough to reduce $\mathcal{E}_m$ from resting values (−90 mV.) to threshold voltage (about −55 mV.) (curve 3, Fig. 19B), there are two possible responses. The response to about half of the stimuli is a propagating action potential (curve 3b). If an action potential is not initiated, there is a *local response* (curve 3a); i.e., the voltage falls back toward the resting level, but initially more slowly than expected from the cable properties. As the name implies, a local response is nonpropagated, i.e., local membrane activity. If the recording electrode impales the fiber farther from the stimulating electrode, a potential quite similar to curve 3b is recorded but delayed in time when an action potential is initiated; otherwise, only the cable response is seen. The value of $\mathcal{E}_m$ at which an action potential is just initiated by a depolarizing current is called the *threshold voltage*. A lesser depolarization does not produce a propagated response, but a greater depolarization does. A current that just depolarizes the membrane to threshold is called a *threshold stimulus*.

Threshold is one of three values of $\mathcal{E}_m$ at which the net influx of Na^+ just balances the net outflow of K^+ and Cl^-. The other two values of $\mathcal{E}_m$ are the resting potential and the peak of the action potential. Thus, as the membrane is depolarized by current outflow, the inflow of Na^+ ions increases, because the depolarization has increased P_{Na} markedly, an increase that more than compensates for the slightly decreased electrochemical gradient of Na^+. The net K^+ and Cl^- fluxes increase because the reduction of $\mathcal{E}_m$ has increased the electrochemical gradients driving these ions. If the net movement of ionic charges through the membrane is zero (i.e., if net Na^+ influx equals net K^+ efflux plus net Cl^- influx), the membrane voltage is not changing, since the membrane charge is constant. The potential will stay constant only until inactivation of P_{Na} reduces Na^+ influx. The potential will then begin to fall, and the fall in potential will in turn further reduce P_{Na}.

The potential in this latter case follows a path similar to curve *3a* (Figure 19*B*). On the other hand, if the applied depolarizing current is made slightly larger or the threshold of the fiber has fallen slightly owing to random fluctuations, the net Na^+ influx through the membrane slightly exceeds the sum of the net K^+ efflux and the net Cl^- influx, so that there is a net movement of positive ions into the fiber. These charges reduce the potential by neutralizing negative charges stored on the inner membrane surface. The decrease in membrane voltage acts to increase P_{Na} further; this increase, in turn, causes additional depolarization. This vicious circle, this self-generating or regenerative process, continues until the maximum P_{Na} is reached and $\mathcal{E}_m$ is changing rapidly toward $\mathcal{E}_{Na}$. Hodgkin[5] diagrams this cycle of events as follows:

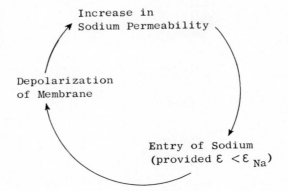

Membrane Voltage Clamping.[13, 19]   It is difficult to study directly such explosive processes as the action potential. However, the dependence of Na^+ current, and hence P_{Na}, on $\mathcal{E}_m$ and time can be measured directly by the voltage clamp technique, in which regenerative interactions between $\mathcal{E}_m$ and P_{Na} are prevented by artificial maintenance of a constant $\mathcal{E}_m$. In this technique, the amount of current required to keep $\mathcal{E}_m$ constant is automatically supplied from an external source. This procedure is equivalent to connecting a battery between the inside and the outside of the cell so that $\mathcal{E}_m$ must equal the battery voltage. If $\mathcal{E}_m$ is not changing in time, all the membrane current must be carried by ions, since none would go to charge the membrane capacity. If voltage is clamped at only one point on a nerve fiber, part of the current supplied by the external source will spread away from that point as a consequence of the cable properties of the nerve fiber. Therefore, voltage clamping requires that $\mathcal{E}_m$ must be held constant over the length of the fiber. If $\mathcal{E}_m$ does not change with distance, no current will flow from one region to another, and all applied current must flow directly through the membrane. Figure 20*A* is a highly simplified schematic diagram of a voltage clamp experiment on squid giant axon. Figures 20*B* and *C* show the results obtained.

When the potential of the battery is set equal to ε_s, no current will flow through the membrane (switch is in position 1, Fig. 20*A*) because ε_s is the voltage at which the net flow of charge is zero. When the switch is moved to position 2, current will flow through the external circuit and bring ε_m to the new voltage (ε) if the resistance between the long internal and external electrodes is mostly in the membrane, i.e., if the resistance of the axoplasm and the external bathing fluid and the resistance between the electrodes and the solution are negligible compared to the membrane resistance. In practice, the resistance between the internal electrode and the axoplasm is an important factor, and rather elaborate measures are necessary to circumvent this and other difficulties.[13, 19]

When the switch is thrown to position 2, the membrane potential is abruptly changed to a new value. In order to change ε_m it is necessary to change the charge on the membrane capacity. This process, however, is brief, because the effectively low resistance of the axoplasm allows a high current flow from the battery to the membrane capacitance. The membrane conductance does not change

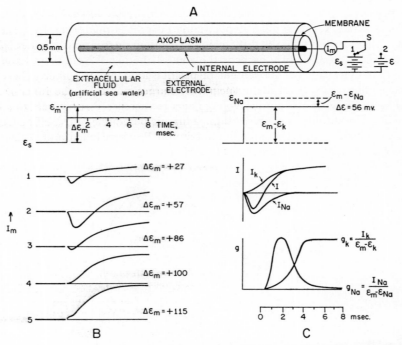

FIG. 20. Voltage clamping in squid giant axon. *A*, Highly simplified diagram of principle of voltage clamp experiments. Transmembrane voltage (ε_m) is held constant over a considerable length of membrane by connecting internal and external media to battery through long electrodes. ε_m can be changed suddenly from ε_s ($I = 0$) to any other value by flipping switch *S* to position 2. Total current flow through membrane is measured as function of time by ammeter (I_m), a cathode ray oscilloscope.

B, Transmembrane current flow as function of time after a sudden change in ε_m. Uppermost curve is ε_m as function of time. Curves *1* to *5*, show membrane current which flows following a depolarization of membrane by increasing amounts (in millivolts) shown at right. Curves *4* and *5* large depolarization in which ε_m is greater than ε_{Na}. (For all but largest depolarizations, early components of current flow in direction opposite to that expected from change in ε_m. Late current flow is in the same direction.) Large depolarization changes early negative (inward) current to a positive current; this happens at $\varepsilon_m = \varepsilon_{Na} \simeq 95$ mV. (from resting potential).

C, Components of total membrane current and conductance. Top curve, ε_m as function of time; ε_K and ε_{Na} are indicated by dashed lines. Middle curve, total membrane current broken up into its two components, I_{Na} and I_K. (I_{Cl} is constant, quite small and neglected here.) Separation was made possible by measurements of effects of changes in $[Na^+]_o$ on total current. Bottom curve, g_{Na} and g_K as functions of time for particular changes in ε_m shown in top curve. Conductances are same shape as current curves because they are calculated, as shown, by dividing ionic current by effective voltage on ion. The g_{Na} versus ε_m curve of Figure 21 was obtained by measuring peak height of g_{Na} for different depolarizations. (After Hodgkin and Huxley, *J. Physiol.*, 1952, *116*:449–472; *ibid.*, *117*:500–544.)

immediately after a sudden change in $\mathcal{E}_m$; therefore, there is an immediate change in membrane current proportional to $\Delta\mathcal{E}_m$; i.e., K^+ flows outward and Cl^- inward. This change is reflected in a sudden small initial jump in outward current (upward in Fig. 20B). Shortly after a sudden depolarization and the consequent outward current, the total membrane current (I_m) begins to decrease, passes through zero, reaches a negative peak in about 1 millisecond, and then slowly changes back to a large maintained positive value. The contributions of Na^+ and K^+ ions to the total current at various times can be deduced from varying the amount of depolarization and the external Na^+ concentration. Cl^- current is nearly negligible and is neglected here.

Sodium Ion Current. The curves of membrane current versus time for different depolarizations differ in detail, but the sequence of events in each curve is nearly the same until $\Delta\mathcal{E}_m$ exceeds about 100 mV. (curves *4* and *5*, Fig. 20B). The early inward current disappears at a particular $\Delta\mathcal{E}_m$ (about 95 mV.), and an early outward current hump appears at larger depolarizations (curve *5*). From measurements of $[Na^+]_i$ and $[Na^+]_o$, $\mathcal{E}_{Na}$ can be calculated. Such analysis demonstrates that the early current hump changes sign when $\mathcal{E}_m = \mathcal{E}_{Na}$, or $\Delta\mathcal{E}_m = \mathcal{E}_{Na} - \mathcal{E}_s$. This finding, together with the finding that changes in the early current reversal voltage vary exactly with changes in $\mathcal{E}_{Na}$ (varied by altering $[Na^+]_o$), leads to the conclusion that early membrane current is carried by Na^+ ions. *The crucial evidence is that this current reverses sign at exactly the $\mathcal{E}_m$ at which the driving force on Na^+ ions changes sign.*

Potassium Ion Current. The late, maintained outward current appears to be largely an outflow of K^+. Direct evidence for this conclusion has not been obtained because $[K^+]_i$ cannot be conveniently changed experimentally. The membrane must be depolarized to produce the delayed, prolonged outward current, and such depolarization tends to drive K^+ out of the cell. Tracer studies with radioactive K^+ have shown that membrane depolarization increases K^+ outflux sufficiently so that it could carry the late outward current.[12,15]

Sodium and Potassium Ion Conductances.[9] It is possible to separate the total membrane current into Na^+ and K^+ currents by analyzing the manner in which changes in $[Na^+]_o$ affect the shapes of curves relating current to time. Presumably, changes in $[Na^+]_o$ affect the shapes of the current versus time curves but do not affect K^+ currents. Figure 20C shows the partition of I_m into Na^+ and K^+ currents for a depolarization of 56 mV. I_{Na} rises rapidly along an S curve and then declines more slowly to zero, whereas I_K rises slowly along an S curve and remains at a high value indefinitely. If Na^+ and K^+ components are correctly identified, then the conductance of Na^+ (g_{Na}) and that of K^+ (g_K) as functions of time can be determined by dividing the ionic current by the driving force on that ion. The terms g_K and g_{Na} are defined by the equations $I_K = g_K (\mathcal{E}_m - \mathcal{E}_K)$, then $g_K = I_K/(\mathcal{E}_m - \mathcal{E}_K)$, and also $g_{Na} = I_{Na}/(\mathcal{E}_m - \mathcal{E}_{Na})$. In voltage clamp $\mathcal{E}_m$ is held constant, so g_{Na} and g_K have the same shape as I_{Na} and I_K, respectively (Fig. 20C).

Since the voltage clamp technique has made possible precise measurements of the changes in membrane conductance that accompany changes in membrane potential, the properties of the membrane which give rise to the action potential can be defined more clearly. From this description of membrane properties, the time course of the action potential, the recovery of excitability, the conduction speed, the ion exchanges during activity and the resistance changes during activity of a squid giant axon can be accurately predicted. As yet, however, there is no definite knowledge of the physiochemical and structural bases for the active changes in membrane conductance.

Voltage dependence of sodium and potassium ion conductances. The upstroke of the action potential results from a depolarization induced increase in P_{Na}. A quantitative measure of the dependence of g_{Na} (equivalent to P_{Na}) on voltage can be obtained from voltage clamp experiments. The time course of g_{Na} is recorded while $\mathcal{E}_m$ is fixed. A series of such measurements at different voltages yields the voltage dependence of g_{Na}. Figure 21 shows this dependence of g_{Na} on $\mathcal{E}_m$. The ordinate is the peak g_{Na} consequent to a sudden depolarization of the membrane. The curve is S-shaped. Small depolarizations have little effect on g_{Na}, moderate depolarizations cause large increases in g_{Na}, and large depolarizations have no further effect. The final value of g_K depends on $\mathcal{E}_m$ in much the manner that the peak g_{Na} does.

Activation and inactivation of sodium ion conductance. A suddenly applied, fixed depolarization produces a large increase in Na^+ conductance. However, despite the continuance of the depolarization, the conductance falls rapidly. This drop is called *inactivation* of Na^+ conductance. Inactivation begins as soon as the membrane is depolarized; the greater the depolarization, the faster the rate of inactivation. Fast depolarization of the membrane has two effects which relate to Na^+ conductance: g_{Na} increases rapidly, and the *rate* at which inactivation of g_{Na} proceeds also increases immediately. Repolarization of the membrane has the reverse effects; any Na^+ conductance not already inactivated will

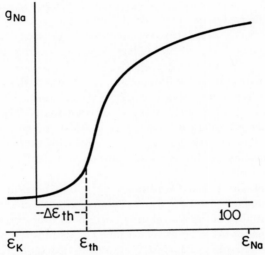

FIG. 21. Effects of sudden changes in membrane voltage on peak membrane sodium conductance, g_{Na}. *Ordinate,* Maximum g_{Na} measured following a sudden displacement of membrane voltage from its steady state value ($\mathcal{E}_s$). *Abscissa,* $\Delta\mathcal{E}$, the value of $\mathcal{E}$ following the displacement minus $\mathcal{E}_s$ ($\Delta\mathcal{E} = \mathcal{E} - \mathcal{E}_s$). For example, a sudden 100 mV. depolarization ($\Delta\mathcal{E} = 100$) increases g_{Na} from its resting value of about 0.04 mmho/cm.[2] to about 100 mmho/cm.[2], an increase of about 2000 times. Threshold voltage $\mathcal{E}_{th}$ is where inward Na^+ current equals the sum of the outward K^+ and Cl^- currents; $\mathcal{E}_s \simeq -60$ mV. Measurements were made on squid giant axon by voltage clamp technique. (After Hodgkin and Huxley, *J. Physiol.,* 1952, *116:*449–472.)

decrease rapidly. Simultaneously the rate of inactivation decreases and the rate of activation increases. There is an important difference between the decrease in Na^+ conductance due to inactivation and that due to polarization of the membrane. Time is required to reactivate inactivated g_{Na}, whereas a decrease in g_{Na} brought about by polarization is immediately available; i.e., a depolarization following shortly after a repolarization will cause an increase in g_{Na}. Inactivation is the main cause of the refractory period (see below).

THE ACTION POTENTIAL

Hodgkin and Huxley analyzed the results of their voltage clamp experiments mathematically and then established the validity of their analysis by successfully predicting the size and shape of the action potential (Fig. 22*A*), the refractory period and many other properties of the nerve impulse.[11] The analysis also permits the calculation of the time course of the changes in Na^+ and K^+ conductance during the action potential and the degree of inactivation of Na^+ conductance factors which are not directly measurable but are the "essence" of the impulse. These calculated conductance changes together with the calculated action potential are graphed in Figure 22B. The experimentally measured action potential (Fig. 22A, bottom) is noticeably but not significantly different from the calculated one (top). The differences are mainly in the falling phase. The regenerative sequence of changes in Na^+ conductance and membrane voltage which generate the rising phase of the action potential has already been described in some detail and will not be further considered. It can be seen from Figure 22B that g_{Na} reaches its peak slightly before the voltage does. Also note that g_{Na} has fallen to about one-sixth of its peak value at a time when repolarization is only half completed. This indicates, and direct calculation confirms, that the major factor acting to decrease Na^+ conductance is inactivation not repolarization.

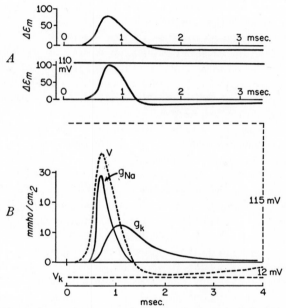

FIG. 22.   A, *top*, Action potential calculated from measurements on voltage clamped axon. *Bottom*, Propagated action potential in an axon. Calculated and measured action potentials differ noticeably in rate of repolarization, but both show same general features. (After Hodgkin and Huxley. *J. Physiol.*, 1952, *117*:500–504.) B, Calculated time courses of membrane voltage (*V*), sodium conductance (g_{Na}) and potassium conductance (g_K) in squid giant axon. Note time relationships between upstroke of action potential and g_{Na} and between g_K and downstroke and afterhyperpolarization. (After Hodgkin, *Proc. roy. Soc.*, 1958, *B148*:1–37.)

Repolarization.   The regenerative nature of the depolarization process insures that it proceeds at the fastest possible rate; i.e., the greater the depolarization, the faster the rate of depolarization. Repolarization, on the other hand, is a *de*generative process; the greater the degree of repolarization, the more slowly it proceeds. The delayed increase in K^+ conductance (Fig. 22B) is the membrane change responsible for rapid repolarization. If g_K did not increase during activity, repolarization would still occur because of the inactivation of Na^+ conductance. However, in such a case the rate of depolarization would be much slower, little faster than the changes in a passive membrane due to its cable properties.

The sequence of events in repolarization is as follows. Depolarization leads to a delayed rise in g_K and an immediate fall in g_{Na}. Na^+ influx falls and K^+ efflux increases, with the result that the membrane starts to repolarize. As repolarization proceeds, both g_K and g_{Na} are decreased by the voltage change, but the fall in g_K is delayed. As a consequence, g_K is still above normal when repolarization is complete and the membrane hyperpolarizes, i.e., the potential goes nearer to $\mathcal{E}_K$ than the resting potential is. Thereafter, g_K and $\mathcal{E}_m$ fall slowly back to their resting values.

Ion Exchange During Activity.[11, 15] It has been repeatedly stressed that the rising phase of the action potential is brought about by a sudden, large influx of Na^+ ions and repolarization by an efflux of K^+ ions. It might be supposed that these "large" fluxes involve the movement of enough ions to change greatly the internal concentrations of Na^+ and K^+. Actually, the concentration changes are very small, the reason being that, although the fluxes are high, they flow only for a short time, and chemically speaking the amount of ions necessary to charge the membrane is small. The minimum net influx of Na^+ required during activity is simply the amount of charge necessary to change the voltage across the membrane capacitor roughly from $\mathcal{E}_K$ to $\mathcal{E}_{Na}$. A similar net efflux of K^+ would suffice to recharge the membrane.

The amount of charge on a capacitor is the product of its capacity and the voltage across it. Such a calculation for squid giant axon shows that the minimum Na^+ entry (or K^+ exit) during one impulse is 1.6 $\mu\mu M$. ($10^{-12} M$.) per cm.^{2} of membrane. A crucial test of the Na^+–K^+ theory of the action potential is to measure net fluxes of Na^+ and K^+ during an impulse by means of radioactive Na^+ and K^+. These measured net fluxes must be greater than the minimum required because, as can be seen from Figure 22B, there is considerable simultaneous inflow of Na^+ and outflow of K^+ during the action potential; such an ion exchange does not affect the charge on the membrane. The measured net Na^+ influx in the squid giant axon is about 4.0 $\mu\mu M$. and the net K^+ efflux about 3.0 $\mu\mu M$. per cm.^{2}-impulse.[15] These values are sufficiently greater than the minimum required to furnish strong additional proof for the Hodgkin Na^+-K^+ theory.[11, 15]

To return to the change in internal concentrations during an impulse, a change in concentration depends not only on the net entry or loss of the ion but also on the volume of axoplasm in which the extra ions distribute themselves. The bigger the fiber, the smaller the concentration change per impulse. For example, in a squid axon 500 μ in diameter, a net Na^+ entry of 3 $\mu\mu M$. per cm.^{2}-impulse raises the internal concentration by only 1.5×10^{-10} M. per cm.^{3}. The internal concentration of Na^+ in the squid is about 50 μM. per cm.^{3}, some 300,000 times greater. However, under the same conditions, the increase in internal Na^+ concentration for a 50 μ fiber would be ten times as great. Nevertheless, the conduction of 30,000 impulses in such a fiber would only double internal Na^+ concentration, even if the Na^+ pump were inoperative. Thus in ordinary sized axons, the Na^+ gain (and K^+ loss) during one impulse is very small. Some mammalian unmedullated axons are only 0.1 μ in diameter. In these fibers rough calculation shows that one impulse will increase internal Na^+ concentration by 10 per cent. If such calculation is valid, the Na^+ pumping rate must be quickly responsive to activity. The large postspike hyperpolarization in these fibers in probably associated with increased active Na^+ extrusion (see Chap. 3).

Nerve fibers conduct impulses up to 100 times per second in normal bodily function. The amount of Na^+ extruded by the Na^+ pump in one second is about the same as the net entry of Na^+ during one impulse. Therefore, during impulse conduction at 100 per second Na^+ entry is 100 times greater than the resting entry. Since, in order to maintain excitability, internal Na^+ must be kept at a low value, the rate of Na^+ pumping must increase as much as 100 times during maintained activity. The function of nerve fibers is to conduct impulses, so the main energy production of nerve likely goes for Na^+ transport. The central nervous system, particularly gray matter, has a high oxygen consumption per gram of tissue. This oxygen must represent metabolism largely devoted to active Na^+-K^+ exchange. It follows that ion exchange is much more rapid in cell bodies than in peripheral nerve.

Propagation of action potential. The interactions between the cable and excitable properties of nerve lead to the propagation of the impulse. Current from polarized inactive regions will flow in the extracellular fluid into an adjacent active region and then return in the axoplasm. This current flow reduces the charge and thus voltage in the inactive region. If this local current flows long enough to depolarize the inactive regions to threshold, they become active and increase the local circuit flow to their immediately adjacent areas of inactive membrane. In this way, a patch of activity travels along the fiber at a constant velocity. Local circuit flow in front of the active

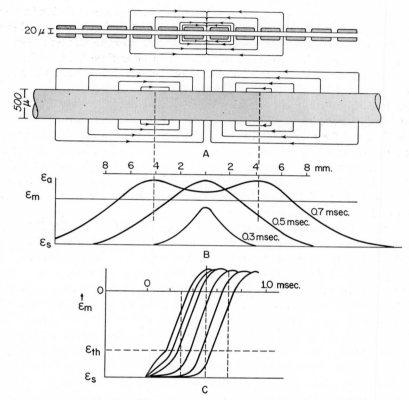

FIG. 23. Impulse propagation in medullated and nonmedullated nerve fibers. *A*, Arrows show local circuit flow into a region of membrane just excited by an external current applied through an intracellular electrode. Current flows in extracellular fluid from polarized unexcited regions, through excited region of membrane, and back to point of origin in axoplasm. (Current flow in axoplasm is not shown.) *Upper*, Frog medullated nerve fiber (diameter, 20 μ) along which local current flows from node to node. (Appreciable capacitive currents flow in internodal regions.) *Lower*, Squid unmedullated giant axon (diameter, 500 μ). Note that membrane current flows outward through inactive regions and inward through active regions and that boundary between active and inactive regions is therefore point where membrane current is zero (*dashed vertical lines*).

B, Plot of ε_m as function of distance along nerve at 0.3, 0.5 and 0.7 millisecond after application of stimulus. Distance scale applies approximately to both nerve fibers in *A*. (Both fibers have conduction speeds of about 20 m. per second.) Regions of membrane between vertical dashed lines are active at 0.5 millisecond; regions outside lines are inactive. Note symmetry around location of stimulating electrode.

C, ε_m as function of time recorded at 0, 1, 2, 4, 6, 8 mm. from the stimulating electrode. Dashed vertical line shows how *B* may be obtained. Points of intersection between constant time (*vertical dashed lines*) and action potentials recorded at different distances give points on the ε_m versus distance curves.

region is the means of exciting inactive regions. Figure 23 illustrates the spread of activity in both directions from a region excited by external current flow.

The curve for x = 0 in Figure 23C shows the sequence of changes in $\mathcal{E}_m$ near the stimulating electrode when the stimulating current is applied abruptly. Until threshold depolarization is reached, $\mathcal{E}_m$ changes are as expected from the cable properties of the fiber. Thereafter, Na^+ influx quickly increases and charges the inside of the membrane to about +30 mV. in the neighborhood of the stimulating electrode. Outside the membrane, the active region around x = 0 is negatively charged, and the adjacent regions, which have not yet been depolarized to threshold, are positively charged. Thus, an electric field is established in the extracellular medium along the membrane. Since the external medium is a good conductor, this field will cause current to flow from inactive to active regions. The 0.3 millisecond line in Figure 23B shows the variation in membrane potential with distance from the stimulating electrode at the time the peak of the action potential at x = 0 is recorded. Only a small region of membrane around the stimulating electrode has become active. At a 0.7 millisecond in later time (Fig. 23B), the active region is much longer and the site of initiation of the action potential is just beginning to recover.

When local circuit current between inactive and active regions has flowed long enough to depolarize the inactive region to its threshold voltage, that region of membrane becomes active, and the resulting large inward Na^+ current is utilized mainly to neutralize the charge on the membrane capacity at that point—i.e., ionic current entering through the membrane exits through the capacitor. The net ionic current through the membrane is local circuit flow. It is usually small compared to I_{Na}; i.e., the "safety factor" of propagation is high, since the available I_{Na} is much greater than that required to excite an adjacent region.

In the curve of membrane voltage versus time at x = 1 mm. (Fig. 23C), it can be seen that the change in $\mathcal{E}_m$ induced by the externally applied stimulating current is attenuated. [The space constant (λ) is assumed to be 2 mm. for convenience.] Because of the attenuation and slowing due to cable properties, the closer the active region is to a particular inactive region, the greater the stimulating effect. It is as though the stimulating electrode were moving nearer. Because local circuit flow is increased when the region at x = 0 becomes active, membrane voltage at x = 1 mm. begins to fall more rapidly than would be expected from the external current, the membrane at x = 1 mm. soon becoming active. Note that the shape of the curve for the subthreshold potential changes has converted from concave downward at x = 0 to concave upward at x = 1 mm. The S shape of the curve for the rising phase is more evident at x = 2 mm. than at x = 1 mm. and slightly more evident at x = 4 mm. than at x = 2 mm. At larger distances the shape becomes constant; this uniformity signifies that the impulse is traveling at constant velocity and that its shape is not changing during propagation. The concave upward foot of the curve for the action potential results from the cable properties of the fiber.

Nerve Impulse as a Wave.   In an active region, membrane current travels inward; conversely, membrane current travels outward through an inactive membrane. Thus the boundary between active and inactive membrane is at the point where membrane current reverses. In terms of the action potential, the border between the inactive and active regions is marked by the inflection point of the rising phase, i.e., the point dividing the rising phase into its concave upward and concave downward portions. Consider the voltage changes at a point on the membrane as a propagating action potential approaches it. The changes are small when the action potential is distant; little current flows from this point into the active region. As the action potential approaches, the flow of current outward through the point increases rapidly; so also does the amount of depolarization. When $\mathcal{E}_m$ at the point reaches threshold, the membrane current reverses and $\mathcal{E}_m$ is changing about as rapidly as it can, because the driving force on Na^+ falls as depolarization proceeds and g_{Na} is near its maximum. Therefore, the curve of $\mathcal{E}_m$ becomes concave downward at the time the membrane current reverses.

If an impulse is propagating as a wave of constant amplitude, duration and velocity, the action potential recorded at one point as a function of time is identical in shape to the action potential recorded at a fixed time as a function of distance along the nerve. The identity of its temporal and spatial aspects is the most typical feature of a wave. For instance, if the duration (t_{ap}) of an action potential is 1 millisecond and if it propagates at a velocity (v) of 20 m. per second, the space (L) occupied by the impulse at any instant in time is $L = vt_{ap} = 20$ m. per second $\times 0.001$ second $= .02$ m. $= 20$ mm.

SOME ASPECTS OF EXCITABILITY

All-or-None Behavior; Excitability. Any depolarizing current strong enough to reduce membrane voltage to threshold initiates the same regenerative sequence of events. A suprathreshold stimulus brings $\mathcal{E}_m$ to threshold sooner, but does not significantly affect the overwhelming course of the events (curve 4, Fig. 19B). A weaker (subthreshold) stimulus produces no propagating response, but there may be a local response (curve 3a, Fig. 19B) in the region of the stimulating electrode. The response of a nerve to a stimulus is either absent or present to its full capabilities—"all-or-none" behavior.

All-or-none behavior is typical of excitable tissues, but, more generally, it occurs in any regenerative process. A mouse nibbling on the bait on the trigger of a mousetrap elicits either an "all" response or (if he is lucky) a "none" response from the trap. In fact "all-or-none" and "excitable" have the same general meaning, although "all-or-none" refers to the nature of the response and "excitable" refers to the existence of a threshold of response. *Excitability* is defined as the reciprocal of threshold depolarization ($\mathcal{E}_{th} - \mathcal{E}_s$) and is usually stated in terms of a ratio of test excitability to excitability in a standard situation.

Refractory Period. Since inactivation of g_{Na} is almost complete at the end of the action potential, a depolarizing current applied at this time will not cause much increase in g_{Na}. Therefore, the fiber is refractory (inexcitable). That is, a stimulating current, no matter how strong, cannot initiate a regenerative response. A little later, after some activation has occurred, a depolarizing current will cause a larger increase in g_{Na}, and an action potential smaller than normal may be generated. The threshold current will be above normal because the available g_{Na} is low and also because g_K is still above normal. Inactivated Na^+ conductance means that excitability is low (threshold high), because greater depolarization is needed to increase g_{Na} enough to make net Na^+ inflow exceed net K^+ inflow. A raised g_K means that more current is required to produce a given depolarization; hence this factor decreases excitability also. Taken together, these two effects, which disappear in a few milliseconds, account for both the absolute and the relatively refractory periods.

Strength-duration curve. A good approximation to the shape of the strength-duration curve (shown in Fig. 13) may be derived as follows. Assume that the area of membrane affected by the stimulating current is small enough to be represented by a single resistance-capacitance circuit (Fig. 18) and that the requirement for a threshold stimulus is that $\mathcal{E}_m$ be depolarized a fixed amount. The change in $\mathcal{E}_m$ ($\Delta\mathcal{E}_m = \mathcal{E}_m - \mathcal{E}_t$) is described by the equation

$$\Delta\mathcal{E}_m = I_s r_m(1 - e^{-t/\tau})$$

where I_s is the portion of the stimulating current flowing through the membrane resistance (r_m) at the site of the stimulating electrode, and $\tau = r_m c_m$ (the membrane time constant). The fiber will fire if $\Delta\mathcal{E}_m$ reaches some critical value ($\Delta\mathcal{E}_{th}$). Setting $\Delta\mathcal{E}_m = \Delta\mathcal{E}_{th}$ in the above equation and solving for I_s as a function of t gives

$$I_s = \frac{\Delta\mathcal{E}_{th}}{r_m(1 - e^{-t/\tau})}$$

This is a relation between the length of time (t) that a stimulating current flows and the strength of the current. If t is large, the strength of the stimulating current (I_m) is minimum; $I_m = \Delta\mathcal{E}_{th}/r_m$. If t is small, larger currents are required. If $I_m = \Delta\mathcal{E}_{th}/r_m$ is substituted into this equation, it becomes, for a time, much less than τ; $I_s = I_m\tau_m/t$, or $I_st = I_m\tau_m$. In other words, for short shocks, a constant amount of charge ($I_m\tau_m$) will stimulate the fiber; i.e., all the applied current enters the membrane capacity. Chronaxy, defined in Figure 13, is directly proportional to the membrane time constant. Chronaxy $= \tau_m\ln2$.

Accommodation and Block. A brief subthreshold stimulus applied to a nerve fiber increases excitability (lowers threshold) in the region of application. If a brief current pulse too weak to initiate an impulse is followed shortly by a second stimulus, also normally subthreshold, delivered to the same or a nearby point, the nerve may be excited; i.e., the first pulse increased the excitability of the stimulated portion of the fiber. This behavior is expected from the cable properties of nerve fibers. A brief, sub-threshold depolarizing stimulus reduces $\mathcal{E}_m$ over a distance (order of 3λ) around the point of application and for a time afterward (order of 3τ). Thus, a relatively weaker second stimulus may further reduce $\mathcal{E}_m$ and initiate an impulse.

In contrast, a prolonged subthreshold stimulus may either increase or decrease excitability. The change in excitability depends on the relative effect of the depolarizing current on $\mathcal{E}_m$, and on the effect of the changes in $\mathcal{E}_m$ on the steady state inactivation of g_{Na}. The curve relating the magnitude of the rapidly available g_{Na} to $\mathcal{E}_m$ is S shaped; a depolarization reduces the g_{Na} available. If, as in the squid giant axon, the resting potential is such that an appreciable amount of g_{Na} is always inactivated, the depolar-ization produced by a prolonged subthreshold stimulus may reduce g_{Na} to such low levels that the stimulus required to initiate an impulse must be stronger than normal; i.e., the reduction in g_{Na} has increased the threshold. An additional factor may be the depolarization-induced increase in g_K, which makes an applied current less effective in changing $\mathcal{E}_m$. If a prolonged subthreshold depolarization reduces the excitability of a nerve, or increases it less than expected, the nerve is said to have *accommodated* to the stimulus. The process of *accommodation* is evidently closely related to the process of inac-tivation and activation of g_{Na}.

Conduction can be blocked at a point on a nerve fiber by a strong, slowly rising, depolarizing current. If the depolarizing current increases slowly enough, inactivation occurs concomitantly. As a result, g_{Na} will not increase sufficiently to reverse the mem-brane current. Similarly, a suddenly applied suprathreshold current may block conduc-tion after first initiating one or more impulses; the block occurs when inactivation has proceeded far enough. The blockage of impulse generation by depolarizing current occurs only in the region of the stimulating cathode. Impulses will propagate on either side of the blocked region, but not through it. This method of blocking impulse conduc-tion is often called *cathodal block*. Better terms are *depolarization block* or *inactivation block*.

Depolarization block can be produced in many ways other than by applying current. Since a sufficient increase in $[K^+]_o$, anoxia and injury all depolarize the mem-brane, they all block impulse conduction. An expected characteristic of depolarization block is that stimuli not strong enough to cause block will increase the excitability. Anoxia probably blocks indirectly by reducing the activity of the Na^+-K^+ pump, so that K^+ ions lost from cells accumulate in the extracellular fluid. An injury such as crushing blocks by destroying the structure of the membrane. As a consequence, its selective permeability properties are lost, an event causing a fall in the absolute value of $\mathcal{E}_m$. At the moment of the crush, a number of impulses are discharged before inactiva-tion is completed in adjacent undamaged, depolarized regions. Local anesthetics block conduction in nerve by increasing inactivation without altering membrane voltage.[22] Depolarization block, no matter how induced, is relieved by a hyperpolarizing current simply because it increases the absolute value of $\mathcal{E}_m$.

A sufficient hyperpolarization of the membrane can also block conduction in a nerve. Block occurs if ε_m is made so large that local circuit flow from the hyperpolarized region into an approaching active region is insufficient to depolarize the hyperpolarized region to threshold. This phenomenon is called *anodal* or, better, *hyperpolarization block*.

Conduction Velocity. A frog medullated fiber 20 μ in diameter has the same conduction velocity (20 m. per second) as a squid giant axon 500 μ in diameter. Available evidence indicates that membrane current densities during activity at a node are about twice those along a squid giant axon.[1] However, it is doubtful that density of current is the major reason for the high conduction velocity of noded fibers. If g_{Na} is assumed to be much larger than g_K during activity, the factors most likely of importance in determining the conduction velocity of an impulse are the membrane capacity and the axoplasmic resistance; the larger the internal resistance and membrane capacitance are, the longer the time needed for local circuit currents to excite a region. It seems reasonable, therefore, to attribute the high conduction velocity of medullated fibers to their myelin sheaths and the resulting low membrane capacity.[17] This argument also indicates that conduction velocity is a direct function of fiber diameter; internal resistance depends inversely on the cross-sectional area, and velocity depends inversely on internal resistance. Hodgkin[6] has shown that, for constant membrane and axoplasmic properties, the conduction velocity should vary directly with the square root of the fiber diameter in nonmedullated fibers. In medullated nerve fibers the experimentally determined velocity is directly proportional to diameter (Chap. 3).

REFERENCES

1. DODGE, F. R. and FRANKENHAEUSER, B. *J. Physiol.*, 1958, *143*:76–90.
2. HEBB, C. O. *Physiol. Rev.*, 1957, *37*:196–220.
3. HODGKIN, A. L. *J. Physiol.*, 1937, *90*:183–210.
4. HODGKIN, A. L. *J. Physiol.*, 1947, *106*:305–318.
5. HODGKIN, A. L. *Biol. Rev.*, 1951, *26*:339–409.
6. HODGKIN, A. L. *J. Physiol.*, 1954, *125*:221–224.
7. HODGKIN, A. L. *Proc. roy. Soc.*, 1958, *B148*:1–37.
8. HODGKIN, A. L. and HUXLEY, A. F. *J. Physiol.*, 1952, *116*:449–472.
9. HODGKIN, A. L. and HUXLEY, A. F. *J. Physiol.*, 1952, *116*:473–496.
10. HODGKIN, A. L. and HUXLEY, A. F. *J. Physiol.*, 1952, *116*:497–506.
11. HODGKIN, A. L. and HUXLEY, A. F. *J. Physiol.*, 1952, *117*:500–544.
12. HODGKIN, A. L. and HUXLEY, A. F. *J. Physiol.*, 1953, *121*:403–414.
13. HODGKIN, A. L., HUXLEY, A. F. and KATZ, B. *J. Physiol.*, 1952, *116*:424–448.
14. HODGKIN, A. L. and KATZ, B. *J. Physiol.*, 1949, *108*:37–77.
15. HODGKIN, A. L. and KEYNES, R. D. *J. Physiol.*, 1955, *128*:28–60.
16. HODGKIN, A. L. and RUSHTON, W. A. H. *Proc. roy. Soc.*, 1946, *B133*:444–479.
17. HODLER, J., STAMPFLI, R. and TASAKI, I. *Amer. J. Physiol.*, 1952, *170*:375–389.
18. LORENTE DE NÓ, R. *Stud. Rockefeller Inst. med. Res.*, 1947, *131*(2):1–548.
19. MARMONT, G. *J. cell. comp. Physiol.*, 1949, *34*:351–382.
20. NACHMANSOHN, D. *Chemical and molecular basis of nerve activity*, New York, Academic Press, 1959, xi, 235 pp.
21. STÄMPFLI, R. *Ann. N. Y. Acad. Sci.*, 1959, *81*:265–284.
22. TAYLOR, R. E. *Amer. J. Physiol.*, 1959, *196*:1071–1078.

CHAPTER 3

Special Properties of Nerve Trunks and Tracts

By HARRY D. PATTON

IN the preceding chapters attention was focused on the general electrical properties common to the membranes of all excitable elements. For that purpose it was desirable to concentrate on data obtained from single nerve and muscle cells with the aid of intracellularly placed ultramicroelectrodes because such methods provide the most direct measure of membrane properties. Also, in initial consideration of the general properties of excitable membranes, quantitative variances arising from differences in cell species could profitably be overlooked.

Even though all axons are qualitatively alike, close scrutiny reveals that individual specimens display considerable quantitative variance in such parameters as, for example, conduction speed and threshold to externally applied electrical currents. It is the purpose of this chapter, then, to describe these special properties of the individual constituents of nerve trunks and tracts and to relate these properties to structural differences such as fiber diameters.

Data for comparison of the special properties of individual nerve fibers may be obtained in two ways. First, intracellular recordings from a great many individual fibers may be made in an attempt to sample the entire population of a trunk. This method has been employed on a limited basis,[18] but is tedious and time consuming. In addition, it suffers from the defect that sampling is distributed in time, so that the conditions may alter from sample to sample or from preparation to preparation. Also, intracellular sampling is biased, because small fibers are less tolerant of penetration than are larger axons. A more satisfactory method is to record the activity of a bundle of nerve fibers excited in concert. Such activity in a nerve trunk is called the *compound action potential*, a term which implies that the recorded potential is compounded from the individual action potentials of the constituent axons.

To record compound potentials the recording electrodes must, of course, be placed extracellularly, for an intracellular electrode is little influenced by activity in fibers adjacent to the one penetrated. Usually, one electrode is placed on the nerve trunk; the other is placed either on some other part of the same trunk or, when provision is made for completion of the electrical circuit, on some inactive structure such as bone or skin. With this arrangement, a difference of potential is recorded between the "active" electrode as it is passed by conducted action potentials and the "reference" electrode on some structure which is inactive at that time.

An important feature of extracellular recording is that the potential sources, i.e., the nerve fibers, are invariably surrounded by an aqueous conducting medium, either the interstitial fluid or some artifically constructed electrolytic medium applied to the trunk to prevent desiccation. Such a system, in which the potential source is immersed in a conducting medium, is called a *volume conductor*, and interpretation of differences of potential between two points in the conducting medium requires special knowledge of the properties of volume conductors.

The influence of the external conducting medium is appreciable only when its volume is very large with respect to the volume of the structure generating the potential. Such is the case when potentials are recorded through electrodes placed on the surface

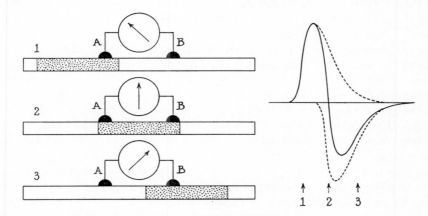

FIG. 24. Diphasic recording of action potential of nerve.

Left, Stippled area represents action potential progressing from left to right in 1, 2 and 3. In 1, electrode *A* is negative to electrode *B;* in 2, *A* and *B* are equipotential; in 3, *B* is negative with respect to *A*.

Right, Solid line trace is recorded diphasic action potential; numbered arrows below indicate instantaneous potential differences corresponding to three stages of conduction shown at left. Broken lines indicate true electrical changes at each electrode; recorded potential is their algebraic sum.

of the brain or the spinal cord, or when the electrical activity of the contracting heart is recorded through electrodes placed on the surface of the body (electrocardiogram). In these instances, the entire body acts as a uniform conducting medium surrounding the relatively small structures generating the potentials. Happily, the volume of the external conducting medium surrounding peripheral nerve trunks can be limited simply by lifting the nerve onto electrodes in air or, better still, by suspending the nerve in an insulating medium such as mineral oil so that only a thin film of external conductor surrounds the fibers and the trunk. The relatively simple compound action potential of peripheral nerve trunks will therefore be considered first, the discussion of potential configurations recorded in volume being postponed.

Diphasic and Monophasic Recording. Figure 24 shows diagrammatically an electrode arrangement suitable for recording the compound action potential of a nerve trunk. The nerve is equipped with a pair of recording electrodes, *A* and *B*; to minimize contact with the surrounding tissues, it is either lifted into the air or immersed in a pool of mineral oil. In the resting state the fibers under both recording leads are externally electropositive, and no difference of potential between them is recorded. When a volley of impulses* (stippled area) approaching A from the left reaches the position indicated in *1*, a difference of potential is recorded between A and B, because the active fibers at A are externally electronegative to the as yet quiescent fibers at B. This difference in potential is registered as an upward deflection of the recording beam, as shown in the accompanying trace (heavy line).† In diagram *2*, the conducted volley has progressed so that both electrodes are in contact with equally depolarized fibers; consequently, the recording beam has returned to the zero potential. In diagram *3*, the wave of depolarization has progressed beyond A (i.e., the fibers under A have repolarized), so that B is now relatively negative to A and the recording beam is accordingly deflected downward. As the depolarization passes beyond B, the beam returns to zero. The potential configuration recorded in this way, shown diagrammatically by the heavy line tracing in Figure 24, is known as a *diphasic compound action potential.*

Diphasic recording is useful if one wishes to determine whether an electrical change is propagated, but for other purposes the method has certain undesirable features. First, if, as in Figure 24, the distance between the recording electrodes is less than the wave length of the action potential (i.e., the length of fiber occupied by an action potential at any time), both the time course and the amplitude of the electrical events at each electrode are distorted, because activity reaches the distal electrode before repolarization occurs at the proximal electrode. The extent of this distortion may be seen in Figure 24 by comparing the traces depicted by the dotted lines (which are extrapolations of the electrical changes at each electrode) with the actually recorded algebraic summation of these changes (heavy line). This kind of cancellation is difficult to avoid, since the wave length of an action potential in a large nerve fiber is as much as 6 cm.

An even more serious defect arises from the fact, shortly to be developed, that the speed of conduction differs in different fibers in the trunk. Consequently, activity in rapidly conducting nerve fibers can reach the distal electrode at a time when the action potentials in more slowly conducting fibers have proceeded only as far as the proximal electrode. Hence, the contributions of rapidly and slowly conducting fibers may tend to cancel one another, for the recording arrangement detects only differences of potential.

Fortunately, the defects inherent in diphasic recording are easily circumvented by changing the experimental conditions to those shown in Figure 25. To block conduction, the fibers underlying electrode B are permanently depolarized by crushing, burning, cutting, or topically applying potassium salts. As a result, a steady difference of potential, the *injury* or *demarcation potential*,‡ develops between electrodes A and B. Now, when a

---

* A *volley of impulses* means a discharge set up in a multifibered nerve trunk or tract by a single brief stimulus, so that, although many constituent fibers are excited, none discharges more than once. The term should not be confused with a *train* or *burst of impulses*, terms which imply repetitive discharge of the constituent fibers, as, for example, when the trunk is *tetanically* or repetitively stimulated.

† The direction of the deflection is, of course, arbitrary and can be reversed by reversing the connections to the recording system.

‡ The demarcation potential might be expected to approximate the membrane potential of the injured fiber, since electrode B is connected to a region in which the steady membrane potential has been reduced to zero by destruction of the membrane. However, current will flow in the external medium from adjacent uninjured regions into the injured region and return through the axoplasm in each fiber. Consequently, the potential drop between the electrodes depends on the relative external and internal resistances of each fiber. Since internal resistance in fibers of the size considered here is quite high, the demarcation potential is only about one-fourth to one-third of the steady transmembrane potential. The shunting can be minimized by increasing the resistance of the external medium, e.g., by bathing the nerve at one recording site with isotonic sucrose. In such instances the demarcation potential approaches closely the true membrane potential. This method has proved useful in measuring action and membrane potentials of fibers too small to tolerate direct measurements with intracellular electrodes.[16]

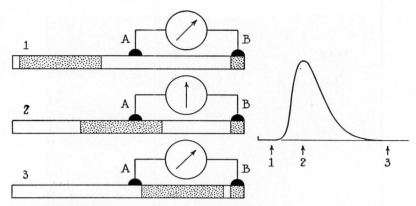

FIG. 25.   Monophasic recording of nerve action potential.

Left, Small stippled area under *B* indicates nerve has been injured at this point. Consequently a steady injury potential is recorded in 1, *B* being negative to *A*. As action potential (long stippled area) progresses to *A* in 2; *A* and *B* become equipotential. In 3, action potential progresses beyond *A* and *B* is once more negative to *A*.

Right, Recorded monophasic action potential; numbered arrows indicate instantaneous potentials recorded at three stages of conduction shown at left.

volley of impulses approaches and passes *A*, the full course of the activity at *A* is recorded as a negative-going variation of the steady demarcation potential, as illustrated in Figure 25. Activity recorded in this manner is called a *monophasic compound action potential*. For the reasons mentioned above, monophasic recording is used almost exclusively in studies of the compound action potential of nerve trunks.

In physiology the convention is to arrange the recording leads so that external negativity (i.e., activity under the "active" electrode) yields an upward deflection. This deviation from the convention in physics of displaying potentials "positive-up, negative-down" originally resulted from esthetic considerations. The first bioelectric transient observed was the negative-going monophasic action potential, or negative variation, and since rising deflections are generally more pleasing psychologically and esthetically than descending ones, the arbitrary convention of "negative-up, positive-down" was adopted. On a sheer priority basis, therefore, physiologists who record positive-going deflections (e.g., cortical surface potentials) have the choice of heretical nonconformism or submission to the fate of purveying depressing descending deflections.

Components of the Compound Action Potential of Peripheral Nerves. The compound action potential recorded monophasically from a nerve trunk excited by a maximal* shock is usually irregular in contour, displaying a series of elevations displaced in time. Figure 26 shows a representative tracing, on a fast time base, of the first portion of the compound action potential in the cat saphenous nerve, recorded 3.4 cm. from the locus of stimulation; the successive components are labeled with Greek letters. Two hypotheses may be formulated to explain the polymodal contour of the compound potential: (i) some fibers may discharge repetitively to the stimulus or (ii) the constituent fibers may conduct impulses at different speeds so that arrival time at the recording electrode is different for impulses in different fibers.

The second hypothesis can be put to a simple experimental test; if different fibers conduct impulses at different speeds, the temporal separation of the elevations should increase as the conduction distance increases. Figure 27 shows an experiment in which the first two components (α and β) of the compound action potential in a frog sciatic nerve were tested for compliance with this requirement. Monophasic recording leads were attached to the nerve at four sites to sample the configuration of the compound

---

* A maximal stimulus or shock is one which produces a maximal response of the stimulated structure; i.e., stronger stimuli do not produce greater responses.

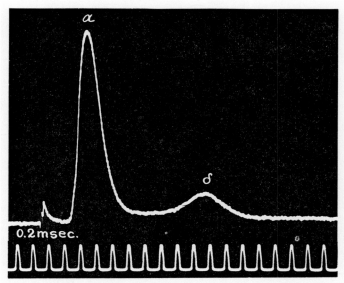

FIG. 26. Compound action potential of cat's saphenous nerve recorded 3.4 cm. from locus of stimulation. Temperature 37.5° C. (Courtsey of Dr. H. S. Gasser.)

action potential at four distances from the stimulating electrode (S). At the farthest recording site (distance: 143 mm.), the α and β components were clearly separated. At the successively shorter conduction distances, the two elevations merged progressively until, at the most proximal electrode site (distance: 21 mm.), the overlap was so nearly complete that the individual components were scarcely distinguishable. Diagonal lines were then drawn between zero distance and the respective beginnings of α and β in the lowermost record, where the two components are clearly separated. The line so constructed for α intercepts with satisfactory precision the beginning of the α deflection in all traces. Similarly, the line for the β deflection falls close to the computed onset of the β component indicated by small circles in the two intermediate traces. These results are best explained if it is assumed that impulses beginning together at S become temporally dispersed as the conduction distance increases because they traverse fibers with different uniform conduction speeds.

Closer scrutiny of the traces in which the components are clearly separated reveals that at increasing distances each deflection becomes broader in base and lower in amplitude. Nevertheless, planimetric measurements indicate that the area lying under each deflection remains constant, irrespective of the conduction distance. This finding suggests that within a group, as well as from group to group, there is a continuous spectrum of conduction speeds. This conclusion is borne out by determinations of conduction velocity in single axons. Among mammalian myelinated somatic fibers, representatives can be found for all speeds between about 5 m. per second and 120 m. per second. It will be pointed out later that the separation of peaks in the compound action potential results not from absolute discontinuities in the velocity spectrum but rather from unequal numerical distribution of fibers representing restricted bands of the spectrum.

Another readily demonstrable difference between fibers contributing to the various components (α, β, γ, etc.) of the compound action potential lies in the *thresholds to electrical stimulation*. As the shock to a nerve trunk is increased progressively from its threshold to maximal intensities, the successive components appear in the recordings in the order α, β, γ, etc. In other words, conduction velocity and electrical threshold are inversely

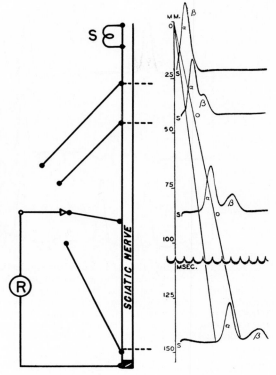

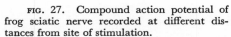

FIG. 27. Compound action potential of frog sciatic nerve recorded at different distances from site of stimulation.

Left, Diagram of recording apparatus: *S,* stimulus; *R,* recorder.

Right, Only the first two elevations, α and β are shown. As conduction increases, α and β become clearly separated in time (temporal dispersion) because they reflect activity of fibers' conduction at different rates. Diagonal straight lines are drawn through onsets of α and β deflections; slopes of these lines give conduction rates of most rapidly conducting α and β fibers. (After Erlanger and Gasser. *Electrical signs of nervous activity.* Philadelphia, University of Pennsylvania Press, 1937.)

related, the rapidly conducting axons being more easily excited than the slower ones. It can be justifiably argued that axon thresholds to electrical excitation have little intrinsic physiologic significance, but the relationship just described provides a valuable experimental tool, for it permits selective excitation of rapidly conducting fibers to the exclusion of slowly conducting fibers.

This tool is used repeatedly in neurophysiologic experimentation. An example pertinent to the present discussion is shown in Figure 28, which illustrates an experiment demonstrating conclusively that the α and β components arise independently from activity in different nerve fibers. The compound action potential was recorded from a site on the nerve trunk at a distance from the stimulating electrodes sufficient to separate clearly the α and β deflections. Two shock strengths were used. The first stimulus was relatively weak and elicited only an α deflection, seen in *A*. The second shock was more intense and produced both α and β deflections (labeled α_2 and β_2 in *B*). In traces *C-H*, both shocks were applied to the nerve at gradually decreasing intershock intervals. At short intervals (traces *E-H*) α_2, coming in the refractory period of α, was progressively delayed and attenuated until, in trace *H*, α_2 was completely obliterated. At all intervals β_2 remained constant in amplitude and latency. The failure of α activity to induce refractoriness in elements responsible for β activity is an elegant and compelling proof that α and β components of the compound action potential are independently conducted by different fibers. Similar observations on γ, δ and other later components indicate that these, too, are mediated by separate groups of axons.

Relation between conduction speed and fiber diameter. The finding that nerve trunks are composed of elements having different properties (conduction speed and electrical threshold) leads naturally to the question: Can these differences in properties be correlated with morphologic differences between axons? There are numerous structural

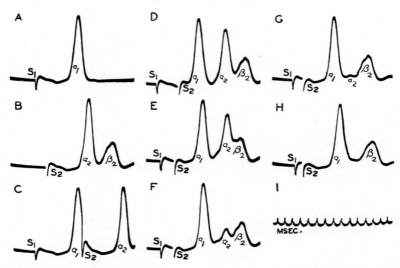

FIG. 28. Demonstration of independent conduction of α and β elevations of frog sciatic nerve. *A*, Stimulation by single shock (S_1) at strength just sufficient to produce maximal alpha elevation (α_1). *B*, Stimulation by stronger shock (S_2) produces an alpha elevation (α_2) and a beta (β_2) elevation. In records *C-H*, S_2 follows S_1 at progressively shorter intervals, so that deflection α_2 falls increasingly into refractory period of deflection α_1 until, in *H*, α_2 is completely obliterated. β_2 deflection is unaltered by refractory obliteration of α_2. *I*, Time scale. (From Erlanger and Gasser. *Electrical signs of nervous activity.* Philadelphia, University of Pennsylvania Press, 1937.)

differences between axons, such as diameter, presence or absence of a myelin sheath* and the relation of the Schwann sheath to the axon. At present, attention is focused on variations in diameter. For this purpose it is instructive to examine the myelinated somatic axons, or A fibers as they are called, because they constitute a set in which diameter is the only prominent morphologic variable. It is the A fibers that are responsible for the elevations labeled α and δ in Figure 26. When cross sections of various somatic nerve trunks treated with the myelin stain osmic acid are examined, the largest stained fibers are about 22 μ in diameter, the smallest about 1 μ. Between these two extremes there is a continuous spectrum of diameters, but the number of fibers in each portion of the diameter spectrum varies; indeed, in some nerve trunks certain bands of the spectrum may lack representation altogether.

The A fibers taken as a whole constitute a similar spectrum with respect to conduction rates. On purely theoretical grounds one would expect the largest fibers to conduct most rapidly, since their internal longitudinal resistance (the local circuit through which, according to theory, current must flow to excite adjacent nodes) is relatively low. In point of fact, it can be shown that the conduction rate and the fiber diameter of A fibers are linearly related. Hursh[10] plotted maximal conduction rates of various nerve trunks against the sizes of the largest myelinated fibers he found when he examined the trunks histologically, the trunks having been selected so that they provided a wide range of maximal fiber diameters. As shown in Figure 29, his results indicate that a straight line with a slope of 6 m. per second per μ of over-all diameter fits the observed points with reasonable accuracy.

Gasser and Grundfest[9] found an even closer approximation to exact linearity when they measured the diameter of the axon within the myelin sheath, rather than the over-all diameter; in their study, the ratio between conduction rate (in meters per second)

---

* Actually, all axons possess at least a vestige of a myelin sheath. It is common practice, however, to label as unmyelinated those axons in which no myelin is detectable by light microscopy.

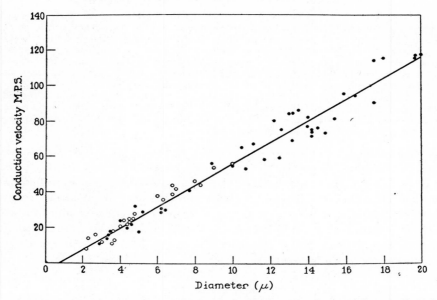

FIG. 29.   Linear relation between conduction rate and diameter of mammalian myelinated nerve fibers. Slope of line is approximately 6 m. per second per μ of diameter. (After Hursh, from Gasser. *Ohio J. Sci.*, 1941, *41*:145–159.)

and axon diameter (in microns) was 8.7. The relationship between conduction speed and fiber diameter is exceedingly useful because it permits reasonably accurate computation of one variable if the other is known. It must be emphasized, however, that the quantitative relationships just described apply only to the A fibers and not to other fiber types.

SYNTHESIS OF THE COMPOUND SPIKE POTENTIAL.[9]   As pointed out above, the direct relationship between conduction rate and fiber diameter provides information for reconstructing the A fiber compound spike potential of a nerve trunk from its constituent fiber diameter spectrum as determined histologically. The only additional data needed are estimates of spike duration and amplitude as a function of fiber size. The first of these estimates is simple to make since studies of single fibers indicate that spike duration for A fibers is about 0.5 millisecond, irrespective of fiber size. Similar studies indicate that spike amplitude varies linearly and directly with fiber diameter.* With these three relationships one can proceed to reconstruct the spike potential from the histologic data, the degree of fit between reconstructed and recorded potentials being a critical test of the proposed concept of the compound spike.

To make a reconstruction like the one shown in Figure 30, the fibers are enumerated and classified in groups according to diameter. Triangles approximating the shape of an axon spike are then drawn for each mean diameter, the height of the triangles being the product of the mean diameter of the group and of the number of fibers in the group. In this way, the diameter-spike amplitude relation is accommodated, and the potential contributed by each size group is found in arbitrary units; for example, 50 fibers of 10 μ diameter would give a triangle 500 arbitrary units high, and 50 fibers 2 μ in diameter would give a triangle only 100 units high. The base of each triangle (spike duration) is made equivalent to 0.5 millisecond on the abscissa. Next, the triangles are located along the abscissa relative to one another by means of the diameter-velocity relationship.

As the conduction time of the largest fibers (and hence those conducting the impulse most rapidly) is the latency of the first elevation of the previously recorded spike potential, it is easy to place the first triangle on the abscissa. In the example presented in Figure 30, that latency (conduction time) was 0.4 millisecond, and the conduction distance was 4 cm.; thus, the largest fibers in the nerve conducted impulses at 100 m. per second. From histologic study of the nerve it is known that the largest fibers were 14 μ in diameter. Therefore, the factor for converting diameter to conduction velocity (for the specific conditions of recording and with the assumption that the relation is linear) is 100/14 or 7.14. By means of this factor, conduction velocities are assigned to each size group. The 10 μ fibers

* It should be realized that a relation between spike size and fiber diameter is a consequence of extracellular recording, for there is no *a priori* reason to suspect that the voltage change across the membrane during activity varies with fiber size.

would have a conduction rate of 71.4 m. per second, and the 5 μ fibers a rate of 35.7 m. per second. From these velocities, the time required for the impulse to be conducted 4 cm. is calculated. Thus, just as impulses in the 100 m. per second (or 14 μ) fibers traveled this distance in 0.4 millisecond, so impulses in the 71.4 m. per second (or 10 μ) fibers would require 0.56 millisecond and those in the 35.7 m. per second (or 5 μ) fibers would require 1.12 milliseconds. On the basis of these calculations, the triangles representing the spike potentials of the groups of smaller fibers are arranged along the time abscissa in proper relation to the triangle representing the largest fibers.

All that remains is to draw the complete spike potential by algebraic summation of the individual triangles and to compare it with the recorded potential. In Figure 30 such a comparison is made, the broken line showing the reconstructed potential at the two points where it did not coincide exactly with the recorded potential as indicated by the solid line.

Afterpotentials. The compound action potential recorded at short conduction distances to minimize dispersion of components does not always terminate with the negative variation or spike potential. Often, a negative deflection is grafted onto the tail of the declining spike. Usually, the deflection looks deceptively like a prolongation of the spike decline, but in some instances a rising phase makes distinct the separate identity of the second wave. This deflection is known as the *negative afterpotential*. Following the decline of the negative afterpotential to the baseline, a prolonged positive deflection, the *positive afterpotential*, occurs.

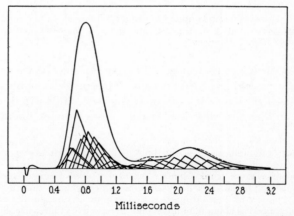

0   0.4   0.8   1.2   1.6   2.0   2.4   2.8   3.2
Milliseconds

FIG. 30.   Reconstruction of compound action potential of myelinated fibers of cat saphenous nerve from histologic data. Large wave (solid line) is recorded action potential. Triangles represent contribution of various fiber components (see text). Dotted line shows deviation of sum of triangles (reconstructed potential) from recorded potential. (From Gasser and Grundfest. *Amer. J. Physiol.*, 1939, *127*:393–414.)

Negative and positive afterpotentials have certain features in common. (i) Both are consequences of, and hence dependent upon, antecedent spike activity. (ii) Both are of very low amplitude and (iii) of long duration relative to the spike (see Fig. 31). (iv) Both are highly labile and heavily dependent upon the metabolic state and previous history of the fiber.

The negative afterpotential rarely exceeds 3 to 5 per cent, and the positive afterpotential is usually only 0.2 to 4.0 per cent of the amplitude of the antecedent spike. An exception is found in small unmyelinated afferent fibers, in which the positive afterpotential may be as much as 10 to 30 per cent of the amplitude of the spike. The relative magnitudes of the spike and of the afterpotentials are illustrated in the scale diagram in Figure 31. Because their amplitudes are small, the afterpotentials can be satisfactorily visualized only at high amplification, which throws the greater part of the antecedent spike off the oscilloscope screen (see Fig. 32).

It should be emphasized that the relative sizes of spikes and afterpotentials quoted above are based on measurements of *compound action potentials* and therefore do not accurately reflect the relative sizes of the potentials in individual fibers. Because the spikes are of short duration, any temporal dispersion markedly reduces the amplitude of the compound spike. Afterpotentials are of much longer duration (see below) and hence suffer much less decrement because of dispersion. Hence, measurements of compound potentials give an exaggerated picture of the relative magnitude of afterpotentials.

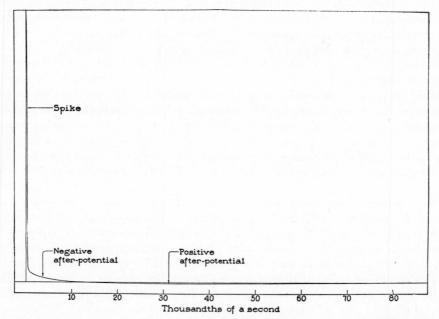

FIG. 31.   Scale diagram of complete action potential of large myelinated nerve fibers in the cat, drawn so that spike potential and afterpotentials appear in their correct relative sizes and time relations. (From Gasser. *J. appl. Phys.*, 1938, *9*:88–96.)

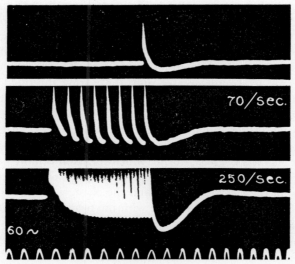

FIG. 32.   Afterpotentials of phrenic nerve following single (*upper* trace) and repetitive (*middle* and *lower* traces) stimulation. Amplification is so high that spike crest is far off this page. Records shown begin with negative afterpotential and continue below baseline into positive afterpotential. Time scale, 16.7 milliseconds. (From Gasser. *J. appl. Phys.*, 1938, *9*:88–96.)

The contrast in the durations of the spike and the afterpotentials is quite striking. Whereas the spike usually lasts only a fraction of a millisecond, the negative afterpotential may have a duration of 12 to 80 milliseconds, and the positive afterpotential may persist for 40 to 1000 milliseconds.

In freshly excised frog nerve, the negative afterpotential is often inconspicuous or absent, but grows as the nerve remains in a bath of Ringer's solution. The negative afterpotential is also markedly accentuated in both amplitude and duration by treatment of the nerve with the alkaloid veratrine. The positive afterpotential, on the other hand, is greatly increased by repetitive stimulation of the nerve trunk (Fig. 32).

The origin of the afterpotentials is not entirely clear. Their timing suggests that they reflect metabolic processes associated with the recovery process. It is significant that 95 to 98 per cent of the increase in heat production by tetanized nerve occurs during the recovery period and runs a time course roughly corresponding to that of the afterpotentials. It may be that the positive afterpotential is a small, long-lasting, electrical manifestation of increased active extrusion of the Na^+ which accumulates in the fiber during activity. Such an explanation accords with the accentuation of the positive afterpotential following tetanic stimulation which, of course, favors intracellular accumulation of Na^+.

This hypothesis is also consistent with the striking prominence of positive afterpotentials in small unmyelinated nerve fibers, in which the transfer of Na^+ into the relatively small intracellular volume during activity might well produce an appreciable increase in the intracellular concentration of Na^+. Also, as described in more detail below, the extracellular space surrounding unmyelinated fibers is peculiarly restricted, so that extracellular accumulation of K^+ during activity may well produce significant increases in the external concentration of this ion. Both these conditions necessitate rapid and efficient Na^+-K^+ pumping to keep the fiber from becoming unexcitable. In this respect it is significant that replacing the extracellular Na^+ with lithium or poisoning the Na^+-K^+ pump with metabolic poisons abolishes the post-tetanic positive afterpotential.[15] Whatever the mechanism of the afterpotentials, their principal significance lies in the changes in excitability accompanying them.

Excitability and afterpotentials. It has already been pointed out that generation of an action potential in an axon makes the axon temporarily refractory to a second stimulus. During the early part of this refractory period the axon is completely inexcitable, regardless of the stimulus strength (absolutely refractory period). Following this absolutely refractory period, excitability gradually recovers (i.e., the threshold becomes finite) along an approximately exponential time course. This period, during which the axon is accessible only to stimuli greater than the resting threshold, is the relatively refractory period. Together, the two refractory periods, absolute and relative, correspond in time with the spike proper. When the action potential has a prominent negative afterpotential, the duration of the absolutely refractory period is curtailed, and excitability continues to increase after the resting threshold is reached. The result is a period of time, known as the *supernormal period*, during which the axon is more easily excited than it is during the resting state and during which the speed of conduction is increased. Careful comparison of the electrical events and the changes in excitability reveals that the supernormal period corresponds in time with the negative afterpotential.

Even following the supernormal period, the sequence of changes in excitability is not complete. As the negative afterpotential gives way to the positive afterpotential, excitability again decreases below the resting threshold and remains depressed throughout the positive afterpotential. During this *subnormal period* the speed of conduction as well as the excitability is depressed.

Types of Nerve Fibers.[6, 7] Systematic examination of the compound action potentials of various nerves of different composition reveals that axons can be classified into four distinctive types known as A, B, s.C and d.r.C fibers. The A fibers have already been described as myelinated, somatic, afferent and efferent fibers. The B fibers are myelinated, efferent, preganglionic axons found in autonomic nerves. The C fibers are unmyelinated, the s.C group being the efferent postganglionic sympathetic axons, and the d.r.C group the small unmyelinated afferent axons found in peripheral nerves and dorsal roots. The distinctive properties of these four fiber types are summarized in Table 2 and Figures 33 and 34.

It should be noted that the A fibers, although comprising a wide range of fiber diameters, constitute a homogeneous group except in respect to conduction speed, which varies predictably with diameter in the manner already described.

TABLE 2. PROPERTIES OF MAMMALIAN NERVE FIBERS

	A	B	s.C	d.r.C
Fiber diameter, μ	1–22	≤ 3	0.3–1.3	0.4–1.2
Conduction speed, m. per sec.	5–120	3–15	0.7–2.3	0.6–2.0
Spike duration, msec.	0.4–0.5	1.2	2.0	2.0
Absolutely refractory period, msec.	0.4–1.0	1.2	2.0	2.0
Negative afterpotential amplitude, per cent of spike	3–5	none	3–5	none
Duration, msec.	12–20	....	50–80	....
Positive afterpotential amplitude, per cent of spike	0.2	1.5–4.0	1.5	*
Duration, msec.	40–60	100–300	300–1000	*
Order of susceptibility to asphyxia	2	1	3	3
Velocity/diameter ratio	6	?	?	1.73 average

* A post-spike positivity 10 to 30 per cent of spike amplitude and decaying to half size in 50 msec. is recorded from d.r.C fibers. This afterpositivity differs from the positive afterpotential of other fibers (see text).

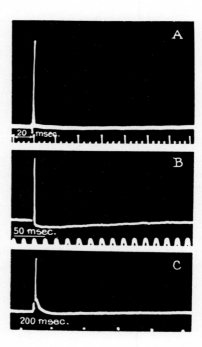

FIG. 33. Compound action potentials of A, B and C fibers showing differences in afterpotentials. (From Gasser. *Ohio J. Sci.*, 1941, *41*:145–159.)

The B fibers are histologically indistinguishable from small A fibers and, as can be seen in Table 2, have conduction rates within the range exhibited by the A group, the smallest of which conduct impulses at speeds as low as 5 m. per second. B fibers are principally distinguished from A fibers by the absence of a negative afterpotential (Fig. 33B). Correspondingly, the recovery cycle of B fibers lacks a supernormal period, the relatively refractory period merging directly with the subnormal period (Fig. 34B). B fibers also differ from A fibers in spike duration, which for B is more than twice as great as for A fibers. Although a sizable range of conduction rates is represented, the compound action potential of B fibers, even at long conduction distances, is relatively smooth and does not break up into discrete elevations. This configuration is seen because all parts of the velocity spectrum have relatively equal numerical representation.

Unlike both A and B fibers, C fibers lack a myelin sheath visible by light microscopy and exhibit a unique relation between the Schwann sheath and the axon.[5,8] Each A or

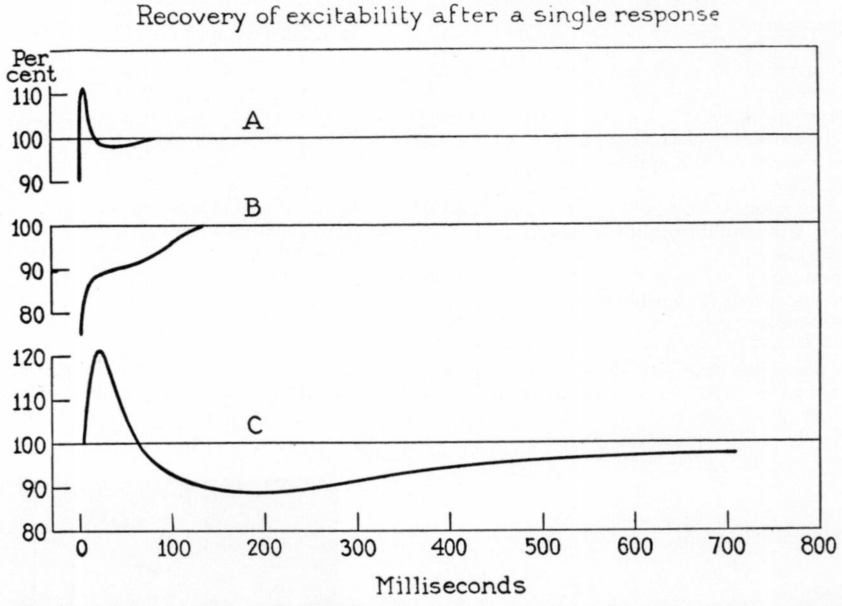

Recovery of excitability after a single response

FIG. 34. Recovery cycles of A, B and C fibers. *Ordinates*, Excitability in terms of resting threshold set at 100. *Abscissae*, Time interval between conditioning and test shocks. (From Gasser. *Ohio J. Sci.*, 1941, *41*:145–159.)

B fiber possesses a private Schwann sheath which surrounds the myelin sheath as a more or less continuous outer investment. Many C fibers, however, share the same Schwann sheath (Fig. 35). This sheath is a cellular structure in which a number of fibers are embedded as a result of the invagination of the outer surface of the Schwann cells. When the fibers are deeply embedded, the edges of the invaginated Schwann membrane lie in close approximation. The space between the Schwann membrane and the axon membrane appears to be of the order of 100 Ångstroms. The presence of this relatively restricted and circumscribed extracellular space raises interesting but as yet unanswered questions concerning the external ionic environment of C fibers.

Functionally, C fibers are distinguished from A fibers by slow conduction rates, long spike durations, high electrical thresholds and relatively great resistance to asphyxia. The various parts of the velocity and diameter spectra are unequally represented in the nerve trunks, and the conducted compound action potential displays a number of discrete elevations of surpassing complexity.

Only recently have C fibers been divided into two groups, s.C and d.r.C, largely on the basis of differences in their afterpotentials.[7] The s.C group, postganglionic sympathetic axons, has pronounced negative and positive afterpotentials. The d.r.C group, comprised of the unmyelinated afferent fibers of peripheral nerves and dorsal roots, has no negative afterpotential but typically displays a large afterpositivity, which differs from the conventional positive afterpotential in that it is converted by repetitive activity into a negative deflection.

Composition of Peripheral Nerves. A typical peripheral nerve such as the sciatic nerve contains both afferent and efferent A fibers, afferent d.r.C fibers and s.C fibers supplying smooth muscle and glandular structures. Because the discrepancy in conduction rate and amplitude between the A and C groups is so great, it is not feasible to record the entire compound action potential of a mixed peripheral nerve on a single sweep of the oscilloscope, but the picture may be resynthesized graphically from several records taken with appropriate amplifications and time bases. Figure 36 shows such a

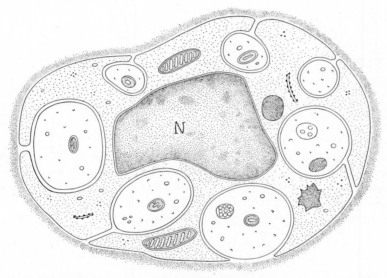

FIG. 35.   Diagram of relation of C fibers to Schwann cells. Drawing represents cross section through single Schwann cell surrounding seven C fibers. *N*, Nucleus of Schwann cell. Note that Schwann cell membrane is everywhere intact but is invaginated by nerve fibers. (After Elfvin. *J. Ultrastructure Res.*, 1958, *1:*428–454.)

resynthesized action potential, drawn to scale, for the saphenous nerve (a purely afferent cutaneous nerve), along with the recordings which provided the requisite data.

To prepare for discussions in subsequent chapters it is important to know the respective diameter spectra of the afferent and efferent A fibers in the various nerves. For cutaneous nerves, in which all the A fibers are afferent, the spectrum is determined simply by inspection of sections of the whole nerve stained with osmic acid. To ascertain the spectra for mixed nerves, it is necessary to cut the contributory ventral or dorsal roots (distal to the ganglion) and allow the efferent or afferent fibers, respectively, to degenerate. The remaining fibers may then be counted. Figure 37 shows the diameter distributions of the afferent fibers in a cutaneous nerve (thin line, crosshatched area) and in a "demotored," deep or muscle nerve (heavy line). The cutaneous afferent fibers have a bimodal distribution, one peak lying between 1 μ and 5 μ and the other between about 6 μ and 12 μ. The histogram for the muscle nerve, however, shows three peaks, two of which are approximately coextensive with the two peaks in the cutaneous nerve

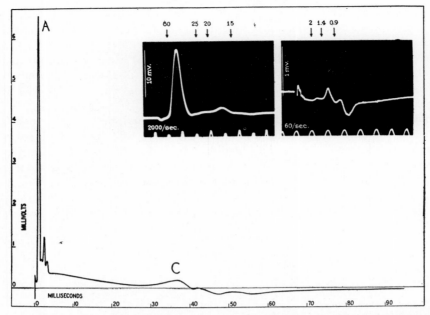

FIG. 36.   Scale drawing of complete compound action potential of mammalian saphenous nerve. *Left inset*, Recording of A fiber components. *Right inset*, Recording of C fiber components. Numbers above arrows give maximal conduction rates (m. per sec.) of each component. (Combined from Gasser. *J. appl. Phys.*, 1938, *9*:88–96 and *Ohio J. Sci.*, 1941, *41*:145–159.)

distribution. The third peak is comprised of large fibers, 12 to 21 μ in diameter, which are almost completely lacking in the cutaneous nerve. Systematic examination of the afferent fiber composition of different nerves shows that the relationships indicated in Figure 37 can be generalized: *the large (12 to 21 μ) afferent fibers are confined to muscle nerves, whereas the other two groups (1 to 5 μ and 6 to 12 μ), although varying somewhat in proportions, are represented in all somatic nerve trunks.*

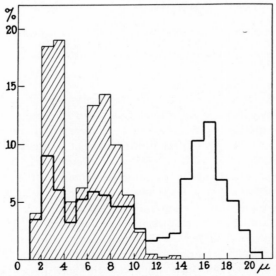

FIG. 37.   Comparison of afferent fiber diameter distribution in a muscle nerve (heavy line) and a cutaneous nerve (hatched area). *Ordinates*, Number of fibers expressed as percentage of total. *Abscissae*, Fiber diameter in μ.

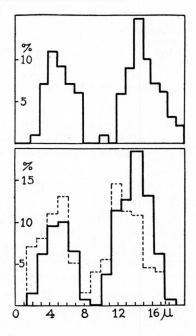

FIG. 38. Diameter distributions of efferent fibers. Coordinates as in Fig. 37. *Upper*, Data from ventral root. *Lower*, Data from gastrocnemius nerve, from which afferent fibers were removed by degenerative section of dorsal roots. *Solid line*, Data from sample taken 50 mm. from muscle. *Broken line*, Data from sample 8 mm. from muscle. Since daughter fibers are of lesser diameter than parent fibers, spectrum shifts slightly to left at the closer distance. (After Eccles and Sherrington. *Proc. roy. Soc.*, 1930, *B106*:326–357.)

It should be remembered that both cutaneous and "demotored" muscle nerves contain a great many unmedullated d.r.C fibers as well as the medullated A fibers. In fact, unmedullated fibers may be three or four times as prevalent as A fibers.

The diameter spectra of efferent fibers is illustrated in Figure 38, which shows the diameter distributions in a ventral root and in a typical muscle nerve deafferented by degenerative dorsal root section. In both the root and the nerve the distribution is distinctly bimodal, the two prominent clusters, from 12 to 20 μ and from 2 to 8 μ, being separated by a definite nadir in the range from 8 to 12 μ. Corresponding to the two distinctly separated clusters in the histogram are two distinct elevations in the conducted compound action potential (see Fig. 112). As will be discussed in a subsequent chapter, these two groups of motor fibers differ functionally.

Deafferented nerve trunks (but not ventral roots) contain, in addition to the A fibers, significant numbers of unmedullated efferent fibers. These fibers are postganglionic autonomic axons (s.C) traversing the nerve trunks to reach smooth muscle and glandular elements of deep structures.

The diameter distribution shown in Figure 38 is, in general, typical of all ventral roots, but there are minor individual differences. The most marked difference is between those roots (thoracic and upper lumbar) which contribute white rami to the sympathetic chain and those which do not. In the former, but not in the latter, there is a sizable peak below 3 μ in the range of distribution; this peak is composed of B fibers.

TERMINOLOGY. It has already been mentioned that the Greek letters α, β, γ, δ (and sometimes ϵ) are often used to designate the successive elevations of the compound action potential of the A fibers in a nerve trunk. Since these elevations result from activity in fibers conducting at different velocities, proportional to fiber diameter, the Greek letter designation may also be used as a categorization of fiber diameters. A difficulty arises, however, because an elevation in the compound action potential reflects not only the diameter but also the number of fibers involved. In nerves with similar function and origins, e.g., cutaneous sensory nerves, the diameter spectra are surprisingly constant. However, when nerves with different origins and functions are compared, striking discrepancies are evident; for example, the first major deflection of the compound action potential of a "demotored" muscle nerve occupies fibers of a diameter range which is sparsely represented in cutaneous nerves. The difficulty is avoided by using Lloyd's[12] Roman numeral designations, which are based on fiber diameter rather than on electrogram elevations. According to this classification, the A fibers are divided into three groups: I, 12 to 21 μ; II, 6 to 12 μ; and III, 1 to 6 μ. The C fibers (both the d.r. and the s. subgroups) are sometimes referred to as Group IV.

The Greek letter and Roman numeral designations are often used interchangeably. The following relations approximately equate the two designations: (i) A-alpha corresponds to Groups I and II. (ii) A-delta corresponds to Group III. (iii) The C group corresponds to Group IV. In cat nerve the deflections originally labeled beta and gamma are apparently largely or wholly artifacts and have no equivalents in the Roman numerical classification.

Conduction in Immature and Regenerating Axons. The conduction speed of nerve fibers at birth is low. As the body grows, axon diameters, and hence conduction rates, increase. In a series of animals at different stages of growth, Hursh[11] found a linear relationship between length of leg and the conduction rate of the fibers of a leg nerve, e.g., the saphenous. The relation is such that conduction time in any pathway between the periphery and the spinal cord remains essentially constant from birth to maturity. Properties other than conduction rate do not change markedly with growth. Afterpotentials, for example, appear to depend more on fiber type than on fiber size.

Degeneration and regeneration. When an axon is severed, the portion disconnected from the cell body undergoes a sequence of morphologic changes known as *Wallerian* or *secondary degeneration.** These changes consist of chemical alteration of the myelin, leading ultimately to its complete dissolution, along with fragmentation and eventual dissolution of the axis cylinder. The degeneration products of both the myelin and the axis cylinder are removed by macrophages.

This process would leave a hollow tube of Schwann sheath if an exuberant proliferation of the Schwann cells did not fill the lumen with a solid column of Schwann cells. At the level of transection, the Schwann cells also grow out of the end of the stumps and, if the gap is not excessive, bridge the space between them, reestablishing continuity. From the end of the axon in the proximal stump, a multitude of sprouts develop and grow between the Schwann cells of the bridge into the column beyond. Although many such sprouts cross the bridge, usually only one survives and continues to advance distally at a rate which may be as great as 3.5 to 4.5 mm. per day. The advancing tip of the regenerating fiber is unmyelinated, and its diameter is small compared to that of the Schwann column in which it grows. Maturation of the fiber, i.e., increase in diameter and acquisition of a myelin sheath, eventually leads to compression of the Schwann cells into the thin sheath typical of mature nerves. Maturation is much slower than longitudinal advance. There is evidence that maturation is progressive along a regenerating stretch of nerve, i.e., at any time the proximal segments are more mature than are the distal segments.

The conduction speed in a regenerating nerve increases as regeneration progresses and constitutes a reliable measure of the time course of maturation. It may be that normal conduction rates are never regained after nerves are cut and resutured. For example, Berry et al.[1] found that the maximum conduction rate in a sciatic nerve more than a year (450 days) after section and suture was about 85 m. per second, whereas a normal sciatic nerve contains fibers conducting at rates up to 120 m. per second. Histologic examination revealed that the largest fiber in the regenerated nerve measured

---

* Changes occurring in the cell body after its axon has been amputated are called *retrograde degeneration.* These changes include disappearance of Nissl granules (chromatolysis), swelling of the perikaryon, and displacement of the nucleus from its typical central position to the periphery. In some neurons (e.g., spinal motoneurons) retrograde degeneration is reversible, and the cell body eventually regains its normal morphologic features and functional properties. In others (e.g., thalamic neurons) retrograde degeneration is irreversible, and the dead perikaryon is removed by phagocytes. Rarely, morphologic changes similar to those of irreversible retrograde degeneration occur in a cell body after section of the axons making synaptic connections with it; this phenomenon is known as *transneuronal degeneration.* An example is degeneration of neurons in the lateral geniculate body following section of the optic nerve.

16 μ, compared with 20 μ in the normal nerve. Failure to mature completely appears to be related to extensive branching (which results in daughter fibers smaller than the parent axon) at the suture line. When the nerve is crushed rather than sectioned, complete maturation occurs, apparently because the continuity of the sheaths is not broken, and the axons grow into their own sheaths without branching.

In the clinical treatment of injuries to peripheral nerves, the major consideration is to establish continuity of the stumps, for, if the gap is large, the probability of sprouts successfully traversing the bridge and reaching the distal stump is reduced. Sprouts meeting an obstruction may form a painful tumor called a *neuroma*. When the nerve has merely been crushed, the prognosis is good. If the trunk is interrupted, the ends of the stumps are approximated by suturing through the epineurium or by gluing the ends together with fibrinogen. When the gap is too large to permit approximation of the severed ends, *cable grafts* are sometimes employed; i.e., segments of expendable nerves (for example, cutaneous nerves) are removed and sutured between the stumps to provide the framework for a bridge.

POTENTIALS IN A VOLUME CONDUCTOR[*][14]

A nerve fiber is surrounded by interstitial fluid and by other fibers. Although the other fibers, especially if they are myelinated, are good insulators,[†] the interstitial fluid is a volume conductor which extends throughout the body. Unless current is flowing in a volume conductor, it is isopotential. In the body, current flows in the interstitial fluid only during impulse conduction in excitable cells; no current flows in quiescent cells. The existence of a current flow in a volume conductor means that there must be a voltage source present. This source, in an impulse, is the voltage difference between the active region and the inactive region.

In comparison with the potentials recorded from an isolated nerve trunk, the potential at a point in a volume conductor (recorded with respect to an electrode so distant that its potential is negligible) is difficult to interpret. (i) It is difficult to determine the location of the active fibers because their currents spread throughout the body. (ii) The size and time course of the volley are uncertain because, as the distance between the recording electrode and the active tissue is increased, the recorded potential becomes smaller and slower. (iii) The relationship between the changes in transmembrane potential and the resulting current flow in the volume conductor is quite complicated.

However, the estimation of potentials occurring in a volume conductor as a result of nerve activity is made quite simple if the action potential is approximated by a square wave, i.e., if depolarization and repolarization are instantaneous (see Fig. 44b). The potential set up at a point in a volume conductor by a square action potential is proportional to the product of the height of the transmembrane action potential and the solid angle of the wave boundaries as measured at the recording electrode. The solid angle is a measure of the apparent size of an object as viewed from a particular point. The square wave approximation to the action potential is quantitatively inaccurate, but this approximation does give an accurate estimate of the sequence of potential changes. The use of this approximation is justified by the great conceptual and computational simplification that results.

* This section written by J. W. Woodbury.

† In tissues other than myelinated nerve, membrane resistance is much lower and capacitance much higher than in nerve, and an appreciable part of the local current may flow through adjacent inactive cells. Part of this current flows through the membrane resistor and, during rapid changes in potential in the interstitial fluid, part flows through the membrane capacitor. Thus, to a limited extent, inactive cells are a portion of the volume conductor surrounding an active cell.

Since the variation of recorded potential with distance from the active tissue depends solely on the solid angle of the wave boundaries, and since the concept of a solid angle is unfamiliar to most students, the first parts of this section present a definition of the solid angle. It is then shown that the potential due to a dipole layer is proportional to the solid angle subtended by the potential at the recording electrode. The section concludes with a description of how this principle is applied to the interpretation of the potentials set up in a volume conductor by nerve activity.

Solid Angle. A solid angle is measured in a manner analogous to measurement of a plane angle, and therefore, the manner of measuring a plane angle will be reviewed here. The angle Θ, subtended at O by a curved line AB (Fig. 39a), may be measured in

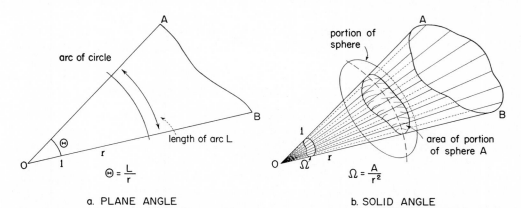

a. PLANE ANGLE   b. SOLID ANGLE

FIG. 39.   Calculation of plane and solid angles. a, Measurement of plane angle Θ, subtended by a curving line AB from point O. Arc of a circle of radius r with center at O is inscribed. Length of arc, L, between lines OA and OB is measured. Θ is defined as equal to L/r. b, Measurement of solid angle, Ω, subtended by surface AB from O. Radii are drawn from O to all points on periphery of AB. This irregular cone is a solid angle. Ω is measured by inscribing a sphere of radius r with center at O and measuring the area, A, on the surface of sphere cut out by the irregular cone. Ω is defined as A/r^2.

degrees; but a more general and natural way to measure the angle is as follows. A circle of any radius (r) with a center at O is drawn. The angle Θ, in radians, is defined as the ratio of the length of an arc (L) between lines OA and OB to the radius; $\Theta = L/r$. This definition conforms with experience; when the angle is fixed, L increases proportionately with r, so L/r remains constant. An angle of 1 radian is such that the arc length is equal to the radius. The circumference of a circle is $2\pi r$, so a full circle is an angle of $2\pi r/r = 2\pi$ radians. Therefore, 1 radian $= 360°/2\pi = 57.4°$. Angular measure in radians is dimensionless.

A solid angle is the three-dimensional equivalent of a plane angle. The solid angle subtended at a point by any object is proportional to the apparent size of the object when the object is viewed from the point. For this reason, the potential at a point in a volume conductor is often referred to as being "seen" by the electrode. An object looms larger as it is brought nearer to the eye, even though the dimensions of the object do not change. The solid angle subtended at point O (Fig. 39b) by the object AB may be outlined by drawing lines from O to every point on the perimeter of AB. The size of a solid angle Ω (omega) is calculated by drawing a sphere of radius r about O as the center; the area (A) cut out by the solid angle on the surface of the sphere is then measured, just as the length of the arc was measured to determine the size of a plane angle. Since the surface area of a sphere is $4\pi r^2$, A depends on the square of the radius. Therefore, just as $\Theta = L/r$, $\Omega = A/r^2$. The dimensionless unit of solid angle measure is the *steradian*. One steradian is the solid angle subtended by an area of 1 cm.^{2} (of any shape) on the surface of a sphere with a radius of 1 cm. The solid angle of an object that completely surrounds O is $4\pi r^2/r^2 = 4\pi$ steradians.

Potential Due to Dipole Layer.   Two equal and opposite charges (q) held a short distance (δ) apart constitute a *dipole* of moment (m); m = qδ (Fig. 40a). The electric field of a dipole falls off rapidly with distance, because the + and − charges exert nearly equal and opposite forces on an exploring charge. At distances large compared with δ, the electric field is inversely proportional to the cube of the distance r; and the potential is inversely proportional to r^2 rather than to r, as it is with a single charge. A *dipole layer* or surface is formed by separating + and − charges across a layer of thickness δ (Fig. 40b). Each region of the layer contains equal numbers of + and −

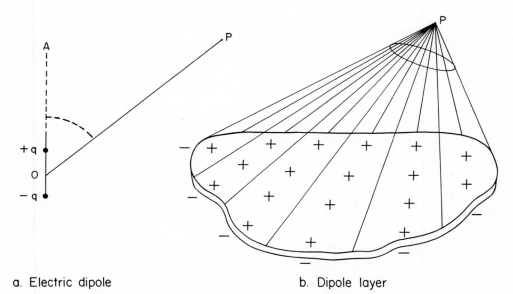

a. Electric dipole   b. Dipole layer

FIG. 40.   Dipole and dipole layer. *a*, In dipole charges +q and −q are the distance δ apart. Potential at P is calculated in terms of angle Θ, between lines OA and OP, and r, the length of OP. *b*, Potential at P is proportional to Ω, the solid angle subtended at P by the dipole layer. q_A is surface charge per unit area and δ is thickness of dipole layer.

charges; i.e., the + and − charges have been separated from each other. However, the number of + or − charges per unit area of the surface may vary from one region to the next. The dipole moment per unit area (m_A) of a dipole layer is the product of the charge per unit area (q_A) and the thickness of the layer; $m_A = q_A\delta$. A charged cell membrane is a closed dipole layer since + and − charges are separated across the membrane. In a quiescent cell m_A is a constant. During activity m_A at a fixed point varies rapidly in time, or, at a fixed time, m_A varies rapidly with distance.

Since the membrane is a capacitor, the amount of charge per unit area is directly proportional to the transmembrane potential at any point. The calculation of the potential arising from cell membrane charge is the same as the computation of the potential of a dipole layer. The potential ($\mathcal{E}$) of a point in a volume conductor is defined as the difference in potential between that point and a point a large distance from the dipole layer. The potential due to a dipole layer is inversely proportional to the square of the distance to it, and so the potential at a sufficiently distant second or indifferent recording electrode can be made arbitrarily small. *At any point, the potential due to a dipole layer of constant moment is proportional to the solid angle subtended by the surface at the point;* $\mathcal{E} = (\mathcal{E}_m/4\pi)\Omega$, where $\mathcal{E}_m$ is the transmembrane potential (Fig. 40b). The sign of the

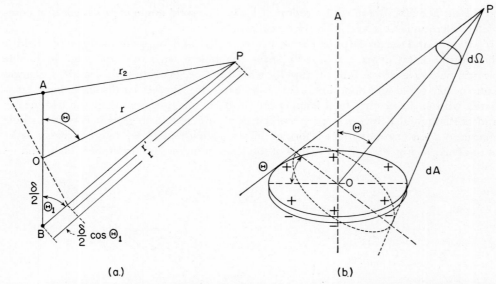

(a.)   (b.)

FIG. 41.   a, Diagram used to calculate potential at P due to a dipole when r is much greater than
δ (r is disproportionately short in this drawing). When r is much greater than δ, lines AP, OP, and
BP are considered to be parallel and $\Theta_1 = \Theta_2$.

b, Solid angle, $d\Omega$, subtended at point P by a small circular segment, of area dA, of dipole layer.
(Both δ and dA are actually much smaller than r, but dA is shown disproportionately large here for
clarity.) Sphere of radius r is drawn around P. Area cut out on surface of sphere by dA is dA cos Θ,
where Θ is the angle between OA and OP. OA is drawn from center of dA, perpendicular to dA and
toward its positively charged surface. If Θ is greater than $\pi/2$ (90°), $d\Omega$ is negative. Therefore, $d\Omega = dA$
cos Θ/r^2

potential is the same as the sign of the charge on the face of the dipole layer nearest to
P. This rule reduces the problem of computing the potentials in a volume conductor to
a problem in solid geometry.

DERIVATION OF POTENTIAL DUE TO DIPOLE LAYER.   Figure 41a shows the geometry involved in
computing the potential at P due to the dipole AB. Since the membrane is only about 100 Ångstroms
thick, any recording electrode is a large distance away from the membrane compared to its thickness.
Although, for the sake of clarity, Figure 41a is drawn with δ nearly as large as r, in the real situation
r is much larger than δ; so lines AP, OP and BP are nearly parallel, and $\Theta = \Theta_1$. The potential at P
is the sum of the potentials due to the charge +q at A and −q at B:

$$\mathcal{E} = K\left(\frac{q}{r_2} - \frac{q}{r_1}\right) \tag{1}$$

To a good approximation, r_1 and r_2 are given by

$$r_1 = r + \frac{\delta}{2}\cos\Theta, \; r_2 = r - \frac{\delta}{2}\cos\Theta$$

Substitution of these into Equation 1 gives

$$\mathcal{E} = Kq\left(\frac{1}{r - \frac{\delta}{2}\cos r} - \frac{1}{+ \frac{\delta}{2}\cos}\right) = \frac{Kq\delta\cos\Theta}{r^2 - \frac{\delta}{4}\cos^2}$$

or

$$\mathcal{E} = K\frac{m\cos\Theta}{r^2} \tag{2}$$

The last step follows from the definition of m and the approximation that $\delta^2/4$ is negligible compared
with r^2. Equation 2 shows that the potential at a point depends inversely on r^2, as stated above, and
also on the angle between the dipole and the point. This dependence is expected because the potential

along a line through O and perpendicular to AB must be zero, since the component of the electric field along this line is always zero.

Exactly the same arguments apply to any small area (dA) of a dipole layer (Fig. 41b), since each element of area has charges, $+q_A dA$ and $-q_A dA$, at points separated by the distance δ. Therefore, the contribution of dA to the potential at P is

$$d\mathcal{E} = K \frac{q_A dA\delta \cos \Theta}{r^2} = K \frac{m_A dA \cos \Theta}{r^2} \tag{3}$$

Part of Equation 3, dA/r^2, is in the form of an element of solid angle, $d\Omega$. This fact suggests that the solid angle of dA at P should be calculated (Fig. 41b). To calculate $d\Omega$, a sphere of radius r and center P is drawn through dA; dA is then projected onto the surface of this sphere. The area of this projection is $dA \cos \Theta$, so the solid angle is, by definition:

$$d\Omega = \frac{dA \cos \Theta}{r^2} \tag{4}$$

Substitution of Equation 4 in Equation 3 gives

$$d\mathcal{E} = K m_A \frac{dA \cos \Theta}{r^2} = K m_A d\Omega \tag{5}$$

Integration of Equation 5 over the whole of the dipole surface (S) gives

$$\mathcal{E} = K \int_s m_A d\Omega \tag{6}$$

If m_A is constant, Equation 5 is a perfect differential and Equation 6 becomes simply

$$\mathcal{E} = K m_A \Omega \tag{7}$$

where Ω is the solid angle of the surface as seen from P. The simplicity of Equation 7 compared to Equation 6 is the reason for approximating the action potential by a square wave. The integration indicated by Equation 6 is accurate* but is difficult and tedious for the action potential. Equation 7 is comparatively easy to evaluate. The quantity $K m_A$ can be evaluated in terms of $\mathcal{E}_m$, the transmembrane potential. As will be shown below, the potential outside a quiescent cell is everywhere zero

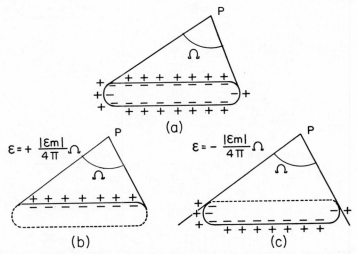

FIG. 42. Axial section of a closed cylindrical cell, drawn to illustrate that the potential outside a quiescent cell is zero. a, From point P, the electrode "sees" two equally and oppositely polarized cell membranes subtending the solid angle Ω. b, Calculation of potential at P due to the near membrane; potential is $+(|\mathcal{E}_m|/4\pi)\Omega$ because positive side of membrane faces P. c, Potential of the far membrane is $-(|\mathcal{E}_m|/4\pi)\Omega$ because negative side of membrane faces P. Total potential is sum of the individual potentials: $\mathcal{E} = (|\mathcal{E}_m|/4\pi)\Omega - (|\mathcal{E}_m|/4\pi)\Omega = 0.$†

* Equation 6 is correct for a nerve fiber only if the specific resistivity of the intracellular fluid is equal to that of the interstitial fluid. The specific resistivity of the axoplasm is about twice that of the interstitial fluid.

† $|\mathcal{E}_m|$ indicates absolute value of $\mathcal{E}_m$.

because the effective solid angle of the cell is zero. Moving the recording electrode inside the cell changes the potential from zero to $\mathcal{E}_m$ and the effective solid angle from 0 to 4π. Therefore, inside the cell Equation 7 becomes

$$\mathcal{E}_m = Km_A \cdot 4\pi \text{ or } Km_A = \frac{\mathcal{E}_m}{4\pi} \tag{8}$$

The relation then becomes

$$\mathcal{E} = \frac{\mathcal{E}_m}{4\pi} \Omega \tag{9}$$

Potential of quiescent cell. The proportionality between potential and the solid angle of the dipole layer means that the potential depends only on the apparent size of the layer and is independent of its detailed shape. Figure 42 illustrates that the transmembrane potential of a quiescent cell does not influence the potential at an external point, because any point outside the cell is faced by two equally but oppositely charged surfaces of the same solid angle. Since the transmembrane potential is everywhere constant in a quiescent cell, the potential due to the part of the surface of the cell facing P (Fig. 42b) is $+(\mathcal{E}_m/4\pi)\Omega$, and that due to the portion facing away from P (Fig. 42c) is $-(\mathcal{E}_m/4\pi)\Omega$ because the negatively charged surface faces P. The total potential at P is the sum of the

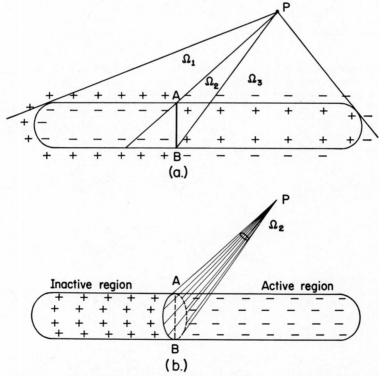

FIG. 43.   Potential at an external point P due to the rising phase of action potential in a cell at some instant. Line AB indicates where the transmembrane potential reverses; for simplicity the reversal is assumed to occur abruptly.

a, Axial section through a cylindrical cell showing cell membrane; diameter has been exaggerated. Total solid angle of cell is divided into three portions, Ω_1, Ω_2 and Ω_3 by lines PA and PB. Potential at P due to solid angles Ω_1 and Ω_3 is zero, since the nearer and farther membranes contribute equal but opposite potentials (see Fig. 42). However, in Ω_2 the nearer membrane is active (outside negative) and contributes a potential at P of the same sign as the more distant, inactive membrane.

b, Diagram to show that under conditions in *a*, the potential at P is the same as would be obtained if the membrane charges were placed on the cross section AB. The size of the potential at P at any instant is proportional to the apparent size of the cross section of the nerve at the wavefront.

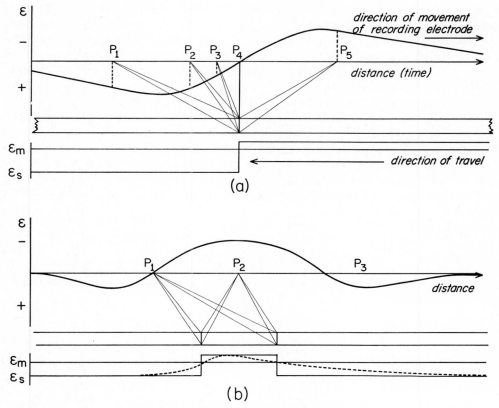

FIG. 44.   Potential generated by propagating wavefronts.

a, Diphasic potential due to a wavefront traveling from left to right at constant velocity. Time sequence of potential changes at a fixed point is shown along line parallel to nerve fiber. Sequence is constructed by supposing that wavefront is stationary and that a recording electrode is moved from left to right along a line parallel to nerve. When the recording electrode is at points P_1, P_2, P_3, it "sees" positive side of wavefront. Dashed line at P has a height proportional to the solid angle of the wavefront from P_1 and thus proportional to the voltage recorded at P_1. As the recording electrode moves toward the right, solid angle of wavefront at first increases slowly owing to closer approach and then decreases rapidly as the electrode sees the wavefront more and more on edge. At P_4 the potential is zero and immediately thereafter becomes negative. The plot is both of ε as a function of distance at a fixed time and of ε as a function of time at a fixed point.

b, Triphasic potential due to an idealized impulse. Solid angles of waves of both depolarization and repolarization must be added to obtain ε. Construction method same as in *a*. P is point of zero potential; note that it is to left of wavefront. Triphasic $(+,-,+)$ potential is typical of a propagated nerve impulse. Note that the maximum external potential is much smaller than the internal potential. An internal electrode at P_2 would see positive changes over 4π; while outside, even on the surface of the fiber, the solid angle is of the order of $4\pi/100$.

potentials due to all portions of the dipole layer, so $\varepsilon = + (\varepsilon_m/4\pi)\Omega - (\varepsilon_m/4\pi)\Omega = 0$. This rather formal method of calculation conforms with earlier statements that the external potential due to a quiescent cell is zero because there is no external current flow. It should be emphasized that potential changes in a volume conductor arise from current flow. The current flow due to a dipole layer is such that the potential is proportional to the solid angle.

Potential of active cell.   As mentioned above, the calculation of the potential generated in a volume conductor by an active cell is simplified by approximating the smoothly rising and falling action potential wave with an abruptly rising and falling square wave. A nerve fiber carrying an impulse can be divided into two regions, quiescent and active.

In the square wave approximation it is assumed that the quiescent region has a constant potential ($\mathcal{E}_s$), that the active region has a constant potential equal to the overshoot of the action potential ($\mathcal{E}_a$), and that the transition between the two regions occurs at a point.* Figure 43 shows how the potential due to a wavefront of depolarization can be calculated. Figure 43a is a diagram of an axial section of an excitable cell with a wave of depolarization near the center. The solid angles Ω_1 and Ω_2 contribute no potential to P, because the proximal and distal portions of the membrane contribute equal and opposite potentials. However, in Ω_2 the proximal membrane is active and contributes a negative potential to P; the distal membrane is inactive and also contributes a negative potential to P. The potential at P is $-(\mathcal{E}_a/4\pi)\Omega_2$, where $\mathcal{E}_a$ is about 130 mV. As Ω_2 is the solid angle of the wavefront, it is seen that the potential at an external point depends only on the solid angle subtended by the boundaries between the active and inactive regions. Figure 43b is a perspective sketch of the solid angle of a wave boundary in a nerve fiber.

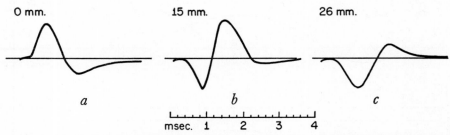

FIG. 45. Nerve action potentials in a volume conductor. An excised bullfrog nerve is arranged so that it enters a volume conductor at x = 0 and exits from it at x = 26 mm. *Ordinate*, Potential of a close electrode with respect to a distant one (negative upward). *Abscissa*, Time.

a, Potential set up by a nerve volley when recording electrode is at level of nerve entry (x = 0) and distant electrode is 3 mm. away from nerve (y = 3). b, Potential recorded at x = 15 mm., y = 3 mm. c, Potential at x = 26 mm., y = 3 mm.

A nerve impulse is a wave traveling at constant speed, so Figure 43 represents the situation at one instant in time. As this wavefront moves from right to left, the solid angle first increases and then gradually decreases to zero. Figure 44 shows the method of estimating the sequence of potential changes as a single wavefront (a) or a nerve impulse (b) travels from right to left at a constant velocity. A recording electrode put anywhere on the line P_1P_5 (Fig. 44a) would record the positive-negative sequence of potential changes as the wavefront approaches, passes and leaves the point nearest the electrode. The curve may be constructed by supposing that the wave is fixed and that the recording electrode is moving in the opposite direction (left to right) at the same constant velocity. The solid angle at each point P_1, P_2, etc. is measured and an ordinate proportional to the solid angle is drawn at that point. In this way the diphasic positive-negative potential sequence is constructed. The graph can be a plot of potential as a function of distance at a fixed time, or as a function of time with the recording electrode fixed. This diphasic volume-conductor potential is frequently seen in recordings from heart tissue during depolarization, because about 0.5 second elapses between depolarization and repolarization in a heart cell.

Figure 44b shows the sequence of potential changes expected from a nerve impulse. The triphasic wave (+, −, +) arises because the waves of depolarization and repolariza-

---

* The action potential of a large myelinated nerve fiber rises in about 0.1 millisecond and has a velocity of 100 m. per second. Therefore, the wavefront occupies 100 mm. per millisecond × 0.1 millisecond = 10 mm. This is 500 times the fiber diameter. Because of this slow rise, potentials recorded in volume from an active nerve are longer and lower than those expected from square-wave solid-angle analysis.

tion are sufficiently close together that both contribute significantly to the potential. To the left of P_1 the wavefront dominates and the potential is positive. At P_1 the two solid angles are equal and opposite in sign, and ε is zero; at P_2 both boundaries contribute a negative potential; and at P_3 the departing wave of repolarization dominates, and the potential is again positive. Triphasic waves are recorded from active nerve fibers in volume, but the last positive phase is much smaller and longer than the first, because repolarization is slower than depolarization (Fig. 45b).

Consider the situation in which an impulse originates at a distance from a recording electrode and travels away from it. Such a situation is encountered when an electrode is inserted in the vicinity of a cell body: an impulse initiated in the cell body by synaptic activity travels along the axon away from the cell body. When the cell body becomes active, the electrode sees negativity. ε remains negative but gradually diminishes as the wave of depolarization recedes. Repolarization in the cell body rapidly changes the potential to a large positive value, which falls off as the repolarization recedes.

Figure 45a shows the potential recorded from a bullfrog sciatic nerve at a region near its entry into a volume conductor.[14] The geometry is the same as that just described for a cell body and an axon. The negative-positive diphasic sequence is as expected. The same type of argument shows that an impulse that approaches but does not reach a recording electrode sets up a positive-negative diphasic sequence of potential changes (Fig. 45c). A recording situation of this sort is found where a fiber terminates before reaching the recording electrode or, more commonly, where the recording electrode has penetrated, injured and blocked the active fibers so that activity can reach the electrode. Lorente de Nó[14] has extensively investigated the potentials of a nerve trunk in a volume conductor.

PROPERTIES OF SPINAL TRACTS

Activity in spinal structures must of necessity be recorded in volume, for it is usually impossible to reduce the extracellular conducting medium to negligible proportions. As already mentioned, this circumstance creates some special problems. The first relates to identification of the structures that originate potentials recorded from the spinal cord. This problem arises because potentials in a volume conductor may be recorded at points distant from the site of activity. One method of localizing activity is to thrust an electrode into the suspected tract. The injury thus inflicted blocks activity in the conducting fibers, and the recorded response then consists of a monophasically positive deflection typical of approaching activity ("killed end" recording).* Conversion of a triphasic (positive-negative-positive) response to a monophasic positive response by penetration indicates that the electrode has damaged active fibers. When the potential sequence remains triphasic, inactive tracts have been penetrated.

A related problem is the computation of conduction times from volume recordings. In insulated nerve trunks conduction times are estimated by measuring the time interval between the shock artefact and the onset of the action potential. In volume, however, positive potentials are recorded before the activity reaches the electrode. The arrival of the conducted wave of depolarization at the level of the recording electrode is approximately signaled by the reversal from positivity to negativity.†

A final peculiarity of volume recording is that the recording electrode records a potential only when the conducting structures are unequally or oppositely polarized.

---

* The response is $+$, $-$ diphasic, but the negative part is usually negligibly small.

† A somewhat better measure is to a point midway between the first reversal and peak negativity For synchronous volleys when the negative component rises rapidly, little error is incurred by using the reversal point.

When a cell is completely polarized or completely depolarized, no potential is recorded, because every solid angle is matched by an equal and electrically opposite solid angle. It follows that prolonged changes in polarization with decay constants which are long in relation to conduction time do not appear in volume recordings. The afterpotentials have these characteristics and are not observed in volume recordings (Fig. 46).

Fiber Constitution of Spinal Tracts. The white matter of the spinal cord consists chiefly of fibers extending longitudinally for varying distances. All sizes of myelinated and unmyelinated fibers are represented. As yet, histologic and oscillographic studies have yielded only scattered information on the fiber constitution and conduction properties of spinal tracts, but several important generalizations can be made.

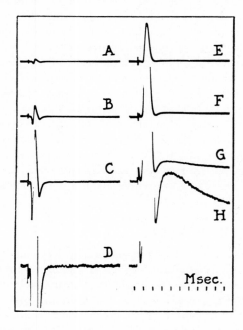

FIG. 46. Responses of frog sciatic nerve recorded in volume (*left*) and in an insulating medium (*right*). Each pair of traces (*A–E, B–F*, etc.) recorded at same gain, but between each pair from above downward gain was progressively increased approximately fivefold. Note in volume recorded responses relatively small amplitudes and absence of any sign of negative afterpotential, which is clearly seen in *G* and *H*. (From Lloyd in *Biology of mental health and disease*. New York, Hoeber, 1952.)

Propriospinal fibers. The spinal cord contains vast numbers of fibers that arise and terminate wholly within the spinal cord. These are known by several names, the most usual being "propriospinal" fibers or "intrinsic" spinal fibers. Tower *et al.*[17] studied the propriospinal fibers after all other fibers (the "extrinsic" fibers) were removed by section of the cord above and below a selected region and division of all the dorsal roots to that region. When sufficient time elapses for degeneration of the extrinsic fibers after such an operation, only propriospinal fibers remain. Upon examination of histologic preparations after this procedure, there are still so many fibers in the cord that it is difficult to appreciate the loss of fibers. The propriospinal fibers exist everywhere throughout the white matter, although they are not evenly distributed. In the dorsal columns most of the propriospinal fibers are small (about 1 μ), but there is a scattering of larger fibers. In contrast, the ventrolateral columns contain fibers of all sizes, many being as large as any found in the normal spinal cord. These large propriospinal fibers are the only ones that have been studied oscillographically; they are known to conduct impulses at rates up to 120 m. per second.

Extrinsic fibers. The *ascending fibers* in the spinal cord arise from neurons within the cord itself or, in the case of the dorsal columns, from neurons in the dorsal root ganglia. In the dorsal columns the largest fibers are ascending branches of Group I afferent fibers.[13] After a Group I afferent volley, a surface electrode on the ipsilateral dorsal column at the level of the activated dorsal roots records a large triphasic deflection, which has a latency compatible with a maximal conduction rate of 110 to 120 m. per second (Fig. 47). As the electrode is moved rostrally along the dorsal column, two changes occur in the recorded response: (i) its amplitude diminishes and eventually reaches zero, and (ii) its conduction rate progressively decreases.

For example, a Group I afferent volley initiated in the quadriceps nerve is traveling at a rate of 117 m. per second at the time of entry at L_5, has decelerated to a rate of 24 m. per second when L_1 is reached, and cannot be traced much beyond the T_{12} segment. The explanation is that the conducting fibers branch along their ascending course,

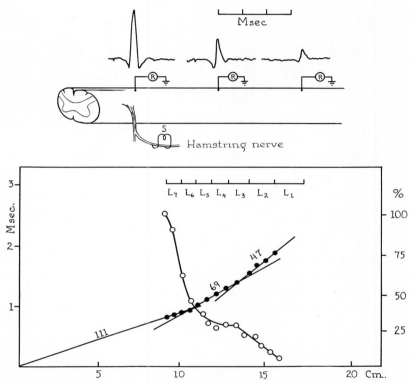

FIG. 47. Conduction in intramedullary projections of Group I afferent fibers. *Upper diagram,* Recordings from surface of dorsal column following a Group I afferent volley originating in hamstring nerve. *Graph* shows conduction time (filled circles, ordinate on left) and relative amplitude (open circle, ordinate on right) of response as a function of conduction distance. Slopes of conduction time lines (conduction rate) indicated by numbers above them. Scale above locates spinal segments. (After Lloyd and McIntyre. *J. Neurophysiol.,* 1950, *13:*39–54.)

giving off collaterals to the cells of Clarke's column. With each branching the parent fiber becomes smaller and hence conducts more slowly. Eventually all the activity of the Group I fibers is relayed into Clarke's column and thence upward in the dorsal spinocerebellar tract. The Group I fibers are thus temporary occupants of the dorsal columns. The most rapidly conducting permanent occupants of these columns (i.e., the fibers which remain in the dorsal columns throughout the length of the cord) have conduction rates which usually do not exceed 70 m. per second. This tract also contains many smaller fibers (Fig. 48).

The dorsal spinocerebellar tract, which originates from cells in Clarke's columns, occupies the dorsolateral white matter. This tract is characterized by a significant number of large fibers (Fig. 48), some of which conduct at velocities exceeding 120 m.

per second. Mixed in with these fibers are others originating in unidentified cell groups in the lumbar gray matter. These are destined to pass, via a relay in the cervical cord, to the contralateral olive and are called spino-olivary fibers. They conduct impulses at rates up to about 60 m. per second.[4]

The fibers comprising the spinothalamic tract in the anterolateral white matter are small (Fig. 48), and their conduction rates are not known. Some of the larger fibers (greater than 5 μ) in the anterolateral white matter of the lumbar segments are said to constitute the ventral spinocerebellar tract and have conduction rates ranging from 30 to 80 m. per second.[3]

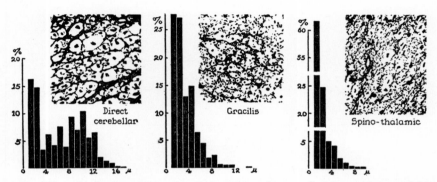

FIG. 48. Fiber distribution plots and typical sections of areas of white matter containing dorsal spinocerebellar tract, fasciculus gracilis and spinothalamic tract. Selected areas contain, in addition to tracts named, numerous propriospinal fibers. Note striking representation of large-diameter fibers in spinocerebellar tract as contrasted with small fibers which make up spinothalamic tract. Fasciculus gracilis is intermediate in fiber constitution. (After Häggqvist. *Z. micr.-anat. Forsch.*, 1936, *39*:1–34.)

The *descending tracts* include the pyramidal or corticospinal tract, the vestibulospinal tract and the reticulospinal tract. The latter two tracts are of fairly uniform size and conduct at rates comparable to those of the large A fibers. The pyramidal tract contains fibers ranging through a wide band of fiber sizes, the largest conducting at rates of about 65 m. per second. Recent studies indicate that the compound action potential of the bulbar and upper cervical portions of this tract includes two elevations, one conducting at 35 to 40 m. per second and the other at 12 to 16 m. per second.[2] This finding is surprising because the fiber spectrum of the tract at the bulbar level is not bimodal.

Despite the lack of systematic observations such as we have on peripheral fibers, it may be said in general conclusion that nerve fibers in the central nervous system have the same properties of conduction as do peripheral nerve fibers. Scattered data on the refractory period, the diameter-velocity relation, the velocity-threshold relation and the velocity-spike relation of fibers in the central nervous system indicate that their properties do not vary greatly from those of peripheral fibers.

REFERENCES

1. BERRY, C. M., GRUNDFEST, H. and HINSEY, J. C. *J. Neurophysiol.*, 1944, *7*:103–115.
2. BISHOP, P. O., JEREMY, D. and LANCE, J. W. *J. Neurophysiol.*, 1953, *16*:537–550.
3. CARREA, R. M. E. and GRUNDFEST, H. *J. Neurophysiol.*, 1954, *17*:203–238.
4. DIBIAGIO, F. and GRUNDFEST, H. *J. Neurophysiol.*, 1955, *78*:299–304.
5. ELFVIN, L.-G. *J. Ultrastructure Res.*, 1958, *1*:428–454.
6. GASSER, H. S. *Ohio J. Sci.*, 1941, *41*:145–159.
7. GASSER, H. S. *J. gen. Physiol.*, 1950, *33*:651–690.
8. GASSER, H. S. *Exp. Cell Res.*, 1958, Suppl. *5*:3–17.
9. GASSER, H. S. and GRUNDFEST, H. L. *Amer. J. Physiol.*, 1939, *127*:393–414.
10. HURSH, J. B. *Amer. J. Physiol.*, 1939, *127*:131–139.
11. HURSH, J. B. *Amer. J. Physiol.*, 1939, *127*:140–153.

12. LLOYD, D. P. C. *J. Neurophysiol.*, 1943, *6:*293–315.

13. LLOYD, D. P. C. and McINTYRE, A. K. *J. Neurophysiol.*, 1950, *13:*39–54.

14. LORENTE DE NÓ, R. *Stud. Rockefeller Inst. med. Res.*, 1947, *132*(2):384–482.

15. RITCHIE, J. M. and STRAUB, R. W. *J. Physiol.*, 1957, *136:*80–97.

16. STÄMPFLI, R. *Experientia*, 1954, *10:*508–509.

17. TOWER, S., BODIAN, D. and HOWE, H. *J. Neurophysiol.*, 1941, *4:*388–397.

18. WOODBURY, J. W. *J. cell. comp. Physiol.*, 1952, *39:*323–339.

CHAPTER 4

Muscle

By J. WALTER WOODBURY *and* THEODORE C. RUCH

THE function of a muscle is to contract. Skeletal muscles are attached to bones by tendons and act to move these bones with respect to each other. Cardiac muscle and visceral smooth muscle occur in the walls of hollow viscera and act by exerting pressure on the fluid visceral contents. The contraction of skeletal muscle is wholly and directly controlled by reflex and voluntary activity of the central nervous system. Cardiac and smooth muscle contractions, although regulated by nervous activity, are intrinsically rhythmic; these muscles, notably the heart, contract at regular intervals even when denervated. This automaticity of cardiac and smooth muscle is in accord with their functions in maintaining the internal environment of the body, the pumping of blood and the movements of the digestive tract. Muscular contraction is the most impressive example of "living machinery."

Skeletal muscle is the means by which an organism reacts to its external environment. "All the endless diversity of the external manifestations of the activity of the brain can be finally regarded as one phenomenon—that of muscular movement" (Sechenov, 1863). The preoccupation of the brain with skeletal muscle was also stressed by Sherrington, who pointed out that any path traced in the brain leads directly or indirectly to muscle. The performance of a smooth, efficient and coordinated bodily movement is the outward sign of complex and extensive activity in the central nervous system.

A bodily movement involves three more or less distinct types of activity: (i) central nervous system activity, reflex and voluntary; (ii) events intervening between the impulse in a motor nerve and the beginning of contraction; and (iii) the contractile process itself. Reflex control of movement is discussed in Chapter 6; the present chapter covers the remaining types of activity and the functions of cardiac and smooth muscle. The following brief description may help to keep the details of the processes in their proper perspective.

Events Leading to Contraction. A number of distinct events intervene between the synaptic initiation of an impulse in a spinal motoneuron and the contraction of the muscle fiber it innervates. (i) The impulse is conducted along the motoneuron axon to its termination on the muscle end-plate. (ii) The impulse causes the liberation of a chemical transmitter substance, acetylcholine, from the axon terminals. (iii) By inducing a depolarization of the muscle fiber membrane, acetylcholine initiates an impulse in it. (iv) The depolarization of the muscle membrane by the conducted impulse is followed by a brief phasic contraction of the muscle fiber—a *twitch*. The phrase *neuromuscular transmission* refers to the events between the arrival of the nerve impulse at the nerve endings and the initiation of an impulse in the muscle; the events between the muscle fiber impulse and contraction are referred to as *excitation-contraction coupling* to distinguish them from the contraction process itself.

A motor axon innervates from 3 to 150 muscle fibers, the number depending on the function of the muscle. The motoneuron and the muscle fibers it innervates are termed a *motor unit*. The contractile response to one impulse in one motoneuron is a twitch contraction in the fibers it innervates. Thus the smallest unit of muscular activity that occurs normally is the contraction of a single motor unit. The twitch response typical of a motor unit contrasts sharply with the smooth maintained contraction of muscle during normal movements. This observation raises a further question: How is the contraction of a muscle smoothly *graded* in strength?

CHANGES ACCOMPANYING MUSCULAR RESPONSE

When a muscle is indirectly stimulated, e.g., by a maximal shock to its motor nerve, a number of almost instantaneous transformations take place. The muscle shortens or attempts to shorten; simultaneously or nearly simultaneously electrical, structural, chemical and thermal changes occur. Fenn has called this transformation an *explosion*. The changes which take place so suddenly are reversible, and the "explosions" can repeat themselves after very brief intervals, resulting in cycles of contraction and relaxation. The chemical and thermal changes involved in the contractile process and the general problem of energy transformation are considered in biochemistry texts.

Structural Changes. CHEMISTRY. Since the end of the last century the protein extracted from muscle, named "myosin" by Kuhn in 1868, has been regarded as the building block of the contractile structure. Interest in this protein was renewed in 1939, when Engelhardt and Ljubimova[21] reported that it apparently has enzymatic properties, being capable of splitting adenosine triphosphate (ATP), the energy-yielding nucleotide intimately associated with contraction. These workers later demonstrated that ATP causes a change in the mechanical properties of myosin threads.[22] It was soon shown by the Szent-Gyorgyi school that "myosin" in skeletal muscle really consists of at least two proteins, actin and myosin, in the approximate ratio of 1:3. These proteins have molecular weights of about 70,000 and more than 800,000, respectively, and consist of long molecular chains.

This complex system was named "actomyosin," and its principal components are now regarded as the "moving parts of the muscle machine." The complete x-ray diffraction diagram of frog sartorius muscle is compounded of the separate diagrams of myosin and actin.[3] H. H. Weber[49] spun actomyosin extracted from muscle into filaments and emphasized their importance as models of the A band of the fibril sarcomere. When ATP is added, such filaments contract and can lift weight.

ULTRASTRUCTURE. Studies of muscle by light, polarizing and electron microscopy, light dispersion analysis and x-ray diffraction have revealed a striking structural parallelism of the units and subunits of a single fiber. The fibrils within a fiber, the myofilaments or threads within a fibril, and the long protein molecules within a filament are all longitudinally oriented, as illustrated diagrammatically in Figure 49. The myo-

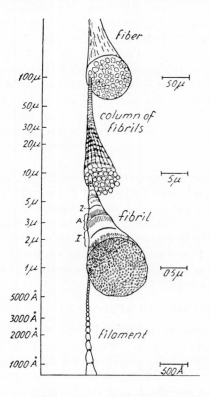

FIG. 49. Logarithmic extension diagram of skeletal muscle fiber structure. (After Buchthal and Kaiser. *Dan. Biol. Medd.*, 1951, *21*(7): 1–318.)

filaments, which may number ten million in all the fibrils of a single fiber, are about 150 Ångstroms in diameter[4] and are the smallest contractile units to be observed directly. They were first seen under the light microscope by Kolliker in 1888, and their identity has been confirmed many times with the electron microscope. Cross striations are typical of skeletal muscle, and regularly alternating light and dark bands or disks are easily seen microscopically. These bands, the A (anisotropic) and I (isotropic) bands, indicate the periodicity within each fibril of materials with higher and lower indices of refraction. An electron micrograph (Fig. 50) shows that the I band is divided by a strip of higher density, the Z line, and that a band of lesser density, the H band, lies at the center of the dark A band.

An efficient model of the structure of the muscle sarcomere was recently proposed simultaneously by A. F. Huxley and Niedergerke[36] and by H. E. Huxley and Hanson.[37] Contrary to the belief that contraction occurs by the folding or coiling of the contractile material, their model shows that the filaments of actin and myosin slide past each other during contraction. The model harmonizes most information on muscle structure and

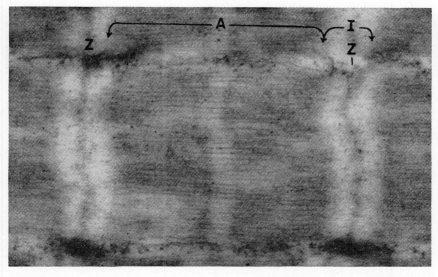

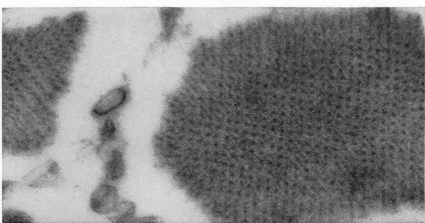

FIG. 50. Electron photomicrographs of skeletal muscle fixed in osmium pentoxide and embedded in plastic material. *Above,* Longitudinal section showing a sarcomere; H band is lighter strip in center of A band. × 65,000. *Below,* Transverse section of parts of two myofibrils. × 100,000. (Courtesy of Dr. Keith R. Porter.)

function, and its main features are shown in Figure 51*A*. The discussion that follows refers to this model, and it should be compared with the electron micrographs in Figure 50.

(i) The high refractive index and birefringence (anisotrophy) of the A bands results from the presence of rods or filaments of myosin with parallel axes. The length of these rods is constant unless the muscle shortens so much that the ends of the rods come into contact with the Z lines, in which case a folding probably occurs. (ii) A second set of filaments (actin) extends from the Z line through the I band and interdigitates with the A band filaments. (iii) The termination of the actin filaments marks the beginning of the H band. (iv) The ends of the corresponding actin filaments in a sarcomere* are joined by a fine extensible connection, the S filament. (v) The actin

* A sarcomere is traditionally defined as the region between two adjacent Z bands. In the new model, the Z line is at the center of a functional sarcomere.

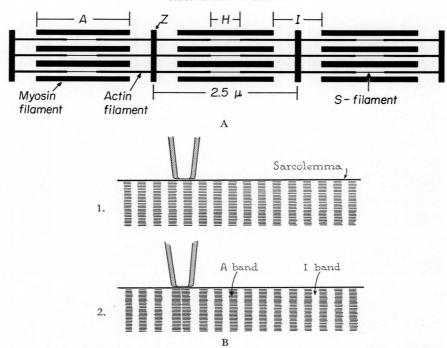

FIG. 51. *A*, Diagram of probable arrangement of filaments within a myofibril. Sarcomere length corresponds to extended length in the body. Transverse distances are exaggerated longitudinally to show individual filaments. Actin and myosin filaments slide past each other in region of overlap when length of muscle is altered. S filaments are only components of fibril which are stretched during lengthening.

B, Effects of local membrane depolarization on contraction of a single frog muscle fiber. Drawing from polarized light photomicrographs which were consecutive frames of motion picture. Edge of fiber with its membrane, portion of contractile substance, and microelectrode for applying current can be seen. Dark regions, A bands; light regions, I bands.

If tip of electrode is made negative with respect to distant electrode, current flows in through the membrane over a large area but flows out only where electrode touches the membrane. *1*, Before application of stimulating current. *2*, After application of stimulating current sufficient to depolarize the membrane (about 30 mV.). Note that I band immediately under electrode has disappeared. (From A. F. Huxley. *Progr. Biophys.*, 1957, 7:257–318.)

and myosin filaments slide past each other when the muscle changes length, i.e., the length of the filaments remains the same but their degree of interdigitation varies. If a sarcomere shortens so much that the I filaments at its opposite ends meet, a folding occurs near the points of contact. (vi) In cross section, any myosin filament is surrounded by six actin filaments. The general hexagonal arrangement can be seen in Figure 50.

CONTRACTION OF SARCOMERE.[36, 37] This detailed picture of sarcomere structure accords with microphysiologic findings as well as with known structure. The most direct and convincing physiologic evidence is the constant length of the A band during passive stretch and shortening and during contractions, provided the sarcomere length is greater than about 1.8 μ. The constancy of the width of the A band was generally accepted in the last century. A. F. Huxley[35] proposed a hypothesis of contraction in which it is assumed that active shortening or the development of tension is brought about by generation of relative translational forces between the actin and myosin filaments at a series of points in the region of overlap. The bridges between the two filaments are assumed to form spontaneously, and energy is supplied to break the bond at a later time when the fibers have slid past each other and the bridges may be retarding additional sliding movement.

Excitation-Contraction Coupling. The events intervening between the propagation of an action potential and the beginning of the contraction process have not been adequately defined. It is well established that depolarization of the surface membrane, rather than the membrane or longitudinal sarcoplasmic currents, is the direct or indirect activator of contraction. A. V. Hill[29] has shown that contraction begins too soon after the action potential to be initiated by a substance diffusing inward after liberation by membrane depolarization. However, if an activator substance is released from a transverse structure, this objection does not necessarily apply.

Considerable evidence, much of it available since the last century, indicates that the Z line is continuous between myofibrils and is also attached to the membrane. These and later observations suggest that the Z lines of individual fibrils are part of an extensive Z membrane which runs transversely through the fibers.* The attractive possibility that the Z membrane is the structure involved in the coupling of membrane depolarization to contraction is now supported by some physiologic evidence. A. F. Huxley and Taylor (see Ref. 35) applied the tip of a 2 μ microelectrode to the surface of an isolated muscle fiber and passed current into the electrode to depolarize the underlying area of membrane. If the electrode tip was placed on the membrane at the Z line, a moderate depolarization (20 to 40 mV.) produced local contraction in the half sarcomeres bounding the Z line (Fig. 51B). On the other hand, depolarization several times larger caused no contraction if the electrode was midway between two Z lines. Depolarizing the membrane at a Z line caused contractions that spread a moderate distance inward from the membrane. This distance was considerably greater than the distance to the adjacent I band, where there was no contraction at all.

There seems little doubt, then, that the Z membrane is involved in excitation-contraction coupling, but by an unknown mechanism. A. F. Huxley[35] tentatively suggests that the coupling may be electrical. If the Z membrane communicates with the external medium through a hollow structure whose walls are membranes with properties (including high electrical resistance) similar to those of the surface membrane, depolarization of the surface membrane would also depolarize the Z membrane. It might be further supposed that depolarization of a Z membrane liberates a substance which activates the contractile machinery by altering the adjacent actin molecules, and that contractile activity falls off as the activator is used up in the process. This hypothesis is made more attractive because the Z membrane capacity would be included in any experimental measurement of surface membrane capacity; this circumstance may explain the finding that the capacity per unit surface area is about ten times greater in muscle than in unmyelinated nerve.

ACTIVATION. The latent period between membrane depolarization and the beginning of the mechanical response is brief (1 millisecond in mammals), but it is occupied by a surprising number of events. As implied above, certain changes in the contractile mechanism precede the mechanical response indicated by a pull on the tendon. These changes are collectively termed *activation*. It was recognized by Gasser in 1924 that activation alters the mechanical condition of the fibers but does not produce contraction. In fact, a variety of mechanical, thermal and optical changes occur during activation.

Mechanical Changes. TYPES OF CONTRACTION.† Contraction results in shortening and/or development of tension. The ability to exert tension between the points of attach-

---

* If the Z membrane is a continuous structure, it must have a low electrical resistance or be highly perforated, for the internal resistivity of the sarcoplasm is less than three times that of the interstitial fluid. This value is about what would be expected from the low mobility of the internal anions and the space occupied by the contractile material.

† "Contraction" is not used by physiologists in the popular sense of "shortening." In physiologic language, "contraction" refers to a series of internal events which are manifested externally by either shortening or tension.

ment is the fundamental property of muscle.* This tension is utilized mechanically in several ways. The contracting muscles may shorten and produce movement. Since weight is carried through space during this movement, whether it is walking, running or lifting, work is performed by the muscle. This type of contraction—shortening under a constant load—has been called *isotonic* (equal tension) since Fick introduced the term in the last century. He applied the term *isometric* (equal length) to contractions in which the whole system does not shorten. Such contractions produce tension rather than shortening and work. The tension or force developed in contracting muscles that do not shorten is utilized to oppose other forces (such as gravity), in holding an object and in posture. In this type of contraction no external work is done; the tension developed is usually used to prevent motion. If the opposing force or load is greater than the maximum isometric contraction tension, the muscle is stretched or lengthened while actively contracting.

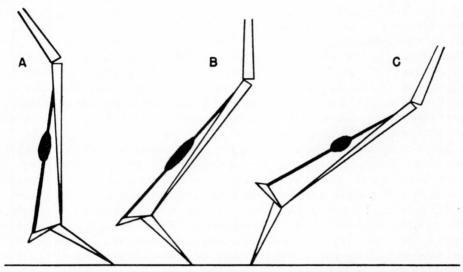

FIG. 52.   Length changes of one contracting leg muscle bundle during running. Tension developed during contraction which has begun in position A is not sufficient to check forward movement of body, thus causing contracting muscle bundle to be stretched to length shown in position B. After this phase in running cycle, muscle is in position to shorten, propelling leg forward to position C. (Prepared and kindly furnished by Dr. H. Elftman.)

Such lengthening occurs, for example, when the extensor muscles of the hip check the velocity of the leg as it approaches the forward limit of its swing during walking or running. Thus physical work is done on the muscle by its antagonist in stretching it. The extensor muscle cannot utilize this energy, and it is degraded as heat. After checking the forward velocity, the stretched muscle will shorten as it accelerates the limb in the opposite direction. We thus have an example of both lengthening and shortening in a contracting muscle, as is schematically illustrated in Figure 52. This type of contraction normally occurs in muscles operating in antagonistic pairs. It will be noted that in these three types of muscular activity—contracting isotonically, isometrically and while

* The force exerted by a muscle on its attachment is surprisingly high. At a very moderate rate of walking, the triceps surae exerts a tension almost four times the person's weight, and during running the gastrocnemius may exert a tension some six times the runner's weight. According to Fick's estimate, the human gluteus may exert a force of 1450 pounds. If all our muscles, containing an estimated 2.7×10^8 individual fibers, exerted their combined tension in the same direction, they could develop a force of at least 25 tons.

TABLE 3. CLASSES OF MUSCLE CONTRACTION

TYPE OF CONTRACTION	FUNCTION	EXTERNAL FORCE OPPOSING MUSCLE	EXTERNAL WORK BY MUSCLE	RATE OF ENERGY SUPPLY
Shortening (isotonic)	Acceleration	Less	Positive	Increases
Isometric (constant length)	Fixation	Equal	None	
Lengthening	Deceleration	Greater	Negative	Decreases

lengthening—the muscles may perform positive external work, no work or negative work. These considerations may be summarized by the classifications proposed by Fenn[26] shown in Table 3.

TWITCH.   The brief contractile response of skeletal muscle to a single maximal volley of impulses in the motor neurons supplying it is called a *twitch*. Graphic recording of muscular responses by any of several methods permits analysis of the mechanical aspects of contraction. In *isotonic recording* the bony origin of the muscle is fixed and the tendon is attached to a freely movable, weighted lever (to set tension), which traces a record of muscle length on moving paper or a revolving smoked drum. This tracing shows the time course of muscle shortening. For isometric recording, the bony attachment of a muscle is firmly fixed to a heavy table by clamps or by drills passed through the bone. The other end of the muscle is attached to a rigidly mounted tension-measuring device (strain gauge) that is moved only negligibly by the contraction of the muscle but which develops a signal proportional to the tension which the muscle exerts on it. The signal from the strain gauge is electrically amplified and recorded on moving film, so that the time course of the development of tension is captured. The mechanical response in Figure 53 is such a record, showing the twitch of the cat tibialis anterior muscle elicited by a single maximal stimulus to its motor nerve. The interval between the beginning of the electrical response and the peak of the tension record is the *contraction time*.

By definition, the whole system (i.e., the muscles, the tendon and the isometric lever) does not shorten during isometric contraction. But, as already mentioned, there is *internal* shortening even though there is no external shortening. The activation induced by stimulation results not only in sudden development of internal tension but also in a

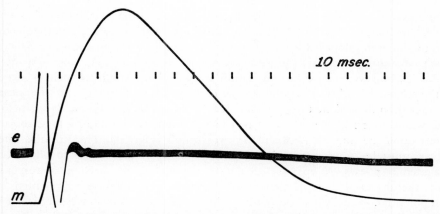

FIG. 53.   Diagram of course of electrical and mechanical response to a single maximal stimulus in skeletal muscle. (After Creed *et al.*, *Reflex activity of the spinal cord*, Oxford, Clarendon Press, 1932.)

capacity to shorten. Under isometric conditions, the contractile elements shorten and pull on the tendon and on the series-elastic components within the fiber, thereby transmitting the tension to the recording lever or, in the body, to the bony lever. The twitch curve, recorded isotonically and isometrically, is the external manifestation of the activated contractile machine. If the passive elastic elements within the fiber and tendons were not extensible, the external manifestations of activation would be much more abrupt.

The twitch response to a single stimulus is as typical of a single isolated muscle fiber as it is of a whole muscle. As can be seen from Figure 53, the action potential is over before the contraction begins. In terms of the hypothesis of the contractile mechanisms given above, this delay is thought to be the time necessary for diffusion of the postulated activator substance from the Z lines and for the initiation of its reactions with the contractile substance. Since it is further assumed that only a limited amount of activator is released and that all of this amount is consumed in the activating reactions, the relaxation of the muscle would signify disappearance of the substance.

The form of the twitch contraction curve, when recorded under the same conditions, is similar for all striated muscles, but the contraction time and the total twitch duration vary a great deal in different types of muscle and in different animals. There are "fast" muscles and "slow" muscles. The most rapidly contracting mammalian muscle studied is the internal rectus of the eye, which has a contraction time of 7.5 milliseconds. The limb muscles of the cat fall into two ranges. Physiologic flexors (e.g., tibialis anterior) and superficial extensor muscles bridging two joints (e.g., gastrocnemius) tend to be fast muscles, having contraction times between 25 and 40 milliseconds. Usually a deep extensor muscle acting at a single joint (e.g., soleus) is a slow muscle with a contraction time in the range of 94 to 120 milliseconds.[13] In the cat, slow muscles are red (owing to greater concentration of myoglobin) and fast muscles are pale or "white;" however, it is better to speak of "slow" and "fast" muscles, since not all fibers in the soleus are red but all are slow. Furthermore, in many vertebrate muscles red and pale fibers are completely intermixed. In the cat, fast muscles are those called upon for rapid phasic movement; slow muscles are concerned with posture. Thus, relative to the maximal tension each muscle can produce, the myotatic stretch reflex (Chap. 6) is larger in the soleus than in the gastrocnemius.

The twitch duration may be altered by direct influence of disease upon the muscle, as in myxedema. The reduced speed of both contraction and relaxation in the single twitch response of the ankle jerk (Achilles tendon reflex) in such patients results from an abnormality of the contractile mechanism.[38]

SUMMATION AND TETANUS.   When a single maximal stimulus is delivered to a motor nerve or directly to a muscle, all the fibers of the muscle are activated and the maximum twitch tension is developed. Even if the electrical stimulus to the motor nerve is increased to a supramaximal intensity, the response will not be greater than that to a maximal stimulus. If, however, two maximal stimuli are delivered rapidly enough in succession that the second stimulus arrives before the contraction cycle is over, the response will be greater than that elicited by a single maximal stimulus. This is true for a single fiber or the whole muscle. The extent of increase in isometric tension or total shortening depends upon the interval between the two stimuli (Fig. 54). The stimulus interval, however, must be greater than the refractory period of the muscle to allow for two propagated responses. As may be seen from Figure 53, the mechanical response far outlasts the electrical. But, in contrast to the conducted response, represented by the action potential, excitation of the actomyosin or contractile substance may occur while the mechanical effect of a prior stimulus persists. There is thus a mechanical fusion or summation of contractions. The degree of fusion is greater when the stimulus interval is shortest, and the tension of such a summated contraction may be more than twice

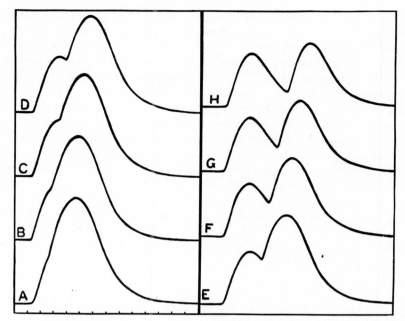

FIG. 54. Summation of muscular contraction by double stimulation. Isometric records of median head of gastrocnemius responding to two stimuli in succession. Interval in milliseconds between stimuli in different records are: *A*, 24; *B*, 32; *C*, 40; *D*, 48; *E*, 57; *F*, 69; *G*, 77; *H*, 88. Time is recorded below record *A* in 20 millisecond intervals. (After Cooper and Eccles. *J. Physiol.*, 1930, *69*:377–385.)

the tension of a single twitch. The degree of summation decreases as the interval between the stimuli approaches the duration of a single twitch response.

If a series of several stimuli is delivered at rapid rate, the third summates with the first two, each subsequent volley adding a diminishing increment of tension until further volleys add no more tension but do maintain the contraction. The response is called a *tetanus.** The tension developed in a tetanus is usually about four times that of a single twitch. With rates of repetitive stimulation too slow to cause complete mechanical fusion, an undulatory jerky response termed an incomplete tetanus is obtained. As the rate of stimulation is increased, the responses to individual volleys become less distinct, and the mechanical fusion becomes progressively greater until complete tetanus occurs (Fig. 55). Similarly, the tension produced increases progressively as the tetanus becomes more fused. Any additional increase in frequency of stimulation beyond this critical rate increases tension only slightly.

This rate is, as might be expected, higher for fast muscles with their relatively brief contraction times and lower for slow muscles with their longer contraction times. A rate of 350 stimuli per second, for example, is necessary to produce a complete tetanus in

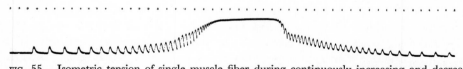

FIG. 55. Isometric tension of single muscle fiber during continuously increasing and decreasing stimulation frequency (2 to 50 per sec.). Time intervals at top of record, 0.2 second. (From Buchthal. *Dan. Biol. Medd.*, 1942, *17*(2):1–140.)

* The physiologic term "tetanus" has been used in naming two neuromuscular disorders: (i) tetany, caused by hypocalcemia, and (ii) tetanus, caused by the toxin of a bacillus. Tetanic contractions of muscles occur in both diseases.

the internal rectus of the eye, whereas a rate of 30 per second is adequate for the slow soleus (i.e., the "slowlyest") muscle. About 100 stimuli per second are required for complete tetanus in a fast limb muscle. In contrast to the mechanical fusion of responses to repetitive stimuli, the spike potentials accompanying such contractions always remain discrete and discontinuous (Fig. 56). This finding emphasizes the fundamental difference between the membrane and the contractile mechanism.

RELATION BETWEEN LENGTH, TENSION AND SHORTENING. Skeletal, cardiac and smooth muscles are elastically extensible. Unstimulated or resting skeletal muscle is normally under slight tension, since it shortens somewhat (20 per cent or more) after its tendons are cut. The length of the unattached relaxed muscle at which the resting tension is zero is the *equilibrium length*. The muscle length at which maximal contraction tension is developed is the *resting length*. This length has been considered close to the maximal extension possible under natural conditions in the body, although Ralston *et al.*[43] think that, in man, the resting length is less than this. When an unstimulated

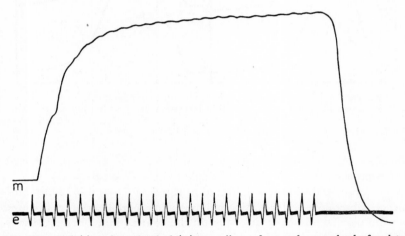

FIG. 56. Electrical (*e*) and mechanical (*m*) recordings of a nearly completely fused tetanic contraction of extensor digitorum longus. Rate of stimulation, 67 shocks per second. Note that spike potentials are quite discrete, although contractions are almost perfectly fused. (From Creed *et al.*, *Reflex activity of the spinal cord*, Oxford, Clarendon Press, 1932.)

skeletal muscle is stretched, the passive elastic tension increases as an exponential function of length over a range up to 200 per cent of the equilibrium length, as shown in Figure 57. (Resting length in this figure is at about length 125; length 100 represents the equilibrium length.) In general this length-tension relationship also holds for cardiac muscle. Stretches up to at least 150 per cent of the equilibrium length are perfectly reversible; the muscle snaps back to its equilibrium length when released. Skeletal muscle ruptures at about three times its equilibrium length.

Since muscles operate at variable and changing lengths, it is essential to know how such changes in length influence contractile capacity. It has long been known that the maximum force developed by a contracting muscle when all its fibers are stimulated at optimal frequencies is specifically related to the initial length at the time of stimulation. The contraction tension increases more or less linearly with increasing initial length until a maximum is reached. If the initial length is greater than this maximum, less contraction tension is developed. The optimal initial length corresponds roughly to the "natural" or resting length of the muscle in the body.

This length-tension relationship of a contracting muscle has been demonstrated many times for whole muscle and also for isolated single frog and mammalian[33] fibers.

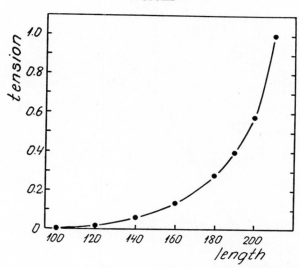

FIG. 57. Static length-tension diagram of isolated skeletal fiber at rest. Mean curve of many experiments performed with increasing and decreasing length at 0° C. *Abscissa,* Length in per cent of equilibrium length, which equals 100. *Ordinate,* Tension in relative units. Tension 1.0 corresponds very closely to maximal tension developed in an isometric tetanic contraction. (From Buchthal and Kaiser. *Dan. Biol. Medd.,* 1951, *21*(7):1–318.)

It is a fundamental mechanical property of contracting muscle and reflects the very nature of contractility. Even in twitch contractions of whole muscles or single fibers, the greatest mechanical reactions occur when the tissue is initially slightly or moderately stretched. The contractile tension developed by cardiac muscle depends on ventricular volume in much the same way. Figure 58 shows the relation between tension developed during maximal voluntary effort and the length of the triceps muscle in man. The net, or active, voluntary tension curve is obtained by first determining the passive tension produced by stretching the muscle fibers and connective tissue to any given length and then subtracting the value obtained from the total tension exerted by the contracting muscle at the same length.

In completely isolated muscles, particularly single fibers, tensions can be recorded for lengths greater than those possible in the body. The net tension developed by contraction becomes progressively smaller with elongations beyond the resting length, until net tension finally decreases to zero when the muscle is stretched to about twice its resting length. The total recorded tension at such elongations is identical with the purely passive tension. The fall in *tetanic* tension as a muscle is stretched past its resting length is easily explained on the sliding hypothesis of muscular contraction: the number of sites for tension-producing cross linkages between the actin and myosin filaments is reduced. The fall in *active* tension at lengths below resting is more difficult to explain by this hypothesis.

The total amount of tension that a muscle can exert under optimal conditions is a function of the total number of fibers. This tension, when expressed as kilograms per square centimeter of physiologic cross section,* represents the absolute muscle force. This force is about 4 kg. per cm.² in man. To do external work a muscle must shorten; thus the realizable work depends upon the fiber's length as well as on its cross section. In man this length varies from 5 mm. for the shortest bundles of the multifidus to more than 400 mm. for the sartorius muscle. When isolated and stimulated, an unloaded muscle does not normally shorten to more than 50 per cent of its resting length. Anatomic limitations of joints and the resistance of antagonistic muscles preclude additional shortening in the body. Parallel-fibered

* A section in a plane at right angles to the axes of the muscle fibers. In pennate muscles, bundles run at an angle to each other, and the physiologic cross section is considerably greater than the anatomic

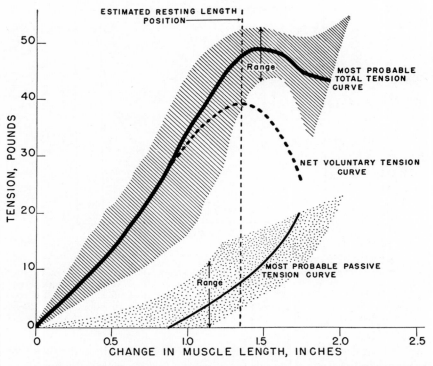

FIG. 58. Isometric length-tension summary for human triceps muscle. (After University of California, *Fundamental studies of human locomotion and other information relating to design of artificial limbs*, v. 2, 1947.)

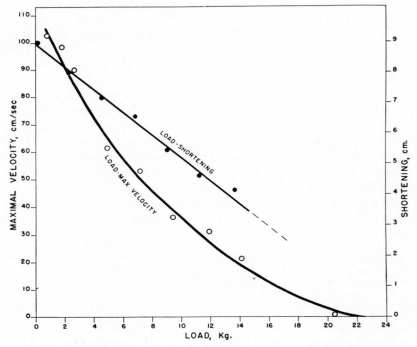

FIG. 59. Load-maximal velocity (muscle initially stretched with a load of 0.32 kg. to a length slightly beyond resting length, all greater loads supported by a block) and load-shortening (freely weighted) relationship for human right pectoralis major muscle. (Based on data of Ralston *et al.*)

muscles in the human body can shorten during contraction to about 60 per cent of their maximal extended lengths. In pennate muscles the excursions are less. The external intercostal muscles must exert considerable force, since their estimated physiologic cross section is about equal to the combined cross section of the gluteus maximus and gluteus medius. The total realizable work, however, is less, because the shortening of the external intercostals is more limited.

Both the rate and the degree of muscle shortening during contraction depend upon the load. With a greater load, the muscle shortens less and more slowly. It is a common experience that lighter objects can be lifted more rapidly than heavier ones. The relation between speed of shortening and l oad in the human pectoralis is given by the load-velocity curve in Figure 59. The velocity is maximal with zero load; with a load which the muscle just fails to lift, the velocity becomes zero and the maximal isometric tension develops. In the body, muscle speed is also limited by the mechanical inertia of the moving parts. Since the absolute amount of shortening depends on the length of the muscle, the intrinsic speed of the muscle is given by its maximum velocity divided by its length. The intrinsic speed, as mentioned in the discussion of the twitch, varies a good deal among muscles of the same animal and between different animals.

For further analysis of the relation between mechanical power, developed efficiency, total power used and speed of shortening, the student may refer to the papers of A. V. Hill.[30, 31] For an analysis of the dynamics of motion, the effective utilization of forces of muscle contraction, and the interrelationship of the geometric arrangement of the bony levers and the dynamics of muscle contraction, refer to Elftman[19, 20] and to the University of California studies.[47]

THE MOTOR UNIT AND GRADATION OF MUSCULAR ACTIVITY

Motor Unit. The functional unit of the motor system is neither the entire muscle nor the individual muscle fiber but the *motor unit*. Just before and just after entering the muscle, the axon from each ventral horn cell (motoneuron) branches many times, thus innervating a number of muscle fibers. Therefore, *the motor unit consists of a single motoneuron, its axon and the group of muscle fibers innervated by this single axon.* It is not the single muscle fiber that represents the unitary, minimum or quantum basis of normal muscular activity but rather the total number or squad of muscle fibers innervated by the single axon of a single motoneuron. Normal skeletal muscle responses are quantitatively graded in terms of motor units and, in Sherrington's words, "a muscle with its motor nerve may be thought of as an additive assemblage of motor units."

The average size of the motor unit—the number of muscle fibers in a motor unit—is learned from the innervation ratio. The innervation ratio is determined by dividing the number of fibers in a muscle by the number of motor axons in the nerve serving the muscle. The extrinsic eye muscles, for example, contain as few as three to six fibers per motor unit. In contrast, Clark found innervation ratios of 1:120 to 1:165 in some cat leg muscles. Doubtless some motor units in man are a good deal larger, particularly those in very large muscles such as the deltoid and the biceps. Smaller innervation ratios permit greater delicacy of graduation of movement.

AVERAGE MOTOR UNIT TENSION. It would seem that the tension yielded by a whole muscle under maximal stimulation of its nerve would, when divided by the number of motor fibers in the nerve, give the average tension of the individual motor units. Following this reasoning, Eccles and Sherrington[18] determined the total tension developed by representative muscles during motor twitches and tetani after the dorsal root ganglia had been removed and the afferent fibers in the muscle nerves allowed to degenerate. Subsequently, the motor fibers passing to the tested muscle were enumerated and the average motor unit tension was calculated, with the results shown in Table 4. It has since been learned that many of the nerve fibers which would be counted in such preparations are γ efferents innervating intrafusal fibers of the muscle spindles. These fibers, which constitute about 30 per cent of the motor fibers, do not add to the tension of muscle contraction. Eccles and Sherrington's values for motor unit tension should therefore be increased by 30 per cent. If, as Hunt and Kuffler claim,[34] a single muscle fiber may be innervated by more than one nerve fiber, the average tension value of a unit would be still greater.

*TABLE 4.   CONTRACTION TENSION OF REPRESENTATIVE MUSCLES AND OF AVERAGE SINGLE MOTOR UNITS**

MUSCLE	TOTAL CONTRACTION TENSION IN GRAMS		NO. OF MOTOR UNITS	AVERAGE MOTOR UNIT TENSION IN GRAMS	
	Twitch	*Tetanus*		*Twitch*	*Tetanus*
Gastrocnemius medialis	2500	9080	393	6.4	23.1
Soleus	580	2230	233	2.48	9.57
Semitendinosus	1020	3310	549	1.8	6.02
Extensor digitorum longus	710	2010	247	2.8	8.1
Crureus	690	2600	256	2.7	10.2

* After Eccles and Sherrington, *Proc. roy. Soc.*, 1930, B106:326–357.

Mechanism of Graduation and Rate of Central Discharge.   Since motor units are the smallest functional units of muscle, the weakest possible *natural* movement is the twitch of a single motor unit. As more force is required, three things happen in an overlapping sequence: (i) more motor units are activated (recruitment); (ii) the active motor units discharge more frequently but not rapidly enough for muscular summation (i.e., the response is subtetanic); and (iii) with further increase of frequency, the motor unit twitches summate to form a tetanus. In both stage ii and stage iii, the more rapid the frequency the greater the tension becomes, although the reasons for this are somewhat different in the two stages.

To visualize these relations it is necessary to know the rate at which single motoneurons discharge. This rate was inferred by Adrian and Bronk,[2] who recorded activity of single motor units through concentric needle electrodes thrust into a muscle. During voluntary contraction the discharge of single motoneurons varied between 5 and 50 impulses per second as the contraction increased from light to maximal effort. During postural reflex contraction, Denny-Brown found a discharge rate of 5 to 25 impulses per second. It is clear that no significant degree of muscle summation occurs at the lower rates; each unit is producing a series of twitches. Nevertheless, tension grades with frequency. A necessary condition for occurrence of this gradation is that the units contract asynchronously, which they will do because they are recruited at different times and are activated at different rates. Not only will the asynchronized trains of impulses in many motoneurons result in a smooth contraction of the whole muscle, but this contraction will vary according to the average frequency of the twitches in the individual units. Think of the twitch as a quantum of contraction. With more rapid rates of motoneuron discharge the number of units twitching at any one time increases, and their individual forces combine to pull on the tendon.

For the stronger grades of muscular tension the third mechanism comes into play as the frequencies of motoneuron discharge enter the tetanic range. As was seen earlier, as twitches fuse to form a tetanus the tension produced is proportional to the frequency of stimulation up to the fusion frequency. Higher frequencies yield little additional tension. In rapid muscles fusion occurs at about 40 to 50 stimuli per second, which agrees well with the top range of motoneuron discharge during voluntary activity.

All-or-None Law.   This relationship between stimulus and contraction, discovered by the American physiologist Bowditch in 1871, has been of profound theoretical importance. Bowditch's original statement, translated into modern scientific terms by Bayliss, is: "An induction [electrical] shock produces contraction or fails to do so according to its strength; if it does so at all it produces the greatest contraction that can be produced by any strength of stimulus in the condition of the muscle at the time." It has already been pointed out that a conduction system obeying such a law must be of the contributing type, in which each segment of the conductor supplies the energy for conduction, rather than the passive or decremental type used to conduct electricity along a wire. All-or-none behavior is associated with a series of properties, all arising from the nature of excitable membranes: (i) absence of graded responses to graded stimuli, (ii) existence of a threshold, (iii) refractory period, (iv) absence of summation, and (v) propagation of response.

In applying the all-or-none law it is necessary to specify accurately the structure exhibiting the behavior. Because cardiac muscle is functionally syncytial, the law holds for the heart as a whole. An entire skeletal muscle or an entire nerve trunk, however, obviously does not obey the all-or-none law. The muscle, for example, grades its contraction with the strength of the stimulus to the point that all units are excited. By application of graded stimuli to a muscle and observation of responses of a few muscle fibers, the contraction is seen to occur in step fashion, each step representing the contraction of one fiber. Thus the muscle fiber appears to obey the all-or-none law, but the muscle does not. Comparable demonstrations for nerve trunks, smooth muscle and sense organs have been made.

But is it strictly correct to speak of the *muscle fiber* obeying the all-or-none law? The fact of a tetanus proves that the contractile process is capable of summation, which is not a property of all-or-none responses. It will be recalled that in a tetanus, no matter how rapid, the action potentials never sum. Thus it is the membrane, discharging in accordance with the all-or-none law, which endows the muscle fiber with all-or-none behavior.

In the next chapters it is shown that a process occurring in axons and synapses grades with the stimulus, shows no refractory period and is not actively conducted. Similar processes occur in the membrane of a muscle fiber. With special electrodes it is possible to produce partial depolarization of the membrane and thereby directly demonstrate the ability of the contractile mechanism to grade its response. Gelfan[28] stimulated muscle fibers with minute electrodes (so-called "pore" electrodes) and noted contractions which were (i) graded, (ii) localized and (iii) unaccompanied by propagated electrical response. Sichel and Prosser[45] set aside the conductive membrane element by stimulating a muscle fiber throughout its whole extent with a massive electrode. The resulting contractions were graded and were not followed by a refractory period.

To summarize in Lloyd's words,

"As a result of these various investigations, it appears certain today that the contractile process of muscle is not an all-or-nothing mechanism; it is capable of full gradation in response and does not exhibit a refractory period. The conducting mechanism that normally transfers excitation to the contractile mechanism, on the other hand, is an all-or-nothing mechanism just as is the conducting mechanism in nerve. In the normal course of events, then, it is a necessary consequence that the contraction follows an all-or-nothing relation, for the stimulus transferred to it from the conducting (and excitable) mechanism is of necessity a constant stimulus."[39]

Finally, it will be noted that Bowditch's definition of all-or-none behavior ends with a qualification which states, in effect, that the response will be "all" that the cell is capable of at the time. It need scarcely be said that a host of factors—temperature, pH, chemicals, and others—affect the response of the muscle fiber. The all-or-none law can be stated as follows: "Of all the factors which influence the magnitude of the response, the stimulus strength, provided it is above threshold, is not one."

NEUROMUSCULAR TRANSMISSION

How a nerve impulse initiates an impulse in a muscle fiber membrane poses a problem not encountered in impulse propagation in either structure. This problem arises from the rapidly changing geometry at the junction of nerve and muscle. If the local circuit current flow of the nerve impulse directly stimulates the muscle fiber membrane, then the nerve fiber must supply a large current in order to depolarize the muscle membrane to threshold. This necessity can be seen from the diagram in Figure 60, which shows the main structural features of the neuromuscular junction (end-plate region of the muscle). The diameter of the naked axon near its termination is less than 10 μ; the diameter of the muscle fiber is about 100 μ. If there were a low-resistance connection between the axoplasm and the sarcoplasm, activity at the nerve terminal would cause local current flow from the inactive muscle membrane. However, the area of muscle membrane that must be depolarized is at least 100 times larger than the area of the nerve terminal. It is unlikely that the nerve can supply the required current. Such a consideration, and also the highly specialized structure of the nerve terminal and the end-plate membrane, suggest that neuromuscular transmission is accomplished by means other than local circuit flow, e.g., chemically.

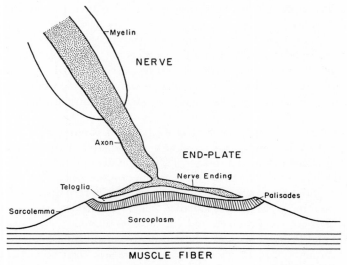

FIG. 60.   Diagram of end-plate region, adapted from Couteaux. (From Acheson. *Fed. Proc.*, 1948, 7:447–457.)

There is an enormous amount of evidence that neuromuscular transmission is mediated by a chemical—acetylcholine (ACh), a methylated quarternary ammonium salt. The sequence of events is as follows. (i) The depolarization of the naked nerve terminal during activity causes the release of a small amount of ACh. (ii) The ACh diffuses across the small gap between the nerve ending and the end-plate and reacts with a *receptor* in the end-plate. (iii) The ACh-receptor complex acts to increase the permeability of the end-plate membrane to all ions and is quickly destroyed by the enzyme acetylcholinesterase (AChE), which exists in high concentrations in the end-plate regions of the membrane. (iv) The membrane potential of the end-plate changes toward zero, no matter what the original potential. (v) If the transmitter action is strong enough, and if the muscle membrane is excitable, the end-plate membrane is depolarized to threshold, and an impulse is propagated away from the end-plate in both directions.

ACETYLCHOLINE LIBERATION.[10, 23, 25]   The arrival of an impulse at the nerve terminals liberates a minute amount of ACh (about 10^{-17} M.). From studies of the electrical potentials at the end-plate it is believed that the ACh is liberated from a large number (at least 200) sites in the form of small packets or quanta containing a constant number (roughly 1000 to 10,000) of ACh molecules. This physiologic evidence conforms with biochemical evidence that ACh exists in bound form and with the findings by electron microscopy that the nerve terminals contain many vesicles a few hundred Ångstroms in diameter. Individual packets are liberated spontaneously at random intervals in the absence of propagated activity in the nerve. During an impulse not all of the sites release a packet of ACh. The number of sites that do release ACh during activity increases directly with the calcium and inversely with the magnesium concentration in the bathing medium. However, the amount of ACh in each packet remains constant over a range of calcium concentrations that changes the total amount of ACh released from near zero to well above normal—indicating that calcium is directly involved in the secretion of the packets of ACh.

END-PLATE RECEPTORS.[11, 23, 41]   The muscle end-plates contain two kinds of ACh receptors. One, the receptor proper, combines with ACh to form the complex which leads to end-plate depolarization. The other "receptor" is the enzyme AChE, which inactivates ACh by speeding its hydrolysis to choline and acetate, which are inactive. It is quite possible that these two receptors are part of the same protein molecule, but differential drug effects leave little doubt that there are two sites having different properties. It is probable that the initial receptor-ACh complex is inactive but quickly changes into an active depolarizing form. Simultaneously, ACh is being destroyed by the AChE. The concentration of AChE in the end-plate region is sufficiently high to account for the destruction of the ACh in a few milliseconds, in accord with the calculated duration of transmitter action at the end-plate. It is supposed that both ACh-receptor complexes are in equilibrium with ACh. Therefore, as ACh is hydrolyzed by AChE, more ACh will dissociate from the receptor and, in turn, be hydrolyzed by the AChE. In this way, ACh can exert its transmitter action in the presence of high concentrations of AChE, but only briefly as required to prevent repetitive firing of the muscle fiber.

Nachmansohn[41, 42] has made careful, detailed biochemical studies of the properties of AChE, choline acetylase (the enzyme directly involved in the synthesis of ACh), and other aspects of ACh metabolism which are discussed in biochemistry texts. He has established the existence of AChE in most excitable tissues, including the membrane of the squid giant axon. From these findings and from studies of the effects of AChE inhibitors on the electrical activity of excitable tissues, he has postulated that ACh is directly involved in and essential to impulse propagation. While this hypothesis is a matter of dispute, there is little doubt that ACh is important in the function of excitable tissues generally and is the transmitter agent in neuromuscular and some other junctions (see Chap. 9). Much of the initial evidence for the transmitter function of ACh came indirectly from studies of AChE concentrations at end-plate sites in muscle. While the rate of ACh hydrolysis is proved rapid enough to agree with known myoneural events, available chemical methods, although quantitative, cannot follow events as rapid as those involved in neuromuscular conduction. For this, electrical methods must be used.

Acetylcholine Action at the End-Plate.[24]   In their classic analysis of neuromuscular transmission, Fatt and Katz concluded that the action of ACh on the end-plate membrane is to increase its permeability to all free ions in the intracellular and interstitial fluids. Such a change in the properties of the end-plate membrane might result from the creation of a pore through the membrane large enough for all ions to penetrate it rather easily; i.e., the membrane structure may be "destroyed" in a small region.

If all the ionic species in the neighborhood could penetrate this pore with equal ease, then the transmembrane potential near it would go to about zero. Since enough ACh is released by a nerve impulse to produce a large number of such "short-circuited" patches of membrane, the whole end-plate membrane potential discharges toward zero.

However, the duration of the transmitter action is so short that the depolarization process does not reach a steady value. The fall in the potential at the end-plate sets up local circuit flow from adjacent regions, so that the depolarization spreads passively along the muscle membrane. If the depolarization at the end-plate region reaches threshold, an impulse is generated which propagates away from the end-plate in both directions. The end-plate potential (frequently abbreviated e.p.p.) is defined as the potential changes in the neighborhood of the end-plate induced by activation of the ACh receptors which cause the nonspecific increase in end-plate permeability. This activation may be induced by means of the ACh released spontaneously from or by activity of the nerve terminals, or by ACh or ACh-like substances applied from an external source.

ANALYSIS OF THE END-PLATE POTENTIAL.[24]   Analysis of the e.p.p. is facilitated by the use of the blocking agent curare. Curare blocks neuromuscular transmission by reducing the e.p.p. below the threshold of the muscle membrane. This reduction comes about because curare competes with ACh for receptors and forms an inactive complex with them. The curare-receptor complex is longer-lasting than the complex formed with ACh; i.e., curare dissociates from the receptor more slowly than does ACh. In consequence, all of the ACh released by a nerve impulse cannot combine with receptors to depolarize the end-plate. If the concentration of curare is properly controlled, some ACh-receptor complexes will form, so that the e.p.p. is not abolished and can be studied without interference by propagated action potentials in the muscle.

If a microelectrode is inserted at the end-plate region in a curarized muscle fiber, a typical monophasic potential change, the e.p.p., is recorded after stimulation of the motor nerve. The size of the e.p.p. depends inversely on curare concentration; the shape of the potential is not affected. That the e.p.p. originates at and is confined to the end-plate region is demonstrated by the recordings in Figure 61. The potentials shown were

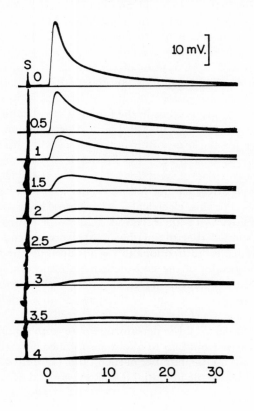

FIG. 61.   Transmembrane potential changes produced in a curarized muscle fiber by stimulation of motor nerve to the muscle. *Abscissa*, Time in milliseconds. *Ordinate*, Change in transmembrane potential in millivolts. *S*, Stimulus artefact, signaling time of stimulus to motor nerve. Number by each curve is distance of intracellular recording microelectrode from muscle end-plate. As distance is increased, the recorded potential becomes smaller and slower. (From Fatt and Katz. *J. Physiol.*, 1951, *115*:320–370.)

recorded at successive 0.5 mm. intervals away from the end-plate. It can be seen that the peak height and rise time of the e.p.p. diminish rapidly as the distance increases. Analysis of these records shows that the change in the size and shape of these potentials is accurately in accord with the cable properties of the fiber. These data lead to the conclusion that the transmitter action at the end-plate discharges the membrane at that point and that this induced potential change spreads passively in both directions along the muscle fiber membrane.

Anticholinesterases. Many compounds, e.g. prostigmine and di-isopropylfluorophos-phate (DFP), inhibit the ability of AChE to hydrolyze ACh. Inhibition of AChE activity at the end-plate by one of these drugs leads, as expected, to a large increase in the size and duration of the e.p.p. A dramatic example of the effect of prostigmine is seen when neuromuscular transmission is blocked by replacing 80 per cent of the sodium chloride in the bathing solution with an equivalent amount of sucrose. The resulting e.p.p. is

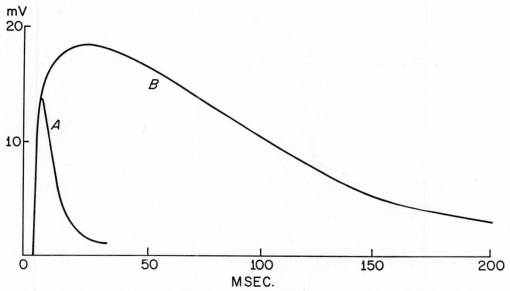

FIG. 62. Effects of an anticholinesterase drug on end-plate potential of single muscle fiber. *Abscissae*, Time in milliseconds. *Ordinates*, Change in transmembrane potential (millivolts) produced by stimulation of motor nerve. *A*, E.p.p. when neuromuscular transmission is blocked after reduction of sodium concentration in bathing medium. *B*, E.p.p. from same fiber after addition of prostigmine to the sodium deficient bathing medium. (From Fatt and Katz. *J. Physiol.*, 1951, *115*:320–370.)

somewhat slower than the e.p.p. during curarization. Addition of neostigmine to the bath enormously prolongs the e.p.p., as can be seen in Figure 62. The relatively great amount of charge displaced from the muscle membrane cannot be supplied by current flow from the active nerve terminals, as required by the electrical theory of neuro-muscular transmission, but is a necessary consequence of the ACh theory.

The different ways curare and neostigmine affect the e.p.p. constitute strong evidence that there are two distinct sites of ACh-binding on the end-plate membrane; curare competes with ACh for the receptor and reduces the e.p.p., whereas neostigmine competes with ACh for AChE and increases the e.p.p.[12] The receptor sites for ACh appear to lie on the outside of the membrane. Application of ACh, carbaminylcholine (an ACh-like compound that is hydrolyzed much more slowly), or curare to the inside of the end-plate region has none of the effects on the end-plate that close external application produces.[11]

NEUROMUSCULAR TRANSMISSION.[24]   In an uncurarized muscle the e.p.p. is usually greater than threshold strength, and an action potential arises out of the e.p.p. as it crosses threshold. The threshold potential at the end-plate is the same whether determined by indirect or direct stimulation. However, the shape of the action potential recorded at the end-plate in response to indirect (motor nerve) stimulation differs from the shape of the potential recorded following direct stimulation of the muscle. Figure 63 shows that, in comparison to the directly evoked action potential, the one indirectly evoked is small and rather bizarrely shaped. Close inspection reveals that the changes in the shape of the indirect action potential are always toward a fixed potential slightly below the zero line. This altered shape is confined to the end-plate region; an action potential recorded a few millimeters away has a normal shape, no matter what the mode of stimulation.

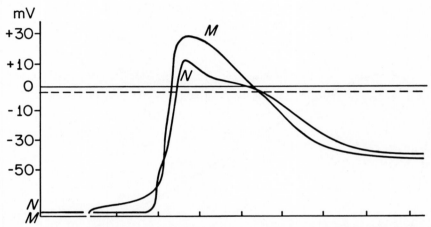

FIG. 63.   Action potentials of a single muscle fiber recorded with intracellular electrode in end-plate region. *Abscissa,* Time in milliseconds. *Ordinate,* Transmembrane potential in millivolts. *M,* Action potential recorded at end-plate when muscle is stimulated by electrodes applied directly to it. *N,* Action potential recorded when muscle is stimulated via its motor nerve. Dashed line shows approximate "equilibrium potential" of end-plate membrane in presence of neuromuscular transmitter agent. (From Fatt and Katz. *J. Physiol.,* 1951, *115:*320–370.)

Fatt and Katz interpreted this finding as indicating that the final steady value of the e.p.p. is slightly less than zero and that the membrane resistance of the end-plate is greatly reduced during transmitter activity, which persists with diminishing intensity throughout most of the action potential. This persisting resistance change explains the divergence of the indirect end-plate spike toward zero. The reduction in membrane resistance during the rising phase of the action potential is quite large (Chap. 2). The transmitter action must produce a roughly equal additional reduction in resistance at the end-plate because the peak height of the end-plate action potential is considerably reduced.

Other evidence supports the "short-circuit" theory of ACh action at the end-plate. That the final steady level of the e.p.p. is near zero is indicated by the finding that changes in the end-plate membrane potential produced by applied currents produce proportionate changes in the e.p.p. Additionally, indirect stimuli delivered at various times during the passage of a directly evoked action potential through the end-plate region always produce changes in the potential toward zero. Under normal conditions, sodium ions and, perhaps, the internal anions must carry most of the depolarizing current during transmitter activity, since these are the only ions appreciably out of equilibrium with the steady membrane potential. However, the e.p.p. steady value near zero is below the sodium-ion equilibrium potential, and it must be supposed that potassium and chloride ions reduce the amount of depolarization as the membrane potential moves away from the potassium and chloride equilibrium potentials. Further evidence that potassium permeability is increased during end-plate activity is the finding that membrane resistance changes when ACh is applied to the end-plate of a muscle depolarized by bathing it in isotonic potassium sulfate.

Muscle Fiber Action Potential. An action potential is propagated by the muscle fiber membrane by local current flow in the same manner as a propagated potential in an unmyelinated nerve fiber (Chap. 2). The rising phase undoubtedly results from an increase in membrane permeability to sodium ions. The repolarization phase is caused at least partly by increased permeability to potassium, since Desmedt[16] found that the maximum rate of repolarization is directly proportional to the internal potassium concentration. The factors leading to increased permeability to potassium are not known, but they appear to be different from the delayed increase in permeability to potassium induced by depolarization (Chap. 2). Conduction velocity is about 5 m. per second in mammalian muscle. In a muscle fiber 10 cm. long, an impulse originating at the center of the fiber would require 10 milliseconds to reach the ends, an appreciable fraction of a contraction time of about 30 milliseconds.

CARDIAC AND SMOOTH MUSCLE

There are two general classes of smooth muscle. *Visceral smooth muscle* is found in the walls of the gastrointestinal tract and the genitourinary tract. *Multi-unit* or *motor unit smooth muscle* is found in structures, such as the precapillary sphincters, the intrinsic muscles of the eye and the pilo-erector muscles, where direct nervous control is required. Smooth muscle is differentiated from striated muscle histologically by the absence of cross striations, and physiologically by a relative slowness of contraction. Bozler[5] drew a close analogy between the properties of striated and smooth muscle and suggested the following functional classification of muscle.

$$\text{Striated Muscle} \left\{ \begin{array}{l} \text{Skeletal} \left\{ \begin{array}{l} \text{Many Units} \\ \text{Motor Nerves} \end{array} \right\} \text{Multi-Unit} \\ \\ \text{Cardiac} \left\{ \begin{array}{l} \text{Automatic} \\ \text{Syncytial} \end{array} \right\} \text{Visceral} \end{array} \right\} \text{Smooth Muscle}$$

The properties of multi-unit smooth muscle with motor nerves are quite similar to those of skeletal muscle; and the properties of cardiac and visceral smooth muscle are quite similar.

Syncytial Muscle. One of the most striking features of the heart is that large parts of it contract almost simultaneously. Certainly, the synchronous contraction of the ventricle is necessary for the efficient expulsion of blood. Synchronous contraction or systole could be produced in skeletal muscle by simultaneous activation of all the motor units. However, the heart beats synchronously and spontaneously when completely denervated. Cardiac muscle is thus different from skeletal muscle in being both automatic and a functional syncytium. The term "automatic" refers to the intrinsic ability of a tissue to generate impulses spontaneously and rhythmically, and "functional syncytium" means that the whole tissue acts electrically like a single large cell. Visceral smooth muscle also has these properties.

SYNCYTIAL CONDUCTION. *Cardiac muscle.* As in skeletal muscle, the normal stimulus for contraction of cardiac and smooth muscle is membrane depolarization. In the heart, but not always in smooth muscle, this depolarization is brought about by conducted action potentials; therefore, the synchronous contraction of cardiac muscle arises from its electrical activity. If a microelectrode is inserted into a ventricular cell and the membrane potential is recorded throughout one cycle, the pattern of the recording is the same, save for slight time differences, no matter from which ventricular cell the recording is obtained (Fig. 64B). The rising phase of the action potential progresses rapidly throughout the ventricle, probably by local circuit activation. There is little doubt that activity in one cardiac cell soon brings adjacent cells into activity; a stimulus above threshold applied anywhere in the ventricle initiates activity which spreads throughout the ventricle.

The spread of activity by local circuit flow in a nerve fiber (Chap. 2) was described in terms of a continuous axoplasm with a specific resistivity several orders of magnitude smaller than that of the membrane. In the heart, however, electronmicrographs show rather clearly that each cell is surrounded by a distinct membrane, so there is no anatomic continuity of the myoplasm between cells. Yet, equally clearly, activity spreads through cardiac muscle from cell to cell. This is the reason for using the term "functional syncytium." The membranes of adjacent cells are closely approximated to each other— only a few hundred Ångstroms apart—and are greatly folded and interdigitated so that their surface areas are increased. This close approximation and the large area of contact between the surfaces of adjacent cells are both factors which tend to increase the flow of the local currents of an active cell through adjacent inactive cells. This flow may be the basis of the functional syncytium.

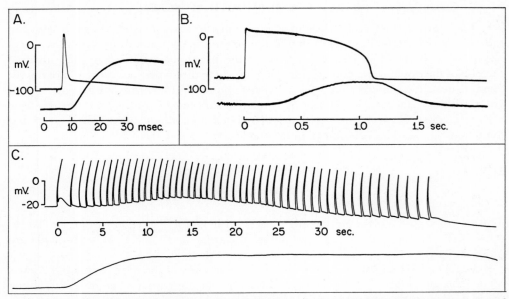

FIG. 64. Simultaneously recorded transmembrane potentials and contraction in three types of muscle. *A*, Isolated frog skeletal muscle fiber. *B*, Whole frog ventricle; action potential recorded from one "cell." *C*, Strip of pregnant rat uterus (smooth muscle); action potential recorded from one "cell." *Abscissae*, Time in milliseconds (*A*) or seconds (*B* and *C*). *Ordinates*, Upper trace, millivolts; lower trace, arbitrary units of contractile tension. (Part A after Hodgkin and Horowicz. *J. Physiol.*, 1957, *136:* 17P-18P.)

Two dimensional and three dimensional spread. Regardless of the mechanism involved, activity initiated in one region of the heart does spread in all directions at a velocity depending on the cable and excitable properties of the cells (see Chap. 2). This spreading behavior is distinctly different from that of nerve or skeletal muscle fibers. In a nerve fiber the activity travels in one direction, that of the fiber. Spread of activity is one dimensional. In syncytial tissues, spread is two or three dimensional. Spread in thin-walled tissues, such as the atrium or the gut wall, is two dimensional; an action potential originating at a point spreads over the surface as a wave.

Such a wave is somewhat analogous to the ripple produced in the surface of a pond by a falling pebble. However, the water wave gradually diminishes in amplitude as it spreads, whereas the electrical wave in tissue is kept constant in amplitude by the excitation of the membrane at each point. In this respect, the electrical wave is more nearly analogous to the wave of "excitation" produced when a lighted match is touched to the center of a sheet of gunpowder spread evenly over a surface. The process of spread is identical in principle. The gunpowder is set afire by the conduction of heat in advance of the burning region; unexcited membrane is "set afire" by the spread of currents in front of the excited area of membrane. The analogy ends there—the membrane presently recovers its excitability. The ventricle, especially the left ventricle, is a thick-walled organ and the spread of excitation is three dimensional. In fact, knowledge of the pathway of the spread of excitation through the ventricle is essential to the understanding of its contributions to the electrocardiogram (Chap. 27). Another way of stating the differences between nerve, atrium and ventricle is that, in nerve, the wave front is a point; in atrium, a line; and, in ventricle, a surface.

Visceral smooth muscle. An impulse originating anywhere in the ventricle spreads throughout it except in abnormal circumstances. In other words, the syncytial connections always transmit an impulse. In visceral smooth muscle, on the other hand, the syncytial connections are much less efficient; whether an impulse spreads from one cell to another depends, sensitively, on local conditions, particularly the tension of the muscle. Syncytial transmission also depends on the concentrations of ions and on various humoral agents such as acetylcholine. The effect of stretching the muscle and increasing its tension is dramatic. The stretch partially depolarizes the muscle and increases the rate of firing.[9] Both of these effects probably increase the active contraction of the muscle and thus act to prevent additional stretching. Overstretching probably blocks syncytial conduction, because a partial depolarization block occurs (Chap. 2).

MEMBRANE POTENTIALS AND CONTRACTION. *Cardiac muscle.* The action potential of cardiac muscle is usually several hundred milliseconds long. In most circumstances, the contraction time is approximately equal to the duration of the action potential (Fig. 64B). For this reason, it is convenient to think of the upstroke of the action potential as "turning on" the contraction and the fast repolarization as turning it off. Since cardiac muscle is striated and has Z bands, and since depolarization of the membrane probably leads to contraction, as it does in striated muscle, this convenience is not without physiologic foundation. The long duration of the action potential insures that each contraction is sufficiently prolonged to be maximal; i.e., the tension corresponds to a tetanus in skeletal muscle.

Since the membrane is refractory until repolarization is well advanced, there can be no summation in cardiac muscle. This behavior is consonant with the function of the heart. A strong synchronous contraction is necessary for the efficient ejection of blood from the heart; the contractile properties of cardiac muscle are otherwise much the same as tetanic contractions of skeletal muscle. The length-tension relationships are qualitatively indistinguishable.

One interesting aspect of cardiac muscle is that the duration of the action potential depends on the heart rate: the faster the rate, the shorter the duration. Over the usual physiologic range, the action potential duration is roughly one-half of the interval between beats. This insures that an increase in heart rate will bring about a maximal increase in cardiac output, because both diastolic filling time and systolic ejection time are reduced. A reduction in the filling time alone would occur if the action potential duration were invariant.

The action potential of cardiac muscle differs from that of nerve or skeletal muscle in its greater duration and in the great variability of duration with rate. The dependence of the rate of rise and the overshoot of the action potential on the external concentration of sodium indicates that the upstroke of the action potential is brought about by a large increase in membrane permeability to sodium.[7, 50] However, the nature of the permeability changes underlying the greatly prolonged period of depolarization—the *plateau phase*—is not known.

Weidmann[51] has shown that total membrane resistance is increased during the plateau. It follows, then, that permeability to sodium is increased and permeability to potassium and/or chloride ions reduced during the plateau. A simple explanation of the long duration of the action potential and the dependence of its duration on rate is to suppose that two types of sodium conductance are available (see Chap. 2). The first type of conductance, responsible for the upstroke of the action potential, is initially large, but it is rapidly inactivated (order of milliseconds) following depolarization and just as rapidly activated following repolarization. The second type, responsible for the plateau, is comparatively small but slowly inactivated (order of seconds) and just as slowly activated following repolarization. After the upstroke of the action potential and the inactivation of the fast sodium conductance, the slowly inactivated sodium conductance, although small, persists. It maintains the membrane potential near zero because the conductances of potassium and chloride have fallen, it being assumed that they depend on the membrane potential. As the slowly inactivated sodium conductance decreases, the potential falls slowly until a potential is reached where one or more other conductances begin to change rapidly with membrane voltage. Sodium conductance is "turned off" and potassium and chloride conductances are "turned on," so repolarization proceeds with increasing rapidity. Following repolarization, excitability returns with activation of the fast sodium conductance, but the action potential will be short because the slow sodium conductance is only slowly activated. The plateau will occur at a lower voltage, so the potential at which rapid repolarization occurs will be reached more quickly.

Visceral muscle.[6, 9, 52]   The action potentials of visceral muscle are extremely variable from time to time and tissue to tissue. The action potentials of the ureter are like those of cardiac muscle. The action potentials of the uterus and the small intestine are spike-like, but their resemblance to skeletal muscle is not marked. Presumably the type of action potential depends on the function of the muscle: spikelike in muscles where tension is widely graded, heartlike where an all-or-none type of contraction is needed. The action potentials of the uterus are about the size of the steady potential (about 30 mV.) and occasionally overshoot (Fig. 64C). Bülbring's intracellular recordings from the small intestine show action potentials which are ordinarily only a few millivolts high, much smaller than the steady potential.[9] Whether the size of the action potential of the uterus and intestine depends on external sodium concentration is disputed, but it is agreed that smooth muscle is unexcitable in the complete absence of sodium. As mentioned above, the steady potential is reduced by stretch. This effect appears to result from an increase in membrane permeability to all ions, similar to the end-plate potential of skeletal muscle.

In uterine muscle long spontaneous contractions are produced by equally long trains of action potentials (Fig. 64C). In intestine, the action potentials are small and short. Although their size and frequency depend on the ionic and humoral concentrations as well as on tension, the effects of these agents on the steady potential appear to be the primary determinants of contractile tension.

Visceral musculature in performing its functions undergoes enormous changes in length. Bozler[5] points out that if a constant load is placed on a strip of smooth muscle it will, after an initial rapid elongation, stretch at a constant speed until there is a 50 per cent change in length. Thereafter, the speed slows, probably because tension-induced depolarization initiates active contraction. This behavior is that of a viscous system, and this finding led Bozler to insist that contraction must involve relative movements of molecules, not a folding or coiling within single molecules.

AUTOMATICITY OF HEART.   Apparently any region of a syncytial tissue can originate propagating action potentials. However, in the heart there is a region specialized for origination of impulses, the *pacemaker* region in the sino-atrial (S-A) node. The S-A nodal region determines the rate of the heart beat, because its intrinsic rate is faster than those of the atrium and ventricle. An action potential from the node reaches these regions before they have time to develop an intrinsic beat. Pacemaker activity is electric; action potentials of a pacemaker region are distinctive. The characteristics of a pacemaker cell membrane are such that the membrane potential has no stable value. During diastole, the membrane potential falls slowly toward zero instead of remaining steady as it does in nonpacemaker regions. This slow diastolic depolarization is called the *pacemaker potential* or *prepotential*.

When the pacemaker potential reaches the threshold voltage, an impulse is generated and propagated away from the pacemaker region in all available directions in the sheet of muscle (Chap. 27). The repolarization process involves a decrease in permeability to sodium and an increase in permeability to potassium, and the membrane voltage approaches the equilibrium potential for potassium. Presumably, the membrane permeability to sodium is rather higher in pacemaker tissue than in other tissues; and, as the permeability changes, causing repolarization to die out, the potential begins to fall from near the potassium equilibrium potential to a rather low steady value (because of high permeability to sodium). However, this steady value is so low that the potential crosses threshold in approaching it, and an impulse is initiated. The rate of initiation of impulses depends primarily on the slope of the prepotential. This slope is extremely dependent on the temperature, the ion concentrations and the presence or absence of small concentrations of acetylcholine and epinephrine.

Visceral smooth muscle apparently has many pacemaker regions, their number and locations changing with local conditions. Variations in tension, which change the membrane potential, might shift some cells into a state where they would begin to fire spontaneously and stop other cells from doing so. The low safety factor of transmission in visceral smooth muscle means that impulses originating at one region will usually spread only a limited distance before conduction is blocked. The cells beyond the block may be stimulated by impulses arising in another pacemaker region.

Multi-Unit Smooth Muscle. Study of multi-unit smooth muscles is complicated by the small size of the units and by the persistence of the transmitter substance following a single motor volley, which usually gives rise to a tetanic response rather than a twitch. A study of the electrical and mechanical responses of the nictitating membrane of the cat demonstrates this feature.[17] When stimulated by a single nerve volley (cervical sympathetic), the nictitating membrane begins to contract after about 150 milliseconds. Contraction is preceded by an electrical response, just as in skeletal muscle. When the electrical activity is not repetitive, the contraction resembles a skeletal muscle twitch but is ten times slower than that of the soleus, a slow muscle. More commonly the electrical activity of the muscle is repetitive, with one to two rhythmic discharges per second. The mechanical record resembles an incomplete tetanus (see Figs. 55, 56). There is an increment of tension corresponding to each electrical discharge, and each discharge has an associated refractory period. These experiments indicate that the nerve volley liberates a chemical transmitter which persists for some time and thus continues to re-excite the muscle fibers rhythmically. This hypothesis is also suggested by the gradual loss of synchronization of the electrical activity. The transmitter substance is probably norepinephrine or epinephrine.

CLINICAL CORRELATIONS: MOTOR UNIT DISEASE

Diseases of the motoneuron (once called lower motor neuron disease) and of muscles bear a bewildering series of names. Taken at random, a few may be listed: acute anterior poliomyelitis or infantile paralysis, myasthenia gravis, familial periodic paralysis, myotonia congenita, progressive muscular paralysis, amyotrophic lateral sclerosis. Each of these names is derived from some conspicuous feature of the disease, but the basis for naming varies. The motor unit provides a systematic rational classification of peripheral motor diseases founded upon the place of attack and the physiologic mechanism disturbed. Diseases attacking each of five different points in the motor unit may be expected to produce different effects. Figure 65 shows these points.

Destruction of Cell Body or Axon. Sudden (acute anterior poliomyelitis) or slow (progressive muscular atrophy) destruction of the cell body or sudden destruction of the axon (peripheral nerve injury) will produce certain classic signs. These are the criteria of "lower motor neuron disease" or, better, "motoneuron disease," because, as will be seen in Chapter 11, they distinguish diseases of the motoneurons from diseases attacking the descending motor pathways from the brain, so-called "upper motoneuron diseases." These signs and other less obvious changes in muscle are:

1. Flaccid paralysis: weakness of voluntary movements combined with flaccidity or deficient muscle tone
2. Atrophy and degeneration
3. Fibrillation and fasciculation
4. Diminution of excitability to brief electrical pulses
5. Increase of excitability to chemicals, especially acetylcholine
6. Biochemical and histologic changes

The first of these signs is obviously consequent to a reduction in the number of functioning motor units available for voluntary and reflex response. After nerve injury, weakness precedes muscular atrophy and therefore cannot be explained by it. Despite much research, why muscles deprived of innervation atrophy and degenerate remains a mystery. Such degeneration is, in a sense, contrary to the neuron doctrine. Atrophy results from denervation, from disuse (as in splinting) and from tendon resection. Mere disuse partly explains the results of denervation seen in the early stage, but disuse atrophy does not lead to fibrillation (see below).

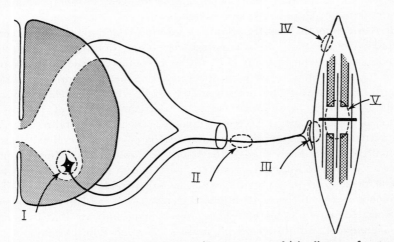

FIG. 65.   Diagram representing sites of injury (Roman numerals) in diseases of motor unit.

Two experiments lead to the conclusion that the axon of the motoneuron must be divided for degeneration, as opposed to atrophy, to occur. Tower[46] sectioned the lumbar spinal cord and all the posterior roots below the level of section, thus depriving the motoneurons of all afferent impulses. The muscle did not degenerate as it would if the nerve had been cut. Conversely, Denny-Brown and Brenner[14] established a compression nerve block for three weeks. Neither fibrillation nor a change in the size of the muscle fibers resulted. Continuity of an axon with its cell body seems sufficient to forestall degeneration in the muscle fiber it supplies. A possible explanation lies in a continual "leaking" of transmitter substance from "resting" motor nerve endings.

FIBRILLATION AND FASCICULATION; ELECTROMYOGRAPHY.[15]   In certain motor unit diseases, muscles exhibit small, local, "spontaneous" contractions. Observing such contractions with the laboratory technique for recording the action potentials of intact muscle has proved useful in the diagnosis and study of these diseases. Such investigations have led to the conclusion that one of the common classic neurologic signs—fibrillation— was misnamed. This name suggests that the unit discharging spontaneously is the muscle fiber, whereas analysis shows that what was called fibrillation is actually a discharge of a whole motor unit.

Fibrillation, as redefined by Denny-Brown and Pennybacker[15] from electrophysiologic studies, consists of 10 to 200 μV. potentials with a duration of 1 to 2 milliseconds. They are irregular and asynchronous, produce no shortening of the muscle, and cannot be observed through the skin. By contrast, the potentials recorded during normal motor unit discharges have an amplitude of 2 to 6 mV. and a duration of 5 to 8 milliseconds. It follows that the unit potential in denervated muscle is the "spontaneous" activation of *single muscle cells* or muscle fibers, and hence properly called fibrillation. The activity reaches a peak in about eight days, ceases when reinnervation occurs through nerve regeneration, or, if this fails, ceases when the muscle fibers have degenerated sufficiently. Fibrillation is lessened by curare and enhanced by prostigmine. That muscle fibers fire in the absence of nerve stimulation is an expression of the denervation sensitivity to acetylcholine, and the stimulus is presumably circulating acetylcholine.

According to Denny-Brown and Pennybacker's analysis, what was called fibrillation is properly termed *fasciculation.* It is visible through the skin or mucosa and represents a "spontaneous" discharge of motor units. The potential developed by the discharge of a squad of muscle fibers innervated by a single motoneuron would be expected to be greater than a single fiber discharge, since many fibers are involved. It would also be longer, owing to the somewhat asynchronous firing of the fibers. A motor unit discharge could lead to a local response in the muscle only if the fibers composing the squad were adjacent within a fasciculus and not dispersed widely throughout the muscle. This expectation has in fact been realized by histologic investigation. The triggering of the motor unit discharge would appear to lie with the cell body. Fasciculation is indicative of lower motor neuron disease attacking the gray column of the spinal cord—amyotrophic lateral sclerosis, progressive muscular atrophy.

In some cases, the origin must be peripheral because procaine block of the motor nerves does not stop fasciculation. Therefore, it may originate at the end-plate of a fiber, be conducted antidromically to the branching point of the motor axon, and, by an "axon reflex," reach all the fibers of a motor unit.

Related to fasciculation is the electromyographic phenomenon of *synchronization.* Potentials 10 to 15 times that developed by a single motor unit are observed in muscles of poliomyelitis patients. The best explanation appears to be that several motor units contract synchronously through some "locking" of the discharge of anterior horn cells. Another possible cause lies in the development of giant motor units when nondegenerated motoneurons sprout and capture (innervate) muscle fibers whose innervation has been destroyed. This kind of synchronization of motor units is to be distinguished from that seen in clonus or tremor and the less definite synchronization in spasticity and rigidity.[32]

CHEMICAL AND ELECTRICAL EXCITABILITY. The greatly enhanced responsiveness of denervated skeletal muscle to chemical agents is one of several instances which justify speaking of the "law of denervation" (Chap. 9). The so-called "reaction of degeneration" in denervated muscle was first noted as a relative loss of excitability to stimulation with an induction coil, which yields so-called "faradic" currents (i.e., currents with pulse durations of less than 1 millisecond), and as a retention of excitability to so-called "galvanic" currents (i.e., current flows with long durations—about 300 milliseconds). This phenomenon is now recognized as simply a testing of two points on the strength-duration curve (Chap. 2), which is now usually determined with electronic stimulators.

Myasthenia Gravis.[1, 48] As one proceeds peripherally in the motor unit, the next critical point is the neuromuscular junction. *Myasthenia gravis* is characterized by muscular weakness and extreme "fatigability" confined to the skeletal muscles but with a predilection for those of the face. Double vision (diplopia), drooping eyelids (ptosis), a toneless voice and difficulty in chewing and swallowing are often present at the initial examination. A repeated movement may initially be strong but becomes progressively weaker. Muscle strength is greatest in the morning and least in the evening.

Figure 66 is an electromyographic record from a normal muscle. The regular rhythm and equal amplitudes indicate that a single unit is being recorded. Sample records taken throughout the course of a continued effort by a patient with myasthenia gravis are shown. Note that the rhythm does not alter, but the spike amplitude soon varies and, eventually, some spikes drop out completely. It follows from the previous discussion of gradation of contraction that the only way a motor unit can be fractionated is by some process occurring in the individual muscle fibers making up the squad. Further evidence that the disorder underlying myasthenia gravis lies in the neuromuscular junction is that the muscle fibers show no histopathologic alteration, respond normally to direct stimulation of the muscle, and are extremely sensitive to drugs. Curare-like drugs aggravate myasthenia; anticholinesterase drugs reduce it and are in fact an effective therapeutic agent.

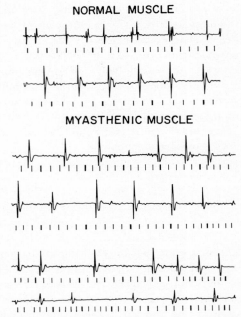

FIG. 66. Single unit discharge from muscles of a normal person (*upper records*) and a myasthenia patient (*lower records*) taken at different stages in the course of a continuous muscular action. (After Lindsley and Curnen. *Arch. Neurol. Psychiat.* (*Chicago*), 1936, *35*:253–269.)

Physiologic analysis suggests four possible mechanisms or "sites" of derangement: (i) a deficient production or liberation of acetylcholine, (ii) an overactive cholinesterase system, (iii) a diminished sensitivity of the muscle end-plate to acetylcholine, and (iv) the circulation of a curare-like substance. The limited experiments that can be done on man (the disease is not known in animals) have seemed to favor the fourth mechanism. There appears to be qualitative, if not quantitative, similarity between myasthenia and curarization in man. The curarization theory might also explain why certain thymic tumors are often associated with myasthenia. While attempts to extract a curare-like substance from the blood of myasthenia patients or to demonstrate a curare-like effect of such blood on nerve-muscle preparations have been unsuccessful, positive results with extracts from thymus glands of myasthenic infants and fetuses have recently been reported. These effects, however, apparently were due to the potassium in the extract.[53] It is not impossible that the thymus of a fetus elaborates a substance which restrains muscular movement and that the production of this substance is reactivated in myasthenic patients.

Myotonia.[1]   Myotonia is a failure of the muscles to relax normally. In dramatic contrast to myasthenia, myotonic muscles can be contracted promptly and forcefully but cannot be relaxed at will. Further, myotonia is most pronounced after a period of rest and decreases with repeated attempts; the patient's condition is better in the evening than in the morning. A tap anywhere on a myotonic muscle produces a local knot of prolonged contraction.

Because a strain of goats exhibits myotonia,[8] it has been possible to study this sign by electrical methods and isometric myography after stimulation of a sectioned nerve, as in a student laboratory experiment. The delayed relaxation is shown clearly in the myographic record in Figure 67. The cause cannot be a persistent central discharge

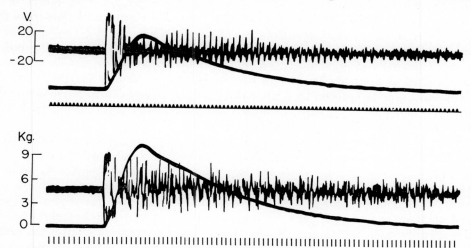

FIG. 67.   Electrical and myographic records from muscle of a myotonic goat. *Upper record*, Result of a single maximal volley to motor nerve. *Lower record*, Result of two volleys to nerve 7 milliseconds apart. Time, 10 milliseconds. (From Brown and Harvey. *Brain*, 1939, 62:341-363.)

because the motor nerve has been sectioned. That this is a prolonged contraction, not a contracture, is shown by the prolonged phasic electrical activity, as opposed to prolonged steady potentials which accompany certain drug-induced contractions. This means that the muscle is being activated through its membrane, and the fault is probably not in the contractile substance itself. The response to acetylcholine is likewise prolonged. The delay in relaxation occurs when the muscle is stimulated locally and is seen even after degeneration of the motor nerve. These observations, together with the fact that mechanical or electrical stimulation anywhere on the muscle results in a prolonged contraction, indicate a fault lying in the membrane of the muscle fibers.

Diseases of the Contractile Mechanism.[1]   The fifth site of muscular pathologic disturbance is in the contractile mechanism of the muscle fiber. Progressive muscular dystrophy serves as an example. Nerves and motor nerve endings which appear normal histologically can occur when the muscle fibers are severely degenerated. (For reasons not pertinent to physiology, the muscles are greatly enlarged.) The muscle membrane is no doubt also abnormal, sharing in the striking destruction of the core of the muscle fiber; however, the functional status of the membrane is not known. Functionally the

FIG. 68.   Myogram and action potential of denervated and curarized leg muscle of myotonic goat.
(From Brown and Harvey. *Brain*, 1939, *62*:341–363.)

disease is manifested as simple weakness unaccompanied by fibrillation, fasciculation or other evidences of abnormal excitability.

   Contracture. "Contracture" is used clinically to designate a condition of fixed high resistance to passive stretch of a muscle. Contracture may result simply from a fibrosis of the tissue supporting the muscles or, more frequently, the joints. Such a condition may be caused by immobilization of a joint, for example. The term covers a number of unrelated phenomena and should be used in a generic sense, preceded by an appropriate adjective. That some contractures actually result from disorders of the muscle fiber, as opposed to connective tissue elements, is suggested by "myostatic contracture," first described by Moll.[40] (See also Ref. 44.) If the attachments of a muscle are approximated and immobilized or, simply, if the tendon is cut, *innervated* muscle becomes fixed at a shorter length. Muscles maintained at shorter lengths by neural activity—as in spasm induced by tetanus toxin or in spasticity caused by lesions of the descending motor systems—show a similar contracture. After experimental tenotomy, the isometric contraction tension is severely reduced.

   "Physiologic contracture" refers to a reversible but prolonged state which lacks some of the features of muscular contraction.[27] The principal difference is that contracture may be local and not accompanied by a propagated action potential. As we have seen, myotonia, although a prolonged contraction, is not a contracture. Physiologic contracture may be induced by a number of agents—thermal, electric, mechanical and chemical. It seems probable that some if not all of these agents achieve their effects by acting directly upon the contractile mechanism without intermediation of the membrane. However, the mechanisms of both myostatic and physiologic types of contracture cannot be stated with certainty.

REFERENCES

1. ADAMS, R. D., DENNY-BROWN, D. and PEARSON, C. M. *Diseases of muscle; a study in pathology.* New York, Paul B. Hoeber, 1953.
2. ADRIAN, E. D. and BRONK, D. W. *J. Physiol.,* 1929, *67*:119–151.
3. ASTBURY, W. T., ed. *Proc. roy. Soc.,* 1953, *B141*:1–103.
4. BENNETT, H. S. and PORTER, K. R. *Amer. J. Anat.,* 1953, *93*:61–106.
5. BOZLER, E. *Cold Spr. Harb. Symp.,* 1936, *4*: 260–266.
6. BOZLER, E. *Biol. Symp.,* 1941, *3*:95–109.
7. BRADY, A. J. and WOODBURY, J. W. *Ann. N. Y. Acad. Sci.,* 1957, *65*:687–692.
8. BROWN, G. L. and HARVEY, A. M. *Brain,* 1939, *62*:341–363.
9. BÜLBRING, E. *J. Physiol.,* 1955, *128*:200–221.
10. DEL CASTILLO, J. and KATZ, B. *J. Physiol.,* 1954, *124*:560–573.
11. DEL CASTILLO, J. and KATZ, B. *Proc. roy. Soc.,* 1957, *B146*:339–356.
12. DEL CASTILLO, J. and KATZ, B. *Proc. roy. Soc.,* 1957, *B146*:369–381.
13. COOPER, S. and ECCLES, J. C. *J. Physiol.,* 1930, *69*:377–385.
14. DENNY-BROWN, D. and BRENNER, C. *Arch. Neurol. Psychiat., (Chicago),* 1944, *51*:1–26.
15. DENNY-BROWN, D. and PENNYBACKER, J. B. *Brain,* 1938, *61*:311–334.
16. DESMEDT, J. E. *J. Physiol.,* 1953, *121*:191–205.
17. ECCLES, J. C. and MAGLADERY, J. W. *J. Physiol.,* 1937, *90*:68–99.
18. ECCLES, J. C. and SHERRINGTON, C. S. *Proc. roy. Soc.,* 1930, *B106*:326–357.
19. ELFTMAN, H. *Amer. J. Physiol.,* 1939, *125*:339–356.
20. ELFTMAN, H. *Biol. Symp.,* 1941, *3*:191–209.
21. ENGELHARDT, V. A. and LJUBIMOVA, M. N. *Nature, (Lond.),* 1939, *144*:668–669.

22. ENGELHARDT, V. A., LJUBIMOVA, M. N. and NEITINA, R. A. *C. R. Acad. Sci., U. S. S. R.*, 1941, *30:*664.
23. FATT, P. *Physiol. Rev.*, 1954, *34:*674–710.
24. FATT, P. and KATZ, B. *J. Physiol.*, 1951, *115:* 320–370.
25. FATT, P. and KATZ, B. *J. Physiol.*, 1952, *117:* 109–128.
26. FENN, W. O. pp. 447–522 in *Physical chemistry of cells and tissues*, R. Höber, ed. Philadelphia, Blakiston, 1945.
27. GASSER, H. S. *Physiol. Rev.*, 1930, *10:*35–109.
28. GELFAN, S. *J. Physiol.*, 1933, *80:*285–295.
29. HILL, A. V. *Proc. roy. Soc.*, 1949, *B136:*399–420.
30. HILL, A. V. *Sci. Progr.*, 1950, *38:*209–230.
31. HILL, A. V. *Lancet*, 1951, *261:*947–951.
32. HOEFER, P. F. A. *Res. Publ. Ass. nerv. ment. Dis.*, 1941, *21:*502–528.
33. HØNCKE, P. *Acta physiol. scand.*, 1947, *15* (Suppl. 48):1–230.
34. HUNT, C. C. and KUFFLER, G. W. *J. Physiol.*, 1954, *126:*293–303.
35. HUXLEY, A. F. *Progr. Biophys.*, 1957, *7:*257–318.
36. HUXLEY, A. F. and NIEDERGERKE, R. *Nature (Lond.)*, 1954, *173:*971–973.
37. HUXLEY, H. E. and HANSON, J. *Nature (Lond.)*, 1954, *173:*973–976.
38. LAMBERT, E. H., UNDERDAHL, L. O., BECKETT, S. and MEDEROS, L. O. *J. clin. Endocrin.*, 1951, *11:*1186–1205.
39. LLOYD, D. P. C. Chap. 2 in *Howell's textbook of physiology*, 15th ed., J. F. Fulton, ed. Philadelphia, W. B. Saunders, 1946.
40. MOLL, A. *Virchow's Arch. path. Anat.*, 1886, *105:*466–485.
41. NACHMANSOHN, D. Chap. 10 in *Textbook of physiology*, 17th ed., J. F. Fulton, ed. Philadelphia, W. B. Saunders, 1955.
42. NACHMANSOHN, D. and WILSON, I. B. pp. 167–186 in *Electrochemistry in biology and medicine*, T. Shedlovsky, ed. New York, John Wiley & Sons, 1955.
43. RALSTON, H. J., INMAN, V. T., STRAIT, L. A. and SHAFFRATH, M. D. *Amer. J. Physiol.*, 1947, *151:*612–620.
44. RANSON, S. W. and DIXON, H. H. *Amer. J. Physiol.*, 1928, *86:*312–319.
45. SICHEL, F. J. M. and PROSSER, C. L. *Amer. J. Physiol.*, 1940, *128:*203–212.
46. TOWER, S. S. *J. comp. Neurol.*, 1937, *67:*109–131.
47. University of California. *Fundamental studies of human locomotion and other information relating to design of artificial limbs.* Berkeley, 1947, 2 vols.
48. VIETS, H. R. and GAMMON, G. D., eds. *Amer. J. Med.*, 1955, *19:*655–742.
49. WEBER, H. H. *Proc. roy. Soc.*, 1952, *B139:*512–521.
50. WEIDMANN, S. *J. Physiol.*, 1955, *127:*213–224.
51. WEIDMANN, S. *J. Physiol.*, 1951, *115:*227–236.
52. WOODBURY, J. W. and McINTYRE, D. M. *Amer. J. Physiol.*, 1956, *187:*338–340.
53. ZACKS, S. I. *Proc. Soc. exp. Biol. (N. Y.)*, 1958, *99:*574–575.

SECTION III

Motor Functions of the
Nervous System

CHAPTER 5

Spinal Reflexes and Synaptic Transmission

By HARRY D. PATTON

PROPERTIES OF THE SYNAPSE

IN the foregoing chapters attention was focused on the distinctive properties of axons and muscle cells, taken as samples of excitable tissues. Stripped of detail, these properties are *excitability* and *conductivity*. An axon, when excited, responds by generating an action potential, which is then conducted in both directions away from the site of stimulation. Individual excitable cells, no matter what type or how excited, always respond to excitation in this stereotyped fashion; no other response is known. The action potential is thus the only mode of expression available to the nervous system; it is the message carried from sense organ to brain, giving rise to sensation; it is the message relayed from brain and spinal cord to muscle, giving rise to movement. Indeed, all feeling and action are reducible to orderly, sequential, neuronal exchanges of minute quantities of potassium for minute quantities of sodium.

Variety of experience and action results from the channeling of action potentials within the central nervous system and from modulation of action potential discharge patterns. Discharge patterns are initially determined by the properties of sense organs. The messages arriving at the sensory and motor centers of the central nervous system, however, may be quite different from those initiated at the sense organ.

In vertebrates, even the simplest experience and behavior derive from the conduction of action potentials over *chains* of neurons, which are linked together by apposition of the efferent process (axon) of one cell to the cell body or dendrites of another. Such a junction between nerve cells is called a *synapse*. During the latter half of the last century, many histologists argued that the nervous system was a syncytium and that nerve cells were joined together at the synaptic region by protoplasmic extensions between them. We now know, largely from Ramón y Cajal's studies, that neurons are individual units and that the synapse is a region of protoplasmic "contiguity, not continuity." This point is most important because it means that conduction through chains of neurons is discontinuous and, consequently, that the message may be fundamentally altered at each synaptic link. At the synapse, the presynaptic impulse initiates a distinctive process, which may tentatively be called the *transmitter process*, that serves to initiate new action in the postsynaptic neuron. The present chapter is primarily concerned with the nature of this transmitter process and its influence on the messages of the central nervous system.

Some of the special properties of synapses may be briefly listed preliminary to a detailed consideration of synaptic function.

1. UNIDIRECTIONAL CONDUCTION. In contrast to action potentials in a nerve fiber, which are conducted in both directions, action potentials in a neuron chain are conducted in only one direction. For example, action potential messages set up in a dorsal root may be transferred, in the spinal cord, to nerve cells with which the root fibers make synaptic connection, thence to other nerve cells and then, over their axons, to the ventral root. On the other hand, impulses excited in a ventral root, although they traverse the axons and probably part of the perikarya and dendrites of the motoneurons, do not initiate action potentials in the nerve terminals which make synaptic connections with these motoneurons. The synapse is a "one way valve" which determines the direction of transmission.

2. REPETITIVE DISCHARGE. A nerve fiber usually responds only once to a single brief stimulus. A single synchronous volley of impulses delivered over a presynaptic path to a neuron often, but not always, evokes a burst or train of spikes in the postsynaptic neuron. The frequency of the postsynaptic discharge usually varies during the burst, but may approach 500 to 1000 impulses a second for short periods. Repetitive discharge is one way in which neural activity is amplified at the synapse.

3. FAILURE TO TRANSMIT FAITHFULLY FREQUENCIES OF PRESYNAPTIC VOLLEYS. When a nerve fiber is stimulated repetitively, each stimulus elicits one action potential, unless the interval between stimuli is less than the refractory period. Refractoriness is thus the only limitation to faithful signaling of the stimulation frequency. In a chain of neurons, however, the postsynaptic neuron may not respond to each of a series of repetitive presynaptic volleys. For example, if the presynaptic path is stimulated 20 times a second, the postsynaptic neuron may respond only to the first volley reaching it. In general, the longer the chain (i.e., the greater the number of synapses), the less is its capacity to follow imposed frequencies faithfully. Obviously, at such rates of stimulation, frequency-following is not limited by the refractory period of the postsynaptic neuron; for repetitive discharge in response to a single presynaptic volley indicates that the cell is capable of generating impulses at rates up to one every millisecond. Some evidence suggests that high frequency blockage occurs in the fine presynaptic terminals. The special significance of this property of synapses is that temporal patterns of discharge initiated in the presynaptic pathway become significantly altered as they traverse successive synapses in a chain.

4. SUSCEPTIBILITY TO ASPHYXIA, ISCHEMIA AND DEPRESSANT DRUGS. The synapse is a region of low safety factor, and transmission is easily blocked. A nerve fiber will continue to conduct impulses many minutes after cardiac arrest, but synaptic transmission succumbs much earlier. In general, long chains with multiple synapses are more easily blocked than are shorter, simpler chains. The effectiveness of general anesthetic agents is largely due to their capacity to block synaptic transmission. Reflex movement, sensation and consciousness are abolished, whereas excitability of nerve trunks is little affected, as evidenced by lively muscle contraction when a motor nerve is stimulated directly.

5. SYNAPTIC DELAY. Conduction over axons is continuous and uninterrupted, the rate of conduction being determined by axon diameter. The synaptic transmitter process consumes a finite interval of time. Conduction time over a chain of neurons is therefore greater than the sum of axonal conduction times, a discrepancy which increases with the number of synapses in the chain.

6. INHIBITION. At some synapses, the consequence of presynaptic activity is not excitation but depression of activity in the postsynaptic neuron. This important property and its mechanism will be discussed in detail below.

ANALYSIS OF SYNAPTIC FUNCTION

The Monosynaptic Reflex.[25] To study the properties of the synapse it is obviously desirable to select a simple monosynaptic system, i.e., one having only a single synapse. The sympathetic ganglion fulfills this requirement, and for qualitative studies is a satisfactory synaptic model. Quantitatively, however, the peripheral synapses in ganglia are somewhat different from the central synapses in the brain and the spinal cord; for example, the delay at a sympathetic synapse is four to ten times as great as that at a central synapse. Also, one of the important synaptic processes, inhibition, is either poorly developed or lacking in ganglionic synapses. For these reasons, the synapses formed between dorsal root afferent fibers and motoneurons will be used as synaptic models in this discussion.

Figure 69 shows the intramedullary course of dorsal root fibers entering the spinal cord as revealed by silver stains. Some afferent fibers (*a*) plunge without interruption through the gray matter to terminate on motoneurons in the anterior horn (*B*). Such reflex arcs are *monosynaptic*. Other afferent fibers (*b*, *c*) terminate on neurons in the dorsal and intermediate regions of the gray matter. Although not shown, the axons of these neurons are in turn distributed to other intermediate neurons or to motoneurons to

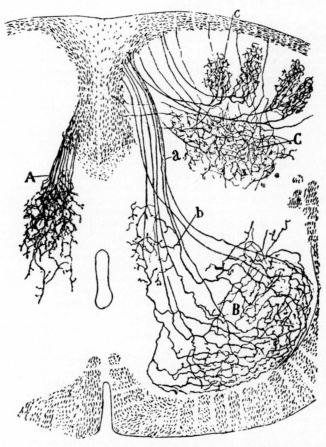

FIG. 69. Distribution of primary afferent collaterals in cross section of spinal cord. On right, collaterals *C* and *c* are distributed to dorsal horn and substantia gelatinosa Rolandi. *a*, Reflexo-motor collaterals extending to ventral horn (*B*). *b*, Collaterals to intermediate nucleus of Cajal. On left, dense collaterals (*A*) to intermediate nucleus. (After Cajal, *Histologie du système nerveux*, Paris, Maloine, 1909.)

complete the circuit through the spinal cord. Such reflex arcs are *multisynaptic*, and impulses directed through them reach the motoneuron only after transfer through one or more *interneurons*, or *internuncial neurons*, the generic names for cells interposed between primary afferent neurons and the final motoneuron. The difference between mono-synaptic and multisynaptic arcs is further clarified by the diagrammatic representation in Figure 70.

Happily, the monosynaptic and multisynaptic arcs can be functionally distinguished. In experiments of the type illustrated in Figure 71, stimulating electrodes (*S*) are placed on a dorsal root near its entrance into the spinal cord, and recording electrodes (R) are attached to the proximal portion of the corresponding segmental ventral root to register the emergent reflex discharge. A minimally effective shock to the dorsal root (trace C) elicits a small ventral root discharge which begins about 3 milliseconds after the stimulus. As the shock strength is increased (D–I), the amplitude of the early synchronous part of the discharge (labeled a in trace E) increases rapidly to a maximal value (E) which is not increased by further increases in shock strength (F–I). The later asynchronous part of the discharge (labeled b in trace E) increases more slowly with increasing stimulus strength, but continues to increase in size after the early discharge has reached a stable amplitude. A reasonable hypothesis is that the early sharp spike reflects a motoneuron discharge reflex elicited through monosynaptic spinal arcs, whereas the later asynchronous waves result from the firing of motoneurons through multi-synaptic channels, with consequent repeated synaptic delays.

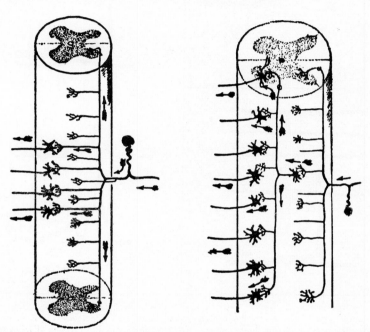

FIG. 70. Diagram of circumscribed reflex mechanism of Cajal (*left*), showing direct connection between afferent collaterals and motoneurons, and diffuse reflex mechanism of Cajal (*right*), in which an interneuron is intercalated between afferent fibers and motoneurons. (After Cajal, *Histologie du système nerveux*, Paris, Maloine, 1909.)

In point of fact, part of the discrepancy in the appearance of the early and the late discharge is attributable to a difference in the sizes of the afferent fibers mediating these discharges, those responsible for the early discharge being larger and hence conducting impulses more rapidly. This difference is suggested by the observation that the early discharge grows most rapidly through a range of stimulus strengths adequate only for low threshold, rapidly conducting, dorsal root fibers; whereas the growth of the later discharges occurs at higher stimulus strengths. The differences in delay due to afferent conduction time are small when conduction distance is minimized by placing the stimulating electrodes close to the cord; but, when appropriate allowances for conduction differences are made, the central delay of the later discharge remains considerably longer than that of the early discharge. Thus, the original hypothesis that the later discharge is conducted over chains more complex than those mediating the early discharge remains plausible.

Synaptic delay.[22, 25]   To prove that the early discharge is monosynaptic, however, requires an independent measure of the duration of synaptic delay. An approximate value is provided by Renshaw's ingenious experiment shown in Figure 72. Electrodes

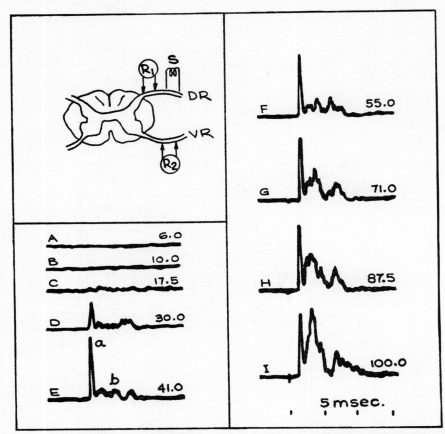

FIG. 71.   Spinal reflex discharges to dorsal root shocks of varying intensity. Single shocks were delivered to dorsal root (*DR*) through stimulating electrodes (*S*). Electrodes R_1 recorded dorsal root action potential; electrodes R_2 on ventral root (*VR*) recorded resultant reflex discharge. Traces *A–I* show reflex discharges at R_2 as shock strength was progressively increased. Numbers to right of traces, computed from R_1 recording, indicate number of afferent fibers excited expressed as a percentage of total fiber content of dorsal root. In *E: a*, monosynaptic discharge; *b*, multisynaptic discharges. (After Lloyd, *J. Neurophysiol.*, 1943, *6*:111–120.)

on the ventral root record the motoneuronal discharge elicited by stimulation through electrodes thrust into the intermediate gray matter of the cord in the region occupied only by elements presynaptic to the motoneurons. Weak shocks produce no response (trace *a*). Slightly stronger stimuli (traces *b* and *c*) evoke, after 1.0 millisecond, the response labeled *s*. Upon stronger stimulation, an additional and earlier (0.2 millisecond) discharge, *m*, appears (trace *d*); and, as *m* grows in size with increasing shock strength, the *s* discharge becomes correspondingly smaller (traces *e* and *f*).

The obvious interpretation of this experiment is that the weak shocks excite only the presynaptic elements near the electrodes, and that these elements then synaptically activate the motoneurons, giving rise to the *s* discharge. With stronger shocks, however, sufficient current spreads to the ventral horn to excite some of the motoneurons directly, giving rise to the earlier *m* discharge (Fig. 72*B*). Because direct excitation renders the motoneurons refractory, the conducted interneuronal impulses find them inexcitable, and hence, as the *m* discharge increases with stronger shocks, the *s* discharge diminishes in amplitude. It follows that the difference in latency between the *m* and the *s* discharge provides an estimate of synaptic delay. The nature of this delay is not completely understood. As measured in this experiment, the delay includes conduction time in the fine presynaptic terminals plus the true synaptic delay, i.e., the interval between the arrival at the motoneuron of a synchronous presynaptic discharge and the depolarization of the motoneuron to the firing level.

In the experiment illustrated in Figure 72, the *m–s* interval is 0.8 millisecond. In a series of such experiments, the interval varied between 0.7 and 0.9 millisecond.[25] When the cord shock was delivered some 3 milliseconds after a dorsal root volley, the interval diminished to 0.5 to 0.7 millisecond. The central delay in transmission across a single

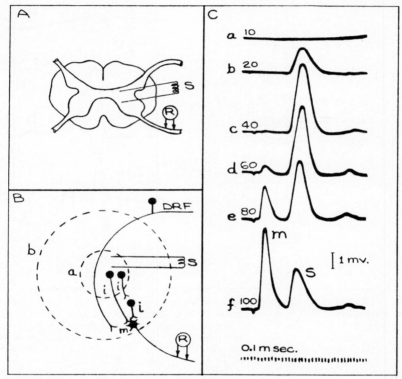

FIG. 72. Measurement of synaptic delay in spinal cord. *A*, Arrangement of stimulating (*S*) and recording (*R*) electrodes. *B*, Diagrammatic interpretation of traces in *C*. *C*, Responses as stimulus strength (indicated by numbers above traces) was increased. In *B*, only dorsal root fibers (*DRF*) and interneurons (*i*) within dotted circle *a* were excited by weak stimulus; shortest path to *R* therefore included one synapse, and delayed response, marked *s* in *C*, *b–f*, resulted. With strong stimulus, elements lying within dotted circle *b* were excited; these included some motoneurons (*m*) whose discharge gave rise to *m* in *C*, *d–f*. Difference in latency between *m* and *s* (about 0.8 msec.) is approximate duration of synaptic delay. (After Renshaw, *J. Neurophysiol.*, 1940, 3:373–387.)

spinal synapse is thus 0.5 to 0.9 millisecond. Comparable delays have been measured in monosynaptic transmission through the oculomotor nucleus,[22] the lateral geniculate body[1] and the cochlear nucleus.[14]

With a measured value for synaptic delay, the hypothesis that the early reflex discharge is monosynaptic can be rigorously tested. Figure 73*b* shows the ventral root discharge evoked by a shock to the corresponding dorsal root; this discharge begins 1.05 milliseconds after the stimulus. The upper trace, labeled *a*, shows the response recorded at the dorsal root entry zone; the latency, 0.30 millisecond (measured to the point where the positive deflection returns to the baseline), gives the conduction time in the dorsal root. The latency of m in c (0.10 millisecond) gives the efferent conduction time in the axons. The central delay of the reflex discharge in this experiment is thus $1.05 - 0.30 - 0.10 = 0.65$ millisecond. In other experiments, similarly measured delays ranged from 0.65 to 0.90 millisecond in resting cord, and from 0.5 to 0.7 millisecond when the reflex was conditioned by an antecedent dorsal root volley. Since these delays are too short to permit more than one synaptic delay, it can be concluded that the early reflex discharge is monosynaptic, as initially postulated.

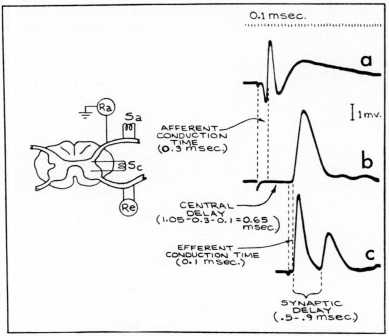

FIG. 73. Demonstration of monosynaptic reflex. Arrangement of stimulating and recording electrodes shown on left. a, Response recorded at Ra following stimulus at Sa. b, Reflex response at Re following stimulus at Ra. c, Response at Re following stimulus at Sc, as in Fig. 72. Subtracting afferent conduction time (derived from a) and efferent conduction time (from c) from latency of reflex in b gives central reflex delay of 0.65 msec., which falls within range of single synaptic delay derived from m-s interval in c and in Fig. 72. (After Renshaw, *J. Neurophysiol.*, 1940, 3:373–387.)

Afferent path of the monosynaptic reflex. The monosynaptic reflex discharge evoked by stimulation of the dorsal root provides a satisfactory model system for a study of some synaptic properties. For certain experiments, however, the later multisynaptic discharge is an objectionable contaminant. As seen in Figure 71, some multisynaptic activity, in addition to monosynaptic discharge, is evident even with very weak dorsal root shocks, an occurrence suggesting considerable overlap in the sizes (and hence thresholds) of the dorsal root fibers mediating monosynaptic and multisynaptic reflexes. However, as the numbers to the right of the traces indicate, the rates of growth of the two types of reflexes with increasing dorsal root volleys are quite different. The monosynaptic discharge is maximal when the dorsal root volley is only 41 per cent of maximal. The remaining 59 per cent of the dorsal root fibers, consisting of the smaller diameter group, contribute nothing to the growth of the monosynaptic discharge but contribute heavily to the multisynaptic arcs responsible for the late waves. This sequence suggests that the monosynaptic reflex is mediated exclusively by a restricted group of large afferent fibers, whereas the multisynaptic arcs are fed by smaller fibers.

It has already been mentioned (Chap. 3) that examination of the fiber constitution of "demotored" peripheral nerves, i.e., nerves in which motor axons have degenerated following ventral rhizotomy (root section), indicates that muscle nerves typically contain a prominent cluster of large afferent fibers, designated Group I, ranging in size from about 12 to 21 μ (see Fig. 37, heavy line). Such large fibers are absent from cutaneous nerves, in which the fibers of maximal diameter measure 6 to 12 μ and are designated Group II (thin line and hatched area in Fig. 37). Group II afferent fibers are also found in muscle nerves, but in less prominent proportions than in cutaneous nerves. A third cluster of fibers, ranging in size from 1 to 6 μ (Group III), occurs in both kinds of nerves. In addition, both contain large numbers of unmyelinated fibers (Group IV or C fibers). This last group is not indicated in Figure 37, because the fiber counts were made in nerves stained with osmic acid, a myelin stain.

The difference in afferent fiber constitution of cutaneous and muscle nerves, coupled with the knowledge that only the largest afferent fibers make monosynaptic connections, suggests that monosynaptic reflexes originate in muscle nerves. Figure 74 shows that

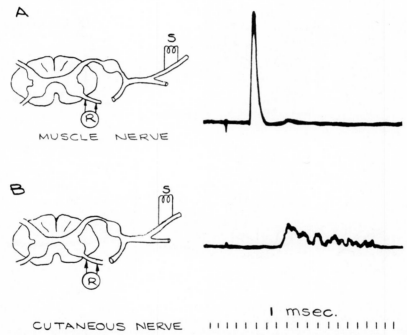

FIG. 74.   Reflex responses to afferent volleys of different origin. *A*, Reflex discharge, almost exclusively monosynaptic, elicited by weak efferent volley in gastrocnemius nerve. *B*, Exclusively multisynaptic reflex response elicited by stimulating efferent fibers in sural nerve. (After Lloyd, *J. Neurophysiol.*, 1943, *6*:111–120.)

this is indeed the case. Both trace *A* and trace *B* were recorded from the first sacral ventral root. In *A*, the stimulus was a maximal shock to the central end of the cut gastrocnemius nerve; in *B*, the afferent volley originated in a cutaneous nerve, the sural. The response to the gastrocnemius afferent volley is almost entirely monosynaptic and can be made completely so by adjusting the stimulus to strengths activating only Group I fibers. On the other hand, the discharge resulting from the sural afferent input is exclusively multisynaptic. Furthermore, systematic investigation using various nerves for afferent input indicates that this finding can be generalized, and that uncontaminated monosynaptic reflexes can be initiated by stimulating Group I afferent fibers of any muscle nerve; whereas weak or strong stimulation of cutaneous nerves elicits only multi-synaptic reflex discharge.

Distribution of monosynaptic discharge.   Experiments of the kind described in the foregoing section establish clearly the afferent origin of monosynaptic reflexes, but do not indicate the peripheral distribution of the reflex discharge, because the recordings are made from the ventral root which supplies many muscles. To determine the "target" muscles of a monosynaptic discharge elicited by stimulating the Group I afferent fibers of a muscle nerve, it is necessary to leave the ventral root intact and place the recording electrode on various peripheral nerves supplying other muscles. When such an experiment is performed, the monosynaptic discharge so prominent in ventral root recordings cannot be detected in any of these peripheral nerves. This finding suggests that the monosynaptic discharge returns only to the muscle from which the afferent volley originates.

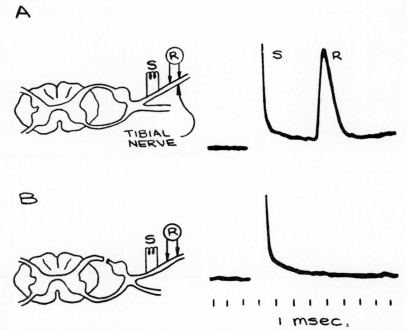

FIG. 75.   Experiment proving that monosynaptic reflex discharge occupies efferent axons in nerve from which afferent volley originates. *A*, Responses recorded at *R* on left following weak shock, at *S* on left, to same nerve. *Right*, *S*, shock artefact and compound action potential of nerve; *R*, monosynaptic reflex discharge. *B*, After dorsal rhizotomy, *R* response is lacking; *R* is therefore reflex. (After Lloyd, *J. Neurophysiol.*, 1943, *6*:293–315.)

That a monosynaptic discharge does, in fact, occupy the efferent fibers of the muscle nerve in which the afferent discharge originates is indicated by the experiment illustrated in Figure 75. To obtain trace *A*, both the stimulating and the recording electrodes were placed on the tibial nerve with all central connections to the spinal cord intact. Stimulation at Group I strength, of course, elicited a compound action potential in the nerve. Because the conduction distance between the stimulating and recording electrodes was small, this compound action potential was fused with the shock artefact. Later, however, another deflection occurred that was clearly of reflex origin, because it was abolished by dorsal rhizotomy (see trace *B*). When allowances for afferent and efferent conduction are made, the reduced central delay of the reflex discharge identifies it as monosynaptic. *The monosynaptic discharge thus returns to—and, except under special conditions, only to—the stimulated muscle nerve.*

The peripheral distribution of a multisynaptic reflex discharge elicited by stimulating Group II and Group III afferent fibers in either muscle or cutaneous nerves serving a limb is much more diffuse; such discharges can be detected in the motor fibers supplying many muscles in the limb. However, multisynaptic discharges do not indiscriminately activate all limb muscles. Systematic testing reveals that *in the ipsilateral extremity, multisynaptic discharges are distributed almost exclusively to flexor muscles;* extensor muscles receive at best only negligibly slight portions of the multisynaptic discharge. Further details of multisynaptic reflex distribution are given in the next chapter.

Minute Anatomy of the Synapse; Convergence and Divergence. At this juncture, a closer scrutiny of the structural organization of spinal synapses is profitable. Figure 76 shows the appearance of fresh, unstained motoneurons isolated from human

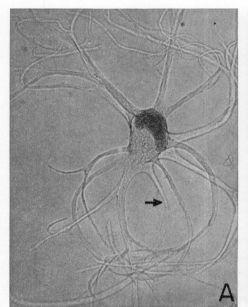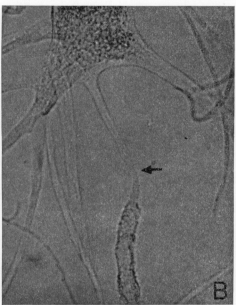

FIG. 76. Isolated human motoneurons. *Arrows* indicate axons; other processes are dendrites. *On right*, initial segment of axon lacks myelin sheath, which begins just distal to axonal constriction marked by arrow. (From Chu, *J. comp. Neurol.*, 1954, *100*:381–414.)

spinal cord. The cell body (sometimes called the *soma* or *perikaryon*) is usually about 70 μ across, has an irregular polygonal shape, and gives rise to a number of long processes. The initially thick (5 to 10 μ) processes which branch and taper are *dendrites*. Dendrites may extend as far as 1 mm. before breaking up into untraceably small branches. The *axon* originates from the conically shaped *axon hillock*, and in its *initial segment* shows a constriction. Beyond the initial segment, some 50 to 100 μ from the soma, the axon increases in diameter, acquires a myelin sheath, and proceeds from the spinal cord into the ventral root. The axon is distinguishable from the dendrites by its uniform diameter (except for the constriction of the initial segment) and by the scarcity of branches. Some axons give off branches within the spinal cord; they part from the parent fiber at right angles, curve dorsally into the gray matter and terminate on interneurons. These branches are called *recurrent collaterals* of the axon.

When motoneurons are stained with basic dyes (toluidine blue, thionin, methylene blue), the cytoplasm surrounding the centrally placed, round nucleus is seen to be filled with granules known as *Nissl bodies* or *tigroid bodies*. These structures are said to be absent from the axon hillock and axon, but are seen in the dendrites, at least in the thicker proximal part of their stalks. Nissl bodies are nucleoproteins and undergo striking changes when the cells are injured as, for example, in amputation of the axon.

In silver stained preparations of spinal cord, the terminations of presynaptic fibers on motoneurons can be seen (Fig. 77). The terminal branches of the presynaptic fibers

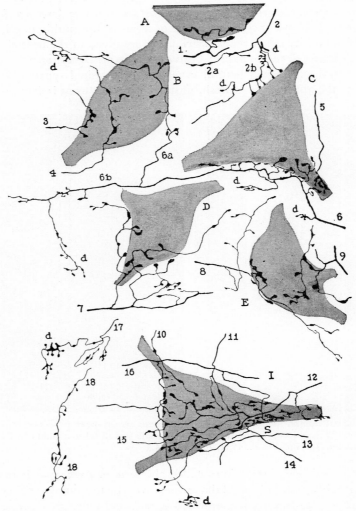

FIG. 77. Synapses on motoneurons (*A–E*) and on a large interneuron (*I*) of spinal cord. *1* to *18*, Presynaptic fibrils carrying synaptic knobs to the several cells; *d*, synaptic knobs in contact with dendrites. Note that fiber *6* supplies both cell *B* and cell *C*, *divergence*, and that many fibers supply each cell, *convergence*. (From Lorente de Nó, *J. Neurophysiol.*, 1938, *1*:195–206.)

are fine and tortuous; they end on both dendrites and soma in small (about 1 *μ*) round or oval expansions known variously as *synaptic knobs, boutons terminaux* or *end feet*. The soma is particularly richly encrusted with knobs; the dendrites are similarly covered, but the density of knobs diminishes as the dendrite divides into fine terminal branches. It has been estimated that up to 40 per cent of the soma-dendritic membrane is covered with knobs. The axon hillock and the unmyelinated initial segment of the axon are sparsely supplied with synaptic knobs.

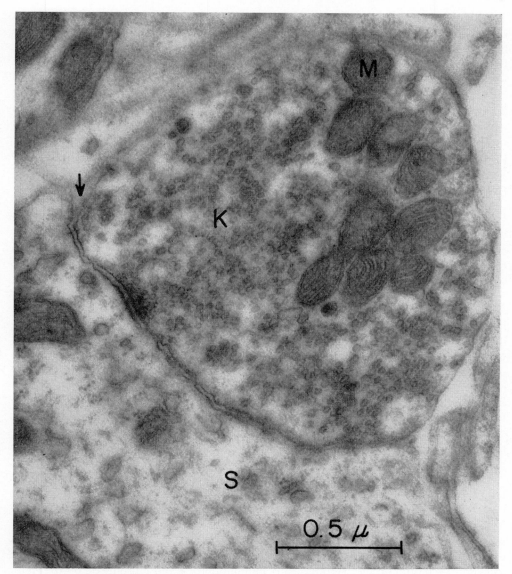

FIG. 78.   Electron micrograph of a synapse on a motoneuron. *K*, Synaptic knob containing mitochondria (*M*) and round profiles of many minute synaptic vesicles. *S*, Motoneuron soma. Arrow indicates synaptic gap. × 65,000. (From Palay, *Exp. Cell Res.*, 1958, *Suppl. 5*:275–293.)

Not all synapses in the central nervous system are characterized by knobs. Fibers terminating on the cells of Clarke's column do so by breaking up into a series of flat plates which are closely applied to soma and dendrites. The fibers of the medial lemniscus terminating in the relay nuclei of the thalamus break up into a rounded bush around the cells. Many synaptic junctions in the cerebral cortex appear to be established largely by naked terminals without specialized bulbs or knobs. The Purkinje cells of the cerebellar cortex receive "basket" endings which encase the soma. These cells also receive the climbing fibers, which run parallel to and in contact with the profusely branched dendritic tree, resembling a vine on a trellis. The climbing fibers and the olfactory glomeruli are examples of *axodendritic synapses* as opposed to *axosomatic* (basket endings) and *axodendrosomatic* synapses (motoneuron, cortical neuron, Clarke's column).

The fine structure of a synaptic knob is shown in the electron micrograph in Figure 78. The junction between the knob and the postsynaptic cell is marked by the arrow. Both the knob and the cell are surrounded by continuous membranes about 50 Å thick.

The knob appears to make a slight indentation in the cell. Between the two membranes there is a clear space about 200 Å wide; this is the synaptic gap. In addition to nine lamellated mitochondria, the knob contains a profusion of small (about 200 to 600 Å) round structures, which are called synaptic vesicles. It has been suggested that the vesicles contain chemical substances important in synaptic transmission.

It is well established that the many knobs on a single motoneuron derive from many different parent afferent fibers. The motoneuron thus constitutes a *final common path* upon which many presynaptic fibers converge. There is reason to suppose that many knobs must be activated within a brief period to initiate an impulse in the motoneuron. Firing thus results from the nearly synchronous activity of many afferent fibers converging on the motoneuron; it is doubtful if activity in a single afferent fiber is sufficient to cause postsynaptic discharge.

Considered from the afferent side, the key feature of organization is divergence. Each dorsal root fiber breaks into many branches which establish synaptic contact with many postsynaptic cells. Thus, although no single afferent fiber alone fires a motoneuron, each fiber contributes to the firing of many motoneurons. These basic principles of *convergence* and *divergence* should be kept clearly in mind while reading the following sections.

Facilitation and Occlusion.   The amplitude of the monosynaptic reflex discharge elicited by an afferent volley in Group I fibers in a muscle nerve provides a convenient index of the *number of motoneurons* fired. This is true because the afferent volley is conducted to the motoneurons over a single, relatively homogeneous pathway with little temporal dispersion, so that the postsynaptic discharge is fairly synchronous. The action potentials of individual fibers in the ventral root are thus approximately added at the recording electrode.* It follows that as stimulus parameters are varied, the excited fraction of the population of motoneurons available to the Group I fibers can be determined simply by measuring the amplitude of the monosynaptic discharge. It has already been shown in Figure 71 that, as the number of excited afferent fibers is increased, the size of the monosynaptic discharge increases, reaching a maximum when approximately one-half of the Group I fibers are recruited.

Reflex amplitude measures only the number of neurons actually discharged by the afferent volley. More subtle influences of the afferent volley on motoneurons can be detected by slightly altering the experimental conditions, as in the experiment illustrated in Figure 79A. Here, a dorsal root has been divided into two strands, each equipped with a stimulating electrode. A weak stimulus to strand *a* elicits the small ventral root discharge shown on the left, and a similar stimulus to strand *b* induces the small response shown in the middle trace. Simultaneous stimulation of *a* and *b* produces, on the right, a response which is far greater than the simple sum of the two individual responses. In other words, the number of motoneurons fired by simultaneous activation of strands *a* and *b* is greater than the total number fired by stimulating *a* and *b* separately. An extreme example of this phenomenon is seen when the shocks to *a* and *b* are reduced so that neither delivered alone can cause discharge of motoneurons, but both delivered simultaneously result in a measurable discharge.

The results of this experiment are most simply explained as follows. An afferent volley delivered to a population of motoneurons, a *motoneuron pool*, has varying effects on the individual motoneurons in the pool, these effects being quantitatively dependent upon the density of activated knobs. Some motoneurons receive many knobs from the

---

* With multisynaptic reflexes, the area under the tracing rather than the amplitude represents the number of neurons fired; both wide ranges of afferent conduction times and multiple synaptic delays result in temporal dispersion, so that the discharge of impulses is asynchronous, and therefore individual impulses do not add at the electrode.

activated afferent source and are liminally excited; these are said to be in the *discharge zone* of the afferent source. Other motoneurons receive too few knobs from the activated fibers to reduce the motoneuron membrane potential to the firing level. The excitability of these subliminally bombarded motoneurons, however, is increased, a phenomenon known as *facilitation*. These facilitated motoneurons are said to be in the *subliminal fringe* of the afferent source. As a result of the convergence, the subliminal fringes of two afferent sources may have common elements; i.e., some motoneurons may receive a subliminal number of activated knobs from each source. With simultaneous activation of both sources, the excitatory processes may summate, so that some cells in the common subliminal fringes are recruited into the discharge zone. These relationships are shown diagrammatically in Figure 79B.

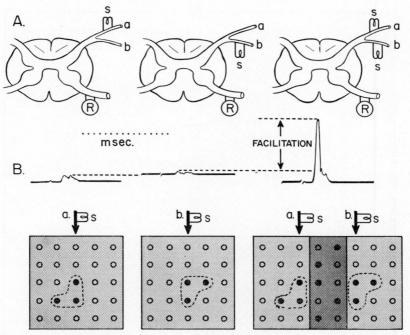

FIG. 79. *A,* Experiment demonstrating facilitation. Dorsal root was split into two strands, *a* and *b*. Weak stimulation of *a* and *b* separately produced reflex responses shown in left and middle traces respectively. Simultaneous weak stimulation of both elicited reflex discharge (trace on right) greater than sum of separate responses.

B, Diagram of mechanism of facilitation. Left and middle figures represent motoneuron pools served by afferent sources *a* and *b* respectively. Each source fires three motoneurons (filled circles enclosed by dotted contours); remaining neurons are subliminally excited. Subliminal fields of *a* and *b* are partially coextensive. When *a* and *b* are simultaneously excited (right), some neurons in common subliminal zones are liminally excited, and eleven rather than six neurons fire.

It follows from the foregoing that merely monitoring the ventral root discharge, which indicates the size of the discharge zone only, gives an incomplete picture of the total effect of an afferent volley. The subtle excitability changes which occur in the many cells of the subliminal fringe are detectable only when two afferent volleys are delivered to the motoneurons, as in the experiment shown in Figure 79. The facilitation of the response, i.e., the difference between the response to the combined volleys and the sum of the responses to the two volleys delivered separately, provides a quantitative measure of the size of the subliminal fringe.

Figure 80 shows diagrammatically the manner in which both discharge zone and subliminal fringe grow as the size of the afferent volley is increased. With weak afferent volleys, no motoneurons discharge, but the facilitation curve shows that considerable numbers of cells are subliminally excited. Indeed, Lloyd's[17] quantitative measurements on monosynaptic reflexes indicate that, when the afferent volley is 7 to 8 per cent of maximum, discharge is just beginning, but the subliminal fringe is already about 30 per cent of maximum. With further increase of afferent volley size, both the subliminal fringe and the discharge zone increase proportionately and reach maxima when the afferent volley is about 40 to 50 per cent of maximum. It should be noted further that no matter how strong the afferent volley, the discharge zone never becomes coextensive with the subliminal fringe. Any afferent volley fractionates its motoneuron pool, discharging only a small proportion of the total number of motoneurons. The reserve represented by the subliminal fringe is brought into active discharge only when other

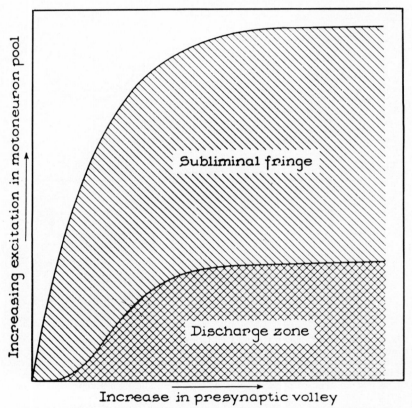

FIG. 80.   Semidiagrammatic representation of relative sizes of discharge zone and subliminal fringe as a function of afferent volley strength. (From Lloyd, *J. Neurophysiol.*, 1943, 6:111–120.)

afferent pathways converging on the same motoneuron pool are activated, providing opportunity for overlap of fringes and summation of subliminal processes.

Because both the subliminal fringe and the discharge zone increase with increased afferent input, it might be expected that when both of two maximal afferent volleys are simultaneously delivered, the discharge zones as well as the subliminal fringes will include common elements as in Figure 81*B*. If the overlap of the discharge zones is extensive, the response to both volleys delivered simultaneously might be less than the sum of the responses to both volleys delivered individually. That this reduction occurs is shown in Figure 81*A*. The left and middle traces show the ventral root discharges resulting from maximal stimulation of each of two separated portions of a dorsal root.

The trace on the right shows the response to simultaneous maximal stimulation of both branches; the resulting discharge is less than the sum of the separate responses. Such reduction in response, attributable to overlapping of the discharge zones, is called *occlusion*.

Time course of facilitation. The experiments just described indicate that, although the neurons of the subliminal zone are not fired by an afferent volley, their excitability is increased. Presumably, the processes leading to this increased excitability differ only quantitatively from those leading to excitation of cells in the discharge zone. Subliminally excited neurons thus provide a suitable medium for studying the processes that lead to synaptic excitation of neurons.

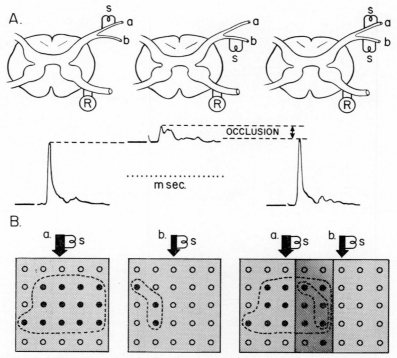

FIG. 81.   *A*, Experiment demonstrating occlusion. Dorsal root split into two strands, *a* and *b*. Maximal stimulation of *a* and *b* separately elicited reflex responses shown in left and middle traces. Simultaneous maximal stimulation of strands elicited reflex discharge (right trace) smaller than the sum of separate responses.

B, Diagram of mechanism of occlusion. Left and middle figures represent motoneuron pools served by afferent sources *a* and *b*, respectively. Because the afferent volleys are larger, discharge zones (filled circles enclosed by dotted contours) constitute a greater fraction of total field than in experiment shown in Fig. 79*B*. Discharge zones of *a* and *b* overlap. Simultaneous stimulation of *a* and *b* (right) fires only 14 motoneurons rather than expected sum, 16, fired by *a* and *b* separately. Note that one neuron in common subliminal fringe discharged.

It is a great advantage if subliminally excited cells can be studied in isolation without the complication of actual firing of cells. One way this isolation can be accomplished is by using very weak afferent volleys (see Fig. 80). A more convenient way of studying subliminally excited motoneurons depends on a peculiarity of the central connections of Group I afferent fibers. As has already been emphasized, a Group I afferent volley can discharge only the *homonymous motoneurons*, i.e., the motoneurons supplying the muscle from which the afferent volley originates. *Heteronymous motoneurons* (those supplying muscles other than the one from which the afferent volley originates) are not fired (except in special circumstances), but conditioning-testing studies indicate that their excitability is altered in a direction which depends upon the relation of their target muscle to the muscle from which the afferent volley originates. For the moment, attention is confined to the motoneurons supplying muscles synergistic to the source of the afferent input.

An experiment designed to test the influence of an afferent volley on the synergistic heteronymous motoneurons is illustrated in Figure 82. Stimulating electrodes were situated on the central ends of the cut nerves supplying the two heads of biceps femoris which are, of course, synergistic. Recording electrodes were affixed to the S_1 ventral root. A volley in the larger branch induced the small reflex discharge shown in *A*. A weak Group I volley in the smaller nerve branch evoked no reflex discharge (*B*). (Even if a

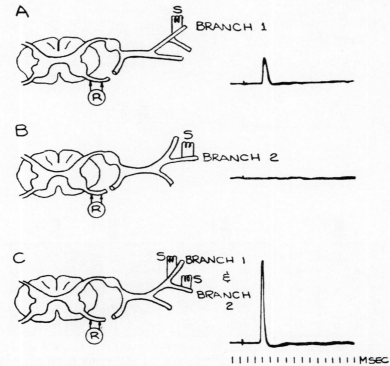

FIG. 82.   Facilitation of heteronymous synergistic motoneurons by Group I afferent volley. Two branches of biceps nerve used as afferent paths. *A*, Response elicited by stimulating Branch *1*. *B*, Stimulating Branch *2* elicited no reflex response. *C*, Simultaneous stimulation of branches elicited response larger than control response in *A*. (After Lloyd, *J. Neurophysiol.*, 1946, *9*:421–438.)

reflex discharge had occurred, it is known from previous experiments that such discharge occupies only the homonymous motoneurons.) When both nerves were stimulated so that the afferent volleys from the two pathways arrived at the spinal cord simultaneously (*C*), the reflex discharge was greatly increased. It can therefore be concluded that the Group I afferent volley traversing the smaller branch, although not sufficiently strong to fire any motoneurons, produced a subliminal fringe and that this subliminal fringe included the motoneurons supplying the muscle fraction innervated by the larger branch.

From systematic investigations of the various muscle nerves, the finding illustrated in Figure 82 can be generalized; i.e., *for any Group I afferent volley, the subliminal fringe includes the heteronymous synergistic motoneurons.*[19] It should be emphasized that this generalization applies only to direct synergists—muscles acting on the same joint and in the

same way as the muscle from which the Group I volley originates. Thus, a lateral gastrocnemius Group I volley facilitates the motoneurons supplying the medial gastrocnemius
and those supplying the soleus, but has no detectable effect on the excitability of motoneurons innervating the hip or toe muscles.

Heteronymous synergistic motoneurons thus provide a pure pool of subliminally
excited cells. By measuring the response of motoneurons to homonymous Group I volleys
delivered at various intervals after these motoneurons have been subliminally excited by
conditioning volleys in the heteronymous synergistic nerve, it is possible to determine
accurately the time course of facilitation.

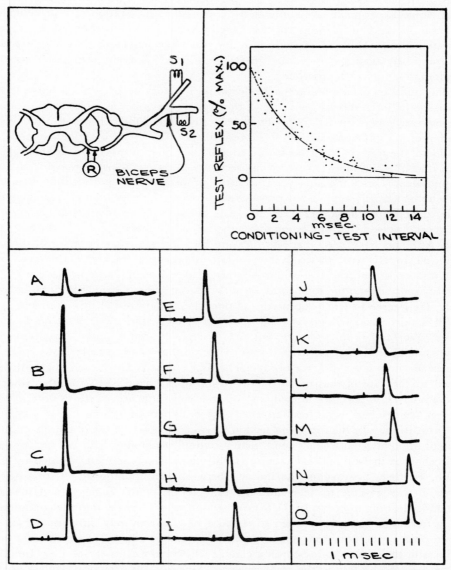

FIG. 83.   Time course of facilitation. Group I fibers in two branches of biceps nerve used as
afferent paths. Conditioning volley (S_1) applied to one branch elicited no reflex discharge. Test volley
(S_2) applied to other branch elicited reflex discharge seen in A and O. Traces $B-N$ show reflex discharges elicited by combined S_1 and S_2 separated by increasing intervals. Graph shows relation between
test reflex amplitude (expressed as percentage of maximal) and conditioning-test interval; data from
seven experiments. (After Lloyd, *J. Neurophysiol.*, 1946, *9*:421–438.)

Figure 83 shows the results of such an experiment in which two branches of the nerve supplying the biceps femoris were used. The conditioning volley was insufficient to elicit a discharge; the test volley delivered to the other branch produced the response seen in traces *A* and *O*. Traces *B* through *N* show how the conditioning volley affects the test response at different conditioning-testing intervals. Facilitation is maximal when the conditioning and testing volleys arrive at the spinal cord at the same time (*B*), but the number of motoneurons responding to the test volley in such pairs of stimuli remains greater than the number responding to the test volley alone (A and O) for a considerable time after the conditioning volley has reached the spinal cord. The graph in Figure 83 shows the pooled results of seven such experiments. When absolute differences related to individual experiments are eliminated by expressing facilitation as a percentage of maximum facilitation in the particular experiment, it is clear that the time course of facilitation is remarkably constant. Indeed, the curve shown in Figure 83 can be described mathematically as an exponentially decaying curve which declines to about one-third of its initial value in 4 milliseconds.

The duration of facilitation (or the "central excitatory state" as Sherrington termed it) is of special interest because it outlasts the presynaptic volley as recorded in the dorsal root. Several explanations for this have been advanced. One holds that, although the duration of the spike potential of dorsal root fibers is brief (0.5 to 1.0 millisecond), the duration of the spike in their fine intramedullary terminals is much longer and approximates that of facilitation (10 to 15 milliseconds). Another holds that, while the presynaptic event is brief, the capacitative-resistive properties of the postsynaptic membrane are such that a briefly applied pulse produces a prolonged change in membrane potential. In electrical terminology, such a circuit would be said to have a long time constant, the time constant being the time required for the voltage to reach $1/e$ ($1/2.718$) of its final value. Attempts have been made to measure the electrical time constant of the soma membrane directly with electrodes inserted into motoneurons.[3, 9] The results have varied. In all instances, however, the values obtained (1.0 to 2.5 milliseconds) have been considerably shorter than the time constant of facilitation (about 4 milliseconds). Unfortunately, the degree to which properties of dendrites influence the measurements is not clear.[24] A third proposed explanation is that both presynaptic and postsynaptic membranes have brief time constants, but that synaptic transmission is accomplished by presynaptic liberation of a chemical agent which diffuses across the synaptic space and depolarizes the postsynaptic membrane. The time course of facilitation might, then, be related to the rate of destruction of this transmitter chemical. No matter what the mechanism, the importance of facilitation is that it permits nerve cells to store information—or "remember" what has happened—for brief periods of time.

Inhibition.   In the foregoing section it was seen how the use of paired stimuli to different afferent trunks (the "conditioning-testing" technique) can be used to detect subtle changes in neuronal excitability (facilitation) which are not revealed by single stimuli. Further, by varying the interval between conditioning and testing afferent volleys, it was possible to determine the time course of the changes in postsynaptic excitability leading to firing. In the present section, it will be seen that the conditioning-testing technique can also be used to reveal a new and entirely different influence of certain presynaptic fibers on motoneurons, *inhibition*. In inhibition, the afferent volley produces in the postsynaptic neuron a change which reduces its excitability. Inhibition can be detected by testing the responsiveness of neurons to excitatory volleys arriving at various intervals after the neurons have been subjected to an inhibitory volley.

It should be emphasized that mere unresponsiveness of motoneurons following an afferent volley is not adequate proof of inhibition as defined above. For example, when two pathways converge on the same pool of neurons, an *excitatory* volley in one pathway may render the neurons less responsive to a subsequent excitatory volley arriving in the other pathway because of refractoriness or postexcitatory subnormality. Such reduction of response is logically categorized as *occlusion*, although it is sometimes termed "indirect inhibition." True or direct inhibition implies a process that is the opposite of excitation and does not depend on previous discharge of any element in the arc displaying the depressed excitability. The distinction between inhibition and occlusion first became possible when a postconditioning deficit in the responses of monosynaptic arcs was demonstrated, for there, and only there, is it possible to be certain that the conditioning volley has not caused discharge of at least some postsynaptic elements (e.g., interneurons) in the chain.

Excitatory processes (facilitation and/or discharge) result when a pool of motoneurons receives Group I impulses from the muscle supplied by these neurons (homonymous) or from that muscle's synergists (heteronymous synergistic). Motoneurons are inhibited when they receive impulses via Group I afferent fibers originating in muscles

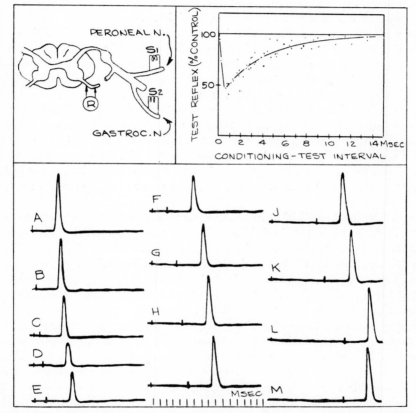

FIG. 84. Time course of inhibition. Group I fibers of two nerves supplying antagonistic muscles used as afferent paths. Weak stimulus S_1 elicited no reflex discharge. Stimulus S_2 elicited monosynaptic reflex seen in traces *A* and *M*. Traces *B–L* show discharges elicited by combined S_1 and S_2 separated by increasing intervals. Graph shows relation between test reflex responses to S_2 at different S_1–S_2 intervals; data from four experiments. (After Lloyd, *J. Neurophysiol.*, 1946, 9:421–438.)

antagonistic to the muscle supplied by the neurons (heteronymous antagonistic).[19] Figure 84 shows a typical experiment demonstrating inhibition. Recordings were made from the first sacral ventral root. Traces *A* and *M* show the monosynaptic discharge recorded following an afferent volley set up in Group I afferent fibers originating in the nerve supplying the gastrocnemius. Records *B–L* show the changes in this discharge when the test shock to the gastrocnemius nerve was preceded by a conditioning volley in Group I fibers in the deep peroneal nerve which supplies the dorsiflexors of the ankle, i.e., the muscles antagonistic in action to the gastrocnemius. Although no motoneuron discharge was elicited by the weak conditioning shock, it nevertheless greatly influenced the number of neurons discharging to the excitatory test volley.

The graph in Figure 84 shows the time course of inhibition occurring in four different motoneuron pools as a result of conditioning volleys delivered through their respective heteronymous antagonistic pathways. The ordinate shows the percentage decrease in the test reflex discharge when the conditioning inhibitory volley preceded the test excitatory volley by the intervals indicated on the abscissa. The curves indicate that, when conditioning and testing volleys arrive at the spinal cord at the same time (zero on the abscissa), there is little or no inhibitory effect. Inhibition does not reach its maximum until about 0.5 millisecond after the inhibitory volley reaches the spinal cord; thereafter, the process decays exponentially along a time course which is a mirror image of the facilitatory curve seen in Figure 83. Indeed, both the facilitatory and the inhibitory curve decay to $1/e$ in about the same time, 4 milliseconds.

The reason for the delayed (0.5 millisecond) maximum of the inhibitory curve is controversial. Lloyd[16, 18] finds no evidence of an interneuron interposed in the inhibitory pathway. Eccles *et al.*,[5] on the other hand, believe that the inhibitory pathway is disynaptic and that the intercalcated interneuron accounts for the delay in maximal inhibition. For the present discussion, the question is largely academic and of secondary importance. The important and universally accepted point is: *different presynaptic fibers can exert one of two fundamentally opposite effects on postsynaptic neurons, either facilitation or inhibition.* A neuron receiving a sufficient number of facilitatory impulses within a sufficiently restricted period is excited and discharges an impulse. If a neuron receives a sufficient number of synchronized impulses from inhibitory afferent fibers, its excitability may be so reduced that the neuron no longer responds to excitatory impulses which otherwise are adequate to discharge it.

Facilitation and Inhibition in Multisynaptic Pathways. The two basic synaptic processes of facilitation and inhibition were deduced from studies of monosynaptic arcs, for reasons already discussed. Similar processes may be presumed to occur at each synapse in more complex neuron chains. It is true that inhibition and occlusion cannot be distinguished clearly in multisynaptic chains, but there is every reason to believe that inhibition rather than occlusion underlies many response deficits in multisynaptic reflexes conditioned by volleys in appropriate afferent channels.

Synaptic processes in multisynaptic arcs differ from those in monosynaptic arcs in two respects: (i) the time course of facilitation and inhibition and (ii) the functional interrelations between the inhibitory and facilitatory pathways.

The time course of reflex facilitation (Fig. 85A) following a single conditioning volley via a multisynaptic path may be much longer than that for a monosynaptic discharge conditioned by a homonymous synergistic volley. Moreover, the development and decay of facilitation via multisynaptic paths is not the smooth and predictable function of time seen in the monosynaptic arc, but rather is typically a varying series of slowly waning maxima and minima. The same characteristics are also obvious in multisynaptic inhibition (Fig. 85B). These characteristics arise not because the fundamental synaptic processes differ in any way, but because the addition of interneurons to the chain increases the time span of motoneuron bombardment by presynaptic impulses. This increase in the duration of bombardment is due partly to the tendency of the interneurons to fire repetitively in response to a single afferent volley.[11, 26] A second reason is that a motoneuron may receive impulses through several chains of various degrees of complexity. Lorente de Nó[23] has classified interneuron chains into two general types: the closed chain and the multiple chain (Fig. 86). In the closed chain (C), collateral branches permit recirculation or reverberation of impulses through the chain, so that bursts of impulses arrive at the motoneurons at intervals determined by the temporal

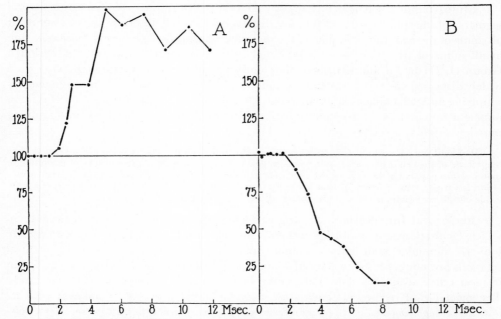

FIG. 85.   Facilitation and inhibition through multisynaptic paths. In both experiments the conditioning volley originated in Group II afferent fibers. In *A*, the test reflex was a monosynaptic discharge
from a flexor motoneuron pool; in *B*, a monosynaptic discharge from an extensor motoneuron pool.
Ordinates give size of test reflex discharge, the control size being taken as 100. *Abscissae* show interval
between conditioning (Group II) and test (Group I) volleys. (From Lloyd, *Res. Publ. Ass. nerv. ment.
Dis.*, 1952, *30*:48–67.)

characteristics of the length of the chain. In the multiple chain (*M*), sequential activation
of parallel chains of interneurons, through collateral branches, results in prolonged
bombardment of the motoneurons, the delay in each chain varying with the number
of synapses involved. In either instance, the motoneuron is subjected to a variable and
asynchronous barrage which prolongs and complicates the time course of facilitation
and inhibition.

The second difference between multisynaptic and monosynaptic arcs is in the origin
and central distribution of their respective inhibitory and facilitatory pathways. Monosynaptic spinal reflexes originate from Group I afferent fibers, found only in muscle
nerves. The efferent discharge is *discretely* delivered to the muscle from which the afferent
input originated. The same input facilitates motoneurons supplying synergistic muscles
and inhibits motoneurons supplying antagonistic muscles. In multisynaptic arcs, the
afferent limb is composed of Group II (12 to 6 μ), III (6 to 2 μ) or IV (unmyelinated)
fibers. These afferent fibers are found in both deep and superficial nerves. Irrespective
of origin—cutaneous, subcutaneous, muscular, synovial or periosteal—these afferent
fibers have, generally speaking, similar *central connections excitatory to motoneurons supplying
ipsilateral flexor muscles and inhibitory to motoneurons innervating ipsilateral extensor muscles.*

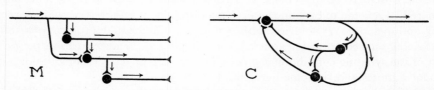

FIG. 86.   Plans of the two fundamental types of neuron circuits. *M*, Multiple chain; *C*, closed chain.
(After Lorente de Nó, *J. Neurophysiol.*, 1938, *1*:207–244.)

Multisynaptic discharges thus occupy efferent pathways that originate from several segments of the spinal cord and that are distributed diffusely to flexor muscles acting at all joints of the extremity. Similarly, the motoneurons supplying extensor muscles acting at all joints of the extremity are inhibited by multisynaptic paths initiated through Group II, III or IV afferent fibers. The multisynaptic reflex may thus originate from widely dispersed afferent fibers and has *diffuse* central connections involving motoneurons supplying muscles acting at different joints. The monosynaptic reflex has a *discrete* origin in muscle nerves and has *discrete* central connections involving only motoneurons supplying muscles acting at a single joint.

It should not be inferred from the foregoing that multisynaptic discharges are stereotyped. The magnitude of the reflex discharge to the various flexor muscles (as well as the intensity of inhibition of motoneurons supplying the various extensor muscles) varies markedly when the site of afferent stimulation is varied. This property of *local sign*, i.e., variation of efferent discharge pattern with changing locale of afferent origin, is discussed in greater detail in the next chapter.

Reciprocal Innervation.   A striking feature of reflex organization is the way in which facilitation and inhibition influence motoneurons reciprocally so that reflexly induced muscular contraction occurs without opposition. Such reciprocal central relations are not confined to the reflex arcs specifically described above, but are found in most reflex arcs, even those influencing smooth muscle, cardiac muscle and glands. The principle of reciprocal innervation may be stated formally as follows: *when the motoneurons supplying a given muscle are reflexly excited by an afferent volley, the motoneurons supplying antagonistic muscles are inhibited by that afferent volley.*

This dual action confers on the afferent volley an especially sensitive and powerful control over the limb reflexes, a control simultaneously initiating muscular contraction of one kind and inhibiting all opposing muscular contraction. These relations for the monosynaptic arc and for the multisynaptic arc are illustrated diagrammatically in Figure 87. It should not be assumed, however, that reflex action lacks flexibility and variability. The diagrams in Figure 87 show the central influences of only a single afferent pathway. In actual fact, each motoneuron receives connections from a host of afferent pathways, and the excitability and behavior of the cell depends at all times upon the relative balance between the excitatory and inhibitory impulses which it receives from these pathways.

It should also be noted that the relationships shown in Figure 87 apply to the motoneurons ipsilateral to the afferent volley. Motoneurons on the contralateral side of the cord are also conditioned by an afferent volley, but generally the effects there are opposite to those found ipsilaterally. Thus, a Group II afferent volley excites ipsilateral flexor motoneurons and inhibits ipsilateral extensor motoneurons, but on the contralateral side, the flexor motoneurons are inhibited and the extensor motoneurons excited. This general arrangement of function is called "*double reciprocal innervation;*" it is discussed further in the next chapter.

Post-tetanic Potentiation.[20]   A disturbing feature of synaptic function is the brevity of the action of presynaptic impulses on motoneurons. In monosynaptic arcs, the influence of a presynaptic conditioning volley persists for only some 12 to 15 milliseconds. Even in multisynaptic arcs, where there is opportunity for recirculation of impulses through interneuron chains, the conditioning influence (facilitatory or inhibitory) rarely lasts for more than 100 milliseconds. It is consequently difficult to fit such actions into any theoretical scheme to explain the prolonged storage of information which occurs in learning and memory. While there appears to be little immediate prospect of satisfactorily explaining such complex phenomena, some hope may be derived from the demonstration of the synaptic conditioning process known as post-tetanic potentiation, which persists for minutes and, in some instances, for hours.

Figure 88 illustrates an experiment demonstrating post-tetanic potentiation of a monosynaptic reflex discharge. Traces 1–4 in *A* show control ventral root discharges

elicited by four successive single shocks of Group I strength delivered to the gastrocnemius nerve at 2.4 second intervals. The nerve was then submitted to repetitive stimulation. After this repetitive or tetanic stimulation, the excitability of the motoneurons
was tested at regular intervals by single shocks of the same intensity as that employed
to evoke traces 1–4. The first post-tetanic test response (*A6*) was markedly increased in
amplitude, and the subsequent traces show still further increase in the number of motoneurons responding to the test volley. The potentiation was still evident at 2½ minutes,
when the test response was approximately twice as large as the control; in some experiments, this potentiation lasted 5 minutes or more after the conditioning tetanus. Several
weeks after motoneurons were isolated from segmental bombardment by section of

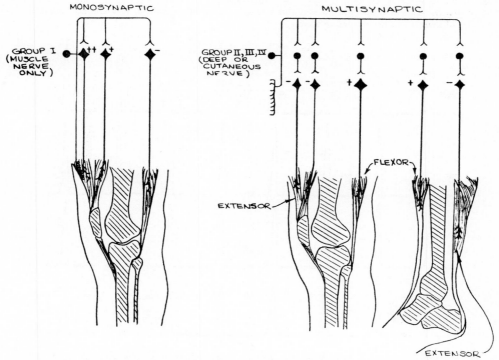

FIG. 87. Reciprocal relations of monosynaptic and multisynaptic reflex arcs. Note that Group I
afferent fibers influence only motoneurons supplying muscles acting at a single joint, whereas Group
II, III and IV afferent fibers diffusely influence motoneurons supplying muscles acting at several joints.

dorsal roots distal to the ganglia, Eccles and McIntyre[6] found that potentiation of
monosynaptic discharge persisted for several hours after tetanization of the dorsal root
stump. Such behavior, in which a single training session (tetanus) alters the responsiveness of the system for relatively long periods, may be likened to a simple form of memory
or learning.

The alteration underlying post-tetanic potentiation appears not to reside in the motoneuron
itself, for antidromic tetanization of motoneurons via the ventral root does not cause potentiation.
Furthermore, the action which is potentiated depends on the action of the tetanized pathway; tetanizing
an inhibitory pathway increases the inhibitory effect of single volleys subsequently delivered over that
pathway, and this exaggerated inhibition persists for minutes. Finally, it may be pointed out that
potentiation seems to be specific for the tetanized afferent pathway, because test responses to stimulation
of other afferent pathways converging on the same motoneuron are not potentiated. For these reasons,
it seems certain that the persistent alteration underlying post-tetanic potentiation is presynaptic and
in some fashion increases the transmitter effectiveness of tetanized afferent fibers.

The exact nature of this change in tetanized afferent fibers is controversial. Lloyd,[20] who discovered the phenomenon, ascribes potentiation to hyperpolarization of the presynaptic endings, a hypothesis which is reasonable because repetitive stimulation of axons increases the amplitude and duration of positive afterpotentials. It is also reasonable to suppose that an action potential in a hyperpolarized fiber would be somewhat larger and consequently exert a more powerful synaptic effect than an action potential engendered in the same fiber at its normal resting potential. Furthermore, Lloyd showed that, following tetanization, the compound action potential recorded from the dorsal root undergoes a slight increase in size, the increase running a time course similar to that of post-tetanic potentiation. Eccles and Rall[7] propose an alternative explanation, based on the hypothesis that repetitive firing causes the synaptic knobs to swell. These workers ascribe potentiation to the increased surface area of postsynaptic membranes covered by swollen knobs.

A pathway potentiated by tetanization recruits into the discharge zone neurons which are normally in the subliminal fringe. A striking example of this is illustrated in monosynaptic arcs. Normally, a Group I afferent volley facilitates but does not fire its heteronymous synergistic motoneurons. After Group I afferents have been tetanized, they may discharge not only homonymous motoneurons, as usual, but also some heteronymous synergistic motoneurons.[21] Such "cross-firing" substantiates the concept that the state of neurons in the subliminal fringe differs only quantitatively and not qualitatively from that of neurons in the discharge zone.

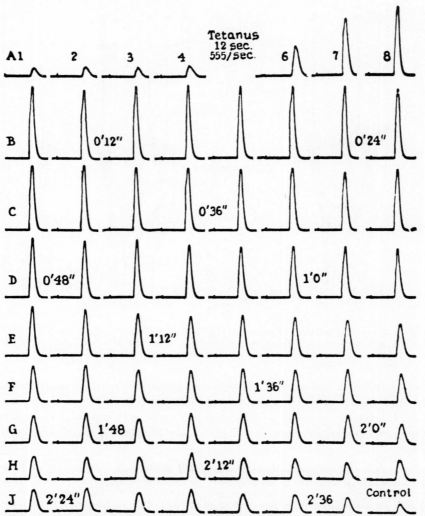

FIG. 88.   Post-tetanic potentiation. Monosynaptic reflex discharges at S_1 ventral root elicited by stimulating Group I afferent fibers in gastrocnemius nerve. Traces *1–4* recorded sequentially at intervals of 2.4 seconds. Between traces *4* and *6* the gastrocnemius nerve was tetanized as indicated. Subsequent traces recorded sequentially once every 2.4 seconds. (After Lloyd, *J. gen. Physiol.*, 1949, *33*:147–170.)

Intracellular Recording from Motoneurons.[2, 4, 10, 26]   Although the technique of recording ventral root discharges emerging from a spinal cord subjected to various afferent volleys serves to demonstrate the basic phenomena of facilitation and inhibition and to delineate their respective time courses, such studies of cell populations or pools are poorly suited to investigation of the intimate mechanisms of excitation and inhibition. For study of such problems, it is desirable to measure directly what happens to the membrane of a motoneuron subjected to excitatory or inhibitory afferent volleys.

Happily, such measurements can be made with ultramicroelectrodes similar to those described in earlier chapters. With electrodes having tip diameters less than 0.5 μ, penetration of the soma membrane can be accomplished without killing the cell, its vitality being evidenced by stable, predictable responses to afferent volleys. Often a cell

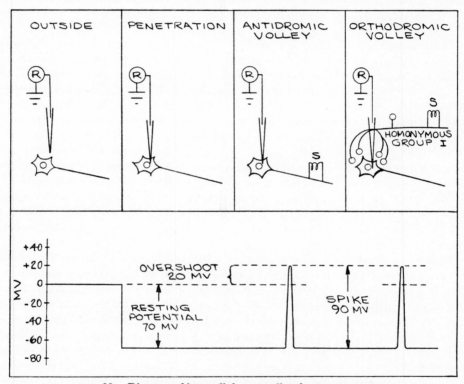

FIG. 89.   Diagram of intracellular recording from motoneurons.

survives impalement for several hours. The advantage of the technique is that it enables the experimenter to measure the potential across the membrane of a single cell and to observe the voltage changes which result when that cell is subjected to synaptic bombardment over various afferent pathways.

Penetration of spinal cord elements must, of course, be carried out blindly by slowly advancing the electrode through the cord (Fig. 89). Penetration of a membrane is signaled by the abrupt registration of a stable DC potential—the resting membrane potential. It is then necessary to identify the element penetrated. If the element responds to an antidromic ventral root volley with a single spike of invariant latency, it may be presumed that the electrode has lodged in a motoneuron. The identity of the motoneuron is next established by testing its responsiveness to Group I afferent volleys originating in various muscle nerves, since Group I volleys usually fire only their homonymous motoneurons.* Thus, for example, a penetrated element which responds to antidromic ventral root stimulation and to an orthodromic Group I afferent volley originating in the lateral gastrocnemius nerve may be presumed to be a motoneuron which supplies the lateral gastrocnemius muscle.

Such tests serve to identify the type of element penetrated but do not indicate the part of the cell penetrated—dendrite, soma or axon. Because the soma is relatively large in comparison to axons and dendrites, the probability of successfully penetrating it without causing rapid deterioration is greatest, but at present there are no absolute criteria for distinguishing penetration sites.

Action potentials recorded from ultramicroelectrodes in acellular regions (peripheral nerves, dorsal and ventral roots, dorsal columns) usually last about 0.6 millisecond. Intracellularly recorded spikes from spinal gray matter fall into two classes: those having durations of 0.6 millisecond and those with durations of about 1.5 milliseconds. The former probably represent axon spikes; the latter, either soma or dendrite spikes.

Membrane resting potentials of motoneurons. When a motoneuron is penetrated with a microelectrode, a sustained difference of potential between the internal microelectrode and the external medium is recorded. Sometimes this DC potential increases gradually for the first few minutes; this phenomenon suggests a sealing of the ruptured membrane around the tip and a consequent decrease in the shunting currents which make the initial potential reading spuriously low. Stable membrane potentials of motoneurons range from 60 to 80 mV., with a mean value of about 70 mV.; they invariably indicate that the inside of the membrane is electronegative to the outside.† The polarity of the resting cell membrane is thus the same as that of the axon membrane, but the magnitude of the polarization usually appears to be somewhat less in the soma membrane. The lower value of the soma membrane potential may reflect continuous subliminal synaptic bombardment, so that the measured potential is not a true "resting" potential; or the lower value may result from injury to the dendritic tree inflicted by the electrode as it approaches the cell body.

Reasoning largely by analogy, one may assume that the mechanisms maintaining the membrane potential in cells and in axons are at least qualitatively the same (see Chap. 2). Unfortunately, with spinal neurons it is not feasible to test this assumption directly by changing the ionic composition of the external medium surrounding the penetrated structure, as has been done with axons. Changes in *intracellular* ion concentrations can be effected by electrophoretic injection of ions through the penetrating electrode;[4] but, unfortunately, the amount of K^+ ion which can be added to the cell sap in this fashson is small compared to the natural high internal K^+ concentration, and the injection has little effect on membrane potential. Attempts to reduce the intracellular concentration of K^+ ion by replacing it with some other injected cation (Na^+ or tetramethylammonium) are more effective and produce expected decreases of 10 to 30 mV. in the membrane potential. When Na^+ is the replacing ion, the membrane voltage recovers its

* It is, of course, also possible to determine the peripheral connection of an impaled motoneuron by antidromically stimulating its axon in the muscle nerve, provided that the ventral root is left intact. Usually, for a variety of reasons, the ventral root is severed, and identification is established by the only slightly less certain method of orthodromic testing.

† The student is here reminded again that it is conventional to use the algebraic signs + or − to indicate the *direction* of membrane polarization. Thus, a membrane potential of −70 mV. means that the inside of the membrane is 70 mV. negative to the outside. It must be clearly understood that the signs refer only to the direction of polarization, and are not to be taken in the algebraic sense when, for example, the membrane potential changes. Thus a change from −70 to −60 mV. is called a decrease, not an increase, in membrane potential, because the absolute voltage across the membrane is decreased, the direction of polarization remaining constant. Similarly, a change from −70 to −80 mV. represents an increased membrane potential. Decreases of membrane potential are often referred to as depolarization, increases as hyperpolarization.

TABLE 5.   *IONIC CONCENTRATIONS AND COMPUTED EQUILIBRIUM POTENTIALS OF CAT MOTONEURONS**

ION	OUTSIDE (mM./l.)	INSIDE (mM./l.)	E (mV.)
Na^+	150	ca. 15	ca. +60
K^+	5.5	150	−90
Cl^-	125	9	−70

* From Eccles.[4]

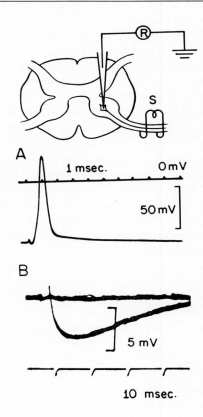

FIG. 90. Intracellularly recorded antidromic action potentials of motoneurons. Diagram shows arrangement of recording (R) and stimulating (S) electrodes. A, Antidromic spike recorded on fast time base and at low amplification. B, Antidromic spike recorded on slow time base and at high amplification to show after-hyperpolarization; most of spike was off the screen. Note that during recovery the trace overshoots the resting potential, indicated by horizontal baseline. Figure made by superposing about 20 responses on one negative. (After Eccles, *The neurophysiological basis of mind*, London, Oxford Univ. Press, 1953; and *The physiology of nerve cells*, Baltimore, Johns Hopkins Press, 1957.)

initial value in several minutes, presumably because the Na^+-K^+ pump rapidly restores the resting ionic state. Following tetramethylammonium replacement of K^+, restitution of the full membrane potential is much slower, presumably because the membrane is only slightly permeable to the tetramethylammonium ion.

The estimated concentrations of Na^+, K^+ and Cl^- ions in the internal and external media of cat motoneurons are given in Table 5. Also shown are the equilibrium potentials for these ions, computed from the Nernst equation. It should noted be that at a resting membrane potential of −70 mV., the K^+ ion is not at equilibrium ($\mathcal{E}_{K^+} = -90$ mV.). This inequality presumably occurs because K^+ is actively pumped into the cell by some metabolic mechanism, so that the resting membrane never reaches the equilibrium potential of K^+. The reasons for assuming an active inward transport of K^+ will be discussed in the next section.

Action potentials of motoneurons.   The intracellularly recorded action potential of a motoneuron antidromically fired (Fig. 90A) usually has an over-all ampitude of 80 to

100 mV. With a resting potential of -70 mV., the "overshoot" is thus 10 to 30 mV.; in cell bodies, as in axons, the membrane potential is reversed during the action potential. This reversal during action is presumably triggered by an increased permeability to Na^+ ions when the membrane potential is reduced to a critical value by the current flow in the axon. The flow of Na^+ ions along their steep concentration gradient into the cell establishes a potential across the membrane which approaches that of the Na^+ equilibrium potential ($+60$ mV.; see Table 5). The potential does not overshoot to this extent, because the increased Na^+ permeability is short-lived and because there follows a period of increased permeability to K^+ during which the membrane potential tends to return toward the K^+ equilibrium potential of -90 mV. High K^+ permeability is persistent. Consequently, after the spike, the membrane becomes hyperpolarized by about 5 mV. (i.e., the membrane potential reaches about -75 mV.) and does not return to the resting level of -70 mV. for some 100 milliseconds (Fig. 90B).

These concepts are supported by observations on the spike potentials of motoneurons in which the intracellular ionic concentrations have been altered by iontophoretic injection of ions through the intracellular electrode. When, for example, a current is passed from a Na_2SO_4-filled intracellular electrode to the outside medium, current is largely carried from the electrode to the cell sap by Na^+ ions, whereas the flow outward across the membrane is largely carried by K^+ ions. Thus, intracellular K^+ is replaced by Na^+ ions. It has already been mentioned that such a procedure diminishes the resting potential as a result of depletion of K^+ and consequent increase in the ratio of K^+ outside to K^+ inside the cell. This procedure also causes a reduction in the amplitude and the rate of rise of the action potential, because the added intracellular Na^+ reduces the Na^+ concentration gradient. In addition, when intracellular K^+ is replaced by either Na^+ or tetramethylammonium ions, the after-hyperpolarization is abolished and the decline of the spike is slowed.

If, as suggested by ion injection experiments and by reasoning from analogy with axons, after-hyperpolarization represents a seeking of the K^+ equilibrium potential during the postspike period of high K^+ permeability, no after-hyperpolarization should be observed if the membrane potential is artifically adjusted to equal ε_{K^+}. Eccles[4] has devised the ingenious technique of adjusting the membrane potential to any desired level by introducing a double-barreled microelectrode into the cell (see drawing in Fig. 91). One barrel of the electrode is used for recording the membrane potential in the conventional fashion. The other barrel is used to pass a brief DC current through the membrane and thus to vary the membrane potential artificially. When the current is passed from the microelectrode outward through the membrane, the membrane potential is decreased, whereas a current passed from the external medium through the membrane into the electrode hyperpolarizes the cell. If the polarizing currents are brief, the membrane potential can be adjusted to any desired level without significantly altering the ion concentrations. Figure 91 illustrates how such variations in membrane potential affect the hyperpolarization following an antidromic spike. As the membrane potential is reduced below the resting level, the afterpotential increases in amplitude, whereas artificial hyperpolarization decreases the afterpotential.

The relationship between the membrane potential and after-hyperpolarization is shown graphically in Figure 91. It usually is impractical to hyperpolarize the cell sufficiently to reduce the after-hyperpolarization to zero, because at such high membrane potentials the impulse may fail to invade the cell. However, it can be seen that the points fit reasonably well onto a straight line which, by extrapolation, intersects the abscissa at a membrane potential of about 90 mV. Intersection at this point means that K^+ exchange, which is presumably responsible for postspike hyperpolarization, is "satisfied," or at equilibrium, only when the membrane potential is -90 mV., or about

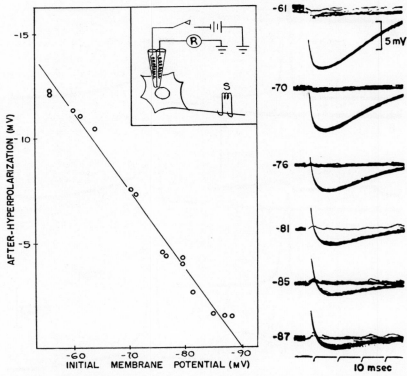

FIG. 91. Effect of membrane potential on amplitude of after-hyperpolarization. Traces show after-hyperpolarization recorded at different membrane potentials established by passing current through polarizing barrel of double-barreled microelectrode. Numbers to left of traces give membrane potential. Graph indicates that after-hyperpolarization is lacking at membrane potential of 90 mV. (After Eccles, *The physiology of nerve cells*, Baltimore, Johns Hopkins Press, 1957.)

20 mV. greater than the resting level. Calculated from the Nernst equation with the assumption of an external K^+ concentration of 5.5 mM. per liter and $\mathcal{E}_{K^+} = -90$ mV., the internal K^+ concentration must be about 150 mM. per liter, or approximately twice that required to maintain the observed resting membrane potential of -70 mV. The internal K^+ concentration is unexpectedly high because K^+ is pumped into the cell against its concentration gradient by some active metabolic process. There is reason to believe that the mechanism pumping K^+ into the cell is linked to that pumping Na^+ out (see Chap. 1).

THE ORIGIN OF MOTONEURON SPIKES.[4, 13]   The rising limb of the motoneuron spike typically displays a slight notch when the depolarization has proceeded to about 30 to 40 mV. This notch is a constant feature if the spike is generated by an antidromic volley, by a presynaptic volley, or by a depolarizing current passed directly through the membrane via one barrel of a double-barreled electrode.

Analysis indicates that the notch reflects the spread of depolarization from a low threshold portion of the cell to a high threshold portion. When the cell is depressed, e.g., during recovery from an antecedent discharge, the spike often does not reach its full size of 80 to 100 mV., but declines from a peak of about 30 to 40 mV. above the resting level. In other words, in the depressed cell the spike amplitude is about equal to, or slightly less than, that of the notch seen in full-sized spikes of the undepressed cell. In antidromically elicited spikes, it can be seen that the portion of the membrane giving rise to the small spike is triggered when the membrane is depolarized by about 10 mV. For various reasons, it is believed that the small, low threshold spike (called the A spike by Fuortes *et al.*[13]) originates in the region of the axon hillock or initial segment of the axon. The higher threshold B spike seems to originate in the soma and/or dendrites. Eccles[4] assumed that the low threshold small spike originates in the initial segment of the axon, and he called it the "IS spike." The high threshold spike he labeled the "SD spike" because he believed that it originates in the soma and dendrites. In view of uncertainties regarding the exact origin of the two components, the noncommittal designations "A" and "B" are

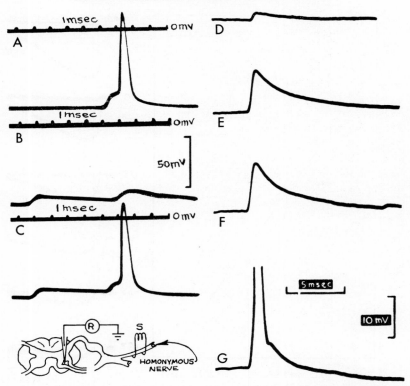

FIG. 92.   Intracellularly recorded responses of motoneurons to homonymous Group I afferent volleys. *A*, Response to barely liminal volley. *B*, Response to two subliminal volleys. *C*, Same as *B* except that interval between volleys is reduced so that the second EPSP sums with first and discharges cell. *D–G*, Responses of another cell to afferent volleys of increasing intensity. In *G* the EPSP reaches threshold and the cell discharges. (After Eccles, *The neurophysiological basis of mind*, London, Oxford Univ. Press, 1953.)

preferable. Fuortes *et al.*[13] have shown that an orthodromically elicited A spike is all that is necessary to generate a full-blown spike in the axon; hence, effective synaptic transmission need involve only a fraction of the total postsynaptic membrane.

Synaptic excitation; the EPSP.   Figure 92*A* shows an action potential recorded intracellularly from a motoneuron subjected to a liminal homonymous Group I afferent volley. Prior to the onset of the spike, a small depolarization appears; when this reaches about 10 mV., the spike is generated. A prepotential of this type is consistently observed in neurons subjected to excitatory presynaptic volleys, and is believed to reflect the pre-excitatory change induced in the membrane by the excitatory volley. For this reason, the prepotential is called the excitatory postsynaptic potential, or EPSP.[4]

To study the full time course of the EPSP, it is convenient to avoid firing the cell, because the spike obscures all but the rising phase of the EPSP. Firing can be prevented by reducing the size of the afferent volley until the induced EPSP is too small to initiate a spike, or, in other words, by recording from the cell when it is in the subliminal fringe rather than in the discharge zone.* Examples are shown in Figure 92*D*, *E* and *F*. The EPSP begins about 0.5 millisecond after the primary afferent volley enters the spinal

---

* A convenient method for studying EPSP without the complication of superimposed spikes is to deliver the Group I volley over the heteronymous synergistic pathway. Such volleys produce an EPSP which is indistinguishable from the EPSP produced by subliminal postsynaptic volley via the homonymous pathway.

cord, rises to a summit in 1.0 to 1.5 milliseconds after being initiated, and then declines slowly along an approximately exponential time course with a time constant of slightly more than 4 milliseconds. It is significant that the time course of the decay of the EPSP is of the same order as that of the facilitation curve determined by the conditioning-testing method applied to motoneuron populations.

Figure 92D, E and F shows another important characteristic of the EPSP—that it is a graded process capable of summation. In contradistinction to the size of the propagated spike, which is "all-or-nothing," the size of the EPSP is a direct function of volley size. Moreover, when two subliminal volleys are delivered within a time interval less than the EPSP decay time, as in Figure 92B and C, the second EPSP may sum with the "tail" of the first EPSP, and cause sufficient depolarization (about 13 mV. in this instance) to discharge the neuron. The behavior of the EPSP thus parallels closely the process of facilitation and may be presumed to be the electrical manifestation of that process.

When the membrane potential is artificially altered by passing brief polarizing currents through an intracellular electrode, the EPSP induced by an excitatory volley displays a marked alteration in amplitude and configuration. As the membrane potential is decreased, both the amplitude and the rate of rise of the EPSP diminish until, when the membrane potential is artificially set at about 0 mV., the excitatory volley produces no change in membrane potential. When the polarizing current is such that it reverses the membrane potential (i.e., makes the outside of the cell negative to the inside), the EPSP is reversed in sign. Thus, the process underlying the EPSP seems to be one which is in equilibrium at about 0 mV.; when the membrane potential is above or below this value, an excitatory volley makes the membrane seek this equilibrium value. In the normal cell, of course, the effect is depolarization.

For a number of reasons, it seems likely that excitatory impulses cause a nonspecific increase in permeability to all ions. For example, injection of various ions into the cell has little or no effect on the amplitude and time courses of the EPSP. These data are best explained by assuming that the excitatory impulses short-circuit* the postsynaptic membrane beneath the synaptic knobs, permitting ions to flow along their concentration gradients and thus reduce the membrane potential. The extent of the depolarization depends on the number of "short circuits" produced, and this number in turn depends on the number of activated synaptic knobs. If the EPSP reduces the membrane potential by about 10 mV. (i.e., to about −60 mV.), the threshold is reached, and the membrane becomes specifically highly permeable—first to Na^+ and then to K^+ ions—and a propagated spike is generated.

It will be recognized that the EPSP is very similar to the end-plate potential recorded at motor end-plates when motor fibers are excited. The end-plate potential results from the liberation of a chemical transmitter agent, presumably acetylcholine. It is likely that excitatory synaptic knobs also liberate a chemical transmitter which renders the subjacent postsynaptic membrane highly permeable to all ions, just as the neuromuscular transmitter renders the end-plate permeable to all ions. Unfortunately, the identity of the central excitatory transmitter is not known; it may be that more than one such substance exists. Although there is some reason to believe that acetylcholine is the excitatory transmitter at some spinal synapses, it seems unlikely that acetylcholine is the transmitter between dorsal root afferents and motoneurons, because analysis indi-

---

* The term "short circuit" is used here in a relative sense. Computations indicate that, with maximal presynaptic action, the total membrane resistance drops from about 8×10^5 ohms to as low as 5×10^5 ohms. This latter resistance is composed of many higher resistances in parallel, the resistances of the patches of membrane under activated and nonactivated knobs.[4]

cates that dorsal root fibers contain very little acetylcholine and choline-acetylase (an enzyme which, in the presence of ATP, acetylates choline).[8] A full discussion of the efforts to identify transmitter agents at various synaptic junctions is given by Eccles in his monograph.[4]

Central synaptic inhibition; the IPSP. When a resting motoneuron is subjected to an inhibitory volley of impulses delivered over its heteronymous antagonistic pathway, the membrane often undergoes a transient hyperpolarization, as shown in Figure 93. The change in membrane potential which follows a synaptic inhibitory volley is called the inhibitory postsynaptic potential, or IPSP.[4] The IPSP, like the EPSP, is a graded non-propagated response of the postsynaptic cell to presynaptic activation. The IPSP usually

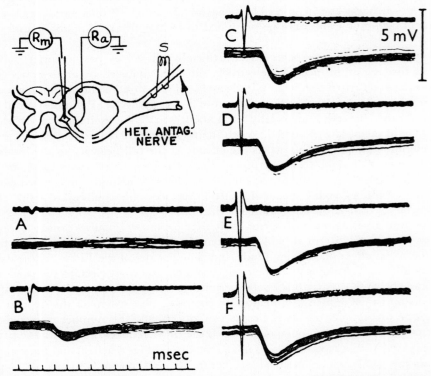

FIG. 93.   Intracellularly recorded inhibitory postsynaptic potentials (IPSP). Responses recorded from biceps semitendinosus motoneuron following Group I afferent volley through quadriceps nerve (heteronymous antagonistic path). Traces *A–F* show afferent volley (upper trace) and intracellular response (lower trace) as stimulus strength was progressively increased. Each record formed by superimposing several traces. (After Eccles, *The physiology of nerve cells,* Baltimore, Johns Hopkins Press, 1957.)

begins 1.25 to 1.5 milliseconds after the primary afferent volley enters the spinal cord, reaches a summit in 1.5 to 2.0 milliseconds, and decays with a time constant of about 3 milliseconds. In cells with normal resting membrane potentials of about 70 mV., the amplitude of the IPSP rarely exceeds 5 mV. (In other words, the membrane potential may rise to as much as 75 mV. following an inhibitory afferent volley.) During the IPSP, the responsiveness of the cell to excitatory volleys is diminished. This decreased responsiveness is partly due to hyperpolarization of the membrane during the IPSP, but as will be seen below, postsynaptic hyperpolarization does not fully account for the effectiveness of an inhibitory volley.

Unlike the EPSP, which is little affected by ion injections, the IPSP is markedly altered by injections which alter the internal Cl^- or K^+ concentration. Injection of Cl^-

ions, for example, converts the hyperpolarizing IPSP into a depolarizing potential; indeed, following injection of Cl⁻ ions, a normally inhibitory volley may cause sufficient depolarization to fire the cell. Similarly, depleting intracellular K^+ by replacement with Na^+ or tetramethylammonium ions also converts the IPSP to a depolarizing response. These observations suggest that the inhibitory process exerts its effect by altering the permeability of the membrane to the small ions K^+ and Cl^-.

It will be recalled that the equilibrium potential for K^+ is about -90 mV.; the Cl^- ion appears to be at equilibrium at a resting membrane potential of -70 mV. Consequently, it might be expected that, if the inhibitory process selectively increases

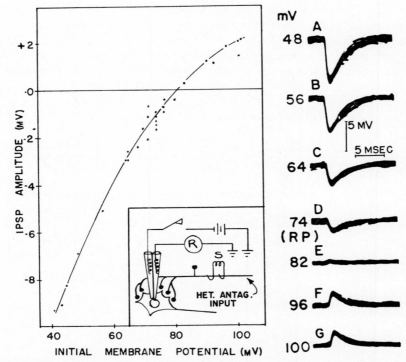

FIG. 94.   Effect of membrane potential on IPSP. Traces show intracellularly recorded IPSP elicited by heteronymous antagonistic Group I afferent volley as membrane potential was artificially varied by polarizing electrode. Numbers to left of trace indicate membrane potential; *RP*, resting potential. Graph shows that IPSP is a hyperpolarizing response at membrane potentials less than 80 mV., but becomes a depolarizing response when membrane potential exceeds 80 mV. (After Eccles, *The physiology of nerve cells*, Baltimore, Johns Hopkins Press, 1957.)

membrane permeability to small ions (K^+ and Cl^-), the membrane potential would seek a value midway between the respective equilibrium potentials of these two ions. As shown in Figure 94, when the membrane potential is artificially set at -80 mV., the inhibitory volley produces no detectable IPSP. When the membrane potential is less than 80 mV., the IPSP is a hyperpolarizing response; when the membrane potential is greater than 80 mV., the IPSP is a depolarizing response. These experimental findings are thus compatible with the hypothesis that inhibitory impulses increase K^+ and Cl^- permeability and tend to drive the membrane potential toward -80 mV. (i.e., the mean of the Cl^- and K^+ equilibrium potentials).

In neurons with a normal resting potential and internal ionic composition, the IPSP is hyperpolarizing. However, an inhibitory volley depresses the motoneuron even when the IPSP is of the depolarizing type, e.g., when the IPSP is elicited in a cell artificially hyperpolarized by a polarizing current. It follows therefore that mere hyperpolarization is not the sole cause of inhibitory depression. Rather, it appears that the temporary stabilization of the membrane near the equilibrium potential for the IPSP (-80 mV.) makes it difficult to depolarize the membrane to the level (about -60 mV.) required to initiate an increase in Na^+ permeability.

It may be assumed that the difference between excitatory and inhibitory nerve fibers is in the chemical transmitters which they liberate. The excitatory transmitter causes a nonspecific increase in permeability to all ions, whereas the inhibitory transmitter causes a specific increased permeability to small ions, of which Cl^- and K^+ are the important naturally occurring species. Recently it has been shown that gamma aminobutyric acid (GABA), which can be isolated from nerve tissue, mimics the action of an inhibitory volley on certain crustacean neurons.[15] The inhibitory transmitter agent at mammalian spinal synapses has not yet been identified.

Although the mechanisms just described account satisfactorily for some aspects of synaptic inhibition, there is reason to believe that other mechanisms also participate. A

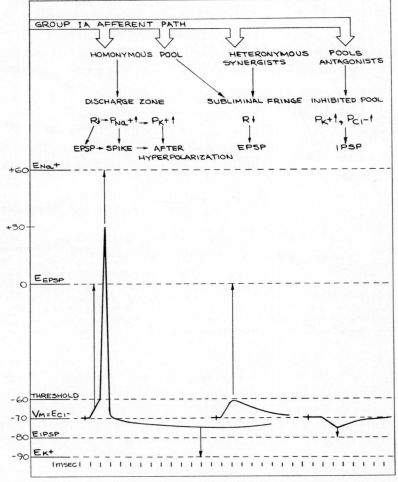

FIG. 95. Summary diagram of monosynaptic connections and events. *Upper*, Functional connections of Group I afferent fibers and permeability changes which they exert on various motoneuron pools; R, membrane resistance; P, permeability. *Lower*, Intracellularly recorded responses and equilibrium potentials (E) toward which each process tends to drive membrane potential; Vm, resting membrane potential.

serious difficulty is the long latency of the onset of the IPSP (1.25 to 1.5 msec. after the volley reaches the cord), for inhibition curves determined on populations of motoneurons show that inhibitory depression begins far earlier. Frank and Fuortes[12] found that some motoneurons subjected to inhibitory volleys showed no change in membrane potential and no change in threshold to direct stimulation through a microelectrode. Nevertheless, such an inhibitory volley reduced by 50 per cent the EPSP generated by a homonymous excitatory volley and prevented the cell from firing. In such instances it thus appears that inhibition is presynaptic, i.e., that the inhibitory volley in some fashion blocks the excitatory impulses before they reach the postsynaptic cell. The mechanism of such "remote inhibition" is not known.

Summary of Synaptic Mechanisms.   It is now possible to reconstruct in some detail what changes occur in the spinal cord when a Group I afferent volley is directed into it (Fig. 95). At the homonymous synapses, the volley liberates a transmitter which increases permeability to all ions and permits the voltage across the membrane to run down. In some cells, many short circuits will occur because the cells receive many active synaptic knobs. In these cells, when the depolarization reaches about 10 mV. less than the resting membrane potential, there is a sudden large increase in Na^+ permeability, so that the membrane potential shifts rapidly toward the Na^+ equilibrium potential; hence, the potential across the membrane reverses. Following in the wake of high Na^+ permeability, K^+ permeability increases, driving the membrane potential back towards the K^+ equilibrium potential of -90 mV. As the K^+ permeability wanes, the membrane potential returns to the resting level of about -70 mV.

Other homonymous motoneurons and also the heteronymous synergistic motoneurons receive fewer active knobs and are consequently in the subliminal fringe of the excitatory volley. In such motoneurons the short-circuiting action of the excitatory impulses is insufficient to reduce the membrane potential to the critical level required to activate the increase in permeability to Na^+. Consequently, these cells do not discharge, but during the time course of the EPSP their excitability is increased.

Finally, the volley exerts an effect on the heteronymous antagonistic motoneuron pool. Here, the presynaptic impulses cause the release of an inhibitory transmitter which increases the permeability to K^+ and Cl^- ions. Consequently, the membrane potential is driven toward -80 mV. and the excitability of the cell is diminished. In addition, inhibitory volleys may block excitatory impulses in presynaptic fibers by a mechanism not yet understood.

REFERENCES

1. Bishop, G. H. and O'Leary, J. *J. Neurophysiol.*, 1938, *1*:391–404.
2. Brock, L. G., Coombs, J. S. and Eccles, J. C. *J. Physiol.*, 1952, *117*:431–460.
3. Coombs, J. S., Curtis, D. R. and Eccles, J. C. *Nature (Lond.)*, 1956, *178*:1049–1050.
4. Eccles, J. C. *The physiology of nerve cells.* Baltimore, Johns Hopkins Press, 1957, ix, 270 pp.
5. Eccles, J. C., Fatt, P. and Landgren, S. *J. Neurophysiol.*, 1956, *19*:75–98.
6. Eccles, J. C. and McIntyre, A. K. *J. Physiol.*, 1953, *121*:492–516.
7. Eccles, J. C. and Rall, W. *Proc. roy. Soc.*, 1951, *B138*:475–498.
8. Feldberg, W. and Vogt, M. *J. Physiol.*, 1948, *107*:372–381.
9. Frank, K. and Fuortes, M. G. F. *J. Physiol.*, 1956, *134*:451–470.
10. Frank, K. and Fuortes, M. G. F. *J. Physiol.*, 1955, *130*:625–654, 1 pl.
11. Frank, K. and Fuortes, M. G. F. *J. Physiol.*, 1956, *131*:424–435.
12. Frank, K. and Fuortes, M. G. F. *Fed. Proc.*, 1957, *16*:39–40.
13. Fuortes, M. G. F., Frank, K. and Becker, M. C. *J. gen Physiol.*, 1957, *40*:735–752.
14. Kemp, E. H., Coppée, G. E. and Robinson, E. H. *Amer. J. Physiol.*, 1937, *120*:304–315.
15. Kuffler, S. W. and Edwards, C. *J. Neurophysiol.*, 1958, *21*:589–610.
16. Lloyd, D. P. C. *J. Neurophysiol.*, 1941, *4*:184–190.
17. Lloyd, D. P. C. *Yale J. Biol. Med.*, 1945, *18*:117–121.
18. Lloyd, D. P. C. *J. Neurophysiol.*, 1946, *9*:421–438.

19. Lloyd, D. P. C. *J. Neurophysiol.*, 1946, *9*:439–444.
20. Lloyd, D. P. C. *J. gen. Physiol.*, 1949, *33*:147–170.
21. Lloyd, D. P. C., Hunt, C. C. and McIntyre, A. K. *J. gen. Physiol.*, 1955, *38*:307–317.
22. Lorente de Nó, R. *J. Neurophysiol.*, 1938, *1*:187–194.
23. Lorente de Nó, R. *J. Neurophysiol.*, **1938**, *1*:207–244.
24. Rall, W. *Science*, 1957, *126*:454.
25. Renshaw, B. *J. Neurophysiol.*, 1940, *3*:373–387.
26. Woodbury, J. W. and Patton, H. D. *Cold Spr. Harb. Symp. quant. Biol.*, 1952, *17*:185–188.

CHAPTER 6

Reflex Regulation of Movement and Posture

By HARRY D. PATTON

IN the previous chapter some simple reflex arcs were analyzed for the purpose of eluci-dating the principles of synaptic transmission. In the present chapter the *functional* role of spinal reflexes in the coordination of posture and phasic motor activity will be con-sidered. It should be emphasized from the outset that, in assessing the function of reflex arcs in intact animals, certain experimental procedures allowable in analysis of synaptic mechanisms are excluded or, at best, must be used with reservation. For example, in the experiments described in Chapter 5, reflex discharges were commonly elicited by applying electric shocks to appropriate bundles of afferent fibers. Such stimulation excites many afferent fibers in synchrony, so that the spinal motoneurons receive a relatively brief-acting "packet" of impulses.

In studies of synapses synchronous bombardment of motoneurons is both advan-tageous and defensible because it allows accurate measurement of the time course of synaptic events. In nature, however, reflex action originates at the receptor organs, and the afferent inputs to the motoneurons are rarely synchronous because the receptors fire repetitively and out of phase with one another. An even more serious drawback to stimulation of a nerve trunk is that afferent fibers of different functional species may be excited in unnatural concert, since the correlation between fiber size (and hence thresh-old) and functional species is not absolute. For example, even the Group I afferent fibers of muscle nerves are not functionally homogeneous (see below). Therefore, in the present chapter, attention will be focused primarily on experiments in which reflexes are elicited by natural stimulation of the receptors.

Also, in evaluation of the functional significance of reflexes, emphasis is placed on observations made while reflex arcs are as nearly intact and uninfluenced by drugs as humane requirements to avoid causing pain permit. The study of reflexes in the truly "natural state" is impossible, for the uncertainty principle applies equally to physiologic and physical systems. However, many procedures (e.g., root sections, deep anesthesia) necessary for learning basic properties of reflex *components* can and must be avoided in studying the properties of the whole *system*. Stated in another way, the goal of this chapter is to present a *synthetic* rather than a purely *analytical* picture of reflex function by emphasizing the behavior of freely interacting components of the reflex arc rather than their behavior in controlled isolation.

The Flexion Reflex.[31] A convenient preparation for the study of spinal reflex patterns is an animal in which the spinal cord has been permanently transected above the lumbosacral enlargement—a "spinal animal."* Segments below the level of the transection are, of course, insensate, and hence the reflex patterns of these segments may be freely studied without the use of anesthetic drugs. In such a preparation, stimulation of the skin or deep structures of the hindlimbs, for example, elicits a variety of movements and postures which must be mediated solely by spinal reflex arcs, because the lower cord has been isolated from supraspinal structures by the transection. Two spinal reflex patterns are particularly prominent—the *flexion reflex* and the *tendon jerk*.

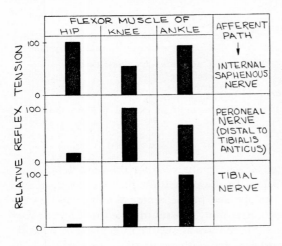

FIG. 96. Local sign in the flexion reflex. Bars indicate relative reflex tensions developed in three flexor muscles as a result of stimulation of each of three nerves (afferent paths) serving sensory endings in different portions of hindlimb. Each path activated all three muscles, but relative participation of the muscles in the reflex movement varied with afferent path. (After Creed and Sherrington, *Proc. roy. Soc.,* 1926, *B100*:258–267.)

The flexion reflex is elicited by noxious stimulation (pinching, burning, strong electrical stimulation), particularly of the skin, although similar stimulation of deep structures after removal or denervation of the skin is also effective. The reflex response consists of contraction of the *ipsilateral* flexor muscles at the ankle, knee and hip so that the whole limb is withdrawn from the noxious stimulus. Palpation of the muscles reveals that, as the flexor muscles contract, the extensor muscles relax, an event suggesting that the extensor motoneurons are inhibited. Thus, the afferent fibers subserving the flexion reflex make *reciprocal* connections (see Chap. 5) with the ipsilateral motoneurons, so that flexor withdrawal of the limb is not impeded by simultaneous contraction of the antagonistic extensor muscles. Because the adequate stimulus for eliciting the flexion reflex is one which is harmful to the tissues, Sherrington[31] called it a *nociceptive* reflex, and, because the reflex contraction results in removal of the extremity from the damaging stimulus, he looked upon the flexion reflex as protective.

In the cat, but usually not in man, reflex withdrawal of the stimulated limb is often associated with contraction of the extensor muscles and relaxation of the flexor muscles of the corresponding contralateral extremity. This contralateral component is known as the *crossed extension reflex*. The crossed extension reflex is not a separate reflex but is accessory to, or a part of, the flexion reflex. The afferent fibers subserving the flexion reflex send to the opposite side of the spinal cord collateral branches which have reciprocal connections opposite those in the ipsilateral spinal cord. This arrangement is known as *double reciprocal innervation*. The crossed extension reflex supports the weight of the body when the ipsilateral limb flexes.

Often when the noxious stimulus is prolonged, the crossed extension reflex is not sustained, but

* In acute experiments the spinal cord is sometimes transected at C_I, and the animal is maintained by artificial respiration. Such an animal is referred to as a "high spinal" or "decapitate" preparation.

gives way to a rhythmically alternating stepping movement. In Sherrington's words, "The irritated foot is withdrawn from harm and the other legs run away."

Prominent features of the flexion reflex are its broad receptive field and its wide sphere of action on muscles. Generally speaking, noxious stimulation anywhere in the limb causes reflex contraction of the flexor muscles at all joints in the limb. The pattern of contraction, however, is not stereotyped, for the relative strength of the contractions of various muscles varies with the site of stimulation. Figure 96 shows the relative participation of three flexor muscles in reflex limb movement elicited by electrical stimulation of three different afferent nerves supplying sensory fibers to different regions of the limb. It can be seen that each of the three afferent nerves drives the motoneurons of each muscle, but in quantitatively different combinations. Such data indicate that the nature of the limb movement and the final position of the limb vary, depending on the site of harmful stimulation. Such dependence of the reflex pattern on the origin of the afferent input is called *local sign*. Because of local sign, effective and appropriate withdrawal of the limb occurs irrespective of the site of injury.

Afferent path and synaptic organization of the flexion reflex. Several features of the flexion reflex are strongly reminiscent of the multisynaptic discharges (see Chap. 5) elicited by electrical stimulation of afferent fibers less than 12 μ in diameter (Groups II, III, and IV). (i) The broad receptive field including deep structures as well as the cutaneous surface of the limb agrees with the ubiquitous distribution of Group II, III and IV afferent fibers. (ii) The channeling of the reflex discharge exclusively into flexor muscles, with concomitant inhibition of extensor motoneurons, is also typical of multisynaptic arcs. The diffuse distribution of the efferent discharge, involving reciprocal action at all joints of the extremity, too, is peculiar to multisynaptic arcs and in striking contrast to the discrete distribution of monosynaptic discharges (cf., Fig. 87). (iii) The flexion reflex typically displays *afterdischarge* (i.e., the contraction outlasts the stimulus), which is expected in multisynaptic systems where recirculation of impulses through interneuron circuits permits sustained motoneuron bombardment after the primary afferent volley has ceased. (iv) Finally, the noxious or harmful nature of the adequate stimulus for the flexion reflex agrees with evidence indicating that many of the Group III and IV fibers supply the plexuses of free nerve endings which are sensitive to noxious or painful stimuli (see Chap. 13). There can be little doubt that the nociceptive flexion reflex utilizes multisynaptic arcs having Group III and IV fibers for their afferent limbs.

Reflex stepping. The functional significance of the Group II afferent fibers which mediate a multisynaptic reflex discharge to flexor muscles is not entirely clear, since there is no reason to suspect that the endings which these fibers supply are nociceptive. The Group II afferent fibers found in muscle nerves originate exclusively in the secondary or flower spray endings of the muscle spindles, which are sensitive to muscle stretch (see below). Group II fibers of cutaneous nerves apparently supply touch-sensitive or pressure-sensitive endings.[35]

It is possible that Group II fibers feed multisynaptic arcs involved in reflex stepping movements. Rhythmically alternating, stepping movements of the hind limbs can sometimes be initiated in the chronic spinal dog by tactile stimulation of the foot pad or, more consistently, by suspending the animal erect off the ground so that gravity imparts a stretch on the hip extensors. Since both the touch-pressure receptors of the feet and the stretch-sensitive spindle endings in the hip muscles are in a position to be alternately excited by normal stepping, and since the Group II fibers innervating these receptors make double reciprocal spinal connections, it is tempting to implicate the Group II fibers in stepping.

The mechanism of stepping, however, is complex. Sherrington found that denervation of the tactile receptors by section of all the cutaneous nerves of the leg impaired walking in the cat so little that an animal was able to walk accurately on a horizontal ladder. Moreover, rhythmically alternating stepping may be induced experimentally by simultaneous repetitive stimulation of afferent fibers originating in each of the hind limbs. Figure 97 shows the results of an experiment in which the tensions in the right and left vastus intermedius muscles (knee extensors) were recorded during afferent stimulation of one or both peroneal nerves. When only one nerve was stimulated, the ipsilateral extensor muscle relaxed and its contralateral counterpart contracted. When both nerves were stimulated concurrently at equal intensities, rhythmically alternating contraction and relaxation of the two muscles occurred and persisted as long as the

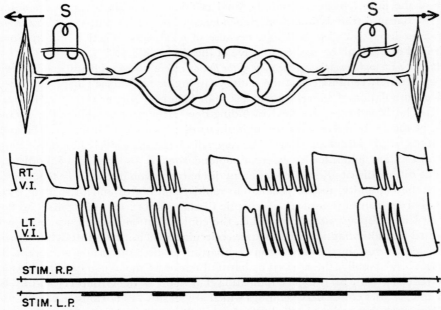

FIG. 97. Production of rhythmic reflexes (stepping by concurrent stimulation of right and left peroneal nerves. Diagram at top represents experimental arrangement. Upper two traces are myographic records of tension in right (*RT.*) and left (*LT.*) vastus intermedius muscles (knee extensors). Lower two traces signal repetitive stimulation of afferent fibers of right (*R.P.*) and left peroneal (*L.P.*) nerves. Note rhythmic alternation of muscle contraction during concurrent stimulation of the two nerves. (After Creed *et al.*, *Reflex activity of the spinal cord*, Oxford, Clarendon Press, 1932.)

concurrent stimulation lasted. In this instance, the input to the two halves of the cord is equal and nonperiodic. Further, such rhythmically alternating contractions of symmetrical muscles can be initiated after complete deafferentation of the limb. The mechanism for rhythmic alternation must therefore be a "built-in" feature of the spinal cord capable of operating in the absence of alternating afferent input such as that which stepping presumably initiates in the cutaneous and deep receptors. These qualifications do not, however, preclude the possibility that Group II afferent pathways modulate and regulate stepping in intact animals.

The Tendon Jerk. Another easily elicited spinal reflex, and one of great importance to the neurologist, is the tendon jerk. One can elicit this reflex in almost any muscle by sharply tapping either the muscle or the tendon, thus imparting a brief stretch to the muscle. The reflex response consists of a twitchlike contraction of the stretched muscle. The neurologist most commonly elicits these reflexes in the extensor muscles of the leg— e.g., quadriceps (knee jerk or patellar reflex) and triceps surae (ankle jerk or achilles reflex)*—but flexor muscles show similar jerk responses to brief stretch (pluck reflexes). In the arm, the biceps, triceps, and pectoral muscles are common test sites; in the face, tapping the lower jaw produces a "jaw jerk" of the masseter muscle.

Tendon jerks are characterized by short latency and absence of afterdischarge. Indeed, the quadriceps jerk has such a brief latency (19 to 24 milliseconds in man) that for many years its reflex nature was questioned; but Sherrington's[28] demonstration that the quadriceps jerk of experimental animals is subject to central inhibition and is abolished by dorsal or ventral rhizotomy clearly established the tendon jerk as a reflex. The short latency and the absence of afterdischarge suggest that tendon jerks are mediated by rapidly conducting monosynaptic pathways. Other similarities between the tendon jerk and the monosynaptic reflex discharge elicited by electrical stimulation of Group I afferent fibers are: (i) both reflect into, and only into, the muscle or muscle fraction from which the afferent activity arises. (ii) Both reflexes, when initiated in extensor muscles, are inhibited by strong stimulation of afferent trunks containing Group II, III and IV fibers. The effect of a single inhibitory volley persists for periods as long as 1 second (Fig. 98). (iii) Both reflexes are inhibited by Group I afferent volleys initiated in nerves supplying antagonistic muscles, and in both the inhibitory input arises only

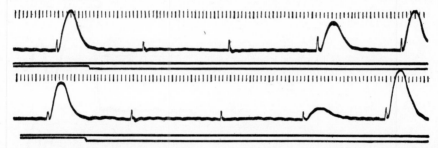

FIG. 98. Inhibition of knee jerk in spinal cat. Myographic recording from quadriceps muscle; tendon taps delivered at three per sec. Sharp upward deflections record tendon taps; subsequent larger deflections represent jerk reflex contractions. Signal at bottom of each record indicates time of delivery of a single shock to an ipsilateral afferent nerve trunk. Time scale: 20 milliseconds. (From Ballif *et al.*, *Proc. roy. Soc.*, 1925, *B98*:589–607.)

from *direct* antagonists; afferent input from muscles acting at joints other than the one at which the test muscle works is ineffective. The jerk reflex of the quadriceps is also inhibited by stretching or kneading its antagonists, the hamstring muscles.[28]

The close similarity between tendon jerks and electrically evoked monosynaptic discharges is strong presumptive evidence that tendon jerks are mediated by reflex arcs of two neurons responding to impulses originating in afferent fibers of Group I size. Lloyd's[21] experiments provide conclusive evidence that this is so. Brief stretches comparable to those imposed by tapping the tendon were applied to a muscle by a solenoid attached to its tendon. Stretch-induced afferent discharges, recorded from appropriate dorsal roots, had conduction velocities in the Group I range (about 116 m./sec.), indicating that muscle stretch excites receptors innervated by the largest and most rapidly conducting afferent fibers. Ventral root reflex discharges resulting from brief muscle stretch had the same central delay as monosynaptic discharges elicited by electrical stimulation of Group I afferent fibers (Fig. 99).

In man, Magladery *et al.*[22] have shown that it is possible to excite selectively the large-diameter afferent fibers by using weak shocks delivered through electrodes placed on the skin over mixed nerves. Recording electrodes inserted into the lumbar vertebral

* Although deeply ingrained in medical jargon, the terms "knee" and "ankle" jerk should be dropped in favor of the more descriptive terms "quadriceps" and "triceps surae" jerk, respectively.

canal register two major deflections in response to such stimulation; the earlier appears to represent the afferent volley traversing the dorsal roots, whereas the later deflection represents the reflex discharge over the ventral roots (Fig. 100). The interval between the two deflections is thus a measure of the time required for transmission through the roots central to the intrathecal electrode plus the delay in the spinal cord. With the recording electrode at L_1 (the termination of the cord in man), this delay was 1.5 milliseconds. If a reasonable allowance of 0.3 millisecond is made for conduction in each root, the cord delay is reduced to about 0.9 millisecond, which allows only a single synaptic

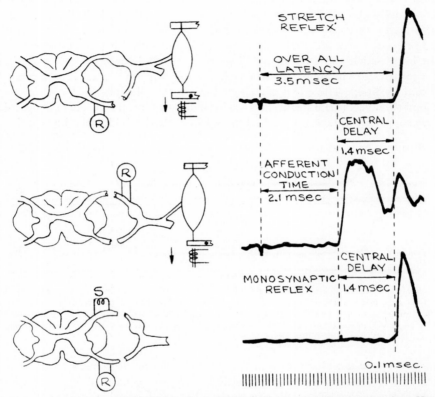

FIG. 99.   Lloyd's experiment proving the monosynaptic nature of the stretch reflex. *Upper trace*, Reflex discharge recorded from ventral root following brief muscle stretch. *Middle trace*, Afferent discharge recorded from dorsal root following muscle stretch. *Lower trace*, Monosynaptic discharge recorded from ventral root following weak shock to dorsal root. The latency of the monosynaptic discharge is the same as the central delay of the stretch-induced discharge (over-all latency minus afferent conduction time). (After Lloyd, *J. Neurophysiol.*, 1943, 6:317–326.)

delay. When the reflex muscular response to nerve stimulation is monitored electromyographically, the over-all latency is 19 to 24 milliseconds; this is also approximately the latency of the contraction elicited by tendon tap.[8] In both man and experimental animals, therefore, it is clearly established that the tendon jerk is mediated by a rapidly conducting monosynaptic arc.

The Stretch or Myotatic Reflex.[19, 20]   The functional significance of the flexion reflex as a protective mechanism is obvious. In contrast, the significance of the tendon jerk is, at first thought, obscure. What can be the functional utility of a reflex that causes a muscle to twitch when its tendon is sharply rapped? The obscurity arises largely from the abnormal way in which the tendon jerk is elicited. It has already been suggested, and will be further proved below, that the adequate stimulus for the reflex mechanism mediating the tendon jerk is *stretch of the muscle*. Tapping the tendon or belly of the muscle to elicit the tendon jerk stretches the muscle between its points of origin and insertion only very briefly. The stretch-sensitive receptors in the muscle are excited synchronously, and, since the afferent pathway is relatively homogeneous in fiber diameter and conduction velocity, the afferent impulses arrive at the spinal cord as a rather synchronous volley. As a result, the motoneurons respond with little temporal dispersion, setting up in the motor nerve a synchronous discharge to which the muscle responds with a brief twitch much like the response of the muscle to a single electric shock to its motor nerve.

Normally, however, the stretches imposed on muscles are of a different nature. Indeed, except possibly for landing from a leap or jumping on a pogostick, it is unlikely that muscles are ever subjected to the sudden brief stretches that the neurologist com-

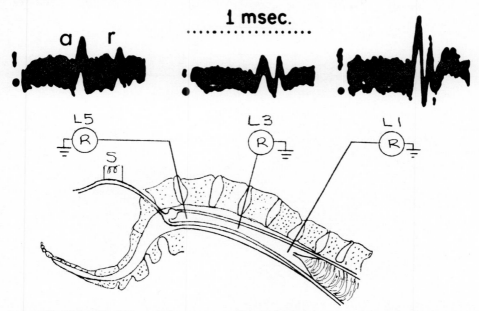

FIG. 100. Monosynaptic reflexes in man. Weak shocks to posterior tibial nerve excite large afferent fibers but not efferent fibers. Electrodes inserted into vertebral canal at levels shown recorded activity in the spinal roots as seen in the traces above (each record consists of several superimposed traces). Deflection a is afferent volley in dorsal roots; r is reflex efferent volley in ventral roots. Interval between deflections measures central delay plus variable root conduction time. At L_1 the interval was 1.5 milliseconds. Estimated root conduction time (dorsal plus ventral) was 0.6 millisecond, leaving a central delay of 0.9 millisecond. (After Magladery *et al.*, *Res. Publ. Ass. nerv. ment. Dis.*, 1952, *30:*118–151.)

monly employs in eliciting a jerk reflex. Natural stretches are usually imposed on muscles by the action of gravity. Thus, during standing, the quadriceps muscle is subjected to stretch because the knee tends to bend in accordance with gravitational pull. The resultant afferent discharge is highly asynchronous, because such a sustained stretch causes many stretch receptors to fire continuously and repetitively at frequencies which are determined by the thresholds of individual receptors and by the amount of stretch. Consequently, the motoneurons receive a prolonged asynchronous bombardment, and they discharge impulses with corresponding asynchrony. The result is a smooth, sustained contraction of the stretched muscle, so that the upright position is automatically maintained despite the action of gravity. When viewed in this light, the stretch reflex, of which the tendon jerk is a fractional and somewhat artificial manifestation, clearly is significant as a *mechanism for upright posture or standing*.

The role of the stretch reflex in posture was first appreciated by Sherrington[29] as a result of his observations on animals subjected to transection of the brain stem at the midcollicular level. In such *decerebrate* preparations the limbs assume a posture of rigid extension, the head and tail are held erect, and the jaw is tightly closed by tonic contraction of the masseter muscle. Although the animal executes no voluntary movements, it will, when placed upon its feet, stand in a rigid, immobile exaggeration of the normal upright posture. Sherrington[32] rightly surmised that such decerebrate rigidity resulted from overactivity of a spinal reflex mechanism that normally maintains upright posture. The overactivity results from interruption by the lesion of certain descending pathways (described in Chapter 8) which exert an inhibitory influence on the segmental spinal reflex.

Sherrington proved his hypothesis that decerebrate rigidity is a spinal reflex by demonstrating that division of the dorsal roots supplying a rigid limb abolishes its

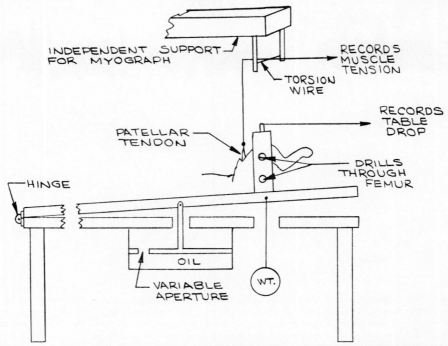

FIG. 101.   Diagram of "fall table" similar to that used by Sherrington to demonstrate the stretch reflex.

rigidity.[29] He next attempted to determine the origin of the requisite afferent inflow from the limb.[33] Section of cutaneous nerves, or even skinning the legs and feet, did not alter the rigid state, findings indicating that the essential receptors are not cutaneous. Furthermore, when the joint was flexed after the tendons of its controlling muscles were cut, the freed muscles did not contract. This observation indicated that the receptors are not located in the joints. When, however, the tenotomized muscle was stretched by a sustained pull on the severed tendon, the muscle contracted and offered palpable resistance to stretch. By the process of exclusion, Sherrington thus deduced that the receptors lie in the muscle itself and, further, that the adequate stimulus for the receptors is stretch of the muscle. Many sensory receptors, such as the retina, the ear and the tactile endings, are acted upon by agents of the external world. The stretch receptors of muscle, however, are excited by events occurring in the muscles themselves; the body itself acts as the stimulus to its own receptors. For this reason, Sherrington[33] termed the muscle stretch receptors *proprioceptors*.

To study the stretch reflex quantitatively, Sherrington constructed an ingenious device known as the "fall table,"[19, 20] the important feature of which was a top which could be lowered for measured distances at various rates (Fig. 101). The leg of an experimental animal was fixed rigidly to a stand on the table by means of drills passed through the bones of the leg. A muscle of the fixed leg was then dissected free and attached to a myograph mounted on a stand independent of the movable table top. Then, when the table top was lowered, the tension developing in the muscle in response to its elongation could be recorded. Figure 102 shows the results of such an experiment. The dotted line T indicates the extent of the table displacement; the heavy line M shows the tension developed in the muscle. Elongation of the muscle by only 8 mm. produced a sustained tension, initially amounting to 3.5 kg. and then decreasing to a stable plateau value of about 3.0 kg. Some of this tension was, of course, attributable to the elastic properties of the muscle, but this moiety could be quantitatively determined by repeating the stretch after denervation of the muscle (dashed line P). The difference between

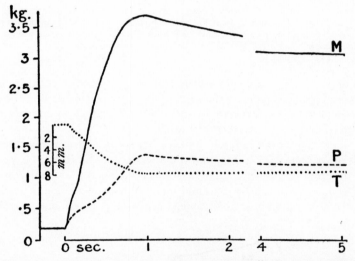

FIG. 102.   Stretch or myotatic reflex of cat demonstrated with "fall table." M, Tension developed in innervated quadriceps muscle. T, Relative elevation of table, which was dropped 8 mm. P, Passive elastic tension developed by similar stretch after denervation of the muscle. Tension difference ($M - P$) represents active reflex tension. (From Liddell and Sherrington, *Proc. roy. Soc.*, 1924, *B96*:212–242.)

curves M and P (about 1.8 kg. at the plateau) represents the *reflex* contractile tension developed in the muscle by stretch.

The same experimental arrangement can also be used to show that the stretch reflex is subject to inhibition. Figure 103 illustrates inhibition of the stretch reflex in a knee extensor induced by repetitive stimulation of an ipsilateral nerve trunk. This effect is comparable to inhibition of the knee jerk (Fig. 98) and of the monosynaptic discharge (Fig. 85) induced by electrical stimulation of Group II, III or IV fibers. Figure 104 shows inhibition of a stretch reflex in an extensor muscle brought about by a physiologic stimulus—stretching of an antagonistic flexor muscle. The result is reminiscent of the inhibition of a monosynaptic discharge by stimuli traversing the heteronymous antagonistic Group I pathway (Fig. 84).

Sherrington's experiments thus proved conclusively the existence of a reflex mechanism for posture and for skeletal muscle tone. By *tone* is meant the resistance of a muscle to passive elongation or stretch. When the stretch reflex arc is interrupted or when the descending central pathways facilitating the stretch reflex are severed, the muscle be-

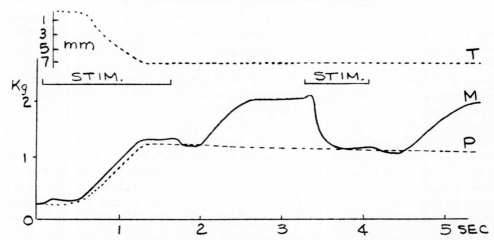

FIG. 103.   Inhibition of stretch reflex in an extensor muscle by stimulation of an ipsilateral cutaneous nerve (afferent). *M*, *P* and *T* as in Fig. 102. During stimulation of cutaneous nerve, tension in innervated muscle was approximately the same as that in denervated muscle; in absence of inhibitory stimulation reflex tension of about 1 kg. (*M–P*) slowly developed. (After Liddell and Sherrington, *Proc. roy. Soc.*, 1924, *B96*:212–242.)

comes flaccid or hypotonic, and offers little resistance to stretch. On the other hand, when central structures inhibitory to the stretch reflex are removed, as in the decerebrate preparation, the muscles are hypertonic and resist elongation so actively that passive flexion of the joint meets with marked resistance.

In man, such hypertonic stretch reflexes are commonly encountered following chronic lesions of the internal capsule, and the affected limb is said to be *spastic*. In both spasticity and decerebrate rigidity, the hypertonus is confined to the antigravity muscles, or physiologic extensors. In spastic man and monkey, passive flexion of a joint resulting in stretch of extensor muscles at the ankle, knee or hip meets active resistance, but

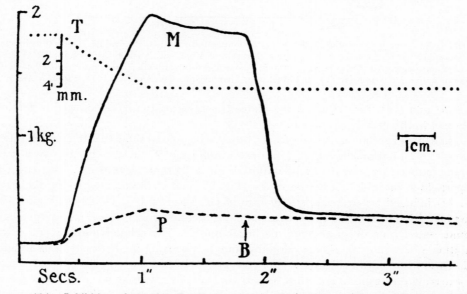

FIG. 104.   Inhibition of stretch reflex in extensor muscle (quadriceps) by stretch of antagonistic flexor muscle (biceps femoris). *M*, *P* and *T* as in Fig. 102. At arrow (*B*) a 4 mm. stretch was applied to biceps femoris inhibiting quadriceps so that tension fell to that of paralyzed muscle. (From Liddell and Sherrington, *Proc. roy. Soc.*, 1925, *B97*:267–283.)

passive extension of these joints is accomplished without opposition. In the arm, resistance is most prominently displayed in the anatomic flexor muscles, for these are the muscles which counteract the forces of gravity. In the sloth, which habitually counteracts gravity with flexor muscles while hanging upside down from branches, decerebration produces a flexor rigidity. In quadripeds that normally maintain upright posture (cat, dog) decerebrate rigidity principally affects the extensor muscles of both the front and the back legs. Indeed, in the decerebrate cat, a sustained stretch reflex from hindlimb flexor muscles cannot be elicited by the fall table technique. The flexor muscles respond readily to the synchronous volley elicited by a tap on the tendon (pluck reflex), but do not give sustained reflex contractions in response to the asynchronous afferent bombardment provided by the sustained stretches imposed by the fall table. It seems likely that the selective distribution of hypertonus to the antigravity muscles in the decerebrate and spastic states reflects the reciprocal connections of the descending pathways maintaining the hyperexcitable state, since the segmental mechanism for stretch reflexes appears to be as well developed in flexor as in extensor muscles.

Since the jerk reflex and the static stretch reflex utilize exactly the same pathways, it may seem strange that flexor muscles display the former but not the latter. The differentiation results from the nature of the stimulus, the opportunities for effective summation at the motoneuron pool being far greater with synchronous (tendon tap) than with asynchronous (slow stretch) inputs. In fact, synchronous inputs are so effective that a relatively severe reflex depression may not be obvious from tests of the tendon jerks alone. For example, after spinal transection in the cat, the lower extremities become flaccid and never again display a sustained stretch reflex;[23] but tendon jerks, although their nature is somewhat altered, are easily elicited. The tendon jerk taken alone is a gross and blunt diagnostic tool.

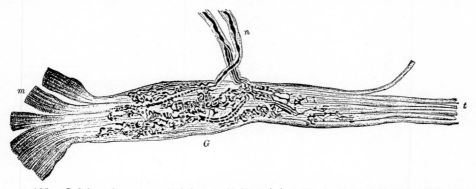

FIG. 105. Golgi tendon organ. At left, muscle fibers (m) end in tendon bundles (t) that extend to right near the junction of muscle and tendon. Two nerve fibers (n) pass to tendon and branch profusely between and around the tendon bundles forming the end organ (G).

Receptors in Muscle and Tendon. Sherrington's studies of the stretch reflex implicated a stretch-sensitive receptor located in either the muscle or the tendon. Muscles and tendons are supplied with a variety of receptors—free nerve endings, encapsulated Pacinian corpuscles, etc.—but with regard to postural reflexes, attention focuses principally on the *Golgi tendon organ* and the *muscle spindle*. The tendon organ is found in the tendons of all mammalian muscles, close to their muscular origins. The organ consists of a number of tendon fasciculi enclosed in a fusiform or cylindrical fibrous capsule which is penetrated by one or two myelinated nerve fibers (Fig. 105). After entering the capsule, the fibers break up into smaller and smaller branches, lose their myelin sheaths, and terminate in a rich arborization in the tendon bundle. Tension on the tendon distorts or displaces these endings and constitutes the adequate stimulus for receptor discharge. Because of its location in the tendon, the tendon organ is equally susceptible to, and does not distinguish between, mechanical stretch applied by a passive pull on the muscle and that applied by active muscular contraction, both being actions which exert tension on the tendon. The Golgi tendon organ is, as Fulton and Pi-Suñer[6] first emphasized, in "series" with the muscle (Fig. 106B).

The muscle spindle[2] is located within the muscle itself, and consists of a bundle of two to ten thin specialized muscle fibers (*intrafusal fibers*) surrounded by a connective tissue capsule which attaches (at its ends) to the endomysium of the regular or *extrafusal* muscle fibers, to the tendon, or to perimysial connective tissue (Fig. 107). The long, slender ends of the intrafusal fibers are striated and contractile; whereas the central or equatorial region, which is somewhat expanded and filled with nuclei, is unstriated and

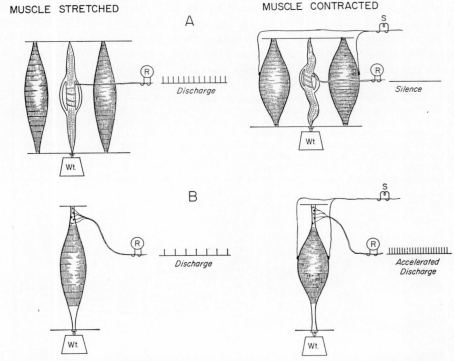

FIG. 106. Relation of muscle spindles and tendon organs to muscle fibers. *A*, Spindle is arranged "in parallel" with muscle fibers so that muscle contraction slackens tension on spindle. *B*, Tendon organ is arranged "in series" with muscle fibers so that both passive and active contraction of muscle cause receptor to discharge.

probably noncontractile. In this *nuclear bag* region of the spindle, and for a short distance on either side where nuclei are arranged in a central core (*myotube region*), the connective tissue capsule is separated from the intrafusal fibers by a lymph space traversed by delicate septa and nerve fibers. The latter are of three major types:[2] (i) Large (8 to 12 μ)* myelinated afferent fibers which, after entering the capsule branch, lose their myelin and end in helical terminals that encircle the nuclear bag region of the intrafusal fibers. These endings are variously known as *annulospiral, primary* or *nuclear bag endings.* (ii) Smaller (6 to 9 μ) myelinated afferent fibers end in coils, rings or varicosities in the myotube regions on one or both sides of the nuclear bag endings. These are called *flower spray, secondary* or *myotube endings.* Some spindles lack myotube endings. Both the myotube and the nuclear bag endings degenerate after section of the dorsal roots. (iii) Small (3 to 7 μ)

* The fiber diameters quoted here are measurements of the axons close to the spindle where they may well be smaller than the parent axons in the main nerve trunk.

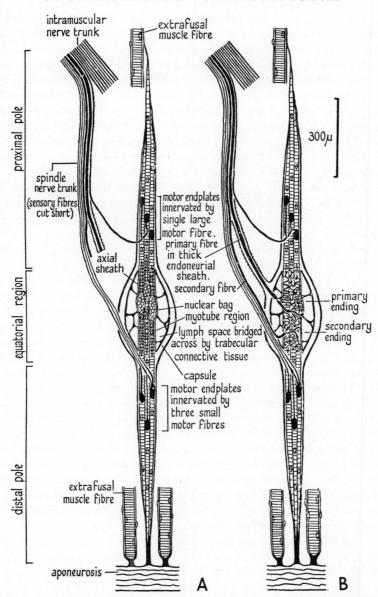

FIG. 107. The muscle spindle and its nerves. *A* shows only the motor fibers (fusimotor fibers) innervating the intrafusal fibers; *B* shows in addition the afferent fibers and their termination in the equatorial or "nuclear bag" region. (From Barker, *Quart. J. micr. Sci.*, 1948, *89*:143–186.)

myelinated efferent fibers terminate in end-plates situated on the striated poles of the intrafusal fibers. These fibers are known to be motor, because they degenerate following ventral rhizotomy but not after dorsal root section. According to Barker,[2] both poles of the intrafusal fibers receive motor innervation. The functional significance of these *fusimotor fibers* or *gamma efferents* is discussed in a subsequent section (see p. 188).

In addition to these three main types of fibers, muscle spindles receive a varying number of fine (0.5 μ) fibers, some of which appear to be the sympathetic motor nerves for the vasculature of the spindles; others, which are afferent, ramify in the capsule as free nerve endings and probably mediate pain sensation.

To return to the afferent endings of the spindle, both the myotube and the nuclear bag endings are so arranged that they can easily be mechanically distorted by stretch of the muscle. However, unlike the Golgi tendon organ, the muscle spindle is arranged in "parallel" with the extrafusal fibers, so that contraction of the extrafusal fibers tends to remove spindle tension induced by external stretch (Fig. 106A). In the next section it will be pointed out that this feature permits experimental distinction between spindle endings and Golgi tendon endings merely by observation of the effect of muscle contraction on a stretch-evoked discharge recorded from their parent axons. It should also be noted, however, that if the intrafusal fibers are made to contract by action of the small motor nerve fibers supplying the two contractile poles, the noncontractile nuclear bag region is put under a tension which constitutes a mechanical stimulus to the nuclear bag and myotube endings equivalent to passive stretch of the whole muscle.

Discharge properties of stretch receptors.[24] The discharge properties of stretch receptors can be studied by recording from their parent axons during muscle stretch. If activity in a whole nerve trunk is recorded, the tracing shows only a chaotic flare of spike-like activity during muscle stretch, because the stimulus excites many end organs which fire out of phase with one another. Such records are usually too complex for analysis. Records satisfactory for analysis can be obtained by isolating one or, at most, a few axons supplying active receptors. Such "single unit" analysis of stretch receptors was first accomplished by Adrian and Zotterman[1] in 1926. They chose to study certain small muscles in the frog which have only a few stretch receptors. By successively paring off bits of the muscle, Adrian and Zotterman were able to whittle away all but one stretch receptor, the activity of which could be recorded in the nerve trunk supplying the muscle. In larger mammalian muscles, this technique for reducing the number of receptors is unsatisfactory, owing to the extensive injury incurred by the drastic carving of the muscle. Matthews[24] obtained the first successful recordings from stretch receptors in cats by subdividing the nerve trunk into small bundles until he isolated a strand containing only one axon which fired in response to muscle stretch. Successful isolation of a single stretch-sensitive unit is recognized by the occurrence during muscle stretch of rhythmically recurring, all-or-nothing spikes of constant amplitude and configuration. Stretch-sensitive units may also be isolated from the dorsal roots, where the rootlets are easily divided into strands. Another satisfactory method,[34] which eliminates the necessity for nerve teasing, is intracellular recording with an ultramicroelectrode in the nerve trunk, the dorsal root or the dorsal column; for an intracellular electrode is not appreciably affected by activity in adjacent fibers.

All stretch-sensitive units have properties in common. All respond to stretch with a regular rhythmic discharge of impulses. The rate of firing is somewhat higher during and immediately after the imposition of stretch, but the discharge rate rapidly reaches a relatively steady level, which is maintained for hours if the muscle stretch is held constant. When the tension on the muscle is increased, the number of impulses per unit time increases, but not in a linear fashion. The firing rate is approximately directly proportional to the log of the applied muscle tension.* *Discharge frequency is thus one way by which the receptor signals intensity of stimulus to the central nervous system.*

If the monitored strand of fibers contains several axons supplying stretch receptors, another correlate of intensity becomes evident. *As stimulus intensity is increased, the number of units responding increases.* The thresholds of stretch receptors are distributed in accordance with a normal frequency curve, so that an increase in the intensity of the stimulus, i.e., muscle stretch, recruits additional units.† Each of these receptors fires at a frequency

---

* This relationship holds only within a limited range of applied tensions. At high tensions, the response falls short of the expected proportionality. Moreover, for different receptors, the slopes of the curves relating discharge rate to log tension are different.

† Receptor variation in threshold is due partly to true variance in sensitivity to stretch and partly to variance in location in the muscle, some receptors bearing more of the brunt of muscle stretch than others.

which is determined by the extent to which the stimulus exceeds the threshold of the individual receptor. These two intensity-signaling variables—number of active units and frequency of unit discharge—account for the grading of reflex response to various degrees of stretch. It may be noted parenthetically that the relationships between stimulus intensity and receptor discharge outlined above are not unique to the stretch receptor. Similar relationships have been observed in a wide variety of receptors, including some

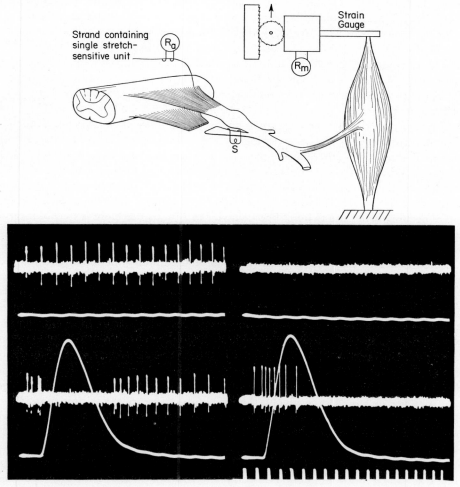

FIG. 108. Behavior of spindle (A type) and tendon organ (B type) receptors during muscle stretch and muscle contraction. In the tracings the thick line is record from dorsal root strand (R_a in diagram), the thin line is record of muscle tension (R_m) in diagram. *Left*, A type discharge from spindle receptor. In upper record, moderate sustained stretch of muscle induced by moving tension recorder upward elicited regular rhythmic discharge of receptor. In lower record, discharge ceased during muscle twitch induced by single shock to ventral root at S in diagram. *Right*, B type discharge from tendon receptor. In upper trace, moderate muscle stretch failed to discharge high-threshold tendon organ. In lower trace, discharge occurred during muscle twitch. (Records provided by Dr. C. C. Hunt.)

involved in reflex regulation of visceral and vascular structures. These will be considered further in subsequent chapters.

Of more interest for the present discussion are the unique properties of different stretch receptors. Matthews[24] found that the stretch-sensitive receptors of muscle can be divided into two general types, designated A and B, which differ principally in their behavior during active muscle contraction. Units of the A type typically have a low threshold to muscle stretch, 1 to 2 grams of tension often being sufficient to evoke a sustained rhythmic discharge. If, during such a stretch-evoked sustained discharge, a twitch contraction of the stretched muscle is elicited by a single shock to the ventral root, the discharge *ceases* during the twitch (Fig. 108, *left*). The A receptor thus behaves as if it were in "parallel" with the contractile extrafusal fibers, so that contraction, by shortening* the muscle, removes the tension from the receptors (Fig. 106*A*). It will be recalled that the muscle spindle is anatomically arranged in parallel with the muscle fibers. In addition, the position of a unit under observation can be roughly localized by pressing on the muscle with a glass rod while the muscle is stretched, for such local mechanical distortion excites the receptors. Local warming, which accelerates the discharge of a firing unit, also serves to localize the unit. In these ways, Matthews[24] found that receptors of the A type lie in the belly of the muscle or near its top insertion, but never in the tendon. For these reasons, it seems almost certain that units of the A type are spindle endings.

In contrast to the A type or spindle ending, the units which Matthews labeled B consistently display *accelerated firing* during muscle contraction (Fig. 108, *right*). Another difference is that B receptors have relatively high thresholds to muscle stretch, usually requiring tensions of 100 to 200 grams or more for sustained firing. Consequently, when the tension on the muscle is slight but adequate to excite A endings, the B endings may not fire unless the muscle is caused to contract. Upon contraction of the muscle, a burst of spikes occurs during the twitch. The behavior of B units therefore is that of receptors arranged in "series" with the muscle, and anatomically the Golgi tendon organ fulfills this requirement. Further, Matthews found by local probing and warming that B units are located either in the tendon or in the musculotendinous junction where the Golgi tendon organ is found histologically.

The presence or absence of a silent period in unit discharge during muscle contraction can thus be used experimentally to distinguish between spindle endings and tendon receptors. The strength of the contraction-producing stimulus to the ventral root is important, however. In A receptors, a single shock to the ventral root adequate to cause only a submaximal or, at most, a maximal isometric muscle twitch results in cessation of discharge during the twitch. If, however, the shocks are supramaximal (i.e., more intense than is required for development of maximal contractile tension), and particularly if they are delivered repetitively, the rate of discharge of the A unit may increase during contraction of the muscle. In other words, when the motor fibers are stimulated supramaximally, the A unit behaves as if it were in series with the muscle. As will be shown later, such stimulation activates the small, high threshold fusimotor fibers that are distributed exclusively to the intrafusal muscle fibers. The resulting contraction of intrafusal muscle fibers does not add detectably to the total muscle tension but markedly influences the spindle endings, because they are in series with the intrafusal fibers, so that contraction of the two poles of the intrafusal fibers takes up slack in the spindle caused by extrafusal contraction and puts the spindle endings under tension.†

* Discharges of A units cease during muscle contraction even when the twitch is isometric, presumably because the tendon is somewhat elastic so that even under isometric recording conditions some internal shortening occurs during a twitch.

† Hunt and Kuffler[13] point out that A units may occasionally discharge during contractions set up by motor volleys too weak to excite fusimotor fibers, especially if the contraction occurs under rigidly isometric conditions and when the initial tension on the muscle is high. Such deviant responses are thought to be due to some unusual distribution of tension within the muscle that increases the amount of stretch deformation on some spindle endings. By varying the conditions, the experimenter can always demonstrate the silent period of such elements, so that there is never serious difficulty in distinguishing them from B endings, which show accelerated discharge during contraction under all conditions.

Afferent fibers supplying stretch receptors.   As just described, the differential behavior of receptors during muscle contraction permits recognition of spindle and tendon endings. Once a unit has been isolated and classified, its conduction velocity can be measured; in turn, the diameter of the axon supplying it can be estimated, for the axon diameter in microns is linearly related to the conduction rate in meters per second, the ratio being 6:1 (cf. Chap. 3). Hunt[12] isolated and classified several hundred stretch-sensitive units from cat soleus and gastrocnemius muscles by painstakingly dissecting and sampling the dorsal roots. The conduction rate in the axon was determined by electrically exciting the nerve trunk and measuring conduction time and distance to the dorsal root. The diameter was then computed by dividing the conduction rate by 6.

Figure 109*A* shows the distribution of computed axon diameters for spindle (A) endings of soleus muscle superposed on the afferent fiber distribution of the soleus nerve as

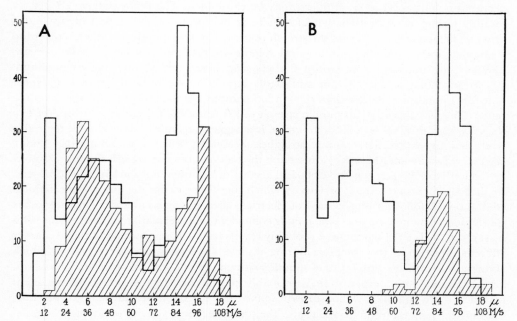

FIG. 109.   Diameter distribution of afferent fibers supplying muscle spindles (*A*) and tendon organs (*B*). Heavy line in each graph plots diameter distribution of myelinated afferent fibers as determined histologically. Hatched area plots distribution of fibers supplying muscle spindles in *A* and tendon organs in *B* as determined by physiologic testing. *Ordinates*, Number of fibers in each 1 μ category. *Abscissae*, Diameter in μ and conduction rate in m. per sec. (After Hunt, *J. gen. Physiol.*, 1954, *38*:117–131.)

determined histologically. Spindle endings fall into a bimodal distribution accounting for approximately half of the Group I fibers (12 to 20 μ) and for virtually all of the Group II fibers (4 to 12 μ) in the nerve. Because the fibers supplying the annulospiral or nuclear bag endings appear to be larger than those supplying the secondary or myotube endings, it is logical to conclude that Group I fibers supplying A receptors (hereafter called *Group IA fibers*) supply annulospiral endings, whereas the Group II fibers of the muscle nerve probably supply myotube or secondary endings. Apart from conduction rate, no essential distinction can be made between annulospiral endings innervated by Group IA fibers and myotube endings innervated by Group II fibers. Both display similar silent periods during muscle contraction and both are accelerated by fusimotor stimulation. Myotube endings have slightly higher thresholds to stretch than do annulospiral endings, but the difference is slight (about 19:3 grams).

Figure 109*B* shows the diameter distribution of axons supplying endings of the B type (Golgi tendon organ). The distribution is unimodal and essentially confined to the Group I diameter range ($>12\ \mu$). *Group I fibers supplying B endings are called IB fibers.* Tendon endings supplied by Group IB fibers not only differ markedly from spindle endings in their response to muscle contraction (acceleration versus silent period), but also have significantly higher thresholds to stretch (100 to 200 grams). Furthermore, tendon endings are completely uninfluenced by stimulation of fusimotor fibers.

Together, the Group IA fibers supplying annulospiral spindle endings and the Group IB fibers supplying Golgi tendon organs account satisfactorily for the entire Group I population of the nerve. The entire Group II population appears to be devoted to spindle endings, presumably those of the myotube or secondary type.

Stretch Reflex Receptor. A question now arises: Which of the three nerve endings in muscle subserves the stretch reflex? The secondary endings of the spindle, innervated by Group II afferent fibers, may be eliminated. The reflex pattern elicited by exciting Group II fibers, whether of spindle or cutaneous origin, is that of the multisynaptic flexion reflex, whereas the stretch reflex is a monosynaptic arc served by Group I afferent fibers. Both the annulospiral spindle endings and the Golgi tendon organ, however, are innervated by Group I fibers, and hence are equally likely candidates.

It is generally believed (but admittedly largely on the basis of indirect evidence) that the annulospiral rather than the tendon endings are the receptors for the myotatic reflex. The low threshold to muscle stretch of the annulospiral endings, as opposed to the very high thresholds of tendon organs, is a suggestive datum, since the stretch reflex is elicited by exceedingly minute stretches. Secondly, selectively eliminating tendon organs by locally anesthetizing or resecting the tendon does not abolish the stretch reflex or tendon jerk. Finally, on the electrical record of a muscle engaged in a tendon jerk, the initial synchronous burst of activity which slightly precedes the onset of mechanical contraction is followed by a period of electrical silence which coincides with the reflex shortening of the muscle and which ends coincident with relaxation of the muscle. This *silent period* during the tendon jerk probably results partly from cessation of the excitatory afferent input from the receptors during muscle shortening, an interpretation which accords well with the properties of spindle endings but not with those of tendon organs.

Although this interpretation is probably partly correct, the genesis of the silent period is more complex. Denny-Brown[5] found that the silent period involved not only the muscle engaged in the jerk but also the tonic electrical activity of adjacent muscles which are not participating in the jerk. He suggested that, during the silent period, there occurs not only withdrawal of excitatory input but also initiation of an active inhibitory input which affects both the motoneurons supplying the stretched muscle and those innervating adjacent muscles.*

There are at least two possible sources for this inhibition. One of these is the recurrent collaterals described by Cajal and by Renshaw. Before emerging in the ventral root, many motor axons give off recurrent collaterals which terminate on interneurons situated in the ventromedial region of the ventral horn.[27] These interneurons, sometimes called "Renshaw cells" after their discoverer, make inhibitory connections with the motoneurons.[26] A synchronous reflex discharge, such as that elicited by tendon tap, is thus directed not only over the motor axons to the muscle but also, through the recurrent collaterals, to the Renshaw cells, which in turn deliver a high frequency burst of inhibitory impulses to the motoneurons.

---

* Electrical silence in direct synergists of the stretched muscle might be explained on the basis of withdrawal of excitation. The silent period, however, has a much wider distribution in limb muscles and may actually be observed in muscles which operate on joints different from that governed by the stretched muscle. Since there are no known excitatory monosynaptic connections between muscles acting at different joints, some process other than withdrawal of excitatory input must be postulated.

The other, and probably more important, source of inhibition accounting for the silent period is the Group IB fibers supplying the tendon organs. Before this pathway is described, it may be pointed out that the implication of tendon organs and Group IB fibers in a proprioceptive arc inhibitory to the homonymous motoneurons is, by exclusion, a further and compelling reason for believing that the Group IA fibers supplying the annulospiral spindle endings constitute the afferent limb of the stretch reflex.

The Clasp Knife Reflex; Autogenic Inhibition. When one attempts to flex forcibly the rigid limb of a decerebrate preparation, resistance is encountered as soon as the muscle is stretched and increases throughout the initial part of the bending. This resistance is, of course, due to the hyperactive reflex contraction of the muscle in response to stretch. If flexion be forcibly carried farther, a point is reached at which all resistance to additional flexion seems to melt and the previously rigid limb collapses readily. Because the action is one which permits the stretched muscle to elongate freely, it is appropriately called a *lengthening reaction*. Also, because the resistance of the limb resembles that of a spring-loaded folding knife blade, this phenomenon is often called the "clasp knife" reaction. A similar phenomenon is regularly observed in human patients with spasticity, in whom the reaction is often best elicited by rapidly and forcibly flexing the spastic limb. Under these conditions, the clasp knife reaction is manifested by a "catch and give" in the resistance, i.e., the muscle first resists, then relaxes. In either instance, it appears that excessive (or rapid) stretch of the muscle brings into play some new influence which temporarily or permanently annuls the stretch reflex and allows the muscle to be lengthened with little or no tonic resistance.

Strong stretch of an extensor muscle also abolishes or diminishes the reflex contraction of that muscle brought about by means other than stretch. For example, when an extensor muscle is reflexly contracting in response to stimulation of a contralateral cutaneous nerve (crossed extension reflex) and the muscle is forcibly stretched, it may suddenly give and lengthen without resistance.

Sherrington[30] demonstrated that the clasp knife phenomenon is reflex in nature and dependent upon stretch of the muscle. When the clasp knife reaction is elicited, not only does the stretched extensor muscle relax but its antagonists (flexors) contract. Often there is a concomitant contraction of the extensor muscles of the contralateral limb (*Phillipson's reflex*) indicating doubly reciprocal connections of the responsible afferent pathways. The clasp knife reflex can be elicited in a muscle after all other muscles and structures of the limb have been denervated. When deafferented by appropriate dorsal rhizotomy, the stretched muscle, of course, becomes flaccid, and there is no tone against which to test for the clasp knife reflex. The deafferented muscle can, however, still be activated reflexly by stimulation of a contralateral cutaneous nerve (crossed extension reflex); strongly stretching the deafferented muscle does not abolish such a crossed reflex contraction as it does in the intact preparation.

These observations indicate that, in addition to the classic stretch reflex already described, there exists a proprioceptive stretch reflex arc of relatively high threshold which inhibits its homonymous motoneurons. Such inhibition, mediated by afferent fibers from a stretched muscle and acting on motoneurons supplying the stretched muscle, is known as *autogenic inhibition*. It follows that during muscle stretch the motoneurons supplying the stretched muscles are bombarded by impulses delivered over two competing pathways, one excitatory and the other inhibitory. The output of the motoneuron pool depends upon the balance between the two antagonistic inputs. With excessive stretch, the high threshold inhibitory pathway becomes an increasingly potent determinant and eventually dominates the motoneuron pool. Functionally the inhibitory pathway serves to *protect the muscle from overload* by preventing damaging contraction against strong stretching forces.

The influence of autogenic inhibition is detectable at degrees of stretch less than that required to annul the stretch reflex completely. For example, Sherrington[4] noted in fall table experiments that the reflex contraction elicited by small or moderate muscle stretch (2 per cent increase in length) was maintained at a steady level for half an hour or longer. When the stretch imposed on the same muscle was greater (4 to 5 per cent increase in length), the reflex contraction often faded in 5 to 10 minutes.

The Golgi tendon organ and autogenic inhibition. There are a number of indications that Group IB fibers innervating the Golgi tendon organ constitute the afferent limb of the clasp knife reflex. The tendon organs are, of course, sensitive to stretch, which is the adequate stimulus for the clasp knife reflex. The relatively high threshold of the tendon organ to stretch accords well with the observation that the clasp knife reflex dominates the motoneurons only when muscle stretch is extreme.

McCouch *et al.*[25] showed that the quadriceps jerk could be inhibited by local electrical stimulation of the tendon or the musculotendinous junction of the vastus intermedius muscle, but not by similar stimulation of the muscle belly. Further indication that the tendon organ feeds a reflex arc inhibitory to the homonymous motoneurons derives from the experiments by Hunt[11] and by Granit.[7] They found that tetanic contraction of a muscle induced by repetitive stimulation of the distal end of the cut ventral root inhibited a monosynaptic reflex discharge set up by stimulation of the Group I afferent fibers from the muscle. Since during muscle contraction the spindle discharge ceases and the tendon-organ discharge is accelerated, it seems reasonable to ascribe this inhibition to activation of the tendon organs.

Central connections of Group IB fibers. The evidence discussed in the previous section strongly implicates the Golgi tendon organs, and the Group IB fibers which supply them as the afferent limb of the clasp knife reflex. To study the central connections of the clasp knife reflex it is desirable to depart from the method of natural stimulation and resort to the conditioning-testing technique, using Group IB fibers for the conditioning pathway. A difficulty is encountered here, however, because Group IB and IA fibers are of the same or only slightly different diameters and electrical thresholds,* so that selective stimulation of IB fibers apart from IA fibers is impossible. Bradley and Eccles[3] maintain that in some muscle nerves IA fibers are slightly larger and have slightly lower thresholds than IB fibers; but, if this is so, the differences are small and the overlap is considerable.

Despite this technical handicap, Laporte and Lloyd[17] were able to distinguish between the effects on motoneurons occasioned by afferent volleys conducted in Group IA fibers and those resulting from activation of Group IB fibers. This distinction is possible because, as will be developed below, the Group IB fibers have interposed between their endings and the motoneuron a single interneuron. In other words, the clasp knife reflex mediated by Group IB fibers is a *disynaptic reflex arc*, whereas the myotatic reflex mediated by Group IA fibers is, of course, monosynaptic. In the monosynaptic pathway the threshold for influence upon the motoneurons is that of the Group IA fibers exerting the influence. In the disynaptic pathway, the threshold for influence upon the final elements, the motoneurons, depends not only upon the threshold of the Group IB fibers but also upon the response threshold of the intermediary elements, the interneurons. For this reason, although Group IA and IB fibers have essentially similar thresholds, the conditioning volleys required to exert detectable influence upon the motoneurons via the Group IB fibers are somewhat greater than those required to demonstrate excitatory

* The threshold of axons to electrical stimulation should not be confused with the threshold of the reflex to natural stimulation via the appropriate sense organs. Thus, Group IA and IB fibers are equally accessible to electrical stimulation of the nerve trunk, but the spindle endings supplied by Group IA fibers are far more sensitive to natural stimulation (stretch) than are the tendon organs innervated by Group IB fibers.

conditioning through the simpler monosynaptic pathway fed by Group IA afferent fibers.

Figure 110 shows the effect of conditioning a monosynaptic test reflex of the plantaris muscle by volleys of varied intensity delivered over the nerve supplying the synergistic muscle flexor longus digitorum. With a feeble conditioning volley, the monosynaptic facilitation curve (*closed circles*) typical of Group IA fibers was obtained. When the intensity of the conditioning volley was increased (*open circles*), the earliest part of the curve was unaltered, but, when the interval between the conditioning and the test volley was 0.5 to 0.6 millisecond, the smooth decay of the facilitation curve was interrupted by the sudden onset of an inhibitory process, and the test response was reduced far below the control level. The 0.5 to 0.6 millisecond delay in the onset of the inhibitory action was constant irrespective of the length of the afferent pathway, and therefore cannot be explained by assuming that the inhibitory impulses traverse a more slowly conducting system of fibers than that responsible for facilitation. Rather, the delay must be due to an intercalated interneuron.

FIG. 110. Reflex conditioning of moto-neurons by three intensities of afferent volley delivered over the heteronymous synergistic pathway. With weak Group I conditioning volleys the expected curve of facilitation was obtained (*filled circles*). When the intensity of the conditioning volley was slightly increased, the facilitation curve was interrupted at a conditioning-testing interval of 0.5 millisecond by a phase of inhibition (*open circles*). An additional increase in conditioning volley strength sufficient to activate Group II fibers (*crosses*) added a still later and more profound phase of inhibition beginning at a conditioning-testing interval of 2 milliseconds. (From Laporte and Lloyd, *Amer. J. Physiol.*, 1952, *169*:609–621.)

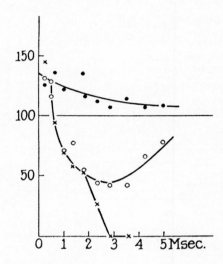

The third curve of Figure 110 (*crosses*) was obtained when the conditioning volley was so increased that it activated Group II as well as Group I afferent fibers. A second phase of inhibition appeared at a conditioning-test interval of about 2 milliseconds, clearly reflecting the delays resulting from the multisynaptic organization of Group II-fed reflex arcs.

When the Group IB disynaptic linkages of various muscles are systematically studied, the following generalizations are reached. Group IB fibers form disynaptic inhibitory linkages with their homonymous motoneurons and with the motoneurons supplying synergists of the muscle from which they arise. On the other hand, Group IB volleys facilitate, through disynaptic linkages, the motoneurons supplying muscles antagonistic to those from which the afferent volley originates. In other words, the reciprocal connections of Group IB are just the opposite of those typical of Group IA fibers. For this reason, the clasp knife reflex is sometimes referred to as the *inverse myotatic reflex*. The reciprocal connections of the Group IB fibers, however, are somewhat more diffuse than those of the monosynaptic arcs arising in Group IA fibers, for the former may exert, through disynaptic linkages, inhibitory influences on motoneurons supplying muscles which are not direct antagonists of the muscle of origin. For example, a Group IB afferent volley set up in the quadriceps (knee extensor) nerve inhibits, through the disynaptic pathway, the motoneurons supplying the triceps surae (ankle extensor). This phenomenon is in marked contrast to the monosynaptic connections of Group IA fibers, these connections being confined to the motoneurons supplying muscles acting around a single joint. In general, it appears that the sphere of influence of a reflex arc increases in proportion to the number of interneurons in the chain.

Summary of Reflex Pathways. At this juncture it is profitable to examine as a whole the segmental afferent inputs to a typical spinal motoneuron. Figure 111 summarizes diagrammatically the various pathways which play upon a spinal motoneuron supplying an extensor muscle. A corresponding diagram of the inputs to a flexor motoneuron would be identical, except that the influence of the multisynaptic paths fed by Group II, III and IV fibers would be reversed. The striking feature of Figure 111 is the multiplicity of pathways which converge on the final common pathway, the motoneuron. In point of fact, Figure 111 gives but a limited picture of this convergence, for only the segmental inputs are shown. Omitted (for discussion in Chap. 8) are the numerous path-

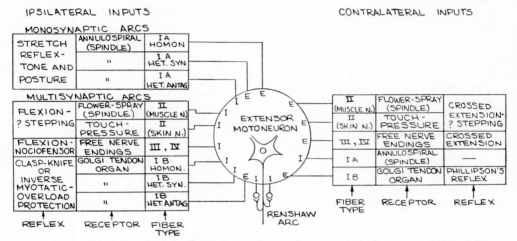

FIG. 111.   Diagram of segmental afferent inputs converging on a typical motoneuron supplying an extensor muscle. The influence of each input is indicated as excitatory (*E*) or inhibitory (*I*).

ways which arise from other spinal segments and from supraspinal structures and which terminate directly or indirectly upon the motoneuron. Each neuron is thus subjected to a multitude of influences, some reinforcing and some antagonistic, and the balance of these influences at any time determines the membrane potential and hence the excitability of the cell. The motoneuron, the final common path of the arc, thus integrates the messages which impinge upon it.

In the preceding chapter mention was made of the apparent hopelessness of explaining complex behavior in terms of what, in axons, appears to be a stereotyped inflexible response—the action potential. Now it can be seen that the system as diagrammed in Figure 111 is a highly flexible machine in which shifts in the intensity and source of afferent bombardment arising from numerous different receptors may alter drastically the participation of the different motoneurons and their subservient muscles in reflex action and thus give rise to an infinite variety of behavioral patterns.

The Fusimotor Fibers and Spindle Regulation.[15, 16, 18]   In the preceding sections, attention was focused on the influence exerted by various receptor organs upon the motoneurons. To complete the picture, it is now profitable to consider the influence exerted by certain motoneurons upon a receptor, the muscle spindle. It has already been mentioned that the intrafusal fibers of the muscle spindle receive a motor innervation that, according to Barker,[2] typically supplies both contractile poles of the fiber. It is easy to visualize how activation of the fusimotor fibers by inducing polar contraction of the intrafusal fibers might put the noncontractile nuclear bag region under tension and thus produce in the receptor endings a mechanical distortion indistinguishable from that occasioned by passive stretch of the whole muscle. In this way, the fusimotor fibers may initiate spindle discharge in the absence of external stretch or, in the presence of stretch, so increase the sensitivity of the spindle that the frequency of afferent discharge is markedly increased. The fusimotor system thus serves as a biasing mechanism regulating the sensitivity of the receptor.

That the fusimotor fibers constitute a specialized efferent pathway distinguishable from that supplying the extrafusal muscle fibers was first proposed by Leksell.[18] Examination of the myelinated fiber spectrum of a ventral root or of a muscle nerve deafferented by degenerative dorsal rhizotomy reveals that the efferent fibers fall into two distinct size categories (Fig. 112). One group, constituting about 70 per cent of the total, ranges in diameter from about 9 to 13 μ, and thus falls approximately in the A-alpha classification of Gasser. The remaining 30 per cent of the myelinated motor fibers, ranging from about 3 to 6 μ in diameter with a peak cluster at 5 μ, are designated gamma efferents.

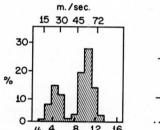 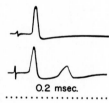

FIG. 112.   Diameter spectrum and compound action potential of motor fibers supplying soleus. *Left,* Note distinct bimodal distribution of fiber diameters. Velocity spectrum shown on upper ordinates. *Right upper trace,* Compound action potential elicited by stimulus just maximal for large-diameter, rapidly conducting fibers. *Right lower trace,* Stronger stimulus elicited a second deflection ascribable to activity in the small slowly-conducting fibers. (Histologic data after Eccles and Sherrington, *Proc. roy. Soc.,* 1930, *B106*:326–357; electrical data after Kuffler *et al., J. Neurophysiol.,* 1951, *14*:28–54.)

The absence of overlap between the two groups makes them relatively easy to distinguish. Figure 112 shows action potentials recorded from the gastrocnemius nerve following stimulation of the S_2 ventral root. In the upper trace, the stimulus was just maximal for the large low threshold alpha fibers. The lower figure shows a trace taken when the stimulus strength was increased sufficiently to recruit the smaller gamma fibers. The peak conduction velocity of the first deflection was 76 m. per second; that for smaller and later deflection was 27 m. per second. The computed fiber diameters corresponding to these velocities are about 13 μ and 5 μ, respectively—values which agree satisfactorily with the histologic data.

Leksell noted that, when the muscle nerve was stimulated with graded shocks, twitch tension of the muscle was directly related to shock strength only until the alpha spike reached full size; further increase in shock strength caused no further increment in muscle tension, even though such strong shocks resulted in the appearance and growth of the gamma spike. In other words, the gamma fibers appeared to contribute nothing to contractile tension. This conclusion can be tested in another way. When pressure is applied to a nerve trunk, the larger fibers are blocked before the smaller ones are. Leksell found that when the alpha fibers were thus differentially blocked, stimulation central to the block produced little or no contractile response in the muscle, even though electrical recording from the nerve trunk distal to the block showed that conduction in the small gamma fibers was unaltered. It may therefore be concluded that the gamma fibers constitute a discrete efferent system innervating some structure in the muscle other than the ordinary tension-producing extrafusal muscle fibers.

It is now clear that the gamma efferent fibers are distributed *exclusively* to the spindle intrafusal fibers, hence the term "fusimotor fibers."[14] Fusimotor activation causes contractions of the intrafusal fibers that are too feeble to add significantly to the total muscle tension but are sufficient to affect profoundly the afferent discharge of the spindle. This effect was demonstrated by Leksell, but more precisely by Kuffler *et al.*,[16] who dissected out for stimulation single fusimotor fibers in the ventral root. Figure 113 shows the effect of fusimotor activity on a single stretch receptor subjected to varying degrees of stretch.

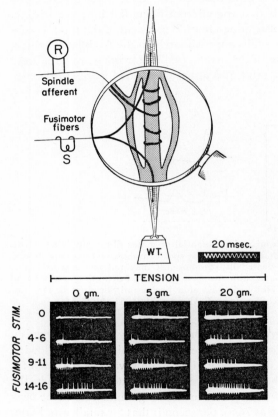

FIG. 113.   Effects of tension and fusimotor stimulation on discharge rate of spindle ending. Upward deflections in traces are action potentials of a single isolated spindle afferent fiber. Small deflections below the baseline in some records are shock artefacts produced by stimulating fusimotor fibers. Note that discharge rate depends on both passive tension and fusimotor activity. (After Kuffler *et al.*, *J. Neurophysiol.*, 1951, *14*:29–54.)

At each level of passive stretch the frequency of afferent discharge was accelerated by fusimotor stimulation, and the degree of acceleration increased with the number of fusimotor volleys delivered to the spindle. It is clear therefore that the afferent discharge of the spindle depends not only upon stretch but also upon the number of impulses reaching the spindle via the fusimotor fibers. Each spindle receives up to five such fusimotor fibers, which provide a precise mechanism for grading through a considerable range the sensitivity of the receptor to stretch. Also, each individual fusimotor fiber, by branching, participates in the innervation of several spindles, and can thus influence the discharge in a number of afferent fibers from different spindles.

It has already been mentioned that spindle receptors cease firing during muscle contraction. This pause comes about because the intrafusal fibers are arranged in parallel with the extrafusal fibers, so that shortening of the latter removes tension from the spindle. If, however, there is concomitant activation of the fusimotor system sufficient to take up the slack in the intrafusal fibers, the spindle endings may continue to discharge even during contraction. Figure 114 illustrates an experimental demonstration of this phenomenon. The upper trace shows the regular rhythmic firing of an A spindle receptor in response to a maintained 15 gram stretch on the muscle. In the middle trace, the muscle was caused to contract by stimulation of a portion of the ventral root containing

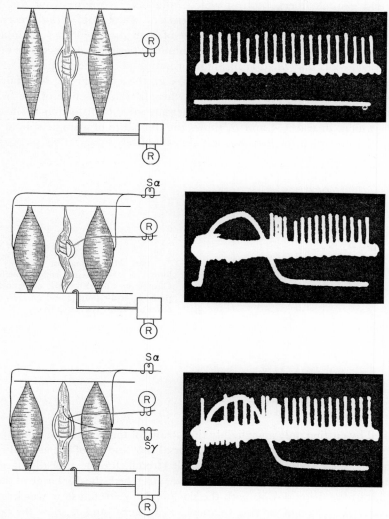

FIG. 114. Effect of fusimotor stimulation on the silent period in spindle discharge during muscle contraction. Thick line in traces, record from spindle afferent fiber; thin line, tension of muscle. *Upper trace*, Sustained tension (15 grams) elicits rhythmic firing of receptor. *Middle trace*, Discharge ceases during muscle twitch because spindles are relieved from stretch. *Lower trace*, Fusimotor stimulation (indicated by shock artefacts extending beneath baseline) takes up "slack" in spindle and permits sustained discharge even during muscle contraction. (After Hunt and Kuffler, *J. Physiol.*, 1951, *113:* 298–315.)

only alpha efferent fibers; during the contraction, the spindle discharge ceased. For the bottom tracing, this same sequence was repeated, except that, in addition, a single fusimotor fiber supplying the spindle was stimulated nine times during the early part of the contraction. As a result of fusimotor stimulation, spindle discharge continued throughout the contraction. It may be inferred from such experiments that, in the intact animal, spindle behavior during muscular contraction is determined by the amount of fusimotor activity as well as by the extent of muscle shortening.

Reflex activity of the fusimotor system.   The discovery of the fusimotor system necessitates reconsideration of the mechanism of the stretch reflex. It will be recognized that the stretch reflex system in the intact animal is composed of a "peripheral loop" of nerve fibers, represented diagrammatically in Figure 115. On the motor side of the loop are the alpha and gamma fibers, both of which influence in unique ways the discharge behavior of the spindle receptors. On the afferent side of the loop, various receptors play back upon and reflexly influence the discharge of both the alpha and gamma systems. It follows that investigations involving the common experimental procedure of dividing ventral or dorsal roots may yield accurate information about the properties of the individual components of the stretch reflex system, e.g., the spindle receptors; but, because the loop is broken, such experiments give a rather distorted picture of the behavior of these components in the intact animal. A measure of this distortion is illustrated in Figure 116, which, in traces *A* and *B*, shows the discharge of a single spindle receptor in a preparation in which the loop was left almost entirely intact. This preparation was

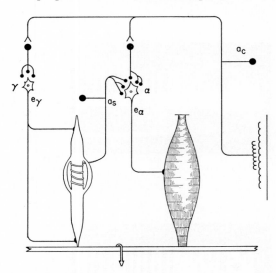

FIG. 115.   Diagram of the "peripheral loop" of the stretch reflex mechanism. a_c, Cutaneous afferent path; a_s, spindle afferent path; e_a and e_γ, alpha and gamma (fusimotor) efferent pathways respectively.

accomplished by cutting only a negligibly tiny strand of the dorsal root to sample spindle activity, leaving intact the remainder of the dorsal root and all of the ventral root. Even with the muscle slack and under no measurable stretch, the receptor discharged a continuous barrage of impulses. When the muscle was stretched, the discharge of the receptor accelerated, but the firing during both the slack and the stretch state was irregular and tended to occur in bursts of varying frequencies. Traces *C* and *D* show the behavior of the same preparation after the loop was interrupted by ventral root section. In the slack state, the spindle was silent. During stretch, the receptor responded with a regularly recurring discharge of impulses quite unlike that in *A* and *B*. Such experiments suggest that, in the intact animal, the fusimotor system maintains a tonic discharge which fluctuates in magnitude as the afferent input to the fusimotoneurons varies.

This "resting" tonic discharge of fusimotoneurons has been studied by Hunt[10, 14] who dissected out small strands of gamma efferent fibers from ventral roots or muscle nerves, taking care to leave the loop intact except for the small sampling strand. Fusimotor spikes are usually recognizably smaller in amplitude than alpha fiber spikes and are thus easily distinguished. In the spinal or decerebrate animal with the limb in a neutral position, many fusimotoneurons are silent, while others maintain a continuous but irregular discharge at frequencies of 10 to 60 per second. That this discharge is highly dependent on segmental afferent inflow is suggested by Hunt's finding that the discharge was abolished by bilateral section of the lumbosacral dorsal roots. *

Various stimuli to the limbs reflexly alter the fusimotor discharge.[10, 14] In this respect cutaneous stimuli are especially effective, light touch, pressure or pin prick causing prominent changes in the discharge frequency of tonically firing units and sometimes driving a resting unit into activity. Generally speaking, such stimuli, particularly when applied to the foot, increase the fusimotor discharge to the ipsilateral flexor muscles but diminish the discharge to ipsilateral extensors. On the side opposite the stimulus, the extensor muscles receive increased fusimotor discharge, whereas the discharge to the flexors is diminished. Thus, in the flexion and crossed extension reflexes, the gamma

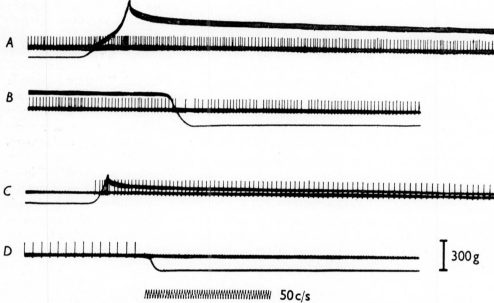

FIG. 116.   Effect of ventral root section on muscle spindle response to muscle stretch. Trace with spikes, electrical activity of single spindle afferent fiber; smooth trace, muscle tension. In *A* and *B* both ventral and dorsal roots were intact except for small strand of dorsal root dissected to sample spindle response. At the beginning in *A*, although the muscle was slack, the unit discharged with an irregular rhythm. When the muscle was stretched 10 mm. as indicated by rise of tension, discharge was moderately accelerated but rhythm remained irregular. *B* is a continuation of *A* showing effect of slackening the muscle again. *C* and *D* show response of same unit to 10 mm. stretch after section of ventral root. Note absence of discharge when muscle was slack and regular rhythmic nature of discharge during muscle stretch. (From Eldred *et al.*, *J. Physiol.*, 1953, *122*:498–523.)

and alpha motoneurons are affected alike. This arrangement probably acts to compensate for the reduction of spindle discharge which might otherwise occur when the reflexly contracting flexor muscle shortens. Fusimotor activity thus provides a mechanism for maintaining a sensory message from the spindles proportional to the amount of external stretch even under changing conditions of muscle contraction.

The distribution of reflexly evoked fusimotor discharge, however, is not stereotyped. Cutaneous stimuli, particularly to proximal portions of the limb, may elicit patterns of fusimotor distribution which do not parallel the flexion and crossed extension patterns. Furthermore, the pattern varies with change in the site of stimulation. For example, the

---

* Other experiments, to be discussed in Chapter 8, indicate that tracts descending from supraspinal structures also influence fusimotor discharge.

fusimotor discharge to the knee extensor, the quadriceps, in accordance with the flexion reflex pattern, is inhibited by touching or squeezing the ipsilateral foot, but the effect of similar stimulation of the skin on the thigh varies with the locus of stimulation. Touching the skin overlying the quadriceps increases fusimotor discharge to this muscle, whereas touching or squeezing the skin overlying its antagonists, the flexor hamstring muscles, inhibits tonic fusimotor discharge to the quadriceps. The fusimotor arcs, like the flexion reflex, thus display local sign.

Electrical stimulation of cutaneous nerves also markedly influences fusimotoneurons, but the effect varies so much with the afferent trunk employed and with the fusimotoneuron sampled that no generalizations are readily apparent. The unnatural electrical activation of functionally heterogeneous afferent fibers may obscure orderly functional patterns. Electrical stimulation, however, has the advantage that the temporal properties of fusimotor arcs can be determined. Measured central delays are in excess of 2 milliseconds, a fact suggesting that afferent fibers connect to fusimotoneurons through one or more interneurons.[14]

Deep receptors also influence fusimotoneuron activity but, in general, somewhat less prominently than cutaneous receptors do. The stretch receptors of muscle and tendon appear to influence the fusimotoneurons little or not at all.[14] Although muscle stretch sometimes inhibits fusimotor discharge to the stretched muscle,[10] there is reason to doubt that the responsible receptors are muscle spindles or tendon organs. The afferent fibers mediating this inhibition do not reach the spinal cord through the muscle nerve as do the Group IA and IB fibers supplying spindles and tendon organs. Moreover, electrical stimulation of muscle nerves at intensities adequate only for Group I fibers does not influence fusimotoneurons. It therefore seems that the receptors responsible for fusimotor inhibition during muscle stretch are neither the spindle nor the tendon organs.

In closing it may be stated that, in the present state of knowledge, the physiologic significance of the fusimotor system is not completely clear. It is obvious that the gamma fibers are potentially powerful regulators of spindle function and hence of reflex function. The full measure of their significance in posture and movement cannot be assessed until the conditions governing their activation are further clarified.

CLINICAL SIGNIFICANCE OF REFLEXES

Examination of reflex status is a standard and valuable clinical diagnostic procedure. Clinically, reflexes are categorized as either *deep* or *superficial*. By "deep reflexes"* is meant all stretch or myotatic reflexes of the phasic or "jerk" type, i.e., those elicited by a sharp tap on the appropriate tendon or muscle to induce brief stretch of the muscle. Detailed lists of the commonly tested deep reflexes and the spinal segments which subserve them can be found in textbooks of neurology. The same type of neural arcs may be tested in the limbs and jaw by gauging the resistance to passive movement of the member; this is a test of *muscle tone* which, like the jerk, depends on the stretch reflex arc. An important difference between this test and the elicitation of jerk reflexes is the nature of the afferent discharge. With slow stretch (passive movement) it is asynchronous and prolonged (static stretch reflex), and with brief stretches (tapping) it is synchronous and of short duration. The *superficial* or *cutaneous* reflexes are withdrawal reflexes elicited by noxious or tactile stimulation of the skin, and display the same general properties as the nociceptive flexion reflex described above. Examples are the plantar reflex (plantar

---

* Deep reflexes are also sometimes inappropriately called "periosteal" reflexes, because neurologists once quite mistakenly believed that the receptive elements were in the periosteum. The term "tendon" reflex, also commonly used interchangeably with "deep" reflexes, is unfortunate, because the receptors are, of course, in the muscle rather than in the tendon and because the jerk reflexes can be elicited by tapping the muscle directly as readily as by tapping the tendon. The clasp knife or inverse myotatic reflex is properly a tendon reflex.

flexion of the toes when the sole of the foot is stroked or scratched), the cremasteric reflex (elevation of the testicle when the inner and upper surface of the ipsilateral thigh is lightly scratched), and the abdominal reflex (contraction of the abdominal musculature when the overlying skin is stroked with a dull pin).

Diseases of the nervous system may affect reflexes in one of three ways: (i) the reflexes may be hypoactive or absent, (ii) the reflexes may be hyperactive, or (iii) the pattern of reflex response to a standard stimulus may change to a new one (the so-called "pathologic reflexes"). In evaluating reflexes in man it should be remembered that the motoneurons are subject to a multitude of influences which vary in intensity from patient to patient and in the same patient from time to time. Patients under strong emotional stress may temporarily display brisk myotatic reflexes suggestive of hyperactivity. It is not unlikely that anxiety and tension are associated with increased fusimotor activity.

On the other hand, in a thoroughly relaxed patient the quadriceps jerk, through lack of descending facilitation, is sometimes difficult to elicit. This difficulty may arise because the muscle is sufficiently slack that the tap fails to impart much stretch to the muscle. Spuriously weak reflexes may also occur in older patients in whom structural changes in the muscle and the tendon permit slack in the system. In such instances, myotatic responses can often be elicited by tapping the muscle rather than the tendon, since stretch receptors are sensitive to deformation resulting from tapping the muscle even though little stretch is imparted to the muscle as a whole. Responses so elicited are usually more localized than those induced by tendon tap, because the stimulus affects only a part of the receptive field of the muscle. Even in the absence of such relaxation, the knee jerk is difficult to elicit in some subjects in whom there is no reason to suspect neurologic disease. Often a clear response can be obtained only by striking the tendon while the subject tightly clasps his hands together and pulls (*Jendrassik's maneuver*) or grips some object tightly. It has been suggested[9] that such reinforcement of the knee jerk is attributable to increased fusimotor discharge to the leg muscles as a result of the muscular effort in the upper extremity.

It follows from all these considerations that evaluation of reflex performance requires a judicious and cautious approach. If the reflexes appear either equally depressed or equally hyperactive at all levels, repeated examinations, preferably over a considerable period and in a variety of environmental circumstances, may be required to distinguish the spurious from the significant. When the reflex aberrations are asymmetrical—occurring, for example, in one limb and not in another, or on only one side of the body—the examiner is on safer ground, because one part of the body then serves as a control for the others.

Hyporeflexia.   It is obvious from the preceding discussion that any process which interrupts or depresses conduction through any part of the reflex arc results in hypo-activity of that reflex in proportion to the severity of damage. The lesion may be in the afferent pathway, as in tabes dorsalis, in which the pathologic process begins in the dorsal root ganglia; or the lesions may affect the efferent limb. Disruption of this portion may result from disease in the gray matter causing injury to the motoneurons, as in anterior poliomyelitis. Disease of nerve trunks commonly affects both the afferent and the efferent limb of a reflex arc; examples are the several varieties of polyneuritis and herniated intervertebral discs or tumors which compress both dorsal and ventral roots in their course through the vertebral canal. Finally, disturbances, such as myasthenia gravis, which interfere with neuromuscular transmission may result in depression or lack of reflexes.

Depressed reflexes, however, do not always indicate an interruption of the segmental arc. It has been mentioned that motoneuron excitability is conditioned by pathways descending the cord from more cephalic spinal and suprasegmental levels as well as by segmental inflows. Even though the segmental arcs are intact after these descending pathways are interrupted by transection of the cord, the reflex responses are severely depressed (spinal shock) in regions innervated by the decentralized spinal segments. With passage of time, some reflexes return (particularly the flexion reflex patterns of the extremities, which may actually become troublesomely hyperactive), but the static stretch reflex often remains permanently depressed. Similarly, cerebellar lesions, by destroying neurons which feed into descending tracts facilitatory to the motoneurons, result in hypoactive stretch reflexes.

Hyperreflexia. Hyperactivity of deep reflexes sometimes results from inflammatory lesions involving the segmental arc, e.g., during the early stages of the intervertebral disc syndrome or of polyneuritis. Persistently hyperactive deep reflexes, however, almost always indicate destruction of descending tracts inhibitory to the segmental stretch reflex mechanism, as in spastic hemiplegia following infarction (from hemorrhage, etc.) in the

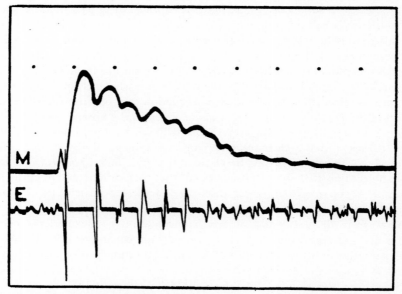

FIG. 117. Clonus. Electrical (*E*) and mechanical (*M*) records of quadriceps muscle. A slight stretch previously applied produced a tonic reflex discharge to the muscle, as indicated by the asynchronous waves in *E*. A tap to the tendon indicated by the first sharp deflection in *M*, elicited a brisk jerk reflex followed by a typical clonic discharge evident in both *M* and *B*. Time above, 100 milliseconds. (After Denny-Brown, *Proc. roy. Soc.*, 1929, *B104:*252–301.)

internal capsule. In this instance, myotatic hyperreflexia is indicated by increased briskness and amplitude of deep reflexes and by increased resistance to passive flexion at the joints (spasticity). In addition, the peripheral distribution of stretch reflex discharge is often increased owing to the occurrence of "crossfiring."

It has already been emphasized that, normally, the stretch reflex discharge returns only to the muscle stretched. When motoneuron excitability is increased (see p. 154), the afferent volley may fire motoneurons that normally are only facilitated (crossfiring). In spasticity, crossfiring is exemplified by *Hoffman's reflex* in which flicking the terminal phalanx of the middle finger results in twitchlike flexion in the other fingers and in adduction and flexion of the thumb. Such a broad field of reflex action resulting from brief stretch of the flexor muscles of one finger joint manifests myotatic hyperactivity.

Another important sign of hyperreflexia, often associated with spasticity, is *clonus*. Clonus occurs when the asynchrony of the motoneuron discharge in a stretch reflex is lost. There then ensues a series of regularly repeated, jerklike contractions superimposed upon a tonic contraction. In the hyperreflexic patient, clonus may be initiated by putting the muscle under moderate but sustained stretch and then tapping the tendon. A jerk response, of course, results; but it is followed by a succession of jerks which continue for a considerable time if the steady stretch is maintained. Figure 117 presents a myograph tracing of a clonic response in a decerebrate cat; the accompanying electromyogram shows that each wavelet of contraction is preceded by a muscle action potential, indicating that the motoneurons are discharging in periodic synchronous bursts. The simplest explanation of clonus is based on the "in series" behavior of the stretch receptor. The tap on the tendon initiates a synchronous volley of afferent impulses which fire the motoneurons in concert, causing a jerk contraction. This contraction relieves the spindles of the tension imposed by the sustained stretch, so that they cease firing and the afferent drive to the motoneurons ceases. As a consequence, the muscle relaxes and the spindles are thereby again put under tension which initiates an afferent volley that again fires the motoneurons so that the sequence is repeated. Even in a healthy subject a slight tendency toward oscillation during a jerk contraction may be observed. If the muscle is under passive tension prior to the tapping of the tendon, the electromyogram displays an asynchronous discharge which indicates that motor units are reflexly firing in response to the sustained stretch. When the tendon is tapped, the electromyogram displays a large synchronous discharge just preceding the muscle contraction, but during the development of contractile tension the asynchronous discharge is in abeyance—the "silent period" already described. As the muscle relaxes and the spindles are again put under tension, firing of motor units resumes and relaxation of the muscle is delayed. Indeed, a second small contraction, the myotatic appendage, may appear on the tension record. When the motoneurons are hyperexcitable, as in spasticity, a series of myotatic appendages appear, constituting clonus which may persist for minutes. Sustained clonus is always a manifestation of hyperreflexia indicating damage within the central nervous system.

Pathologic Reflexes.   These are reflex responses which do not occur in the normal person. In a sense, the Hoffman reflex is a pathologic reflex. A better example is the *Babinski sign* or reflex. In the normal adult, stroking the sole of the foot causes plantar flexion of the toes; this is the plantar flexion reflex. In certain diseases of the central nervous system, however, the response to plantar stimulation (particularly along the lateral surface and the ball of the foot) is dorsiflexion of the great toe, often accompanied by fanning of the other toes. The Babinski reflex is part of the generalized flexion reflex pattern and is accompanied by flexor contraction at other joints of the limb; the significant deviation in the Babinski reflex is the aberrant pattern. In adults, presence of the Babinski reflex is always a sign of disease, but this pattern is normal in infants, particularly when they are asleep. The Babinski reflex is commonly believed to indicate interruption of the pyramidal tract (see Chap. 11).

Deductions from Examination of Reflexes.   In summary, it may be pointed out that the examination of reflexes provides several kinds of information to the thoughtful physician. *First*, unilateral aberration of reflex performance provides a basis for identifying the *side* affected by the disease process. *Second*, the distribution of reflex aberrations along the longitudinal axis of the body often betrays the *segmental level* of the lesion. *Third*, once a segmental defect is established, attention may be turned to identifying the *defective component* in the arc. Loss of reflex accompanied by loss of sensation but without voluntary motor weakness implies injury to the afferent limb. Loss of reflex without sensory defect but with muscular weakness, atrophy, fibrillation or fasciculation suggests injury to the efferent limb. *Fourth*, examination of segmental reflexes often reveals disturbances of *more distant structures* which influence the segmental arcs. Thus, disease of descending pathways inhibitory to the segmental reflex mechanism is brought to the physician's attention by hyperreflexia, as in spasticity.

REFERENCES

1. ADRIAN, E. D. and ZOTTERMAN, Y. *J. Physiol.*, 1926, *61:*151–171.
2. BARKER, D. *Quart. J. micr. Sci.*, 1948, *89:*143–186.
3. BRADLEY, K. and ECCLES, J. C. *J. Physiol.*, 1953, *122:*462–473.
4. CREED, R. S., DENNY-BROWN, D., ECCLES, J. C., LIDDELL, E. G. T. and SHERRINGTON, C. S. *Reflex activity of the spinal cord.* London, Oxford University Press, 1932, vi, 183 pp.
5. DENNY-BROWN, D. *Proc. roy. Soc.*, 1928, *B103:* 321–336.
6. FULTON, J. F. and PI SUÑER, J. *Amer. J. Physiol.*, 1928, *83:*554–562.
7. GRANIT, R. *J. Neurophysiol.*, 1950, *13:*351–372.
8. HOFFMANN, P. *Arch. Anat. Physiol. (Lpz.)*, *Anat. Abt.*, 1910, 223–246, 1 pl.
9. HOFFMANN, P. *Dtsch. Z. Nervenheilk.*, 1951, *166:*60–64.
10. HUNT, C. C. *J. Physiol.*, 1951, *115:*456–469.
11. HUNT, C. C. *J. Physiol.*, 1952, *117:*359–379.
12. HUNT, C. C. *J. gen. Physiol.*, 1954, *38:*117–131.
13. HUNT, C. C. and KUFFLER, S. W. *J. Physiol.*, 1951, *113:*298–315.
14. HUNT, C. C. and PAINTAL, A. S. *J. Physiol.*, 1958, *143:*195–212.
15. KUFFLER, S. W. and HUNT, C. C. *Res. Publ. Ass. nerv. ment. Dis.*, 1952, *30:*24–47.
16. KUFFLER, S. W., HUNT, C. C. and QUILLIAM, J. P. *J. Neurophysiol.*, 1951, *14:*29–54.
17. LAPORTE, Y. and LLOYD, D. P. C. *Amer. J. Physiol.*, 1952, *169:*609–621.
18. LEKSELL, L. *Acta physiol. scand.*, 1945, *10* (Suppl. 31):1–84.
19. LIDDELL, E. G. T. and SHERRINGTON, C. S. *Proc. roy. Soc.*, 1924, *B96:*212–242.
20. LIDDELL, E. G. T. and SHERRINGTON, C. S. *Proc. roy. Soc.*, 1925, *B97:*267–283.
21. LLOYD, D. P. C. *J. Neurophysiol.*, 1943, *6:*317–326.
22. MAGLADERY, J. W., PARK, A. M., PORTER, W. E. and TEASDALL, R. D. *Res. Publ. Ass. nerv. ment. Dis.*, 1952, *30:*118–151.
23. MATTHES, K. and RUCH, T. C. *Quart. J. exper. Physiol.*, 1932, *22:*221–231.
24. MATTHEWS, B. H. C. *J. Physiol.*, 1933, *78:*1–53.
25. McCOUCH, G. P., DEERING, I. D. and STEWART, W. B. *J. Neurophysiol.*, 1950, *13:* 343–350.
26. RENSHAW, B. *J. Neurophysiol.*, 1941, *4:*167–183.
27. RENSHAW, B. *J. Neurophysiol.*, 1946, *9:*191–204.
28. SHERRINGTON, C. S. *Proc. roy. Soc.*, 1893, *52:* 556–564.
29. SHERRINGTON, C. S. *J. Physiol.*, 1898, *22:*319–332.
30. SHERRINGTON, C. S. *Quart. J. exp. Physiol.*, 1909, *2:*109–156.
31. SHERRINGTON, C. S. *J. Physiol.*, 1910, *40:*28–121.
32. SHERRINGTON, C. S. *Brain*, 1915, *38:*191–234.
33. SHERRINGTON, C. S. *Nature (Lond.)*, 1924, *113:* 732, 892–894, 929–932.
34. WOODBURY, J. W. and PATTON, H. D. *Cold Spr. Harb. Symp. quant. Biol.*, 1952, *17:*185–188.
35. ZOTTERMAN, Y. *J. Physiol.*, 1939, *95:*1–28.

CHAPTER 7

Transection of the Human Spinal Cord:
The Nature of Higher Control

By THEODORE C. RUCH

CONSEQUENCES OF SPINAL TRANSECTION
  Spinal shock
    Areflexia and hyporeflexia
    Return of reflexes and hyperreflexia
      Flexion reflex and the Babinski sign
      Mass reflex
      Extensor reflexes
      Autonomic reflexes

Level of transection
Completeness of spinal transection
NATURE OF HIGHER CONTROL
  Release of function
  Nature of spinal shock and mechanisms of
    recovery

THE principles of reflex action outlined in earlier chapters are applied clinically in dealing with destructive diseases and mechanical injury of the spinal cord. Such injuries are especially common during war. During World War I, spinal transection meant early death; during World War II, however, the prognosis for patients with spinal paraplegia was radically altered. Through application of physiologic principles, many of these men have been rehabilitated and are now self-reliant citizens.

When the spinal cord is severed, all muscles innervated from segments below the transection become paralyzed (paraplegic), and the skin and other tissues are anesthetic. Voluntary motion and sensation are abolished and never recover. Reflexes, although initially abolished, do recover to some degree, and some become overactive. This chapter will be concerned with the higher control of reflex action; sensory changes from complete and partial spinal cord section are discussed in Chapter 14.

CONSEQUENCES OF SPINAL TRANSECTION

Spinal Shock. The disappearance of reflexes was designated "spinal shock" some 100 years ago by Marshall Hall,[10] and the term, despite its inappropriateness, is still used. Spinal shock is not related to surgical shock or to spinal concussion, which results from physical shock to the spinal cord. As Sherrington[23] proved, spinal shock will occur when the cord is functionally sectioned atraumatically, as by cooling or by injection of procaine. If reflexes of segments below a transection have returned, another section just below the first produces no shock effect. In short, it is the *fact* of cord section—not the *act* of transection—which produces spinal shock. The alternative terms are *post-transectional areflexia* or *hyporeflexia*. The state of increased reflex excitability which may supervene can be called *post-transectional hyperreflexia*. A phenomenon following a brain lesion comparable to spinal shock is *diaschisis* (von Monakow).

Areflexia and hyporeflexia. The most conspicuous sign of spinal shock in man and other primates is the suppression of all reflexes, both skeletal and visceral, below the transection. This suppression is usually complete during the first two weeks after the injury. Before the first World War it was believed that the reflexes were permanently abolished, this belief having arisen because intercurrent infections of the bladder or other structures reduced the excitability of the spinal cord. Then, Head and Riddoch[11] proved that some paraplegic patients could be maintained indefinitely by fastidious nursing care, and that in such patients spinal reflexes began to return after two to three weeks. Since World War II, Freeman[4] and others[15] have found that reflexes may reappear within two to three days after the accident.

Return of Reflexes and Hyperreflexia. *Flexion reflex and the Babinski sign.* Contrary to early studies, withdrawal movements in response to plantar stimulation (rather than the knee jerk) are the first reflexes to emerge from the period of areflexia; anal and genital reflexes also recover early. As the withdrawal reflex becomes more brisk, the toes (especially the great toe) tend to become extended upward during the response (the sign of Babinski[7]). In the course of the third and fourth weeks following the injury, the withdrawal response becomes more vigorous, and the zone from which it can be elicited spreads up the inner side of the leg, the knee and the hip. The withdrawal response is brought about mainly by strong contraction of the hamstring muscles of the thigh.

Mass reflex. Several months after spinal transection, the withdrawal reflexes tend to become exaggerated and spread to the visceral autonomic outflow. Thus, if the plantar surface of the foot is vigorously scratched, both extremities may withdraw violently, the patient may sweat profusely, and both the bladder and the rectum may contract. This widespread reflex activation of the musculature in spinal man is referred to as the "mass reflex."[11] Mass reflexes may be evoked unintentionally and, at times, they appear to develop spontaneously without obvious stimulation. Flexor reflex contractions with or without autonomic concomitants are very disturbing to the patient, since they interfere with his sleep and rest.

Extensor reflexes. During the first weeks after a spinal transection, the lower extremities are flaccid: they are limp and do not resist manipulation. Even after the withdrawal reflexes have returned, the limbs usually are still flaccid except when exhibiting flexor spasms. Some months after spinal transection, if there are no complications, a slight degree of extensor posture usually develops, but the extremities seldom become strongly spastic, as in hemiplegia. Strong extensor spasticity occurring soon after the transection generally indicates that the spinal cord is not completely severed and that some degree of functional recovery can be anticipated. However, patients with surgically verified spinal transections may reach a stage in which the tendon reflexes are hyperactive as judged by decreased threshold and clonus. Stretch reflexes and positive supporting reactions sufficiently sustained to permit momentary support of the body have been reported. The lower extremities show both ipsilateral and crossed extension reflexes, but extreme resistance of the extensors to passive stretch is seldom found in spinal man.[14]

Autonomic reflexes. Surprisingly, autonomic reflexes are even more completely suppressed in spinal shock than are somatic reactions. During the first month or two the skin is completely dry, sweating having been wholly abolished, and the skin may be warm and pink owing to separation of the autonomic outflow innervating it from the descending vasoconstrictor impulses. In monkeys, sweating generally does not appear until the third month. In the later stages, this sweating may be so excessive that the patient's clothing and bed linen are constantly wet.[4, 8]

Of the autonomic reflexes, those of the bladder are most important to the patient; these are described in full in Chapter 47.

Level of Transection. The manifestations of spinal injuries vary to some extent with the level of transection. In general, cervical transections are associated with less spinal shock in the lower extremities than is encountered in cases of lower thoracic or lumbar transection. Reflexes tend to return earlier after cervical transections, and the lower extremities normally develop slight spasticity.

Cervical transections resulting from dislocation of the spine vary in severity with the actual cervical level. Transections above the fourth cervical segment are followed by prompt paralysis of breathing movements, and for this reason sudden death is the usual result unless artificial respiration is instituted immediately. Dislocations of the cervical vertebra at C_3 or C_4 occur commonly on the football field. Section of the cord at C_4 leaves diaphragmatic breathing unaffected (as Galen originally showed), but a state of quadriplegia develops in which all four extremities become paralyzed and pass into spinal shock. Transections at C_5, C_6 and C_7 give partial to almost complete paralysis of all four extremities, the actual level being determinable from the level of anesthesia and analysis of which muscle groups are paralyzed. Transections at C_8 or T_1 and T_2 have less effect on the upper extremities, but, owing to the sympathetic outflow emerging from these levels, Horner's syndrome develops. The signs making up this syndrome are pupillary contraction, exophthalmos, flushing of the skin and absence of sweating over the face and neck. Unilateral injuries of the cord at this level can often be recognized by the presence of unilateral ocular symptoms. From T_2 to L_1 the dermatomal pattern of the effects is easily followed.

Completeness of Spinal Transection. In civil life complete spinal transections fortunately are rare. Much more common are partial injuries, and it is important to be able to distinguish between an incomplete and a total transection. Broadly speaking, incomplete transections are marked by an early return of extensor reflexes and are eventually associated with spasticity and great reflex hyperactivity. A patient with a cervical dislocation who appears completely paralyzed below the level of dislocation but who nevertheless exhibits extensor reflexes has an incompletely divided cord, and he has a good possibility of functional recovery if the dislocation can be reduced. Often a patient shows flaccidity and areflexia shortly after the injury but later develops spasticity and active reflexes.

A spinal transection represents the sudden withdrawal of the many excitatory and inhibitory influences which play upon the spinal reflex arcs. A partial interruption of the spinal cord disrupts some but not all of the descending pathways. Since these pathways originate at different levels of the neural axis, transection at higher levels will interrupt some of them and not others. To obtain a complete view of the nature of higher control and the clinical syndromes resulting from destructive lesions of the nervous system, it is necessary to consider the same topic at each level of transection.

NATURE OF HIGHER CONTROL

Spinal transection suddenly interrupts all descending pathways which control spinal reflexes by facilitation and inhibition. The results are necessarily complex. The nature of higher control is the subject of several of the following chapters, but it cannot be fully understood until sections at higher levels interrupting only a few descending pathways are studied.

It might be thought that stretch reflexes, for example, disappear in the higher animal because they have, in course of evolution, been long-circuited through the brain. That these reflexes in higher animals are served by monosynaptic spinal reflex arcs has been proved by Magladery.[18] It is generally conceded that spinal shock results from sudden interruption of control normally exerted on spinal centers by forebrain structures. In the course of evolution, the forebrain has come to dominate lower midbrain and spinal centers more and more, the domination being most complete in man and other higher primates. This evolutionary process is generally referred to as "encephalization." The degree of spinal shock reflects the degree to which a given spinal reflex depends on the brain for facilitation of the segmental afferent input. Generally, the dependence becomes greater as the primate series is ascended, but exceptions do occur. For example, the reflexes of the semiprehensile hind foot of the chimpanzee may be more profoundly disturbed than those of the human foot after spinal transection.

The depression of reflexes comes about because, as will be brought out many times in subsequent chapters, descending pathways converge and summate with the segmental afferent input. Presumably, these descending tracts are discharging continuously, subliminally exciting the motoneurons and keeping many near the point of discharge.[16] As a result, a local afferent volley which has few motoneurons in its discharge zone is able to discharge many neurons lying in its subliminal fringe. If the flow of descending impulses is terminated, the reflex shrinks to its original discharge. This recession explains much of the areflexia and hyporeflexia which follow spinal transection.

Fulton[5] has pointed out that another mechanism may be operative. In addition to or instead of withdrawing facilitation from anterior horn cells, withdrawal of descending impulses might remove an inhibitory influence acting upon the interneurons of an antagonistic reflex arc, necessarily a multisynaptic one. An afferent volley in this arc, e.g., for a flexion reflex, would traverse the uninhibited interneurons with less reduction and would inhibit the motoneurons of the antagonistic extensor reflex. Thus, the flexion reflex should be, and is, augmented while the extensor reflex is inhibited. In passive flexion of a joint to test an extensor stretch reflex, the mere manipulation might prevent one's feeling the weak but recovering stretch reflex.

Ballif *et al.*[1] demonstrated myographically that the knee jerk of a spinal animal is inhibited for several seconds by a single ipsilateral stimulus, whereas the knee jerk of a decerebrate animal is inhibited for only a tenth of a second. It is apparent that it is extremely difficult to distinguish between inhibition and lessening of facilitation as mechanisms of spinal shock, and probably both contribute. One of the complexities of the nervous system is that the higher centers can control a spinal reflex by exerting their influence on the motoneurons and/or on the internuncial neurons of the reflex arc.

Release of Function. When reflexes below a transection become stronger and more easily elicited, "release of function"* is said to have occurred. The simplest example of release of function is provided by the consideration of what happens to the flexion reflex when the spinal cord of the decerebrate cat is sectioned in the midthoracic region.[21] As will be discussed in greater detail in Chapter 8, a decerebrate cat is a reduced system in which the only descending pathways still affecting the reflex arcs are the vestibulospinal and reticulospinal tracts from the medulla oblongata. What occurs on transection—by surgery, cooling or procaine injection—is a prompt and marked *decrease* in the excitability of stretch and other extensor reflexes and an *increase* in the excitability of the flexion reflex. In other words, the two classes of reflexes are oppositely affected, and the simplest conclusion is that the descending pathways innervate two classes of motoneurons reciprocally. There is the same advantage to reciprocal innervation from the descending pathways as there is to such innervation by the local afferent inputs.

Further evidence of reciprocal effects of spinal transection is seen in the reflex changes in the forelimbs following midthoracic transection in a decerebrate cat. These changes, termed the Schiff-Sherrington phenomenon, are, as indicated in Figure 118, a striking augmentation of the stretch reflex and a decrease in the size of the flexion reflex to equal stimuli. The former is clearly observable without instrumental recording as an increased stiffening of the forelimbs. (The changes are opposite in homologous muscles of the forelimb and hindlimb, and while this must have meaning, the reciprocal changes between flexors and extensors constitute the significant point.)

* Release of function was first recognized in 1833 by Marshall Hall,[9] who also was the first to describe spinal shock.

The diminution of reflexes in these experiments illustrates *spinal shock* resulting from withdrawal of facilitation; the augmentation of reflexes illustrates *release of function* resulting from withdrawal of inhibition. These two phenomena always occur together and are manifestations of a reciprocal relationship of descending pathways to extensor and flexor spinal motoneurons. Descending pathways other than the vestibulospinal tract act in the same reciprocal fashion but vary in sign, so that a spinal transection which interrupts many descending pathways at once can have quite complex effects. Nevertheless, the effects of transecting lesions, and of certain large brain lesions, can best be interpreted in terms of a kind of algebra of the nervous system in which positive and negative quantities are summated. (For examples, see Chap. 47.)

Nature of Spinal Shock and Mechanisms of Recovery. The question now arises: Is spinal shock more than mere withdrawal of facilitation and inhibition? Withdrawal of descending influences explains adequately the decrease or release of spinal reflexes. However, there is considerable recovery from the depression of reflexes, and this requires

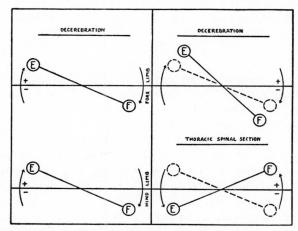

FIG. 118. A schematic diagram of the reciprocal effect of thoracic transection of the spinal cord upon the reflex activity of fore and hind limbs of the decerebrate preparation. *E* and *F* are the extensor and flexor motoneurons. The ordinates are reflex excitability and indicate merely decrease and increase and not absolute amount of change in reflex excitability. (From Ruch and Watts, *Amer. J. Physiol.*, 1934, *110*:362–375.)

exploration. Why recovery should occur is a puzzle, but clues to a solution are offered by the following experiment.

The effects of interrupting all the descending pathways suddenly are much more profound than those of a gradual interruption. McCouch and Fulton[7, 20] removed the motor cortex of one cerebral hemisphere and noted a depression of reflexes in the contralateral limbs (the corticospinal pathway is crossed). After the reflexes had recovered, the spinal cord was sectioned. The reflexes in the limb contralateral to the brain lesion were only moderately depressed, whereas the spinal shock was profound in the previously normal extremity. The two stage removal of descending influences had exerted less effect than did the one stage removal. (For a somewhat similar demonstration, see Chap. 11.) These experiments show that cerebral lesions can depress spinal reflexes. Kempinsky[12] has recently demonstrated what von Monakow deduced from clinical observations and termed diaschisis—that cerebral lesions will depress the electrical activity in a remote region with which the damaged area is neuronally connected. This "cerebral shock" or diaschisis will be discussed again in Chapter 11. It is theoretically significant that a depression of excitability of motoneurons also follows dorsal root section and that this period of depression is followed by one of increased excitability.[24]

One theory of spinal shock holds that the sudden withdrawal of facilitation decreases the excitability of spinal motoneurons and interneurons more than would be accounted for by the mere withdrawal of excitatory background. Recovery of function is in part interpreted as a return to normal from the "S state" or "shock state" of the neurons. The S state is hypothetical but can be supported by analogy: in certain situations, interruption of axons can cause the cell bodies on which they terminate to undergo microscopically visible disorganization (transneuronal degeneration); degeneration of the muscle cell as a consequence of a sectioning of its motor nerve has already been pointed out. If these transjunctional changes can proceed to the point of visible degeneration, it is not inconceivable that interference with descending fibers terminating on spinal motoneurons can cause changes in them which are not visible under the microscope but which are manifest in a decreased synaptic excitability.

There is good reason to believe that spinal reflex arcs subsequently attain a level of excitability which is more than a return to normal from a hypothetical S state. In part, this hyperactivity reflects a release of function when, as is usually the case, inhibitory as well as excitatory pathways are interrupted by a lesion. Release of function would not be apparent until the S factor had disappeared. But this perhaps does not explain the protracted, month-long increase in excitability following the initial state of depression.

Convincing evidence has been adduced that motoneurons partially denervated by spinal transection[2] or posterior root section[3] become highly sensitive to chemical agents (see law of denervation, Chap. 9). If chemical substances of this kind are present in the synaptic region, they might influence the excitability of motoneurons irrespective of whether neurohumors are involved in transmission at central synapses.

McCouch and his coworkers[20] have described another mechanism which would account for a progressive increase in the excitability of reflex arcs below a spinal transection. These investigators have furnished anatomic and electrophysiologic evidence that, subsequent to spinal transection, the local posterior root fibers sprout new collaterals and produce more synaptic connections with motoneurons and interneurons.[17] This increase in connections would, for reasons already familiar (Chap. 5), increase the magnitude of a reflex response to the same peripheral stimulation. (An analogous sprouting of teledendrons of sensory neurons into denervated skin is described in Chapter 14.)

In patients suffering from neurologic disorders, the "spontaneous" recovery of function can be a difficulty, as in the disturbing flexor spasms of paraplegia; or it can be the sole hope for improvement of the patient, as in hemiplegia. Despite the latter fact, the problem of analyzing the basic mechanism of *shock* and *recovery of function* has been largely left to the future.

REFERENCES

1. BALLIF, L., FULTON, J. F. and LIDDELL, E. G. T. *Proc. roy. Soc.*, 1925, *B98*:589–607, pls. 36–37.
2. CANNON, W. B. and HAIMOVICI, H. *Amer. J. Physiol.*, 1939, *126*:731–740.
3. DRAKE, C. G. and STAVRAKY, G. W. *J. Neurophysiol.*, 1948, *11*:229–238.
4. FREEMAN, L. W. *J. Amer. med. Ass.*, 1949, *140*:949–958, 1015–1022.
5. FULTON, J. F. *Muscular contraction and the reflex control of movement*. Baltimore, Williams & Wilkins, 1926, xv, 644 pp.
6. FULTON, J. F. and KELLER, A. D. *The sign of Babinski: A study of the evolution of cortical dominance*. Springfield, Ill., Charles C Thomas, 1932, xi, 165 pp.
7. FULTON, J. F. and McCOUCH, G. P. *J. nerv. ment. Dis.*, 1937, *86*:125–146.
8. GUTTMAN, L. and WHITTERIDGE, D. *Brain*, 1947, *70*:361–404.
9. HALL, M. *Phil. Trans.*, 1833, 635–665.
10. HALL, M. *Synopsis of the diastaltic nervous system; or the system of the spinal marrow; and its reflex arcs*. London, J. Mallett, 1850, xii, 100, vii pp.
11. HEAD, H. and RIDDOCH, G. *Brain*, 1917, *40*: 188–263.
12. KEMPINSKY, W. H. *Arch. Neurol. Psychiat. (Chicago)*, 1958, *79*:376–389.
13. KUHN, R. A. *Brain*, 1950, *73*:1–51.
14. KUHN, R. A. and MACHT, M. B. *Johns Hopk. Hosp. Bull.*, 1949, *84*:43–75.

15. KUHN, W. G., JR. *J. Neurosurgery*, 1947, *4:*40–68.
16. LIDDELL, E. G. T. *Brain*, 1934, *57:*386–400.
17. LIU, C.-N. and CHAMBERS, W. W. *Arch. Neurol. Psychiat. (Chicago)*, 1958, *79:*46–61.
18. MAGLADERY, J. W., PARK, A. M., PORTER, W. E. and TEASDALL, R. D. *Res. Publ. Ass. nerv. ment. Dis.*, 1952, *30:*118–151.
19. McCOUCH, G. P. *Amer. J. Physiol.*, 1924, *71:*137–152.
20. McCOUCH, G. P., AUSTIN, G. M., LIU, C. N. and LIU, C. Y. *J. Neurophysiol.*, 1958, *21:*205–216.
21. RUCH, T. C. and WATTS, J. W. *Amer. J. Physiol.*, 1934, *110:*362–375.
22. SAHS, A. L. and FULTON, J. F. *J. Neurophysiol.*, 1940, *3:*258–268.
23. SHERRINGTON, C. S. *The integrative action of the nervous system*. New Haven, Conn. Yale University Press, 1906, xvi, 411 pp.
24. TEASDALL, R. D. and STAVRAKY, G. W. *J. Neurophysiol.*, 1953, *16:*367–375.

CHAPTER 8

Pontobulbar Control of Posture and Orientation in Space

By THEODORE C. RUCH

ALTHOUGH stretch reflexes are present in the chronic spinal animal, including spinal man, they are poorly sustained. For example, the knee jerk may be brisk, but a protracted stretch of the quadriceps muscles does not give rise to a persistent reflex contraction. In contrast, when section of the brain stem at a midbrain level leaves the pons and medulla oblongata intact and connected with the spinal cord through their descending pathways, there ensues a state of hyperactivity of the stretch reflexes, *decerebrate rigidity* (Fig. 119 and Chap. 6). The myotatic reflex, which is the basis of decerebrate rigidity, has already been discussed; there remains the question of the higher control of these spinal reflexes. This question is of particular interest because decerebrate rigidity in animals resembles the spasticity associated with hemiplegia in man, a most common neurologic disorder.

HISTORICAL NOTE. Decerebrate rigidity was first clearly described by Sherrington in a paper published in 1898.[19] He noted that shortly after section of the brain stem a state of exaggerated extensor posture developed, affecting all four extremities and also the neck and tail. He argued that, since this state persisted indefinitely, it could not result from irritation incident to the cut and must therefore be looked upon as a "release" of the lower brain stem from control normally exercised by higher centers in the forebrain. His analysis of the condition is one of the classics of physiology.

In analyzing decerebrate rigidity, Sherrington first asked what forebrain areas must be destroyed to release the rigidity. He reasoned that exclusion of the pyramidal tracts

FIG. 119. Cat in decerebrate rigidity. Note hyperextended posture of neck, arching of back (opisthotonos) and extension of tail. Sherrington described the total pattern as "an exaggerated carica-ture of reflex standing." (From Pollock and Davis, *J. comp. Neurol.*, 1930, *50*:377–411.)

was not responsible, because semisection at the level of the corpora quadrigemina caused the rigidity to appear on the *ipsilateral* side, whereas the pyramidal pathways cross below this level. Sherrington concluded that decerebrate rigidity must result from interruption of extrapyramidal projections from some part of the forebrain. As will be seen in subse-quent chapters, descending systems from the cerebral cortex, the basal ganglia and the cerebellum are concerned. It suffices now that impulses in these paths funnel into the structures of the lower brain stem (reticular formation) which will be described in this chapter.

The second question is what brain stem nuclei maintain the rigidity by facilitating the spinal myotatic reflex arcs. The vestibular nuclei are certainly involved (not the red nuclei, as was once supposed)[16], and the lateral reticular formation has been implicated.

RETICULAR FORMATION AND THE STRETCH REFLEX[9]

According to Brodal,[5] "reticular formation" as used by anatomists comprises those areas of the brain stem which are made up of "diffuse aggregations of cells of different types and sizes, separated by a wealth of fibres travelling in all directions. Circumscribed groups of cells, such as the red nucleus or the facial nucleus, formed of relatively closely packed units of a more or less uniform size and type, are not considered to be part of the reticular formation, which forms, so to speak, a sort of matrix in which the 'specific' nuclei and the more conspicuous tracts, e.g., the medial longitudinal fasciculus, are imbedded." Some nuclei with a reticular structure have received names and tend to be excluded when physiologists use the phrase. Finally, the trend anatomically is to break up the reticular formation into a number of fairly circumscribed cellular areas which can be referred to as nuclei.

The functions of the reticular formation remained obscure for many years. In 1946, Magoun and Rhines[15] reported that stimulation of the reticular substance lying ventro-medially in the caudal part of the bulb inhibited the knee jerk, decerebrate rigidity and movements resulting from stimulation of the motor area of the cerebral cortex. With stimuli of ordinary intensity the inhibitory effect was bilateral, but with very weak stimuli the primary inhibitory effects were ipsilateral. These investigators also described a facilitatory region which lay more laterally in the reticular formation and was con-siderably more extensive, running upward into the midbrain tegmentum, the central gray matter and the subthalamus (Fig. 120).[18] Stimulation of these regions facilitated the knee jerk and augmented the responses to stimulation of the motor area.

At first sight, these reticular areas and their reticulospinal tracts provided an exceedingly simple explanation of decerebrate rigidity and the higher control of posture that was not unlike the action of the brake and accelerator on a car. The reticular facilitatory area was considered to provide a supraspinal facilitation maintaining rigidity. The reticular inhibitory area was believed to be deprived of its input from the cerebellar and cerebral cortex, and hence functionless. However, further analysis showed that, as previously thought, the vestibulospinal tract also facilitates stretch reflexes. Furthermore, as we have seen in Chapter 6, the net effect of bulbospinal descending pathways in the decerebrate preparation is facilitatory to extensor reflexes and inhibitory to flexor reflexes. If the lateral reticular area were purely facilitatory, loss of its influence could not explain the changes in reflex activity following spinal transection in a decerebrate preparation, because there is a reciprocal decrease of the stretch reflex excitability and increase of flexor reflex excitability.

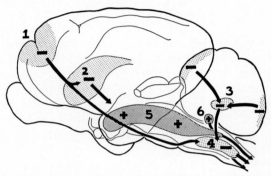

FIG. 120.   Reconstruction of cat's brain showing inhibitory and facilitatory systems concerned in spasticity. Inhibitory pathways are: *1*, corticobulboreticular; *2*, caudatospinal; *3*, cerebelloreticular; and *4*, reticulospinal. Facilitatory pathways are: *5*, reticulospinal and *6*, vestibulospinal. (From Lindsley et al., *J. Neurophysiol.*, 1949, *12*:197–216.)

Further experimentation by Sprague and Chambers[20] has removed this objection by showing that the purely inhibitory and purely excitatory effects of reticular stimulation described by Magoun and Rhines are the exception, not the rule. Generalized inhibition is uncommon in decerebrate cats, and it never occurs in unanesthetized intact cats stimulated through implanted electrodes. Rather, the effect is reciprocal—extensor inhibition-flexor contraction and vice versa—in a given limb. Thus, the reticulospinal tract obeys Sherrington's law of reciprocal innervation.* Threshold stimulation near the midline (the inhibitory area of Magoun and Rhines) tends to inhibit extensor tonus and to cause flexor contraction. Lateral stimulation (the facilitatory area of Magoun and Rhines) tends to facilitate decerebrate rigidity and inhibit flexion. (Reciprocal effects on the opposite limbs are also the rule.)

Gernandt and Thulin[8] recorded monosynaptic and multisynaptic ventral root reflex discharge while stimulating the reticular substance. They found definite reciprocal effects, especially from the medial reticular area. Moving the stimulating electrode position only 0.1 mm. might change the response to the reverse, reciprocal effect. Often, an inhibitory or facilitatory effect which was strong at first decayed even though the stimulation was continued. Such decaying responses were followed by a postexcitatory

* Should this prove otherwise, it would be profitable to think of possible nonpostural functions for this system, where nonreciprocal effects would be meaningful. Thus it is possible that the descending reticular system is concerned with awakening the animal or putting it to sleep, as is the ascending aspect of this system (Chap. 21).

rebound of opposite sign—typical of stimulation of a "mixed" structure. Since nociceptive flexion reflexes were not extensively examined in the original experiments by Magoun and Rhines, it is easy to see how the ideas of a purely facilitatory and a purely inhibitory area in the reticular formation arose when they looked only at extensor reflexes. In the light of the subsequent work by Sprague and Chambers and others, it would be appropriate to refer to the "bulbar reticular extensor inhibitory area" and the "lateral reticular extensor facilitatory area."

Alpha and Gamma Mechanisms of Higher Control.   In considering the influence of various brain centers on myotatic reflexes and tonus, one must think of two ways in which such reflexes can be influenced: (i) by facilitation or inhibition of the large α motoneurons which innervate the majority of muscle fibers; (ii) by facilitation or inhibition of the small γ motoneurons which cause contraction of the intrafusal fibers of the muscle spindles, thereby increasing the rate of spindle firing, which in turn influences the amount of the α motoneuron firing that underlies extensor tonus. The reticular system apparently acts mainly through the γ efferents. Since the spindle discharge is only mildly inhibitory to the flexion reflex, the reticular system will affect chiefly extensor myotatic reflexes. This helps us understand how the lateral reticular areas could appear to be purely facilitatory.

Granit and Kaada[10] attached an extensor muscle to a sensitive myograph and placed a cut-down filament of dorsal root containing a Group I fiber from a muscle spindle in this muscle upon recording electrodes. When a point in the brain was stimulated, they could learn: (i) whether the muscle spindle firing was decreased or increased; (ii) whether there was any change in muscle contraction which might account for the change in spindle activity through slackening the muscle spindles. Weak stimulation of the pontile and mesencephalic ("facilitatory") reticular areas augmented the spindle discharge without causing a change in muscle tension.

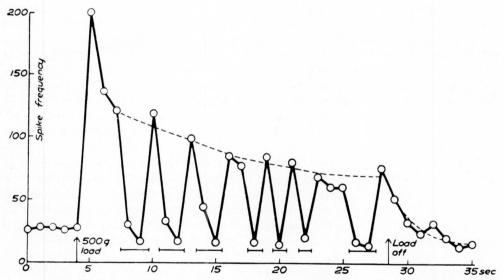

FIG. 121.   Discharge frequency of a single fiber from a muscle spindle loaded with 500 grams. The bulboreticular inhibitory system was stimulated intermittently as shown by the lines below the curve. Note accompanying decrease in rate of spindle discharge. (From Granit and Kaada. *Acta physiol. scand.*, 1953, *27:*130–160.)

In similar experiments, the bulbar region from which Magoun and Rhines obtained inhibition of the knee jerk and decerebrate rigidity was stimulated. The rate of spindle discharge was dramatically reduced as the result of γ efferent inhibition. An example of such an experiment is shown in Figure 121. Many of the cerebellar and cerebral structures which affect posture do so via the γ efferent system and presumably through the reticular areas. Other descending impulses may act upon the α moto-neurons; e.g., elimination of the anterior cerebellum augments decerebrate rigidity although simul-taneously paralyzing the γ efferent system.[6] This effect must be exerted directly upon the α motoneurons, probably by the vestibulospinal tract.

Input to Reticular and Nuclear Structures.   If, as pointed out above, the lower brain stem gives rise to descending axons inhibitory as well as excitatory to myotatic reflexes, why are myotatic reflexes hyperactive after decerebration? More specifically, why does the facilitatory pathway remain active while the inhibitory pathway is no longer functional? The reason is that the extensor inhibitory reticular system is dependent for its activity on impulses descending from higher centers (cerebral and cerebellar cortex). In contrast, vestibulospinal pathways facilitating extensors are activated through the labyrinth, and the reticular extensor facilitatory system receives impulses from the ascending afferent systems, including those originating in the muscles. A midbrain transection would remove the input into the reticular inhibitory system, thus leaving the innervated facilitatory system unopposed and the extensor reflexes overactive.

Summary.   The brain stem is the origin of descending pathways, vestibular and reticular, that facilitate myotatic reflexes of extensor muscles (and inhibit nociceptive flexor reflexes), so that hypertonus (exaggerated standing) occurs when the effects of this system are unopposed by descending inhibition of myotatic reflexes (and facilitation of flexor reflexes). The actions on stretch reflexes are by two routes: (i) gamma efferent fibers innervating intrafusal fibers, and (ii) alpha motoneurons innervating the ordinary extrafusal motor fibers.

POSTURAL REFLEXES (STATIC REACTIONS)

Postural reactions, sometimes designated "attitudinal" reflexes,[12, 13] are of three types: (i) local static reactions, (ii) segmental static reactions, and (iii) general static reactions, which include the tonic neck and labyrinthine reflexes. These terms were used by Magnus in his famous book *Körperstellung* (body posture). Some of the underlying reflexes have already been discussed under other names. All are proprioceptive in nature, the local static reactions stemming primarily from gravitational stimuli, seg-mental reactions arising from the effects of movement of one extremity on the opposite extremity, and general static reactions arising from the actual position of the head in space. Acceleratory reactions, e.g., postrotational nystagmus, are initiated by the semi-circular canals and are distinct from the tonic labyrinthine reactions, which are inde-pendent of movement or acceleration.

The afferent sources of stimulation are as follows: (i) static reactions originate in the muscles themselves; (ii) segmental reactions develop as a result of afferents from one muscle acting upon fellow muscles of the same segment on the opposite side; and (iii) neck and labyrinthine reactions stem from receptors in the membranous labyrinth (the otolith) and in the neck muscles. Transecting the neural axis of an experimental animal and testing for the presence of the static reactions reveals the general site of the neural structures subserving them.

Spinal Animal.   The basic pattern of the local and segmental static reflexes is to be found in the spinal animal. The stretch reflex—the most prominent of the *local static reactions*—is elicitable, though not strongly developed. The crossed extensor reflex may also be obtained, its presence indicating that *segmental static reactions* are also laid down at the spinal level. General static reactions are also seen. When a crossed extensor reflex is obtained in the high spinal preparation, the ipsilateral forelimb also extends. This is a reaction pattern which tends to keep the animal from toppling over; it is also a part of the quadrupedal pattern of movement involved in forward locomotion.

Low Decerebrate Animal (Bulbospinal Preparation).* All three types of static reactions are well developed in the decerebrate animal.

LOCAL STATIC REACTIONS. Local static reactions are most conspicuously developed in the extremities, and they have to do primarily with stance—the fixed standing posture that prevents collapse of the extremity under force of gravity. Sir Thomas Browne wrote (1646):

"For station is properly no rest, but one kinde of motion, relating unto that which Physitians (from Galen) doe name extensive or tonicall, that is an extension of the muscles and organs of motion maintaining the body at length or in its proper figure, wherein although it seem to be immoved is neverthelesse [not] without all motion, for in this position the muscles are sensibly extended, and labour to support the body, which permitted unto its proper gravity would suddenly subside and fall unto the earth, as it happeneth in sleep, diseases and death; from which occult action and invisible motion of the muscles in station (as Galen declareth) proceed more offensive lassitudes then from ambulation."†

Magnus put the problem of the local static reaction as follows:[13]

"A movable limb is at times used as an *instrument* for very different purposes (such as scraping, scratching, fighting, etc.), and moves freely in all joints, whereas at other times it is transformed into a stiff and strong *pillar*, which gives the impression of being one solid column, able to carry the weight of the body. Experiments have shown that this is accomplished by a series of local static reflexes."

In becoming pillar-like, joints must become fixed; this involves simultaneous contraction of opposing muscle groups. The stretch reflex, which is at the basis of the anti-gravity response, is not of itself sufficient to fix a given joint: opposing muscles must contract simultaneously to ensure fixation of the joint but must relax reciprocally when position of the extremity is changed even slightly.

The basis of this coordinated response involving the entire musculature of an extremity was discovered by Magnus in a decerebellated dog. Here the already exaggerated stretch reflexes are still more pronounced when the pads of the feet are lightly touched. The extremity in these circumstances follows one's finger as if it were a magnet. Although now designated the "positive supporting reaction," when first described the response was referred to as the "magnet reaction." Close analysis revealed that the reaction starts from a touch stimulus to the skin of the toe pad, i.e., *exteroceptive* stimulus; this, however, is followed by a *proprioceptive* stimulus, i.e., stretch of the interosseus muscles by separation of the toe pads. When the skin of the foot was anesthetized, the exteroceptive phase was abolished, but as soon as the toe pads became separated, the proprioceptive stimulus promptly initiated the response. Once the extremities encountered active resistance, other muscles were stretched, and they in turn reinforced the reaction initiated from the skin and small muscles of the toe pads. The reaction itself transforms the extremity from a flexible and toneless state into a supporting member having the stiffness of a rigid pillar. The reaction is present in normal animals and also in man, but is less readily demonstrated in them than in a decerebrate preparation in which all of the static reactions are released and exaggerated.

SEGMENTAL STATIC REACTIONS. The crossed extension reflex is one of the classic reactions of decerebrate animals. One must also recognize intersegmental static reactions. For example, when a hindlimb is caused to extend either through the positive supporting reaction or from a crossed extension reflex, the opposite forelimb also extends, thus demonstrating the influence of the lumbar segments upon the cervical. The same pattern also occurs in reverse—the extension of one forelimb is accompanied automatically by the extension of the opposite hindlimb, all of which is a pattern essential for quadrupedal standing as well as for locomotion.

* Preparations made by transecting the neural axis can be designated by the level of the decerebrating transection or by the highest brain stem level maintaining connection with the spinal reflex arcs., e.g., bulbospinal.
† *Enquiries into vulgar and common errors*, 1646, Book 3, Chap. I. Of the Elephant, p. 105.

GENERAL STATIC REACTIONS.   Once an animal succeeds in standing, various modifications of stance can develop in accordance with the needs of a given situation. If, for example, a cat lifts its head to look up to a shelf, both forelimbs become automatically extended; if it tries to look under a sofa, both forelimbs become flexed. The general static reactions are due in part to the influence of one muscle group upon muscle groups in other segments, but they are also modified by the tonic neck and labyrinthine reflexes.

Tonic neck reflexes.   In order to differentiate neck from labyrinthine reflexes, both labyrinths must be destroyed and sources of stimulation for the static reactions removed, so that only the influence of the neck muscles will be observed when the neck is turned. Rotation of the jaw to the right in such a preparation causes prompt increase in the extensor posture of both limbs on the right side and relaxation of the limbs on the other side. Dorsal flexion of the head of non-hopping animals causes extension of both forelimbs and relaxation of the hindlimbs (cat looking up to shelf); ventral flexion of the head causes relaxation of both forelimbs and extension of the hindlimbs (cat looking under sofa).

These reactions are obviously purposeful. If a cat walking forward in a straight line hears a mouse to its right, mere turning of the head to the right causes the extremities on that side to become extended, and the cat is automatically prepared for a quick takeoff with its left foot. Clear-cut utility is also seen in extension and flexion of the forelimbs when the gaze is directed upward and downward, respectively. Section of the dorsal nerve roots in the anterior cervical region abolishes these reactions. These reactions are prominent in decerebrate cats and have also been clearly demonstrated in labyrinthectomized monkeys following bilateral removal of the motor and premotor areas.

Tonic labyrinthine reflexes.   The tonic neck and labyrinthine reactions can be separated by severing bilaterally the upper four cervical sensory roots. The labyrinth itself has two distinct mechanisms, one the otolith and the other the semicircular canals. The static labyrinthine reactions are probably mediated by the otolith, and the reactions to angular acceleration appear to stem primarily from the semicircular canals, but a clear-cut distinction between the functions of the two end organs has never been achieved. The static labyrinthine reactions manifest themselves through changes in resting posture brought about by alterations of the animal's position. When it is placed on its back, i.e., in a horizontal supine position, the extremities are maximally extended. Extension is minimal when the animal is prone with its snout tilted 45 degrees to the horizontal plane. This behavior is contrary to expectation, and its rationale must yet be worked out.

The low decerebrate animal never rights himself, stands or walks spontaneously. That this is not due to "shock" but rather to the loss of the necessary neural apparatus was proved by Bard and Macht,[3] who maintained bulbospinal animals for as long as 40 days without observing the spontaneous head or body righting shown by high decerebrate preparations.

High Decerebrate Animal (Midbrain and Thalamic Preparations).   The neural apparatus essential for the reactions described below appears to lie in the midbrain, since the reactions are seen if the neural axis is transected just above the red nucleus and the animal is kept alive and in good condition for one or two weeks. If an even higher transection is made, yielding a thalamic or decorticate preparation, righting, standing and walking are seen immediately after the operation, and the adjustments are in general brisker and more powerful. The structures lying between the red nucleus and the cerebral cortex apparently facilitate the function of the structures which execute rigidity and walking.

RIGHTING REFLEXES.   The second category of general static reactions are the so-called righting reflexes. The low decerebrate preparation exhibits no tendency to regain the upright position once it topples over. In cats and dogs, decerebrate rigidity is not present when the midbrain remains intact. When the animal is placed on its side, it tends first to right its head and then its body. Through a series of such maneuvers the animal may achieve an upright position, standing essentially normally on all four limbs. The midbrain primate (Fig. 122) shows a similar tendency, but is unable actually to stand, even though some of the righting reflexes to be described below are present. The primate differs from the dog or the cat in greater encephalization of motor function in the forebrain.

The classic righting reflex can be demonstrated in the intact cat by dropping it blindfolded with its legs pointed upward. The cat turns with almost incredible speed and lights deftly on all fours. Magnus[12] noted that in every case a rotation of the head initiates the turn. This rotation he considered due to labyrinthine righting reflexes. Rotation of the upper body follows to align it with the head. This Magnus ascribed to neck righting reflexes. These two reactions are followed by rotation of the lower body, completing the turn. Rademacher and Ter Braak[17] have analyzed the muscular movements employed in turning. After its labyrinths have been destroyed, a blindfolded cat fails entirely to turn when dropped, and plummets to the floor on its back. It is not yet clear which part of the labyrinth is responsible for the reaction, but most investigators believe that the utricle is the primary receptor.

The reflexes responsible for the righting tendency have been separated into five principal groups. The reactions are sequential, as are those involved in the act of swallowing.

Labyrinthine righting reflexes.   If all the sensory channels contributing to the righting reflex are obliterated, the animal lies on its side, disoriented, and makes no attempt to bring its head or its body into the horizontal position. This "zero" condition is accomplished if both labyrinths are destroyed, the animal is blindfolded, the upper cervical sensory nerve roots are cut, and a weight is applied to the upper surface of the animal's body. If, however, any one of the sensory fields obliterated by these maneuvers remains intact, its contribution can be analyzed. If an animal is blindfolded but its labyrinth is still intact, the head assumes the horizontal position irrespective of the position of the remainder of the body, i.e., the head is given orientation in space. This reaction, like that of a tonic labyrinthine response, disappears if the otoliths are destroyed. The reaction is thus static, having nothing to do with acceleratory responses. The labyrinthine righting reactions are undoubtedly primary and take the lead, as it were, in bringing the body as a whole into the upright position.

Body-on-head righting reflexes.   If a labyrinthectomized animal is blindfolded and is placed in the lateral position on a table, the head also tends to right itself. The reaction can be inhibited by placing a weighted board on the animal's upper surface. The reaction thus is due to asymmetrical stimulation of the receptors of the body surface. These reactions are seen in a thalamic primate as well as in the cat and dog.

Neck righting reflexes.   Once the neck has been turned in response to the labyrinthine and body-on-head righting reflexes, the neck muscle proprioceptors become stimulated, and the body itself then tends to be brought into a horizontal position following the head. This response likewise is seen in the primate and is accompanied by a grasping reflex presently to be described.

Body righting reflexes acting on body.   If the head and shoulders are held in the lateral position, the hindquarters tend to assume the horizontal position independently of the forward segments. This reaction can be inhibited by applying weight to the animal's upper surface.

Optical righting reflexes.   In the normal animal the eyes contribute to the righting reactions, but since the occipital lobes are absent in the thalamic preparation, visual data play no part in midbrain righting. If, however, the labyrinths and neck muscles are denervated and the animal is dropped with its eyes open, righting still occurs, but this reaction fails if such a preparation is blindfolded. The optical cues are particularly important in the primates, for optical righting can still be demonstrated in monkeys after their motor and premotor areas have been completely removed bilaterally (Chap. 11).

Grasp reflex. The thalamic primate (unlike the cat and dog) has an abnormal distribution of postural reflexes. When the animal is in the lateral position, the lowermost extremities are vigorously extended and the uppermost extremities are flexed (Fig. 122). The uppermost extremities, furthermore, exhibit an involuntary grasp reflex. When the animal is turned to the opposite side, the thalamic reflex pattern is reversed; the extremities previously extended now become flexed and also show a grasp reflex which was previously absent. The grasp reflex seems to be a general static reaction[4] and is well known to clinical neurologists in a slightly modified form termed "forced grasping."

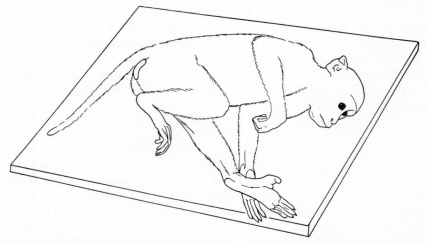

FIG. 122.   Thalamic reflex posture in decorticate monkey. Note the lowermost extremities are extended and the uppermost flexed. (From Bieber and Fulton, *Arch. Neurol. Psychiat. (Chicago)*, 1938, *39*:433–454.)

Postural Reactions Depending upon Cerebral and Cerebellar Cortex.   Two groups of reactions important to the postural mechanism clearly depend upon the integrity of the cerebral cortex[2] and the cerebellum.[20] These are the placing and the hopping reactions.

PLACING REACTIONS.   The placing reactions ensure that the foot shall be in a position suitable for normal standing and normal locomotion. These reactions are of two types, visual and nonvisual. When an animal is lowered toward a visible supporting surface, the forelimbs are put down, so that, without further adjustment, the limb is in a position to support the weight of the body. When the animal is blindfolded, a similar reaction occurs as a result of a combination of exteroceptive and proprioceptive stimuli.[2] (Contact placing, which occurs when the foot touches an object, is described in Chapter 13.)

HOPPING REACTIONS.   Hopping reactions are evoked when the body is displaced in a horizontal direction; these maintain the animal in a normal standing posture. If an animal is held so that it stands on one leg and its body is then moved sideways, the leg hops in the direction of the displacement, so that the leg remains more or less under the body. Rademaker has pointed out that the reaction is due to stretching of the muscles and probably is little affected by exteroceptive stimuli.

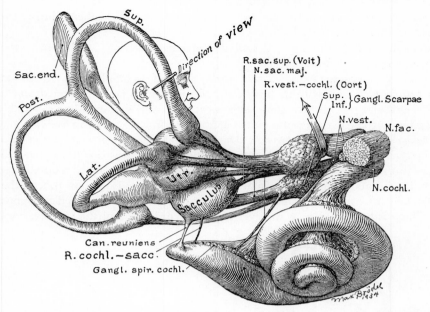

FIG. 123. Structural relations of innervation of human labyrinth. Note orientation of the three nerves supplying the macula sacculi—also Oort's nerve, passing through the cochlea. (From Hardy, *Anat. Rec.*, 1935, *59:*403–418.)

LABYRINTHINE ACCELERATING REFLEXES

Although technically an organ of special sense, the labyrinth gives rise to reflexes which orient the body in space and which hence are allied to postural reflexes. The labyrinth, often referred to as the vestibular organ, is made up of two principal parts: the semicircular canals and the otolith organs (saccule and utricle), as seen in Figure 123.

POSITION AND STRUCTURE OF LABYRINTH. The membranous semicircular canals lie within the bony labyrinth. These canals contain endolymph which communicates through fine openings with the endolymph in the utricle. The canals lie in three planes that are, approximately at least, at right angles to the mesial or sagittal plane of the body, and each of the vertical canals makes an angle of about 45 degrees with this mesial plane. The plane of each anterior canal is parallel to that of the posterior or inferior vertical canal of the opposite side of the head, as represented in Figure 124. At one end of each canal, near its junction with the utricle, is the swelling known as the ampulla. Within the ampulla lies the crista acustica, containing hair cells which communicate with the nerve fibers and which therefore are considered to be the receptors of the organ. Sitting astride the hair cells and crista is a gelatinous partition known as the cupula, which rises like a swinging door to the roof of the ampulla, filling the whole cross section of this structure. Once considered a fixation artefact, the cupula is now known to be a real structure of functional importance. It responds in a highly damped fashion to hydrostatic forces acting upon it through the endolymph. The nerve fibers distributed to the hair cells pass into the vestibular branch of the VIIIth nerve.

Function of the Semicircular Canals. The work of Flourens and of the investigators who followed him* made it evident that a primary function of the semicircular canals is to register movement of the body in space; expressed more precisely, the vestibular organ responds to any *change in the rate of movement*, i.e., to acceleration or deceleration. In fast aircraft, for example, very intense acceleratory forces may develop, particularly in the "pull-out" from a dive or in a close turn. In these circumstances the semicircular canals may be so profoundly stimulated that the pilot becomes completely

* The literature on the semicircular canals and the vestibule is very extensive. The principal bibliography may be obtained from the works by Camis,[6] and by McNalley and Stuart.[11]

disoriented in space, especially if he should inadvertently turn his head during the high acceleration (Coriolis effect).*

Acceleratory reflexes may be described under two headings: (i) linear acceleration and (ii) angular acceleration.

ACCELERATORY REFLEXES. *Linear acceleration.* If a blindfolded cat is suddenly lowered through the air with its head down, its forelegs become extended and its toes spread (vestibular placing reaction). This is the normal response to linear acceleration. The obvious purpose of the reaction is to facilitate landing after a jump from a high place.

Angular acceleration and nystagmus. During rapid rotation around the vertical axis of the body, a series of reactions affect the muscles of the eyes, neck, limbs and trunk. As the head turns, the eyes turn slowly in the *opposite* direction in order to maintain the gaze at a fixed point and to maintain visual contact with the environment. But, as the body turns farther, the eyes swing rapidly in the direction of the rotation and fix upon a new point, which is held in view as the eyes again move slowly and the rotation continues.

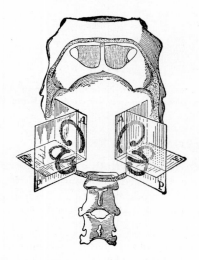

FIG. 124. Position of semicircular canals in birds. The three canals lie in planes at right angles to one another. External or horizontal canals (*E*) on the two sides lie in same plane. Anterior canal of one side (*A*) lies in a plane parallel to that of the posterior canal (*P*) of the other side.

This alternate movement of the eyes—a quick refixation phase followed by a slow fixation deviation—is termed *nystagmus*. The direction of the nystagmus is designated clinically by the direction of its quick phase.

When rotation continues for a time at a constant rate, the nystagmus disappears; this disappearance indicates that the stimulus for the response is acceleration rather than continuous motion. If the acceleration is suddenly stopped, the involuntary eye movements commence once again, but in the opposite direction; i.e., *in postrotational nystagmus the direction of the quick phase is the opposite of the direction of the preceding acceleration* (and of the quick phase during rotation). Combining this rule with a knowledge of the physiologic significance of the eye movements makes it unnecessary to remember the direction of the initial nystagmus. During rotation, the eyes move slowly in the direction opposite that of rotation in order to maintain fixation, and the quick or refixation movement is in the *same direction as the rotation*. Therefore, in postrotational nystagmus the quick phase is opposite to the direction of the prior rotation.

Nystagmus may be horizontal, vertical or rotatory in direction, since the particular response depends upon which semicircular canals or groups of canals are stimulated, i.e., upon the direction of the acceleration. If the head is bent forward at an angle of 30 degrees, the horizontal semicircular canals are in the plane of rotation about the vertical

* Coriolis, G. G. *Traité de la mécanique des corps solides et de calcul de l'effet des machines*, Paris, 1829.

axis of the body and they become responsible for the nystagmus caused by the rotation.

Nystagmus induced by rotation or, more often, by irrigation of the ear with cold water is a clinical test of labyrinthine function. Nystagmus may occur "spontaneously" after a variety of lesions affecting the sense organs or the neural pathways connecting the labyrinth with the motor nuclei innervating the eye muscles. Such nystagmus is of great aid in localizing lesions of the brain.

Mechanism of stimulation of the canals. If the fluid in the semicircular canals moves, the mechanisms for stimulation of the hair cells during and after rotation are easily visualized. While the small diameter of the membranous canals and the consequent capillary forces and frictional resistances argue against fluid movements, direct visualization indicates that movement actually occurs—at least in the semicircular canals of fish. Steinhausen[21] devised an ingenious method of visualizing the semicircular canals in the living animal through the use of dyes, and Dohlman[7] succeeded in introducing a drop

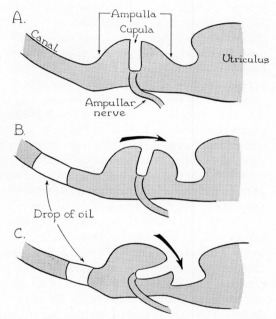

FIG. 125. Ampulla and semicircular cana of living fish (pike) before and during angular acceleration. *A*, Normal relations of ampulla, cupula and utriculus in semicircular canal. In *B*, a drop of oil has been inserted in canal. Note in *C* that cupula, nearly vertical in *B*, bends toward utricle as result of flow of endolymph into ampulla. (After Dohlman. *Proc. R. Soc. Med.*, 1935, *28:*1371–1380.)

of oil into the canal so that he could follow the movement of the endolymph during angular acceleration.

Steinhausen found that the cupula (Fig. 125) bends over toward the utricle when endolymph moves into the ampulla and slowly returns to its resting position after the acceleration stops.

The relations of the canal to the ampullar nerve, the crista and the cupula are shown in Figure 125*A*. In Figure 125*B* one sees a semicircular canal at rest with a drop of oil in the lumen of the canal. In Figure 125*C* the same canal is shown during angular acceleration; the oil droplet has moved forward, and the cupula is bent over through an angle of some 30 degrees. Dohlman points out that, when the rates of displacement and return of the cupula are actually determined, they coincide precisely with the duration of nystagmus during the acceleration and with that of the postrotational nystagmus which follows. To quote:

"The cupula deviates during, perhaps, the first, or possibly also the second, revolution as long as the rotation is accelerated. On reaching a constant speed the rotation no longer affects the fluid or the cupula in any way. The deviation of the cupula is now, however, gradually diminished by its elasticity; and after about half a minute it has returned to the original position. It is to be expected that the nystagmus *during rotation* should cease when the cupula resumes its normal position, and it does, as Buys showed by nystagmographic registration several years ago.

"When rotation stops we again have, as a result of the effect of retardation on the endolymph, a deviation of the cupula, this time in the opposite direction. A post-rotational nystagmus occurs, and lasts as long as the cupula needs to return once more, through its elasticity, to its starting position. This explains why a post-rotatory nystagmus does not occur until after a longer continued rotation. And it explains why we must have a rotational time of about 20 seconds to obtain the longest nystagmus for any rotational speed. For the cupula has by that time regained its initial position by its elasticity, so that it might be ready for the maximal displacement in the opposite direction through the inertia of the endolymph when the rotation ceases. So the nystagmus *during* rotation, like the *post-rotational* nystagmus, is a consequence of the deviation of the cupula; and its duration depends on the time the cupula requires to reassume its normal position."[7]

In human subjects in whom the membranous labyrinth had been opened to expose the horizontal canal to mechanical stimulation, suddenly applied pressure caused a horizontal nystagmus lasting about 20 seconds.[7]

CLINICAL CORRELATIONS: CALORIC REACTIONS.   In 1908, the Swedish neurologist Robert Bárány[1] found that nystagmus occurred about one minute after the external auditory canal was irrigated with water cooler than body temperature and that the characteristics of the nystagmus varied with the position of the head in space. This procedure has become a useful, if somewhat uncomfortable, clinical test of labyrinthine function, largely replacing the rotation test. Various theories have been proposed to explain the mechanism of caloric nystagmus, and that postulating convection currents appears to be the most satisfactory. During caloric stimulation, the endolymph within the canal is gradually cooled at the point nearest the auditory meatus. This focal chilling causes the endolymph to flow, thus leading to a deviation of the cupula caused by the convection currents. The difference between the two forms of stimulation—rotational and caloric—lies in this: rotation suddenly stimulates both labyrinths, whereas in the caloric test there is a gradual stimulation of only one labyrinth. Thus, caloric stimulation permits the neurologist to determine which labyrinth is affected and to estimate from the duration of the nystagmus the degree of impairment.

States of abnormal paroxysmal stimulation of the semicircular canals or of the nerves which innervate them also occur, the classic syndrome being the one described in the nineteenth century by the French neurologist Menière. Characteristically, the afflicted patient experiences buzzing in the ear (tinnitus), hearing loss and attacks of dizziness during which he is thrown to the ground. Failure or sluggishness of the nystagmic response to caloric stimulation is diagnostic and also indicates that the disturbance destroys function as well as stimulating it. Section of the VIIIth nerve on the affected side relieves the dizziness and improves hearing, because the normal ear hears better when the buzzing in the other ear has ended.

Utricle and Saccule.   In summarizing the vast and conflicting literature concerning the discrete functions of the various parts of the labyrinth, McNalley and Stuart[11] drew attention to the work of Ross, who succeeded in recording action currents from individual fibers of the vestibular nerve. He found that the labyrinthine receptors can be divided into three groups, those responding to slow mechanical vibration, those responding to tilting movements (linear acceleration) and those responding to rotatory movements. It is quite clear that the semicircular canals are stimulated by rotatory movements and probably not by gravity per se; the cupula projection from the floor of the ampulla would not respond to an increased gravitational force. The otolith organ in the utricle responds to both linear acceleration and tilting; and, in frogs, destruction of the utricle without encroachment upon the semicircular canals has abolished the normal response to linear acceleration and tilting.

Evidence concerning the function of the *saccule* is also conflicting, but, according to McNalley and Stuart, the consensus at the present time is that the saccule is not an essential part of the vestibular mechanism but rather is an organ associated with the cochlea designed for the reception of slow vibrational stimuli.

REFERENCES

1. BÁRÁNY, R. *Med. Klinik*, 1908, *4*:1903–1905.
2. BARD, P. *Harvey Lect.*, 1937–38, *33*:143–169.
3. BARD, P. and MACHT, M. B. Pp. 55–75 in *Ciba Foundation Symposium on the neurological basis of behaviour*, G. E. W. WOLSTENHOLME and C. M. O'CONNOR, eds. Boston, Little, Brown and Co., 1958.
4. BIEBER, I. and FULTON, J. F. *Arch. Neurol. Psychiat. (Chicago)*, 1938, *39*:433–454.
5. BRODAL, A. *The reticular formation of the brain stem. Anatomical aspects and functional correlations.* London, Oliver and Boyd, 1957, vii, 87 pp.
6. CAMIS, M. *The physiology of the vestibular apparatus*, trans. by R. S. CREED. London, Oxford University Press, 1930.
7. DOHLMAN, G. *Proc. R. Soc. Med.*, 1935, *28*:1371–1380.
8. GERNANDT, B. E. and THULIN, C. A. *J. Neurophysiol.*, 1955, *18*:113–129.
9. GRANIT, R., HOLMGREN, B. and MERTON, P. A. *J. Physiol.*, 1955, *130*:213–224.
10. GRANIT, R. and KAADA, B. *Acta physiol. scand.*, 1953, *27*:130–160.
11. McNALLEY, W. J. and STUART, E. A. *War Med.*, 1942, *2*:683–771.
12. MAGNUS, R. *Körperstellung*. Berlin, J. Springer, 1924.
13. MAGNUS, R. *Lancet*, 1926, *2*:531–536; 585–588.
14. MAGOUN, H. W. *Physiol. Rev.*, 1950, *30*:459–474.
15. MAGOUN, H. W. and RHINES, R. *J. Neurophysiol.*, 1946, *9*:165–171.
16. RADEMAKER, G. G. J. *Das Stehn.* Berlin, J. Springer, 1931.
17. RADEMAKER, G. G. J. and TER BRAAK, J. W. G. *Acta oto-laryng. (Stockh.)*, 1936, *23*:313–343.
18. RHINES, R. and MAGOUN, H. W. *J. Neurophysiol.*, 1946, *9*:219–229.
19. SHERRINGTON, C. S. *J. Physiol.*, 1898, *22*:319–332.
20. SPRAGUE, J. M. and CHAMBERS, W. W. *Amer. J. Physiol.*, 1954, *176*:52–64.
21. STEINHAUSEN, W. *Z. Hals-, Nas.- u. Ohrenheilk.*, 1931, *29*:211–216.

CHAPTER 9

The Autonomic Nervous System

By HARRY D. PATTON

IN the foregoing chapters attention was focused on reflex systems in which the effector organ is skeletal muscle and the response is skeletal movement. Such reflex arcs are termed *somatic reflexes*. Smooth muscle, glands and the conducting tissue of the heart also receive motor nerve supplies which, when reflexly activated, alter the functional state of the innervated organ; such reflexes are termed *autonomic reflexes*.

Autonomic nerve discharge to smooth muscles and glands has an important role in visceral and glandular responses to environmental changes; for example, reflex alteration of arteriolar diameter, mediated over autonomic motor fibers supplying vascular smooth muscle, is at least partly responsible for the shifting of blood from one vascular bed to another in accordance with physiologic demand. Similarly, although not initiating the beat of the heart, reflex discharges over the autonomic nerves supplying the cardiac pacemaker modulate and regulate the rate of beating, so that the varying demands upon the pumping system are automatically met. Numerous examples of the regulation of visceral and glandular structures by autonomic reflex arcs will be encountered in subsequent chapters. This chapter is concerned with the general properties and organization of the autonomic nervous system.

The distinction between autonomic and somatic motor outflows is based on both anatomic and functional grounds. Before entrance upon a detailed description of the autonomic system, a brief account of its unique and distinctive properties is appropriate. Anatomically the autonomic outflow differs from the somatic outflow in the location

As in the somatic motor nerve, the nerve action potential is brief and solitary, but the electromyogram shows a series of somewhat asynchronous deflections, which persist long after the nerve fibers have repolarized. The tension record shows, further, that each muscle action potential is associated with increments of contraction, so that the resulting tension curve is prolonged and bumpy, resembling an unfused tetanus of skeletal muscle.

Persistence of electrical and mechanical activity long beyond the duration of the excitatory nerve impulses is typical of autonomic neuroeffectors and persuasively suggests that the nerve exerts its action on effectors by liberating a chemical transmitter agent which remains and continues to act on the effector after the nerve action has ceased. Observations of this sort led to the theory of humoral transmitters. It has been pointed out that there is reason to believe that somatic neuromuscular transmission is also accomplished by the liberation of a chemical transmitter (probably acetylcholine) which depolarizes the end-plate, but that transmitter is destroyed rapidly and its action is brief. At autonomic junctions the slow destruction and prolonged action of the transmitter make the chemical nature of transmission much more immediately obvious.

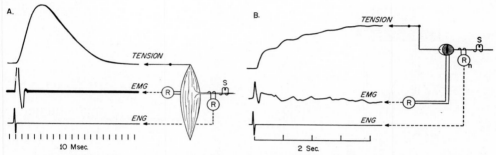

FIG. 128. Neuromuscular transmission in somatic and autonomic effector systems. *A*, Simultaneously recorded electroneurogram, electromyogram and mechanical response of skeletal nerve muscle preparation following single shock to motor nerve. *B*, Simultaneously recorded electroneurogram, electromyogram and mechanical response of nictitating membrane following single shock to postganglionic motor nerve. Note difference in time scales. (Partly after Eccles and Magladery, *J. Physiol.*, 1937, *90*:31–99.)

Cholinergic fibers. Humoral transmission in an autonomic neuroeffector system was first clearly demonstrated by Otto Loewi.[8] Because cardiac inhibition resulting from vagal stimulation far outlasts the period of nerve stimulation, Loewi suspected a humoral transmitter. In the experiment illustrated in Figure 129 fluid perfusing a donor frog heart (*D*) was used to perfuse a second, recipient heart (*R*). When the vagus nerve supplying heart *D* was stimulated, cardiac arrest occurred; shortly thereafter heart *R* also stopped beating, an event implicating an inhibitory chemical agent liberated into the perfusion fluid at the vagal endings in heart *D* and then carried to heart *R*. Loewi noncommittally termed the vagal inhibitory transmitter *Vagusstoff*.

Identification of Loewi's *Vagusstoff* followed from Dale's studies[3] on the pharmacologic actions of choline and its esters. He noted that the acetyl ester of choline is *parasympathomimetic*, i.e., when injected into the blood stream, acetylcholine acts upon autonomic effectors, including the heart, in a manner similar to or mimicking the action exerted on these effectors by their respective parasympathetic nerves. The drug atropine blocks the action of acetylcholine on smooth muscle and similarly blocks the action of parasympathetic nerves on their effectors. The drug eserine, on the other hand, potentiates the action of acetylcholine by inactivating the enzyme cholinesterase, which splits acetylcholine into the relatively inert choline and acetic acid. Eserine also potentiates the effect of parasympathetic nerve stimulation. Such observations provided presumptive evidence that Loewi's *Vagusstoff*—as well as the transmitter at all other parasympathetic postganglionic endings—is either acetylcholine or a closely related substance.

Subsequent investigations have revealed that acetylcholine is also the transmitter agent liberated by autonomic preganglionic fibers, sympathetic as well as parasympathetic. The brief action of the transmitter in ganglia (and at the somatic neuromuscular junction) results from high concentrations of cholinesterase at these sites, so that the liberated transmitter is destroyed within the refractory period of the postjunctional cell.

Nerves which liberate an acetylcholine-like transmitter are called *cholinergic fibers.* In summary, these include somatic motor nerves, all autonomic preganglionic fibers and all parasympathetic postganglionic fibers. In addition, the sympathetic postganglionic fibers supplying sweat glands are also cholinergic (see below).

Sympathetic postganglionic mediators. It has already been pointed out that there is reason to suspect that sympathetic postganglionic endings liberate a humoral transmitter which is destroyed relatively slowly and which may act to prolong depolarization in sympathetic effectors. The proof that sympathetic nerve endings liberate a humoral

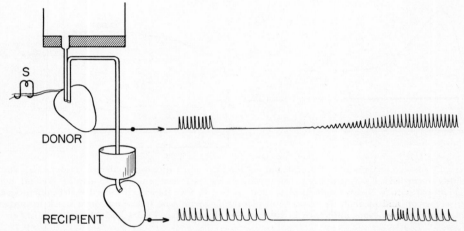

FIG. 129. Loewi's experiment demonstrating humoral mechanism of vagal inhibition of heart. Stimulation of vagus supplying donor heart released chemical inhibitory mediator which not only arrested donor heart but, after diffusion into perfusion fluid, also arrested recipient heart. (After Bain *Quart. J. exp. Physiol.*, 1932, 22:269–274.)

agent under physiologic conditions was first provided by Cannon and his associates when they analyzed the mechanism of the cardiac acceleration which accompanies exercise and emotional excitement. Even after the heart was completely denervated by severing of the vagi and the cardiac accelerator nerves, these investigators observed that struggling, excitement or physical exercise induced a prompt (one minute) increase in heart rate of 80 to 100 beats per minute. Such acceleration results partly from the liberation into the circulation of epinephrine by the adrenal medulla. However, adrenal secretion does not entirely account for the response. Cannon found that, after the adrenals were removed or denervated, a moderate (25 to 30 beats per minute) but delayed (three minutes) increase in heart rate followed emotional excitement. Delayed emotional tachycardia persisted in animals subjected to hypophysectomy and bilateral abdominal and cervical sympathectomy. However, complete removal of the abdominal and thoracic sympathetic chains abolished the response.

These experiments implicated an extra-adrenal humoral agent released into the blood stream during exercise or excitement and capable of exerting a sympathetic-like (acceleratory) influence on the heart. Derivation of this substance from sympathetic nerve endings was indicated by experiments in which sympathetic nerves were stimulated electrically. When injected into the blood stream, perfusates of organs collected during stimulation of their sympathetic nerves caused cardiac acceleration and increased blood pressure. Years earlier, Elliott had presciently observed that epinephrine, the secretion of the adrenal medulla, is a *sympathomimetic agent;* i.e., it mimics the action of sympathetic postganglionic stimulation. Although the actions of the sympathetic mediator and of epinephrine were very similar, there were some differences, and Cannon cautiously termed the mediator *sympathin.* It is now known that both the adrenal medulla and the sympathetic postganglionic endings secrete at least two catechol amines—epinephrine and norepinephrine. Although closely related structurally, these two substances do not invariably exert identical actions on effector organs; a full catalogue of their pharmacologic properties can be found in textbooks of pharmacology or in von Euler's monograph.[5] The proportions of epinephrine and norepinephrine secreted appear to vary from nerve to nerve, but norepinephrine is the major sympathetic postganglionic mediator and probably corresponds to Cannon's sympathin. Adrenal medullary secretion, on the other hand, appears to be principally epinephrine, at least in man.

Nerve fibers secreting epinephrine and/or norepinephrine are called *adrenergic fibers.* Most sympathetic postganglionic fibers are adrenergic. A notable exception is the sympathetic postganglionic innervation of the sweat glands, which is cholinergic and readily blocked by atropine. Other sympathetic postganglionic cholinergic systems have been postulated but are not so well documented.

In passing it may be noted that the discovery of the adrenergic nature of sympathetic postganglionic fibers renders less anomalous the absence of a peripheral synapse in the adrenal medullary innervation. Indeed, the adrenal medullary cells and the sympathetic postganglionic neurons are very similar, since they secrete the same substance and derive from the same embryologic tissues.

Effect of autonomic nerve impulses on membrane potentials of postjunctional cells.[6] The technique of intracellular recording, so fruitful in studying junctional transmission at muscle end-plates and central synapses, has had limited application to the study of autonomic transmission, principally because the effector cells are generally small and hence tolerate penetration poorly. An exception is cardiac tissue, from which satisfactory intracellular recordings can be obtained. However, a special problem is created when movement of the spontaneously beating heart dislodges the electrode. This accident can be avoided by the ingenious "dangle electrode" technique devised by Woodbury and Brady,[14] who mounted the electrode on a fine flexible wire. Once inside the fiber, the electrode rides freely with the fiber's contractions.

In the spontaneously beating heart, the beat originates in the sinoatrial node, a small nodule of specialized tissue in the wall of the right atrium (see Chap. 26). Intracellular recordings from this tissue show rhythmically recurring slow depolarizations (the "pacemaker" potential). When depolarization proceeds to threshold, an action potential is generated (Fig. 130A). No pacemaker potential is seen in recordings from atrial fibers (Fig. 130B). The cause of the pacemaker depolarization is not clear; it appears to reflect a slow leakage of Na^+ into the cell.

Figure 130C shows intracellular recordings from pacemaker tissue before, during and after vagal stimulation. During the stimulation period the membrane became hyperpolarized, and the rhythmically recurring depolarizations were abolished. With cessation of vagal stimulation, the pacemaker cell slowly depolarized as the transmitter was destroyed, until threshold was reached and an action potential was generated. During the first few beats, the rate of rise of the pacemaker potential was slow, so that the heart rate remained depressed; also, the duration of the action potential was curtailed. In subsequent beats, the recorded potentials gradually resumed the prestimulation configuration.

Although direct evidence is not available, it is likely that hyperpolarization during vagal stimulation reflects an increased permeability of the pacemaker membrane to K^+ and Cl^-, so that the membrane potential is driven toward a voltage determined jointly by these two ions—a voltage offsetting the one resulting from the inward leakage of Na^+. Also in accord with this interpretation is the shortening of the action potential. This shortening is a manifestation of rapid repolarization which, in pacemaker tissue, as in nerve and skeletal muscle cells, is the consequence of increased permeability of the membrane to K^+. It will be readily recognized that the action of the vagal transmitter, presumably acetylcholine, is quite different from the action of acetylcholine on the motor end-plate. The discrepancy emphasizes the extremely varied responses of different tissues to a chemical agent.

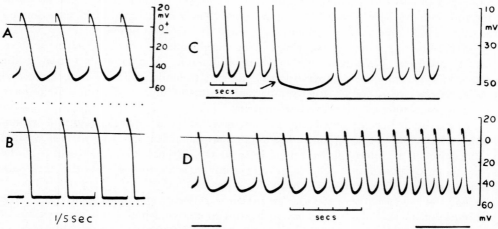

FIG. 130.   Intracellular recordings from frog atrial cells beating normally during vagal inhibition and during sympathetic acceleration. *A*, Record from pacemaker cell in normally beating heart; note pacemaker potential (slow depolarization preceding each beat). *B*, Record from atrial fiber in normally beating heart; note absence of pacemaker potential (flat baseline preceding spike). *C*, Records from pacemaker cell during vagal stimulation; gain is high so that peaks of action potentials and zero reference lines are not shown. During vagal stimulation, indicated by break in bottom line, cell becomes hyperpolarized and pacemaker potentials and spikes are in abeyance. Note decreased slope of pacemaker potential in first two beats after recovery. *D*, Records from pacemaker cell during sympathetic stimulation, indicated by break in bottom line. Slope of pacemaker potential increases and rate accelerates. (From Hutter and Trautwein, *J. gen. Physiol.*, 1956, *39*:715–733.)

Figure 130*D* shows the effect of sympathetic stimulation on potentials recorded intracellularly from a pacemaker cell. The firing level remains constant, but the slope of the pacemaker potential increases. As a result, the threshold voltage is reached more rapidly, and the rate of firing increases accordingly. Simultaneously, the "overshoot" of the spike increases, so that the over-all amplitude of the action potential is greater. These events are satisfactorily explained if it is assumed that the sympathetic transmitter increases the permeability of the pacemaker membrane to Na^+ ions and thus permits more rapid depolarization to the firing level and a closer approximation during the spike to the Na^+ equilibrium potential.

Denervation Hypersensitivity.[2]   When an autonomic effector is denervated, it becomes increasingly sensitive to chemical agents. This sensitivity is most pronounced when the organ is directly denervated by section of its *postganglionic* nerves (Cannon's law of denervation). Such denervation hypersensitivity was first described by Budge, who produced Horner's syndrome in rabbits. *Horner's syndrome*, which results from interruption of the sympathetic supply to the face, consists of pupillary constriction (miosis), drooping of the eyelid (ptosis), and flushing of the face owing to loss of vasoconstrictor tone.

Since the postganglionic sympathetic supply to the face originates in the superior cervical ganglion, which receives a preganglionic sympathetic input from the fibers ascending the cervical chain, Horner's syndrome may be experimentally produced either by dividing the cervical chain to interrupt the preganglionic fibers, or by a transection of the postganglionic fibers emerging from the ganglion. Budge found that, when a preganglionic section on one side and a postganglionic section on the other were performed, the resultant Horner's syndrome was initially symmetrical bilaterally. With the passage of time, however, the pupil on the side of the postganglionic denervation was larger than the one on the preganglionically denervated side, and the discrepancy was intensified when the animal was frightened or subjected to emotional excitement. Budge could not explain the phenomenon of the paradoxical pupil; but it is now known that denervation hypersensitivity to circulating epinephrine (released into the blood stream

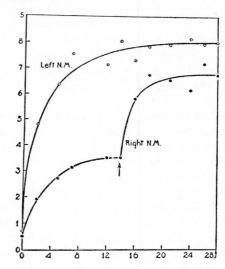

FIG. 131. Contractile responses of denervated nictitating membrane to epinephrine. *Ordinates*, Amplitude of isotonic contraction (cm.) in response to 10 μg. of epinephrine. *Abscissa*, Days after initial denervation. At day 0, left membrane denervated postganglionically, right membrane denervated preganglionically. At day 14 (*arrow*), right membrane denervated postganglionically. (From Hampel, *Amer. J. Physiol.*, 1935, *111*:611–621.)

during emotional excitement) accounts for the paradoxical pupil as well as for a number of similar phenomena in other denervated organs.

Even skeletal muscle displays the phenomenon of denervation hypersensitivity. Following section of the motor nerve, the muscle end-plates become hypersensitive to acetylcholine. Fibrillation in denervated skeletal muscle presumably results from the depolarization of hypersensitive end-plates by minute quantities of circulating acetylcholine or other excitatory chemical substances.

A quantitative study of denervation hypersensitivity is illustrated in Figure 131. The response of the nictitating membrane to a standard dose of epinephrine was measured on successive days following postganglionic denervation on the right side. Both nictitating membranes underwent a gradually increased sensitivity to epinephrine, as evidenced by the amplified responses, but the sensitivity was much more prominent in the membrane postganglionically denervated. On the 14th day the right superior cervical ganglion was removed, and the sensitivity of the related membrane increased, approaching that displayed by the right membrane. If denervation is caused by crushing of the nerves, so that they may regenerate, hypersensitivity occurs but wanes as the regenerating fibers re-establish connections with the muscle cells.

The mechanism of denervation hypersensitivity is not understood. It is probably partly attributable to the demonstrable disappearance from the denervated structure of the enzymes which normally inactivate the transmitter (cholinesterase or monoaminoxidase). This explanation is at best only partial because the increased sensitivity is not specific; the denervated nictitating membrane becomes hypersensitive not only to epinephrine but also to acetylcholine, pilocarpine, calcium, potassium, arterenol, tyramine and several nonphenolic aromatic amines.

Surgery of the autonomic nervous system and denervation hypersensitivity. To conclude this chapter an example may be given of the application of the functional and anatomic principles outlined above to a practical clinical problem. To relieve any of a number of disorders, the therapeutic procedure is surgical interruption of the autonomic nerve supply to the diseased organ. The signs of these diseases and the appropriate surgical procedures are discussed in detail by White *et al.,*[13] but for our purposes a single disease may be considered.

Raynaud's disease is a peripheral vascular disease in which there are painful paroxysms of cutaneous vasospasm (usually in the fingers or toes) so intense that gangrene may result. The paroxysms are often precipitated by exposure to cold or by emotional stress. While it is not certain that the vasospasm results from excessive sympathetic discharge, sympathectomy of the affected regions is nevertheless a rational procedure, since impulses in sympathetic fibers regulate vasoconstriction of cutaneous vessels and since interruption of these fibers increases blood flow through the skin.*

The vasoconstrictor pathway to the hand originates in preganglionic neurons situated in spinal segments T_2 to T_7; most of the postganglionic cell bodies are in the stellate ganglion, although a varying small number lie in the second and third thoracic ganglion. The hand can thus be sympathectomized by removal of the stellate, T_2 and T_3 ganglia. This operation has the defect of producing a Horner's syndrome, since the preganglionic fibers ascending the chain to the superior cervical ganglion are interrupted. A more serious objection is that the sympathectomy of the hand is postganglionic, and the denervated vessels become so sensitive to epinephrine that cold exposure or emotional stress (both of which increase adrenal medullary secretion) may precipitate vasospastic attacks even more severe than those occurring before operation.

A much more successful procedure is preganglionic sympathectomy. The sympathetic chain is divided between the third and fourth ganglia; this interrupts preganglionic fibers originating in segments T_4 to T_7 and ascending the chain. To interrupt the fibers originating in the T_2 to T_3 segments, the segmental nerves are cut at a point central to the entry of the postganglionic fibers via the gray rami. Not only are the consequences of denervation hypersensitivity thus avoided, but Horner's syndrome does not occur because preganglionic fibers passing from the T_1 segment to the superior cervical ganglion are intact.

REFERENCES

1. CANNON, W. B. and ROSENBLUETH, A. *Autonomic neuro-effector systems.* New York, Macmillan, 1937, xiv, 229 pp.
2. CANNON, W. B. and ROSENBLUETH, A. *The supersensitivity of denervated structures.* New York, Macmillan, 1949, x, 245 pp.
3. DALE, H. H. *J. Pharmacol.* 1914, *6*:147–190.
4. ELIASSON, S., LINDGREN, P. and UVNÄS, B. *Acta physiol. scand.,* 1952, *27*:18–37.
5. VON EULER, U. S. *Noradrenaline.* Springfield, Ill., Charles C Thomas, 1955, xxi, 382 pp.
6. HUTTER, O. F. and TRAUTWEIN, W. *J. gen. Physiol.,* 1956, *39*:715–733.
7. KUNTZ, A. *The autonomic nervous system.* Philadelphia, Lea and Febiger, 1953, 605 pp.

.* In chronic Raynaud's disease anatomic changes in the vessels eventually prevent dilation even in the absence of vasoconstrictor nerves. In such cases sympathectomy is of no value. A standard procedure is to perform a diagnostic procaine block of the stellate ganglion. If this procedure does not cause increased blood flow to the hand, as indicated by a rise in skin temperature, surgery is not recommended.

8. LOEWI, O. *Pflüg. Arch. Physiol.*, 1921, *189:* 239–242.

9. LUNDBERG, A. *Acta physiol. scand.*, 1957, *40:* 21–34.

10. MITCHELL, G. A. G. *Anatomy of the autonomic nervous system.* Edinburgh, E. and S. Livingstone Ltd., 1953, xvi, 356 pp.

11. MITCHELL, G. A. G. *Cardiovascular innervation.* Edinburgh, E. and S. Livingstone Ltd. 1956, xii, 356 pp.

12. MORGAN, M. W., JR., OLMSTEAD, J. M. D. and WATROUS, W. G. *Amer. J. Physiol.*, 1940, *128:*588–591.

13. WHITE, J. C., SMITHWICK, R. H. and SIMEONE, F. A. *The autonomic nervous system.* New York, Macmillan, 1952, xxii, 569 pp.

14. WOODBURY, J. W. and BRADY, A. J. *Science*, 1956, *123:*100–101.

CHAPTER 10

Higher Control of Autonomic Outflows:
The Hypothalamus

By HARRY D. PATTON

IN the previous chapter it was pointed out that visceral organs, glands and blood vessels—structures important in the maintenance of a constant internal environment (homeostasis)—are regulated by the autonomic nervous system. The preganglionic autonomic neurons are maintained in a continuous but quantitatively variable state of activity by a host of inputs. Some of these inputs are segmental in origin (dorsal roots); others originate in supraspinal structures and descend the neural axis to reach the levels of autonomic outflow.

Some idea of the relative role of supraspinal as contrasted to segmental control of the spinal autonomic outflows (sympathetic and sacral parasympathetic) can be obtained by studying autonomic reflexes in animals subjected to transection of the neural axis at different levels. After the spinal cord is transected above the level of T_1, for example, the spinal autonomic outflows are regulated solely by segmental inputs. The immediate consequence of such a transection is profound depression of all autonomic reflexes,[54] paralleling the depression of somatic reflexes (spinal shock). Blood pressure drops precipitously, owing to a decrease in the sympathetic discharge to the visceral vascular bed and a consequent diminution in the peripheral resistance to flow.* Temperature regulation is lacking, sweating is absent, and the body temperature changes toward that of the environment. The bladder and bowel are paralyzed, and sexual reflexes (erection and ejaculation) are lacking.

After several weeks spinal shock wanes and the segmental autonomic reflexes reappear. The blood pressure rises from the low levels typical of the spinal shock period and fluctuates in response to noxious stimulation of the skin. (Permanently lacking, however, is the adaptive vasoconstriction which normally prevents gravitational hypotension when the body is moved from a horizontal to a vertical position, because the spinal

---

* Regulation of heart rate remains because it is governed largely by vagal impulses.

pathways which connect the pressure-monitoring receptors in the aortic arch and the carotid sinus with the sympathetic outflows are severed.) At the same time vestiges of temperature regulatory mechanisms reappear; sweating returns, and noxious stimulation of the skin may elicit troublesomely profuse sweating. Immersion of one extremity in cold water induces vasoconstriction in the contralateral limb, and, conversely, heating one limb is followed by vasodilatation in the other. Nevertheless, even after long recovery periods, temperature regulation remains sluggish, and the smoothly coordinated adjustments of blood vessels, sweat glands, pilomotor muscles and skeletal muscles which make the normal mammalian body temperature independent of environmental temperature are never recovered. Similarly, micturition, defecation and sexual reflexes return and can be elicited by stimulation of the skin of the thigh or genitalia. Micturition in the paraplegic, however, often fails to evacuate the bladder completely. Even ignoring the acute effects of spinal shock, we may conclude that autonomic reflex arcs are highly dependent on supraspinal inputs.

The contribution of medullary structures to the regulation of autonomic reflexes may be inferred from studies on decerebrate preparations in which the brain stem is sectioned at the intercollicular level. Such preparations rarely survive more than a few weeks (and then only with most exacting postoperative care), so that only the acute effects of interruption of suprabulbar pathways can be studied.* The status of autonomic reflexes in such preparations resembles in general that in the spinal preparation. Temperature regulation is lacking, and body temperature fluctuates with environmental temperature. A major difference, however, is that arterial blood pressure is maintained rather well in the decerebrate preparation in contrast to the profound hypotension of the spinal animal. Moreover, both the heart and the visceral vessels respond appropriately to postural changes, so that perfusion pressure remains constant despite changes of the position of the body in space. Retention of these responses is due to the retention of the medullary vasomotor and cardioregulatory centers and their afferent inputs via the IXth (carotid sinus) and Xth (aortic arch) cranial nerves. The threshold for the micturition reflex is decreased in the decerebrate cat, an example of release of reflex function from supracollicular inhibition. The released center, however, is in the pons, not the medulla (see Chap. 47).

Finally, if the test section is made at a higher level by removal of the cerebral cortex, residual autonomic function gives some indication of the relative participation of supracollicular brain stem structures in the regulation of autonomic function. Cats and dogs survive decortication surprisingly well and can be kept in good health for long periods. Blood pressure is well maintained, temperature regulation is normal, and the bladder, bowel and sexual functions are essentially those of the intact animal.

The full measure of autonomic reactivity in the decorticate preparation is seen when a mildly noxious stimulus such as lightly pinching the skin is applied. Such stimulation evokes a paroxysm of behavior which, because it simulates rage, was named "sham rage" by Cannon and Bard. Sham rage is a coordinated reaction pattern with many components mediated by autonomic (principally sympathetic) outflows. Thus, in addition to somatic attitudes of anger (arching of back, spitting, snarling, and protrusion of claws), the decorticate animal provoked into sham rage displays piloerection, pupillary dilation, tachycardia and elevated blood pressure. In striking contrast, the decerebrate preparation never shows such explosive behavior.†

---

* "Chronic" decerebrate preparations which will survive a month or more can be obtained if the hypophysis and a small isolated island of the overlying hypothalamus are left intact.[4]

† In response to strong nociceptive stimuli, chronic decerebrate cats show some fragments of affective behavior, e.g., vocalization, protrusion of claws, running movements and acceleration of pulse and respiration. The responses are poorly coordinated, and the threshold for evoking them is high.[4]

The full significance of sham rage is discussed in Chapter 22; for now it need only be emphasized that the presence of sham rage in the decorticate preparation and its absence in the decerebrate preparation indicate that structures lying between the cortex and midbrain influence powerfully, via descending connections, the lower brain stem and spinal autonomic centers. Moreover, this control is well integrated, so that discharges over both autonomic and somatic pathways are blended into an effective behavioral pattern. This integrative center lies in the hypothalamus.

Prior to and since the discovery of its role in sham rage, the hypothalamus has been subjected to focal lesions and focal stimulation. The results of these experiments indicate that the different areas in the hypothalamus are important portions of many of the visceral regulatory mechanisms which maintain the constancy of the internal environment. The remainder of this chapter is devoted to a résumé of these functions.

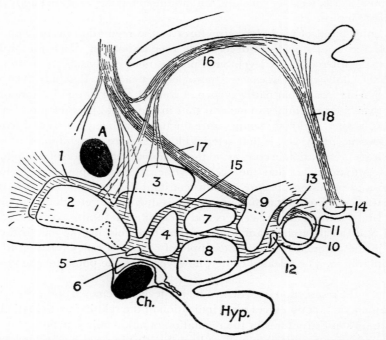

FIG. 132.   Diagram showing relative positions in sagittal plane of hypothalamic nuclei in typical mammalian brain, and their relation to fornix, stria habenularis and fasciculus retroflexus. *A*, anterior commissure; *Ch*, optic chiasma; *Hyp*, hypophysis; *1*, lateral preoptic nucleus (permeated by the medial forebrain bundle); *2*, medial preoptic nucleus; *3*, paraventricular nucleus; *4*, anterior hypothalamic area; *5*, suprachiasmatic nucleus; *6*, supraoptic nucleus; *7*, dorsomedial hypothalamic nucleus; *8*, ventromedial hypothalamic nucleus; *9*, posterior hypothalamic nucleus; *10*, medial mammillary nucleus; *11*, lateral mammillary nucleus; *12*, premammillary nucleus; *13*, supramammillary nucleus; *14*, interpeduncular nucleus (a mesencephalic element in which the fasciculus retroflexus terminates); *15*, lateral hypothalamic nucleus (permeated by the medial forebrain bundle); *16*, stria habenularis; *17*, fornix; *18*, fasciculus retroflexus of Meynert (habenulo-peduncular tract). (From Le Gros Clark *et al.*, *The hypothalamus*, London, Oliver and Boyd, 1938.)

Anatomic Organization of the Hypothalamus.   The hypothalamus (Fig. 132) consists of those structures in the walls and floor of the third ventricle extending from a position slightly rostral to the optic chiasm caudally to the mammillary bodies. Dorsally the thalamus and subthalamus bound the hypothalamus. On its ventral surface it is connected to the hypophysis by a strand of fine nerve fibers originating in hypothalamic nuclei and running via the median eminence and infundibular stalk into the posterior lobe of the hypophysis. Much of the substance of the hypothalamus is composed of small diffusely arranged cells not clearly arranged in nuclear groups. Nevertheless, the following regions and nuclei, some more clearly delimited than others, can be defined: (i) anterior region, including the preoptic, supraoptic and paraventricular nuclei; (ii) middle region, including the tuber nuclei and the lateral nuclear masses; and (iii) the posterior region, including the posterior hypothalamic nuclei and the mammillary nuclei.

Many afferent pathways lead into the hypothalamus; they include: (i) the *medial forebrain bundle*, which originates in the ventromedial areas of the rhinencephalon and is distributed to the preoptic region and the lateral hypothalamic and lateral mammillary nuclei; (ii) the *fornix*, which connects the hippocampus with the mammillary nuclei; (iii) the *stria terminalis*, which connect the amygdaloid nuclei with the preoptic and anterior hypothalamic regions; (iv) the *mammillary peduncle*, which feeds impulses ascending from spinal and tegmental structures into the lateral mammillary nucleus; and (v) numerous other, less well defined pathways connecting the hypothalamus with the frontal cortex, the globus pallidus and the thalamus. Branches from the optic tract ending in the supraoptic and ventromedial nuclei have also been described and implicated in the retinal regulation of hypothalamic and hypophysial function.

The efferent pathways include: (i) The *mammillothalamic tract of Vicq d'Azyr*. This pathway links the medial mammillary nucleus with the anterior thalamic nuclei which project to the cortex of the cingular gyrus. (ii) The *mammillotegmental tract* runs from the medial mammillary nuclei to the lateral and medial reticular structures in the tegmentum. (iii) The *periventricular system* arises mainly in the supraoptic, posterior and tuberal nuclei and descends in periventricular gray matter. Some fibers in this system terminate in the dorsomedial thalamic nucleus; others supply the midbrain tegmental reticular nuclei; but most pass into the dorsal longitudinal fasciculus. It is believed that this tract supplies brain stem parasympathetic nuclei and also, through relays, the spinal sympathetic preganglionic neurons. There is also evidence for a dorsolaterally placed descending tract leading from the hypothalamus to spinal levels. (iv) The *hypothalamico-hypophysial* tract leads from the supraoptic nuclei into the posterior lobe of the hypophysis. Some of the fibers originate from the paraventricular nuclei. The role of this tract in regulating water metabolism is discussed below. Fiber tracts leading into the posterior lobe from the tuberal nuclei have also been described.

Regulation of Body Temperature.[50]   It has already been pointed out that experimental animals subjected to transection of the brain stem below the level of the hypothalamus become poikilothermic. The thermoregulatory function of the hypothalamus is even more clearly indicated when discrete positions of the hypothalamus are destroyed experimentally in otherwise intact animals.

Discrete destruction or stimulation of the hypothalamus (or any other subcortical structure) is accomplished with the aid of the stereotaxic apparatus invented by Horsley and Clarke. This consists of an electrode carrier framework which is firmly attached to the animal's head by bars in the ears and clamps fitting against the upper jaw and the inferior orbital ridge. The framework on which the electrode carrier moves is calibrated in millimeters in all three planes of movement: anteroposterior, lateral and vertical. To calibrate the instrument for a given species, wires are introduced into the brain at measured coordinates in each of the three planes. The animal is then sacrificed and serial brain sections are prepared. Measurement on the sections from the distance between the holes made by the reference wires and any subcortical structure yields coordinates for the structure. Using these coordinates one can accurately introduce the uninsulated tip of an insulated electrode into the desired structure with only minimal damage to those overlying it. Stimulation can then be carried out by conventional methods. To produce a lesion a direct current is passed through the electrode tip (positive) through the brain and out through a diffuse electrode (negative) applied to the skin. The high current density at the small uninsulated tip of the electrode causes local electrolytic destruction of tissue in the surrounding region. The size of the lesion varies with current intensity and duration.

The influence of discrete hypothalamic lesions on temperature regulation varies with their location. Lesions in the rostral hypothalamus (level of optic chiasm and anterior commissure), particularly in its lateral reaches, render an animal incapable of regulating its temperature in a warm environment, although it may maintain a normal body temperature in a cold environment. Indeed, so profound is the deficit following rostral hypothalamic destruction that death from hyperthermia often results if the animal is kept at room temperature. Similarly, hyperthermia in man and inability to withstand warm environments have been described as following anterior hypothalamic lesions due to tumors or infarcts.[14, 61] The disturbances are traceable to inadequate operation of the heat loss mechanisms which normally are activated by exposure to a warm environment. In man these are principally cutaneous vasodilatation, which increases radiation of heat to the environment, and sweating, which lowers body temperature by evaporative cooling. In furry animals such as the dog and cat, panting is an important means of heat loss. Following rostral hypothalamic destruction these adaptive changes do not occur when the environmental temperature is elevated, so body temperature rises.

When lesions are placed in the caudal hypothalamus dorsolateral to the mammillary bodies, the animal's ability to maintain normal body temperature in either a warm or a cold environment is seriously impaired; such preparations are essentially poikilothermic. It is probable that the heat loss mechanisms fail in such animals because the lesions interrupt the pathways descending from the rostrally located *heat loss centers*, and that the failure to regulate against cold results from destruction of a caudally located *heat production and conservation center*. In normal animals, exposure to cold elicits cutaneous vasoconstriction, shivering, piloerection and increased epinephrine secretion—all mechanisms which tend to increase the heat content of the body and prevent excessive cooling. Epinephrine and shivering act by increasing metabolism and thus heat production, whereas piloerection* and vasoconstriction conserve body heat by increasing the surface insulation. Following posterior hypothalamic lesions these adaptive mechanisms are defective, and in cold the body temperature inclines toward environmental temperature.

In exceptional instances regulation against heat and cold may be dissociated following posterior hypothalamic lesions. An example is illustrated in Figure 133. In contrast to the intact dog (46), which shivered vigorously and maintained normal body temperature when exposed to cold, dog 28 with posterior hypothalamic lesions failed to shiver and suffered profound hypothermia (*left graph*). When exposed to a warm environment, however, dog 28 panted and showed only slightly elevated body temperature, in contrast to dog 72-D with rostral hypothalamic lesions. The latter animal became markedly hyperthermic without panting after only brief exposure to a warm environment (*right graph*).

The role of hypothalamic structures in initiating thermoregulatory responses is also demonstrated by stimulation experiments. In unanesthetized animals electrical stimulation through electrodes permanently implanted in the rostral hypothalamus (level of optic chiasm and anterior commissure) causes panting and cutaneous vasodilation with a resultant drop in body temperature, particularly when the animal is in a cold environment.[2] Cold-induced shivering is inhibited by rostral hypothalamic stimulation, but exposure to cold increases the electrical threshold for inducing panting and vasodilation. These latter observations suggest reciprocal connections between the heat loss and heat production centers. On the other hand, stimulation of the posterior hypothalamus (in the tuberal region between the fornix and the mammillothalamic tract) induces a muscular tremor resembling shivering.[7]

It is thus apparent that the hypothalamus contains two opposing thermoregulatory centers which by their descending connections bring about coordinated and integrated

---

* The fluffing of body hair to trap an insulating layer of stationary air is an important means of heat conservation in furry animals. In man piloerection has no thermoregulatory importance but persists vestigially in the form of "goose bumps."

neural discharges to structures involved in maintaining a constant body temperature. In the intact animal these two centers operate reciprocally. When environmental temperature increases and body temperature begins to rise, the anteriorly located heat loss centers are activated and overheating is prevented. Similarly, low environmental temperatures activate the posteriorly placed heat conservation and production center, and the resultant shivering, piloerection, vasoconstriction and epinephrine secretion combat excessive cooling of the body. The hypothalamic centers have been likened to a thermostat which operates automatically to prevent large fluctuations of body temperature.

A thermostat requires a receptive mechanism to sample the temperature as well as an executive mechanism to bring about the appropriate regulation. For the hypothalamic thermostat two receptive mechanisms are available: (i) cutaneous thermoreceptors, which vary their rate of firing with changes in skin temperature and which presumably feed impulses into the hypothalamic thermoregulatory centers; and (ii) centrally located

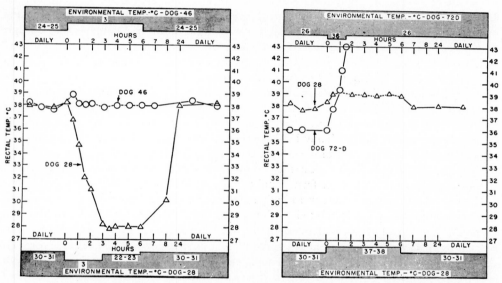

FIG. 133.   Effect of hypothalamic lesions on temperature regulation in dogs. Dog *46*, intact animal; dog *28*, posterior hypothalamic lesions; dog *72D*, rostral hypothalamic lesions. Dotted lines joining points indicate, on left, shivering; on right, panting. (From Keller. *Phys. Therap. Rev.*, 1950, *30*:511–519.)

receptors, which respond to changes in internal, particularly intracranial, temperature. The properties of cutaneous thermoreceptors have been studied by the single unit recording technique[32, 62] and are described in detail in Chapter 13. Thermoreceptors are classified as warmth or cold receptors according to the range of temperatures which cause them to discharge. The messages from thermoreceptors are presumed to reach the hypothalamic thermoregulatory centers where they initiate the appropriate reciprocal actions—i.e., impulses initiated in cold receptors excite the caudally located heat production and conservation center and inhibit the rostrally located heat loss center; impulses from warmth receptors have the reverse action on the hypothalamic centers. In addition, the messages from thermoreceptors presumably feed into other ascending pathways to thalamus and cortex and constitute the basis of conscious sensation of temperature, which provides a cue for complex adaptive behavior, such as seeking a more comfortable environment (shelter, shade, etc.).

The existence of centrally located thermoreceptors is also well documented. Warming the carotid blood entering the head induces sweating, panting and vasodilation, even though skin temperature (except on the head) is not altered by the procedure. Similarly, cooling the carotid blood induces vasoconstriction, piloerection and shivering. That the thermosensitive regions are contained in the hypothalamus (and indeed are coextensive with the thermoregulatory centers) is indicated by experiments[19, 20, 38] in which local heating of the rostral hypothalamus by diathermy induced sweating, panting and vaso-dilation (see Chap. 49 for further description). Such local heating does not affect skin or body temperature; indeed inappropriate panting and sweating could be induced by heating the hypothalamus when the body temperature was subnormal (35° C.). It may therefore be concluded that the thermoregulatory centers are directly sensitive to temper-ature and therefore vary in activity in accordance with the temperature of the blood perfusing them.

The relative roles of the cutaneous receptors (sensitive to skin temperature) and the central receptors (sensitive to body core temperature) in initiating and controlling thermoregulatory functions are not entirely clear,[6, 36] Magoun et al.[38] found it necessary to elevate hypothalamic temperature to feverish levels (104.5° to 109° F.) to elicit panting and sweating, a fact which suggests that the central receptors constitute a rather crude protective mechanism. On the other hand, recent data on human subjects suggest that sweat secretion is related more closely to core temperature than to skin temperature.[6] Studies by Carlson[11] indicate that both cutaneous and central receptors are involved in the activation of shivering induced by cold exposure.

Regulation of Water Balance.[18]   It was mentioned above that a prominent tract of unmyelinated fibers originates from cells in the supraoptic and paraventricular nuclei and traverses the median eminence and pituitary stalk to terminate in the posterior lobe of the hypophysis. This hypothalamico-hypophysial tract is essential to the formation and release of posterior hypophysial hormones, the most important of which is the *antidiuretic hormone* (ADH). Its function is described in detail in Chapters 39 and 52. Briefly, ADH promotes reabsorption of water from renal tubular fluid into the blood stream and thus limits the amount of water lost from body stores to the urine. Other things being equal, urinary volume is inversely related to the amount of ADH in the blood reaching the kidney. Secretion of ADH is dependent on the integrity of the hypothalamico-hypo-physial tract. Injury to the system at the supraoptic nuclear level or to its course through the median eminence and hypophysial stalk, or destruction of the posterior hypophysis itself, causes *diabetes insipidus*, in which excessive volumes of dilute urine are secreted (polyuria). The excessive urinary water loss (up to 20 liters a day in man) results in excessive thirst and ingestion of large quantities of water (polydipsia); the victim is a veritable aqueduct and spends most of his waking hours dashing from water fountain to water closet and back again.

The dependence of ADH secretion on the hypothalamico-hypophysial system has also been demonstrated by stimulation experiments. In rabbits, Harris[30] found that electrical stimulation through electrodes permanently implanted in the tract caused ADH secretion sufficient to block the diuresis induced by a previously administered oral water load.

Neurosecretion.   In most neurally regulated secretory systems (e.g., salivary glands, sweat glands, adrenal medulla) nerve fibers terminate on gland cells; nerve impulses initiate the secretory process in the gland cells. The neurohypophysis is an exception to this arrangement. Apart from supporting elements, the posterior lobe is relatively cell free and its mass is largely composed of terminations of the hypothalamico-hypophysial tract. In some species, the terminal fibers are arranged in parallel rows (palisades) in close relation to highly vascular connective tissue trabeculae.[8]

The fibers of the hypothalamico-hypophysial tract thus appear to innervate no particular structure but terminate blindly near blood vessels. This perplexing situation has been clarified by Bargmann's discovery[5] that chrome hematoxylin (Gomori stain) applied to sections of posterior hypophysis stains selectively an amorphous material which is presumed to be either the secretory product of the neurohypophysis or a ground substance to which the active hormone is attached. The material is found in high concentration surrounding the nerve terminals in the palisades but also along the entire extent of the hypothalamico-hypophysial tract and within the cells of the supraoptic and paraventricular nuclei. Water deprivation, which is known to increase the secretion of ADH (see below), causes a reduction in the amount of Gomori-stainable material present, particularly in the neurohypophysis but also in the supraoptic and paraventricular cell bodies. It is therefore suggested that the paraventricular and supraoptic nuclei are composed of *neurosecretory* cells capable of elaborating ADH, which then diffuses down in or around the axons to the terminals to be stored in the posterior hypophysis. The exact relation of the electrical activity of these cells to the formation and release of ADH is not yet clear.

Regulation of ADH secretion.   Renal excretion of water is closely related to body stores of water. Ingestion of large quantities of water leads to a prompt reduction of tubular reabsorption of water and consequent diuresis. On the other hand, water deprivation leads to accelerated water reabsorption and a scant, concentrated urine. This homeostatic regulation tending to maintain constant water stores and osmotic pressure of blood is achieved by variations in the secretion of ADH in accordance with the blood osmotic pressure. Intracarotid injection of hypertonic solutions stimulates the release of ADH, so that more water is reabsorbed by the kidney. When carotid blood is made hypotonic, ADH secretion declines and diuresis results. These changes are abolished when the internal carotid artery is ligated. Somewhere within the cranial cavity, therefore, cells exist (possibly those of the supraoptic and paraventricular nuclei) which are *osmoreceptors* and which comprise a mechanism for automatic regulation of ADH secretion and hence water excretion in accordance with bodily needs.[59]

However, there must exist mechanisms other than osmoreceptors for regulating ADH secretion, since reduction of total extracellular volume, e.g., by hemorrhage, increases ADH levels and induces oliguria. Conversely, expansion of extracellular volume by transfusing isotonic solutions leads to diuresis. These facts have led to the postulation of "volume receptors" which respond to increased plasma volume and reflexly inhibit ADH secretion. Several possible sites for the hypothetical volume receptors have been suggested; a full discussion of the problem is given in Chapter 40.

Water intake.   In view of the important role of the hypothalamus in regulating water output, it is perhaps not surprising that it also plays a part in the regulation of water intake. Such a function is indicated by the experiments of Andersson and McCann,[3] who stimulated the hypothalamus of goats through permanently implanted electrodes. Stimulating the region between the columns of the fornix and the mammillothalamic tract induced polydipsic drinking sufficient to cause overhydration up to 40 per cent of the body weight and to cause dilution of renal fluid and polyuria. Microinjections of hypertonic saline in the same regions also induced polydipsia, a response suggesting (but not proving) that the responsible neurons (like the hypothalamico-hypophysial osmoreceptors) are sensitive to the osmotic pressure of the body fluids.

Oxytocin Secretion.   In addition to ADH the posterior pituitary elaborates a hormone, oxytocin, which causes (i) powerful contraction of the gravid or estrous uterus and (ii) ejection of milk from the lactating mammary gland. Electrical stimulation of the supraoptic hypophysial tract causes liberation of oxytocin as measured by the responses of both the estrous uterus and the lactating mammary gland.[13, 30] The natural stimuli which trigger release of oxytocin are not entirely clear. In the case of lactation the sensory irritation of the nipples incident to sucking probably constitutes the adequate stimulus.

Whether oxytocin is involved in the initiation of spontaneous labor is controversial; in any event, there is no conclusive evidence that the hormone is released at term.

Regulation of Adenohypophysial Function.[31] Although it is well established that the posterior lobe of the hypophysis receives nerve fibers from the hypothalamus, repeated investigations have failed to demonstrate convincingly that the anterior hypophysial lobe is similarly innervated. Nevertheless, there is considerable evidence that the central nervous system, particularly the hypothalamus, plays some part in the government of adenohypophysial secretion. Since there are no direct neural connections which might mediate this control, it is postulated that certain hypothalamic cell groups elaborate chemical mediators which, reaching the adenohypophysis via the blood stream, stimulate the production and release of hormones. Such hypothalamic cells are thus neurosecretory cells.

Hypothalamico-hypophysial portal system.[25] Although the hypothalamus and adenohypophysis are not neurally connected, they are connected by a special vascular system which is thought to transmit humoral agents from the hypothalamus to the pituitary. The internal carotid and posterior communicating arteries form a rich vascular plexus over the surface of the median eminence. From this plexus arise myriads of capillary loops which arch up into median eminence, where they are closely related to neurosecretory axons. The capillary loops then coalesce into larger trunks which pass down the hypophysial stalk and drain into the sinusoids of the adenohypophysis. Other branches of the internal carotids penetrate the hypophysis more directly. The portal system is illustrated in Figure 585 (Chap. 52).

Harris[30] believes that a vascular connection with the hypothalamus is essential to the secretory functions of the hypophysis. Severing the pituitary stalk (and consequently the portal vessel) has no permanent effect on adenohypophysial function.[57] According to Harris, it recovers because the severed portal vessels rapidly regenerate. If, however, regeneration is prevented by inserting a paper barrier between the base of the brain and the decentralized hypophysis, or if the gland is transplanted to a remote site, signs of pituitary deficiency ensue (cessation of growth and gonadal, adrenocortical and thyroid atrophy). The interpretation is that such hypophysial transplants, although histologically intact, fail to function because they have lost the direct vascular "pipeline" from the hypothalamic neurosecretory centers. Other investigators[12, 21, 45] however have demonstrated that intraocular transplants of adenohypophysis can, under some conditions, secrete adrenocorticotrophic hormone, although all agree that the secretory capacity of transplants is subnormal.

Adrenocorticotrophic hormone. Secretion of adrenocortical hormones (with the exception of aldosterone) is entirely regulated by the adrenocorticotrophic hormone (ACTH) secreted by the adenohypophysis (see Chap. 54). Secretion of ACTH with consequent activation of the adrenal cortex may be initiated by a wide variety of seemingly unrelated physiologic and pharmacologic stimuli which are collectively called "biologic stresses." Examples of stresses which activate the pituitary-adrenal axis are exposure to extremes of heat or cold, anoxia, hemorrhage, pain, bacterial toxins, histamine and anesthetic agents. Pituitary-adrenal responsiveness to such stresses is not altered by section of the pituitary stalk,[57] but is abolished by lesions of the median eminence or of the posterior hypothalamus.[28, 44] It is therefore postulated that stress situations induced either by afferent neural input or (in the case of chemical stresses) by direct action stimulate neurosecretory hypothalamic cells to secrete a humoral substance, corticotrophin releasing factor (CRF). CRF is carried by the portal vessels to the hypophysis, where it stimulates secretion of ACTH which, in turn, stimulates adrenocortical secretion.

The chemical nature of CRF is unknown. McCann[43] believes it is identical with ADH; when the pituitary-adrenal axis is made unresponsive to stress by hypothalamic lesions, it may still be activated by injections of ADH. A difficulty with this theory is that overhydration, which diminishes ADH secretion, causes secretion of ACTH.

Additional evidence implicating hypothalamic structures in the regulation of ACTH secretion is provided by experiments involving electrical stimulation of the hypothalamus through implanted electrodes in unanesthetized animals. Stimulation in the tuberal and posterior hypothalamic regions activates the pituitary-adrenal system.[28] Also, extracts prepared from hypothalamic tissue stimulate secretion of ACTH by pituitary cells grown in tissue culture.[29] Although such experiments indicate that the hypothalamus participates in the regulation of ACTH secretion, other mechanisms have been proposed; these are discussed in Chapter 54.

Secretion of *aldosterone*, the adrenal hormone which regulates renal excretion of sodium and potassium, appears to be independent of the pituitary. Regulation of aldosterone secretion is poorly understood. Recent investigations by Farrel *et al.*[16, 17] suggest a posterior diencephalic neurohumoral mechanism. Removal of the pineal body is said to decrease aldosterone secretion, and the adrenal output of aldosterone increases when extracts prepared from beef diencephalon are injected intravenously. The active substance has been named *glomerulotrophin*, because aldosterone is secreted principally by the glomerulosa of the adrenal cortex.

Gonadotrophin secretion (see Chaps. 57 and 58). Numerous observations suggest neural regulation of pituitary gonadotrophin secretion. In many birds and mammals the sexual cycle may be altered by varying the exposure of the animal to light. For example, a midwinter estrus in the ferret, which normally breeds in the spring, can be induced by exposing the animal to light. Such disturbances in seasonal sexual cycles depend on the visual pathways; ferrets blinded by section of the optic nerve do not have estrus cycles even when exposed to light. Light-induced estrus also fails to occur in ferrets with transected hypophysial stalks. According to Donavan and Harris[15] interruption of the hypothalamico-hypophysial portal system and prevention of vascular regeneration is critical, but this statement has been contested.[58]

Cats and rabbits normally ovulate only after coitus. In estrous cats stimulation of the hypothalamus in the vicinity of the ventromedial nuclei elicits ovulation, and lesions in the ventromedial tuberal region block coitus-induced ovulation.[55]

Thyrotrophin secretion. Hypothalamic lesions between the levels of the paraventricular nuclei and the median eminence prevent the thyroid hypertrophy which normally results from administration of phenylthiourea.[9, 26] This compound blocks the synthesis of thyroid hormone. The resultant diminution of circulating thyroid hormone stimulates secretion of thyrotrophin, which causes the thyroid gland, although hormonally nonfunctional, to enlarge (see Chap. 55). The effectiveness of hypothalamic lesions in preventing phenylthiourea-induced goiter suggests that the lowered thyroxin blood levels act on neurosecretory cells in the hypothalamus. The latter cells presumably liberate an agent which reaches the hypophysis via the portal vessels and stimulates secretion of thyrotrophin. Conversely, when the thyroxin concentration of fluids bathing the hypothalamus is increased by local intrahypothalamic injection of thyroxin, the neurosecretory elements are depressed, and thyrotrophin secretion diminishes.[60]

Although hypothalamic lesions are effective in preventing drug-induced goiter, the capacity of the thyroid to metabolize iodine is little affected by such lesions. For this reason, Greer[27] has postulated that the pituitary generates two thyrotrophins, one being dependent on neural regulation and concerned with the thyroid growth and the other being relatively independent of hypothalamic control and concerned with the metabolic functions of the thyroid.

Prolactin secretion. It is well known to the dairyman as well as to the physiologist that maintenance of lactation depends on continued suckling or milking. The breasts of lactating rats undergo involution if the young are allowed to suckle only breasts rendered anesthetic by spinal transection; if suckling of breasts above the level of the transection is permitted, lactation persists.[35] Furthermore, the mammary involution which normally occurs when the litter is removed from a lactating rat can be prevented by the satanic procedure of painting the nipples with turpentine; the irritation thus produced serves as an adequate substitute for that produced by suckling.[34]

The role of the hypothalamus in the regulation of prolactin secretion is difficult to assess. Lactation involves three different hormonal mechanisms: (i) ovarian hormones, regulated by the pituitary gonadotrophins, develop and maintain the secretory tissue and duct systems; (ii) prolactin stimulates milk secretion; and (iii) oxytocin from the posterior pituitary regulates the ejection of milk. Disturbances of lactation following central neural lesions are therefore hard to analyze.

Growth hormone secretion. Virtually nothing is known about the regulation of the secretion of somatotrophin or growth hormone. Growth is usually impaired when the pituitary is transplanted to remote sites, but whether this disorder is due to loss of the vascular connections with the hypothalamus or to other factors is not clear.

Regulation of Food Intake. Hetherington and Ranson[33] first demonstrated that animals subjected to small bilateral lesions of the ventromedial hypothalamic nucleus become obese. Careful measurements indicate that the obesity results from increased food intake (which often increases threefold), although decreased activity may play a minor contributory role. Gastrectomy does not prevent the development of *hypothalamic*

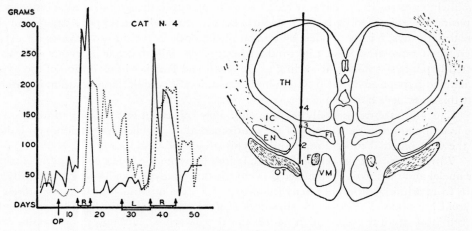

FIG. 134.   Effect of stimulating feeding center on food intake in cat. *Solid lines*, meat intake; *dotted lines*, milk intake. *OP*, Implantation of electrodes; *R*, daily stimulation at a point between *2* and *3* in section with marked increase in food intake; *L*, stimulation of a point 2 mm. posterior; 1.5 mm. inferior, and 0.5 mm. lateral to *R* with no effect on food intake. (From Delgado and Anand, *Amer. J. Physiol.*, 1953, *172*:162–168.)

hyperphagia and obesity; thus there is no evidence that increased afferent input from the gastrointestinal tract drives the animals to increase their food intake. Indeed behavioral experiments,[46] described fully in Chapter 22, indicate that the operated animals have no increased food drive and will not work as hard as normal animals for a food reward. For this reason it has been postulated that the ventromedial nucleus is concerned with *satiety* rather than with the initiation of feeding. In other words, the hyperphagic animal doesn't know when to stop eating.

When bilateral lesions are made in the lateral hypothalamus, anorexia results and the animals die of starvation unless force fed[1] (see Chap. 49). If, rather than being destroyed, this same region is stimulated through implanted electrodes, food intake increases strikingly (Fig. 134). The lateral hypothalamic region is therefore termed a *feeding center*.

The rather precise adjustment of food intake to energy expenditure and the maintenance of relatively constant body weight thus appears to depend upon the balanced operation of the hypothalamic feeding and satiety centers. Of the two, the laterally placed feeding center appears to be dominant, since destruction of both the feeding and the satiety center results in anorexia and weight loss. Further consideration of the role of the hypothalamic centers in regulating food intake resolves into two questions: what are the efferent connections of the centers and what are the afferent inputs which "inform" the centers of the energy stores of the body? Concerning the first question, little is known except that probably both centers give rise to descending tracts which connect with the cranial and spinal nuclei involved in the complex behavior of seeking and ingesting food. Hyperphagia has been produced by lesions caudal to the hypothalamus in the rostral mesencephalic tegmentum; such lesions presumably interrupt descending pathways from the satiety center. Two additional areas concerned with eating were disclosed by stimulation experiments, one in the premammillary region and one in the mammillary region.[51] In goats, Larsson[37] induced polyphagia by electrical stimulation in the medulla near the dorsal motor nucleus of the vagus; this region might be supposed to receive fibers from the hypothalamic feeding center.

The way in which the hypothalamic centers are activated, although a subject of much speculation, is obscure. Two theories have been advanced. One, proposed by Brobeck,[10] may be termed the *thermostat theory*. Briefly, this theory assumes that the feeding and satiety centers, like the thermoregulatory centers, are sensitive to body temperature; decrease in body temperature is supposed to activate the feeding center and depress the satiety center, whereas increased temperature acts on the centers in the opposite sense. Ingestion of food by increasing heat production[48] [the so-called specific dynamic action (SDA); see Chap. 48] leads to satiety; whereas the cooling of the body as heat is dissipated activates the feeding center. The SDA varies with composition of the diet; Strominger and Brobeck[56] found that rats ingest various diets not in proportion to either bulk or total caloric content but rather in proportion to the SDA.

The second theory is the *glucostat* theory, proposed by Mayer.[41] According to this theory, the hypothalamic centers are sensitive to blood glucose levels: hypoglycemia is supposed to excite the feeding center and inhibit the satiety center, whereas hyperglycemia has the reverse actions. To explain the paradoxical polyphagia of diabetes mellitus (in which, of course, the blood sugar level is high), Mayer suggests that, in the absence of insulin, the failure of sugar to penetrate the receptor cells "tricks" them into behaving as if the blood sugar were actually low. A difficulty with this explanation is that brain cells, unlike cells of other tissues, apparently do not suffer alterations of glucose transport and utilization even in the absence of insulin.

Obesity is induced in mice by gold thioglucose which destroys cells in the ventromedial nucleus. Other gold-thio compounds, many closely related to gold thioglucose and equally toxic, are ineffective. Mayer and Marshall[42] suggest that the affinity of glucoreceptors in the ventromedial nucleus for the glucose moiety of gold thioglucose causes them to accumulate damagingly high quantities of gold.

Regulation of Gastric Acid Secretion.   It has been mentioned above that hypothalamic hyperphagia is a disturbance of feeding behavior and does not appear to be directly related to alterations in gastrointestinal function. Nevertheless, the hypothalamus does appear to be involved in gastric secretory activity. According to Porter *et al.*[22, 49] electrical stimulation of the rostral hypothalamus at the level of the optic chiasm induces a prompt increase in secretion of gastric acid indicated by a drop in pH which reaches maximum in about one hour. The efferent pathway is the vagus nerve, for vagotomy abolishes the response (Fig 135, *left*). Stimulation of the posterior (tuberal or mammillary) hypothalamus induces a much more delayed gastric acid secretion which is not maximal until three hours after stimulation. This latter secretory response is not influenced by vagotomy but disappears after bilateral adrenalectomy. It is therefore postulated that the hypothalamus is involved in two gastric secretory mechanisms—one neural (vagus) and the other humoral—acting through the adenohypophysis and the adrenal cortex. Insulin-induced hypoglycemia, a strong stimulus to gastric acid secretion, appears to act through both the neural and the humoral channels. Thus lowered blood sugar initiates, via the hypothalamus, not only food seeking behavior (according to the glucostat theory) but also the secretion of gastric acid to prepare the stomach for the reception of food.

Overactivity of the hypothalamic secretory mechanism leads to injury of the stomach. In monkeys prolonged hypothalamic stimulation (two to four times daily for four to ten weeks) through implanted electrodes often leads to gastric hemorrhage and ulceration.[23] It has long been known that gastric hyperacidity and peptic ulcers occur more frequently in patients under chronic emotional stress; indeed, these abnormalities may be induced in experimental animals by subjecting them repeatedly to conflict situations. Peptic ulcer is therefore often described as a "psychosomatic disorder." In view of the known role of the hypothalamus in elaborating emotional behavior and in regulating gastric secretory mechanisms, it may be suggested that peptic ulcer is more aptly described as a "hypothalamosomatic disorder."

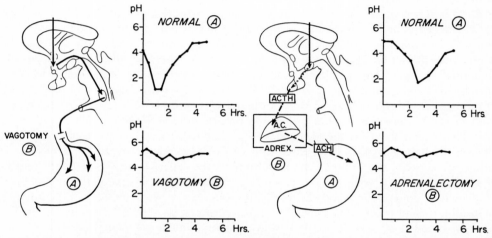

FIG. 135. Diagram of neural and humoral mechanisms regulating gastric HCl secretion. *Left*, Rostral hypothalamic stimulation causes prompt acid secretion (indicated by decreased pH in curve A); response is abolished by vagotomy (curve B). *Right*, Stimulation of posterior hypothalamus causes delayed acid secretion (curve A). Response is not altered by vagotomy but is abolished by adrenalectomy (curve B). (From French *et al.*, *Surgery*, 1953, *34*:621–632.)

Cardiovascular Regulation in Fear, Anger and Exercise. It has been observed repeatedly in experiments on anesthetized animals that electrical stimulation at various hypothalamic sites induces marked alterations in the cardiovascular system, e.g., changes in blood pressure and heart rate. The significance of these changes is not easy to evaluate in anesthetized or restrained preparations in which the behavior of the animal is suppressed. When Hess developed the technique of permanently implanting stimulating electrodes in the brain it became possible to observe the effects of hypothalamic stimulation on unanesthetized and unrestrained animals. As described in more detail in Chapter 22, such experiments indicate that the hypothalamus plays an important role in the elaboration of emotional or affective behavior. Stimulation at some hypothalamic foci elicits behavior which mimics that displayed by an animal subjected to a threatening situation and which might therefore be called the behavioral pattern of fear. Stimulation at other sites elicits aggressive reactions similar to those displayed by animals angered by natural stimuli or situations.[47] In both fear and anger, changes in heart rate and blood pressure are constantly occurring accompaniments of the total behavioral picture; along with the onset of "fight or flight," to use Cannon's expression, there are concomitant automatic adjustments of the cardiovascular system to support the increased demands for oxygen attending combat or hasty retreat. The cardiovascular changes observed in anesthetized animals during hypothalamic stimulation appear therefore to represent isolated fragments of a total behavioral pattern which is readily recognizable only in the unanesthetized and unrestrained preparation.

Adaptive cardiovascular adjustment occurs, however, in situations other than those eliciting fear or anger. Simple muscular exercise, no matter how motivated, is accompanied by prompt adaptive changes in the heart and vascular tree. Using a variety of ingeniously devised recording instruments which are attached permanently to the heart and great vessels, Rushmer[52] and his colleagues succeeded in monitoring in intact, unanesthetized dogs the cardiovascular response to exercise (walking on a treadmill). The typical pattern of cardiovascular adjustment to exercise is discussed in Chapter 32. Recent experiments indicate that electrical stimulation of the diencephalon in the region of the fields of Forel induces cardiovascular changes which mimic to a remarkable degree those induced in intact dogs by exercise (Fig. 435). When bilateral lesions are inflicted on these same regions, exercise no longer elicits the cardiovascular adjustments seen in intact dogs.[53]

Pulmonary edema.[24, 39, 40] An observation which documents dramatically the vital function of the hypothalamus is that lesions in the preoptic region lead to lung edema and hemorrhage. The edema often develops with an explosive suddenness within one to 24 hours after induction of the lesions and results in the rapid asphyxial death of the animal. Hypothalamic lung edema is apparently a release phenomenon, for caudal hypothalamic lesions, spinal transection or splanchnic nerve section protects the animals from the effects of preoptic lesions. It has been suggested that the released hypothalamic centers normally regulate the capacity of the systemic venous reservoirs. After destruction of the preoptic region, the unfettered activity of the caudally located centers may result in constriction of venous reservoirs so that an excess volume of blood is dumped into the pulmonary circuit, causing lung hemorrhage and edema.

REFERENCES

1. ANAND, B. K. and BROBECK, J. R. *Yale J. Biol. Med.*, 1951, *24*:123–140.
2. ANDERSSON, B., GRANT, R. and LARSSON, S. *Acta physiol. scand.*, 1956, *37*:261–280.
3. ANDERSSON, B. and McCANN, S. M. *Acta physiol. scand.*, 1955, *33*:333–346.
4. BARD, P. and MACHT, M. B. Pp. 55–75 in *Ciba Foundation symposium on neurological basis of behavior*, G. E. W. WOLSTENHOLME and C. M. O'CONNER, eds. Boston, Little, Brown and Co., 1958.
5. BARGMANN, W. *Z. Zellforsch.*, 1949, *34*:610–634.
6. BENZINGER, T. H. *Proc. nat. Acad. Sci. (Wash.)*, 1959, *45*:645–659.
7. BIRZIS, L. and HEMINGWAY, A. *J. Neurophysiol.*, 1957, *20*:91–99.
8. BODIAN, D. *Bull. Johns Hopk. Hosp.*, 1951, *89*:354–376.
9. BOGDANOVE, E. M. and HALMI, N. S. *Endocrinology*, 1953, *53*:274–292.
10. BROBECK, J. R. *Yale J. Biol. Med.*, 1957, *29*:565–574.
11. CARLSON, L. D. *Proc. Soc. exp. Biol. (N. Y.)*, 1954, *85*:303–305.
12. CHENG, C. P., SAYERS, G., GOODMAN, L. S. and SWINYARD, C. A. *Amer. J. Physiol.*, 1949, *159*:426–432.
13. CROSS, B. A. and HARRIS, G. W. *J. Endocrin.*, 1952, *8*:148–161.
14. DAVISON, C. *Res. Publ. Ass. nerv. ment. Dis.*, 1940, *20*:774–823.
15. DONOVAN, B. T. and HARRIS, G. W. *Nature (Lond.)*, 1954, *174*:503–504.
16. FARREL, G. *Endocrinology*, 1959, *65*:29–33.
17. FARREL, G., KOLETSKY, S. and LAPHAM, L. W. *Fed. Proc.*, 1959, *18*:44.
18. FISHER, C., INGRAM, W. R. and RANSON, S. W. *Diabetes insipidus and the neuro-hormonal control of water balance: a contribution to the structure and function of the hypothalamico-hypophyseal system.* Ann Arbor, Mich., Edwards Brothers, 1938, x, 212 pp.
19. FOLKOW, B., STRÖM, G. and UVNÄS, B. *Acta physiol. scand.*, 1949, *17*:317–326.
20. FOLKOW, B., STRÖM, G. and UNVÄS, B. *Acta physiol. scand.*, 1949, *17*:327–338.
21. FORTIER, C. and SELYE, H. *Amer. J. Physiol.*, 1949, *159*:433–439.
22. FRENCH, J. D., LONGMIRE, R. L., PORTER, R. W. and MOVIUS, H. J. *Surgery*, 1953, *34*:621–632.

23. French, J. D., Porter, R. W., Cavanaugh, E. B. and Longmire, R. L. *Arch. Neurol. Psychiat. (Chicago)*, 1954, 72:267–281.

24. Gamble, J. E. and Patton, H. D. *Amer. J. Physiol.*, 1953, 172:623–631.

25. Green, J. D. and Harris, G. W. *J. Endocrin.*, 1947, 5:136–146, 3 plates.

26. Greer, M. A. *J. clin. Endocrin.*, 1952, 12:1259–1268.

27. Greer, M. A. *Ciba Foundation on Endocrinology*, 1957, 10:34–50.

28. de Groot, J. and Harris, G. W. *J. Physiol.*, 1950, 111:335–346.

29. Guillemin, R., Hearn, W. R., Cheek, W. R. and Housholder, D. E. *Endocrinology*, 1957, 60:488–506.

30. Harris, G. W. *Phil. Trans.*, 1947, B232:385–441.

31. Harris, G. W. *Neural control of the pituitary gland.* London, Edward Arnold Ltd., 1955, ix, 298 pp.

32. Hensel, H. *Ergebn. Physiol.*, 1952, 47:166–368.

33. Hetherington, A. W. and Ranson, S. W. *Anat. Rec.*, 1940, 78:149–172.

34. Hooker, C. W. and Williams, W. L. *Yale J. Biol. Med.*, 1940, 12:559–564, 1 plate.

35. Ingelbrecht, P. *C. R. Soc. Biol. (Paris)*, 1935, 120:1369–1371.

36. Kerslake, D. McK. *J. Physiol.*, 1955, 127:280–296.

37. Larsson, S. *Acta physiol. scand.*, 1954, 32 (suppl. 115):1–63.

38. Magoun, H. W., Harrison, F., Brobeck, J. R. and Ranson, S. W. *J. Neurophysiol.*, 1938, 1:101–114.

39. Maire, F. W. and Patton, H. D. *Amer. J. Physiol.*, 1956, 184:345–350.

40. Maire, F. W. and Patton, H. D. *Amer. J. Physiol.*, 1956, 184:351–355.

41. Mayer, J. *Physiol. Rev.*, 1953, 33:472–508.

42. Mayer, J. and Marshall, N. B. *Nature (Lond.)*, 1956, 178:1399–1400.

43. McCann, S. M. *Endocrinology*, 1957, 60:664–676.

44. McCann, S. M. and Brobeck, J. R. *Proc. Soc. exp. Biol. (N. Y.)*, 1954, 87:318–324.

45. McDermott, W. V., Fry, E. G., Brobeck, J. R. and Long, C. N. H. *Proc. Soc. exp Biol. (N. Y.)*, 1950, 73:609–610.

46. Miller, N. E., Bailey, C. J. and Stevenson, J. A. F. *Science*, 1950, 112:256–259.

47. Nakao, H. *Amer. J. Physiol.*, 1958, 194:411–418.

48. Passmore, R. and Ritchie, F. J. *Brit. J. Nutr.*, 1957, 11:79–85.

49. Porter, R. W., Movius, H. J. and French, J. D. *Surgery*, 1953, 33:875–880.

50. Ranson, S. W. *Res. Publ. Ass. nerv. ment. Dis.*, 1940, 20:342–399.

51. Ruch, T. C., Maire, F. W. and Patton, H. D. *Abstr. Comm., Congr. int. Physiol.*, 1956, 20:788.

52. Rushmer, R. F. *Cardiac diagnosis, a physiologic approach.* Philadelphia, W. B. Saunders, 1955, vii, 447 pp.

53. Rushmer, R. F. and Smith, O. A., Jr. *Physiol. Rev.*, 1959, 39:41–68.

54. Sahs, A. L. and Fulton, J. F. *J. Neurophysiol.*, 1940, 3:258–268.

55. Sawyer, C. H. Pp. 164–174 in *Physiological triggers and discontinuous rate processes*, T. H. Bullock, ed. Washington, D. C., American Physiological Society, 1957.

56. Strominger, J. L. and Brobeck, J. R. *Yale J. Biol. Med.*, 1953, 25:383–390.

57. Tang, P. C. and Patton, H. D. *Endocrinology*, 1951, 49:86–98.

58. Thompson, A. P. D. and Zuckerman, S. *Proc. roy. Soc.*, 1954, B142:437–451.

59. Verney, E. B. *Proc. roy. Soc.*, 1947, B135:25–105.

60. Yamada, T. and Greer, M. A. *Endocrinology*, 1959, 64:559–566.

61. Zimmerman, H. M. *Res. Publ. Ass. nerv. ment. Dis.*, 1940, 20:824–840.

62. Zotterman, Y. *Skand. Arch. Physiol.*, 1936, 75:105–119.

CHAPTER 11

The Cerebral Cortex: Its Structure and Motor Functions

By THEODORE C. RUCH

SINCE antiquity, the cerebral hemispheres have been looked upon as the organ of intelligence and conscious sensation. Consequently, the structure of this region of the brain has long aroused curiosity. Ancient writers, and even those of the Renaissance, speculated widely about the localization of consciousness. Some placed the "psyche" in the cerebral ventricles; others drew diagrams suggesting precise localization of various mental faculties in different regions of the forebrain. Neurologists of the seventeenth century, such as Willis and Vieussens, carried out experiments which indicated that the brain substance, not the ventricles, is the seat of consciousness. Willis, moreover, proclaimed the cerebrum the seat of volitional movements and the cerebellum the source of involuntary movements; he also described the gross structure and blood supply of the brain in detail.

HISTORICAL NOTE.[20]   Use of the microscope came late in the analysis of the structural organization of the nervous system. The story actually began in February 1776, when an Italian medical student, Francesco Gennari, observed the well defined white line which indicates special structural organization of the occipital lobes of the brain; this line is now recognized as a primary landmark within the so-called visual cortex. In 1840, the French psychiatrist J.-P. Baillarger,[23] found macroscopically that six discrete layers can be identified in most areas when thin sections of human cerebral cortex are placed between two plates of glass, but that the relative width of a given layer varies widely from one region to another. He also established that Gennari's white line extends into other cortical areas and corresponds to his own "external band."

In the early part of the present century improved staining methods were brought to bear upon the cortical histology of man and other primates, and this is still a subject of active investigation. This study has taken two main directions: (i) cytoarchitecture and myeloarchitecture, i.e., the cellular and fiber make-up of various cortical areas (Campbell,[11] Brodmann,[7] C. and O. Vogt[62] and von Economo and Koskinas[17]); and (ii) dendritic and axonic ramifications as studied with silver impregnation methods by Ramón y Cajal[48] and, more recently, by Lorente de Nó[37] and Sholl.[51] Further insight into cortical function has been gained by investigating thalamocortical projections to specific regions and efferent projections from them. Collectively, these studies provide an anatomic framework with which functional studies—ablation, stimulation and the recording of evoked potentials—can be correlated.

STRUCTURE

Through studies of cytoarchitecture and myeloarchitecture, the neocortex, as opposed to the archicortex, has been subdivided into areas of specific structure in the belief that structural differences bespeak differences in function. Within each area, the cortex is divided into six more or less distinct layers. The stratification is based on the presence of specific types of cells peculiar to each layer.

The four main types of cells are:

(i) Cells with descending axons, often reaching the white substance, to be continued by a fiber of projection or association.

(ii) Cells with short axons ramified near the cell body, often within a homogeneous zone of the dendritic plexus.

(iii) Cells with ascending axons ramified in one or several cortical layers.

(iv) Cells with horizontal axons.

The six recognized layers are:

I. The molecular or superficial plexiform layer. This layer lies immediately beneath the pia mater and is about 0.25 mm. thick; it is sparsely populated with nerve cell bodies,[51] and is made up of dendrites and axons from neurons lying deeper in the cortex.

II. The external granular layer, or the layer of small pyramidal cells. This layer contains many pyramidal cells, those nearer the lower boundary generally being larger than those above. The apices of these cells are directed toward the external surface. The apical dendrites terminate in the molecular layer and form the basis of intracortical association; the axon arising from the basal side of the cell passes inward to constitute one of the fibers of the medullary portion of the cerebrum. The other cells in this layer belong to the short axon group (Golgi type II or granule cells). This thick lamina of cells is sometimes subdivided into three layers of small, medium and large pyramidal cells.

III. The external pyramidal layer, a layer of larger pyramidal cells. This layer is sometimes difficult to distinguish from layer II.

IV. The internal granular or stellate layer. This layer is composed of many small multipolar cells with short branching axons. These latter are Golgi type II cells and receive endings of specific thalamic afferents to the sensory cortex.

V. The deep layer of large pyramidal cells. Here lie large or medium-sized pyramidal cells, similar in form to those in layer II, with axons which pass into the medulla or white matter of the cerebrum.

VI. The layer of fusiform or spindle-shaped cells. Layer VI consists of cells whose form is more irregular than that of the pyramidal cells. The axons of these irregularly shaped cells pass into the medullary portion of the cerebrum, and their dendrites stretch externally into the layers of pyramidal cells. This layer also contains some Golgi type II cells.

Physiologic Deductions from the Histology of the Cortex. Ramón y Cajal[48] stressed some anatomic features as justifying certain generalizations of a physiologic nature. In the first place, every part of the cortex receives incoming impulses and gives rise to outgoing impulses; every part of the cortex is, therefore, both the terminal of an afferent path and the beginning of an efferent path. In other words, a cortical point is a reflex center of greater or lesser complexity. Second, there are provisions for the spread of impulses both horizontally through the gray matter and also along association fibers running through the white matter. Thus, efferent discharges from one part of the cortex can be aroused by impulses coming to it from other cortical areas and hence, indirectly, from any part of the body. A given area, in addition to discharging caudally over its own efferents, may transmit impulses to another area and discharge over the latter's efferents.

Third, all parts of the neocortex exhibit an essentially similar basic structure. Nevertheless there are definite regional differences in the thickness of the layers, in the size or shape of the cells or in the nature of the fibers. Numerous detailed studies made of the lamination of different parts of the cerebral cortex have given an anatomic foundation for certain speculations which subsequent investigations of function may or may not confirm.

Although the size, shape and density of cell bodies in the cerebral cortex permit the establishment of useful cytoarchitectural maps, these factors offer few clues to function. Information more significant to physiology is provided by study of the plexuses of dendritic and axonal branches that cut across cortical cell layers and determine the synaptic connections through which nerve impulses are transmitted.

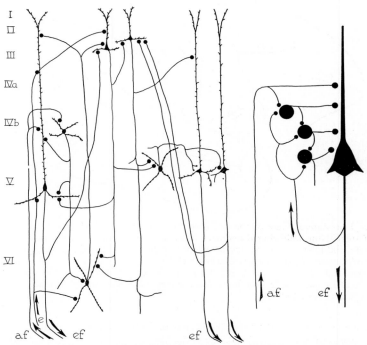

FIG. 136.   Diagram of some intracortical neuron chains. Note that few dendrites and axonal branches have been included. Synaptic junctions are indicated by thickening of axon. *af*, Axon entering cortex; *ef*, axon leaving cortex; *e*, axon of intra-areal cortical association cell whose cell body lies in sixth layer, outside picture. Diagram at right is a simplification of diagram at left. Afferent fiber activates large pyramidal cell which is origin of efferent fiber and also of a system of cortical internuncial cells; recurrent collateral of *ef* delivers impulses again to internuncial system. This diagram exemplifies the broad plan upon which the cerebral cortex is organized. Roman numerals at left indicate cortical layers. (After Lorente de Nó in Fulton, *Physiology of the nervous system*, 3rd ed., New York, Oxford University Press, 1949.)

The fourth layer of the cortex may be termed a receptive layer, since the *specific thalamocortical afferents* mainly end there in a compact axon brush; but other layers are also receptive. The *nonspecific thalamocortical afferents* begin to give off collaterals while still in the white matter; these ascend through the cortex to the outermost layer, ending in terminal branches which run horizontally. Because the initial side branches spread horizontally before ascending, the nonspecific afferents terminate in blocks of cortex. Association and callosal fibers are now also thought to terminate in several layers. The fifth and sixth layers are the main efferent layers. They contain the cell bodies whose **axons** enter the pyramidal tract. The apical dendrites of the cells in these layers ascend, giving off collaterals, but the basal dendrites may spread laterally or obliquely down-ward, presenting a much greater area for synaptic contact than the cell body itself. Callosal and association fibers also originate in the deep layers, V and VI.

An impulse traversing one cortical afferent may pass directly or monosynaptically to a cortical efferent, but, through collaterals and cortical cells with short dendrites and axons, cortical afferents can effect multisynaptic connection with the efferent neuron, as shown in Figure 136. Moreover, through the recurrent collaterals of cortical afferents ending on other neurons of the same type, and through recurrent collaterals from the efferent neurons themselves, circular chains capable of re-excitation or "reverberation" are formed, a functional formation which has important physiologic implications.

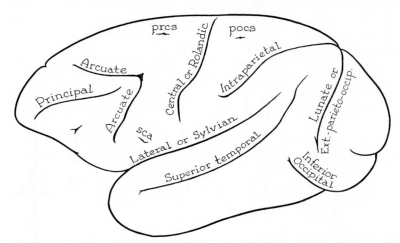

FIG. 137. Dorsolateral view of the left cerebral hemisphere of *Macaca mulatta* showing pattern and names of sulci. Note following differences from human brain: (i) fewer and less complex sulci, (ii) smaller prefrontal lobe, (iii) ascending course of intraparietal, lateral and superior temporal fissures (also lesser development of posterior parietal region), (iv) lesser development of the superior precentral (*prcs*) and postcentral (*pocs*) sulci. Sulcus subcentralis anterior (*SCA*) may correspond to the human inferior precentral sulcus. (After von Bonin and Bailey. *The neocortex of* Macaca mulatta. Urbana, University of Illinois Press, 1947.)

Altogether, the cerebral cortex reduced to its absolute skeleton is not unlike the spinal cord. As said by Lorente de Nó,[37] to whom we owe much of this knowledge, cortical neuron chains "are in no way different from chains of internuncial neurons in any part of the central nervous system." He also points out that:

". . . in the cortex of the mouse, cells with ascending axons are relatively numerous, while those with short axons are relatively rare. In the human cortex there is an increase in the number of cells with ascending axons, but the increase in the cells having short axons is much more pronounced, so much so that in some cortical regions they outnumber the cells with descending axons. Furthermore, the increase in the short axon cells is not restricted to any one layer, but takes place in all of them, although in different cortical regions the increase is more pronounced in certain layers, for example, in the area striata in layer IV and the motor area in layer V. *Cajal assumed that the large number of cells with short axons was the anatomical expression of the delicacy of function of the brain of man.* At present that assumption is almost a statement of fact, for it is known that synaptic transmission demands the sum-mation of impulses under strict conditions, and it is evident that the more heterogeneous is the origin of the synapses on the cells with descending axons, the more rigid become the conditions for threshold stimulation, and the more accurate the selection of the paths through which the impulses may be conducted. The reduction of the number of cells with short axons, without essential modification of the long links in the chains of cortical neurons, makes the cortex of the mouse the 'skeleton' for the human cortex."[37]

Electrophysiologists,[1] by using microelectrodes which can record from single cells throughout the depth of the cortex, are developing a physiology of the cortex comparable to the histologic studies of the cortex made with silver stains. This development brings closer an understanding of cortical function.

CYTOARCHITECTURAL MAPS.   As already indicated, cytoarchitectural maps offer few clues to function. Major differences between the cytoarchitectural fields have functional correlations, although it is not necessary to believe that every small cytoarchitectural difference denotes a difference in function or that each function requires a unique cytoarchitecture. Some students of cytoarchitecture have overzealously divided the cortical layers into more and more sublayers and the cortical areas into smaller and smaller subareas. Many of these proposed divisions, almost always based on subjective and nonquantitative criteria, have not been verified by other observers looking at the same sections. Many cytoarchitectural boundaries are not constant from animal to animal, and variations often result from distortions produced mechanically by the cortical folds, which notoriously differ from brain to brain within a species. It is interesting that the revolt against parcellation was initiated by two psychologists[29] rather than by neuroanatomists.

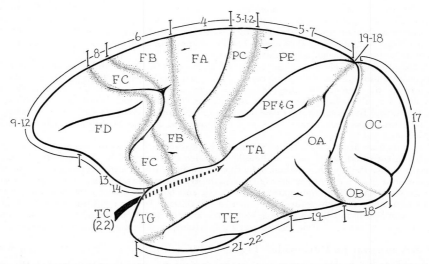

FIG. 138.   Cytoarchitectural map of monkey brain relating terminology of Brodmann (*numbers*) to that of von Bonin and Bailey (*letters*). The areas and the relation of the designations are only approximate

Experiments on the cerebral cortex are often described in terms of fissures, sulci, gyri and lobes. The fissural pattern for the rhesus monkey, a common laboratory animal, is shown in Figure 137. It can be seen that the simian brain is basically similar to the human, but much simpler. Cytoarchitectural maps also provide a language in which to describe the cortex, a language that is often more compact than description in terms of fissures and convolutions. It is virtually impossible to follow present and past experimental literature based on the monkey without knowledge of Brodmann's map. This map, as modified by the Vogts,[62] and another produced by von Bonin and Bailey[6] are reproduced for reference in Figure 138.*

In the interpretation of such maps it should be realized that the boundaries are not

* In this map the initial letter is drawn from the name of the lobe. The numbers used by Brodmann and others can be remembered more easily if the way they were assigned is understood. His monkey brain was cut horizontally, so the precentral and postcentral regions appeared in the first few sections. These received the low numbers (1–8) as different cytoarchitecture was encountered. It will be noticed that the numbers jump from front to back. The next important group of numbers (9–12) is frontal; 17–19 are occipital; 20–22 are in the temporal lobe in the order of their appearance in serial horizontal sections.

sharp; instead, one type of cortex blends into another. The Brodmann terminology can be modified to encompass modern studies. The expression "areas 3–1–2" may be retained, even though the differences between 3 and 1 may not be real and 2 is nonexistent. Similarly, use of "areas 9–12" reflects scepticism of the significance of the subareal differences but describes a region for which there is no other generally accepted term, since some object to the word "prefrontal." In the description below, the letters signify von Bonin and Bailey's terminology. The numbers are those of Brodmann, occasionally modified. Some of the areas concerned with motor function will be discussed in detail; others will be described in later chapters.

FA (area 4) is agranular cortex beginning in the depth of the central fissure and extending up its anterior bank onto the free surface of the precentral gyrus. Here the gray matter is thick (3.5 to 5.0 mm.); the presence of the giant pyramidal cells of Betz in the fifth layer constitutes the major basis for determining the anterior border. Since the size necessary to qualify a cell as a Betz cell is not agreed upon, the forward boundary is not definitely established. Histologic evidence of a 4s strip is lacking.

FB, together with FA, corresponds roughly to Brodmann's area 6, although the posterior boundary, as noted, fluctuates markedly. In this area, the cortex is still thick and agranular but lacks giant pyramidal (Betz) cells in the fifth layer.

FC, corresponding to area 8 as modified since Brodmann, is a transitional band with a poorly developed internal granular layer; it extends around the frontal pole. On the lateral surface, FC is largely buried in the two limbs of the V formed by the arcuate fissure, but issues from it laterally. The remainder of the frontal lobe (FD or area 9–12) is quite uniform in structure, except for an area around the posterior end of the principal fissure.

PB lies almost entirely buried in the depth of the central fissure and is easily recognized. Like other primary sensory areas, PB is koniocortex ("dusty cortex," referring to its highly granular nature). PC, occupying the free face of the postcentral gyrus, loses the excessive granulation and becomes homotypical; i.e., all six layers are present and none is "overdeveloped." Since area 2 has been shown by von Bonin and Bailey to be nonexistent, the posterior boundary of area PC lies somewhat anterior to the superior postcentral fissure. The two terminologies can be made congruent by speaking of Brodmann areas 3 and 1.

The remaining areas which figure prominently in discussion of motor function are the two concentric bands surrounding the large and easily identified striate area (the primary visual area), which in monkeys, unlike the situation in man, extends over the free surface of the occipital lobe. The transition from OC or area 17 is sharp, OB or area 18 being homotypical and marked by the presence of very large cells in the third layer. The boundaries between OB and OA and between OA and the parietal lobe are not sharp, and cytoarchitectural analysis is made difficult by the deep fissures in the region. The Vogts and von Bonin and Bailey agree in restricting area 17 mainly to the posterior wall of the lunate sulcus. The general region can be termed area 18–19 without neglect of major cytoarchitectural criteria.

Corticospinal or Pyramidal Tract.[44]

By definition, the pyramidal tract consists of those fibers which originate in the cortex and pass to the spinal cord through the medullary pyramids.* As their names suggest, these medullary structures have a pyramidal shape, and the name of the tract derives from this fact. It is only accidental and incidental that some of the tract originates in large, conspicuous, pyramid-shaped cells such as the Betz cells. The term "pyramidal tract" in no way implies fibers originating at such cells; in fact, the tract was named before the shape of the cells of origin was known.† Unquestionably, fibers from the cortex to the cranial motor nerve nuclei are functionally similar to those going to spinal segments. Although fibers in the former group do not pass through the pyramids, they should not be confused with those termed extrapyramidal fibers. Some corticobulbar fibers end on intercalated nuclei and are difficult to separate morphologically or experimentally from those that end more directly on the motor nerve nuclei.

* Although recent anatomic evidence that the pyramids may contain ascending fibers has not been contradicted, functional evidence thought to indicate their existence has been thoroughly disproved.[42]

† Some fibers in the pyramids give collaterals to the pontine nuclei and possibly to the reticular formation of the medulla. Should these collaterals reach the cord without synapse they would be corticospinal but not pyramidal. Further, because of this collateralization, it is possible that the distinction between pyramidal and extrapyramidal fibers has been overdrawn.

It is now believed that all of the pyramidal tract arises from the cerebral cortex; degeneration in the pyramids is said to be complete after decortication.[41] That the pyramidal tract arises solely in the giant Betz cells is a misconception; the tract also arises from small cells distributed through the third to the sixth layer. In man, the motor area of each hemisphere contains approximately 34,000 Betz cells, enough to account for the 2 per cent of fibers with large diameters ranging from 11 μ to 20 μ, but not nearly enough to account for the one million axons in each medullary pyramid. Figure 139

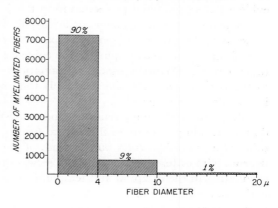

FIG. 139. Myelinated fiber spectrum of pyramidal tract. (After Lassek. *J. comp. Neurol.*, 1942, *76:*217–225.)

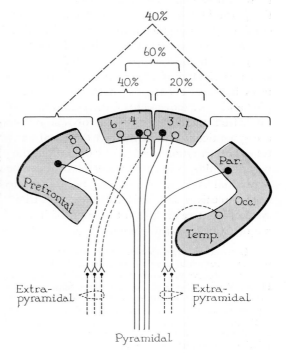

FIG. 140. Summary diagram showing origins of pyramidal and extrapyramidal systems influencing spinal motoneurons. Note overlapping resulting from pyramidal tract originating outside the precentral and postcentral areas, and extrapyramidal systems originating from sensorimotor areas. Quantitative estimates and other details will vary, depending on technique used.

shows the distribution of the diameters of the myelinated fibers which constitute the major portion of the pyramidal tract.[30] The remaining fibers in the tract are unmyelinated and recently[14] were estimated to constitute 6 per cent of it. Little is known of their origin and function.

That the pyramidal tract originates exclusively in the motor area is another misconception. The proportion of fibers originating from the precentral gyrus is variously estimated at only 20 to 40 per cent of the total (Fig. 140). Another large component comes from the postcentral gyrus—20 per cent according to Levin and Bradford.[33] Thus, at most, the two central gyri contribute only 60 per cent of the tract. Whether pyramidal tract fibers originate in area 6, which some believe is part of the motor area, is controversial.[61] At the moment, electrophysiologic and anatomic studies do not agree particularly well. Patton and Amassian,[44] who recorded pyramidal activity evoked by stimulation of the cerebral cortex, obtained evidence of a strong contribution from area 6 but a relatively small contribution from the postcentral region, even though the anatomic evidence of a pyramidal projection from this latter region is good.

The 40 per cent of fibers not arising in the precentral and postcentral gyri must come from the prefrontal, posterior parietal, occipital and temporal lobes,[63] although there is little direct electrophysiologic evidence of such contributions. It is possible that these pyramidal fibers represent continuations of fibers which have given off collaterals to the pontine and reticular nuclei. If this suggestion is valid, important theoretical implications are involved.

Regardless of the uncertainty concerning the origins of pyramidal tract fibers that do not arise in proximity to the central fissure, it seems clear that one should no longer think of a pyramidal tract but, instead, of pyramidal tracts. Whether pyramidal tract neurons with different cortical origins serve different functions, and whether some fibers originating in the occipital and temporal lobes have functions like those of fibers originating in the precentral gyrus cannot be determined without further research. However, there is now increasing reason to question the value of the classic dichotomy between the pyramidal and the extrapyramidal systems, a distinction in which each has been considered homogeneous and unlike the other.[10]

Extrapyramidal Projections from the Cortex. Overlapping with pyramidal tract projections in respect to point of origin are projections to a wide range of subcortical structures including the brain stem reticular formation (Fig. 152). Through these structures impulses eventually reach the segmental level in the spinal cord and can both *effect* and *affect* movement. Extrapyramidal pathways from the cortex to the spinal cord differ from the pyramidal or corticospinal system in two ways: (i) the chains of neurons are synaptically interrupted in the basal ganglia or other subcortical nuclei, or in the reticular formation; and (ii) by definition, the pathways do not pass through the medullary pyramids. These systems of neurons can be termed the "cortically originating extrapyramidal system," which can be abbreviated "COEPS." Since the extrapyramidal system receives subcortical inputs, "COEPS" is not a synonym for "extrapyramidal system," but refers to that portion of it which originates in the cerebral cortex. The major COEPS pathways may be summarized as follows.

CORTICOSTRIATAL AND CORTICOPALLIDAL. The existence of a corticostriatal system had long been suspected but could not be demonstrated by the usual degeneration techniques.* Glees,[26] using a silver stain, has observed an unmyelinated corticocaudate and corticoputamen projection in cat and monkey. Dusser de Barenne and his coworkers applied strychnine to the cortex in monkeys and recorded strychnine spikes† in the caudate nucleus. Impulses originating in the cortex can reach the pallidum by way of the putamen or by direct pathways. Glees traced fibers from area 6 to the external segment of the globus pallidus. From the basal ganglia, impulses can be relayed along the lenticular fasciculus and the ansa lenticularis; and, after traversing a synapse in the field of Forel, the impulses reach the midline tegmentum. A more direct projection from areas 4 and 6 enters the midbrain nuclei including the red nucleus.

* A discrete area of cortical tissue is ablated. Some time later, the animal is sacrificed, and lower neural structures are stained and studied histologically for degenerated fibers.

† Strychnine causes a large number of neurons to synchronize their discharges. The result is periodic spikes at the terminus of the neurons in another part of the cortex or in a subcortical nucleus. Since the spikes suffer temporal dispersion at the first synapse, the recording of a spike means a direct connection between the recording and strychninized points. "Strychnine neuronography" is a useful tool for functional anatomy.

CORTICOTHALAMIC.   In general, a specific cortical area sends fibers to the thalamic nucleus from which it receives fibers. This reciprocal arrangement occurs in the motor cortex as well as in the sensory and the association cortex.

CORTICORETICULAR.   Rossi and Brodal,[49] using a silver method, found that corticoreticular fibers originate from much of the cerebral cortex but mainly from the sensorimotor region, particularly the motor area. These fibers end predominantly in the pontine reticulum and in the medulla dorsal to the inferior olive. The projection is bilateral and poorly, if at all, organized somatotopically. The terminations of this projection are in the regions from which the reticulospinal tracts originate, providing an extrapyramidal connection of the cortex with spinal motoneurons. Several investigators[2, 3] have shown that single reticular units can be activated by cortical stimulation; the latency (2 to 6 milliseconds) of the response suggests that the connection is a direct corticoreticular neuron. Some of these connections may be effected by collaterals from the pyramidal tract.

CORTICOPONTINE.   Each of the four major lobes of the brain projects to the pons, the frontopontine tract being the largest projection. It arises equally from areas 4 and 6. Besides conveying impulses to the cerebellum, this important tract in primates is thought to give off collaterals to midbrain structures, e.g., the substantia nigra. According to Cajal, some corticopontine fibers are actually collaterals of corticospinal fibers.

The COEPS provides not only multisynaptic pathways to the spinal cord but also recurrent or "feed-back" pathways from the cortex that pass through the subcortical structures to return to the cortex. There are at least three such potential pathways from the cortex: (i) via the cortico-ponto-cerebellar tract and returning via the dentato-thalamo-cortical pathway; (ii) via collaterals from the corticopontine tract and from direct corticospinal fibers to the substantia nigra and thence via nigrostriatal fibers to join the loop described next; and (iii) via cortico-striatal-pallidal projections, thence via the anteroventral nucleus of the thalamus and its projections to the motor areas.

MOTOR FUNCTION

Pyramidal Tract.   A single point in the motor area of the cortex can be stimulated and the resulting discharge in the pyramidal tract recorded from any point along its course—from the interneurons of the spinal cord, from the motor roots and nerves, or from the muscles. In fact, a point on the motor cortex and the pyramidal fibers to which it gives rise can be treated like the afferent limb of a reflex arc and subjected to the same kind of analysis. Stimulations of two cortical points can be interacted like stimulations of two afferent nerves.

D AND I RESPONSES.   The first question to be asked is, what is stimulated when electrodes are applied to the cortical surface of the motor area? The cells of origin of the pyramidal tract? The intracortical neurons which end on these cells? Because too

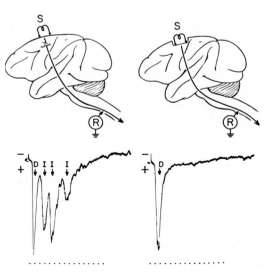

FIG. 141.   Pyramidal tract responses to stimulation of motor cortex (*left*) and white matter (*right*) in monkey. Recording electrode in lateral column of spinal cord at C_1. Downward deflection indicates positivity at electrode in pyramidal tract. Time, 1 millisecond. *D* and *I* waves are labeled. (After Patton and Amassian. In *Handbook of physiology*. In press.)

many stages intervene, the response of a muscle or even of a nerve to stimulation of the motor cortex will obviously not give much information.

Patton and Amassian[43, 44] inserted a recording microelectrode into the bulbar pyramid or the pyramidal tract of the cervical spinal cord and stimulated the motor cortex. In the records so obtained (Fig. 141), the first deflection (D wave) is a stable, short-latency (0.7 millisecond), short-duration, positive wave. This wave is followed by a series of positive, irregular or imperfectly rhythmic waves beginning after a longer time (2.0 to 2.5 milliseconds) and lasting for many milliseconds. The first wave was termed the D wave because analysis indicated that it appeared when the electric current excited *directly* the cells giving rise to the pyramidal tract axons. The later deflections were termed the I waves because analysis showed that they were caused by indirect excitation of pyramidal tract neurons. The longer latency of the I waves was accounted for by the time consumed in traversing chains of intracortical neurons.

The experiments leading to this conclusion illustrate how a neurophysiologic analysis can be made. Briefly, the D wave relative to the I waves was more resistant to anesthesia, anoxia, etc.; had a shorter recovery cycle; and persisted when the cortex was removed and the underlying white matter was stimulated (Fig. 141). In "penetration experiments," the I waves appeared only when the tip of the stimulating electrode was within the cortex. Further, when the stimulating electrode was moved rostrally, the D wave disappeared, but the I wave persisted for some distance. This observation will help in resolving some of the controversial aspects of localization in the motor cortex.

RATES OF CONDUCTION.   In general, the pyramidal axons are small, less than 2 per cent being of Group I diameter (11 to 22 μ). Maximal conduction velocity in the spinal portion of the tract is, according to Lloyd[36] and Bernhard et al.,[5] 60 to 70 m. per second. This difference in velocity suggests that the axons between the cortex and the pyramid are larger than those below the pyramids, the fibers becoming attenuated by collateralization in the spinal cord.

SPINAL STAGE OF PYRAMIDAL SYSTEM FUNCTION.   Knowledge of how the inter-neurons and motoneurons of the spinal cord are excited is necessary to a complete picture of pyramidal tract activity. In the cat, Lloyd[36] used microelectrodes to record from the nuclear groups of the spinal gray matter while he stimulated the bulbar pyramids (Fig. 142). (All of the medulla except the pyramids had been sectioned below the stimulating electrodes to prevent activation of descending fibers in the extrapyramidal system, and a midcollicular decerebration had been performed to prevent impulses from ascending in sensory tracts and activating the pyramidal tract at the cerebral cortex.)

In view of the great power and promptness of voluntary contractions in intact animals, Lloyd's study revealed a surprising amount of "inertia" in the spinal stage of pyramidal tract function. A single shock discharged only the cells of the external basilar nucleus, which lies in the gray matter just deep to the pyramidal tract fibers. The pyramidal volley arrived 4.5 milliseconds after the pyramids were stimulated and almost immediately discharged a few external basilar cells. This latency largely represents conduction time in the tract. To cause the intermediate nucleus of Cajal to discharge, repeated stimulation was required. By testing the excitability of this nucleus with spinal volleys, Lloyd showed that a nuclear delay of 4.5 milliseconds passed before the external basilar nucleus discharged into the intermediate nucleus. Another 3 milliseconds elapsed before the motoneurons were facilitated, a finding indicating another nuclear delay in the intermediate nucleus. As the repeated stimuli continued, the latency between arrival of an impulse at the spinal segment and motoneuron facilitation was reduced to 1.0 milliseconds.

From these studies it can be concluded that two systems of interneurons are involved, one at the cortical stage and one at the spinal stage of pyramidal tract activation. Movements elicited by cortical stimulation will therefore have properties similar to those which interneurons lend to spinal reflex action, and the following phenomena could also be predicted on this basis.

Excitable Properties of the Motor Cortex and its Efferent Pathways (Pyramidal and Extrapyramidal). RECIPROCAL INNERVATION. In 1889, Sherrington demonstrated that, given a background of reflex muscular contraction, stimulation of a cortical point* might excite flexor motoneurons and inhibit the antagonistic extensor motoneurons—a "flexor point." Conversely, stimulation of a neighboring point might excite the extensor motoneurons and inhibit the antagonistic flexor motoneurons—an "extensor

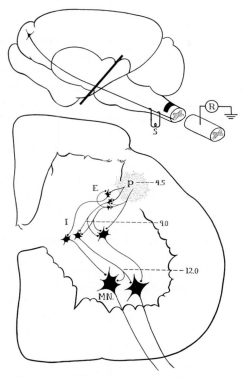

FIG. 142. Diagram of Lloyd's experiment on activation of spinal nuclei by pyramidal tract discharge. Upper drawing shows positions of stimulating and recording electrodes and of brain ablations to rule out nonpyramidal conduction. Time noted at each level is first detectable facilitation of nuclear neurons. Subtraction gives nuclear delay in *previous nucleus*. P, Pyramidal tract; E, external basilar cells; I, intermediate nucleus of Cajal; MN, motoneuron. (After Lloyd. *J. Neurophysiol.*, 1941, *4*:525–546.)

point." The site of the inhibition is in the spinal cord, because the same phenomenon has been demonstrated by stimulating the white matter underlying flexor and extensor points. That reciprocal innervation of muscles by the pyramidal tract has been questioned is understandable because: (i) the flexor and extensor points may overlap somewhat; and (ii) intracortical neurons may spread impulses from one point to another, both giving cocontraction of flexors and extensors.

LATENCY. The latency of cortically induced movements in response to a repetitive stimulus (summation time) may be as long as several seconds, during which time more than 100 volleys pass down the pyramidal tract. In contrast, man can initiate a voluntary response to a signal in less than one fifth of a second. Analytical studies indicate conduc-

* A cortical point is not a physiologic, anatomic or physical entity, but is simply the point at which electrodes are placed. The current may, for example, excite neurons at a distance from the "point."

tion times and nuclear delays in the spinal interneurons measured in milliseconds. Such long latencies of movement in response to cortical stimulation, then, must represent an interaction of excitatory and inhibitory effects resulting from a mixed stimulation of what may be loosely termed "extensor" exciting and "flexor" exciting pyramidal tract fibers.

AFTERDISCHARGE. The movement induced by stimulation of the motor cortex often continues long after the cessation of the stimulation. This afterdischarge is at first sustained ("tonic") and then becomes a series of rhythmic contractions ("clonic"). The same sequence of events is seen in epileptic seizures of the Jacksonian type. Experimentally induced epilepsy is best ascribed to cortical interneurons acting in closed or self-reexciting circuits.

FACILITATION.[16] Bubnoff and Heidenhain[9] recognized that stimulation of one point on the cortex can facilitate (or inhibit) the response of another point. Facilitation is manifested by a greater response to a cortical testing shock when it is preceded by a cortical conditioning shock than when it is given alone. In fact, stimulation of one point may not merely facilitate but actually may discharge pyramidal tract fibers originating from another cortical point. For example, stimulation of neurons in area 6 may cause neurons in area 4 to discharge. Both intracortical spread and arcuate association fibers are involved in this activation. When the discharge of a stimulated area into another falls short of causing the latter to discharge, facilitation occurs. The duration of facilitation in this system is measured in seconds, 13 seconds being a typical figure. Facilitative interaction also occurs at the spinal interneuron pool, and activity at this level as well as at the cortex is important in the interpretation of cortical localization experiments.

EXTINCTION.[16] At intervals longer than those required to demonstrate facilitation, and especially with pulses of long duration, the response to a testing stimulus may be *smaller* when the stimulus follows a conditioning stimulus than when it is delivered alone. Dusser de Barenne and McCulloch[16] called this phenomenon "extinction" to give it a name not limited to a specific mechanism. The unresponsiveness is cortical, not spinal, and is local, becoming progressively less apparent if the electrodes delivering the testing shocks are moved a few millimeters from the conditioning electrodes. *Extinction* was defined as a diminution or absence of response to stimulation of a motor focus following antecedent stimulation of the *same* focus. *Inhibition* is also a diminution or absence of an expected response, but is manifest when the testing stimulus has been preceded by stimulation of *another* cortical point, one from which an antagonistic response may be elicited. Because Betz cells serving antagonistic muscles may not be totally separate, this distinction is not sufficient. In fact, the relationship of extinction to inhibition, suppression, voltage drifts and pH changes in the cerebral cortex is not entirely clear, and whether extinction exists at all has been questioned.[44]

LABILITY.[8] With facilitation, inhibition and extinction resulting from cortical stimulation, it could be anticipated that the motor cortex exhibits a certain lability of response. Not all intensities and frequencies of stimulation give the same result, and apparently identical stimuli do not give identical responses. The names given various manifestations of this "instability of the cortical point"[8] need not concern us. One manifestation of lability is explicable by the immediate history of the point stimulated (intracortical facilitation); another is a change in response as the parameters of the stimulus are changed.

Lilly *et al.*[35] varied and monitored the pulse duration, amplitude and frequency of cortical stimulation. (i) Combinations of amplitude and duration constituted an intermediate range which excited efferent cells; (ii) stimuli in a second range of durations and amplitude excited both cells and efferent fibers in the white matter; and (iii) strong unidirectional pulses of long duration destroyed cells and, eventually, fibers in the immediate vicinity of the stimulating electrode. (This damage is avoided by using Lilly's reverse pulse stimulator.) It follows that, if stimuli of different parameters excite different structures and if some stimuli injure fibers, quite different results may be obtained by different investigators, or by the same investigator during successive stimulations of the cerebral cortex.

SPREADING DEPRESSION.   Electrical, mechanical or chemical stimuli applied to the cerebral cortex were observed by Leão[32] to cause a slowly expanding depression of its spontaneous electrical activity. This depression spreads over the cortex at a rate of 2 to 3 mm. per minute and persists at any one point for two to six minutes. It is also manifested by a decreased cortical excitability to stimulation, a slow change in the steady potential, vascular dilatation and an increase in the electrical resistance of the cortex.[60]

Spreading depression is a marked phenomenon in the rabbit, but it is more capricious in the cat and monkey. Marshall[39, 40] has shown that such depression is an important experimental artefact caused by dehydration and cooling of the cerebral cortex when it is widely exposed. The depression can be prevented by protecting the cortex with mineral oil, or it can be induced by dehydrating the animal by means of an intravenous administration of sucrose. Marshall's analysis suggests that spreading depression is a phenomenon of the pathologic cortex. Spreading depression is significant as a source of error in experiments on the cerebral cortex and may play some role in the general cortical depression that follows epileptic seizures.

Prior to Marshall's analysis, it was believed that stimulation of specific bands of the cerebral cortex (running mediolaterally) gave rise to a widespread diminution of electrical activity and excitability. This phenomenon was given the name "suppression" and was thought to be mediated by circuits passing through the basal ganglia and returning to the cerebral cortex. Experiments by Marshall[39] and by Sloan and Jasper[52] indicate that this suppression is the same as the spreading depression of Leão and that it can be initiated from any point on the cortex, not specifically from the so-called suppressor bands.

Somatotopic Organization of the Motor Cortex.   That different parts of the body move when different parts of the precentral gyrus are stimulated has been known for nearly a century, but the nature and detail of this somatotopic representation are still subjects of experiment and controversy. "Representation of the body," "somatotopic organization" and "topographic organization" are synonyms. All means that the cortical cells which give rise to the descending fibers activating different muscle groups lie in broadly the same relation to one another as do the muscles in the body. On the other hand, according to some authors, movements rather than muscles are represented.

Figure 143 shows the sequence of motor representation expressed in terms of body structures. The body parts are represented "upside down," with the leg area medial, the face area lateral, and the arm area lying between. In man, much of the leg area is buried in the medial longitudinal fissure, and much of the primary motor area for the arm and face lies buried on the anterior wall of the central fissure. In the monkey, more of the motor area lies on the free surface.

An important functional deduction can be made from the amount of cortical space devoted to a given part of the body. The lips, the tongue, the thumb and the great toe, which are all highly mobile and capable of finely graded movement, have larger cortical spaces devoted to them than do the less mobile fingers. The hand and foot areas of the cortex are roughly the same size as the total of those governing the movements of all the other limb muscles. This arrangement suggests that finely graded movements are obtained by the simplest of all methods—the provision of a larger number of efferent neurons. Since the efferent cells, especially the Betz cells, occur in clusters, it is probably not only the number of cells but also the number of interspersed intracortical neurons that determines the variety of movement of which the hand or tongue is capable. In either case, cortical space is required. In view of these considerations, it should not be

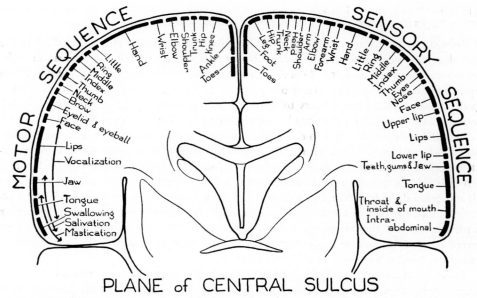

PLANE of CENTRAL SULCUS

FIG. 143.   Diagrammatic representation of sensory and motor sequences as mapped by threshold stimulation of cerebral cortex in man. Length of bars indicates in general way extent of cortical areas devoted to each structure in average patient. This is subject to considerable variation, however. (From Rasmussen and Penfield. *Fed. Proc.*, 1947, 6:452–460.)

surprising that the degree of paralysis caused by equal-sized lesions in the motor areas is greater and more persistent in the hand than in the shoulder.

The history of the discovery that movement can be elicited by cortical stimulation is informative because it illustrates how careful clinical observation and astute deductions can interact with the more analytical and controlled animal experiments. In 1870, Hughlings Jackson, the great physiologically minded neurologist, postulated the existence of a somatotopically organized motor area from his observations of the epileptic seizures which originate in that area and now bear his name. In a given patient, a seizure might start in the lips, spread to the face, then to the arm, and then to the leg (the "march of epilepsy"). Hughlings Jackson[27] reasoned that there must exist, somewhere in the brain, structures having a concern with the lip, and further, that the remainder of the musculature must be represented there in an orderly fashion, accounting for the successive and orderly involvement during the epileptic discharge. Independently and experimentally, Fritsch and Hitzig[19] discovered the electrical excitability of the motor cortex in the dog and the monkey, mapped areas for the face, the arm and the leg, and demonstrated some evidence of localization of even smaller body parts.

Similar experiments have been conducted on monkeys and apes by Sherrington, Fulton, Marion Hines, Woolsey and many others, and on man (during a surgical operation under local anesthesia) by Cushing and by Penfield.

The trend in both animal and human experiments has been from localization in terms of region (face, arm, leg) to movements of joints and digits, culminating in the suggestion (Marion Hines) that single muscles may be separately represented in the motor cortex. Hughlings Jackson and others following him have expressed the opposite view. Impressed by the fact that a patient can recover the use of a limb after destruction of cortical representation of that limb previously defined by stimulation, they have favored the idea of a widespread overlapping of the representation of muscle groups. Sherrington generalized that the cerebral cortex "thinks" in terms of movements, not muscles; and this view has been found persuasive, particularly by British neurologists and neurophysiologists.

EVIDENCE FROM SINGLE MUSCLE RECORDING.   Responses of an individual muscle or its nerve to systematic stimulation of the motor cortex have been studied in efforts to resolve the question.

Just which muscles at a given joint respond to cortical stimulation is difficult to discern with the naked eye. Using monkeys, Chang et al.[12] isolated the tendons of 13 muscles acting over the ankle and attached them, eight at a time, to myographs. Part of the foot area in the motor cortex was divided into millimeter squares and systematically stimulated. The response produced in each muscle by a given stimulus was recorded on a two-dimensional plot for that muscle in the space corresponding to the cortical point stimulated. Three major results were obtained: (i) Occasionally, only one of eight muscles responded, and the points for such "solitary responses" by a given muscle always fell in a cluster (Fig. 144, *left*). (ii) When the responses of each muscle were classified according to latency, those with the shortest latency clustered on contiguous points, whereas the points that yielded inter- mediate and long-latency responses tended to form surrounding rings (Fig. 144, *right*). (iii) When the responses of any two muscles were graded and represented on the cortical map as greater or less than the other muscle responses, a similar clustering was observed (Fig. 145).

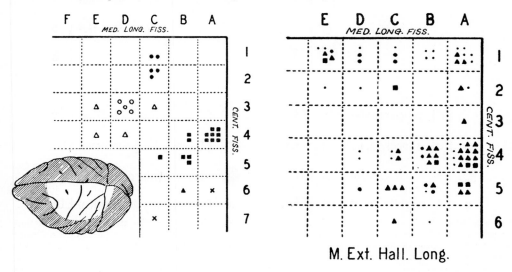

- M. Extensor Digitorum Longus (EDL)
- M. Extensor Hallucis Longus (EHL)
- M. Tibialis Anticus (TA)
- M. Abductor Hallucis Longus (AHL)
- M. Flexor Digitorum Longus (FDL)
- M. Tibialis Posticus (TP)

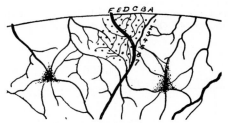

FIG. 144.   Muscle responses from stimulation of motor cortex. *Lower right*, grid of blood vessels and stimulated points. Broad dark line is caused by vein leaving central fissure to enter longitudinal sinus. Above are two maps of this small cortical area that are related to brain diagram by letters and numbers. *Upper left* shows points from which response was obtained in single foot or ankle muscle. Note that such "solitary" responses cluster. *Upper right* shows points from which extensor hallucis longus was activated. Note, however, that in region *AB45* responses were of short latency; large squares, 0–1.00 second; large triangles 1.01–2.00 seconds. Small circles represent latencies of 2.01–3.00 seconds, and dots, latencies of 3.01 seconds or longer. Responses of several muscles were obtained from *Row 1 A–E*, possibly owing to proximity to supplementary motor area. (From Chang et al. *J. Neurophysiol.*, 1947, *10*:39–56.)

The latency study has been conducted in another way by Bernhard and Bohm,[4] who recorded the latency of impulses in a muscle nerve and correlated it with the point stimulated on the motor cortex (Fig. 146). Again, the lines representing given latencies formed concentric rings. Thus, a given muscle can be thrown into contraction from a fairly wide area of the motor cortex, but into strong short-latency contraction only from a narrow focus.

Both of these studies lead to the concept that Betz and other corticofugal cells activating the motoneuron pool for a given muscle are topographically closely related

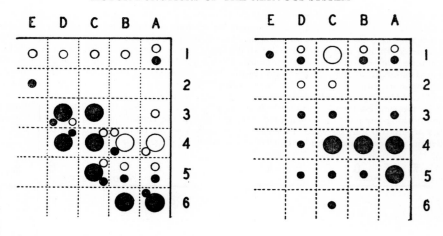

○ EHL much greater than TA   ○ EDL much greater than EHL

o EHL slightly greater than TA   o EDL slightly greater than EHL

● TA much greater than EHL   ● EHL much greater than EDL

• TA slightly greater than EHL   • EHL slightly greater than EDL

FIG. 145. Foci and fields of muscle representation determined by relative strengths of contraction in pairs of muscle to same cortical stimulation. Note that extensor hallucis longus (*EHL*) contractions relative to extensor digitorum longus (*EDL*) contractions were greatest in *4 ABC* and adjoining *5A*, establishing a focus. In the surrounding squares, relative strength of *EDL* contractions was less, establishing a field. Responses of *EDL* exceeded *EHL* only for points in rows *1* and *2*. Note in diagram at left that extensor hallucis longus (*EHL*) and tibialis anticus (*TA*), which in monkeys are slips of the same muscle, are spatially less differentiated than *EDL* and *EHL*. Compare this map with Figs. 146 and 147. (From Chang *et al. J. Neurophysiol.*, 1947, *10*:39–56.)

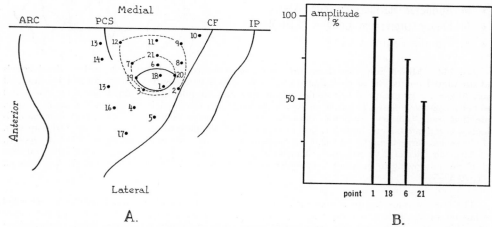

A.   B.

FIG. 146. *A*, Latency (summation time) for monosynaptic activation of triceps motoneurons from different points on left motor cortex, 1 second for inner circle, 3 seconds for next (*dashed*), and 7 seconds for outer circle. Note closeness of isotemp lines inferiorly, suggesting sharp boundary between arm and face. This diagram confirms experiment shown in Figs. 144 and 145. *B*, Amplitudes of monosynaptic discharge from points in a line running vertically through field for triceps. (After Bernhard and Bohm. *Arch. Neurol. Psychiat.* (*Chicago*), 1954, *72*:473–502.)

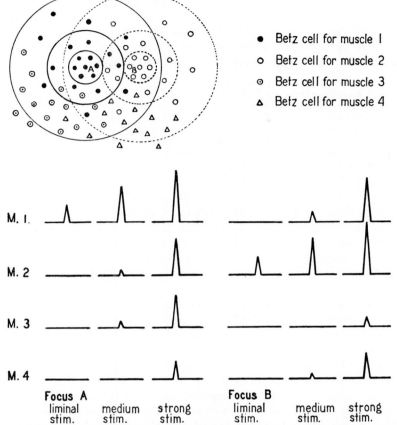

FIG. 147.   Diagrammatic representation of hypothetical distribution of Betz and other cells of fifth and sixth layers for individual muscles. A cell group for each muscle has a focal distribution and an overlapping fringe. Each symbol stands for a Betz cell; large concentric circles are spheres of excitation. Expected contraction of muscles to cortical stimulation at different strengths is shown by myograms drawn in lower part of figure, in which magnitude of contraction is determined by number of Betz cells involved in sphere of excitation. Scale is in millimeters; zones A and B represent about 4 to 8 mm.^{2} (From Chang *et al. J. Neurophysiol.*, 1947, *10*:39–56.)

to one another in the motor cortex.* In fact, as shown in Figure 147, there appears to be a focus of neurons surrounded by a field for each muscle. The foci for two muscles never overlap, although the field for one muscle may overlap the field and even the focus for another.

For several reasons, the size of the focus and the field for a given muscle, and the degree of overlapping with other muscles, are probably even more restricted than Figures 143 to 146 suggest. Extrapyramidal projections from area 4 and any collateralization of the pyramidal tract axons, both feeding into systems with a diffuse ultimate relationship to motoneurons, would obscure a tight grouping of the Betz cells concerned with a given muscle. Further, transcortical spread of the stimulating current or nerve impulses in intracortical neurons would also obscure discrete localization. That currents of threshold strength can activate neurons 4 mm. away from the electrodes has been proved by Phillips,[47] who used a single cortical unit technique.

EVIDENCE FROM PYRAMIDAL TRACT RECORDING.   The common result of cortical stimulation at a single point, especially with strong, long-duration pulses delivered

* It is remarkable that the axons in the peduncle, the pyramids and the spinal cord are not so related but are considerably intermixed.

through unipolar electrodes, or with any type of stimulus in an unanesthetized animal, is activation of several muscles, producing a movement of one or more joints. The basic and controversial question is whether this finding means that the motor cortex integrates the activities of various muscles into movements by re-representing the muscle many times and diffusely, contrary to the picture presented above.

The experiments on the D and I waves of the pyramidal tract discharge appear to resolve the controversy and, more important, to explain how the motor cortex organizes the contractions of individual muscles into a pattern which constitutes a skilled coordinated voluntary movement. After location of the point on the cortex giving a large D wave in the axons near the microelectrode tip in the pyramidal tract, the stimulating electrodes were moved several millimeters away from this cortical point until the D response disappeared. A threshold stimulus now elicited only I waves over the intracortical neurons, a D wave occurring only if the intensity was so high that the stimulus spread electrically to the cell body of the primary motor area. A stimulus near threshold can therefore indirectly excite a cell body at a distance of several millimeters.

The conclusion can be drawn that the cells of origin of the corticofugal pathways are highly organized topographically; that the neurons connected ultimately with a given muscle are grouped closely together in the cortex. Thus, the motor cortex is organized in terms of muscles. By definition, the motor cortex thinks in terms of movements, since it produces movement. But the organization of different movements is accomplished, not in the arrangement of Betz and other cells in the deep layers, but in the manifold connections of intracortical neurons with such cells. The neuropil of the cortex thinks in terms of movements, and the controversy over cortical localization can be traced to neurophysiologists' thinking in terms of a morphologically complex structure—the motor cortex—rather than in terms of its various cellular components—single units or classes of like neurons.

EXTENT OF PRIMARY MOTOR AREA.   That the mediolateral dimension of the precentral gyrus represents the cephalocaudad dimension of the animal has been known since 1870. By contrast, how the anteroposterior dimension is utilized and what constitutes the forward border of the motor area are still somewhat uncertain. The latter has, in fact, been shifted forward and backward, like the boundaries of some countries. If the mediolateral dimension represents the cephalocaudad dimension of the animal, it is logical that the axial and appendicular dimension should be represented in the remaining anteroposterior dimension of the motor area; and, in fact, this is the most recent view.

In the simunculus based on Woolsey's experiments (Fig. 148), the areas of representation of the fingers, toes, lips and tongue are mainly buried in the central fissure, with the successively more proximal musculature being represented more anteriorly in orderly sequence. The threshold for movement rises, and is higher for the axial than for the apical musculature. Note the position of the superior precentral sulcus or "dimple," which corresponds roughly to the anterior border of the motor area by certain cytoarchitectural and functional studies. If the simunculus in Figure 148 is correct, the axial musculature is represented in Brodmann's area 6, which has not previously been considered part of the body representation. In the light of recent experiments on unipolar versus bipolar stimulation, it is possible that Woolsey's studies place the forward boundary too far rostral. That such an expanse of cortex is needed to manage the proximal musculature is improbable.

Other Cortical Motor Areas.   With appropriate electrical stimulation, movements can be induced by activating areas other than the primary motor area. In fact, experiments on unanesthetized animals indicate that this is true of virtually the whole of the convexity of the cerebral hemispheres.[34] For each area and type of movement, the question arises whether (or in what degree) the responses from a given point are due to (i) physical spread of current, (ii) spread of impulses over intracortical and intercortical fibers to the primary motor areas, (iii) activation of extrapyramidal fibers

(COEPS) originating at the stimulated point, or (iv) activation of pyramidal tract fibers (or equivalent corticobulbar fibers going to the cranial motor nuclei), since, as we have seen, much of the pyramidal tract originates outside the primary motor area.

Whether the first two factors are operative is frequently learned by ablating the primary motor area or by cutting between it and a stimulated area. The consensus of opinion is that pyramidal tract efferents are concentrated near the central fissure, and that their concentration diminishes in passing forward. Conversely, the precentral gyrus contributes some fibers to the extrapyramidal system, and this contribution increases in passing forward into areas 6 and 8. With these differences in the kind of efferent projection comes a difference in the kind of movement that results. Tower[56] and Marion Hines showed that the primary motor area is to some degree the cortical origin of the extra-

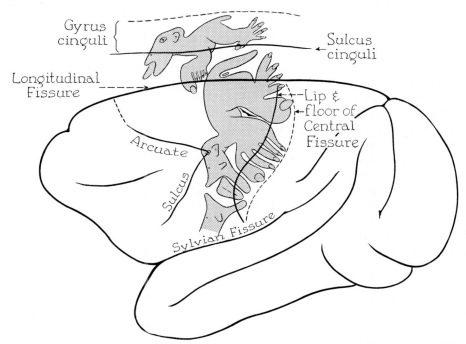

FIG. 148.   Somatotopic organization of primary and supplementary motor areas. Note that central and longitudinal fissures are shown "opened out" with dotted line representing floor of a fissure and solid line lip of fissure on brain surface. At bottom of figure is an ipsilateral face area. In bay formed by foot, hand and abdomen is precentral dimple, the anterior border of area 4 (cf. Fig. 138). Much of the primary simunculus and virtually all of supplementary area falls in area 6. (After Woolsey *et al. Res. Publ. Ass. nerv. ment. Dis.*, 1952, *30*:238–264.)

pyramidal system. They sectioned the pyramids of cats, monkeys and chimpanzees, and found that not all ability to move was lost. While movement lost the delicacy, accuracy and variety that are embodied in the phrase "skilled movement," certain gross movements, such as clutching and climbing, were retained. Moreover, stimulation of the precentral gyrus subsequent to section of the pyramids gave rise to such movements, but not to movements of single muscles or single joints.

That the corticospinal tract is not the sole agent of volitional skilled movement is true in man as well as in monkeys. The pyramids have not been sectioned surgically, but the corticospinal fibers (along with some extrapyramidal fibers) have been interrupted, occasionally bilaterally, in the cerebral peduncle and in the posterolateral region of the spinal cord. The resulting paralysis has been surprisingly slight and the ultimate recovery surprisingly great. For example, after a posterolateral cordotomy, a patient was still able to play a Beethoven piano concerto. Clearly, the role of the COEPS in the execution of movement is considerable and should be examined in detail. However, as pointed out, it is not always possible to decide whether a given response is executed over the extrapyramidal or the "extraprecentral pyramidal" system. By this latter term is meant pyramidal tract fibers arising elsewhere than in the classic cortical motor area.

SECOND MOTOR AREA. A small motor area in the lateral prolongation of the precentral gyrus onto the lip of the sylvian fissure has been described. The body is represented in reverse order to the representation in the precentral gyrus. Discovered by Sugar et al.,[55] the existence of the area has been confirmed,[31] but little is known of its function. According to Lauer[31] and Woolsey et al.,[67] the area immediately below the main motor representation is an ipsilateral motor face area. This finding correlates with our knowledge that the facial musculature tends to escape paralysis when cortical or capsular lesions are restricted to one side of the brain.

SUPPLEMENTARY MOTOR AREA.[46, 67] In both monkey and man the musculature is represented a third time in the cortex. This representation (Fig. 148), constituting the *supplementary motor area*, occupies mainly the mesial extent of area 6, and only the thumb representation in the monkey is detectable on the free surface of the hemisphere. This area is also topographically organized, although not in such detail as the primary motor area. In contrast with the primary motor area, the thresholds are higher and more affected by anesthesia, and the responses are in the nature of the assuming and holding of a limb posture rather than quick phasic movements like those induced by precentral stimulation. The postures are often held many seconds after the stimulus has ceased. The responses are often bilateral, and one stimulation tends to facilitate the next.

While the supplementary area gives rise to fibers projecting widely to the frontal and precentral cortex, those reaching the primary motor areas of the same and opposite hemispheres constitute the main projection. However, the supplementary area can act independently and in the absence of these connections. Contrary to some reports, it does not contribute fibers to the pyramidal tract, but rather has extensive connections with brain stem structures, inducing motor effects via the extrapyramidal motor system.[53] The postural nature of the movements, the long after-action and facilitation, and the tendency of widespread areas of musculature to be involved—all are properties associated in reflex action with multisynaptic connections and are to be expected of an area connected with the motoneurons through the extrapyramidal system.

Other Supplemental Areas. An experiment on unanesthetized monkeys was devised to learn the total extent of the cortex which yields movements upon electrical stimulation.[34] As seen in Figure 149, nearly all of the lateral surface of the cerebral cortex was stimulated through as many as 610 implanted electrodes. Most of the cortex was excitable at about the same threshold, but the type of movement varied from region to region.

All regions of the cerebral cortex giving rise to movement on stimulation were termed supplementary motor areas by Crosby.[13] Movements obtained by stimulating the postcentral gyrus are mainly effected through the precentral motor area. A posterior parietal supplementary motor area discharges partly through the pyramidal systems and partly through the extrapyramidal system. The temporal lobe contains two supplementary motor areas, one in the lateral region and one in the temporal portion of the preoccipital field. Both regions remain excitable after damage to the primary motor area. They tend to provoke ipsilateral as well as contralateral movements, especially in the facial musculature, the movements on both sides being gross rather than fine.

EYE MOVEMENTS.[54] Stimulation of area 8 in both man and animals causes responses of the musculature of the orbit and the lacrimal glands. The eyes sweep together (conjugate deviation) so that they often "look away from the stimulating electrodes." Ablation results in lateral deviation of the eyes so that they look toward the side of the lesion and cannot voluntarily move in the opposite direction. Movements obliquely upward and downward also occur, as shown in Figure 150. Fibers from these areas have been traced either directly to the eye nuclei or to coordinating nuclei which distribute impulses to the motor nuclei for the eye. According to Woolsey et al.[67] and Crosby,[13] a part of the frontal eye fields is included in the primary motor area representation.

It is significant that autonomic motor responses (lacrimation and pupillary dilatation or constriction) are obtained from foci closely adjacent to, and sometimes overlapping, the foci giving rise to motor effects on the eye musculature. Similar but generally weaker responses of the eye are obtained by stimulating areas 18 and 19 of the occipital lobe. Conjugate deviations elicited by stimulating area 17, the primary visual cortex, are perhaps to be viewed as sensorimotor responses of fixation.

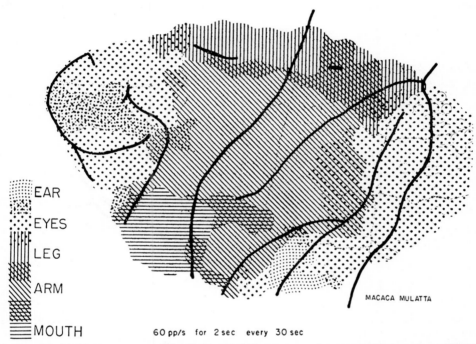

EAR

EYES

LEG

ARM

MOUTH   60 pp/s for 2 sec every 30 sec

MACACA MULATTA

FIG. 149. Map of movements elicited at threshold from cortex of unanesthetized monkey. All of 610 electrodes used yielded same kind of response at about same threshold. Movements elicited by stimulating a given receiving area were appropriate to the corresponding sensation; i.e., eyes and head moved from stimulation of visual areas, ear from acoustic area, somatic musculature from tactile area. To identify fissures compare with Fig. 137. (From Lilly in *Biological and biochemical bases of behavior*, Harlow and Woolsey, eds. Madison, University of Wisconsin Press, 1958.)

ADVERSIVE MOVEMENTS. In man, a sustained lateral movement of the eyes and twisting of the neck and upper trunk may constitute an epileptic seizure. Such *adversive seizures* are usually caused by a discharging focus in the general region separating the motor areas from the prefrontal lobe. The exact relationship of this region to the eye fields (area 8), to the forward-lying representation of the axial musculature in the monkey,[67] and to the supplementary motor area is not clear. However, it seems that a broad area, encompassing the anterior part of area 6 and the posterior portion of the prefrontal lobe including area 8, constitutes an extrapyramidal adversive field. It lies in proximity to the pyramidal field for the axial musculature.[67] In patients, Penfield and Jasper[45] observed adversion traceable to a region still farther forward and medial. Their patients, however, were not aware of an epileptic discharge. Adversive movements elicited by stimulation of area 22 of the temporal lobe also have been described.

Use of the term "adversive movements" to describe seizures and experimentally elicited movements does not clearly convey their direction or physiologic significance. The term "orientational movements" may be substituted. Visual and somatosensory impulses initiated externally from the right side pass into the left hemisphere. If such impulses elicited adversive movements by way of area 8, the eyes and the body would twist to the right and thus would be oriented toward the external stimulus. Adversive or orientational movements may therefore be a part of the motor aspect of attention. Many movements elicited by stimulation in or near the primary sensory areas direct the appropriate sense organ in much the same way as if the sense organ itself were stimulated.

AUTONOMIC REACTIONS.[28]   In addition to the autonomic effects of stimulation of the eye fields, there are autonomic reactions to stimulation anterior to the motor area in area 6 or in the premotor area. These are true responses, not nociceptive reflexes

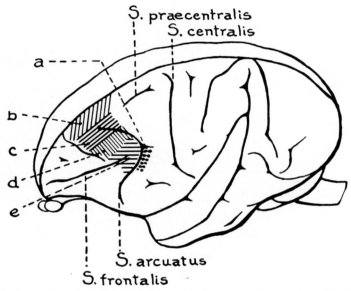

FIG. 150.   Subdivisions of frontal eye field and area yielding closure of eyes in monkey (*Macaca mulatta*). Designations: *a*, closure of eyes; *b*, pupillary dilatation; *c*, "awakening"; *d*, conjugate deviation to opposite side; *e*, nystagmus to opposite side. (From Smith, in Bucy, *The precentral motor cortex*. Urbana, University of Illinois Press, 1944.)

activated by stimulation of pain afferents associated with cerebral blood vessels.[64] The arrangement of points yielding autonomic responses coincides closely with the distribution of somatic motor foci. Vasomotor reactions in arms and legs can be obtained by stimulating points on the premotor area opposite the arm and leg areas, respectively. These changes may be associated with fluctuations in the systolic blood pressure and the heart rate. Vasopressor points are usually discrete and separable from vasodepressor points, but their spatial relation varies from animal to animal, and they are highly susceptible to changes in the type of anesthetic used and in the depth of anesthesia. This cortical representation of autonomic function has been confirmed by ablation studies, and aids in explaining autonomic changes often observed in clinical cases of hemiplegia.

CLINICAL PHYSIOLOGY OF THE MOTOR SYSTEMS

Investigation of the motor systems based on regional cortical ablations, principally by Fulton and Kennard,[21, 25] and on section of the medullary pyramids by Tower[56] and by Hines have profoundly altered the interpretation of such common clinical disorders as *hemiplegia*. Neurologists and neuropathologists were handicapped in learning the neuroanatomic basis of the signs making up hemiplegia because capsular lesions simultaneously and inevitably damage both the pyramidal and the COEP systems. In fact, the same is true of all other naturally occurring damage to the corticospinal neurons in the cortex, brain stem or spinal cord. That all of the signs of hemiplegia should have been ascribed to disruption of the pyramidal tract is an understandable error, but neurophysiologic analysis has now shown that many classic signs of pyramidal tract damage are in fact caused by damage to the extrapyramidal system.

Neurologists confronted with paralysis of voluntary movement ask first: Is this a disease or disturbance of the lower motoneurons—in modern language, motoneuron disease? Or is it a disturbance of the descending motor tracts—upper motor neuron disease?* Preliminary to an analysis of the clinical syndromes, such as hemiplegia, which are characterized by spastic paralysis, their components may be presented in outline under four categories.

DISEASE OF UPPER MOTOR NEURONS
(SYNDROMES INVOLVING SPASTIC PARALYSIS)

I. *Movement*
    1. Paralysis — Absence of voluntary movement.
    2. Paresis — Weakness of voluntary movement or deficient motor power.

II. *Postural reflexes*
    1. Spasticity — Resistance to passive movement of a joint, strongest in flexors of arms and extensors of leg. Fundamentally a stretch or myotatic reflex, the mounting resistance to increased force terminating in a collapse of the resistance (lengthening or "claspknife" reaction), distinguishes spasticity from *rigidity*. Spasticity is an example of "release of function."

    2. Exaggerated deep reflexes
       Tonic tendon jerk, etc. — Threshold of deep reflexes is low, and presence of myotatic appendage causes "dead beat" rather than pendular termination.

       Clonus — A rhythmic series of contractions following the knee or ankle jerks; also elicited by an abruptly applied but sustained passive stretch of extensors.

       Rossolimo's reflex (toes)
       Hoffmann's sign (fingers) — Sudden release of fingers (or toes) after bending them downward causes them to spring backward, stretching the physiologic extensors and causing a brief, smart contraction in all digits. Spasticity and alteration of deep reflexes are fundamentally the same phenomenon, differing only in the way the stretch reflex is elicited.

III. *Other reflexes*
    1. Babinski sign present†
       (Loss of plantar flexion) — Normal adult reflex response to scratching sole is downward or plantar flexion of toes. Babinski sign is an upward or dorsiflexion, especially of great toe, with or without fanning. It is caused by contraction of physiologic flexors and is often combined with flexor contraction at knee and hip.

    2. Abdominal and cremasteric reflexes absent — Contraction of abdominal muscles and retraction of testicle to stroking of abdomen and inner side of thigh, respectively, do not occur.

IV. *Muscle*
    1. No atrophy of degeneration — The absence of these signs plus the spasticity, etc., distinguish
    2. No electrical reaction of degeneration — hemiplegia from flaccid paralysis of motoneuron disease; any atrophy is due to disuse and any contracture to holding limb
    3. No fasciculation or fibrillation — in fixed position. (See Chapter 4 for details.)
    4. No contracture

* If the paralysis is manifest in the facial musculature, the equivalent of upper motor neuron disease is supranuclear disease.

† A clinical nicety is never to speak of a "positive Babinski sign"—a tautology.

Experimental Analysis.   The need to abandon the idea that all elements of the syndrome resulting from lesions at the upper motor levels could be ascribed to interruption of the pyramidal tract became apparent from the critical experiments by Fulton and his colleagues.[21, 24, 25] They have proved that neither the paralysis (see below) nor the reflex changes of hemiplegia can be ascribed solely to damage to the pyramidal tract. These workers removed area 4 in monkeys and chimpanzees, extensively damaging the pyramidal tract while creating relatively little interference with COEPS. *Flaccidity rather than spasticity ensued.* Neither exaggerated deep reflexes nor clonus was in evidence. Although some digital spasticity occasionally occurred several weeks later,[15] it need not have been caused by failure of pyramidal tract function, because even area 4 gives rise to some extrapyramidal fibers.

In additional experiments, Fulton proved further that interruption of COEP fibers is responsible for the spasticity of hemiplegia. Bilateral ablations which included area 6 as well as area 4 caused, in addition to a more profound and enduring paralysis, a typical spasticity and exaggeration of the deep reflexes. In the chimpanzee, these included Rossolimo's and Hoffmann's signs. Toe fanning was added to the Babinski sign, which had followed removal of area 4. The question has recently been raised whether this increased spasticity is due to interference with all of the anterior portions of the motor area or only with its most medial part, the supplementary motor area.[57, 58] Whichever is the case, "pyramidal tract disease" and "upper motor neuron disease" are not synonymous, and the cortically originating portion of the extrapyramidal system must be taken into account in understanding hemiplegia.

As pointed out above, the pyramidal tract consists of those fibers which originate in the cortex and pass to the spinal cord through the medullary pyramids. Therefore, the conclusive experiment is to section the medullary pyramids. The ensuing disturbances throw light on pyramidal tract function; hence, the other clinical signs reflect the functions of the extrapyramidal system.

Pyramidotomy was performed by Tower[56] on monkeys and by Hines on a chimpanzee. The results fully confirmed the cortical ablation experiments. Spasticity was neither an early nor a late consequence of the pyramidal interruption. In the monkeys, there was a definite flaccidity, and in the chimpanzee, a slighter flaccidity. The Babinski sign (in the chimpanzee) and the loss of abdominal reflexes remained as the true pyramidal tract signs. (The status of the cremasteric reflex must be assumed, since the chimpanzee subjected to pyramidotomy was a lady!) Forced grasping, induced by stretching the physiologic extensors of the digits, resulted in a strong plantar flexion that was severe enough to cause an animal to get "hung up" through inability to release its grip on the cage bars.

As pointed out above, interference with the pyramidal tract at all levels from the cerebral cortex to the spinal cord (except at the pyramids, which are rarely if ever selectively disrupted by pathologic processes) necessarily involves simultaneous interference with the pyramidal tract and the COEPS. In the light of these experiments, the respective contributions of the pyramidal and COEP systems are those shown in Figure 151.

Much of what is known of the extrapyramidal system has been deduced by subtracting proved pyramidal tract signs from the total and ascribing what is left to the extrapyramidal system. This method may have to be qualified. There is anatomic evidence that corticospinal fibers give off collaterals before reaching the pyramids. These collaterals enter the pontine nuclei and probably the medial reticular formation, *potentially* reaching descending pathways and exerting an effect on extensor reflexes that is opposite (ei.., inhibitory) to that of the parent corticospinal tract of fibers.

Fulton's and Tower's reinterpretations of corticospinal function afford an explanation, previously lacking, for a typical feature of hemiplegia. The immediate results of disruption of the internal capsule are flaccidity and a reduction in deep reflexes, both of which persist for a varying number of days and gradually give way to the spasticity typical of chronic hemiplegia. Transitory areflexia or hyporeflexia implies the withdrawal of a descending facilitatory influence on segmental neurons. Since the pyramidal tract was traditionally assigned an inhibitory relationship to the segmental postural reflexes, its interruption could not logically underlie the initial flaccidity. However, if in man (as in the monkey) the pyramidal tract is facilitatory to extensor reflexes, the initial flaccidity can be ascribed to its interruption.

Whether in man it is necessary to abandon the idea that the pyramidal tract is the sole servant of voluntary activity cannot be answered with certainty, since neither nature nor the neurosurgeon has selectively sectioned the pyramids. In most clinical studies

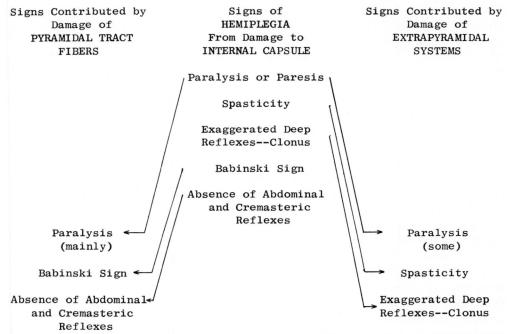

FIG. 151.   Contributions of pyramidal tract and extrapyramidal systems to syndrome resulting from damage to internal capsule in man.

it is necessary to lump the extrapyramidal systems with the pyramidal systems that originate elsewhere than from the primary motor area. It suffices to say that, in man, section of the cord sector containing the pyramidal tracts, or of the middle two-thirds of the cerebral peduncle containing corticospinal fibers, produces much less interference with volitional movement than does a capsular lesion. The conclusion is that, in man as in animals, the corticospinal tract from the primary motor area, the corticospinal fibers originating elsewhere in the cortex, and the COEPS work together to produce skilled voluntary movements. This concept is helpful in the interpretation of the recovery of voluntary power after lesions of the motor system.

Recovery of Voluntary Power.   Explanation of the recovery of voluntary power that occurs after lesions in the cortical arm or leg area has always presented a problem. In fact, the degree of recovery possible when supposedly all of the cortical arm area is destroyed has led some clinicians to form the view that the arm is represented throughout the length of the precentral gyrus. Such an assumption is no longer necessary now that it is known that: (i) the cortiscospinal tract originates in substantial degree from areas outside the primary motor area, and (ii) the COEPS supports some voluntary movement. In addition, the amount and complexity of voluntary activity that can be supported by subcortical motor centers have been underestimated in both the monkey[59] and in man.

Several factors affect the duration and ultimate degree of paralysis. (i) *Extent of cortex removed.* In monkeys, removal of area 6 including the supplementary motor area adds to the depth and duration of voluntary paralysis. Bilateral removal of areas 4 and 6 is more paralyzing than a comparable unilateral lesion. Similarly, retention of one area 6 leaves an animal significant useful movement.* If the parietal lobe, which gives rise to pyramidal tract fibers, is removed, there is a further deficit, only in part attributable to interference with somatic sensation. (ii) *Time between operations.* If bilateral removal of areas 4 and 6—an operation reducing a monkey's motor status virtually to that of a complete decorticate animal—is performed in stages with a long period elapsing between each, a surprising amount of voluntary ability is recaptured. (iii) *Phylogenetic position.* Clinical signs following isolated ablation of area 4 increase in severity as the primate scale is ascended. Lemurs and New World monkeys exhibit less deficit than do the mangabeys and macaques, and the chimpanzees exhibit a greater deficit. Motor functions are more highly encephalized (actually "corticalized") in the animals with more highly developed brains. (iv) *Age.* If the removal of areas 4 and 6 is carried out in an infant, the animal is at first little affected by the procedure, a condition which correlates with the late myelination of the pyramidal tract. Serious motor deficits begin to appear as the animal matures, but it may never become as gravely affected as an animal undergoing the ablation as an adult. (v) *Postoperative care.* When small cortical areas are removed in serial operations, passive exercise to prevent contractures and nursing care to prevent bedsores, wasting, etc.[59] are important factors in recovery.

MECHANISMS OF RECOVERY. Even though recovery of function is the first concern of the patient and should be the concern of the neurologist, little research has been devoted to this subject. Definite explanations of the recovery mechanisms cannot be given. One factor is embraced in the term "neighborhood symptoms." Whether the cause of the disorder is a vascular accident or a meticulous surgical ablation, some reversible damage—trauma, dehydration, edema, venous occlusion, free blood, etc.—is done to cortical areas or tracts neighboring on the areas completely destroyed. As these transient lesions abate, what remains functions at more normal levels, and the paresis shrinks in severity and in distribution over the musculature.

Since motor skills can be improved by learning, it is reasonable to believe that usage and training can increase the level at which the undamaged apparatus can perform. This is termed "compensation." That tracts or cortical areas which have previously not controlled a given muscle do so after a lesion—as implied by the term "vicariation"—is exceedingly doubtful. However, performance of the same act with a different set of muscles is a commonplace phenomenon.

The sequence of events—areflexia, hyporeflexia and ultimate hyperreflexia—is typical of both capsular hemiplegia and spinal transection. The hyperreflexia (spasticity) is interpretable as *release of function,* i.e., release from inhibition by a descending pathway. The problem is why this release is not immediately manifest. Release phenomena are manifest within seconds in certain experimental situations, e.g., decerebrate rigidity or the *increase* in the excitability of the hindlimb flexion reflex following spinal transection in a decerebrate preparation. In both instances, no major facilitatory tract is removed

---

* Whether this is an argument for the motor capacity of COEPS or of corticospinal fibers is not entirely clear, since the anatomic and electrophysiologic evidence in respect to the origin of fibers in area 6 is conflicting, as is the evidence in respect to the border of the primary motor area.

by the transection. In primary transection of the spinal cord or in capsular hemiplegia, descending facilitatory tracts as well as inhibitory ones are removed. According to one interpretation, interruption of facilitatory pathways causes some change in the motoneuron's excitability, thus preventing any manifestation of the withdrawal of inhibition until the motoneuron has recovered excitability.

What is Released? Spasticity is a release phenomenon. Two questions must be asked about any release phenomenon. What structures must be damaged to effect the release, and what structures are released? In respect to spasticity and other signs of hemiplegia, the first of these questions has been answered in this chapter. The importance of the second question was first stressed by the philosophical neurologist Hughlings Jackson, who pointed out that a negative event (a lesion) cannot cause a positive event (a phenomenon such as spasticity). Except when irritative, a lesion can be only an antecedent circumstance; the direct *cause* or underlying mechanism of the overactivity must be the structures remaining functional. Releasing the brake of an automobile does not cause the car to go forward; it is the motor which does that. Magoun and Rhines[38] have expressed Hughlings Jackson's idea in a homely fashion, likening the motor systems to a jack-in-the-box. The motor cortex is the lid—but what is the spring that makes jack jump out of the box?

At first sight, the segmental stretch reflex might seem to be the thing which is released. However, in the higher primates including man, spinal reflexes in themselves are not very strong, or they would not be depressed after spinal transection. For spasticity to develop, some facilitatory tract from the brain stem must remain functional. Just what tract or tracts are responsible is discussed in detail in the next chapter, but they may be previewed briefly as follows. One such tract is the vestibulospinal tract, but it may not be as important in primates as it is in the cat or dog. The second possibility is the reticulospinal tracts descending from the lateral reticular facilitatory area, described by Magoun and Rhines.[38] As will be discussed more fully, the reticular system may be involved in both the maintenance and the release of stretch reflexes. Impulses have been traced by strychnine neuronography from the anterior portion of the motor areas to the bulbar reticular inhibitory area, from whence inhibition of the stretch reflexes is exerted by the reticulospinal tracts. Some such fibers may go from the cortex to the caudate nucleus and hence, through poorly defined pathways, to the bulbar reticular inhibitory area. Both of these pathways require verification before they can be fully accepted as the source of the impulses involved in the production of spasticity.

REFERENCES

1. AMASSIAN, V. E. *Electroenceph. clin. Neurophysiol.*, 1953, *5*:415–438.
2. AMASSIAN, V. E. and DeVITO, R. *J. Neurophysiol.*, 1954, *17*:575–603.
3. v. BAUMGARTEN, R., MOLLICA, A. and MORUZZI, G. *Pflüg. Arch. ges. Physiol.*, 1954, *259*:56–78.
4. BERNHARD, C. G. and BOHM, E. *Arch. Neurol. Psychiat. (Chicago)*, 1954, *72*:473–502.
5. BERNHARD, C. G., BOHM, E. and PETERSEN, I. *Acta physiol. scand.*, 1954, *29* (Suppl. 106): 79–105.
6. von BONIN, G. and BAILEY, P. *The neocortex of Macaca mulatta.* Urbana, University of Illinois Press, 1947, xi, 163 pp.
7. BRODMANN, K. *Vergleichende Lokalisationslehre der Grosshirnrinde in Prinzipien dargestellt auf Grund des Zellenbaues.* Leipzig, J. A. Barth, 1909.

8. BROWN, T. GRAHAM and SHERRINGTON, C. S. *Proc. roy. Soc.*, 1912, *B85*:250–277.
9. BUBNOFF, N. and HEIDENHAIN, R. Chap. 7 in *The precentral motor cortex*, 2d ed., P. C. BUCY, ed. Urbana, University of Illinois Press, 1949, xiv, 615 pp.
10. BUCY, P. C. *Brain*, 1957, *80*:376–392.
11. CAMPBELL, A. W. *Histological studies on the localisation of cerebral function.* Cambridge, Cambridge University Press, 1905, xx, 360 pp.
12. CHANG, H.-T., RUCH, T. C. and WARD, A. A., JR. *J. Neurophysiol.*, 1947, *10*:39–56.
13. CROSBY, E. C. Pp. 218–231 in *Progr. Neurobiol. Proc. 1st. Int. Meet. Neurobiologists*, Amsterdam, Elsevier, 1956.
14. DeMYER, W. *Neurology*, 1959, *9*:42–47.
15. DENNY-BROWN, D. and BOTTERELL, E. H. *Res. Publ. Ass. nerv. ment. Dis.*, 1948, *27*:235–345.

16. DUSSER DE BARENNE, J. G. and McCULLOCH, W. S. *J. Neurophysiol.*, 1939, *2*:319–355.

17. VON ECONOMO, C. and KOSKINAS, G. N. *Die Cytoarchitektonik der Grosshirnrinde der erwachsenen Menschen.* Berlin, J. Springer, 1925, xxxix, 810 pp.

18. FERRIER, D. *West Riding Lunatic Asylum med. Rep.*, 1873, *3*:1–50.

19. FRITSCH, G. and HITZIG, E. *Arch. Anat. Physiol. (Lpz.)*, 1870, *37*:300–332.

20. FULTON, J. F. *Bull. Hist. Med.*, 1937, *5*:895–913.

21. FULTON, J. F. *Functional localization in the frontal lobes and cerebellum.* Oxford, Clarendon Press, 1949, xiii, 140 pp.

22. FULTON, J. F. *Physiology of the nervous system,* 3d ed. New York, Oxford University Press, 1949, xii, 667 pp.

23. FULTON, J. F. *Gesnerus,* 1951, *8*:85–91.

24. FULTON, J. F., JACOBSEN, C. F. and KENNARD, MARGARET A. *Brain,* 1932, *55*:524–536.

25. FULTON, J. F. and KENNARD, MARGARET A. *Res. Publ. Ass. nerv. ment. Dis.*, 1934, *13*:158–210.

26. GLEES, P. *J. Anat. (Lond.),* 1944, *78*:47–51, 2 pl.

27. JACKSON, J. HUGHLINGS. *Selected writings of John Hughlings Jackson.* J. TAYLOR, ed. New York, Basic Books, Inc., 1956, 2 vols.

28. KENNARD, MARGARET A. Chap. 9 in *The precentral motor cortex,* 2d ed., P. C. BUCY, ed. Urbana, University of Illinois Press, 1949, xiv, 615 pp.

29. LASHLEY, K. S. and CLARK, G. *J. comp. Neurol.*, 1946, *85*:223–305.

30. LASSEK, A. M. *J. comp. Neurol.*, 1942, *76*:217–225.

31. LAUER, E. W. *J. Neurophysiol.*, 1952, *15*:1–4.

32. LEÃO, A. A. P. *J. Neurophysiol.*, 1944, *7*:359–390, 391–396; *ibid.*, 1947, *10*:409–414.

33. LEVIN, P. M. Chap. 5 in *The precentral motor cortex,* 2d ed., P. C. BUCY, ed. Urbana, University of Illinois Press, 1949, xiv, 615 pp.

34. LILLY, J. C. Pp. 83–100 in *Biological and biochemical bases of behavior,* H. F. HARLOW and C. N. WOOLSEY, eds. Madison, University of Wisconsin Press, 1958.

35. LILLY, J. C., AUSTIN, G. M. and CHAMBERS, W. W. *J. Neurophysiol.*, 1952, *15*:319–341.

36. LLOYD, D. P. C. *J. Neurophysiol.*, 1941, *4*:184–190.

37. LORENTO DE NÓ, R. Pp. 288–315 in *Physiology of the nervous system,* 3d ed., J. F. FULTON, ed. New York, Oxford University Press, 1949, x, 667 pp.

38. MAGOUN, H. W. and RHINES, RUTH. *Spasticity: The stretch-reflex and extrapyramidal systems.* Springfield, Ill., Charles C Thomas, 1947, 59 pp.

39. MARSHALL, W. H. *Electroenceph. clin. Neurophysiol.*, 1950, *2*:177–185.

40. MARSHALL, W. H. and ESSIG, C. F. *J. Neurophysiol.*, 1951, *14*:265–273.

41. METTLER, F. A. *Proc. Soc. exp. Biol. (N. Y.),* 1944, *57*:111–113.

42. PATTON, H. D. and AMASSIAN, V. E. *Amer. J. Physiol.*, 1955, *183*:650.

43. PATTON, H. D. and AMASSIAN, V. E. *J. Neurophysiol.*, 1954, *17*:345–363.

44. PATTON, H. D. and AMASSIAN, V. E. Chap. 35 in *Handbook of physiology, Section 1, Neurophysiology,* vol. 2, H. W. MAGOUN, ed. Baltimore, Williams & Wilkins, in press.

45. PENFIELD, W. and JASPER, H. *Epilepsy and the functional anatomy of the human brain.* Boston, Little, Brown & Co., 1954, xv, 896 pp.

46. PENFIELD, W. and WELCH, K. *Arch. Neurol. Psychiat. (Chicago),* 1951, *66*:289–317.

47. PHILLIPS, C. G. *Quart. J. exp. Physiol.*, 1956, *41*:58–69, 6 pls.

48. RAMÓN Y CAJAL, S. *Proc. roy. Soc.*, 1894, *55*:444–468.

49. ROSSI, G. F. and BRODAL, A. *J. Anat. (Lond.),* 1956, *90*:42–62, 1 pl.

50. SHERRINGTON, C. S. *J. Physiol.*, 1889, *10*:429–432.

51. SHOLL, D. A. *The organization of the cerebral cortex.* London, Methuen & Co., 1956, xvi, 125 pp.

52. SLOAN, N. and JASPER, H. H. *Electroenceph. clin. Neurophysiol.*, 1950, *2*:59–78.

53. SMITH, O. A., JR. and DeVITO, JUNE L. *Fed. Proc.*, 1958, *17*:35, 151.

54. SMITH, W. K. Chap. 12 in *The precentral motor cortex,* 2d ed., P. C. BUCY, ed. Urbana, University of Illinois Press, 1949, xiv, 615 pp.

55. SUGAR, O., CHUSID, J. G. and FRENCH, J. D. *J. Neuropath.*, 1948, *7*:182–189.

56. TOWER, SARAH S. Chap. 6 in *The precentral motor cortex,* 2d ed., P. C. BUCY, ed. Urbana, University of Illinois Press, 1949, xiv, 615 pp.

57. TRAVIS, ANN M. *Brain,* 1955, *78*:155–173.

58. TRAVIS, ANN M. *Brain,* 1955, *78*:174–198.

59. TRAVIS, ANN M. and WOOLSEY, C. H. *Amer. J. phys. Med.*, 1956, *35*:273–310.

60. VAN HARREVELD, A. and OCHS, S. *Amer. J. Physiol.*, 1957, *189*:159–166.

61. VERHAART, W. J. C. and KENNARD, MARGARET A. *J. Anat. (Lond.),* 1940, *74*:239–254.

62. VOGT, C. and O. *J. Psychol. Neurol. (Lpz.),* 1919, *25*:279–461.

63. WALBERG, F. and BRODAL, A. *Brain,* 1953, *76*:491–508, pls. 10–11.

64. WALL, P. D. and PRIBRAM, K. H. *J. Neurophysiol.*, 1950, *13*:409–412.

65. WALSHE, F. M. R. *Brain,* 1942, *65*:409–461.

66. WALSHE, F. M. R. *Brain,* 1943, *66*:104–139.

67. WOOLSEY, C. N., SETTLAGE, P. H., MEYER, D. R., SENCER, W., PINTO-HAMUY, TERESA and TRAVIS, ANN M. *Res. Publ. Ass. nerv. ment. Dis.*, 1952, *30*:238–264.

CHAPTER 12

Basal Ganglia and Cerebellum

By THEODORE C. RUCH

MOTOR FUNCTIONS OF THE BASAL GANGLIA

THE basal ganglia are involved in the control of movement and posture, since abnormal spontaneous movement results from lesions of these ganglia in man. The abnormal functions attendant upon such lesions are well known clinically, but the normal function of the basal ganglia is difficult to visualize. The conventional experimental methods of ablation, stimulation and degeneration in animals have provided tantalizing clues but little definitive information. Certain of the basal ganglia have functions which cannot be classified as motor. These functions will be discussed elsewhere.

Anatomic Considerations. By "basal ganglia" is meant all subcortical motor nuclei of the forebrain including the caudate nucleus, the putamen and the globus pallidus. They discharge to such structures as the corpus Luysii (subthalamic nucleus), the substantia nigra, the red nucleus and the reticular formation in the brain stem, as shown in Figure 152. Some authors include these brain stem structures among the basal ganglia. The caudate nucleus and the putamen, although separated by the internal capsule, are phylogenetically related and are known morphologically as the striatum. Although the putamen and the globus pallidus have been joined under the term "lenticular nucleus," this grouping is not meaningful. It is, however, meaningful to divide the pallidum into a medial and a lateral portion. The lateral portion is, in a sense, afferent, since it receives fibers from other structures including the thalamus and the cerebral cortex. These connections are arranged to form a circuit: motor cortex–pallidum–thalamus–motor cortex. The medial division sends a large projection via the ansa and the fasciculus lenticularis to the lateroventral nucleus of the thalamus, which projects to the cerebral cortex. The pallidum also has descending connections with the subthalamic nucleus.

Lying deep to the cerebral cortex and lateral to the cerebral ventricles, the basal ganglia are the highest motor center in birds and lower forms, which possess little cerebral cortex. In these species these nuclei preside over a motor apparatus capable of producing such highly skilled movements as flying. Consistently, the basal ganglia receive fibers from the intralaminar nuclei, the centromedian nuclei and the smaller midline nuclei. These fibers complete a potential subcortical connection of the ascending afferent systems with the basal ganglia. However, this system is not necessarily motor in function. With the development of a whole new apparatus for the control of movement—the cerebral cortex—the evolutionary fate of the basal ganglia becomes an intriguing question.

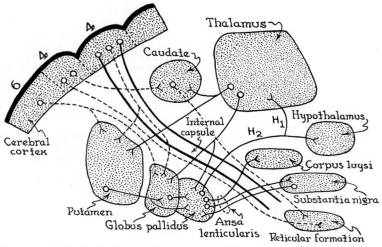

FIG. 152.   Diagram of interconnections of the basal ganglia, thalamus and cerebral cortex. Connections between ventrolateral nucleus of the thalamus and areas 4 and 6 complete a circuit. H_1 and H_2 are the fields of Forel. (After Kennard, *J. Neurophysiol.*, 1944, 7:127–148.)

Motor Responses.   The results of early attempts to elicit movement by stimulation of the basal ganglia were mainly negative, and the apparent exceptions actually reflected spread of current to the internal capsule. Rioch and Brenner[16] controlled the latter by stimulating the basal ganglia in experimental animals three weeks after removal of the cerebral cortex.   In these experiments, motor responses of the extremities were not evoked, but chop-licking, swallowing, salivation and sniffing occurred. These responses were attributed, no doubt correctly, to stimulation of the adjacent olfactory system rather than the striopallidum. Forman and Ward[5] stimulated the caudate nucleus in unanesthetized free-moving cats by means of implanted electrodes. Stereotyped movements—head-turning or flexion of the whole fore or hind leg—were obtained even after ablation of the motor areas and allowance of time for degeneration of corticofugal fibers.

INHIBITORY EFFECTS.   If the responsiveness of the basal ganglia is examined against a background of either posture or movements concurrently induced by stimulation of the cerebral cortex, it is seen that stimulation of the caudate nucleus and the globus pallidus causes inhibition. Primary motor movements are never obtained, but somatic motor reactions initiated by the cerebral cortex "melt away" when even a weak stimulus is delivered to the caudate nucleus.[12, 18] Pallidal stimulation likewise does not induce movement but interrupts a cortically induced movement, thus causing the limb to be held in space. These results accordingly point to a predominantly inhibitory influence of the basal ganglia upon cortically induced movements and postures. Anesthesia may favor the inhibitory and "holding" responses; they were not seen following stimulation of the striopallidum in unanesthetized cats by Forman and Ward.[5]

ACTIVATION BY MOTOR CORTEX. There is some evidence that the basal ganglia are activated by stimulation of the motor cortex.[3] An anatomic projection from the cortex to the caudate nucleus—a projection which could account for this activation—has been described by Glees.[6] There are also anatomic connections through which the caudate nucleus, when activated, could discharge to the globus pallidus, which in turn is connected with the part of the thalamus that projects to area 4 of the cerebral cortex. Whether this circuit is in fact the route through which the stimulated caudate inhibits movements induced by the cortex has not been proved by critical studies of single unit discharge in the pyramidal tract (see Chap. 11). Much of the functional evidence for the existence of this circuit is based on suppression of the electrical activity of the cortex, a phenomenon of doubtful status (see Chap. 11). Therefore, voluntary movement could as well be affected by the basal ganglia discharging impulses to structures in the brain stem, the interaction with corticospinal impulses being at the spinal segmental level.

Experimental Lesions. RELATION TO MOVEMENT. Transection of the neural axis below the basal ganglia in an animal with its cerebral cortex already removed adds little deficit in voluntary movement. This finding is consistent with the failure of stimulation of these ganglia to produce movement. Whatever their functions in the production of movement, they are not exercised independently, as one might expect from phylogenetic considerations. Instead, these functions must be expressed through, or be in some way tied to, those of the motor cortex. If the cortex is absent, the basal ganglia seem to have no motor function demonstrable by ablation; but, as pointed out below, the basal ganglia must participate in movement, since, in man, abnormal spontaneous movements are modified by lesions damaging these ganglia.[4]

Although in themselves of little effect, lesions of the basal ganglia combined with lesions of the anterior portions of the motor areas in monkeys and apes induce disturbances of movement reminiscent of those seen in man.[9, 10] This suggests (i) that the basal ganglia in some way modulate the activity of the primary motor areas, either by direct action on them or by convergence at lower levels, and (ii) that the anterior motor areas and the basal ganglia act synergistically, but independently, to modulate the discharges from the primary motor area.

RELATION TO POSTURE. In Chapter 11 was described a cortex–caudate–reticular mechanism, the interruption of which causes spasticity. This mechanism is part of the cortically originating extrapyramidal system (COEPS). However, the disturbance of postural reflexes occurring in the most common disease of the basal ganglia is clinically termed *rigidity*, and differs from spasticity in its properties and, presumably, in its cause. The actual disturbances of posture and movement resulting from damage to the basal ganglia are best discussed from clinical information.

Pathophysiology of Basal Ganglia in Man. The abnormalities resulting from damage to the basal ganglia are more outspoken and more easily examined in man than in experimental animals. Unfortunately, lesions of the human basal ganglia are mainly produced by diffuse pathologic processes, so that clinical cases tell little of functional localization. (The areas of greatest or most common damage may simply be those most easily damaged by the specific agent, not those responsible for the syndrome.) Presumably, the various ganglia do not all have similar functions, because there are two groups of disorders that contrast with one another in many ways.

ATHETOSIS, CHOREA, BALLISMUS. This group of disorders is a spectrum of dyskinesias having many points of similarity; athetosis and chorea occur together. These dyskinesias have in common marked—even violent—voluntary-like movement with *no typical changes in muscle tonus.* * Paradoxically, these movements are involuntary, i.e., not willed by the patient and beyond his control.

In *chorea*, meaning "dance," a wide variety of rapidly performed, jerky, but well coordinated movements occur ceaselessly. They are not willed by the patient and serve no purpose. Their coordinated, purposive look led Hughlings Jackson to speak of "some method in their madness."

In *athetosis*, the limbs indulge in ceaseless, slow, sinuous, writhing movements which are especially severe in the hand and are involuntary. They are reminiscent of certain oriental dances and bear less resemblance to coordinated voluntary movements than do those of chorea; antagonistic muscles may contract simultaneously. The brain damage is said to be greatest in the striatum.

In *ballismus*, the movements are violent and flinging (ballistic) and are caused by contractions of the proximal limb muscles. If the movements are confined to one-half of the body, as is commonly the case, the condition is called *hemiballismus*.

Clinical and pathologic observations, animal experiments and neurosurgical attempts to relieve chorea and athetosis have not yielded any consistent picture of the underlying mechanism of these diseases and what lesions produce them. There is some evidence that human athetosis is relieved by lesions of the premotor area and of the anterior columns of the spinal cord. Bucy[1, 2] has suggested that athetosis represents an abnormal discharge over the COEPS.

The location of the lesion resulting in hemiballismus is better known. Clinical and experimental evidence[23] agree that ballismus is caused by destruction of the subthalamic nucleus of Luysii or its fiber connections. However, the structures that are released from control by the destruction of the subthalamic nucleus and thus subserve the violent ballistic movements remain to be identified.

PARKINSON'S DISEASE (PARALYSIS AGITANS). As the second part of the formal name suggests, paralysis agitans is, like the previous group, often marked by an involuntary movement—in this case a *tremor.* Unlike athetosis, chorea and ballismus, Parkinson's disease results in a definite and disabling reduction in voluntary and associated movements (poverty of movement) and also in a definite disturbance in the postural sphere, *rigidity.* Observations on Parkinson's disease and related animal experiments can be taken as exemplifying two important clinical signs, rigidity and tremor. The pallidum and the substantia nigra are often said to be the most consistent sites of damage in this syndrome. However, there is good reason to believe that the lesions in the pallidum are not the responsible ones.

Although nearly a century and a half have elapsed since Parkinson described the syndrome, none of its three major components can yet be clearly explained in terms of mechanism or responsible neural structure. Since the major components tend to occur in different proportions in different patients, and since the brain damage is diffuse, it is presumed that several structures may be involved.

Poverty of movement. Parkinson's disease contrasts with chorea and athetosis in that initiation of voluntary movement is difficult and there is a resultant immobility. Absent are the small restless movements, the play of emotional expression on the face, and the movements associated with intentional movements, such as arm-swinging during walking seen in normal persons. Despite the formal name for the condition, there is no real paralysis, and in this fact, as well as in the type of tonus change, Parkinson's disease differs from spastic paralysis resulting from capsular lesions. Magoun and Rhines[11] ascribe the poverty of movement to interference with the descending reticular facilitatory system; however, such interference might be expected to induce accompanying flaccidity rather than rigidity. Some think that movement is damped by the rigidity, since movement improved in amplitude, speed and endurance when injection of procaine

---

* In the contrasting disease, parkinsonism, tonus is severely disturbed, and involuntary movements are generally less conspicuous.

hydrochloride into the muscles had caused them to become flaccid.[22] However, the tendency for hypokinesia and rigidity to occur in different proportions in different patients suggests that rigidity is not the sole basis for the poverty of movement.

Rigidity. In Chapter 11 rigidity was distinguished from spasticity. A rigid limb affords resistance throughout the entire extent of a passive movement. The resistance does not develop suddenly, does not mount with the application of additional force, and does not collapse terminally in a lengthening reaction. Sometimes, however, the response to passive movement is a series of catches and gives—so-called "cog-wheel" rigidity. The rigidity is manifest in both extensor and flexor muscles, being stronger in the latter. To the examiner the resistance has a dead, leadlike feel, as opposed to the live vibrant resistance felt in the spastic limb. The rigid limb therefore exhibits a more marked plasticity than does a spastic limb. The rigidity of extrapyramidal disease is dependent upon the integrity of the myotatic reflexes; it disappears in muscles deprived of afferent innervation by posterior root section.[13] However, the tendon reflexes are not exaggerated or marked by clonus. It is interesting that Jendrassick's maneuver (clenching of hands),

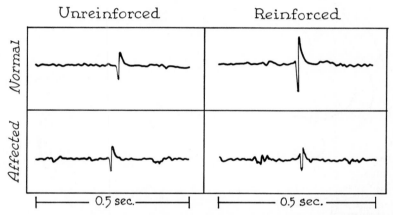

FIG. 153.   Electromyograms of deep reflex jerks in biceps brachii in a case of hemiparkinsonism. Left side of records shows size of reflex before reinforcement by hand-clasping; right side shows reflex during hand-clasping. The reflex in limb exhibiting parkinsonism is unchanged by reinforcement. (After Hassler, *Dtsch. Z. Nervenheilk.*, 1956, *175*:233–258.)

used to bring out or enhance a weak tendon jerk, does not affect such reflexes in Parkinson's disease (Fig. 153). In all these respects, the rigidity resulting from extrapyramidal lesions at the level of the basal ganglia differs from the spasticity caused by interference with the COEPS.

Section of the pyramidal tract at the spinal level in Parkinson's disease does not augment rigidity but rather decreases it slightly.[15] Thus interruption of the pyramidal tract appears to cause neither rigidity nor spasticity. Contrary to expectation from results of animal experiments, in man section of the efferent outflow from the pallidum (ansa lenticularis) or destruction of the medial pallidum itself may virtually abolish rigidity.[4] Moreover, surgical destruction of the lateroventral nucleus, which receives impulses from the pallidum and projects to areas 4 and 6 of the cerebral cortex, also may abolish rigidity. It thus seems that the globus pallidus should not be considered a structure which, when damaged, releases the mechanisms underlying rigidity; rather it should be considered contributory to the mechanism underlying rigidity. It is not clear how this system of fibers operates in the intact animal—whether through the midbrain motor nuclei or by influencing descending pathways (COEPS) at the level of the cerebral cortex. Hassler,[7] who ascribes the Parkinson syndrome to destruction of the substantia nigra, suggests that loss of *ascending* collaterals from the nigra to the pallidum permits overactivity in the pallidothalamic system of neurons. As with spasticity and decerebrate rigidity, descending influences may cause the rigidity of Parkinson's disease by acting upon the alpha motoneurons or upon the fusomotor fibers. Marked inhibition of spindle discharge follows stimulation of the lateroventral nucleus of the thalamus; this effect is exerted through the cerebral cortex.[21] This finding cannot be correlated in any simple way to the demonstrated effects of lateroventral thalamic lesions on Parkinson's disease.

Tremor. The tremor, which is initially most obvious distally in the limb, is fine, highly regular and rapid (four to eight cycles per second). It occurs during rest and stops when the limbs are used voluntarily. It is therefore variously termed "tremor of rest," "static tremor," etc. Electromyography shows that antagonistic muscles are alternately activated and that the rate is surprisingly constant over long periods in a given muscle group. Both in its sinusoidal regularity and its occurrence at rest, the tremor of Parkin-

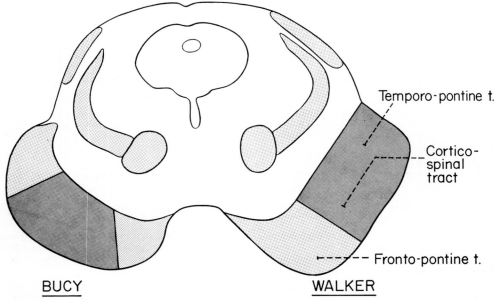

BUCY   WALKER

Temporo-pontine t.

Cortico-spinal tract

Fronto-pontine t.

FIG. 154. Cross sections through the human midbrain. On right is shown a pedunculotomy performed by Walker and on the left one performed by Bucy. Involuntary movements were greatly diminished and recovery of voluntary power included independent movements of fingers in Bucy's case. (After Bucy. Chap. 11 in *Pathogenesis and treatment of parkinsonism*, W. S. Fields, ed. Springfield, Ill., Charles C Thomas, 1958.)

son's disease contrasts with the intentional tremor of cerebellar disease (see below). In the later stages of the disease, which is rather common in people who contracted influenza during World War I, the tremor becomes more violent, shaking the whole body and thus greatly disturbing and exhausting the patient.

Pathologic or neurosurgical damage to the motor areas,[1] the internal capsule, the cerebral peduncle (Fig. 154)[2] or the posterolateral region of the spinal cord[14, 15] abolishes or diminishes tremor, at least transiently. The relationship is well established, but different authors interpret it quite differently. Bucy,[1] for example, considered the tremor to result from an oscillatory continuous discharge of the pyramidal tract unmodulated by a cortex-to-cortex circuit through the basal ganglia, the oscillating discharge being superseded by impulses mediating smooth movement when the pyramidal tract is involved in voluntary movement. However, no experimental lesion of the striopallidum

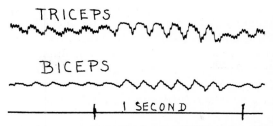

FIG. 155. Synchronous electromyograms of triceps and biceps in a monkey exhibiting tremor consequent to ventrolateral midbrain lesion. Note alternating contraction in antagonistic muscles. (From Ward *et al.*, *J. Neurophysiol.*, 1948, *11*:317–330.)

link in the modulating circuit has ever produced a static tremor. On the other hand, Ward[19, 20] and others[17] have produced a Parkinson-like tremor in monkeys by placing lesions in the ventrolateral midbrain reticular area between the red nucleus and the substantia nigra. The tremor is about eight cycles per second, and antagonistic muscles contract alternately (Fig. 155). As seen in Figure 156, the tremor, as in Parkinson's disease, disappears upon voluntary movement and tends to be increased during emotional excitement; it disappears during sleep. Other signs of Parkinson's disease noted by Ward and confirmed by Schreiner were masked facies, sluggish movements and rigidity. On the basis of these experiments, Ward postulates that the lesion giving rise to the tremor of clinical Parkinson's disease lies in the mesencephalic tegmentum.

Since, according to Hughlings Jackson's principle, the tissue destroyed by a lesion cannot directly cause an overactivity (tremor), these experiments lead to the conclusion that the lesion, by interrupting descending pathways, has permitted some lower brain stem mechanism to oscillate. The oscillatory discharge is, by exclusion of major descending systems, in the reticulospinal tract. Stimulation of the reticular substance below the

MOVEMENT DISORDER – MONKEY

Effect of Voluntary Movement on Tremor at Rest

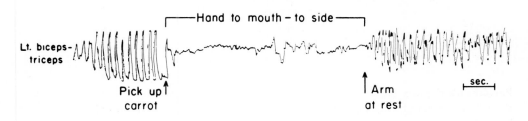

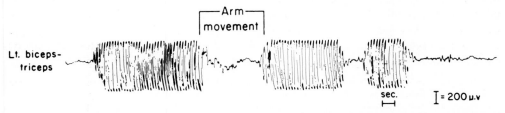

FIG. 156. Electromyographic records of arm tremor in monkey with bilateral lesions of ventromedial midbrain region. Note absence of tremor while a carrot is grasped and placed in mouth, and while arm is being returned to animal's side. (From Schreiner *et al.*, in *Pathogenesis and treatment of parkinsonism*, W. S. Fields, ed., Springfield, Ill., Charles C Thomas, 1958.)

level of the lesion causes rapid oscillatory movements (15 to 25 per second).[8] As seen in Figure 157, the region yielding this tremor is the medial reticular substance lying between the red nucleus and the VIth cranial nerve. Presumably, impulses inhibiting these tremorogenic neurons come from higher levels and funnel through the ventrolateral midbrain area—perhaps from the substantia nigra, but this assumption has not yet been verified. The role of the pyramidal tract is envisioned as the supplying of a facilitatory, nonoscillatory background which is necessary for tremor just as a tonic background is favorable to clonus.

The substantia nigra and the globus pallidus are usually considered the most common sites of damage resulting in paralysis agitans, but, quite empirically, it was learned by Cooper in 1952 (see Ref. 4) that destruction in the region of the globus pallidus decreases both tremor and rigidity, and restores mobility to many patients with

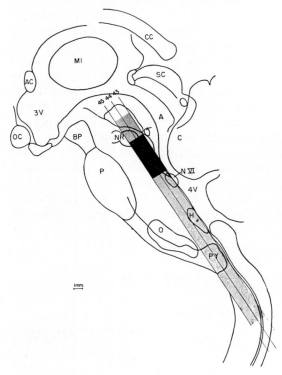

FIG. 157. Sagittal section through brain stem showing tremorogenic zone demarcated by electrical stimulation. Black area between Horsley-Clarke coordinates 43 and 45 yields tremor most consistently. Pertinent abbreviations are: *NR*, nucleus ruber; *VI*, nucleus of abducens nerve; *H*, nucleus of hypoglossal nerve; *O*, inferior olive; *PY*, pyramids. (From Jenkner and Ward, *Arch. Neurol. Psychiat. (Chicago)*, 1953, *70*:489–502.)

Parkinson's disease. Destruction of the ansa lenticularis or the ventrolateral nucleus of the thalamus may be equally effective. Experimental Parkinson's disease from midbrain lesions is also relieved by pallidectomy.[17] The pallidum and the lateroventral thalamus, like the corticospinal tract, are presumed to exert a facilitatory drive on the motoneurons or on the extrapyramidal structures in the tremorogenic area. Empirical, too, is the fact that atropine-like compounds relieve Parkinson's disease, an action suggesting that excessive acetylcholine or acetylcholine-sensitivity may be involved. However, acetylcholine mediation of synaptic transmission in the brain has never been proved.

It is paradoxical that destruction of the very structures showing maximum pathologic alterations in Parkinson's disease often lessens the disability. This paradox could be resolved by the possible (but unpopular and unsubstantiated) hypothesis that the circuit consisting of the globus pallidus, the ansa lenticularis and the ventrolateral thalamus is the site of a discharging lesion. Such a discharge might act on the cerebral cortex or upon the brain stem tegmentum. To account for a symptom-free interval of as long as 30 years, and to account for the efficacy of anticholinesterase drugs on the basis of degeneration hypersensitivity, it is necessary to postulate further that an irritative-destructive process begins long after the original influenzal infection. In short, while the disappearance or reduction of tremor by pallidectomy does not establish the pallidum as the site of the discharging oscillatory lesion, the possibility that this is the case must now be considered.

CEREBELLUM

Orientation. The cerebellum, like the cerebral hemispheres, is a suprasegmental structure, but it has no long direct pathway to the spinal cord comparable to the pyramidal tract. Thus, the cerebellum can influence motoneurons only through its connections with the motor systems of the brain stem and with the cerebral cortex. It is therefore not surprising to find that the cerebellum does not execute detailed movements;* none disappears when it is extirpated. Its chief function lies in the *control* or regulation of movement, especially voluntary skilled movements, but also such brain stem functions as walking. The cerebellum also regulates posture and tonus; it must also regulate visceral activities, since many of them are altered by cerebellar stimulation or ablation.[35]

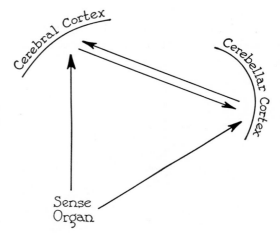

FIG. 158. Basic plan of cerebrocerebellar control system. Arrows indicate the pathways of impulse conduction, not neurons.

Consistent with widespread regulation or control is the cerebellum's richness of efferent and afferent connections,[49] as seen in Figure 158. It is reciprocally connected† with the cerebral motor and sensory areas.[40, 42, 49] It projects to the brain stem structures giving rise to descending motor pathways. Control requires information. Functional studies indicate that the cerebellum receives an afferent input not solely from the proprioceptive and vestibular systems, but from many sensory systems, including those for vision and audition.[51] Certain areas of the cerebellar cortex are somatotopically organized, although not in the detail found in the cerebral cortex. Furthermore, there is evidence of functional localization reflecting differences in the efferent and afferent projections; however, thought on this matter is now in a state of flux.

Anatomic Organization. The cerebellum, like the cerebrum, consists of a cortex and deep nuclei. Unlike the cerebral cortex, the three-layered cortex of the cerebellum has a uniform structure showing no cytoarchitectural subdivisions. The efferent cells of the cerebellar cortex, the Purkinje cells, send their axons to the deep nuclei in such a manner that the cerebellum can be divided into longitudinal corticonuclear zones (Table

---

* Cerebellar stimulation does produce coordinated rotations of the head or flexions and extensions involving the whole limb. Such stimulation also facilitates and inhibits movements. The distinction between a strong facilitation and a weak movement is not great. The above distinction may therefore be more conventional than real. In fact, Sprague and Chambers[53] found that contact placing reactions are lost after cerebellectomy.

† "Reciprocal connection," not to be confused with "reciprocal innervation," means that A sends fibers to B and B sends fibers to A.

TABLE 6. CORTICONUCLEAR ZONES OF THE CEREBELLUM

Medial Zone	Vermal Cortex	Fastigial Nuclei
Intermediate Zone	Paravermal Cortex (incl. paramedianus?)	Interpositus or Intermediate Nuclei*
Lateral Zone	Hemspheric Cortex lobulus ansiformis and parafloccules	Dentate Nucleus

* Globosus and emboliformis nuclei of man.

6 and Fig. 159). The efferent path is then continued by neurons of these nuclei, the axons leaving the cerebellum via the inferior and superior peduncles to reach various nuclei of the thalamus, midbrain and medulla.[30] Some cortical areas also project directly to the vestibular nuclei of the medulla (Fig. 159). The corticonuclear zones were delimited anatomically by Jansen and Brodal,[43] and this description was modified recently by Cohen et al.[30] The functional significance of these zones has been stressed by Chambers and Sprague.[29] This way of dividing the cerebellum may be termed the longitudinal or zonal, in contrast to the transverse or lobular division.

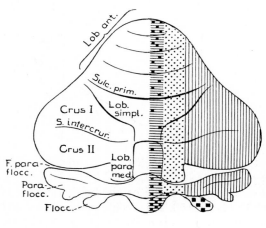

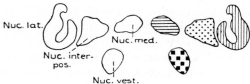

FIG. 159. Diagram of primate corticonuclear zones. Note that medial or vermal zone of cerebellum (*horizontal lines*) projects to nucleus medialis, i.e., fastigial nucleus, and to the vestibular nuclei; intermediate or paravermal zone (*stipple*) projects to nucleus interpositus; and lateral zone (*vertical lines*) projects to nucleus lateralis or dentate nucleus. (From Jansen and Brodal, *Avh. norske VidenskAkad., Kl. I*, 1942, No. 3.)

The afferent pathways to the cerebellum terminate chiefly in the cortex (the granule and Purkinje cell layers) and to a lesser extent in the deep nuclei. The regions of termination of the various afferent pathways are shown in Figure 160, in which the lobular organization of the cerebellum is illustrated. Although knowledge of afferent projections has influenced the concept of a lobular organization, this concept is based to a greater extent on comparative anatomy and embryology.*[33, 34, 35, 45]

Knowledge of the connections of the cerebellum is essential for the understanding of its functional organization. Comparative anatomy and embryology have demonstrated that the cerebellum has two major divisions separated by the posterolateral fissure—the flocculonodular lobe and the corpus cerebelli. Phylogenetically, the flocculonodular lobe

* The afferent pathways can also be related satisfactorily to the longitudinal corticonuclear zones.

develops early, and it receives its connections chiefly from the vestibular system. This lobe is relatively the same in various animals and is sometimes called the *archicerebellum*. The corpus or body of the cerebellum first appears as a medial (vermal) area consisting of a cortex and deep nuclei, which are presumably the homologue of the fastigial nuclei. This area, the *paleocerebellum*, is connected primarily with the vestibular mechanism and the proprioceptors and exteroceptors of the body and head. In mammals the paleocerebellum also receives corticopontile connections. The body of the cerebellum shows great development, especially in its lateral parts (*neocerebellum*), which consist of intermediate and lateral areas with their respective nuclei (Fig. 160). The lateral area receives its chief connections from the cerebral cortex via the pontine nuclei and additional connections from the upper brain stem via the inferior olive. The intermediate area shares the

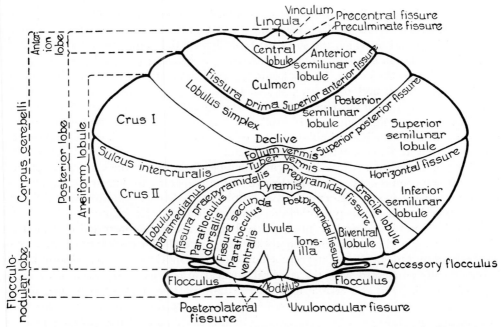

FIG. 160. Diagram of primate cerebellar cortex to summarize various terminologies, based principally on lobes and afferent projections to cerebellar areas (*right*). (From Larsell. *Anatomy of the nervous system*, 2d ed. New York, Appleton-Century-Crofts, 1951.)

afferent connections of the lateral area and many of those of the vermis. These connections are the ventral and dorsal spinothalamic tracts, the tectocerebellar tracts and the connections with the trigeminal and other sensory systems innervating the face.

The flocculonodular lobe projects back to the vestibular nuclei. The vermal area of the corpus cerebelli projects to the same vestibular nuclei, to the reticular formation of the medulla, and to the pons, midbrain and thalamus. The lateral and intermediate areas project to the reticular formation of the midbrain and to the red nucleus and the thalamus. Thus all areas of the cerebellum except the flocculonodular lobe project to the origin of the pyramidal and extrapyramidal systems in the cerebral cortex via the ventral thalamic nuclei. All cerebellar areas likewise send projections to the subcortical extrapyramidal systems, that from the vermal area going chiefly to the medulla (reticulospinal paths).

The concept of lobular parcellation now seems inadequate in the light of some of the newer information on afferent and efferent somatotopic organization. For example, the representation of the body surface extends behind the fissura prima into the declive and the simplex lobule; moreover, a second spinothalamic projection area exists, and there is a representation of the body surface in the posterior part of the posterior lobe. Under the system of lobular division, the anterior lobe—that part of the corpus cerebelli rostral to the primary fissure—has often been treated as a unit. In primates, however, this lobe consists of three zones—vermal, intermediate and lateral—each having different fiber connections and functions. Such a subdivision exists in the posterior lobe, lying between the primary and posterolateral fissures. In each instance, the lateral (and probably the intermediate) area should be referred to as the hemisphere. Even the flucculonodular lobe is subdivided into a vermal portion, the nodulus, and a lateral portion, the flocculi.

FUNCTIONAL ANATOMY OF THE CEREBELLUM

Localization and Projection. If the cerebellar cortex is explored, millimeter by millimeter, with a recording electrode while a point on the skin is touched, a cerebellar point will be found at which the so-called evoked potential is maximal (see Chaps. 14 and 21). Stimulation of an adjacent point on the skin evokes a maximal potential at an adjacent point on the cortex. In this fashion, a *somatotopic* map of the cerebellar cortex has been produced, and the cortex is said to be somatotopically or topographically organized. Elicitation of movements by cerebellar stimulation has confirmed such maps. If the evoked potential technique is applied to the cerebral and the cerebellar cortex, recording from one while stimulating the other (and then reversing the procedure) reveals many specific connections between them.

MULTIPLICITY OF INPUTS. By varying the type of stimulus to the body, or by stimulating different sense organs such as the eye or the ear, one can determine the kind of sensory input received by a central area. Until 1942, when Snider and Stowell[51] performed experiments of this type, the afferent input into the cerebellum was thought to be exclusively vestibular and proprioceptive. These workers demonstrated that tactual, visual, auditory and even visceral impulses reach the cerebellar cortex. Subsequently it was learned that the portion of the cerebellar cortex responding to peripheral stimulation is reciprocally connected with the cerebral cortical area which responds to the same type of stimuli. Thus the vermal and intermediate parts of the anterior lobe, which receives somesthetic input, are connected with the postcentral gyrus, the somatosensory area of the cerebral cortex; the cerebellar visual area (vermis of the posterior lobe) is interconnected with the cerebral cortical visual area; etc. Finally, after it was discovered that the cerebral cortex contains two somatosensory areas (see Chap. 14), the classic postcentral one (somatic area I) was found to be interconnected with the anterior projection field of the spinocerebellar tract in the anterior lobe and the second (somatic area II) with the posterior or paramedian projection of the spinocerebellar tracts.[39]

Beginning with Adrian's work[24] in 1943, demonstrations of a comparable reciprocal connection—cerebellum to cerebral cortex and vice versa—between all zones of the anterior lobe and the motor areas of the cerebral cortex became available. All these experiments also revealed an element of topographic organization.

To summarize: (i) The cerebellum receives afferent inputs other than vestibular and proprioceptive. (ii) The anterior lobe is reciprocally connected with somatosensory area I of the cerebral cortex. (iii) The posterior lobe (paramedian lobule) is reciprocally connected with the second somatosensory cortex. (iv) The motor area of the cerebral cortex and the entire anterior lobe are reciprocally connected. (v) In all these areas there is considerable somatotopic organization. The general plan of reciprocal connections can be diagrammed as in Figure 161.

It can be deduced from this information that the cerebellum (since it has an input from exteroceptors) is concerned with adjustments of the body to the external world as well as to the internal proprioceptive world. Secondly, the cerebral motor cortex and the cerebellum must work closely together in effecting and controlling movements.

Somatotopic Organization. Evidence of a somatotopic organization of the cerebellar cortex comes from electrophysiologic studies of afferent inputs and stimulation of the cerebellar cortex and anatomic studies of the projections of the spinocerebellar tracts. This organization is, however, relative rather than absolute.* The body surface of the cat is projected into its anterior cerebellum, so that the tail is predominantly "localized" in the lingula, the hindleg in the simplex. Furthermore, the axial portions of the animal are represented along the midline in the vermis, and the apical portions

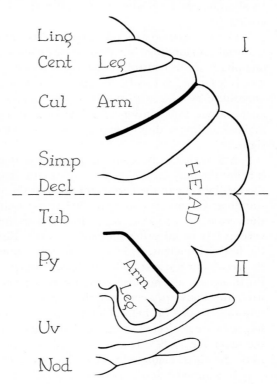

FIG. 161. Summary diagram showing somatotopic organization of cerebellar cortex and nature of cerebrocerebellar relationships. The latter are indicated by the Roman numerals (referring to cerebral somatosensory areas) and horizontal dashed line. For meaning of abbreviations, see Fig. 160. Much of data obtained on cats and extrapolated to primate cerebellum. Representation in paramedian lobule, behind lower heavy line indicating prepyramidal fissure, is bilateral. (After Hampson *et al., Res. Publ. Ass. nerv. ment. Dis.*, 1952, *30*:299–316.)

more laterally, in the intermediate cortex. Similarly, as shown in Figure 161, the tail areas in the somatosensory and motor areas of the cerebral cortex are reciprocally connected with the lingula—and so on through the cerebral and cerebellar areas for the hindlimb, forelimb and neck–face. In the second representation of the body surface, found in the posterior part of the corpus cerebelli, there is also a topographic localization.

FUNCTIONS OF THE CEREBELLUM

Equilibration. Since part of the cerebellum developed from the vestibular structures of the medulla oblongata, it is not surprising that regulation of the mechanism underlying upright posture is a cerebellar function. One such mechanism is equilibration, or balancing, and its regulation is served mainly by the flocculonodular lobe.

FLOCCULONODULAR LOBE. The disturbances resulting from ablation of this lobe

* In electrophysiologic mapping experiments conducted on *un*anesthetized cats by Combs,[31] stimulation of a point on the skin or of a cutaneous nerve resulted in bilateral activation of all folia of the vermal and intermediate anterior lobe. For reasons which will be brought out in the discussion of similar experiments on the cerebral cortex, this finding is not incompatible with the existence of a focus of representation as revealed in experiments involving use of barbiturate anesthetics.

reflect its vestibular afferent and efferent connections. Dow[32] performed isolated ablations in this area and observed conspicuous disturbances of equilibrium without either changes in the basic postural reflexes or difficulties in volitional movements. After such a lesion, a monkey can feed itself manually without tremor or deviation of the hands, but it is unable to stand, even on a broad base, without swaying and falling. For this reason, the monkey generally sits, propping itself up in a corner to secure support from two sides of the cage or maintaining equilibrium by clutching the cage wall or floor. The syndrome is therefore one of *disequilibration*. The vestibular concern of the flocculonodular lobe is further documented by the fact that development of motion sickness in dogs is prevented by ablation of this area but not by removal of any other in either the cerebellar or cerebral cortex.[56, 57]

OTHER CEREBELLAR AREAS REGULATING STANDING.   The stretch reflexes are the raw materials of standing, but these basic reflexes must be controlled. Equilibration is only one phase of this control, the phase in which the vestibular system is important. Vision, too, is a factor, as can be quickly learned by standing on one foot and comparing the amount of swaying with the eyes closed and with them open. Proprioception is another factor, since interruption of spinal proprioceptive pathways, as in locomotor ataxia, makes standing without swaying difficult, especially when the eyes are closed (Romberg's sign).

Although the flocculonodular lobe is unquestionably important in equilibration, it is not the only cerebellar structure regulating standing. Recent evidence suggests that the medial zone of the vermis throughout the whole of the cerebellum is concerned with standing. Chambers and Sprague[28] found that lesions confined to the anterior zone of the vermal area produce difficulties in standing like those caused by posterior (medial) vermal lesions affecting the nodular area. Since the medial vermal cortex projects to the fastigial nucleus, which in turn sends many fibers to and receives many fibers from the vestibular nucleus of the medulla oblongata, this finding is anatomically reasonable. Furthermore, the spinocerebellar tract, carrying proprioceptive and tactual impulses from the body, projects heavily to the anterior portion of the vermis. Such sensory impulses would be helpful in maintaining equilibrium. Finally, visual and auditory impulses are projected to the vermal structures, centering on the declive, the folium and the tuber vermis.[44, 51] It may be predicted that one function of this projection will prove to be the visual element in the maintenance of the body's orientation in space.

In summary, standing—whether on two legs or four—depends upon three afferent inputs: vestibular, somesthetic and visual. All these are heavily represented in the most medial vermal regions of the cerebellar cortex that control the musculature of the entire body. The higher control of equilibration and standing seems to be served by the medial vermal region of the corpus cerebelli and by the flocculonodular lobe.

Tonus.   More fundamental to standing than equilibration is the control of the myotatic reflexes. As discussed in Chapter 5, these include two-neuron-arc spinal reflexes regulated by impulses descending from the vestibular nuclei and from the brain stem reticular system. Normally, such reflexes serve to prevent collapse of the joints by the pull of gravity. A decerebrate animal, in which descending influences from the cerebellum and cerebrum are interrupted, can stand, but its legs must be adjusted under it. If pushed slightly from the side, the animal does not adjust the strength of its extensor reflexes sufficiently to prevent toppling. The intact animal has a greater capacity for promptly adjusting its muscular contractions to the vicissitudes of gravitational forces. The cerebellum is concerned with reflex tonus of the musculature and presumably functions to control that tonus.

Inhibition of extensor tonus is the predominant effect of threshold stimulation of the medial anterior lobe. This inhibition of rigidity is especially evident when the vermal area of the anterior lobe of a decerebrate cat is stimulated. Consistently, when decerebration is combined with ablation of this lobe, as in the anemic method of decerebration,[46] the release of extensor myotatic reflexes is greater than that following simple transcollicular decerebration. These effects in decerebrate animals prove also that much of the postural influence of the medial anterior lobe is exerted on the brain stem—understandable since the major outflow from the lobe is the fastigiobulbar tract to the vestibular and reticular nuclei of the medulla. There is little doubt that the loss of the anterior lobes is responsible for the extensor spasm, the opisthotonos and the hyperactive posture-supporting reaction seen during the *initial* stages after decerebellation. However, in the dog and cat, the medial anterior lobe is not purely inhibitory to extensors, but usually activates the flexors reciprocally. Moreover, after stimulation of the lobe has ceased, a contrary effect often appears—contraction of extensor muscles and inhibition of flexor motoneurons. The response obtained depends somewhat on the parameters of the stimulus. This and the rebound phenomena indicate that the anterior cerebellum contains oppositely acting components, each of which acts reciprocally on flexor and extensor motoneurons.

The release of extensor reflexes is greater and more enduring in the pigeon than in the dog or cat, and is less marked in the monkey than in the cat. In man, a medial anterior lobe syndrome denoted by release of extensor reflexes has never been identified. All these facts lead to the conclusion that the extensor-inhibiting postural function of the medial anterior lobe has changed during phylogeny.

A factor in the complex effects of ablation of the anterior lobe was disclosed by Sprague and Chambers[52] when they destroyed only one fastigial nucleus, the main outflow from the anterior lobe (and from the remainder of the vermis). Whereas bilateral nuclear lesions have effects similar to those of an ablation of the anterior lobe, destruction of one fastigial nucleus causes spasticity in the contralateral extensor muscles and in the flexor muscles of the ipsilateral limbs. Another complicating observation was that lesions of the vermian cortex of the anterior lobe exert effects opposite to those of lesions of the underlying fastigial nucleus. The cortex presumably inhibits the nucleus which, in turn, is inhibitory to contralateral extensors and ipsilateral flexors. With the cerebellum, as with many other structures, what is seen on stimulation or ablation reflects the predominant rather than the *sole* function of the structure.

Suprasegmental influences on myotatic reflexes can be exerted on either the alpha motoneurons or the gamma fusomotor neurons. The cerebellum acts through both avenues. Granit and Kaada[38] have shown that the afferent discharge from a muscle spindle is *decreased* by stimulation of the vermal portion of the anterior lobe, an action which would decrease muscle tonus. This finding corresponds to the known predominant effect (inhibition) of such stimulation on myotatic reflexes. Stimulation of the intermediate portion of the anterior lobe increased the spindle discharge, a finding which correlates with studies described later in this chapter. The tonus changes exerted through gamma efferents occurred at a lower threshold of anterior cerebellar stimulation than did direct effects upon alpha motoneurons. However, the anterior cerebellum also acts upon alpha motoneurons. Functional ablation of it by cooling resulted in extensor hypertonus without increased gamma efferent discharge. Knowledge of the higher control of tonus via the gamma efferent is a new development which may in the future explain some of the puzzling features of abnormal tonus states (Chap. 5).[35]

One hypothesis to account for the severe *hypo*tonia seen in clinical cases of cerebellar damage is that hypotonia is caused by injury to the lateral corticonuclear zone of the whole cerebellum. Since these areas are developed progressively in primates, including man, this theory might explain why hypotonia rather than hypertonia is typical of the human cerebellar syndrome. Unfortunately, lesions in experimental animals have rarely been confined to the lateral zone but have included portions of the medial and intermediate zones, and thus an element of extensor reflex release has been introduced.

It is not certain whether lesions confined to the lateral portion of the cerebellum in the dog or cat result in hypotonia after the initial stage of hypertonus.[26, 29] Hypotonia is much more marked in the primate. After unilateral cerebellar ablations sparing the anterior vermis and the fastigial nucleus in baboons, Botterell and Fulton[25] observed hypotonia, which was more severe and enduring when the dentate nucleus was damaged.

The lateral and intermediate portions of the cerebellum, unlike the vermis, do not project to the reticular and vestibular areas of the brain stem known to be concerned with facilitating and inhibiting the basic, spinal, myotatic reflexes. How, then, can these cerebellar areas influence muscular tonus?

The efferent projection of the lateral lobes of the cerebellum is to the dentate nucleus, from which fibers pass to the thalamus, some with a synapse in the red nucleus (Fig. 162). At this point, an influence on posture could be exerted by way of the rubro-

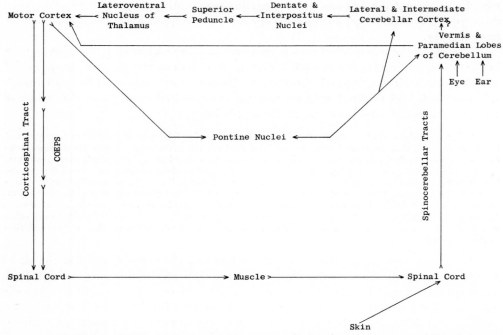

FIG. 162.   Feedback loops from and to motor cortex. Long loop involves a return of proprioceptive information from muscle to motor cortex by way of cerebellum. This loop assumes existence of connections between paleocerebellum and neocerebellum. A second potential loop is shorter and entirely within brain. It may or may not receive information from periphery, depending on connection of neocerebellum with vermis and paramedian lobes, which receive proprioceptive and exteroceptive sensory information. Note that short loop is informed of events in periphery only if there are connections between the medial and the more lateral cerebellar regions. Also note that arrow connecting vermis and paramedian lobe is questioned. This pathway is known functionally but not anatomically.

spinal tracts or the neighboring descending systems of the reticular facilitatory area. A synapse in the lateroventral nucleus of the thalamus interrupts the ascending pathways to the cerebral cortex. Fibers from this nucleus project to the motor areas of the motor cortex. Physiologic experiments teach that the pyramidal tract arising in the motor area is facilitatory to the extensor monosynaptic reflex arcs serving stretch reflexes. It is reasonable to assume that the fibers reaching the cerebral cortex from the lateral cerebellum provide the input drive for this tonic pyramidal influence on extensor reflexes. If this drive were eliminated by a lateral cerebellar lesion, the effect would be hypotonia.

It would be going too far to ascribe the hypotonia of the human cerebellar syndrome entirely to injury to the lateral hemispheres, since the more medial cerebellar regions connect with the motor area through the fastigial and interpositus nuclei as well as with the brain stem. However, the influence of the medial cortex upon pyramidal tract discharge seems to be mainly inhibitory,[30, 53] and the net effect exerted through the brain stem connection is inhibitory to extensor tonus. Damage to either system would not produce hypotonia. Altogether, it is probably that damage in the greatly expanded lateral hemisphere is responsible for the hypotonia consequent to cerebellar injury in man.

Control of Volitional Movements. Because these controls are displayed best in man when cerebellar disease has disrupted them, the detailed descriptions may be deferred. It suffices to say that the signs of such defects are errors in the rate, range, force and direction of volitional movements (ataxia) and coarse, irregular oscillations, especially at the termination of a movement.

Anatomic considerations strongly suggest that the lateral and paravermal zones of the cerebellum are particularly concerned with the control of voluntary movement of the limbs. The lateral zone has developed commensurate with manipulatory ability in the primate series, and the afferent and efferent connections of these lobes form a cerebello-cerebellar circle. However, the paravermal cortex also projects to the motor cortex via the interpositus nucleus and, unlike the lateral zone, is somatotopically highly organized. The most recent evidence from animal experiments indicates that ablation of the paravermal cortex induces ataxic movement; the influence of the more lateral region is less clearly established—a situation which may mean simply that the influence is more subtle. Paradoxically, lesions of the dentate nucleus, through which the lateral cortex exerts its influence, produce the most striking effects on volitional activity.[25, 37] Regardless of the relative roles of the lateral and the paravermal cortex, it is clear that they, together, control voluntary movement through the projections ultimately reaching the cortex; whereas the midline structures influence mainly the basic postural reflexes.

Before the ways in which the cerebellum and the cerebral cortex interact in the control of voluntary movement are discussed in detail the manifestations of cerebellar disease in man should be examined. Not only are certain disturbances more pronounced in man than in animals, but the examination of movement can be more detailed and enlightening in man than in experimental animals. However, it should be remembered that knowledge of which cerebellar regions have been destroyed or damaged is less certain.

Clinical Correlations. DISTURBANCES OF GAIT AND STATION. A specific type of tumor (medulloblastoma) occurring in young children induces disorders almost exactly like those which Dow[32] produced in monkeys by ablating portions of the flocculonodular lobe. Arising from the roof of the fourth ventricle, often at the base of the nodulus, these tumors produce few obvious signs of incoordination of movement as long as the child lies in bed. However, he is unable to balance and walk. Disturbances of gait and station, unaccompanied by hypotonia, also occur when the more anterior vermal region is affected by tumor or degeneration. Such cases are rare. In fact, as a result of the sheltered position of the anterior and flocculonodular lobes and their proximity to vital brain stem structures, the usual case of cerebellar disease probably reflects mainly damage to the cerebellum as a whole.

DISTURBANCES OF TONUS. The common procedure of passive flexion or extension of a joint, or simply shaking a limb, is generally used to demonstrate disorders of tonus. A *pendular knee jerk* is a manifestation of hypotonia. Through default of the myotatic appendage, the limb is not lowered but falls as an inert body does, and swings back and forth (Fig. 163). Failure of the antagonistic flexors to respond with a stretch reflex as the leg passes the midposition is also a factor. The mechanism of cerebellar hypotonia

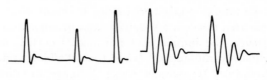

FIG. 163.   Excursion of leg in knee jerk in normal person (*left*) and in patient with cerebellar lesion (*right*). Note that in three knee jerks at left leg falls "deadbeat," whereas in two knee jerks at right leg oscillates after initial upright excursion due to the knee jerk itself. (From Holmes, *Lancet*, 1922, *202:* 1177–1182.)

is not known with certainty. As pointed out earlier, the neocerebellum is connected with the motor areas of the cerebral cortex, and can facilitate their action. From the Fulton–Tower–Hines analysis of pyramidal tract function, default of the cerebellar discharge to the motor cortex could, like interruption of the pyramidal tract, result in flaccidity. Default of the cerebellar connection with the upper brain stem, which contains the reticular facilitatory area, is another possibility.

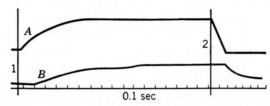

FIG. 164.   Myograms of voluntary contraction by a patient with unilateral cerebellar lesion. *A*, normal; *B*, affected hand. Vertical lines *1* and *2* mark signals to start and stop gripping. Note slower start, weaker contraction, and delayed relaxation in the lower record. (From Ruch, Chap. 5 in *Handbook of experimental psychology*, S. S. Stevens, ed., New York, Wiley, 1951.)

DISTURBANCES OF VOLUNTARY MOVEMENT.[41, 42]   Deficiencies in force (asthenia), rate, direction (dysmetria), and steadiness (tremor) of movement are typical effects of cerebellar lesions on volitional movement. Starting, stopping and changing the direction of motion are especially disturbed.

The weakness of voluntary movements is not accompanied by loss of any specific movement, and, although severe subjectively, it is not easily demonstrable objectively. This *asthenia* is explicable by the hypothesis that the cerebellum facilitates the motor cortex. As with many cerebellar signs, the facilitation could be at the segmental level by way of the cerebellar connections with the brain stem.

In patients with cerebellar lesions, simple movements are slow to start (Fig. 164), a condition presumably reflecting the lack of facilitation. Figure 164 also shows that movements are slow to stop, so that hypermetria—overshooting the mark—occurs in a finger-to-nose test. (However, the finger can also undershoot—hypometria.) The rebound phenomenon, i.e., inability to restrain an arm exerting tension when it is suddenly released by the examiner, is a failure to stop a willed muscular contraction quickly. As

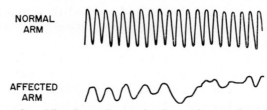

NORMAL
ARM

AFFECTED
ARM

FIG. 165.   Tracings of rapidly alternating supination and pronation of arms illustrating adiodochokinesis. By contrast with normal arm, affected arm even initially made slow, low-amplitude movements, which rapidly deteriorated further. (From Holmes, *Lancet*, 1922, *203:*59–65.)

shown in Figure 165, a patient with cerebellar disease is unable to perform alternating movements (supination and pronation of forearms) rapidly and with equal excursions (adiodochokinesis). This sign again reflects a defect in starting and stopping a movement.

A cerebellar tremor is "intentional" (i.e., occurs during voluntary movement rather than rest), terminal (most marked at the end of a movement), and coarse and irregular, as seen in Figure 166. In all these respects, cerebellar tremor contrasts so greatly with the regular oscillatory tremor of rest seen in Parkinson's disease that "tremor" may be a poor term. The term "ataxic tremor" is descriptive.[27] In visualizing the cerebellar tremor, one can imagine the arm drifting from the intended path and being corrected too late and too vigorously, so that the hand overcorrects and then overshoots the intended path. This overcorrection continues through slowness in stopping a movement and in initiating a return toward the course. As this sequence is repeated, the result is an irregular tremor which mounts in severity as the movement progresses. The whole appearance somewhat resembles the first attempt to steer a boat. There are also typical disturbances in speaking, writing, standing and walking, but they present no new features.

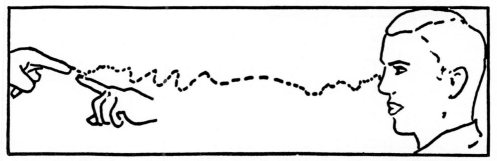

FIG. 166.   Record of tremulous movement obtained by having patient move his finger from his nose to touch the finger of the examiner, represented at the left. Note irregularity and coarseness of tremor and that it is most marked near termination of the movement. (From Ruch, Chap. 5 in *Handbook of experimental psychology*, S. S. Stevens, ed., New York, Wiley, 1951.)

The effort of neurophysiologists is to reduce the many manifestations of cerebellar disease to one or two basic defects. A unitary explanation of cerebellar symptoms must take into account the cerebellocerebral relationships.

Cerebellocerebral Relationships.   The principal fact is the one we started with. The cerebral cortex cannot execute coordinated movements without help. This is true even though the cerebral cortex has at its disposal rich information from proprioceptors and exteroceptors. Although the cerebellum also has rich somatosensory inputs, it is presumed to contribute to cortically induced movement something over and beyond sensory information. It is surely significant that the cerebellum is reciprocally linked with the cerebral motor cortex, the connections potentially forming a loop.

It has long been known that stimulation of the neocerebellum can make the motor cortex more excitable,[47] and that some of this effect is exerted through connections between the two structures rather than by convergence on the reticular substance or spinal levels. Electroencephalographic waves are augmented. Surprisingly, the influence of the midline paleocerebellar areas on corticomotor excitability is better documented.[35] These areas have a topographic organization, and their influence on the motor cortex, like their influence on the limb reflexes, is often *inhibitory* but can be facilitatory. Snider and Magoun[50] have found facilitatory areas lying just lateral to the vermis in the anterior lobe and the paramedian lobule. The occurrence of inhibitory or occlusive interaction in the cerebral cortex has been shown by recording from the pyramidal tract while interacting cerebellar and motor area stimulation.[55] It is clear that the cerebellum exerts both facilitatory and inhibitory influences on movement initiated by the cerebral motor cortex. This helps us to understand why the clinical manifestations of cerebellar injury present contrary elements—slowness to start and overshoot.

Altogether, the available data on the functioning of reciprocal cerebellocerebral connections does not permit more than speculation. Since the function of the neocerebellum is the control of discrete limb movement, and since control systems developed in engineering often employ a feedback loop, considerable *a priori* significance is attached to the potential neural loop afforded by the reciprocal cerebellocerebral connections. Wiener[58] and others[36] have commented on the similarity between servomechanisms and the neural control of movements. This parallel is illustrated in Figure 167.

A command to take a new position activates a motor which effects the movement to a degree dependent upon the difference between the present position and the desired

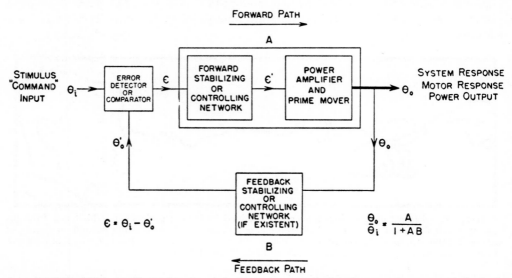

FIG. 167. Diagram illustrating the analogies between a physiologic control system and the basic elements of a servosystem. The "command" is a low energy input such as the sight of an object. The forward path might represent the corticospinal pathways. Θ reflects achieved movement, which is compared with intent of stimulus and a modified order goes over the forward path. (From Frank *et al.*, *Ann. N. Y. Acad. Sci.*, 1948, *50*:187–277.)

position. A signal from the response is returned to the comparator, where present position is again related to intended position and a new order is issued to the power source. Thus the error, i.e., difference between present and intended position, is progressively reduced. Such systems are subject to overshoot and oscillation in making rapid transients if underdamped, or to a sluggish response if overdamped. Unfortunately for the sake of simple analogy, the signs of cerebellar disease appear to be overdamping at the initiation of movement and underdamping at its end.

The cerebellum might serve as a comparator, comparing the order from the cortex with the resulting limb position; however, the cerebral cortex itself, with its extensive exteroceptors, would be a more logical candidate for the task of comparing the goal with the present position. Perhaps the cerebellum should be considered analogous to the feedback stabilizing or controlling network, which determines whether the system is too slow in its control or is prone to oscillation.

It has been suggested[48] that the motor cortex is handicapped in planning movements in time because nerve impulses cannot be stored to be discharged after a fixed delay. However, if the motor cortex discharged in a circular pathway involving the cerebellum, a programming of movement in time might be possible. The cerebellum might provide an accelerating or facilitating mechanism to impart velocity without overshoot. Default of such a function would account for the slowness of movements to start in a patient with cerebellar disease (Fig. 163). A programming circuit with the correct decay characteristics would be helpful in decelerating movement to prevent overshoot or a jerky stop. Movements so roughed in could be further refined by afferent sensory reports, either via the cerebellum or to the cerebral cortex by way of the spinothalamocortical fibers. Whatever its resemblance to servomechanisms, the cerebellum has the requisite facilitatory and inhibitory relationship to the motor cortex and to the brain stem mechanisms to aid both systems in starting and stopping movements in the manner necessary to effective, well directed movement.

REFERENCES

BASAL GANGLIA

1. BUCY, P. C. Chap. 15 in *Precentral motor cortex*, 2d ed. Urbana, Ill., University of Illinois Press, 1949, xiv, 615 pp.
2. BUCY, P. C. Chap. 11 in *Pathogenesis and treatment of Parkinsonism*, W. S. FIELDS, ed. Springfield, Ill., Charles C Thomas, 1958, x, 372 pp.
3. DUSSER DE BARENNE, J. G. and McCULLOCH, W. S. *J. Neurophysiol.*, 1941, 4:311-323.
4. FIELDS, W. S. *Pathogenesis and treatment of Parkinsonism*. Springfield, Ill., Charles C Thomas, 1958, x, 372 pp.
5. FORMAN, D. and WARD, J. W. *J. Neurophysiol.*, 1957, 20:230-244.
6. GLEES, P. *J. Anat. (Lond.)*, 1944, 78:47-51, 2 pls.
7. HASSLER, R. *Dtsch. Z. Nervenheilk.*, 1956, 175:233-258.
8. JENKNER, F. L. and WARD, A. *Arch. Neurol. Psychiat. (Chicago)*, 1953, 70:489-502.
9. KENNARD, MARGARET A. *J. Neurophysiol.*, 1944, 7:127-148.
10. KENNARD, MARGARET A. and FULTON, J. F. *Res. Publ. Ass. nerv. ment. Dis.*, 1942, 21:228-245.
11. MAGOUN, H. W. and RHINES, RUTH. *Spasticity: The stretch-reflex and extrapyramidal systems*. Springfield, Ill., Charles C Thomas, 1947, viii, 59 pp.
12. (16) METTLER, F. A., ADES, H. W., LIPMAN, E. and CULLER, E. A. *Arch. Neurol. Psychiat. (Chicago)*, 1939, 41:984-995.
13. POLLOCK, L. J. and DAVIS, L. *Arch. Neurol. Psychiat. (Chicago)*, 1930, 23:303-319.
14. PUTNAM, T. J. *Arch. Neurol. Psychiat. (Chicago)*, 1940, 44:950-976.
15. PUTNAM, T. J. and HERZ, E. *Arch. Neurol. Psychiat. (Chicago)*, 1950, 63:357-366.
16. RIOCH, D. McK. and BRENNER, C. *J. comp. Neurol.*, 1938, 68:491-507.
17. SCHREINER, L. Chap. 5 in *Pathogenesis and treatment of Parkinsonism*, W. S. FIELDS, ed. Springfield, Ill., Charles C Thomas, 1958, x, 372 pp.
18. TOWER, S. S. *Brain*, 1935, 58:238-255.
19. WARD, A. A. Chap. 4 in *Pathogenesis and treatment of Parkinsonism*, W. S. FIELDS, ed. Springfield, Ill., Charles C Thomas, 1958, x, 372 pp.
20. WARD, A. A., JR., McCULLOCH, W. S. and MAGOUN, H. W. *J. Neurophysiol.*, 1948, 11:317-330.
21. WARD, A. A. and STERN, J. Personal communication.
22. WALSHE, F. M. R. *Brain*, 1924, 47:159-177.
23. WHITTIER, J. R. and METTLER, F. A. *J. comp. Neurol.*, 1949, 90:319-372.

CEREBELLUM

24. ADRIAN, E. D. *Brain*, 1943, 66:289-315.
25. BOTTERELL, E. H. and FULTON, J. F. *J. comp. Neurol.*, 1938, 69:63-87.
26. BREMER, F. *Arch. int. Physiol.*, 1922, 19:189-226.
27. CARREA, R. M. E. and METTLER, F. A. *J. comp. Neurol.*, 1947, 87:169-288.
28. CHAMBERS, W. W. and SPRAGUE, J. M. *J. comp. Neurol.*, 1955, 103:105-129.
29. CHAMBERS, W. W. and SPRAGUE, J. M. *Arch. Neurol. Psychiat. (Chicago)*, 1955, 74:653-680.
30. COHEN, D., CHAMBERS, W. W. and SPRAGUE, J. M. *J. comp. Neurol.*, 1958, 109:233-266.
31. COMBS, C. M. *J. Neurophysiol.*, 1954, 17:123-143.
32. DOW, R. S. *Arch. Neurol. Psychiat. (Chicago)*, 1938, 40:500-520.
33. DOW, R. S. *Biol. Rev.*, 1942, 17:179-220.
34. DOW, R. S. *J. Neurophysiol.*, 1942, 5:121-136.
35. DOW, R. S. and MORUZZI, G. *The physiology and pathology of the cerebellum*. Minneapolis, University of Minnesota Press, 1958, xvi, 675 pp.
36. FRANK, L. K., HUTCHINSON, G. E., LIVINGSTON, W. K., McCULLOCH, W. S. and WIENER, N. *Ann. N. Y. Acad. Sci.*, 1948, 50:187-278.
37. FULTON, J. F. *Functional localization in the frontal lobes and cerebellum*. Oxford, Clarendon Press, 1949, xii, 140 pp.

38. GRANIT, R. and KAADA, B. R. *Acta physiol. scand.*, 1952, *27*:130–160.

39. HAMPSON, J. L. *J. Neurophysiol.*, 1949, *12*:37–50.

40. HENNEMAN, E., COOKE, P. M. and SNIDER, R. S. *Res. Publ. Ass. nerv. ment. Dis.*, 1952, *30*:317–333.

41. HOLMES, G. *Lancet*, 1922, *202*:1177–1182, 1231–1237; *203*:59–65, 111–115.

42. HOLMES, G. *Brain*, 1939, *62*:1–30.

43. JANSEN, J. and BRODAL, A. *Avh. norske VidenskAkad.*, *Kl. I*, 1942, No. 3, 50 pp.

44. KOELLA, W. P. *J. Neurophysiol.*, 1959, *22*:61–77.

45. LARSELL, O. *Arch. Neurol. Psychiat. (Chicago)*, 1937, *38*:580–607.

46. POLLOCK, L. J. and DAVIS, L. *Brain*, 1927, *50*:277–312.

47. ROSSI, G. *Arch. Fisiol.*, 1912, *10*:389–399.

48. RUCH, T. C. Chap. 5 in *Handbook of experimental psychology*, S. S. STEVENS, ed. New York, John Wiley & Sons, 1951, xi, 1436 pp.

49. SNIDER, R. S. *Arch. Neurol. Psychiat. (Chicago)*, 1950, *64*:196–219.

50. SNIDER, R. S. and MAGOUN, H. W. *J. Neurophysiol.*, 1949, *12*:335–345.

51. SNIDER, R. S. and STOWELL, A. *J. Neurophysiol.*, 1944, *7*:331–357.

52. SPRAGUE, J. M. and CHAMBERS, W. W. *J. Neurophysiol.*, 1953, *16*:451–463.

53. SPRAGUE, J. M. and CHAMBERS, W. W. *Arch. ital. Biol.*, 1959, *97*:68–88.

54. THOMAS, D. M., KAUFMAN, R. P., SPRAGUE, J. M. and CHAMBERS, W. W. *J. Anat. (Lond.)*, 1956, *90*:371–385, 1 pl.

55. TOWE, A. L. and CASEY, K. L. *Physiologist*, 1959, *2*:22.

56. TYLER, D. B. and BARD, P. *Physiol. Rev.*, 1949, *29*:311–369.

57. WANG, S. C. and CHINN, H. I. *Amer. J. Physiol.*, 1956, *185*:617–623.

58. WIENER, N. *Cybernetics or control and communication in the animal and the machine.* New York, John Wiley & Sons, 1948, 194 pp.

SECTION IV

Sensory Functions of the
Nervous System

CHAPTER 13

Somatic Sensation

By THEODORE C. RUCH

Introductory Concepts and Definitions.[4] All knowledge comes to us through our sense organs. Our simplest motor acts are initiated through sense organs; our most complex ones are controlled by means of them. Pain is a matter of immediate interest in many clinical conditions, and testing other forms of somatic sensation is a considerable part of the neurologic examination. In the next chapter it will become clear that the distinction between sensation and perception is a valuable clue to the level of nervous system damage. Under the broad heading of sensation are grouped certain complex phenomena which are immensely important to the individual experiencing them: hunger, nausea, vertigo, sexual sensations, feelings of fatigue, and a host of ill-defined discomforts originating in the deeper structures of the body. Many of these have only recently become the object of physiologic inquiry, presumably because they are important to psychosomatic medicine.

By a "sensory modality" or, simply, a "sense" one usually means a subjectively distinctive response to stimulation. Conscious sensations are therefore said to differ in quality or modality. Differences in quality on a conscious level are associated with a distinctness in one or more of the following: the sense organ and the sensory nerve fiber which conducts to the central nervous system, the pathway through the central nervous system, and certainly the ultimate or terminal neurons of the cerebral cortex underlying the conscious experience.

Within the limits of a modality, we distinguish certain subqualities. In vision we have many different subqualities, which we designate by special names, the primary colors for example. In sound sensations, we distinguish different tones. In addition to the subqualities of a sense, there are sensory processes of a higher order than sensation which, for convenience of expression, may be grouped in the general category of *perceptions*. Perceptions, which are elaborations of sensation, may involve simply a temporal pattern of a single modality (tickle) or may involve the fusion of information from more than one sensory channel. It is said, for example, that "wetness" is a fusion of cold and pressure. Other forms of perception have a spatial element—the awareness of the location of a stimulus, of its size, shape, etc.

The response of the brain to afferent impulses is always double—besides the quality of the sensation and perceptions, we feel that some sensations are pleasant, others unpleasant. Technically this aspect of sensation is known as *affect*. In certain neurologic disorders, the affect becomes more intense and the quality less vivid, suggesting different brain mechanisms for the two phenomena.

Touch was, until nearly the turn of the last century, treated as a single, unitary sense which appreciated many characteristics of the stimulus object.[4] Thus, warmth or coldness, pressure, etc., were thought of as subqualities of the single sense of "feeling" or "touch." About 1890, it was discovered that the skin is not everywhere uniformly sensitive to all aspects of a stimulating object. If the skin is marked off in millimeter squares and systematically explored with very small objects—blunt (pressure), sharp (pain), warm and cold—it is found that some spots give rise to sensations of warmth but not of cold or pain, while others respond only to a cold stimulus and with a sensation of coldness; still other areas respond only with sensations of pressure or pain. Cutaneous sensibility is therefore *punctiform* or pointlike in its distribution. This was one of the fundamental experiments in the physiology of sensation. On the basis of such experiments, touch was easily divided into several separate senses—pressure or touch, warmth and cold.

The establishment of pain as a separate modality of sensation was more difficult because pain sensations can be aroused from virtually every spot stimulated. Indeed, today some still argue that pain is not a separate sense.

Classification of the Senses. The senses and sensory receptors are classified in several ways, all of which are useful. Since parts of each system are in common use, it is well to become familiar with all.

Sherrington's classification.[38] This classification is much used in physiologic literature and is based on the source of the stimulus and the location of the receptor. The *proprioceptors*, found in muscles, tendons and joints, and in the labyrinth, give information concerning the movements and position of the body in space. The *exteroceptors*, the sense organs of the skin, give information on changes in the immediate external environment. The *interoceptors* transmit impulses from the visceral organs. The *teleceptors*, or *distance receptors*, which give information concerning changes in the more remote environment, are the sense organs of the eyes, ears and nose. (By usage, labyrinthine receptors are often not included in the proprioceptive group.)

Clinical classification of sensation. The clinical classification of sensation is strongly influenced by morphologic considerations. The following list shows how the modalities of sensation are grouped by clinicians; in the right-hand column is given a sample term to illustrate clinical terminology of the sensation and its disturbances.

I. *Special senses* served by the cranial nerves
   1. Vision...Hemianopia
   2. Audition..None
   3. Taste...Ageusia
   4. Olfaction...Anosmia
   5. Vestibular..None
II. *Superficial or cutaneous sensations* served by the cutaneous branches of spinal and certain cranial nerves
   1. Touch-pressure..Hypesthesia
   2. Warmth...⎫
   3. Cold...⎬ Hypothermesthesia
   4. Pain...Hyperalgesia
III. *Deep sensations* served by muscular branches of spinal nerves and certain cranial nerves
   1. Muscle, tendon, and joint sensibility, or position sense.................Bathesthesia
   2. (Deep pain)
   3. (Deep pressure)

IV. *Visceral sensations* served by fibers conducted with the autonomic nervous system
  1. Organic sensation, e.g., hunger, nausea, etc.
  2. Visceral pain

The parentheses indicate that the position of deep pain and pressure in the scheme is anomalous. Thus, the phrase "deep sensation," as ordinarily used, does not include muscular pain and sometimes does not include deep pressure.

Other classifications. Sensory receptors are sometimes designated by the agent which most easily stimulates them, e.g., chemoreceptors, mechanoreceptors, etc. The term *nociceptors* was applied to pain receptors by Sherrington because they respond to a variety of stimuli which have in common the property of being noxious or damaging to the tissues. Finally, a useful dichotomy applicable to both motor and sensory phenomena is *somatic* and *visceral* for sensations arising in structures derived from the somatopleura and visceropleura, respectively. Somatic sensation (or *somesthesia*) is a convenient name for superficial and deep sensation together.

Adequate Stimulus (Differential Sensitivity). The basis for the law of the adequate stimulus is that most sensory receptors are especially sensitive to one form of energy. By definition, then, the criterion for an *adequate* stimulus is not whether it elicits a response but whether it is the form of energy to which the receptor is most sensitive. For example, radiant energy of the visible spectrum is the adequate stimulus for visual receptors. Pressure on the eyeball can also stimulate these receptors, but is not an adequate stimulus to them because their threshold for light is lower. The best quantitative illustration is that the warmth end-organs of the skin are nearly 2000 times as sensitive to radiant heat as are the intermingled pain end-organs. The biologic function of the elaborate sense organ is, as Sherrington pointed out, to lower the threshold of the nerve fiber to some *one form* of energy. For each sense organ there is an adequate stimulus, because each type of sensory receptor is especially sensitive to one form of energy.

Whether the differential sensitivity necessarily depends on morphologic differentiation of the end-organ has long been questioned.[4, 37] It is now doubtful that specialized endings exist in much of the body surface (see below). However, it is not the physiologic specificity denoted by the law of the adequate stimulus but the existence of an underlying histologic differentiation that is being questioned. We are thus left with neither an anatomic nor a physiologic clue to the basis of sense organ specificity.*

What is the biologic significance of the adequate stimulus? The sense organs collectively act not unlike a series of light filters. Collectively they analyze the complex energy pattern of the external world—as color filters do in photography—and translate the complex impression into an intricate pattern of action currents which are recombined in the cerebral cortex—just as in color printing the various colors are recombined—to give a picture of the external world.

"Specific" Nerve Energies (Nonspecific Sense Organ Discharge). Closely related to the principle of the adequate stimulus is another law, enunciated by Johannes Müller,[36] known as the *doctrine of specific nerve energies.* Although a sense organ can be stimulated by other than its adequate stimulus, the subjective response is always the same and hence is not influenced by the *kind* of stimulus. Thus, the excitation of the visual system by pressure on the eye, by electrical stimulation, or by irritation from a pathologic process, gives rise to *visual* sensation only. From present knowledge of the nerve impulse, this seems obvious. However, prior to the time of Johannes Müller it was naïvely believed that "copies" or corpuscles from objects traversed nerve fibers to the brain. His principle implies that the nature of sensation resulting from a given type of stimulus depends upon *what* nerve fibers are stimulated and not upon *how* the nerve fibers are stimulated.

The phrase "specific nerve energy" is unfortunate since it suggests that the action currents in the

---

* Could coding of nerve impulses be established, the concept of end-organ specificity could be abandoned. One type of end-organ could be affected in four different ways and respond in four different temporal patterns to give the four cutaneous sensory modalities.

axons from a given type of receptor are specific and different from those in other types of sensory fibers, a suggestion which has been directly disproved. The locus of the specificity Müller left an open question, although he favored a central one. Dramatic evidence of this is the production of visual sensation by stimulation of the cortical visual area in conscious human patients and of somatic sensation by stimulation of the cortical somatosensory area.

Neurohistology of Cutaneous Sensation.[20, 33, 42-46] It is usually taught that pain is served by fine free nerve endings and that touch, cold and warmth are served by specialized encapsulated endings of various sorts. However, according to recent studies by Weddell and his collaborators (cited above) hairy skin which gives rise to the usual modalities of sensation contains no specialized endings of any kind, only bare nerve endings lying free in the skin or about the roots of the hairs. Similarly, the cornea which contains only free nerve endings is clearly sensitive to both touch and pain.[32] Glabrous skin, such as the lips and finger tips, contains both encapsulated end-organs and "organized" endings made up of whorls of unmyelinated terminal fibers. That these structures endow the endings with differential sensitivity is now in doubt (i) because glabrous and adjacent hairy skin do not differ greatly in sensitivity and (ii) because the specialized endings do not fall into four categories (corresponding to the cutaneous senses) but present many gradations.

A free nerve ending is formed by the repeated dichotomizing of an axis cylinder, which loses its medullary sheath and, ultimately, the neurilemma. The fine naked branches of the axis cylinder ramify among the cells of the deeper layers of the epidermis; other free nerve endings also end subepidermally. Knowledge of these terminations has been greatly enlarged by anatomic studies with the methylene blue staining technique. The free nerve endings are not disposed in the skin like trees in the forest with trunks widely separated and branches touching; instead, the arrangement is plexiform. The ramifications of a single axon interconnect to form a true nerve net. Nets derived from different parent axons overlap and interdigitate. Although the endings are arranged in a plexiform fashion, the resulting network does not form a syncytium; i.e., they are closely interlocked but are not interconnected protoplasmically. Nerve fibers from the superficial plexus branch repeatedly over a wide area and end in "fine, naked, beaded terminals disposed below and among the cells of the deeper layers of the epidermis."[48]

Sensory unit. This was defined by Tower[41] as a single sensory axon and all its peripheral branches. To investigate its size and topographic distribution, Tower chose to study the central zone of the cornea. Action currents were led from a filament of a long ciliary nerve, cut down to a few fibers so that the responses of single fibers could be identified. A single fiber was discharged by stimuli applied over an area forming roughly a quadrant of the cornea together with adjacent portions of the sclera and conjunctiva. In size, the unit areas varied between 50 and 200 mm.[2] or more. A single fiber can be followed anatomically over areas of this size.[49] Within this field there were, of course, silent points, and stimulation of these would sometimes cause a different sensory fiber to discharge. A large number of fibers must interdigitate closely, and each point on the cornea must be innervated by a large number of fibers.

In other areas, Maruhashi *et al.*[34] have recorded from single axons (3 to 11 μ) connected with an ending sensitive to pinprick but not to light touch. The area of the receptive field was 9 mm.[2] on the footpad in the cat and ten times as large on hairy areas. Thus, the overlapping arrangement of sensory units is well documented physiologically and histologically and is of theoretical importance (see Fig. 183).

SENSE ORGAN DISCHARGE

The most direct knowledge of sense organ function is that gained when the spike potentials of the axon leading from the sense organ are recorded. This was first done adequately by Adrian and Zotterman.[1] This procedure is analytical in two ways: (i) the response of sense organs is studied without recourse to subjective experience and without the complications introduced as impulses traverse the spinal nerves, spinal cord and brain tracts; (ii) *single* sensory nerve fibers have been recorded, so that much of the complexity encountered when many units are active is eliminated.

As traction was applied to the Achilles tendon, electrodes attached to the sciatic nerve of a frog recorded a succession of irregularly shaped and spaced potentials. Too many fibers were simultaneously active. Adrian and Zotterman turned to a tiny skin muscle from the frog's thorax (sternocutaneous muscle) whose nerve contains from 15 to 25 fibers, only a few of which are sensory. Traction on this muscle resulted in a simpler but still too complex record. As strips of muscle were cut off, eliminating the muscle spindles one by one, the record became progressively less complex and finally was reduced to a regularly repeated sequence of spike potentials of uniform amplitude and duration. A single unit preparation had been achieved. In the very first experiments the main facts of sense organ discharge were broadly outlined.

The contribution of the sense organ to the total sensory process has naturally been learned largely from electrical studies and can now be summarized systematically. These are the characteristics imposed by the sense organ upon sensation; other characteristics are contributed by the central pathways.

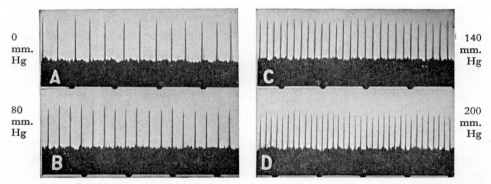

FIG. 168.   Oscillographic records showing relation of frequency of discharge to intensity of stimulation. Single end-organ in carotid sinus was stimulated by four different pressures within sinus. Time is 0.2 second intervals. (After Bronk and Stella, *Amer. J. Physiol.*, 1935, *110*:708–714.)

Neural Basis of Differential Sensitivity and Nonspecific Discharge.   The recording of sensory impulses often affords final proof of what constitutes the adequate stimulus for individual receptors. Since impulses arising from different types of sense organs are approximately identical, the different sensations they produce must be a property of their central destinations (doctrine of specific nerve energies). The shapes of the action potentials are essentially the same. There are differences in the amplitude and rate of conduction in sensory nerve fibers; but these correlate with differences in fiber size and myelinization, and there is no reason to believe that they determine the kind of sensation resulting. Temporal patterning is often postulated to be the neural substrate of quality, but there is no evidence for this as yet. In fact, it appears more likely (see below) that temporal patterning is the substrate of intensity. Since taste and vision receptors with unlike adequate stimuli connect with the same fiber running to the central nervous system, the mechanism underlying the doctrine of specific nerve energies is still controversial.

Intensity.[1, 4, 7]   Adrian's initial experiments on the single unit showed that the sensory end-organ and axon obey the all-or-nothing law. Stronger stimulation does not result in larger action potentials. It has already been brought out how the stretch receptor "signals" to the brain the elementary aspect of the stimulus, its intensity. All sense organs so far examined signal intensity of stimulus by changes in the rate of discharge. Weak stimulation causes a discharge at a slow rate, and a stronger stimulation causes a discharge at a more rapid rate. This is shown clearly in Figure 168.

The second way in which intensity of the stimulus affects the discharge is in the number of sense organs active. A light weight attached to the tendon in a sternocutaneous preparation containing only a few units may cause only one unit to discharge. With increasing tension on the muscle, a second unit commences to discharge. This added discharge usually can be identified by a slightly different amplitude of the potential because the fiber is closer to or farther from the recording electrodes. Also the two discharges work in and out of phase, owing to slightly different rates. Further tension brings in additional receptors, each at a different frequency, until the record becomes totally irregular. This process is picturesquely known as *recruitment of end-organs*. The neural correlates of stimulus intensity are therefore two: the number of end-organs discharging, and the frequency of discharge in each. By spatial and temporal summation, the rapid multifiber discharge to intense stimulation presumably becomes translated into greater activation of spinal tract fibers and ultimately of cells in the cerebral cortex. A third factor determines the responsiveness of the muscle spindle to the stimulus, the so-called "small fiber" efferent discharge (see below).

The responses of several sense organs are controlled by discharges from the central nervous system.

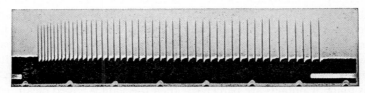

FIG. 169.   Record showing adaptation of sense organ (photoreceptor). Stimulus was maintained at constant strength throughout, but interval between discharges steadily diminished. Signal indicates duration of stimulus application and time is in 0.2 second intervals. (Record of Hartline cited from Bronk, *Res. Publ. Ass. nerv. ment. Dis.*, 1934, *15*:60–82.)

Adaptation.[1, 7, 17]   The number of impulses which a sense organ discharges per second depends not only upon the energy of the stimulus but also on the length of time the stimulus has been acting and the rapidity with which it is applied. To a maintained stretch of constant amount, the rate of discharge from muscle receptors is initially high and then grows progressively slower until a plateau rate of discharge is struck and maintained many minutes or hours. The end-organ has partially *adapted*. The discharge frequency declines and so does the intensity of conscious sensation. An oscillographic record showing adaptation is given in Figure 169. Probably similar in cause is the fact that a rapidly applied stretch is more effective (produces a higher rate of discharge) than a slowly applied stretch of the same degree. The end-organ adapts to the slowly applied stretch during its application.

Customarily, any decrement in response coming as a result of activity is designated "fatigue." In the instance of a slowly increasing stimulus, fatigue is distinguishable from adaptation, because such a stimulus produces fewer discharges and therefore less opportunity for fatigue than the more rapidly applied stimulus; the lesser response to slow stretch is therefore not due to activity *per se* (fatigue). In fact, the touch receptor can adapt to a slowly applied contact without emitting a single discharge. The rate of stimulus growth which is just sufficient to excite is termed the critical slope. Mechanical stimuli can be delivered in the desired wave form and with something of the accuracy of an electric current. Measured in this fashion, the adaptation of touch receptors in the frog's skin and the pacinian corpuscle is quantitatively so similar to the accommodation

(Chap. 2) shown by their respective axons that Gray and Matthews[19] believe adaptation of the sense organ is simple accommodation of the axon, a rapidly adapting sense organ being supplied by a rapidly accommodating axon. Sense organ adaptation is thus more allied to accommodation than it is to fatigue.

That the elaborately encapsulated pacinian corpuscle behaves like a simple axon points away from any specific, preneural end-organ process in the explanation of the behavior of sense organs. The function of the capsule appears to be simply that of transmitting mechanical forces to the nerve ending. Part of the apparent adaptation of cutaneous pressure organs seems to result from the mechanical flow of the skin. Nafe and Wagoner[37] noticed that a weight placed on the skin is felt only as long as it continues to "sink in" at a supraliminal rate, which it does for a considerable time. Stimulus failure, a pre–sense-organ phenomenon, is a factor in adaptation of pressure and possibly other sense organs.

Rate of adaptation in different sense organs.   Adaptation is not equally rapid in all sense organs. Certain types of end-organs adapt very little after the initial few seconds of response and are able to maintain discharge for minutes or hours. In the class of slowly adapting end-organs come the muscle spindle, the tension receptors at the root of the lung, the pressure receptors of the carotid sinus, cold receptors and the pain receptors of the cornea. Touch receptors, especially those associated with hairs, give rise to a burst of impulses largely ended within half a second. Even the highly encapsulated pacinian corpuscle adapts very rapidly.[18] Rapid adaptation would obviously unfit an end-organ for serving long sustained postural reflexes or for recording the pressure of blood within the carotid sinus. Similarly, if pain end-organs were to cease generating pain impulses before removal of the noxious stimulating agent, pain would lose much of its protective function. On the other hand, rapid adaptation may be an advantage to an exploratory sense such as touch. Contacts are perceived; then the slate is wiped clean by adaptation and is ready to receive a new impression.

Weber-Fechner Law.   Another problem to be decided by electrical methods is whether the Weber-Fechner law, where it applies, is a characteristic of the sense organ or of the central phases of the total sensory process. Weber made the important discovery that the smallest discriminable difference between two weights (just noticeable difference, j.n.d.) is a constant fraction of the weights themselves, the so-called "Weber fraction." For weights this fraction is approximately 1/30, meaning that 31 grams is discriminated from 30, 62 grams from 60, and so on. This is usually stated as $\Delta I / I = C$, in which delta I means a just discriminable increment of intensity.

Fechner's name is linked to Weber's because he sought by mathematical manipulation to derive the relationship between stimulus and sensation. By assuming that discriminable increments are equal units of sensation, he derived the following formula:

$$\text{Sensation} = K \log I + C$$

Weber's law had nothing like the generality which has been ascribed to it; for most sensory modalities it applies only over a very limited range of intensities and often then only because small continuous changes of j.n.d. are ignored. Fechner's equation has been endlessly criticized; but, whatever its original derivation, it appears to express a fundamental feature of sense organ behavior. Over a certain range of intensities, the frequency of discharge is a linear function of the logarithm of the stimulus. This has been shown for the muscle spindle by Matthew[35] and for *Limulus* eye by Hartline and Graham.[25]

Sense Organ Mechanisms.[17]   The fact that a sense organ discharges repetitively to a continuous stimulus at a rate proportional to the logarithm of the stimulus intensity and exhibits adaptation should have a single explanation. Adrian[1] suggested an ingenious

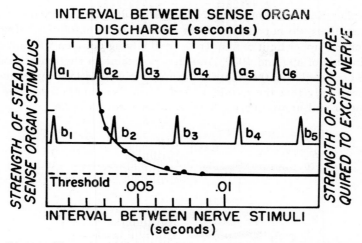

FIG. 170. Diagram illustrating refractory period hypothesis of sense organ rhythmicity. Curve is conventional recovery curve (absolutely and relatively refractory periods) for frog nerve and represents actual experimental data. Schematized action potential records (a, b) are hypothetical. They show how a strong, continuous sensory stimulus might excite earlier in the refractory period and fire the sensory axon at a higher rate. (Redrawn from Adrian, *The basis of sensation*, London, Christophers, 1928.)

one based on the relatively refractory period. Assume that the sensory axons have a refractory period like that of frog nerve. Assume also that a stimulus such as pressure produces a steadily maintained change to which the neural element can respond only periodically because of its refractory period. The mechanism can be envisaged with the aid of Figure 170. A strong steady stimulus (*upper*) will fire the fiber at a_1 and, after the ensuing refractory period, re-excite it (a_2). At the end of a second and subsequent absolutely refractory period, the fiber will fire at a_3, etc. The weaker steady stimulus (*lower*) must wait well into the refractory period—until excitability has fallen sufficiently for excitation to occur (b_2)—and will fire the unit only at the lower frequency.

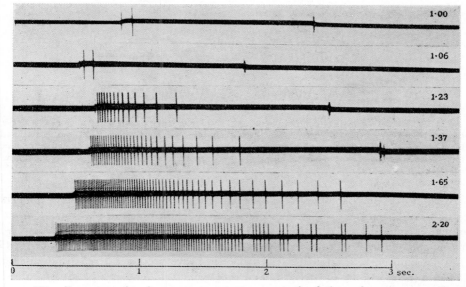

FIG. 171. Responses of crab nerve to constant current stimulations of varying strengths above threshold showing a similarity to sense organ behavior. Number at right gives current strength in relation to threshold. Artifacts mark make and break of current. (From Hodgkin, *J. Physiol.*, 1948, *107*:165–181.)

This explanation encounters one grave difficulty. Sense organs, except under abnormal conditions, do not fire nearly as rapidly as the absolutely refractory period would predict, the upper limit of frequency usually lying between 100 and 200 impulses per second instead of 800 and 1000. And they do maintain rhythm at rates far slower than the rate predicted from the length of the absolutely and relatively refractory periods. This may mean only that the terminal fibrils of the sense organ, because they are of smaller diameter and unmyelinated, have a slower recovery cycle.

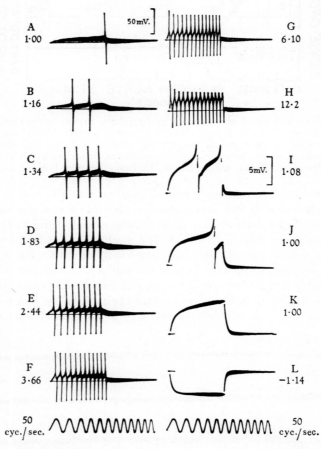

FIG. 172. Records showing repetitive responses, similar to sense organ behavior, of crab nerve to constant currents of varying intensity. Note that each response consists of a local potential and a conducted spike. Firing seems to occur when local potential reaches a given height. Note in first record the long period required for current of threshold strength to induce discharge. (From Hodgkin, *J. Physiol.*, 1948, *107*:165–181.)

Another explanation comes from so-called "sense organ models" such as the nerves of certain crustaceans or frog nerve from which calcium is removed. Since neurons of mammalian sense organs contain a slender, unmyelinated segment, the analogy with thinly myelinated invertebrate nerve may be close. As Hodgkin[27] has shown (Figs. 171, 172), a constant current applied to a crustacean nerve produces a repetitive discharge with a rate (proportional to strength of current) which undergoes a progressive slowing comparable to adaptation. Since a crustacean axon with a relatively refractory period of less than 10 milliseconds may fire rhythmically at 200 millisecond intervals, the frequency of discharge must be regulated by a process slower than the refractory period.

The possibility that local electrotonus has the requisite time characteristics was therefore examined. With stimulating currents near threshold, as much as 98 milliseconds elapsed between the onset of the current and the spike action potential—"response time." This time correlated well with the interspike interval. In fact, as shown in Figure 173, throughout a considerable range of constant current strengths, the response time and the interval separating the first two spikes correlated closely, suggesting that time to build up a local electrotonus sufficient to discharge the axon determines the frequency for weak stimuli. However, refractory period rather than response time appeared to limit the upper frequency of discharge, since the response time was shortened to nearly zero but the repetition interval was never less than 6.5 milliseconds. These experiments, although

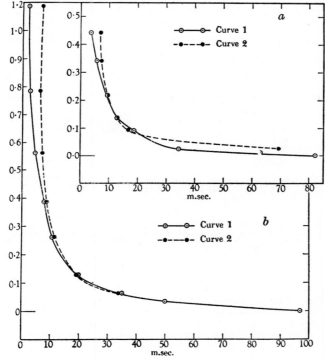

FIG. 173. Experiments on crab nerve as a sense organ model showing correlation between response time (*circles*) and interval between discharges (*abscissa*) for weak stimuli (*ordinate*) and lack of such correlation for strong stimuli—rapid discharge. Two experiments are shown. Curve 1, interval between make of current and appearance of first impulse. Curve 2, interval between first and second impulse. (From Hodgkin, *J. Physiol.*, 1948, *107*:165–181.)

only analogous to sense organ behavior, do suggest that the factors controlling the minimum and maximum rates of firing are different.

Receptor potential.[17] Is there any local depolarization preliminary to spike discharge in the nerve terminals comparable to that seen in crustacean and other nerve fibers? By a suitable dose of local anesthetic, Katz[29, 30] abolished the spike in the sensory axon and observed that stretch produced a depolarization of the nerve endings which spread electrotonically along the axon. The magnitude of the depolarization varied directly with the amplitude and the rate of application of the mechanical stimulus. Thus, there was a large potential when stretch was applied and a smaller potential while stretch was simply maintained. In the unanesthetized muscle spindle, the frequency of spike discharge was correlated qualitatively with the amplitude of the depolarization potential. Receptor potentials have been observed in a variety of receptors and the characteristics of the potential correlated with the characteristics of the sense organ discharge.[17] It is therefore possible to believe that a local depolarization or receptor potential is an intermediate step between stimulus and nerve impulse.

SOMATIC SENSES[16]

Temperature Senses.[26, 51]   Rather than a single temperature sense there are two: one for cold and one for warmth. Four pieces of evidence support this statement: (i) The skin contains receptors which fire more rapidly as the temperature increases and others which fire more rapidly as the temperature decreases. (ii) There is a clear subjective difference between warmth and cold. (iii) Temperature sensibility is distributed in a punctate fashion. (iv) Some areas are sensitive to cold but not to warmth. When the skin is explored millimeter by millimeter, spots are found which respond only with a sensation of cold.[11] Other spots, fewer in number, respond only to warmth, and the intervening areas are sensitive to neither. On the forearm, cold spots average about 13 to 15 per square centimeter and warm spots only one or two per square centimeter. It was once believed that beneath each spot lay a distinctive type of end-organ specifically sen-

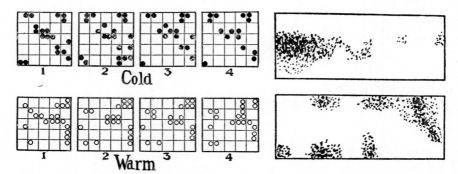

FIG. 174.   Maps of thermal sensitivity of skin. *Left:* Results of four successive mappings (left to right) of same area on upper arm. Each small square equals 4 mm.². Observe high degree of similarity in independent mappings and that sensitive spots occur in groups. (From Dallenbach, *Amer. J. Psychol.*, 1927, *39:*402–427.) *Right:* Maps of distribution of sensibility to cold in 12 mappings of an area on volar surface of forearm. Each rectangle corresponds to area on skin 4 by 10 mm., and each represents a different subject. Subjects were permitted to report neutral and three degrees of coldness. Score for each point is crudely given by depth of shading. (From Jenkins, *J. exp. Psychol.*, 1939, *25:*373–388.)

sitive to one or the other thermal stimulus. However, it has not been possible to prove this contention by mapping spots and identifying histologically an underlying sense organ (see Fig. 174, *left*). Jenkins[28] found an areal distribution of sensitivity (Fig. 174, *right*) indicating that a branching type of fiber is responsible for cold reception. It has since been proved that only branching fibers are found in most (hairy) skin areas.

It must be remembered that it is the anatomic and not the functional specificity that has been questioned. The minimum effective heat energy required to elicit the sensation of warmth, according to Hardy and Oppel,[22] is 0.00015 gm. cal. per cm.² per second acting for three seconds; that for pain is 0.218 gm. cal. Thus, the threshold is one-thousandth as great for warmth as for pain.

Bazett[2] has estimated the depth of the thermal receptors by measuring with thermocouples the rate at which heat penetrates double folds of skin obtained by the Spartan procedure of stretching the prepuce out into a flat sheet by means of fish hooks. Rate of penetration was correlated with latency of sensation, and the results suggest that the warmth endings lie deeper than the cold ones. By the more accurate method of electrical recording from the axons of cold receptors, Hensel *et al.*[26] proved by similar reasoning that these receptors lie at a depth of 180 μ, i.e., subepithelially at the base of the papillae.

The adequate stimulus for both warmth and cold is heat. Cold is not a positive quantity, and temperature does not have the dimension of energy. The threshold stimulus for cold receptors is a fall in temperature at the rate of 0.004° C. per second and, for warmth receptors, a rise of 0.001° C. per second, both continuing for three seconds.[22] The thermal sense organs record not the temperature of objects, but the temperature of the skin at the depth at which the receptors are situated. Hence they are stimulated by internal heat as well as by the heat of the environment. The patient with Raynaud's disease experiencing a vasospasm in the fingers complains bitterly of the cold even in a warm room. A metal object and a wooden object of the same temperature do not seem equally cold to the touch because the metal object conducts heat from the skin more readily. A most important factor is the temperature of the skin. Objects having a temperature close to the physiologic zero, i.e., the temperature of the skin, elicit neither warmth nor cold sensations. On the other hand, even warm air falling on the warmer skin during fever arouses distressing sensations of cold. Since thermal sense organs play a role in the regulation of body temperature, it is important to know the exact nature of the temperature stimulus.

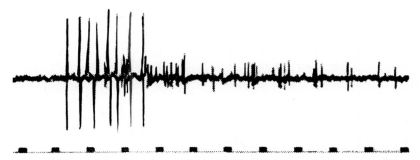

FIG. 175.   Oscillographic record from a "cut-down" lingual nerve showing a volley of large fiber potentials (touch) and of small fiber potentials (cold). Stimulus was a current of air strong enough to deform surface of tongue visibly. (From Zotterman, *Skand. Arch. Physiol.*, 1936, 75:105–120.)

The cold receptor stimulus can be studied by recording from cutaneous nerves because impulses in axons of cold receptors have a small amplitude and travel and adapt slowly (see Ref. 49 and Fig. 175). Hensel and Zotterman[26] recorded such impulses from the lingual nerve along with the surface and intracutaneous temperature of the tongue while it was being cooled with cold water. A drop in water temperature from 37° to 13° C. caused a maximum discharge within one to two seconds which fell exponentially to a plateau rate of 25 impulses per second in about 70 seconds, at which time the temperature at the level of the receptor was no longer changing. Such steady discharges were recorded after 70 minutes of cooling. Thus, while temperature change is a powerful stimulus to the rapidly adapting cold receptor, it is not a necessary condition for stimulation, since discharge to steadily maintained cooling occurred. The actual stimulus therefore is either a temperature gradient (energy flow) from within out or the absolute temperature. The latter would imply that excitation depends on some internal physiologic process, such as a chemical reaction, inversely dependent on temperature. The direction of temperature gradient and heat flow is of no importance. From experiments comparing responses from one surface of the tongue when comparable gradients from within out were maintained during cooling of first the upper and then the lower surface, Hensel and Zotterman[26] concluded that temperature *per se* rather than a temperature gradient is the actual stimulus to the cold receptor. By combining frequency of firing and recruitment, as few as ten cold fibers can show a linear relation of impulses per second to temperature between 38° and 27° C.[26]

The warmth receptor also seems to respond to a steady thermal flow.[12] Although it shows the phenomenon of adaptation to a high degree, it maintains a very slow (up to five impulses per second) and somewhat arrhythmic discharge to sustained temperatures. As shown in Figure 176 the maximum rate of discharge occurs at 38 to 43° C. Below 38° C., the discharge rate falls gradually, reaching zero at 20° C. At temperatures above 43° C., the rate declines rather steeply, all discharges disappearing at 47° C.

Pain.[41]   The sensory mechanism for pain is in many ways unique. The sensory end-organs for pain are spread through virtually all of the tissues of the body, so that three kinds of pain are recognized and designated: (i) superficial or cutaneous pain;

(ii) deep pain from muscles, tendons, joints, and fascia; and (iii) visceral pain. The first two together form somatic pain. The pain endings are unique also in exhibiting only to a limited degree the phenomenon of the adequate stimulus. Several kinds of energy are adequate to elicit pain, electrical, mechanical, extremes of heat and cold, and a wide variety of chemical stimuli. The pain ending therefore is not specialized to react to a single form of energy, but reacts to extreme degrees of several kinds of stimulation. Sherrington pointed out that the property common to all stimuli adequate to excite pain endings is the threat of damage to the tissues. Hardy et al.[21] have proved this quantitatively for heat energy. Thus, increasing degrees of heat first stimulate warmth endings and then, at 44.9° C., commence to stimulate pain endings. At about 44 to 45° C., irreversible damage to the skin, demonstrable histologically, occurs, and accompanying release of chemical substances such as histamine is expected. One explanation of the wide stimulus spectrum of the pain end-organ is that various noxious stimuli release a chemical substance in the skin and that this substance stimulates the end-organs. A chemical stage

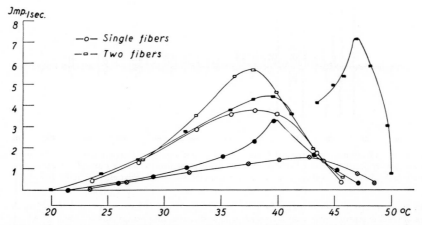

FIG. 176.   Graphs showing relation between frequency of discharge and temperature for different single and dual warm fiber preparations. Steady discharge after adaptation has occurred is graphed. An occasional fiber (one in 13) had a maximum above 45° C. and was undoubtedly a pain fiber. (From Dodt and Zotterman, *Acta physiol. scand.*, 1952, *26*:345–357.)

in excitation might explain certain pathologic pain responses—itch, hyperalgesia, etc.—which persist long after the noxious agent is removed. The evidence for this will be presented in the next chapter under the heading *Hyperalgesia*.

In Sherrington's classification of the senses, pain was termed *nociceptive*, meaning sensitive to noxious agents. The function of the pain sense is protective, whereas the other modalities of sensation are primarily informative or gnostic. Other differences are that pain is unpleasant or, in other words, possesses a considerable *affect;* that pain leads to more precipitate action; and, finally, that certain types of pain tend to radiate and to be poorly localized.

Because pain is so unlike other forms of sensation, it was long considered not a separate form of sensation but rather a response elicited by intense stimulation of other kinds of sensory end-organs. This overstimulation or intensive theory is refuted by considerable evidence, including the fact that stimulation of certain areas causes only pain. That overstimulation of touch and pressure organs does not cause pain was proved by Cattell and Hoagland.[9] Intense stimulation of an end-organ increases the frequency of its discharge. Stimulating the skin of a frog with puffs of air at a high frequency produced high rates of discharge (300/sec.). When such stimuli were applied to an unanesthetized frog, it exhibited no sign of pain.

Measurement of pain sensibility.   Pain is elicited for purposes of clinical examination by pricking the skin with a pin or needle. The patient reports whether the pricks "feel" different on the two sides of the body; or he is asked to distinguish between the point and the head of a pin. Thresholds can be determined quantitatively with a thistle glued to a von Frey hair (see below).

In such tests touch and pressure receptors are stimulated along with the pain receptors, and the results are not sufficiently quantitative. Hardy et al.[23] have introduced an apparatus employing radiant energy (Fig. 177). By repeated tests with increasing intensities of radiant heat, a threshold for pain is obtained. If precautions are taken to ensure that skin temperature is stabilized, or its variations corrected for, thresholds of a single individual are remarkably invariable. As with cold sensation, pain from radiant heat seems to depend on actual skin temperature and not on the rate of change. In contrast with other sensory channels, the threshold is not dependent on size of area stimulated. Spatial summation between fibers supplying a given area, or between the branches of a single fiber, apparently does not occur. Hardy et al.,[24] using their radiant heat apparatus, found that they could discriminate only 21 steps (j.n.d.) between thresh-

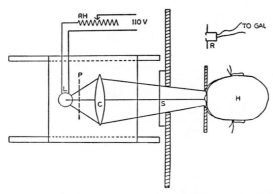

FIG. 177. Radiant energy apparatus for measuring warmth and pain sensibility. Light from 1000 watt lamp, *L*, is focused by condensing lens, *C*, through fixed aperture of 3.5 mm.[2] on forehead of subject which is blacked by India ink. Intensity of radiation is controlled by means of rheostat, *RH*, and duration by shutter, *P*, which automatically limits exposure to 3 seconds. Shutter, *S*, is hand-operated. (From Hardy *et al., J. clin. Invest.*, 1940, 19:649–657.)

old and maximum, and the range of energy was little more than 2:1. The grossness of the j.n.d. is experimental justification for speaking of pain as a nondiscriminative modality of sensation.

Visceral pain, deep pain and special forms of pain are discussed in Chapter 15.

Touch-Pressure. Touch is one of the four fundamental cutaneous sense modalities. Whether touch forms a single sense modality, like warmth or cold, or whether there are subqualities, served by distinct neural mechanisms, is uncertain. That there are several types of mechanoreceptors is certain.

The existence of two end-organs of quite different properties is conclusively proved by Adrian and Zotterman's records of sensory discharges.[1] Continuous touch or light pressure applied to the cushion of a cat's toe produces a burst of impulses in the medial plantar nerve which lasts for only 0.2 second. Pressing a von Frey hair onto human skin produces only a brief sensation described as a "minute pat" or tap. Therefore a submodality of light touch or light pressure, with a quick-adapting end-organ, may be considered established. Maruhashi et al.[34] have identified such a touch fiber in the cat's skin. It is large in diameter, 8 to 14 μ, adapts completely in 30 to 60 milliseconds, and serves one or two spotlike areas.

A second receptor was isolated by Adrian and Zotterman from the toe pad of the cat. This receptor continued to respond after the first had adapted. Its discharge decreased rapidly to a plateau rate which was maintained for seconds; the frequency correlated with the intensity of pressure. Such surface pressure is to be distinguished from "deep pressure" arising from massive pressure on muscles and tendons. The existence of a slowly adapting receptor with a punctiform distribution has been confirmed by the single unit technique.

When an object is brought into contract with the skin, giving rise to a feeling of touch or pressure, the actual stimulus is not pressure *per se*, but a pressure gradient causing deformation of the end-organ. The classic illustration of this (Meissner) is gained by thrusting the finger into a vessel of mercury. The sense of pressure does not come all over the submerged portions of the finger but only at the interface between air and mercury.

The densely punctiform distribution of touch sensibility was demonstrated by von Frey, who explored the skin with hairs mounted on a wooden handle. Such instruments are still used in clinical and experimental research. Hairs of different lengths and diameters, calibrated for bending strength with a balance, are used. The hair, by bending, determines the pressure exerted regardless of the rate and force with which the hair is applied. Clinically, light contact is conveniently assayed by Head's "cotton wool"

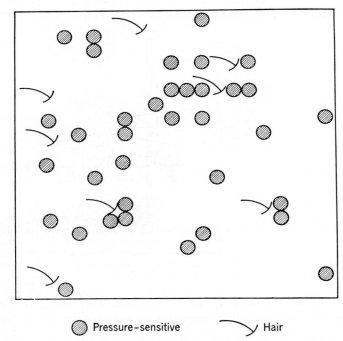

FIG. 178.   Diagram showing degree to which pressure-sensitive spots are located in relation to hairs (volar surface of forearm). (From Geldard, *The human senses*, New York, Wiley, 1953.)

test, in which the skin is lightly stroked with a few loose strands from a wad of absorbent cotton (not with the wad itself). A heavier stimulus is given by contact with a small camel's-hair brush or with von Frey hairs.

Several types of endings are believed to give rise to touch sensations. Over hairy regions, touch-sensitive "spots" are largely found in juxtaposition to the hairs, especially on the "windward" side of the sloping hair (Fig. 178). Masses of bare nerve endings surround the roots of hairs. By leverage, the force of a light contact with hair is greatly magnified. Histologically[43] and physiologically it is known that a single fiber serves hairs over a very wide area—as great as 5 cm.². Other sensitive spots represent aggregations of free nerve endings. Over hairless areas, various corpuscles located in the corium are held to be "touch corpuscles" (Fig. 179). A third type of end-organ, the giant pacinian corpuscle, is found in the subcutaneous tissues and in still deeper structures. A deformation of 0.5 μ, if applied for 100 milliseconds, will excite this ending.[18]

It was once thought that a touch spot signifies the existence beneath it of a sense organ from which a single axon leads to the central nervous system. However, the touch spot appears to be a point of heightened sensibility, resulting not from a single end-organ and a single fiber but from a cluster of end-organs innervated by several fibers, undoubtedly representing several sensory units (Fig. 179). As a consequence, each touch spot can grade activity by recruitment of sense organs as well as by increased frequency of discharge.

Deep Sensibility. Although it is a matter of common experience that a person with his eyes closed knows the direction of a movement, active or passive, and is aware of the position of his arms and legs, it was not until 1826 that Charles Bell[3] explicitly described the "sixth" sense—muscle sense. "For example," he said, "between the brain and the muscles, there is a circle of nerves; one nerve conveys the influence from the

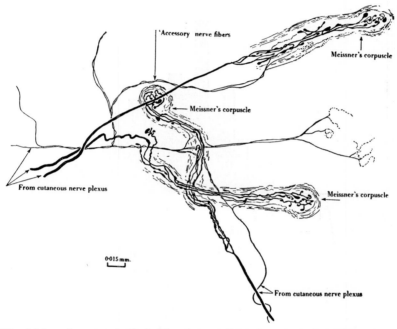

FIG. 179.   Meissner's corpuscles (touch) and unmyelinated accessory fibers. Note that three end-organs, each borne upon separate nerve fibers, were found within an area approximately 0.15 mm. wide. (From Weddell, *J. Anat. (Lond.)*, 1941, *75:*441–446.)

brain to the muscle; the other gives the sense of the condition of the muscle to the brain." Sherrington, very much later (1894), showed that muscular branches of nerves contain a high percentage (40 per cent) of afferent fibers. The principal sensory end-organ of muscles was not fully described until 1892 (by Ruffini and by Sherrington). The forms of deep sensibility exclusive of pain and deep pressure are known by several synonyms, all of which are in common use: muscle sense or, more completely, muscle, tendon and joint sensibility; kinesthesia (Bastian); proprioception (Sherrington); and, operationally, position sense (Head) and the appreciation of passive movement.

It has already been pointed out that four types of sense organs are found in muscles, tendons and joints: (i) the muscle spindle; (ii) the Golgi tendon organ; (iii) the joint organs, the pacinian corpuscle, etc.; and (iv) free nerve endings. It will be remembered that the muscle spindle contains two types of endings and that its discharge rate is subject to reflex and higher control via gamma efferents. The analysis previously presented suggests that muscle, tendon and joint receptors as a group record three aspects of the state of the muscle: active contraction, passive stretch (length of fiber), and tension, whether produced by passive stretch or active contraction. Finally, it should be mentioned that the deep receptors, e.g., the pacinian organs, may be more important than the muscle receptors in the detection of passive movement of a limb (Goldscheider) or its position in space.

Browne *et al.*[8] found that application of procaine to the joint capsule ends the appreciation of passive movement of the metatarsal-phalangeal joint and appreciation of the position of the great toe in space. Significant clinically is the fact that some normal subjects appreciated only very large displacements (10 to 30 degrees). Impairment of the appreciation of passive movement, whether occurring naturally or induced by application of procaine to the capsule, was not associated with any defect in appreciation of

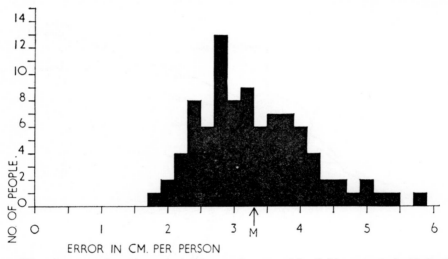

FIG. 180.   Accuracy of position sense in 91 normal young adults. Subjects touched with forefinger a reference point on a target at arm's length. After closing eyes and returning arm to side, subjects attempted to touch the point again. Test was repeated until 48 different points were tried. *Abscissa*, mean error on 48 points. (From Cohen, *J. Neurophysiol.*, 1958, *21*:550–562.)

active movement. The former function is capsular; the latter is muscular or tendinous. The joint capsule contains end-organs of the nonadapting type which vary the discharge rate according to joint position.[6, 14]

Clinical examination of deep sensibility.   Deep pressure and deep pain are elicited by firm, massive pressure over muscles or tendons. Muscles and tendons possess an exquisite pain sensibility, and this is discussed in a subsequent chapter.

The "appreciation of passive movement" of a single joint is commonly tested in the neurologic examination. If a finger or toe is grasped by the side (to minimize cues from pressure) and moved up or down, a patient with normal sensibility is able to state the direction of quite small angular displacements. A roughly quantitative idea of the threshold can thus be obtained.

The "sense of position" is tested in a variety of ways. A limb is placed in an unusual position and the subject, with eyes closed, is asked to duplicate the posture with his other limb. Another maneuver— the finger-to-finger test—consists of passively moving the arm to be tested and bringing it to rest with finger extended. The patient is then asked to touch the extended forefinger with the forefinger of the other hand. By interposing a piece of cardboard between the two fingers and marking their positions, a roughly quantitative estimate of the error can be obtained. Recently, another method for quantitation of position sense was described by Cohen[10] (Fig. 180). In animals something akin to the sense of position is tested by determining whether a false or abnormal position—not extreme enough to be painful—is corrected, a test which is valid only when motor ability is normal. A similar procedure applicable to animals is the "proprioceptive placing" reaction (Chap. 8).

The appreciation of muscle tension is studied by determining the ability to detect difference in weight of objects by lifting them. Two weights are usually presented, and the subject is asked to state which is the heavier. This is a classic laboratory procedure which has proved useful in studying neurologic patients and which has been adapted to monkeys and chimpanzees in the study of cortical localization of sensory functions.

Vibratory Sensibility.[15] The appreciation of vibration, or *pallesthesia*, is tested crudely by placing the base of a vibrating tuning fork upon the skin. A thrill or feeling of vibration is normally experienced, but only a sense of continuous contact is felt after certain neurologic lesions. Electrically driven vibratory devices yield thresholds in terms of the just perceptible amplitude of vibration.[31] Vibratory sensibility is often erroneously considered a separate sense modality rather than a special way of exciting the sense organs for pressure and possibly proprioception. Because application of the fork over bone intensifies the stimulus in a purely mechanical fashion, vibratory sensation has been mistakenly called "osseous sensation." The sense organs are not in the periosteum. Vibratory sensibility has a punctate distribution with vibration-sensitive spots corresponding to pressure-sensitive spots.[15] That vibratory sensibility of the skin is served by pressure sense organs is also suggested by Weitz' experiments,[47] but deep sense organs may also be involved.

Vibratory sensibility is certainly not a separate sense and it is certainly not bone sensibility, nor does it seem to be associated exclusively with either deep or superficial pressure fibers. Vibratory sensibility is a perception of a *temporal* pattern of pressures, somewhat like the flicker phenomenon in vision (Chap. 19). This interpretation is supported by the behavior of vibratory sensibility in various clinical neurologic conditions.[13]

The underlying impulses must be conducted in the posterior columns since defective vibratory appreciation is typical of spinal cord lesions. Cordotomy leaves it unimpaired. If spinal cord damage is sufficient to affect position sense, vibratory appreciation is always affected. In contrast, lesions of the cerebral cortex rarely affect vibratory sensibility unless they penetrate deeply; in such cases damage to the thalamus may be responsible (Fig. 181). Though not subject to any simple explanation, this difference in vulnerability of vibratory sensitivity at the spinal and cerebral levels makes vibratory sensibility helpful in clinical diagnosis. Laidlaw and Hamilton[31] have published norms for various regions of the body.

Localization or Topognosis.[4] Every somatic sensation has in addition to its quality and its intensity a localization upon the body surface. The accuracy of localization has been extensively investigated in both normal individuals and neurologic patients. Weber (1852) touched the skin with a pointer dipped in powdered charcoal to mark the point stimulated; the subject, with his eyes closed throughout, tried to touch the same spot with another pointer. The measured discrepancy between the two marks gave the error of localization, which was found to vary greatly in different regions of the body surface.

Usually only localization of light pressure is tested, and it is sometimes forgotten that all sensations can be localized though with quite different accuracy. (The explanation for this will be given in the next chapter.) Localization may be severely impaired by damage to central pathways when mere awareness of the stimulation is preserved. Testing topognosis is, therefore, part of the neurologic examination (Fig. 181).

Projection of Sensation. This is a phenomenon related to localization.* The ultimate event in the sensory process occurs in the brain, but in no case are we aware of this. On the contrary, our sensations are projected either to the external world or to some peripheral organ in the body, i.e., to the place where experience has taught us that the acting stimulus arises. Sound seems to come from the bell, light from the lamp, etc. Pain, muscle sense, labyrinthine sensations, hunger, thirst, sexual sense, etc., are pro-

* The distinction between projection and localization is that the former has more to do with the envelope or layer, external or internal, from which a sensation appears to come. Localization has more to do with where on these envelopes the sensation is localized. (See Chap. 14).

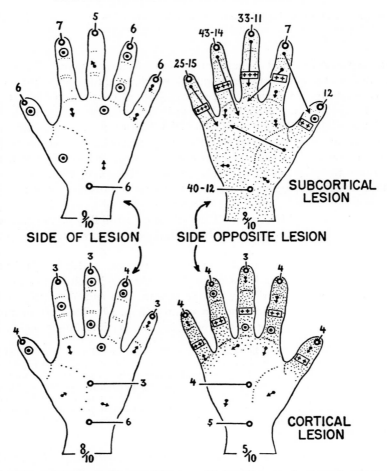

FIG. 181.   Example of Fox's chart used for recording sensory examination of neurologic patients with subcortical (*upper*) and cortical lesions (*lower*). Degree of loss of position sense in phalangeal joint is indicated by $+$, $++$ and $+++$; accurate localization of point touched is designated by circle and dot; displacement of an erroneous localization is indicated by arrow. Areas of hypesthesia are indicated by stipple. Fraction at wrist is a measure of stereognosis and shows number of successfully identified objects in series of ten presenting increasing difficulty. Numbers connected by line with heavy circle give threshold of vibration in arbitrary unit at point indicated; a large number signifies large amplitude of vibration. (After Fox and Klemperer, *Arch. Neurol. Psychiat.* (*Chicago*), 1942, *48*:622–645.)

jected to the interior of the body. The temperature senses may be projected either to the exterior or to the interior, according to circumstances.

An aspect of sensation important to clinical neurology and which deserves to be called the *law of projection* is that stimulation of sensory pathways at any point central to the sense organ gives rise to a sensation which is projected to the periphery and not to the point of stimulation.

Numerous examples of this law can be cited. An amputee may experience projected sensations so elaborate that they amount to a feeling that the limb is still present and executing movements, often painful—the phenomenon of "phantom limb." Irritation of a dorsal spinal root by a ruptured intervertebral disc of the fifth lumbar segment often gives rise to a sensation of pain over the buttock and down the back of the thigh, which is the region innervated by the affected root. Stimulation of the cerebral cortex in conscious human patients at the time of intracranial operation gives rise to sensations which appear to come not from the head but from the skin of some part of the body. In all these cases the cerebral cortex interprets the nerve impulses as though they had come from the sense organ. For further implications of the phenomenon of projection, see the section on referred pain (Chap. 15).

Two Point Sensibility. If the blunt points of a compass are applied simultaneously to the skin with sufficient distance between them, they are perceived as two separate points of contact. If the points are brought progressively closer together in successive applications, they eventually give rise to a sensation of a single point applied to the skin. The smallest distance between points at which they are still perceived as two separate contacts is the *two point threshold*. A two point threshold can be determined for all forms of sensation, but only thresholds for light pressure and occasionally pain (prick) are tested clinically. The two point threshold is a smaller distance for touches than for warmth or cold stimuli. But the ability of the skin to resolve two points is only one three-thousandths of that of the eye. Regional differences are pronounced (Fig. 182) and

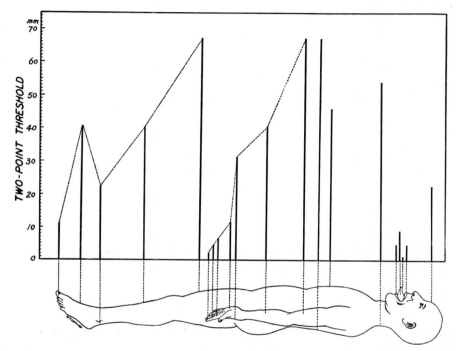

FIG. 182.   Regional variation in two point threshold for touch. Length of vertical lines is approximately equal to magnitude of two point threshold. (Data from Weber cited by Sherrington in Schäfer, *Text-book of physiology*. Edinburgh, Young J. Pentland, 1900.)

broadly parallel the accuracy of localization. They do not, however, parallel regional variations in the intensity threshold. In the neurologic examination corresponding areas on both sides of the body must be tested.

Neural basis of localization and two point discrimination.   Weber assumed that the two point threshold for a given region was fixed by the size of the skin area to which terminals of a single nerve fiber are distributed (so-called Weber's sensory circles). As long as one unexcited sensory unit remained between the two on which the compass rested, the points were, according to Weber, appreciated as two. The size of the sensory unit's distribution is to some degree correlated with the size of the two point threshold. For example, Weddell[42] has found the area on the back of the human hand covered by the terminals of a single sensory fiber to be approximately 7.5 mm. in diameter, while on the thumb of the monkey it is 1.5 mm. These values agree fairly well with the two point thresholds of the same regions in man. But Weber's notion of two excited receptors and an intervening unexcited one, each with a private path to the cerebral cortex, is now recognized to be a great oversimplification. The ramifications within the skin of a single posterior root fiber do not occupy discrete areas but overlap. Weber's concept also supposes that the three neurons making up the sensory pathway from receptor to sensory cortex constitute a simple chain having no cross connections with other chains at the synaptic levels. Such connections are known to occur even in the most highly organized system—the visual pathways. Figure 183 shows how two closely adjacent points can be

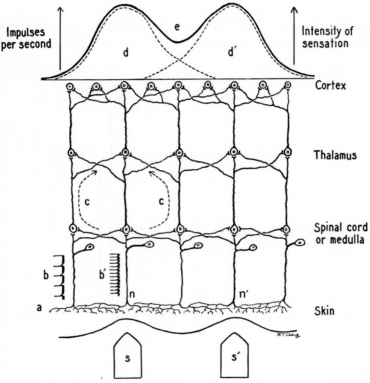

FIG. 183. Schematic diagram illustrating some neural factors involved in localization and in discrimination of two points; s and s' are the points of esthesiometer or compass used in determination of two point threshold; a is plexus of interlocking pain terminals; b and b' show rate of discharge from sensory neuron stimulated at periphery of terminal brush and second neuron stimulated at center of its peripheral distribution. Arrows c illustrate that tendency of excitation to spread in first synaptic layer results in intensification by facilitation of core neuron in next synaptic layer; d and d' represent graphically frequency of corticopetal impulses arriving upon (and hence activity of) each cortical cell when due to s and s' respectively; e represents summed activity pattern; d, d' and e are termed *modal excitation fields*.* In the diagram an attempt has been made to combine the views of Weber, Bernstein, Lorente de Nó, Tower, and Marshall and Talbot.

perceived as two, despite the multiple factors making for merging of the streams of impulses arising from the two points stimulated.

Size, Shape, Figure Writing, Etc. The ability of the cutaneous and proprioceptive sensory systems to appreciate the spatial aspect of objects is demonstrable by a variety of simple maneuvers. Objects of graded size, such as coins, placed successively in the hand are discriminated. The direction and length of a line drawn upon the skin are recognized.

* In a frequency curve in which classes are arranged along the abscissae from small to large and the number falling within each class is graphed, the mode is that class which contains the largest number of frequencies or members.

Touch and pressure are mainly responsible for such discrimination. Geometric patterns of warmth produced without contact (radiation) are virtually unrecognizable. Perhaps the most convenient test of the spatial aspect of skin sensibility is the "figure writing" test introduced by Foerster. While the patient's eyes are closed, numerals between 0 and 9 are written on his palm or another smooth surface of his body with a blunt, pointed object, using a slow, even movement. Although mistakes are rarely made by a normal person after the first few trials, certain neurologic patients do little better than chance. The manner of recording the observation is as follows:

As written	1	2	7	4	8	6	9	5	3	0
As reported	1	2	6	3–2	6	6	1	7	7	0

Figure writing, left hand. J. P., a white youth aged 18. Tests were conducted subsequent to a right occipital craniotomy which disclosed an aneurysm of the posterior cerebral artery with a hemorrhagic cyst in the anterior portion of the occipital lobe. The resection included the midportion of the posterior parietal lobe.

Stereognosis. The appreciation of the form of three-dimensional objects by palpation without the aid of vision is termed *stereognosis* or the knowledge of (geometric) solids. A key, a coin or a pencil may serve as a test object—"recognition of common objects." For exact testing a series of standardized objects or geometric forms of graded difficulty, as employed by Fox,[13] is desirable because it allows a rough quantitative statement of ability. Stereognosis is not a "sense" despite the common clinical usage. It is a complex perception or concept based upon the synthesis of the several modalities of somatic sensation.

Touch and kinesthesis perhaps yield the most information, but all senses may be involved. For example, the roundness of a cylinder is recognized by the even pressure on the pulp of the fingers when it is rolled, kinesthetic sense giving information on the diameter and weight of the object. It is soon appreciated that the object rolls in one direction but not the other. As the finger slides along the smooth surface, an end is discovered which proves to be a flat, smooth surface, the circular border of which confirms the original impression. And when the identical impression is gained from the opposite end, the data are synthesized into the conclusion that the object is a cylinder. Additional data with regard to smoothness and temperature complete its recognition as a metal cylinder.

It is not difficult to understand how stereognosis becomes defective when either tactual or kinesthetic sense is blunted, although one can partly substitute for the other. This situation is more properly termed stereo-anesthesia.[5] But in certain instances, especially after lesions of the posterior parietal lobe, stereognosis seems to be affected out of proportion to the deficit in the basic sensations—so-called pure astereognosis. At some point difficult to define, disturbances of the higher levels of sensation merge into agnosia and aphasia (see Chap. 21).

REFERENCES

1. ADRIAN, E. D. *The basis of sensation.* London, Christophers, 1928.
2. BAZETT, H. C. Pp. 489–501 in: *Temperature: its measurement and control in science and industry.* New York, Reinhold, 1941.
3. BELL, C. *Phil. Trans.*, 1826, Pt. 2, pp. 163–173.
4. BORING, E. G. *Sensation and perception in the history of experimental psychology.* New York, D. Appleton-Century Co., 1942.
5. BOSHES, B. and PADBERG, F. *Neurology*, 1953, 3:90–101.
6. BOYD, I. A. and ROBERTS, T. D. M. *J. Physiol.*, 1953, 122:38–58.
7. BRONK, D. W. *Res. Publ. Ass. nerv. ment. Dis.*, 1935, 15:60–82.
8. BROWNE, K., LEE, L. and RING, P. A. *J. Physiol.*, 1954, 126:448–458.
9. CATTELL, McK. and HOAGLAND, H. *J. Physiol.*, 1931, 72:392–404.
10. COHEN, L. A. *J. Neurophysiol.*, 1958, 21:550–562.
11. DALLENBACH, K. M. *Amer. J. Psychol.*, 1927, 39:402–427.
12. DODT, E. and ZOTTERMAN, Y. *Acta physiol. scand.*, 1952, 26:345–357.
13. FOX, J. C., JR. and KLEMPERER, W. W. *Arch. Neurol. Psychiat. (Chicago)*, 1942, 48:622–645.
14. GARDNER, E. *Amer. J. Physiol.*, 1948, 152:436–445.
15. GELDARD, F. A. *J. gen. Psychol.*, 1940, 22:243–308.

16. GELDARD, F. A. *The human senses.* New York, J. Wiley & Sons, 1953.
17. GRAY, J. A. B. Chap. 4 in *Handbook of physiology. Section 1: Neurophysiology,* vol. 1, J. FIELD, ed. Baltimore, Williams & Wilkins, 1959.
18. GRAY, J. A. B. and MALCOLM, J. L. *Proc. roy. Soc.,* 1950, *B137*:96–114.
19. GRAY, J. A. B. and MATTHEWS, P. B. C. *J. Neurophysiol.,* 1951, *14*:454–464.
20. HAGEN, E., KNOCHE, H., SINCLAIR, D. C. and WEDDELL, G. *Proc. roy. Soc.,* 1953, *B141*: 279–287.
21. HARDY, J. D., GOODELL, H. and WOLFF, H. G. *Science,* 1951, *114*:149–150.
22. HARDY, J. D. and OPPEL, T. W. *J. clin. Invest.,* 1937, *16*:533–540.
23. HARDY, J. D., WOLFF, H. G. and GOODELL, H. *J. clin. Invest.,* 1940, *19*:649–657.
24. HARDY, J. D., WOLFF, H. G. and GOODELL, H. *J. clin. Invest.,* 1947, *26*:1152–1158.
25. HARTLINE, H. K. and GRAHAM, C. H. *J. cell. comp. Physiol.,* 1932, *1*:277–295.
26. HENSEL, H. *Ergebn. Physiol.,* 1952, *47*:166–368.
27. HODGKIN, A. L. *J. Physiol.,* 1948, *107*:165–181.
28. JENKINS, W. L. *J. exp. Psychol.,* 1939, *25*:373–388.
29. KATZ, B. *J. Physiol.,* 1950, *111*:248–260.
30. KATZ, B. *J. Physiol.,* 1950, *111*:261–282.
31. LAIDLAW, R. W. and HAMILTON, M. A. *Bull. neurol. Inst. N. Y.,* 1937, *6*:145–153, 268–273, 494–503.
32. LELE, P. P. and WEDDELL, G. *Brain,* 1956, *79:* 119–154.
33. LELE, P. P., WEDDELL, G. and WILLIAMS, C. M. *J. Physiol.,* 1954, *126*:206–234.
34. MARUHASHI, J., MIZUGUCHI, K. and TASAKI, I. *J. Physiol.,* 1952, *117*:129–151.
35. MATTHEWS, B. H. C. *J. Physiol.,* 1931, *71*:64–110; *72*:153–174; *idem*, 1933, *78*:1–53.
36. MÜLLER, J. *Handbuch der Physiologie des Menschen für Vorlesungen.* Coblenz, J. Holscher, 1834–40, 2 vols. Translated selections in: RAND, B. *The classical psychologists.* Boston, Houghton Mifflin, 1912.
37. NAFE, J. P. and WAGONER, K. S. *J. gen. Psychol.,* 1941, *25*:323–351.
38. SHERRINGTON, C. S. *The integrative action of the nervous system.* New Haven, Yale University Press, 1906.
39. SINCLAIR, D. C., WEDDELL, G. and ZANDER, E. *J. Anat. (Lond.),* 1952, *86*:402–411.
40. TOWER, S. S. *J. Neurophysiol.,* 1940, *3:*486–500.
41. TOWER, S. S. *Res. Publ. Ass. nerv. ment. Dis.,* 1943, *23:*16–43.
42. WEDDELL, G. *J. Anat. (Lond.),* 1941, *75*:346–367.
43. WEDDELL, G. *J. Anat. (Lond.),* 1941, *75*:441–446.
44. WEDDELL, G. *Brit. Med. Bull.,* 1945, *3*:167–172.
45. WEDDELL, G., PALLIE, W. and PALMER, E. *Quart. J. micr. Sci.,* 1954, *95*:483–501.
46. WEDDELL, G., PALMER, E. and PALLIE, W. *Biol, Rev.,* 1955, *30*:159–195.
47. WEITZ, J. *J. exp. Psychol.,* 1939, *25*:48–64.
48. WOOLLARD, H. H., WEDDELL, G. and HARPMAN, J. A. *J. Anat. (Lond.),* 1940, *74*:413–440.
49. ZANDER, E. and WEDDELL, G. *J. Anat. (Lond.),* 1951, *85*:68–93.
50. ZOTTERMAN, Y. *Skand. Arch. Physiol.,* 1936, *75*:105–120.
51. ZOTTERMAN, Y. Chap. 18 in *Handbook of physiology. Section 1. Neurophysiology,* vol. 1, J. FIELD, ed. Baltimore, Williams & Wilkins, 1959.

CHAPTER 14

Neural Basis of Somatic Sensation

By THEODORE C. RUCH

CHAPTER 13 described the stimuli, the sense organs and the peripheral nerve plexuses for somatic sensation; this chapter takes up the sensory pathways in functional sequence, beginning with the peripheral nerve trunk and ending with the thalamic and cortical orientation.

The diagnosis of neurologic diseases depends in part on answering two questions: what sensory functions are lost? and, equally important, what sensory functions are retained? The result of neurologic disease is called a *dissociation of sensation*, and pathologic lesions at each level of the nervous system produce characteristic dissociations. From a knowledge of these, the level and location of a lesion is deduced. The kind of dissociation is also taken into account. They are of four types: (i) *topographical dissociations*, in which certain regions show altered sensitivity and other regions remain normal; (ii) *modality dissociations*, in which one or more kinds of sensation are lost or impaired while others are preserved; (iii) an *affect-quality* dissociation, in which the affect is exaggerated; and (iv) *dissociations of levels of sensation*, in which the more complex sensory functions, e.g., perception, are lost but the simpler ones are retained.

PERIPHERAL NERVE AND SPINAL ROOTS

A "peripheral nerve field" is the area of skin supplied by one cutaneous nerve. Charts showing the distribution of the major cutaneous nerves are commonly used clinically to record the distribution of sensory disturbances. Although not shown on such charts, there is overlap between peripheral nerve fields. Each major nerve field has a central zone of skin, the *autonomous zone*,[63] which is innervated only by the parent nerve and which is, therefore, completely anesthetic when the nerve is sectioned. Between this zone and the fully innervated skin is the *intermediate zone* of overlap, where sensation is present owing to invasion by branches from neighboring nerves. The sensation elicited by stimulation in this zone of overlap has three abnormal aspects: (i) sensory dissociation, only pain and possibly pressure being appreciated; (ii) hypesthesia, responses to light pressure stimuli showing a gradual transition from anesthesia to normal threshold; and (iii) hyperpathia, the pain sensation being abnormally unpleasant.

Recovery of sensibility occurs by a remarkable circumferential shrinkage of the anesthetic area, i.e., the intermediate zone extends progressively into the anesthetic area. The early phase of this shrinkage occurs within the first few days after nerve section, long before regenerating fibers could possibly reach the skin. Pollock[45] reasoned that the shrinkage is due to an ingrowth of fibers from the adjacent peripheral nerve fields, because the recovery was not lost after a second section of the regenerating nerve. Weddell *et al.*[63] have demonstrated by intravital staining that unmyelinated fibers do grow out from the intermediate into the autonomous zone.

Shortly after nerve section, pain (and, to some degree, touch sensibility) elicited from the intermediate area is qualitatively altered. Although a stronger stimulus is needed to arouse sensations of pain (hypalgesia), once the threshold is exceeded the pain is peculiarly strong and unpleasant (hyperpathia). This phase passes off, but at about the time the sensation served by the regenerating nerve returns to the anesthetic area, the tendency to abnormal pain responses appears again.

EPICRITIC AND PROTOPATHIC SENSIBILITY.[8, 24, 58, 62] Head termed the abnormal sensations found in the intermediate zone, in the autonomous zone during nerve regeneration, and in regions of special sensitivity, e.g., the glans penis, *protopathic sensibility;* and he postulated for it a special set of fibers having a wide peripheral nerve field and regenerating quickly. He also postulated a second set of fibers for each modality to carry out fine intensity and spatial discriminations; these he termed *epicritic sensibility,* e.g., two point threshold. The more highly evolved epicritic system was believed to inhibit the phylogenetically older protopathic system, except when absent as after nerve section.

Few now accept Head's theory. Some of his observations were in error and others have different explanations, e.g., the thinning out of fibers in the intermediate zone. Nevertheless, the terms are still used by clinical neurologists. Perhaps, in a very broad sense, pain may be considered protopathic and other modalities epicritic. Some of the reasons for this statement were given in previous chapters; others will be given when hyperpathia is discussed below.

Dermatomes.[18, 29, 30, 32, 52] The area of skin supplied with afferent fibers by a single posterior root is a *dermatome*. Because the dermatomes are important to clinical neurology, they have been mapped repeatedly. Such charts, which are used in recording the results of a sensory examination, show the dermatomes as contiguous fields. Actually the dermatomes of adjacent roots overlap greatly, so that always two and sometimes three roots supply a single point on the skin. The dermatomes are therefore considerably larger than those shown on most clinical charts. The size of a dermatome is somewhat smaller for pain than for temperature and smaller for temperature than for touch, which is just the reverse of the dissociation in the border surrounding a peripheral nerve injury. Dermatomes, or *sensory root fields*, must not be confused with peripheral nerve fields. The two are quite different in shape, and often the fibers of one dermatome are conducted to the spinal cord in two peripheral nerves.

The dermatomes cannot be demarcated by sectioning a single posterior root and mapping the resulting area of anesthesia, since, owing to overlap, none may be found. The classic method for mapping dermatomes is that of *remaining sensibility*. Sherrington sectioned three roots above and three below the intact root to be studied, producing an island of sensitivity in a sea of anesthesia. Mapping the hyperesthesia induced in the skin surface by injection of 5 per cent saline solution into the interspinous ligaments[32] is another method of dermatomal mapping. Finally, mapping zones of hypesthesia produced by pressure on posterior roots has yielded results at variance with those obtained by the classic procedure.[29, 30]

According to Sherrington,[52] dermatomes are the distorted remnants of what was originally an orderly metameric arrangement that has survived with clarity only in the trunk. There, the dermatomes consist of a series of 12 narrow (overlapping) bands running from the vertebral column to the midventral line. The bands slope downward as they pass around the body to the ventral surface, because, as a result of his upright posture, man's front has blossomed while his back has regressed. In the limbs, the segmental organization is less clear because a number of metameres have been combined to form the limb. The apparent complexity of the dermatomes is clarified if man is placed in the posture of his forebears as in Figure 184, which brings out the neurologically important fact that the perianal region—once ornamented by a tail—and not the foot is the most caudal part of the body and hence is innervated by the lowermost posterior roots.

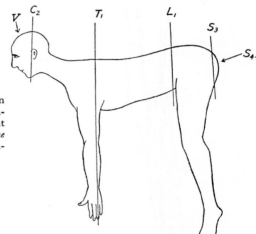

FIG. 184. Key dermatomal boundaries in man in quadruped position. First spinal dermatome is shown as C_2 because first cervical segment lacks posterior root. (After Monrad-Krohn, *The clinical examination of the nervous system*, 3rd ed., London, H. K. Lewis, 1926.)

According to Sherrington's observation, the dermatomes of the arms, when viewed from the side, are "rays" which originate at a mid-dorsal line, as brought out in Figure 185, and terminate in the midventral line. Thus, the dermatomes, as the name suggests, are not bands but cuts or slices. In the arm, a dermatome consists of the surface of a wedge which passes through the arm in the same plane as, but diverging from, the plane established by the mid-dorsal and midventral line of the limb from which the dermatome takes origin. For example, the same dermatome includes the back and front of the middle finger. Dermatomes anterior to the mid-dorsal and the midventral plane are *preaxial;* those posterior are *postaxial.*

Keegan and Garnett[29] present a different kind of dermatomal map based upon the distribution of dermal hypesthesia caused by nucleus pulposus material extruding from a ruptured intervertebral disc and pressing on individual posterior roots. In this map (Figs. 187, 188), the dermatome extends as a band from the backbone down the arm or leg to its tip, and this pattern is repeated serially much as on the trunk. It is surprising that a difference of opinion exists on such a fundamental matter as the shape of the dermatomes.

The dermatomal pattern is significant in several ways to both clinical medicine and physiology: (i) in distinguishing peripheral nerve injury from root injury; (ii) in localizing the level of spinal cord injury; (iii) in determining the levels for root sections or cordotomy for relief of pain; (iv) in treating herpes zoster, which is often distributed on the skin according to dermatomes; (v) in recognizing the origin of visceral pain, which is often referred to a dermatome; and (vi) in studying the lamination of spinal tracts and the projection of the body surface upon the cerebral cortex (see below).

Conduction of Sensory Nerve Impulses.[22, 32, 69] Temporal dissociation of sensory impulses occurs normally by virtue of different conduction rates in the fibers making up the spinal nerves. To what degree can conduction rate be associated with the modality of somatic sensation? Fundamental to the consideration of this problem is knowledge of the distribution of fiber size—the so-called "fiber spectrum" of sensory nerves described in Chapter 3 and illustrated in Figure 37.

It will be recalled from Chapter 3 that the spike potential of a mixed spinal nerve, recorded sufficiently far from the stimulating electrodes, separates into a series of elevations corresponding to fiber groups of different conduction velocity. Only fibers belonging to the A and the C groups are concerned with somatic sensation, the B group consisting of sympathetic preganglionic fibers. The C wave is contributed by fine unmye-

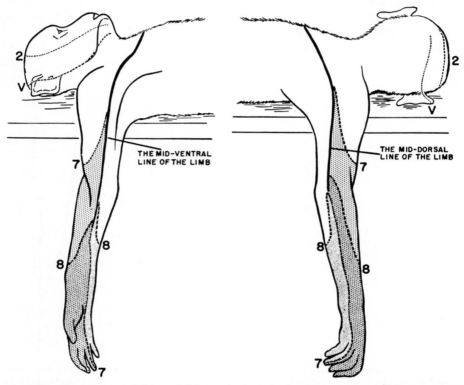

FIG. 185. Dermatomes of 7th and 8th cervical roots of the macaque monkey determined by method of remaining sensibility. Note that dermatomes run between midventral and mid-dorsal lines. Note also the overlap. On the head is seen a similar overlap between lower border of trigeminal nerve field (*V*) and upper border of the 2nd cervical dermatome. (Redrawn from Sherrington, *Phil. Trans.,* 1898, *B190:*45–186.)

linated fibers which are approximately 1 μ in diameter and conduct at the rate of 0.5 to 2.0 m. per second. Of the A fibers, the large rapidly conducting ones, Group I in Lloyd's terminology,[33] are found only in muscle nerves and apparently are not sensory. Impulses in these fibers cannot be traced to the thalamus and cortex. Group II fibers (6 to 12 μ) are infrequent in muscle nerves, but constitute a large peak in the fiber distribution for cutaneous nerves. Group III fibers (mostly 3 to 4 μ) conduct impulses at about 6 to 30 m. per second; these fibers are the same as A delta fibers and are found in both muscle and cutaneous nerves.

Evidence that pain reflexes (and therefore presumably pain) are elicited by C impulses was provided by the experiments of Clark *et al.*[11] The saphenous nerve of the cat was stimulated with graded stimuli while the resulting nerve impulses were recorded with a cathode-ray oscillograph and breathing was recorded pneumographically. When

C strength of current was reached, the rate and depth of breathing increased. Also, when the A group was blocked by pressure, stimulation continued to produce blood pressure and respiratory change when only the C wave was detectable in the electro-neurogram. Zotterman[69] confirmed the association of C fibers with pain and showed that fine myelinated fibers of Group III also conduct pain impulses. This observation explains certain features of normal and abnormal pain not previously understood. Brookhart et al.[9] have shown that fibers from the tooth pulp, a classic pure pain source,

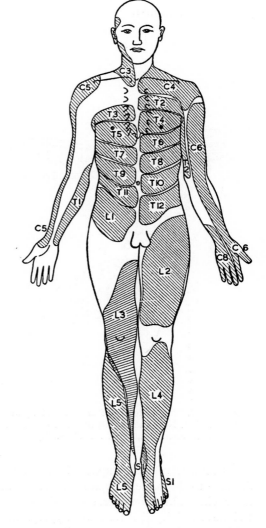

FIG. 186. Dermatomes of man determined by method of "remaining sensibility." Half the dermatomes are shown on left and remainder on right in order to display the overlap. (Data of Foerster, *Brain*, 1933, *56*:1–39, redrawn by Lewis, *Pain*, New York, Macmillan, 1942.)

have the conduction characteristics of Group III fibers, which is consistent with their being myelinated. No conduction at C fiber rates was discovered. Neuroanatomists find fewer unmyelinated fibers in cranial than in spinal nerves.

DOUBLE PAIN RESPONSE.[22, 32, 46] Evidence for the existence of a fast and a slow system of pain fibers comes from several sources: (i) *Psychologic studies*. Several investigators have described under the names *double pain, delayed pain, echo pain* or *first and second pain* the fact that the pain sensation from a brief stimulus is often experienced as two pulses or peaks of pain. You can demonstrate this double pain response for yourself by flicking the dorsum of a finger against a very hot object. (ii) *Latency studies*. If the two pain pulses are due to rapidly and slowly conducting fibers, the interval between pulses should be greater when stimuli are applied to the distal end of an extremity than when they are applied to the proximal end. This has been found experimentally,[32, 69] and the delays are compatible with the difference between C and delta rates of conduction. (iii) *Cocaine and asphyxial block.* Although both kinds of block affect the components of the A wave in the same order,[22] C fibers are the last to be blocked by asphyxia and the first to be blocked by cocaine. Pain is the last sensation blocked by asphyxia, and the pain which disappears last is the delayed type. Cocaine, on the other hand, blocks the slow pain component first.

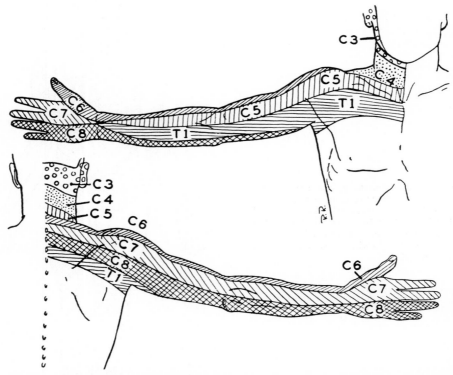

FIG. 187. Dermatomes of arms based upon zones of hypesthesia resulting from ruptured inter-vertebral discs. Note that bands begin at back, not at mid-dorsal and midventral lines. (After Keegan and Garnett, *Anat. Rec.*, 1948, *102*:409–437.)

CLINICAL CORRELATIONS.   *Tabes dorsalis and peripheral neuropathy.*[55]   Neurosyphilitic damage to the posterior roots may result in loss of touch, proprioception, etc. without destroying pain. Moreover, such pain is often felt after a delay of 1 or 2 seconds and may well be especially disagreeable—hyperpathic. This was not understood until the existence of the "slow" pain fibers was discovered. The latencies of the pain response in most tabetic patients and of second pain in normal individuals are approximately the same.[44] Further, the delay in the pain response in the tabetic patient is about 1 second after stimulation of the knee but nearly 2 seconds after stimulation of the toes. Groups II and III are probably damaged to a greater extent than are the C fibers. That light touch, position sense and vibratory sensibility are affected early in both tabes dorsalis, and nutritional neuropathy is explicable on the grounds that the impulses mediating these sensory functions travel in fast-conducting fibers of the A group. In passing it should be mentioned that pain fibers in tabes also seem to fire spontaneously, e.g., tabetic crises, as though the pathologic factor which is progressively killing fibers causes bursts of impulses to be generated in the ones remaining viable.

Hyperpathia.[55, 56] Dissociations of sensation in which pain sensibility is selectively preserved are often associated with a qualitative change in pain, its disagreeableness (affect) being heightened—the phenomenon of *hyperpathia* or *dysesthesia.* From time to time it is suggested that the unmyelinated fibers serve a kind of pain different from the more rapid one. One can easily verify for himself that the qualities of the two flashes of pain elicited from normally innervated skin are similar if not identical, although the second tends to be more prolonged. Lewis[32] states that the two types of pain are equally well localized. Although subtle differences may exist, second pain as normally experi-

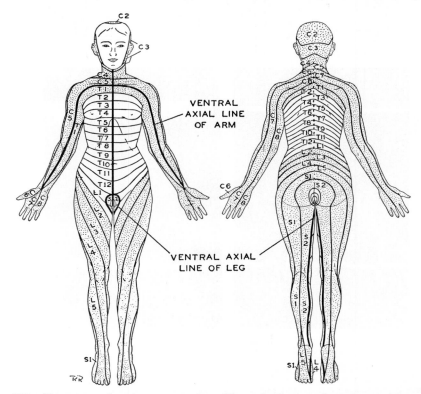

FIG. 188. Dermatomes based upon mapping of hypesthetic zones from ruptured intervertebral discs. Contrast with Fig. 186, showing data obtained by method of "remaining sensibility." (After Keegan and Garnett, *Anat. Rec.*, 1948, *102*:409–437.)

enced is certainly not identical with hyperpathia. However, some hint of the mechanism of hyperpathia can be found in the fact that it tends to occur when pain sensibility persists after the other modalities of sensation are blocked (asphyxia, tabes,[55] neuropathy,[56] nerve degeneration). Head, as noted earlier, postulated a central inhibitory interaction between pain and other modalities of sensation. However, Landau and Bishop[31] believe, from experiments involving asphyxial nerve block, that the slow pain impulses (C fibers) give rise to dull, burning, disagreeable pain when not preceded by the Group III pain impulses.

C FIBER TOUCH. Not all pain fibers are in the C category and not all C fibers are tpain fibers. In Chapter 13 it was seen that free nerve endings serve modalities of sensa ion other than pain. Consistently, nonmedullated C fibers appear to serve touch. It is- extremely difficult to record activity in C fibers produced by natural stimuli, which give rise to asynchronous volleys. Douglas and Ritchie[17] deduced the amount of C fiber activity in response to skin stimulation by causing the volley from this stimulus to collide with an antidromic volley from an electrical stimulus; the decrease in the C wave of the antidromic volley reflected the number of collisions in individual C fibers (Fig. 189). Even gentle stroking of the skin excited C fibers. Further, it was found that, of the two components of the C wave, the slightly more rapid one was blocked by tactile stimuli. Thus there may be sets of both pain and tactile fibers in the unmyelinated group. C touch fibers differ from medullated touch fibers in exhibiting long afterdischarge.

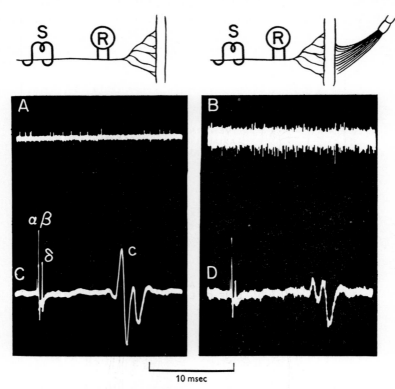

FIG. 189.   Action potentials of myelinated and unmyelinated fibers of a sensory nerve twig before (A) and after (B) skin was stroked with cotton gauze. In C and D the unit nerve impulses seen in A and B have been shunted out so that the C wave is emphasized and the alpha, beta and delta waves (seen at left of each record) are reduced; also an antidromic volley was sent down the nerve to collide with the impulses in it. Note that the C wave of the antidromic volley in C is greatly reduced by collision after stroking. (After Douglas and Ritchie. *J. Physiol.*, 1957, *139:*385–399.)

SENSORY PATHWAYS OF THE SPINAL CORD

Sensory fibers, exclusive of those connecting with spinocerebellar neurons, may (i) ascend without synaptic interruption or crossing in the ipsilateral posterior column to the medulla, or (ii) form a synapse with a fiber which crosses the spinal cord to ascend in the contralateral spinothalamic tract in the anterolateral region of the cord. Of the various somatic and visceral modalities of sensation, some are exclusively dependent on the posterior columns, others are dependent on the anterolateral columns, and still others utilize both pathways.

Spinothalamic Tract.[19, 27, 28, 60, 61, 64-66].   Impulses conducted in the lateral and ventral spinothalamic tracts subserve the following kinds of sensation and perception.

Partially spinothalamic:
   1. Pressure and touch*
Exclusively spinothalamic:
   1. Pain from skin, muscles, tendons, joints and viscera
   2. Warmth
   3. Cold
   4. Sexual sensations
   5. Tickle, itch, feelings of muscular fatigue

Upon entering the spinal cord sensory fibers are regrouped so that (i) the fibers for cutaneous and deep sensibility are no longer separate and (ii) the fibers serving the same quality of sensation are sorted out and grouped together. Thus, pain fibers from cutaneous, muscular and visceral nerves are collected together in the anterolateral tract, and the muscle sense impulses from the deep branches pass into the posterior columns. Both temperature senses go together.

FUNCTIONAL ANATOMIC DETAILS—ORIGIN AND DECUSSATION. Each posterior root branches into a fan of rootlets which enter the spinal cord. At the point of entry, the fibers of each filament sort out according to size. The *medial division* contains the large myelinated fibers which, instead of entering the posterior horn, swing across its tip to enter the posterior columns (Fig. 190). The unmyelinated and small myelinated fibers are grouped into a *lateral division* which swings laterally and, bifurcating, forms the tract of

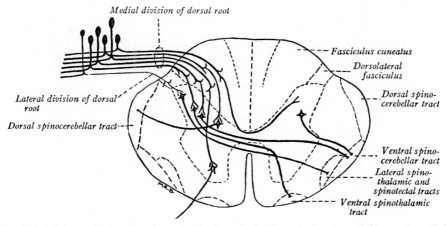

FIG. 190. Schematic cross section of spinal cord showing destination of fibers of medial and lateral divisions of dorsal root and position of ascending tracts. (From Ranson and Clark, *Anatomy of the nervous system,* 1959.)

Lissauer (*dorsolateral fasciculus*) at the tip of the posterior horn. This is not a tract in the usual sense of the word. The fibers ascend only one to three segments before terminating in the substantia gelatinosa Rolandi, a cell column capping the posterior horn. This column is named for its discoverer and for its seemingly uniform texture (due to the smallness of the cell bodies and the absence of large myelinated fibers traversing it) (see Fig. 191). The axons of its fine cells cross the cord and ascend in the lateral spinothalamic tract.

Some fibers of the medial division terminate, either immediately or after ascending several segments, upon large pericornual cells in the posterior horn. The axons of these cells decussate in the ventral gray commissure to ascend in the ventral portion of the anterolateral column (ventral spinothalamic tract). This scheme may be too rigid; both divisions of the posterior root probably contribute to both the lateral and the ventral spinothalamic tract.

* The degree to which the anterolateral pathways are concerned with pressure and tactile sensibility and whether there is a *qualitative* difference between the touch-pressure sensations served by the anterolateral and by the posterior columns is not fully known (see p. 335).

Syringomyelia. The proximity of the anterior gray commissure to the central canal makes the decussating fibers liable to interruption by a widening of the central canal (syringomyelia). This produces a clinical syndrome consisting of loss of pain and of warmth and cold sensations on *both sides* of the body at the level of the segments affected. Touch, pressure, and deep sensibility are not affected. Syringomyelia is, therefore, a good example of modality dissociation.

LAMINATION. The ascending tracts of the anterolateral region (spinobulbar, spinotectal and spinothalamic) are laminated. This means that the contributions of successive dermatomes form more or less distinct layers or laminae of fibers. A tract so arranged is said to be "topographically organized." The lamination is in the form of imperfect annular rings with the fibers from the most caudal regions lying superficially because the long fibers from sacral segments are pushed outward by the accretion of crossing fibers at each successive segment (Fig. 190). Some other influence pushes the longer sacral fibers laterally and dorsally away from the margin of the ventral horn

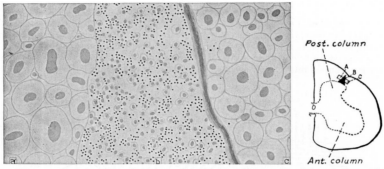

FIG. 191.   Silver stained cross section through white matter at tip of dorsal horn of spinal cord (cat), as shown at right. *a*, Large fibers of medial division of dorsal root after entering fasciculus cuneatus; *b*, unmyelinated and fine myelinated fibers of lateral division after entering fasciculus dorsolateralis (Lissauer); *c*, second order fibers of dorsal spinocerebellar tract. Unmyelinated fibers appear as black dots. (From Ransom and Clark, *Anatomy of the nervous system*, 1959.)

where they originally lay. This results in the arrangement seen in Figures 192 and 193. The physiologic significance of such lamination is the preservation of the topographic organization of fibers whereby the dermatomes of the body surface may ultimately be projected onto the cortical sensory areas.

CLINICAL CORRELATIONS; CORDOTOMY.[27] Lamination explains certain features of the symptoms produced by spinal cord tumors. Extramedullary tumors, those originating outside the spinal cord, tend to cause hypalgesia in the caudal dermatomes first, because the pressure from the outside blocks first the peripherally lying fibers from the sacral segments. As the cord is pressed further, the sensory border creeps up. Intramedullary tumors, on the other hand, may leave a characteristic region of intact sensibility in the anogenital region because they spare the peripherally lying fibers derived from the lowest sacral roots.

The separation of sensory impulses to travel in the anterolateral and posterior columns of the spinal cord allows surgical interruption of the pain pathway without production of a disabling anesthesia and ataxia. As shown in Figure 193, a small knife with a depth guard of wax is inserted into the spinal cord just below the dentate ligament and pyramidal tract and is drawn downward through the antero-lateral columns. Such anterolateral cordotomies are performed to relieve unbearable pain not tractable to medical control. The operation is effective for superficial, deep and visceral pain, although, for the last, bilateral operations are required. Despite the fact that the ventral spinocerebellar and various descending motor tracts—vestibulospinal, tectospinal, ventral corticospinal tracts, etc.—are partially sectioned, little motor disturbance is apparent. Bilateral cordotomy rarely interferes permanently with bladder function or with sensations of bladder fullness. However, sensations of the sexual orgasm are usually lost.

Posterior White Columns.[19]   These columns (more correctly funiculi), lying be-tween the posterior horns, are formed by the ascending and descending branches of the fibers making up the medial division of the posterior horns. Some of the ascending fibers reach the medulla before synaptic interruption; others transmit impulses to the second order neurons which form well defined ascending tracts passing to the cerebellum. By collaterals, impulses also reach the motoneurons and possibly the propriospinal system.

As discussed in Chapter 3, Group I and Group II fibers fare differently in the posterior columns. Lloyd and McIntyre proved that few, if any, of the rapidly conducting

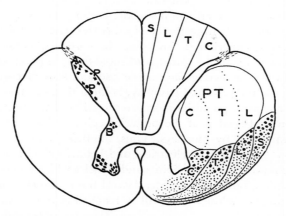

FIG. 192. Semischematic cross section of spinal cord in lower cervical region, showing one concept of lamination of spinothalamic and other tracts. In anterolateral column, heavy dots represent fibers concerned with temperature; medium-sized dots, pain fibers; fine dots, touch and pressure fibers. *C*, cervical; *T*, thoracic; *L*, lumbar; *S*, sacral; *PT*, pyramidal tract. *A*, *P* and *B* are apical, pericornual and basal groups of large cells of posterior horn. (From Walker, *Arch. Neurol. Psychiat.* (*Chicago*), 1940, *43*:284–298.)

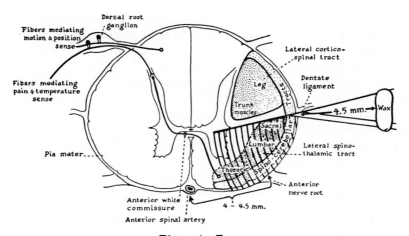

Thoracic II.

FIG. 193. Diagram illustrating cordotomy. Cross section of spinal cord shows lamination of spinothalamic tract, position of pyramidal tract in relation to it, and presence of other tracts in lower quadrant. A piece of bone wax is mounted 4.5 mm. from tip of knife as a depth gauge. Heavy curved lines in ventral quadrant indicate sweep of knife. Note that a desire to spare lateral corticospinal tract would result in sparing of sacral dermatomes. (From Kahn and Rand, *J. Neurosurg.*, 1952, *9*:611–619.)

proprioceptive fibers (Group I) project rostrally to the thalamus and cortex, being directed chiefly into the Clarke's column-spinocerebellar system. On the other hand, Group II fibers from muscle (and skin) reach the medulla via the posterior columns in great numbers. Mountcastle and his coworkers could record no evoked cortical potential from Group I volleys. The anulospiral endings and Golgi tendon organs, which are innervated by Group I fibers, apparently play no role in proprioceptive sensations. At first sight this arrangement might appear to leave the deep receptors with no pathway to the cerebral cortex except by way of the cerebellum. However, Hunt[26] has shown that muscle spindles are innervated by Group II as well as Group I fibers (see Chap. 6). Furthermore, impulses from receptors at the joints probably play a great part in the appreciation of the position of a joint. Group II fibers from muscle, like those from cutaneous nerves, continue in the posterior column to the medulla in great numbers. That impulses in these fibers continue on to the cortex has been shown by recording short-latency action potentials from the cerebral cortex caused by stimulation of the muscle nerve. However, experiments involving the cortical potential as an end-point and section of various tracts in the spinal cord show that the posterior columns are not the sole spinal pathway connecting the muscle and the sensory cortex. Some investigators[21] believe it is not the principal pathway, holding that section of the anterolateral columns reduces the evoked potential more than section of the posterior column does. DeVito[16] has shown that section of the posterior columns interferes only temporarily with weight discrimination by monkeys. Thus, another pathway can also serve discriminative function. It seems from electrical and behavioral studies that the posterior column contains Group II fibers from joints and muscles which can serve such functions as weight discrimination, but that the anterolateral tracts also contain such fibers. This is substantially the same conclusion that will be reached in respect to cutaneous tactile-pressure fibers.

CLINICAL CORRELATIONS: SENSORY FUNCTIONS. According to clinical studies, the sensory impulses conducted in the posterior columns serve the functions listed below. Note that the list includes processes of a perceptual nature, some of which involve more than one modality of posterior column sensibility. A test of each sensory or perceptual function, described in Chapter 13, is also mentioned.

A. Muscle, tendon and joint sensibility (proprioception, kinesthesia)
    1. Passive movement—threshold angular movement for appreciation of movement
    2. Threshold of tension—discrimination of lifted weights
    3. Position of limb in space—finger-to-finger test

B. Touch and pressure
    1. Light touch—cotton wool
    2. Light pressure—von Frey hairs
    3. Massive pressure—weight discrimination with supported hand

C. Perceptual functions
    1. Topognosis or localization—spot finding test
    2. Two point discrimination—compass test
    3. Spatial functions—figure writing, length and direction of a line
    4. Appreciation of vibration—tuning fork test or pallesthesiometer
    5. Stereognosis—recognition of common objects by palpation

The sensations served by the posterior columns are gnostic,* discriminative, epicritic, and spatial. They give knowledge of the position of the limbs in space and knowledge of objects making up the external world. For this knowledge, fine discrimination of the weight, size and texture of objects handled is required. However, intensity, spatial and temporal discriminations are not exclusively the attributes of posterior column sensibility; nor are there some fibers serving localization and others serving intensity discrimination. These are functions common to all forms of sensation. But the sensory systems of the posterior column are sufficiently elaborate and topographically organized so that they exhibit such functions as localization, resolution of two stimuli or

---

* From "gnosis" meaning knowledge.

discrimination of intensity to a very high degree.* Recent physiologic (see p. 334) and occasional clinical studies indicate that proprioception as well as pressure and touch impulses has a double pathway in the spinal cord, the uncrossed posterior and the crossed anterolateral. Two views are held: (i) The two pathways are functionally equivalent, or (ii) the posterior column system, phylogenetically newer, is capable of a higher degree of perceptual function. The lateral spinothalamic tract is frequently sectioned and the ventral tract is sometimes included. The disturbance of perceptual proprioceptive and tactual function (localization, two point discrimination and figure writing) is minimal,[19] but the threshold for light pressure is markedly reduced.[66] The posterior columns are rarely sectioned surgically, but indications are that the spinothalamic tract may be able to serve more perceptual function than has previously been suspected.

Injury of the posterior columns, like injury to posterior roots, give rise to ataxia, the inability to regulate the direction, rate, force and extent of voluntary movements. This consequence is to be expected, since the posterior columns are an extension of the posterior roots and conduct impulses from muscles destined for both the cerebellum and the sensory areas of the cerebral cortex. Lesions of the cerebellum or, to a lesser degree, lesions of the parietal lobe produce ataxia.

SENSORY SYSTEMS OF THE BRAIN STEM

At the upper border of the medulla oblongata, impulses derived from the fifth and other mixed cranial nerves are added to the ascending sensory systems. Here, the ascending systems undergo some rearrangement.

Trigeminal Nerve.[60]   Pain, temperature and touch-pressure sensibility of the face and buccal cavity are served by trigeminal neurons. Their cell bodies are located in the semilunar (Gasserian) ganglion and their central processes enter the pons. Approximately half of the fibers of large diameter bifurcate, giving one branch to the main sensory nucleus located in the pons and one branch to the elongated spinal nucleus which extends through the medulla to meet the substantia gelatinosa Rolandi. The other half of the large fibers connect only with the main nucleus. All but a few of the fine fibers connect only with the spinal nucleus. Pain and temperature impulses pass exclusively by way of the spinal nucleus. Harrison and Corbin[23] recorded tactual impulses from the spinal tract of the trigeminal nerve. As in the spinal cord, a small and functionally unimportant component of the touch-pressure system pursues the same course as the impulses for pain and temperature.

The proprioceptive innervation of the striate muscles of the face and the orbit has long been a neurologic puzzle. Recent studies suggest that the mesencephalic extension of the trigeminal nucleus contains the cells of origin for afferent fibers coming from the muscles of mastication (which also receive motor fibers from the trigeminal nerve). If so, this is the one known instance in which cell bodies of afferent neurons are found *within* the substance of the central nervous system. Although proprioceptive end-organs have been demonstrated in eye muscles, the location of cells or origin of the fibers supplying them is unknown.

SECOND ORDER NEURONS.[61]   As shown in Table 7, the second order neurons carrying somatosensory impulses ascend by way of the medial lemniscus and the dorsal secondary trigeminal tract, and the spinothalamic and ventral secondary trigeminal tract. These are joined by other, less well worked out systems of secondary neurons from the vagus, etc., and all terminate in the thalamus. In addition to these well organized tracts, there are others which are less well organized. When impulses from the teeth were traced

* Note that one should not speak of a "sensation," much less a "two point threshold," ascending the posterior columns.

TABLE 7. SENSORY CONNECTIONS OF SPINAL AND CRANIAL NERVES

SPINAL NERVE	TRIGEMINAL NERVE	FACIAL, GLOSSOPHARYNGEAL AND VAGUS NERVES
Lateral division		
Tract of Lissauer	Descending fibers	Tractus solitarius
Substantia gelatinosa Rolandi	Spinal nucleus	Nucleus of tractus solitarius
Spinothalamic tract	Ventral secondary tract	Unknown
Medial division		
Posterior columns	Ascending fibers	
N. gracilis and cuneatus	Main sensory nucleus	
Medial lemniscus	Dorsal secondary tract	

through the brain stem, electrical activity was recorded from no less than five areas.[36] Three of these lie within the reticular area.

Clinical correlations: trigeminal neuralgia.   This consists of paroxysmal attacks of excruciating pain projected to an area innervated by one or more divisions of the trigeminal nerve. Vasomotor and secretory disturbances may accompany the pain; the facial musculature undergoes clonic contractions—hence the common name *tic douloureux*. The area of skin affected is often apparently hyperesthetic and hyperalgesic, but measurements of threshold indicate a *decreased sensitivity*, suggesting a central overresponse rather than true hyperesthesia. In cases of severe trigeminal neuralgia, the trigeminal neurons are severed central to the ganglion (retrogasserian neurectomy) to avoid regeneration. Although effective, this operation sacrifices touch sensitivity, which results in an unpleasant feeling of numbness over the face, and keratitic changes in the cornea due to loss of protective pain reflexes may ensue.

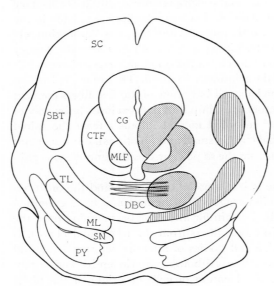

FIG. 194.   Brain stem areas conducting impulses from tooth pulp. Vertically lined areas are the classic pain pathways, the spinobulbothalamic tract (*SBT*) and the trigeminal lemniscus (*TL*) adjacent to the medial lemniscus (*ML*). Dotted areas are three additional regions from which tooth pulp impulses were recorded: one in the central gray (*CG*), one in the central tegmental fasciculus (*CTF*), and one in the reticular substance lateral to decussation of the brachium conjunctivum. Section is at the level of the superior colliculi (*SC*). (After Melzack, Stotler and Livingston. *J. Neurophysiol.*, 1958, *21*:353–367.)

Ascending Reticular System.   It has long been known that the ascending sensory systems lose fibers and also give off collaterals to the reticular substance forming the core of the brain stem. Electrical methods show that both visceral and somatic, as well as auditory and visual, impulses reach the reticular substance. In fact, single unit analysis shows that volleys in all these channels may discharge the same reticular cell. The impulses are conducted slowly to the diencephalon cephalad in a manner consistent with multisynaptic conduction. This recently discovered ascending reticular system is the first stage of a fiber system which eventually reaches and activates the cerebral cortex

(Chap. 21). That ascending multisynaptic pathways may conduct pain impulses has already been suggested in the discussion of the trigeminal system. By ingenious methods, impulses from C fibers have been traced and found to evoke responses in a small portion of the bulbar reticular area.[13]

Both electrophysiologic and behavioral studies indicate that extraspinothalamic pathways in the brain stem, coursing through the central gray and reticular substance, conduct pain impulses. On the other hand, destruction of the nearby central tegmental fasciculus (see Fig. 194) caused a curious overresponse to pin prick and, sometimes, behavior suggestive of "spontaneous pain." The pathway would seem to exert some inhibitory effect on central pain responses. This is perhaps a clue to the problem of hyperpathia. Also, these observations were the first to link multisynaptic ascending reticular systems with sensation. The retention of some pain responses after lesions below the thalamus had been noted by Walker.[59] Spiegel et al.[54] produced movement indicative of unpleasant sensation by stimulating the mesencephalic tectum in the midbrain gray matter. Similar observations are made on man; it will be seen in Chapter 22, which deals with emotion, that stimulation of the hypothalamus also yields responses indicative of pain, or at least of unpleasant affect. It suffices to say at this point that, apart from the classic pain pathways, somewhat diffuse structures extending through the brain stem from the medulla to the diencephalon are in some way connected with pain and the affective side of sensory experience.

THALAMUS AND CEREBRAL CORTEX

Thalamus.[11, 29, 47, 59] All sensory tracts except the olfactory are interrupted by a synapse in the thalamus of the diencephalon before continuing to the cerebral cortex. The thalamus is therefore the gateway to the cerebral cortex through which passes almost all information gained from the external world and from our bodies. Much study and ingenuity has been devoted to tracing the ascending fibers to the various thalamic nuclei and learning to which part of the cortex each nucleus sends its impulses.

The usual anatomic method of tracing pathways in the central nervous system (Marchi's method) is difficult to apply to thalamocortical connections. Walker and LeGros Clark applied an entirely different procedure to the problem. Section of an axon often causes changes in the cell body—chromatolysis, eccentric placement of the nucleus and blurring of the cell outline—first stained and described by Nissl. In some neurons, this process is reversible ("retrograde degenerative reaction"), but in most thalamocortical neurons it goes on to degeneration, disappearance and gliosis. These workers made lesions in the cerebral cortices of monkeys in accordance with cytoarchitectural areas. This procedure truncated the cortically directed axons of thalamic nuclei. The exact nucleus projecting to the area ablated could then be identified by the presence of retrograde degeneration. This supplied one link in the sensory chain. Tracing the great ascending sensory systems into the thalamus by Marchi's method completed our knowledge of the pathway (Figs. 195 through 198).

The thalamus is a large ovoid mass lying along the wall of the third ventricle and the floor of the lateral ventricle. Its sides are partially bounded by the internal capsule. Internally, the thalamus is divided into lateral and medial masses by a vertical sheath of white matter (internal medullary lamina). This lamina bifurcates anteriorly to enclose the third, or anterior, nuclear mass. It is the lateral mass that is concerned with somatic sensation. This mass is subdivided into a *ventral* and a *medial* mass (dotted line in Fig. 195, *upper*). These are represented by the first letters of the abbreviations. The second and third letters (or words) denote additional spatial relations. Often the order of the names is reversed to make an English adjective. Thus, n. *ventralis lateralis* becomes the *lateroventral* nucleus.

The thalamic nuclei (Table 8) can be classified into three categories, given below, on the basis of their connections. A second classification which will also be mentioned is based on the specific and nonspecific thalamocortical connections.

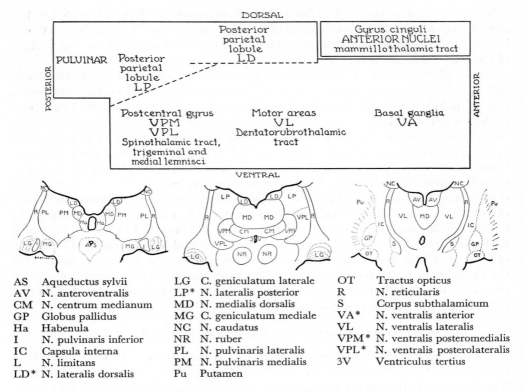

AS	Aqueductus sylvii	LG	C. geniculatum laterale	OT	Tractus opticus
AV	N. anteroventralis	LP*	N. lateralis posterior	R	N. reticularis
CM	N. centrum medianum	MD	N. medialis dorsalis	S	Corpus subthalamicum
GP	Globus pallidus	MG	C. geniculatum mediale	VA*	N. ventralis anterior
Ha	Habenula	NC	N. caudatus	VL	N. ventralis lateralis
I	N. pulvinaris inferior	NR	N. ruber	VPM*	N. ventralis posteromedialis
IC	Capsula interna	PL	N. pulvinaris lateralis	VPL*	N. ventralis posterolateralis
L	N. limitans	PM	N. pulvinaris medialis	3V	Ventriculus tertius
LD*	N. lateralis dorsalis	Pu	Putamen		

FIG. 195. Correlation of longitudinal and cross-sectional views of thalamus. *Top:* Lateral nuclear mass of macaque thalamus in schematic parasagittal section. Cortical projection is given above abbreviation; afferent connection, below it. (Data from Walker, *The primate thalamus*, Chicago, University of Chicago Press, 1938, and after Ranson, *Anatomy of the nervous system*, 1943.) *Bottom:* Cross sections of chimpanzee thalamus at three levels—*left*, posterior; *middle*, midthalamus; *right*, anterior. (From Fulton, *Physiology of the nervous system*, 3d ed., New York, Oxford University Press, 1949.)

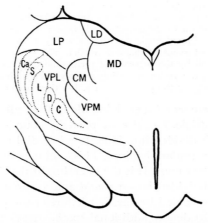

FIG. 196. Cross-sectional diagram through left half of thalamus, showing areas of nucleus ventralis posterolateralis (*VPL*) in which spinothalamic tract fibers from different levels of spinal cord terminate. From Marchi degeneration studies on monkey with prehensile tail. Comma-shaped areas enclosed in fine dots show termination of spinothalamic tract fibers. Order of termination from lateral to medial is: *Ca*, caudal; *S*, sacral; *L*, lumbar; *D*, thoracic; *C*, cervical. For abbreviation of thalamic nuclei see legend of Fig. 195. Note that degeneration was not found in nucleus ventralis posteromedialis (*VPM*), "face" and "taste" nucleus. (After Chang and Ruch, *J. Anat.* (*Lond.*), 1947, *81*:140–149.)

TABLE 8. THALAMIC NUCLEI AND THEIR PROJECTIONS

I. *Anterior nuclei.* Enclosed by internal medullary lamina, these receive fibers from the mammillo-thalamic tract and project to the gyrus cinguli.

II. *Nuclei of the midline.* These clusters of cells, lying along the walls of the third ventricle, have hypothalamic connections.

III. *Medial nuclei.* These lie within or medial to the internal medullary lamina.
   i. Medialis dorsalis is a large nucleus which projects to the hypothalamus and the prefrontal lobe.
   ii. Centrum medianum (centre médian of Luys) which has no direct cortical connections.
   iii. Intralaminar nuclei.

IV. *Lateral nuclear mass.*
   i. N. ventralis anterior, the anterior portion of the ventral mass, is connected with the basal ganglia.
   ii. N. ventralis lateralis, somewhat misnamed since it consists of the anterior half of the lateral mass exclusive of the preceding nucleus, is an important nucleus which receives fibers from superior cerebellar peduncle and projects to the motor areas.
   iii. N lateralis dorsalis et posterior, of which the lateral posterior is the larger, occupy the superior portion of the posterior part of the lateral mass. They project to the posterior parietal lobule.
   iv. N. ventralis posterior (the posteroventral nucleus) lies nferior to the preceding nuclei and occupies the ventral part of the posterior half of the ilateral mass. This nucleus is further divided into the medial portion (arcuate) and a lateral portion, n. ventralis posterolateralis. They project to the postcentral gyrus.

V. *Posterior nuclei.* These lie posterior to the ventral and lateral nuclei and medial to the internal medullary lamina.
   i. N. pulvinaris, a large posterior outgrowth of n. lateralis posterior, projects to the parietal association area.
   ii. Corpus geniculatum lateralis, a prominent laminated nucleus, receives the fibers of the optic tract and projects to the visual area of the occipital lobe.
   iii. Corpus geniculatum medialis lies inferior and medial, and projects to the auditory area of the temporal lobe.

NUCLEI WITH SUBCORTICAL CONNECTIONS.   These nuclei do not project directly to any portion of the cerebral cortex. Thus, if a monkey is hemidecorticate, only these nuclei remain undegenerated and, though surprisingly small, must account for all sensory functions that persist after complete decortication. These nuclei are, chiefly, (i) the nuclei of the midline or paleothalamus; (ii) the intralaminar nuclei, which are small, and the *centre médian*, a large nucleus which has developed in the phylogenetic series; and (iii) the anteroventral nucleus.

Although these nuclei do not send fibers directly to the cerebral cortex, the impulses from them do reach the cortex by a multisynaptic route not yet completely worked out. Because stimulation of a single point in one of these nuclei will affect a wide expanse of cortex, one speaks of a "diffuse" or "nonspecific thalamocortical projection." These nuclei are considered to be a diencephalic extension of the brain stem reticular substance and hence are collectively referred to as the "diffuse thalamic reticular nuclei." This newly discovered system of fibers will be discussed in detail in Chapter 21.

CORTICAL RELAY NUCLEI.   These nuclei possess a definite afferent input and project to the cerebral cortex in or close to a known sensory area. The main somesthetic relay nucleus is n. ventralis posteromedialis. It receives fibers from the trigeminal and medial lemnisci and the spinothalamic tract, and projects to the postcentral gyrus. This projection is highly organized topographically. Nuclei with such projections are referred to as "specific thalamocortical projection nuclei."

ASSOCIATION NUCLEI.   These nuclei receive impulses, not directly from the ascending sensory systems, but from the relay nuclei or the thalamic nuclei with subcortical connections. They project to the so-called "association areas" of the cerebral cortex, notably those of the prefrontal lobe (dorsomedial), the posterior parietal lobe (dorsolateral and posterolateral), and the common ground between the sensory areas of the parietal, occipital and temporal lobes (pulvinar). Since the association nuclei send fibers to the cerebral cortex in a reasonably point-to-point fashion, they are "specific thalamic

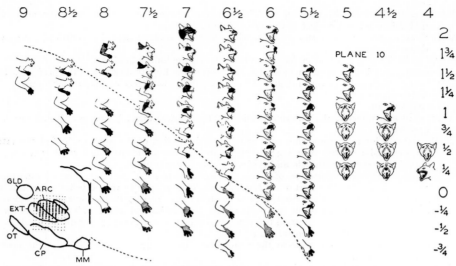

FIG. 197.   Evoked-potential mapping of representation of body surface on thalamus of cat. Inset in lower left corner is a cross section through posterior part of thalamus. Grid of small dots shows points from which electrical records were made; enlarged dots are points from which potentials were recorded on tactual stimulation. For each of the larger points a figurine is located in main diagram (mm. scale), showing which area of skin or mucosa yields a strong (black) or weak (cross-hatched) response at given thalamic point. Line of dashes running diagonally represents boundary between pars externa (*EXT*) and pars arcuata (*ARC*) of ventrolateral nucleus (which in the monkey is known as posteroventral nucleus). Other abbreviations are: *OT*, optic tract; *CP*, cerebral peduncle; *MM*, mammillary nucleus; *GLD*, lateral geniculate body. *Note that medial portion of pars arcuata (to right) did not yield evoked potentials to touch stimulation and may be area that relays taste and/or visceral impulses from vagus nerve.* Trunk and leg appear in similar drawings made from more anterior planes. (From Mountcastle and Henneman, *J. Neurophysiol.*, 1949, *12*:85–100.)

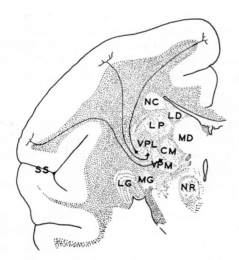

FIG. 198.   Schematic frontal section through thalamus and postcentral gyrus of cerebral cortex to show topographic arrangement of projection fibers from posteroventral nuclei. Nucleus ventralis posteromedialis (*VPM*) projects to inferior end of postcentral gyrus near sylvian fissure (*SS*), whereas nucleus ventralis posterolateralis (*VPL*) projects to middle and superior thirds of postcentral gyrus. (From Walker, *The primate thalamus*, Chicago, University of Chicago Press, 1938.)

projection nuclei." Superposed as it were on the relay nuclei, the association nuclei have no *raison d'être*, unless in some manner they integrate impulses before relaying them to the cortex. But their final expression of activity comes through the cerebral cortex. Further, the nonspecific thalamic nuclei affect cortical function, and, finally, the two levels are connected by an elaborate system of corticothalamic fibers. The thalamic nucleus which projects to a given cortical area receives corticothalamic projection fibers from that or an adjacent cortical area. A circuit with the potentialities of interplay is thus formed between thalamus and cortex, and, therefore, the role of the thalamus in sensation cannot be gauged from observations on decorticate animals. Cortical and thalamic functions are inseparable, and the ability of the thalamus to function independently after destruction of the cerebral cortex is subordinate to the question of how the thalamus and cortex function together in subserving sensation.

The two modality groupings found in the spinal cord continue in the brain stem. However, the spinothalamic tract and the medial lemniscus interdigitate so much in terminating in the thalamus that the dichotomy is obliterated. Therefore, the dissociations of modalities so conspicuous after lesions of the spinal cord cannot be expected and do not occur after lesions at the thalamic level.

Topographic Organization.[12, 51, 59]   In contrast to modality grouping, topographic organization is preserved. The ventral secondary trigeminal tract, carrying impulses from the face and mouth, terminates in the most medial portion of the posteroventral nucleus (VPM; arcuate nucleus). The medial lemniscus and the spinothalamic tract, carrying impulses from the trunk and limbs, end in the *lateral* portion of the posteroventral nucleus (VPL). A finer topographic organization of the posteroventral nucleus has been shown by studying the degeneration which followed transections at various levels of the spinal cord (Fig. 196). A still finer organization was proved by Mountcastle and Henneman,[39, 40] who searched the thalamus in half-millimeter steps for electrical activity during stimulation of points on the body surface. They obtained a finely detailed map of the thalamus (Fig. 197) with the head posteromedial, the tail anterolateral, the back superior, and the feet inferior. In short, the body surface is *projected* onto the thalamus, specifically onto the posteroventral nucleus, since electrical activity was not detected in any other nucleus.

Projection in the nervous system is roughly analogous to the projection of a lantern slide, nerve fibers taking the place of light "rays." There is considerable distortion. Certain parts of the body are "blown up" or enlarged, an arrangement which is functionally significant (p. 343). The essential feature of a topographically organized system is that the spatial relations existing peripherally are preserved. A detailed organization is often described as a "point-to-point" projection, i.e., a point on the body surface is projected to a point on the thalamus or cortex.

The topographic organization manifested in the thalamic terminations of sensory systems is preserved in the thalamocortical projections (Fig. 197). The medially situated arcuate nucleus (VPM), receiving impulses from the face, projects near the sylvian fissure. The lateral part of the posterolateral nucleus (VPL), receiving impulses from the leg, projects near the midline. The projection of impulses from the arm is intermediate in both thalamus and cortex. Thus, the body surface is projected upon the postcentral gyrus with its spatial relations preserved. It will be noted that the lateromedial relationship is opposite in the thalamus and cortex.

IPSILATERAL NATURE OF PROJECTIONS.   All of the cortical projection from one half of the thalamus passes to the cerebral cortex on the same side; none crosses in the corpus callosum to the opposite cortex. Thus, any representation of one lateral half of the body surface in the ipsilateral cortex must come about because some fibers either do not cross at levels below the thalamus or cross twice, once at a spinal level and once at a brain stem level. A slight ipsilateral projection to the thalamus has been demonstrated electrically.[39]

EXTENT AND DENSITY OF CORTICAL PROJECTIONS.   The *potential somatosensory area* is defined as that region of the cerebral cortex which receives projection fibers from the thalamus exclusive of the geniculate bodies. It includes the whole of both the frontal and the parietal lobes. These projections originate in relay nuclei, in association nuclei and in nuclei connected with the cerebellum, so the areas certainly are not equivalent. Neither are the various sectors* of the potential sensory areas equivalent in density of projection, as shown in Figure 199. The floor and posterior wall of the central fissure constitute a region of great density of projection. This density lessens markedly in passing posteriorly and anteriorly. The prefrontal area, including its orbital surface, receives quite a dense projection from the dorsomedial nucleus but has no known sensory function. A second sensory area in the superior wall of the sylvian fissure (somatic area II) must also be counted as a part of the potential somatosensory area.

Cortical Localization of Sensory Functions.[47, 48, 49, 51]   The somatosensory area has two parameters. The mediolateral dimension is devoted to topographic localization. The anteroposterior parameter may reflect functional localization.

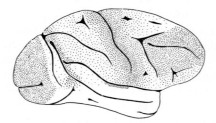

FIG. 199.   Cerebral cortex of macaque, showing extent and relative density of thalamocortical projections. (From Walker, *The primate thalamus*, Chicago, University of Chicago Press, 1938.)

ELECTRICAL STIMULATION.[43]   The cortical sensory areas has been stimulated electrically in conscious patients by Cushing (1909), by Foerster and by Penfield.[43] Stimulation of the area for the foot gives rise to sensations which seem to come from the foot; stimulation near the face area causes sensations which are localized in the face (see the *law of projection*). Sensations can often be elicited by stimulating the motor areas (4 and 6), even through the postcentral gyrus has been ablated, and these sensations are similar in quality to those elicited by stimulation of the postcentral gyrus. Ease of elicitation correlates well with the density of thalamocortical projection fibers. Sensations of the spinothalamic category—pain, warmth and cold—are rarely reported, the usual responses being a sense of numbness, tingling and, especially, a sensation of movement unaccompanied by actual movement. The sensations are not clearly formed, but the same is true of those aroused by stimulation of a sensory nerve. No evidence of zonal localization of modalities has been obtained.

ELECTRICAL ACTIVITY OF SENSORY CORTEX.[6, 47, 68]   Recording action currents evoked in the cerebral cortex by cutaneous stimulation reveals a detailed *dermatomal* projection.[68] Tactual stimulations were applied to the skin, and a recording electrode connected to an oscilloscope was moved systematically over the cortex in millimeter steps. Maximal *evoked* potentials† in response to stimulation occurred in the areas receiving projection fibers from the posteroventral nucleus, cytoarchitectural areas 3–1. Short latency potentials with clear topographic localization were recorded from areas 4 and 6; those from

* A cortical sector is a strip running mediolaterally which receives a projection from a single nucleus or a closely related group of thalamic nuclei.

† Cortical potentials induced by stimulation of end-organs or afferent pathways are, by convention, termed *evoked potentials*. The earliest response is surface positive and brief in latency and duration. Later waves will be discussed in a subsequent chapter.

areas 5 and 7 were smaller and of longer latency. Electrical responses were confined to the contralateral cortex, except that stimulation of the face gave rise to ipsilateral cortical responses as well.

The main conclusion reached from these experiments was that "the parts of contralateral body surface are represented in an orderly sequence. In the case of the lower extremity this sequence clearly reflects the metameric origin of the dermatomes; the arrangement is in the order of spinal innervation, not in the order—hip, thigh, knee, leg, ankle, foot, toes." Thus, the order may be termed "dermatomal" or "metameric," as opposed to "regional," the term "segmental" being ambiguous. The dermatomal law is borne out by the recent discovery that a fast fiber component of the splanchnic nerve reaches the trunk area of the cortex, the region which had been predicted on the basis of the segments at which the splanchnic nerve impulses enter the spinal cord. The observation also suggests that one should speak of the "somatovisceral" area[1, 2, 3] rather than of simply the "somatosensory" area.

Another result has been to demonstrate that the extent of cortical area devoted to a given region parallels the tactual acuity and innervation density of the region. Thus,

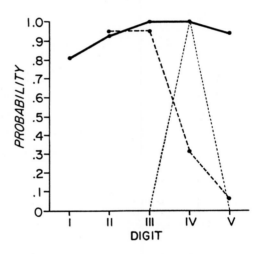

FIG. 200. Size of the field from which three different cortical units could be fired. *Solid line*, unit with a large receptive field; *dotted line*, unit with receptive field confined to one finger; *dashed line*, unit with large field, showing rapid decline of discharge probability near edge of field. (From Towe and Amassian, *J. Neurophysiol.*, 1958, *21*:292–311.)

a wider strip is devoted to the distal than to the proximal portions of the limbs or to the trunk dermatomes. Representation of T_{1-12}, dermatomes for the chest and abdomen, is compressed into a cortical strip only 2.5 mm. wide. In contrast, the cortical area for the thumb and forefinger dermatome (C_8) is several times larger.

The large numbers of sense organs and cortical neurons devoted to the relatively small skin areas of thumb and fingers underlie the low two point threshold and small error of localization of stimuli in those regions, and topographic organization of thalamocortical projections explains why a cortical lesion may, for example, affect the arm but spare the leg. However, although such organization is clinically important, is there sufficient point-to-point representation of the body surface on the cortex *physiologically* to contribute the neural substrate for topognosis and two point discrimination? While this is the best view we have, there are several disquieting thoughts. It is surprising that the brain should use the most simple conceivable device—multiple private lines. Modern communication engineering goes beyond this by using coding, so that one line carries many messages to avoid endless duplication of lines.

The ability to record from single cortical units is being used to attack this problem. A single neuron in the brain stem reticular substance[5] or in a cortical association area can be activated from widely separated receptors, e.g., from the arm and leg. However, in somatic area I, Mountcastle[37] found that the receptive field for a single cortical neuron can be quite small—smaller at the distal than at the proximal portion of a limb—and about the same size as the field of a spinal afferent neuron.[47] Towe and Amassian[57] found some cortical neurons with very broad receptive fields and others with very narrow ones (Fig. 200). Depth of anesthesia is an important factor in such experiments. Temporal patterning of the discharge of a cortical neuron has been demonstrated, and this device may serve as the basis for localization.[57] Finally, inhibition may narrow the discharge zone on the cerebral cortex.[7, 37] The same problem of how the cerebral cortex identifies the point of peripheral stimulation is also encountered in the study of audition and vision.

Somatic area II.[67] The sensory representation of the body in the postcentral gyrus (somatic area I) is duplicated in reverse order, i.e., face, arm, leg, in passing from the

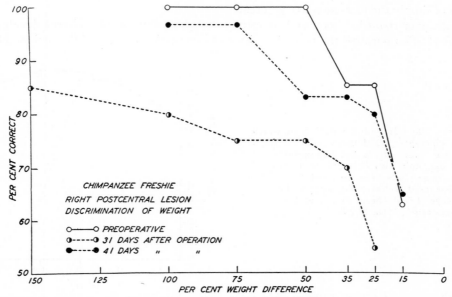

FIG. 201. Threshold curves for discrimination of lifted weights by a chimpanzee before and after ablation of postcentral gyrus. Discrimination with 50 per cent accuracy is a chance performance and represents absence of discriminatory ability. Abscissae are weight ratios, with difference in weight expressed as a per cent of standard 100 gram weight. Discrimination ability was severely affected a month after operation, but with practice approached preoperative ability. (From Ruch, Kasdon and Fulton, unpublished.)

foot of the postcentral gyrus to the bottom of the sylvian fissure.[56] This so-called "somatic area II" is less well organized topographically and the evoked potentials are of longer latency and more susceptible to anesthesia than those in the postcentral gyrus. Here, ipsilateral as well as contralateral cutaneous stimulation evokes potentials, and the second area may be more important in lower animals than in primates. Ablation experiments of the type described below suggest that this area is not concerned with sensory discrimination.[41]

ABLATION EXPERIMENTS.[6, 10, 42, 50] By special techniques, the sensory status of animals after cortical ablation can be safely inferred from overt behavior and even measured. According to Bard[6] contact placing is focally localized in the postcentral gyrus, but others believe that some ability returns unless the posterior parietal lobe is also removed. Parietal lobectomy affects the hopping reactions less permanently than it does the placing reactions. Bard believes the former is represented precentrally.

Discriminations of weight, roughness and geometric forms after various cortical lesions have been studied in a phylogenetic series including the monkey, chimpanzee and man.[50] Ablation of the postcentral gyrus reduces weight discriminatory ability in the chimpanzee (Fig. 201) and, to a lesser degree, in the monkey. The sensory impairment produced by lesions confined to the posterior parietal lobe (areas 5 and 7) does not differ greatly from that produced by lesions of the postcentral gyrus (areas 3–1). A parietal lobectomy interferes much more with the ability to discriminate weight and roughness than does ablation of the postcentral gyrus alone. Obviously the posterior parietal lobule does not depend solely upon sensory impulses relayed through the short association fibers from the postcentral gyrus. Besides the direct pathway between relay nuclei and areas 3–1 (Fig. 202), there is a "by-pass" through which impulses from the

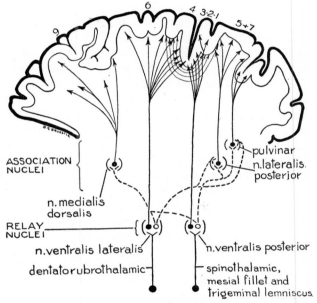

FIG. 202. Diagram of connections and projections of main thalamic nuclei. Geniculate bodies and nuclei with purely subcortical connection are not shown. Details of connections indicated by dotted lines are not known. Numbers along cerebral cortex designate Brodmann areas. (Based upon Walker and LeGros Clark. From Ruch, Kasdon and Walker, unpublished.)

great ascending sensory systems pass from relay nuclei to association nuclei to areas 5 and 7. It may be concluded from much recent anatomic and physiologic information that the conventional pathway, from the thalamus to the primary sensory area to the posterior-lying association area, is not the only course open to sensory impulses (see also Chap. 21). The association area may be reached via the relay nuclei and the thalamic association nuclei.

Ablation of the parietal lobe does not end ability to discriminate weights or roughness, except as a transitory phenomenon. Impairment, i.e., increased threshold, is all that remains after an extensive lapse of time and retraining. Several lines of evidence, therefore, suggest that the so-called "motor areas" may serve discriminative function and are, in fact, sensorimotor areas. For example, section of the medial lemniscus and spinothalamic tract leaves some weight discrimination and other proprioceptive function.[53] When the dentatorubrothalamic tract is involved in the lesion, the impairment is much greater. Posterior column section, like parietal lobectomy, although interfering seriously with weight discrimination at first, has little permanent effect.[16] This argues against the cerebellar route's being of importance, since the fibers from the arm to the dorsal spinocerebellar pathway run in the posterior column until the medulla (external cuneate nucleus) is reached. Perhaps the answer is that the precentral gyrus receives impulses from a rapidly conducting pathway which does not traverse the cerebellum.[35] The anatomic basis of this pathway is unknown.

The thalamocortical projection systems not yet discussed are the diffuse thalamocortical projections. Whether these afferents help support residual sensation following lesions of primary sensory areas remains to be learned. The role of this system in the maintenance of alertness will be discussed in Chapter 21.

To summarize, several multiple channels in addition to the classic pathway conduct somatosensory impulses to the cerebral cortex. The somatoviscerosensory area is extensive and may be reached by four pathways: (i) the cerebellum, (ii) the diffuse thalamocortical projection system, (iii) a recently discovered, short latency projection to the motor areas of unknown pathway, and (iv) the classic pathway via the relay nuclei.

Clinical Studies: Cortical Function in Man.[14, 24, 25, 43, 50, 59]   The status of sensation can be learned in much greater detail in man than in animals, especially when refined, quantitative methods borrowed from the psychologists are used, as was done by Head.[24] However, interpretation may be confused by increased intracranial pressure, lesions which do not respect cytoarchitectural zones, and lack of histologic verification of the lesion, especially when it is progressive. Studies in man often show only the *kind* of sensory function carried on by the cerebral cortex and leave unanswered many of the questions on cortical localization and the "corticalization" of sensory functions.

Cortical lesions do not produce anesthesia for any modality of sensation except as a transitory phenomenon, and persisting anesthesia implies subcortical damage (Fig. 181). The reasons for the latter are that the thalamus subserves sensation and deep lesions are more effective because they interrupt projection fibers to a larger area of cortex. Cortical lesions are manifested by an increase in the threshold for elicitation of sensation, and in severe cases only the fact and kind of stimulation can be recognized. The modalities of sensation are not equally affected. Pain recovers most quickly and almost completely; pressure, warmth and cold recover next; and light touch and proprioceptive sensation are most severely and permanently damaged. Discrimination of intensity is subnormal for all modalities.

Perceptions having a strong spatial element—topognosis, two point discrimination, figure writing and stereognosis—are especially affected by cortical lesions, and deficiencies in them may well be the first sign of damage to the parietal region. On the other hand, perception of temporal patterns (vibratory sensibility) is relatively little influenced by cortical lesions unless they extend into the white matter, as in the case illustrated in Figure 181. In general, tactual and proprioceptive sensations, and the perceptions built upon them, are affected in much the same way by parietal and posterior column lesions. This is not true of vibratory sensibility, which is greatly blunted by posterior column lesions but not by cortical lesions. The defects of stereognosis represent more than the default of a necessary sensory channel. They occur, especially from parietal lesions, in a marked degree when sensation is not greatly disturbed. If sensation is disturbed, the term to use is "astereognosis through anesthesia," or "stereoanesthesia."

Because spatial and discriminative functions are severely damaged by cortical lesions, Head and others have given the impression that sensation has a thalamic and perception a cortical representation. Intensity and spatial functions have even been assigned different areas in the parietal lobes. To separate sensation and perception is not in accord with modern psychologic teaching or with the close interrelation between the thalamus and cerebral cortex. Apparently the discrimination of fine spatial functions and of differences in intensity requires a multitude of neurons arranged in dense, spatially organized fields. The cortex possesses such fields and the thalamus does not. Why else do regions with a high degree of spatial discriminative ability, e.g., the forefinger or the fovea of the retina, have a wide expanse of the cortex devoted to them? Thus, even if the thalamus is capable of some form of sensation, it apparently does not possess the extensive apparatus necessary for fine discrimination and accurate localization, since only very few functional cells are left when the cortex is removed. Crude sensation of the type ascribed to the thalamus is "crude" in the sense that it is poorly located and capable only of coarse discrimination. Here, as in the discussion of epicritic and protopathic sensation, the same facts are open to two theories, one assuming qualitative difference and a different neural substrate, the other stressing quantitative and topographic differences in the neuronal organization of tracts and projection fields.

It is possible to argue that lamination and topographic organization at the thalamus and cortex represent mere engineering conveniences and are not functionally significant. Two facts would support this belief. The posterior parietal lobe is poorly organized topographically; yet damage to it can interfere with spatial discriminations, even though the highly organized apparatus of the postcentral gyrus remains intact. Moreover, the single cortical unit technique applied to the association area of a cat under chloralose anesthesia (a cortical excitant) shows that the same cell in the somatic association area can be fired from all four limbs and from superficial, deep and visceral nerves.[4] Topographic organization appears to be progressively less in ascending through the various levels of the nervous system. Some of the modern speculation based upon work of communication engineers suggests that this very dispersal rather than canalization may make more accurate discriminations possible.

Role of Thalamus in Sensation and Affect.[24, 59, 61]   Although the function of the thalamus is largely expressed through the cortex, the thalamus in man may not have lost all the function it indisputably has in animals with poorly developed cerebral cortices. The history of cortical localization teaches that a sensory or motor function should not be ascribed to subcortical regions until every possibility of cortical participation has been ruled out. The hemidecorticate man does not fulfill this requirement, because the cerebral cortex of only one hemisphere is removed and remaining sensory ability may be due to ipsilateral representation in the intact cortex.

The sensory disturbances produced by hemidecortication are less severe in the face than over the body. In the face contralateral to the ablation, touch and pinprick are quite well appreciated and to some degree localized; but over the body all forms of sensation are lost except the appreciation of heavy touches and pinpricks, and localization of them is defective. It is agreed that, in man and in the primates, deep sensibility and probably all functions of the posterior column have no ipsilateral representation. However, ipsilateral representation of cutaneous sensations has been demonstrated in lower animals, especially in somatosensory area II. Woolsey et al.[68] recorded action potentials from the postcentral gyrus on the *same* side as the point stimulated, but only for *superficial stimulation in the region of the head.*

Head believed that the thalamus subserves the affective side of sensation and therefore of pain, which is a strongly affective experience. Affectivity—pleasantness and unpleasantness—was considered a primitive function which, in the course of evolution, remained at a thalamic level despite development of the cerebral cortex. Pain is only slightly and transiently affected by cortical lesions, and clear-cut pain experiences are not elicited by stimulating the human cerebral cortex. In contrast to stimulation of the spinothalamic tract or the lateral nuclear mass of the thalamus, stimulation of the sensorimotor cortex will not motivate behavior, as will peripherally induced pain.[15]

THALAMIC SYNDROME.   In a classic ' thalamic syndrome," spontaneous pain and subjective overresponse to pleasant and unpleasant sti muli are prominent features. This syndrome is usually caused by occlusion of a small blood vessel (thalamogeniculate branch of the posterior cerebral artery) which supplies the posterolateral portion of the lateral nuclear mass of the thalamus.

The syndrome consists of unilateral symptoms:[59] (i) fleeting hemiplegia or hemiparesis, (ii) sensory disturbances of the cortical type, and (iii) overresponse or hyperpathia. Attacks of "spontaneous" or central pain of a severe, agonizing nature are common. Pinprick or strong stimulation produces a intensely disagreeable, irradiating, diffuse sensation which is quite intolerable. One of Head's patients, a clergyman, complained that his trousers produced such disagreeable sensations that he was forced to remove them! Pleasantness of a sensation is also magnified, and emotional responses to music give rise to excessive "feelings" on one side of the body! Sensory overresponse differs from hyperesthesia because the threshold is often elevated, but once it is attained the experience is overly intense. Little definite can be said about the thalamic syndrome. Spontaneous pain and overresponse have in common with the hyperpathia produced by disturbances at lower levels a reduction of touch and deep sensibility paralleled by a heightened response to painful stimuli. Perhaps all have a common explanation in the hypothesis that affective activity of the midline nuclei is normally held in check when the ventral posterior nucleus is activated.

REFERENCES

1. AMASSIAN, V. E. *J. Neurophysiol.*, 1951, *14:* 433–444.

2. AMASSIAN, V. E. *J. Neurophysiol.*, 1951, *14:* 445–460.

3. AMASSIAN, V. E. *Res. Publ. Ass. nerv. ment. Dis.*, 1952, *30:*371–402.

4. AMASSIAN, V. E. *J. Neurophysiol.*, 1954, *17:* 39–58.

5. AMASSIAN, V. E. and DeVITO, R. V. *J. Neurophysiol.*, 1954, *17:*575–603.

6. BARD, P. *Harvey Lect.*, 1938, *33:*143–169.

7. v. BÉKÉSY, G. *J. acoust. Soc. Amer.*, 1957, *29:*1059–1069; *ibid.*, 1958, *30:*399–412.

8. BORING, E. G. *Sensation and perception in the history of experimental psychology.* New York, D. Appleton-Century Co., 1942.

9. BROOKHART, J. M., LIVINGSTON, W. K. and HAUGEN, F. P. *J. Neurophysiol.*, 1953, *16:* 634–642.

10. CHOW, K. L. and HUTT, P. J. *Brain*, 1953, *76:*625–677.

11. CLARK, D., HUGHES, J. and GASSER, H. S. *Amer. J. Physiol.*, 1935, *114:*69–76.

12. CLARK, W. E. LeG. and BOGGON, R. H. *Phil. Trans.*, 1935, *B224:*313–359.

13. COLLINS, W. F. and RANDT, C. T. *J. Neurophysiol.*, 1958, *21:*345–352.

14. CRITCHLEY, M. *The parietal lobes.* London, Arnold & Co., 1953.

15. DELGADO, J. M. R., ROBERTS, W. W. and MILLER, N. E. *Amer. J. Physiol.*, 1954, *179:*587–593.

16. DeVITO (LOGAN), J. *Study of sensory pathways in monkeys.* Ph.D. Thesis, University of Washington, 1954.

17. DOUGLAS, W. W. and RITCHIE, J. M. *J. Physiol.*, 1957, *139:*385–399.

18. FOERSTER, O. *Brain*, 1933, *56:*1–39.

19. FOERSTER, O. *Bumke u. Foersters Handb. Neurol.*, 1936, *5:*1–403.

20. FULTON, J. F. *Physiology of the nervous system*, 3d ed. New York, Oxford University Press, 1949.

21. GARDNER, E. D. and MORIN, F. *Amer. J. Physiol.*, 1953, *174:*149–154.

22. GASSER, H. S. *Res. Publ. Ass. nerv. ment. Dis.*, 1943, *23:*44–62.

23. HARRISON, F. and CORBIN, K. B. *J. Neurophysiol.*, 1942, *5:*465–482.

24. HEAD, H. *Studies in neurology.* London, Oxford University Press, 1920.

25. HOLMES, G. *Brain*, 1927, *50:*413–427.

26. HUNT, C. C. *J. gen. Physiol.*, 1954, *38:*117–131.

27. HYNDMAN, O. R. and Wolkin, J. *Arch. Neurol. Psychiat. (Chicago)*, 1943, *50:*129–148.

28. KAHN, E. A. and RAND, R. W. *J. Neurosurg.*, 1952, *9:*611–619.

29. KEEGAN, J. J. *Arch. Neurol. Psychiat. (Chicago)*, 1943, *50:*67–83.

30. KEEGAN, J. J. and GARNETT, F. D. *Anat. Rec.* 1948, *102:*409–437.

31. LANDAU, W. and BISHOP, G. H. *Arch. Neurol. Psychiat. (Chicago)*, 1953, *69:*490–504.

32. LEWIS, T. *Pain.* New York, Macmillan, 1942.

33. LLOYD, D. P. C. *J. Neurophysiol.*, 1943, *6:*293–326.

34. LLOYD, D. P. C. and McINTYRE, A. K. *J. Neurophysiol.*, 1950, *13:*39–54.

35. MALIS, L. I., PRIBRAM, K. H. and KRUGER, L. *J. Neurophysiol.*, *16:*161–167.

36. MELZACK, R., STOTLER, W. and LIVINGSTON, W. K. *J. Neurophysiol.*, 1958, *21:*353–367.

37. MOUNTCASTLE, V. B. *J. Neurophysiol.*, 1957, *20:*408–434.

38. MOUNTCASTLE, V. B., COVIAN, M. R. and HARRISON, C. R. *Res. Publ. Ass. nerv. ment. Dis.*, 1952, *30:*339–370.

39. MOUNTCASTLE, V. [B.] and HENNEMAN, E. *J. Neurophysiol.*, 1949, *12:*85–100.

40. MOUNTCASTLE, V. B. and HENNEMAN, E. *J. comp. Neurol.*, 1952, *97:*409–439.

41. ORBACH, J. and CHOW, K. L. *J. Neurophysiol.*, 1959, *22:*195–203.

42. PEELE, T. L. *J. Neurophysiol.*, 1944, 7:269–286.

43. PENFIELD, W. and RASMUSSEN, A. T. *The cerebral cortex in man: a clinical study of localization of function.* New York, Macmillan, 1950.

44. POCHIN, E. E. *Clin. Sci.*, 1938, *3:*191–196.

45. POLLOCK, L. J. *J. comp. Neurol.*, 1920, *32:* 357–378.

46. RANSON, S. W., DROEGEMUELLER, W. H., DAVENPORT, H. K. and FISHER, C. *Res. Publ. Ass. nerv. ment. Dis.*, 1935, *15:*3–34.

47. ROSE, J. E. and MOUNTCASTLE, V. B. Chap. 17 in *Handbook of physiology. Section 1. Neurophysiology*, vol. 1, J. FIELD, ed. Baltimore, Williams & Wilkins, 1959.

48. RUCH, T. C. Chap. 19 in: FULTON, J. F. *Physiology of the nervous system*, 3d ed. New York, Oxford University Press, 1949.

49. RUCH, T. C. Chap. 4 in: STEVENS, S. S. *Handbook of experimental psychology.* New York, John Wiley & Sons, 1951.

50. RUCH, T. C., FULTON, J. F. and GERMAN, W. J. *Arch. Neurol. Psychiat. (Chicago)*, 1938, *39:*919–937.

51. RUCH, T. C., PATTON, H. D. and AMASSIAN, V. E. *Res. Publ. Ass. nerv. ment. Dis.*, 1952, *30:*403–429.

52. SHERRINGTON, C. S. *Phil. Trans.*, 1898, *B190:* 45–186.
53. SJÖQVIST, O. and WEINSTEIN, E. A. *J. Neurophysiol.*, 1942, *5:*69–74.
54. SPIEGEL, E. A., KLETZKIN, M. and SZEKELY, E. G. *J. Neuropath.*, 1954, *13:*212–220.
55. STEIN, M. H. and WORTIS, H. *Arch. Neurol. Psychiat. (Chicago)*, 1941, *46:*471–476.
56. STEIN, M. H., WORTIS, H. and JOLLIFFE, N. *Arch. Neurol. Psychiat. (Chicago)*, 1941, *46:* 464–470.
57. TOWE, A. L. and AMASSIAN, V. E. *J. Neurophysiol.*, 1958, *21:*292–311.
58. TROTTER, W. and DAVIES, H. M. *J. Psychol. Neurol. (Lpz.)*, 1913, *20*, Ergänzungsheft 2:102–150.
59. WALKER, A. E. *The primate thalamus.* Chicago, University of Chicago Press, 1938.
60. WALKER, A. E. *J. Neurophysiol.*, 1939, *2:*234–248.
61. WALKER, A. E. *Res. Publ. Ass. nerv. ment. Dis.*, 1943, *23:*63–85.
62. WALSHE, F. M. R. *Brain*, 1942, *65:*48–112.
63. WEDDELL, G., GUTTMANN, L., and GUTMANN, E. *J. Neurol. Psychiat.*, 1941, *N.S. 4:*206–225.
64. WHITE, J. C. *Arch. Neurol. Psychiat. (Chicago)*, 1954, *71:*1–23.
65. WHITE, J. C. and SWEET, W. H. *Pain. Its mechanisms and neurosurgical control.* Springfield, Ill., C. C Thomas, 1955, xxiv, 736 pp.
66. WHITE, J. C., SWEET, W. H., HAWKINS, R. and NILGES, R. G. *Brain*, 1950, *73:*346–367.
67. WOOLSEY, C. N. and FAIRMAN, D. *Surgery*, 1946, *19:*684–702.
68. WOOLSEY, C. N., MARSHALL, W. H. and BARD, P. *Johns Hopk. Hosp. Bull.*, 1942, *70:*399–441.
69. ZOTTERMAN, Y. *J. Physiol.*, 1939, *95:*1–28.

CHAPTER 15

Pathophysiology of Pain

By THEODORE C. RUCH

IN the previous two chapters the pathologic physiology of pain as seen in disturbances of the nervous system has been stressed. The present chapter will deal with the pain arising from pathologic processes at the periphery: visceral pain, muscle and joint pain and cutaneous hyperalgesia. In a sense, all pain is pathologic, but these forms of pain are especially so. This chapter will also deal with the physiologic mechanisms involved in psychosomatic pain states.

Characteristics of Pain. Pain is often described as pricking, stabbing, tearing, stinging, burning or throbbing. These descriptions reflect the duration of the sensation or identify it with an agent which has caused such pain in the past. Many agents (needle prick, pinching, traction on a hair, heat, electric current, etc.) cause indistinguishable "pricking" pains when briefly and focally applied.[27] The same stimuli prolonged cause a "burning" pain, even though heat is not involved. What Lewis[26] called the time-intensity curve of pain makes pains seem different and often suggests a possible origin. A needle prick produces a flash of pain. The impact of the pulse wave over sensitive pain organs will cause a throbbing pain, etc. Figure 203 gives additional examples.

Sharp pain elicited from the skin is called "bright." Heavy, diffuse, aching pain from the deeper layer of the skin or the subjacent receptors, as is elicited by sustained pinching of the web between the fingers, is called "dull." The autonomic responses to deep and visceral pain—sweating, nausea, fall in blood pressure causing pain to be sickening—differ from those to cutaneous pain. Thus pain is a protean phenomenon differing in quality and time course, depending on how it is elicited.

Localization, Projection and Reference of Pain. These words are related but should not be used indiscriminately. The basic concept is *projection* (see Chap. 13), a psychologic process which makes sensation seem to come from some layer of the body or from the external world. *Localization* (topognosis) reflects slight random errors in the projection of the sensation to the skin (Fig. 204). The clarity and extent of the projection can vary. Deep and visceral pain are often described as diffuse and poorly localized. *Projected pathologic pain* accurately describes the fact that impulses set up anywhere along the pain pathway from nerve to cortex give rise to a sensation projected to the peripheral

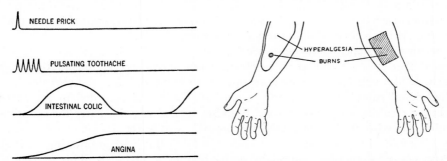

FIG. 203. *Left:* Time-intensity curves of some common forms of pain. (From Lewis, *Pain*, New York, Macmillan, 1952.) *Right:* Arm to right illustrates primary hyperalgesia confined to area of burn; arm to left, secondary hyperalgesia extending well beyond burn. (From Hardy *et al.*, *J. clin. Invest.*, 1950, *29*:115–140.)

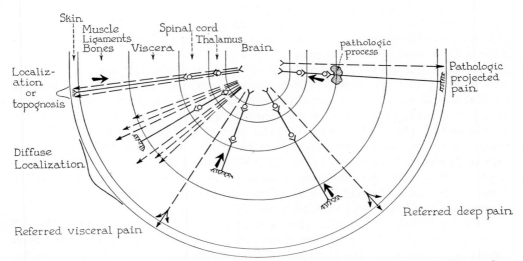

FIG. 204. Highly schematic representation of the projection of pain to points at a distance from the actual stimulation. Note that the place from which the pain seems to come (projection) may be incorrect in respect to two dimensions, depth and distance.

region served by the end-organs of that pathway. Thus, the pain from a ruptured intervertebral disk is projected, not referred. (Note that it is the stimulus that is pathologic; the projection is normal, the brain merely having been tricked.) *Referred pain* is pain projected to an area distant from and usually superficial to the point of end-organ stimulation. Referred pain can be described as a systematic error in the projection of pain; examples will be given below.

Cutaneous Hyperalgesia. In many pathologic states of the skin, light innocuous contacts not normally painful, such as friction from clothes, arouse pain. Often the pain is an especially intense, unpleasant, burning sensation which is diffuse, poorly localized or prolonged. This condition, called *hyperalgesia*, can be caused by a large number of agents (heat, abrasions, ultraviolet light, freezing, etc.). Two forms of hyperalgesia appear to exist. In *local* or *primary hyperalgesia*, the threshold is lowered and the response is intense but normal in quality. In *secondary hyperalgesia*, the threshold is actually *elevated*, but the response, once it occurs, is especially unpleasant. This phenomenon extends well beyond the area damaged.

*Local or primary hyperalgesia.** Although it is common experience that several hours after an injury the skin becomes reddened and hypersensitive to pain, it was not until 1933 that a major study of this phenomenon was conducted.[27] Pain resulting from brief stimulation of a hyperalgesic area has a burning quality. It is translated into actual pain when the area is heated. Cooling reduces the hyperalgesia.

Because the hyperalgesic state develops after a painless interval, Lewis and Hess[27] reasoned that it is not caused by persisting damage of nerve endings dating from the trauma. Echlin and Propper[12] demonstrated a sense organ basis for hyperalgesia. They applied equal stimuli to intact and scraped frog skin and recorded in the cutaneous nerves the resulting slowly conducted impulses typical of pain. After the scraping, the stimulus elicited more impulses and the threshold was lower. In minor injuries, hyperalgesia is confined to the traumatized area (Fig. 203), but, with greater injury, it gradually spreads out somewhat, especially along lymphatic channels. This pattern would result from the diffusion of a substance which causes both pain and vasodilatation, part of the inflammation process. Histamine is such a substance. Lewis and Hess[27] believed some other, unidentified, substance is involved, because hyperalgesia is not combined with itching, the main response to histamine injected intradermally.[4] If, as Bishop[5] suggests, itch is caused by low grade stimulation of pain fibers, this is not a serious objection, and Rosenthal has marshalled much evidence to support the view that histamine is a chemical mediator for pain.[37, 38]

Secondary hyperalgesia.† Secondary hyperalgesia was also first studied by Lewis, who observed that prolonged electrical stimulation causes, after a painless interval, cutaneous pain and reddening extending two or three inches beyond the point of stimulation (Fig. 203). The main characteristics distinguishing secondary from primary hyperalgesia are: (i) The painful area extends far beyond the borders of the irritation into undamaged skin. (ii) The secondary form never lasts more than 48 hours, whereas primary hyperalgesia may last for days. (iii) The threshold only seems lower in secondary hyperalgesia because the subjective response is greatly augmented.[16] (iv) Secondary hyperalgesia extends beyond the area of flush (erythema), but the pain and vascular phenomena in primary hyperalgesia are usually coincident, at least initially.

Peripheral theory. To explain hyperalgesia, Lewis postulated a so-called "nocifensor" system of nerves, which has not been demonstrated anatomically. Some explain hyperalgesia by an axon reflex like that responsible for the flare (Chap. 34). Impulses passing along a pain fiber reach a point of dichotomy and return peripherally over a branch which, in turn, releases a chemical substance which causes local vasodilatation and sensitizes adjacent pain endings. Such a phenomenon could spread beyond the distribution of a sensory unit.

While the occurrence of hyperalgesia from antidromic stimulation of peripheral nerves in man[26] has been questioned,[16] Habgood[15] has demonstrated release of a chemical substance by antidromic stimulation of frog's cutaneous nerve. He arranged two pieces of frog skin, each with a cutaneous nerve attached, in such a way that their undersides were in contact and the two nerves were available for

* "Primary hyperalgesia" is a term suggested by Hardy *et al.*[16] Lewis[26] speaks of "erythralgia" to emphasize the accompanying local reddening.
† "Hyperpathia" is preferable to "hyperalgesia" since it emphasizes the subjective nature of the change, leaving "hyperalgesia" to reflect the lowering in threshold.

stimulation and recording (Fig. 205). When one nerve was stimulated antidromically, the dromic discharge caused in the other nerve by a standard stimulus applied to its piece of skin was increased (sensitization). Often actual discharge was produced in the second nerve (induced discharge). Sensitization and induced discharge also occurred during stimulation and recording from adjacent nerve twigs. As in man, cutaneous nerve fibers in the frog have interdigitating ramifications in the skin (Fig. 205). Pharmacologic analysis suggested that histamine (not acetylcholine) was the chemical agent involved.

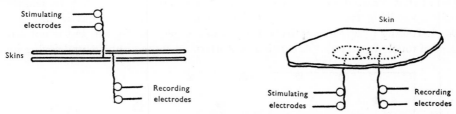

FIG. 205.   Double skin preparation (*left*) and double nerve preparation (*right*) used to prove the release of a chemical by antidromic stimulation of a cutaneous nerve. (From Habgood, *J. Physiol.*, 1950, *111*:195–213.)

Central theories.   Hardy et al.[16] stimulated a nerve *proximal* to a procaine block. They obtained hyperalgesia mostly proximal to the block (Fig. 206), not below as Lewis[26] had found. Repeated pinpricks within the hyperalgesic area caused its borders to shrink, an occurrence suggestive of central inhibition. After the pricking was stopped, the zone expanded again. Hardy and his coworkers concluded therefore that secondary hyper-

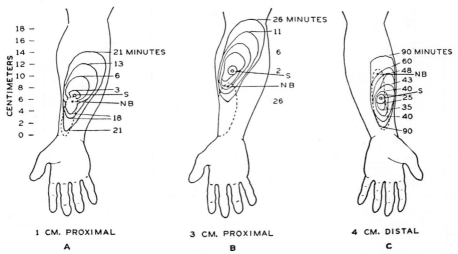

FIG. 206.   Development of secondary hyperalgesia as shown by concentric solid lines when a cutaneous nerve is stimulated at point S proximal (*A, B*) and distal (*C*) to a nerve block (*NB*). Broken line marks area of anesthesia supposedly due to nerve damage. Figures give rate of development and spread of hyperalgesia. (From Hardy et al., *J. clin. Invest.*, 1950, *29*:115–140.)

algesia occurs because a barrage of impulses from the injured area facilitates centrally the afferent pathways from adjacent skin areas. They postulated an interneuronal system between first-order pain neurons and spinothalamic tract fibers. However, this system has not been proved anatomically or physiologically. It is unwise to postulate a set of fibers to explain each physiologic phenomenon and dichotomizing of first-order neurons would seem to make such interneurons unnecessary. Quite possibly hyperalgesia is explicable along the same lines as referred pain, discussed in detail below (see Fig. 213). Also, the point of interaction may well lie in the thalamus or cortex rather than in the spinal cord.

Itch. Itching rivals pain in the amount of discomfort it causes. According to Rothman,[39] it is a temporal pattern of pain which tends to follow stimuli as an after-action. Bishop[5] induced it with repeated shocks by "sparking" from electrodes not quite touching the skin, each stimulus being too weak to be felt by itself. As shown in Figure 207, itch is distributed in a punctate fashion; this is true of chemically induced itch[40] as well as of that induced by electrical and mechanical stimulation.[5, 6, 41] In sensory dissociations resulting from neurologic lesions or operations, pain and itching are lost together. Itching disappears entirely in cases of complete analgesia, but is not affected in cases of touch anesthesia.[4] According to Zotterman,[55] the impulses underlying itching

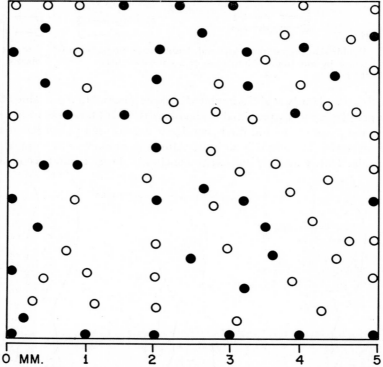

FIG. 207.   Map of itch points on flexor surface of wrist. *Solid circles,* Points at which itching was reported. *Unfilled circles,* Sites at which itching was not experienced. Stimulus, 5 millisecond square-wave pulses; rate, 25 impulses per second; intensity, 1.5 V. (After Shelley and Arthur. *Arch. Derm.* (*Chicago*), 1957, 76:296–323.)

are conducted in C fibers, since only these continue to discharge in the afterstimulation period when itching occurs. The latent period for itch following mechanical stimulation is consistent with this view.[41]

Itching is explained by the release of a chemical substance, perhaps histamine, which stimulates nerve endings. Histamine injected into the skin certainly causes intense itching, and histamine is liberated into the skin by the types of injury which cause itching (mechanical damage, electrical stimulation,[36] sunburn, etc.). Arthur and Shelley[2, 40, 41] argue that, unlike histamine, proteinase produces a prompt and sustained itching without evident whealing or other gross tissue damage.

DEEP PAIN

The impulses underlying deep pain originate in muscles, tendons and joints, and, with occasional exceptions, traverse the muscle branches of mixed nerves. The quality of deep pain is dull, aching or boring. It seems to come from below the skin, but is difficult to localize, for it tends to radiate. Deep pain is accompanied by a definite autonomic response and is especially disagreeable, even sickening. The deep structures vary in sensitivity. According to Inman and Saunders,[21] the periosteum has the lowest threshold to irritating chemicals, followed in order of ascending threshold by ligaments, fibrous capsules of joints, tendons, fascia and the body of muscle. Feindel et al.[13] applied the methylene blue staining technique to deep pain fiber plexuses. Fine, beaded, naked fibers like those in skin form networks of varying density, being sparsest in connective tissue septa of muscles, denser in fascia, and still denser in periosteum. The density of innervation, then, seems to agree with the sensitivity of the structures.

Adequate Stimuli for Deep Pain. Mechanical forces excite deep pain endings. After trauma or infection these become so sensitive that the slightest touch or movement may be distressing. The endings are also sensitive to chemicals used experimentally or occurring in the body. Prolonged, continuous contraction of muscles, as in holding surgical retractors, causes muscles to ache and become sore. Rhythmic contraction, as in walking, or sustained contraction interrupted at frequent intervals causes no pain unless the muscle is ischemic. The pain which results from activity of ischemic muscle is called angina if it occurs in the heart and intermittent claudication if it occurs in the leg.*

Lewis' experimental analysis[26] of muscle pain is one of the classics in human physiology. It illustrates how much can be accomplished with minimal equipment but with close observation and reasoning. He had a subject grip an ergograph at the rate of once each second. When the circulation to the forearm was arrested by an inflated sphygmomanometer cuff around the upper arm, the standard exercise caused pain within 24 to 45 seconds which became severe in 60 to 90 seconds. Muscle tension is not the direct cause of such pain, because the pain is continuous while the contractions are intermittent. Under standard conditions, the time of onset of pain is remarkably constant, as is the onset of claudication in a patient. When exercise is stopped but occlusion is continued, the pain continues undiminished (Fig. 208). When blood is readmitted to the limb, the pain disappears within a few seconds. Since the pain stimulus appears to be "stored up," Lewis and his coworkers concluded that the stimulus is a chemical substance arising out of the contraction process.

This substance seems to be eliminated from the muscle by metabolism rather than by being washed out in the blood. Intact circulation does not prevent the development of pain in muscles during sustained contraction (Fig. 208) or during rhythmic contraction when the blood is insufficiently oxygenated. However, oxygen lack in itself is probably not the direct and sufficient pain stimulus.[17]

Lewis termed the hypothetical metabolite "factor P." It seems to be a normal product of muscle metabolism in both the resting and active states and to stimulate the pain endings only when it accumulates in fairly large quantities. Exercise facilitates this accumulation because it induces greater metabolic activity and thus greater release of factor P. For example, if a muscle with an occluded blood supply is exercised, but not to the point of pain, continued arrest of circulation to the resting muscle will eventually cause pain.[33] Cessation of pain requires only that the concentration of factor P be reduced below the critical threshold level, not that it be completely removed from the muscle. If a muscle performs measured work until pain starts and is rested only until pain stops before the experiment is repeated, the time to onset of pain is much shorter for the second trial.[26] This means that the factor P produced during the second trial is added to an accumulation remaining from the first trial, even though pain induced by the first trial had stopped.

Of the many agents which may constitute factor P (anoxia, pH changes, lactic acid, potassium, histamine), potassium, in the opinion of Dorpat,[11] is most likely the one. Both activity and ischemia release potassium from the muscle fiber, and intra-arterial injection of it provokes a severe pain in muscle resembling ischemic muscle pain.

* "Angina," a Latin word, refers to the sense of suffocating contraction which accompanies the pain from the heart. "Claudication" refers to the limping which accompanies the pain.

The pain-inducing nature of sustained muscle contraction is particularly important because many pains and aches in organic disease and anxiety states result from it. The underlying mechanism is probably diminished blood flow caused by compression of blood vessels within the muscles.[11] Muscle temperature *decreases* momentarily at the beginning of exercise, probably because the blood, which is warmer than the arm, is prevented from entering it.

Causes of sustained muscle contraction. Sustained contractions of skeletal muscle likely to cause pain may arise from higher centers or from reflexes of somatic or visceral afferents. Such reflexes are important (i) as diagnostic signs (Kernig's sign, stiff neck of meningeal irritation, abdominal rigidity of appendicitis), and (ii) as secondary sources of pain and discomfort.

Nociceptive impulses experimentally induced from a restricted focus in the head often give rise to a pain confined and fairly well localized to the traumatized focus, and also to a second, more generalized, pain ("headache"). According to the following

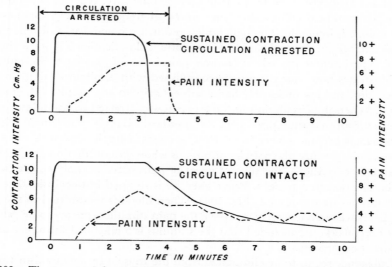

FIG. 208. Time course of sustained muscle contraction and resulting pain with arrested and intact circulation. In both experiments contraction was maintained as long as possible. (From Dorpat, *Mechanisms of muscle pain*, M.D. thesis. University of Washington School of Medicine, 1952.)

analysis, the second pain results from tension of the neck muscles.[42] A single injection of 0.6 ml. of 6 per cent saline solution into the right temporal muscle caused intense local pain accompanied by sweating, salivation, lacrimation, nausea and contraction of the temporal and neck muscles. However, it caused no discomfort in the neck. Additional injections were made before temporal muscle pain had subsided. Pain in the neck began after the second injection and increased with each subsequent injection. At the end of 40 minutes, the neck pain was rated at nearly half the intensity of the local pain. With other stimuli—an irritating substance injected into the conjunctival sac or excessive activity of the external ocular muscle to overcome a tendency to double vision caused by a vertical prism set before one eye—the neck pain outlasted and, in the latter case, exceeded the local (frontal) pain (Fig. 209). The neck pain was promptly relieved by massage. It is not known how much the building up of the reflex muscle contraction is due to a change in the interneuron pools of the spinal cord, since no clear experimental demonstration of such long-lasting facilitatory effects has been made. The muscle contraction may be due to a vicious circle: deep pain→sustained reflex contraction→deep pain→reflex contraction→etc. The success of such single procedures as osteopathic

treatments, ethyl chloride sprays and procaine hydrochloride injection of trigger zones
may depend on the breaking of the circle.

Muscle pain in anxiety states.   Headache associated with a mild emotional disturbance
such as that caused by an uncongenial job was found to be accompanied by tension of
the neck and scalp muscles which disappeared along with the pain after psychiatric and
drug therapy.[42] Holmes and Wolff[19] believe that in many instances of backache local
dysfunction is minimal and that muscle tension produced by emotional tension is the
cause of *secondary pain* in the back. Muscle tension could readily be induced by provoking
hostility in the patient and relieved by appropriate psychiatric treatment. Thus, the
sustained muscle contraction which causes pain reduces down to a familiar pattern
representing a segmental reflex discharge and facilitation of this reflex from the brain.

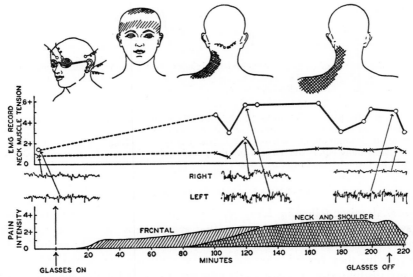

FIG. 209.   Distribution and time intensity course of muscle tension and pain from sustained
contraction of external ocular muscle induced by vertical prism in front of left eye. Note neck pain
and muscle tension, middle record, is on this side. Dips in upper EMG record are due to involuntary
movements of head and neck. (From Simons *et al., Res. Publ. Ass. nerv. ment. Dis.*, 1943, *23:*228–244.)

Referred Muscle Pain.   By a mechanism entirely different from that operating
in secondary pain, the stimuli arising from a restricted focus in muscle can give rise to
pain which appears to come from points distant from the point of stimulation. In short,
muscle pain shows the phenomenon of referred pain in the same way as visceral pain
does (see below). Lewis and Kellgren[28] injected small quantities of 5 per cent saline
solution, which is highly irritating, into deep structures (Fig. 210). Localization of the
resulting pain was fairly accurate when injections were made into fascia or tendons
lying near the surface and into the perosteum of superficial bones such as the tibia. Pain
from the same kinds of deeply situated structures, and also pain from the belly of a
muscle, were diffuse and often were referred to a distant area of the skin surface in a
regular, reproducible fashion (Fig. 210). Deep somatic pain was referred to the dermatomes supplied by the posterior roots which conduct pain impulses from the muscle
stimulated. Kellgren[23] systematically worked out the segmental reference of pain by
injecting the interspinous ligaments successively with hypertonic saline. The referred
pain for deep muscle stimulation is accompanied by rigidity and tenderness of muscles,
and the skin may become hyperesthetic.

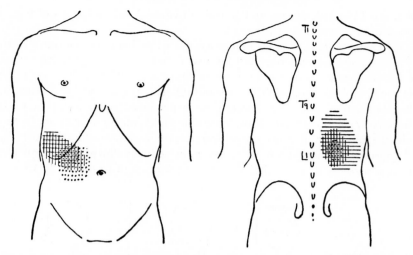

FIG. 210. Reference of deep pain elicited by injections of hypertonic saline into three muscles supplied with pain fibers from T_9: multifidus muscle (*horizontal lines*), intercostals (*vertical lines*) and rectus abdominis (*dots*). (From Kellgren, *Clin. Sci.*, 1938, 3:175–190.)

These results have been criticized by Sinclair *et al.*[43] on the grounds that the saline reached nerve trunks, which would make the pain projected rather than referred. Kellgren,[24] however, showed that it is quite difficult to stimulate nerve trunks (as opposed to nerve endings) by saline injection, and that when the needle actually enters the nerve trunk the pain is quite different. Further examples of referred deep pain will be brought out in the next section.

VISCERAL AND REFERRED PAIN

Neuroanatomists, following Langley, define the sympathetic nervous system as an efferent system. Langley was fully aware that sympathetic nerves and the white rami carry sensory fibers from the viscera. He chose to "rule them out" by definition because, except in origin, they resemble ordinary somatic afferents, whereas the sympathetic efferents are distinguished from somatic efferents by a peripheral synapse. Because so much autonomic surgery is performed to control pain, the modern tendency is to alter Langley's definition and to speak of "sympathetic," "autonomic" or, better still, "*visceral*" *afferents*. Pain impulses arising within the abdominal and thoracic cavities may reach the central nervous system by three channels: (i) the parasympathetic nerves, (ii) the sympathetic nerves, and (iii) the somatic nerves innervating the body wall and the diaphragm. The last of these channels makes visceral sensation a somewhat larger question than autonomic afferent innervation.

Visceral Pain.[26, 31, 48] It is noted by surgeons operating with local anesthesia that visceral organs can be handled and even cut, crushed or burned without causing sensation, as long as traction on the mesentery and stimulation of the body wall are avoided. And it is true that the viscera are sparsely innervated. However, Kinsella[25] has shown that a broad, firm, manual pressure on the appendix elicits pain when restricted stimuli affecting only a few fibers of the sparse innervation are ineffective. If account is taken of the principle of the adequate stimulus and the fact that pathologic states may lower the threshold of pain fibers, the viscera are unquestionably sensitive. The viscera are not normally exposed to the forms of stimulation that are adequate for skin receptors and therefore have not evolved sensitivity to them. The adequate stimuli for visceral afferents are those arising from their own environment and especially from their own activities and pathologic states. Such adequate stimuli include: (i) sudden distention against resistance; (ii) spasms or strong contractions, especially when accompanied by ischemia;

(iii) chemical irritants; and (iv) mechanical stimulation, especially when the organ is hyperemic (stomach). The pain from such stimulation is not, as is often stated, due to traction on the mesentery. Normal contractions and relaxations of visceral organs apparently do not discharge pain fibers, although normal activities may become painful when the blood supply is inadequate.

Most visceral reflexes and organic sensations are served by afferents in the parasympathetic nerves (see Chap. 16), but *impulses serving visceral pain are conducted mainly in the sympathetic nerves*. The major exceptions to this rule, given in detail below, lie in the pelvic regions and in the esophagus and trachea. Because sympathetic nerves are not essential for visceral regulatory reflexes, sympathectomy for the relief of pain does not produce serious visceral dysfunction.

Pain pathways can be interrupted at several points, as can be seen by tracing a typical pathway from an abdominal organ. The axons of free nerve endings in the walls of a viscus follow the artery to the abdominal aorta, where they traverse the collateral ganglia without synapse and enter the splanchnic nerve. The ganglion of the sympathetic chain is entered and traversed, again without synapse; and, by way of the white ramus, the fibers reach the spinal nerve close to the spinal ganglia. The cell body of the viscerosensory fiber is situated in the spinal ganglion, and the central process enters the spinal cord by way of the dorsal root. There it forms reflex connections with somatic motoneurons and preganglionic fibers and ascending connections with the neurons of the spinothalamic tract. A visceral organ can therefore be denervated of pain fibers by (i) stripping the artery supplying it (periarterial neurectomy), (ii) removal or alcohol injection of the sympathetic chain of ganglia at appropriate levels, (iii) rhizotomy of several posterior roots, and (iv) section of the spinothalamic tract (cordotomy). Impulses from a single visceral organ enter the spinal cord by several roots, necessitating

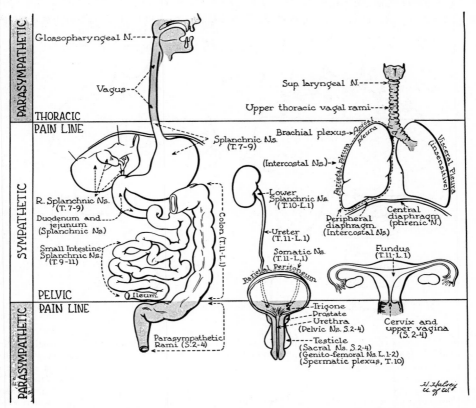

FIG. 211. Summary diagram of pain innervation of various viscera. Pain afferents from structures between thoracic and pelvic pain lines traverse sympathetic nerves, and structures above and below these lines traverse parasympathetic nerves. (Data from White, *Res. Publ. Ass. nerv. ment. Dis.*, 1943, *23*:373–390.)

extensive root sections. Cordotomy is often the operation of choice because somatic as well as visceral structures are frequently involved.

Visceral pain fibers are not confined to the sympathetic nerves. Many pain impulses reach the spinal cord via the pelvic nerve; others reach the brain stem via the vagus nerve. Sympathetic surgery for the relief of hypertension permits study of this question in man (Fig. 211). Below an imaginary line, which may be termed the *pelvic pain line*, pain impulses from the bladder neck, prostate, urethra, uterine cervix and the lower end of the colon are conducted to the spinal cord by way of the parasympathetic pelvic nerve. This explains why hypogastric neurectomy fails to relieve bladder pain. Note that the portions of the urogenital system falling above this line (bladder fundus, kidney, ureters, ovaries, fallopian tubes, uterus and testes) are served with pain afferents by way of sympathetic nerves. (The testes have migrated below the pelvic pain line, carrying with them a sympathetic innervation derived from the tenth thoracic cord segment.) Above the pelvic pain line, the pain fibers from the abdominal and most of the thoracic viscera pursue sympathetic nerves, although they have equal opportunity to join the vagus nerve.

It has long been taught that no visceral pain impulses are conducted in the vagus. By means of implanted electrodes, Bradford Cannon[8] stimulated the vagus in cats below the recurrent laryngeal branches. No pain responses were observed. However, other observations[14, 46, 51] suggest that a "thoracic pain line" may be drawn, with the esophagus and trachea giving fibers to the vagus nerve. Finally, it is to be noted that somatic nerves are also concerned with innervation of the visceral cavities.

Impulses arising in visceral structures may give rise to pain localized to more superficial structures of the body, often those at a considerable distance from the disturbed organ. Such pain is said to be *referred*. Why visceral pain is referred is not known, but what determines where the pain is referred is known. Pain is referred to the dermatomes supplied by the posterior roots through which the visceral afferent impulses reach the spinal cord. This may be called the "dermatomal rule." Thus, referred pain from the heart (angina pectoris) seems to come from the chest and from a thin strip along the inner aspect of the upper arm. The highest root carrying pain fibers from the

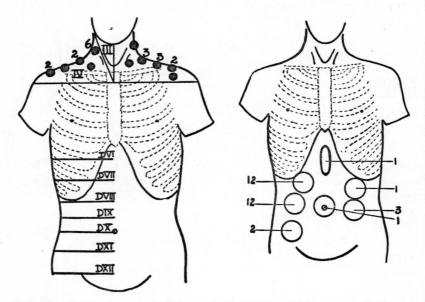

FIG. 212. Superficial reference of pain from diaphragm. *Left:* Reference of pain from stimulating *central zone* of diaphragm. Black dots and attached numbers represent position and frequency of reference in a series of observations. Pain is also referred to corresponding territory on dorsal surface of neck and shoulders (not shown). Roman numerals identify 3rd and 4th cervical and 6th to 12th thoracic dermatomes (*D*). *Right:* Reference of pain from visceral disease affecting *margins* of diaphragm. Circles represent points of reference, numbers the frequency of reference; in two cases pain was referred to back. Margins of diaphragm are innervated by lower six thoracic posterior roots. Compare their cutaneous distribution shown in figure at left with zones of reference shown in figure at right. (From Capps and Coleman, *An experimental and clinical study of pain in the pleura, pericardium and peritoneum*, New York, Macmillan, 1932.)

heart is the first thoracic posterior root, and the upper border of the corresponding dermatome extends out along the inner aspect of the arm.

Pain is only one of four associated signs of visceral disease. Irritation of the viscera by a pathologic process is manifested in four ways: (i) pain; (ii) hyperalgesia, hyperesthesia or tenderness; (iii) autonomic reflexes—sweating, piloerection or vasomotor changes; (iv) somatic reflexes, muscular rigidity.

Types of Pain from Viscera. Two main types of "visceral" pain must be recognized: (i) quasivisceral pain aroused by stimulation of the inner surfaces of the body wall, and (ii) pain actually arising from the viscera. Either type may be unreferred or referred. Quasivisceral pain is an important factor in visceral disease. Spread of inflammation, exudation, pressure, friction or an invasion of the body wall by a pathologic process causes pain impulses which reach the spinal cord via the somatic nerves supplyin the walls of the visceral cavities. Moreover, the thoracic and abdominal cavities are deeply penetrated by a somatic nerve—the phrenic—in which one fiber in three is sensory and many are unmyelinated. Table 9 summarizes the role of the somatic afferent fibers.

Unreferred parietal pain. Capps and Coleman[9] studied this kind of pain in conscious patients. Taking advantage of the space for maneuvering afforded by collections of exudate in the body cavities, these workers stimulated various internal structures. A wire was passed into the space by means of a trocar, and pressure or friction was applied to visceral and parietal structures. The peritoneum was insensitive to this kind of stimulus, but stimulation of the inner body wall caused a sharply localized pain. This pain seemed to come from the body wall over the site of stimulation, presumably because one posterior root innervates superimposed areas on the internal and external surface of the body wall. The lower right quadrant pain in the second stage of appendicitis falls in this category.

Referred parietal pain. Experimental stimulation of the margin of the diaphragm, innervated by the lower six intercostal nerves, was referred to the anterior abdominal wall, which is innervated by the same thoracic nerves (Fig. 212, *right*). Pain from stimulation of the central zone of the diaphragmatic pleura or peritoneum was invariably referred to the point of the shoulder and neck (Fig. 212, *left*). This reference is well recognized clinically. Thus, impulses ascending the phrenic nerve and entering the spinal cord via C_{3-4} are referred to the dermatomes of these roots.[18] Because the diaphragm has migrated caudally, carrying its nerve supply with it, the discrepancy between the points of origin and of reference is dramatic.

Referred visceral pain. Unlike referred somatic pain, this type of pain results from impulses arising in the viscera and conducted over visceral nerves, usually sympathetic. Frequently, the pain seems to come from the surface of the body, often at a considerable distance from the diseased organ. Despite the error of reference, the localization may be quite definite, and its apparent location obeys the dermatomal rule. Angina pectoris is perhaps the classic example of a referred visceral pain. The pain from a renal stone descending the ureter does not move but has a fixed reference (to the groin although

TABLE 9. ROLE OF SOMATIC AFFERENT FIBERS IN SENSIBILITY OF VISCERAL CAVITIES

Somatic afferent fibers	Phrenic nerve	Central zone of diaphragm Portions of pericardium Biliary tract
	Thoracic and upper lumbar spinal nerves	Parietal pleura Parietal peritoneum Borders of diaphragm Roots of mesentery

the upper end of the ureter is beneath the last rib). An inflated balloon in the gut, which embryologically is a midline structure, gives rise to pain which has the same reference whether the stimulated portion of the gut is on the left or right side of the body. Stimulation of the central end of the splanchnic nerve in conscious patients gives rise to referred pain.[48] There seems little justification for Morley's contention[32] that pain from the viscera is referred only when the body wall is involved.

Unreferred visceral pain (splanchnic pain). In anginal pain there is, in addition to the superficially referred pain, a deep, substernal, agonizing component. Such pain is therefore unreferred although it is poorly localized. Ross[38] in 1888 hypothesized the double nature of visceral pain and named the unreferred component "splanchnic pain." This category of pain is less well substantiated. It should be recognized, however, that gastrointestinal tract pain, although referred elsewhere than the point of stimulation, appears to come from much deeper within the body than does the referred parietal pain.

Referred Pain. The reference of pain from the central zone of the diaphragm, innervated by a somatic nerve, provides a clue to the nature of referred pain. So, too, does the common observation that pain arising in the teeth cannot be localized to the correct tooth, even though the sensory innervation of the teeth is somatic (trigeminal). Referred pain is therefore not a phenomenon associated exclusively with the viscera, and the reference of visceral pain is therefore not due to any unique properties of the visceral pain pathways. Lewis and Kellgren[28] induced pain in observers with experience of angina pectoris by injecting hypertonic saline into the first thoracic interspinous ligaments. The subjects recognized the similarity of the two types of pain. The common denominator of referred visceral pain and referred muscular pain is that they both originate deep to the skin and in a general sense are deep pain. Faultiness of localization perhaps represents the failure to evolve a topographically organized neural apparatus for localization. The faulty projection of deep pain to the surface is the result of (i) infrequency of deep pain, and (ii) inability to use vision to verify the source of stimulation. Thus, learning appears to be an important factor in referred pain.

Habit reference. Evidence that reference of sensation is a learned phenomenon can be found in the clinical observation that a pain may be referred not to its usual point of reference but to the site of a previous surgical operation, trauma or localized pathologic process. Experimentally this was demonstrated repeatedly in Jones' study[22] of gastrointestinal pain resulting from distention by balloons. Aberrant projections of pain, for example those falling to one side of the midline when the balloon was in the upper level of the gastrointestinal tract, were explicable as references to pre-existing surgical scars.

Habit reference had the status only of a clinical observation until recently, when it was suspected of being the cause of a bizarre pain phenomenon and was subjected to formal experimental proof by Reynolds and Hutchins.[20, 35] During high-altitude flying some individuals suffer severe pain localized to the teeth (aerodontalgia). After every possible dental cause for the pain had been excluded, it was discovered that the pain stimulus was the expansion of air trapped in the maxillary sinus. Some individuals referred this pain to the face; others referred it to the teeth. The latter group had a high incidence of traumatic dental work on the side of reference, suggesting habit reference of pain. To test this hypothesis, dental work was done without anesthesia on one group of young men and with anesthesia in another group. Two weeks later, the ostium of the maxillary sinus was pricked with a pin. Over 90 per cent of the no-anesthesia group referred this pain to the dental area where the work had been done. This response could still be elicited two months after the dental trauma. The anesthesia group did not refer the pain to the teeth.

Habit reference, secondary hyperalgesia and referred pain are subject to two explanations, one peripheral and the other psychologic. Using the above experiments as an example, the first explanation is that the traumatized teeth were the source of a subthreshold discharge of pain impulses which was facilitated by impulses from the sinus. The other interpretation is, as the name of the phenomenon implies, that a projection of pain is learned and that the pain impulses from the sinus, conducted in an overlapping pathway, were simply given the previously learned reference for impulses in that path.

Mechanism of Referred Pain. To account for the dermatomal reference of pain, MacKenzie[29] suggested that sensory impulses from the viscera were unable to pass directly to the brain, having no connection with the spinothalamic tract, but created an "irritable focus" in the segment at which they entered the spinal cord. Afferent impulses from the skin were thereby magnified, causing pain which was literally cutaneous pain. Stated in modern language, MacKenzie's theory of irritable focus amounts to the suggestion that visceral impulses facilitate somatic pain impulses normally coming from the skin in insufficient quantities to excite the spinothalamic tract fibers. Hyperalgesia and referred pain would be the consequence. Wiggers,[50] Hinsey and Phillips,[18] and others have stated the MacKenzie theory very clearly in modern physiologic terms. It can be called the *convergence-facilitation* theory to distinguish it from the convergence-projection theory.

Convergence-projection theory. Although facilitation may well be essential for hyperalgesia of dermatomal distribution, it is not essential for reference of pain. An adequate explanation of referred pain is that some visceral afferents converge with cutaneous pain afferents to end upon the *same* neuron at some point in the sensory pathway—spinal, thalamic, or cortical—and that the system of fibers is sufficiently organized topographically to provide the dermatomal reference. The first opportunity for this is in the spinothalamic tract. The resulting impulses, upon reaching the brain, are interpreted as having come from the skin, an interpretation which has been learned from previous experiences in which the same tract fiber was stimulated by cutaneous afferents. The same explanation serves equally well for referred parietal or diaphragmatic pain.

The pain fibers in the posterior roots outnumber the spinothalamic tract fibers, so that several pain fibers must converge upon one tract fiber. Therefore, it is likely that a share of the afferent pain fibers coming from the diaphragm converge with cutaneous pain fibers entering the same segment to

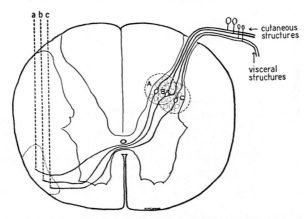

FIG. 213.   Convergence-projection mechanism of referred visceral and somatic pain based upon Sherrington's neuron-pool concept. *A, B* and *C* represent a neuron pool consisting of all the spinothalamic tract fibers originating in one segment of spinal cord. *A* is field of neurons having connections only with afferent fibers from cutaneous sense organs. *B* is field of overlap constituted by neurons which receive impulses from *both* visceral and cutaneous afferents, and impulses in *B* will give rise to pain referred to skin. *C* are those neurons of pool which connect only with afferent fibers from visceral cavities, and give rise to unreferred or true splanchnic pain. Only one neuron in each category is represented; others are indicated by "ghost cells." *a, b* and *c* are fibers in spinothalamic tract having cell bodies in fields *A, B* and *C,* respectively.

end upon the spinothalamic tract neurons. According to the doctrine of specific nerve energies, impulses in a spinothalamic tract fiber are identical whatever their origin. On all previous occasions when these particular spinothalamic neurons have been activated, stimulation of the body surface, verified by other senses, was responsible. Thus, when impulses of visceral origin reach the cerebral cortex, the interpretation is made which experience has built up—that of a pain arising from cutaneous pain neurons.

Figure 213 illustrates the convergence-projection theory of referred pain applied to visceral sensation. The spinothalamic tract fibers originating at one segment of the spinal cord are regarded as a pool of neurons. The visceral pain afferents entering the posterior root of that segment come into synaptic relation with one group of cells, and the cutaneous pain afferents synapse with an overlapping field in the pool. Those spinothalamic tract neurons within the field of overlap, when stimulated by visceral afferents, give rise to pain referred to the cutaneous surface. In Figure 213, certain spinothalamic tract fibers are "private" to visceral afferent neurons. These fibers are responsible for "splanchnic" or unreferred visceral pain. Facilitation of cutaneous nerve impulses within the overlap probably accounts for hyperalgesia, but facilitation is not involved in referred pain. Thus is avoided the unphysiologic and unnecessary supposition that cutaneous pain afferents are perpetually discharging at an amount inadequate to discharge spinothalamic fibers unless facilitated.

Attempts to demonstrate facilitation within pain systems in man, by means of radiant heat, have failed. Unfortunately, pain fibers are too small to be studied easily by bioelectric methods, but in such studies on other somatosensory systems the evoked cortical response to peripheral stimulation has given little indication of facilitation in sensory systems.[1] One afferent volley tends to block another either by occlusion or by what resembles inhibition in reflex arcs. Clinical experience also teaches that the effect of a cutaneous pain or a strong stimulus (e.g., mustard plasters) is to reduce visceral pain, not facilitate it.

The crucial experiment to decide the role of facilitation versus simple convergence and projection would seem to be injection of procaine into the area to which the pain is projected. Such experiments have been carried out on man and animals for a variety of referred visceral and somatic pain, but with conflicting results. Unfortunately, no agreement has been reached, despite extensive investigations. It seems certain that visceral and somatic pain are referred after injection of procaine into the projection site or surgical deafferentation of it so that the convergence-projection mechanism is substantiated. Why in other situations the pain is alleviated is not clear. If, as the convergence-projection theory holds, the reference of pain is a psychologic phenomenon, several factors must be considered: (i) the subjective nature of the pain and its tendency to be reduced by any form of therapy, (ii) procaine injection does not produce a blankness, as does a visual field defect, but a feeling of numbness which may suppress the projection to the area, and (iii) the strength and persistence of the referred pain. In view of the conflicting nature of the evidence, perhaps it is best to accept both mechanisms as operative.

The only evidence that facilitation is a necessary feature of referred pain lies in the experiments of Weiss and Davis[45] and others,[44] where procaine injection into the skin over the area of reference ended the referred pain or caused it to migrate. However, studies by Carmichael, on anginal pain, and by Livingston,[18] on diaphragmatic pain, have shown that procaine injection of an area of reference has no effect upon the reference. White et al.[47] denervated the thoracic wall by section of the intercostal nerves in dogs and observed that ischemia of the myocardium continued to produce pain; Wolff[53] also found that superficial anesthesia in most instances did not prevent the superficial reference of deep pain experimentally produced.

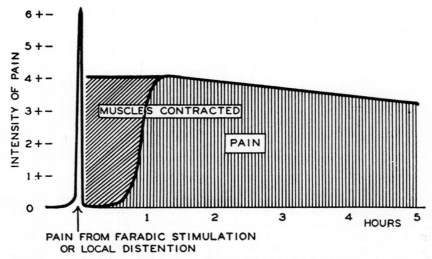

FIG. 214. Diagram to show sequence of sudden pain, muscle contraction and muscle ache from stimulation of ureter or kidney pelvis. (From McLellan and Goodell, *Res. Publ. Ass. nerv. ment. Dis.*, 1943, 23:252–262.)

Rigidity and Deep Tenderness.   This phenomenon is a special example of the sustained muscle contraction and resulting soreness which were discussed in connection with deep pain. Unlike referred pain, the rigidity which accompanies visceral disease is distributed regionally rather than segmentally. It appears to be a sustained reflex comparable to the flexion reflex of the limbs to nociceptive stimuli. Like referred pain, rigidity is typical of pain stimulation arising from the deep somatic tissues as well as that from diseased viscera, and is readily produced experimentally by hypertonic saline injections. In fact, the rigidity of visceral disease is most marked when the body wall is involved (parietoskeletal reflex). Pain from some hollow organs is not accompanied by rigidity, whereas that from others is accompanied by a marked rigidity and a resulting deep tenderness that outlasts and outweighs the original pain.

McLellan and Goodell[30] described an experiment in which the ureter of a female patient was stimulated electrically near the kidney (Fig. 214). Pain with typical references anteriorly along the border of the rectus muscle at the level of the umbilicus was reported. This pain subsided quickly, but the muscles of the abdominal wall on the side of stimulation remained contracted, and, after about half an hour, the "side commenced to ache." This ache became quite severe and lasted six hours; the side was tender the next day. The course of this pain is shown in Figure 214. Similar experiments on the kidney pelvis yielded a similar result. The initial transient pain was referred to the back at the junction of the ribs and vertebral column, and the back muscles ached and became tender. If, in visceral disease, the source of pain continues, it is clear that the resulting pain may be a mixture of referred visceral pain and pain arising from sustained skeletal muscle contraction. Since the muscle ache and tenderness may be at a considerable distance from the site of the projected pain, rigidity and tenderness are an additional source of confusion in diagnosis.

Specific Applications.   Although a detailed consideration of pain characteristics of specific viscera is beyond the scope of a textbook of physiology, a few examples illustrating the mechanisms of visceral pain will be given.

Gastrointestinal pain from distention.   Pain arising from the gastrointestinal tract has been investigated by Jones[22] in normal individuals (medical students), and by Ray and Neill[34] in patients during sympathectomy operations. Pain induced by inflation of a balloon at various levels in the upper end of the gastrointestinal tract (i) is usually anterior (but sometimes goes through to the back), (ii) is usually projected to the midline, and (iii) moves caudally as the stimulus is moved through the tract. As the position of the balloon moves through the esophagus, the point of projection moves with it (Fig. 215). Thus, esophageal sensation in this respect, as in others, is transitional between that typical

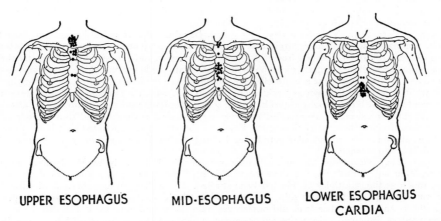

UPPER ESOPHAGUS   MID-ESOPHAGUS   LOWER ESOPHAGUS
                                                                    CARDIA

FIG. 215.   Reference of pain produced experimentally by distention of esophagus at various levels with balloon. (From Jones, *Digestive tract pain: diagnosis and treatment; experimental observations,* New York, Macmillan, 1938.)

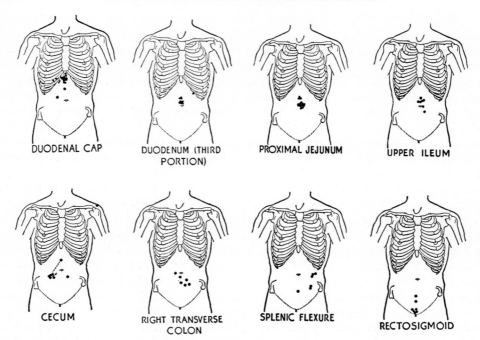

FIG. 216.   Reference of pain produced experimentally by distention of small and large intestine at various levels. Note rapid downward progression of reference points as distending balloon progresses along duodenum and also that pain from jejunum and ileum are referred to about the same point. Note also shift of reference point from right center to left center combined with downward progression in passing from cecum to rectosigmoid. (Selected records from Jones, *Digestive tract pain: diagnosis and treatment; experimental observations*, New York, Macmillan, 1938.)

of the exterior and that of the interior of the body. In contrast, the lower esophagus, the stomach and the duodenal cap all project to the region overlying the xiphoid (Fig. 216). The duodenal projections extend from the xiphoid to the umbilicus and are deep, resembling "a gas pain." The upper, middle and lower jejunum and the ileal projections are grouped around the umbilicus, and variations of several feet in the position of the balloon make no appreciable difference in the localization. The pain is well localized and sharp or cramplike. When the balloon is in the large bowel, the pain differs by being more diffusely localized and less intense; it is more often localized to one side of the midline and is always localized below the umbilicus, but with less correlation between locus of the balloon and locus of the projection. At three points, the hepatic and splenic flexures and the sigmoid, the loci of the balloon and of the projected sensation coincide. In part this correlates with the fixation of the colon and could be explained on the basis of unreferred somatic pain. However, Ray and Neill found that these lateral projections are lost after sympathectomy.

Heart burn (pyrosis).   This term describes a hot, burning, almost painful sensation deep to the sternum, popularly ascribed to regurgitation of acid gastric contents into the esophagus. However, such sensations are described when free gastric acidity is absent, and Jones[22] induced exactly the same burning sensation with mere inflation of a balloon inserted into the lower end of the esophagus. Actually, cold water or N/10 NaOH was a more effective stimulus than N/10 HCl. Often accompanying heart burn is what is popularly known as "acid regurgitation," in which a burning sensation seems to run up the esophagus with or without regurgitation of gastric contents into the mouth. X-ray observation shows that this sensation is accompanied by reverse esophageal peristalsis and that periods of heart burn are accompanied by constriction of the lower esophagus. Jones concluded that both phenomena result from abnormal neuromuscular activity and that the chemical constituency of any regurgitated fluid is of little importance.

Stomach pain.   Pain from the stomach does not lend itself to study by the balloon technique. However, Wolf and Wolff[52] have studied the sensitivity of the gastric mucosa in a modern Alexis St. Martin, much as the sensitivity of skin has been studied. To mechanical and thermal stimulation, the gastric mucosa responded as does skin, but was not so sensitive. Nocuous stimuli such as pinching, electric shocks and strong chemicals did not arouse pain in normal mucosa, but did so if the mucosa was engorged or inflamed. Since the engorgement underlying such hypersensitivity could be produced by stress situations or psychologic probing, the experiments clearly illustrate a psychosomatic mechanism. Physiologically, this phenomenon seems to resemble primary cutaneous hyperalgesia, but whether secondary hyperalgesia is involved is not known.

Peptic ulcer pain. A variety of clinical and experimental facts, including the observations referred to in the previous paragraph, suggest that acidity is the immediate precipitating cause of pain in end-organs rendered excessively excitable by ulceration. Local vascular and inflammatory factors play a critical role. Mechanical factors such as hyperperistalsis are insufficient to evoke pain in the absence of acid, but play a subordinate role. The effect of surgical section of the vagus in ending pain is so immediate and dramatic some have thought that the vagus carries the pain impulses. However, direct evidence disproves such a theory, and the immediate relief must be interpreted to mean that the vagotomy immediately changes some factor in the equation of acid $+$ local sensitivity $=$ pain.

Appendicitis. The two stages in acute appendicitis illustrate two of the types of visceral pain described above. The first stage, consisting of pain localized diffusely to the midline at the epigastric level and not accompanied by muscular rigidity, is a classic example of unreferred visceral pain. The second stage, with pain much less diffuse, localized to the lower right quadrant and accompanied by rigidity and deep tenderness, illustrates referred parietal pain.

Gallbladder pain. Consistent with the studies of Ray and Neill,[34] gallbladder pain is localized to the right and above the umbilicus. It is a pain involving purely sympathetic innervation. Because the pain fibers from the gallbladder, pancreas, duodenum and stomach enter the spinal cord within a few thoracic segments, the references of pain are similar enough to make diagnosis difficult.

Pain Reaction Versus Pain Perception. No discussion of the difficulties attending the interpretation of pain is complete without the recognition that different individuals evaluate the degree of pain quite differently. Chapman *et al.*,[10] using the Hardy-Wolff type of apparatus, measured the pain threshold of a normal and a psychoneurotic group of individuals. No clear difference was found in threshold. There seems little justification for the belief of psychoneurotics that they are "so sensitive to pain." When the test was conducted so that it measured the stimulus necessary to cause a reaction to pain—flinching, blinking or withdrawing—as opposed to mere detection of pain, there emerged a clear difference in the average threshold for reaction. On the average, the psychoneurotic group reacted more readily to pain. However, the amount of overlap was so great that it is perhaps more correct to say that *some* psychoneurotics react more to pain. Clearly, evaluation of pain at this level requires an understanding of the highest levels of cortical function. This subject will be discussed in the chapter on the cerebral association areas.

REFERENCES

1. AMASSIAN, V. E. *Res. Publ. Ass. nerv. ment. Dis.*, 1952, *30*:371–402.
2. ARTHUR, R. P. and SHELLEY, W. B. *J. invest. Derm.*, 1955, *25*:341–346.
3. ASSOCIATION FOR RESEARCH IN NERVOUS AND MENTAL DISEASE. *Pain. Research Publications.* Baltimore, Williams & Wilkins, vol. 23, 1943.
4. BICKFORD, R. G. *Clin. Sci.*, 1938, *3*:377–386.
5. BISHOP, G. H. *J. Neurophysiol.*, 1943, *6*:361–382.
6. BISHOP, G. H. *J. invest. Derm.*, 1948, *11*:143–154.
7. BONICA, J. J. *The management of pain.* Philadelphia, Lea & Febiger, 1953.
8. CANNON, B. *Amer. J. Physiol.*, 1933, *105*:366–372.
9. CAPPS, J. A., with collaboration of G. H. COLEMAN. *An experimental and clinical study of pain in the pleura, pericardium and peritoneum.* New York, Macmillan, 1932.
10. CHAPMAN, W. P., FINESÍNGER, J. E., JONES, C. M. and COBB, S. *Arch. Neurol. Psychiat.* (*Chicago*), 1947, *57*:321–331.
11. DORPAT, T. L. *Mechanisms of muscle pain.* M.D. Thesis, University of Washington, 1952.
12. ECHLIN, F. and PROPPER, N. *J. Physiol.*, 1937, *88*:388–400.
13. FEINDEL, W. H., WEDDELL, G. and SINCLAIR D. G. *J. Neurol. Psychiat.*, 1948, *11*:113–117.
14. GRIMSON, K. S., HESSER, F. H. and KITCHIN, W. W. *Surgery*, 1947, *22*:230–238.
15. HABGOOD, J. S. *J. Physiol.*, 1950, *111*:195–213.
16. HARDY, J. D., WOLFF, H. G. and GOODELL, H. *J. clin. Invest.*, 1950, *29*:115–140.
17. HARPUDER, K. and STEIN, I. D. *Amer. Heart J.*, 1943, *25*:429–437, 438–448.
18. HINSEY, J. C. and PHILLIPS, R. A. *J. Neurophysiol.*, 1940, *3*:175–181.
19. HOLMES, T. H. and WOLFF, H. G. *Res. Publ. Ass. nerv. ment. Dis.*, 1950, *29*:750–772.
20. HUTCHINS, H. C. and REYNOLDS, O. E. *J. dent. Res.*, 1947, *26*:3–8.
21. INMAN, V. T. and SAUNDERS, J. B. deC. M. *J. nerv. ment. Dis.*, 1944, *99*:660–667.
22. JONES, C. M. *Digestive tract pain: diagnosis and treatment; experimental observations.* New York, Macmillan, 1938.
23. KELLGREN, J. H. *Clin. Sci.*, 1938, *3*:175–190
24. KELLGREN, J. H. *Lancet.* 1949, *256*:943–949.
25. KINSELLA, V. J. *The mechanism of abdominal pain.* Sidney, Australasian Medical Publishing Co., 1948.
26. LEWIS, T. *Pain.* New York, Macmillan, 1942.
27. LEWIS, T. and HESS, W. *Clin. Sci.*, 1933 *1*:39–61.

28. LEWIS, T. and KELLGREN, J. H. *Clin. Sci.*, 1939, *4*:47–71.

29. MacKENZIE, J. *Brain*, 1893, *16*:321–354. See also his: *Symptoms and their interpretation*, 2d ed. London, Shaw and Sons, 1912.

30. McLELLAN, A. M. and GOODELL, H. *Res. Publ. Ass. nerv. ment. Dis.*, 1943, *23*:252–262.

31. MOORE, R. M. *Surgery*, 1938, *3*:534–555.

32 MORLEY, J. *Abdominal pain.* New York, William Wood & Co., 1931.

33. PERLOW, S., MARKLE, P. and KATZ, L. N. *Arch. intern. Med.*, 1934, *53*:814–824.

34. RAY, B. S. and NEILL, C. L. *Ann. Surg.*, 1947, *126*:709–724.

35. REYNOLDS, O. E. and HUTCHINS, H. C. *Amer. J. Physiol.*, 1948, *152*:658–662.

36. ROSENTHAL, S. R. and MINARD, D. *J. exp. Med.*, 1939, *70*:415–425.

37. ROSENTHAL, S. R. and SONNENSCHEIN, R. R. *Amer. J. Physiol.*, 1948, *155*:186–190.

38. ROSS, J. *Brain*, 1888, *10*:333–361.

39. ROTHMAN, S. *Res. Publ. Ass. nerv. ment. Dis.*, 1943, *23*:110–122.

40. SHELLEY, W. B. and ARTHUR, R. P. *Arch. Derm. (Chicago)*, 1955, *72*:399–406.

41. SHELLEY, W. B. and ARTHUR, R. P. *Arch. Derm. (Chicago)*, 1957, *76*:296–323.

42. SIMONS, D. J., DAY, E., GOODELL, H. and WOLFF, H. G. *Res. Publ. Ass. nerv. ment. Dis.*, 1943, *23*:228–244.

43. SINCLAIR, D. C., WEDDELL, G. and FEINDEL W. H. *Brain*, 1948, *71*:184–211.

44. TRAVELL, J. and RINZLER, S. H. *Proc. Soc exp. Biol. (N.Y.)*, 1946, *63*:480–482.

45. WEISS, S. and DAVIS, D. *Amer. J. med. Sci.* 1928, *176*:517–536.

46. WHITE, J. C. *Res. Publ. Ass. nerv. ment. Dis.*, 1943, *23*:373–390.

47. WHITE, J. C., GARREY, W. E. and ATKINS, J. A. *Arch. Surg.*, 1933, *26*:765–786.

48. WHITE, J. C., SMITHWICK, R. H. and SIMEONE, F. A. *The autonomic nervous system; anatomy, physiology, and surgical application*, 3d ed. New York, Macmillan, 1952.

49. WHITE, J. C. and SWEET, W. H. *Pain. Its mechanisms and neurosurgical control.* Springfield, Ill., C. C Thomas, 1955, xxiv, 736 pp.

50. WIGGERS, C. J. Chap. 6 in: LEVY, R. L., ed. *Diseases of the coronary arteries and cardiac pain.* New York, Macmillan, 1936.

51. WILLIAMS, A. F. *Thorax*, 1950, *5*:40–42.

52. WOLF, S. and WOLFF, H. G. *Human gastric function*, 2d ed. New York, Oxford University Press, 1947.

53. WOLFF, H. G. *Harvey Lect.*, 1944, *39*:39–95.

54. WOLFF, H. G. and WOLF, S. *Pain.* Springfield, Ill., Charles C Thomas, 1949.

55. ZOTTERMAN, Y. *J. Physiol.*, 1939, *95*:1–28.

CHAPTER 16

Taste, Olfaction and Visceral Sensation

By HARRY D. PATTON

IN the previous chapter, the pain aroused by noxious stimuli in visceral and deep structures was discussed. Scattered through the mesentery and within the walls and mucosa of the viscera are end-organs which mediate other sensations. The adequate stimulus for these receptors is usually either mechanical (distention or contraction) or chemical. The sense of taste falls into the latter category.

TASTE[51]

Receptors. The taste buds are ovoid structures on the tongue, palate, anterior faucial pillars, pharynx and larynx. They are most numerous on the circumvallate and fungiform papillae of the tongue. The mid-dorsal region of the tongue lacks taste buds. Strangely enough, the larynx, particularly the laryngeal surface of the epiglottis and the medial and lateral surfaces of the arytenoids, is significantly populated with taste buds. Stimulation of these regions by solutions applied through a laryngoscope elicits taste sensations.[66]

Morphologically, the buds consist of central fusiform gustatory cells surrounded by columnar sustentacular cells (Fig. 217). The cavity between fusiform and sustentacular cells communicates with the oral cavity through the gustatory pore. The delicate peripheral ends of the fusiform cells project through this pore. Nerve fibers arising from a subepithelial plexus traverse a second plexus at the base of the bud and terminate, by knobs or delicate interlacing networks, on both fusiform and sustentacular cells. Some fibers bifurcate, sending one branch to the bud and the other to unencapsulated endings in the surrounding stratified epithelium.[66] These structures are identified with taste reception because their distribution is restricted to the taste-sensitive mucosa. Also, taste buds atrophy and degenerate following section of the peripheral nerves transmitting taste impulses.

Four distinct gustatory submodalities are recognized: sweet, salt, bitter and sour or acid. The complex sensations aroused by mixed gustatory stimuli are a fusion of these four primary modalities along with various somatosensory and olfactory components.

Application of pure solutions to various regions of the tongue reveals differences in sensitivity. The tip of the tongue is sensitive to all four modalities, but mostly to sweet and salt. The lateral margins of the tongue are most sensitive to sour or acid stimuli, but may also respond to salt. The basal portion of the tongue is sensitive to bitter stimuli.

The existence of four gustatory submodalities, coupled with the fact that certain drugs selectively abolish sensitivity to one or another of the submodalities, suggests the existence of four specifically sensitive receptors. Studies of the sensitivity of single taste receptors as measured by the recording of action potentials from single taste afferents in the chorda tympani (Fig. 218), however, do not bear out this hypothesis.[51] Most taste receptors respond to more than one submodality; for example, the receptor giving rise to the potentials shown in Figure 218 responded not only to salt (both NaCl and KCl) but also to acid (HCl). In receptors which responded to both salt and sugar solutions, gymnemic acid (which differentially abolishes the sweet taste) caused a pronounced

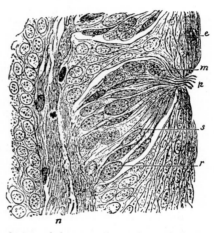

FIG. 217. Section through one of the taste buds of papilla foliata of rabbit, highly magnified: *p*, gustatory pore; *s*, gustatory cell; *r*, sustentacular cell; *m*, leukocyte containing granules; *e*, superficial epithelial cells; *n*, nerve fibers. (After Ranvier from *Quain's Elements of Anatomy*, 1909.)

decrement in the response to sugar but did not alter the sensitivity to salt. It thus appears that different portions of or sites on the receptor membrane are selectively sensitive to different substances.

The nonspecific sensitivity of taste receptors leads to a search for the means by which sensory information underlying discrimination of submodalities is coded. Pfaffmann[51] suggests that the frequency pattern of the discharge of a population of receptors constitutes the basis of discrimination.

In other respects, taste buds behave very much as do other types of receptors. Increased intensity of stimulation is signalled by increased rate of firing and increased number of units firing (Fig. 218).[17, 51, 68] With prolonged stimulation, taste buds show adaptation. The frequency of firing in response to 0.1 M NaCl drops to about 40 per cent of its initial value after 1 second.[17]

Thresholds for taste. The zonal distribution of sensitivity complicates determination of thresholds, because the threshold for a modality varies with the region of the tongue. For example, Kiesow reported the following thresholds (grams per cent) for quinine sulfate:

Base of tongue	0.00005%
Tip of tongue	0.00029%
Right edge of tongue	0.00020%
Left edge of tongue	0.00021%

Similar regional variations in threshold can be demonstrated for other pure stimuli. As a result, different values for the same threshold often appear in the literature, e.g., values from 0.016 to 0.250 per cent for human salt threshold.[53] However, this variability need not interfere with the clinical examination of taste. Gustatory disturbances are usually unilateral, and the two sides of the tongue can be compared quantitatively.

The preference method is used to study taste discriminative ability in animals.[47] The only liquid available to the animal is measured quantities of water and a taste solution, e.g., quinine. If the animal consistently drinks the water and avoids the quinine solution, it must be able to discriminate between the two. When the concentration of quinine is reduced on successive days, the animal drinks more and more quinine solution until it drinks the solution as readily as water. Plotting the quantities of water and quinine solution drunk, i.e., solution drunk/total fluid drunk, against the concentration of quinine yields a threshold curve which is a remarkably stable measure of the animal's gustatory discriminative capacity. Preference studies are often used to determine the effects of lesions in the central nervous system.

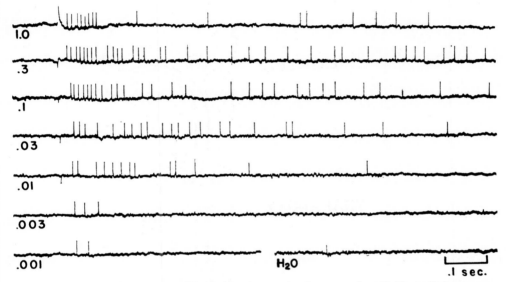

FIG. 218.   Response of single afferent fiber in rat chorda tympani to NaCl applied to tongue. Numbers under records give molar concentration of solution. *Lower right record,* Control with water as stimulus. (From Pfaffmann, *J. Neurophysiol.*, 1955, *18:*429–440.)

Peripheral Pathways.   At least two cranial nerves are involved in the transmission of taste impulses from the tongue. The taste buds of the posterior one-third of the tongue are innervated by the *glossopharyngeal nerve;* those from the anterior two-thirds by the chorda tympani branch of the *facial nerve.* Also, a few fibers in the vagus may supply the buds of the larynx and pharynx. The trigeminal nerve mediates general somatic sensation from the tongue, but apparently contains no gustatory afferents.

Taste fibers entering the glossopharyngeal nerve continue with it into the brain. The course of taste fibers leaving the tongue in the chorda tympani is complicated, apparently being subject to individual variation. Of the four known peripheral pathways for these fibers,[44] only two need be described here. The first is a direct route via the chorda tympani until it joins the facial nerve and thence in this nerve to the brain. The second pathway is via the chorda tympani through its anastomoses with the otic ganglion. The taste fibers pass through this ganglion to the greater petrosal nerve and in it to the geniculate ganglion of the facial nerve. The former is the usual route, but the petrosal nerve may be important in a few people.

Section of the chorda tympani and glossopharyngeal nerves in rats increases the threshold for quinine as measured by the preference method, but strong solutions are still discriminated. Two explanations are possible: (i) perception of quinine in large concentrations involves nongustatory end-organs, or (ii) the vagally innervated taste buds are adequate for discrimination of high concentrations.

That taste fibers in both the facial and glossopharyngeal nerves are small may be inferred from the small amplitude and slow conduction of impulses aroused by gustatory stimulation.[51, 68] Zotterman[68] assigns taste fibers a diameter of less than 4 μ. In the "demotored" chorda tympani of the cat, 18 per cent of the fibers are unmyelinated (less than 1.5 μ), and myelinated afferents range from 1.5 to 6.0 μ.[34]

Bulbar Nucleus. The afferent fibers of the VIIth, IXth and Xth nerves, after entering the medulla, form a well defined common descending tract, the *tractus solitarius*. In this respect, taste fibers behave like the pain and temperature fibers of the trigeminal nerve, which descend in the neighboring spinal trigeminal tract (Fig. 219). Most of the

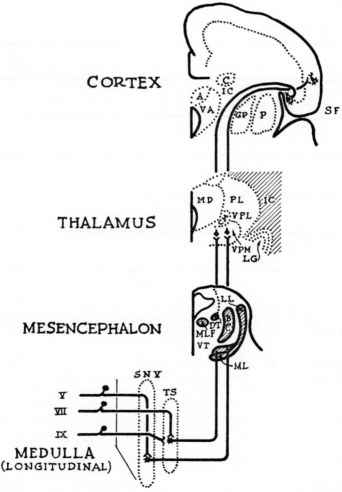

FIG. 219.   Summary diagram, highly schematic, representing taste and somatosensory pathways from face. *A*, Anterior thalamic nucleus; *BC*, brachium conjunctivum; *C*, caudate nucleus; *CM*, n. centrum medianum; *DT*, dorsal secondary trigeminal tract; *GP*, globus pallidus; *IC*, internal capsule; *LG*, lateral geniculate body; *LL*, lateral lemniscus; *MD*, n. medialis dorsalis; *ML*, medial lemniscus; *MLF*, medial longitudinal fasciculus; *P*, putamen; *PL*, n. lateralis posterior; *SF*, sylvian fissure; *SNV*, spinal nucleus of 5th nerve; *TS*, nucleus of tractus solitarius; *VA*, n. ventralis anterior; *VPL*, n. ventralis posterolateralis; *VPM*, n. ventralis posteromedialis (arcuate nucleus); *VT*, ventral secondary trigeminal tract. (Patton and Ruch, unpublished studies.)

taste and viscerosensory fibers terminate in the gray matter adjacent to the solitary tract, *nucleus tractus solitarius*.[6, 7] The fibers of the three nerves terminate at different levels in the nucleus. Fibers from the facial and glossopharyngeal nerve terminate in the rostral part of the nucleus, only vagal fibers entering the caudal portion. Consequently, secondary taste neurons are concentrated in the rostral part of the nucleus.

Bulbothalamic Pathways. Both anatomic and physiologic methods have been used to trace the secondary taste pathways from the medulla to the thalamus. Allen[7] traced degenerating fibers from lesions in the rostral portion of n. tractus solitarius along the opposite medial lemniscus to the ventral and lateral nuclei in the guinea pig. When he placed lesions in the region of the medial lemniscus, he found retrograde degeneration of the cells in the rostral ("gustatory") half of n. tractus solitarius. His experiments thus suggest that the secondary taste fibers run with the medial lemniscus. In rabbits, Gerebtzoff[36] followed degenerating fibers after lesions of n. tractus solitarius into the medial portion of the medial lemniscus in close association with the ventral trigeminothalamic path.

Thalamic Nucleus. There is clear evidence that in the thalamus, as in the bulbothalamic pathways, taste and facial somatic sensibility are localized in adjacent areas. As mentioned in Chapter 14 the ascending somatosensory systems (spinothalamic tract, medial lemniscus, dorsal and ventral secondary trigeminal tracts) are topographically projected upon the posteroventral thalamic nucleus. This nucleus is formed by two easily recognized masses, the laterally situated posteroventral nucleus and the medially situated posteromedial nucleus or arcuate nucleus. The sensory fibers from the face form a synapse medially in the arcuate nucleus, and it is in this nucleus that clinical, anatomic and physiologic observations have localized taste.

In the rabbit, Gerebtzoff[36] traced degenerating fibers to the medial part of the arcuate nucleus after damage in the nucleus of the tractus solitarius. Direct evidence that the arcuate nucleus is the thalamic locus for taste was obtained from studies on monkeys by the preference method.[20, 49] For example, two separate preoperative determinations of taste sensibility yielded almost identical threshold curves. After operation, the threshold was shifted to higher concentrations, indicated by the fact that the monkey drank large quantities of intensely bitter solutions which it rejected completely before operation.

Cortical Representation. From the subcortical course of the taste fibers it may be predicted that the cortical center for taste must lie in or near the area receiving somatosensory impulses from the face, the inferior end of the central fissure near the sylvian fissure. To this cortical area the arcuate nucleus, the taste nucleus of the thalamus, sends projection fibers. The first evidence that taste is localized on the convexity of the hemisphere and not in the hippocampal region, as is widely held, came from ablation studies by Bremer[24] and clinical observations by Börnstein.[22, 23]

According to Bremer, gustatory impairment in rabbits follows ablation of those areas which on stimulation produce masticatory movements; in this species the area appears to be sensorimotor. The electrocorticogram of this area in unanesthetized rabbits changed when quinine solutions were placed on the tongue.[31] Gerebtzoff[37] demonstrated retrograde degeneration in the arcuate nucleus of Bremer's rabbits in which the taste-masticatory areas had been extirpated. Electrical stimulation of the chorda tympani in cats evokes typical surface-positive responses in the inferior portion of the cortical receiving area for face and tongue.[46] Single cortical cells responding to gustatory but not thermal or tactual stimulation of the tongue have been isolated in this same region.[29] Adjacent cells responded to other modalities as well as to gustatory stimulation.[42] Taste thus seems to have no true private cortical receiving zone but is thoroughly admixed with somatosensory reception from the face, mouth and tongue.

In humans with bullet wounds of the inferior postcentral region, Börnstein[23] found heterolateral reduction of gustatory and tactual sensibility of the tongue.

In monkeys and chimpanzees, extensive lesions of the free surface of the lower rolandic cortex, including the entire face motor and sensory areas, did not alter the taste threshold measured by the preference method. Only when the lesions were sufficiently deep to involve the buried opercular and para-insular cortex (Fig. 219) did significant and lasting gustatory deficits appear.[48] Discrete lesions of the para-insular area alone produce taste impairment.[56] Stimulation of this region in conscious humans elicits taste sensations.[50] The experiments of Bagshaw and Pribram[15] implicate the insular and anterior supratemporal cortex as well as the para-insular cortex. Disregarding the folding of the cortex, the deep para-insular and insular cortex may be considered an inferior extension of the sensory cortex.

Taste fibers, which end medial to face somatosensory fibers in the thalamus, project to a cortical area inferior to the face somatosensory cortex. Taste localization thus conforms with the orderly ladder-like organization of sensory cortex and with the established topographic arrangement of the thalamocortical projection systems. The relations of ascending gustatory and trigeminal pathways are shown diagrammatically in Figure 219. Because taste has no "private" cortical receiving zone, it should not be classed as a special sense comparable to vision, olfaction and audition.

Biologic Value of Taste.   Superficially, taste appears to be an unimportant sensory modality. Richter,[52] however, has shown that taste plays a critical role in nutrition and in the maintenance of a constant internal environment for the organism. Using the preference technique, he demonstrated that rats suffering from dietary or endocrine deficiencies select foodstuffs or liquids containing the substances required to correct their deficiencies. For example, an adrenalectomized rat shows a marked appetite for saline and, if allowed to do so, will selectively drink sufficient sodium chloride not only to maintain life but to gain weight; adrenalectomized animals not offered saline die within a few days. Similarly, an animal in which the parathyroid glands have been extirpated displays an increased appetite for solutions containing calcium, and this appetite can be abolished by parathyroid implants. Vitamin-deficient rats will also eat selectively those foods containing the necessary vitamins. All these vitally important self-regulatory behavior patterns depend upon intact gustatory sensibility. Taste provides the sensory cue by which these discriminative selections are made. Animals with their peripheral taste nerves sectioned are no longer capable of regulating their diets to correct deficiencies, but tend to eat and drink indiscriminately.

OLFACTION

The olfactory mucosa occupies an area of 2.5 cm.^{2} in each nostril, including the upper third of the septum and the superior concha. Little of the air entering the nostrils in quiet respiration reaches the olfactory crypt. Rapidly diffusing molecules of volatile substances may, however, reach the mucosa, and sniffing creates currents which aid in carrying molecules upward into this secluded location. The end-organs are rod-shaped structures embedded in a mass of pigmented epithelium which gives the mucosa a yellow color. The distal ends of the rods are thinned and terminate in a cup-shaped structure, from the rim of which project five or six hairlike fibrils.[28] These "hairs," which extend into overlying mucosa, are thought to constitute the true olfactory surface. The proximal end of the receptors thins into an unmyelinated nerve fiber which reaches the olfactory bulb through the cribriform plate. The receptors serve the double function of reception and conduction, i.e., they are at once receptor cells and ganglion cells.

Olfactory Thresholds.   Absolute thresholds vary considerably, depending on the methods of measurement, but agree in indicating very high sensitivity. For example, artificial musk can be detected at a concentration of only 0.00004 mg. per liter of air and mercaptan at 0.00000004 mg. per liter of air.

Relative thresholds can be measured more easily and yield consistent results. While variations from person to person occur because of differences in the construction of the nasal passages,[32] ranges of normal values have been obtained, and repeated determinations on a man give constant values. In women, the individual results are also consistent, but acuity increases just before and during the menstrual period.

The first apparatus for testing olfaction in the human was designed by Zwaardemaker. It consists of two concentric tubes. The inner wall of the outer tube is porous so that it may be saturated with an odorous solution. The inner tube, graduated in arbitrary units of length termed *olfacties*, may be inserted into the outer tube to any depth. This controls the area of odorous material exposed. The tube is held to one nostril and the subject inhales through it. Unfortunately, this procedure does not control the force of inhalation, which can affect the threshold. To overcome this, Elsberg[32] designed an apparatus by which the odorous material is pumped into the nostril while the subject holds his breath. With this apparatus, the minimum identifiable odor (MIO), or threshold, is determined as the least quantity of air saturated with the olfactory substance which can be smelled when injected with uniform force.

These olfactory testing methods have some application in clinical neurology. In 74 per cent of patients with tumors in or around the frontal lobes, the MIO was found to be elevated.[32] No changes were found in patients with lesions below the tentorium. Through lack of sufficient postmortem verification of the lesions, such studies have failed to contribute much to the understanding of how the various parts of the olfactory system function.

Olfaction may be tested in animals by two methods, the conditioned reflex method and the discrimination method. In the conditioned reflex method, presentation of the olfactory stimulus is accompanied by another stimulus which causes a motor response. Soon the animal becomes conditioned so that the motor response occurs on presentation of the olfactory stimulus alone. Since such behavior depends on olfactory acuity and consequently on the integrity of the olfactory system, lesions of the latter should interfere with the habit. An interesting result of such studies in dogs is that many sensations commonly alluded to as olfactory are partially trigeminal-borne.[8] Such sensations therefore have, at least in the dog, a strong tactile component.

Conditioned reflexes to inhalation of cloves, lavender, anise, asafetida, benzol and xylol are abolished by section of the olfactory nerves. These substances are therefore true olfactory stimuli. But conditioned responses to camphor, eucalyptus, pyridin, butyric acid, phenol, ether and chloroform persist after olfactory nerve section, and can be abolished only by both section of the olfactory nerve and division of the maxillary and nasociliary branches of the trigeminal nerve. It follows that only the purely olfactory stimuli should be used in studies of the olfactory system, since residual trigeminal-borne cues may be sufficient to provoke a response even though the olfactory pathways are completely divided.

In the discrimination method, the animal is trained to discriminate between two food containers on the basis of an olfactory stimulus placed in one. If only one box contains food, an animal with intact olfactory sensation soon learns to respond appropriately and makes a correct olfactory discrimination in almost 100 per cent of the trials. If olfaction is destroyed by a neural lesion, the animal is no longer able to discriminate between the containers and chooses the food-bearing box on a purely chance basis (only 50 per cent correct).[43, 62]

Olfactory Bulb. The axons issuing from the olfactory receptors enter the cranial cavity through the cribriform plate of the ethmoid bone. On the ventral surface of the frontal lobes near the midline they enter the olfactory bulb. The bulb, like the retina, is a part of the brain proper. In lower animals it is quite prominent and possesses a cavity which communicates with the ventricular system of the brain. In man, the central cavity is obliterated by a mass of neuroglia. Next to the neuroglia is a deep layer of myelinated fibers passing from the bulb to the olfactory tract (Fig. 220). Superficially there is a layer of unmyelinated fibers which are the terminations of the olfactory nerve. Situated between the two fiber layers is a mass of gray matter which contains three types of neurons, the tufted cells, the mitral cells and the granule cells. The tufted cells are the most superficial. The mitral cells form a compact layer just beneath them. The dendrites of both types of cells course toward the periphery of the bulb and break up into rounded, bushy terminals, the olfactory glomeruli, which form synapses with the primary olfactory fibers. The axons of the mitral and tufted cells join the deep myelinated fiber layer of the bulb to pass into the olfactory tract. The axons of the tufted cells probably leave the tract to reach the opposite olfactory bulb via the anterior commissure; they do not degenerate if the olfactory tract is severed. The mitral cells are thus the secondary olfactory neurons. The granule cells are most deeply situated and send short axons toward the surface of the bulb.

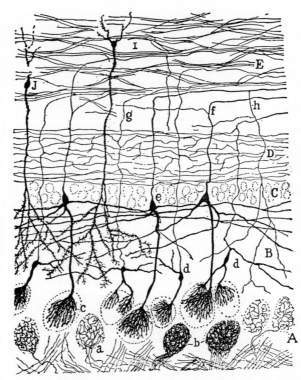

FIG. 220. Olfactory bulb of a kitten, Golgi stain. Surface of bulb is at bottom; core white matter at top. *A*, Layer of glomeruli; *B*, external plexiform layer; *C*, layer of mitral cells; *D*, internal plexiform layer; *E*, layer of granule cells and white matter; *I, J*, granule cells; *a, b*, glomerular terminals of primary olfactory fibers; *c*, glomerular terminal of mitral cell dendrite; *d*, tufted cells; *e*, mitral cell; *h*, recurrent collateral of mitral cell axon. (From Ramón y Cajal.)

Olfactory discrimination. An amazing variety of odors can be distinguished even by man in whom olfaction is much less acute than it is in lower animals. It is therefore interesting to inquire how the centrally transmitted message varies when the mucosa is excited by psychologically discriminable odorants. An estimated 26,000 receptors converge upon a single glomerulus. Also, each glomerulus receives axons from some 24 mitral cells and 68 tufted cells.[11] This extreme convergence and divergence allows for a complex variation of pattern in the centrally directed message.

The small size, short length and secluded location of the olfactory receptors preclude isolation of single primary receptors. However, fine electrodes thrust into the central white matter of the bulb satisfactorily record spike activity of individual secondary units (axons of mitral and/or tufted cells).[4] In the anesthetized animal breathing odorous air, each inspiration is accompanied by a burst of activity in secondary axons; this ceases when charcoal-filtered air is substituted for odorous air. Electrodes in different parts of the bulb record differential activity with different odorants.[3] In rabbits the anterior part of the bulb responds briskly to inhalation of substances with a fruity odor, e.g., amyl acetate, whereas a posteriorly situated electrode records little. The posterior part, however, responds readily when oily-smelling substances, e.g., benzene or pentane, are added to inspired air. Adrian[3] suggests that such spatial differences (as well as certain observable temporal differences) may constitute a basis for odor discrimination.

The spatial arrangement of the projection of the olfactory mucosa onto the bulb can be mapped because receptors whose axons are interrupted rapidly undergo retrograde degeneration.[28] By making discrete lesions of the bulb and mapping the areas of atrophy in the mucosa, one can map the spatial pattern of projection. Such studies first led to the conclusion that there is no topographic organization of the projection onto the bulb.[28] Subsequently, Le Gros Clark[26] repeated these experiments and found mucosal degeneration was not completely diffuse following discrete bulbar lesions, but tended to appear in patches, the boundaries of which were sometimes sharp. It is evident, however, that there is no point-to-point projection of mucosa onto the bulb in the sense that each local area of sensory epithelium is represented centrally in an orderly sequence of equivalent areas having the same spatial relationship. The reason for this is the plexiform distribution of the primary fibers after they reach the surface of the bulb. Normal material shows olfactory fibers randomly approaching and entering individual glomeruli from different directions.

Concerning specificity of receptors, Adrian[5] found that for each mitral unit isolated there is one odor which will stimulate it at a concentration too low to affect other units in touch with the electrode. The selective sensitivity is usually greatest for one substance, but chemically related substances may also be effective. He distinguished four main groups of olfactory stimulants: aromatic hydrocarbons, paraffin hydrocarbons, terpenes and related substances, and ethereal esters and ketones.

Central Olfactory Pathways.   The axons of the mitral and tufted cells, on leaving the bulb, are collected together in the olfactory tract which courses caudally on the base of the frontal lobes. Both tract and bulb are derivatives of the brain, and the fibers of the tract are capped dorsally by gray matter continuous with the gray matter of the bulb; the tract is really a gyrus in which the gray matter has been greatly reduced. The site of termination of the tract fibers is not entirely settled. The most recent careful studies[27] indicate the following direct connections: (i) the opposite bulb (via the anterior commissure), (ii) the prepyriform area and parts of the amygdaloid complex, and (iii) the olfactory tubercle. Contrary to the usual statement, there appear to be no direct connections with either the hippocampus or the septal area.[25] Unlike all other sensory modalities, olfaction does not seem to have a thalamic representation.

Three kinds of experiments have been designed to determine the functions of the various parts of the central olfactory system—ablation, stimulation and electrical recording. Swann[63, 64] studied the effect of neural lesions on the ability of rats to discriminate between two odors and dig through a pile of shavings saturated with the correct odorous substance to reach food. Lesions of the septum, amygdaloid complex, pyriform lobes, hippocampal complex, fimbria, fornix, habenula and cortex around the central part of the corpus callosum did not affect the discrimination. Section of the olfactory tract was the only procedure which abolished the ability to make the discrimination. Allen[9] conditioned dogs to elevate the paw when the odor of cloves was presented. Bilateral temporal lobectomy, removal of the hippocampus or destruction of the pyriform-amygdaloid complex had no effect on this habit. In more complex conditioned responses involving discrimination between cloves and asafetida, however, bilateral destruction of the pyriform-amygdaloid complex abolished the habit. All these studies are inconclusive, but it must be remembered that minimal cues even in the face of badly deranged function may allow a correct response.

Stimulation studies are poorly adapted to the study of any form of sensation because they necessitate the observer's subjective interpretation of the response. Rioch and Brenner[54] stimulated the basal olfactory areas in otherwise chronically decorticate cats. Such stimulation evoked chewing, swallowing, sniffing, salivation and chop-licking, i.e., produced responses which "appeared to be related to smelling and eating."

In the rabbit, Hasama[41] detected electrical changes in the pyriform lobe when olfactory stimuli were presented to the animal, and the responses were abolished by anesthetization of the nasal mucosa. Allen[10] obtained similar results in the dog as did Adrian[2] in the hedgehog and cat. Rose and Woolsey,[55] on faradic stimulation of the olfactory bulbs, detected conspicuous electrical alterations in the olfactory tract, the pyriform area, the amygdala and portions of the hippocampal gyrus. Fox et al.,[35] in similar experiments on the cat, placed the recording electrode in the deep portions of the brain with a Horsley-Clarke instrument. Stimulation of the bulb was accompanied by electric potentials in the prepyriform cortex, anterior perforated substance and the pyriform lobe. No responses were obtained from the para-olfactory area, the diagonal band of Broca, the amygdaloid nuclei or the hippocampus. More recently Berry et al.[19] have recorded evoked responses over a much wider area including the hippocampus. The latencies of hippocampal responses were much longer than those recorded in pyriform cortex, suggesting that the former are relayed over chains of many synapses.

VISCERAL SENSATION

Since the afferent fibers of the autonomic and somatic nervous systems are similar except in course, the terms "sympathetic visceral afferents" and "parasympathetic visceral afferents" do not imply any functional peculiarity of these afferents as compared with somatic afferents (see Chap. 15). Actually, the sensory innervation of the visceral cavities is derived from both the autonomic and the somatic nervous system.

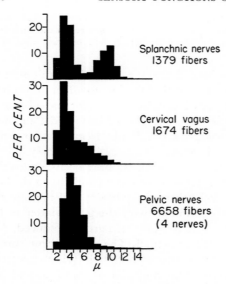

FIG. 221. Histogram of myelinated afferent fibers in "demotored" autonomic trunks supplying viscera. Abscissae show fiber diameters in μ; ordinates, percentage incidence of fibers at each diameter. (From Griffin, Griffin and Patton, unpublished studies.)

The number of visceral afferent fibers traversing somatic pathways cannot be estimated, but about 11,000 myelinated visceral afferents traverse autonomic pathways. To this should be added an uncounted but large number of unmyelinated (type C) visceral afferents reaching the spinal cord by both pathways. Figure 221 shows the size distribution of myelinated, visceral, autonomic afferents in the cat. The data were obtained by enumerating and measuring osmic acid-stained fibers remaining after section had caused degeneration of the efferent fibers. In all three nerves there are prominent peaks at 3 to 4 μ (A delta fibers). The splanchnic nerves show a second peak at 8 to 11 μ (A beta fibers). The vagal afferents shown are almost wholly derived from thoracic and cervical structures. Compound action potentials elicited by stimulating the vagus just above the diaphragm show only a C elevation, and sections of "demotored" supradiaphragmatic vagus show few or no myelinated afferents. Vagal afferents from abdominal viscera are thus nearly all unmyelinated.

Reflex Afferents. Not all of the visceral afferents are truly sensory. Many form reflex connections in the cord and bulb without projections to the higher sensory centers. Such fibers do not mediate conscious sensation. The origin of visceral afferents and the reflex and sensory functions which they subserve are shown diagrammatically in Figure

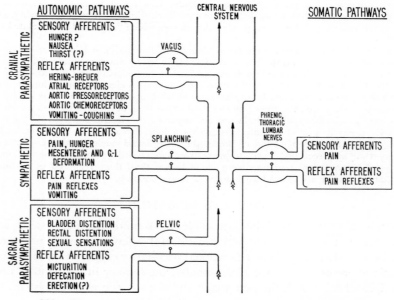

FIG. 222. Diagram showing origin and function of visceral afferent fibers.

222. The afferent limbs of the reflex arcs controlling vital visceral phenomena—cardiac reflexes, aortic reflexes, Hering-Breuer reflex, micturition, etc.—are without exception found in *parasympathetic nerves*. True, stimulation of the central end of the splanchnic nerve will elevate blood pressure and initiate polysynaptic reflex discharges in adjacent ventral roots, but these appear to be pain reflexes. Gentle stimulation of the mesentery[39] or weak stimulation of the central end of the splanchnic nerve, although adequate to excite the A beta afferent fibers, does not elicit reflex discharge. This occurs only when stimuli are sufficiently strong to excite A delta fibers.[13] The sympathetic afferent fibers, although abundant, are not essential to the reflex regulation of the visceral organs. Reflexes from parasympathetic afferents are regulatory reflexes operative under normal conditions of life, whereas the reflexes from sympathetic afferents occur in response to strong stimuli and in pathologic conditions. The contrast between sympathetic and parasympathetic motor function (Cannon) applies equally well to afferent function. The sympathetic afferents are "dispensable."

In this chapter, the visceral sensory afferents are discussed. Visceral reflex afferents are described in the chapters dealing with the organ systems which they serve.

SENSORY VISCERAL AFFERENTS AND THEIR CENTRAL PATHWAYS

Somatic and Sympathetic Afferents. Noxious stimulation (pinching, burning, application of hypertonic $NaCl$ or acid) of the diaphragm sets up a shower of small centripetally conducted spike potentials in the phrenic nerve.[38] Light tactile stimulation is without effect. When the nerve is subdivided, individual spikes can be recorded and conduction velocities estimated from spike size and duration. Such studies indicate that the active fibers are of A delta or C size. Similar small spikes appear in the splanchnic nerve when the intestine is pinched.[39] Passage of strong peristaltic waves and spastic contractions of the intestinal wall induced by local application of acetylcholine also excite splanchnic A delta and C fibers. It thus appears that visceral and cutaneous pain are conducted by similar fibers.

Light mechanical stimulation of the mesentery elicits in the splanchnic nerve large spikes with conduction velocities in the A beta range.[39] These fibers supply the pacinian corpuscles of the mesentery.[59] However, some of the large splanchnic afferents must end in other kinds of receptors, because there are more large splanchnic afferents than pacinian corpuscles.[13] The sensory function of mesenteric pacinian corpuscles is not entirely clear. They are rapidly adapting receptors and are exquisitely sensitive to mechanical distortion; the air vibration induced by the spoken voice is often sufficient to excite a brief shower of spikes.

Both A beta and A delta groups project to the cerebral cortex and hence presumably subserve conscious sensation. Stimulation of the splanchnic nerve evokes typical surface-positive potentials in the contralateral postcentral gyrus.[12] The splanchnic receiving zone lies between and overlaps the areas for the arm and leg in the somatosensory cortex. A similar topographic projection of splanchnic impulses obtains in the lateral part of the posteroventral thalamic nucleus.[45] This accords with expectation in a topographically organized system. There appears to be no special cortical or thalamic area devoted to visceral as opposed to somatic sensation.

Weak stimuli liminal for A beta fibers evoke a smooth cortical wave with a latency of 8 to 12 milliseconds. Mechanical stimulation of the mesentery produces a similar response, although the latency may be slightly greater (15 milliseconds). Stronger shocks recruiting A gamma-delta fibers into the afferent volley produce a double wave, the second wave (latency about 20 milliseconds) being superimposed on the rising limb of the first. Thus, at least some of the impulses carried by A gamma-delta afferents reach the cortex. The spinal pathway for the large afferent fibers is via the dorsal columns; shocks strong enough to excite A gamma-delta fibers evoke electrical activity in the contralateral anterolateral column.[13]

Conduction of visceral afferent impulses to the cortex is conditioned by activity in somatic afferents. A shock to the splanchnic nerve which produces a maximal cortical response when delivered alone may produce little or no response if it is preceded by a shock to somatic afferents.[14] Blockage of conduction of splanchnic impulses may also occur with antecedent tactile stimulation of the skin. Blocking interaction is readily demonstrated at the thalamic level. It may explain the efficacy of cutaneous irritation (mustard poultices) in relieving visceral distress.

Vagus Nerve. The evidence for a specific cortical projection of vagal afferents is much less clear. By repetitive stimulation of the vagus in cats, Bailey and Bremer[16] induced changes in the spontaneous electrical activity of the cortex overlying the orbit. This cortical region receives somatosensory impulses from the face. To eliminate the effect of reflex hypotension, the experiments were conducted on unanesthetized animals with the spinal cord transected at the cervical level ("isolated encephalon" preparation of Bremer). Because this operation spares reflexes in the head and face, the observed alterations in cortical activity may have been secondary to reflexly induced movements. More recently Dell,[30] also using "isolated encephalon" preparations, recorded short latency (8 to 10 milliseconds) cortical responses to vagal stimulation. The responsive cortical area was in the inferior part of the face somatosensory area. In the thalamus responses of 5 to 6 milliseconds latency were recorded in the midline nuclei medial to the face somatosensory relay nuclei. Other investigators using anesthetized animals have failed to record specific cortical responses to vagal stimulation.[57, 58]

In conscious humans, stimulation of the postcentral cortex within the sylvian fissure elicits sensations referred to the pharynx.[50] Nausea, "sinking sensations of the stomach," belching and vomiting may result when the island of Reil is stimulated. It is, however, quite possible that the primary effect is motor and that the sensations are secondary.

Most of the myelinated vagal afferents appear to subserve purely reflex functions. Sensation[8] aroused by irritation of the pharynx or the lining of the respiratory tree (the adequate stimulus for the gag and cough reflexes) may be subserved by myelinated afferents since these structures are clearly supplied with some of the larger afferent fibers of the vagus. However, we have seen that the abdominal viscera have few if any myelinated vagal afferents. Specific cortical projection of impulses traversing C fibers has never been clearly demonstrated by electrical recording methods. This may be due to the small size of potentials conducted in small fibers, or it may indicate that sensations mediated by C fibers are elaborated at subcortical levels.

Pelvic Nerve. Stimulation of the central end of the pelvic nerve evokes small primary cortical responses in the most medial part of the leg somatosensory cortex to which tactile impulses from the sacral segments project. Discharges are also recorded in the dorsal columns, although this is presumably not the exclusive spinal pathway for impulses from the bladder. Whether these responses represent the neural substratum of bladder or genital sensation, however, is open to question; cortical stimulation in conscious patients produces neither micturition nor sensations referable to the bladder.[50] Similarly, electrical stimulation of cortex does not elicit sexual sensations, although contralateral nonerotic sensations projected to the genitalia occur when the postcentral gyrus is stimulated on the mesial surface of the hemisphere.

Erickson[33] reported the case of a female patient in whom a tumor arising from the falx and compressing the paracentral lobule produced seizures characterized by erotic sensations and intense desire for intercourse. The patient described the sensations as more intense on the side opposite the tumor. She was first diagnosed as a nymphomaniac, and an unsuccessful attempt was made to induce artificial menopause by ovarian irradiation. Subsequent discovery and removal of the tumor abolished the symptoms.

Summary. Two features are notable in the cortical projections of autonomic visceral afferents. First, despite their common origin in visceral structures, the three nerves have quite separate cortical receiving zones. This is because they enter the nervous system at different levels: sacral, thoracic, and bulbar. The orderly segmental pattern of afferent inflow is preserved in cortical localization which respects neither functional similarity nor anatomic propinquity of the organs represented.[57] Secondly, relatively small areas of cortex are devoted to the viscera. This corresponds to the poverty of spatial discrimination in visceral sensations as compared, for example, with cutaneous tactile sensation, vision, or audition, which have extensive cortical receiving zones. Precise spatial discrimination apparently requires large numbers of cortical cells.

ORGANIC SENSATIONS

In the previous chapter it was emphasized that visceral pain is chiefly mediated by afferent fibers traveling with sympathetic and somatic nerves. The remaining sensations from visceral organs (hunger, thirst, bladder fullness, sexual sensations, etc.) are termed "organic sensations." Organic sensations signal body needs and lead to behavior which satisfies those needs. They are mediated by both sympathetic and parasympathetic afferents.

Hunger. Hunger, defined generically as all those processes which lead to the ingestion of food, has at least three components: appetite, hunger sensations or pangs, and a third, unnamed, physiologic state or hunger-drive which leads to the ingestion of food.

Appetite. The term "appetite" refers to a food preference which "arises from the experience of previous pleasures; a wishing, longing or yearning for something especially desirable" (Cannon). Associated with appetite are conditioned gastrointestinal reflexes. The sight, smell or taste of favored food elicits copious secretions of saliva and gastric juice, whereas similar presentation of food for which the subject has little liking is a much less potent stimulus. Since most obesity appears to result from strong appetites and their free indulgence, it often is primarily a psychologic problem. Although previous experience is most important in determining appetite, genetic factors obviously determine food preferences of different species; for example, lions do not eat tomatoes, nor do monkeys eat meat. Appetite as reflected by food preference patterns may also be altered by dietary or metabolic deficiencies, as discussed in the previous section on taste. The preference pattern is invariably of a type which combats or offsets the deficiency. The mechanism of such homeostatic changes of appetite is poorly understood.

Hunger sensations. Although appetite may determine *what* we eat under situations of free choice, it does not determine *when* or *how much* we eat. In the human, frequency of eating is largely determined by social custom and by appetite. There is, however, a physiologic mechanism for signalling that it is time to eat—*hunger sensations*. These are described as "a very disagreeable ache or pang or sense of gnawing or pressure which is referred to the epigastrium." Hunger pangs recur periodically and with a fair degree of regularity. Prior to 1911, hunger sensation was considered to be a sensation of the depletion of bodily stores of foodstuffs in blood or tissues. Cannon discovered that hunger pangs are sensations derived from contractions of the empty stomach.

Frequency and amplitude of hunger contractions are greatest in the empty stomach. They disappear promptly with ingestion of food and are temporarily stopped by sham chewing or swallowing, by smoking, by alcohol, or by tightening the belt. Strong emotional states also abolish them. Sleep, however, does not inhibit them. Restlessness and dreams are associated with their occurrence, as was proved by a simultaneous recording technique (Carlson). Newborn infants are restless before feeding time as though disturbed by unpleasant sensations, and random activity of rats interpretable as food seeking is associated with onset of hunger contractions. Recent observations suggest that hunger sensations do not cause the increased random activity, but that both are manifestations of some more deep-seated phenomenon. For example, lowering the blood sugar level by injection of insulin increases hunger contractions, spontaneous activity and food intake. In prolonged fasts hunger sensations disappear after the first few days, but the hunger contractions persist. This appears to be due to some central adaptive process.

Hunger contractions, both spontaneous and insulin-induced, are abolished by vagotomy.[60] It is thus difficult to test the time-honored hypothesis that the afferent path of hunger sensations is vagal. At least part of the impulses traverse sympathetic pathways. Grossman and Stein[40] stated that sympathectomy abolishes hunger sensations although the contractions persist. This is not surprising, since hunger pangs are disagreeable sensations allied to pain, which is, of course, mediated via sympathetic pathways.

Hunger drive. Although hunger contractions signal to the nervous system emptiness of the stomach (and possibly hypoglycemia), they are not essential for the maintenance of food intake sufficient to support caloric balance. Neither vagotomy (Bash, Morgan) nor gastrectomy (Tsang) seriously affects food intake, food seeking activity or weight maintenance. In vagotomized humans, insulin-induced hypoglycemia no longer elicits hunger contractions, but usually creates a desire for food.[40] Finally, cessation of hunger contractions (which occurs with the ingestion of a few mouthfuls of food) does not correlate with termination of eating. Rather, eating normally continues until sufficient calories have been ingested to maintain requirements. Mature rats fed diets diluted with cellulose or kaolin eat increased quantities and maintain constant caloric intake and weight.[1] Similarly, fat-fortified high caloric diets lead to decreased bulk intake until constant caloric intake is achieved.*[61] Thus it must be concluded that *hunger as a physiologic state leading to ingestion of food and in amounts adjusted to energy expenditure is something different from hunger as a sensation.* Hunger as a drive is discussed in Chapters 10 and 22.

Thirst.[67] Thirst, like hunger, appears to consist of a sensory component and a physiologic state or drive. The sensory component is mediated by the glossopharyngeal and vagus nerves which signal the dryness of throat which accompanies dehydration. Salivary secretion, for example, decreases markedly with advancing dehydration; with water deficits of 8 per cent of the body weight (computed from weight loss during dehydration), salivary flow drops to near zero. The resulting dryness of the mucous membranes is sensed. This sensation can be abolished by anesthetizing the mucous membrane or by administering drugs which stimulate salivary flow.

The presence or absence of a sensation of oral and pharyngeal dryness does not, however, govern the frequency or amount of drinking. Neither section of the IXth and Xth nerves nor removal of the salivary glands affects water intake. Drugs (e.g., pilocarpine) which stimulate salivary secretion prevent oral dryness but do not alter the amount of water drunk by dehydrated humans. Obviously, then, there is a thirst drive or "urge to drink" which is relatively independent of the sensory component of thirst.

The mechanism of the thirst drive is entirely unknown, but experiments show that the intensity of the drive is directly related to the water deficit. A dehydrated dog, when offered water, at once drinks enough to replace its water deficit and bring the body fluid content to the threshold of diuresis. In other words, in a few moments all the water the body will hold is metered with some accuracy through the pharynx.[18] The same behavior is exhibited by dogs with an esophageal fistula which prevents ingested water from reaching the stomach; hence receptor activation in the stomach is not the cue to stop drinking. In fact, when enough water to replace the deficit is introduced into a dehydrated dog's stomach through the distal end of the fistula, it still sham drinks that amount if water is offered immediately. If the interval between prewatering and presentation of water is 20 minutes or more, the dog does not drink. Two satisfactions thus appear to be involved, a temporary one produced by passage of an appropriate quantity of water through the throat, and a more lasting one following absorption and distribution of water from the stomach.

Dehydrated man is more deliberate in replacing water deficits than is the dog, rabbit or burro; within 30 minutes after breaking a water fast, man replaces only about 80 per cent of the water deficit. Nevertheless, dehydrated man has a strong urge to replace water deficits, and this urge is unaffected by drugs. Dehydration in both man

* Such readjustment of bulk intake to maintain constant caloric intake requires several days. Caloric balance is thus a relatively long-term regulation and does not account for the amount ingested in any one feeding period.

and animals is accompanied by anorexia, but ingestion of moderate amounts of food does not alter the thirst drive. The diet of choice during water deprivation is carbohydrate, because its oxidation yields a mol of water for every mol metabolized, and because its other combustive product, CO_2, requires no water for excretion.

Nausea.[21] Nausea is an unpleasant sensation vaguely referred to the epigastrium and abdomen and often culminating in vomiting. However, vomiting does not always follow nausea, nor is nausea a necessary antecedent of vomiting. Vomiting produced by mechanical irritation of the pharynx and the "projectile vomiting" of children with tumors in or near the fourth ventricle may occur without nausea. In animals, the salivation, swallowing and rhythmic licking preceding vomiting are often taken as signs of nausea. With some emetic agents, e.g., cardiac glycosides, a conditioned vomiting response may be established, suggesting that such drugs cause true nausea as well as vomiting.

Stimulation of the vomiting center in the dorsolateral reticular formation of the medulla consistently produces vomiting in decerebrate cats.[21] The vomiting is projectile in nature, stimulus-bound (i.e., persists only during the stimulus), and can be repeatedly initiated. This is probably comparable to the projectile vomiting, often unassociated with nausea, that is seen with cerebellar tumors. Spontaneous nausea and vomiting occur in response to a wide variety of stimuli. Emetic drugs initiate nausea and vomiting either by central action alone or by combined peripheral and central action. Central action is not directly upon the vomiting center in the reticular formation, but upon a "chemoreceptor trigger zone" situated near the fasciculus solitarius and the area postrema, dorsal to the vomiting center.

Lesions of the trigger zone abolish vomiting induced by intravenous or oral apomorphine, whereas combined vagotomy and abdominal sympathectomy have no effect.[21] Trigger zone lesions do not prevent vomiting induced by orally administered copper sulfate, whereas combined vagotomy and abdominal sympathectomy greatly elevate the threshold and prolong the latency of emesis. The effectiveness of intravenous copper sulfate is not altered by peripheral denervation. Neither copper sulfate nor apomorphine causes vomiting when the vomiting center is selectively destroyed and the trigger zone is left intact. Thus, whereas apomorphine acts solely via the trigger zone, copper sulfate acts both peripherally and centrally.

The emetic effectiveness of digitalis glycosides is greatly reduced by destruction of the trigger zone, but large doses produce delayed vomiting even when the gut is denervated and the trigger zone ablated.

Impulses from the abdominal cavity which cause nausea and vomiting traverse both vagal and sympathetic pathways, although the former predominate. Copper sulfate, mustard, Escherichia coli peritonitis, staphylococcus enterotoxin and distention of the biliary tract elicit nausea and vomiting which are ameliorated by vagotomy but abolished only by combined vagotomy and abdominal sympathectomy. Vomiting which results from experimental intestinal distention (simulating intestinal obstruction) is abolished by sympathectomy, but anorexia (presumably indicating nausea) persists until the vagi are sectioned.

Motion sickness.[65] The term "motion sickness" is a misnomer; continuous movement at uniform velocity in one direction does not induce nausea. Only when the speed or direction of motion is repeatedly varied does nausea occur; hence, the term "acceleration sickness" is more appropriate. The responsible receptors are in the vestibular apparatus; section of the VIIIth nerve or labyrinthectomy renders susceptible animals immune to acceleration. Also, nausea may be invoked by irrigating the ear with hot or cold solutions which stimulate vestibular receptors by inducing convection currents in the endolymph. Finally, nausea and vomiting commonly accompany the attacks of vertigo in acute labyrinthitis and Menière's disease.

When the provocative acceleration is linear, as in an elevator or a vehicle accelerating in a straight line, the responsible impulses arise largely from the saccular macula.

Angular accelerations (spinning) stimulate principally the cristae of the semicircular canals, and the resultant nausea is accompanied by nystagmus. Many accelerations producing nausea have angular as well as linear components, e.g., in swings, ships, airplanes and automobiles, but linear components constitute the major share of the movement. Susceptibility to nausea from such motions is affected by the position of the head. For example, horizontal position reduces susceptibility to wave accelerations simulating the conditions in boats. As is well known, some acceleration sickness has a strong psychosomatic component, certain individuals suffering attacks even before the ship leaves the pier or the plane the ground. Psychologic attitude, conditioned by past experience, fear of accident, and "old wives' tales," undoubtedly influence susceptibility to acceleration sickness, but the physiologic reaction does exist apart from psychologic facilitation.

The central mechanism of acceleration nausea is not clear. Stimulation of the descending vestibular roots elicits retching movements but not vomiting. Removal of the cerebellar nodulus, uvula and pyramis renders experimental animals immune to acceleration sickness.[65]

The belladonna alkaloids, the barbiturates and certain antihistaminic drugs are useful in combating acceleration sickness. All are central nervous system depressants and produce drowsiness. Whether their effectiveness is due solely to such general action or whether some drugs have a specific action on the vestibular apparatus has not been settled.

REFERENCES

1. ADOLPH, E. F. Amer. J. Physiol., 1947, 151: 110–125.
2. ADRIAN, E. D. J. Physiol., 1942, 100:459–473.
3. ADRIAN, E. D. Brit. med. Bull., 1950, 6:330–332.
4. ADRIAN, E. D. Année psychol., 1951, 50:107–113.
5. ADRIAN, E. D. Brit. med. J., 1954, 1:287–290.
6. ALLEN, W. F. J. comp. Neurol., 1923, 35:171–204.
7. ALLEN, W. F. J. comp. Neurol., 1923, 35:275–311.
8. ALLEN, W. F. Amer. J. Physiol., 1937, 118: 532–540.
9. ALLEN, W. F. Amer. J. Physiol., 1941, 132: 81–92.
10. ALLEN, W. F. Amer. J. Physiol., 1943, 139: 553–555.
11. ALLISON, A. C. and WARWICK, R. T. T. Brain, 1949, 72:186–197.
12. AMASSIAN, V. E. J. Neurophysiol., 1951, 14: 433–444.
13. AMASSIAN, V. E. J. Neurophysiol., 1951, 14: 445–460.
14. AMASSIAN, V. E. Res. Publ. Ass. nerv. ment. Dis., 1952, 30:371–402.
15. BAGSHAW, M. H. and PRIBRAM, K. H. J. Neurophysiol., 1953, 16:499–508.
16. BAILEY, P. and BREMER, F. J. Neurophysiol., 1938, 1:405–412.
17. BEIDLER, L. M. J. Neurophysiol., 1953, 16: 595–607.
18. BELLOWS, R. T. and VAN WAGENEN, W. P. Amer. J. Physiol., 1939, 126:13–19.
19. BERRY, C. M., HAGAMEN, W. D. and HINSEY, J. C. J. Neurophysiol., 1952, 15:139–148.
20. BLUM, M., WALKER, A. E. and RUCH, T. C. Yale J. Biol. Med., 1943, 16:175–191.
21. BORISON, H. L. and WANG, S. C. Pharmacol. Rev., 1953, 5:193–230.
22. BÖRNSTEIN, W. S. Yale J. Biol. Med., 1940, 12:719–736.
23. BÖRNSTEIN, W. S. Yale J. Biol. Med., 1940, 13:133–156.
24. BREMER, F. C. R. Soc. Biol. (Paris), 1923, 89:432–433.
25. BRODAL, A. Brain, 1947, 70:179–222.
26. CLARK, W. E. LE GROS. J. Neurol. Psychiat., 1951, 14:1–10.
27. CLARK, W. E. LE GROS and MEYER, M. Brain, 1947, 70:304–328.
28. CLARK, W. E. LE GROS and WARWICK, R. T. T. J. Neurol. Psychiat., 1946, 9:101–111.
29. COHEN, M. J., LANDGREN, S., STRÖM, L. and ZOTTERMAN, Y. Acta physiol. scand., 1957, 40 (Suppl. 135):1–50.
30. DELL, P. J. Physiol. Path. gén., 1952, 44:471–557.
31. ECTORS, L. Arch. int. Physiol., 1936, 43:267–298.
32. ELSBERG, C. A. In GLASSER, O., ed. Medical physics. Chicago, Year Book Publishers, 1944.
33. ERICKSON, T. C. Arch. Neurol. Psychiat. (Chicago), 1945, 53:226–231.
34. FOLEY, J. O. Proc. Soc. exp. Biol. (N. Y.), 1945, 60:262–267.
35. FOX, C. A., MCKINLEY, W. A. and MAGOUN, H. W. J. Neurophysiol., 1944, 7:1–16.
36. GEREBTZOFF, M. A. Cellule, 1939, 48:91–146.
37. GEREBTZOFF, M. A. Arch. int. Physiol., 1941, 51:199–210.
38. GERNANDT, B. Acta physiol. scand., 1946, 12: 255–260.
39. GERNANDT, B. and ZOTTERMAN, Y. Acta physiol. scand., 1946, 12:56–72.

40. GROSSMAN, M. I. and STEIN, I. F., JR. *J. appl. Physiol.*, 1948, *1:*263–269.
41. HASAMA, B. *Pflüg. Arch. ges. Physiol.*, 1934, *234:*748–755.
42. LANDGREN, S. *Acta physiol. scand.*, 1957, *40:* 210–221.
43. LASHLEY, K. S. and SPERRY, R. W. *Amer. J. Physiol.*, 1943, *139:*446–450.
44. LEWIS, D. and DANDY, W. E. *Arch. Surg.*, 1930, *21:*249–288.
45. PATTON, H. D. and AMASSIAN, V. E. *Amer. J. Physiol.*, 1951, *167:*815–816.
46. PATTON, H. D. and AMASSIAN, V. E. *J. Neurophysiol.*, 1952, *15:*245–250.
47. PATTON, H. D. and RUCH, T. C. *J. comp. Psychol.*, 1944, *37:*35–49.
48. PATTON, H. D., RUCH, T. C. and FULTON, J. F. *Fed. Proc.*, 1946, *5:*79.
49. PATTON, H. D., RUCH, T. C. and WALKER, A. E. *J. Neurophysiol.*, 1944, *7:*171–184.
50. PENFIELD, W. and RASMUSSEN, T. *The cerebral cortex of man.* New York, Macmillan, 1950.
51. PFAFFMANN, C. *Handbook of physiology* 1959, *1*(1):307–533.
52. RICHTER, C. P. *Harvey Lect.*, 1943, *38:*63–103.
53. RICHTER, C. P. and MacLEAN, A. *Amer. J. Physiol.*, 1939, *126:*1–6.
54. RIOCH, D. McK. and BRENNER, C. *J. comp. Neurol.*, 1938, *68:*491–507.

55. ROSE, J. E. and WOOLSEY, C. N. *Fed. Proc.*, 1943, *2:*42.
56. RUCH, T. C. and PATTON, H. D. *Fed. Proc.*, 1946, *5:*89–90.
57. RUCH, T. C., PATTON, H. D. and AMASSIAN, V. E. *Res. Publ. Ass. nerv. ment. Dis.*, 1952, *30:*403–429.
58. SACHS, E., JR., BRENDLER, S. J. and FULTON, J. F. *Brain*, 1949, *72:*227–240.
59. SHEEHAN, D. *J. Anat. (Lond.)*, 1932, *67:*233–249.
60. STEIN, I. F., JR. and MEYER, K. A. *Surg. Gynec. Obstet.*, 1948, *86:*473–479.
61. STROMINGER, J. L., BROBECK, J. R. and CORT, R. L. *Yale J. Biol. Med.*, 1953, *26:*55–74.
62. SWANN, H. G. *J. comp. Psychol.*, 1933, *15:*229–241.
63. SWANN, H. G. *J. comp. Neurol.*, 1934, *59:*175–201.
64. SWANN, H. G. *Amer. J. Physiol.*, 1935, *111:* 257–262.
65. TYLER, D. B. and BARD, P. *Physiol. Rev.*, 1949, *29:*311–369.
66. WILSON, J. G. *Brain*, 1905, *28:*339–351.
67. WOLF, A. V. *Thirst.* Springfield, Ill., Charles C Thomas, 1958, x, 536 pp.
68. ZOTTERMAN, Y. *Skand. Arch. Physiol.*, 1935, *72:*73–77.

CHAPTER 17

Audition and the Auditory Pathway

By A. L. TOWE and THEODORE C. RUCH

AUDITION

THE auditory system transmits information about pressure variations in the air to the central nervous system through a mechanism consisting of (i) the external and middle ears, (ii) the cochlea, and (iii) the auditory nerve and pathways to various central neural structures. The first stage is an effective mechanical impedance-matching device which transmits pressure variations from the air to the cochlear fluid with little energy loss. The second stage is the site of excitation of nervous tissue, a process depending upon an external energy source. Energy for the subsequent nerve conduction is supplied by the metabolizing organism. For our purposes, highly schematic diagrams (Fig. 223 *A*, *B*) suffice to portray the functional anatomy of the auditory mechanism; knowledge of the somewhat complicated anatomy of the middle and inner ear should be obtained from special works on anatomy and histology. The mechanical principles of energy transmission can be outlined without recourse to detailed anatomy.

Resonance. Longitudinal waves enter the external auditory meatus, where they lose their energy to the walls of the tube and the tympanic membrane. Some of this energy is reflected back to the air, but some appears as motion of the membrane. The external meatus behaves as a closed tube, so that sound pressures are greater at the closed end than at the open end. A resonance curve may be constructed by plotting the pressure difference between the two ends against the applied frequency. The curve thus obtained is not sharply peaked, but, largely as a result of the damping effect of the nonrigid tympanic membrane, is broad and rounded. The maximum increase in pressure occurs when the applied sound has a wavelength four times the effective length of the external meatus (about 12 db* at 3400 to 4000 c.p.s.). The curve slowly falls off on either side

---

* The standard unit of sound intensity is the decibel (db), 1/10 bel. The bel is the logarithm of the ratio of the applied power or energy to some reference power or energy; measurement of the "absolute" energy level is difficult. The reference usually taken in auditory work is the power necessary for a 1000 c.p.s. pure tone to be just audible; this is about 10^{-16} watts per cm.². Thus, $N_{db} = 10 \log_{10} P/P_o$, where P = applied power and Po = 10^{-16} watts per cm.².

of the resonant frequency, being above 5 db over the interval from 2000 to 6000 c.p.s.[38] The resonant frequency is nearly 3000 c.p.s. above the major speech frequency.

The tympanic membrane completely separates the air-filled external and middle ears. It is shaped like a shallow funnel with its apex, or umbo, somewhat below the center and directed inward. The handle of the malleus is directed downward and attaches to the umbo. Radial fibers radiate from the umbo, except in a pie-shaped wedge under the handle of the malleus, and circular fibers interfuse the membrane. This membrane acts like a pressure receiver, being insensitive to velocity changes but exceedingly sensitive to pressure changes. Its specific behavior varies with the applied frequency. At low frequencies the membrane vibrates like a rigid body about a horizontal axis at its upper edge. At frequencies exceeding 2400 c.p.s. the drum membrane vibrates in segments, the particular pattern depending upon the applied frequency. However, measurement of maximum membrane displacement shows that it approximates the amplitude

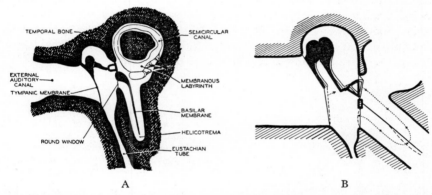

A   B

FIG. 223.   A, Highly schematic diagram of middle and internal ear in which cochlea is shown as though uncoiled. Oval window (unlabeled) lies just above round window and opens into vestibule and scala vestibuli, which is separated from scala tympani by basilar membrane. (After Békésy. Redrawn for Stevens and Davis, *Hearing: its psychology and physiology*, John Wiley & Sons, Inc., 1938. Reprinted by permission.) B, Highly schematic diagram of auditory portions of middle and inner ear showing position of ossicles and various membranes at rest and following inward displacement of tympanic membrane (*shadow lines*) by a sound wave. Dotted lines and arrows represent path of sound waves. (Reprinted by permission from Stevens and Davis, *Hearing: its psychology and physiology*, New York, John Wiley & Sons, Inc., 1938.)

of motion of the air molecules at nearly all frequencies. At the threshold of hearing, this ranges from 10^{-5} cm. for low frequencies to 10^{-9} cm. at 3000 c.p.s.[40]

Impedance matching.   The unique problem solved by the middle ear is one of transferring sound energy from a gas to a liquid without significant loss. This feat is accomplished by the drum membrane-ossicular chain system (Fig. 224), which amplifies the applied pressures by means of a lever arrangement and a "hydraulic press" action. Movements of the drum membrane are communicated to the tip of the malleus. The malleus and incus rotate as a unit about an axis through the short process of the incus and along the tympanic side of the malleus (Fig. 225). Because, when measured to this axis, the manubrium is a longer lever than the long process of the incus, the force appearing at the stapes is greater than that at the tympanic umbo; the force amplification is about 1.3 to 1.

The area of the drum membrane averages about 64 mm.[2], and the stapedial footplate measures about 3.2 mm.[2]. If the two structures moved as simple pistons, the resulting pressure amplification could readily be estimated. However, neither structure behaves so simply. As mentioned above, the mode of vibration of the tympanum varies with frequency, the effective area being 60 to 75 per cent of the total. Because the annular ligament which fixes the stapedial foot-plate into the oval window is narrowest at its posterior margin, the stapes rotates about a vertical axis near its posterior border (Fig. 225).[4] Hence, the ratio of effective areas could vary from ear to ear between 13 to 1 and 16 to 1. Since the force delivered to the stapes is amplified by the lever action described above, the total pressure gain would range from 17 to 21 for the average ear. This increase signifies a long step toward matching the impedance of the inner ear mechanism to the air. At all frequencies, however, some energy is reflected, and some is lost to frictional resistance. The energy flow through the system can be calculated when the impedance is known; at the threshold of hearing, the impedance is large for low frequencies and minimal around 1000 c.p.s., increasing again at higher frequencies. This relationship means, as we shall see later, that the ear is most sensitive in the region of 1000 c.p.s.

When the phase shifts of the reflected portion of a sound wave are measured,[32, 34] it becomes clear that the stiffness (elastic reactance) of the ear mechanism is large at low frequencies, whereas the mass of the system (mass reactance) predominates at high frequencies. Somewhere between 300 and 3000 c.p.s. these two reactances, which are 180° out of phase, just cancel, and the only limitation becomes the frictional losses. Thus, transmission losses are least in the region of 1000 to 2000 c.p.s.

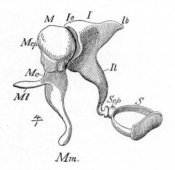

FIG. 224. Bones of middle ear in functional connection. *M*, Malleus; *Mcp*, head; *Mc*, neck; *Ml*, processus gracilis; *Mm*, manubrium; *I*, incus; *Ic*, body of incus; *Ib*, short process; *Il*, long process; *S*, stapes. (From Helmholtz, *Die Lehre von den Tonempfindung*, Braunschweig, F. Wieweg & Son, 1896.)

Overloading and damping. Contraction of either or both of two small muscles in the middle ear, the *tensor tympani* and *stapedius*, will increase the stiffness of the middle ear mechanism. The tensor tympani has a long tendon inserted onto the manubrium of the malleus; this tendon can pull at right angles to the plane of motion of the malleo-incudal system. The stapedius muscle inserts onto the neck of the stapes and likewise pulls at right angles to its main axis. This muscle thus tends to rotate the stapes out of the oval window, opposing the action of the tensor tympani, which forces the stapes into the oval window.

Reflex contraction of these muscles can be produced (i) by clicks, tones and noises; (ii) by irritation of the external auditory canal, pinna or face; and (iii) by such activities as swallowing and yawning. The latency to the beginning of contraction of the stapedius is about 15 milliseconds when activity is induced by sound; the latency to contraction of the tensor tympani is about twice as great. Johannes Müller proposed that this acoustic reflex acts as a protective mechanism like blinking of the eyelids and constriction of the pupil; increasing tension in the system damps the vibrations. Thus, energy transmission, particularly for low tones, is greatly reduced. The fact that the electric potentials from the inner ear (the cochlear microphonic, discussed below) provide an accurate index of the cochlear response to sound enabled Wiggers[39] to study this question in animals. He found that, under light anesthesia, the intra-aural muscles execute spontaneous rhythmic contractions. The microphonic threshold during peaks of contraction was *increased* for tones below 1000 c.p.s., but was unchanged for frequencies above 2000 c.p.s. Since low-pitched sounds are apt to damage the organ of Corti, any device which reduces energy transmission from such sounds would be protective. The spontaneous contractions observed by Wiggers affected the threshold to the extent of 40 db; and it is probable that the reflex contractions in the absence of anesthesia are more vigorous. Thus, with the exception of explosive changes, which develop full effect before this reflex can come into play, the damping protects the system from intense sounds.

Static pressure matching.[3] By connecting the cavity of the middle ear with the pharynx and thus with the exterior, the *eustachian tube* provides a means of adjusting the air pressure in the middle ear. In this way the pressures on the two sides of the tympanic membrane can be kept equal. Normally, the soft, slitlike pharyngeal orifice is closed; it is opened by the tensor palati muscle during swallowing, yawning and sneezing. Without thinking, man swallows whenever the sensations from the tympanic membrane warn him of inequality in the pressures upon its two sides.

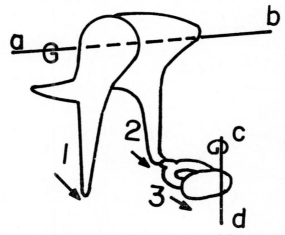

FIG. 225.   Illustration of way in which ossicles act in transmitting movements of tympanic membrane to cochlea. *1*, Handle of malleus; *2*, long process of incus; *3*, stapes; *a–b*, axis of rotation of malleoincudal system; *c–d*, axis of rotation of stapedial foot-plate. Arrows indicate direction of motion of ossicles when a positive pressure is applied at the tympanum.

In upper respiratory infections, however, the auditory tube may be blocked by inflammation or collection of mucus. As the trapped air is partially absorbed, the tympanum is pushed inward; the resulting pressure sensations and impairment of hearing are quite discomforting.

In severe changes of atmospheric pressure, such as those encountered in flying, the adjustment of air pressure within the middle ear can present serious problems. In ascent, with the ambient pressure decreasing, the excess pressure in the middle ear can force the eustachian tube open even if it is not opened by swallowing. In descent, however, swallowing is the sole mechanism for equalizing pressure. If muscular action is absent, as may occur in sleeping passengers or when unconscious wounded are transported by air, the tubes remain closed or are, in fact, held closed by the higher pressure in the nasopharynx. Weak solutions of phenylephrine hydrochloride (Neo-Synephrine) or ephedrine are frequently sprayed into the nostrils to shrink the tissue around the eustachian orifice, thus aiding in pressure equalization. If negative pressures of 60 to 80 mm. Hg develop within the middle ear, pain is severe, and deafness, tinnitus and vertigo supervene. At pressures of 80 to 90 mm. Hg, muscular contraction may not open the tube, and, at negative pressures between 100 and 150 mm. Hg, the eardrum may rupture. Such rupture is marked by the sensation of a loud explosive sound, piercing pain, nausea and even shock. Short of rupture, pressure differences may produce traumatic inflammation of the middle ear.[3] The eardrum is sometimes pierced with a fine needle to allow trapped air to escape; small defects of the tympanum so produced quickly close and heal.

Physical and Psychologic Dimensions of Sound.[25]   Sound waves are longitudinal; i.e., they consist of molecular motion in the direction of energy transmission. The consequent alternate waves of condensation and rarefaction move with specifiable velocity according to the characteristics of the medium and independently of intensity. The simplest sound wave, a sine wave, can vary in frequency and amplitude (Fig. 226). The perceived *pitch* is determined by the frequency of a sine wave; *loudness* is determined by both amplitude and frequency. Such simple waves are exceedingly difficult to produce (except with a tuning fork or an electronic oscillator); most sound sources produce compound sounds consisting of a fundamental and overtones, which bear a simple arithmetic relationship to the fundamental (first harmonic). A single string vibrates not only as a whole, but in halves, thirds, fourths, etc. Since the fundamental has the greatest

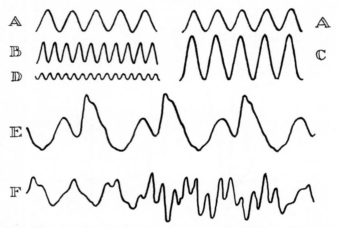

FIG. 226.   Diagram showing dimensions of a sound wave. *A* and *B* differ in frequency and pitch. *A* and *C* differ in amplitude, and *D*, though of smaller amplitude, is equal to *A* in loudness, showing that frequency is a factor in loudness. *E* and *F* illustrate difference between a musical sound and a noise. Note that in *E* (from an organ pipe) wave form is complex but is regularly repeated, whereas in *F*, representing sound of a bell, the wave is irregular or nonperiodic. (After Miller, *The science of musical sounds*, New York, Macmillan, 1916.)

amplitude, it determines the pitch of the sound; the overtones can also be heard with their own pitches. The relative amplitudes of the various harmonics yield a unique wave form for each sound source, and result in the *timbre* or *quality* of the sound. It is this property of complex sound which enables us to distinguish between different muscial instruments, human voices, or other sound sources emitting at equal fundamental frequency and intensity. No matter how complex a wave form may be, it is "musical" if its pattern is regularly repeated. Nonperiodic vibrations, which constitute the vast majority of sound waves emanating from the natural environment, are "noise." However, even noise has a crude sort of pitch, for some frequencies in the jumble have a greater energy than others. When many frequencies are represented about equally, as in the thermionic emission of a vacuum tube, the resulting sensation is termed "white noise" (by analogy to white light).

Loudness.[26]   That loudness is correlated with the amplitude of a sound wave is only partly true. Loudness is a psychologic reaction to the *intensity** of a sound wave, which

* Intensity refers to energy flux density, but is also loosely used in acoustics to refer to power or energy.

is proportional to the square of amplitude. Frequency is also an important factor in determining the loudness of a sound. This fact appears in the audibility curve (Fig. 227), which relates frequency to intensity for pure sine waves. Two threshold intensities can be plotted for each frequency, one for hearing and one for feeling. Between these two extremes, loudness varies approximately as the logarithm of intensity. At the threshold of audibility, the effective pressures and movements are exceedingly minute. Displacements of the tympanum less than the dimensions of a hydrogen atom are effective (Fig. 228). Why pressure variations and vibrations of the blood vessels of the tympanum and

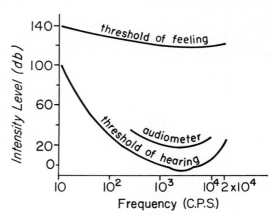

FIG. 227.   Audibility curve in man, showing threshold under ideal conditions and under conditions in which audiometer tests are administered. Energy which excites tactual and pain receptors is about a million million times energy at threshold of hearing at 1000 c.p.s. (After Licklider, Chap. 25 in *Handbook of experimental psychology*, S. S. Stevens, ed. New York, John Wiley & Sons, 1951.)

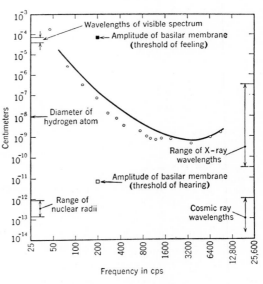

FIG. 228. Amplitude of vibration of tympanum at threshold of hearing. *Circles*, Data of Wilska. *Solid line*, Amplitude of vibration of air molecules at threshold intensity as calculated by Stevens and Davis. *Squares*, Data of Békésy. (From Békésy and Rosenblith, Chap. 27 in *Handbook of experimental psychology*, S. S. Stevens, ed. New York, John Wiley & Sons, 1951.)

cochlea do not produce distracting sounds is puzzling in view of this extreme sensitivity. Perhaps flow is laminar and pulse is totally absent in these vessels.

The striking feature of the audibility curve is the degree to which the threshold of hearing depends upon frequency. Hearing is keenest at 1000 to 3000 c.p.s. and decreases sharply for higher and lower frequencies. The threshold for feeling* discomfort, on the other hand, is fairly constant at different frequencies (about 10^{-3} watts per cm.²). It is interesting that the frequencies most important for perception of the human voice are nearly those which the ear hears best. The audibility curve is determined to a large

* Sound waves, when sufficiently intense, will stimulate somesthetic sense organs. The resulting sensations include touch, tickle, pressure and even pain.

extent by the energy loss in the middle and inner ears (elastic reactance at low frequencies and mass reactance at high frequencies), and to a small extent by the resonance properties of the external ear. The purely resistive losses, representing minimal energy loss, occur at frequencies near the resonant frequency of the external meatus. All these factors combine to make the ear most sensitive in this range.

Audiometry. Because the auditory threshold is so dependent upon frequency, the rough and ready clinical methods of testing hearing—whispering and the ticking watch—do not measure but merely sample hearing ability. Testing of hearing has come to mean the determination of the audibility curve (audiogram). The instrument used (audiometer) to make these measurements consists of a vacuum tube oscillator arranged to produce ten to 12 different frequencies at octave intervals. It is calibrated to read "0 db" at the mean threshold value for each of these frequencies as determined in a large

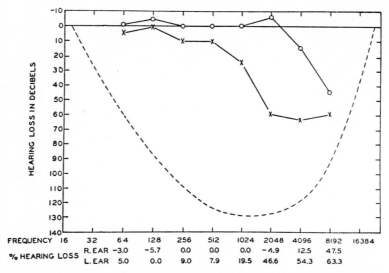

FREQUENCY	16	32	64	128	256	512	1024	2048	4096	8192	16384
% HEARING LOSS R.EAR		-3.0	-5.7	0.0	0.0	0.0	-4.9	12.5	47.5		
L.EAR		5.0	0.0	9.0	7.9	19.5	46.6	54.3	63.3		

FIG. 229. Graphic representation of hearing ability (audiogram) of individual suffering from high-tone deafness. Circles indicate auditory sensitivity of right ear; crosses, that of left ear. Figures at bottom show calculation of per cent hearing loss, with broken line, the threshold of feeling, representing complete loss of hearing. For convenience, normal threshold of hearing is taken as zero (or reference point) on a decibel scale. In absolute physical units threshold energy varies considerably throughout audible range of frequencies. (Reprinted by permission from Stevens and Davis, *Hearing: its psychology and physiology*, New York, John Wiley & Sons, Inc., 1938.)

number of "normal individuals." The audibility threshold curve shown in Figure 227 is thus pulled into the straight line at 0 db. Actually, the 0 line in Figure 229 is based on the curve labeled "audiometer" in Figure 227, because audiometer measurements are not conducted under conditions as ideal as those prevailing in the experimental situation. The broken line of Figure 229 represents complete hearing loss; between 0 and the broken line, each increase in intensity brings an increase in loudness up to the point beyond which tactual sensation is experienced. The crosses and circles represent the threshold of the left and right ears of an individual with high-tone deafness that was greater in the left than in the right ear.

In an audiometer test, the patient holds a receiver to his ear and flashes a light whenever he hears a sound. The intensity of an intermittently sounded tone is steadily decreased until the patient no longer signals its occurrence consistently. The sound intensity at this point is read from the intensity dial (labeled in decibels or sensation units), and entered on the audiogram. This fixes one point on the patient's audibility curve; the procedure is repeated for the remaining frequencies; then the other ear is tested. In interpreting such curves, the following facts should be noted. Hearing loss may be stated either in terms of decibels of loss or in terms of percentage loss of useful hearing. If at any point the patient's threshold coincides with the broken line representing the threshold of feeling, the loss of hearing is complete. If the threshold falls halfway between the 0 line and the broken line, the loss in that ear is 50 per cent.

Structure of Inner Ear. The manner in which the ear analyzes complex sound waves into component frequencies was originally deduced by Helmholtz from the structure of the inner ear. He was struck by the fact that the ear contains a very large number of neurosensory units arranged along a membrane interposed in the path of the sound wave. He viewed this membrane as a system of tuned elements that resonated so that a given unit would be the one most vigorously stimulated by sound waves of a given frequency. This arrangement would result in a different nerve fiber discharging more actively for each frequency within the audible range, and the discharge of this unit, transmitted over the auditory pathway, would be recognized by the cerebral cortex as a given pitch. Although significant changes have been made in the theory of auditory receptor excitation, Helmholtz set the basic philosophy that the functional anatomy and the physiology of the inner ear are inextricably bound together.

The auditory portion of the inner ear, like the middle ear, is housed in a system of cavities and tunnels known as the osseous labyrinth (Figs. 223A and 230). The cochlear portion of the osseous labyrinth consists of a fluid-filled tube about 3 cm. long that is coiled in a spiral fashion about a central pillar (modiolus). Except for a small opening at the apical end (helicotrema), the tube is completely divided into two canals by a stout connective tissue membrane (basilar membrane) and a bony shelf (spiral lamina) extending from the modiolus. At the base of the tube, the cochlear partition consists mainly of spiral lamina, the basilar membrane being narrowest at this end. Farther up around the spiral, the bony lamina becomes smaller, and the basilar membrane widens until reaching the helicotrema at the apex. The latter opening serves to equalize slowly developing pressure differences between the two divisions of the cochlea.

Sound waves enter the part of the cochlea *above* the basilar membrane (*scala vestibuli*) by way of the oval window and vestibule—hence its name (Fig. 223B). The passageway below the basilar membrane (*scala tympani*) communicates with the middle ear by way of the round window, which is closed by the *secondary tympanic membrane*.

Within the osseous labyrinth lies the membranous labyrinth, a portion of which extends into the cochlea to contribute Reissner's membrane, the basilar membrane and the organ of Corti (thus forming the cochlear duct, or *scala media*). In a sense, the scala media occupies the lower third of the scala vestibuli; since Reissner's membrane is so delicate that the two scalae probably function as a single tube in the transmission of sound. In fact, the term "scala vestibuli" is often loosely used to include the cochlear duct.

Sensory epithelium of cochlea. The fibers of the cochlear branch of the VIIIth nerve arise in bipolar cell bodies lodged within the modiolus (spiral nucleus) and arborize around the sensory cells, or *hair cells*, of the *organ of Corti* in the cochlea. These hair cells are in a position to be affected by sound waves and, in turn, generate nerve impulses in the fibers of the auditory nerve. The general arrangement and relations of these cells are indicated in Figure 230. Note that the upper ends of the cells bear a number of short, stiff hairs. The hair cells are divided by a supporting arch (*rods of Corti*) into a single row of *inner hair cells* and three or four rows of *outer hair cells*. Radial nerve fibers emerging from the spiral lamina either turn sharply toward the apex and innervate the inner hair cells for more than a quarter of a turn, or pass through the arch of Corti and course toward the base of the cochlea to innervate outer hair cells along a quarter of a

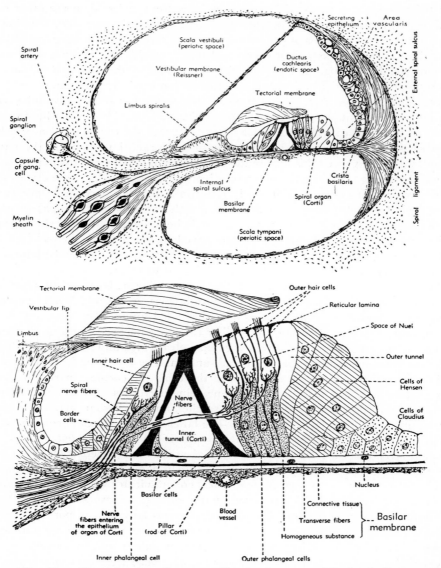

FIG. 230. *Upper*, Vertical section of human cochlea showing organ of Corti and adjacent structures. *Lower*, Organ of Corti and basilar membrane in greater magnification. (From Rasmussen, *Outlines of neuro-anatomy*, 3d ed., Dubuque, Ia., William C. Brown Co., 1943.)

turn down the spiral. A few radial fibers do not course so widely but arborize about hair cells at the level of entry. Lying above and, in the living state, possibly in contact with the hairlike processes of the sensory cells is the nearly structureless *tectorial membrane*, which is attached at one margin to the spiral lamina (*limbus*) and is free at the other.

Excitation in the Cochlea. The cochlea as a whole is a device whereby sound waves, transmitted through the fluid of the inner ear, are translated into nerve impulses. It is apparent from the arrangement of the cochlea that the vibration imparted to the basilar membrane by a pressure variation in the scala vestibuli is one stage in this process. The truth of this statement is shown directly by the fact that excessive vibrations produced by loud sounds may dislodge the organ of Corti from the basilar membrane.

Moreover, there is conclusive evidence that the segment of the basilar membrane undergoing the widest excursion shifts progressively with frequency.[26] As this shift occurs, different auditory nerve fibers will undergo maximal excitation. Direct evidence[2, 41] indicates that the nerve impulses remain canalized as they pass through the fibers of the auditory system, so that ultimately each tone results in a peak of activity in some patch of auditory cortex. The doctrine of specific nerve energies holds that which patch of cortex is maximally active determines which pitch is experienced. This view of cochlear function is the "place theory" of hearing; it is also somewhat irreverently known as the "pitch-is-which" theory.

Within the framework of the place theory there are two theories—the resonance theory and the traveling wave theory—regarding the manner in which the basilar membrane responds to different sound frequencies. Neither theory specifies the mechanism of end-organ excitation. In the resonance theory, it is assumed that a pressure wave is rather quickly and widely developed throughout the scala vestibuli and that the basilar membrane responds selectively, as though in some measure tuned. Helmholtz, in framing this theory, was led by several histologic features to regard the basilar

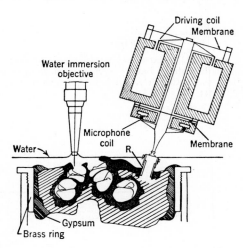

FIG. 231. Experimental set-up used by Békésy to study stapes and basilar membrane. (From Békésy and Rosenblith, Chap. 27 in *Handbook of experimental psychology*, S. S. Stevens, ed., New York, John Wiley & Sons, Inc., 1951.)

membrane and its burden of receptor elements as a series of resonators. That the transverse fibers of the basilar membrane are under tension, however, has recently been disproved. The most liberal calculations show that the resonance theory could account for only four and one-half of the ten and one-half octaves available to the human ear.[34]

Békésy[7] removed the cochlea under water from a fresh cadaver and mounted the organ in a saline bath so that he could view the basilar membrane with a water-immersion microscope at magnifications of 30 to 70 times (Fig. 231). He then explored the elastic properties of various structures by pressing them with a minute von Frey hair (Chap. 13). At the apex (where the basilar membrane is widest) the area of deformation was circular, showing that the membrane is under no greater transverse than longitudinal tension. Near the stapes, the deformation was an ellipse with a longitudinal-transverse axis of 2:1, suggesting only slight transverse tension. Moreover, the profile of the deformation (Fig. 232) was broad, unlike the sharply peaked deformation which results when a stretched, elastic membrane is similarly treated. When minute slits were made in the basilar membrane "at rest," the edges did not gape.

The second theory of cochlear transmission invokes traveling waves like the pressure pulse wave in blood vessels.[7] The basilar membrane introduces enough elasticity into an otherwise rigid tube to justify this analogy. (The amount of damping, stiffness, etc., in the cochlear partition constitutes the basis for the assumptions in several theories of cochlear mechanics.) Traveling waves in the scala vestibuli (Fig. 233) will first grow in size and then subside as the apex of the cochlea is approached because they are damped by the cochlear partition. An envelope enclosing the peak amplitudes will reveal one region at which the basilar membrane has been maximally deflected, and this region will be different for each frequency. Short wavelengths will die out more quickly than will long wavelengths. These observations meet the requirement for a localization of high tones at the base and low tones at the apex of the cochlea. The requirement for pitch perception would be, as in the previous theory, that the region of maximum excursion be recognizable.

Békésy,[7] using the preparation from cadavers described above, replaced the stapes with a tube containing an electromagnetically driven piston and observed the cochlear partition through a window cut in the cochlea. When the artificial stapes vibrated at different rates, the displacement amplitudes shown in Figure 234 were obtained. The result lends support to the traveling wave hypothesis insofar as it is possible to reason from nonviable preparations.

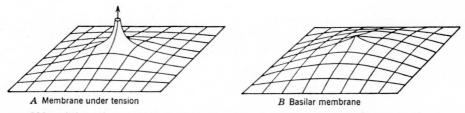

A Membrane under tension   B Basilar membrane

FIG. 232.   *A* shows how a thin, elastic, uniformly stretched membrane behaves when local pressure is applied. *B* shows basilar membrane near apex when same pressure is applied and its deformation pattern shows that it is not a thin, stretched membrane. (From Békésy, *J. acoust. Soc. Amer.*, 1948, 20:227–241.)

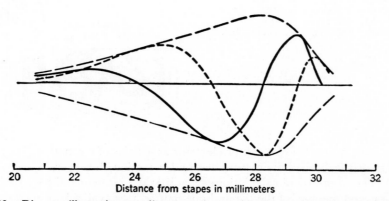

Distance from stapes in millimeters

| 20 | 22 | 24 | 26 | 28 | 30 | 32 |

FIG. 233.   Diagram illustrating traveling wave theory of basilar membrane movement. Solid and short dash lines represent same sound wave at two instants of time. Long dash line is described by connecting the peaks at successive instants of time. Scale at bottom represents distance along basilar membrane. (After Békésy, *J. acoust. Soc. Amer.*, 1947, *19*:452–460.)

The traveling wave theory, in contrast to the resonance theory, requires a definite time for conduction of the wave through the cochlea. Wever and Lawrence[37] advance convincing evidence that interference effects, expected from traveling waves, do not occur. On the other hand, there are several indications that the traveling wave theory may be correct. At the nerve, the cochlear nucleus and the cerebral cortex (see below), the activity reflects a sharp "cut-off" at high frequencies and a gradual "cut-off" at low frequencies, mirroring the shape of the deflections of the cochlear partition seen in Figure 234. Partial transections of the topographically organized auditory nerve do not lead to a tonal gap.[17, 21, 27] This finding offers a difficulty to both theories, but is more easily reconcilable with the traveling wave hypothesis. Figure 235 shows that the basal turn of the cochlea responds to all frequencies but that the more apical third turn

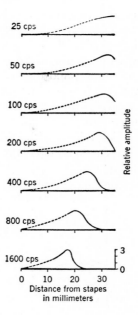

FIG. 234. Displacement amplitude along basilar membrane for different frequencies (constant amplitude) of stapes vibration. Solid lines were obtained by measurement, dotted lines by extrapolation from other observations. (From Békésy and Rosenblith, Chap. 27 in *Handbook of experimental psychology*, S. S. Stevens, ed., New York, John Wiley & Sons, Inc., 1951.)

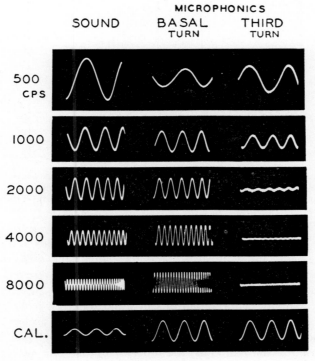

FIG. 235. Microphonic electrical records from base and from a point near apex of guinea pig cochlea in response to sound waves of various frequencies. Note that basal turn responds to all frequencies as demanded by traveling wave theory, and that amplitude of sound waves need not be altered greatly (10 db) to give equal responses. Note absence of response to high frequencies at third turn. (From Tasaki, *J. Neurophysiol.*, 1954, *17*:97–122.)

responds only to low frequencies. These facts were learned by recording the electrical phenomena of the cochlea.

Electrical activity of cochlea.   With the advent of electrical recording, it has been possible to break into the chain of events linking airborne sound waves and sound perceptions by the brain, and thus to make a more analytic attack on the physiologic mechanisms involved. Three quite different kinds of electrical phenomena can be recorded from the ear: (i) the *cochlear microphonic* or *Wever-Bray effect*, (ii) action potentials of the VIIIth nerve, and (iii) resting DC potentials.

Potentials which mirror faithfully the sound waves falling on the eardrum can be recorded from the general region of the ear. When this so-called "microphonic" potential is suitably amplified and fed into a loudspeaker, words spoken into a cat's ear can be heard in the loudspeaker. Because the cochlear microphonics were first recorded from the auditory nerve,[35, 36] the potentials were initially mistaken for action currents. Analysis

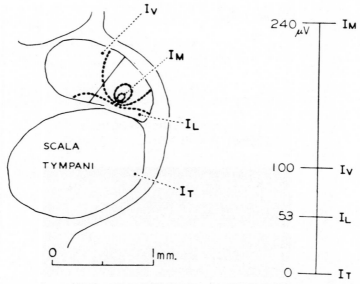

FIG. 236.   Microphonic isopotential lines (*dotted*) of guinea pig cochlea. Electrodes at I_V, I_M, and I_L recorded potentials shown on scale at right relative to electrode I_T. Contour lines represent 70 μV. potentials. Highest potential was recorded from I_M, region of organ of Corti. (From Davis *et al.*, *Cold Spr. Harb. Symp. quant. Biol.*, 1952, *17*:143–154.)

soon showed that these electric potentials originate in the cochlea and spread, with an exponential decrement, along the nerve and throughout the tissue surrounding the cochlea. Subsequently, the action currents of the auditory nerve were recorded separately from the microphonic potential.[24]

The minute anatomy of the organ of Corti and other evidence suggest that the microphonic potential originates from a non-neural structure. This has been shown[10] by mapping the isopotential lines of the microphonic (Fig. 236). One pole is at or near the hair bearing portion of the hair cells; the other is diffuse. The microphonic effect of the cochlea is further distinguished from nerve impulses by having "zero" latency, as opposed to a 0.7 millisecond latency for nerve; by absence of refractory period; by capability of continuous gradation; by resistance to fatigue, cold, anesthesia and ischemia; and by an ability to follow frequencies up to 16,000 c.p.s. These are not attributes of the nerve impulse—a trigger-like release of energy contributed by the metabolizing cell and obeying the all-or-none law; they are, however, characteristics of the passive transformation (transduction) of mechanical energy into electrical energy. Pressure upon the face of a quartz crystal, for example, produces a potential difference between the two ends. The essential condition for this *piezoelectric effect* appears to be the orderly orientation of the atoms, a property of biologic structures. However, Békésy[6] has calculated that the mechanical energy of sound cannot supply all the electrical energy of the microphonic potential.

This calculation focuses attention on the third type of potential, a DC potential that may be the source of energy and that may be modulated in some manner by movements of the cochlear structures. These resting potentials of the cochlea are surprisingly large. Taking the fluid of the scala vestibuli as a zero point, Békésy[5] found that the fluid of the scala media shows positivity of 50 mV., whereas the organ of Corti shows negativity of 50 mV. The scala tympani (and spiral ligament) are nearly equipotential to the scala

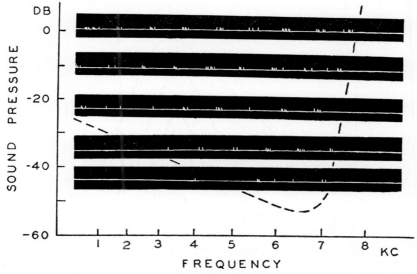

FIG. 237.   Single auditory nerve responses to tone "pips" of different frequencies and intensities. Each strip of record shows a short burst of repetitive discharges in the single fiber in response to a tone which is increased in frequency between pips. Each strip of record represents a different sound level, lower record representing weakest intensity used. Dashed line encloses "response area" for this fiber. (From Tasaki, *J. Neurophysiol.*, 1954, *17*:97–122.)

vestibuli. The potential difference between the organ of Corti and its surrounding fluid is readily understood; an ionic separation across Reissner's membrane presents some difficulties.

It is tempting to believe that the microphonic potential is the means by which sound waves stimulate nerve fibers, giving the sequence: sound pressure–microphonic potential–nerve impulse. It was once thought that the time (0.6 to 0.7 millisecond) elapsing between the first sign of the cochlear microphonic potential and the nerve impulse demanded chemical intermediation, but this is now accounted for by the slow conduction within the peripheral segment of the auditory nerve. Tasaki *et al.*[28] found a third phasic potential, which is an early phase of the action potential and is thus a "prepotential" such as those preceding synaptic spike potentials.

Action Potentials of Auditory Nerve.   Tasaki[27] recorded the response of single auditory nerve fibers to tonal "pips" of different frequencies and intensities. He found (Fig. 237) that at threshold a fiber is excited by a narrow band of frequencies. This band widens as the intensity of the stimulus is increased, expanding rapidly into lower frequencies (gradual cut-off) and almost not at all into higher frequencies (sharp cut-off). The frequency at which the sharp cut-off occurred varied with the fiber. Those from the basal turn of the cochlea have a very high cut-off and respond to any lower frequency; those from the apical end respond only to low frequencies.

Galambos and Davis[15, 16] recorded potentials from single cell bodies of the second order neurons scattered throughout the intracranial portion of the auditory nerve. Like all other sensory receptors so far examined, the auditory receptor initiates more nerve impulses per second the more strongly it is stimulated. However, as would be expected from the audibility curve, the *frequency* of the sound wave also influences the rate of discharge. When the number of impulses per second appearing in a single second-order neuron are plotted against the frequency of a constant intensity exploring tone, a peaked curve is obtained. Thus, the rate of discharge of the single neuron shown in Figure 238

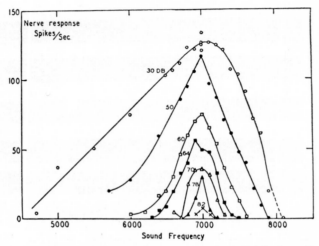

FIG. 238.   Relation of intensity and frequency to discharge of a single auditory nerve fiber. As intensity level is increased (numbers attached to curves get smaller), a wider range of frequencies excite fiber, and each frequency excites more discharges. Distance along abscissa is probably function of distance along basilar membrane. Intensity level equals db *below* a reference level. (From Galambos and Davis, *J. Neurophysiol.*, 1943, 6:39–57.)

decreases on either side of 7000 c.p.s. The family of isointensity curves derived by repeating the procedure with exploring tones of different intensities shows that wide stretches of the basilar membrane are excited by more intense sounds, but also that the position of the maximum excitation stays the same for a given frequency.

The present-day concept—the place theory—allows for the fact that a pure tone, if intense, will throw a long stretch of the basilar membrane into vibration. But such vibration has a maximum at some region, and the nerve fibers leading from this region will discharge at the highest rate (Fig. 238). Thus, the notion of "pitch-is-which" should be understood to mean which fibers are firing at maximum frequency, and hence which patch of cortex is maximally active.

Tonal Localization in the Cochlea.   That the apex of the cochlea is concerned with low sounds and the base with high sounds has been indicated. In an effort to work out a detailed map of the cochlea, a variety of ingenious and painstaking methods have yielded results in essential agreement.

In a series of guinea pigs, Stevens *et al.*[26] disrupted the basilar membrane by drilling into the cochlea at various points. The audibility curve was then determined, with the minimal cochlear microphonic used as the threshold response (Fig. 239). The loss of sensitivity was confined to two octaves and was not absolute. Sounds louder than 30 db excited areas to either side of the damaged stretch. By relating the "tonal gaps" in the audiograms to the areas of damage, as determined histologically, these workers evolved the map of the cochlea shown at the bottom of Figure 239. The curve for man was deduced from the experimental curve obtained from guinea pigs. The octaves in different parts of the audible range do not occupy equal extents on the basilar membrane. The lower five octaves are crowded into little more than the short, apical turn of the cochlea; the upper four octaves, which include the frequencies essential to hearing human speech, occupy the balance of the basilar membrane. This apportionment apparently is related to the fineness of pitch discrimination throughout the audible range. The minimal detectable difference in frequency appears to correspond to a constant distance on the cochlea. The long stretch of basilar membrane devoted to the

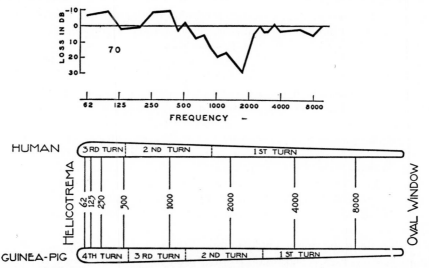

FIG. 239. *Upper,* Electrical audiogram as affected by lesion to portion of basilar membrane. The threshold intensity for elicitation of a detectable microphonic response from cochlea is increased for tones from middle range of frequencies. *Lower,* Map of cochlea of guinea pig showing localization of pitch reception on basilar membrane. Map for guinea pig is constructed from results of 20 experiments like those shown in upper part of figure, together with histologic data on extent of basilar membrane damaged. Map for man was deduced from data on guinea pig. (From Stevens *et al., J. gen. Psychol.,* 1935, *13:*297–315.)

middle range makes possible the discrimination of a large number of pitches in the frequency range of audible speech. As in the case of two point threshold and visual acuity, fine discrimination of tones appears to be gained by multiplication of sensory units.

Frequency theories. The alternative to the place theory of cochlear function is some version of the "frequency theory." According to these theories, it is not necessary for the cochlea to respond differentially along its extent for frequency reception. The frequency of the sound waves is supposedly reproduced in the frequency of nerve discharge, and the cerebral cortex interprets different frequencies of discharge as different pitches. However, nerve fibers cannot discharge at the frequencies of high pitches and the theory cannot explain loudness by frequency of discharge. The *volley theory*[34] attempts to overcome these difficulties, but the evidence for the place theory seems overwhelming.

Routes of Conduction.[34] Sound waves in the air reach the organ of Corti by three routes, the first of which may be termed the *physiologic* or *ossicular route.* The vibrations are transmitted from the tympanum through the ossicular chain and oval window to the scala vestibuli and scala media, and thence through the organ of Corti and basilar membrane to the scala tympani and, finally, to the round window. This route has already been discussed in some detail; the important role of the round window is discussed below.

The second route of conduction through the middle ear may be termed the *air route* of conduction. This begins at the tympanum and passes via the air in the middle ear to the round window, scala tympani, etc. The air route is principally by way of the round window, because this window is covered by only a thin membrane, whereas the oval window is stoppered by the stapes, especially when the chain is ankylosed ("frozen"). But transmission through the round window is inefficient because, as pointed out above, sound is not transmitted efficiently from air to fluid.

When the ossicular chain is broken, the air route conducts less well than might be expected from the acoustical matching value of the chain (30 db). The hearing loss from interruption of the chain varies between 30 db for low tones and 65 db for the middle range. Two factors are involved. One is that the tympanum, weighted by the interrupted ossicular chain, becomes an obstacle to sound transmission to the air of the middle ear. The second is that the sound waves transmitted through the round window and scala tympani push the basilar membrane upward during the phase of positive pressure while the same wave conducted by the oval window and scala vestibuli pushes the membrane downward. If this interference is prevented experimentally by leading the sound through a tube to only one window, the hearing loss is 30 db. Fortunately, the sound paths are not equally long, and therefore the sound waves are not 180° out of phase. The cancellation is thus imperfect, and the net loss due to this factor is about 12 db.

More common than interruption is a fixation of the ossicular chain, resulting from adhesions in the wake of a middle ear infection or from a pathologic change in the temporal bone that seals the stapes in the oval window (otosclerosis). Understanding of the resulting deafness and its surgical relief hinge on an appreciation of the physiologic significance of the round window.

The function of the round window apparently is to provide "give" in the otherwise rigidly encased cochlea. Deformation rather than mere compression is required for stimulation of skin receptors and, apparently, of the hair cells as well. For deformation to occur, the basilar membrane must actually move, no matter how slightly, and the membrane closing the round window must bulge to permit this.

In otosclerosis, hearing is severely impaired partly because the ossicular route of conduction is lost. Further, the air route of conduction to the round window cannot function to best advantage because "give" is lacking. Such "give" is successfully provided in Lempert's "fenestration operation" by drilling a small window into the horizontal semicircular canal, which is in continuity with the vestibule of the cochlea. A flap of skin is placed over this fistula, and hearing is significantly improved (usually within 20 to 30 db of normal) as long as the new passage remains patent.

The third route by which sound can be conducted to the inner ear is by means of bone conduction—the *osseous route*. Instead of following the ossicular chain or the air route of the middle ear, the sound waves reach the inner ear through the bones of the skull. The middle ear is, as it were, "short-circuited" or "by-passed." Unlike the ossicular and air routes, bone conduction plays little if any part in hearing ordinary sounds because so much energy is lost in the passage of a sound wave from air to the bones of the head. However, if a tuning fork which is unheard when sounded in air is held with its base against the skull (better acoustical matching), it can be heard clearly. Bone conduction is important in distinguishing between types of deafness, and it is employed for one type of hearing aid. Conduction by this route must be ruled out in testing an ear with sounds louder than 50 to 60 db, at which level bone-conducted sound may reach the normal ear. Ear plugs are, of course, useless, but hearing of bone-conducted sound can be eliminated by introducing a "masking" noise into the ear.

The mechanism of bone conduction appears to be twofold. Tiny oscillations of the bone subject the fluid contents of the cochlea to alternate pressures. The scala vestibuli and the scala tympani are equally exposed to these pressures, but the positive pressure phase of the sound wave causes a downward movement of the basilar membrane, just as in normal hearing, because the round window presents relatively less resistance than the oval window. The round window bulges into the middle ear and allows the basilar membrane to move downward. In the second proposed mechanism inertia prevents the stapes and cochlear fluid from following exactly the oscillations of the head bones. The result is movement of the basilar membrane and the membrane of the round window. Experiments involving fixation of the stapes which would differentiate these two mechanisms favor the second as the more important.

Types of Deafness.[34]   Deafness, including partial impairment of hearing, is classified into three main types according to where the block occurs. *Conduction deafness* is any interference with the passage of sound waves through the external or middle ear. Common causes are collections of pus, exudates or wax; adhesions of the ossicles to the bony walls; thickening of the tympanum as a result of infection; and new growths of bone that bind the stapes (otosclerosis). The Weber and Rinné diagnostic tests are based on the greater interference with air and ossicular routes of conduction characteristic of conduction deafness. Because it "by-passes" the middle ear, bone conduction is little affected. The deafness is never total because some sound is conducted through the skull. Also, in these patients, audiograms tend to be "flat"; i.e., the loss is equal for all frequencies. The patient, paradoxically, seems to hear best in noisy surroundings, because voices are raised and he is not disturbed by the noise which is unheard. He tolerates hearing aids and is greatly benefited by them.

The second type of hearing impairment, once termed *perception deafness*, is now known as *nerve deafness*. The defect is not in the cortical process of sound perception but is caused by a degeneration of sensory cells of the inner ear, tumors of the auditory nerve, etc. Because the damage is in the portion of the hearing mechanism (hair cells or auditory nerve) common to air and bone conduction, a failure of both routes is diagnostic. In respect to tone, the deafness is "spotty." The hearing of high tones is typically the most impaired (hence "high tone deafness"). This distorts the perception and discrimination of spoken words (consonants tend to sound alike), and hearing is poor when noise masks the slight remaining differences in sounds. For some reason, as the intensity of a tone is increased, the perceived intensity (loudness) increases more rapidly than it does when hearing is normal. The loud sounds may be just as unpleasant as they are to the normal ear, making the patient intolerant of loud speech or hearing aids. Since this is the deafness of old age, the familiar phrase, "Don't shout, young man," is understandable. Nerve deafness may be temporary when caused by fatigue or partial trauma, as in exposure to prolonged loud sounds ("boilermaker's deafness"), or permanent when caused by degeneration through senility, disease or toxic agents.

The third type of deafness, *central deafness*, is rare. It may result from interference with the pathway of nerve impulses to the cerebral cortex, but is more often a manifestation of aphasia (Chap. 21) or of a psychogenic disorder. Recent studies[13, 14] on suppression of auditory nerve discharge may have some bearing on these latter disorders.

THE AUDITORY PATHWAY

The peripheral ramifications of bipolar cells in the spiral ganglion are rather varied and complex.[12] The central axons of the bipolar cells pass in the VIIIth nerve to enter the pons at its junction with the medulla. The entering fibers bifurcate and connect with both the ventral and the dorsal cochlear nuclei. In the nerve, the fibers from the base and apex twist like a rope, but do not intermingle randomly. The detailed anatomy of the first-order neurons is consistent with the place theory; the cochlear nucleus is an "uncoiled" reflection of the cochlea.

The auditory pathway is complex (Fig. 240). At least four neurons are involved, and the pathway is ipsilateral as well as contralateral. In broad outline, it consists of the two cochlear nuclei, the superior olivary nuclei and related nuclei, the lateral lemnisci, the inferior colliculi, the medial geniculate bodies and the auditory cortex.

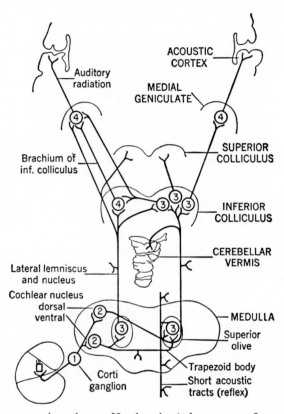

FIG. 240.   Afferent acoustic pathways. Numbers in circles represent first, second, third and fourth neuron of chain. Drawing summarizes work of several investigations, mainly on cat. (From Davis, Chap. 28 in *Handbook of experimental psychology*, S. S. Stevens, ed., New York, John Wiley & Sons, Inc., 1951.)

Action potentials can be recorded from both the ipsilateral and contralateral lateral lemnisci when one cochlea is stimulated. From the size and timing of the activity, the ipsilateral fibers apparently equal the contralateral in number, and the same number of synapses is involved. No crossing occurs at the level of the inferior colliculi or the medial geniculate bodies.[22] Chow[9] has shown that the number of fibers progressively increases at each stage of the auditory system. For each fiber in the spiral ganglion two issue from the cochlear nucleus, 14 issue from the medial geniculate, and some 40 occur in the auditory cortex.

The bilaterality of the auditory system was well demonstrated physiologically in the ingenious experiments by Mettler *et al.*[19] (Fig. 241). After various components of the auditory pathway in dogs had been interrupted, the degree of hearing loss was determined by the conditioned reflex method. By removing one cerebral cortex in combination with one or the other cochlea, Mettler and his coworkers discovered that the "acoustic values" of the ipsilateral and contralateral pathways are equal. Nearly complete bilaterality of representation also characterizes the auditory system of man. Unilateral cortical lesions affect hearing only slightly, and, since both auditory areas are seldom attacked by the same pathologic process, deafness is rarely produced by cortical lesions.

In addition to the specific projection to the auditory cortex outlined above, a more diffuse route can be traced through the reticular formation. Although several major stages in this system are undefined, the ascending reticular system is clearly implicated by the observation that sounds continue to arouse decerebellate cats after the specific auditory system has been severed.

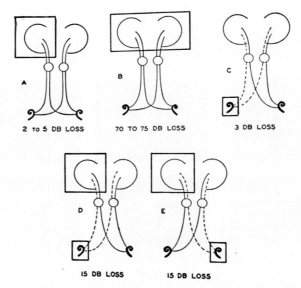

FIG. 241. Summary diagram of series of experiments demonstrating bilaterality of auditory pathway in dog. Number below each diagram is hearing loss in decibels, and a box around symbol for cerebral cortex or cochlea indicates destruction of it. Observe that in *D* hearing depends on *uncrossed* fibers of left lateral lemniscus, whereas in *E* hearing depends upon crossed fibers of right lateral lemniscus; hearing loss is equal in the two cases. (Experiments by Mettler *et al.*, *Brain*, 1934, *57:*475–483; diagram after Stevens and Davis, *Hearing, its psychology and physiology*, New York, John Wiley & Sons, Inc., 1938.)

Centrifugal auditory pathway. Anatomically, it is known that a bundle of fibers originates in the superior olive and terminates in the cochlea of the opposite side (bundle of Oort), but the function of these fibers is unknown. By applying shocks to this olivo-cochlear bundle in the cat, Galambos[14] was able to alter the response of the auditory nerve to click stimuli (Fig. 242). When the muscles and ossicles of the middle ear were removed and the animal was curarized, the suppression began 20 to 30 milliseconds after the first shock of the train and continued as long as 500 milliseconds beyond stimulation. The hair cell response (cochlear microphonic) was unaltered during these maneuvers, but the auditory nerve response was suppressed (strong clicks) or totally abolished (weak clicks). It is evident that the central nervous system could modulate its input via this system; malfunction of the system could result in significant alteration from normal hearing.

Topographic Organization.[12] The auditory system is composed of a topographically highly organized pathway superimposed on a more diffuse one. The spiral organ of Corti is projected upon higher neural structures in such a way that the "localization of tones" observed at the cochlea is preserved at the levels of the cochlear nuclei, the medial geniculate body and the cerebral cortex. This organization is a logical extension of the place theory of audition. A peripheral apparatus to analyze complex sound waves and a signalling of the component frequencies by different auditory nerve fibers are without meaning unless the streams of impulses remain distinct. In cats trained to respond to tones near the thresholds of audibility, Ades *et al.*[2] destroyed minute portions of the medial geniculate body by means of the Horsley-Clarke stereotaxic apparatus. Hearing was reduced for restricted bands of tones, and the frequencies affected varied in a systematic fashion with small changes in the loci of the injury. These investigators were thus able to map the medial geniculate body in terms of tone localization.

The auditory cortex, once considered single, is now known to consist of three areas in the cat and dog.[1] (These animals are much used in audition studies because the auditory cortex is not buried as it is in man and in the monkey.) The auditory areas lie in the ectosylvian gyrus. Auditory area I (AI) lies in the superior part, AII lies in the subjacent sylvian gyrus, and AIII lies rostrally overlapping with somatic area II. AI is

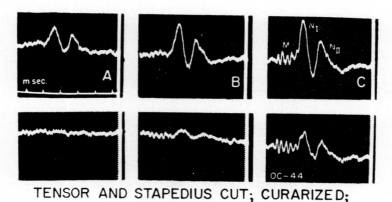

TENSOR AND STAPEDIUS CUT; CURARIZED;
STAPES DISARTICULATED

FIG. 242.   Suppression of auditory nerve response to click stimulation by shocks to olivo-cochlear bundle. *A*, Response to weak click totally abolished by 100/sec. shocks to medulla. *B*, *C*, Stronger clicks, showing incomplete suppression. *M*, Hair cell response. N_I and N_{II}, Auditory nerve response. (From Galambos, *J. Neurophysiol.*, 1956, *19*:424–437.)

the projection area for the medial geniculate body, and the orderly topographic organization of this projection has been shown anatomically in both the dog[30] and the cat.[23]

The details of tonotopic localization in AI, representing a projection of the cochlea (untwisted), is better shown by electrical methods. However, two major difficulties are encountered. One is that under anesthesia the cortex responds only to the start of a sustained tone. Unfortunately, the energy at the start of a tone is not confined to the final, single frequency. There seems to be no way of overcoming this difficulty. The other problem is that a sound stimulus strong enough to evoke electrical activity distinguishable from background activity is strong enough to activate a wide expanse of basilar membrane (and of AI cortex). This difficulty, which masks the degree of tonotopic organization, has been circumvented in two ways.

Woolsey and Walzl[41] exposed the spiral lamina along which the nerve fibers from the organ of Corti enter the modiolus. By means of fine electrodes, a few fibers at a time could be stimulated. A change in the point of maximal electrical activity on the auditory cortex was occasioned by a shift of the electrodes along the row of nerve fibers. Stimulation of a small group of fibers activated a vertical band of cortical tissue in the ectosylvian gyrus. Stimulation at the base of the cochlea, which responds most strongly to high tones, caused activity in the most forward bands, while stimuli at the apex (low tones) were projected to the bands nearest the occiput; intermediate cochlear regions were also intermediate at the cortex.

Tunturi[30, 31] met the difficulty by applying millimeter-wide strips of filter paper soaked in strychnine to the auditory cortex. This procedure causes the poisoned cortex to give rise to large "strychnine spikes" and augments evoked potentials. He determined the range of frequencies (and their requisite intensities) which activated the particular bit of cortex under the filter paper. This experiment resulted in a map (Fig. 243) show-ing that each octave has maximum localization in a mediolaterally oriented strip 5 to 7 mm. long and that the octave strips are about equidistant (2 mm. apart). Shifting the strychnine paper 0.2 mm. shifted the point of maximum 0.1 octave, which is not far from discriminable frequency difference. Disappointingly, the length of the cortical strip does not indicate intensity. As might be predicted from cochlear mechanics, increas-ing the intensity increased the width of the frequency band which would excite a given

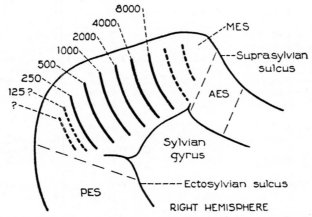

FIG. 243. Tonal localization in dog's primary auditory area. *AES*, Anterior ectosylvian area; *PES*, posterior ectosylvian area; *MES*, middle ectosylvian area. Bands indicate point at which strychnine spikes occurred with lowest intensity. Bands indicated by dashes were not determined experimentally. (After Tunturi from Bremer, *Some problems in neurophysiology*, London, Athlone Press, 1953.)

strip of cortex. The curve for the low frequencies was changed most, the cut-off being sharper in the higher tones. This is one of several indications favoring the concept of a traveling wave activation of the basilar membrane.

These observations are consistent with the belief that the pitch heard depends simply upon which group of cells in the cerebral cortex is thrown into maximal activity. No clear-cut cortical correlate of intensity has been discovered, and it may be noted that an important stimulus dimension—duration—is, because of the action of anesthesia, largely unexplored.

Cortical Localization.[12]   The tonotopic organization of the auditory cortex sug-gests that small cortical lesions might produce "tonal gaps" like those following cochlear damage. On the contrary, nearly all of auditory area I can be ablated without effect on tonal discrimination in the cat[20] or monkey.[11] In the cat, all three auditory areas had to be destroyed bilaterally before tone discrimination was permanently lost. This obser-vation calls to mind the ablation studies of somatosensory localization.

The function of AI may lie in some "higher" auditory activity. AII seems essential to pattern discrimination, whereas AI is not. If tones A and B are used to make two tonal patterns, ABA or BAB, the transition between them is easily discriminable by a cat before operation. After removal of all three auditory areas, pattern discrimination, unlike single frequency discrimination, is lost and cannot be relearned. Again, if we homologize the auditory and somatosensory cortex, the results of cortical lesions are broadly similar. Clinical cases offer little evidence on this point. The primary auditory areas are buried, so that the occurrence of symmetrical, bilateral lesions of these areas is a virtual impossibility. Moreover, each area is connected with both cochleae.

REFERENCES

1. ADES, H. W. *J. Neurophysiol.*, 1943, *6*:59–63.
2. ADES, H. W., METTLER, F. A. and CULLER, E. A. *Amer. J. Physiol.*, 1939, *125*:15–23.
3. ARMSTRONG, H. G. *Principles and practice of aviation medicine*, 3rd ed. Baltimore, Williams & Wilkins, 1952, x, 476 pp.
4. BÉKÉSY, G. VON. *Acta oto-laryng. (Stockh.),* 1939, *27*:281–296.
5. BÉKÉSY, G. VON. *J. acoust. Soc. Amer.*, 1951, *23*:576–582.
6. BÉKÉSY, G. VON. *J. acoust. Soc. Amer.*, 1952, *24*:72–76.
7. BÉKÉSY, G. VON and ROSENBLITH, W. A. Chap. 27 in *Handbook of experimental psychology*, S. S. STEVENS, ed. New York, John Wiley & Sons, 1951.
8. BREMER, F. *Some problems in neurophysiology.* London, Athlone Press, 1953, ix, 79 pp.
9. CHOW, K. L. *J. comp. Neurol.*, 1951, *95*:159–175.
10. DAVIS, H., TASAKI, I. and GOLDSTEIN, R. *Cold Spr. Harb. Symp. quant. Biol.*, 1952, *17*:143–154.
11. EVARTS, E. V. *J. Neurophysiol.*, 1952, *15*:443–448.
12. GALAMBOS, R. *Physiol. Rev.*, 1954, *34*:497–528.
13. GALAMBOS, R. *Ann. Otol. (St. Louis),* 1956, *65*:1053–1059.
14. GALAMBOS, R. *J. Neurophysiol.*, 1956, *19*:424–437.
15. GALAMBOS, R. and DAVIS, H. *J. Neurophysiol.*, 1943, *6*:39–57.
16. GALAMBOS, R. and DAVIS, H. *Science*, 1948, *108*:513.
17. GUILD, S. R. *Acta oto-laryng. (Stockh.),* 1953, *43*:199–207.
18. LORENTE DE NÓ, R. *Laryngoscope (St. Louis),* 1933, *43*:1–38.
19. METTLER, F. A., FINCH, G., GIRDEN, E. and CULLER, E. *Brain*, 1934, *57*:475–483.
20. MEYER, D. R. and WOOLSEY, C. N. *J. Neurophysiol.*, 1952, *15*:149–162.
21. NEFF, W. D. *J. comp. physiol. Psychol.*,1947, *40*:203–215.
22. RAAB, D. H. and ADES, H. W. *Amer. J. Psychol.*, 1946, *59*:59–83.
23. ROSE, J. E. and WOOLSEY, C. N. *J. comp. Neurol.*, 1949, *91*:441–466.
24. SAUL, L. J. and DAVIS, H. *Arch. Neurol. Psychiat. (Chicago),* 1932, *28*:1104–1116.
25. STEVENS, S. S. and DAVIS, H. *Hearing: its psychology and physiology.* New York, John Wiley & Sons, 1938, xv, 436 pp.
26. STEVENS, S. S., DAVIS, H. and LURIE, M. H. *J. gen. Psychol.*, 1935, *13*:297–315.
27. TASAKI, I. *J. Neurophysiol.*, 1954, *17*:97–122.
28. TASAKI, I., DAVIS, H. and LEGOUIX, J.-P. *J. acoust. Soc. Amer.*, 1952, *24*:502–519.
29. TROGER, J. *Phys. Z.*, 1930, *31*:26–47.
30. TUNTURI, A. R. *Amer. J. Physiol.*, 1945, *144*:389–394.
31. TUNTURI, A. R. *Amer. J. Physiol.*, 1950, *162*:489–502.
32. WAETZMANN, E. *Akust. Z.*, 1938, *3*:1–6.
33. WALKER, A. E. *The primate thalamus.* Chicago, University of Chicago Press, 1938, xxiii, 321 pp.
34. WEVER, E. G. *Theory of hearing.* New York, John Wiley & Sons, 1949, xiii, 484 pp.
35. WEVER, E. G. and BRAY, C. W. *J. exp. Psychol.*, 1930, *13*:373–387.
36. WEVER, E. G. and BRAY, C. W. *Proc. nat. Acad. Sci. (Wash.),* 1930, *16*:344–350.
37. WEVER, E. G. and LAWRENCE, M. *Physiological acoustics.* Princeton, N. J., Princeton University Press, 1954, 454 pp.
38. WIENER, F. M. and ROSS, D. A. *J. acoust. Soc. Amer.*, 1946, *18*:401–408.
39. WIGGERS, H. C. *Amer. J. Physiol.*, 1937, *120*:771–780.
40. WILSKA, A. *Skand. Arch. Physiol.*, 1935, *72*:161–165.
41. WOOLSEY, C. N. and WALZL, E. M. *Johns Hopk. Hosp. Bull.*, 1942, *71*:315–344.

CHAPTER 18

The Eye as an Optical Instrument

By FRANK W. WEYMOUTH*

THE eye is the peripheral organ of vision. By means of its physical structure (Fig. 244), rays of light from external objects are focused upon the retina and there set up nerve impulses that are transmitted by the fibers of the optic nerve and the optic tract to the visual area in the cortex of the brain. Here is aroused the reaction we call seeing. In studying the physiology of vision we must first consider the eye as an optical instrument that is physically adapted to form an image on its retina and that is provided with certain physiologic regulatory mechanisms.

FORMATION OF AN IMAGE

The image on the retina is formed by virtue of the refractive surfaces of the cornea and the lens. The curved surfaces of these transparent bodies act substantially like a convex glass lens, and the physics of the formation of an image by such a lens is used to explain the refractive processes in the eye.

Image Formation by a Convex Lens. The most common artificial lens is a piece of glass with polished spherical surfaces surrounded by air. Such lenses are of two types, the converging lens with convex surfaces (thick in the middle) and the diverging lens with concave surfaces (thin in the middle). The *principal axis* of a lens with two spherical surfaces is a line passing through the centers of curvature that is therefore perpendicular to these surfaces where it pierces them. Real images that may be caught on a screen are formed only by convex (converging) lenses.

Light from a point on the principal axis so distant that the rays are parallel when they strike the lens will converge at a point, the *principal focus*, on the principal axis

* Revised by Theodore C. Ruch.

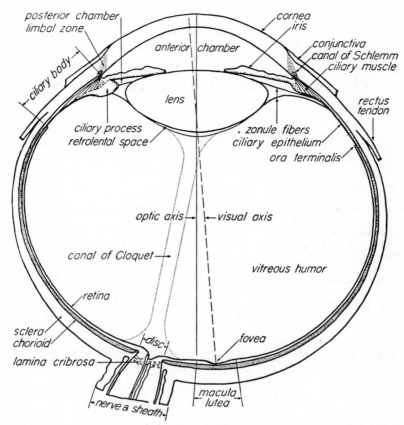

FIG. 244. Horizontal section of human eye. (From Walls, *The vertebrate eye*. Bloomfield Hills, Mich., Cranbrook Institute of Science, 1942.)

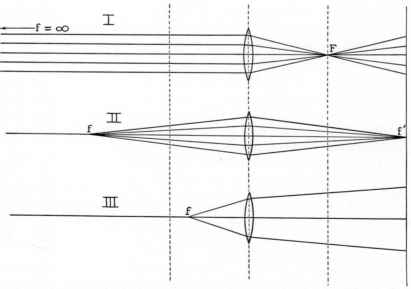

FIG. 245. Refraction of light by convex lens. *I,* Refraction of parallel rays; *II,* refraction of divergent rays; *III,* refraction of divergent rays from a luminous point nearer than principal focal distance. *F,* Principal focus; *f,* luminous point; *f',* focused image of *f.*

behind the lens (*F* in Fig. 245, I).* The distance between the principal focus and the lens is the *principal focal distance*. This distance, which is a measure of the refractive power or "strength" of the lens, depends upon the curvatures of the lens surfaces and the refractive index of the glass. Absolutely parallel rays emanate from an infinitely distant source of light; practically, however, objects not nearer than about 20 feet give rays which diverge so little that they may be considered to be parallel. On the other hand, if a luminous object is placed at *F* in Figure 245, the rays that pass through the lens will emerge as parallel rays. If a luminous point (*f* in Fig. 245, II) is placed in front of the lens at a distance greater than the principal focal distance but not far enough to give practically parallel rays, the cone of diverging rays from this source will focus at *f'*, which is farther away than the principal focus. Conversely, the rays from a luminous

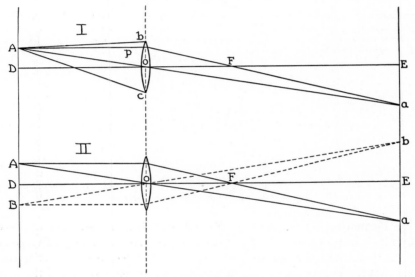

FIG. 246.   Formation of image by convex lens. *I*, Relation of a point (*A*) to its image (*a*). *Ab* and *Ac* are limiting rays of cone of light reflected by *A*; *Ap* ray parallel to optic or principal axis (*DE*) of lens; *F*, principal focus; *o*, optical center. *II*, Relation of luminous object and its image points. *A, B,* luminous points; *a, b,* images of points.

point at *f'* will be brought to a focus at *f*. Such points as *f* and *f'* are spoken of as *conjugate foci*. All luminous points within the limits specified have corresponding conjugate foci at which their images are formed by the lens. Lastly, if a luminous point is placed nearer to the lens than the principal focal distance, as at *f* in Figure 245, III, the cone of strongly divergent rays, although refracted, is still divergent after leaving the lens, and consequently is not focused and forms no real image of the point.

Any lens contains an *optical center*, or nodal point, on the principal axis; in Figure 246, *DE* is the principal axis, and *o* is the optical center. All other straight lines passing through the optical center, i.e., rays coincident with the principal axis or any secondary axis, are not bent in passing through the lens. Moreover, the conjugate focus of any luminous point not on the principal axis will lie somewhere upon the secondary axis drawn from this point through the optical center.

The exact position of the image of such a point can be determined by the construction illustrated in Figure 246, I. *A* represents a luminous point throwing a cone of rays upon the lens; the limiting

* In all such diagrams, the curvatures and thickness of the lens are greatly exaggerated. Statements concerning the course of rays are strictly true only for an ideally thin lens and for a small area about the principal axis.

rays of this cone are represented by *Ab* and *Ac*. Ray *Ap* is parallel to the principal axis and will therefore pass through the principal focus, *F*. If the focal distance is known, the line *Ap* can be extended, as indicated, to pass through *F* after leaving the lens. The point at which the prolongation of this line cuts the secondary axis, *Ao*, marks the conjugate focus of *A* and gives the position, *a*, at which all the rays are focused to form the image.

To calculate the position of the image of any object in front of the lens, the same method may be used, a construction being drawn to determine the images of two or more limiting points, as shown in Figure 246, II. If *AB* is an arrow in front of a lens, the image of *A* is formed at *a* on the secondary axis *Ao* and the image of *B* at *b* along the secondary axis *Bo*. The images of all the intervening points will, of course, lie between *a* and *b*, so that the entire image is that of an inverted arrow. This image may be caught on a screen at the distance indicated by a construction drawn to scale.

The principal focus of a convex lens in air may be determined experimentally, or it may be calculated from the formula

$$\frac{1}{F} = \frac{1}{f_1} + \frac{1}{f_2}$$

where F represents the principal focal distance, and f_1 and f_2 the conjugate focal distances for an object farther away than the principal focus. That is, if the distance between the object and the lens, f_1, is known, and the distance of its image, f_2, is determined experimentally, the principal focal distance of the lens, F, may be determined from the formula.

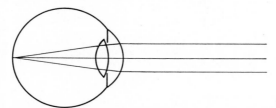

FIG. 247.   Chief ocular interfaces at which light rays are refracted. Rays are refracted at air-cornea, aqueous-lens and lens-vitreous interfaces.

Image Formation by the Eye.   Although the refractive surfaces of the eye act essentially like a convex lens, they are more complex. As indicated in Figure 247, the eye contains three refractive surfaces. The light is refracted at the anterior surface of the cornea, where the rays pass from the air into the denser medium of the cornea; at the anterior surface of the lens, where they again enter a denser medium; and at the posterior surface of the lens, where they enter the less dense vitreous humor. The relative refractive effects on these various surfaces depend upon the curvatures and the indices of refraction* of the various media of the eye and therefore differ.[6, 8]

$$\text{index of refraction} = \frac{\text{velocity in air}}{\text{velocity in x}} = \frac{\text{sine i}}{\text{sine r}}$$

The following illustrate the data on the index of refraction:

air	= 1.000
water	= 1.333
aqueous and vitreous humors	= 1.336
crystalline lens (index of an equivalent thin lens)	= 1.413

Because the difference between the index of refraction of air and that of the cornea is greater than the difference between the indices for the lens and its surroundings, light is more strongly bent on entering the eye than in passing through the lens.

In a lens system like the eye, composed of media with different indices of refraction separated by surfaces of varying curvatures, it is possible, but laborious, to trace accurately the entire path of the light. However, the course of light rays through the eye can be followed with sufficient accuracy by means of a simplification, the *reduced eye*.[4] All

---

* The index of refraction is the ratio of the velocity of light in air (or, more exactly, in vacuum) to the velocity of light in the substance considered; this index is commonly measured by the ratio between the sine of the angle of incidence and the sine of the angle of refraction.

refraction is presumed to occur at a single interface between air and the contents of the eye, here assumed to be homogeneous and to have the same index of refraction as water, 1.333. The interface (c in Fig. 248) corresponding to the surface of the cornea has a radius of 5 mm., and its center of curvature is the optical center or nodal point (n) of the system. The retina lies 15 mm. posterior to the nodal point and 20 mm. from the cornea; this is also the principal focal distance of the system, so that distant objects are focused on the retina of the reduced eye at rest. The anterior principal focus, i.e., the point at which rays parallel within the eye would converge on emerging, lies 15 mm. in front of the cornea. The anterior and posterior focal distances are different because the light travels in air outside the eye and in denser media inside the eye. If the interior focal distance, 20 mm., is divided by the index of refraction of the reduced eye, the result will equal the anterior focal distance, 20/1.333 = 15.0.

As mentioned above, the surfaces and distances in the completely relaxed ideal eye are so related that the posterior focal point coincides with the retina and images of distant objects are focused on it. The formation of the image on the retina can therefore be shown by a construction like the one presented in Figure 248. Secondary axes are drawn from the limiting points of the object—A and B—through the nodal point. Where these axes meet, the retinal image of the object will be formed. That is, all the rays of

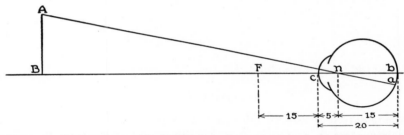

FIG. 248.   Diagram of reduced eye with dimensions and construction required for location and size of retinal image. AB, Object; ab, image; n, nodal point; F, principal focus (anterior); c, corneal surface.

light from A that penetrate the eye will be focused at a, and all those from B at b. The image on the retina will therefore be inverted and smaller than the object. The angle formed at the nodal point by the lines An and Bn (angle AnB or anb) is known as the *visual angle;* it varies inversely with the distance of the object from the eye.

Retinal Image and Spatial Perception.   The apparent position of objects is related to the position of their retinal images, as produced by these physical processes. Stimulation of retinal point a in Figure 248 indicates an object at A, the point in the outside world from which light would normally come to focus on a. If point a is stimulated in some other manner, as by finger pressure on the eyeball producing a phosphene, the sensation is projected, i.e., appears to come from the direction of A. This relation occurs in the congenitally blind just as it does in persons who have "used" their retinas for years.[16]

It is clear that the relation of the direction in which an object is "seen" to the part of the retina stimulated is innate; it is present as soon as a child's behavior indicates a recognition of up and down, right and left. Salamanders in which an eye has been rotated through 180° during an early larval stage snap down for food held above the nose and never learn to correct this confusion. In man, when an abnormal position of an eye causes the stimulation of its retina to indicate an object position disagreeing with that indicated by other sources of information, including the other eye, the afferent impulses from the divergent eye are, after a period of confusion, excluded from consciousness. The nonconforming eye is then said to be amblyopic and is, for certain purposes, blind. However, when the images in both eyes have been reversed by lenses, experimental subjects have, after some confusion, performed tasks in a manner indicating proper orientation in space. When the inverting lenses were then removed, a second period of disorientation followed. In man there seems to be a certain plasticity of brain function which is poorly understood, but which is clinically important in ambylopia.

Size of Retinal Image.   The size of the retinal image may readily be calculated from the size of the actual object and its distance from the eye. As can be seen from Figure 248, the triangles *AnB* and *anb* are similar: consequently, we have the following equality of ratios:

$$\frac{AB}{ab} = \frac{An}{an}$$

or

$$\frac{\text{size of object}}{\text{size of image}} = \frac{\text{distance of object from nodal point}}{\text{distance of image from nodal point}}$$

Suppose it is desired to find the size of the retinal image of a tree 40 m. high at a distance of 2 km. Reducing all measurements to meters and substituting in the above equation, we have

$$\frac{40}{\text{image}} = \frac{2000}{0.015}$$

$$\text{image} = \frac{0.6}{2000} = 0.0003 \text{ m. or } 0.3 \text{ mm.}$$

The image of the tree is thus about the size of the fovea.

ACCOMMODATION

Accommodation of Eye for Objects at Different Distances.   In the *emmetropic* or ideal refractive state, parallel rays from distant objects are brought to a focus on the retina when the eye is at rest. In other words, the structures are usually so correlated that the retina lies very near the second principal focus of the relaxed eye's combined refractive surfaces. When objects are brought closer to the eye, however, the rays proceeding from them become more and more divergent. Were the eye to remain unchanged, the rays would strike the retina before coming to a focus; in consequence, each luminous point in the object, instead of forming a point upon the retina, would form a circle, known as a *diffusion circle*. Thus, the retinal image as a whole would be blurred. Up to a certain point, the eye *accommodates* itself to focus rays from nearer objects so that blurring does not occur.

That a change in the curvature of the lens is the essential factor of accommodation for near objects is demonstrated by a simple and conclusive experiment utilizing the Purkinje images. The eye

FIG. 249.   Effect of accommodation on Purkinje images. *A*, eye at rest; *B*, eye accommodated for near objects; *a*, image reflected from air-cornea interface; *b*, from aqueous-lens interface; *c*, from lens-vitreous interface.

to be observed is relaxed, i.e., gazes into the distance. A lighted candle is held to one side and the observer takes a position on the other, where he can see the light of the candle reflected from the observed eye. With a little practice, and under the right conditions of illumination, the observer can see three images of the candle reflected from the eye as from a mirror. One image, the brightest, is reflected from the convex surface of the cornea (image *a*, Fig. 249*A*). A second, larger and much dimmer, is reflected from the convex surface of the lens (image *b*); this image is larger and fainter because the reflecting surface is less curved. The third image (*c*) is inverted and is smaller and brighter than the second. This image is reflected from the posterior surface of the lens, which acts as a concave mirror in this instance. If the observed eye now gazes at a near object (Fig. 249*B*), the first image (*a*) does not change at all, the third image (*c*) also remains practically the same, but the middle image (*b*) becomes smaller and approaches nearer to the first. This result can only mean that in the act of accommodation the anterior surface of the lens becomes more convex. In this way, its refractive power is increased and the more divergent rays from the near object are focused on the retina. Helmholtz demonstrated that the curvature of the posterior surface of the lens also increases slightly, but this change is so slight that the increased refractive power is referred chiefly to the change in the anterior surface. The means by which the change is effected was first satisfactorily explained by Helmholtz.

The structures involved (Fig. 250) and their action as envisioned by Helmholtz will be described briefly. The tiny *ciliary muscle* lies in a thickened anterior portion of the vascular layer, called the *ciliary body*, which lies as a collar between the anterior margin

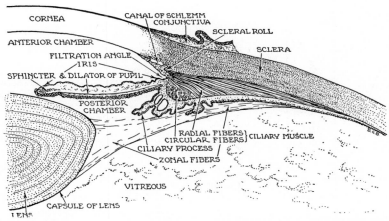

FIG. 250. Detail of anterior segment of human eye. Ciliary process has been distorted in cutting of section. Scleral roll is a narrow shelf of scleral tissue, on under side of which radial or meridional fibers of ciliary muscle originate. (After Maximow and Bloom, *A textbook of histology*.)

of the functional retina and the root of the iris surrounding the lens. Some of the smooth fibers making up the ciliary muscle take a radial course, originating in the sclera near the margin of the cornea and inserting in the chorioid* near the posterior margin of the ciliary body. Other fibers, tending to lie more central to these, have a circular course like that of the fibers of a sphincter muscle.

The lens is suspended by the *zonula*, which consists of delicate transparent membranes and fibers bridging between the ciliary body and the elastic capsule covering the lens. *When the ciliary muscle is relaxed, the zonula is under tension* and pulls on the equator of the lens so that the lens is flattened. When the ciliary muscle contracts, it pulls the ciliary body toward the lens, relaxing the zonula. The tension which held the lens in its flattened shape having been reduced or abolished, the elasticity of the capsule, like the rubber of a toy balloon, tends to mold the plastic lens into a more convex form.

Although other theories have been proposed both before and since the time of

* The spelling *chorioid* is preferred to *choroid* as etymologically more correct and closer to the intended meaning, "resembling the chorion."

Helmholtz, his view of the mechanism, with minor changes resulting from recent work,[8] is still the most adequate.

Other mammals accommodate in the same way as man, but not all vertebrates do. In most bony fish, for example, the mechanism is wholly different. The lens moves backward and toward the retina, thus focusing the eye for more distant objects.[2, 22]

Near and Far Points of Distinct Vision. When an object is brought closer and closer to the eye, a point is reached at which even the strongest contraction of the ciliary muscle will not result in a clear image of the object. The rays from it are so divergent that the refractive surfaces cannot bring them to a focus on the retina. Therefore, each luminous point makes a diffusion circle on the retina, and the whole image is indistinct. The nearest point at which an object can be distinctly seen, with full accommodation, is called the *near point*. The distance between the near point and the eye increases with age, slowly in early life, most rapidly in the early 40's, and very slowly after 50. The rate of this decline is shown in Figure 251. Recession of the near point is usually ascribed to a progressive loss of the plasticity of the lens, so that, although contraction of the ciliary muscle reduces the tension of the zonula, the lens is less and less capable of being

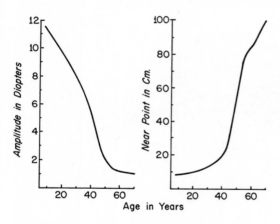

FIG. 251. Decrease in accommodation and increase in distance to near point of vision with age. (Based on data gathered by Duane[6] in over 4000 subjects.)

molded into a more convex form. The progressive loss starts as early in life as the near point can be satisfactorily measured; this process is one of many showing that senescence begins practically at birth. This decline in the power of accommodation is little noticed until it begins to interfere with reading, usually between the 40th and 50th years, when the condition is called *presbyopia* or old-sightedness (p. 419).

In the normal eye, parallel rays are brought to focus on the retina from infinity. If large enough, objects at distances greater than 20 feet are seen distinctly without accommodation—i.e., with the eye at rest. Practically, then, a distance of 6 m. (20 feet) is the *far point* of the normal eye.

Refractive Power and Amplitude of Accommodation. The refractive power of a lens is usually expressed in terms of its principal focal distance. A lens with a focal distance of 1 m. is taken as the unit and is designated as having a refractive power of 1 diopter, 1 D. Compared with this unit, the refractive power of lenses is expressed in terms of the reciprocal of their principal focal distances measured in meters; thus, a lens with a principal focal distance of 1/10 m. is a lens of 10 diopters (10 D.), and one with a focal distance of 5 m. is 1/5 diopter (0.2 D.).

The reduced eye at rest has a refractive power of 66 2/3 D. This value is the reciprocal of the focal distance in air when measured in meters (1/0.015 = 66 2/3 D.), or the reciprocal of the focal distance within the medium of the eye multiplied by the refractive index of that medium (1.333/0.020 = 66 2/3 D.). This power is somewhat greater than that—about 58 D.—derived from measurements of the eye. The cornea contributes about twice as much to this power as does the lens. Thus, the loss of the lens, as in cataract operations, does not lessen the refractive power as much as does the abolition of the action of the cornea occurring, for example, when the eye is opened under water.

In accommodation, greater curvature of the lens increases the total refractive power of the eye. Thus when a 20 year old emmetrope, with a near point of 1/10 m., accommodates, the eye not only brings to a focus parallel rays (66 2/3 D.) but overcomes in addition the divergence of light from the near point (10 D.). It is as though the eye were left at rest, and a glass lens of 10 D. were placed before the cornea. The amplitude of accommodation may thus be expressed by the number of diopters added to the refractive power of the eye by the action of the ciliary muscle. Figure 251 shows the amplitudes of accommodation at various ages corresponding to the near points plotted in Figure 251. Both of these charts are derived from data collected by Duane.[5, 6]

OPTICAL DEFECTS AND ABNORMALITIES

Optical Defects of the Emmetropic Eye. As in other optical systems, spherical, chromatic and other aberrations are present in the eye, but they seldom appreciably affect vision. There are several reasons why these aberrations rarely distort the retinal image. First, the shape and structure of the cornea and the lens and the location of the iris near the nodal point reduce aberrations. In addition, several physiologic factors favor clear vision. The most severe distortions fall on the peripheral retina, where visual acuity is low and more distinct images cannot be appreciated; the important "finder" function of this part of the retina is not thereby impaired. Another factor is the lesser sensitivity of the retina to the wavelengths at the ends of the spectrum—the extreme reds and blues—where chromatic aberration is most marked. Thus, since scattered light and diffraction fringes are of low intensity, they tend to fall below the retinal threshold. For these reasons, what may be called the "physiologic image" is commonly better than the physical image.

Ametropia. As pointed out above, emmetropia is that refractive state of the eye in which, without accommodation, parallel rays focus on the sensitive layer of the retina, or in which the far point is infinitely distant; a person with such eyes is often called an "emmetrope." Any deviation from the condition of emmetropia is called *ametropia*. Obviously, emmetropia does not require any particular total refractive power or size of eye so long as there is a proper proportion between the axial length and the refractive powers of the cornea and lens.

Only recently have accurate measurements been available for a sufficient number of living eyes to permit analysis of the interrelations among the various optical elements.[10, 17] As with other human measurements, all values vary from person to person, the distribution for nearly all elements following a normal frequency curve. The deviations from emmetropia, as measured by the lens needed to bring parallel rays to focus in the resting eye, give a distribution more peaked than normal and with a scatter far less than would result from a chance association of the refractive elements. Correlations of the axial length, the refractive power of the cornea and the lens, and the other optical elements tend to reduce ametropia. In consequence, emmetropia is surprisingly common. Thus, if emmetropia is construed as embracing values from −0.5 to +0.5 D., about 25 per cent of young adults are emmetropic; if the range is expanded to include values between −1 and +1 D., about 65 per cent fall in this category.[14, 17]

At one time those biologic variations constituting ametropia excluded the afflicted from occupations requiring good vision. Now, most defects can be remedied by eyeglasses and are hardly noticed.

Ametropia may result from an unusually large or small value for any optical element, or from some combination of these elements not resulting in the compensatory correlations mentioned above. Analysis of Stenström's data[17] indicates that: (i) unusual values for the axial length are the most common cause of ametropia, (ii) about half as common is variation in the corneal refraction, and (iii) less important are separation of the cornea and lens or other optical elements. Ametropia of necessity falls into two types. In one, parallel rays come to a focus before reaching the retina; in the other, they reach the retina before coming to a focus. In the first, the axial length is relatively too long for the refractive power—this is called *myopia*.[9] In the second, the axial length is relatively too short—this is called *hyperopia* (hypermetropia). The frequency distribution of the refractive state in adults shows, as stated above, a crowding of cases toward emme-

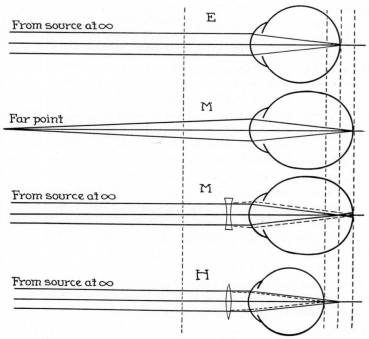

FIG. 252.   Diagram of emmetropia (*E*) (reduced eye to scale), myopia (*M*), and hyperopia (*H*). Dotted lines in two lower diagrams show effect of proper correcting lenses.

tropia (the mean is about 0.5 D. hyperopic), with some extreme cases of myopia and hyperopia, so that the form of the curve is distinctly peaked.[3, 11, 14, 19, 20]

Myopia.   During growth (from about six to 20 years, but particularly at puberty) in a small proportion of persons, the increase in length is relatively more rapid than the decrease in refractive power. As a result, they become myopic. In myopia, without accommodation, parallel rays of light come to a focus in the vitreous and diverge again to form diffusion circles on the retina. In any degree of myopia there is some point, nearer than that giving parallel rays, from which the light is sufficiently divergent to come to a focus on the retina of the unaccommodated eye; this is the myopic far point. The distance of this far point may be only a few centimeters, and all more distant objects will appear in some degree blurred—the more so the more distant they are. This condition is represented by diagram *M* in Figure 252. The obvious remedy is to use concave lenses for distant vision. By this means, the rays can be made divergent enough that the focus will be thrown accurately on the retina. Since the myopic eye at rest can focus rays of some degree of divergence, it can in full accommodation focus on very near objects; i.e., its near point is nearer than that of an emmetropic eye with equal amplitude of accommodation. This situation has led to the term "nearsightedness."

Hyperopia. This condition is represented in diagram *H* of Figure 252. In the eye at rest the retina is reached before the light has come to a focus, and each point source of light is represented by a diffusion circle. A converging lens of the proper strength will obviously bring light rays to the eye with that additional amount of convergence needed for their focus on the sensitive layers of the retina. The uncorrected hyperope may see distant objects clearly only by use of his accommodation. Clear vision is accomplished at the expense of eyestrain arising from constant excessive accommodation without corresponding convergence of the two eyes. Further, since some accommodation is used to see even far objects, less is available for viewing near things. Consequently, the near point is more distant than it is in an emmetrope with equal amplitude of accommodation. The extra effort required for near work limits the amount of effective reading or other close work and leads to headaches or other evidences of eyestrain.

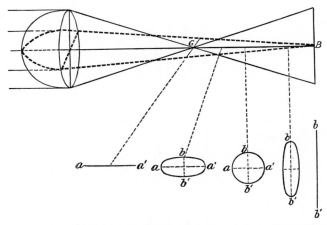

FIG. 253. Diagram of conoid of light emerging from an astigmatic lens. Lower figures represent cross sections of light at points indicated; note that image of distant point of light is never a point.

The term "farsightedness" for hyperopia is misleading. The "far" refers only to the excessive distance to the near point. The hyperope sees distant objects no better than does an emmetrope. In fact, when the farsighted person sees them as well, it is at the cost of some eyestrain.

Presbyopia. A decline in the amplitude of accommodation is termed presbyopia and, as indicated earlier, is a consequence of aging. The near point of distinct vision recedes farther and farther from the eye until near work is difficult or impossible. Because his near point is initially more distant, the uncorrected hyperope will experience difficulty with near work earlier than will the emmetrope, and the myope will experience reading difficulty late in life, or perhaps never. A myope with a near point of 20 or 30 cm. can see near objects even if no accommodation remains; those people who can read fine print at 80 or 90 are, in all cases, myopes. All properly corrected eyes will become presbyopic at about the same time, at an age of approximately 45; after that age, an additional convex lens will be necessary for comfortable reading.

Astigmia or Astigmatism. In an ideal eye, the refractive surfaces of the cornea and lens would be spherical surfaces with equal curvatures along all meridians. In many eyes, however, the corneal surface is not spherical. In such a case there is a meridian of least curvature and a meridian of greatest curvature at a right angle to the first. Rays from a luminous point, refracted in passing through such a surface, will not form a point image; rays falling along the meridian of greatest curvature will tend to reach a focus before those falling along the meridian of least curvature do, and may already be diverging when the latter reach a focus.

The effect is illustrated by Figure 253, which represents the refraction of rays from a distant luminous point by a lens in which the curvature is greater along the vertical than along the horizontal meridian. The rays along the vertical meridian are brought to a focus (G) while those along the horizontal meridian are still converging. A screen placed at this point will reflect an image having the shape of a horizontal line (a–a'). The rays along the horizontal meridian are brought to a focus at B, but those from the vertical meridian, having passed through the focus at G, are by this time spread out vertically. A screen placed at this point will show the image as a vertical line (b–b'). In between, the image of the point may be elliptical or circular, as represented in the diagram.

Astigmia may be due to a toric cornea or to the decentering of the cornea or the lens. Such conditions, producing the image forms just described, are called *regular astigmia*. Regular astigmia may be corrected by a cylindrical lens or by a combination

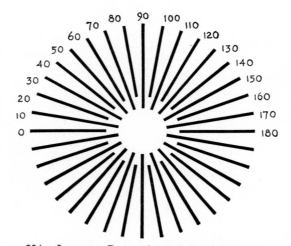

FIG. 254.   Lancaster-Regan chart used to test for astigmia.

of spherical and cylindrical lenses of such strength and so placed that they equalize the refraction in the meridians of greatest and least curvature. Since in a markedly astigmatic eye the image of a point is an ellipse or line, the image of a line, which may be considered a series of points, will be a series of small image lines. If these image lines have the same direction as the entire image, this image will be dark and clear (except for a slight blurring at the ends); but if the image lines are transverse, the entire image will appear broad, gray and indistinct. Because of this, a chart like Figure 254 may be used to detect astigmia and to locate the axes of least and greatest curvature. If the lines appear to differ in clearness, astigmia is present, and the two axes at right angles correspond to the blackest and grayest sets of lines.

Related to astigmia is the characteristic image defect of rays about a central point when a point image might be expected. This defect is a result of the peculiar structure of the crystalline lens, since it is absent in aphakics (individuals whose lenses have been removed). The stars, which furnish accurate point sources of light, do not give rise to point images in the human eye, but rather to radiate figures, the exact form of which varies from eye to eye. The "star" form is thus not characteristic of the heavenly bodies but of our eyes.

OPTICAL EFFECTS OF OTHER FACTORS

Iris and Pupil. The iris has important optical and sensory functions, and, because its innervation is exposed to lesions in several locations, the size and reactions of the pupils are important diagnostically in a surprising variety of conditions. The iris, the colored portion of the eye, arises from the anterior surface of the ciliary body and lies between the cornea and the lens, being in contact with the latter. As seen through the cornea, the iris is slightly magnified. It is pierced by a central opening, the pupil. The stroma of the iris contains, besides the visible pigment, a rich network of blood vessels and black pigment on the interior surface. Because of the abundant pigment the iris is impervious to light and forms an excellent diaphragm. Between the layers mentioned lie the muscles of the iris, the larger and better developed sphincter near the pupillary margin and the smaller and less completely differentiated dilator near the posterior surface next to the pigment layer.

The iris exerts its principal effect in producing clear images. By constricting, it excludes the periphery of the lens, where spherical and chromatic aberration are greatest. The constriction also increases the depth of focus; i.e., the diffusion circles produced by

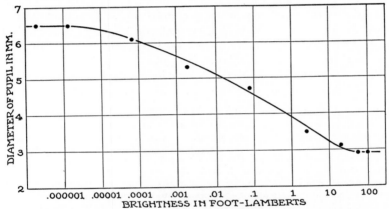

FIG. 255.   Relation of pupil diameter to illumination. Data obtained by infrared photography. (From Wagman and Nathanson, *Proc. Soc. exp. Biol.* (*N. Y.*), 1942, *49*:466–470.)

cones of light from points just too near or too far to be in focus are reduced in area. Both these effects are greatest during near work. Constriction of the pupil occurs in conjunction with accommodation and convergence in near vision. The illumination must be adequate at such a time, since constriction reduces the amount of light falling on the retina, a factor which strongly affects the acuity of vision (see Chap. 19).

Light reflex. An increase in light intensity causes the pupil to constrict, and a decrease in light intensity permits it to dilate. An increase of light in one eye leads to changes in the size of both pupils. The reaction of the pupil illuminated is called the *direct* light reflex and that of the opposite pupil the *consensual* light reflex. Over a considerable range of ordinarily encountered illumination, a person's pupils have a nearly constant average or habitual size. A slight increase in light intensity causes a slight constriction of the pupil, which then gradually dilates again as the retina adapts to the new higher level of illumination, and in a short time the pupil has resumed its habitual size.

When the new intensity is above this normal range, the change in pupillary size persists. This is illustrated by Figure 255, which shows the pupil diameter at illuminations over a range of a millionfold.[21] It will be seen that at both ends of this huge range of illumination, the pupil reaches a constant size representing its limit of dilation or constriction. These diameters are approximately 2.9 mm. and 6.5 mm.; there is, therefore, a fivefold change in area. Obviously, such a small change in area is utterly inadequate to compensate for the enormous range of experimental intensities or even for the smaller range of intensities met during daily variations in light. (This compensation is accomplished by retinal adaptation; see Chapter 19.) A fivefold alteration of area, however, helps the eye adjust to the sudden moderate changes in illumination to which it is constantly exposed. If the amount of light decreases, dilation of the pupil, although far less effective than retinal adaptation, is more prompt and gives, within 15 or 20 seconds, an appreciable improvement in the ability to see in dim light. If the amount of light increases, the still more rapid constriction of the pupil, in 3 or 4 seconds, shields the retina from light too intense for the existing level of sensitivity.

Intraocular Pressure. The position of the refracting surfaces relative to each other and to the retina must be maintained with great exactness. That minute variations in the axial length will cause ametropia is often not realized. When refraction was carefully measured in 1000 school children 12 years and older, 47 per cent showed ametropia of 0.50 or 0.25 D.[11] The change in axial length necessary to produce these degrees of ametropia is 0.187 mm. or less. Clearly if there is to be any constancy in refraction, even of an individual eye, the constancy of the size and shape of the globe must be assured.

The fixed distance of the refractive surfaces from the retina is maintained because the inelastic scleral envelope is under a constant intraocular pressure of 20 to 25 mm. Hg. This pressure results from a balance between the production and the escape of intraocular fluid. The volume of vitreous humor is relatively constant, although it may absorb or lose water to some extent. The chief changes occur in the aqueous humor.

The mechanism maintaining intraocular pressure is complex and, although much studied, is not completely agreed upon; the following appears to be the most satisfactory view. The aqueous consists of about 1 per cent solids, about one-eighth the solid content of the serum. All the constituents of the serum are found in the aqueous. The proteins are present in little more than traces, but the electrolytes appear in amounts about equal to those in the serum, the anions being clearly more abundant. According to some studies,[15] the total osmotic activity is above that of the blood. The material of the aqueous is derived from the blood—chiefly from that in the ciliary body, although to some extent from that in the iris—partly by secretion and partly by diffusion; and the aqueous escapes by leakage into the canal of Schlemm, nonselectively, at a rate of 5 or 6 ml. a day.[13] From the canal of Schlemm and the connecting canaliculi, the aqueous reaches the venous system through the aqueous and intrascleral veins.[1, 18] It is claimed that the hypertonicity results from secretion of the electrolytes. Interference with the outflow leads to a rise in the intraocular pressure which may damage the fibers of the optic nerve where they pass out of the globe (glaucoma).

Nutrition of the Lens and Cornea. The eye contains the largest nonvascular mass in the body. No blood vessels are found in the cornea, the aqueous, the lens or the vitreous after the early fetal period of rapid growth; obviously, blood vessels would seriously interfere with the optical function of all these structures. None of these tissues has a high metabolic rate, the rates of the aqueous and vitreous being negligible; but interference with the oxygen supply of the cornea, for example, is promptly followed by loss of transparency.

Like other organs of epithelial origin, the lens continues to grow throughout life, and, even though its metabolic rate is low, must maintain an interchange with the blood. This exchange is carried on through the intraocular fluid which, as pointed out above, contains at least a trace of all the constituents of the blood.

The transparency of the cornea, so necessary to its optical function and impaired in so many pathologic conditions, has attracted much study. Histologically the stroma of the cornea is not strikingly different from that of the opaque white sclera. The corneal stroma, however, differs in its osmotic relations, since it is covered by closely investing semipermeable membranes, epithelium on the exterior and endothelium on the interior surface. The normal transparent cornea is markedly dehydrated. When excised and placed in water, the cornea swells to three or four times its normal thickness and becomes opaque. When placed in contact with a hypertonic solution, the uninjured surface of the cornea loses water rapidly enough to remain dehydrated and transparent. Under normal conditions, the water of the cornea is derived from the vascular margin. It slowly diffuses toward the center and is lost through both surfaces to the hypertonic tears and to the aqueous.[12] This slow circulation of fluid from the periphery together with the diffusion from the aqueous supplies the slight metabolic needs of the cornea. In addition, oxygen reaches it directly from the external air.

CHIEF INSTRUMENTS FOR EYE EXAMINATION

Among the instruments designed for study of the eye, three have proved outstandingly useful. The *ophthalmoscope* makes visible the interior of the eye and is of value to the internist or surgeon as well as specialists on the eye. The *retinoscope*, or skiascope, provides an objective and accurate method of determining the refraction of the eye. The *ophthalmometer*, designed to measure corneal curvature, has been a valuable source of data on optical constants, but its usefulness in modern practice is limited. Because ophthalmoscopic inspection of the eye is an important part of the general physical examination, this instrument will be described here briefly. Descriptions of the retinoscope and the ophthalmometer may be found in ophthalmologic manuals.

OPHTHALMOSCOPE. Light entering the eye is largely absorbed by the black pigment of the retina and the chorioid. In leaving the eye, the part that is reflected, chiefly by the blood vessels, approximately retraces the path by which it entered. Merely holding a light near the eye does not, therefore, enable

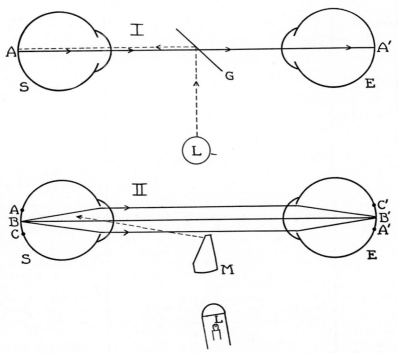

FIG. 256. Course of light in ophthalmoscope; *S*, eye of subject; *E*, eye of examiner. Entering light is indicated by dotted line; emerging light by solid line. *I*, Diagram of original model devised by Helmholtz; *L*, light; *G*, unsilvered glass; *A*, illuminated point in observed eye; *A'*, image in examiner's eye. *II*, Diagram of ophthalmoscope with May prism; *L*, electric bulb in handle; *M*, May prism. *A*, *B* and *C*, three illuminated points in observed eye, here assumed to be emmetropic; *A'*, *B'* and *C'*, images in examiner's eye, also emmetropic.

us to see into it, since to see this emerging light an observer must place his head where it blocks the entering light. If, however, the light could enter the observed eye as though it proceeded from the observer's own eye, then the returning rays might be utilized to give a view of the retina and its blood vessels, or the *fundus*, as it is called.

The principle of the ophthalmoscope is well represented by the original form, shown schematically in Figure 256, *I*. *S* represents the observed eye and *E* the eye of the examiner. Between these two eyes is placed a piece of glass inclined at an angle. Some rays from a source of light falling upon this glass are reflected to enter eye *S*; these rays then emerge from eye *S* along the same course, pass through the glass and enter eye *E*. The glass plate used by Helmholtz was soon replaced by a mirror, either one with a small hole in the center or one with a small area of silvering removed to permit the returning light to reach the examiner's eye. The source of light was later placed in the handle of the instrument, and at present light is thrown into the observed eye not by a mirror but by a prism of special form. This prism directs the light into the lower half of the pupil while the returning rays emerge through the upper half and reach the examiner's eye over the top of the prism (Fig. 256, *II*).

Irrespective of the manner in which the light reaches the fundus, this surface becomes a luminous object sending out rays of light. If eye *S* is emmetropic, any three objects on the retina, *A,B,C*, are at the principal focal distance, and the rays sent from each are in parallel bundles after emerging from the eye. These rays enter the examiner's eye as though they came from distant objects. If his eye is

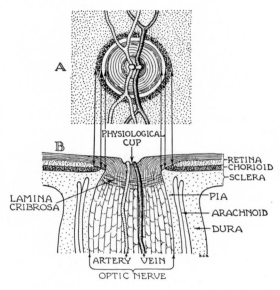

FIG. 257. Ophthalmoscopic appearance of optic disc (*A*) correlated with histologic section through it (*B*). Arrows indicate corresponding points on the two views. Pigmented ring is emphasized in *A* to show manner of its formation.

also emmetropic, or is made so by suitable glasses, these bundles of rays will be focused on his retina without an act of accommodation. In fact, in looking through the ophthalmoscope, he must gaze, not at the eye before him, but through the eye and into the distance, as it were, in order to relax his accommodation. In this way he will see the illuminated portion of the retina; the images of the objects seen will be inverted on his own retina and therefore will appear erect. If the observed eye is myopic, its retina is farther back than the principal focus of its refracting surfaces; consequently the emerging rays converge and cannot be focused on the retina of the examiner's eye. By inserting a concave lens of proper power between his eye and the mirror, the examiner can render the rays parallel and thus bring out the image. Just the reverse happens if the observed eye is hyperopic. In such an eye the retina is nearer than the principal focal distance of the refractive surfaces; consequently the light emerges in bundles of diverging rays which cannot be brought to focus on the retina of the examiner unless he exerts his own power of accommodation or interposes a convex lens between his eye and the mirror.

The battery of lenses in the ophthalmoscope is valuable in estimating the degree to which objects lie above or below the general level of the fundus. For example, the head of the optic nerve normally occurs in a slight conical pit, the *physiological depression* or *cup* (Fig. 257). When intraocular pressure is greatly elevated, as in glaucoma, this depression may be transformed into an excavation. Conversely, in papilledema caused by increased intracranial pressure, the physiologic cup may be eliminated and the nerve head swollen. The difference in the power of the lenses required to bring the center of the optic disc into sharp focus as compared with that required for its margin may be recorded in diopters. Thus, the progress of cupping may be followed and the depth estimated from the fact that 3 D. correspond to about 1 mm. The usefulness of the ophthalmoscope is twofold. First, it renders conditions within the eye as visible as they would be in a superficial structure; second, the blood vessels of the retina are a sample of those in all parts of the body and reveal certain general circulatory conditions.

REFERENCES

1. ASCHER, K. W. Amer. J. Ophthal., 1942, (3) 25:31–38.
2. BEER, T. Pflüg. Arch. ges. Physiol., 1894, 58: 523–650, 3 pls.
3. BROWN, E. V. L. Arch. Ophthal. (N. Y.), 1942, n.s. 28:845–850.
4. DONDERS, F. C. On the anomalies of accommodation and refraction of the eye. With a preliminary essay on physiological dioptrics, tr. by W. D. MOORE. London, New Sydenham Society, 1864, xvii, 635 pp.
5. DUANE, A. Ophthalmoscope, 1912, 10:486–502.
6. DUANE, A. Amer. J. Ophthal., 1922, (3) 5: 865–877.
7. DUKE-ELDER, W. S. Text-book of ophthalmology, vol. 1. St. Louis, C. V. Mosby Co., 1939.
8. FINCHAM, E. P. Brit. J. Ophthal., 1937, Suppl. 8:5–80.
9. VON HELMHOLTZ, H. Treatise on physiological optics, J. P. C. SOUTHALL, ed. Rochester, N. Y., Optical Society of America, 1924–25, 3 vols.
10. HIRSCH, M. J. and WEYMOUTH, F. W. Amer. J. Optom., 1947, 24:601–608, and Arch. Amer. Acad. Optom., 1947, Monogr. 39, 8 pp.
11. KEMPF, G. A., JARMAN, B. L. and COLLINS, S. D. Publ. Hlth. Rep. (Wash.), 1928, 43: 1713–1739.
12. KINSEY, V. E. and COGAN, D. G. Arch. Ophthal. (N. Y.), 1942, n.s. 28:449–463.
13. KINSEY, V. E. and GRANT, W. M. Brit. J. Ophthal., 1944, 28:355–361.
14. KRONFELD, P. C. and DEVNEY, CLARISSA. v. Graefes Arch. Ophthal., 1931, 126:487–501.
15. ROEPKE, R. R. and HETHERINGTON, W. A. Amer. J. Physiol., 1940, 130:340–345.
16. SCHLODTMANN, W. v. Graefes Arch. Ophthal., 1902, 54:256–267.
17. STENSTRÖM, S. Acta ophthal. (Kbh.), 1946, Suppl. 26:104 pp.
18. THOMASSEN, T. L. and BAKKEN, K. Acta ophthal. (Kbh.), 1951, 29:257–268.
19. TRON, E. v. Graefes Arch. Ophthal., 1934, 132: 182–223.
20. TRON, E. J. Pp. 245–255 in Modern trends in ophthalmology, F. RIDLEY and A. SORSBY, eds. New York, Paul B. Hoeber, Inc., 1940.
21. WAGMAN, I. H. and NATHANSON, L. M. Proc. Soc. exp. Biol. (N. Y.), 1942, 49:466–470.
22. WALLS, G. L. The vertebrate eye and its adaptive radiation. Bloomfield Hills, Mich., Cranbrook Institute of Science, 1942, xiv, 785 pp.

CHAPTER 19

Vision

By THEODORE C. RUCH

IN the previous chapter the eye was portrayed as an optical instrument focusing light rays from objects at various distances and regulating the amount of light falling upon the retina. However, the formation of a physical image on the retina is of no value unless that image is translated into a pattern of nerve impulses from which the cerebral cortex can reconstruct a reasonably accurate perception of the external world. In this perception, color, fineness of detail and sharpness of contour all play a part.

The eye is not one but two end-organs, each specialized for quite different visual functions although closely knit anatomically. One system of receptors, the cones, is specialized to function in daylight when the surroundings are brightly illuminated. Objects are then seen clearly with much detail and exhibit grades of color. Visual acuity is at a premium. The second system of receptors, the rods, is specialized for twilight and night vision. Then, low threshold is at a premium. By a process of dark adaptation the eye becomes many times more sensitive to light and dilation of the pupil admits more light to the eye. The human retina is extraordinarily able to use the slightest light energy afforded by the environment, nearly attaining the theoretical lower limit of sensitivity—sensitivity to 1 quantum of light. But specialization in one direction has meant loss of capacity in another. The apparatus for night vision does not record the color of objects or fine details and sharp boundaries. Yet perception of objects as dark, indistinct masses makes the difference between blindness and visual orientation to the environment at night.

The double function of the eye is manifested in several ways. When the pupil is constricted, the eye is adjusted for detail vision but requires a high level of illumination; pupillary dilation allows utmost use of the light present at low intensities of illumination. The retina itself is specialized into the fovea centralis for color and detail vision, and the periphery for light and dark vision. The fovea contains only cones, and in the periphery rods predominate. The neural pathways give further evidence of a double function. The "duplicity" theory is, then, the organizing principle to be used in describing vision. Originally, this theory referred only to the existence of two types of receptor cells, but it is now applied to the central mechanism of vision as well.

Visual Stimulus. The eye is sensitive to a narrow band of wavelengths, the visible spectrum (723 mμ to 397 mμ) lying between the long, infrared heat waves and the short, ultraviolet "chemical" waves. The wavelengths within this range are not equally effective in stimulating the retina. The wavelength influences the intensity of light necessary to elicit a sensation and also determines the hue or chroma. The curve which expresses that relation is the *visibility curve* (Fig. 258). Before any curve or other quantitative data can be understood, the nature of the visual stimulus and the units in which it is measured must be defined.

In the audibility curve, the base line is frequency; in the visibility curve, it is wavelength, i.e., the inverse of frequency, since the speed of light is divided by frequency to obtain the wavelength. A wavelength is stated in Ångstrom units (1 Å = 1/10,000,000 mm.) or, more usually, in millimicrons (1 mμ = 1/1,000,000 mm.). The unit for the ordinate must express the intensity of the light. As in

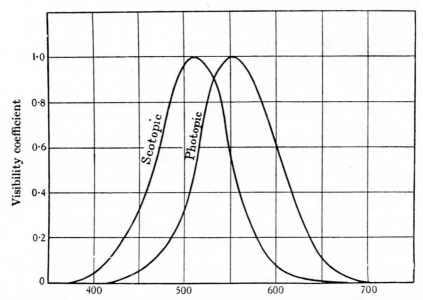

FIG. 258. Visibility or luminosity of a bright spectrum as seen by cones (photopic) and of a dim spectrum as seen by rods (scotopic). Ordinates are the reciprocal of the energy which is just visible for each wavelength of light (scotopic) or which matches a moderately bright standard light (photopic). Curves were adjusted to a common scale by making maximum of each curve equal to one. On an absolute scale of intensities, rod curve would fall far below that for cones, which are much less sensitive than rods. (From Rawdon-Smith, *Theories of sensation*, Cambridge, Cambridge University Press, 1938, after Hecht and Williams, *J. gen. Physiol.*, 1922, 5:1–34.)

audition, the physical unit most useful is one with a psychologic reference. The basic unit is the *international candle*, which is the total luminous energy emitted in all directions by a standardized candle with a flame 1 inch high. To state the amount of light *falling upon* an object, the illumination (a more usual requirement), the distance between the object and the candle must be defined because the total energy becomes less per unit area as it spreads over a larger sphere. The *foot-candle* is the amount of light falling on a square foot of area placed 1 foot from the standard candle. But not all of the light is reflected by the surface and only reflected light can be seen. The *brightness* of an object, which is the amount of light reflected from it, is measured in *millilamberts*. This is the amount of light reflected by an ideal surface 1 foot square illuminated by 0.93 foot-candle. Since the size of the pupil of the eye affects the amount of light entering the eye, another unit, the *photon*, has been devised which takes this factor into account. Photons are the number of millilamberts × sq. mm. of pupil area. In experiments this is easily calculated because an artificial pupil—a screen with an aperture smaller than the pupil—is usually employed.

The visibility curve is affected by the distribution of energy among the different wavelengths of the particular light source employed—daylight, carbon lamp, etc.—but can be calculated for an equal energy spectrum. Also, light is filtered by the cornea, lens and vitreous body. When all physical factors are properly accounted for, the visibility

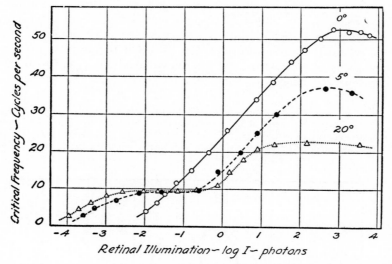

FIG. 259. Curves showing relation between critical fusion frequency (c.f.f.) and logarithm of intensity for three retinal locations: fovea, and 5° and 20° from fovea. (From Hecht and Verrijp, *J. gen. Physiol.*, 1933–34, *17*:251–268.)

curve becomes an index of the manner in which the retina utilizes light of different wavelengths. The visibility curve expresses one fundamental parameter of visual sensation, luminosity, whether aroused by colored or uncolored light.

Intensity Functions.   The intensity of the physical stimulus must be distinguished from the intensity of the resulting visual experience. Although these two intensities are related causally, intervening photochemical and neural processes may considerably alter the correlation between the two. *Luminosity, brilliance* and *apparent brightness* always refer to the response; *brightness* is restricted to the intensity of the physical stimulus. Three main intensity functions are distinguished: the *absolute threshold*, the least that can be seen; the *difference threshold*, the least discriminable difference between two intensities; and the *critical flicker fusion frequency*.

The principal factors affecting the absolute threshold will be discussed in detail later, but may be enumerated as follows: (i) intensity of light, (ii) wavelength of light, (iii) size of illuminated area, (iv) duration of exposure, (v) state of the retina (dark adaptation, etc.), and (vi) the region of retina stimulated. Much the same factors influence the difference threshold, which is basically similar to the absolute threshold. The Weber fraction is not constant for brightness discrimination. The curve of $\Delta I/I$ rises sharply for weak and strong stimuli and is constant for the middle range of intensities only if small changes are ignored (by coarse plotting). The absolute threshold under the most favorable conditions appears to approach the theoretical minimum, the receptors being sensitive to 1 quantum of light according to the calculations of Hecht.[11]

As few as 54 quanta of light incident upon the cornea are perceptible. An estimated half of these are reflected or absorbed by the ocular media. Of the 27 quanta reaching the retina, perhaps only 5 are absorbed by the visual purple of the rods. These rods, spread over a retinal area containing an estimated 500 rods, are so few that at threshold a given rod must rarely receive more than 1 quantum of energy. According to Einstein's photochemical equivalence law, 1 quantum of energy will break down one molecule of visual purple. Thus, the evolution of the eye has progressed to the theoretical maximum of sensitivity.

The critical fusion frequency for flicker is determined by rotating a sectored disc in front of a light source at a speed controlled by the observer. With slow rotation intermittent flashes of light are seen, but at a certain rate for each intensity a sensation of continuous brightness is experienced, the *critical fusion frequency* (c.f.f.). The higher the intensity of the light, the higher the c.f.f. For the middle range of intensities, c.f.f. = log I + k (Ferry-Porter law). When the light falls on the periphery of the retina, the duality of the visual mechanism produces a sharp inflection in the curve relating c.f.f. to log I (Fig. 259). For the fovea, the curve shows no inflection. The first part of the duplex curve is interpreted as a response of the rods and the second as a response of the cones.

PHOTOCHEMICAL BASIS OF VISION

Visual Purple—Rhodopsin. The change taking place in the rods and cones which translates physical energy, light, into nerve impulses involves a photochemical step, i.e., light waves set up chemical changes in rods or cones which, in turn, give rise to nerve impulses. The retinal rods contain a red pigment which is bleached by light (Boll, 1877), *visual purple* or *rhodopsin*. The cones probably contain another pigmented substance.

Solutions of visual purple are also bleached when exposed to light. Visual purple is, therefore, an unstable substance readily altered by light energy. That this photochemical property of rhodopsin accounts for the visibility curve was first suggested by Kühne (1878), who studied the effectiveness of different wavelengths in bleaching rhodopsin. According to Draper's law, the photochemical effect of a given wavelength is proportional to the degree to which that wavelength is absorbed. The absorption spectrum of visual purple from the frog's retina has been accurately determined (Fig. 260). Moreover, a fair degree of success has been attained in superposing the absorption spectrum and the visibility curve of the human eye. The success of one such attempt is shown in Figure 261. The visibility curve for rod function appears, therefore, to be determined by the photochemical properties of rhodopsin. If so, rhodopsin must be the photochemical intermediary standing between the light stimulus and the optic nerve impulse.

The same demonstration has not yet been made for cone vision, although the intermediation of a rhodopsin-like photosensitive substance, *iodopsin* (visual violet), is strongly suspected.[26]

Dark Adaptation. The retina possesses to a remarkable degree the ability to become sensitive to dim light* and thus to make maximum use of weak light reflected from objects. This is especially true of the periphery of the retina. When one passes from daylight into a dark room, vision is at first very imperfect, but it rapidly improves "as the eye becomes accustomed to the dark." This change is known as *dark adaptation*. Loss of the sensitivity attained through dark adaptation occurs upon re-exposure of the eyes to light and is called *light adaptation*.

* The change from full sunlight to the least light perceptible at night is a change of approximately 10 billion to 1.

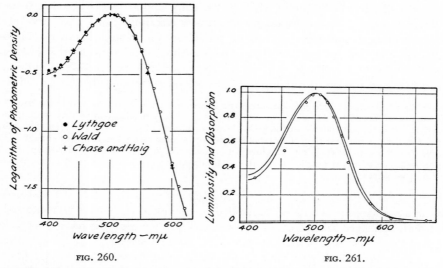

FIG. 260.   FIG. 261.

FIG. 260.   Absorption spectrum of the visual purple from frog. Data obtained by three independent observers were made equal at 500 mμ. Ordinates show degree to which each wavelength is absorbed, with 0.0 representing maximal absorption. (From Hecht, *Amer. Scientist*, 1944, *32*:159–177.)

FIG. 261.   Relation of subjective brightness of spectrum (luminosity, circles) to absorption curve of visual purple (frog). Visibility curve is corrected for transmissional losses, quantum effectiveness, etc., and therefore is not identical with that shown in Figure 258. Two solid lines give absorption spectrum calculated by assuming that 20 and 5 per cent of light are absorbed by visual purple. (From Hecht *et al.*, *J. gen. Physiol.*, 1942, *25*:819–840.)

A curve of dark adaptation is plotted by repeatedly determining the weakest flash of light which is visible. The rate of dark adaptation for rods is initially rapid, although not so rapid as the rate of light adaptation. Dark adaptation is about 60 per cent accomplished in the first five minutes and virtually completed in 20 minutes, after which the curve is asymptotic. A curve with this simple form is obtained by starting from levels of illumination too low to stimulate the cones and by observing with the peripheral portions of the retina where there are few cones. It is therefore the rod adaptation curve.

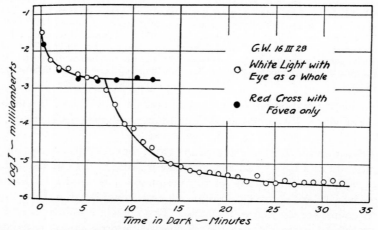

FIG. 262.   Curve of dark adaptation obtained by plotting visual threshold against time spent in darkness. Initial limb of curve for whole eye (*circles*) is due to cones; lower portion is due to rods. To obtain complete curve for cones alone (*black dots*), stimulation of the more sensitive rods was avoided by employing red light and foveal fixation. (From Hecht, *A handbook of general experimental psychology*, C. Murchison, ed., Worcester, Clark University Press, 1934.)

When both cones and rods are stimulated, the curve is made up of two curves (Fig. 262). First there is an initial rapid fall in threshold which tends to strike a plateau. After about seven minutes of darkness, a further drop occurs which is less rapid but is quantitatively much greater. Analysis shows that the curve before its breaking point is due to dark adaptation of the cones. Dark adaptation is therefore not a phenomenon peculiar to the rods. Cone adaptation is much more rapid than rod adaptation but produces less reduction of threshold.

Factors Influencing Dark Adaptation.   The extent and rapidity of dark adaptation are critical in many military and civilian activities. Several factors are involved.

AVOIDANCE OF LIGHT.   The most effective means of securing dark adaptation is to prevent unnecessary exposure to light. Obvious as this is, it has often been overlooked in the design of airplane cockpits.

Miles'[17] introduction of red goggles as an aid to the acquisition of dark adaptation illustrates effective application of physiology to a practical situation. A tedious 20 to 30 minute wait in a completely dark room is avoided by wearing the goggles, which allow cone vision to continue while the rods are adapting to dark. As the visibility curve shows, wavelengths longer than 640 mμ stimulate the rods only very weakly. Thus, red goggles, by admitting only longer wavelengths, prevent light adaptation of the rods.

PREADAPTATION ILLUMINATION.   The more intense the illumination and the longer the time during which the eye is light-adapted, the longer the period necessary to attain complete dark adaptation.[13, 28] This phenomenon appears explicable on the basis of a slow and a fast resynthesis of rhodopsin (see p. 433).

NYCTALOPIA.*   This is a rare organic and often hereditary abnormality in which rod function is seriously disturbed or, in extreme cases, absent. Dark adaptation is correspondingly reduced in extent and greatly slowed. The result is *night blindness*. Color vision is normal. There is no evidence that vitamin A therapy will affect the congenital form of nyctalopia.

VITAMIN A DEFICIENCY.   Severe vitamin A deficiency experimentally induced interferes with the mechanism of dark adaptation, and irreversible changes can be produced. Dark adaptation of cones as well as of rods is affected. The measurement of dark adaptation has not proved useful in detecting vitamin A deficiencies in the degree present in the population.

ANOXIA AND METABOLIC FACTORS.   McFarland and Evans[16] have shown that the visual threshold of the completely dark-adapted eye is elevated by anoxic anoxia. Exposure to a simulated altitude of 15,000 feet raised the threshold 2.5 times. Glucose neutralized the effects of anoxia and insulin intensified them. Hyperventilation at sea level improved visual sensitivity, lowering the threshold by half[29] and CO_2 added to air doubled the threshold. Such changes, although small in relation to the whole range of dark adaptation, are significant in night flying. Because these changes occur more rapidly than photochemical changes, it is believed that the anoxic effects are exerted on the synaptic apparatus of the retina. The retina—except for the rods and cones—being part of the brain has a high metabolic rate and is correspondingly sensitive to anoxia.

Curve of Light Adaptation.   After a period of darkness, light of moderate intensity at first seems intense, dazzling and even painful, but after a few minutes the eye becomes less sensitive. In other words, the sensitivity gained by dark adaptation is lost when the eye is stimulated by light. Light adaptation is simply the absence of dark adaptation, and the expression is somewhat misleading. However, it is also an active process, since the first intense stimulation results from bleaching of the rhodopsin accumulated during dark adaptation. It takes much less time to lose dark adaptation than to acquire it. Light adaptation is largely completed in just a few minutes.

* "Hemeralopia," the term for inability to see in bright light, is sometimes used instead of "nyctalopia."

Mechanism of Rod Stimulation and Dark Adaptation.[11, 26]   Rhodopsin is the intermediary in the excitation of rods by light and changes in its concentration are believed to be the basis of dark adaptation. The simplest possible photochemical mechanism employing rhodopsin is as follows:

$$\text{Light}\longrightarrow\text{rhodopsin}\longrightarrow\text{excitatory decomposition product}\longrightarrow\text{nerve impulse}$$

During dark adaptation rhodopsin is regenerated. Until recently it seemed possible to account for the principal features of excitation and dark adaptation on the basis of a simple equation from photochemistry.[26] In brief, light was conceived of as breaking down photosensitive material (rhodopsin) at a rate dependent on the light intensity and the amount of photochemical substance present. It now seems that bleaching a small amount of rhodopsin causes the threshold to rise enormously; for the human eye, the bleaching of 0.006 per cent of the visual purple decreases the visual sensitivity 8.5 times, and a 0.6 per cent bleaching lowers the sensitivity an estimated 3300 times.[27] Nevertheless, bleaching and regeneration of rhodopsin follow the same time courses as light adaptation and dark adaptation (Fig. 263), and this is true of the faster adaptation of the cones.[21, 22]

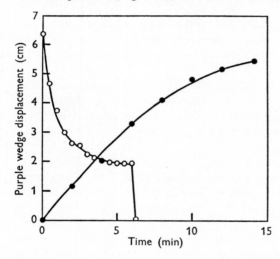

FIG. 263.   Time course of bleaching (o) and subsequent regeneration (●) of rhodopsin in the human eye. Sudden drop at 6 minutes was caused by flash of very bright light. (From Campbell and Rushton, *J. Physiol.*, 1955, *130:* 131–147.)

However, the concentration of rhodopsin is proportional to the *logarithm* of the sensitivity. Whether a neural factor must be introduced into the equation to gain quantitative agreement is still to be learned.

Photochemical Cycle of Retina.   That vitamin A plays a part in the long-term changes in retinal excitability has been demonstrated by chemical methods. Using a spectrographic technique to follow the changes in the photochemical substances, Wald[25, 26] established the broad outlines of the photochemistry of the visual cycle. Three main reactions were observed (Fig. 264). The first is a rapid reaction:

$$\text{Rhodopsin} \underset{\text{dark}}{\overset{\text{light}}{\rightleftharpoons}} \text{Retinene} + \text{Protein.}$$

Visual purple, which has a high molecular weight (270,000), is a conjugated protein, i.e., a protein molecule united to a pigment group (*retinene*), and is related to the carotene compounds. Rhodopsin is stable unless exposed to light, when it bleaches owing to a dissociation into protein and retinene. In the dark it is reconstituted (Fig. 263). Because the rate and extent of decomposition depend on the intensity of light and the duration of exposure, this phase is believed to be the photochemical basis of light and dark adaptation. Retinene is reduced to vitamin A by the conjoint action of an enzyme (alcohol dehydrogenase) and the coenzyme DPN. Rushton and his colleagues[23] have been able to measure rhodopsin in the human retina. The changes in the density of rhodopsin in passing through the fovea and the optic nerve head into the peripheral retina conform to the known density of rods. Proceeding much more slowly is a thermo-labile reaction in which rhodopsin is re-formed with vitamin A as an intermediate step. Vitamin A from blood is also a source for restoring the retinal level of vitamin A and rhodopsin. These reactions therefore form the photochemical cycle, which may be divided into a photodynamic and a thermolabile phase. In Figure 264 the length of line connecting the substances indicates roughly the speed of the reaction.

The effect of preadaptation illumination on the rate of dark adaptation is explained by a "slow" and a "fast" synthesis of rhodopsin. If the completely dark-adapted retina, charged with rhodopsin, is light-adapted by a *short exposure to intense light*, much retinene

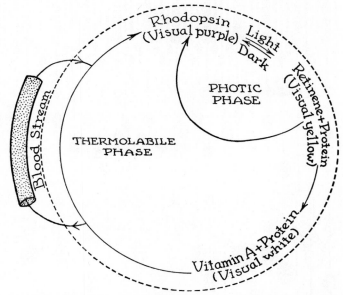

FIG. 264. Retinal photochemical cycle according to Wald. Length of arrows suggests speed of reaction.

and little vitamin A are produced. Therefore, subsequent dark adaptation is rapid be-cause rhodopsin is re-formed by the "fast route" from retinene. Exposure to weaker adapting lights for a seven minute period is followed by a slowed adaptation curve, because more retinene has gone to vitamin A and must be resynthesized by the slower route.

In addition to the visual functions which seem interpretable on the basis of photo-dynamic action there are certain processes which depend on the neural mechanisms of the retina.

NEURAL BASIS OF RETINAL FUNCTION

Functional Anatomy of Retina.[18]   The neural layers of the retina are three strata of densely packed cell bodies and two intervening synaptic layers consisting of inter-twining dendritic and axonic brushes (Fig. 265). The retinal layer nearest the chorioid is made up of pigmented cells which probably produce and store photochemicals such as visual purple. The layer next to the pigment cells contains two kinds of neurons, one bearing a cone-shaped process and the other a rod-shaped process. The rods and cones, packed closely together, are the structures actually sensitive to light. The axons of the rod-bearing and cone-bearing neurons end upon the dendrites of the middle layer ot bipolar cells, which in turn give axons to the dendrites of ganglion cells. The axons of the ganglion cells sweep to a point just slightly to the nasal side of the center of the retina. There they pierce the chorioid and sclera in the company of the blood vessels and make up the optic nerve. It is an instance of nature's lack of wisdom that light must pass through blood vessels, nerve fibers, and cell bodies to reach the rods and cones. The rod and cone neurons are the receptor cells. The bipolar and ganglion cells are, respectively, second and third order neurons; this makes them part of the brain. Like other parts of the brain, they form complex synaptic relations.

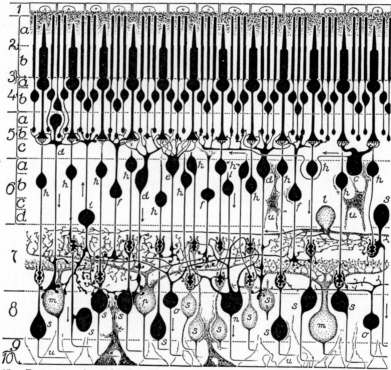

FIG. 265. Reconstruction of primate retina, based on Golgi impregnations, showing principal neuron types and their synaptic relations. Layers are: *1*, pigment epithelium; *2a*, outer segment of rods and cones; *2b*, inner segment of rods and cones; *3*, outer limiting membrane; *4*, outer nuclear layer; *5*, outer plexiform layer (cone-pedicles and rod-spherules); *6*, inner nuclear layer; *7*, inner plexiform layers; *8*, ganglion cells (origin of optic nerve fibers); *9*, layers of optic nerve fibers; *10*, inner limiting membrane. Various cell types are: *c*, horizontal cells; *d, e, f*, diffuse or polysynaptic bipolar cells; *h*, individual cone (midget) bipolar cell; *i, l*, "amacrine cells"; *m, n, o, p, r, s*, ganglion cells, of which *s* is the individual or monosynaptic ganglion cell. (From Polyak, *The retina*, Chicago, University of Chicago Press, 1941.)

To study human and monkey retinas, Polyak employed the Golgi technique which fully impregnates only occasional neurons so that the cell body, dendrites and axon of single neurons can be distinguished. The distinctness of the rod and cone systems is not maintained at the level of the bipolar cells. Many bipolar cells synapse with both rod and cone neurons, and this is not an occasional variation. The rod and cone systems are thus incompletely separated in their pathways to the brain. This finding obviously embarrasses the theory of specific receptors and private pathways for each phenomenon, but its exact significance is yet to be realized. Polyak recognized two types of bipolar cells. The most common type is variously termed the *diffuse, polysynaptic* or *rod and cone* bipolar cell because of its widely spread dendritic branches through which it receives impulses from a group, sometimes large, of rod and cone neurons. The bipolar cell termed the *individual, monosynaptic, cone* or *midget* bipolar cell connects only with cones, sometimes only one (fovea). The third order neurons also fall into two categories: (i) *diffuse* ganglion cells which connect with a great number of bipolar cells, and (ii) *monosynaptic* or *individual* ganglion cells which establish synaptic connections, by way of midget bipolar cells, with only one or two cones.

Neural basis of areal interaction.   Thus, there are two systems of neurons in the retina. One, identified exclusively with cones, is highly canalized and spatially organized so that each cone in it has a private path in the optic nerve. The other system, one of mixed rods and cones, is marked by the convergence of many receptors on bipolar cells and of many bipolar cells upon ganglion cells. Convergence is, as pointed out in connection with spinal reflexes, the neural substrate for an interaction of streams of impulses that results in facilitation and inhibition phenomena. An arrangement of this sort, therefore, affords a basis for interaction between retinal areas. Interaction is further provided for by a system of intraretinal association neurons. These include (i) *horizontal* cells, (ii) *centrifugal* bipolar cells, and (iii) possibly some of the *amacrine* cells. The horizontal cells are named for their axons which run horizontally for long distances in the outer plexiform layer. They appear to connect various points of the layer of rod and cone neurons.

Regional variations of retina.[18]   By confining the stimulus to the fovea, cone function can be studied in isolation; by confining the stimulus to the extreme periphery,

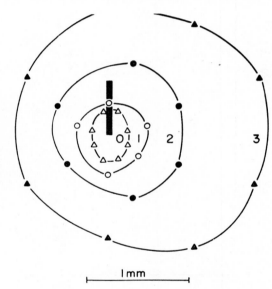

FIG. 266.   Receptive field of bullfrog optic nerve fiber showing the effects of four intensities on size of field. Numbers indicate logarithms of relative intensities used. *Vertical black line,* Radius along which determinations in Fig. 267 were made. (From Wagner and Wolbarsht, *Amer. J. Ophthal.,* 1958, *46:*46–59.)

1 mm

rod function almost free of cone activity can be studied. However, there are important differences between foveal and peripheral vision besides the ratio of cones to rods, e.g., the synaptic relationships.

The retina extends through roughly 180°. In the center of this hemisphere (in line with the visual axis) is a yellow pigmented area, the *macula lutea,* within which is a round pitlike depression 1500 μ in diameter, the *fovea centralis,* which in turn encompasses a slighter depression containing the finest cones, the *foveola.* In man an area of 1200 μ, or 2° of arc, is rod-free, the rods appearing just within the margin of the fovea. It contains approximately 34,000 cones varying from 1 μ (12 to 15′) to 3.3 μ (40′) in diameter.

The fovea is specialized for detail vision in four ways: (i) the cones are more slender and densely packed, especially in the foveola; (ii) it is rod-free; (iii) blood vessels and nerve detour around it, and the cellular layers are deflected to the side, reducing the scattering of light; and (iv) the cones have a "private line" to the optic nerve.

In passing peripherally, two principal changes occur. The cone-to-rod ratio rapidly decreases in the first 5° of arc. A few cones (6 to 8 per 100 μ linear distance) occur even in the extreme periphery. Another difference is an increased convergence of receptor elements on single ganglion cells. The ideal ratio of one cone to one ganglion cell is probably approached in the fovea centralis. In the periphery (beyond 10° from the fovea), there are as many as 250 rods and cones per ganglion cell.

SIZE OF RECEPTIVE FIELD.   Histology hints at the spatial distribution of receptors which send their messages to the brain by a single optic nerve fiber. Electrophysiology permits the mapping of the receptive field of single optic tract neurons. Such plots indicate that the receptive fields in the frog retina, for example, are relatively large, their size depending on the light intensity (Fig. 266).[24] The sensitivity field viewed in cross section and in terms of frequency of firing suggests a mesa-like or flat-topped profile (Fig. 267). Similar findings have been obtained in higher animals, although light scatter is a problem in such experiments. In a system which has a highly developed spatial discriminative ability and in which the receptor elements are minute and closely packed, should all this be apparently lost by having such large receptive fields rather than a one-to-one relationship between receptor and optic nerve fiber? In some manner not yet understood, a "sloppy" arrangement may be better than a one-to-one, highly

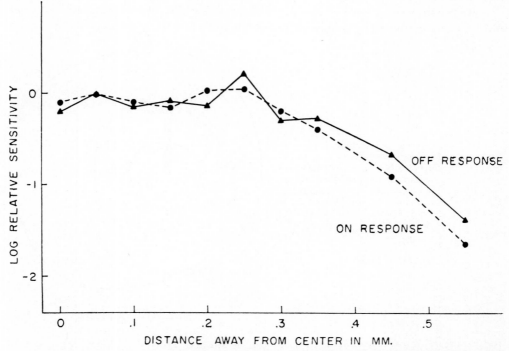

FIG. 267.   Sensitivity along radius of receptive field of bullfrog optic nerve fiber (see Fig. 266). Test stimulus was 0.05 mm. in diameter. Lower curve based on electrical activity at beginning and after end of a one second flash. (From Wagner and Wolbarsht, *Amer. J. Ophthal.*, 1958, *46*:46–59.)

channelized one. Knowledge of the electrical activity of the retina provides some understanding of this matter.

Electrical Activity of Retina.   Four types of potential changes are recorded from the retina: (i) a steady corneoretinal potential, (ii) phasic potentials produced by light (electroretinogram), (iii) unit responses from the level of the bipolar cells, and (iv) action potentials of ganglion cells and optic nerve fibers. The steady potential recorded between the front and back of the eyeball is produced by the retina, probably across Bruch's membrane of the chorioid. In penetration experiments with ultramicroelectrodes, Brown and Wiesel[3] recorded a 30 to 60 mV. potential across the membrane with the chorioidal side negative. When recorded from the tissues about the eyes, the steady potential can be used to measure eye movements.

ELECTRORETINOGRAM (ERG).[3]   This is a complex of potential deflections, shown in Figure 268, which is still imperfectly analyzed. Studies in man suggest that the *A* wave represents a photopic response, since it is well marked when red light is used; penetration experiments show that it comes from a deep structure, probably the outer segment of the receptors. The *B* wave waxes in the dark and wanes in the light. This behavior suggests that it reflects a scotopic mechanism. This wave appears to originate in the layer of bipolar cells; it is dependent upon nerve impulses and has unit components which can be inhibited by light turning on and off. The *C* wave probably originates in the cells of the pigment layer.

FACILITATORY AND INHIBITORY PHENOMENA; SUMMATION.[10] Since the optic nerve in *Limulus* is made up of receptive cells without lateral connections, single axon recordings show the ability of a simple receptor to signal intensity. Frequency of discharge is the correlate of intensity. The total number of discharges from a single visual unit when it responds to flashes of light which vary only in intensity ranges from 1 to 100,000. For moderate intensities the frequency of discharge varies as the logarithm of intensity (Weber-Fechner law). Adaptation is another property of the visual end organ. In retinas with lateral connections and convergence, the firing of impulses depends not on intensity

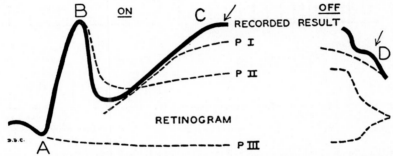

FIG. 268. Compound electric potential (heavy line) recorded from retina (electroretinogram, ERG) in response to stimulation by light. Upward deflections indicate electropositivity. *A, B, C, D,* are potential waves of ERG, and broken curves, *P I, P II, P III,* are one analysis (Granit) of compound potential into its components. (From Bartley, *Psychol. Rev.,* 1939, *46:*337–358.)

alone but upon *area* of stimulus and upon other factors that call into play facilitatory and inhibitory properties.

Inhibitory phenomena. Recording from ganglion cells reveals that the optic nerve axons send three kinds of signals to the brain. Some fibers respond to the onset of light—the "on fibers." Others, if responding prior to the stimulus, cease to fire during it and resume firing when it ends—the so-called "off fibers." (This should be understood as "off fiber behavior"; it depends upon function, not some fixed mechanism.) The most common type of fiber behavior is firing at the start and after the end of a stimulus—the "on-off" fibers. These three types are shown in Figure 269, which illustrates the ways the receptor cells manipulate the ganglion cells. There appear to be two antagonistic systems which compete at the ganglion cell. Record *2b* in Figure 269 shows that the response of an on-off receptor is inhibited by light. It is fair to assume that the off fiber did not fire until the stimulus was off because the light inhibited the fiber. Thus we see that inhibitory interaction is involved in every discharge of the retina.

Inhibitory reactions between areas have been observed. Kuffler,[14] in mapping the size of the receptive field served by an optic nerve fiber in the mammal, discovered that when the on response occupied the center of the receptive field the off responses were obtained from the periphery, and the on-off responses lay between. Sometimes the reverse was found. Barlow[1] showed that illumination of a ring around a receptive field would inhibit the discharge elicited from its center. There is a possibility that the amacrine or horizontal cells are responsible for these lateral effects.[2] The concept of antagonistic on and off systems helps one to understand the dynamic nature of the receptor unit, the dependence of the response on intensity and illumination of the surrounding area, and dark adaptation.

Facilitation and summation. It is well known that when the objects are small the threshold for the human fovea is inversely proportional to the area of the test object (Ricco's law). Such areal effects represent mutual facilitation between units occupying the field of stimulation, just as fibers within a nerve trunk facilitate one another synaptically.

Graham and Granit[7] used the flicker technique to show summation between retinal areas by throwing two illuminated half circles upon the retina and varying their separation. The two areal stimuli facilitated one another to a degree depending on their proximity. Under special conditions, one of which is foveal position, stimulation of one area reduces the sensitivity of the other—a form of inhibition.

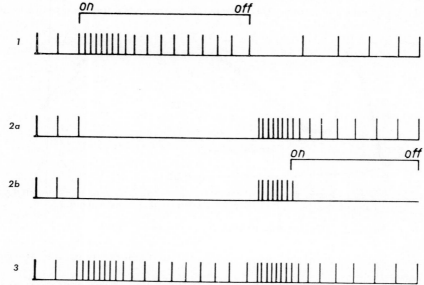

FIG. 269. Diagram of discharges of three optic nerve fibers with different discharge patterns. Beginning and end of stimulus indicated by horizontal bar. In *2b* note inhibitory effect of light on discharge of "off" fiber, which otherwise would have fired as in trace *2a*. This diagram collects observations by Adrian and Mathews, Hartline and Granit. (From Granit, *Receptors and sensory perception*, New Haven, Yale University Press, 1955.)

Summative interactive phenomena are less pronounced in the fovea than in the periphery, where the degree of convergence and lateral connection is greater. Facilitation appears to be the mechanism by which the periphery of the retina attains a higher degree of sensitivity (higher c.f.f.) than the fovea,[5] even though the peripheral cones are less sensitive. When the test object has a very small area, the c.f.f. drops very sharply as the stimulus passes from central fixation to 3 to 5°. In fact, under these conditions, the c.f.f. is lower throughout the periphery than at the fovea, because use of a small area reduces the amount of intra-areal facilitation. But with large test patches permitting intra-areal summation, the peripheral sensitivity is greater than the foveal.

Thus, the retinal periphery has two means of increasing its ability to respond to weak stimuli: (i) photochemical reactions (rhodopsin) and (ii) summative neural mechanisms. Both are operative in dim light, but only the latter is operative in daylight. The second mechanism is probably also a factor in endowing the scattered rods of the extreme periphery with good perception of movement. Neural interactions of an inhibitory nature occur in the foveal regions and are significant to detail vision.

One can think of the optic nerve fiber as behaving like a motoneuron of the spinal cord subjected to antagonistic afferent influences. As indicated, such convergence effects (facilitation and inhibition) will ultimately explain both the intensity (dark adaptation, etc.) and the spatial discrimination (visual acuity) functions of the retina.

VISUAL ACUITY AND DETAIL VISION

Biologically, visual acuity is the sharpness with which detail and contours are perceived and constitutes the basis for form or object vision. From the point of view of testing, it is often measured by finding the smallest distance by which two lines may be separated without appearing as a single line. This distance is the *minimum separable*. Visual acuity is thus the *resolving power* of the eye, i.e., its ability to resolve two lines, and is akin to the two point threshold of the skin. Lines or contours of solid fields placed closer together than the minimum separable blur into one another and may, if sufficiently close, appear homogeneous. Thus, if visual acuity is low, the fine details of environment are blurred and the intricate patterns of detail and contour give way to structureless masses with fuzzy outlines. Tests of visual acuity are simply standardized and quantified means of sampling a basic physiologic function—detail vision. Visual acuity can also be expressed in terms of the *minimum visible*, the narrowest line or the finest thread that can be discriminated from a homogeneous background. Weymouth[31] has shown that the *minimal angle of resolution* (M.A.R.) is a better designation for many purposes than is the minimum separable.

Dioptric Factors. The minimum separable varies with many conditions which are of two main kinds—dioptric and stimulus factors. The first have to do with the physical formation of a sharply focused image on the retina (Chap. 18). Under this heading come: (i) The "normal" errors of dioptric mechanisms: spherical and chromatic aberration, diffraction by imperfections in the ocular media and scattering of light by reflection from the retina. (ii) Errors of refraction: myopia, hyperopia and astigmatism. (Detection of such errors is the main purpose for clinical tests of visual acuity.) (iii) Pupillary size: constriction increases visual acuity by minimizing factors (i) and (ii), although undue constriction hinders detail vision by increasing diffraction. (iv) The composition of the light: monochromatic light increases visual acuity by decreasing chromatic aberration. (v) Random variations of fixation: these occur even when control of eye muscles is normal and cause a slight shifting (30′ of visual angle) of the image on the retina, thus blurring it.

Ratliff and Riggs[19] have recorded such movements by attaching a mirror to a contact lens. While the eyes are supposedly fixated no less than four types of movement are being made, varying from rapid movements (30 to 70 per sec.) averaging 17.5′ of visual angle to slow drifts and rapid jerks averaging 5′ of visual angle. Such movements have proved to be not a hindrance to vision but an actual necessity. An optical stabilizing of the retinal image, counteracting movement, results not in more detailed vision but in an actual fading of the image. As indicated earlier, something appears to be gained by the introduction of variability into the system.

Stimulus Factors. With the printed page as the stimulus, there are four ways in which the stimulus can be altered to make its recognition more difficult.[15] The letters may be reduced uniformly in size; the ink may be bleached to the white of the background or the latter may be darkened; the light falling on the page can be diminished; and, finally, the time allowed for observation can be shortened. The four factors influencing visual acuity are, then, size of detail, brightness contrast, illumination, and exposure time. All must be considered in attaining efficient vision in the school room or industry.

Retinal Grain. A third group of factors influencing visual acuity involves the anatomic and physiologic grain of the retina. Just as one factor in obtaining detail in photography is fineness of the grain in the film, so retinal grain is a factor in visual acuity. The dense packing together of exceedingly minute receptor elements is undoubtedly based upon the need for a finely grained receptive mechanism. The minimum separable, converted from seconds of visual angle to retinal distance and the diameter of a cone are of about the same order of magnitude. This suggests that two white lines on a black field could not be seen as two unless an unstimulated row of cones separated the stimulated ones ("ideal retinal illumination," Fig. 270). Yet we know this is not true. The eye distinguishes the lines even though optical imperfections and eye movements have caused the edges of the light bands to spread randomly over the intervening cones (diagrams *C* and *C'*, Fig. 270). If the lines are brought closer together, the curves

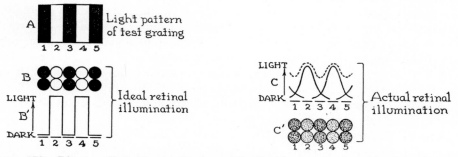

FIG. 270. Diagram illustrating mechanism of detail vision or visual acuity. *A* is test grating; *B* and *C'* are receptors with intensity of the illumination represented by shading; *B'* and *C* are plots of intensity of illumination, with dotted line in *C* representing algebraic summation of two underlying curves. For further explanation, see text.

representing the random distribution of light will be drawn together until the summated stimulus on the center cones equals that on the neighboring cones. So long as there is a discriminable difference in intensity of illumination between the shaded cone and its neighbors, a dark stria is visible. Visual acuity therefore resolves into the discrimination of a light-dark pattern. With these facts in mind, the retinal factors influencing visual acuity may be enumerated.

RETINAL REGION. Visual acuity is far from uniform over the entire retina. The fovea centralis is a region specialized for high visual acuity and is employed for accurate inspection of fine detail. The zone immediately surrounding the fovea possesses the next greatest capacity for detail vision, etc. The falling off in acuity in passing from fovea to periphery is quite abrupt (Fig. 271). With the foveal visual acuity taken as 1, the acuity at the edge of the macula (2.5°) has fallen to one-half; at 7.5° from the fovea it is one-fourth, and in the extreme periphery it is only one-fortieth. This curve, difficult to characterize, tends to become a straight line if plotted as the minimal angle of resolution, as in Figure 272;[31] at least two factors operate to produce this result. Extrafoveal cones are both larger in diameter and fewer per unit area, being "diluted" by rods. Secondly, more cones converge on a single ganglion cell in the periphery than in the central zones; as shown in Figure 273, visual acuity falls off more rapidly than intercone distance. On the other hand, the separation of ganglion cells in minutes of visual angle, plotted against degrees of eccentricity, forms a straight line. This confirms the deductions made from Figure 273.

Figure 272 also shows the marked difference between the visual acuities of the rod and cone mechanisms. With light below cone threshold, the fovea has the lowest visual acuity. In training for night vision, observers are taught to use the parafoveal regions of the retina. The acuity of rod vision increases throughout 10° owing to the increasing proportion of rods. Rod vision by night is inferior to cone vision by day within a 30° zone surrounding the fovea, not because the rods are "diluted" by inactive cones but because many rods converge ultimately upon a single ganglion cell. This is a second indication that the number of "lines" available to carry information to the brain, as well as the anatomic grain of the receptor elements, is important.

FUNCTIONAL GRAIN AND CONTOUR VISION. Hecht explains the familiar effect of illumination on visual acuity in terms of "functional retinal grain." He assumes that cone thresholds are distributed according to a normal frequency curve like heights or weights of individuals. By integrating* such a curve, the S shaped line in Figure 274 is

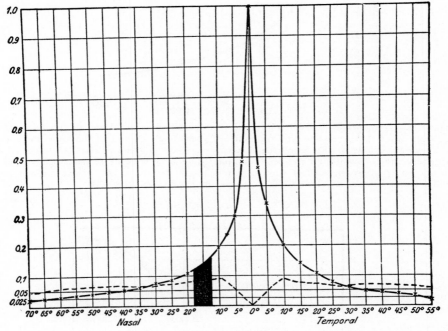

FIG. 271. Curve of relative acuity of vision in central and peripheral fields of retina. Solid line represents acuity of cone vision (light-adapted eye), and dotted line represents acuity of rod vision (approximate). Black area is the blind spot. (After Wertheim, Z. Psychol., 1894, 7:177–187.)

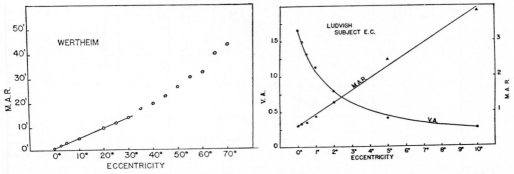

FIG. 272. Left, Graph showing approximation to straight line when data in Figure 271 are plotted as minimal angle of resolution. Right, Graph of data obtained by Ludvigh to show value of expressing visual acuity as minimal angle of resolution. (From Weymouth, Amer. J. Ophthal., 1958, 46:102–113.)

* This can be done graphically by adding the low threshold cones to those of the next lowest threshold to get the second part on the curve, and so on for each class.

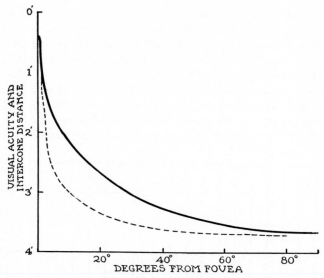

FIG. 273. Comparison of visual acuity and cone density for central and peripheral portions of retina. Dotted line shows visual acuity in minutes of visual angle. Note that the lower the curve the larger is the minimum separable. Heavy line shows cone gradient of retina in terms of intercone distance for periphery and cone width for rod-free areas, plotted on same ordinate as visual acuity. Failure of curves to correspond proves that factors other than density and diameter of cones determine minimum separable. (After Polyak, *The retina*, Chicago, University of Chicago Press, 1941.)

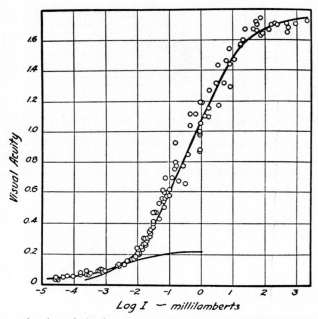

FIG. 274. Curves showing relation between visual acuity and level of illumination. Circles represent experimental determinations by König of visual acuity (reciprocal of minimum separable on ordinate) for a wide range of intensities of illumination (abscissa). Two solid lines, one for rods (lower) and one for cones (upper), show the success with which a normal probability integral can be fitted to data. According to Hecht's theory, curve represents number of receptor units whose threshold is attained by a given intensity of illumination, thresholds of receptors being distributed according to normal probability curve. (From Hecht, *A handbook of general experimental psychology*, C. Murchison, ed., Worcester, Clark University Press, 1934.)

obtained, and agreement of the theoretical curve and the experimental data justifies the assumption.

Figure 275 shows why dim lighting results in fuzzy, blurred contours. For convenience of illustration, Hecht's theory of cone thresholds is adopted. Circles represent the anatomic grain of the retina; the filled circles, the cones active at successively higher levels of illumination, A, B and C. The central vertical line demarcates a shadow cast upon the retina by a black object; the heavy line represents the boundary between lighted and shaded cones. A progressively sharper definition is obtained as more active cones are available to "draw" the contour, which is therefore sharpest at high illumination. (The same diagram also illustrates the difference in contour vision in peripheral (A), paracentral (B) and central (C) regions of the retina under conditions of bright illumination, the unfilled circles then being considered rods (inactive) and the filled circles cones.)

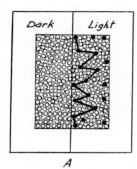 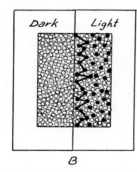 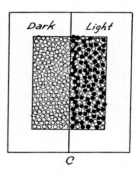

FIG. 275. Diagrams illustrating relation between level of illumination and perception of contours. A, B, C represent increasing levels of illumination of right-hand side of field, left-hand field being shielded by the shadow of an object. Filled circles represent active units and unfilled circles inactive units, rods and cones, retinal ganglion cells, or cells of striate cortex. Where many units are active, contour is quite sharply defined, but when few units are active contour is fuzzy. Same diagram serves to compare contour vision of peripheral (A), intermediate (B), and macular (C) regions of retina, with filled circles representing active cones, and unfilled circles inactive rods.

Clinical tests of visual acuity. Visual acuity is usually measured by the familiar chart on which the letters in each line are smaller than those in the previous line. The chart is always viewed from the virtual far point of vision (6 m., or 20 ft.), so that accommodation is not needed. The number at the end of each row of type is the distance at which a whole letter of the size found on that line subtends an angle of 5' on the retina, and each stroke of the letter subtends a visual angle of 1'. Snellen (1876), in making the chart, believed that the components of a letter should be separated by a distance equal to the minimum separable for the letter to be perceived by the normal eye. The situation is more complex than this. For example, the letters differ considerably in legibility; if B, the hardest letter to distinguish, is taken as 1, G and H are next hardest at 0.92, and L is the easiest at 0.71. However, the shortcomings of the test appear to compensate for one another, and the test serves its purpose very well. The chart must be well lighted; each eye is tested separately.

If at 20 feet the individual reads the letters of the line marked 20 feet, visual acuity is stated as 20/20 and is considered normal. If an individual can read only the line marked 100 (which a normal eye can read at 100 feet), his visual acuity is given as 20/100. Lines of test type smaller than the 20/20 line are provided and are rated 20/15, 20/13 and 20/10. Such ratings mean that the individual has better than normally acute vision and *do not mean that the individual is hyperopic*. As pointed out in the previous chapter, the hyperope does not see better than the emmetrope at a distance, but sees with less need for accommodation when objects are at a distance. To reduce the visual acuity to a fraction by saying that a person with 20/40 vision has 50 per cent normal visual acuity is like saying that a temperature of 80° is twice as hot as 40°. In some Snellen test charts the lines of type are labeled in terms of percentage of useful vision.

COLOR VISION

The sensations of color or hue resulting from the stimulation of the retina by the successive wavelengths of the visible spectrum and the *extraspectral* color, purple, form the *chromatic series*. It is paradoxical that the series of whites and grays—which in common parlance denotes a lack of color—is most conveniently considered a form of color vision, the *achromatic series*.

Achromatic and Chromatic Series.   Objects reflecting to our eye all the visible rays of sunlight give us a white sensation. Black, on the contrary, is the sensation caused by withdrawal of light. In order to see black one must have a retina. In the region of the blind spot one sees not black but nothing. Thus, it is not improbable that black is a sensation connected with a definite retinal activity.

In the chromatic series many different colors (technically hues) may be detected—some observers record as many as 160. We generally give specific names only to those that represent quite distinct sensations. The limiting wavelengths (mμ) of the commonly named colors are: red, 723–647; orange, 647–585; yellow, 585–575; green, 575–492; blue, 492–455; indigo, 455–424; violet, 424–397.

Color saturation. The term "saturation" means the amount of color or freedom from dilution by white sensation. Pale or pastel shades is the nontechnical name for unsaturated colors. However, even monochromatic light does not produce a color experience entirely free from white sensation, since the monochromatic rays induce the retinal processes underlying white as well as those underlying its own special color (see below).

Laws of color vision. There are quite a number of laws which any theory of color vision must explain. Some of these are more in the province of psychology than physiology. We must, therefore, content ourselves with a brief statement of the main laws of color vision.

(i) *Color mixture or fusion.* When two or more wavelengths fall upon the same retinal area, the resulting sensation is often quite different from any aroused by the individual wavelengths. (ii) *Primary colors.* Color fusion experiments show that three wavelengths may be selected from the spectrum, one from the red end, one from the blue end, and one from the middle, whose combinations in different proportions will give a sensation of white, of any intermediate color shade, or of extraspectral purple (obtained by mixing the two ends of the spectrum). It is customary to designate these three wavelengths as primary colors.* (iii) *Complementary colors.* For any given color there is a complement which combines with it to produce white. Because the colors of the spectrum differ in saturation, widely differing intensities may be necessary. Colors that are closer together in the spectral series than the complementaries give on fusion some intermediate color. Thus, red and yellow, when fused, give orange. Colors farther apart than the distance between the complementaries give some shade of purple. (iv) *After-images.* After one stops looking at a color, he may continue to see it for a short time (positive after-image) or he may see its complementary color (negative after-image). This is a retinal phenomenon. (v) *Color contrasts.* If a piece of blue paper is laid upon a yellow paper, the color of each of them is heightened— color contrast.

Theories of Color Vision.   Many theories have been proposed to explain the facts of color vision. None of them is entirely successful. The oldest and simplest theory is that of Young and Helmholtz.

Young-Helmholtz theory.   Proposed by Thomas Young[32] in 1801 and later modified by Helmholtz, this theory assumes three fundamental color sensations—red, green and violet. Corresponding with these are three classes of cones containing three different photochemical substances. Decomposition of each of these substances stimulates different nerve fibers, and the impulses are conducted to different systems of nerve cells in the visual cortex. The theory, therefore, assumes specific nerve fibers and specific cortical cells, corresponding respectively to the red, green and violet photochemical substances.†

When these three cone types are equally excited, a sensation of white results. All other color sensations, including yellow, are compounded by combined stimulation of the three receptors in different proportions. It is assumed, furthermore, that each photochemical substance is acted upon to some degree by all of the visible rays of the spectrum, but that the rays of long wavelengths at the red end of the spectrum affect the red substance most strongly, etc.

---

* There are many combinations of three wavelengths with which the spectrum can be matched.

† Helmholtz's hypothesis of zonal representation of color in the cerebral cortex has not proved justified. Le Gros Clark, however, has made the interesting suggestion that the three layers of the lateral geniculate body are related to the three receptors of the trichromatic theory.

The theory of Helmholtz accords with the doctrine of specific nerve energies, since each photochemical substance serves simply to excite a nerve fiber and the quality of the sensation aroused depends on the ending of this fiber in the brain.

Negative after-images are explained as follows: if we look fixedly at a green object, the corresponding photochemical substance is chiefly acted upon. When the same cones are subsequently exposed to white light, the red and violet substances, having been previously less acted upon, now respond in greater proportions to the white light, and the after-image takes a red-violet—that is, purple—color. Many objections have been raised to the Young-Helmholtz theory. It fails to explain some of the subjective phenomena of color vision in normal and "color blind" persons, and why, in the periphery, yellow and, further out, white or gray are perceived in otherwise color blind zones. Finally, recent neurophysiologic and anatomic information suggests that the theory is oversimplified.

Specific Color Receptors. In the past the number of the hypothetical color receptors and their wavelength sensitivity have been deduced chiefly from highly

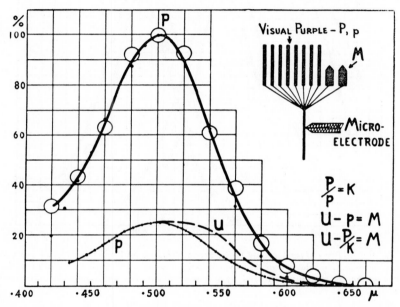

FIG. 276. Average sensitivity curve (large circles) of receptors connected with single ganglion cell of cat's retina when dark-adapted. Black dots are Lythgoe's curve for the absorption of light by visual purple. U is experimentally obtained curve from which curve P in appropriate magnitude (p) is subtracted to give sensitivity of specific color receptor. (From Granit, *J. Neurophysiol.*, 1945. 8:195–210.)

technical experiments on color mixture. Granit[8] has succeeded in recording impulses from single ganglion cells of the mammalian retina by means of microelectrodes. The least amount of light at different wavelengths adequate to discharge the ganglion cell was determined, i.e., the visibility curve for a single functional retinal unit. All units studied exhibited sensitivity to a wide band of wavelengths. The curve of sensitivity obtained in the dark-adapted eye agreed closely with the absorption curve of visual purple (Fig. 276). Under conditions of light adaptation, a curve resembling the photopic visibility curve was obtained. Polyak has shown that both rods and cones converge through bipolar cells upon the same ganglion cell. The shift from the scotopic to the photopic curve presumably means that rods cease to function at the intensities that stimulate cones. Granit terms this response the *scotopic and photopic dominator response*. The conscious response is presumably achromatic.

In addition to these dominator responses, some units in the light-adapted eye respond to a *narrow* band of wavelengths. This is termed the *modulator* response; it may represent the activity of individual cones. The sensitivity curves tend to vary slightly, but cluster into three groups (Fig. 277): red-yellow (580–600 mμ), green (520–540 mμ), and blue (450–470 mμ). The visibility curve reconstructed from these curves agrees satisfactorily with that of the human eye. This direct evidence therefore indicates that Helmholtz's trireceptor theory may be true in the statistical sense that the cones fall into three groups within which the receptors are similar, although not identical, in sensitivity. Apparently many ganglion cells discharge in response to several receptors, each sensitive to a narrow band, which collectively give the ganglion cell a sensitivity (visibility) curve like that of the whole eye. Such units, which are numerous, probably give rise to a sensation of white. Other ganglion cells connected with single receptors serve color discrimination.

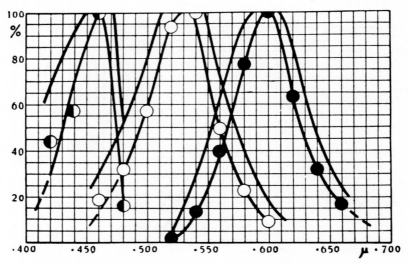

FIG. 277.　Sensitivity curves for blue (*left*), green (*middle*), and red (*right*) color receptors. These were obtained by selective adaptation and by averaging curves of several individual receptors, which varied from average by amount indicated by upper contours. (From Granit, *J. Neurophysiol.*, 1945, *8*:195–210.)

Clinical Correlations; Color Blindness and Anomalies. The discovery of color blindness (1794) is credited to the British chemist and physicist, John Dalton (of the gas law), who was himself "color blind."

CLASSIFICATION OF COLOR BLINDNESS.　The conventional classification of color blindness derives from the Young-Helmholtz theory of three specific receptors, color blindness being ascribed to an alteration in one of them. Defects in color vision are no longer described in terms of red, green and violet blindness, because, for example, the individuals Helmholtz called red blind are actually red-green blind. They see the spectrum as yellow and blue (see p. 448). Instead are employed the more noncommittal categories suggested by von Kries: protanopia, deuteranopia and tritanopia, implying merely a defect in the first (*protos*), second (*deuteros*) or third (*tritos*) receptor. The suffixes -anomaly and anopia distinguish color weakness and color blindness, respectively. The conventional-classification is as follows:

I. TRICHROMATS	II. DICHROMATS	III. MONOCHROMATS
1. normal color vision	1. protanopia	
2. protanomaly	2. deuteranopia	
3. deuteranomaly	3. tritanopia	

This classification, like the parent Young-Helmholtz theory, characterizes adequately the objective phenomena of color mixture in the color blind and is not meant to describe the appearance of the spectrum. The normal and color weak trichromats require three primary colors to match all colors in the spectrum, but they use the colors from the red and green parts of the spectrum in different proportions. In matching yellows by mixing red and green wavelengths, they employ quite different ratios; the protanomalous requires more of the red, and the deuteranomalous more of the green. Their defect may be quite slight or may be nearly as severe as in dichromatism.

Dichromats are so named because they can match the spectrum as they see it with only two primary colors, a red and a blue for the deuteranope and a green and a blue for the protanope. These two conditions are believed to be reduction systems representing the loss of one of the three Young-Helmholtz color receptors. Tritanopia is an extremely rare form of color blindness in which a wavelength from the long end and one from the middle of the spectrum suffice to duplicate the spectrum. The monochromat duplicates the spectrum with only one wavelength by adjusting its intensity. Apparently, only grades of light and dark are seen.

Luminosity of spectrum in color blindness. To the deuteranope-deuteranomalous the luminosity of the spectrum (visibility curve) is virtually normal (Fig. 278); to the protanope-protanomalous it is distinctly abnormal, the spectrum being shortened. The

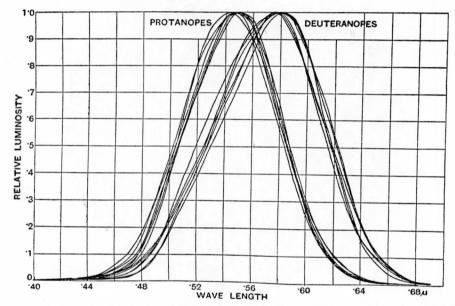

FIG. 278. Visibility curves of six protanopes and six deuteranopes. Curves are adjusted to same height. Observe similarity of curves within each group and that there are no intermediate cases. Curves for deuteranopes are very similar to those for persons with normal color vision (cf. Fig. 258); but a band of the long wavelengths (red), normally visible, cannot be seen or is poorly visible to the protanope, whose point of maximum brilliance is shifted to the short wavelengths. (From *Spec. Rep. Ser. med. Res. Council*, 1935, no. 200, 58 pp. By permission, the Controller, His Britannic Majesty's Stationery Office.)

longer (red) wavelengths are not even appreciated as light; it is as though they did not reach the retina. This explains why a protanope can confuse a red with a black and appear at a funeral wearing a red tie. The point at which the spectrum seems brightest is shifted from 552 mμ to approximately 540 mμ. No intermediate forms link the protanope to the normal (Fig. 278), and the visibility curves for protanopes and protanomalous are identical. The term *scoterythrous* has been suggested for this state. The visibility curve of the deuteranope shows no such abnormality; hence, it is a form of pure color blindness, whereas protanopia is a *color plus light* blindness.

Color confusions. The color blind person is satisfied with the appearance of his visual world, rarely misnames a colored object or even a color, and is often tardy in discovering his abnormality. His deficiency is usually first noticed because he confuses certain colors, and tests of color vision depend on these confusions. The protanomalous and deuter-anomalous find difficulty in distinguishing the red-green range, and the tritanomalous finds difficulty in distinguishing the blue-yellow range; the dichromat fails entirely.

Subjective phenomena.[11, 30] How does the spectrum appear to the color blind? To the dichromat, protanope and deuteranope, the spectrum is divided into two halves by a band of gray in the neighborhood of 493 to 497 mμ (greenish-blue), the so-called neutral point above which all wavelengths seem yellow and below which all wavelengths seem blue. The colors gain in saturation in passing away from the neutral point. Dalton described the spectrum as follows: "My yellow comprehends the red, orange, yellow and green of others; and my blue and purple (dark blue?) coincide with theirs." The few cases of monocular color vision examined confirm this description of the spectrum.

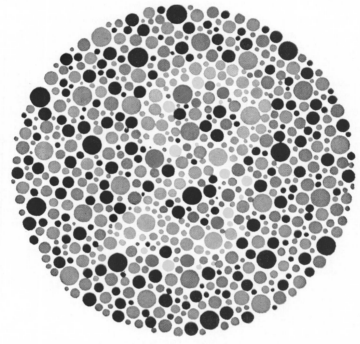

FIG. 279. Hidden-figure chart for detection of color blindness. Normal eye sees figure 5, color blind eye sees figure 2. (Copied by permission from Ishihara's *Series of plates designed as tests for color blindness*, Tokyo, Kanehara & Co., 1920.)

So, too, the color confusions of deuteranope and protanope are only subtly different. From the point of view of their subjective experiences, protanopes and deuteranopes both are red-green color blind, but in slightly different ways. Protanopia is characterized by a shortening of the spectrum and a decreased luminosity of the longer (red) wavelengths.

An explanation of why the spectrum appears to be made up of yellow and blue, rather than green and blue and red and blue, is as follows: In protanopia the "red receptor" is supposed to have the same wavelength sensitivity as the "green receptor," but retains its central "red" reaction unaltered. Therefore, neither green nor red is ever separately experienced, their receptors being always excited together, resulting in a color mixture. The spectrum corresponding to the whole red and green range appears as yellow or orange, the hues resulting from mixing red and green wavelengths. Deuteranopia may consist of a change in the cone normally most sensitive to the green wavelength so that it has the same sensitivity as the red-sensitive cone.

Classified on the basis of etiology, color disability may be (i) *acquired* through a variety of retinal, cerebral, systemic and toxic disorders, including avitaminosis, or (ii) *congenital* because of inherited lack of some mechanism vital to color vision. Red-green blindness and weakness are strongly sex-linked. According to one study it is present in some degree in 8 per cent of boys and 0.5 per cent of girls. It passes from father to grandson by way of a daughter. The lesser incidence among females is presumably due to the necessity for the disability to be received from both parents if it is to be exhibited. Total color blindness seems to be inherited as a simple recessive trait. Difficulty with blue and yellow is usually acquired; too few individuals born with this form have been discovered to learn much of its genetics.

TESTS OF COLOR BLINDNESS. For the purpose of explaining the principles involved, the simplest of the many tests for color vision is Holmgren's. A number of skeins of wool are used, and three standard colors are chosen: standard I, a pale, pure green skein, which must not incline toward yellow-green; standard II, a medium purple (magenta) skein; and standard III, a vivid scarlet skein. The subject is given skein I and is asked to select quickly from the pile of assorted colored skeins those that have approximately the same color. Those who are dichromatic will see the test skein as a gray with some yellow or blue shade and will select, therefore, not only the green skeins, but the grays or grayish-blue skeins. To ascertain whether the individual is a protanope or a deuteranope, standards II and III may then be employed.

With standard II (medium purple) the protanope will select, in addition to other purples, only blues or violets; the deuteranope will select as "confusion colors" only greens and grays.

With standard III (red) the protanope will select as confusion colors greens, grays or browns less luminous than the standard color, and the deuteranope will select greens, grays or browns of a greater brightness than the standard.

The second test of color vision in common use is the Ishihara or other version of Stilling's (1876) pseudo-isochromatic charts. This test, familiarly known as the "hidden digit" test, consists of a book of plates containing digits made up of spots of color set in a field composed of spots of the confusion color (Fig. 279). Spots of several shades are used because the luminosity of certain hues is altered for color deviates. In constructing the original tests, Stilling was guided in choice of colors by a red-green blind painter and a blue-yellow blind school teacher. In the Ishihara test one number is seen by the normal eye and another by the color weak eye. By appropriate choice of colors and chroma levels, the test can be made qualitatively and quantitatively diagnostic.

REFERENCES

1. BARLOW, H. B. *J. Physiol.*, 1953, *119*:58–68; 69–88.
2. BARLOW, H. B., FITZHUGH, R. and KUFFLER, S. W. *J. Physiol.*, 1957, *137*:338–354.
3. BROWN, K. and WIESEL, T. N. *Amer. J. Ophthal.*, 1953, 46 (No. 3, Pt. 2):91–98.
4. CAMPBELL, F. W. and RUSHTON, W. A. H. *J. Physiol.*, 1955, *130*:131–147.
5. CREED, R. S. and RUCH, T. C. *J. Physiol.*, 1932, *74*:407–423.
6. DITCHBURN, R. W. and GINSBORG, B. L. *J. Physiol.*, 1939, *119*:1–17.
7. GRAHAM, C. H. and GRANIT, R. *Amer. J. Physiol.*, 1931, *98*:664–673.
8. GRANIT, R. *J. Neurophysiol.*, 1945, *8*:195–210; also *Nature (Lond.)*, 1943, *151*:11–14.
9. GRANIT, R. *Receptors and sensory reception.* New Haven, Yale University Press, 1955.
10. HARTLINE, H. K. and RATLIFF, F. *J. gen. Physiol.*, 1958, *41*:1049–1066.
11. HECHT, S. Pp. 704–828 in *A handbook of general experimental psychology*, C. MURCHISON, ed. Worcester, Clark University Press, 1934.
12. HECHT, S. *Amer. Scientist*, 1944, *32*:159–177; also pp. 1–21 in *Visual mechanisms*, H. KLÜVER, ed. Lancaster, Pa., Jaques Cattell Press, 1942.
13. HECHT, S., HAIG, C. and CHASE, A. M. *J. gen. Physiol.*, 1937, *20*:831–850.
14. KUFFLER, S. *J. Neurophysiol.*, 1953, *16*:37–68.
15. LUCKIESH, M. and MOSS, F. K. *The science of seeing.* New York, Van Nostrand Co., 1937.
16. McFARLAND, R. A. and EVANS, J. N. *Amer. J. Physiol.*, 1939, *127*:37–50.
17. MILES, W. R. *Fed. Proc.*, 1943, *2*:109–115.
18. POLYAK, S. L. *The retina.* Chicago, University of Chicago Press, 1941.
19. RATLIFF, F. and RIGGS, L. A. *J. exp. Psychol.*, 1950, *40*:687–701.
20. RIGGS, L. A., RATLIFF, F., CORNSWEET, J. C. and CORNSWEET, T. N. *J. opt. Soc. Amer.*, 1953, *43*:495–501.
21. RUSHTON, W. A. H. *Nature (Lond.)*, 1957, *179*:571–573.
22. RUSHTON, W. A. H. *Ann. N. Y. Acad. Sci.*, 1958, *74*:291–304.
23. RUSHTON, W. A. H., CAMPBELL, F. W., HIGGINS, W. A. and BRINDLEY, G. S. *Optica acta*, 1955, *1*:183–190.
24. WAGNER, H. G. and WOLBARSHT, M. L. *Amer. J. Ophthal.*, 1958, *46*:46–59.
25. WALD, G. *J. gen. Physiol.*, 1935, *19*:351–371.
26. WALD, G. Pp. 1658–1667 in *Medical physics*, O. GLASSER, ed. Chicago, Yearbook Publishers, 1944.
27. WALD, G. *Handbook of physiology*, 1959, *1* (1): 671–692.
28. WALD, G. and CLARK, A. B. *J. gen. Physiol.*, 1937, *21*:93–105.
29. WALD, G., HARPER, P. V., JR., GOODMAN, H. C. and KRIEGER, H. P. *J. gen. Physiol.*, 1942, *25*:891–903.
30. WALLS, G. L. *The vertebrate eye and its adaptive radiation.* Bloomfield Hills, Mich., Cranbrook Institute of Science, 1942.
31. WEYMOUTH, F. W. *Amer. J. Ophthal.*, 1958, *46*:102–113.
32. YOUNG, T. *Phil. Trans.*, 1801, *92*:12–48.

CHAPTER 20

Binocular Vision and Central Visual Pathways

By THEODORE C. RUCH

THE dioptric and neural mechanisms for accurate vision at the central portions of the retina are rendered more useful by a provision for training this area upon objects requiring close examination. The gaze can be transferred quickly from point to point or it can be fixed steadily on a single detail. Two kinds of movements are executed so that light from an object will always fall upon the fovea in each eye, making possible fusion of the images: (i) convergence-divergence movements occurring when the eyes are fixed upon near or far objects, and (ii) conjugate movements in which the eyes sweep from side to side, etc., in unison.

Movements of Eye. Each eyeball is moved by six extrinsic, striated muscles which are innervated by three cranial nerves. By means of these muscles the eyeballs execute various movements best considered as *rotations* of the eyeball around various axes. These axes are: (i) the horizontal, which corresponds with the visual axis; (ii) the transverse; (iii) the vertical; and (iv) the oblique axes, which include all axes of rotation making oblique angles with the horizontal axis. Rotations around the oblique axes move the eyeballs obliquely upward or downward. The share of the individual eye muscles in producing rotation of the eyeball around the various axes is shown in Figure 280, which indicates the paths traversed by the visual axis when each muscle separately moves the eyeball.

The eyes can be moved sufficiently to fix on objects within a circular area having a diameter equal to 100° of visual angle. Rotations to the left and right are approximately equal in extent, but vertical upward movements are more limited (40°) than vertical downward movements (60°). The range of eye movements is tested with a *tangent screen* and is an important diagnostic sign in neurology.

In conjugate deviations the eyes move in a way to keep the visual axes of the two eyes parallel or else to converge them upon a common point, the medial rectus of one eye acting with the lateral rectus of the other. In movements of convergence, the medial recti of the two eyes are associated. Normally, it is impossible to diverge the visual axes beyond the parallel. A movement of this kind would produce useless double vision (diplopia).

The smooth intrinsic and striate extrinsic muscles of the eyeball and lids are controlled by a group of nuclei centered about the midbrain. These are closely interconnected to integrate the activities of the various muscles. Provision is made for the simultaneous activation of one muscle and inhibition of the motoneurons supplying its antagonist (reciprocal innervation). Provision is also made for associating the activities of two or more muscles. Even simple upward or downward movement requires unison contraction by two muscles. Reading requires simultaneous conjugate movements and a slight convergence. Transference of the gaze from a far to a near point involves the "fixation triad": (i) constriction of the pupil, (ii) accommodation of the lens, (iii) convergence. The strong linkage of these explains one form of "muscle strabismus" (see below).

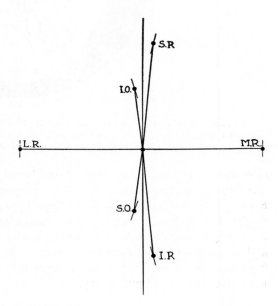

FIG. 280. Hering's diagram showing actions of individual eye muscles. Lines radiating from primary fixation point show path which visual axis would describe on screen placed in front of eyes when they are rotated by each muscle acting singly. Short line through terminus of each line represents tilt of eyes from vertical imparted by action of each eye muscle in executing each movement. Abbreviations are: I.O. and S.O., inferior and superior oblique; I.R. and S.R., inferior and superior recti; L.R. and M.R., lateral and medial recti. (From Martin and Weymouth, *Elements of physiology*, Philadelphia, Lea & Febiger, 1928.)

Coordination of Eye Muscle—Strabismus. Useful binocular vision requires a beautifully balanced or coordinated action of the opposing muscles to move the eyeballs in absolute unison. The visual axes must unite upon the object or point looked at. In looking about or in reading, the individual readjusts his eyes continually to bring point after point at the junction of the visual axes. When he looks at a distant object, the visual axes should be parallel. If this balance does not exist, a condition designated as *heterophoria* is present.

In heterophoria a constant contraction of one or more muscles is required, even in far vision, to prevent diplopia. When the eye at rest tends to drift toward the temporal side because of the unbalanced pull of the lateral rectus, the condition is known as *exophoria*. If there is a tendency to drift to the nasal side, the condition is described as *esophoria*. A tendency to drift upward is *hyperphoria* and downward is *hypophoria*. A lack of resting balance of this kind may also make itself felt in near work, such as reading and sewing, since it will require an increasing activity of the muscle overbalanced by its antagonist. The resulting muscular strain causes much distress. When muscular effort no longer brings the visual axes to bear upon the same point, a condition of squint or *strabismus* (*exotropia, esotropia, hypotropia,* or *hypertropia*) exists. Since both eyes cannot fix, double vision would result were it not for suppression of the image; this, however, leads to a reduction of visual ability (see below) in the squinting eye.

Severe defects of long standing and those caused by actual muscle weakness may be remedied by surgical operations upon the muscles or by the use of proper prisms with bases adjusted to direct light upon the fovea. Recognition of the physiologic causes

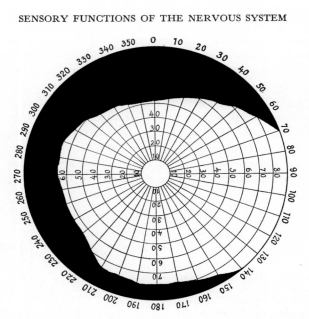

FIG. 281.   Perimetric chart to show field of vision for *right* eye when eye looks straight ahead and does not move. Temporal field is to right, nasal to left of chart. Numbers along vertical and horizontal meridians are degrees of visual angle from center of fovea.

operative in a "functional" type of strabismus permits a more fundamental treatment. *Convergent concomitant strabismus* in which one eye turns inward is usually due to uncorrected hyperopia in early childhood. For a hyperope to focus on near objects, excessive accommodation is necessary. Because accommodation and convergence are closely linked in the midbrain region, this convergence is appropriate to the excessive accommodation and in excess of that required to converge on the object. Early correction of the hyperopia, forced use of the squinting eye, and orthoptic training in binocular vision often render operative treatment unnecessary.

VISUAL FIELDS AND BINOCULAR VISION

Visual Fields—Perimetry.   By the visual field of an eye is meant the entire extent of the external world which can be seen without a change in the fixation of the eye. Because of the lens, the visual field is inverted upon the retina, so that objects in the upper visual field fall upon the lower half of the retina and objects in the right half of the visual field fall upon the left half of the retina. The retina is sensitive out to the ora serrata and, if the eye protruded sufficiently from its orbit, its visual field projected upon a flat surface would be a circle, the center of which would correspond to the fovea centralis. However, the nose, eyebrows and cheek bones cut off a considerable part of this field, giving it an irregular outline. The normal field of vision (Fig. 281) is therefore of little interest, but testing of the visual fields is an important clinical maneuver, especially in cases of suspected brain tumor.

To outline the visual field it is only necessary to keep the eye fixed and then to move a small object inward along a meridian until it is seen, keeping it at the same distance from the eye. This is repeated for each meridian and the results are combined upon an appropriate chart. An instrument, the perimeter, facilitates this process and is also useful for charting the peripheral fields. For plotting the central region of the visual field in detail, use is made of a large piece of black velvet marked off in degrees of visual angle and viewed from a distance of 1 m. (Bjerrum screen).

The outer zone of the retina has no color sensitivity. In this region, as ordinarily tested with light at moderate levels of illumination, a colored object gives rise only to an achromatic sensation. In passing toward the fovea color sensitivity develops gradually, the blue colors being perceived first and the greens last. The color zones of the retina may be plotted by means of a perimeter, but have no special significance. Ferree and Rand[6] state that the color blindness of the periphery of the retina is relative and not absolute.

Binocular Vision. When the two eyes are fixed upon a point straight ahead, each eye has its own visual field that may be charted by means of the perimeter. But the two fields overlap for a considerable portion of their extent. This area of overlap constitutes the field of binocular vision (see Fig. 282). At both sides of this field is a region which can be seen by only one eye. It is known as the *monocular crescent*, or the *temporal half-moon*. Every point in the binocular field forms an image upon both retinas. Whether a given object is seen single or double depends upon whether its image does or does not fall upon corresponding points in the two retinas.

Corresponding points. Physiologically defined, corresponding points in the two retinas are those which, when simultaneously stimulated by the same luminous object, give a single sensation. Noncorresponding points are, of course, those which when so stimulated give two visual sensations. It is evident that the foveae form corresponding points or areas. When we look at any object, the visual axes of the two eyes converge upon and meet at the point looked at. If, while observing an object, one eyeball is gently pressed upon from the side, two images are seen, and they diverge farther and farther from each other as the pressure is increased. Experiment shows that portions of the retina symmetrically placed to the right side of the foveae correspond, and the same is true for the two left halves. The right half of the retina in one eye is noncorresponding to the left half of the other retina. Doubling of objects that do not fall on corresponding points is readily demonstrated for objects that lie either closer or farther away than the object looked at (physiologic diplopia). If one holds the two forefingers in the median plane, one close to the face and the other as far away as possible, the nearer finger is seen double when the eyes are fixed on the far one and vice versa. The reason for this is seen in Figure 283. In this same experiment, most people will find that closing one eye makes a finger appear out of line to one side, the right-hand finger being seen by the left eye and vice versa. If, when one eye is closed, the fingers stay lined up, the open

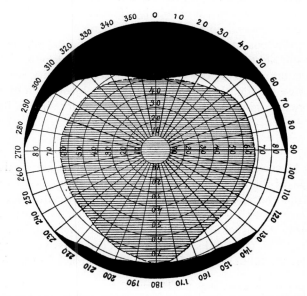

FIG. 282. Perimeter chart to show extent of binocular visual field. Shaded area is portion of visual field seen by both eyes; white areas at both sides are the monocular crescents seen only by extreme nasal portion of homonymous retina.

eye is the dominant one. When both eyes are open this finger (image) out of line does not seem as clear as when only the heteronymous (opposite) is open. The image in this eye is partially suppressed.

Suppression of visual images. One of the images of an object falling upon noncorresponding points is usually ignored or suppressed. When failure to fix comes on suddenly, as in pressing on one eyeball, double vision results. But in cases of long standing, the image from the abnormal eye is usually suppressed. The "suppressed" eye eventually shows a reduction or loss of visual ability, even blindness, when tested separately; this condition is called *amblyopia*.

Binocular rivalry. When the images of two dissimilar objects are thrown on corresponding parts of each retina, binocular rivalry ensues. If the image consists of vertical lines on one eye and horizontal lines on the other, only one field is seen at a time, first one, then the other; or the field is broken, vertical lines in part and horizontal lines in part. There is no genuine fusion in a continuous constant picture.

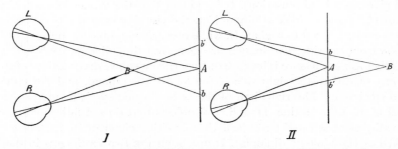

FIG. 283. Diagrams to show homonymous and heteronymous diplopia: In *I*, eyes are focused on *A*; images of *B* fall on noncorresponding points—that is, to different sides of foveae—and are seen double, being projected to plane of *A*, giving heteronymous diplopia. In *II*, eyes are focused on nearer point, *A*, and farther point, *B*, forms images on noncorresponding points and is seen double—homonymous diplopia—images being projected to focal plane *A*.

*Judgments of solidity and depth.** Vision gives us knowledge not only of the surface area of objects, but also of their depth or solidity. The visual sensations upon which this conception is built are of several different kinds, partly monocular and partly binocular. If we close one eye and look at a bit of landscape or a solid object, we are conscious of the perspective, of the right relations of foreground and background. Nevertheless, it is true that with binocular vision the perception of depth and solidity are far more perfect. This is mainly because the slightly different views of an object given by the two eyes are subjectively combined to give the third dimension. This principle is illustrated by the stereoscope.

CENTRAL VISUAL PATHWAYS[18]

Retina, Optic Nerve and Chiasm.[9] The fibers composing the optic nerve originate in the ganglion cells of the inner layer of the retina. They converge to form the optic nerve and pierce the chorioid and scleral coats of the eyeball. Morphologically the point of convergence forms the optic nerve head, disc or papilla; physiologically it produces a *blind spot* in the visual field because only nerve fibers are present at that point. The nerve head lies 15° to the nasal side of the fovea centralis; because the lens reverses spatial relationships, the blind spot is 15° to the temporal side in the visual field. Fibers

---

* Depth perception is measured with the Howard-Dolman apparatus. A short, upright rod is mounted 20 feet from the subject on a wire passing around a pulley. The two ends of the wire are manipulated by the subject until this rod and a stationary rod appear to be equidistant. The error is then measured and the average of repeated tests is made.

from the macula lutea are numerous and form a distinct bundle running horizontally to the nerve head (Fig. 284), the *maculopapillary bundle*. Fibers to the nasal side of the nerve head pursue a direct course like the spokes of a wheel. Since no fibers pass through the fovea, fibers from the temporal portion of the retina arch above or loop below the fovea centralis, forming a geometrically sharp "watershed" along a horizontal line drawn through the fovea to the temporal margin of the retina. In this fashion, the temporal retinal fibers (and some of the fibers of the nasal half) become separated into an upper and a lower quadrant by the interposition of the macular fibers,* an arrangement continued throughout the central visual pathways.

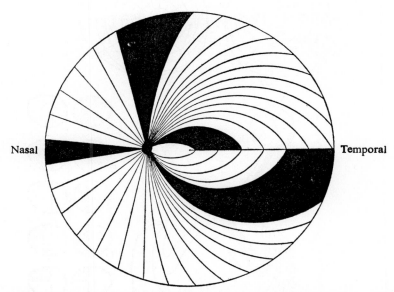

FIG. 284. Highly schematic diagram of arrangement of fibers coursing across retina of left eye to form optic nerve. Arching and radiating lines are paths taken by nerve fibers converging to optic nerve head. Black areas represent four types of defect which result from interruption of nerve bundles at optic nerve head. Note horizontal raphe running from macula to temporal margin of retina. (From Traquair, *Clinical perimetry*, St. Louis, C. V. Mosby & Co., 1927.)

A vertical line drawn through the macula divides the retina into two hemimaculas and hemiretinas. Fibers from the temporal hemiretina of the left eye continue through the *optic chiasm* and, without crossing, pass in the optic tract to the *lateral geniculate body* of the left side; those from the temporal side of the right eye enter the right optic tract (Fig. 285). Fibers from the nasal half of each retina decussate in the optic chiasm and enter the optic tract of the opposite cerebral hemisphere, where they join the uncrossed fibers from the temporal half of the other eye, thence to the lateral geniculate body. Thus, the termination for fibers from the nasal half of the retina is contralateral. Because of this regrouping of fibers, lesions of the optic chiasm, or central to it, cause visual defects different from those induced by lesions of the retina or optic nerve.

The effects of lesions at various points in the visual system upon the visual fields of the two eyes are shown in Figure 285. It is also profitable to consider their effect on the field of vision when both eyes are open. From complete interruption of one optic nerve there is, on the same side as the lesion, a slight lateral narrowing of the field of vision when both eyes are open. This is due to loss of vision in one temporal half-moon

* In discussion of the central visual pathways, the terms "macula" and "macular" do not always mean the region of the macula lutea. In clinical literature, these are almost synonyms for "central," and denote any central zone less than about 10° of visual angle.

(seen only by the extreme nasal portion of the ipsilateral retina). However, interruption of the visual pathway central to the chiasm on one side blocks impulses from *both* eyes, conveying impressions from one-half the binocular visual field plus one temporal half-moon. The result of such a lesion in, for example, the left hemisphere is a visual field defect known as *right lateral homonymous hemianopsia*—"half-blindness" because the blindness extends over a geometric half of the visual field; "homonymous" because the corre-

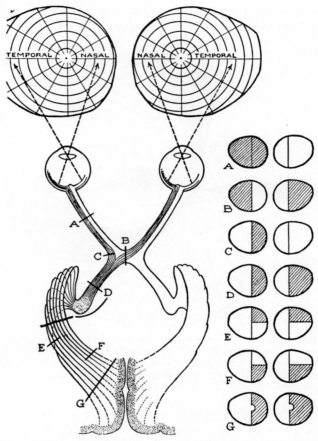

FIG. 285.   Diagram of central visual pathways passing to left hemisphere. Shaded areas in inserts indicate visual field defects resulting from lesions at point indicated by corresponding letter on left-hand figure. For convenience, visual fields for two eyes are shown separated, but actually they superimpose so that vertical meridians coincide: *A*, complete blindness of left eye; *B*, bitemporal hemianopsia; *C*, unilateral nasal hemianopsia; *D*, right homonymous hemianopsia—interruption of either optic tract or geniculocalcarine projection; *E* and *F*, right upper and lower quadrant hemianopsias; *G*, right homonymous hemianopsia from a large lesion of occipital lobe. (From Homans, *A text-book of surgery*, 5th ed., Springfield, Ill., Charles C Thomas, 1941.)

sponding halves of the two retinas are blinded; "lateral" because nothing to one side is seen; and "right" because the disturbance is named for the side of the visual field defect, not for the side of the "retinal blindness." The lesion is always on the side opposite the visual field defect.

Occurring less commonly, an expanding tumor of the pituitary body, the stalk of which is located in the bay formed by the two optic tracts, may split the decussating fibers from the nasal half of each retina, producing a *bitemporal hemianopsia;* then only the nasal half of each visual field is seen. Similarly, a pathologic expansion of both internal carotid arteries lying in the angle formed by the optic nerve and tract of each side may interrupt the fibers from the two temporal hemiretinas, yielding a *binasal hemianopsia*. These are *heteronymous* because noncorresponding retinal fields of the two eyes are affected and little restriction is noticeable when both eyes are open.

Between the optic chiasm and the lateral geniculate bodies optic tract fibers, or collaterals from them, representing every portion of the hemiretinas, pass to the pretectal region lying just rostral to the superior colliculus. This group of fibers constitutes the afferent limb of the pupillary reflexes to light. These fibers were once believed to end in the superior colliculus, but now are known to end in the pretectal region.[12, 20] Hemianopsia *with* retention of the light reflex therefore characterizes lesions central to this regrouping. The "visual fibers" continue to the lateral geniculate body of the diencephalon where they enter synaptic relations with the fourth order neurons which continue on to the occipital lobe.

Lateral Geniculate Bodies and Striate Cortex.   This nucleus is made up of six layers of cells separated by layers of fibers, giving the structure its conspicuous laminated appearance. Alternate layers of fibers are contributed by the hemiretinas of the two

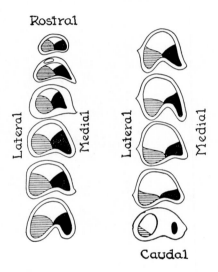

FIG. 286. Sections through left lateral geniculate body of monkey. Terminations of fibers from retina are indicated as follows: *hatched area*, lower peripheral quadrant; *white*, macula, upper and lower quadrants; *black*, upper peripheral quadrant. According to the work of Le Gros Clark and Penman, this diagram shows too much macula at rostral end and too much peripheral representation at caudal end. (After Brouwer and Zeeman, *Brain*, 1926, *49*:1–35.)

eyes.[4] Crossed fibers end in cell layers 1, 4 and 6, and uncrossed fibers end in the intervening layers of cells; impulses from corresponding retinal points presumably first converge in the occipital cortex, which makes fusion a cortical function. Glees and Le Gros Clark[8] have shown further that in the monkey each optic nerve fiber breaks up into a spray of five or six branches. In degenerating preparations each branch ends by means of a *single* degenerating bouton related to the cell body (never the dendrites) of a neuron of the lateral geniculate body. This is a remarkable instance of *divergence* and is the only known instance in which a cell is excited by single synapse stimulation.

By transneuronal[5] and Marchi[1] degeneration studies, the projection of the retina upon the lateral geniculate body has been established. Note in Figure 286 that the macular sector is interposed between sectors containing fibers from the upper and lower extramacular quadrants and that the lower retinal quadrant is lateral. Note also that, relative to its small retinal area, the macula is represented by a disproportionate amount of the nucleus. The oral-caudal relationship is the same as in the retina, i.e., the macular region is posterior to the periphery in both.

Fourth order neurons constituting the geniculostriate bundle, especially the inferior part, swing forward and around the ventricle of the temporal lobe before running posteriorly to the striate area of the occipital lobe. Meyer's loop or detour, so formed, accounts for the occurrence of visual field defects from lesions well forward in the temporal lobe (Cushing). Within the geniculostriate bundle, the macular fibers continue to separate those from the upper and lower quadrants. Those originating in the mesial sector of the geniculate body and representing the upper quadrant of the retina pass above the tip of the posterior horn and end in the superior lip of the calcarine fissure; those from the lateral sector (lower retinal quadrant) pass below the horn and end on the lower lip of the calcarine fissure. The macular fibers swing around the end of the ventricle and can be traced mainly to the posterior part of the calcarine fissure. The interposition of macular fibers between peripheral ones explains how a quadrant visual field defect having a sharp horizontal border can occur. An irregularly shaped pathologic process could produce a quadrant defect with a geometrically shaped horizontal boundary only if the fibers from the two quadrants were to some degree topographically separated as they are by intervening macular fibers.

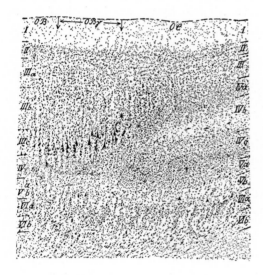

FIG. 287. Cytoarchitecture of transition zone (*asterisk*) between area 17 (*right*) and area 18 (*left*) of upper lip of calcarine fissure. On right (*striate area*) note that inner and outer layers of pyramidal cells are virtually absent. The almost clear area, *IVb*, corresponds to line of Gennari. Observe band of large pyramidal cells in layer *IIIc* of area 18. Cell stain and 44× magnification. (From von Economo, *Zellaufbau der Grosshirnrinde des Menschen*, Berlin, J. Springer, 1927.)

The cortical visual area in man is almost completely concealed from view in a longitudinal infolding on the mesial and cerebellar surfaces of the occipital lobe, the *calcarine* fissure. Cytoarchitecturally the region is characterized by a conspicuous line of Gennari visible to the naked eye without staining which is often called the *striate area*. The cellular structure (Fig. 287) is the highly granular type associated elsewhere in the cerebral cortex with sensory function because of the great development of the outer and inner granular layers. The striate area, which is area 17 in Brodmann's numeration, is surrounded by a concentric band, area 18 or the *parastriate* cortex, and between them is an exceedingly abrupt transition in cytoarchitecture. A second more anterior concentric zone is the *peristriate* area, Brodmann's area 19. The optic radiations terminate in area 17; none pass to areas 18 and 19.

Topographic Organization of Visual Area. The way fibers of the optic radiations terminate in the cerebral cortex is learned in three main ways: (i) correlation of visual field defects with the locus of restricted lesions of the occipital lobe; (ii) correlation of the site of retrograde degeneration in the lateral geniculate bodies from restricted striate lesions with the site of transneuronal degeneration, or tracing Marchi degeneration in the same nuclei from experimental lesions of the retina (monkey); and (iii) recording action potentials from the cortical fields in response to systematic stimulation of the various retinal regions (monkey).

As shown in Figure 288, the representation of the upper quadrant of the *retina* is on the upper lip of the calcarine fissure; that of the lower retinal quadrant is on the lower lip of the fissure. Thus lesions of the lower lip, for example, produce a defect in the upper quadrant of the visual field. Much evidence[11], [17] indicates that the anteroposterior dimension of the striate area corresponds to the periphery-macula (meridional) dimension of the retina. The rule is that the macula is posterior in the eye, and its representation is posterior in the lateral geniculate body and posterior in the occipital lobe. The periphery is most anterior at these three levels. As in the geniculate body, the area of cortex devoted to the macula is very large compared to the area for the periphery.

How this arrangement came about may be easily visualized as follows: Imagine the left hemiretinas of the two eyes superimposed with their foveae coinciding. They are then folded forward from top to bottom along the horizontal meridian and inserted into the calcarine fissure with the fold coming at the bottom of the fissure and the point (fovea) posterior. If the meridians are imagined as closing like the blades of a Japanese fan, it becomes clear that the periphery will be located anteriorly. But this

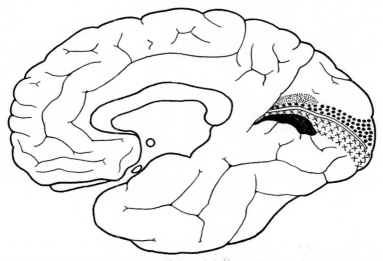

FIG. 288.   Projection of retina upon calcarine fissure of man. Fine dots and black are, respectively, representation of upper and lower *peripheral* quadrants of retina; heavy dots and crosses are, respectively, representation of upper and lower quadrants of *macula*. Rostral extension of macular representation is hypothetical. (Modified from Brouwer, *Res. Publ. Ass. nerv. ment. Dis.*, 1934, *13*:529–534.)

fails to suggest that a larger cortical area is devoted to the fovea than to the periphery. The ribs at the handle end of the fan would have to be farther apart to have the relations that exist in the cortex. Note that the free edges of the infolded retinas are the two halves of the vertical meridian which are vis à vis to the vertical meridian of the right hemiretinas located in the opposite hemisphere. This explains why midline lesions affecting both occipital lobes may produce a confluent midline scotoma of the right and left visual fields.

If this arrangement is correct, it means that at the occipital lobe the macular fibers for the first time cease to lie interposed between the upper and lower peripheral quadrant fibers. Such a rearrangement is somewhat unlikely. It is possible that the macular fibers do not all pass to the posterior end of the calcarine fissure, but form a wedge, the point of which is directed forward, separating the upper and lower quadrants as shown in Figure 288. Some evidence demands that a portion of the macular fibers extend even farther forward than the peripheral fibers.

Functional significance of topographic organization.   What is the significance of the topographic organization of the occipital lobe? Is it simply an engineering convenience, or is it the neural basis for detail vision, vision of forms and patterns and visual localization? Is it possible to think that the pattern of light on the retina is translated into a pattern of impulses on the occipital cortex with each unit holding its topographic position relative to other units? That this is the case is suggested by the fact that minute injuries of the cortex produce contiguous areas of blindness of the visual field. That the retina is projected point-to-point on the cortex is confirmed anatomically within the limits of our techniques. Thus Polyak[17] finds that a lesion of the occipital cortex 1 mm.[2] in extent causes a degeneration confined to a single band of cells in the geniculate body only four to five cells wide. Moreover, the extent of the striate cortex devoted to the fovea justifies belief that the fineness of grain in the occipital cortex is the basis for the high degree of visual acuity exhibited by the fovea.

For the monkey, this has been demonstrated in a quantitative fashion by Talbot and Marshall,[15, 23] who recorded the points of maximal electrical activity in the striate area while systematically exploring the retina with a point of light. The foveal representation is situated at the anterior border of the striate area on the lateral surface of the occipital lobe, which places it about 5 mm. below the tip of the simian or lunate sulcus (external parieto-occipital sulcus) not far from the ear (Fig. 289). This region becomes posterior when the striate area largely disappears from the free surface of the cortex in the chimpanzee and man as a result of an expansion of the parietal association area. Even in the monkey, only 8° of the periphery (little more than the macular area) is on the wide expanse of the free surface of the occipital cortex. The first 8° are arranged in concentric bands medial to the fovea. The portion of the striate area devoted to the hemifovea is 6 mm. in radius. Retinal distance and cortical distance compare as follows: within the foveal representation, 1 mm. of cortex is devoted to only 2′ of visual angle; whereas at the representation for 5° from the fovea, 18′ of visual angle are crowded into 1 mm. Much greater ratios must obtain for the extreme peripheral regions of the retina. Another outcome of these studies is a quantitative estimate of the degree to which the retina is magnified upon the occipital cortex. Such magnification has been shown by Glees and by Chow et al.[2] for the monkey. In

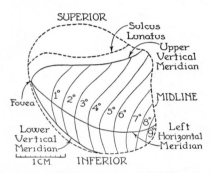

FIG. 289.   Map showing projection of retina upon occipital lobe of monkey as charted by electrical methods. Left occipital lobe is shown as viewed from behind; foreshortening decreases apparent size of central representation. (Redrawn from Talbot and Marshall, Amer. J. Ophthal., 1941, 24:1255–1264.)

the monkey the number of cells in the lateral geniculate body is approximately the same as the number of fibers in the optic nerve, on the order of 1,000,000. In the striate cortex the number of cells increases to more than 145,000,000. Talbot and Marshall calculate that a circular foveal area 1′ in diameter (5 μ, or the width of 2 foveal cones) is represented by a cortical region 100 times as wide (0.5 mm.) with an area 10,000 times as great. With nerve cells spaced at 20 μ, the ratio between cone and cortical cell is 1:100. In the physical transmission of light to the retina, the energy tends to spread over a wide region, and in neural transmission there is a further tendency for lateral spread of excitation; yet the cortical grain is finer than the retinal grain. Since, as Figures 183 and 270 show, acuity is a question of discrimination of intensity differences between peaks and valleys of excitation, discriminations much less than cone width are theoretically possible because of the fine cortical grain. An offset in a line of only 2.5″ of visual angle (vernier acuity of "aligning power") is discriminable. Perhaps the fine cortical mosaic is used for such discriminations or for registering the slight differences in the images seen by the two eyes which form the basis of stereoscopic vision. On the other hand, the multiplicity of units may be significant for intensity discrimination, the number of active units being one way of reflecting intensity.

Macular Sparing.[19]   A hemianopsia which includes macular vision is rarely caused by lesions of the occipital lobe. More often, the vertical or median border of the blind area is not a straight line ("macular splitting") but is indented so that 3 to 5° of central vision is "spared."

The macula sometimes escapes when ischemia damages the cortical receiving areas. Such survivals are often caused by the fact that the macular areas receive a double blood supply so that its fibers may be relatively less affected. In a patient with bilateral thrombosis of the posterior calcarine artery, macular vision was spared.[16] Other times the macula may escape although peripheral vision is affected because the latter is represented by so few fibers that functional loss caused by pressure or ischemia has a greater effect on it.

Macular sparing after extensive surgical resections of the occipital lobe cannot be accounted for by either of the factors mentioned above. Two explanations have been advanced: (i) that the macular region is bilaterally represented in the cerebral cortex, and (ii) that the macula is extensively localized throughout the striate area so that only rarely is the whole representation destroyed. To the first there are serious objections.[7, 23] For example, electrical activity is detectable in the macular representation of the left occipital lobe only when light is flashed upon the left hemimaculae of the eyes. Electrical responses of both striate areas suggestive of bilateral representation have never been observed.

There is some presumptive evidence for the second theory, since macular sparing occurs in some lesions of the optic radiations, but electrical studies do not bear out this theory. However, the macular region may be more extensively localized anteriorly than was suggested in the previous section. That the macula is heavily represented at the posterior end of the calcarine fissure has been firmly grounded anatomically by mapping the visual cortex in monkeys.[23] Yet lobectomies which fall short of destroying the whole extent of the calcarine fissure tend to spare the macula; whereas, if resection is carried out farther forward to include the extreme anterior tip of the striate area, macular vision is not spared. It is almost necessary to suppose that the macular area extends farther forward than the representation of the peripheral retinal zones.

Visual Function of Striate Area.   The role of the cerebral cortex in vision increases steadily throughout the phylogenetic series. The great visual acuity of birds and fish, which is legendary, is subserved entirely by subcortical functions. In the mammalian series, visual function becomes progressively corticalized or encephalized until, in primates, the superior colliculi serve largely reflex functions. A corollary of the increasing importance of the cortex is therefore that the cerebral cortex is essential for certain types of visual function, whereas other types can be carried on by subcortical structures.

In man, occipital lobectomy abolishes all types of visual discrimination—light from dark, lights of different intensities, colors and patterns (form), but in animals some visual ability is sustained by subcortical levels. Visual discrimination in animals is tested by establishing the habit of choosing between two differently illuminated alleys or stimulus objects in order to receive food. In rats, cats and dogs[14, 22] discrimination of light from dark, a rod function, survives complete removal of the striate areas. The ability to discriminate may be temporarily lost, but it seems to be merely the discriminatory habit which is upset because the discrimination itself is readily relearned. The fineness of discrimination is decreased, but not greatly so. In monkeys, the disturbance is more severe, but even these animals can relearn.

When discrimination between two bright lights or between patterns (form) is tested, functions involving cone vision, the opposite result is obtained. Such discriminations are not possible after destruction of the striate areas. Even in the rat, pattern vision is impossible and no amount of retraining restores the ability.

Much evidence indicates that the two categories of results reflect the duality of vision so obvious at the retina. The clinching evidence is based on the fact that monkeys exhibit rod and cone visibility curves similar to man's (see Fig. 258). After ablation of the occipital lobes, the monkey's visibility curve even at high illumination is that characteristic of rods.[13] The conclusion therefore is that rod vision is not corticalized to the same extent as cone vision, and that even in the monkey rod vision can be carried out at subcortical levels of the brain. However, pattern vision demands a topographically organized system of fibers consisting of multiple discrete units such as the foveal cones and their central connections provide.

Areas 18 and 19.[3]   These areas surrounding the striate area, since they are strongly developed in the primates, might be concerned with higher levels of visual function. Evidence indicates they are efferent as well as associative. Stimulation of them induces eye movements (Chap. 11). Several skilled investigators have sought by a wide variety of objective behavior techniques to discover disturbances of higher visual ability after destruction of this region. However, higher visual function seems to be carried out by the primary receptive areas, perhaps by a geniculocortical reaction rather than by the intervention of association areas.

Higher levels of visual sensation in man.[10, 21] Visual disturbance occurs as a result of large injuries to the free surface of the occipital lobe and especially to the posterior parts of the parietal lobe, but only the higher levels of visual sensation are affected. Perceptions of light and dark, of color and of pattern are retained apart from visual field defects because of interference with the underlying optic radiations. Since objects are recognized visually, the disturbance is not visual agnosia.

Holmes[10] characterized the syndrome as *visual disorientation* and described it as follows. Spatial localization is markedly defective, and the patient finds it particularly difficult to coordinate movements of his hand in relation to an object. The estimation of distance toward and away from the patient presents more difficulty than side-to-side localization, possibly because the latter is simply a matter of retinal local sign, whereas the former involves many factors. The patient will reach out in good faith for an object five or six feet away. Length and size are inaccurately judged. Asked to divide a line into halves, the patient may make one part several times as long as the other. Movement of an object is appreciated, but to say whether the movement is up or down, toward or away is difficult. Occasionally stereoscopic vision is lost, objects appearing flat. Visual inattention is also characteristic. By this is meant that objects although seen are not reacted to, as though the mechanism for translating sensory impressions into action is damaged.

Whether the lesions of the posterior part of the brain which produce these disturbances do so by destroying areas 18 and 19 or by interrupting the long association pathways linking the visual cortex with other regions of the brain, especially the temporal lobe, is not yet clear. The functions of the association areas and the intercortical systems are the subject of the next chapter.

REFERENCES

1. BROUWER, B. and ZEEMAN, W. P. C. *Brain*, 1926, *49*:1–35.
2. CHOW, K.-L., BLUM, J. S., and BLUM, R. A. *J. comp. Neurol.*, 1950, *92*:227–239.
3. CHOW, K.-L. and HUTT, P. J. *Brain*, 1953, *76*:625–677.
4. CLARK, W. E. LE GROS. *Brit. J. Ophthal.*, 1932, *16*:264–284.
5. CLARK, W. E. LE GROS and PENMAN, G. G. *Proc. roy. Soc.*, 1934, *B114*:291–313.
6. FERREE, C. E. and RAND, G. *Psychol. Rev.*, 1919, *26*:16–41, 150–163.
7. FOX, J. C., JR. and GERMAN, W. J. *Arch. Neurol. Psychiat. (Chicago)*, 1936, *35*:808–826.
8. GLEES, P. and CLARK, W. E. LE GROS. *J. Anat. (Lond.)*, 1941, *75*:295–308.
9. HINES, M. *Arch. Ophthal. (Chicago)*, 1942, *28*:913–937.
10. HOLMES, G. *Brit. J. Ophthal.*, 1918, 2:449–468, 506–516.
11. HOLMES, G. and LISTER, W. T. *Brain*, 1916, *39*:34–73.
12. MAGOUN, H. W. and RANSON, S. W. *Arch. Ophthal. (Chicago)*, 1935, *13*:791–811, 862–874.
13. MALMO, R. B. *Psychol. Bull.*, 1940, *37*:497–498.
14. MARQUIS, D. G. *Res. Publ. Ass. nerv. ment. Dis.*, 1934, *13*:558–592. See also: *Arch. Neurol. Psychiat. (Chicago)*, 1935, *33*:807–815.
15. MARSHALL, W. H. and TALBOT, S. A. Pp. 117–164 in KLÜVER, H., ed. *Visual mechanisms*. Lancaster, Penn., Jaques Cattell Press, 1942.
16. McDONALD, P. R. *Arch. Ophthal. (Chicago)*, 1943, *29*:92–97.
17. POLYAK, S. *Res. Publ. Ass. nerv. ment. Dis.*, 1934, *13*:535–557.
18. POLYAK, S. *The vertebrate visual system*. Chicago, University of Chicago Press, 1957, xviii, 1390 pp.
19. PUTNAM, T. J. and LIEBMAN, S. *Arch. Ophthal. (Chicago)*, 1942, *28*:415–443.
20. RANSON, S. W. and MAGOUN, H. W. *Arch. Neurol. Psychiat. (Chicago)*, 1933, *30*:1193–1202.
21. RIDDOCH, G. *Brain*, 1935, *58*:376–382.
22. SMITH, K. U. *J. genet. Psychol.*, 1937, *51*:329–369.
23. TALBOT, S. A. and MARSHALL, W. H. *Amer. J. Ophthal.*, 1941, *24*:1255–1264.

SECTION V

Cerebral Cortex in General;
Neurophysiology of Behavior

CHAPTER 21

Association Areas and the Cerebral Cortex in General

By A. L. TOWE and THEODORE C. RUCH

CEREBRAL action is a thing apart from simple reflex activity. Sensory information is stored over long periods to appear in the cerebral output from time to time inextricably interwoven with more recent information. It is this property which underlies learning and retention, language and cognitive processes—functions traditionally ascribed to the "association areas." The primary sensory and motor areas constitute but a fraction of the cerebral mantle and are largely buried in the fissures. In this chapter, after a consideration of certain activities pertaining to the cortex as a whole, we shall discuss the functions of the mass of cortical tissue that is collectively termed the "association cortex."

ELECTRICAL ACTIVITY

The cellular elements of the cerebral cortex, like all other cells, have distinctive electrical properties. Cortical tissue shows both a continuous, rhythmic alternation of electrical potential and a variety of localized, larger voltage responses following receptor activity. The former rhythm is called "spontaneous" because its origin is not known; the latter responses are called "evoked" because they are closely associated with sensory input. Knowledge of the way in which the evoked potentials occur should lead to an understanding of the spontaneous activity of the brain.

Continuous Activity. ELECTROENCEPHALOGRAM.[13, 14, 21, 24]   In 1929, Hans Berger announced that irregular potentials could be recorded via leads placed on the human head. The record thus obtained (Fig. 290) has come to be called an *electroencephalogram*, abbreviated EEG. Such potentials are exceedingly small (up to 50 μV. peak-to-peak in normal adults), whether recorded from frontal, parietal, occipital or temporal regions.

However, typical voltage differences exist between any two regions, the pattern depending upon the "state of the system" and the manner of recording.* Although the normal EEG consists of many different frequencies, one frequency predominates. This characteristic has proved as important as the amplitude of the wave and, in fact, is used in naming the EEG pattern. Thus, *alpha* waves are those with frequencies of eight to 14 per second; *beta* waves, 14 to 60 per second; and *delta* waves slower than eight per second. The amplitude of these waves is inversely proportional to the typical frequency. By convention, high frequency waves are called "fast activity" and low frequency waves are called "slow activity."

State of the system. A whole constellation of factors affects the pattern of the EEG. At birth the predominant rhythms are one-half to two waves per second and 20 to 50 waves per second; by 14 to 19 years, the adult pattern is fully developed. The precise pattern that develops is typical of the individual and is stable, provided no disease or injury to the brain supervenes. Records from the frontal and parietal regions tend to show higher frequencies than records from the occipital region. However, during visual, attention-provoking stimulation, a faster rhythm of greatly reduced amplitude supersedes

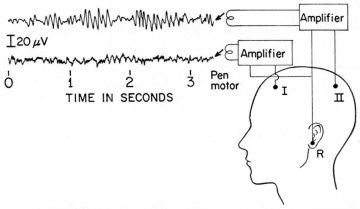

FIG. 290. Arrangement for recording EEG. The potential difference between frontal lead (*I*) and reference lead (*R*) shows low amplitude, fast activity of waking, relaxed human. Simultaneously, occipital lead (*II*) shows higher amplitude, slower activity.

the normally preponderant *alpha* rhythm; this phenomenon is called "alpha blocking" or "desynchronization." When the sensory stimulus ceases to hold the individual's attention, the slower rhythm reappears. The pattern of the EEG is also markedly altered when the blood or oxygen supply to the brain is altered. For example, slowing results when, in cerebral venous blood, O_2 saturation falls below 30 per cent, when blood sugar decreases to 35 mg. per ml., or when CO_2 level increases above 52 volumes per cent. On the other hand, fast activity predominates when CO_2 level decreases; forced overbreathing is used clinically to reveal certain latent abnormalities of the EEG.

A striking correspondence exists between the dominant frequency of the EEG and the apparent state of arousal of the individual (Fig. 291). In deep sleep, waves of three per second or less are seen; Bremer[2, 3] found a similar situation in the unanesthetized, isolated cerebrum (mesencephalic transection) and concluded that sleep results from a functional deafferentation of the cerebral cortex. In moderately deep sleep, so-called "sleep spindles," bursts of 10 to 12 per second activity, begin to appear. As sleep lightens,

* A *bipolar* recording shows the difference in potential between two active leads, and a *monopolar* recording shows the variation of potential at a single lead compared with a stable reference point. A good reference or indifferent lead is difficult to establish.

such bursts of activity appear at progressively shorter intervals, until the EEG is gradually transformed into that typical of the waking state. Similar spindle activity is seen in an animal anesthetized with a barbiturate, the period between bursts being inversely related to depth of anesthesia. As an individual goes from a drowsy to a relaxed to an excited state, the EEG progressively increases in frequency and decreases in amplitude. This state of affairs can be mimicked in an experimental animal by appropriate stimulation of the brain stem reticular formation.[41]

Focal damage to the cerebral cortex is localized electroencephalographically by the occurrence of irregular and abnormal activity (usually slow waves) in the neighborhood of the lesion or by the "reversal of phase" in records taken from opposite sides of the lesion with the reference lead over the lesion. Asymmetry of the records from corresponding positions over the two hemispheres is very suggestive of focal damage. Epileptogenic lesions produce briefer waves, or "focal spike activity."

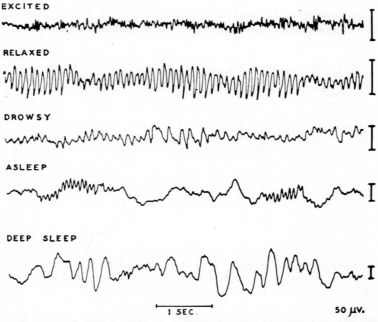

FIG. 291.   Electroencephalographic records during excitement, relaxation and varying degrees of sleep. In fourth strip runs of 14/sec. rhythm, superimposed on slow waves, are termed "sleep spindles." Note that excitement is characterized by a rapid frequency and small amplitude and that varying degrees of sleep are marked by increasing irregularity and by appearance of "slow waves." (From Jasper, in Penfield and Erickson, *Epilepsy and cerebral localization*, Springfield, Ill., Charles C Thomas, 1941.)

EPILEPSY.   The principal types of epilepsy cause distinctive electroencephalograms during the attack and brief, less pronounced, less characteristic abnormalities between attacks.[15] However, the latter are of major importance in diagnosis. Figure 292 shows the sequence of electrical events during an electroshock convulsion, which mimics the *grand mal* seizure of man. Fast activity is seen in the tonic period, and the clonic phase is marked by spike—slow-wave complexes, synchronous with the clonic jerks. The postseizure stupor is accompanied by high-voltage, slow, rolling waves which become very pronounced after repeated convulsion. *Petit mal* attacks consist of momentary lapses of responsiveness and consciousness without falling, often manifested to the observer only by a fixed stare. The EEG shows a doublet of a fast and a slow wave ("spike and dome") repeated at the rate of about three per second. *Psychomotor epilepsy*, perhaps better called *epileptic automatisms*, usually originates in a focus in the temporal lobe. The attack takes the form of a stereotyped behavior pattern, sometimes an emotional outburst, of which the patient has no subsequent memory.*

* In this, as in other instances of epilepsy arising outside the sensory and motor areas, there is a strong element of "paralysis" rather than stimulation of function.

PHYSIOLOGIC BASIS OF THE EEG.   Several lines of evidence show that the EEG depends for its existence upon the electrical properties of cortical cells. Certain characteristics of the essential processes can be surmised from the basic properties of individual cells. As shown in Chapter 2, the electrical space-constant of the cell body is so large that the cell body must behave as a unit, i.e., show no dipole properties. On the other hand, the minute dendritic projections of the soma, because of their high internal resistance, have space constants less than their own length. This means that they should be seen as moving dipoles by a distant electrode immersed in the same volume conductor. It is for

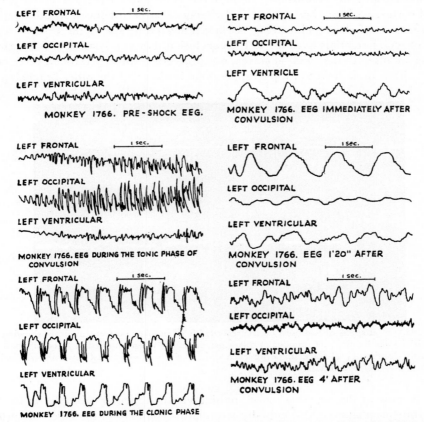

FIG. 292.   Electroencephalographic records of successive stages of an electroshock convulsion in a monkey. One lead was taken from the lateral ventricles. Note especially the "slow waves" 1' 20" after the convulsion. These were associated with stupor which became more prolonged after repeated convulsions. (After Lennox et al., Electroenceph. clin. Neurophysiol., 1951, 3:63–69.)

this reason that many believe the EEG to result from the summation of dendritic activity (and especially of any vertically oriented projection, which should be, on the average, closer to a surface electrode and show a greater solid angle).

In order for such waves as are seen in the EEG to exist, something other than a random distribution of cellular activity must prevail. Attempts have been made to explain both synchrony and regular recurrence of cellular activity either in terms of reverberating activity in closed neuronal circuits or as a consequence of "spontaneous" rhythmic excitability changes in various neurons. A consideration of the environment in which a cortical cell is immersed leads to a qualitative understanding of the latter kind of explanation. If the extensive dendritic ramifications of a cortical neuron partake of the activity of adjacent cells, whether ephaptically or by some more active process, then the entire cell membrane will be affected by the electrotonic spread of such changes. Consequently, in the absence of any disrupting input, the excitability of cells in a local cluster would tend to vary as a unit. Likewise, the local cluster would synaptically excite other neurons in near synchrony with itself. This becomes a statistical process in which, eventually, the entire system tends to fluctuate in excitability as a unit at some unique frequency; the process could be disrupted by an afferent input. At the termination of such afferent domination, the system would again slowly reestablish its resting or "idling" condition.

Evoked Cortical Potentials.   Besides the continuous electrical activity of the cerebral cortex, various discrete electrical changes can be produced by stimulation of sense organs or of some point along the ascending pathways to the cerebral cortex. Studies of such potentials have led to the conclusion that two systems of fibers connect the sense organs with the cerebral cortex, one proceeding directly through three or four neurons with a high degree of topographic organization and the other branching from

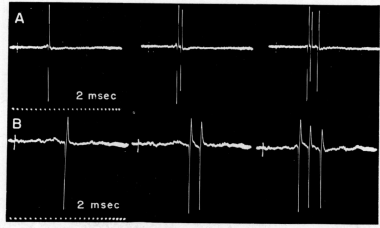

FIG. 293.   Unit spikes of two units (*A, B*) recorded from monkey postcentral gyrus, showing variation in initial spike latency and number of spikes per discharge when sampled at three different times. Note general consistency of spike shape for each unit. Positive downward. (Towe and Amassian, *J. Neurophysiol.*, 1958, *21*:292–311.)

the direct route at the medullary level, passing via the reticular substance of the brain stem and diencephalon, and eventually terminating diffusely in the cerebral cortex. A separate component of the latter pathway diffuses at the thalamic level. The properties of these two systems are largely known from the potentials they induce in the cortex and the manner in which they initiate or modify rhythmic potential phenomena. These properties will be described before discussing the pathways neuroanatomically.

SINGLE CORTICAL UNIT RESPONSE.   Two classes of potential change occur in the cortex following sense organ stimulation: (i) a very abrupt alteration lasting 1 to 2 milliseconds and (ii) a more slowly developing, much longer lasting voltage variation. The former change is associated with the electrical field in the immediate vicinity of an active cortical cell, and is usually called the "unit response" or "unit spike discharge." Not until recently did techniques for *prolonged* systematic observation of such unit activity in the cortex become available.[1] Microelectrodes (0.5 to 5 μ tip diameter) are used to avoid damaging the cell whose activity is being observed. The patterns of activity of cortical cells have been found to be highly complex, but one generalization is possible: *no parameter of unit response is invariant* (Fig. 293). However, statistical studies[2, 54] show that real systematic differences in discharge pattern do exist between units; differences in temporal patterns are believed by some to convey sensory information.

PRIMARY EVOKED RESPONSE.   When a macroelectrode is placed on the cortical surface, it is possible to record the second sort of potential change mentioned above. Stimulation of a sense organ, a sensory nerve or a thalamic relay nucleus results in a very large (over 0.5 mV.) diphasic potential (Fig. 294 A, B) restricted to the sensory receiving areas of the cortex. As pointed out previously, such responses are used to map the projection of the body surface, retina, or cochlea on the cortical sensory areas. This mapping is possible because the primary response results from synchronous activity in the classic, fast-conduction sensory pathways, which show a high degree of topographic organization.

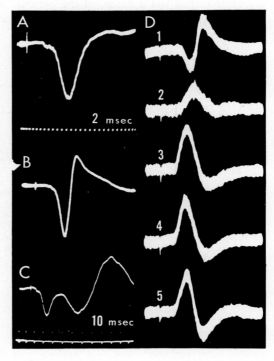

FIG. 294.   Primary evoked discharge recorded from cat. A, Primary response recorded from cortical surface of somatosensory area I. B, Primary from somatosensory area II. C, Primary response and secondary discharge from area I. D, Superimposed microelectrode traces from surface (1) in 480 μ steps to 1920 μ (5), showing reversal of primary discharge and change in initial response latency with depth

No single cortical structure can be designated as *the* source of the gross cortical potentials. The source of the primary response lies about 0.3 to 0.6 mm. below the pial surface, as is testified by the reversal of potential with depth shown in Figure 294 *D*. This is about the level of termination of thalamocortical afferents. The evoked primary response begins as activity ascends into the fine terminal ramifications of these afferent fibers and outlasts the period of their activity. Single cortical units discharge throughout the duration of the primary response; among these are cells whose axons project into the brain stem and spinal cord via the pyramidal tract.

Repetitive waves.   In the lightly anesthetized animal, a short train of eight to 12 per second positive waves sometimes follows the primary discharge. These waves, initiated by the primary response volley in the thalamus, have been described as a thalamic afterdischarge (Adrian) and as a result of a reverberating circuit between thalamus and cortex (Chang). They are confined to the same area of cortex as the primary discharge.

SECONDARY DISCHARGE.   In deep anesthesia, the primary evoked response is often followed by a second positive-negative wave (Fig. 294 *C*) that appears throughout both hemispheres after a fairly uniform latency (30 to 80 milliseconds). This phenomenon does not depend upon spread of activity from the primary focus but appears to be mediated via the diffuse projection system described above. The secondary discharge is very closely related to the following two phenomena.

SPONTANEOUS CORTICAL BURSTS.   Under moderate to deep anesthesia and in the absence of known sensory stimulation, a succession of waves with a frequency of eight to 12 per second waxes and wanes over wide areas of both hemispheres in near synchrony. These surface-negative waves are strikingly like "sleep spindles" and the *alpha* rhythm (Fig. 295). This phenomenon is not truly an evoked potential, although similar burst activity can be produced by stimulation of the thalamic reticular system.[9] The presence of spontaneous cortical bursts precludes the appearance of the generalized secondary discharge—apparently an "occlusive" process. Such burst activity can be regarded as a manifestation, not a cause, of the periodic waxing and waning of excitability in the "idling" system, because most evoked responses are potentiated during burst activity and depressed during the interburst periods.

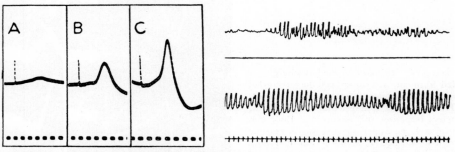

FIG. 295.   *Left,* Cortical recruiting response to three successive shocks to intralaminar thalamic region. Initial vertical line is shock artefact. Negativity is upward. *Right,* A "spontaneous" 1–12/sec. burst (*upper record*) and a waxing and waning response (*lower record*) to continuously repeated shocks to intralaminar thalamic region. Bottom line is stimulus signal. (From Morison and Dempsey, *Amer. J. Physiol.,* 1942, *135*:281–292.)

RECRUITING RESPONSE.   Repetitive shocks delivered to the intralaminar thalamic nuclei produce a series of diphasic (negative-positive) potentials in both hemispheres after a 15 to 60 millisecond delay. If five to 15 stimuli are delivered each second, the amplitude of the potentials builds up during the first few shocks (Fig. 295) and then proceeds to wax and wane at a frequency of eight to 12 per second.[40] Not only are the shape and frequency of this response similar to those of spontaneous cortical bursts, but its distribution in the cortex is identical to that of burst activity. Discovery of this phenomenon[40] and an observation by Bremer described later initiated the physiologic analysis of the electroencephalogram.

NEURAL BASIS OF RECRUITING RESPONSE AND SPONTANEOUS BURSTS.   Study of the cortical potentials resulting from stimulation of the thalamus has led to a new, functional classification of the thalamic nuclei. Because focal stimulation of the relay and association nuclei results in short-latency (1 to 5 milliseconds) localized activity in the cortex, these structures are considered "specific thalamic nuclei."* Stimulation of other thalamic nuclei results in widespread, bilateral cortical activation of the recruiting type. Such

---

* The name derives from the writings of Lorente de Nó, who described two types of thalamocortical afferents in Golgi preparations. The "specific" afferents come from relay nuclei and end with many synaptic terminals in layer IV, but have little lateral spread throughout the cortex. They thus form a point-to-point projection. The "nonspecific" thalamocortical afferents terminate less profusely but more widely, giving branches to more than one and perhaps many cytoarchitectural areas. Their origin in the thalamus is not known anatomically, and whether such afferents form the diffuse thalamo-cortical projection system is problematic.

nuclei are considered "nonspecific thalamic nuclei." They include the midline and intralaminar nuclei, the anteroventral nucleus and the lateral reticular nucleus. Although stimulation of these nuclei sometimes has an effect on cortical electrical activity different from that of stimulation of the brain stem reticular system, the nuclei are collectively considered to be a continuation of the midbrain reticular substance.

Because the nonspecific thalamic nuclei did not appear to be sufficiently endowed with projection fibers to the cortex, McLardy[38] proposed that their effect on cortical activity depends upon an intrathalamic diffusion system which activates specific thalamic relay and association nuclei. Starzl and Magoun[51] later concurred in this proposal. However, when Hanbery and Jasper[17] selectively destroyed the relay or association nuclei and then stimulated the centrum medianum or the n. ventralis anterior, recruiting potentials appeared in the cortex to which the relay nuclei project. In fact, a "way in" to the cortex for the diffuse (nonspecific) thalamic system has been found in the n. ventralis anterior. This nucleus, which is especially effective in producing recruiting responses, and which is essential for the appearance of such responses in the cortex following stimulation of the centrum medianum, projects heavily to the "motor" cortex.

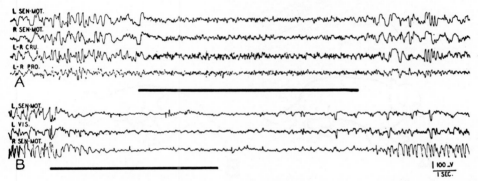

FIG. 296. Desynchronization of electrical activity of cortex by left bulboreticular stimulation during period marked by horizontal black line. *A* is from an "encéphale isolé" cat lightly anesthetized; *B* is from intact cat heavily anesthetized with chloralosane. Abbreviations at left give origin of activity: sensorimotor areas, gyrus cruciatus or proreus and visual area. (From Moruzzi and Magoun, *Electroenceph. clin. Neurophysiol.*, 1949, 1:455–473.)

Rose[47] and Chow[6] have shown that the n. reticularis of the thalamus also projects to the cortex in a systematic manner. The anteroposterior axis of the nucleus is represented mediolaterally on the cortex; the dorsoventral axis appears in a caudorostral arrangement. Hanbery and his coworkers[16] have proposed that the thalamic reticular nucleus is the final outflow to the cortex of the reticular system. Magoun[33] takes the position that both n. ventralis anterior and that portion of the reticular nucleus lying in front of it constitute the corticopetal thalamic reticular projection.

AROUSAL RESPONSE.[33] It is now evident that the EEGs of the waking and the sleeping animal are strikingly different and that afferent stimulation can transform the EEG into the "alerted" pattern. The latter phenomenon is variously termed the "arousal response," "desynchronization" or "activation." Moruzzi and Magoun[41] discovered that stimulation of the reticular substance of the brain resulted in a phenomenon resembling arousal (Fig. 296) and interpreted the effect as a desynchronization of cortical cellular activity. Bremer[2] had shown earlier that a waking pattern prevailed in the unanesthetized cat following a bulbospinal transection (*encéphale isolé*), but that the cortex falls into a kind of sleep after a mesencephalic transection that leaves the blood supply intact (*cerveau isolé*). The latter transection deprives the rostral part of the nervous system of the *trigeminal* and vestibular inputs that maintain the waking pattern in the *encéphale isolé* preparation.[46] Although it previously had been thought that the arrival of impulses over the classic sensory pathways was responsible for the alerting of the cerebral cortex by a sensory stimulus, the analysis by Magoun and his coworkers[32, 52] showed otherwise. As illustrated in Figure 297, impulses carried in a system of fibers branching from the classic sensory systems and traversing a multisynaptic route through the reticular substance of the brain are actually responsible. This explains why a sensory stimulus evokes a potential in the somatosensory areas within 10 milliseconds, whereas the changes in the alpha rhythm associated with sensory stimulation appear only after 40 to 60 milliseconds.

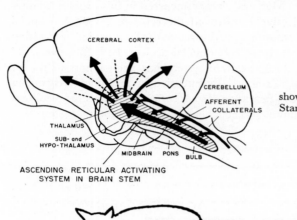

FIG. 297. Sagittal section of cat brain showing neural basis of arousal response. (From Starzl *et al.*, *J. Neurophysiol.*, 1951, *14:*479–496.)

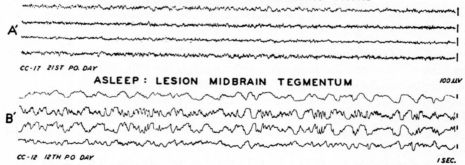

FIG. 298. Typical behavior and EEG records of cats with midbrain lesion sparing tegmentum (*A* and *A'*) and with lesion of tegmentum (*B* and *B'*). Cat *B* appeared continuously asleep or comatose during postoperative survival. (After Lindsley *et al.*, *Electroenceph. clin. Neurophysiol.*, 1950, *2:*483–498.)

Experimental sensory stimuli cause replacement of the highly synchronized, large-amplitude, long-lasting potentials of barbiturate-induced sleep by low-amplitude, fast activity, an event termed "desynchronization." It is clear that the arrival of nerve impulses at the cortex over the familiar sensory pathways does not "wake up" the cerebral cortex since a sensory stimulus will still cause the cortical arousal response when these pathways are interrupted by a lesion placed laterally in the midbrain. The relay nuclei of the thalamus have been by-passed, and impulses are still reaching the cortex. Medial lesions which interrupt the centrally placed reticular substance preclude the arousal response. Consistently, evoked potentials can be recorded in the reticular substance after sensory stimulation. Throughout the brain stem, collaterals given off by the somatosensory and auditory systems enter the central reticular substance. Impulses ascend slowly and enter the dorsal hypothalamus, the subthalamus and the reticular and ventromedial part of the thalamus. They then pass on into the internal capsule and finally reach the cerebral cortex. On the other hand, the relay and association nuclei are not activated by midbrain reticular stimulation. Thus, cortical arousal occurs after destruction of all but the basal part of the thalamus and the hypothalamus.

The similarity of cortical activation or desynchronization resulting from stimulation of the ascending reticular system and that accompanying "normal" waking can be seen by comparing Figures 291 and 296. The sleeplike state of the cortex in Bremer's *cerveau isolé* preparation was analyzed in the experiment shown in Figure 298. When the ascending afferent systems were interrupted in the midbrain, the animal was awake and the EEG corresponded. However, if the reticular activating system was interrupted by medially placed lesions, the animal was continuously somnolent and the EEG showed slow waves and spindles typical of sleep. Thus, despite the integrity of the long sensory and motor pathways, the animal was not "conscious" and did not move about.

Such observations explain the akinetic states which occur clinically and which can be produced experimentally by lesions in the region of the periaqueductal gray matter and posterior hypothalamus. If the EEG records shown in this chapter are studied, it will be seen that the EEG varies from the high-frequency response of the excited state, through the slower activity of the relaxed state, to the slow activity of sleep and the long rolling waves of stupor following multiple electroshock convulsions.[29] By extrapolation, it is conceivable that this ascending reticular system, by driving the cortex excessively, might produce overalertness of the cortex and thereby the quick responses, flight of ideas and flow of words that characterize mania. If so, the beginning of an ultimate understanding of the psychoses may have been achieved.

ASSOCIATION AREAS

The association areas of the brain—those areas once thought to be devoid of thalamic projection fibers—occupy the homotypical cortex of the frontal and temporal regions. Where these areas border on sensory or motor areas, the cortex is transitional in structure (Chap. 11). Three general association areas are recognized: (i) a frontal, (ii) an anterior temporal, and (iii) a parietotemporo-preoccipital area. These cortical regions are phylogenetically recent, showing especially marked development in the primates, and become myelinated later than the primary sensory and motor areas. The term "association areas" is in a sense misleading since it fails to convey the full scope of the activity of these regions. For example, the personality changes, hyperactivity, etc., which follow lesions of association areas certainly are not disturbances of associative function. These areas are projection areas in that they receive corticopetal fibers from various thalamic nuclei. The frontal sector receives fibers from the large lateral (neothalamic) portion of n. medialis dorsalis of the thalamus in a systematic manner.[55] The anterior cingulate gyrus receives fibers from the hypothalamus by way of the bundle of Vicq d'Azyr and the anterior thalamic nuclei; the relevant hypothalamic region receives fibers from the midline thalamic nuclei by way of the medial (magnocellular) portion of n. medialis dorsalis. The pulvinar, a large and recently developed thalamic nucleus, projects to the entire parietotemporo-preoccipital sector (except the insula and superior temporal gyrus) and the lateral surface of the temporal lobe. Nucleus lateralis posterior also projects to the parietal association cortex. In addition to these connections, the entire cerebral cortex, as mentioned earlier, appears to receive fibers from n. reticularis of the thalamus.[6, 47]

Prefrontal Lobule. The frontal association area, sometimes known as the prefrontal area or lobule, occupies the anterior pole of the frontal lobe. It extends fully upon the orbital surface of the frontal lobe and merges posteriorly with olfactory structures. Area 8 constitutes its posterior border on the dorsolateral surface of the hemispheres; this area is transitional, in that it displays both premotor and prefrontal functions. Because the "free" and orbital surfaces of the frontal lobe are projection areas of a single nucleus (n. medialis dorsalis, pars lateralis), Rose and Woolsey[48] believe that these regions should be treated as a unit. They named this region the "orbitofrontal" cortex. Its efferent connections include the hypothalamus (direct and via n. medialis dorsalis)[56] and the neocerebellum (frontopontine tract). It sends fibers not only to the dorsomedial nucleus of the thalamus, but also to the anterior and ventral portions of the lateral thalamic nuclei and to the reticular nucleus.

Reflexes, posture and discrete movement are not affected by ablation of the orbito-frontal cortex. However, definite disturbances of *behavior* are produced. Unlike the language functions, the behavior disturbances are marked only when the frontal areas are *bilaterally* damaged. As recently as 1922, Bianchi described the results of extirpating the orbitofrontal areas in animals in purely mentalistic terms from "naked eye" observations. Since that time, definite, objectively demonstrable disturbances of behavior have been discovered, and methods have been devised for quantifying these behaviors.

HYPERACTIVITY.[7, 25, 31, 49]   Ablation of the entire orbitofrontal lobule or its sub-areas in monkeys induces a state of hyperactivity manifested by incessant, stereotyped walking or pacing very much like that of certain zoo inhabitants (notably the carnivores).

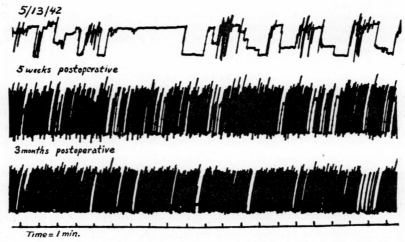

FIG. 299.   Activity records of monkeys before and after posterior orbital lesions. Freely movable bottom of oblong activity cage rests on pneumatic pad connected to tambour which records upon kymograph. Any movement toward or away from end resting on pad causes a pen excursion, height roughly reflecting extent of animal's movement. In top record, notice varied pattern of activity and frequency of small movements of a normal monkey indicated by small pen excursions. Second and third strips show hyperactivity induced by bilateral ablation of area 13. Observe absence of pauses longer than a few seconds and that hyperactivity was undiminished three months after operation. (From Ruch and Shenkin, *J. Neurophysiol.*, 1943, 6:349–360.)

The pacing appears aimless. It is continued for hours, almost without pause, but ceases in the darkness. In its extreme form, it is almost maniacal. This hyperactivity, like the hyperactivity of certain problem children, is stopped by amphetamine and certain other cerebral excitants. It has been observed in cats, rats and monkeys, but not as yet in chimpanzees or man. To some degree the whole orbitofrontal cortex is concerned with the regulation of activity,[25] but bilateral lesions of posterior portions of the orbital surface (area 13 of Brodmann) produce nearly maximal hyperactivity.[49] Livingston *et al.*[31] studied quantitatively the activity before and after lesions of area 13 and estimated that activity increased eight to 16 times following the lesion. The onset of hyperactivity is most rapid after lesions of area 13; some prefrontal ablations sparing this region do not result in marked hyperactivity.

Paradoxically, the period of hyperactivity is preceded by a period of hypoactivity: apparent apathy, drooping of the head, sluggishness of movement, blankness of expression, and a tendency to sit staring into space and to ignore human presence. This state lasts from several days to two or three weeks after operation. It gradually gives way to "bouts" of stereotyped pacing which punctuate the periods of inactivity; the bouts of activity become progressively longer. Once established, the pacing persists indefinitely (Fig. 299). When hyperactivity is marked, random activities—the varied patterns of manipulations and posturings, the quick play of grimacing, and head and eye movements—give way to stereotyped waking or to quiescence.

Recent evidence suggests that the hyperactivity may result from an interruption of fibers passing to the hypothalamus, since, in rats, lesions in septal-preoptic regions[35] produce incessant running behavior reminiscent of that following stimulation of certain hypothalamic areas by implanted electrodes.[34] Lesions in the head of the caudate nucleus of the monkey also produce a hyperactivity that is diminished by darkness; interestingly, these lesions need not be bilateral to produce their effect.[8] Smith and DeVito,[50] using the Nauta technique, have observed fine terminal degeneration in the head of the caudate nucleus in the monkey following prefrontal lobule ablation. This finding brings the caudate into intimate relation with the frontal association area. Degeneration in the preoptic area is also found.

DELAYED RESPONSE.[7, 22, 25, 36]   Responses to the temporally and spatially immediate environment constitute a large portion of an animal's behavior. However, many responses, although called forth by the immediate situation, owe their direction to sensory information gained previously. Experimentally, this capacity is assessed by the delayed response test, which may take a variety of forms. In one test, a monkey or chimpanzee is allowed to view through bars a piece of food being deposited beneath one of two or more cups on a sliding tray. An opaque door is then lowered in front of the animal for a chosen interval. The tray is then pushed forward and the door raised, permitting the animal to reach the cups. The animal is allowed to select one cup; the reward is obtained if the proper cup is selected. A normal monkey makes successful choices after delays as long as 90 seconds between seeing the food and choosing among the cups. After bilateral orbitofrontal ablation, even delays as short as 5 seconds make successful response a matter of chance; the animal is at a complete loss in selecting the cup containing food. Neither unilateral frontal lobule ablation nor extirpation of other brain areas has this effect. No other part of the cerebral cortex can substitute for the orbitofrontal areas in this capacity, since the problem cannot be relearned. Nor is complete failure in the delayed response test due to a general impairment of intelligence or ability to learn. After frontal lobectomy, monkeys can learn or retain a visual discrimination quite as well as normal monkeys. Furthermore, successful performance of the "stick and platform" problem, which assesses the animal's ability to solve complex problems, indicates that a defect of general intelligence is not involved.

A chimpanzee in a barred cage is confronted with a platform on which a piece of food and a stick or rake have been placed. The food is out of arm's reach but can be reached if the rake is used. After this task is mastered, a series of sticks is introduced, a short stick being used to secure a longer stick, etc., until one long enough to reach the food is obtained. An orbitofrontal lobectomized chimpanzee is able to grasp these relations and organize a serial response involving four sticks, but only if the whole problem is within its view at one moment. If two platforms are used, the lobectomized animal fails totally when a stick from one platform must be carried to the other in order to secure the next longer stick, and it experiences great difficulty when only one stick is involved but the food is on the other platform. Correct solution of two-platform problems, like that of the delayed response test, demands that behavior be determined by memory of what occurred previously—a memory for recent sensory experience. Much the same kind of ability is required in the performance of *delayed alternation*, in which the animal is taught to make alternate right and left turns and to remember which turn comes next despite an enforced delay after each turn is completed. Rats show definite deficiencies in this problem after bilateral injury to the frontal poles. Monkeys with similar lesions are deficient in double alternation problems in which the correct choices are RRLLRRLL.[28]

The basic defect may lie in (i) failure to attend, (ii) passive decay of the "mental set," or (iii) active interference with the set, i.e., distractability. Indeed, reduction of external stimuli through the elimination of light during the delay period, administration of sedative drugs, exposure of the correct object of two which are presented later, or "heightening attention to the stimulus," result in improved performance by lobectomized monkeys. Clearly, the loss of this capacity to respond correctly after a delay is not absolute.

EXPERIMENTAL NEUROSIS AND FRONTAL LOBOTOMY[30, 37, 43]   Certain experimental situations produce behavior in animals which strongly resembles neurotic behavior in man, although the identity of the two states is not yet proved. The classic experiment was conducted in Pavlov's laboratory in 1914 and involved the discrimination of a circle from an ellipse. A dog was "conditioned" to salivate when confronted with a circle, but not when an ellipse appeared. The ellipse was then made progressively more circular until the difference was no longer discriminable. Continued training failed to bring improvement of discrimination and, in fact, the habit deteriorated. The animal displayed neurotic behavior which Pavlov[43] described as follows:

"At the same time the whole behaviour of the animal underwent an abrupt change. The hitherto quiet dog began to squeal in its stand, kept wriggling about, tore off with its teeth the apparatus for mechanical stimulation of the skin, and bit through the tubes connecting the animal's room with the observer, a behaviour which never happened before. On being taken into the experimental room the dog now barked violently, which was also contrary to its usual custom; in short, it presented all the symptoms of a condition of acute neurosis."

Experimental neurosis is not merely a momentary emotional response. In sheep, the neurosis continues to affect the behavior of the animal outside the experimental situation.[30] Twenty-four hour records of spontaneous activity or respiratory rhythm and of the heartbeat yield objective evidence of an excited state that persists outside of the experimental room.

Monkeys and chimpanzees working on discrimination problems near threshold or other difficult problems tend to exhibit neurotic behavior like that of Pavlov's dogs. In a highly emotional chimpanzee which was unable to perform delayed reactions successfully in preoperative tests, Jacobsen[22] observed the following behavior:

"This animal was extremely eager to work and apparently well motivated; but the subject was highly emotional and profoundly upset whenever she made an error. Violent temper tantrums after a mistake were not infrequent occurrences. She observed closely loading of the cup with food, and often whimpered softly as the cup was placed over the food. If the experimenter lowered or started to lower the *opaque door* to exclude the animal's view of the cups, she immediately flew into a temper tantrum, rolled on the floor, defecated and urinated. After a few such reactions during the training period, the animal would make no further responses to this test, although she responded eagerly if examined on different problems. Training on this situation was continued daily for three weeks. At the beginning, the animal had been eager to come to the experimental room, and when released from the living quarters ran to the transfer cage, opened the door and entered. But by the end of this period it was necessary to drag the animal from the living cage to the transfer cage, and in turn force her into the experimental cage. It was as complete an 'experimental neurosis' as those obtained by Pavlov's conditioned reflex procedures."

After bilateral frontal lobectomy the animal's behavior changed profoundly. She now entered the experimental room and worked with alacrity. Mistakes and failures to obtain food caused no emotional manifestation although many more errors were made than before operation. "It was," in Jacobsen's words, "as if the animal had . . . placed its burdens on the Lord."

These observations by Jacobsen provided a rationale for "psychosurgical" operations upon the frontal areas. In 1935, Egas Moniz, a Portuguese neurologist, introduced an operation—frontal lobotomy—designed to interrupt most of the connections between the orbitofrontal area and the deeper portions of the brain without completely isolating it from the remainder of the cerebral cortex. Certain neurotic symptoms of man, like those experimentally engendered in the chimpanzee, are altered by lobotomy. The effects of this procedure are most favorable in disorders characterized by emotional tension, e.g., anxiety neuroses, involutional depression and manic-depressive psychosis. This does not mean that the patient becomes incapable of displaying emotion; he may even be emotionally overreactive. But the force of the emotion or its connection with imagination and thought processes is reduced. Anxieties, thoughts or delusions which have distressed and incapacitated the patient may persist, but are now remote and of no concern. Unfortunately, other matters, such as household duties, sexual proprieties or regard for the feelings of others, may also become of no concern to the patient.

Frontal Lobe Function in Man.[11, 12, 19, 20]   Damage of the orbitofrontal area produces a bewildering diversity of symptoms difficult to describe. These vary from patient to patient even though the lesions are closely similar. The manner of damage may be natural—trauma or tumor—or intentional—lobotomy, lobectomy, topectomy or gyrectomy.* Whether the damage is bilateral is certainly important. Surgical cases provide the best evidence on the physiology of the orbitofrontal lobule in man. However, evaluations of such evidence must take account of the possibility that the scar rather than the loss of cerebral tissue is the source of abnormal frontal lobe activity[20] and the cause of behavioral abnormalities. Three factors contribute to the diversity of symptoms: (i) the symptoms have not been reduced to objective description, (ii) different investigators emphasize different symptoms, and (iii) the patients are usually psychiatrically abnormal at the outset. The following are some of the more frequently encountered disturbances.

INTELLIGENCE AND INTELLECTUAL FUNCTIONS.   Loss of intelligence as tested by familiar mental tests is not conspicuous after orbitofrontal lobectomy, although some decrease in general intelligence may be observed. An I.Q. approaching normal has been found in a bilaterally lobectomized patient.[20] In one study[11] lobotomy improved rather than hindered performance on intelligence tests, probably by relieving the patients of anxiety. The frontal lobes are clearly not the "seat of intelligence," and intellectual disturbances are manifested only in subtle ways. Although various studies have shown slight defects of intellect tested formally, these all may well be due to changes in the patients' attitudes and motivations. A lobectomized patient who becomes unconcerned with things about which he was previously anxious or obsessed may also be unconcerned about his test performance.

PERSONALITY CHANGES.   Since 1848, the date of the famous "crow-bar" case of Phineas P. Gage, the relation of the frontal areas to emotional life and personality has been recognized. The nature of such changes is not the same in all cases of frontal lobe damage, but some form of personality alteration is usually reported.

Phineas P. Gage, an "efficient and capable" foreman, was injured on September 13, 1848, when a tamping iron was blown through the frontal region of his brain. He suffered the following change in personality, according to the physician, J. M. Harlow, who attended him. "He is fitful, irreverent, indulging at times in the grossest profanity (which was not previously his custom), manifesting but little deference to his fellows, impatient of restraint or advice when it conflicts with his desires, at times pertinaciously obstinate yet capricious and vacillating, devising many plans for future operation which are no sooner arranged than they are abandoned in turn for others appearing more feasible. . . . His mind was radically changed, so that his friends and acquaintances said he was no longer Gage."†

The absence of consistency of purpose and behavior reported in this classic description is noted in many cases of damage to the orbitofrontal areas. The patients are highly distractible, turning from one activity to another according to the novelty of a fresh stimulation rather than to any plan. A lack of foresight, an inability to plan activity, and a failure to anticipate future events on the basis of past experience—all intellectual functions—contribute to a lack of continuity in behavior. The patient may not feel the ambitions, responsibilities or proprieties of his life circumstances and may be so altered

---

* In lobotomy (or leukotomy) the fibers of the white matter are incised; in the other three operations, a lobule, gyrus or cytoarchitectural area, respectively, is removed.
† Harlow, *Boston med. surg. J.*, 1848, *39*:389.

that he seems a different and sometimes unacceptable person to his relatives and fri ends. Another character change is *Witzelsucht*, a tendency toward frivolous and sometimes stupid and tedious joking, often at the expense of others. Such patients often react with a light remark to situations of considerable gravity, and their ebullient spirits may conceal an emotional dulling. In some cases, unresponsiveness, inertia, apathy and masking of the facies are characteristic, especially in the early postoperative period, and may alternate with restlessness. This calls to mind the sequence of events observed in the monkey after frontal lobectomy and after lesions of area 13—apathy followed by an excess of activity—which in both instances is likely to be perseverant and sterotyped.

It is equally certain that the personality changes following extensive bilateral lobectomies may be slight and transitory, as in the case thoroughly studied by Hebb and Penfield.[20] More recently,[39] more than 50 investigators from several disciplines applied a highly diversified battery of objective tests for intelligence, personality, etc., to a series of topectomy patients. Although striking initial defects and some persisting ones were observed, no stable, characteristic pattern could be objectively demonstrated. The results varied from individual to individual with similar lesions. It is as though the orbitofrontal lobes embody the emotional development and experience of each individual and their loss effects a change according to the original personality structure.

Evaluation of lobectomy is exceedingly complex and not wholly to be accomplished by statistics, since the operation may deprive the patient of further psychiatric treatment, may alter the patient-family relationship, and will produce an admixture of desirable and undesirable effects. On the other hand, many patients have been relieved of intense suffering, saved from suicide, and restored to something approaching a normal existence. Lobectomy, even unilateral, appears to be of value in rendering seriously ill patients relatively indifferent to pain. It does this even though the operation does not reduce the actual perception of pain. The alternatives of protracted suffering or opiate addiction must be considered. In respect to lobotomy for neurosis and psychosis, it is to be hoped that further knowledge of frontal lobe function and localization of function within the lobes will permit operations with enhanced therapeutic results and minimal undesirable consequences.

Temporal Lobes.[26, 27]   Apart from the small area on the superior surface devoted to audition (Heschl's gyrus), the temporal lobe consists of a wide expanse of cerebral cortex to which until recently no function could be reliably assigned. Bilateral temporal lobectomy in the monkey (sparing the primary auditory areas)[26, 27] caused widespread disturbances of behavior not related to the auditory sphere.

Some of the observed phenomena were: (i) *Psychic blindness*, manifested by inability to recognize objects visually. To find a familiar edible object in a series of inedible ones, the monkey had to bring all objects to its mouth and test them instead of picking out the bit of food immediately by visual examination. A snake, which monkeys ordinarily fear, was manipulated freely and apparently not recognized. Object vision at the higher levels is therefore disturbed by lesions in three different areas of the cerebral cortex besides the striate area: area 19, area 8 and the temporal lobe. (ii) *Oral exploration*, examination of objects by sniffing, touching them with the lips, or biting them. This action appeared to be compulsive rather than a mere substitute for vision. (iii) *Compulsive manipulatory reaction*, analogous to hypermetamorphosis, took the form of excessive attraction to objects which were examined closely. (iv) *Emotional changes* in the direction of docility and emotional unresponsiveness were pronounced. (v) *Sexual activity* was augmented and took bizarre forms. This finding has been successfully localized. Further analysis suggests that many of these changes are due to destruction of the rhinencephalic or transitional portions of the temporal lobe lying in its mesial surface. The connection between these structures and emotional reactions is abundantly documented in Chapter 22.

The temporal lobe more nearly than the frontal lobe is an association area. It receives far fewer thalamocortical projection fibers than other association areas, and has abundant reciprocal connections with other association areas and with the pericentral cortex. Whereas lesions of the parietal and occipital association areas do not appreciably influence the retention of quite elaborate visual discrimination habits' involvement including the temporal lobe or lesions of the temporal lobe alone may abolish such habits and prevent their being learned or relearned.[7] The suggestion has been made that the parietotemporo-preoccipital area may be subdivided into areas subserving different functions,[45] but the evidence is not entirely conclusive. The temporal lobe, especially the ventromedial surface, is essential for the acquisition and integrity of certain visually directed behaviors and unnecessary for somesthetic discriminations. On the other hand, the parieto-preoccipital association areas appear to be related to somesthetic discriminations.[45] Penfield[44] finds that complex, well formed visual images corresponding to real events in the past life of the individual are aroused by electrical stimulation at the surface of the temporal lobe in certain epileptic patients. Experience with clinical patients, like the animal experiments, also teaches that portions of the morphologic temporal lobe are concerned with basic intellectual and emotional activities.

Discharging foci in the temporal lobes may also produce alterations in the clarity of conscious experience. Penfield states:

"The things the patient is looking at, the sounds that he hears, the position of himself in regard to his environment may seem to him to be strongly altered. . . . He feels that he has experienced it all before ('déjà vu' phenomenon), or that it is absurd, or things are far away or suddenly near, or he himself seems to be far away in space and to be observing himself. He is not unconscious, of course, and he maintains an awareness of the reality of things as well as of this distortion of his own perceptions."

AGNOSIA, APRAXIA, APHASIA

The loss of the memory of learned reactions, sometimes referred to as intellectual functions, which results from cortical damage takes three principal forms—agnosia, apraxia and aphasia.

Agnosia. By this is meant loss of the ability to recognize common objects, i.e., to perceive the significance of sensory stimuli. Four forms of agnosia are distinguished: (i) *astereognosis* or tactile agnosia, the failure to recognize common objects by palpating them (see Chap. 14); (ii) *auditory agnosia* or *psychic deafness*, which verges into aphasia; (iii) *visual agnosia*, the inability to appreciate the meaning of objects seen, of colors, or of visual space in the absence of a primary visual defect; and (iv) *autotopagnosia* (e.g., *finger agnosia*), failure to recognize the parts of the body, to differentiate right and left or, in general, to recognize the relationship of objects to the body.

Apraxia. In 1886, Hughlings Jackson described a selective disturbance of the higher levels of voluntary motor function now known as apraxia. His patient could not stick out his tongue when asked to do so, but used it well in semiautomatic acts such as chewing and swallowing. There was no paresis or paralysis typical of pyramidal tract damage.

Aphasia.[19, 57] The word "aphasia" means literally a loss of the power of speech, but the term as now used includes any marked interference with the ability either to use or to comprehend symbolic expressions of ideas by spoken or written words or by gestures, and any interference with the use of language in thinking. Formerly a sharp distinction was made between sensory and motor aphasia. By "motor aphasia" was meant the inability to speak in the absence of paralysis of the muscles of articulation; "sensory aphasia" was an inability to understand written, printed or spoken symbols of language in patients without defective vision or hearing. The aphasias are still so described, but later work indicates that the clean-cut separation formerly claimed rarely if ever exists in clinical cases; intermediate forms are far more numerous.

MOTOR OR EXPRESSIVE APHASIA. The first definite identification of the portion of the brain involved in motor aphasia seems to have been made in 1825 by Bouillaud, who, as the result of numerous autopsies, attributed the defect to lesions of the frontal lobe.

Broca made a more restricted localization—the posterior part of the third or inferior frontal convolution. This region surrounds the anterior or ascending limb of the lateral fissure (region *S* in Fig. 300) and is known as Broca's area. Many authors insist that this localization is too limited and that defects in the power of speech also result from lesions of contiguous areas. Broca's region is not the direct cortical representation of the muscles of speech, but lies just anterior to it. The "motor speech area" has a characteristic cytoarchitecture, even in monkeys (area 44), and is possibly a development of the portion of area 6 from which vocalization can be produced in monkeys by stimulation (von Bonin). As a result, aphasia can exist without paralysis of these muscles; also, the motor act of speech may be disturbed with relatively little influence on the symbolic aspect of speech.

Broca's area and adjacent regions apparently are necessary in forming the organized complex of appropriate sounds and words with which we express concepts. Lesions affecting this area destroy more or less the ability to use spoken words appropriately, and clinical experience shows that motor aphasia may be exhibited in all degrees of completeness and in many curious varieties. The individual may retain a limited number

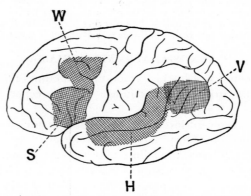

FIG. 300.   Lateral aspect of human hemisphere indicating one view of localization of language areas; cortical area *V*, damage to which produces mainly word blindness; cortical area *H*, damage to which produces mainly word deafness; cortical area *S*, damage to which causes loss of articulate speech; cortical area *W*, damage to which particularly affects ability to write. (After Donaldson.)

of words with which he expresses his whole range of ideas, as, for instance, in the case described by Broca in which the word "three" was made to serve for all numerical concepts. Or, the last words spoken before a cerebral accident may survive. Thus, an intelligent woman stricken while ordering luncheon had available for expressing her whole range of ideas but one word—"horseradish." Automatic word series—e.g., the days of the week or counting—tend to survive, as does reactive speech demanded by a particular situation—for example, "hello" and "good-bye." When no words can be commanded for the expression of ideas (propositional speech), speech expressive of emotion—ejaculations or swearing—may persist. Usually associated with disturbance of speech is a loss of ability to write (agraphia), whether spontaneously, to dictation or from copy. Since writing involves a different set of muscles, it was natural to assume that a different cortical area is responsible for this form of expression, as in Figure 300. Although pure agraphia is a questionable entity, in some aphasics the expression of thoughts by writing is more definitely affected than is speech. When the difficulty is in finding the word and writing it correctly, agraphia is considered comparable to aphasia; when the errors are in forming the letters, the disturbance is related to apraxia.

SENSORY OR RECEPTIVE APHASIA.   In this form of aphasia, the individual suffers from an inability to *understand* spoken or written language. Inability to understand spoken language, or word deafness, has been attributed to lesions involving the superior and middle temporal convolutions contiguous to the cortical center for hearing (*H*, Fig. 300); whereas loss of power to understand written or printed language, word blindness (alexia), is traced to lesions involving the inferior portion of the posterior parietal lobule, the gyrus angularis, contiguous to the occipital visual area (*V*, Fig. 300). This separation is probably too schematic. Weisenberg and McBride[57] found that some patients have greatest difficulty in comprehending spoken words; others, the greatest difficulty with written language; but many patients have equal trouble in both spheres. It is possible that cases of reputed word blindness or word deafness are in reality special manifestations of visual and auditory agnosia. Furthermore, Weisenberg and McBride found little evidence of pure sensory aphasia. Because of the associated expressive difficulties, they refer to this group as "predominantly receptive aphasics."

APHASIA AS AN INTELLECTUAL DEFECT. Aphasics once labeled "expressive" or "receptive" are found, on close examination, to have disturbances of language as a symbolic function and disturbances of intellectual functions in general. One disturbance of the language mechanism at a high level is *amnesic aphasia*, which may exist in a relatively pure form. In this form of aphasia, the articulation of words is normal and the understanding of language is not gravely affected. Nevertheless the patient finds the naming of objects difficult and often searches for words while speaking. According to Goldstein,[15a] there are disturbances of an intellectual character—e.g., the inability to categorize, to sort miscellaneous collections of objects according to classes. These defects are supposed to result not from lesions affecting the speech areas, but from widespread although not severe cortical damage.

REFERENCES

1. AMASSIAN, V. E. *Electroenceph. clin. Neurophysiol.*, 1953, *5*:415–438.
2. BREMER, F. *C. R. Soc. Biol. (Paris)*, 1935, *118*:1235–1242.
3. BREMER, F. *Boll. Soc. It. Biol. Sp.*, 1938, *13*: 271–290.
4. BREMER, F. *Some problems in neurophysiology.* London, Athlone Press, 1953.
5. BURNS, B. D. *J. Physiol.*, 1950, *111*:50–68.
6. CHOW, K. L. *J. comp. Neurol.*, 1952, *97*:37–59.
7. CHOW, K. L. and HUTT, P. J. *Brain*, 1953, *76*:625–677.
8. DAVIS, G. D. *Neurology*, 1958, *8*:135–139.
9. DEMPSEY, E. W. and MORISON, R. S. *Amer. J. Physiol.*, 1942, *135*:293–300.
10. FORBES, A. and MORISON, B. R. *J. Neurophysiol.*, 1939, *2*:112–128.
11. FREEMAN, W. and WATTS, J. W. *Psychosurgery, in the treatment of mental disorders and intractable pain*, 2d ed. Springfield, Ill., Charles C Thomas, 1950.
12. FULTON, J. F. *Functional localization in the frontal lobes and cerebellum.* Oxford, Clarendon Press, 1949.
13. GIBBS, F. A. Pp. 361–370 in: GLASSER, O., ed., *Medical physics.* Chicago, Year Book Publishers, Inc., 1944.
14. GIBBS, F. A. and GIBBS, E. L. *Atlas of electroencephalography*, 2d ed. Cambridge, Mass., privately printed, 1950 and 1952, 2 vols.
15. GIBBS, F. A., GIBBS, E. L. and LENNOX, W. G. *Arch. Neurol. Psychiat. (Chicago)*, 1938, *39*: 298–314.
15a. GOLDSTEIN, K. *Language and language disturb-ances.* New York, Grune and Stratton, 1948, xii, 374 pp.
16. HANBERY, J., AJMONE-MARSAN, C. and DILWORTH, M. *Electroenceph. clin. Neurophysiol.*, 1954, *6*:103–118.
17. HANBERY, J. and JASPER, H. *J. Neurophysiol.*, 1953, *16*:252–271.
18. HARLOW, H. F. *Annu. Rev. Physiol.*, 1953, *15*: 493–514.
19. HEAD, H. *Aphasia and kindred disorders of speech.* New York, Macmillan Company, 1926, 2 vols.
20. HEBB, D. O. and PENFIELD, W. *Arch. Neurol. Psychiat. (Chicago)*, 1940, *44*:421–438.
21. HILL, D. and PARR, G., eds. *Electroencephalography, a symposium on its various aspects.* London, Macdonald, 1950.
22. JACOBSEN, C. F. *Comp. Psychol. Monogr.*, 1936, *13*, no. 63:3–60.
23. JACOBSEN, C. F., WOLFE, J. B. and JACKSON, T. A. *J. nerv. ment. Dis.*, 1935, *82*:1–14.
24. JASPER, H. H. Chap. 14 in: PENFIELD, W. and ERICKSON, T. C. *Epilepsy and cerebral localization*, Springfield, Ill., Charles C Thomas, 1941.
25. KENNARD, M. A., SPENCER, S. and FOUNTAIN, G., JR. *J. Neurophysiol.*, 1941, *4*:512–524.
26. KLÜVER, H. and BUCY, P. C. *J. Psychol.*, 1938, *5*:33–54.
27. KLÜVER, H. and BUCY, P. C. *Arch. Neurol. Psychiat. (Chicago)*, 1939, *42*:979–1000.
28. LEARY, R. W., HARLOW, H. F., SETTLAGE, P. H. and GREENWOOD, D. D. *J. comp. physiol. Psychol.*, 1952, *45*:576–584.

29. LENNOX, M. A., RUCH, T. C. and GUTERMAN, B. *Electroenceph. clin. Neurophysiol.*, 1951, *3:* 63–69.

30. LIDDELL, H. S. Chap. 26 in: FULTON, J. F. *Physiology of the nervous system*, 3d ed. New York, Oxford University Press, 1949.

31. LIVINGSTON, R. B., FULTON, J. F., DELGADO, J. M. R., SACHS, E., Jr., BRENDLER, S. J. and DAVIS, G. *Res. Publ. Ass. nerv. ment. Dis.*, 1948, *27:*405–420.

32. MAGOUN, H. W. *Res. Publ. Ass. nerv. ment. Dis.*, 1952, *30:*480–492.

33. MAGOUN, H. W. *The waking brain.* Springfield, Ill., Charles C Thomas, 1958.

34. MAIRE, F. W. (Unpublished observations.)

35. MAIRE, F. W. and PATTON, H. D. *Amer. J. Physiol.*, 1954, *178:*315–320.

36. MALMO, R. B. *J. Neurophysiol.*, 1942, *5:*295–308.

37. MASSERMAN, J. H. *Behavior and neurosis; an experimental psychoanalytic approach to psychobiologic principles.* Chicago, University of Chicago Press, 1943.

38. McLARDY, T. *Electroenceph. clin. Neurophysiol.*, 1951, *3:*183–188.

39. METTLER, F. A., ed. *Selective partial ablation of the frontal cortex; a correlative study of its effects on human psychotic subjects.* New York, Paul B. Hoeber, Inc., 1949.

40. MORISON, R. S. and DEMPSEY, E. W. *Amer. J. Physiol.*, 1942, *135:*281–292.

41. MORUZZI, G. and MAGOUN, H. W. *Electroenceph. clin. Neurophysiol.*, 1949, *1:*455–473.

42. PATTON, H. D. and AMASSIAN, V. E. *J. Neurophysiol.*, 1954, *17:*345–363.

43. PAVLOV, I. P. *Conditioned reflexes: an investigation of the physiological activity of the cerebral cortex.* London, Oxford University Press, 1927.

44. PENFIELD, W. and KRISTIANSEN, K. *Epileptic seizure patterns.* Springfield, Ill., Charles C Thomas, 1951.

45. PRIBRAM, H. B. and BARRY, J. *J. Neurophysiol.*, 1956, *19:*99–106.

46. ROGER, A., ROSSI, G. F. and ZIRONDOI, A. *Electroenceph. clin. Neurophysiol.*, 1956, *8:*1–13.

47. ROSE, J. E. *Res. Publ. Ass. nerv. ment. Dis.*, 1952, *30:*454–479.

48. ROSE, J. E. and WOOLSEY, C. N. *Res. Publ. Ass. nerv. ment. Dis.*, 1948, *27:*210–232.

49. RUCH, T. C. and SHENKIN, H. A. *J. Neurophysiol.*, 1943, *6:*349–360.

50. SMITH, O. A. and DEVITO, J. L. (Unpublished observations.)

51. STARZL, T. E. and MAGOUN, H. W. *J. Neurophysiol.*, 1951, *14:*133–146.

52. STARZL, T. E., TAYLOR, C. W. and MAGOUN, H. W. *J. Neurophysiol.*, 1951, *14:*461–477.

53. STARZL, T. E. and WHITLOCK, D. G. *J. Neurophysiol.*, 1952, *15:*449–468.

54. TOWE, A. L. and AMASSIAN, V. E. *J. Neurophysiol.*, 1958, *21:*292–311.

55. WALKER, A. E. *The primate thalamus.* Chicago, Ill., Univ. of Chicago Press, 1938.

56. WALKER, A. E. *J. comp. Neurol.*, 1940, *73:* 59–86.

57. WEISENBERG, T. and McBRIDE, K. E. *Aphasia, a clinical and psychological study.* New York, Commonwealth Fund, 1935.

CHAPTER 22

Neurophysiology of Emotion and Motivation

By THEODORE C. RUCH

MOTIVATION or drive is a neural process which impels the organism to some action or goal, the attainment of which results in drive reduction. For example, thirst is a drive; drinking reduces it. The resulting actions may be positive, like those from hunger and sex drives; or they may be negative or avoidance reactions, such as those resulting from painful or cold stimulation. More hedonistic theories have also been proposed; pleasurable consummative experience is considered the essence of motivation. Emotion is more difficult to define, but an interesting definition has been provided by a neuropathologist, Vonderahe:

"Emotion is a way of feeling and a way of acting. It may be defined as a tendency of an organism toward or away from an object, accompanied by notable bodily alteration. There is an element of motivation—an impulsion to action and an element of alertness, a hyperawareness or vividness of mental processes. There is of course the opposite, a depression of movement."[54]

We can see from this thoughtful definition that emotion has four aspects. (i) *Cognition:* a situation must be perceived, related to past experiences, and evaluated. This evaluation mainly reflects past experience and the cultural influences of the family, society, etc. Such factors determine the "appropriateness of emotion" (in kind and degree). As already seen, the prefrontal lobes are concerned with the evaluative aspect of emotion.

(ii) *Expression:* Emotion is expressed outwardly in the form of somatic and autonomic activities—facial expression, lacrimation, vocalization, hair standing erect, flushing or paling, laughter, fighting or flight. Emotions are also expressed internally in the form of visceral changes executed by the sympathetic and parasympathetic nervous systems (Chap. 9). Another kind of emotional expression is muscle tension which, as we have seen, causes discomfort and pain. Even if the obvious expression of emotion is suppressed as "inappropriate" (if frustration is introduced), the internal expressions may well occur.

(iii) *Experience* is sometimes called the "inward aspect of emotion." On an introspective basis, psychologists once divided emotion into two categories, those accompanied by pleasant *affect* and those which are unpleasant. These feelings are conscious experiences difficult to study quantitatively and objectively. However, as seen earlier in the discussion of sensation, there is evidence that the expressive and experiential aspects of emotion are dissociable by various lesions; this dissociation can be demonstrated in both animals and patients.

(iv) *Excitement:* It is a matter of common experience that when we experience certain emotions we look and feel excited and our friends say, "Now, don't get excited." As the above definition suggests, our mental processes may be excessively vivid. Conversely, sluggish and dull mental processes are commonly experienced during some emotions. The subjective side of the excitement factor, like its affect, would seem impossible to study. However, as seen in the discussion of the ascending reticular systems, there seem to be reliable objective signs of alertness and excitement (electroencephalographic patterns) which can be used in animal experiments.

Emotion and motivation will be discussed in terms of the above categories, the first section dealing with what can be studied objectively and the second with what can be inferred about internal or subjective events from objective study. The excitement parameter is discussed last. Although the hypothalamus and rhinencephalon are discussed separately here, they do not function separately.

OUTWARD EXPRESSION OF EMOTION

In considering the neural basis of emotion we must keep in mind all of the factors just discussed. The expression and the experience of emotion are the main concern of this chapter, and their interrelations are far from obvious. While we would say that we run away because we are afraid, whether this or the reverse is the actual sequence has been debated since 1890, when William James and Lange independently suggested that emotional states (e.g., fear) result from rather than cause overt manifestations of emotion. Emotional experience and expression are not inseparably linked. Certain neurologic patients (pseudobulbar palsy) exhibit involuntary bouts of laughing and crying without experiencing emotion; conversely, patients with other lesions (parkinsonism) may experience emotion while remaining completely impassive and expressionless.[18]

Hypothalamus and Emotion.   The visceral, vascular and glandular changes resulting from activity of the autonomic nervous system are elicited by stimulation at many levels of the central nervous system. These changes have already been discussed in their relation to the control of bodily processes. They can also be profitably examined as contributors to the bodily manifestation of emotion. In 1890, Goltz described a dog whose cerebral cortex he had removed. Were externally expressed emotion executed by the cortical motor areas, none would have been seen in this decorticate dog. However, not only did it manifest reactions recognized as rage, but these were aroused by inconsequential stimuli. Thus, the apparatus for this kind of emotion was released from inhibitory control exerted by the cerebral cortex. On the other hand, Sherrington noted that the acute decerebrate animal is nearly, if not entirely, without emotional expression.* This finding narrowed the locus for the execution of a full angry display to the basal ganglia, diencephalon and anterior midbrain. Karplus and Kreidl in 1914 discovered that stimulating the hypothalamic portion of the diencephalon resulted in a variety of visceral responses.

In 1928, Bard made transections which localized the neural mechanism of rage chiefly to the diencephalon. By longitudinal sections removing the thalamus he localized

---

*In a cat with a *chronic* section at the level of the midbrain, high threshold fragmentary expressions of anger can be elicited.[2] These responses indicate some participation of midbrain centers in emotional expression, but fall short of the integrated rage behavior seen in cats with transections above the hypothalamus.

this mechanism in the hypothalamus. The excitement or dynamic aspect of emotion is pointed up by the fact that the retention of a relatively few cubic millimeters of hypothalamic tissue makes the difference between a preparation which is an emotional vegetable and one which at a slight touch, or even "spontaneously," will go into a paroxysm of activity—struggling, baring of the claws, spitting, pupillary dilation, erection of hair and a variety of internal visceral responses. Whether this response is, in fact, "sham rage" (Bard) and a "pseudoaffective state" (Sherrington) will be discussed later.

It is important that these experiments should not be generalized to encompass emotional displays other than rage; it is still not known where all emotional activities are managed. However, basic sexual behavior appears to be integrated in the diencephalon. When given estrogens, a decorticate female cat displays normal feline estrous behavior, which Bard divides into (i) courtship activity (playful rubbing and rolling, vocalizing, estrous crouching, and treading with hind legs) and (ii) the after-reaction (frantic rubbing, licking, squirming, and rolling following vaginal stimulation). As with rage, the chronic high mesencephalic decerebrate cat shows only fragments of this behavior, the induced activity falling short of the full pattern of estrous behavior exhibited by normal and decorticate cats. The neural mechanisms for the basic elements of sexual behavior are localized in the hypothalamus.

DETAILED LOCALIZATION OF EMOTIONAL AND MOTIVATIONAL ACTIVITY IN HYPOTHALAMUS.   Although the hypothalamus is a small structure, the apparatus for several kinds of motivational and emotional behavior lie within it. As seen in Chapters 10 and 49, the ventromedial nucleus of the hypothalamus is a "satiety center," and destruction of this nucleus produces excessive eating and gross hyperphagia. Slightly lateral is a "feeding center"; destruction of it causes fatal anorexia. By stimulation with implanted electrodes, an area in the anterior hypothalamus concerned with drinking has been demonstrated. Farther posterior in the hypothalamus, at the level of the mammillary bodies, are areas concerned with both eating and drinking.[46] Stimulation of them can force an animal to eat and drink like an automaton.

Focal stimulation and localized lesions have demarcated a restricted hypothalamic region concerned with emotional display. Lesions of the ventromedial nuclei of the hypothalamus induce rage and savageness in animals, which make well-directed attacks toward the experimenter.[55] Focal stimulation of unanesthetized animals through implanted electrodes with their tips in the hypothalamus is highly valuable in more precise localization of the hypothalamic subcortical areas concerned with emotion.[16] The same point can be stimulated in successive animals with different strengths and durations of stimulation and the exact point of stimulation determined histologically. Two types of behavioral responses are obtained: (i) a fight or ragelike pattern (growling and hissing, flattening of the ears, piloerection and other sympathetic responses) and (ii) a flight or fearlike pattern (pupillary dilation, darting of eyes to and fro, turning of head from side to side, and finally flight). In addition, visceral and other acts, such as micturition, defecation, salivation, retching and sniffing, can be elicited by stimulation of regions rather widely distributed through the hypothalamus. According to one group of investigators the flight zone is a concentric ring around a core in which hissing, back-arching and the fight response are centered.[17] According to Nakao,[36] loci for the two types of responses are found in the same concentric lamina, but flight mechanisms are manifest after stimulation of regions more rostral than those serving aggressive reactions. Similar reactions are obtained by stimulating the amygdalar region of the rhinencephalon.

Regardless of the details of localization there are indications that an area extending entirely through the hypothalamus instigates flight and aggressive motor behavior with accompanying autonomic manifestations, although many other points in the hypothalamus do not give rise to these emotional responses. Further, a system of fibers involving the ventromedial nucleus appears to restrain emotional behavior, since rage and savageness occur in exaggerated form when these nuclei alone are destroyed.

Limbic System; Rhinencephalon.[5, 6, 20, 43]   A medial complex of cortex, subcortical nuclei and the tracts which connect them with the hypothalamus and other structures is known anatomically as the "rhinencephalon," literally "nose brain" (Fig. 301). It received this name because the olfactory tract enters it. However, comparative neuroanatomic studies have shown that the "nose brain" is well developed in animals having few or no olfactory receptors. According to electrophysiologic studies, only a fraction of the rhinencephalon is activated by olfactory stimuli. Ablation and stimulation studies indicate that the nonolfactory portions of the rhinencephalon are concerned with emotional life. MacLean,[32] to avoid the olfactory implications of "rhinencephalon," has popularized the terms "limbic lobe" or "limbic system." First used by Broca to describe this area, "limbic" means border. The cerebral hemispheres arise as a tremendous outgrowth from the diencephalon. The hilus or neck of this growth forms a concentric ring of cerebral cortex which, in a sense, is a *border* of the great neocortical vesicle.

The major part of the limbic system is composed of two rings of limbic cortex and associated subcortical nuclei. The inner ring of three-layered cortex includes part of

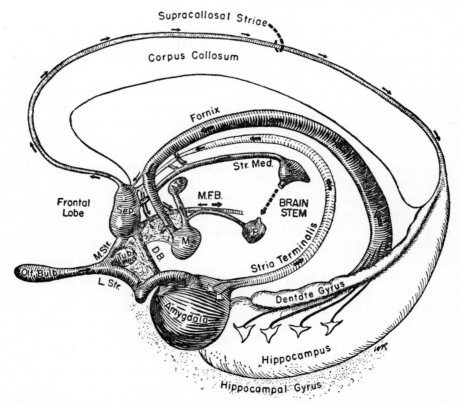

FIG. 301.   Schematic representation of relationship of main subcortical structures and connections of rhinencephalon, drawn as though all of them could be seen from medial aspect of right hemisphere. For diagrammatic purposes some connections have been given an arbitrary course. Abbreviations: *AT*, anterior thalamic nucleus; *DB*, diagonal band of Broca; *H*, habenula (part of epithalamus); *IP*, interpeduncular nucleus; *L Str*, lateral olfactory stria; *M*, mammillary body (part of posterior hypothalamus); *MFB*, medial forebrain bundle; *M Str*, medial olfactory stria; *Olf Bulb*, olfactory bulb; *Sep*, region of septal nuclei; *Str Med*, stria medullaris; *Tub*, olfactory tubercle (head of caudate immediately underneath). (After Krieg; from MacLean, P. D. *Psychosom. Med.*, 1949, *11*:338–353.)

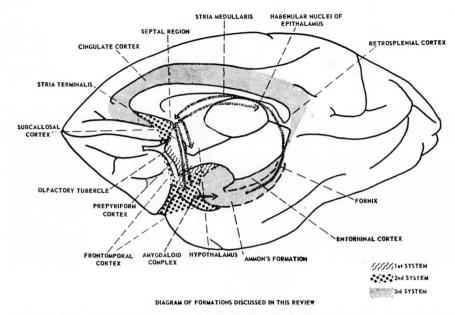

FIG. 302. Drawing of medial and basal surfaces of brain showing divisions of the rhinencephalon. Note smallness of first system, which has direct connections with olfactory bulb. Second system is defined as structures connected with the first system but not the bulb. Third system includes hippocampus and other structures of Ammon's cortex and juxtallocortex in entorrhinal (inferior), retrosplenial (posterior) and cingulate (superior and anterior) regions. Most of discussion in text pertains to the second system. (From Pribram and Kruger, *Ann. N. Y. Acad. Sci.*, 1954, *58:*109–138.)

the hippocampal formation and is phylogenetically the most primitive, being generally referred to as the "archipallium" or "allocortex." This area includes structures with olfactory connections (the olfactory tubercle, the prepyriform cortex, the periamygdaloid cortex, the corticomedial nuclei of the amygdala) and certain structures and areas which are connected with the thalamus and hypothalamus, mainly the entorrhinal area and the hippocampus. The next ring is designated "juxtallocortex," "mesopallium" or "transitional" cortex; it is homotypical six-layered cortex. In its structure and phylogenetic history it is intermediate between the archipallium and the surrounding "neopallium" or "neocortex," from which it is separated by the cingulate sulcus. This outer ring consists of the cingulate gyrus and, anteriorly, the orbitoinsulotemporal cortex and, posteriorly, the presubiculum. Two important subcortical masses, the septal nuclei and the basolateral amygdalar nuclei, are associated with mesopallium. (Note in Figure 302 that Pribram and Kruger classify some of the mesopallium with their second system and some with the third.) The efferent projections from the mesopallium pass to subcortical centers, largely by way of the striatum. The fornix is the mean efferent projection for the archipallium, which sends fibers to the septal region, the hypothalamus and the midbrain. The neuroanatomy of the rhinencephalon or limbic system is too complex to permit detailed description. Figures 301 and 302 represent it and some of its connections in a highly simplified fashion.

MESOPALLIUM. As pointed out in Chapter 11, the neopallium subserves some visceral functions, the responsible foci appearing to be discrete, specialized and generally associated with motor or sensory areas. Thus salivation is initiated from points ventral to the face area, pupillary dilation and lacrimation from the frontal eye fields, and vasoconstrictor responses by points in the arm and leg areas. We have also seen that stimulation of mesopallium results in autonomic responses. That stimulation of its orbital portion causes changes in respiration and visceral function was discovered in 1894 and again noted in 1940,[1] but not until 1949 was it learned that the whole mesopallium gives rise to respiratory, vascular and visceral changes when electrically excited. Kaada and his associates[21] have shown (Fig. 303) that such results are obtained by stimulating the whole ring of cortex running from the anterior cingulate gyrus across the posterior orbital surface to the insula, the temporal pole, the pyriform cortex, the periamygdaloid

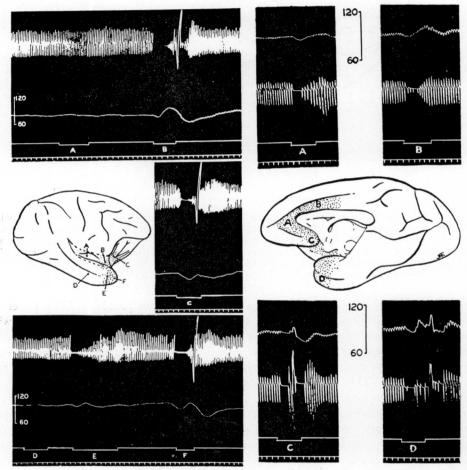

FIG. 303.   Responses to stimulation of limbic cortex. *Left,* Respiratory (*upper record*) and blood pressure response (*lower record*) resulting from electrical stimulation of points designated on brain map. Insula, containing points *A* and *B,* is visualized by separation of temporal and frontoparietal operculum. Respiratory movements recorded through tracheal cannula. Stroke upward indicates expiration. *Right,* Same for mesial surface except that blood pressure is now the upper record. (From Kaada *et al., J. Neurophysiol.,* 1949, *12:*347–356.)

and the posterior hippocampal cortex. As with hypothalamic stimulation, a wide variety of visceral responses to limbic stimulation have been obtained in both animals and man,[26, 27] but in general these responses are of lesser magnitude than are those induced by hypothalamic stimulation.

Many limbic areas affect the same visceral structure, and stimulation of the same point in the limbic lobe will cause several kinds of visceral or vascular responses. In fact, the various segments of the limbic cortex appear to be closely interrelated but only poorly connected with the neopallium. By applying strychnine to various limbic areas and searching the limbic lobe for strychnine spikes, MacLean and Pribram[11, 30] identified the interconnections between limbic areas shown in Figure 304. The interconnectedness of the limbic system is shown by the fact that stimulation in it produces prolonged repetitive afterdischarges detectable electroencephalographically.[14] These discharges spread readily throughout the limbic system and to other structures such as the hypo-

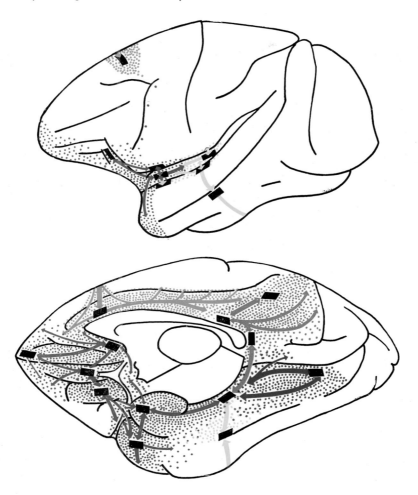

FIG. 304. Schematic representation of lateral (*top*) and mediobasal (*bottom*) surfaces of macaque brain showing segments of phylogenetically old and new cortex which appear related on basis of strychninization studies. Black rectangles indicate areas to which strychnine was applied. Respective colors indicate reciprocally connected areas. Note overlapping of shading at fringes. Extent of firing into neopallium is not shown. (Based on experiments by MacLean and Pribram; from Fulton, *Frontal lobotomy and affective behavior; a neurophysiological analysis.* New York, W. W. Norton and Company, 1951.)

thalamus. These structures are thus identified as closely associated with the limbic system. In passing it may be noted that the supplementary motor area described by Woolsey (Chap. 11) is half in the mesopallium and half in the neocortex.

The responses of limbic structures to stimulation may mean that they serve as a regulatory system for visceral and vascular function superimposed upon the hypothalamus. On the other hand, the responses may mean that the limbic lobe is concerned with emotion. An involvement in emotional expression is suggested by the kind of somatic muscular response resulting from stimulation of these areas. For example, by stimulating area 24 or the anterior cingulate gyrus, Wilbur Smith[51] elicited vocalization suggestive of emotional response.

SUBCORTICAL LIMBIC STRUCTURES.   The participation of the limbic system in emotion is especially clear when the subcortical limbic structures, e.g., the septal and amygdalar nuclei, are stimulated or ablated. The amygdalar nuclei lying beneath the pyriform cortex seem to be peculiarly important. The amygdala is a complex of nuclei with connections with the olfactory bulb and the temporal neocortex. The amygdala also projects to the septal region and the hypothalamus via the stria terminalis. The

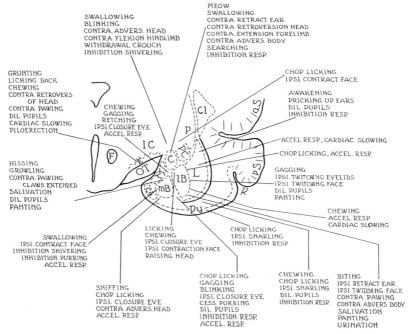

FIG. 305.   Cross section through midregion of amygdala showing types of oral, facial and other behavior resulting from stimulation. Note the divisions of the amygdala and its relationship to other brain structures. Abbreviations: LB and mB, lateral and medial parts of basal nucleus of amygdala; L, lateral nucleus; C, central nucleus of amygdala; F, fornix; OT, optic tract; Py, pyriform cortex; R, rhinal fissure; Cl, claustrum; P, pulvinar; IC, internal capsule; Co, cortical nucleus of amygdala; E, entopeduncular nucleus; M, medial nucleus of amygdala; PC, putamen-central amygdaloid complex; aS, anterior sylvian gyrus; pS, posterior sylvian gyrus. (From MacLean and Delgado, Electroenceph. clin. Neurophysiol., 1953, 5:91–100.)

septal nuclei, rhinencephalic structures lying along the midline just beneath the anterior genu of the corpus callosum, are widely connected with structures known to be concerned with emotion and motivation—the preoptic region, the hypothalamus, the hippocampus, the brain stem tegmentum and the habenulae.

Stimulation experiments.   Stimulation experiments by Gastaut[12] in France and MacLean.[30, 33] in America focused attention on the amygdalar and periamygdalar region. Stimulation of these structures through implanted electrodes in unanesthetized cats and monkeys elicited responses clearly related to "eating" and the upper end of the gastrointestinal tract—sniffing, licking, biting, chewing, chop-licking, gagging and retching (Fig. 305). (Somewhat inconsistently, hyperphagia following amygdalar lesions has been reported.[13]) A second category of responses were classified as components of defense—attack, retraction of ears, snarling and other vocalization, and protrusion of claws. A third category of responses were the respiratory and autonomic responses elicited from the mesopallium generally. Finally, occasional organized affective responses—angry attacking behavior or fear-escape behavior—were elicited. Angry behavior typically results from amygdalar stimulation.[10] Wood *et al.*[56] have recently demonstrated localization of function in the amygdala, with jaw and face movements most easily elicited by stimulation of the basolateral nuclei and autonomic and respiratory effects by stimulation of the corticomedial zone.

Ablation of septal region. Lesions of this anterior, medial limbic region reduce responses in a "fear" or "anxiety" situation.[7] To establish an anxiety-producing stimulus, a clicking noise lasting three minutes was followed immediately by a painful shock to the feet. After a few such presentations the clicking noise alone caused an anxiety response—crouching, micturition and defecation. To obtain an objective measure of this conditioned fear or anxiety, rats were trained to depress a lever in order to secure a lever of water. The animals were rewarded only once in 60 seconds so that the rate of drop pressing would remain high. The degree to which the clicking noise interfered with the lever pressing was taken as a measure of anxiety. In unoperated control rats, conditioned anxiety completely inhibited bar pressing for water. After lesions of the septal region, the effect of the clicking noise on lever pressing was much less pronounced.

Other methods supplied evidence of increases in other emotional behavior after such lesions. Following the operation, the rats were placed in a group cage. On emerging from anesthesia they were soon engaged in a free-for-all. Tame rats which had been petted freely with bare hands could now be handled only with gloves; they repeatedly attacked a bar of steel placed in front of them. Such attacks are not like sham rage but are extremely skillful and well directed. It can be concluded that the animals have become more excited and more savage; that they are less fearful and anxious.

Amygdalar ablations. As is true in many subcortical structures concerned with visceral function, oppositely acting structures lie side by side or intermingled in the amygdala. The apparently contradictory results of pioneering experiments should not cause confusion since further study often discloses separate structures with antagonistic actions.

In determining what structures must be destroyed to produce the sham rage which follows high decortications, Bard and Mountcastle[3] found that removal of the neocortex does not cause the rage reaction, provided the subcortical nuclei are not involved. Such lesions actually lead to a state of abnormal calm and placidity. This placidity followed lesions which left intact the amygdala, the hippocampal formation, and the cortex of the pyriform lobe. When the pyriform lobes and the amygdala were removed from a placid decorticate cat, the calmness ended. Bard and Mountcastle concluded that the amygdala must act as a "funnel" through which inhibitory impulses originating in the transitional cortex and the neocortex exert an inhibitory influence on the posterior hypothalamus, which subserves the rage response.

In 1937, Klüver and Bucy[24, 25] produced bizarre behavioral disturbances (visual agnosia, exploration by smelling, compulsive exploratory behavior) in monkeys following bilateral temporal lobectomy which destroyed important limbic structures. Some of these behavior changes have already been described. Noted, too, were profound changes in emotional behavior in the direction of passivity or unresponsiveness. Objects which normally excite fear or wariness—a snake, a stranger, a cat or a dog—were approached without hesitation and without the vocalization and facial behavior which denote fear in the monkey. By contrast, other types of emotional behavior, especially sexual activity, were intensified and were aroused by an unusual diversity of objects. The monkeys manifested sexual behavior toward the opposite sex, the same sex, and themselves in a degree far beyond that seen in normal male monkeys. Also manifest was excessive oral behavior—biting and sucking of various parts of the body or inanimate objects. In the same year Papez[42] reached a somewhat comparable conclusion in a theoretical paper, namely that the regions involved in the lesions made by Klüver and Bucy are linked with the hypothalamus and thalamus to form the neural mechanisms of emotion. Thus both the behavior datum and an indication of involvement of limbic structures, rather than structures of the temporal lobe proper, were available. These observations have been confirmed in animals[51] and in man.[50]

Since World War II, these pioneering studies probing the neural basis of emotion have been widely extended in a number of laboratories throughout the world. Subsequent studies indicate that, of the limbic structures destroyed in Klüver and Bucy's operation, it is the amygdalar nuclei and overlying pyriform cortex whose loss produces the emotional symptoms. Ablation restricted to the limbic areas involved in Klüver and Bucy's experiments produces the emotional but not the cognative part (e.g., psychic blindness) of the syndrome exhibited by their monkeys. While many investigators have reported fragments of the Klüver-Bucy syndrome resulting from lobectomy in animals[53] and even in man,[52] the most dramatic demonstration has been that by Schreiner and Kling.[47, 48, 49] After removal of the amygdalar nuclei and the overlying cortex, cats and monkeys became exceedingly docile. The agouti and the lynx, two animals selected for their savage natures, similarly became docile for a period of weeks following amygdalectomy. Operated cats and monkeys clearly demonstrated the hypersexuality, which they exhibited toward either sex without discrimination or toward animals of a different species, such as the hen. The sexual activity diminished after castration but was not caused by an increased production of testosterone. These results were confirmed, and the area concerned with sexual behavior has been delimited.[13] Hypersexuality follows lesions restricted to the pyriform cortex (Fig. 306) overlying the basal amygdaloid nucleus but not lesions confined to the nucleus.

While a certain amount of placidity or calmness may follow many brain operations, that following amygdalectomy is specific. It is interesting that a placid amygdalectomized animal is made savage and rageful by lesions of the ventromedial nucleus of the thalamus.[47] Conversely, rats made savage by septal lesions have been made placid by amygdalectomy.[22]

Some investigators have been unable to confirm these findings; others not only have observed the same disorders but have obtained them by producing fractional lesions of the amygdalar nuclei or the overlying cortex. This variation is perhaps not surprising when dealing with a behavior which is complex and difficult to quantify and study objectively, on the one hand,* and with an exceedingly complex neural structure on the other. Somewhat the same difficulties were encountered in early studies of the hypothalamus, and these were resolved by the discovery that the hypothalamus contains pairs of oppositely acting centers. The same may be true of the limbic lobe.

ARCHIPALLIUM. Despite the anatomically well established connections of the hippocampal formation with the hypothalamus via the fornix and with the anterior cingulate gyrus (area 24) via the mammillary bodies and the anterior nuclei, the emotional significance of these connections, hypothesized by Papez[42] and others[29] has not been clearly established experimentally. Although rather intangible changes in emotionality have been described as following lesions of area 24 and other areas of the mesopallium, interference with this system is not accompanied by gross changes in emotional behavior like those following interference with the subcortical limbic nuclei. It is quite possible that Papez's system serves the cognative and other subjective aspects of emotion. There is, in fact, evidence that the hippocampal formation is concerned with the sub-

---

* For example, Rosvold et al.[45] have shown that an amygdalectomized baboon which was aggressive in a cage situation was submissive in a group hierarchy situation.

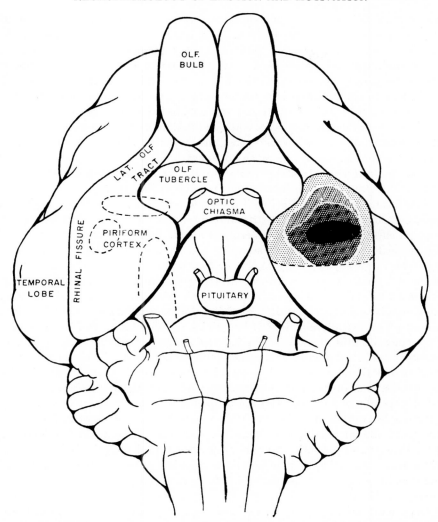

FIG. 306.   Ventral aspect of cat brain showing surface projection of areas where destruction caused specific behavior problem. On right is concentric stipple circle showing quartile incidence of involvement in animals exhibiting hypersexuality. (From Green *et al.*, *J. comp. Neurol.*, 1957, *108*:505–545.)

jective or inner aspect of emotion. Perhaps these connections constitute the path over which the limbic and neocortical functions are related to one another. Similarly, the prefrontal lobe is concerned with emotion, but much more subtly than the amygdalar region.

INNER ASPECTS OF EMOTION

Sherrington, recognizing the dangers of inferring subjective experiences from motor behavior, spoke of "pseudoaffective" reflexes in the decerebrate cat. Cannon, in turn, cautiously spoke of "sham rage" in the decorticate or high decerebrate animal, implying that only the external and not the subjective manifestations of rage were observed. The groundwork for what may seem paradoxical—an objective attack on a subjective phenomenon—was laid by Loucks from 1934 to 1938, when he introduced the buried-electrode technique and used it to analyze the neural basis of conditioned reflexes.

Since Pavlov, it has been known that if a "neutral" stimulus (the conditioned stimulus) producing no visible reaction, or a reaction unrelated to the conditioned response, is presented at the proper time interval with or before a stimulus which causes a given reaction (the unconditioned stimulus and response, respectively), the conditioned stimulus subsequently presented alone will produce the same reaction (conditioned response). By stimulating at various points along the pathway of the *unconditioned* reflex from sense organ to muscle, Loucks and others found that stimulation of sense organs, posterior root or columns of the spinal cord, and thalamus can serve as an unconditioned stimulus; stimulation of the motor cortex, the anterior root, or the muscle, though producing a response, cannot serve as an unconditioned stimulus. In other words, a stimulus on the afferent side of the reflex is effective as an unconditioned stimulus; a stimulus on the efferent side is ineffective. It is also known that conditioning is exceedingly difficult and may be impossible if a neutral stimulus produces the unconditioned response, e.g., light→pupillary constriction or tendon tap→knee jerk. Going one step farther, one can restate this issue in terms of affect. The reflexes which serve well are those produced by unconditioned stimuli which a man would call pleasant or unpleasant—for example, an electric shock, or food or acid placed in the mouth.

Role of Hypothalamus in Affect.   Masserman[35] applied the same type of analysis to the emotional display elicited by hypothalamic stimulation. He asked: Is the hypothalamus simply a motor structure organizing the external expression of emotion, or is it "upstream" on the afferent side? If hypothalamic stimulation can serve as an *unconditioned* reflex stimulus, then, following Loucks' analysis, the hypothalamus is upstream. Masserman established a series of criteria which have proved very useful in determining whether an emotional manifestation resulting from a central lesion or stimulus is a pseudoaffective or sham emotion. These criteria are: (i) Is the aggressive activity directed toward any specific object? (ii) Does the display inhibit and replace other activity? (iii) Does the display outlast the stimulus as does emotional excitement in intact animals? (iv) Does the animal become conditioned against the environment (the experimental box)? (v) Will brain stimulation serve as an unconditioned reflex in formal conditioning experiments? He answered these questions negatively for the hypothalamus. Subsequent investigators have uniformly answered the same questions positively, and the reason for the discrepancy is not known.

Masserman's criteria have been widely used by others in working out the neurophysiology of emotion and motivation. Nakao,[37] for example, observed that the emotional display is not blind and undirected. When it is ragelike, it can be directed toward the experimenter or toward an innocent feline bystander; if the display is fearlike, attempts to escape are directed toward a weak point in the cage. Both Nakao and Delgado *et al.*[8] have found that hypothalamic stimulation giving rise to hissing, baring of teeth, biting, scratching, attempts to escape, etc., serve very well as unconditioned stimuli. Moreover, it is possible to show how the animal "interprets" the hypothalamic stimulation. Nakao placed an animal with electrodes implanted in its hypothalamus in a box with an electrified grid floor. He then taught the animal to turn off a shock by manipulating a paddle. The first time a hypothalamic shock is delivered, some animals immediately turn off the shock. Delgado *et al.*[8] have shown further that the hypothalamic shock can motivate learning *de novo* and can act as a punishment strong enough to inhibit an animal's approaching food.

How well a hypothalamic stimulation in cats will serve as an unconditioned stimulus for a conditioned avoidance response depends on whether a flight or a rage type of reaction is elicited. When a flight reaction resulted, paddle pushing motivated by food stimulation was transferred to the hypothalamic stimulation immediately, whereas transfer did not occur when the stimulus produced fight reactions. The two types of response were elicited by stimulation of slightly different portions of the hypothalamus, flight responses from a somewhat diffuse lateral region in the anterior hypothalamus and aggressive responses (hissing and snarling) from the medial and inferior portion of the middle hypothalamus.[37]

Other subcortical regions give rise to emotional reactions which can be used as unconditioned stimuli.[9] Many of these regions are on the classic pain pathways. Others, like the hypothalamus and the medial nucleus of the amygdala (see below), are not. Electrical stimulation of the amygdala in man yields subjective reports of fear and rage.[15]

It should not be thought that the hypothalamus working alone is capable of initiating directed emotional behavior. The cerebral cortex is necessary for this. The emotional behavior of Goltz's decorticate dog or that resulting from hypothalamic stimulation in decorticate cats is not directed. It is quite possible that the hypothalamus discharges upward to the cerebral cortex, which directs the attack. Nor can it be assumed that the hypothalamus is the site of the affective experience, or whatever cerebral process is necessary for a stimulus to serve as an unconditioned stimulus. The hypothalamus may discharge to a thalamic or other area essential to affect. Additional investigation is necessary to work out these relations, but it is clear that the hypothalamus is more than an efferent structure downstream in the apparatus for emotional behavior. Further evidence of this is obtained from self-stimulation experiments (see below).

Role of Hypothalamus in Motivation. Certain lesions of the hypothalamus cause excessive eating and drinking (Chap. 10). At first sight, this would seem to indicate that these animals are driven and highly motivated. However, the amount eaten or drunk is not the sole and perhaps not even the best indication of a hunger drive. (Have we not all absent-mindedly eaten a bowl of peanuts when not at all hungry?) Another test of motivation is what effort will be made or what obstacles will be overcome in order to satisfy a drive. Using these criteria, Miller[36] did not find high motivation in rats obese from hypothalamic hyperphagia. These rats were not, however, in the dynamic phase of hyperphagia when weight is increasing, so it is not certain that the hyperphagia is not highly motivated.

The hypothalamic apparatus concerned with eating and drinking is complex. As we have seen, no less than three areas are concerned with eating and one with satiety. Stimulation of the feeding center lateral to the satiety center causes delayed eating but does not increase food drive.[51]

Stimulation of Maire's eating centers in the medial mammillary area causes eating that is prompt and apparently discriminative, in contrast to bulimia when inedible objects are ingested.[46] Unlike the eating produced by stimulation of the lateral hypothalamus, the discriminative eating was clearly motivated when tested by the method of conflicting drives. A male rat with electrodes implanted in the premammillary area was placed in a cage strewn with food and containing a female rat in heat (Fig. 307). When the male rat's activities were clearly oriented toward the female, the posterior hypothalamic feeding center was stimulated. Sexual play promptly ceased; the male turned away, sniffing for food, and, when he found it, began eating. When the stimulation stopped, he dropped the food pellet and returned to the female. Thus while excessive eating and drinking can be forced by stimulation and by lesions of various hypothalamic and adjacent subcortical structures, whether this is truly motivated behavior must be assessed for each activity, for each hypothalamic point and for each lesion. The indications are that eating is controlled by a series of nuclei and that at some point in the hypothalamus the mechanism changes from one producing motivated eating to one producing a behavior which, although occurring in excessive amounts, is a mechanical "motor" behavior. Thus emotion and drive present similar problems, namely to discover the neural basis of the essential feature of each—the affect and the motivation, respectively.

Self-Stimulation.   If electrodes are implanted in the brain and the key which closes a stimulating circuit arranged so that it can be manipulated by the animal, the affects of stimulation can be deduced from the animal's behavior. With the electrode tip in certain places in the animal's brain and the key where the animal can close it accidentally, in a few trials he will have learned the connection between the key and the shock and will thereafter shun the key. Quite otherwise, when the electrodes are in some other parts of the brain, the animal will stimulate itself repeatedly, as often as 5000 times per hour—more than once a second.[41] If permitted, this behavior will be continued to the point of exhaustion. In hour-long tests continued for a month no sign

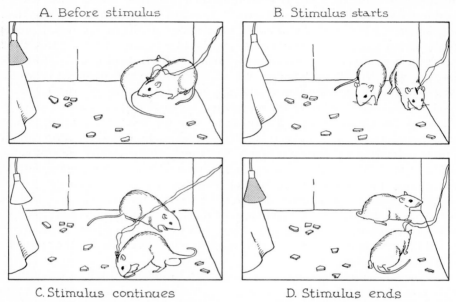

A. Before stimulus   B. Stimulus starts

C. Stimulus continues   D. Stimulus ends

FIG. 307.   Tracings of sequence from research motion picture of rat with electrodes implanted in premammillary region of hypothalamus. Light is on during stimulation through electrodes.

of satiation developed.[40] Shocks in still other areas are indifferent, i.e., the animal neither seeks nor avoids stimulation. That forms of behavior other than key pressing can be motivated by self-stimulation has been proved in a variety of ways. A rat can be trained to run a maze for a brain shock as a reward, or will cross an electrified grid in order to receive a brain shock. In a Skinner box, a rat may press a bar more rapidly for a brain shock than for food.[6]

The rate of bar pressing affords a measure of the efficacy of given electrode positions. Self-stimulation results when the tip of the electrode is at any point in a rather wide extent of the brain. The neocortex, however, is a quite indifferent locus. The most effective regions are in the hypothalamus and the limbic system. The posterior hypothalamus just anterior to the mammillary bodies yields very high rates; the anterior hypothalamus much lower rates. The active points extend caudally into the midbrain tegmentum and rostrally into the preoptic region, the septal region and the median forebrain bundle. Other parts of the limbic system produce bar-pressing, but at low rates.

Because stimulation of certain points acts as a motivation, Olds[40] has asked this question: Are the electrodes in some system of fibers serving a major drive? For example, are there electrode placements which will cause an animal to stimulate itself more rapidly when it is hungry than when it is satiated? Some evidence for a hunger-correlated variation in self-stimulation rate was obtained when the electrode tip was placed in the posterior hypothalamus. With another electrode placement, castration decreased bar pressing after a delay of 10 to 11 days required for the androgen level to fall; the rate of bar pressing was restored by testosterone injections. The effective point in this experiment was at the dorsomedial boundary of the caudate nucleus.

Androgen injection influences the response from one series of points most strongly, and hunger influences the response from a different series of points. It is a reasonable hypothesis that self-stimulation or positive reinforcement occurs when the neural apparatus for a basic drive is stimulated. If mentalistic interpretations are permitted, drives and emotions can be divided into pleasant and unpleasant ones. Self-stimulation may indicate some pleasurable affect or some satisfaction resulting from the stimulus, although this is a point of view contested by many.

Another approach to analysis of the phenomenon of self-stimulation is to establish a state of anxiety and discover either its effect on self-stimulation or the effects of self-stimulation on the anxiety. As in his experiments on ablation of the septal region, Brady[6] established two operant conditioned responses in a Skinner box, pressing the lever for water and for a brain shock. A clicking noise had previously been given anxiety-producing qualities by linking it with a shock to the feet. The clicking sound alone was then sufficient to elicit an anxiety response and inhibit bar pressing for water. If self-stimulation in the median forebrain bundle was substituted for the water reward, bar pressing was not suppressed by the conditioned anxiety, i.e., the clicking noise. Analysis shows that this persistence of bar pressing is not due simply to self-stimulation being a more powerful reward. It may be "peace" rather than "joy" that is obtained by self-stimulation.

The difficulties besetting interpretation of self-stimulation experiments are somewhat analogous to those encountered in considering ablation experiments. With certain electrode placements, Roberts[44] found that stimulation would motivate some kinds of learning but not others. He suggested that the stimulation was rewarding at the onset but quickly became punishing. This basic observation has been confirmed.[4] It was also shown that rats displaying signs of receiving punishment from prolonged stimulation will, if given opportunity, choose short bouts of brain stimulation. Mixed and apparently contrary effects from stimulation of the same locus have been reported for many brain structures, e.g., anterior cerebellum. Such mixed effects are taken to indicate that oppositely acting systems of neurons lie side by side or intermixed. If this arrangement is typical of the limbic system, as we know it to be of the hypothalamus, it perhaps explains the divergence of results obtained in ablation and stimulation experiments by different investigators.

EXCITEMENT

The importance of the excitement or dynamic aspects of emotion is clear since we often categorize psychiatric patients as manic or depressed. Whether the overt manifestations of excessive activity reflect a conscious state of excitement is not certain, but a parallelism can be assumed. The external manifestations of excitement can be increased or reduced by neural lesions. Thus while acting unopposed by more cephalad levels, as after a high decerebration, the posterior hypothalamus causes sham rage. Furthermore, destruction of the hypothalamus in otherwise intact animals results in somnolence, drowsiness, cataplexy, general stolidity and inactivity. The posterior hypothalamus is therefore a way station in the *descending* system producing emotional display and in the *ascending* reticular systems producing alertness and wakefulness (Chap. 21). Somewhat more anteriorly, destruction of the ventromedial nucleus produces hyperactivity as well as savageness. Maire and Patton[34] have demarcated the levels at which lesions produce general bodily hyperactivity, namely the preoptic and anterior hypothalamic areas. Some anterior lesions produce hyperactivity combined with fatal pulmonary edema. This combination is a familiar sequel to mania.

Lindsley[28] has proposed an activation theory of emotion, perhaps better considered as the activation aspect of emotion. According to this theory, a discharge of hypothalamic nuclei downward, which produces the external aspect of emotions, is accompanied by a discharge upward which produces the subjective alertness or excitement typical of emotion. As we have seen in Chapter 21, this theory is well substantiated.[19] It is perhaps not too much to hope that underactivity of such a system will eventually be identified as causing the flatness of emotion in the schizophrenic and the obtunding of mental processes and depression of postural and motor activities in the depressed patient.

REFERENCES

1. BAILEY, P. and SWEET, W. H. *J. Neurophysiol.*, 1940, *3*:276–281.
2. BARD, and MACHT, M. D. Pp. 55–75 in *Ciba Foundation symposium on the neurological basis of behavior*, G. E. W. WOLSTENHOLME and C. M. O'CONNOR, eds. Boston, Little, Brown and Co., 1958.
3. BARD, P. and MOUNTCASTLE, V. B. *Res. Publ. Ass. nerv. ment. Dis.*, 1948, *27*:362–404.
4. BOWER, G. H. and MILLER, N. E. *J. comp. physiol. Psychol.*, 1958, *51*:669–674.
5. BRADY, J. V. Pp. 193–235 in *Biological and biochemical bases of behavior*, H. F. HARLOW and C. N. WOOLSEY, eds. Madison, University of Wisconsin Press, 1958.
6. BRADY, J. V. Pp. 689–703 in *Reticular formation of the brain*, Henry Ford Hospital International Symposium, H. H. JASPER, L. D. PROCTOR, R. S. KNIGHTON, W. C. NOSHAY and R. T. COSTELLO, eds. Boston, Little, Brown and Co., 1958.
7. BRADY, J. V. and NAUTA, W. J. H. *J. comp. physiol. Psychol.*, 1953, *46*:339–346.
8. DELGADO, J. M. R., ROBERTS, W. W. and MILLER, N. E. *Amer. J. Physiol.*, 1954, *179*: 587–593.
9. DELGADO, J. M. R., ROSVOLD, H. E. and LOONEY, E. *J. comp. physiol. Psychol.*, 1956, *49*:373–380.
10. FERNANDEZ DE MOLINA, A. and HUNSPERGER, R. W. *J. Physiol.*, 1959, *145*:251–265.
11. FULTON, J. F. *Frontal lobotomy and affective behavior; a neurophysiological analysis*. New York, W. W. Norton, 1951, 159 pp.
12. GASTAUT, H., NAQUET, R., VIGOUROUX, R. and CORRIOL, J. *Rev. neurol.*, 1952, *86*:319–327.
13. GREEN, J. D., CLEMENTE, C. D. and DE GROOT, J. *J. comp. Neurol.*, 1957, *108*:505–545.
14. GREEN, J. D. and SHIMAMOTO, T. *Arch. Neurol. Psychiat. (Chicago)*, 1953, *70*:687–702.
15. HEATH, R. G., MONROE, R. R. and MICKLE, W. A. *Amer. J. Psychiat.*, 1955, *111*:862–863.
16. HESS, W. R. and BRÜGGER, M. *Helv. physiol. Acta*, 1943, *1*:33–52.
17. HUNSPERGER, R. W. *Helv. physiol. Acta*, 1956, *14*:70–92.
18. IRONSIDE, R. *Brain*, 1956, *79*:589–609.
19. JASPER, H. H., PROCTOR, L. D., KNIGHTON, R. S., NOSHAY, W. C. and COSTELLO, R. T., eds. *Reticular formation of the brain*, Henry Ford Hospital International Symposium. Boston, Little, Brown and Co., 1948, xiv, 766 pp.
20. KAADA, B. R. *Acta physiol. scand.*, 1951, *24* (Suppl. 83):1–285.
21. KAADA, B. R., PRIBAM, K. H. and EPSTEIN, J. A. *J. Neurophysiol.*, 1949, *12*:347–356.
22. KING, F. A. *J. nerv. ment. Dis.*, 1958, *126*:57–63.
23. KLUVER, H. *J.-Lancet*, 1952, *72*:567–577.
24. KLUVER, H. and BUCY, P. C. *J. Psychol.*, 1938, *5*:33–54.
25. KLUVER, H. and BUCY, P. C. *Arch. Neurol. Psychiat. (Chicago)*, 1939, *42*:979–1000.
26. KOIKEGAMI, H., KIMOTO, A. and KIDO, C. *Folia psychiat. neurol. Jap.*, 1953, *7*:87–108.
27. KOIKEGAMI, H. and YOSHIDA, K. *Folia psychiat. neurol. Jap.*, 1953, *7*:109–126.
28. LINDSLEY, D. B. Chap. 14 in *Handbook of experimental psychology*, S. S. STEVENS, ed. New York, John Wiley and Sons, 1951, xi.
29. MACLEAN, P. D. *Psychosom. Med.*, 1949, *11*: 338–353.
30. MACLEAN, P. D. *Electroenceph. clin. Neurophysiol.*, 1952, *4*:407–418.
31. MACLEAN, P. D. *Psychosom. Med.*, 1955, *17*: 355–366.
32. MACLEAN, P. D. *J. nerv. ment. Dis.*, 1958, *127*:1–11.
33. MACLEAN, P. D. and DELGADO, J. M. R. *Electroenceph. clin. Neurophysiol.*, 1953, *5*:91–100.
34. MAIRE, F. W. and PATTON, H. D. *Amer. J. Physiol.*, 1956, *184*:345–350.
35. MASSERMAN, J. H. *Psychosom. Med.*, 1941, *3*:3–25.
36. MILLER, N. E., BAILEY, C. J. and STEVENSON, J. A. F. *Science*, 1950, *112*:256–259.
37. NAKAO, H. *Amer. J. Physiol.*, 1958, *194*:411–418.
38. OLDS, J. *J. comp. physiol. Psychol.*, 1956, *49*: 281–285.
39. OLDS, J. *J. comp. physiol. Psychol.*, 1958, *51*: 675–678.
40. OLDS, J. *Science*, 1958, *127*:315–324.
41. OLDS, J. and MILNER, P. *J. comp. physiol. Psychol.*, 1954, *47*:419–427.
42. PAPEZ, J. W. *Arch. Neurol. Psychiat. (Chicago)* 1937, *38*:725–743.

43. PRIBRAM, K. H. and KRUGER, L. *Ann. N. Y. Acad. Sci* , 1954, *58*:109–138.

44. ROBERTS, W. W. *J. comp. physiol. Psychol.*, 1958, *51*:391–399, *idem*, 400–407.

45. ROSVOLD, H. E., MIRSKY, A. F. and PRIBRAM, K. H. *J. comp. physiol. Psychol.*, 1954, *47*: 173–178.

46. RUCH, T. C., MAIRE, F. W. and PATTON, H. D. *Abstr. Comm., Congr. int. Physiol.*, 1956, *20*:788.

47. SCHREINER, L. and KLING, A. *J. Neurophysiol.*, 1953, *16*:643–659.

48. SCHREINER, L. and KLING, A. *Arch. Neurol. Psychiat. (Chicago)*, 1954, *72*:180–186.

49. SCHREINER, L. and KLING, A. *Amer. J. Physiol.*, 1956, *184*:486–490.

50. SMITH, O. A., JR. In *Electrical stimulation of the brain*. Austin, Texas, University of Texas Press, in press.

51. SMITH, W. K. *J. Neurophysiol.*, 1945, *8*:241–255.

52. TERZIAN, H. and ORE, G. D. *Neurology*, 1955, *5*:373–380.

53. THOMSON, A. F. and WALTER, E. A. *Folia psychiat. neurol. et neurochir. neerl.*, 1950, Brower Memorial Volume, 444–452.

54. VONDERAHE, A. R. *New Scholasticism*, 1944, *18*:76–95.

55. WHEATLEY, M. D. *Arch. Neurol. Psychiat. (Chicago)*, 1944, *52*:296–316.

56. WOOD, C. D., SCHOTTELIUS, B., FROST, L. L. and BALDWIN, M. *Neurology*, 1958, *8*:477–480.

SECTION VI

Properties and Constituents of Blood

CHAPTER 23

General Properties of Blood: The Formed Elements

By HELEN PAYLING WRIGHT

GENERAL PROPERTIES OF BLOOD

Functions of Blood. In the most primitive animals the constituent cells are exposed directly to the vicissitudes of their immediate external environment. One of Claude Bernard's many great contributions to physiology was his recognition that the evolution of higher forms became possible only through the establishment of stable, self-regulated, internal conditions (the "milieu interne") within their body fluids. Although chemical substances and cellular elements are continually entering and leaving the blood stream, its general composition in the higher animals remains remarkably uniform. This constancy is the result of numerous regulatory processes, together with the rapidity of the circulation, which ensures that any disturbances in constitution engendered by metabolic processes in the tissues become minimized in the large volume of blood flowing through the individual organs during their activity.

By virtue of its circulation through every organ, the blood participates in every major functional activity of the body. The primary roles of the blood are, in a broad sense, nutritional and excretory. It conveys oxygen from the lungs to the tissues and returns carbon dioxide from the tissues to the lungs; the mode of carriage of these gases is discussed in Chapter 36. The blood also provides the vehicle for supplying tissues throughout the body with food materials derived from the digestive tract. Such substances may be utilized immediately by active cells or stored in depots, whence they can be mobilized and again transported in the blood as need arises. The removal of the products of catabolism from the tissues is also effected by the passage of blood through them, and such products are carried to the main excretory organs, the lungs and kidneys, for elimination. The selective excretion of soluble substances and the buffering power of the blood, which assists in the preservation of an almost neutral reaction in the tissues, are considered in Chapters 24 and 39. The maintenance of a normal water balance and fluid distribution throughout the body depends on the mobility of the water contained in the blood. Moreover, in the regulation of fluid movements between the capillaries and tissue spaces, and in the filtration process in the renal glomeruli, the colloidal osmotic pressure of the plasma proteins is of great physiologic significance.

The metabolic processes which occur during cell activity constantly produce heat, but mammalian tissues can function with maximal efficiency only within closely restricted limits of temperature. The blood plays an important part in maintaining the temperatures of the organs within this range, since, as it passes through their capillaries, it tends to minimize even minor variations in local temperature. Further, the circulation of the blood in vessels in the skin and lungs enables heat to be lost from the body by radiation and evaporation. Finally, besides the nutritive substances absorbed from the alimentary tract, the blood carries to the tissues the hormones which are produced by the glands of internal secretion and which regulate many functions. Indeed, the effective integration of metabolism carried out by the various endocrine glands is entirely dependent upon the transporting function of the blood.

CELLS, PLASMA, AND SERUM

In its fluid state, which can be maintained outside the body only by artificial anticoagulant measures, the blood is separable into microscopically visible *formed elements* and the liquid *plasma* in which they are suspended. The formed elements are the red corpuscles or erythrocytes, the white cells or leukocytes, and the platelets or thrombocytes (Fig. 308). The leukocytes are true cells with nuclei, active metabolism and powers of locomotion; but mammalian erythrocytes and platelets are non-nucleated cell remnants. The plasma is a complex watery fluid containing colloids, electrolytes and other substances. The process of coagulation (see Chap. 25), which is so characteristic of shed blood, is primarily a plasmatic phenomenon, although ordinarily modified by the presence of platelets and other formed elements. A plasma protein fraction, fibrinogen, is the soluble precursor of the jelly-like fibrin of the blood clot. Corpuscles and platelets become entangled in the filamentous meshes of the fibrin network and undergo disintegration. After formation, the clot undergoes retraction, separating from the wall of the containing vessel and shrinking in volume, thereby squeezing out a straw-colored fluid termed *serum*. The serum or plasma from a fasting individual is clear and transparent, while that obtained during fat digestion is opalescent. This milky or lipemic condition of the fluid fraction of the blood is caused by the presence of submicroscopic fatty droplets (chylomicrons, hemoconia, or "blood dust"). These droplets are best seen under the dark-field microscope, where they are conspicuous for their Brownian movement. The pigments which give plasma and serum their normal yellow or greenish tinge are chiefly porphyrins related to the degradation of hemoglobin and to the synthesis of the bile pigments.

Plasma is obtained when fresh blood is mixed with an anticoagulant and then

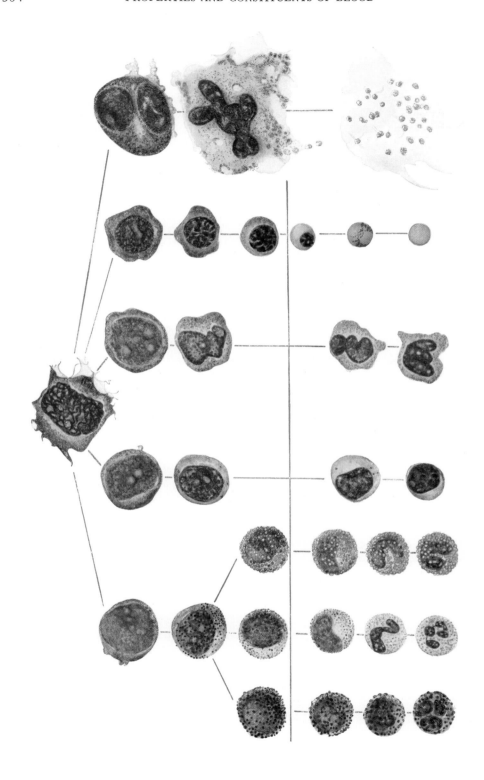

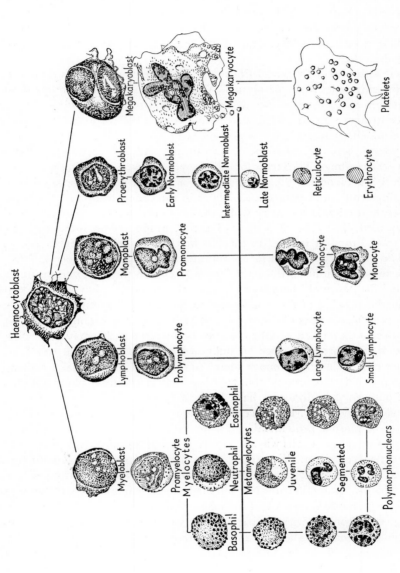

FIG. 308. Diagram showing development of blood cells from bone marrow cells. All cells (except the late normoblasts) shown below the horizontal line are found in normal peripheral blood. (From Whitby and Britton, *Disorders of the blood*, 8th ed. London, J. & A. Churchill, 1957.)

centrifuged or allowed to stand until the cells have settled. In references to plasma, the anticoagulant which it contains is often designated by a prefix, as citrate-plasma, oxalate-plasma, heparin-plasma, etc.

Another method of retaining blood in a fluid state is by *defibrination*. If freshly shed blood is whisked with a glass rod or shaken with glass beads, the fibrin, as it forms, adheres to the foreign surface while the bulk of the blood remains free from coagulum and the red cells preserve their integrity. Anaerobic defibrination may be accomplished by collecting blood over mercury in a special vessel; the blood displaces all except the last few milliliters of the mercury, which is made to defibrinate the sample by repeated inversion of the tube.

Relative Volumes of Cells and Plasma. The centrifuge affords a rapid method of separating the corpuscles from the plasma. Although quantitative techniques date back to 1890,[29] more modern methods are described by Wintrobe.[73] The *hematocrit* is a small graduated centrifuge tube in which the relative volumes of corpuscles and plasma are quickly determined. It is necessary to prevent coagulation of the blood, but most anti-coagulants, except heparin, cause the cells to shrink, and a correction factor thus must be applied to the readings. The factor for sodium oxalate, when used in the concentration of 1 mg. per 1 ml. blood is 1.09. No correction is needed if the anticoagulant is a 3:2 mixture of ammonium and potassium oxalates in the concentration of 2 mg. per 1 ml. of blood. Gentle stirring is necessary while the salts dissolve. The Wintrobe hematocrit is a flat-bottomed glass tube of 3 mm. diameter, graduated in millimeters from the bottom up to 100 mm. It is filled to the 100 mark, care being taken to allow for the meniscus. The tube is centrifuged for 30 minutes at 1500 g, which corresponds to 3000 rev. per minute if the radius of the centrifuge is 15 cm. In the past, various figures have been recorded for "normal" hematocrit values, the differences having been caused by variations in the packing of the cells owing to the use of different times and rates of centrifugation, different sizes of tubes and different radii of gyration. Under any given conditions, a constant packed volume may be obtained,[50] but this may not represent the true volume of the corpuscles since an unknown quantity of plasma may be trapped between the cells. In normal venous blood subjected to the standard centrifugation described above, red cells occupy about 47 per cent of the total blood volume. More accurate hematocrit measurements have been obtained by Leeson and Reeve,[39] who used a radioactive indicator. Before centrifugation of venous blood, they added to it a small amount of plasma protein labeled with radioactive iodine (I^{131}). The residual radioactivity of the packed cells was then determined as an indication of the amount of fluid trapped between them. From these observations it appears that about 5 per cent of the packed cell volume separated from normal blood represents trapped plasma, a finding for which a correction must be applied when estimating total blood volumes (see below). Hematocrit values for blood taken from different vessels, moreover, differ considerably, that from arteries having a lower value than that from veins, and that from minute vessels having a lower value than that from large ones. Organ differences are also recognized, splenic blood having the highest hematocrit value, whereas the values of kidney and heart bloods are low.[15] Finally, it must be noted that in some abnormal conditions when the numbers of leukocytes are greatly increased it is important to distinguish between the red cell volume and the total volume of all cells. In the separation achieved by centrifugation, the white cells and platelets, being less dense than the red cells, appear as a separate layer (*buffy coat*) above the erythrocytes, and a correction should be made for this in reading the hematocrit.

Total Blood Volume. The accurate measurement of circulating blood volume became important as a result of the recognition of the close association of changes in blood volume with the onset of surgical shock.[22] The direct methods of Welcker[69] and Bischoff,[2] in which the body was bled, minced and extracted, the total blood then being estimated colorimetrically, are now of only historical interest. Similarly the method in which a known small volume of carbon monoxide, mixed with oxygen, was rebreathed until all the CO was absorbed and the HbCO:Hb ratio of a sample was then estimated is rarely used since it became evident that unknown amounts of the test gas were retained by the bone marrow. At the present time three main methods of estimating blood volumes are in use: (i) those based upon measurement of marked plasma; (ii) those in which a known number of marked red corpuscles are injected into the circulation and their proportion later found in a sample; and (iii) electrical impedance methods.

(i) DYE METHODS. This technique involves injection of a known amount of a harmless dye which is allowed to mix completely in the circulation. Its concentration in the plasma is then determined colorimetrically, and from this finding the plasma volume can be calculated. The hematocrit value of the blood sample yields the volume fraction of plasma, and from these data the total blood volume can be deduced. Various dyes have been used for this type of measurement, but T-1824, also called Evans Blue, is the one most commonly utilized,[1] since it becomes coupled with plasma albumin and is consequently retained in the blood stream.

Radiotracer methods. A somewhat similar technique has recently been introduced in which radio-iodinated plasma proteins replace the dye.[14, 59] A known amount of the tagged protein is injected intravenously, and, after time for mixing, the radioactivity of a drawn blood sample is determined. From this value the extent of dilution of the injected protein can be ascertained and, when the hematocrit value of the sample is determined, the total blood volume can be calculated.

(ii) MARKED RED CELL METHODS. Here again the principle of dilution is employed, with a known amount of marked material being introduced intravenously. Red corpuscles may be labeled with Fe^{55}, Fe^{59}, P^{32}, Cr^{51}, K^{42} and various other radioisotopes.[16, 31, 55, 61] Tagged red cells of measured radioactivity are injected into the blood stream and, after time for mixing, a blood sample is taken. From the activity of this sample, it is possible to estimate the extent of dilution of the injected material and thus deduce the total volume of blood present in the body. A similar technique (the Ashby technique), in which red blood corpuscles of a different, but compatible, blood group are introduced instead of radioactively marked cells, has also been used with much success. The proportion of "foreign" cells, after their mixing in the circulation, may be determined in the withdrawn blood sample by their agglutination with appropriate sera[1] and from that point onward the calculation is the same as with other techniques.

When these methods are used, the blood volume of normal healthy adults of differing heights may be expressed by the equation:[22]

$$\text{Blood volume} = 5{,}720 + 60(H - 174) \text{ ml.,}$$

where H is the height of the subject in centimeters. This formula was derived from regression equations relating measured height to experimentally determined blood volumes in a group of average normal men in good physical training. It gives a mean of 5 to 6 liters for normal men; women of corresponding height have about 1 liter less. Of this volume, about one-fifth is in the capillaries and the rest in the large vessels and heart.

Comparison of plasma and cell methods. Some discrepancy appears when the estimates obtained by dye and tagged-cell techniques are compared, the former giving values that are about 5 per cent higher than those given by the latter. This discrepancy is probably due to the *skimming* phenomenon in capillary flow; when this occurs, many of these vessels contain only plasma. If corrections, both for this error and for the plasma trapped in the cell column, are made in the hematocrit values, the methods are found to agree very satisfactorily. (For a fuller discussion of this subject, see Torgny Sjöstrand.[60])

(iii) ELECTRICAL IMPEDANCE METHOD.   Another technique involves estimation of the blood volume from alterations in the conductivity of the blood, brought about by injection of hypertonic or hypotonic solutions.[44] A substance, such as sucrose, which will cause a change in the conductivity of the blood, is injected intravenously. After a mixing period, the degree of alteration in conductivity gives a measure of the degree of dilution of the injected material. From this value the total volume of circulating blood is calculated. This method is claimed to have the advantage of measuring changes in whole blood so that errors dependent upon hematocrit values are eliminated. Its application to human physiology has not yet been undertaken, however, and available data refer to animal experiments only.

THE FORMATION OF THE CELLULAR ELEMENTS OF THE BLOOD

Embryonic Blood Formation.   In man the first blood cells to appear are situated in numerous cell islands[3] in the mesenchyme of the yolk sac when the embryo is about 2.25 mm. long.[38] These cells differentiate into two groups. Those in the peripheral parts of the islands form the embryonic *endothelium*, i.e., the cells lining the first blood vessels; those in the centers of the islands become primitive blood cells with basophilic cytoplasm and large, loosely reticulate nuclei. These large, poorly differentiated and unfixed cells are known as *hemocytoblasts*. They are totipotential and, according to the needs of the body, may give rise to cells of either the red or the white series. Similar totipotential cells are found in *hemopoietic* (blood forming) tissue throughout life.

With the differentiation of the organs and the growth of the fetus, and the simultaneous regression of the yolk sac, hemopoietic activity is transferred to the embryonic liver. At about two months' gestation, when the fetus is 5 to 7 mm. long, groups of primitive blood cells, probably derived from the mesenchyme of the developing liver, appear in small groups or nests. At this stage some differentiation of blood cells becomes apparent, and primitive elements of both the red and the white series are recognizable. At the same time, similar sites of hemopoietic activity are also present in the spleen, the thymus and the lymph nodes. These secondary sites are transitory and of little importance. Their most interesting feature is that during adult life, should hemopoiesis be under great strain for any reason, they may once more become capable of blood production, thus proving that they have retained their embryonic powers.

The final period of blood formation in the embryo begins at about the fifth month of gestation, when the blood cells are produced almost exclusively in the red bone marrow. By the time the child is born, his blood, which contains both red and white cells of the normal adult type, is entirely derived from this organ.

Blood Formation in Childhood.   The amount of active hemopoietic tissue in the neonatal period is about 70 to 80 grams, and this highly cellular bone marrow is extremely active to meet the demands of the growing child. At birth, active marrow is present in all bones of the body; but, as growth continues, the quantity of marrow space in the bones outstrips the needs of the hemopoietic marrow, and the small bones and the shafts of the long bones gradually become filled with yellow fatty marrow. By the midteens, the adult distribution of blood-forming marrow is reached.

Blood Formation in the Adult.   In the normal adult the erythrocytes and granulocytes arise in the red marrow of the thoracic bones (ribs, vertebrae, sternum, clavicles, scapulae), the base of the skull, and the upper ends of the femurs and humeri. The total amount of marrow is considerable and constitutes about 5 per cent of the body weight, or 2500 grams—a weight comparable with that of the liver—although normally only about half this is actively forming blood. The reduction in the relative volume from that of childhood allows a reserve of space so that, should physiologic or pathologic needs make demands upon the blood-forming elements, they are able to increase rapidly at the expense of the fatty marrow until the output of blood is seven or eight times normal. As mentioned earlier, in extreme cases, where very unusual stress is laid on the hemo-poietic system, extramedullary marrow may appear in those organs in which blood was formed during fetal life.

With so active an organ as the bone marrow, the metabolic needs are great. The active blood-forming areas are well supplied with *sinusoids*, permitting the substances essential for the formation and release of the various cells to be readily available to maintain the supply of normal mature cells in the circulation. As might be expected, the oxygen consumption by active bone marrow is high.

Cytology of the Bone Marrow. As has been mentioned in the discussion of embryonic blood formation, the primary cell or progenitor of all the types of blood cell is the *hemocytoblast*, a cell capable of developing into the precursors of all the circulating blood elements according to the requirements of the body. By mitotic division within the bone marrow, the hemocytoblast gives rise to five specific, primitive or "blast" cells, each of which derives its prefix according to the blood cells which originate from it. These five cells are: the *proerythroblast* from which the red cells eventually develop, the *myeloblast* for the granulocyte series, the *monoblast* for the large mononuclear cells, the *lymphoblast* for the lymphocyte series, and the *megakaryoblast* from which are derived the blood platelets. Each of these early cells undergoes further division before its offspring are released into the blood stream as circulating blood cells. Within the marrow, cells of the same type tend to form clumps, so that there are islands composed mainly of erythroid cells and others composed mainly of leukoid cells. It is probable that the dividing hemocytoblast gives rise to only one type of daughter cell, e.g., to two erythro-blasts or to two megakaryoblasts, rather than to a mixed progeny, and that this factor explains the grouping of marrow cells during development.

For purposes of study, bone marrow in the adult may be obtained from several sites, the commonest being the sternum. Sternal marrow puncture is carried out under local anesthesia, the skin, the underlying tissues and the periosteum being well infiltrated before a special needle is passed through the outer lamina of the sternum into the marrow

TABLE 10. DIFFERENTIAL COUNTS OF NORMAL STERNAL MARROW
SMEARS (PERCENTAGES)*

	NEUTROPHIL	EOSINOPHIL	BASOPHIL	
Polymorphs	10–40	0–4	0–1	
Metamyelocytes	10–25	0–2.5	–	MYELOID SERIES
Myelocytes	2–8	0–1	–	
Promyelocytes		0.5–5.0		
Myeloblasts		0–2.5		
Lymphocytes		5–20		LYMPHOID SERIES
Monocytes		0–5		
Late Normoblasts		7–19		
Early Normoblasts		4–15		ERYTHROID SERIES
Proerythroblasts		0–4		
Haemocytoblasts		0–1		UNDIFFERENTIATED

* Adapted from Whitby & Britton, *Disorders of the Blood*, 8th. ed., J. & A. Churchill Ltd., London, 1957.

space. Marrow cells are then withdrawn by gentle suction into an attached syringe, and these may be used to make smears, just as is done with blood. Alternatively, a block of marrow tissue suitable for cutting into histologic sections may be removed with a small trephine. Such biopsies may also be made in the iliac crests, the great trochanter or, in children, the proximal end of the tibia. The material so obtained is fixed, stained and used for making differential cell counts. An average total count is 20,000 to 100,000 cells per mm.[3], the numbers of cells of the myeloid series being about five times greater than the number of erythroid cells. Normal differential cell counts of sternal marrow smears are given in Table 10; from these figures it is evident that there are wide variations from person to person and that marked differences are found in the same person at different sites and at different times.

From Figure 308 and Table 10 a general picture of bone marrow may be obtained, although terms occurring in both are yet to be defined. The further development of the different series of blood cells from their specific "blast" cells must be considered according to their respective types.

ERYTHROCYTES

Development of the Erythrocyte. The *proerythroblasts*, which are derived by mitosis from the hemocytoblasts in the bone marrow, are large (14 to 19 μ) basophilic cells with finely reticular nuclei. These cells are devoid of hemoglobin and undergo further division to form *primary erythroblasts*. Although the youngest of these cells have basic-staining cytoplasm, they now contain hemoglobin. By still further division, a second, intermediate form of primary erythroblast is produced. This new form is smaller and less basophilic than its parent, and has a more pyknotic, cartwheel nucleus. From these cells, without further division, arise the normoblasts, or nucleated red cells, which contain hemoglobin and have acid-staining cytoplasm. The dense nucleus of the normoblast is often eccentric and finally undergoes *karyolysis* (fragmentation and digestion), either within the cell or after total extrusion from the cell.

The remaining cell envelope is the normal *erythrocyte*, which at this stage passes out via the blood sinusoids of the marrow into the general circulation. When young, the erythrocyte frequently shows a reticular formation in its cytoplasm; this formation is demonstrable by vital staining of peripheral blood with brilliant cresyl blue. Such *reticulocytes*, which constitute up to 1.5 per cent of circulating red cells, are often slightly larger than more mature erythrocytes. Normal red cells occasionally contain another type of granule, which can be demonstrated by the Prussian blue reaction or with α,α'-dipyridyl. These are the *siderocytes*, which are believed to contain "easily split" iron and which are most commonly found in aging cells and in the blood of premature infants after birth when the fetal cells are being eliminated. The whole process of so-called "maturation" of red cells should be considered as one of degeneration, the changes in the nucleus and in the cytoplasm corresponding closely with those seen in slowly dying cells in other organs.

Although the red corpuscle, after it has passed the reticulocyte stage, is little more than a hemoglobin-containing shell, it nevertheless has a small but significant oxygen consumption. Even cold stored blood progressively converts oxyhemoglobin to the reduced form, the change being most rapid in freshly drawn blood.[9] This metabolism is related to the maintenance of electrolytic balance within the cell, potassium being retained and sodium expelled. These ion exchanges can be achieved only if the corpuscular membrane is a dynamic part of the cell and controlled by its metabolic activity. There seems to be little doubt that the distinctive behavior of the membrane of the red cell is dependent upon the integrity of its internal enzymic system. The energy required for selective ion exchange processes is derived from glycolysis—the conversion of glucose to lactic acid—which is carried on by enzymes present within the corpuscle. Also present are various other enzymes, some with functions which are still obscure.

One further aspect of red cell metabolism requires special mention. During its life in the circulation, the erythrocyte actively destroys lipids (see below), which are incorporated in the stroma. However, erythrocytes appear to be incapable of synthesizing or utilizing protein.

The Mature Erythrocyte; Numbers, Measurements and Morphology. In normal adult peripheral blood, the average number of red cells is 5 million per mm.[3] (4.2 to 6.4 million); in the newborn, the numbers are considerably higher, the average being 6.5 million per mm.[3] The erythrocyte is a biconcave disc with a diameter averaging 7.2 μ (4.75 to 9.50 μ) in dried films. A rough idea of the total area presented by the circulating red cells can be gathered from the calculation that, if they were put edge to edge like a line of coins they would measure some 130,000 miles, or about five times the circumference of the world at the Equator.

The membrane of the erythrocyte is not elastic, although the cell easily becomes distorted in order to pass through narrow capillaries. The Price-Jones curve provides a statistical analysis of the variation in diameter in a blood-cell population and has proved valuable in the clinical diagnosis of various anemias. It is, however, a tedious and time-consuming technique, and has largely been superseded by halometric (diffraction) methods in which thin, evenly spread blood films are used as diffraction gradings; if a light source is viewed through such a film, a circular spectrum, or "halo," is seen. Since the angle of diffraction is determined by the distance between diffracting edges, the size of the halo varies inversely as the diameter of the corpuscles between which the light passes. The average cell diameter measured by such techniques is known as the mean corpuscular diameter (M.C.D.).

In clinical practice the mean corpuscular volume (M.C.V.) is often used in place of diameter measurements in the assessment of abnormalities in cell size. The M.C.V. is the average volume of single red corpuscles expressed in cubic micra (μ^3) and is derived from the hematocrit value of the blood sample and its red cell count according to the following simple formula:

$$\text{M.C.V.} = \frac{\text{Volume packed cells per 1,000 ml. blood}}{\text{Red cell count (millions per mm.}^3)}.$$

The M.C.V. of normal blood is 86 μ^3 with a range of 78 to 94 μ^3.

The thickness of red cells varies from about 1 μ in the center of the biconcavity to 2.4 μ near its edge. These measurements may be made by micrometry on fresh blood cells which, after shedding, have come together to form *rouleaux*. Rouleaux resemble piles of coins, the corpuscles adhering to each other by their flat surfaces, thus presenting a side-on view to the observer. The mean corpuscular thickness (M.C.T.) may also be simply calculated from M.C.D. and M.C.V. In certain blood diseases the red cells may be of normal or subnormal diameter and have the form of flattened ellipsoids (*spherocytes*) rather than of biconcave discs; in others they may be unusually thin (*leptocytes*) and appear in stained films as rings with a denser central area (*target cells*).

The other standard measurements made upon blood samples are closely associated with the hemoglobin content of the blood, the estimation of which is one of the most common laboratory procedures. This estimation is usually made colorimetrically, although basically it depends upon the oxygen-combining capacity of the blood, 1.36 ml. of oxygen being bound by 1 gram of hemoglobin. As there has been wide disagreement concerning what constitutes normality, hematologists have tended to abandon reports based on percentages of an arbitrary normal in favor of records expressed as grams of hemoglobin per 100 ml. of blood. According to the current assessment, normality would generally lie between 15 and 16 grams per 100 ml. for men and has a rather lower range for women.

When the hemoglobin content of a blood sample has been determined, the mean corpuscular hemoglobin (M.C.H.) and the mean corpuscular hemoglobin concentration (M.C.H.C.) may also be derived. The former expresses the average weight of hemoglobin in individual corpuscles and is calculated from the formula:

$$\text{M.C.H.} = \frac{\text{Hemoglobin, gm. per 1,000 ml. blood}}{\text{Red cells, millions per mm.}^3}.$$

The M.C.H. is expressed in $\gamma\gamma$ (gm. $\times 10^{-12}$), the normal figure for man being 29 $\gamma\gamma$ (range, 27 to 32 $\gamma\gamma$).

The M.C.H.C. is obtained directly from the weight of hemoglobin in a standard amount of blood and from the volume of the corpuscles in which it is contained, and is derived from the following formula:

$$\text{M.C.H.C.} = \frac{\text{Hemoglobin in gm. per 100 ml. blood} \times 100}{\text{Volume in ml. packed cells per 100 ml. blood}}.$$

For normal individuals this value is about 33 per cent (range, 32 to 38 per cent) and shows no variation with sex.

It should be noted that a high hemoglobin content is found in the blood of infants at birth, 20 grams per 100 ml. blood being common. This high value is caused by a compensatory response to the low oxygen tension in fetal tissues during intrauterine life, and the blood picture during the neonatal period may be likened to that of an individual living at high altitudes. During the first weeks of independent life this polycythemia gradually drops, the value falling to the adult level, or rather lower, owing to the destruction of red cells containing fetal hemoglobin. This hemoglobin is distinctive in having an oxygen dissociation curve that differs from that of the adult. The heme components are the same in both fetal and adult hemoglobins; the difference lies in the globulin moiety of the molecules (see below).[57]

The morphology of the cells is usually seen in dry films stained with one of the Romanowski eosin-methylene blue-azure stains, e.g., Wright's stain. In these, human erythrocytes appear as salmon-colored discs, somewhat denser at the edge than in the center (Fig. 308). It is not certain whether the interior of the cell is traversed by any supporting fibrils, although phase contrast[13] and electron microscopic[51] studies make their presence unlikely. The cell membrane, which is composed of lipoproteins, presents a uniform, finely granular appearance without folds or holes when examined with the electron microscope.[64]

Life Span of the Erythrocyte. If the normal blood volume is taken to be 5 liters and the red cell count as 5,000,000 per mm.[3], then a total of 25 $\times 10^{12}$ red corpuscles are in active circulation at any one time. Their speed of travel varies in different parts of the vascular system, traverse of the whole circuit taking, on the average, 45 seconds. It has been computed that, after liberation into the blood stream, each corpuscle travels about 700 miles before disintegration. From this estimate it is obvious that the wear and tear on the corpuscles is considerable and that constant replacement is essential.

Through the use of distinctively recognizable red cells, it has been possible to determine the mean life span of the erythrocyte. In the Ashby technique, donor cells from a different but compatible group are injected intravenously, and subsequently their progressive disappearance is followed by the use of differential cell-agglutinating sera.[42] Such transfused "foreign" cells can be detected in the recipient's blood for 100 to 120 days after injection. This survival time has now been confirmed by the use of red cells tagged with radioactive iron.[48] From these findings it appears that about 1 per cent of the total number of red cells in the circulation is replaced daily, and that all the corpuscles of the body are renewed every four months. Although this rate of cell replacement is enormous when compared with that of other tissues, in emergencies, such as after severe hemorrhage, even this may be surpassed many times.

Factors Influencing Erythropoiesis. The main physiologic stimulus to erythropoiesis is the lowering of the oxygen content of arterial blood. Such *hypoxemia* may occur in various physiologic and pathologic conditions—for example, at high altitudes where the partial pressure of oxygen is low, in heart disease where the proper aeration of blood in the lungs is impaired, or after hemorrhage or hemolysis. No matter what the cause of the hypoxemia, if the bone marrow is functioning properly, erythropoiesis becomes enhanced so that an adequate oxygen supply to the tissues is restored.

Although hypoxemia is undoubtedly the chief physiologic stimulus to erythropoiesis, it has recently been recognized that there is also a humoral control,[11] and a factor in plasma which increases the activity of the erythropoietic bone marrow has been demonstrated. This factor is augmented by hemorrhage, and it has been shown in experimental animals that the plasma from one animal which has previously been bled causes an increase in the numbers of circulating red cells when transfused into a second, normal animal.[4]

To be able to respond to the demands put upon it, the bone marrow must have available the building stones for erythropoiesis. These essential materials may form part of the heme moiety, which contains iron, or may be needed for the synthesis of the globin, or protein, fraction of the hemoglobin molecule. Lipoproteins are necessary for the formation of the cell envelope or stroma.

IRON CYCLE AND STORAGE OF FERRITIN. The process of hemopoiesis is closely related to iron metabolism since each hemoglobin molecule contains four atoms of this element. In normal persons, about 70 per cent of the body iron is circulating as hemoglobin, while the rest is retained in depots for use in blood formation as need arises. When red cells break down, the hemoglobin splits into globin, bilirubin and ferritin, an iron-coupled protein most of which is retained for resynthesis into hemoglobin. With a good mixed diet 1–2 mg. Fe in usable form is also absorbed daily from the gut.

The iron cycle and the importance of the conservation of available iron in the tissues have recently been more fully elucidated by the use of the radioisotope.[6] A protein, *apoferritin*, with an avidity for ferric hydroxide, with which it combines loosely, enables iron to be stored in the liver, spleen, bone marrow and intestinal mucosa, whence it is distributed as needed to the hemopoietic marrow. In normal healthy adults, this store contains about 600 mg. Fe, and, if depleted, it is only slowly replaced. Isotopic iron studies have shown that, in day-to-day erythropoiesis, the iron used is almost wholly derived from the breakdown of senile corpuscles; that derived from the gut forms only a small fraction of the total. The administration of extra iron to persons in normal iron balance is not followed by increased absorption. In circumstances in which hemopoiesis is more active, as after hemorrhage, during growth, or in pregnancy, the stored ferritin is mobilized,[27] and, with this decrease of depot iron, absorption of dietary iron is increased. As Hahn and his colleagues[21, 24] point out, the mucosa of the small intestine is the organ responsible for the acceptance or rejection of iron by the body, and it is, therefore, this tissue which is ultimately concerned with the maintenance of iron reserves. This control is effected by the amount of iron held in the mucosa. When demands for iron increase the mucosal ferritin is drawn upon, the ferritin barrier is lowered, and absorption from the gut is adjusted accordingly. When the ferritin content of the mucosa again rises, the barrier is re-established and absorption is correspondingly diminished.

VITAMIN B_{12} AND FOLIC ACID.   Recognition of the factors concerned in hemopoiesis has been largely dependent upon analysis of specific anemias in which blood formation is defective. In pernicious anemia the error lies in a delay in the maturation of the erythroblasts. As these are retained in the marrow, too few cells enter the circulation and anemia is produced. Moreover, those cells which are released are abnormally large (*megalocytes*) and constitute the finding in the peripheral blood typical of this disease. Twenty years ago, Castle showed that a dietary *extrinsic* factor, found particularly in liver and red meat, is essential for blood formation in conjunction with an *intrinsic* factor secreted in the gastric juice by the fundal glands of normal persons. In megalocytic anemia, the gastric juice is abnormal. Achlorhydria is common and the intrinsic factor is absent, while histologic examination frequently reveals degenerative changes in the mucosa of the fundus.

This simple concept of extrinsic factor + intrinsic factor → hemopoietic factor cannot easily be fitted into present knowledge of the complex vitamin B_{12} and folic acid reactions. Vitamin B_{12}, a cobalt-containing compound, has been shown to be effective in small doses in relieving megalocytic anemia, and it has been claimed that vitamin B_{12} and Castle's extrinsic factor are closely related. Certainly, when given orally, vitamin B_{12} is without effect upon hemopoiesis in patients with achlorhydria and is only active after it has reacted with gastric juice. On the other hand, when this vitamin is administered intravenously, it is potent in the treatment of megalocytic anemia, which suggests existence of a circulating factor with which the vitamin combines.[7] Thus,

$$\begin{array}{c} \text{Injected Vitamin } B_{12} + \text{Circulating "Intrinsic" Factor} \searrow \\ \text{Hemopoietic} \\ \text{Factor} \\ \text{Oral Vitamin } B_{12} + \text{Gastric "Intrinsic" Factor} \nearrow \end{array}$$

It has been shown biochemically that vitamin B_{12} and folinic acid are both essential in the formation of nucleosides, and that, in the absence of these substances, the methene bridges of purines and pyramidine rings cannot be closed. This relation undoubtedly is significant to the formation of the hemoglobin complex in the developing erythron.

Folic acid (*pteroylglutamic acid*) is chemically unrelated to vitamin B_{12}, but promotes maturation of erythroblasts in patients with megalocytic anemia. This action probably results from conversion of folic acid to folinic acid by enzymic oxidation in the presence of vitamin C.[35] Folinic acid is biochemically associated with vitamin B_{12}, as mentioned above.

Although many individual pieces in the complex jigsaw puzzle of hemopoietic factors are now known, how they fit together is still obscure. It is impossible, at present, to offer from the many experimental data available a clear and comprehensive picture of the manner in which vitamin B_{12}, folic acid, folinic acid and the intrinsic and extrinsic factors react to regulate and maintain normal blood formation.

TRACE ELEMENTS.   *Copper.*   It has long been known that traces of copper are essential for hemopoiesis. In the absence of this element the absorption and utilization of iron is deficient and the heme fraction of hemoglobin cannot be synthesized. Copper appears to act as a catalyst in a nonspecific manner in the utilization of the iron stores in the liver and spleen. The daily requirement for copper is about 2.0 mg. daily for adults, an amount easily surpassed on a normal diet. Copper is protein-bound for transportation in the blood.

Cobalt.   Cobalt deficiency in sheep and cattle produces disease characterized by anemia. In man no such disease is known, although the presence of cobalt in the vitamin B_{12} molecule suggests that this element is essential. It has been used in the treatment of various types of anemia in man with irregular results, but the weight of evidence suggests that cobalt does not stimulate hemopoiesis. The estimated daily requirement is 1 μg. for adults, a figure so small that it is difficult to believe that deficiency can develop, since cobalt is a common contaminant of "tap" water.

Other trace elements. From time to time claims have been made that various minerals are essential for blood formation. Of these, manganese, zinc, nickel, vanadium, molybdenum and germanium may be mentioned, although there is little to support the contention that deficiency of any of them may cause a failure of hemopoiesis.

OTHER FACTORS IN HEMOPOIESIS. The body seems well able to synthesize the porphyrin fraction of hemoglobin. When N^{15}-labeled glycine was fed to rabbits, the isotope was rapidly incorporated in the heme fraction of the molecule. In animals rendered anemic by hemorrhage or with phenylhydrazine, most of the tagged glycine appeared in the corpuscles within the first 24 hours, while with nonanemic animals the process was prolonged over five to nine days. In protein-starved rabbits the time over which the N^{15}-heme continued to increase in the circulation was longer than in the controls. It was found, moreover, that the highest proportion of the isotope appeared in the reticulocytes (newly formed erythrocytes) in the circulation.[43] Similar observations show that in man the isotope continues to increase in the circulating heme for about 20 days and that its first appearance in the peripheral blood is more delayed than it is in rabbits. These differences are best interpreted as reflecting a slower rate of erythroblastic maturation in man.[23] Although chlorophyll from green plants contains porphyrin, there is little evidence that its ingestion promotes hemoglobin formation unless iron is also readily available.

The globin fraction of hemoglobin constitutes 96 per cent of the molecule. Its lack is a limiting factor in hemopoiesis only under starvation conditions. Observations on prisoners from German concentration camps[30] showed that hemoglobin levels fell to about 60 per cent of normal in extreme inanition. In these cases hemosiderin was present in both liver and spleen, a finding which showed that the iron stores of the body were being conserved. In these victims, restoration of a normal diet was accompanied by hemopoiesis without other specific therapeutic measures. The Minnesota experiment,[36] involving the study of starvation in volunteers but excluding the side effects of camp conditions found in prisoners, has confirmed these findings.

In recent years it has become evident that there are several types of normal hemoglobin. As has been noted (p. 512), there is a distinctive fetal type (HbF) in which the oxygen dissociation curve is shifted to the left of the adult (HbA) type. This shift allows greater saturation with O_2 at low O_2 tensions and facilitates release of CO_2 at high CO_2 tensions. HbF is, therefore, an admirable adaptation for intrauterine life. The HbF:HbA ratio in the blood at birth is about 4:1, but this falls rapidly to 1:10 during the first months of life.[71] The recognition that the differences between HbF and HbA lie in the globin fraction led to investigation of the hemoglobin in certain blood diseases. By chromatographic methods some 17 types of hemoglobin have now been distinguished; these differ from each other in their amino acid constituents,[40] and the types are determined genetically by paired allelomorphs. Some of the recognized types (e.g., HbS in sickle cell anemia) cause serious disease when they occur homozygously, but give rise to "traits" rather than to the overt disease when present heterozygously. Other types appear to be "normal" hemoglobins unassociated with any blood disease. Interaction of the genetic types producing variations in blood diseases is becoming more widely recognized as of major clinical significance, and these types may have played an important role in the natural selection of man and in the distribution of racial types.

Aging and Normal Destruction of Erythrocytes. When a blood sample is withdrawn from the circulation and examined microscopically, appearance does not distinguish the young from the older erythrocytes. Certain features, however, are typical of the aging cell. When first released into the blood stream, red cells tend to be a little larger than those which have been circulating for some time. During their lives, red cells gradually metabolize lipoids, so that by careful centrifugation, cells of various ages can be separated into different layers.[53] When this technique was combined with the use of radioiron, so that Fe^{59} was built into the erythrocytes before their release from the bone marrow, it was possible to show that the older cells are considerably heavier than those just entering the circulation. This change in density is mainly dependent upon the relative loss of lipoid from the older cells. Alteration in lipid content is reflected in the increased osmotic fragility of older cells (see below) which probably plays an important part in the removal of the senescent cells from the circulation. Certainly cells artificially denuded of lipid are rapidly destroyed in the blood stream.[26]

Throughout its life the red cell membrane is permeable to water but not readily to cations, so that *hemolysis* (the destruction of the red cell with liberation of hemoglobin) in hypotonic saline may be explained by the osmotic attraction of water into the corpuscle with consequent stretching and ultimate rupture of its membrane, escape of hemoglobin, and formation of a clear red solution. In this solution, the cell envelope (*stroma*) can be seen in centrifuged deposits as a distorted, flaccid "ghost" which ultimately undergoes disintegration. On the other hand, if the cell is exposed to hypertonic solutions in which a nonpenetrating ion is present, water is withdrawn from the cell, causing it to shrink and wrinkle (*crenate*). Crenation often damages the cell membrane and facilitates subsequent hemolysis.

Osmotic fragility test. The resistance of red cells to osmotic hemolysis can be placed on a quantitative basis by exposing them to saline solutions of varying degrees of hypotonicity and ascertaining by centrifugation those concentrations needed to produce (i) the start of hemolysis, i.e., lysis of the more fragile cells, and (ii) complete hemolysis. This fragility test gives normal values of 0.45 to 0.39 per cent NaCl for the start of hemolysis and 0.35 to 0.30 per cent NaCl for complete cell destruction. There is, therefore, a considerable reserve of protection against sudden osmotic shifts of fluid in and out of the corpuscle under normal conditions. The fragility test is of clinical diagnostic value in certain blood diseases. In acholuric jaundice and in sickle cell anemia, for instance, the fragility of the red cells is increased, whereas in pernicious anemia the cells are less fragile than normal. These variations are, moreover, associated with the age of the cells, young forms (*reticulocytes*) being more resistant and aging cells less resistant to saline hemolysis.

While the red cell is in the circulation its membrane is mechanically injured both by constant buffeting in the blood stream and by the alterations in its tension dependent upon the ionic changes associated with the transference of oxygen and carbon dioxide. Consequent to this damage, the aging erythrocyte becomes more spheroidal or deformed (*poikilocytosis*), and either one of these physical changes facilitates rupture of the cell envelope. Normally, the end stages of cell destruction take place in the reticuloendothelial system, particularly of the bone marrow, liver and spleen; however, except in certain disease states (e.g., typhoid fever), it is rarely possible to demonstrate phagocytosis of erythrocyte remnants. The precise manner in which final hemolysis takes place is still a subject for speculation. A lytic agent (*lysolecithin*) has been demonstrated in plasma, but it is unlikely that this agent is wholly responsible for blood destruction. Nevertheless, prolonged stasis of blood, especially in the splenic sinusoids, may allow lysolecithin levels to rise, and this higher concentration, together with alterations in corpuscular pH and osmotic swelling due to lowered oxygen tension in this organ, may promote the rupture of the aged erythrocyte. The spleen has long been regarded as the main graveyard of red cells, but doubt has been thrown upon its predominance in this respect, for in previously normal persons subjected to splenectomy after injuries, polycythemia does not tend to develop. Such a sequel might be expected if the spleen were the organ principally responsible for the removal of senescent cells. It is, moreover, probable that the breakdown of the erythrocyte is brought about by its own metabolic exhaustion.

Abnormal Mechanisms of Red Blood Cell Destruction. Erythrocyte destruction can be caused by various types of hemolysis, hemoglobin alterations and parasites. In hemolysis or laking, hemoglobin escapes from the corpuscle; the process is complex, simple fragmentation under certain conditions being insufficient to release the hemoglobin. Hemolysis may result from physical damage to the cell membrane by shaking, freezing and thawing, by heat, by exposure to light in the presence of certain photochemical sensitizers (hemoporphyrin, eosin, etc.), by exposure to radium and x-irradiation or to ultraviolet light, and by the passage of electric currents. Hemolysis is also caused by any chemical agent or proteolytic enzyme capable of destroying the lipoprotein of the cell membrane.

SEROLOGIC AGGLUTINATION AND HEMOLYSIS.   The sera of many species possess the property of agglutinating and hemolyzing the erythrocytes of other species, both *in vivo* following transfusion and *in vitro*. To such phenomena may be attributed in large part the reactions and fatalities that, in the past, followed blood transfusions from one species to another. Not all human erythrocytes possess an identical antigenic structure, and their associated sera also differ in their corresponding agglutinins. The existence of these "iso" antigens and "iso" antibodies was discovered in 1901 by Landsteiner, who found that human bloods fall into four main serologic groups. The current international classification of these groups is as follows:

RED CELL FACTORS (Agglutinogens)	SERUM FACTORS (Agglutinins)	PERCENTAGE OF POPULATION IN EACH GROUP
O	anti-A and anti-B	46
A	anti-B	42
B	anti-A	9
AB	neither	3

It will be noted that every individual has in his serum antibodies against those antigens which his erythrocytes do not contain. Since transfusion with blood from a person of another group may result in fatal reactions, it is essential to test the bloods for compatibility. Typing is performed by mixing a suspension of red cells from the patient with sera known to contain anti-A and anti-B agglutinins. No agglutination with either serum shows that the patient has blood of Group O; agglutination with the anti-A serum, of group A; with the anti-B serum, of group B; and with each serum, of group AB. Transfusions should, whenever possible, be made with blood of the recipient's own group and, as a further safeguard, a cross-matching test, in which the patient's red cells are mixed with the donor's serum, and vice versa, should always be made. When crossmatching is performed on a microscope slide only, errors often occur. The proper technique is to mix cells and serum in agglutination tubes which are incubated at 37° C. for 15 minutes; suspensions are then examined microscopically for cell clumping.

It is apparent that cells of a group O individual will not be agglutinated by sera of any of the other groups, while his own serum, unless extremely potent in anti-A and anti-B agglutinins, will be so diluted in the recipient's blood stream that the titer will fall to an ineffective level. Group O individuals are, therefore, sometimes regarded as "universal donors." Conversely, group AB individuals may be considered as "universal recipients." However, transfusions of whole blood based on these principles are potentially dangerous and should be made only in emergencies. A further source of danger is the use of pooled plasma, which frequently replaced blood for transfusion in war casualties. This practice has now been abandoned because the virus of serum hepatitis, a serious and often fatal disease, may be transmitted. Substances with the characteristics of A and B agglutinogens are also found outside the erythrocytes. About 80 per cent of persons are "secretors" who show the group-specific substance of their particular blood type in their saliva, gastric juices, blood platelets, etc.

Although the differences in the Landsteiner groups constitute the main hazards in blood transfusion, other antigens are now recognized to be present in normal red cells. In 1940, Wiener and Peters[67] demonstrated the presence of another antigen in the erythrocytes of about 85 per cent of the white population. This is the *Rh factor*, so called because it was first detected by the use of antibodies produced in guinea pigs following injections of *rhesus* monkey red cells. This first Rh antigen has proved to be one of a complex group, but it differs from the others in being more strongly antigenic and remains the one of greatest clinical importance. Human serum ordinarily contains no corresponding antibody, so that detection of these antigens depends upon the use of specially prepared animal sera or of serum from an Rh− person who has become sensitized to one or more of the Rh factors. The importance of these antigens lies in the fact that Rh− individuals may develop antibodies as a result of transfusion with Rh+ blood, so that any subsequent transfusion of blood which contains such factors may give rise to severe reactions. Moreover, since the Rh factors are determined genetically, an Rh− mother may have an Rh+ child through inheritance from an Rh+ father. During pregnancy, such a mother may become sensitized by the antigen derived from the fetus, and the maternal antibody so induced then passes back through the placenta into the child. To this transfer has been attributed the various types of hemolytic disease (icterus gravis neonatorum, erythroblastosis fetalis, etc.) sometimes seen in the neonatal period. Furthermore, if the mother herself should then receive a transfusion of Rh+ blood, a severe reaction might follow. For these reasons, in every first pregnancy the Rh characteristics of both parents should, if possible, be determined. In all transfusions, particularly in women, the blood of the donor should be proved compatible for Rh (including its subtypes), as well as for the ABO groups.

The determination of the Rh subtypes is somewhat complicated, since the inherited Rh antigens are differentiated into at least 12 main allelomorphic genes of equal dominance which give rise to 78 possible genotype combinations. In practice, however, many of these genotypes are so rare that they can usually be ignored; and only six, representing about 93 per cent of all persons, are common. Tests for these six are normally carried out, and further investigations are undertaken only if a rare type is encountered.

Besides the Rh complex antigens, others are also known, the M, N, S and P factors being of occasional forensic interest.

Chemical Alteration of Hemoglobin. Methemoglobin is formed when the ferrous iron of hemoglobin is converted to the ferric form, as when blood is treated with an oxidizing agent *in vitro*. *In vivo*, methemoglobin is formed in the blood of patients poisoned with phenylhydrazine, pyrogallol, nitrobenzene and other nitro and amide compounds. In clinical practice, minor degrees of methemoglobinemia are encountered after the therapeutic use of sulfonamide drugs, nitrates, methylene blue, sulfonal, potassium chlorate, etc. Sulfhemoglobin seems to require preliminary formation of methemoglobin and is more frequently found post mortem than during life. A frequent form of asphyxial death is caused by the breathing of carbon monoxide; with this gas, hemoglobin forms a stable compound, CO-hemoglobin, which is bright cherry red. Since hemoglobin has a much higher affinity for carbon monoxide than for oxygen, the corpuscles are no longer available for normal respiratory purposes.

Preservation of Red Blood Cells. An isotonic solution containing sodium chloride alone (0.9 gram per 100 ml. for mammalian tissues, 0.65 gram for those of frogs and turtles) fails to keep tissues in a state of normal activity. It was shown by Ringer (1880–1883), and subsequently by others, that small amounts of potassium and calcium salts, together with bicarbonate and phosphate, are needed to maintain the beating of the frog heart. Formulas for solutions suitable for mammalian tissues are given in Table 11.

TABLE 11. MODIFIED RINGER'S SOLUTIONS FOR MAMMALIAN TISSUES

SUBSTANCE	LOCKE'S SOLUTION FOR RABBIT HEART (GM. PER 100 ML.)	TYRODE'S SOLUTION FOR RABBIT INTESTINE (GM. PER 100 ML.)
NaCl	0.9	0.8
KCl	0.042	0.02
$CaCl_2$	0.024	0.02
$MgCl_2$		0.01
$NaHCO_3$	0.015 (0.01 to 0.03)	0.1
NaH_2PO_4		0.005
Glucose	0.1	0.1
Oxygen	Saturated	Saturated

Although a modified Ringer's solution is useful in acute experiments with tissues, it is inadequate for the preservation of blood cells. When blood is to be used for transfusion, coagulation must be prevented and 4 per cent sodium citrate solution in the proportion of 1 part to 10 parts of blood is the anticoagulant most frequently used. The addition of citrate alone, however, does not preserve blood for more than a few days, as the cells undergo lysis. It was found that this lysis could be greatly delayed by the addition of dextrose to the citrate and by reduction of its pH. This observation resulted in the wide use of various acid-citrate-dextrose (A.C.D.) solutions, which maintain stored blood fit for transfusion for about three weeks. One formula for an A.C.D. solution is as follows:

> Disodium citrate, monohydric.......................... 2 gm.
> Dextrose, anhydrous................................... 3 gm.
> Water..120 ml.

An alternative formula (U.S. Pharmacopeia XIV, 1950, p. 550) calls for the following:

> Trisodium citrate, dihydrate.......................... 13.2 gm.
> Citric acid, monohydrate............................. 4.8 gm.
> Dextrose, monohydrate............................... 14.7 gm.
> Water for injection, to make.........................1,000.0 ml.

These solutions must, of course, be sterile and pyrogen-free. In either instance 120 ml. of solution is used for 420 to 480 ml. of blood (i.e., the usual donation volume), and the mixture is ordinarily stored at 2° C. Under these conditions, many cells become crenated because of the high dextrose content of the fluid and its low pH, so that, on transfusion, these corpuscles are hemolyzed in the blood stream of the recipient. New methods of storage, however, are becoming available since it has been found possible to remove 36 per cent of water from erythrocytes so that their hemoglobin is in the form of a gel rather than a saturated solution.[62, 63] This dehydration may be produced by sucrose, maltose, lactose and other sugars, to whose penetration the red cell envelope is resistant. The shrunken cells are separated from their plasma and suspended in solutions of purified human globulin and albumin, and, if stored at 0° C., they retain their functional integrity for some months. On replacement in plasma at room temperature the cells reassume their original size, and on subsequent transfusion their life span *in vivo* is within normal limits. Since the advent of ion exchange resins, it has been found possible to collect blood directly through such an agent operating on a sodium cycle (Dowex 50).[63] With this technique, all cations, including that of calcium, are replaced by sodium; therefore, no anticoagulant need be used. For erythrocyte storage, however, a replacement of Mg^{++}, Mn^{++}, Co^{++} and K^+ in various proportions appears to be necessary.[49] Although it is evident that this technique will undoubtedly supersede the use of A.C.D. solutions, various aspects of cell storage with this method require further investigation.

Bone Marrow Transfusion.   Under certain conditions in which the bone marrow has been destroyed, as after heavy nuclear or X-irradiation, marrow cells, fresh or preserved by deep-freezing in glycerol, may be transfused into the blood stream and become "seeded" in the marrow space. Such seeded marrow cells replace the recipient's own blood-forming organ, and, moreover, take over and restore his body defenses which ". . . now bear the imprint and password of the donor. His tissues—skin certainly, and presumably, by analogy, kidney, endocrine glands and other organs—are now accepted by the altered host. Thus . . . the recipient becomes a chimera producing and tolerating cells of the blood type of the donor and in general recognising his tissues as friendly."[65] Blood which is derived from such transplants retains the donor's characteristics, such as his ABO group and Rh type, or exhibits polymorphs with the X-chromosome "drumstick" if formed by cells from female donors transplanted to male recipients. At present, work along these lines is still in its initial stages, but it opens large fields for investigatory projects in physiology and pathology.

LEUKOCYTES

Development and Morphology of the Leukocytes.   The various types of leukocyte in the blood stream arise from three "blast" cells in the blood-forming organs (see p. 508). All three (myeloblasts, monoblasts and lymphoblasts) are large cells with pale basophilic nuclei showing a loose chromatin network and numerous rodlike mitochondria in the cytoplasm. The three types are difficult to distinguish except by vital stains and peroxidase tests.

MYELOCYTIC (GRANULOCYTIC) SERIES.   Because polymorphonuclear cells contain distinctive granules, it has been easier to trace the development of these cells than that of other leukocytes. The myeloblast, which is 11 to 18 μ in diameter and exhibits no granules in its basophilic cytoplasm, has a round or oval, finely reticular and poorly staining nucleus. It undergoes mitotic division to form, successively, promyelocytes, myelocytes and metamyelocytes. With difficulty, these forms may be differentiated by their diminishing degrees of basophilia, by the numbers of their mitochondria, and by the size and numbers of their granules. The number of granules is progressively greater in the more mature forms, and those in the myelocytic and metamyelocytic phases are recognizable as neutrophilic, eosinophilic or basophilic in their staining properties. In all three phases the cells have large, round or kidney-shaped, poorly staining nuclei, and all are motile, exhibiting ameboid movements.

At the time of release from the marrow, cells of the myelocytic series are characterized by their irregularly shaped basophilic nuclei and cytoplasmic granules. There are three varieties: the *neutrophil*, with numerous small purple-staining granules; the *eosinophil*, with many large red-staining granules; and the *basophil*, with large, scanty granules that stain deep blue-black (see Fig. 308). The nucleus of circulating neutrophilic granulocytes is divided irregularly into two to five lobes connected by fine strands. The number of lobes indicates the cell's age; in newly liberated leukocytes in the blood stream, the nucleus is horseshoe-shaped with indefinite lobulation (*stab cells*), whereas in aging cells the lobes are clearly separated and multiple (Fig. 308). In the differential Arneth count, the proportions of cells with varying numbers of lobes are determined; an increase in the frequency of oligolobate cells indicates that young granulocytes are entering the circulation. Such counts are sometimes used to assess the leukopoietic response to pyogenic infections.

Recent work has shown that the shape of the nuclear lobes affords a method of determining the sex of the individual from which blood has been derived; in the female a small node or "drumstick" of nuclear material is often clearly demonstrable in stained preparations (Fig. 309).[8] This drumstick lobe is believed to be associated with the X chromosome of the female. This finding is useful in forensic medicine, and it also helps the endocrinologist determine whether certain intersexed patients should be considered to be males or females.

MONOCYTIC SERIES. The monoblast, like the myeloblast which it closely resembles, undergoes mitotic division to form the promonocyte and, finally, the mature monocyte or large mononuclear cell of the circulating blood. The close resemblance of the blast and pro phases of the monocytes and granulocytes, combined with the observation that stimulation of their production is often simultaneous, suggests a close affinity between these two series. The monocytes are the largest cells in the circulation (16 to 22 μ), have oval or kidney-shaped eccentric nuclei (which stain a pale violet), and possess abundant cytoplasm.

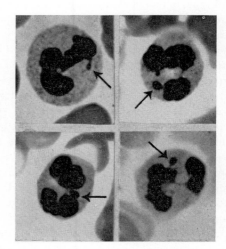

FIG. 309. Stained polymorphonuclear leukocytes from women. *Arrows*, "Drumstick" or node of nuclear material peculiar to women. ($\times$ 1700.)

LYMPHOCYTIC SERIES. Although in the adult both monocytes and granulocytes are normally produced solely in the marrow sinuses, lymphocytes are formed predominantly in the lymphatic tissues. The fetal germinal centers in the spleen, the systemic lymph nodes and the lymphadenoid structures of the alimentary tract retain their activity for the production of these cells; and recently it has been shown that lymphocytes are able, even after leaving their organ of origin, to divide mitotically,[18] especially in the lymph of the thoracic duct. This may be of great importance in maintaining lymphocyte numbers in the blood.

Although closely resembling the myeloblast in appearance, the lymphoblast has a nucleus which is more coarsely reticular and stippled and which has a more definite membrane. The lymphoblast undergoes division to form a prolymphocytic stage, a large cell with pale basophilic cytoplasm and a well defined, round or oval nucleus. This cell in turn gives rise to lymphocytes of the blood stream, which vary considerably in size and are sometimes subdivided into large and small varieties. They have large, deeply staining round or indented nuclei and a clear pale blue cytoplasm which may exhibit a few granules.

Leukocyte Numbers. The counts of the different types of leukocyte vary widely even in a normal person; this instability in both total and relative numbers is shown by the following tabulation:

	TOTAL PER CU.MM.	PERCENTAGE
Neutrophil polymorphonuclear..................	1,500–7,500	33–75
Lymphocyte.................................	1,000–4,500	15–60
Monocyte....................................	0–800	0–9
Eosinophil polymorphonuclear...................	0–400	0–6
Basophil polymorphonuclear....................	0–200	0–2

Physiologic fluctuations occur from day to day, and there is clear evidence of a diurnal rhythm, the highest counts being found in the afternoon. Raised counts are also found during digestion, following violent exercise, in pregnancy and in the neonatal period. Leukocyte counts should, therefore, preferably be made under basal conditions and at a fixed hour of the day.

Factors Influencing Leukopoiesis. The chief stimulus to leukopoiesis is acute infection with a pyogenic organism. The response is rapid, and within a few hours the white cell count may increase many fold (*leukocytosis*). Although the absolute numbers of all types of leukocyte usually rise, the neutrophilic polymorphs and later the monocytes increase relatively more than the others, so that the differential count shows a marked swing in their favor. In such cases it is essential to remember that a *percentage* rise in one type of cell appears to be at the expense of the others, and such an apparent imbalance must not be confused with a specific *leukopenia* (abnormal reduction in numbers). Leukocytosis is also promoted by hemorrhage, tissue damage and certain intoxications with bacterial products and drugs. In allergic states and in helminthic infestations there is often an increase in the number of eosinophils (*eosinophilia*), which suggests that certain types of foreign protein sensitization may stimulate the production of this kind of leukocyte. Also, eosinophils appear to be controlled by the pituitary-adrenocortical hormones, and so sensitive are these cells to cortisone and ACTH that their disappearance from peripheral blood is used in the biologic assay of these substances. The removal of lymphocytes, as by cannulation of the thoracic duct, stimulates a transitory lymphocytosis which is succeeded by a lymphopenia probably resulting from fatigue of the lymphopoietic tissue.[18]

The physiologic stimulus which promotes leukopoiesis is not at present fully understood. Abnormal breakdown of white cells apparently stimulates the outpouring of young cells from the marrow. A similar effect follows tissue destruction, while, experimentally, leukocythemia can be induced by the injection of nucleic acid and its derivatives. It seems likely that in normal health the disintegration of senescent polymorphs may, by their lysis, provide the chemical stimulus for leukocyte liberation. The isolation of a specific *leukocytosis-promoting factor* (L.P.F.)[41] from pseudoglobulin fractions of exudates confirms the view that chemical factors are of importance in regulating white cell numbers. It has also been shown that the tonicity of tissue fluids is associated with white cell count, hypertonicity being followed by leukocytosis.[66] Furthermore, the effect of adrenocortical activity causes an increase in circulating neutrophils while diminishing the numbers of lymphocytes and eosinophils. It seems, therefore, that the maintenance of a steady leukocyte count depends upon a balanced mechanism with several interacting factors.

Life Span and Destruction of Leukocytes. The life span of leukocytes is still undetermined. A figure of two to three days was previously accepted for granulocytes, but tracer studies[37] have suggested that their survival *in vivo* may be as long as two weeks. Compatible with the belief that the life of the leukocyte is comparatively short is the fact that, although erythrocytes are many hundred times more numerous than white cells in blood, cells of the erythropoietic series occupy only a small part of the active red marrow, the rest being devoted to myeloid activity.

The survival time of lymphocytes is probably short, and, in experiments with rabbits, the estimated output of these cells from the thoracic duct would replace all those in the circulation about 11 times a day.[19] It is likely, however, that many of these are being recirculated from blood to lymph and back to blood. Radioisotope studies have suggested that the lymphocyte population may be of two types (possibly corresponding to the large and small lymphocytes) with mean ages of two to three days (20 per cent) and 100 to 200 days (80 per cent) respectively.[46]

Granulocytes become senile and die while in the circulation and are ultimately disposed of through phagocytosis by cells of the reticuloendothelial system. Observations made on transfused leukocytes tagged with P^{32} suggest that redundant and senescent leukocytes are rapidly withdrawn from the circulation and sequestered in the lungs. From there they are slowly released for final destruction in the liver and spleen.[68]

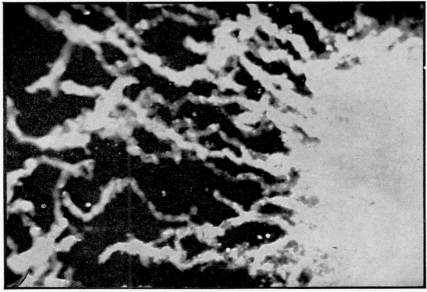

FIG. 310.   Migration pattern produced by leukocytes moving toward clump of *Staphylococcus albus* (*right*). Tracks of individual granulocytes are readily identified. ($\times$ 240, exposure 15 min.) (From Harris, *J. Path. Bact.*, 1953, *66*:135–146.)

The fate of lymphocytes is still uncertain,[19] although they too are probably removed by the reticuloendothelial cells, particularly in the lymph nodes. There is little modern evidence to support the idea that senescent lymphocytes are excreted into the gut.

Function of Leukocytes.   Leukocytes play a significant role in protection against infection. They are capable of ameboid movement and can undergo great alterations in shape without structural damage. Their cell membrane is sticky, so that they readily adhere to foreign surfaces. In dried films the leukocytes assume a rounded form, and it is not until they are seen in the living state in transparent tissues, such as the mesentery, that their ability to insinuate themselves through the endothelium of blood vessels into the tissues (*diapedesis*) in order to reach sites of tissue injury can be fully appreciated. The extravascular movement of neutrophils is largely dependent upon stimuli arising from focal liberation of chemical substances by bacteria or damaged tissues. Under these conditions their rate of movement is some 30 μ per minute. *Chemotaxis* may be either positive (attractive) or negative (repulsive). Figure 310 demonstrates how granulocytes in a warm, moist film migrate toward a small clumped mass of staphylococci.[25] The photograph was taken with dark-ground microscopy, and, since the exposure was continued for some minutes, the movement of each leukocyte is disclosed by its distinctive track.

The chemotatic emigration of white cells is, however, only the prelude to the main function of neutrophils and monocytes in the defense of the body against microorganisms. Both of these types of cell are actively *phagocytic* and engulf foreign particles, such as bacteria, to which they are attracted. While the monocytes are particularly concerned with the enzymic breakdown of lipids, the granulocytes appear to engulf bacteria whole, and in certain infections may be seen containing numerous ingested microorganisms (Fig. 311). Once the bacteria have entered the leukocyte, they are digested by the action of its cytoplasmic proteolytic enzymes. Sometimes, after phagocytosis of virulent bacteria, the white cells themselves succumb, and the products of their autolytic breakdown contribute to the formation of pus. Phagocytosis takes place much more effectively in animals that have been specifically immunized against the invading organism than in unimmunized controls. This process by which bacteria are rendered more susceptible to ingestion by leukocytes is known as *opsonization*.

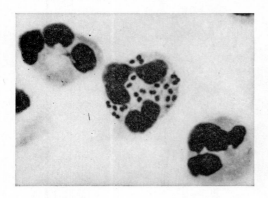

FIG. 311. Phagocytosis of *Neisseria meningitidis* by neutrophil leukocytes. The paired microorganisms are clearly visible in the cytoplasm. ($\times$ 1200.)

The monocytes and cells of the reticuloendothelial system play a major part in the production of immune substances (*antibodies*). The presence of enhanced concentrations of antibody in lymph nodes after regional injection of antigen into their drainage area is evidence that these structures partake in antibody production. The exact method by which this is achieved is uncertain, but the lymphocytes are known to be associated with the production of both the β and γ globulin fractions of plasma.[70] These fractions are probably derived from non-nucleated, globulin-containing cytoplasmic "buds" which are cast off from the parent cell and undergo disintegration in the plasma.[72] The production of such buds increases during an antibody response and appears to be controlled, at least in part, by pituitary–adrenocortical activity.

Finally, the basophilic granulocytes possess a very specialized function. The granules of these cells are a source of *heparin*, a polysaccharide which is a potent anticoagulant. The lysis of these leukocytes in the circulatory system is one of the factors believed to maintain the balance between the fluidity of the blood and the onset of coagulation. Besides the presence of heparin, the presence of histamine in the basophil is now recognized as important, and these cells have by far the highest (1080 μg. per 10^9 cells) histamine content of all leukocytes.[20] In certain species, such as the dog, liberation of heparin is accompanied by simultaneous release of histamine.[56]

Metabolism of the Leukocytes. As might be expected from their considerable activity, the respiratory rate of leukocytes is high. They also show marked aerobic glycolysis and actively convert pyruvates and glycogen within their cytoplasm into lactic acid. The white cells, moreover, contain many enzymes, of which pepsin, trypsin, phosphatase, lipase and lysozyme are the most important. It is probable that these enzymes are liberated only on the death and autolysis of the leukocytes, and in the process of suppuration take part actively in the degradation of the larger molecules present.

PLATELETS

Development and Morphology of Platelets. The blood platelets or thrombocytes are unique in the manner of their development, since they enter the blood stream only as discarded cytoplasmic buds from the fixed, extravascular *megakaryocytes* of the bone marrow. The first recognizable cell in the development of the thrombocyte series is the *megakaryoblast*, which is about twice the size of the myeloblast and has a single oval nucleus. From this cell, by mitosis, is formed the promegakaryocyte, which is larger than its parent cell and shows lobulation of its nucleus. The fully mature megakaryocyte, which develops from the promegakaryocyte, is a giant multinucleate cell, 40 to 70 μ in diameter. During growth of the cell, these nuclei all undergo division synchronously. Their cytoplasm is abundant and weakly basophilic. The megakaryocytes lie in the marrow substance outside the vascular sinuses, and young cells show powers of phagocytosis and ameboid movement. Their pseudopodia pass between the endothelial cells of the marrow sinusoids and in this position are nipped off to form the platelets of circulating blood.

The platelets are the smallest of the formed blood elements, with a diameter of 2 to 4 μ in dried films. They are non-nucleated, round or oval cellular structures which, with usual blood stains, are deeply blue-purple, their hyaline cytoplasm showing fine granulation (Fig. 308). When examined in the fresh state by phase-contrast microscopy, they are found to possess many fine flagella-like spicules which project from their surfaces. These processes are somewhat in the nature of pseudopodia, being pushed out or withdrawn according to the oxygen tension of the surrounding blood; they are more abundant in platelets from arterial blood than in those from reduced blood.[17] Electron microscopic studies suggest that the structure of the platelet membrane is identical to that of the other types of white blood cell. A comparison of the osmotic fragility of platelets with that of erythrocytes—the other non-nucleated blood elements—shows that platelets are rather easily ruptured, as their total disintegration occurs at concentrations between 0.44 to 0.34 per cent NaCl.[33]

Platelets adhere readily to foreign surfaces; the younger ones exhibit this characteristic more markedly than do the older forms,[74] an observation correlated with a decreased ability of senescent platelets to form pseudopodia or spicules. As a preliminary to disintegration, when in contact with a wettable foreign surface, the platelets clump together (conglutinate) and exhibit the *spreading phenomenon*, in which form they may achieve a diameter of 16 μ or more. In the spread condition, the cytoplasm becomes ballooned and vacuolated, but the platelets show no ameboid movement. In shed blood, the spicules form an incomplete network along which the fibrin crystals are subsequently laid down.

Platelet Numbers. Normally the platelet count lies between 250,000 and 500,000 per mm.[3], but these cells are irregularly distributed through the circulation; they are especially numerous in pulmonary blood. Daily fluctuations in count are random, showing no tendency to diurnal rhythm. A low platelet count (*thrombocytopenia*) is associated with sudden changes from the horizontal to the upright position, and follows x-, β- or γ-irradiation. An increased count (*thrombocythemia*) is found after exercise, during digestion, at high altitude and after exposure to ultraviolet light. There is, moreover, a slight but definite sex difference, men having a higher count than women. Women also show a drop of as much as 50 per cent at the onset of menstruation. A thrombocythemia occurs in pregnancy; in the newborn the platelet count is low.

Factors Influencing Platelet Formation.   The chief stimulus to platelet production appears to be the liberation of chemical substances, especially nucleic acid derivatives, into the circulation from the autolysis of injured tissues. Thrombocythemia invariably follows surgical operations, childbirth and any trauma to the tissues by infectious, mechanical or toxic agents. The maximal response in platelet numbers occurs about seven to ten days after the injury and is correlated with the extent of cellular destruction. Simple hemorrhage alone is insufficient to elicit a response; whereas the production of tissue destruction by sterile inflammatory reactions, even without surgical interference, is followed by a many fold rise in the number of circulating thrombocytes.[75]

Stimulation of platelet formation is also associated with lowered blood oxygen tensions, and asphyxia produced by either mechanical or chemical means is followed by an outpouring of platelets into the blood stream. This mechanism explains the increase in platelet numbers that is seen both in persons at high altitudes and also in patients who have been poisoned with such gases as carbon monoxide or nitrous oxide which lower the oxygen tensions in tissues and bone marrow.

Life Span of Platelets.   The life span of the platelets depends to some extent upon the wear and tear on the person, for once brought into contact with damaged tissue they undergo disintegration, so that the "rate of utilization" is perhaps of greater moment than the actual survival time of individual platelets. In cats rendered thrombocytopenic by roentgen irradiation, the total replacement time of circulating thrombocytes is three to four days; in patients with bone marrow aplasia, however, transfused platelets have been found to survive for five to six days.[32] The life span of platelets in the blood of caged rats has been carefully followed by observation of the uptake of $Na_2S^{35}O_4$ by megakaryocytes in the bone marrow and the appearance in the peripheral blood of radioactive platelets derived from them.[45] The results of this study indicated that the platelets survived for about four days, a figure which confirms that obtained by replacement studies.

Platelets are lost in the circulation by disintegration at any site of tissue damage, where they undergo lysis. If they escape local breakdown, they are finally destroyed by the cells of the reticuloendothelium, especially in the spleen, an inference based upon the observation that the platelet count is higher in arterial blood entering this organ than in the blood in its vein. Moreover, splenectomy in hematologically normal persons is followed by a considerable thrombocythemia which persists for several months until the other parts of the reticuloendothelial system have hypertrophied to assume the function of the spleen.

Functions of Platelets.   Platelets are intimately bound up with hemostasis after the severance of blood vessels, with blood coagulation, and with the retraction of formed clots. Hayem[28] was the first to recognize the presence of platelets during the formation of thrombi, and later Eberth and Schimmelbusch[10] watched their conglutination and adhesion at areas of damaged endothelium in living blood vessels. Here the platelets formed *white plaques* on which coagulum later became deposited.

The platelet surface carries a negative electric charge which normally repels them both from vascular endothelium, which is also so charged, and from each other. Any reduction of this potential, such as that brought about by damage to tissue,[58] allows the thrombocytes to clump together and stick to the vessel wall at the site of injury. The spreading phenomenon then occurs and the platelets disintegrate to liberate a substance, *thromboplastin* (or thrombokinase), which, in the presence of Ca^{++}, triggers the complicated coagulation mechanism by allowing the conversion of prothrombin to thrombin.

At the same time the adhesion of platelets at the damaged site acts as a mechanical plug to the ruptured vessels and prevents prolonged hemorrhage. As the blood flows over the cut edges of the vessels, the platelets stick to the margins until the openings are completely occluded and retrograde coagulation takes place in the now stagnant columns of blood between the proximal severed ends and the next anastomotic branch. This process is facilitated by the liberation of 5-hydroxytryptomine (serotonin) from the disintegrating platelets,[54] this material causing the shutting down of the severed and adjacent vessels. Serotonin, a powerful local vasoconstrictor and general hypotensive material, is produced by the enterochromaffin cells of the gastrointestinal mucosa and passes from them into the circulating plasma. Here it is rapidly and actively absorbed by the platelets, especially the young ones, and is carried by them throughout the body. This highly active material is thus usually maintained in an inactive form within the platelet, which normally liberates it with reluctance. When, however, serotonin is required at a site of tissue damage it is immediately available on the disruption of the carrier platelet. Hemostasis is thus aided not only by local vasoconstriction but also, after some of the liberated serotonin has entered the circulation, by a fall in systemic blood pressure which tends further to reduce hemorrhage.[12]

When the coagulation process has been initiated, the fibrin network is deposited along the platelet spicules. In this way the thrombocytes act as nodal points for the formation of fibrin crystals, and can be demonstrated clearly in stained fibrin films. Finally, platelets are of importance in the retraction of formed clots.[5] In their absence, the clot remains soft and friable and does not fall away from the containing vessel. The most recent view is that this retraction is caused by the withdrawal of the pseudopodal spicules of the platelets before their final disintegration. This process in turn tightens the fibrin net to which the spicules are adherent, thus drawing the whole clot together.

The post-traumatic increase in number and stickiness of the platelets may be regarded as a protective mechanism against hemorrhage. Occasionally, however, the response may be excessive, and in the presence of other factors, such as local retardation of the circulation rate, disbalance occurs and intravascular thrombosis supervenes. The characteristic modes of behavior of platelets can be modified by the use of anticoagulant substances. The removal of Ca ions from shed blood ensures that thromboplastin liberated from platelets is ineffective and so will not initiate coagulation. The adhesiveness of the thrombocytes is, moreover, decreased by all types of anticoagulants, so that, even when increased numbers of thrombocytes are present, the likelihood of white plaque formation on damaged endothelium is retarded and the consequent formation of further thrombosis prevented.

REFERENCES

1. BARNES, D. W. H., LOUTIT, J. F. and REEVE, E. B. Clin. Sci., 1948, 7:135–154, 155–173.
2. BISCHOFF, T. De nova methodo sanguinem chemice investigandi quam Emilius Harless Monachensis proposuit. Jena, Schreiberi et fil., 1856, 24 pp.
3. BLOOM, W. and BARTELMEZ, G. W. Amer. J. Anat., 1940, 67:21–53.
4. BORSOOK, H., GRAYBIEL, A., KEIGHLEY, G. and WINDSOR, E. Blood, 1954, 9:734–742.
5. BUDTZ-OLSEN, O. E. Clot retraction. Oxford, Blackwell, 1951, xiv, 149 pp.
6. CALLENDER, SHEILA T. Brit. med. Bull., 1959, 15:5–8.
7. CALLENDER, SHEILA T. and LAJTHA, L. G. Blood, 1951, 6:1234–1239.
8. DAVIDSON, M. M. and SMITH, D. R. Brit. med. J., 1954, 2:6–7.
9. DENSTEDT, O. F. Chap. 4 in Blood cells and plasma protein. Their state in nature, J. L. TULLIS, ed. New York, Academic Press, 1953.
10. EBERTH, C. J. and SCHIMMELBUSCH, C. Die Thrombose nach Versuchen und Leichenbefunden. Stuttgart, Enke, 1888, xii, 144 pp.
11. ERSLEV, A. J. and LAVETES, P. H. Blood, 1954, 9:1055–1061.
12. ERSPAMER, V. J. Physiol., 1956, 133:1–9.
13. FEISSLY, R. and LÜDIN, H. Rev. Hémat., 1949, 4:481–501.
14. FREINKEL, N., SCHREINER, G. E. and ATHENS, J. W. J. clin. Invest., 1953, 32:138–148.
15. GIBSON, J. G., 2ND, SELIGMAN, A. M., PEACOCK, W. C., AUB, J. C., FINE, J. and EVANS, R. D. J. clin. Invest., 1946, 25:848–857.
16. GIBSON, J. G., 2ND, WEISS, S., EVANS, R. D., PEACOCK, W. C., IRVINE, J. W., GOOD, W. M. and KIP, A. F. J. clin. Invest., 1946, 25:616–626.
17. GOODMAN, J. R., REILLY, E. B. and MOORE, R. E. Blood, 1957, 12:428–442.
18. GOWANS, J. L. Brit. J. exp. Path., 1957, 38:67–78.
19. GOWANS, J. L. Brit. med. Bull., 1959, 15:50–53.

20. GRAHAM, HELEN T., LOWRY, O. H., WHEEL-WRIGHT, FRANCES, LENZ, MIRIAM A. and PARISH, H. H., JR. Blood, 1955, 10:467–481.

21. GRANICK, S. Rep. Ross pediat. Res. Conf., 1956, 19:15–19.

22. GRANT, R. T. and REEVE, E. B. Spec. Rep. Ser. med. Res. Coun. (Lond.), 1951, 277:xiii, 313 pp.

23. GRAY, C. H. and NEUBERGER, A. Biochem. J., 1950, 47:81–87.

24. HAHN, P. F., BALE, W. F., LAWRENCE, E. O. and WHIPPLE, G. H. J. exp. Med., 1939, 69:739–753.

25. HARRIS, H. J. Path. Bact., 1953, 66:135–146.

26. HARRIS, I. M., MCALISTER, JOAN M. and PRANKERD, T. A. J. Clin. Sci., 1957, 16:223–230.

27. HASKINS, D., STEVENS, A. R., JR., FINCH, S. and FINCH, C. A. J. clin. Invest., 1952, 31:543–547.

28. HAYEM, G. Recherches sur l'anatomie normale et pathologique du sang. Paris, Masson, 1878, 1, 143 pp.

29. HEDIN, S. G. Skand. Arch. Physiol., 1891, 2:134–140.

30. HELWEG-LARSEN, P., HOFFMEYER, H., KIELER, J., THAYSEN, E. H., THAYSEN, J. H., THYGESEN, P. and WULFF, M. H. Acta med. scand., 1952, 144 (Suppl. 274):1–25.

31. HEVESY, G. and NYLIN, G. Acta physiol. scand., 1951, 24:285–292.

32. HIRSCH, E. O. and GARDNER, F. H. J. Lab. clin. Med., 1952, 39:556–569.

33. HOLLINGWORTH, J. W., FINCH, S. C. and CHANG, C. H. Blood, 1956, 11:665–672.

34. HORAN, M. Arch. Dis. Childh., 1950, 25:110–128.

35. JACOBSON, W. and GOOD, PHYLLIS, M. Quart. J. Med., 1952, 21:1–18.

36. KEYS, A., BROZEK, J., HENSCHEL, A., MICKELSEN, O. and TAYLOR, H. L. The biology of human starvation. Minneapolis, University of Minnesota Press, 1950, 2 vols.

37. KLINE, D. L. and CLIFFTON, E. E. Science, 1952, 115:9–11.

38. KNOLL, W. Acta haemat., 1949, 2:369–377.

39. LEESON, D. and REEVE, E. B. J. Physiol., 1951, 115:129–142.

40. LEHMANN, H. Brit. med. Bull., 1959, 15:40–46, pl. 1.

41. MENKIN, V. Blood, 1948, 3:939–947.

42. MOLLISON, P. L. Clin. Sci., 1947, 6:137–172.

43. NEUBERGER, A. and NIVEN, JANET, S. F. J. Physiol., 1951, 112:292–310.

44. NYBOER, J., BAGNO, S. and NIMS, L. F. The impedance plethysmograph, an electrical volume recorder. U. S. National Research Council Committee on Aviation Medicine, Rep. No. 149, 1943.

45. ODELL, T. T., JR., TAUSCHE, F. G. and GUDE, W. D. Amer. J. Physiol., 1950, 180:491–494.

46. OTTESEN, J. Acta physiol. scand., 1954, 32:75–93.

47. PAULING, L., ITANO, H. A., SINGER, S. J. and WELLS, I. C. Science, 1949, 110:543–548.

48. PEACOCK, W. C., EVANS, R. D., IRVINE, J. W., JR., GOOD, W. M., KIP, A. F., WEISS, S. and GIBSON, J. G., 2ND. J. clin. Invest., 1946, 25:605–615.

49. PENNELL, R. B. Chap. 3 in Blood cells and plasma proteins. Their state in nature. J. L. TULLIS, ed. New York, Academic Press, 1953.

50. PONDER, E. Hemolysis and related phenomena. New York, Grune & Stratton, 1948, viii, 398 pp.

51. PONDER, E. Blood, 1954, 9:227–235.

52. PRANKERD, T. A. J. Int. Rev. Cytol., 1956, 5:279–301.

53. PRANKERD, T. A. J. J. Physiol., 1958, 143:325–331.

54. RAND, M. and REID, G. Nature (Lond.), 1951, 168:385.

55. REEVE, E. B. and VEALL, N. J. Physiol., 1949, 108:12–23.

56. RILEY, J. F. Blood, 1954, 9:1123–1126.

57. RIMINGTON, C. Lancet, 1951, 261:551–556.

58. SAWYER, P. N. and PATE, J. W. Nav. med. Res. Inst. Rep., 1953, 11:109–128.

59. SCHULTZ, A. L., HAMMARSTEN, J. F., HELLER, B. I. and EBERT, R. V. J. clin. Invest., 1953, 32:107–112.

60. SJÖSTRAND, T. Physiol. Rev., 1953, 33:202–228.

61. STERLING, K. and GRAY, S. J. J. clin. Invest., 1950, 29:1614–1619.

62. STRUMIA, M. Chap. 2 in Blood cells and plasma proteins. Their state in nature, J. L. TULLIS, ed New York, Academic Press, 1953.

63. STRUMIA, M. M. Blood, 1954, 9:1105–1119.

64. SUNDHARAGIATI, B. and WRIGHT, C.-S. J. clin. Invest., 1953, 32:979–990.

65. THOMAS, E. D., LOCHTE, H. L., JR. and FERREBEE, J. W. Blood, 1956, 14:1–23.

66. TULLIS, J. L. Amer. J. med. Sci., 1948, 215:424–430.

67. WIENER, A. S. and PETERS, H. R. Ann. intern. Med., 1940, 13:2306–2322.

68. WEISBERGER, A. S., HEINLE, R. W., STORAASLI, J. P. and HANNAH, R. J. clin. Invest., 1950, 29:336–341.

69. WELCKER, H. Arch. Ver. gemeinsch. Arb. Förd. wissensch. Heilk. Göttingen, 1854, 1:195–208.

70. WHITE, A. and DOUGHERTY, T. F. Ann. N. Y. Acad. Sci., 1946, 46:859–882, 1 pl.

71. WHITE, J. C. and BEAVAN, G. H. Brit. med. Bull., 1959, 15:33–39, pl. 2.

73. WINTROBE, M. M. Clinical hematology, 4th ed. Philadelphia, Lea & Febiger, 1956, 1184 pp.

74. WRIGHT, H. PAYLING. J. Path. Bact., 1944, 56:151–159.

75. WRIGHT, H. PAYLING. J. Obstet. Gynaec. Brit. Emp., 1945, 52:253–258.

CHAPTER 24

Physical Chemistry of Blood

By DAVID I. HITCHCOCK

THE physiology of blood can be only partially understood through knowledge of its general properties and its formed elements. A better understanding has resulted from the application of the principles of physical chemistry to the behavior of gases, water, electrolytes and proteins in blood. For a more complete exposition of these laws, students are advised to consult a standard textbook of physical chemistry or one of the books written especially for medical students.[6, 17]

Equilibrium and Steady State. To a physical scientist the word *system* denotes any part of the universe which is selected for discussion. When a system is at *equilibrium,* its properties no longer change spontaneously with the lapse of time. A further criterion of equilibrium is that the same equilibrium state is approached from opposite directions. At equilibrium, all spontaneous processes have progressed as far as possible under the given conditions. A system at equilibrium cannot yield useful work to surroundings at the same temperature and pressure, and we say that its free energy is at a minimum. From these considerations it is obvious that no living organism or tissue can be in a state of complete physicochemical equilibrium.

However, the circulating blood in the higher animals is in a remarkably *steady state* in which its temperature and composition are normally maintained, within narrow limits, by physiologic regulatory processes. The result of this regulation is what Claude Bernard called "la fixité du milieu intérieur." This constancy is not a state of dynamic equilibrium like that of a reversible chemical reaction. For example, if ethyl acetate and water are mixed and the mixture is kept at a constant temperature, the chemical reaction proceeds to a definite state of equilibrium in which the hydrolysis and the synthesis of the ester, the direct and reverse reactions, are both going on at the same rate. In the blood, however, the constancy of composition is the result of equal rates of formation and destruction, or inflow and outflow, of biologic cells or chemical substances. In this case one reaction is not simply the reverse of the other, and the constancy is that of a steady state but not of an equilibrium state.

Within the blood there are many chemical reactions which may fairly be regarded as always in equilibrium. These include reactions involving ions in solution, such as the ionization of a weak acid and the recombination of its ions to form an undissociated molecule. Somewhat slower reactions are the transfer of water and certain solutes across cell membranes, but these are quite rapid because of the short distances involved. Other fairly rapid reactions are the transfer of gases between the blood and the air of the alveoli, and between the blood and tissue fluids. Physiologists have found it useful to consider the laws which apply to the equilibria approached in such processes, although the laws of equilibrium give no information about rates. The study of the rates of physical and chemical processes is beyond the scope of this chapter.

CHEMICAL COMPOSITION OF BLOOD

As a first approximation, it may be said that blood is about 80 per cent water. The proteins constitute about 18 per cent of blood, leaving 2 per cent for other solutes. About half of these are inorganic salts, the rest being organic molecules smaller than proteins. The important blood gases, oxygen and carbon dioxide, amount to little more than 0.1 per cent of the total mass of the blood.

The osmolar concentration, which is the total concentration of all dissolved particles, ions as well as molecules, amounts to about 0.3 mol per liter of blood. The results of blood analyses are often expressed in milligrams per 100 ml.; concentrations in these units are also commonly (though illogically) designated as milligrams per cent. Such data may be translated into milliequivalents (mEq.) or millimols (mM.) per liter by multiplying by 10 and dividing by the equivalent or the molecular weight of the sub-

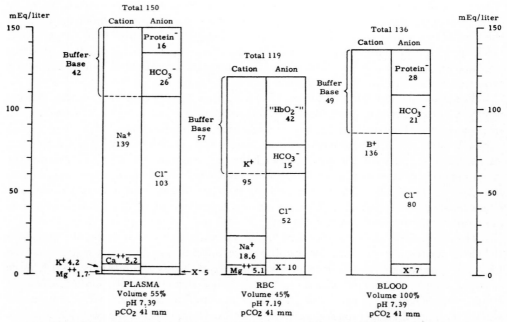

FIG. 312. Normal ionic patterns of arterial blood in adult man. Buffer base, the appropriate fraction of total cation or its equivalent amount, the labile fraction of total anions, i.e., proteinate, bicarbonate, oxyhemoglobinate, and other buffer anions. RBC, Red blood cells; pCO₂, partial pressure or tension of CO₂; X⁻, undetermined anion residue. HbO₂ includes such other buffer anions as organic phosphate. (From Singer in *Handbook of respiration*, P. L. Altman *et al.*, eds., Philadelphia, W. B. Saunders, 1958.)

TABLE 12.   DISTRIBUTION OF SOLUTES IN THE WATER OF PLASMA AND CELLS OF
           NORMAL HUMAN BLOOD

	SERUM		CELLS	
	$\dfrac{\text{mM.}}{\text{kg.H}_2\text{O}}$	$\dfrac{\text{mEq.}}{\text{kg.H}_2\text{O}}$	$\dfrac{\text{mM.}}{\text{kg.H}_2\text{O}}$	$\dfrac{\text{mEq.}}{\text{kg.H}_2\text{O}}$
Urea	7		7	
Glucose	4		4	
Other neutral organic solutes	?		?	
Sodium	150	150	27	27
Potassium	4	4	135	135
Calcium	3	5	0	0
Magnesium	1	2	3	5
Chloride	111	111	74	74
Bicarbonate	28	28	27	27
Inorganic phosphate	2	3	2	3
Acid-soluble organic phosphate	trace	unknown	21	unknown
Sulfate	1	1	?	?
Protein	1	18	7	62
Total base		161		167
Total acid		161		166
Total milliosmols	312		307	

From J. P. Peters, *Body water*, 1935, by courtesy of Charles C Thomas, publisher, Springfield, Illinois; revised values kindly supplied by Dr. Peters.

stance in question. For example, if blood plasma contains 370 mg. Cl per 100 ml., its chloride concentration is 3700/35.46 or 104 mEq. per liter; that is, 0.104 N. If the chloride concentration is reported as 610 mg. per cent of NaCl, the concentration of this salt is also 6100/58.45 or 104 mM. per liter, which is 0.104 M.

Figure 312 shows diagrammatically the concentrations of the ionized constituents of blood plasma, red cells and whole blood. The concentrations are expressed in milliequivalents per liter of plasma, cells or blood, respectively. The equal heights of the blocks representing cations and anions are consistent with the rule of electroneutrality, which is valid for any electrolytic solution. The unequal heights of the blocks for plasma and cells reflect the existence of different total concentrations.

In studying the properties of solutions, physical chemists have found that simpler results are obtained if the concentrations are referred to equal amounts of the solvent (*molality*), rather than to equal volumes of solution (*molarity*). The molality of an aqueous solution is the number of mols of solute per kilogram of water. For dilute solutions of small molecules, the molality is almost the same as the concentration or molarity (mols of solute per liter of solution). For blood plasma, however, and especially for the cells, the values are quite different, because the proteins occupy an appreciable portion of the total volume. According to Peters,[26] 1 liter of average plasma or serum contains 935 grams of water, whereas 1 liter of red blood cells contains only 707 grams of water. A plasma concentration of 0.104 N may also be expressed as 104/935 or 0.111 equivalents per kilogram of plasma water; a concentration of 0.052 N in blood cells means that there are 52/707 or 0.074 equivalents per kilogram of cell water. In any calculation involving osmotic pressure or other colligative properties of solutions, concentrations are best referred to 1 kg. of the solvent.

Distribution of Substances Between Cells and Plasma.   Table 12 shows the distribution of solutes in blood serum and cells in terms of millimols or milliequivalents per kilogram of water. There is still unequal distribution, but the discrepancies are smaller than those between the concentrations shown in Figure 312.

The unequal distribution of proteins is qualitative as well as quantitative in nature. The protein of the cells is almost entirely hemoglobin, which constitutes about 32 per cent of their weight. The stromata, the structural elements in the red cells, also contain some protein, probably about 1 per cent of the wet weight of the cells. These cell proteins are not found in plasma, and the plasma proteins are absent from the cells. Plasma contains about 7 grams of protein per 100 ml. Of this, about 0.2 to 0.4 gram is fibrinogen. The remaining plasma proteins are the serum proteins, which are classified as albumins and globulins on the basis of the concentrations of ammonium sulfate or other salt required to precipitate them. The albumin:globulin (A/G) ratio shows considerable variability in normal sera, and it also varies somewhat with the particular salting-out technique adopted; the normal ratio runs from about 1.5 to 2.0. (Electrophoretic measurements give a lower value for this ratio, about 1.2.)

Another marked instance of unequal distribution is that of the principal cations or bases,* sodium and potassium. In human blood the greater part of the potassium is found in the cells, whereas most of the sodium is in the plasma. These cations, as well as the proteins of the blood, are in some way restrained from free diffusion between the cell contents and the plasma. Yet the impermeability of the cells to potassium cannot be absolute, for the injection into the plasma of a salt solution containing a radioactive isotope of potassium has been followed by the detection of radioactivity in the cells. The mechanism responsible for the unequal distribution of cations is not known, but under most conditions the cells behave as if they were impermeable to all cations, with the possible exception of the hydrogen ion.† The situation with respect to anions is quite different, since the human red cell is freely permeable to chloride, bicarbonate and hydroxyl ions, although not to various other anions. It is also readily permeable to water and to many undissociated molecules, such as those of dissolved carbon dioxide or carbonic acid, ammonia or ammonium hydroxide, urea and glucose.

It will be noted that Table 12 shows a small discrepancy between the amounts of total base and total acid in the cells. This is not due to the omission of hydroxyl and hydrogen ions, for their molal concentrations lie in the seventh and eighth decimal places. If the analytical data were complete, the sums of the cation and anion equivalents would have to agree, for any solution must be electrically neutral with respect to ionic charges. The Table is admittedly incomplete; organic acids (other than proteins) are not included, and the amount of base neutralized by organic phosphate is unknown. The actual concentrations of bicarbonate ion are less than the values given, since these include carbon dioxide bound to proteins in carbamino complexes. It is possible that sodium and potassium proteinates are not completely ionized. There is good evidence that this is true of calcium proteinates, and there may be some nonionized chloride in combination with lipids. In view of these uncertainties, the agreement of the totals is much better than might have been expected, and it is quite possible that serum and cells may have the same total number of equivalents of ions per 1000 grams of water.

OSMOTIC EQUILIBRIUM

Total Osmotic Pressure of Blood. It has long been known that red blood cells can be made to swell or shrink by placing them in slightly hypotonic or hypertonic salt

---

* Physiologic and medical chemists use the term "base" to include metallic radicals or cations, as well as all compounds which can react with acids to form salts. This older usage is not consistent with the more recent definition of a base as a proton acceptor.

† The apparent permeability of the red cell to NH_4^+ has been ascribed to penetration by NH_3 or NH_4OH, and the apparent permeability to H^+ may result from permeability to OH^-.

solutions. Because water is so easily driven into or out of the cells in this way, it is inferred that the cell contents and the plasma must have the same total osmotic pressure. Hematocrit experiments have shown that human red cells retain their original volume in a sodium chloride solution containing approximately 0.9 gram of NaCl per 100 ml. (0.154 molar). The results of thermoelectric measurements,[20] which detect differences in vapor pressure or rate of evaporation of water, indicate that sera from normal men have the same osmotic activity as sodium chloride solutions of molal concentrations between 0.152 and 0.159. These results are consistent with the belief that a 0.9 per cent solution of sodium chloride (0.155 molal) is isotonic with either cells or plasma. Since the salt is believed to be completely dissociated into ions, the osmotically effective (osmolal) concentration of an isotonic salt solution is 0.310, a figure which agrees well with those given in the last line of Table 12.

The total osmotic pressure of a solution is approximately related to its total concentration by the same equation which applies to gas pressure:

$$P = 0.082 \ TC.$$

Here P is the pressure in atmospheres, T the absolute temperature, and C the concentration of the gas or the dissolved substance in mols per liter. (In the case of aqueous solutions, the equation fits better if the total molality (m) replaces C.) Accordingly, the osmotic pressure of blood plasma at 37° C. should be $0.082 \times 310 \times 0.31$, or about 7.9 atmospheres. This figure does not represent an actual pressure in the blood. It will be recalled that osmotic pressure is defined as the excess pressure which must be imposed upon a solution to prevent the entrance of pure solvent into the solution through a membrane permeable only to the solvent. Because the membranes of the body are permeable to most of the dissolved substances as well as to water, they do not fit the physical chemist's definition of a perfect semipermeable membrane, and the total osmotic pressures of body fluids are not manifested as actual pressures in the body.

However, since natural membranes are more readily permeable to water than to most other substances, a comparison of total osmotic pressures or concentrations often serves to indicate the direction in which water tends to flow. In a perfect osmometer, water moves away from a region in which its escaping tendency or vapor pressure is high. Since the vapor pressure of the solvent is lowered by the presence of a solute, the usual direction of osmotic flow is into the more concentrated solution. This need not be the case if the system contains both a penetrating and a nonpenetrating solute; for example, Meschia and Setnikar[22] found that water as well as urea moved from a 0.2 M solution of urea through a collodion membrane into a 0.002 M solution of dextran, a solute to which the membrane was impermeable. If the membrane is permeable to all solutes as well as to the solvent, the liquids on both sides will be identical at equilibrium, and they will be at the same pressure. If the membrane is impermeable to any solute but permeable to the solvent, the concentrations on both sides need not be the same at equilibrium, but the solvent on both sides of the membrane must have the same vapor pressure. In an osmometer this is achieved by the excess pressure on the solution, the osmotic pressure, which raises the vapor pressure of the solvent in the solution.

The belief that osmotic equilibrium prevails in the animal body is supported by thermoelectric comparisons of the rates of evaporation of body fluids from the dog. It was found that blood, lymph, aqueous humor, gastric juice, hepatic bile and pancreatic juice were practically isotonic.[14]

Colloid Osmotic Pressure of Plasma. A small fraction of the total osmotic pressure of plasma consists of the partial osmotic pressure of the plasma proteins. This colloid osmotic pressure or "oncotic" pressure was first measured in 1895 by the English physiologist Starling, who was also the first to recognize its importance in the exchange of fluids between the tissue spaces and the blood stream.[19] Starling[36] measured the colloid osmotic pressure by placing serum in an osmometer on one side and a 1 per cent salt solution on the other side of a membrane supported rigidly by a wire mesh. The membrane was permeable to salt and water, but impermeable to proteins. Starling found that the pressure increased on the side containing the serum, reaching an equilibrium value of 30 to 40 mm. Hg, which was close to the accepted value for the capillary blood pressure. More recent figures for the colloid osmotic pressure of normal human serum fall between 22 and 30 mm., and 25 mm. is generally accepted as a useful average or norm.[32] The early measurements of colloid osmotic pressure required days for the establishment of osmotic equilibrium, but improvements in technique have reduced the time to one or two hours.

MEMBRANE EQUILIBRIUM

Distribution of Ions Across a Membrane.   If two different solutions are separated by a membrane, dissolved substances which can pass through it tend to become equally concentrated on both sides. For example, if a salt solution is placed in a cellophane bag which is then submerged in a beaker of water, the final result is that the liquids inside and outside the bag are equally dilute solutions. However, if one of the solutions contains ions or other charged particles to which the membrane is impermeable, the distribution of diffusible ions is not uniform. In such a case, at equilibrium, a diffusible electrolyte is less concentrated in the solution which also contains the nondiffusible or colloidal ion.

This unequal distribution of ions at equilibrium has been called the Donnan effect; it was discovered in 1911 by Donnan and Harris and was explained by Donnan's theory of membrane equilibria.[11] After it was realized that, in 1875, Gibbs had formulated a general equation which might have been applied to the equilibria of ions across membranes, the term "Gibbs-Donnan equilibrium" came into use.

The application of the theory may be understood by considering a simple system:

1	2
C_R/z R^{z-}	
$C_1 + C_R$ Na^+	Na^+ C_2
C_1 Cl^-	Cl^- C_2

In this diagram the vertical line represents a membrane which separates two aqueous solutions of sodium chloride. One solution also contains a sodium salt having a large colloidal anion, R, of valence z. The membrane is permeable to the sodium ion and the chloride ion but not to the colloidal ion. The molar concentrations at equilibrium are C_1 for the sodium chloride in the left compartment, C_2 for that in the right compartment, and C_R/z for the colloidal sodium salt. The equivalent concentration or normality of this salt is C_R, and the equivalent concentrations of the ions satisfy the requirement of electroneutrality in each solution. According to the theory of membrane equilibria, the diffusible ions of sodium and chloride become distributed in such a way that the product of their concentrations in one solution is equal to the corresponding product for the other solution at equilibrium. In the notation of the diagram, the Donnan equation

$$C_1(C_1 + C_R) = C_2{}^2$$

shows that C_1 is less than C_2, or that the concentration of diffusible salt is less in the solution which also contains the nondiffusible ion. Donnan's relation may also be expressed as an equality of ratios of ion concentrations,

$$\frac{C_1}{C_2} = \frac{C_2}{C_1 + C_R}$$

For a system containing a number of ions of unit valence, a similar equation will hold for every pair of oppositely charged ions to which the membrane is permeable, as

$$\frac{[Cl^-]_1}{[Cl^-]_2} = \frac{[Na^+]_2}{[Na^+]_1} = \frac{[HCO_3^-]_1}{[HCO_3^-]_2} = \frac{[K^+]_2}{[K^+]_1}$$

An approximate equality of such ratios was found[42] to hold for the concentrations of chloride, sodium and bicarbonate in blood serum and in edema fluid, which was nearly free from protein; the average was 0.96 ± 0.02.

COLLOID OSMOTIC PRESSURE AND DONNAN EQUILIBRIUM.   A membrane equilibrium between solutions containing sodium proteinate and sodium chloride is essential to measurement of the colloid osmotic pressure of serum by Starling's method or its later modifications. If the external fluid is a physiologic salt solution, C_2 is 0.155. According to Table 12 the equivalent concentration of ionized protein, C_R, is 0.018. The Donnan equation,

$$C_1(C_1 + 0.018) = 0.155^2$$

is satisfied by the value 0.146 for C_1. On this basis, the concentration of sodium in the equilibrated serum would be the sum of this value and 0.018, or 0.164. The Donnan ratio is therefore

$$\frac{C_1}{C_2} = \frac{0.146}{0.155} = \frac{0.155}{0.16425} = 0.944$$

a value close to those observed for serum and edema fluid.

The osmotic pressure measured in such an experiment is the difference between the total osmotic pressures of the two solutions, and it is calculable if the molal concentrations are known. If that of the protein is 0.001 (Table 12), the concentration difference is $0.001 + 0.164 + 0.146 - 0.155 - 0.155$, or 0.0015. If the temperature is 37° C., multiplication by the product of 0.082 and $(273 + 37)$, which is 25.4, gives the calculated osmotic pressure in atmospheres. To get the pressure in millimeters of Hg, we must multiply the concentration difference by the product of 25.4 and 760, or 19,400. The calculated osmotic pressure difference is therefore $1.5 \times 10^{-3} \times 19.4 \times 10^3$, or 29 mm. Hg, a value not far from those commonly observed in such measurements. The actual colloidal particles, if their concentration is 0.001, are responsible for only about 19 mm. of this pressure, the rest being due to the unequal distribution of diffusible ions. While this distinction is important in the calculation of molecular weight from a measurement of osmotic pressure, it is the observed pressure difference which is significant in physiology.

Distribution of Ions Between Cells and Plasma.   The value of Donnan's theory of membrane equilibria in the interpretation of experiments with proteins and electrolytes was firmly established by the work of Jacques Loeb.[16, 21] Other workers tried to apply this theory to the distribution of ions across membranes in living systems. Here a difficulty appears, for the theory was deduced for a condition of equilibrium. It seems likely, however, that Donnan's equation for ion ratios may apply to systems in a steady state as well as to those in equilibrium. In a few experiments with cellophane membranes Teorell[39] found that the continuous diffusion of one electrolyte across the membrane resulted in the unequal distribution of another. The ions accumulated in such a way as to simulate the Donnan effect without the presence of a nondialyzable ion.

Of the ions in blood cells and plasma, the protein anions and the principal cations, sodium and potassium, are unable to pass freely across the cell membrane. Diffusible ions whose ratios might fit the theory are chloride, bicarbonate and hydrogen or hydroxyl. Definite ratios of the concentrations of the latter pair cannot be obtained by present methods of measurement, but it is inferred that the concentration of hydrogen ions is greater in the cells than in the serum because this is true of a mass of hemolyzed cells. The molality of chloride is definitely less in the cells than in the serum, as shown in Table 12, but Peters'[26] figures for bicarbonate do not show the difference found in earlier work. Van Slyke[42] reported that the bicarbonate as well as the chloride ratios could be altered by changes in the carbon dioxide content of the blood, and the direction of these shifts fitted predictions from the theory. It seems likely that a quantitative agreement of these ratios would be found if the concentration of hydrogen ion in the cells could be measured, and if the analytical concentrations of chloride and bicarbonate could be accurately corrected by subtracting the amounts not in ionic form.

BLOOD GAS EQUILIBRIA*

The amounts of oxygen and carbon dioxide absorbed by the blood are much greater than those held in a comparable volume of water or salt solution. The curves in Figure 313 show how the total concentrations of these gases in the blood vary with their partial pressures. The lines marked "free CO_2" and "free O_2" indicate the small amounts of the gases held in simple physical solution. These amounts were obtained from experiments in which blood was first treated with a reagent to prevent holding of the gas by a chemical combination—lactic acid in the case of carbon dioxide and potassium ferricyanide in the case of oxygen. The concentrations of the free gases in the blood are directly proportional to the partial pressures, in agreement with Henry's law, and the concentrations differ little from the solubilities in a physiologic salt solution. In each

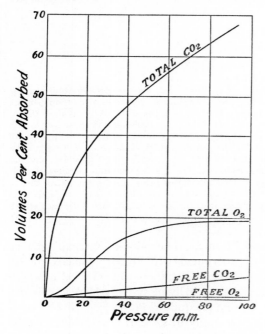

FIG. 313. Blood-gas absorption curves. (After Henderson, *Blood: a study in general physiology*, New Haven, Yale University Press, 1928.)

instance, the greater part of the gas absorbed by the blood, represented by the difference in height between the curve and the corresponding line in Figure 313, is explained by a chemical reaction.

Oxygen. If the curve for oxygen is corrected by subtracting the amounts of free oxygen, it becomes horizontal at high partial pressures, a shape indicating that blood has a definite oxygen capacity. Normal blood has an oxygen capacity of about 20 volumes per cent, or 9 mM. per liter. The oxygen capacity of blood depends directly on its hemoglobin concentration, and the amount of hemoglobin which contains 1 gm.-atom of iron can bind just 1 mol of oxygen. This combining weight, 16,500 grams, is represented by the symbol Hb, and on that basis, the chemical combination might take place according to the reaction

$$Hb + O_2 \rightleftharpoons HbO_2$$

This simple formulation gives a correct idea of the reversibility of the reaction and the composition of the compound, oxyhemoglobin, but it is inadequate in two respects.

* See also the discussions of the properties of gases and liquids, and of the transport of O_2 and CO_2 in Chapter 36.

Application of the law of mass action to this reaction requires that the oxygen absorption curve should be a rectangular hyperbola, a curve which lacks the inflection typical of blood oxygen curves. Moreover, the molecular weight of hemoglobin in dilute solution, as obtained from the osmotic pressure measurements by Adair (cf. Barcroft[2]) and the ultracentrifugal experiments of Svedberg,[38] is about 66,000, corresponding to the formula Hb_4. Saturation of this amount of hemoglobin with oxygen would require 4 mols, and the formula for oxyhemoglobin would then be Hb_4O_8. For the reaction

$$Hb_4 + 4\ O_2 \rightleftharpoons Hb_4O_8$$

the law of mass action yields an oxygen absorption curve with such a marked inflection that it bears little resemblance to the observed curves. Roughton,[31] having concluded that attempts to fit the oxygen data with a two-constant equation have not been completely successful, has been engaged in determining the values of the four constants required for an equation based on intermediate reactions:

$$Hb_4 + O_2 \rightleftharpoons Hb_4O_2$$
$$Hb_4O_2 + O_2 \rightleftharpoons Hb_4O_4$$
$$Hb_4O_4 + O_2 \rightleftharpoons Hb_4O_6$$
$$Hb_4O_6 + O_2 \rightleftharpoons Hb_4O_8$$

Although none of the intermediate compounds indicated in these reactions has been isolated, this hypothesis of transitory intermediate compounds, originally suggested by Adair in 1925, still seems likely to be correct.

Carbon Dioxide. The curve for the total carbon dioxide in the blood is quite different from that for oxygen. The carbon dioxide curve in Figure 313 rises far more steeply than does the line for free carbon dioxide, and the difference between the two graphs does not indicate directly a limiting or saturation value. In this, the relation differs from the carbon dioxide absorption curve for sodium carbonate or bicarbonate solution, as shown in Figure 314. Here the upper curve approaches 25 mM. at low

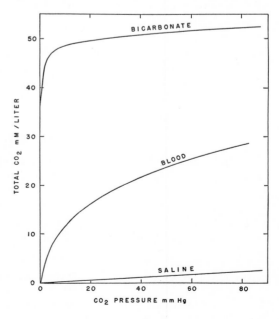

FIG. 314. Carbon dioxide absorption or dissociation curves for 0.05 M sodium bicarbonate, blood and physiologic saline. (After Parsons, *J. Physiol.*, 1919, *53*:42–59.)

pressures, as carbon dioxide is removed from a 50 mM. solution of bicarbonate by the reaction,

$$2\ NaHCO_3 \rightarrow Na_2CO_3 + CO_2 + H_2O.$$

At partial pressures of carbon dioxide of 40 mm. Hg or more, the total carbon dioxide in the bicarbonate solution is a little above 50 mM., the excess being about the same as the free carbon dioxide indicated by the curve marked "saline," at the bottom of the figure. In the region of physiologic interest, the combined carbon dioxide in the bicarbonate solution is almost constant. Comparison of the bicarbonate curve with that for blood shows that the blood is much more efficient in giving up its carbon dioxide when the partial pressure is decreased, as it is when the blood passes from the tissues to the lungs.

The carbon dioxide absorption curve of blood can be fitted by a two-constant equation of a form suggested by Parsons.[24] He regarded the bound carbon dioxide as bicarbonate formed by the reaction of carbonic acid with the salt of another weak acid. A similar reaction between carbonic acid and a protein salt had been postulated by Henderson[15] and other early workers. If we assume complete ionization of the salts, this reaction becomes

$$H_2CO_3 + R^- \rightleftharpoons HCO_3^- + HR$$

and has an equilibrium constant equal to the ratio of the ionization constants of the two weak acids. Parsons concluded that the proteins of the blood, especially hemoglobin, behave as a second weak acid which shares with carbonic acid a fixed amount of "available sodium." The "available sodium" of Parsons is identical with the "buffer base" of Singer and Hastings;[35] this base is equal to the sum of the concentrations, in milliequivalents per liter, of buffer anions (that is, anions of weak acids). Parsons' values for the bloods of two investigators, 47.8 and 50.5, were not appreciably changed by oxygenation of the blood; the normal range of buffer base, according to Singer,[1] is 46 to 52. The equilibrium constant in Parsons' equation was changed by oxygenation, in agreement with the idea that oxygenation increases the acid strength of hemoglobin.

It is now believed that some of the bound carbon dioxide in the blood is combined with protein as a carbamino or carbamate ion, and it is known that the reaction

$$CO_2 + H_2O \rightleftharpoons H_2CO_3$$

is accelerated in both directions by carbonic anhydrase, an enzyme present in red blood cells.[30, 31] However, it is still true that most of the carbon dioxide carried by the blood is bicarbonate, produced by the reaction of carbonic acid with protein anions, and that this reaction provides a physicochemical explanation for the shape of the carbon dioxide absorption curve of blood.

ACID-BASE EQUILIBRIUM

Hydrogen Ion Concentration and Buffer Action. The reaction of normal blood is remarkably constant; an average figure is pH 7.40, with normal deviations of only a few hundredths of a pH unit. Since present methods for measuring pH do not give access to the interior of the cells, the pH of whole blood is really that of the plasma. If fresh blood is handled carefully, with precautions against loss of carbon dioxide, identical pH values are obtained for whole blood, plasma and serum.

The symbol pH was originally defined as the logarithm of the reciprocal of the hydrogen ion* concentration, $\log \frac{1}{[H^+]}$ or $-\log [H^+]$. It is now recognized that this definition is not strictly consistent

* In this discussion it seems unnecessary to use a special name or formula to emphasize the hydration of hydrogen ions in all aqueous solutions.

with accepted methods of measuring pH. One may think of pH as $-\log a_H$, where a_H is the activity or effective concentration of hydrogen ions but not necessarily their true concentration. In pure water a_H and $[H^+]$ are identical, but in ordinary dilute solutions the activity is less than the concentration. The activity coefficient, which is the ratio of activity to concentration, is about 0.75 for the ions of a physiologic salt solution. It is the activities rather than the concentrations of the ions of water in dilute aqueous solutions which are related by the law of the constancy of the ion product,

$$a_H \, a_{OH} = K_w.$$

For any one temperature K_w is a true constant, independent of the acidity or alkalinity of the solution. Because of this relation, pH values can be used to describe the reaction of alkaline as well as of neutral or acid solutions. For 25° C. the value of K_w is 1.0×10^{-14}, but for 37° C. it is about 2.4×10^{-14}. The values of a_H and a_{OH} in pure water are equal to each other and to the square root of K_w, which is 1.55×10^{-7} for 37° C. The pH of a neutral solution at body temperature is the negative logarithm of this number, $-(0.19-7.00)$ or 6.81. Since the pH of normal blood is higher than this by 0.6, blood is a slightly alkaline liquid. The hydrogen ion activity in blood is the antilogarithm of -7.40 or of $0.60-8.00$. Since the antilogarithm of 0.60 is 4.0, the value of a_H is 4.0×10^{-8}.

In dealing with pH values it should be remembered that an increase in pH means a decrease in acidity. If the pH of a solution is increased by one unit, its actual acidity, or the value of a_H, is reduced to $1/10$ of its former value. If the acidity of a solution is doubled, its pH is decreased by the logarithm of 2, which is 0.30.

In blood, as in other solutions of moderate acidity or alkalinity, pH is most conveniently measured by means of the glass electrode.[3, 6, 17] A colorimetric method requiring only 0.1 ml. of blood was described by Shock and Hastings.[33]

Blood plasma has a high buffer capacity, and that of whole blood is still higher. This means that considerable amounts of a strong acid or base may be added to these liquids without inducing great changes in pH.

A buffer solution is one which possesses reserve acidity and alkalinity; this results from the presence in the solution of a weak (i.e., slightly ionized) acid or base, together with a highly ionized salt of the same acid or base. If the formula HA is used to represent any weak acid, buffer action may be seen to be a consequence of the mobile equilibrium,

$$HA \rightleftharpoons H^+ + A^-.$$

If an alkali is added, hydrogen ions are removed to form water, with the production of more A^- ions from the weak acid. If a strong acid is added, its hydrogen ions combine with A^- ions, furnished by the buffer salt, to form undissociated HA. Such an equilibrium may be described by the law of mass action in the form

$$K' = a_H \frac{[A^-]}{[HA]}.$$

The K' of this equation is called the *apparent dissociation constant* of the weak acid. For any acid the value of K' varies, not only with the temperature, but also with the total concentration of dissolved substances, especially ionized salts. In the case of blood and many common buffer solutions, there is enough salt present to keep the ionic environment essentially constant, and K' is then independent of the ratio $[A^-]/[HA]$. If the proper value of K' is known, the value of a_H may be calculated from the composition of the buffer.

The pH of a solution containing buffer substances may be calculated from the ratio of the components of any one buffer system by means of the equation,

$$pH = pK' + \log \frac{[BA]}{[HA]}.$$

This modified form of the law of mass action is known as the Henderson-Hasselbalch equation. Here [HA] is the concentration of a weak acid and [BA] is the concentration of an ionized salt of this acid. Each buffer system may be characterized by its own pK' value, but this is a constant only under certain conditions. The temperature and the concentrations of dissolved substances, especially ionized salts, must be nearly constant and the concentrations of hydrogen and hydroxyl ions must be much less than [HA] and [BA]. These conditions are satisfied for the buffer systems in blood.

Buffer equilibria are shown graphically as dissociation curves of the buffer acids.

The abscissae are pH values and the ordinates represent the fraction of the total buffer substance of each system which has been transformed into the more alkaline form, $[BA]/([HA] + [BA])$. Figure 315 shows such curves for two buffer acids, H_2CO_3 and NaH_2PO_4. Each of these curves shows the pH values which are obtained by mixing the more acid and more alkaline components of one buffer system in the proportions indicated. Such a curve may also be regarded as a titration curve. The phosphate curve could be nearly reproduced, if the scale of ordinates were adjusted in the proper proportion, by plotting against pH the number of cubic centimeters of a sodium hydroxide solution added to a fixed amount of NaH_2PO_4. Even better agreement would be obtained by plotting against pH the amounts of an HCl solution added to a fixed amount of Na_2HPO_4; in this case the curve would have the same shape if the ordinates were plotted downward from the top of the figure.

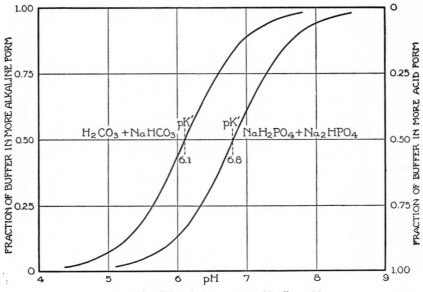

FIG. 315.   Dissociation curves of buffer acids.

The curves for the two buffers are identical in form, differing only in their location along the pH axis. When the buffer acid is exactly half neutralized, the concentrations of the acid and its salt are equal, and the pH is equal to the pK' of the buffer acid. At this point the dissociation curve has its steepest slope and the buffer capacity of the system is at a maximum. The addition of any acid or base causes some change in the proportions of the buffer constituents, but the resulting change in pH is least at the midpoint of the curve. The slope of the curves becomes decidedly less at both ends; the buffer capacity is rather poor if the buffer acid is less than 15 per cent or more than 85 per cent neutralized. For very efficient buffering, the ratio $[BA]/[HA]$ should lie between 1/5 and 5. A concentrated buffer solution is, of course, more effective in controlling pH than a dilute solution having the same buffer ratio.

Buffers in Blood. The buffers of the blood include the phosphate, bicarbonate and protein buffer systems. Inorganic phosphate, in solutions within the physiologic range of pH values, cannot exist in significant amounts as the free acid, H_3PO_4, or as the trivalent anion, $PO_4^{\equiv}$; it is present as $H_2PO_4^-$ and $HPO_4^{=}$. These two ions constitute a buffer system whose behavior may be represented by the equation

$$pH = 6.8 + \log \frac{[B_2HPO_4]}{[BH_2PO_4]}$$

in which B stands for sodium or potassium. Since these salts are regarded as completely ionized into B^+, $HPO_4^=$ and $H_2PO_4^-$, the last ion is the weak acid of the buffer system. At pH 7.4 the logarithmic term is 0.6, and the ratio $[B_2HPO_4]/[BH_2PO_4]$ is 4.0. This ratio is favorable for efficient buffer action, but the inorganic phosphates in blood are present at such low concentrations that they cannot account for much of the total buffer capacity.

Most of the carbon dioxide in blood is present as bicarbonate ions, HCO_3^-. In the physiologic range of pH the concentration of carbonate ions, $CO_3^=$, is about $10^{-4}M$. The distribution of carbon dioxide in blood plasma or serum at body temperature is quantitatively described by the equation

$$pH = 6.10 + \log \frac{[BHCO_3]}{[H_2CO_3]}$$

if $[BHCO_3]$ represents the concentration of bound carbon dioxide, which is largely bicarbonate ions, while $[H_2CO_3]$ is the concentration of free carbon dioxide, including dissolved carbon dioxide and nonionized H_2CO_3. According to this equation, the ratio of free to bound carbon dioxide at pH 7.4 is only 1/20. This is a very poor buffer ratio, and the total concentration of carbon dioxide in the blood is not more than 0.025 M. One might be tempted to conclude that the buffer action of the bicarbonate system in blood would be unimportant, but such a conclusion would be quite erroneous, because of the facts which are discussed in the following pages.

The proteins in blood exist as negatively charged particles or colloidal anions. On the alkaline side of its isoelectric point, a protein behaves as a multivalent acid. Because the number of ionizable groups in the protein molecule is large, the buffer action of a protein cannot be described by a single pK' value. The proteins of the body are powerful buffers; they may give off hydrogen ions, becoming more negatively charged, or they may take up hydrogen ions, becoming less negatively charged. At physiologic pH values the net charge of the blood proteins is negative.

Because of the predominantly acid nature of the substances formed in physiologic processes, the buffers of the body are usually called upon to resist increases in acidity rather than in alkalinity. Peters and Van Slyke[27] have estimated that the alkali which is physiologically available for the neutralization of acids other than carbonic acid is distributed among the buffers of the blood about as follows, in milliequivalents per liter: bicarbonate, 18; hemoglobin 8; other buffers, principally serum proteins, 2. These figures are less than the equivalent concentrations of the same buffer substances, as given in Figure 312, because they apply only to a change in pH from 7.4 to 7.0. If the total volume of the circulating blood is 6 liters, these buffers could neutralize 6 × 28, or 168 ml. of a 1.0 N solution of a strong acid. This is by no means the total buffer capacity of the body. In experiments in which a solution of a strong acid was injected into the circulating blood of a dog, it appeared that about five times as much acid was neutralized by other tissues as by the blood. Most of this buffer action is probably due to tissue proteins, although organic phosphate may also be important. According to these estimates,[27] the body of an average man might neutralize one equivalent (i.e., 1 liter of a 1.0 N solution) of a strong acid such as HCl before the blood pH fell below 7.0, which is almost the lowest value found for blood from a living subject. The upper limit of blood pH compatible with life appears to be close to 7.8.

Physiologic Buffer Action of Carbon Dioxide. The buffer system composed of carbon dioxide and bicarbonate is especially important in physiology. Carbon dioxide is continually being produced in the body, and, if it were not eliminated, the ratio of the concentrations of free and bound carbon dioxide would soon rise far above the normal value of 1/20. It is, of course, the lungs which constitute the path by which this tremendous excess of acid is removed from the body. The regulation of respiration is so sensitive to small changes in the concentration of free carbonic acid or dissolved carbon dioxide in the blood that this concentration is held nearly constant. As L. J. Henderson pointed out in 1908, this physiologic or heterogeneous buffer action transforms the carbonic acid-bicarbonate system from a rather poor buffer into a very good one.[15] Since carbonic acid is a weaker acid than most other acids produced by metabolic processes, the bicarbonate of the blood can neutralize these acids. This neutralization tends to decrease the numerator, [$BHCO_3$], in the buffer equation, but because carbon dioxide is removed by respiration this decrease is not accompanied by an equal increase in the denominator, [H_2CO_3]. The change in pH is therefore less than it would be in an ordinary, homogeneous buffer system.

Because of the availability of bicarbonate as a means of defending the body against excess acid, the bicarbonate of the blood was called by Van Slyke and Cullen the alkaline reserve of the body. This name is generally accepted because a disturbance of the acid-base balance, if it is due to retention or loss of nonvolatile acids or bases, is indicated by a change in the plasma bicarbonate content. Actually, bicarbonate is not the only reserve of alkali in the body or even in the blood. The proteins of the body can neutralize considerable amounts of acid. The reaction between carbonic acid and an alkali pro-teinate may be represented by the chemical equation

$$H_2CO_3 + Protein^- \rightleftharpoons HCO_3^- + H \ Protein$$

which applies to a single acid group. It must be understood that the protein molecule contains many such groups. In the physiologic pH range a protein anion neutralizes acid by binding hydrogen ions, which cancel only a part of its negative charge. This buffer action of the proteins explains why the pH of venous plasma is only 0.02 or 0.03 less than that of arterial plasma, although the concentration of free carbon dioxide in venous blood is some 15 per cent greater. When blood gains carbon dioxide from the tissues, some of the dissolved gas diffuses into the red blood cells. Here its hydration to form carbonic acid is hastened by the action of the enzyme carbonic anhydrase, and some of the carbon dioxide is bound to hemoglobin as a carbamino protein complex. Carbonic acid reacts with hemoglobin anions according to the chemical equation given above; this reaction is possible because some of the acid groups in hemoglobin are weaker acids than carbonic acid, and it is favored by the removal of oxygen from the hemoglobin, since reduced hemoglobin behaves as a weaker acid than does oxyhemoglobin. The resulting bicar-bonate ions tend to diffuse out into the plasma. They cannot do this without some other change, because of the electrostatic forces between oppositely charged ions. Because of the peculiar impermeability of the red cell, cations cannot accompany the bicarbonate ions into the plasma. The diffusion of bicarbonate ions is made possible by the simultane-ous diffusion of chloride ions from plasma to cells. The chloride-bicarbonate shift proceeds in the reverse direction when the blood reaches the lungs and loses carbon dioxide. In spite of this reversed shift, the bicarbonate content of the cells becomes less on oxygena-tion; as hemoglobin becomes a stronger acid, it reacts with HCO_3^- to form H_2CO_3.

SPECIAL FORM OF BUFFER EQUATION FOR CARBON DIOXIDE. Because carbon dioxide is a gas, the Henderson-Hasselbalch equation is sometimes written in a special form, applicable only to the ionization of carbonic acid. No distinction is made between dissolved carbon dioxide and undissociated carbonic acid. The sum of their concentrations [free CO_2] is proportional to the partial pressure of carbon dioxide in the gas mixture with which the solution is in equilibrium (Henry's law). If this partial pressure is p mm. Hg, the free carbon dioxide in plasma at 37° C. amounts to 0.0334 p mM. per 1 kg. of water. For a plasma which contains 0.940 kg. of water in 1 liter, the concentration of free carbon dioxide at 37° is 0.0314 p mM. per liter. It is this quantity which is used in place of [HA] or [free CO_2] in the Henderson-Hasselbalch equation. The difference between the concentrations of total carbon dioxide and free carbon dioxide is [bound CO_2] or [BA]. If [total CO_2] is expressed in millimols per liter, the equation becomes

$$pH = 6.10 + \log \frac{[\text{Total CO}_2] - 0.0314\,p}{0.0314\,p}$$

since the value of pK' is 6.10. In this form, the equation is used to calculate the pH of serum or plasma from measurements of carbon dioxide content and carbon dioxide tension. Some workers have measured pH and carbon dioxide content and then solved the equation to get values for the carbon dioxide tension. Once the value of pK' has been established, any one of the three variables may be obtained from experimental measurements of the other two.

It is recognized that the difference between [total CO_2] and [free CO_2] is greater than the true value of [HCO_3^-] in blood serum, because some of the carbon dioxide is bound in the form of carbamino protein complexes. However, the equation is still valid because the numerical value of pK' was determined by applying the equation in this form to experimental measurements of the three variables.

Kidney Action and Neutrality of Blood. The constant pH of the blood is maintained, not only by physicochemical buffer action and the elimination of carbon dioxide in the lungs, but also by the action of the kidneys. Excess acid may leave the body in the form of weak organic acids, acid phosphates or ammonium salts in the urine; excess alkali may be eliminated as bicarbonate in the urine.

Since urine is usually more acid than blood, the ratio [BA]/[HA] is generally decreased for each buffer system whose constituents pass from the blood to the urine. For example, the ratio $[\text{HPO}_4^=]/[\text{H}_2\text{PO}_4^-]$ is 4 in blood of pH 7.4 but only about 0.16 in urine of pH 6.0. This decrease in the phosphate buffer ratio, together with other similar changes, is ascribed to a selective action of the kidneys, especially in the reabsorption in the renal tubules of the fluid which has been filtered from the blood in the glomeruli. The protein-free ultrafiltrate is believed to contain the crystalloidal buffer substances in essentially the same proportions as the blood. Most of the water in the filtrate, much of the alkali bicarbonate, and certain other solutes are reabsorbed through the tubules into the blood. It has been assumed that carbonic acid or dissolved carbon dioxide is not actively reabsorbed, but becomes concentrated as water is reabsorbed. This would explain why the partial pressure of carbon dioxide is often much higher in urine than in blood. It was calculated by Sendroy, Seelig and Van Slyke that the glomerular filtrate provides enough carbon dioxide to account for the acidity of the urine by reaction with other buffer systems, as:

$$\text{H}_2\text{CO}_3 + \text{Na}_2\text{HPO}_4 \rightleftharpoons \text{NaHCO}_3 + \text{NaH}_2\text{PO}_4.$$

Such a reaction might be driven nearly to completion by the reabsorption of bicarbonate. In 1945, however, this hypothesis was found inadequate to explain some quantitative experiments by R. F. Pitts. He worked with dogs which had received dilute hydrochloric acid by mouth and neutral sodium phosphate by intravenous infusion. Pitts calculated that the glomerular filtrate contained less than one-fourth as much carbon dioxide as the titratable acid found in the urine. He concluded that the carbon dioxide of the ultrafiltrate is largely reabsorbed in the tubules, but that additional carbon dioxide is formed by metabolic processes in cells of the distal tubules. According to Pitts, the urine acquires its acidity by a secretory process in which these tubule cells give out hydrogen ions in exchange for sodium ions. Support for this theory was found by Pitts and collaborators in experiments on themselves;[29] they received ammonium chloride by mouth and neutral phosphate by intravenous injection.

Acid is also eliminated in the urine as ammonium ion. This ion is present in blood only in small amounts, and at pH 7.4 the concentration of free ammonia (NH_3 or NH_4OH) must be extremely low. The immediate source of urinary ammonia has in the past been thought to be urea, or possibly amino acids. Experiments reported in 1943 by Van Slyke et al. indicate that the kidney obtains ammonia by the hydrolysis of the amide group in glutamine, which is brought to the kidney by the blood. The ammonia combines with H^+ to form NH_4^+, which is excreted in the urine with equivalent amounts of an anion such as chloride. In this way acid is removed while adequate amounts of bicarbonate and sodium are retained in the blood.

The greater part of the nitrogen of protein foods is removed from amino acids by a process of deamination. The resulting ammonia does not appear in the blood because the liver converts it to urea, a neutral substance. If intermediate steps and necessary catalysts are disregarded, the chemical reaction for this conversion may be written in the form

$$2 \; NH_3 + CO_2 \rightarrow CO(NH_2)_2 + H_2O.$$

The normal excretion of urea may therefore be regarded as a means of removing ammonia and preventing a change in the reaction of the blood.

Experimental Shifts in Acid-Base Balance. When a person hyperventilates his lungs by rapid and deep breathing, a good deal of acid is lost from the body as carbon dioxide. In one experiment on a human subject, Shock and Hastings[34] found that 20 minutes of intentional overbreathing caused the pH of the plasma to rise from 7.36 to 7.69, producing a temporary condition of carbon dioxide deficit or respiratory alkalosis. The reverse of this condition, carbon dioxide excess or respiratory acidosis, could be produced by rebreathing through a closed system of about 35 liters of oxygen for 15 to 18 minutes; in one case the pH of the plasma fell from 7.37 to 7.19 as the carbon dioxide content of the gas rose to 9 per cent. A condition of acid excess or metabolic acidosis was produced by having the subjects take 5 or 10 grams of NH_4Cl, dissolved in water, by mouth. In one such experiment the plasma pH fell from 7.45 to 7.22 in three hours, while there was also a marked drop in the plasma bicarbonate concentration. The acidity produced by NH_4Cl in the body may be explained on the assumption that some of its ammonia is converted to neutral area, leaving an excess of hydrogen ions to disturb the buffer equilibria. When subjects received 10 or 20 grams of $NaHCO_3$ by mouth, their condition became one of temporary alkali excess or metabolic alkalosis. In one case the plasma bicarbonate was nearly doubled within one hour, during which the free carbon dioxide also rose somewhat and the plasma pH rose from 7.35 to 7.50.

During each of these experiments Shock and Hastings took several small samples of finger blood, which has nearly the composition of arterial blood. After anaerobic dilution of 0.1 ml. to 2.0 ml. with neutral saline, they determined the cell volume, pH and total carbon dioxide content of each sample.[33] From charts based on previous work they evaluated the plasma carbon dioxide. With this information and the measured pH, the partial pressure of carbon dioxide was calculated by means of the Henderson-Hasselbalch equation. The results were reported in the form of graphs plotted on paper with triangular coordinates showing the values of pH, bound carbon dioxide and carbon dioxide pressure for each point. These results fell along four primary acid-base paths for the four types of experimental disturbance.

The general nature of these disturbances may be illustrated by diagrams which represent only two variables at a time. In Figure 316 the bound carbon dioxide of plasma is plotted against the partial pressure of carbon dioxide. The curve represents normal values[1] for the true plasma of oxygenated blood, i.e., plasma from blood which has been altered only by the addition or removal of carbon dioxide as a result of equilibration with different gas mixtures. Points A, B, C and D, which represent initial values for subjects in Shock and Hastings' experiments, lie near this curve and close to the usual carbon dioxide pressure of arterial blood. The primed points represent values obtained for the same subjects at the time of maximum displacement. The point A' shows that ingestion of ammonium chloride produced a marked lowering of plasma bicarbonate, with little change in carbon dioxide pressure. (In other experiments, the carbon dioxide pressure did not rise but remained constant during the displacement and sometimes fell

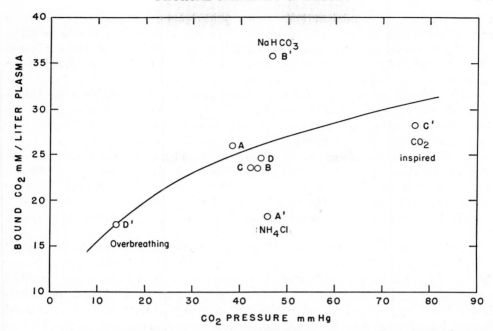

FIG. 316.   Experimental displacement of acid-base balance in man. *Curve*, Accepted average values for normal subjects; A and A', values for normal subject before and after ingesting NH₄Cl; B and B', before and after ingestion of NaHCO₃; C and C', before and after rebreathing; D and D', before and after overbreathing. (Curve from Root in *Handbook of respiration*, P. L. Altman *et al.*, eds., Philadelphia, W. B. Saunders, 1958. Experimental data from Shock and Hastings, *J. biol. Chem.*, 1935, *112*:239–262.)

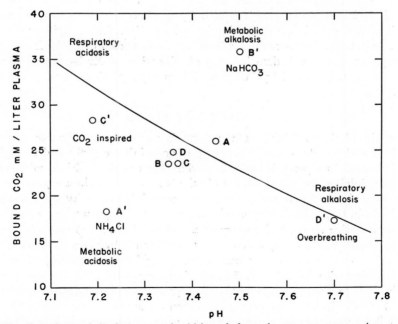

FIG. 317.   Experimental displacement of acid-base balance in man; same experiments as Figure 316. *Curve*, Accepted normal values; A and A', before and after NH₄Cl; B and B', before and after NaHCO₃; C and C', before and after rebreathing; D and D', before and after overbreathing. (Curve from Root in *Handbook of respiration*, P. L. Altman *et al.*, eds., Philadelphia, W. B. Saunders, 1958. Experimental data from Shock and Hastings, *J. biol. Chem.*, 1935, *112*:239–262.)

during the recovery.) Administration of sodium bicarbonate produced a large increase in the bound carbon dioxide (B'), again with little change in carbon dioxide pressure. Point C' shows that breathing carbon dioxide raised the partial pressure and the bound carbon dioxide along a path close to the normal curve, while D' shows that just the reverse effect was produced by overbreathing.

In Figure 317 the results of the same experiments are plotted to show the bound carbon dioxide as a function of plasma pH. Again the initial points, A, B, C and D, are fairly close to the normal curve. Point A' shows that the ingestion of ammonium chloride was followed by a marked fall in pH as well as in bound carbon dioxide; point B' shows that the administration of sodium bicarbonate produced a decided rise in pH as well as in bound carbon dioxide. Point C' shows that the inspiration of excess carbon dioxide produced a fall in pH with a rise in bound carbon dioxide along a course parallel to the normal curve. The location of point D' shows that overbreathing was followed by a large rise in pH with a fall in bound carbon dioxide along a path close to the normal curve.

In Figures 316 and 317 the points C' and D', representing data from blood subjected to respiratory changes *in vivo*, fall close to the normal curves obtained from experiments with blood *in vitro*. Such conditions of displacement occurring in disease are described as respiratory acidosis or carbon dioxide excess and respiratory alkalosis or carbon dioxide deficit. By contrast, the points A' and B', representing the condition of the blood after the ingestion of an acid-forming and an alkaline salt, respectively, lie well below and well above the normal curves. The corresponding states of acid-base imbalance in disease are described as metabolic acidosis or alkali deficit and metabolic alkalosis or alkali excess. Each of these four conditions is best identified and characterized if two of the three variables of the Henderson-Hasselbalch equation are known. This knowledge requires at least two measurements, such as the determination of total carbon dioxide content and pH of blood or plasma. If the carbon dioxide content of whole blood is determined, as in the Shock-Hastings technique,[33] it is also necessary to measure the hematocrit or hemoglobin concentration in order to describe the acid-base balance of the blood. Acid-base disturbances of mixed types result from physiologic compensation for primary disturbances. Estimation and classification of displacements of acid-base balance have been discussed by Peters and Van Slyke,[27] Singer and Hastings,[35] and Davenport[9].

PROTEINS OF BLOOD

Properties of Hemoglobin. Hemoglobin is a readily crystallizable protein which contains iron and has the unusual property of combining rapidly and reversibly with oxygen. This useful property is easily lost when the protein is dried, subjected to the action of an oxidizing agent, or even kept in the laboratory; the best crystalline preparations have only about 95 per cent of the oxygen-combining capacity of the same amount of hemoglobin in fresh blood. The maximum amount of oxygen which can be made to combine with native hemoglobin approaches 401 ml. for each gram of iron contained in the hemoglobin, as shown by R. A. Peters (see Barcroft[2]). Since the atomic weight of iron is 55.85, it follows that the amount of hemoglobin which contains 1 gm.-atom of iron can combine with 0.401×55.85 liters of oxygen; this is 22.4 liters or 1 mol of the gas. The iron content of human hemoglobin (crystallized, dialyzed and dried to constant weight at 105° C.) is 0.340 per cent, as reported by Bernhart and Skeggs.[4] From these results it follows that the oxygen capacity of 1 gram of hemoglobin is 0.340 per cent of 401 ml., or 1.36 ml., and the weight of hemoglobin which contains 1 gm.-atom of iron is 55.85/0.00340 or 16,400 grams. This amount of hemoglobin (its minimal molecular weight) is commonly represented by the symbol Hb, or HHb when the acidic nature of the protein is under discussion.* The actual molecular weight of human hemoglobin in aqueous solutions, as determined from its osmotic pressure or from the study of its sedimentation in the ultracentrifuge,[38] is about 66,000; this figure indicates that the molecule contains four atoms of iron.

The combination of oxygen with hemoglobin is not an oxidation in the electrochemical sense; studies of oxidation-reduction potentials[8] have indicated that the iron in oxyhemoglobin as well as in reduced hemoglobin (ferrohemoglobin) is in the ferrous condition. There is some evidence that normal blood contains a little of its iron in a form which cannot combine with oxygen or carbon monoxide. The true oxidation of hemoglobin by chemical reagents such as ferricyanide results in the formation of a brown substance, methemoglobin (ferrihemoglobin), in which the iron is ferric and the oxygen-binding capacity is lacking. If oxyhemoglobin or methemoglobin is first reduced by sodium dithionite, also called hydrosulfite ($Na_2S_2O_4$), the maximum amount of carbon monoxide which can be bound agrees quite well with the total iron content. The combination of hemoglobin with carbon monoxide, like that with oxygen, is a reversible reaction, but the affinity of hemoglobin for carbon monoxide is about 210 times as great as its affinity for oxygen. Carbon monoxide can therefore displace oxygen from combination with hemoglobin, and this accounts for the well known facts of carbon monoxide poisoning. In this connection it may be noted that carefully measured, small amounts of carbon monoxide have been breathed without untoward results by physiologists experimenting upon themselves; this procedure was involved in an early method for determining total blood volume.

Hemoglobin resembles other proteins in its amphoteric nature. Oxyhemoglobin is isoelectric at about pH 6.7, and reduced hemoglobin at 6.8. Since both of these values are below the pH of circulating blood, hemoglobin *in vivo* is negatively charged or "combined with base." Although it seems unlikely that the 32 per cent of hemoglobin in the red cells can be in true solution, the hemoglobin may be regarded as a large, colloidal anion of an ionized potassium salt. The valence of this anion, or the number of equivalents of "base bound" per mol of hemoglobin, is variable, being increased by a rise in pH or an increase in the degree of oxygenation.

Hemoglobin can be broken down into a nonprotein fraction and a protein called *globin*, which does not combine with oxygen and contains no iron. Globin has a rather high content of the basic amino acid, histidine, and an alkaline isoelectric point, pH 8. The nonprotein fraction of hemoglobin has been called *reduced hematin, reduced heme* or *ferroheme;* it contains all of the iron of hemoglobin. The name heme (haem in British publications) is used to describe a class of iron-porphyrin complexes which includes the nonprotein parts of hemoglobin, cytochrome and other derivatives of animal or plant origin. The nature of the chemical linkages which hold the iron atom in the porphyrin nucleus of the heme compounds, and of those which unite ferroheme and globin in hemoglobin, has aroused the interest of both physical and organic chemists. It appears that each iron atom in hemoglobin is linked in some way to six other atoms, as in the ferrocyanide ion. These atoms include the four nitrogens of the porphyrin structure and one in globin, probably an imidazole nitrogen of histidine. In reduced hemoglobin the sixth group may be a second histidine residue in the globin; in oxyhemoglobin it is oxygen. Measurements of magnetic susceptibility[25] have shown that reduced hemoglobin is strongly paramagnetic, whereas oxyhemoglobin has zero magnetic moment; it is inferred that the bonds about the iron are electrostatic in the former substance but

---

* According to a recent report (*Science*, 1958, *127*:1376–1378), an international commission has recommended that the iron content of hemoglobin be accepted as 0.338 per cent; this makes the combining weight 16,520.

covalent in the latter. This difference in the type of bonding is associated with the more strongly acid nature of oxyhemoglobin.

Because hemoglobin and its derivatives have typical and specific absorption spectra, the spectroscope has been a valuable tool in the study of these substances. The concentration of hemoglobin in blood is usually determined by colorimetry, or the comparison of the intensities of light transmitted by known and unknown solutions. Visual colorimetry is greatly improved by the use of a suitable light filter (green in this case), and a photoelectric colorimeter with monochromatic or filtered light is even better. One instrument of this sort, the Millikan oximeter, gives an estimate of the degree of oxygenation of circulating blood by means of a photoelectric cell responding to light transmitted through the lobe of the human ear.

Plasma Proteins.   The plasma proteins, because of their colloid osmotic pressure, play an important part in the regulation of the distribution of water in the body; this osmotic pressure is due largely to the albumins.[32] Fibrinogen and other proteins, present in smaller quantities, are responsible for the coagulability of blood. The antibodies of immunology, which constitute an important defense of the body against disease, appear to be protein in nature and are associated with certain of the globulins of plasma, the gamma globulin fraction.

The classic separation of the plasma proteins was based on the successive precipitation of different fractions when increasing amounts of a salt were added. Fibrinogen can be precipitated by adding to oxalated plasma an equal volume of saturated sodium chloride solution, or one quarter of its volume of saturated ammonium sulfate. Globulins may be precipitated from serum by adding an equal volume of saturated ammonium sulfate; if the filtrate is saturated with this salt by addition of a sufficient amount of solid ammonium sulfate, the albumins are precipitated and the last filtrate is free from protein. These separations are not absolutely sharp and definite, and they are not even reproducible unless the temperature, pH and other conditions are carefully controlled.

Although globulins are usually said to be insoluble in pure water but soluble in salt solutions, an appreciable fraction of the globulins of serum does not precipitate when the salts are removed by dialysis. These more soluble globulins are termed *pseudoglobulins*. The globulins which can be precipitated by dialysis, or by simple dilution and acidification of serum with carbon dioxide, are called *euglobulins*. Still other fractions have been separated by adjusting the pH of dialyzed solutions for isoelectric precipitation; serum globulins have isoelectric points which range from pH 5 to pH 8.4.[41]

Serum albumins were first crystallized from concentrated, aqueous salt solutions. More recently, ethanol-water mixtures containing ions at low concentrations have been employed. The isoelectric point of human serum albumin is not far from pH 5.

Useful information about the plasma proteins was obtained by subjecting plasma and its fractions to electrophoresis. It had long been known that proteins would migrate in an electric field, but the phenomenon of electrophoresis became useful for the quantitative characterization and analysis of protein mixtures only after the technique was greatly improved by Tiselius.[40] The electrophoretic velocity depends principally on the number of charges carried by the particle, and different proteins can usually be made to move with different velocities by conducting the experiment in a medium of suitable pH. By means of ingenious optical systems it is possible to obtain photographic records which show not only the mobilities of the different constituents in a protein solution but also their relative amounts. In this way it has been found that the most rapidly moving protein component of human plasma is the albumin. In order of decreasing mobilities, the next are two globulin fractions designated alpha 1 and alpha 2. These are followed by beta globulin, fibrinogen and gamma globulin. Electrophoretic analysis indicates that albumin is about 53 per cent of the total plasma protein.[12] Since fibrinogen is about

4 per cent of the total, the remaining globulins amount to 43 per cent, and on this basis the normal albumin:globulin ratio may be as low as 1.2. Since the procedure involves only the addition of a weakly alkaline buffer solution and the passage of a small electric current at a low temperature, it seems likely that electrophoretic analysis gives a better idea of the proteins as they exist in plasma than does any precipitation method. Plasma proteins have also been separated by having the electrophoresis take place in filter paper wet with a buffer solution, or in a compressed block or packed column of starch particles, cellulose fibers or similar material. Electrophoresis in such a supporting medium has been termed "zone electrophoresis."[18]

The precipitation methods developed by Cohn and his coworkers[7, 12] for the fractionation of blood plasma depend on the use of graded concentrations of alcohol at low temperatures, with careful control of pH and salt content or ionic strength. Modified methods were tried with the aim of keeping the blood cells and proteins more nearly in their "states of nature." For example, one precipitation which previously required 19 per cent of ethanol at pH 5.8 was carried out with the aid of a little zinc acetate at pH 7 with no alcohol at all.[41] The stable plasma protein solution which resulted from this treatment could be freed from zinc by an ion exchange resin; after being heated to 60° C. for ten hours as a precaution against the transmission of virus, this solution could be stored without refrigeration.[37]

The fractions of human plasma proteins which have been utilized clinically include albumin, gamma globulin and fibrinogen. Albumin has been injected intravenously with the object of restoring plasma volume in patients in shock. The gamma globulin fraction obtained from the pooled plasma of normal adults contains antibodies, and for this reason it has been administered as a temporary protection against measles. Another globulin, which is partially precipitated with the fibrinogen fraction, promotes the coagulation of blood in hemophiliacs. Fibrin foams impregnated with a thrombin solution are useful for the control of bleeding in surgical work, and fibrin films have been successfully employed in brain surgery as a temporary substitute for the dura.[7, 12]

A lipoprotein of definite composition was first obtained from horse serum in 1929 by Macheboeuf. Since that time, evidence has been accumulating that much of the lipid material in human plasma is combined with protein. Using Cohn's methods for fractionation of plasma, Oncley[23, 41] and others found that two lipoprotein fractions constituted about 10 per cent of the plasma proteins. In electrophoresis, these had mobilities typical of alpha 1 and beta 1 globulins. The alpha lipoprotein was about 40 per cent lipid; the beta, about 75 per cent. The lipid portion consisted of phospholipids and cholesterol, largely esterified. In a preparative ultracentrifuge, lipoprotein fractions have been separated from plasma which had been mixed with a salt solution of high density in order to produce negative sedimentation of the lighter constituents. De Lalla and Gofman[10] studied such fractions further by means of the analytical ultracentrifuge. From analysis of records obtained during sedimentation in this instrument, these investigators concluded that plasma has a whole spectrum of lipoproteins of different densities. Gofman and his coworkers investigated the possibility of a relation between the amount of plasma lipoproteins present and the incidence of atherosclerosis. Lipoproteins separated in the preparative ultracentrifuge were studied by Bragdon and collaborators,[5] who determined the free and total cholesterol, lipid phosphorus, total lipid, and protein nitrogen in four fractions. The function of lipoproteins in the transport of fatty acids was reviewed by Fredrickson and Gordon.[13]

Specific gravity and protein concentration. The classic method of estimating the amount of protein in plasma is based on a total nitrogen determination by the Kjeldahl method. After a small correction for nonprotein nitrogen, the nitrogen content is multiplied by 6.25, since the plasma proteins contain about 16 per cent of nitrogen. Because Kjeldahl determinations are slow, approximate methods which can be carried out more rapidly have often been used for clinical purposes. It was shown by Moore and Van Slyke in 1930 that the specific gravity of serum or plasma is essentially a straight line function of its protein content. The specific gravity can be determined with an accuracy adequate for clinical work by an extremely simple method.[28] A series of copper sulfate solutions, differing by 0.001 in specific gravity, is prepared, and a small drop (not measured) of plasma is allowed to fall into a solution from a height of about 1 cm. above its surface. The drop is observed for 15 to 20 seconds, during which it remains intact because of the formation of a film of copper proteinate. If the drop continues to fall during this time, it is heavier than the standard; if it rises, it is lighter. The specific gravity can be estimated with an accuracy equal to about one-fourth of the difference between successive copper sulfate solutions. The determination may be carried out without temperature control, because the coefficient of expansion of the copper sulfate solutions approximates that of plasma. The protein concentration, P, in grams per 100 ml., is given by the equation

$$P = 373 \, (G - 1.0070),$$

in which G is the specific gravity of the plasma.[43]

The same procedure, with more concentrated copper sulfate solutions, can be used to obtain the specific gravity of whole blood, and the originators of this method have shown that approximate values for hematocrit and hemoglobin concentration may be calculated graphically from the specific gravities of whole blood and its plasma. According to this work, the average specific gravities of samples obtained from 20 normal men were 1.0269 for plasma and 1.0595 for blood. The average hematocrit was 46.9 per cent cells, while the oxygen capacity of the blood samples averaged 21.6 volumes per cent. These figures correspond to 7.42 grams of protein per 100 ml. of plasma, 15.9 grams of hemoglobin per 100 ml. of blood, and 1.0964 for the average specific gravity of the cells in normal blood.

The specific gravities of blood and its plasma or serum have served as a guide in the treatment of patients whose blood volume has been diminished by injury, as in shock.

REFERENCES

1. ALTMAN, P. L., GIBSON, J. F., JR., WANG, C. C., DITTMER, D. S. and GREBE, R. M. *Handbook of respiration.* Philadelphia, W. B. Saunders, 1958, xv, 403 pp.
2. BARCROFT, J. *The respiratory function of the blood. Part II. Haemoglobin,* 2d ed. Cambridge, Cambridge University Press, 1928, viii, 200 pp.
3. BATES, R. G. *Electrometric pH determination.* New York, John Wiley & Sons, 1954, xiii, 331 pp.
4. BERNHART, F. W. and SKEGGS, L. *J. biol. Chem.,* 1943, *147*:19–22.
5. BRAGDON, J. H., HAVEL, R. J. and BOYLE, E. *J. Lab. clin. Med.,* 1956, *48*:36–42.
6. CLARK, W. M. *Topics in physical chemistry; a supplementary text for students of medicine,* 2d ed. Baltimore, Williams & Wilkins Co., 1952, xviii, 777 pp.
7. COHN, E. J. *Amer. Scientist,* 1945, *33*:61–83.
8. CONANT, J. B. *J. biol. Chem.,* 1923, *57*:401–414.
9. DAVENPORT, H. W. *The ABC of acid-base chemistry,* rev. ed. Chicago, University of Chicago Press, 1958, 86 pp.
10. DE LALLA, O. F. and GOFMAN, J. W. *Meth. biochem. Anal.,* 1954, *1*:459–478.
11. DONNAN, F. G. *Chem. Rev.,* 1924, *1*:73–90.
12. EDSALL, J. T. *Advanc. Protein Chem.,* 1947, *3*:383–479.
13. FREDRICKSON, D. S. and GORDON, R. S., JR. *Physiol. Rev.,* 1958, *38*:585–630.
14. GILMAN, A. and COWGILL, G. R. *Amer. J. Physiol.,* 1933, *104*:476–479.
15. HENDERSON, L. J. *Blood. A study in general physiology.* New Haven, Yale University Press, 1928, xix, 397 pp.
16. HITCHCOCK, D. I. *Physiol. Rev.,* 1924, *4*:505–531.
17. HITCHCOCK, D. I. *Physical chemistry for students of biology and medicine,* 4th ed. Boston, Little, Brown & Co., 1953, 266 pp.
18. KUNKEL, H. G. *Meth. biochem. Anal.,* 1954, *7*:141–170.
19. LANDIS, E. M. *Physiol. Rev.,* 1934, *14*:404–481
20. LIFSON, N. *J. biol. Chem.,* 1944, *152*:659–663.

21. LOEB, J. *Proteins and the theory of colloidal behavior*, 2d ed. New York, McGraw-Hill Book Co., 1924, xiv, 380 pp.

22. MESCHIA, G. and SETNIKAR, I. *J. gen. Physiol.*, 1958, *42:*429–444.

23. ONCLEY, J. L. *Harvey Lect.*, 1954–55, *50:*71–91.

24. PARSONS, T. R. *J. Physiol.*, 1919, *53:*42–59.

25. PAULING, L. and CORYELL, C. D. *Proc. nat. Acad. Sci.* (*Wash.*), 1936, *22:*210–216.

26. PETERS, J. P. *Body water; the exchange of fluids in man.* Springfield, Ill., Charles C Thomas, 1935, viii, 405 pp.

27. PETERS, J. P. and VAN SLYKE, D. D. *Quantitative clinical chemistry. Vol. 1, Interpretations.* Baltimore, Williams & Wilkins Co., 1931, xvi, 1264 pp.

28. PHILLIPS, R. A., VAN SLYKE, D. D., HAMILTON, P. B., DOLE, V. P., EMERSON, K., JR. and ARCHIBALD, R. M. *J. biol. Chem.*, 1950, *183:*305–330.

29. PITTS, R. F., LOTSPEICH, W. D., SCHIESS, W. A. and AYER, J. L. *J. clin. Invest.*, 1948, *27:*48–56.

30. ROUGHTON, F. J. W. *Harvey Lect.*, 1943–44, *39:*96–142.

31. ROUGHTON, F. J. W. Chap. 5 in *Handbook of respiratory physiology*, W. M. BOOTHBY, ed. Randolph Field, Texas, USAF School of Aviation Medicine, 1954, ix, 189 pp.

32. SCATCHARD, G., BATCHELDER, A. C. and BROWN, A. *J. clin. Invest.*, 1944, *23:*458–464.

33. SHOCK, N. W., and HASTINGS, A. B. *J. biol. Chem.*, 1934, *104:*565–573.

34. SHOCK, N. W. and HASTINGS, A. B. *J. biol. Chem.*, 1935, *112:*239–262.

35. SINGER, R. B. and HASTINGS, A. B. *Medicine* (*Baltimore*), 1948, *27:*223–242.

36. STARLING, E. H. *J. Physiol.*, 1896, *19:*312–326.

37. SURGENOR, D. M. *Sci. Amer.*, 1954, *190*(2):54–62.

38. SVEDBERG, T. *Industr. Engng. Chem.* (*Anal. Ed.*), 1938, *10:*113–127.

39. TEORELL, T. *J. gen. Physiol.*, 1937, *21:*107–122.

40. TISELIUS, A. *Harvey Lect.*, 1939–40, *35:*37–70.

41. TULLIS, J. L., ed. *Blood cells and plasma proteins. Their state in nature.* New York, Academic Press Inc., 1953, xxi, 436 pp.

42. VAN SLYKE, D. D. *Factors affecting the distribution of electrolytes, water and gases in the animal body.* Philadelphia, J. B. Lippincott Co., 1926, vii, 62 pp.

43. VAN SLYKE, D. D., HILLER, A., PHILLIPS, R. A., HAMILTON, P. B., DOLE, V. P., ARCHIBALD, R. M. and EDER, H. A. *J. biol. Chem.*, 1950, *183:*331–347.

CHAPTER 25

Coagulation of Blood

By ROSEMARY BIGGS

BLOOD coagulation results from the solidification in the blood of a particular plasma protein, fibrinogen. This alteration in fibrinogen is the only directly observable change that occurs in the blood during clotting, but it is certainly preceded by a long chain of preliminary reactions which can be studied only by their effect on the final clotting of fibrinogen. Information about important early stages is therefore not direct but inferred, and is often a matter more of interpretation and opinion than of fact. Thus conflicting views are inevitable. In this presentation much of the conflict is eliminated by giving only one point of view. In some ways such a method is unsatisfactory, but it is unavoidable if so complicated a problem is to be reviewed both briefly and clearly. If the subject is pursued more deeply, conflict of opinion will very soon be encountered. Another difficulty arises from the fact that much information about the normal process of coagulation is derived from study of patients with abnormal clotting or from study of plasma fractions isolated from blood. The phenomena observed in artificial experiments or in the blood of patients may have no simple interpretation in terms of the normal process.

    Bearing these difficulties in mind, the writer has attempted to describe the main substances involved in coagulation and the reactions that they are thought to undergo.

It might be logical to describe these substances and their reactions in the order in which they occur, but in practice this cannot be done because of the method of study. The early reactions are little understood, because they are viewed through a haze of deductions and hypotheses. Information about the process decreases with separation from the final stage, clotting, and it is necessary to pursue the reactions backward from the formation of the clot, about which there is no doubt.

FIBRINOGEN, THROMBIN AND FIBRIN

Fibrinogen. Fibrinogen is the plasma protein which is coagulated by a specific enzyme, thrombin; the protein is a globulin with a molecular weight of about 400,000 to 500,000. The molecule is three to four times as large as other plasma proteins and is needle-shaped. Fibrinogen is destroyed by heating to 47° C. It is precipitated from human plasma by one-fourth to one-third saturation with ammonium sulfate, by molar phosphate buffer,[17] by 11 volumes per cent of ether at 0° C.[19] or by 8 to 10 volumes per cent of ethyl alcohol at 0° to −3° C. and pH 7.[14] Methods for the preparation of fibrinogen from plasma depend on the use of one of these precipitation properties.

Fibrinogen deficiency. In normal blood fibrinogen is present at a concentration of from 190 to 330 mg. per 100 ml. In advanced liver disease the level may be reduced; as a result of experiments on poisoning with chloroform, which causes both liver damage and reduction in the amount of fibrinogen, it was suggested that fibrinogen is normally formed in the liver.[54] Occasionally, fibrinogen may be present in abnormally small quantities or completely absent from the blood as a constitutional defect. Patients with this anomaly usually have a more or less severe tendency to bleed. An acute hemorrhagic state associated with a reduction in fibrinogen may arise in pregnant women at delivery if hemorrhage has previously occurred at the placental site. It is thought that coagulant material from the placenta enters the blood stream and causes clotting of fibrinogen. In such an event, the fibrin is thought to be deposited in the vessels, and blood withdrawn at venipuncture is thus poor in fibrinogen.[49] Similar defibrination may occur very occasionally in patients with widespread deposits of carcinoma or in those who have undergone major surgical operations, particularly on the lungs. The amount of fibrinogen in the blood may increase as a nonspecific response to various infections, and this increase may be one factor leading to an increased red cell sedimentation rate.

Thrombin. Thrombin is an active coagulant of fibrinogen, and appears in blood during clotting. From its precipitation by ammonium sulfate, Astrup and Darling[1] concluded that thrombin belongs to the albumin group of proteins. Thrombin is precipitated between pH 5.1 and pH 3.4; it is destroyed by heating to 60° C. In normal blood, thrombin is formed from a precursor, prothrombin; the factors which control this reaction will be discussed later. Thrombin is prepared by converting prothrombin; the purer the prothrombin used, the purer will be the thrombin produced.

Thrombin-Fibrinogen Reaction. The most important property of thrombin is its ability to clot fibrinogen. This reaction is usually studied by obtaining relatively pure solutions of fibrinogen and thrombin and observing the speed at which coagulation occurs when the two are mixed. By this method it is found that the clotting time is inversely proportional to the concentration of the thrombin. This relationship is important in the interpretation of methods for the measurement of prothrombin. Many factors, such as the concentration of fibrinogen, pH, salt concentration and colloid osmotic pressure, influence the clotting time. Much work has been done on the nature of the thrombin-fibrinogen reaction. It appears that fibrin is formed from fibrinogen by progressive polymerization. In the early stages of this reaction a soluble "fibrino-peptide" is separated from the fibrinogen, probably by a splitting of arginyl-glycine bonds in the fibrinogen.[25] The altered fibrinogen (fibrin monomer) then polymerizes to form fibrin. In the final clot the altered fibrinogen molecules are held together by primary and secondary linkages.[16, 47]

The strength of a thrombin solution can be measured by the clotting time which it gives with a standard fibrinogen solution under closely defined conditions of pH, salt concentration and temperature. In this way units of thrombin have been variously defined. Thrombin may be used, either alone or in association with fibrinogen or fibrin preparations, for local application in the control of hemorrhage. This form of local hemostatic has proved useful in operations on the nose, throat and eye, and in plastic surgery.

Fibrin.   When thrombin is added to fibrinogen, the stages in the formation of fibrin can be observed with an electron microscope. It is found that the fibrinogen molecules unite end-to-end to form long fibrils; later, these fibrils associate into bundles which have regular cross striations. Fibrinogen and fibrin have much the same gross chemical constituents. Fibrin formed during the clotting of plasma is insoluble in urea; that formed by the interaction of purified thrombin and fibrinogen is soluble. This difference is attributed to the presence in plasma of a fibrin-stabilizing factor which is absent from purified fibrinogen.[24]

PROTHROMBIN AND THE CONVERSION OF PROTHROMBIN TO THROMBIN

Prothrombin and the Classic Theory.   Prothrombin is the plasma precursor of thrombin. Its existence was first postulated because it was observed that, whereas an active coagulant of fibrinogen could be isolated from fresh serum, no such coagulant could be obtained from fresh, unclotted whole blood.[48] The existence of prothrombin has been confirmed by numerous observations. Mellanby[32] isolated from plasma a substance which, while not itself a coagulant, could be converted into a coagulant on suitable treatment. Isolation from plasma of prothrombin more or less freed from other constituents has now become a frequent step in blood coagulation research.

In citrated or oxalated plasma, prothrombin is readily converted to thrombin. On the addition of $CaCl_2$ this conversion may take five to ten minutes. If a tissue extract, like that derived from acetone-dried brain, is present as well as $CaCl_2$, the conversion may be achieved in less than one minute. Thus tissue extracts, usually referred to as thromboplastin, accelerate the conversion of prothrombin to thrombin, and the coagulation process may be represented diagrammatically as follows:

Scheme 1

$$\text{Prothrombin} \xrightarrow[\text{CaCl}_2]{\text{Thromboplastin}} \text{Thrombin}$$

$$\text{Fibrinogen} \xrightarrow{\text{Thrombin}} \text{Fibrin}$$

This scheme to explain the reactions of coagulation is often called the classic theory of blood coagulation; it was proposed by Schmidt[48] and supported by Morawitz,[33] as well as by much experimental work in the first 40 years of this century.

Factor V.   The classic theory, though very fruitful because it gave rise to numerous experiments, is now recognized to be incomplete. The first doubts about its adequacy arose when it was found that prothrombin isolated from plasma was not always readily converted to thrombin in the presence of thromboplastin and $CaCl_2$. Prothrombin may be isolated from plasma by precipitation with ammonium sulfate at 50 per cent saturation, by dilution and acidification to pH 5.3, and by adsorption on various inorganic precipitates such as $BaSO_4$, $Ca_3(PO_4)_2$, and $Al(OH)_3$. When prepared by precipitation, prothrombin is readily converted to thrombin; when prepared by adsorption, it is not converted readily by $CaCl_2$ or by $CaCl_2$ and tissue extracts. It appears that prothrombin prepared by adsorption lacks some substance essential for the conversion of prothrombin to thrombin that is present in preparations made by other methods. This observation was originally made by Nolf,[34, 35, 36] and he called this essential factor "thrombogen," an unfortunate term because it had previously been used by Morawitz[33] for prothrombin. Similar observations were made by Ware and Seegers,[52] who referred to the accelerating substance as "accelerator globulin" (Ac-globulin).

In 1943, Quick[45] observed that the prothrombin in oxalated plasma which had been stored was not readily converted to thrombin; he suggested that this failure to form thrombin resulted from the destruction of a "labile" factor which is present in whole fresh plasma.

In 1947, Owren[38] published a very full account of a patient who had a hemorrhagic tendency due to the absence of something that was necessary for the conversion of prothrombin to thrombin; this he called "factor V." (Later Owren called this substance "proaccelerin," but the term factor V is to be preferred because he suggested that "proaccelerin" is converted to "accelerin" during clotting, and the evidence for this change available at present is not entirely convincing.)

It appears that the terms "thrombogen," "Ac-globulin," "labile factor," "factor V," and "proaccelerin" all refer to a single substance. This substance is unstable on storage, is not adsorbed by inorganic precipitates, and is essential for the rapid conversion of prothrombin to thrombin in the presence of tissue extracts and $CaCl_2$. In the clotting of normal blood, factor V disappears and therefore is not present in serum; presumably it is converted into some other substance during the clotting process.

Factor VII.   A second accelerator substance is also necessary for the conversion of prothrombin to thrombin in the presence of tissue extracts and $CaCl_2$.[22] This substance is adsorbed together with prothrombin by inorganic precipitates and is stable on storage. The activity of this factor was therefore initially not readily separated from that of prothrombin. As with factor V, it was investigation of a coagulation abnormality which led to a full study of the substance. Patients treated for thrombosis with drugs of the dicoumarin [3,3'-methylenebis (4-hydroxycoumarin)] group have a coagulation defect which was attributed originally to a lack of prothrombin. But this defect can be corrected by normal serum which does not contain prothrombin (because all of the prothrombin has already been converted to thrombin). Serum does contain a substance, called "factor VII" by Koller et al.,[22] which is not used up during the process of clotting; and the main abnormality which follows treatment with dicoumarin is a reduction in the amount of factor VII available.

Factor VII is probably synonymous with co-thromboplastin,[31] serum prothrombin conversion accelerator,[37] and proconvertin.[39]

To summarize, in addition to tissue extracts and $CaCl_2$ two substances are now known to be necessary for the rapid conversion of prothrombin to thrombin. These two substances, factors V and VII, differ quite markedly from each other: factor V is unstable on storage, is not adsorbed by inorganic precipitates, and is used up during clotting; factor VII is stable on storage, is adsorbed by inorganic precipitates, and is not consumed during clotting.

Tissue Extracts and Factors V and VII.   Coagulation theory is now complicated by the existence of two accelerators of prothrombin conversion for which there are several possible modes of action. The accelerators may so alter prothrombin that it is more readily acted on by the tissue extract, or the tissue extract itself may be inactive until it is acted on by these factors. Of these two possibilities, the second is the more probable. If brain extract is incubated with factors V and VII, a very powerful prothrombin con-

TABLE 13. THE REACTION OF BRAIN EXTRACT WITH FACTORS V AND VII

Brain extract and various other factors indicated under the first column are incubated at 37° C At intervals samples are removed and added to mixtures of prothrombin and fibrinogen (second column). The clotting times in seconds, after various periods of incubation, are shown in columns 3–7.

INCUBATION MIXTURE	SUBSTRATE	INCUBATION TIME IN MINUTES				
		1	2	3	4	6
Brain and CaCl₂	Prothrombin and fibrinogen	175	189	158	174	172
Brain, Factor V, Factor VII, and CaCl₂	Prothrombin and fibrinogen	13	11	10	10	11
Brain and CaCl₂	Fibrinogen, Prothrombin, Factor V, and Factor VII	37	36	33	35	37

verting substance is formed. This is illustrated in Table 13. Brain extract with $CaCl_2$, added to a mixture of prothrombin and fibrinogen, has a very feeble coagulant ability—indicated by the long clotting time—because the brain extract alone has a poor ability to convert prothrombin to thrombin. When the brain extract is incubated with factors V and VII and $CaCl_2$, the prothrombin converting substance formed is very powerful, this power being indicated by the very short clotting times. When the factors V and VII are added to prothrombin and fibrinogen before the brain extract is added, the clotting times are longer, the reaction with the brain extract having occurred in the substrate clotting. These results suggest that the brain extract reacts with the accelerator substances. The classic theory of blood coagulation should therefore be modified as shown below in scheme 2. An additional factor, the Stuart-Prower factor, is included in this scheme for completeness; it will be mentioned later.

Scheme 2

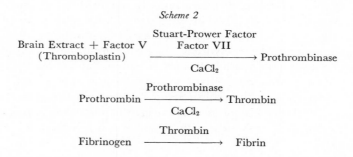

When originally devised, the term "thromboplastin" denoted tissue extracts which were thought to be direct activators of prothrombin. Since this hypothesis no longer fits the observed facts, it is necessary to invent a new term for the direct activator of prothrombin. It is proposed to adopt for the purpose the term suggested by Owren *et al.*,[41] *prothrombinase*. Since the term "thromboplastin" has been variously used by different workers, it is proposed to use it in rather a general way by saying that any substance has thromboplastic activity if it will shorten the clotting time of recalcified normal plasma. According to this scheme, a specific type of activity must be noted, e.g., that of tissue thromboplastin.

One Stage Prothrombin Time and Measurement of Prothrombin. In 1935, before the existence of factors V and VII was widely recognized, Quick[43] described a method for the quantitative measurement of prothrombin. This method was very simple and has proved widely useful, but it is to be doubted whether it often measures prothrombin. In the test, 0.1 ml. of citrated or oxalated plasma is mixed with 0.1 ml. of a brain extract, and the mixture is warmed to 37° C. Next, 0.1 ml. of $CaCl_2$ is added, and a stop watch is started; the time required for coagulation to occur is then measured. The test has been useful because it shows that a number of patients have an abnormal clotting time. These include some persons with inherited or constitutional hemorrhagic diathesis, newborn infants, patients with obstructive jaundice or liver disease and patients treated with anticoagulants of the dicoumarin group.

This test was based on the assumption that brain extract is the direct and only activator of prothrombin. If this assumption were true, the clotting time in this test would be controlled only by the quantity of prothrombin present. It is now clear, however, that the test cannot be relied upon to measure prothrombin. Reference to Scheme 2 shows that, in the presence of $CaCl_2$, the addition of brain extract to normal plasma will set in motion a series of reactions. First, the extract reacts with factors V and VII to form prothrombinase. The prothrombinase then converts the prothrombin to thrombin. The clotting time will therefore depend on the amount of prothrombinase formed and the speed of its formation, and on the amount of prothrombin available for conversion to thrombin. The formation of thromboplastin is controlled by the amounts of factors V and VII present. The one stage prothrombin time will therefore be affected by a deficiency in factor V, factor VII or prothrombin.

When the technique was first used it was thought to give a measure of prothrombin, and patients whose blood gave abnormal results with the test were said to have prothrombin deficiency. Now these cases must all be reviewed to determine which of the three factors is involved.

Prothrombin Deficiency. A lack of prothrombin with factors V and VII at a normal level is a very uncommon defect. One case of uncomplicated prothrombin deficiency has been described,[2] and sometimes in liver disease the prothrombin level may be reduced when other factors are normal. In the majority of patients originally thought to lack prothrombin, the amounts of both prothrombin and factor VII are reduced; these conditions will be discussed in more detail below.

Factor V Deficiency. A number of patients whose blood lacks factor V have been described. The disease gives rise to a severe bleeding tendency, which may be present from birth and may occur in other members of the family. In severe liver disease the quantity of factor V may be reduced, and, in some cases, severe infections such as hemorrhagic measles or scarlet fever may be associated with factor V deficiency. In occasional patients with advanced secondary carcinoma the amount of factor V may be reduced.[10]

Factor VII Deficiency. An isolated deficiency of factor VII is uncommon. One or two patients with a hemorrhagic diathesis from early childhood in whom factor VII was deficient have been described.[10]

Combined Prothrombin and Factor VII Deficiency. The commonest type of abnormality is a defect of both prothrombin and factor VII.

Vitamin K deficiency. Before Quick's one stage technique was widely used, a hemorrhagic disease of chickens fed purified diets was investigated. It was found that the condition was cured by giving green vegetables; the curative substance was not vitamin C, however, because the curative substance was removed by extraction of the diet with fat solvents. A brilliant series of experiments led to the isolation of a fat soluble substance called vitamin K. It was found that a number of synthetic substances with a structure similar to 2-methyl-3-hydroxy-1,4-naphtho-quinone can counteract the disease in chickens, although they are somewhat less effective than the substance extracted from its natural sources.

Deficiency of vitamin K may arise in patients who have a reduced ability to absorb fats and in those with jaundice or with steatorrhea. In these patients the one stage prothrombin time is prolonged and a hemorrhagic diathesis may develop. The hemorrhagic tendency is corrected and the one stage prothrombin time reduced to normal by the administration of vitamin K. A careful analysis of the clotting defect in these patients has shown that deficiencies of both prothrombin and factor VII are present.

Hemorrhagic disease of the newborn.   Before the discovery of vitamin K, a hemorrhagic tendency was observed in about one in 400 newborn infants. The bleeding occurred at the third or fourth day of life. The one stage prothrombin time of newborn infants is often normal at birth, but the clotting time determined by this technique lengthens during the first week of life. It is thought that vitamin K is normally made in the intestine as a result of the action of bacterial enzymes on the food ingested, and that in the newborn this ability to synthesize vitamin K is deficient. At birth, the amounts of both prothrombin and factor VII are slightly less than those observed in older individuals. The levels of these substances fall during the first week of life unless vitamin K is given, a practice which prevents the decline.

Dicoumarin.   A hemorrhagic disease of Canadian cattle was traced to feeding on spoiled sweet clover hay and was found to be attributable to the development in the hay of a certain derivative of coumarin. This substance was identified as 3,3'-methylenebis (4-hydroxycoumarin), also called "dicoumarin," "dicoumarol" or "Dicumarol."[23] It can be synthesized, and, if given by mouth to animals, it causes bleeding. The bleeding tendency is associated with a long one stage prothrombin time, which in turn is caused by a definite reduction in the factor VII level and a lesser fall in prothrombin in the blood.

This substance, or modifications of it such as Tromexan [bis-3,3'-(4-hydroxycoumarinyl)ethylacetate], or substances with a similar physiologic action such as Dindevan (phenylindanedione), are often given to patients who suffer from intravascular clotting to reduce the coagulability of the blood. In patients with clots in the cardiac arteries the treatment is undoubtedly beneficial; it reduces the mortality among such patients by about one-half.[10, 56] For therapeutic purposes, the dosage is controlled by measuring the level of the one stage prothrombin test and maintaining this level between defined limits by varying the dose of the drug. This control is essential for safe treatment, because the amount necessary varies greatly from one patient to another, and an overdose may give rise to serious bleeding.

Administration of synthetic, water soluble vitamin K preparations to patients who have received an overdose of dicoumarin is relatively ineffective. The hemorrhage is not rapidly controlled, nor is the one stage clotting time rapidly restored to normal. It appears that, for some unknown reason, the oil soluble substance extracted from its natural sources (called "vitamin K_1") is much more effective than the synthetic compounds in correcting the bleeding tendency caused by this group of drugs.

Stuart-Prower Factor and Factor X.[50]   Some patients whose plasma has a long one stage prothrombin time have been found to lack a factor which differs from both factor V and factor VII. This additional element has been called the *Stuart factor* and the *Prower factor*. It is certain, however, that only one factor is involved, and this may be called the *Stuart-Prower factor*. Patients with vitamin K deficiency and those treated with drugs of the dicoumarol group may also lack the Stuart-Prower factor in addition to being deficient in factor VII. The blood of patients with vitamin K deficiency and of those treated with dicoumarol drugs have also been said to lack *factor X*. It is possible that the Stuart-Prower factor and factor X are the same and the two terms are now used synonymously.

BLOOD THROMBOPLASTIN

So far, the development of coagulant activity from tissue extracts has been discussed. This is an artificial system, because normal clotting cannot be attributed to the appearance in the blood of a saline extract of dehydrated brain. In normal clotting it is possible that a substance analogous to these tissue extracts appears in the early stages of clotting, and it is now necessary to consider the origin of this substance. It is referred to as *blood thromboplastin* because there are, as yet, no experiments on the mode of action of the final coagulant formed in blood.

Blood collected with care to avoid contamination with tissue extracts will clot solidly in five to ten minutes if placed in a glass tube. It would therefore appear that all of the reagents necessary for the production of thromboplastin must occur in whole blood—and it is in whole blood that they must be sought. This search is not easy because, as was pointed out earlier, the initial stages of coagulation can be studied only by their effect on fibrin formation, and observations of these early stages must therefore be very indirect.

When whole blood is placed in a glass tube, the clotting time (five to ten minutes) is considerably longer than that of the same blood if brain extract has been added (12 to 15 seconds). This difference indicates either that the blood thromboplastin is very weak in comparison with that formed from tissue extracts, or that a time consuming reaction or series of reactions precedes the appearance of blood thromboplastin. The distinction between these possibilities can be made quite readily. If whole normal blood is placed in a glass tube, the progress of thrombin formation can be followed by removing samples at intervals and adding these to fibrinogen. When this is done, it is found that there is an interval of three to five minutes during which no thrombin can be detected; after this time, the first threads of fibrin appear, and, as these are produced, a sudden explosive generation of thrombin follows.[28] This pattern of thrombin formation suggests that a powerful thromboplastin is formed during the clotting of normal blood, but that some minutes are required for its formation. Were the blood thromboplastin very feeble, a low level of thrombin formation continuing over a considerable period of time would be expected.

If a powerful thromboplastin is formed in the blood, the next step is to determine the factors required for its formation. Two of these factors have been defined by the work of Quick,[46] Brinkhous[12] and others. These authors have found that patients with hemophilia and patients whose blood lacks platelets have a deficient ability to form thromboplastin. Hemophilic blood lacks a substance, present in normal blood, which has been called *antihemophilic globulin* or "factor VIII." Thus antihemophilic globulin and platelets are established as components of thromboplastin. Factors V and VII were also suggested as probable components, because both of these substances are necessary for the formation of complete thromboplastin from brain extracts.

These four factors—platelets, antihemophilic globulin and factors V and VII—can be provided quite readily from normal blood. Platelets can be prepared by centrifuging citrated blood at a low speed to obtain platelet-containing plasma. During rapid centrifuging of this plasma, the platelets are deposited and can be freed from plasma by repeated washing and centrifuging. Antihemophilic globulin and factor V can be prepared by treating plasma from which platelets have been removed with an inorganic adsorbent such as $Al(OH)_3$, which removes prothrombin and factor VII but does not remove factor V or antihemophilic globulin. These two factors can be separated from the $Al(OH)_3$ treated plasma by precipitation with $(NH_4)_2SO_4$. Factor VII can be provided by normal serum, which does not contain appreciable amounts of prothrombin, antihemophilic globulin or factor V, because all of these factors are consumed in normal

TABLE 14. THE FORMATION OF BLOOD THROMBOPLASTIN

Equal parts of reagents indicated in column 1 are incubated at 37° C. and at intervals samples are added, together with $CaCl_2$, to the mixture indicated in column 2. The clotting times in seconds after various periods of incubation, are shown in columns 3–7.

INCUBATION MIXTURE	SUBSTRATE	INCUBATION TIME IN MINUTES				
		1	2	3	4	6
Al(OH)₃ treated plasma Serum Platelets CaCl₂	Prothrombin, fibrinogen, and $CaCl_2$	130	43	13	10	10
	Plasma and $CaCl_2$	73	48	18	10	9

clotting. If the four reagents and $CaCl_2$ are mixed in a tube, a powerful thromboplastin develops in the mixture.[6] Thrombin is not formed because no prothrombin is present in the reagents. The presence of thromboplastin can be detected by removing samples from the mixture and adding these, together with $CaCl_2$, to a mixture of prothrombin and fibrinogen or to plasma. An experiment to demonstrate thromboplastin formation is illustrated in Table 14. In this experiment samples of 0.1 ml. were removed at one or two minute intervals from the mixture forming thromboplastin and added, together with 0.1 ml. of $CaCl_2$, to 0.2 ml. of a mixture of equal parts of prothrombin and fibrinogen. The clotting times of the prothrombin and fibrinogen mixtures were recorded. The progressive shortening of the clotting times observed indicates the formation of thromboplastin in the mixture. Normal citrated plasma may also be used as a test system to replace the mixture of fibrinogen and prothrombin. In this way the formation of thromboplastin from normal blood reagents can be followed and the method, called the "thromboplastin generation test,"[5] can be used to detect abnormality in thromboplastin formation in specific patients. This experiment shows that the formation of thromboplastin from its components is a time-consuming reaction.

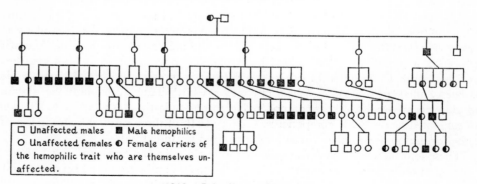

□ Unaffected males ■ Male hemophilics
O Unaffected females ◑ Female carriers of
the hemophilic trait who are themselves unaffected.

FIG. 318. Inheritance of hemophilia.

Coagulation Defects Caused by Deficient Thromboplastin Formation. *Hemophilia.* Hemophilia is a severe bleeding disease which usually affects males; it is inherited as a sex linked recessive character. A typical family tree is shown in Figure 318. The patients undergo hemorrhagic episodes from early infancy and by adolescence are often crippled by the damaging effect of repeated hemorrhages into joints. The coagulation abnormality in hemophilia can be detected by various laboratory tests; the whole-blood clotting time is lengthened, and the results of the thromboplastin generation test are abnormal when normal Al(OH)₃-treated plasma is replaced by that from the patient.

If normal blood is added to hemophilic blood *in vitro*, the coagulation abnormality is corrected, the correcting substance being antihemophilic globulin. This substance is unstable on storage. The only effective treatment for hemophilia is blood transfusion, very large amounts of blood usually being required to check bleeding. Attempts to prepare purified antihemophilic globulin from human blood have had some success,[11, 20] but very little of the material is available. Antihemophilic globulin of very high potency can also be made from beef and pig blood,[2, 3] and, with the use of these preparations, surgical operations may be undertaken in hemophilic patients.[29] The animal material is, however, antigenic, and is at present used only for life-saving procedures.

Christmas disease.   Occasionally, when blood samples from two apparently hemophilic patients are mixed together, the mixture has a completely normal clotting time.[9] It appears that the two patients lack different substances. A closer study of this phenomenon has shown that patients thought to have hemophilia from clinical and genetic evidence and from the usual laboratory tests can be divided into two groups. In one, antihemophilic globulin is lacking, and the patients can be said to have hemophilia; in the second group, an entirely different substance is lacking. This substance differs from the antihemophilic globulin in that it is adsorbed by Al(OH)₃, is precipitated in a different plasma fraction, and is present in normal serum. This new factor has been called the *Christmas factor* (after the first patient examined, whose name was Christmas) or factor IX. The term "plasma thromboplastin component," used by White *et al.*,[55] refers to the same substance.

The recognition of the Christmas factor raised the question of the number of factors required for blood thromboplastin formation. The factors so far postulated were antihemophilic globulin, factor V, factor VII, platelets, and CaCl₂. Study of Christmas disease made it clear that the Christmas factor is an essential blood thromboplastin component. The original view that factor VII was also necessary was based on the observation that patients who are treated with the dicoumarol type of drugs (and who therefore lack factor VII) have poor serum activity in the thromboplastin generation test. At the time when the original hypothesis was proposed, no other active substances present in serum were recognized. Reinvestigation of the serum from patients receiving these drugs showed that, in addition to a deficiency of factor VII, the amounts of the Christmas factor and the Stuart-Prower factor were also reduced. Study of the blood of patients having factor VII deficiency as a single congenital defect showed that blood thromboplastin formation was entirely normal, whereas study of patients with the Stuart-Prower defect showed that blood thromboplastin formation was abnormal. Thus, at this stage it was necessary to remove factor VII from the list of blood–thromboplastin-forming substances and substitute the Christmas and Stuart-Prower factors. The exact mode of action of the Stuart-Prower factor is unknown; it has been included in Scheme 3 (p. 563) in the most logical position, but further work will be required to settle this question.

Christmas disease is probably less common than hemophilia. Of 187 patients thought to have hemophilia examined in Oxford, only 20 proved to have Christmas disease. The distinction between the two conditions is of more than academic interest, because preparations providing antihemophilic globulin activity will be ineffective in the treatment of Christmas disease.

Platelet deficiency (thrombocytopenia).   When the blood of patients with reduced numbers of platelets clots in a glass tube, the clotting time is usually normal, although an abnormal excess of prothrombin remains in the serum after clotting. If the progress of thrombin formation is followed in platelet-deficient plasma, it is found that the amount of thrombin formed is reduced but that thrombin formation is not delayed. In the artificial system, platelets are essential for thromboplastin formation. These results suggest that the platelets control the amount of thromboplastin formed but have little effect on the speed of its formation. Experiments in which crude cephalin fractions of brain extract were used have shown that these can replace platelets in the thromboplastin generation test. Thus, the active platelet factor is probably a phospholipid. Attempts to identify a single specific phospholipid with platelet activity have so far given rise to confusion.

In the absence of platelets, the formed clot does not retract from the sides of the tube and express serum as does a normal clot. It is probable that the normal mechanism of clot retraction is the result mainly of the vital activity of platelets which become entangled in the clot during fibrin formation and subsequently tend to agglutinate. During agglutination, the strands of fibrin to which the platelets are attached are forcibly pulled together.[13]

In many cases of thrombocytopenia the capillaries do not contract normally when injured. This abnormality leads to prolonged oozing from minor injuries. This failure of capillary function does not appear to be related to the abnormality in clotting caused by platelet deficiency.

CALCIUM AND BLOOD COAGULATION

Ionized calcium is needed in at least three of the reactions preceding thrombin formation. This accounts for the well known anticoagulant efficiency of decalcifying agents, such as citrates or oxalates. It is thought that calcium is adsorbed by various plasma proteins and may act by maintaining an optimum surface charge for their interaction.[26]

SURFACE CONTACT AND COAGULATION

Usually clotting is greatly delayed if blood is in contact with a surface such as vascular endothelium, silicone, Lustroid or paraffin. In glass tubes, on the other hand, clotting occurs promptly. It is reasonable to suppose that some substance or substances occur in the blood in an inactive form and that they are activated on exposure to suitable surfaces. Experiments have suggested that both the Christmas factor and the platelets are in some way altered by contact with glass.[7] It seems probable that the natural stimulus to coagulation is this exposure to an abnormal surface such as might be provided by damaged endothelium or other injured tissues.

The Hageman Defect and Plasma Thromboplastin Antecedent Deficiency. The mechanism through which contact activation may operate has been studied in connection with two coagulation defects known as the *Hageman defect* and *plasma thromboplastin antecedent (P.T.A.) deficiency*. The Hageman defect is an abnormality of coagulation in which the blood clots poorly in glass tubes and gives abnormal results in various other laboratory tests. It has no clinical significance, as patients with the anomaly show no unusual bleeding tendency. Fortunately, routine laboratory work is not confused by such cases as they are extremely rarely encountered. Study has shown that the blood of these patients lacks the ability to be activated by glass contact. It must be presumed that in the body the reaction to contact is carried out by some other mechanism and that this explains why the patients are unaffected.

Plasma thromboplastin antecedent deficiency gives rise to a disease not unlike mild hemophilia, but women may be affected. The deficient factor appears to be concerned in the very early stages in clotting; it may be the factor upon which the contact factor acts. The substance produced by interaction of the Hageman and P.T.A. factors probably brings about the activation of Christmas factor from an inactive precursor.

1HEORY OF COAGULATION AND TESTS FOR CLOTTING FUNCTION

Scheme 3 for blood coagulation is a scheme for blood thromboplastin formation. This scheme cannot be coordinated exactly with Scheme 2 for tissue thromboplastin, because factor VII is required for prothrombinase formation but not for the formation of blood thromboplastin. It should be recognized that this scheme is entirely hypothetical; it merely serves as method of visualizing the many probable factors and as a basis for further experiments.

Some of the tests of clotting function and the stages of coagulation that they record are also indicated in Scheme 3. In the whole-blood clotting time test a measured amount of blood is placed in a glass tube and the time elapsing until it solidifies is recorded. This method is a crude test of over-all clotting function and will give abnormal results if any stage of the clotting process is sufficiently defective. Unfortunately it is not a sensitive test. For example, patients with hemophilia may have almost complete absence of anti-hemophilic globulin, and their clotting time will be prolonged. The addition of 1 to 2

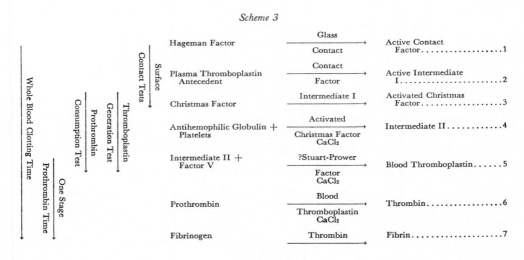

Scheme 3

per cent of antihemophilic globulin may return the clotting time almost to normal. Again, treatment with any of the dicoumarin group of drugs effectively interferes with the patient's clotting mechanism, yet the clotting time is not usually prolonged.

The one stage prothrombin test assays clotting function in the presence of a tissue extract, usually brain extract. The test will give abnormal results if reactions 5 through 7 of Scheme 3 are abnormal. The use of brain extract, which supplies reagents that are very roughly equivalent to those formed during reactions 1 though 4, will mask deficiency in any of these factors. The one stage prothrombin time in hemophilia, Christmas disease and thrombocytopenia is therefore normal. If it is desired to obtain specific measurements of factors V or VII, the one stage test must be modified as described by Owren and Aas[40] or by Koller et al.[22] If a specific measurement of prothrombin is desired, a two stage test[4, 53] must be made.

The prothrombin consumption test consists of measuring the amount of prothrombin remaining in serum one hour after clotting. In normal blood most of the prothrombin has disappeared by this time, but, if there is any abnormality in reactions 1 through 5 of Scheme 3, much prothrombin will remain in the serum because thromboplastin formation is defective. The test is rather more sensitive than the whole-blood clotting time, and has often been used in the diagnosis of hemophilia.

The thromboplastin generation test[5] will also record abnormalities in reactions 3

TABLE 15. RESULTS OF ONE STAGE PROTHROMBIN TIME AND THROMBOPLASTIN GENERATION TEST ON PATIENTS WITH VARIOUS COAGULATION DEFECTS

TECHNIQUE	SOURCE OF THROMBO-PLASTIN COMPONENTS			TYPE OF COAGULATION DEFECT					
				Hemophilia	Christmas disease	Factor V deficiency	Factor VII deficiency	Stuart Prower factor	Thromboplastin inhibitor
One stage "prothrombin" time				Normal	Normal	Prolonged	Prolonged	Prolonged	Normal
Thromboplastin generation test	Absorbed plasma*	Serum	Platelets						
	Patient	Normal	Normal	Abnormal	Normal	Abnormal	Normal	Normal	Abnormal
	Normal	Patient	Normal	Normal	Abnormal	Normal	Normal	Abnormal	May be abnormal

* Plasma treated with Al(OH)$_3$.

through 5 of Scheme 3. This test is more sensitive than the prothrombin consumption test and can be used to distinguish abnormality in separate components. For example, in hemophilia the fraction equivalent to the normal antihemophilic globulin can be prepared from the patient's blood and used to replace the normal fraction in the thromboplastin test. If the patient has hemophilia, the test will be abnormal; if, on the other hand, he has Christmas disease, the antihemophilic globulin prepared from the patient's blood will be normal, but the serum, lacking the Christmas factor, will give abnormal results when used to replace normal serum (see Table 15).

In Table 15 are shown applications of the one stage prothrombin time and the thromboplastin generation test in the diagnosis of the more frequently encountered hemorrhagic states associated with abnormal clotting. The techniques used to investigate hemorrhagic states have been described in detail by Biggs and Macfarlane.[10]

NATURAL INHIBITORS OF COAGULATION

The blood contains a considerable excess of many factors which promote clotting. The prothrombin in 10 ml. of plasma, if converted to thrombin, would be sufficient to clot all of the blood in the body. The thromboplastin from 10 ml. of platelet-containing plasma is also theoretically capable of converting all of the prothrombin in the body to thrombin. This enormous potential coagulant ability must naturally be controlled in the body if life is to proceed. The controlling mechanism probably consists of a series of inhibitory systems capable of neutralizing active coagulants or preventing their formation.

Antithrombin. A powerful mechanism for neutralizing thrombin exists in normal blood. Within 15 to 30 minutes after all of the prothrombin in a sample of blood is converted to thrombin, no thrombin can be detected in the serum. This disappearance of thrombin is due in part to adsorption of thrombin by fibrin formed during clotting and in part to the neutralization of thrombin by a substance in the albumin fraction called *antithrombin*.[21] It appears that antithrombin reacts quantitatively with thrombin to form a neutralized substance which has been called *metathrombin*.

The presence of antithrombin means that the formation of thrombin and its neutralization in blood progress simultaneously. Thus the amount of thrombin to be detected in blood is always less than the amount formed. Moreover, the amount to be detected will depend greatly on the speed of thrombin formation; if thrombin formation is slow, the thrombin will be exposed to antithrombin for a longer period during its formation, and the amount of thrombin to be demonstrated at any one time will be low. The efficiency of thrombin formation in blood is therefore closely related to the speed of its formation, and deficiency of thromboplastin factors will greatly reduce the clotting efficiency of the blood.

Theoretically, abnormal clotting could be caused by an increase or decrease of antithrombin in the blood. No convincing instances of such abnormality have been recorded.

Heparin. In experiments designed to purify tissue extract, McLean,[30] working in Howell's laboratory, found that an inhibitor of blood coagulation could be obtained from liver. Subsequent work showed that this material, *heparin*, as extracted from beef liver, is a mixture of mucoitin polysulfuric acids.[18] The action of heparin is complex. It inhibits the thrombin–fibrinogen reaction and prevents thrombin formation. If thrombin and fibrinogen isolated from blood react together, heparin has little inhibitory effect. On the other hand, heparin strongly inhibits the reaction of thrombin with fibrinogen in whole plasma. It appears that heparin requires a cofactor from plasma for its action to be effective. Much evidence suggests that the cofactor for heparin in plasma is antithrombin.[27] Heparin therefore probably works by enhancing the normal antithrombin. In addition, heparin inhibits thrombin formation by interfering with the formation of thromboplastin.

Heparin is often used to depress the coagulability of blood in patients with thrombosis; its action is short-lived and it is effective only when given intramuscularly or intravenously. Drugs of the dicoumarin group are now more commonly used than heparin because, being effective when given by mouth, they are more convenient. Heparin does not occur in measurable quantity in the blood of normal people, but appears in the blood following anaphylactic shock. Very occasionally the occurrence of heparin in the blood, for which there is no known cause, may give rise to a hemorrhagic state in patients.

Antithromboplastin. Tocantins[51] has made many experiments to demonstrate the existence of an antithromboplastin in plasma. This substance is said to be removed by contact with glass surfaces. A substance can be isolated from plasma by a method described by Tocantins; this material has an undoubted effect in preventing the formation of thromboplastin and inhibits the action of brain extracts. It is possible that this substance normally neutralizes the Christmas factor and that the activating effect of contact with glass is attributable to the liberation of the Christmas factor from combination with the inhibitor. This suggestion is at present only supposition.

Hemorrhagic Disease Due to Anticoagulants. A number of patients have been described in whom a circulating anticoagulant has developed.[10] Some of these patients have hemophilia, and in some the condition has followed pregnancy. So far, when examined, the anticoagulant has been found to neutralize antihemophilic globulin or to inhibit the formation of thromboplastin. In the hemophilic patients the condition follows repeated transfusion, and it has been thought that the antihemophilic globulin may behave as a foreign protein to these patients and thus provoke the development of antibodies specific for antihemophilic globulin. The cause in the other cases is even more obscure; it is possible that, in the cases which follow pregnancy, thromboplastin components from the placenta enter the circulation at delivery and antibodies to some thromboplastin component develop.

MISCELLANEOUS COAGULANTS AND ANTICOAGULANTS

A number of other substances have been investigated with the hope of throwing some light on the normal clotting mechanism, but these cannot be considered to be physiologic substances.

Coagulants of Fibrinogen. Some of the fibrinogen in plasma may be clotted by substances other than thrombin, such as papain, Chloramine-T, ninhydrin and naphthoquinone. The clots formed are usually much more fragile than normal plasma clots, and it is clear that only a fraction of the fibrinogen has been affected.

Staphylocoagulase. Staphylocoagulase, prepared from staphylococci, is a substance which will clot plasma. It appears that this material acts by converting prothrombin to a modified form of thrombin. This thrombin is unaffected by antithrombin or heparin and will coagulate a portion of the fibrinogen. It is probable that the conversion of prothrombin to the modified thrombin is independent of factors V and VII. The conversion of prothrombin by staphylocoagulase therefore probably may be used to give a measure of prothrombin.[15]

Trypsin. Trypsin will clot normal plasma in the absence of calcium, but the reaction is considerably enhanced by the presence of calcium. It is probable that trypsin is analogous to tissue extracts in its mode of action, but that it reacts more rapidly with factors V and VII than brain extract does.[8]

Russell's Viper Venom. Russell's viper venom is a very powerful coagulant of plasma in the presence of $CaCl_2$, and will cause coagulation even when diluted many million times. This preparation has been used to replace brain extract in the one stage prothrombin time test, a purpose for which it is very convenient, being stable in dried form and readily reconstituted for use. Unfortunately the results of using Russell's viper venom have not proved very satisfactory, because its action depends upon the lipoid component of the plasma, which varies from one sample to another. This difficulty can be overcome by adding lipid in the form of lecithin to the Russell's viper venom. This greatly enhances its activity, and the mixture will not clot normal plasma in the presence of calcium in 5 to 7 seconds. Russell's viper venom does not require factor VII for its action; it is therefore a particularly unsatisfactory form of thromboplastin for use in the one stage prothrombin time when the test is used to control anticoagulant therapy. The clotting time is lengthened when the Stuart-Prower factor is lacking, and the test is useful for diagnosis of this condition.

Soybean Trypsin Inhibitor. Soybean trypsin inhibitor is an inhibitor of blood coagulation. Its effect on coagulation appears to result from a specific inhibition of formed thromboplastin.[8] A similar inhibitor, pancreatic trypsin inhibitor, has been isolated from beef pancreas. It is possible that the pancreatic inhibitor has a similar action, but this has not been investigated.

EXCESSIVE COAGULATION

The mechanism of normal clotting and its failure in certain hemorrhagic states have been discussed together because knowledge of the normal mechanism is largely derived from a study of the difference between the normal and defective systems. This study leads to the conclusion that the fluidity of normal intravascular blood and its prompt coagulation on vascular injury are regulated by a delicately balanced equilibrium system. The process of clotting is started by contact with a foreign surface, and clotting when vessels are injured may be explained on this basis. The normal failure of the clot to extend beyond the site of injury may be attributed to the various inhibitors of clotting which neutralize natural coagulants as they are diluted in the circulation.

Excessive clotting or thrombosis occurs when a clot extends beyond the site of an injury, or when blood coagulates in uninjured vessels. No single cause for excessive coagulation is likely to operate in all cases. Roughening of the vascular endothelium by atheroma or infection might predispose to clotting, and, similarly, stasis of the blood will favor clotting because rapid dilution of locally formed coagulants will not occur. Severe trauma may also predispose to thrombosis, because products of tissue breakdown may enter the circulation. When enough unfavorable factors coexist in one patient, pathologic thrombosis may occur. Considering the complexity of the problem, it is not surprising that tests to detect a liability to thrombosis have not given consistent results. Regardless of whether a change in coagulability of the blood is commonly associated with thrombosis, there is little doubt that reduction in coagulability by the use of anti-coagulant drugs is an effective form of treatment.

BLOOD COAGULATION AND HEMOSTASIS

The fact that patients with deficient clotting bleed abnormally shows that normal clotting is essential for hemostasis, but the exact role of clotting in hemostasis is not clear. Some evidence about this mechanism can be derived from a study of bleeding hemophilic and thrombocytopenic patients. In hemophilic patients, small puncture wounds do not bleed excessively, for only small vessels are injured and bleeding is controlled by vascular contraction. Larger wounds in hemophilic patients do bleed. In a large wound, immediate hemostasis is achieved by vascular contraction; during this period the blood normally clots below the surface of the contracted vessels, and, when after an hour or so the vessels relax, the proximal lumen is blocked by a clot. In hemophilic patients this clotting does not occur, and when the vessels relax there is continuous and persistent bleeding which is controlled only by the eventual healing of the wound.

In patients with thrombocytopenia, on the other hand, slow oozing from small puncture wounds is characteristic. In thrombocytopenia there is some defect in coagulation, but this is usually only a minor factor in the bleeding tendency. The main abnormality is a failure of the small vessels to contract normally. This failure may be due to one of two causes. The platelets may normally produce a vasoconstrictor substance which is liberated by their breakdown at the site of injury. Alternatively, in some cases a toxic factor may be responsible for the reduction in platelets, and this may cause direct damage to the capillaries which are then incapable of normal contraction.

In conclusion it may be said that the maintenance of a normal clotting function is essential. Excessive coagulation, which is probably more generally dangerous than defective clotting, may lead to the occlusion of some vital vessel. Defective clotting may produce a hemorrhagic state which is very difficult to control. The extraordinary efficiency of the normal mechanism is apparent only when its defects are studied, and it is only by a study of these defects that some knowledge of normality has been achieved.

REFERENCES

1. ASTRUP, T. and DARLING, S. *Acta physiol. scand.*, 1941, 2:22–40.
2. BIDWELL, E. *Brit. J. Haemat.*, 1955, 1:35–45.
3. BIDWELL, E. *Brit. J. Haemat.*, 1955, 1:386–389.
4. BIGGS, R. and DOUGLAS, A. S. *J. clin. Path.*, 1953, 6:15–22.
5. BIGGS, R. and DOUGLAS, A. S. *J. clin. Path.*, 1953, 6:23–29.
6. BIGGS, R., DOUGLAS, A. S. and MACFARLANE, R. G. *J. Physiol.*, 1953, 119:89–101.
7. BIGGS, R., DOUGLAS, A. S. and MACFARLANE, R. G. *J. Physiol.*, 1953, 122:538–553.
8. BIGGS, R., DOUGLAS, A. S. and MACFARLANE, R. G. *J. Physiol.*, 1953, 122:554–569.
9. BIGGS, R., DOUGLAS, A. S., MACFARLANE, R. G., DACIE, J. V., PITNEY, W. R., MERSKEY, C. and O'BRIEN, J. R. *Brit. med. J.* 1952, 2:1378–1382.
10. BIGGS, R. and MACFARLANE, R. G. *Human blood coagulation and its disorders*, 2d ed. Oxford, Blackwell's Scientific Publications, 1953, xxv, 476 pp.
11. BLOMBÄCK, MARGARETA and NILSSON, INGA M. *Acta med. scand.*, 1958, 161:301–321.
12. BRINKHOUS, K. M. *Proc. Soc. exp. Biol. (N. Y.)*, 1947, 66:117–120.
13. BUDTZ-OLSEN, O. E. *Clot retraction*. Oxford, Blackwell's Scientific Publications, 1953, xiv, 149 pp.
14. COHN, E. J. Quoted by Edsall, J. T. *Advanc. Protein Chem.*, 1947, 3:383–479.
15. DUTHIE, E. S. and LORENZ, L. L. *J. gen. Microbiol.*, 1952, 6:95–107.
16. FERRY, J. D. *Advanc. Protein Chem.*, 1948, 4:1–78.
17. JAQUES, L. B. *Biochem. J.*, 1943, 37:344–349.
18. JORPES, J. E. *Heparin in the treatment of thrombosis. An account of its chemistry, physiology, and application in medicine*, 2d ed. London, Oxford University Press, 1946, 260 pp.
19. KEKWICK, R. A., MACKAY, M. E. and RECORD, B. R. *Nature*, 1946, 157:629.
20. KEKWICK, R. A. and WOLF, P. *Lancet*, 1957, 272:647–650.
21. KLEIN, P. D. and SEEGERS, W. H. *Blood* 1950, 5:742–752.
22. KOLLER, F., LOELIGER, A. and DUCKERT, F *Acta haemat.*, 1951, 6:1–18.
23. LINK, K. P. *Harvey Lect.*, 1944, 39:162–216.

24. LORAND, L. *Physiol. Rev.*, 1954, *34*:742–752.
25. LORAND, L. and MIDDLEBROOK, W. R. *Biochem. biophys. Acta*, 1952, *9*:581–582.
26. LOVELOCK, J. E. and PORTERFIELD, B. M. *Biochem. J.*, 1952, *50*:415–420.
27. LYTTLETON, J. W. *Biophysical studies of thrombin and antithrombin and the kinetics of their reaction.* Thesis for degree of Ph.D. in the University of London, 1950.
28. MACFARLANE, R. G. and BIGGS, R. *J. clin. Path.*, 1953, *6*:3–8.
29. MACFARLANE, R. G., MALLAM, P. C., WITTS, L. J., BIDWELL, E., BIGGS, R., FRAENKEL, G. J., HONEY, G. E. and TAYLOR, K. B. *Lancet*, 1957, *273*:251–259.
30. MCLEAN, J. *Amer. J. Physiol.*, 1916, *41*:250–257.
31. MANN, F. D. and HURN, M. *Amer. J. Physiol.*, 1951, *164*:105–110.
32. MELLANBY, J. *J. Physiol.*, 1909, *38*:28–112, 441–503.
33. MORAWITZ, P. *Ergebn. Physiol.*, 1905, *4*:307–422.
34. NOLF, P. *Arch. int. Physiol.*, 1908, *6*:1–72.
35. NOLF, P. Pp. 130–133 in *The blood plasma in health and disease*, J. W. PICKERING, ed. London, Heinemann, 1928.
36. NOLF, P. *Arch. int. Pharmacodyn.*, 1945, *70*:5–44.
37. OWEN, C. A., JR., MAGATH, T. B. and BOLLMAN, J. L. *Amer. J. Physiol.*, 1951, *166*:1–11.
38. OWREN, P. A. *Acta med. scand.*, 1947, Suppl. 194, 327 pp.
39. OWREN, P. A. *Scand. J. clin. Lab. Invest.*, 1951, *3*:168.
40. OWREN, P. A. and AAS, K. *Scand. J. clin. Lab. Invest.*, 1951, *3*:201–208.
41. OWREN, P. A., RAPAPORT, S. I., HJORT, P and AAS, K. *Sang*, 1954, *25*:752–765.
42. PICKERING, J. W. *The blood plasma in health and disease.* London, Heinemann, 1928, xi, 247 pp.
43. QUICK, A. J. *J. biol. Chem.*, 1935, *109*:lxxiii–lxxiv.
44. QUICK, A. J. *The hemorrhagic diseases and the physiology of hemostasis.* Springfield, Ill., Charles C Thomas, 1942, xx, 340 pp.
45. QUICK, A. J. *Amer. J. Physiol.*, 1943, *140*: 212–220.
46. QUICK, A. J. *Amer. J. med. Sci.*, 1947, *214*: 272–280.
47. SCHERAGA, H. A. and LASKOWSKI, M., JR. *Advanc. Protein Chem.*, 1957, *12*:1–131.
48. SCHMIDT, A. *Zur Blutlehre*, Leipzig, Vogel, 1892.
49. SCHNEIDER, C. L. *Amer. J. Obstet. Gynec.*, 1955, *69*:759–775.
50. TELFER, T. P., DENSON, K. W. and WRIGHT, D. R. *Brit. J. Haemat.*, 1956, *2*:308–316.
51. TOCANTINS, L. M. and CARROLL, R. T. Pp. 11–28 in: *Trans. 2nd Conference on blood clotting and allied problems, Josiah Macy, Jr. Foundation*, New York, 1949.
52. WARE, A. G. and SEEGERS, W. H. *J. biol. Chem.*, 1948, *172*:699–705.
53. WARE, A. G. and SEEGERS, W. H. *Amer. J. clin. path.*, 1949, *19*:471–482.
54. WHIPPLE, G. H. and HURWITZ, S. H. *J. exp. Med.*, 1911, *13*:136–161.
55. WHITE, S. G., AGGELER, P. M. and GLENDENING, M. B. *Blood*, 1953, *8*:101–124.
56. WRIGHT, I. S., MARPLE, C. D. and BECK, D. F. *Trans. Amer. ther. Soc.*, 1950, *48–49*: 81–94.

SECTION VII

Circulation of Blood and Lymph

CHAPTER 26

Mechanical Events of the Cardiac Cycle

By ALLEN M. SCHER

THE circulatory system has as its prime objective the transport of materials to and from the tissues. This transport involves movement of many substances across the capillary walls; it is dependent on the integrity of the heart as a pump as well as on the proper functioning of arteries, veins, capillaries, lungs, etc.

Even in the course of a routine physical examination, the physician must often decide whether the heart is functioning as a competent and efficient pump. Before the advent of certain newer procedures, the diagnostic techniques of the physician were largely limited to experiences gained from his own sense organs and from one or two simple instruments. Even now, information the physician gains from his eyes and ears will be important in leading him to use the newer techniques or in supplementing them. In interpreting information which comes to him from his own sensations and diagnostic instruments, the physician must have a reference; i.e., he must know whether the individual being examined is within or outside the normal range. In addition, the scientific physician should know what sequence of physiologic phenomena produces the information he receives. For this purpose, it is essential that the physician know the normal sequence of mechanical and electrical events taking place within the chambers of the heart. This chapter and the succeeding one will introduce this material.

Functional Anatomy. In many properties cardiac muscle is intermediate between striated and smooth muscle. This intermediacy is both structural and functional. Cardiac muscle is cross-striated like skeletal muscle but, like smooth muscle, it is involuntary, i.e., is not under the control of the will. Functionally, if not anatomically, cardiac muscle appears to be a syncytium like smooth muscle. That is, the units of the muscle are functionally interconnected, so that, once electrical depolarization is initiated in some unit, it continues through all units of the syncytium. This aspect of cardiac function will be discussed in the next chapter. Striated muscle is able to develop a large amount of tension in a short time, but will fatigue; in contrast, smooth muscle contracts slowly but is capable of exerting moderate amounts of tension for long periods of time. In this respect, cardiac muscle is closer to skeletal muscle, because the heart can contract rapidly, although not as rapidly as skeletal muscle. Like smooth muscle, cardiac muscle is almost continuously in rhythmic action. The heart is composed of a large number of separate muscle bundles which can be separated only with difficulty. The individual bundles have been named, but in the adult heart they have merged to such an extent as to be virtually indistinguishable.[7]

Although the anatomy of the heart may be considered from several viewpoints, the ideal one is to think of the fibrous skeleton of the heart as a supporting framework to which the muscle masses and valves are attached.[9] The fibrous skeleton separates the atria and ventricles and surrounds large openings for the tricuspid and mitral valve orifices, the atria and ventricles being attached about these openings. The fibrous skeleton also includes the smaller aortic and pulmonary valve orifices. The two atria and the two ventricles, as well as the aorta and the pulmonary artery, thus insert into the fibrous skeleton. Figure 319 indicates this general structure.

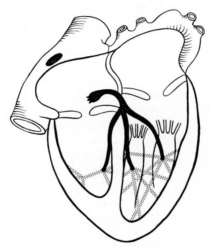

FIG. 319. Diagrammatic view of heart showing cavities of both ventricles and atria. *Upper left*, Superior and inferior venae cavae may be seen entering right atrium. Black ellipse in this area indicates general region of sino-atrial node. Atrioventricular node is indicated above tricuspid valve cusps in interatrial septum. Right bundle passes down into right ventricle; the two branches of left bundle pass into left ventricle. Numerous Purkinje branches cross ventricular cavity on both sides.

In addition to the general myocardial muscle mass we must note the conduction system of the heart (Fig. 320). It consists of the *sino-atrial* (sino-auricular) node, which is the mammalian analog of the sinus venosus. The sino-atrial node (S-A node), or the node of Keith and Flack, is the pacemaker of the mammalian heart. A section of Keith and Flack's description of this node follows:

"Our search for a well-differentiated system of fibers within the sinus, which might serve as a basis for the inception of the cardiac rhythm, has led us to attach importance to this peculiar musculature surrounding the artery at the sino-auricular junction. In the human heart, the fibres are striated, fusiform, with well-marked elongated nuclei, plexiform in arrangement, and embedded in densely packed connective tissue—in fact, of closely similar structure to the Knoten (A-V node). The amount of this musculature varies, depending upon how much of the sinus has remained of the primitive type; but in the neighborhood of the taenia terminalis there is always some of this primitive tissue found. Macroscopically, the fibres resemble those of the a.-v. bundle in being paler than the surrounding musculature, i.e., in being of the white variety. . ."[3]

The tissue of the S-A node consists of small, closely interlaced cells interspersed with

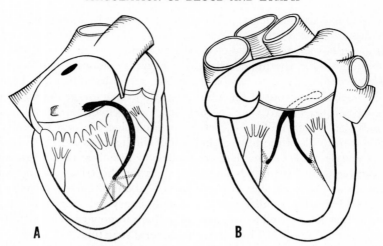

FIG. 320. The conduction system as seen from the right and from the left side. In *A* right bundle terminates near anterior papillary muscle on the right. In *B*, the two branches of left bundle pass to general regions of anterior and posterior papillary muscles on the left. Much of the Purkinje tissue lining endocardium is not represented.

connective tissue. The region is easily recognized microscopically with low magnification.

In the region of the interatrial septum, near the coronary sinus, there is a second mass of specialized conduction tissue, the atrioventricular node (A-V node), or node of Tawara. The A-V node, as indicated, closely resembles the S-A node. The A-V node gives rise to the common bundle, which passes through the fibrous skeleton.

The so-called Purkinje* tissue, a system of specialized muscle fibers, begins at the common bundle and continues through the right and left bundle. Its network of branching fibers covers much of the endocardium. Purkinje tissue has anatomic and electrical characteristics somewhat different from those of ordinary myocardium. In general, the fibers of the common bundle and the right and left bundles are larger, have clearer cytoplasm, and contain more glycogen (indicated by glycogen-specific stains). These fibers conduct more rapidly than ordinary cardiac muscle, and in some species, particularly the ungulates, are surrounded by a substantial connective tissue sheath; in ungulates, the Purkinje tissue penetrates the walls of the ventricles. This tissue, like the rest of the myocardium, is functionally syncytial. Electrically, the differences are less marked, the intracellular action potential differing somewhat from that of ordinary myocardial fibers.

Electrical Precursors of Mechanical Activity. The sequence of contraction and relaxation of cardiac muscles results from the cyclic electrical depolarization and repolarization of the membranes of the cardiac muscle units. The normal sequence of electrical events in single muscle cells has been discussed previously (see Chap. 4), and the electrical events within the entire cardiac mass will be discussed in detail in the next chapter. It is necessary, however, to summarize briefly the sequence of electrical changes in the heart as an introduction to the consideration of cardiac mechanical events.

CARDIAC PACEMAKER. Certain tissues of the heart have the ability to act as a pacemaker, i.e., to initiate the depolarization without external influences. Localization of the cardiac pacemaker cells in cold-blooded animals was anticipated in some very early experiments performed by Harvey in 1628. He found that isolated small bits of

---

* Named for its discoverer Johannes Evangelista Purkinje (1787), a Bohemian physiologist. Pronounced "pur-kin'-je."

cardiac tissue continued to beat rhythmically and that pieces of atrium had a higher inherent rate than did pieces of ventricular muscle. Several other kinds of experimental evidence can be produced.

In the elementary physiology laboratory, it is a common experiment to place and temporarily tighten ligatures in the frog heart (i) between the sinus venosus and the atria and (ii) between the atria and the ventricles. These are known as Stannius' ligatures. After either ligation, the pre-ligature heart rate is maintained only above the ligature, since the pacemaker is in the sinus venosus. In the mammalian heart, the S-A node is the pacemaker. Warming or cooling the pacemaker in the heart of a cold-blooded or a warm-blooded animal will change the rate of the entire heart, whereas warm or cool applications placed on regions which cannot function as pacemakers will not. Similar results are obtained with drugs, such as epinephrine or acetylcholine, which increase or slow the heart rate. At times, if a warm rod or an acceleratory drug is applied to a tissue which is not acting as the pacemaker but which *can* function as a pacemaker, the entire heart may accelerate. This technique thus demonstrates potential as well as actual pacemaker sites.

The pacemaker at any instant is that portion of the heart with the highest rate. Techniques for electrical mapping of pacemaker sites have been suggested by Lewis.[6] Recently, intracellular recording has been used to find pacemaker cells, which indeed have unique characteristics (see Chap. 27 and Fig. 342).[11] Study of the embryonic development of the chick heart shows that pacemaker activity begins in the precursor of ventricular muscle and moves, first to the atrial muscle and then to the sinus venosus.

SPREAD OF ACTIVITY.   Once electrical activity is initiated in the atrial pacemaker, the activity spreads through both atrial walls and through the interatrial septum. The wave of excitation spreads in all directions concentrically from the S-A node at a rate slightly less than 1 m. per second. The spread of depolarization through the entire human atrium requires about 80 milliseconds. This spread produces an electrical event which may be recorded at the body surface and is called the "P wave" (Fig. 330). The electrically excited state in the atrium continues for approximately 150 milliseconds. Atrial repolarization occurs during the depolarization of the ventricles.

The sole muscular connection between the atrium and the ventricle consists of the A-V node, the common bundle and the right and left conducting bundles. Unless an electrode lies very close to these tissues, it records no electrical activity while the electrical wave passes through them. The velocity of conduction in the A-V node is very low (about 0.1 m. per second). The conduction velocity in the bundles is about 2 m. per second. In the body surface electrocardiogram, there is a period between the end of the excitation of the atrium and the beginning of the excitation of the ventricles when no potential changes are recorded. After the electrical wave has traveled down the right and left bundles, it rapidly traverses the Purkinje fibers, which are widely distributed to the endocardium on both sides. Consequently, excitation is distributed quite synchronously to most of the mural and septal endocardium. The velocity of conduction along the endocardium is about 1 m. per second.

The electrical wave then travels through the ventricular muscle, generally from endocardium to epicardium at about 0.3 m. per second. Ventricular excitation produces an electrical potential at the body surface, the "QRS complex" (Fig. 330). In man, about 80 milliseconds are required for all the ventricular muscle to become electrically excited. During the period when the ventricles are depolarizing, the atria are repolarizing, i.e., returning to the resting state. The ventricular cells remain depolarized for about 300 milliseconds, the range being from slightly above 200 milliseconds to slightly below 500 milliseconds. In the electrocardiogram, the "T wave" signals ventricular repolarization.

Summarizing these electrical events, we have a wave of depolarization moving through the atrial myocardium, keeping it depolarized for some time. The repolarization of the atrium occurs while the ventricles are depolarizing. The ventricular myocardium starts to depolarize about 80 milliseconds after the end of atrial depolarization and remains in a depolarized state for about 300 milliseconds before returning to the resting state. The chemical link between the electrical and mechanical events in muscle has not been elucidated, but cardiac cells begin to contract about 10 milliseconds after they become depolarized and continue contracting while they remain depolarized. After a variable period of electrical inactivity, this process is repeated. The recurring electrical events lead to a rhythmic contraction of the cardiac muscle which pumps the blood.

Mechanical Characteristics of the Heart. Let us now consider the mechanical characteristics of the system in which these events take place and the techniques used to record them. The atria may be likened to a single, irregularly shaped, thin-walled cone split in two chambers by the interatrial septum. The chambers have little ability and opportunity to do work. The right atrium produces a pressure differential of 5 to 6 mm. Hg as it contracts; the left atrium, a differential of 7 to 8 mm. Hg.

The right ventricle, which pumps blood returned from the systemic circulation into the pulmonary artery, is a crescent-shaped chamber which sits atop the free wall of the interventricular septum. This ventricle is more a volume pump than a pressure pump and can move large volumes at low pressure. Right *intraventricular* systolic pressure is about 25 mm. Hg*; diastolic pressure is nearly the same as atmospheric pressure. The shape of the left ventricle may be compared to a cylinder with a small cone at the end. This ventricle is in effect a pressure pump,[9] and its function is to pump oxygenated blood, returned from the lungs, into the aorta. Left ventricular systolic pressure is approximately 125 mm. Hg.

The right heart can easily adapt to changes in stroke volume, the left to demands for increased pressure. The atrium and ventricle on each side are separated by valves which move in response to pressure-induced flow changes. If the pressure in the atria is higher than that in the ventricles, the atrioventricular (A-V) valves will open and blood will enter the ventricles. Conversely, if the ventricular pressure is higher, back-flow will tend to occur and the valves will close. The aortic and pulmonary valves function in a similar manner. If, for instance, the pressure in the aorta is higher than that in the left ventricle, the aortic valves will be closed; if ventricular pressure is higher, the valves will open and blood will flow from the ventricle into the aorta.

Some of the blood ejected into the aorta and pulmonary artery during systole distends the elastic walls of these vessels, storing potential energy. This stored potential energy is released during diastole. The aortic and pulmonary arterial pressures rise to a peak during the contraction of the ventricle, but the pressures in either the greater or lesser circulation do not fall to zero between beats. Peak systolic pressure is normally about 120 mm. Hg in the aorta and 25 mm. Hg in the pulmonary artery. The diastolic pressure in the aorta is about 80 mm. Hg; that in the pulmonary artery is about 7 mm. Hg. The intraventricular diastolic pressure, though, falls to nearly zero.

Measurements. The events of the cardiac cycle consist of a number of physical changes. The electrocardiogram has been considered briefly and will be discussed further in the next chapter. The mechanical contraction which results from activation of the cardiac muscle produces cyclic pressure changes in the chambers of the heart, in the aorta and in the veins. These pressure changes were

---

* In discussion of pressures in the cardiovascular system, the values given are the pressure in excess of atmospheric pressure. Systolic pressure is the highest pressure produced by contraction. If used without qualification "systolic pressure" refers to the peak pressure in the aorta. Diastolic pressure is the lowest pressure reached during ventricular relaxation. At times the terms "electrical systole" and "electrical diastole" are used loosely to designate the period of the cardiac action potential and the period between action potentials, respectively.

recorded in experimental animals during the last four decades by Wiggers and his coworkers.[12] Recently, some of the measurements have been repeated in humans and in intact dogs with essentially similar results.[2]

In the older experiments, the pressure changes within the chambers and vessels were recorded optically by liquid-filled manometers of exceptional fidelity. In these instruments, hollow tubes filled with fluid were connected to cannulas tied into the chambers or vessels under study. The other end of the tubing was connected to a thin, stiff membrane, to which was attached a small mirror. A change in the pressure within the chamber caused the membrane to bulge, thereby moving the mirror. The movements of the mirror were magnified optically by shining a light on the mirror, and were recorded on photographic paper. These recording systems, in careful hands, had an excellent frequency response and a small volume change per unit pressure change, both highly desirable characteristics. Recently pressure transducers have been designed which respond to a change in pressure by an alteration in resistance, inductance or capacitance.[9] These transducers are suitable for use with modern electronic recorders employing direct-writing galvanometers. Many such assemblies are quite accurate and are easier to use than the membrane manometers. The frequency response of the penwriting recorders is the limiting factor in over-all response of these systems, but it is adequate for most studies. Recently introduced transistor-driven pens have greatly improved responsiveness.

In the classic studies, the combined volume of the two ventricles was recorded by placing both of them in a glass container which was closed by a rubber ring around the atrioventricular groove. The container was connected to a recording tambour, i.e., a rubber diaphragm which moved a pen or mirror. This system could be used only on experimental animals with opened chests. Recently designed transducers[9] permit the estimation of ventricular volume from measurements of ventricular diameter or circumference.

EVENTS OF THE CARDIAC CYCLE

Because electrical events precede mechanical events, let us draw the conventional electrocardiogram and then try to deduce what mechanical changes take place during the various phases of the cycle. We are here concerned with changes in a number of variables through a single cardiac cycle. The events will be described vertically—that is, we will describe the changes in all variables in one phase of the cycle, then discuss the next portion of the cycle, etc. In this discussion, too, the attempt will be made to discuss first that mechanical change which is of primary importance in each phase.

It is a general rule that where two chambers are directly interconnected, the pressure pulses will be identical with a pressure gradient in the direction of flow. When the chambers are separated by closed valves, there may be a mechanical "artefactual" effect of one on the other. The phases of contraction and relaxation are named in a fashion which describes the activity of the ventricle.

Diastasis (Fig. 321).   As drawn, the cycle begins at the end of diastole. The pressure in the aorta is falling, owing to the "runoff" of blood into the peripheral vessels. Volume and pressure in the atria and ventricles are rising slightly since the venous pressure exceeds the pressure within the chambers. The atrioventricular valves have long been open. No potentials are recorded in the electrocardiogram, and no sounds are heard stethoscopically. The diastolic period extending from the end of the rapid filling phase in one cycle to the atrial contraction in the next cycle is known as the period of *diastasis*.

Atrial Contraction.   Slightly after the beginning of the P wave (during the diastolic period) the atria commence their contraction. This contraction leads to a surprisingly slight rise in the intra-atrial pressure. With atrial contraction, the ventricular volume and pressure increase slightly owing to the atrial ejection of blood. During this time, the pressure in the aorta continues to decrease as blood flows into the arterioles. A very faint atrial vibration, not normally perceived as a sound, occurs at this time. The ventricles begin to depolarize during this period, as shown by the beginning of the QRS complex.

Ventricular Isometric (Isovolumetric) Contraction (Fig. 322).   The next event is the onset of ventricular contraction. It begins shortly after the onset of the ventricular (QRS) electrocardiographic complex. The first period of ventricular contraction is called the "isometric phase." At the beginning of ventricular contraction, the A-V valves on both sides are open. As the interventricular pressure begins to rise and exceeds the atrial pressure, the valves close. The aortic and pulmonary valves are, of course, also closed. Since fluid is incompressible, this is by definition an "isometric phase." Any "change" recorded in ventricular volume is an artefact due to change in dimensions.

At the beginning of ventricular contraction, aortic pressure is about 80 mm. Hg, pulmonary pressure is about 7 mm. Hg, and ventricular pressure is only slightly above atmospheric pressure. The ventricles change dimensions as the muscle fibers contract, but no blood is ejected into the arteries and none flows retrograde into the atria once the valves close. Pressures in the arteries and the atria are thus not directly affected even

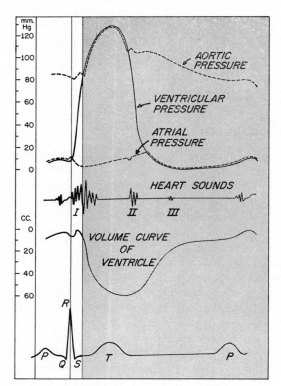

FIG. 321. Events of the cardiac cycle; lowest curve is electrocardiogram. First event is excitation of atrium, signaled by electrical P wave. Atrial contraction follows, leading to a slight increase in volume curve of ventricle and producing an atrial "sound." (Atrial pressure and ventricular pressure increase slightly.) Aortic pressure is falling during this period and is not influenced by the contraction of the atrium. QRS complex indicates depolarization of ventricles, which leads to mechanical contraction. The beginning of contraction closes valves to atrium, and aortic valves remain closed. This phase of contraction is thus isovolumetric, and volume of blood in ventricles cannot change. Sound is produced at this time, and there is an apparent change in ventricular volume that is undoubtedly dimensional. Atrial pressure falls owing to mechanical effects of ventricular contraction. (After Wiggers, *Circulatory dynamics*, New York, Grune and Stratton, 1952.)

though ventricular pressure rises steeply; both pressure and muscle fiber length change. During this phase, several investigators[9, 12] have observed a slight increase in *apparent* ventricular volume despite the fact that both inflow and outflow valves are closed. When the diameter or circumference of the ventricle is measured during this period, a change in shape is observed in the record. This change probably results from contraction of portions of the myocardium near the endocardium, possibly the trabeculae carnae and/or parts of the papillary muscles.[8]

When the pressure in the left ventricle first exceeds the pressure in the aorta, the aortic valves open. Since there is now a large orifice between the aorta and the ventricle, the two form virtually a single chamber; pressure curves measured in the two regions follow one another closely, with a slightly higher pressure in the ventricle. Blood flows rapidly from the ventricle into the aorta. During this period of maximal ejection, the ventricular volume decreases sharply. Also, the atrial pressure decreases abruptly; this decrease is thought to be produced by passive lengthening of the atrium as the ventricle contracts. Atrial pressure even falls below venous pressure, and the atria begin filling at this time. At the end of the period of maximal ejection, ventricular repolarization is signaled by the onset of the T wave.

When the major portion of the stroke output has been ejected, the rate of outflow from the ventricle decreases markedly and there is a period of reduced ejection. The ventricular volume curve starts to level off, and then ventricular and aortic pressures begin to fall. Decreased ejection results because the fibers have reached a shorter length, are contracting isotonically, and can no longer contract forcefully. It is also possible that there is some influence of the end of depolarization at this time. The venous pressure continues to be greater than atrial pressure; the atria continue to fill. Electrically this period is marked by the major deflection of the T wave; i.e., ventricular repolarization becomes complete.

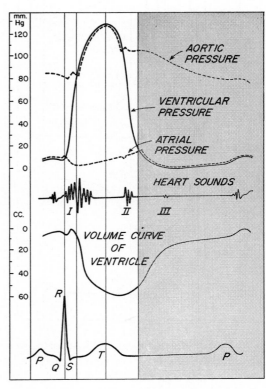

FIG. 322. When ventricular pressure rises above aortic pressure, aortic valves open. Volume of ventricle can now decrease, since blood flows from ventricle to aorta. Heart sound continues; ventricular pressure continues to rise and is followed closely by aortic pressure. This pressure reaches a peak slightly before the ventricle reaches its lowest volume. After the peak, ventricular pressure begins to decline. Maximum pressure is determined by amount of blood which ventricle ejects, force of contraction, etc. (After Wiggers, *Circulatory dynamics*, New York, Grune and Stratton, 1952.)

Phase of Isometric (Isovolumetric) Relaxation (Fig. 323). When the ventricular ejection per unit time falls to zero, the left ventricular pressure falls below the pressures in the aorta and pulmonary artery. The aortic and pulmonary artery valves therefore close. The ventricular pressure continues to fall rapidly as the ventricles relax. The A-V valves remain closed while the ventricular pressure exceeds atrial pressure. This is the period of isometric relaxation. As the valves at both ends of the ventricles are closed, the amount of fluid contained in the ventricles obviously cannot change except for small amounts of blood flowing into the right heart from coronary veins. The term isovolumetric relaxation seems appropriate here.

Phase of Rapid Ventricular Filling. The isometric relaxation phase ends when the ventricular pressure falls below pressure in the atria; the A-V valves then open, and a phase of rapid ventricular filling begins. It should be noted that, during all of this period, flow of blood from the aorta to the peripheral arteries continues and the aortic pressure falls slowly. It has recently been claimed that ventricular diastolic suction contributes to the ventricular filling.[1] Apparently the ventricle is able to do work filling itself with blood, i.e., the fact that the ventricle is empty but relaxed makes the atrioventricular pressure difference greater than the difference between the atrial and intrathoracic pressures. If "suction" is important in the normal heart, it is during this period of rapid filling.

The phase of rapid inflow is followed by a variable phase of diastasis during which filling is much less rapid. Filling is limited, too, because the ventricle has come close to

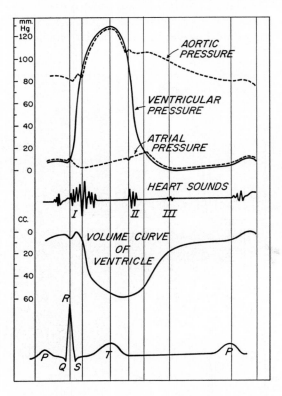

FIG. 323. After ventricular pressure falls below aortic pressure, aortic and pulmonary valves again close. Second heart sound occurs at this time. There follows a period of isovolumetric reaction during which interventricular pressure is greater than atrial pressure. After this period, atrial valves open and ventricles again begin to fill (at first rapidly and then more slowly). Aortic pressure continues to fall owing to run-off of blood into peripheral vessels. (After Wiggers, *Circulatory dynamics*, New York, Grune and Stratton, 1952.)

a maximum diastolic size, which, for a given cycle length is determined by the atrial pressure (although it may be changed by nervous, hormonal and other factors). This period of diastasis ends the cycle and is terminated by atrial systole which begins the next cycle. The durations of the various phases, taken from Wiggers, are as follows:[12]

	MAN	DOG
Isometric contraction	.05	.05
Maximum ejection	.09	.12
Reduced ejection	.13	.10
Total systole	.27	.27
Protodiastole*	.04	.02
Isometric relaxation	.08	.05
Rapid inflow	.11	.06
Diastasis	.19	.29
Atrial systole	.11	.11
Total diastole	.53	.53

* The protodiastolic period, which has not been discussed, is the period after the ventricles cease to eject and before the aortic valves close. It is here included in the period of isometric relaxation.

Pressure changes in the human heart have been recorded during cardiac surgery.[2] In general the results are similar to those previously described. Right atrial contraction precedes left atrial contraction by about 20 milliseconds. Right ventricular ejection also begins slightly earlier than does ejection from the left. Further, mitral valve closure follows tricuspid closure and the pulmonic valves open before and close after the aortic valves. In general, therefore, when the two ventricles have equal output, there will be a higher mean flow rate on the left (Mean Rate $\times$ Time = Stroke Output, which is the same on both sides).

HEART SOUNDS

The mechanical events that take place during the cardiac cycle produce sounds which may be heard at the body surface. The sound-producing events include oscillations of the blood, movements of the heart wall and the valves, and turbulence of blood flow. These sounds may be heard by placing the ear on the chest wall or by using a stethoscope, or they may be recorded by placing a microphone against the chest wall and connecting it to a proper recording system. The various sounds are heard with differing intensities at various locations on the body surface. In certain experimental procedures, microphones or catheters connected to microphones have been placed within the chambers of the heart.

We shall first consider the mechanism of production of each of the sounds and its relationship to the events of the cardiac cycle. We shall also consider the location on the body surface at which each sound may be heard most clearly and the effects on the perceived vibrations of the type of instrument used to listen to them.

Causes of Specific Heart Sounds. From the graph of the events of the cardiac cycle, it is obvious that during diastole blood is flowing smoothly from the atrium into the ventricle and from the aorta into the peripheral vascular beds. This smooth flow of blood produces no audible vibrations.

First heart sound. The first heart sound occurs with the onset of contractions of the ventricles. Before ventricular contraction, the A-V valves (mitral and tricuspid) are open and, as ventricular pressure rises, the contraction moves blood toward the atrium. As a result of this movement, the atrioventricular valves close. The initial movement of the blood, the closure of the valves, and the resulting abrupt cessation of movement of blood into the atrium produce sounds which are part of the *physiologic first sound*. It is probable that vibration of the taut valves and of the atrial and ventricular walls contribute to this sound.

Valve closure is generally considered the major contributor to the first sound;[4] however, the continued increase in ventricular pressure moves blood within the great vessels, and the distention of these vessels by the increased pressure may produce vibrations which are part of the first heart sound. Thus the great vessels, the valves, the blood and the ventricular walls may all be vibrating interdependently. A further component of the first sound may result from turbulence in the flow of blood through the arteries (Chap. 29); if this component becomes clearly perceptible at the body surface, it is referred to as a *murmur*.

Although several components of the first sound have been described, it must be remembered that, with each perceived sound, several structures generally move. It would be presumptuous at this time to attempt to identify components of the perceived sound with movement of specific structures. In many normal persons, the mitral and tricuspid valves close slightly asynchronously. If the asynchrony of valve closure is marked, a *split first sound* will be heard. The mitral valve normally shuts last, and the interval between closures is not long. A stethoscope especially adapted for the perception of high frequency sounds can often detect the asynchrony, or it can be accentuated with phonocardiographic recording devices.

If the P-R interval is long (0.2 second or more), and if ventricular contraction is therefore delayed, the valve leaflets will have moved close together before ventricular contraction occurs. In this case, the valves will not travel far to close, and the first sound will be unusually faint. If the P-R interval is short (25 to 75 milliseconds in the dog), valve closure will be abrupt and the first sound will be loud. If the atrial pressure on either side is abnormally high, the valve leaflets may remain widely open and then close abruptly during ventricular contraction. The first sound will be abnormally loud in this case. Increase in thickness of a valve by growth of connective tissue will also increase the sound intensity.

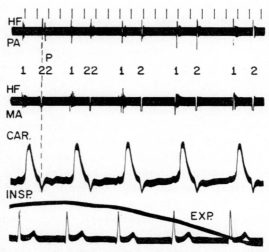

FIG. 324. Phonocardiograms correlated with carotid pulse, respiration and electrocardiogram. Phonocardiograms were obtained with a high frequency recording phonocardiograph from pulmonary (*PA*) and mitral (*MA*) areas. Below heart sounds is indirect carotid pulse recorded with a device which is sensitive to changes in pressure but not to absolute pressure. Below this are indicated the phases of respiration and convention lead II ECG. Note that first sound is always simultaneous with upstroke of carotid pulse.

Second sound in pulmonary area has two components during inspiration but only one during expiration. During inspiration first component is synchronous with downward notch in carotid pulse. This dicrotic notch is synchronous with closure of aortic valves. Second component of second sound is perceived in pulmonary but not in mitral area and occurs after closure of aortic valves. These observations indicate that second component is of pulmonary origin. As recorded in mitral area, second sound correlates only with aortic valve closure; in pulmonary area, closure of pulmonary as well as aortic valves is indicated and resultant sounds may be fused or separate. Time intervals are 40 milliseconds. (After Leatham, *Lancet*, 1958, (*2*):703–708.)

SECOND HEART SOUND.   Once the flow of blood from the ventricle into the aorta has been established and the valves are open, no sounds will be heard until the onset of the relaxation phases, unless the blood flows turbulently. When the ventricular pressure falls below the aortic (or pulmonary arterial) pressure, the tendency for backflow to occur will close the aortic and pulmonary valves. The sequence of events includes a slight backflow of blood toward the ventricles and rapid cessation of the movement as the valves close. This recoil initiates movements of the ventricular chambers and of the stretched valve cusps. As with the first sound, various components of the perceived sound have been considered to be produced by movements of specific structures. Also, valve movement is generally considered of prime importance.[4] When highly sensitive electronic recorders are used, low frequency vibrations are seen which are considered to be produced by movements of the aortic walls and by the opening of the mitral and tricuspid valves. If the pressure in the pulmonary artery or aorta is abnormally high, the closure of the valves may be exceptionally rapid and the sounds may be very loud.

As previously stated, right ventricular systole terminates after left ventricular systole. Consequently, it is possible for the right and left ventricular components of the second sound to be separated or split. This splitting is more marked in inspiration and, usually, during right bundle branch block; it is possibly due to increased right ventricular filling. In the instance of the respiratory variation, filling is increased during inspiration because the transmural pressure is then greater. Contributions made by the left ventricle to the second sound are considered to be greater than those of the right ventricle. Figure 324 shows normal first and second sounds.

THIRD HEART SOUND. As the ventricles relax, their internal pressure drops below the pressure in the atrium. The atrioventricular valves will then open, and blood will move into the relaxed ventricular chambers. This movement has a rapid initial phase; then the period of diastasis or slow filling occurs. Movement of blood into the ventricle produces vibrations of the chamber walls at about the time that the rapid filling phase terminates.

ATRIAL SOUND; FOURTH HEART SOUND. The first mechanical event of the cardiac cycle, the contraction of the atrium, moves blood through the partially open atrioventricular valves into the well distended ventricles. This movement gives rise to a vibration of low frequency and amplitude preceding the first heart sound. These sounds possibly originate in movements of blood back and forth from atrium to ventricle and in vibrations of the atrial wall, the distended ventricular wall and the A-V valves. The third and fourth sounds are generally inaudible.

AUDIBILITY OF HEART SOUNDS. Recently Lewis and coworkers[5] have devised a procedure for intracardiac phonocardiography in man. In the right heart—the region which they studied—the first and third heart sounds were loudest in the right ventricle. The second sound was loudest in the pulmonary artery; the fourth was loudest in the right atrium. These results are compatible with the concepts of the origins of the sounds given above and indicate that movement of the blood within the chambers is probably necessary for transmission of the heart sounds.

When one uses a stethoscope, only two distinct sounds are normally heard. The first heart sound is of lower pitch, more booming and longer. Its frequency content is apparently between 30 and 100 cycles, whereas the second heart sound contains higher frequencies. (Remarks about the frequency of these sounds are misleading unless one specifies where and how they are recorded.) The third sound, when present, is not loud; the atrial sound is rarely heard unless some form of amplification is used. The first heart sound has a duration of between 50 and 100 milliseconds. The second sound lasts from 25 to 50 milliseconds.

The heart sounds have their maximum intensities at different locations; these depend on the site of origin of the sound and on the way in which the fluids of the body conduct the sound to the surface (Fig. 325). When valvular defects produce murmurs and turbulence, it is usually possible to identify the defective valve from the location of the sound. The pulmonary valve produces sounds in the pulmonary area at the third (and second) left intercostal space in the left parasternal line. The aortic valve produces sounds which are of maximum intensity at the right of the sternum in the second right intercostal space. The sounds of the tricuspid valve are loudest at the right sternal border in the fourth intercostal space; those from the mitral valve are heard best near the apex of the heart. It should be noted that the sounds from the pulmonary and tricuspid valves tend to be of maximal amplitude near the underlying valvular positions. However, the sounds from the aortic and mitral valves are not heard best over the valve rings, probably because the sounds are transmitted more successfully through a liquid medium than directly through the lungs. That the first and second sounds are generally audible in all four valvular areas indicates that valvular vibrations alone are not important in sound production. The physician usually moves his stethoscope from one area to another, noting where the sounds are loudest and picking out components from each valve in seeking to assess the sound.

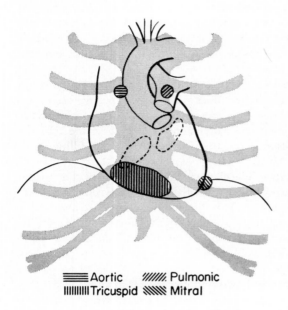

FIG. 325. Locations on body surface at which sounds from particular valve regions are best perceived.

≡≡ Aortic   ⁄⁄⁄⁄ Pulmonic
‖‖‖‖‖Tricuspid ▨▨▨ Mitral

Characteristics of Systems Used in Detecting the Heart Sounds.   Sound involves a wavelike motion in which energy is imparted from particle to particle in a homogeneous or inhomogeneous medium without any net movement of the medium. Within the thorax, this medium of transmission is liquid or, in the case of the lungs, liquid and air. When sound reaches the body surface, it causes that surface to move, and this movement may be perceived by the physician placing his ear directly in contact with the thorax. In such a situation, he will perceive the sound through the gas, solids and liquid of his outer, middle and inner ear. The sensation which he receives may not at all represent the actual events at the surface of the thorax because, as will be recalled from our study of the audibility curve, the auditory system cannot perceive sounds below 20 cycles per second. Even where it can perceive low-frequency sounds, the auditory system is not linear—i.e., the perceived intensity of sound at different frequencies is not proportional to the actual intensity of the vibrations (Chap. 17). Heart sounds are generally in the range between 20 and 200 c.p.s. In this range, low frequency sounds are minimized by the nonlinearity of the ear. The stethoscope is commonly employed as a convenience in listening to heart sounds; it does not amplify sound but actually distorts it, changing its characteristics and generally accentuating the nonlinearity of the auditory system. In this respect, it is important that various types of stethoscope have different effects on sounds and that for certain purposes one type may be better than another. For example, a stethoscope of the diaphragm type selectively attenuates the low frequencies, whereas the bell type attenuates the high frequencies.

PHONOCARDIOGRAPHY.   Phonocardiography is the technique of directly recording the heart sounds so that a visual record is obtained. Such records supplement auscultation, i.e., the use of the stethoscope to hear the heart sounds. The technique has not been widely accepted, and a large number of variations on the basic technique have been described. The major problem with respect to phonocardiography concerns the differences between behavior of the ear and the responses of the conventional microphones, amplifiers and recorders—both optical and direct—which have been used. As mentioned above, the perception by the ear of vibrations in the audible range (20 to 1500 cycles) is nonlinear. To date, the microphones available for phonocardiography have been either linear in their response or nonlinear in a manner different from the nonlinearity of the ear. The physician who wishes to see a phonocardiogram which accurately represents the perception of the sound will be disappointed if the phonocardiographic system is one which faithfully reproduces the sounds. Since identification of strange sound patterns and their correlation with diagnostically valuable patterns obtained by auscultation are difficult, attempts have been made to modify the responses of electronic systems to duplicate the auditory responses.

A number of modified phonocardiographic techniques have been described. An interesting one, which has been used by Rushmer[9] amplifies and rectifies the sound

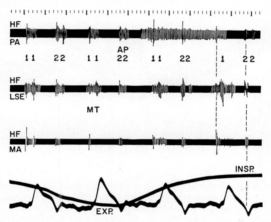

FIG. 326. Splitting of first and second sounds sometimes occurs in complete right bundle branch block. Closure of tricuspid valve (*T*) [seen in second record taken at left sternal edge (*LSE*)] and of pulmonary valve (*P*) (seen in upper record from pulmonary region) are both delayed, although mitral and aortic valve closures, indicated by *M* and *A*, are at approximately the normal time. Delayed tricuspid component of first sound at lower left sternal edge is not altered by respiration, but splitting of second sound in record from pulmonary area is greater during inspiration, because closure of pulmonary valve is delayed owing to increased filling during inspiration. First component of split second sound is synchronous with dicrotic notch in carotid tracing (there is some delay in carotid recording system). Pulmonary nature of second component is indicated by its great intensity at pulmonary area. (From Leatham, *Pediat. Clinics North Amer.*, 1958, pp. 839–870.)

logarithmically, so that the actual frequencies of sound are not heard but a trace is produced which indicates the intensity of the sound. This device, the sonvelograph,[10] is extremely useful in detecting split sounds and murmurs.

Abnormalities. SPLITTING OF HEART SOUNDS. In a number of circumstances a dissociation of the component vibrations of a sound takes place, dividing it into separate parts, each of which is heard or recorded as a separate entity. As far as the first sound is concerned, this may be a purely physiologic event, and frequently can be recorded as an exaggerated separation of the two major components, the isometric phase and the ejection phase components; this may often occur at the end of expiration (Fig. 324).

Splitting of the second sound proceeds from quite a different cause, namely, asynchronous closure of the aortic and pulmonary valves, so that the sound is, in fact, reduplicated. The phenomenon occurs occasionally in normal subjects, but is understandably more frequent during right bundle branch block when the interval between right and left ventricular contraction is abnormally prolonged (Fig. 326). The second sound associated with some ventricular extrasystole (i.e., beats which originate in abnormal sites and during which more time than normal is required for ventricular depolarization) may also be split for the same reason. In left bundle branch block the natural asynchrony may be masked.

OPENING SNAP OF MITRAL VALVES. In mitral stenosis (pathologic narrowing of the mitral orifice) a third sound is heard, and, when it is recorded phonocardiographically, it is found to be coincident in time with the opening of the A-V valves. It represents an abnormal intensification of a component of the normal second heart sound, which, because of attentuation in the stethoscope-ear combination is not normally heard (Fig. 327).

GALLOP RHYTHMS. When a loud third sound is heard in a rapidly beating heart, the resulting triple rhythm has a cadence resembling the sound of a galloping horse. The loud third sound can be shown phonocardiographically to represent (i) an intensified third sound (rapid filling gallop), (ii) an intensified atrial sound (presystolic or atrial

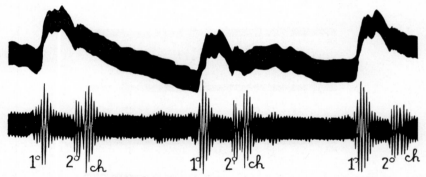

FIG. 327. Opening snap of mitral valve in mitral stenosis. Snap (*ch*) represents an increase to an audible stage of vibrations normally present but inaudible. *Above:* Central arterial pulse. *Below:* Phonocardiogram. (From Orias and Braun-Menéndez, *The heart sounds in normal and pathological conditions,* 1st ed. London, Oxford University Press, 1939.)

gallop), or (iii) a combination of the third heart sound and the atrial sound, when the rapid filling phase and atrial systole occur more or less simultaneously (summation gallop). Such gallop rhythms are heard most frequently in cases of serious cardiac disease, and it is presumed that the abnormal intensification of the third or the atrial sound is related in some way to an altered ventricular response to rapid filling or atrial systole. A systolic gallop may occasionally be heard when there is marked splitting of the first heart sound.

MURMURS. When fluid flows slowly through a smooth tube of uniform diameter, no sound may be heard through a stethoscope placed on the tube. If, however, the velocity of flow is greatly increased or the viscosity of the fluid reduced, flow is no longer smooth but becomes turbulent; i.e., eddy currents are set up, and these produce vibrations which may be audible. The velocity at which turbulence begins is greatly diminished by annular expansions or constrictions of the tube or inequalities of its surface. These factors therefore favor the development of murmurs.

In the normal heart with altered diameters at the orifices and the presence of valves as impediments to streamline flow, the critical velocities for turbulent flow are not quite attained in average circumstances. In strenuous muscular exercise and in other conditions in which cardiac output is increased and the velocity of flow augmented, systolic murmurs may appear in normal hearts. Increased velocity of blood flow during the ejection phase, with resulting turbulence, is probably also responsible for the systolic murmurs that may appear in anemia and in thyrotoxicosis. The murmurs of a patent ductus arteriosus (Fig. 328), the hum over arteriovenous aneurysms, the Korotkow sounds (sounds heard during auscultatory determination of blood pressure) and Duroziez' sign (systolic and diastolic murmurs heard over the femoral artery in aortic incompetence and modified by the degree of pressure exerted by the stethoscope) are other examples of sounds produced by turbulence at constrictions in smooth tubes.

Abnormal narrowing of an orifice such as occurs in mitral or aortic stenosis will both increase flow velocity and lower the velocity at which turbulence occurs. These effects account in the main for the murmurs heard in these conditions, although the

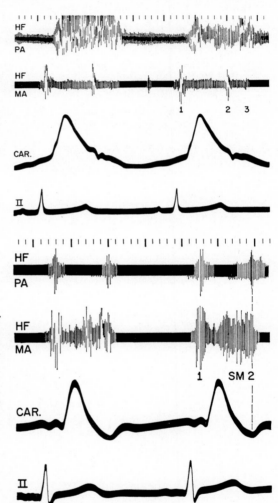

FIG. 328. In patent ductus arteriosus blood flows continuously from the high pressure aorta to the low pressure pulmonary artery. Resultant murmur is loud, often increases in intensity late in systole, and differs in its characteristics from murmurs which result from regurgitation. (From Leatham, *Pediat. Clinics North Amer.*, 1958, pp. 839–870.)

FIG. 329. Heart sounds in a mild case of mitral regurgitation. The murmur, as seen in mitral area, extends throughout systole, although its intensity diminishes during rising phase of carotid pulse. Note relative absence of this murmur in pulmonary region and tendency for murmur to blend with and virtually obscure second sound. (From Leatham, *Pediat. Clinics North Amer.*, 1958, pp. 839–870.)

roughening of the walls of the orifice by scarring and partial destruction of the valves undoubtedly also contribute in some measure. In mitral stenosis the murmurs will be diastolic, occupying typically the periods of rapid filling and atrial systole, although the murmur may be continuous throughout diastole owing to overlapping of the two phases. The typical murmur of aortic stenosis occurs in systole during the phase of ejection.

It is understandable that in the presence of valvular incompetence in addition to stenosis, murmurs may be heard during systole in mitral valvular disease and during diastole in aortic valvular disease, due in part to the regurgitation of blood through the narrow orifice (Fig. 329). Another mechanism may also contribute to the murmur heard in these circumstances; the regurgitated column of blood may set up vibrations in structures upon which it may impinge and thus produce sounds not related to turbulent flow. In mitral incompetence, the atrium itself may be set in vibration by the blood forced back during ventricular systole, causing a "collision" murmur; the regurgitation of blood against the anterior mitral valve leaflet in aortic incompetence is thought to give rise to the presystolic murmur of "relative" mitral stenosis, the "Austin Flint murmur."

REFERENCES

1. BLOOM, W. L. and FERRIS, E. B. *Proc. Soc. exp. Biol. (N. Y.)*, 1956, *98:*451–454.
2. BRAUNWALD, E., FISHMAN, A. P. and COURNAND, A. *Circulation Res.*, 1956, *4:*100–107.
3. KEITH, A. and FLACK, M. *J. Anat. (Lond.)*, 1907, *41:*172–189.
4. LEATHAM, A. *Lancet*, 1958, (2):703–708, 757–766.
5. LEWIS, D. H., DEITZ, G. W., WALLACE, J. D. and BROWN, J. R. *Circulation*, 1957, *16:*764–775.
6. LEWIS, T. *The mechanism and graphic registration of the heart beat*, 3d ed., London, Shaw and Sons, Ltd., 1925.
7. ROBB, J. S. *Med. Wom. J.*, 1934, *41:*143–152.
8. RUSHMER, R. F. *Amer. J. Physiol.*, 1956, *184:* 188–194.
9. RUSHMER, R. F. *Cardiac diagnosis*, Philadelphia, W. B. Saunders Co., 1955.
10. RUSHMER, R. F., BARK, R. S. and ELLIS, R. M. *Amer. J. Dis. Child.*, 1952, *83:*733–739.
11. WEIDMANN, S. *Electrophysiologie der Herzmuskelfaser*, Bern, Hans Huber, 1956.
12. WIGGERS, C. J. *Circulatory dynamics*, New York, Grune and Stratton, 1952.

CHAPTER 27

Electrical Correlates of the Cardiac Cycle

By ALLEN M. SCHER

As a consequence of developments in the measurement of bioelectric potentials,[12, 13] it became possible early in this century to record voltages produced on the body surface by the electrical activity of the heart. Tracings of these potentials are shown by the *electrocardiogram*. In addition to its relevance to the normal physiology of the heart, the electrocardiogram (ECG)* is a valuable diagnostic tool, since certain common cardiovascular abnormalities alter the ECG in recognizable fashion. Electrocardiographic information thus supplements the history and the physical examination in the evaluation of disease.

The normal ECG is altered by age, body build, heart position, electrode position, variations in the anatomy of the heart and other variables. If electrodes are connected to the right arm and left leg of a normal adult and the difference in potential between these extremities is recorded in the fashion described later in this chapter, curves of voltage-in-time like those appearing in Figure 330 will result. The initial upright, low, rounded deflection is called the *P wave*. It results from the passage of the wave of excitation through the atrial muscle. The second deflection, called the *QRS complex*, is produced by the activation of the ventricular mass. The final deflection, the *T wave*, results from the return of the ventricular muscle to the polarized or resting state. At times, the T wave is followed by a small *U wave* which seems, like the T wave, to be produced by

---

* "EKG," an abbreviation of "Elektrokardiogramm," is often used as a carryover from the original German name.

repolarization. It should be remembered that these potentials result *only* from electrical changes within the heart.

It will be our purpose in this chapter first to understand why the electrocardiographic complex has its normal configuration and why it alters with electrode placement and heart position; then we shall consider electrocardiographic abnormalities. Prerequisite to this study is a knowledge of some fundamental properties of cardiac muscle and of the body as a volume conductor. Familiarity with the conventions regarding electrocardiographic recording is also necessary.

Fundamental Properties of Cardiac Muscle. The cellular phenomena responsible for conduction in excitable cells have previously been discussed (see Chap. 1). Conduction proceeds along the membrane of a cell because current flows from resting portions of the membrane into adjacent depolarized regions. We may wonder whether conduction within the heart proceeds by an identical mechanism. Recent investigations show that the heart is *anatomically* divided into discrete units by cellular membranes.[37] The intercalated disks which cross the muscle perpendicularly to the long axes of the muscle fibers are seen under the electron microscope to be continuations of the longitudinal membranes which are visible under the light microscope (Fig. 331). This anatomic

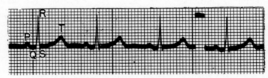

FIG. 330.   Normal lead II electrocardiogram. Initial, low, rounded deflection about 1 mm. high and 2 mm. long is the P wave. Second deflection, about 1 mm. wide and 10 mm. high, shows a rapid rise and fall and is called the QRS complex. Third, peaked deflection, about 3.5 mm. high and 6 mm. long is the T wave. Here sequence is repeated three times. Standardization at right, 1 mV. Small black vertical lines are 40 milliseconds apart; larger lines (five spaces) are 200 milliseconds apart; heaviest lines are 1 second apart. (From Winsor, ed., *Electrocardiographic text book*, New York, American Heart Association, 1956.)

evidence conflicts with the older view that the heart is syncytial, i.e., that there are no true barriers dividing the atria or the ventricles into discrete units. The older view arose from studies with the light microscope and explained the finding that depolarization originating anywhere in the atria will normally proceed through all of the atrial and ventricular musculature. Likewise, if the ventricle is stimulated at a point, excitation will normally travel through all of that chamber and may also pass to the atrium. (Forward and—particularly—retrograde conduction through the atrioventricular nodal region may at times fail. If it does not, we may consider the entire cardiac mass a functional syncytium.)

The finding that conduction is syncytial is still physiologically valid.[42, 43] Perhaps future studies with the ultramicroelectrode will demonstrate how conduction across the membranes occurs. Ephaptic conduction in nerves is probably the best model we have at present for cardiac conduction. Current flow in one nerve cell can depolarize another across an ephapse or artificial synapse. The original proof, in the experiments by Galvani and Matteucci, that electrical activity occurs in living tissues involved ephaptic conduction.

Volume Conduction. As discussed in Chapter 3, the instantaneous potential at a point in a homogeneous and infinite volume conductor as a result of a boundary between active and resting cells is a function of (i) the number of charges per unit area across the boundary, (ii) the solid angle subtended by the boundary at the point, and (iii) the resistivity of the medium.

$$\mathcal{E}_p = K_1 K_2 \Omega \, \phi$$

where $\mathcal{E}_p$ denotes the potential at a point, K_1 is a constant for tissue resistivity, K_2 a geometric constant, Ω the solid angle subtended at the point by the boundary, and ϕ, which has the dimension of volts, is proportional to the charge density per unit solid angle across the boundary. ϕ is normally constant and is equal to 120 mV. (overshoot minus resting potential) where the solid angle is 4π steradians.

To understand why a potential of a certain magnitude exists at a particular point on the body surface at some instant during the electrocardiogram, we must know the position and geometry of the boundary at that instant; the dipole moment (number of

FIG. 331. Reconstruction by Sjostrand of submicroscopic anatomy of cardiac muscle. Long narrow structures running from left to right in anterior aspect are myofibrils. Vertical and horizontal double membranes divide the mass of muscle into "units" in these planes. Cutaway section shows continuation of these vertical and horizontal membranes into the intercalated disks, the many tonguelike processes which extend from left to right. These disks form a boundary between "domains" of muscle and constitute justification for discarding the term "syncytial" insofar as anatomy is concerned. Insofar as conduction is concerned, however, the cardiac mass does seem to be syncytial or ephaptic.

charges multiplied by distance between poles) per unit area across the boundary; and the corrections necessary to compensate for the resistivity of the body, for its finite rather than infinite extent, and for its shape (Fig. 332). Studies by Burger and van Milaan[5] and by Schwan and Kay[36] differ somewhat in absolute values for tissue resistance and in the relative resistances of various tissues. It does appear, however, that the blood is a better conductor than any of the other tissues within the thorax.

Qualitative understanding is possible without correction for the geometric factors and for the resistivity. If we wish to understand the entire electrocardiographic complex, we must know the nature of the cellular electrical activity, the theory of volume conduc-

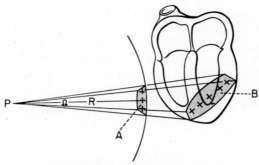

FIG. 332. Hypothetical boundary between active and resting muscle within heart. Potential at point P is a function of the dipole moment per unit area across this boundary and of the solid angle subtended at P by the boundary. A is the projection of B on sphere of radius R. Solid angle is A/R. B is boundary between resting and active tissue.

tion as it applies to the body, and also all successive positions of the boundary between active and resting muscle. This last requirement will be satisfied if we know the exact pathway of cardiac depolarization and repolarization. If electrocardiographic interpretation can be based on events within the heart rather than on the memorization of empirically derived electrocardiographic patterns, it will be easier to understand and teach, and such understanding may lead to better diagnosis.

Electrocardiographic Recording Apparatus and Conventions. APPARATUS. The development of Einthoven's string galvanometer (Fig. 333)[12, 13] in 1903 made possible the adoption of the electrocardiogram as a diagnostic tool. In the use of this instrument, electrodes on the body are connected by wires to a very fine gold plated quartz fiber suspended between the poles of a magnet. Current flow in the fiber causes it to move in the magnetic field in a direction perpendicular to both the magnetic field and its own axis. The deviations of the fiber are recorded optically on moving photographic paper. This instrument produces records of high quality, but photographic processing of its records is necessary.

Recently, the string galvanometer has been supplanted by the direct-writing galvanometer employing vacuum tube or transistor amplifiers (Fig. 334). Here, the small voltages at the body surface are amplified to produce currents that can drive a large galvanometer which moves a hot stylus across heat-sensitive paper.

The usual amplifier has a "push-pull" or balanced input to make it relatively insensitive to the alternating currents that may be picked up in any location near conventional wiring. Alternating

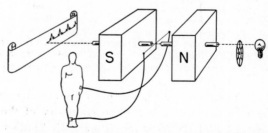

FIG. 333. Einthoven's string galvanometer. Two electrodes on extremities of patient are connected by wires to fine gold-plated quartz fiber which is suspended between the north (N) and south (S) poles of a magnet. Shadow of this fiber produced by incandescent lamp at the right is projected on photosensitive paper at left through an optical system. Wheel between bulb and magnet is rotated at a constant speed to give timing lines on record. Technically, records from this recording instrument are superior to those from many more modern recording devices, but difficulty of using the string galvanometer (necessity for photographic development, etc.) has led to its replacement by electronic amplifier-galvanometer.

current is picked up either through a capacitive coupling between a lead-in to the amplifier and a wire which carries AC, or because alternating magnetic fields cut across the electrocardiographic recording leads. The alternating current is, however, picked up nearly equally by both input leads of the push-pull circuit. Since the amplifier measures the differences in potential between these leads the alternating current in the leads will tend to cancel.

Electrocardiographic amplifiers are also condenser-coupled. That is, each lead is interrupted by a condenser. Condenser coupling has two purposes: (i) Maintained differences in voltage, i.e., "direct currents," at the two recording leads do not pass condensers. Such voltages may be produced by electrolytic processes (identical to those in batteries) involving the electrodes, electrode paste, perspiration, etc. These effects are generally much larger than the electrocardiographic voltage, and, since they will usually change in time, much rebalancing would be necessary were they not eliminated. (ii) Condenser coupling also makes it easier to construct a drift-free amplifier because the amplifier may be condenser-coupled between stages. This feature minimizes changes in vacuum tube performance attributable to temperature, aging, etc. Condenser coupling for electrocardiographic recording has a time constant of 3 seconds; i.e., if a constant voltage is applied between the two input terminals, the pen will return about two-thirds of the way to its zero position in 3 seconds (Fig. 335). This time constant makes it possible to record the slower components of the ECG, and does not affect the rapid components. The European standard is 2 seconds.

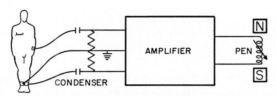

FIG. 334. Conventional electronic amplifier-pen recorder. Voltages recorded from left arm and leg of patient lead to input tubes of amplifier through a resistance-condenser input. There is also a ground connection, and input is "balanced." Output of amplifier is sufficient to drive a large galvanometer, which moves a recording stylus across a paper. In this way, a record is instantaneously available.

FIG. 335. Three second time constant of conventional electrocardiographic amplifier causes it to respond as shown when a maintained voltage is applied to input. Because of condensers in input, amplifier cannot respond to a maintained (direct current) voltage. Electrocardiographic amplifiers will return approximately two-thirds of the way to zero in 3 seconds. This time constant is sufficiently long that none of slower activity in electrocardiogram is lost. It does not affect the recording of rapid voltage changes.

CONVENTIONS. Electrocardiographic convention specifies that 1 mV. input to the amplifier shall produce a 1 cm. deflection of the pen. Recording paper is moved at 25 mm. per second. The conventional bipolar limb leads, designated leads I, II and III, record differences between the right arm, left arm and left leg (Fig. 336). We can think of the extremities merely as lead wires connected to the body, i.e., the potentials are not altered if the electrodes are moved along the extremities; for convenience the wrists and ankles are used as recording points. Electrocardiographic electrodes are fabricated of corrosion resistant metal. They are coated with a film of conducting paste, and are applied lightly but firmly to the body with rubber straps. It is important that the electrical contact with the body be good, and, for this purpose, the paste may be rubbed into the skin. The right leg is used as a ground connection. The amplifier is connected to these leads as indicated. In lead I, positivity of the left arm (or negativity of the right arm) produces an upward deflection. In leads II and III, positivity of the leg or negativity of the appropriate upper extremity produces an upward deflection. These conventions were originally established by Einthoven, who arranged them so that the major deflection in each lead would be upright in a normal individual.

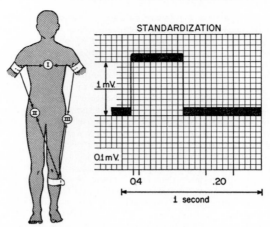

FIG. 336. Electrocardiographic limb lead connections and conventions for sensitivity and paper speed. Conventionally, 1 mV. equals 1 cm. vertically; 1 mm. horizontally equals 40 msec. Over-all horizontal speed is 25 mm. per second. Conventional bipolar limb leads, designated *I, II* and *III,* are recorded as indicated by the Roman numerals.

In the present technique for recording limb and precordial "unipolar" leads,[3] the negative terminal of the amplifier (the one which will produce an upward pen deflection if its potential is negative) is connected, through a resistive network (Fig. 337), to all three extremities. This arrangement constitutes Wilson's "central terminal." The positive electrode is designated the "exploring electrode"; it is connected to the limb electrodes individually and moved through several precordial positions, designated V_1 through V_6 (Fig. 338). The purpose of the unipolar leads is to record predominantly the potential at the point where the exploring electrode is placed. Wilson's central terminal is considered to be approximately a "zero terminal"; that is, it approximates the potential at some point which, because of its symmetry with respect to the voltages produced by

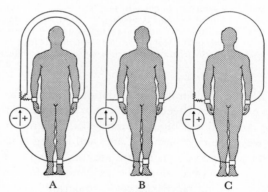

FIG. 337. Various types of connection used in electrocardiographic recording of unipolar leads. *A,* Recording of unipolar leads according to convention established by Wilson. All three extremities are connected by a resistive network; resistors are usually 5000 ohms or larger. This network is connected to negative terminal of amplifier. Exploring or positive electrode is either connected to each extremity (for unipolar limb lead recording) or placed at precordial positions shown in Figure 338.

B, Modified unipolar *limb* lead recording system devised by Goldberger. Potential at one limb electrode, connected to positive terminal of amplifier, is recorded against potential of other two, connected together *without* resistors.

C, Form of unipolar limb recording devised by Wilson wherein potential at one extremity is compared with potentials at other two connected *with* resistors. System shown in *C* has been generally replaced by system shown in *B* for unipolar limb lead recording. System shown in *A* is used for recording of unipolar *chest* leads.

the heart or because of its great distance from the heart, is not influenced by the voltages produced by the heart. The idea that a true zero potential can be found on the body surface is theoretically unsound, and has been criticized;[38] practically, however, the Wilson terminal seems to be quite convenient.[43]

The unipolar limb leads are designated VR, VL and VF. R indicates that the exploring electrode is connected to the right arm, L to the left arm, and F to the left foot. Potentials so recorded may be slightly smaller than desirable, and for this reason a system of augmented unipolar extremity leads, originally described by Goldberger, is more commonly used. In this system the potential difference is recorded between one extremity and the other two, which are connected directly with each other (see Fig. 337). Goldberger's leads are standard and are wired into most electrocardiographic recorders.

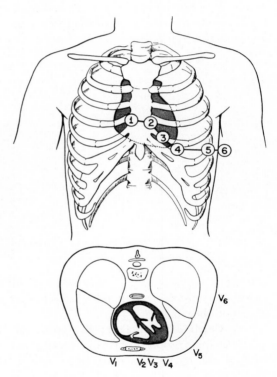

FIG. 338.   Positions of unipolar precordial (chest) leads as routinely recorded in electrocardiography. V_1 is immediately to right of sternum at fourth intercostal space. V_2 is just to left of sternum in fourth intercostal space. V_4, in fifth intercostal space, is in midclavicular line. V_3 is between V_2 and V_4. V_5 is in fifth intercostal space in anterior axillary line. V_6, in fifth intercostal space, is at midaxillary line. The two portions of figure indicate vertical and horizontal positions of these leads.

Important Anatomic Electrical Features.   The anatomy of the conduction system has been considered in the previous chapter. The atrial walls can be considered as two triangular sections of a sphere, curved to join superiorly, posteriorly and anteriorly to each other and superiorly to the interatrial septum. Inferiorly, the walls and septum join the fibrous ring to which are attached the corresponding ventricular structures. The specialized conduction system links the atria to the ventricles. It is composed of the A-V node, the common bundle and the right and left bundles. The right and left bundles each divide into a branching network of Purkinje fibers, which cover much of the ventricular endocardium in the dog and man and which penetrate widely into the ventricular myocardial mass in ungulates. (Purkinje fibers can be observed grossly in the ungulates and less clearly in the dog and man.) There is still some disagreement regarding the extent to which Purkinje fibers penetrate the canine or human myocardium.

The following structural details are important in considering ventricular electrical activity (see also Chap. 26). (i) The right bundle terminates and connects with the ventricular musculature near the right anterior papillary muscle and sends strands of Purkinje fibers to the endocardium of the free wall from this location. (ii) The left bundle usually splits into an anterior and a posterior division. These run, respectively, toward the anterior and posterior papillary muscles on the left and give rise to numerous false tendons (Purkinje strands) which cross the left cavity. (iii) The right wall is normally quite thin, generally no more than 3 or 4 mm. thick; the left wall is up to 15 mm. thick, except in infants, whose two ventricular walls are about equally thick. (iv) The endocardial Purkinje network is more widespread in the central and apical portions of the wall and septum bilaterally. This network is sparse or nonexistent in the basal septum.

EXCITATION OF THE HEART

All our direct knowledge of the pathway of cardiac excitation is derived from animal experiments, most of them on dogs. Although the various components of the canine electrocardiogram last about one-half as long as do those of the human cycle, it is customary to consider results obtained in dogs as applicable to man. This extrapolation

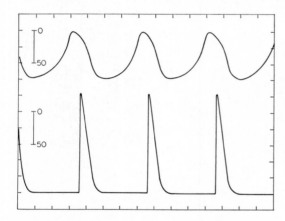

FIG. 339.   *Upper trace*, Potentials recorded by ultramicroelectrode in the pacemaker region. *Lower trace*, Potentials recorded by second ultramicroelectrode in normal atrial tissue. Note diastolic prepotential of smaller amplitude in record from pacemaker; also, notice differences in shapes of potentials in rabbit. (After West *et al., J. Pharmacol.*, 1956, *117*:245–252.)

is justified by two facts: (i) human and canine hearts are anatomically similar, both grossly and histologically, and (ii) electrocardiograms of similar shape can be recorded Jrom both hearts.[39, 43]

The Cardiac Pacemaker; Excitation of Atrium.   As indicated previously (Chaps. 10 and 26), one property of cardiac tissue is automaticity—the ability to beat rhythmically without external stimuli. The cells with the most rapid inherent rhythm are called "pacemaker cells." In cold-blooded animals, pacemaker activity seems to be possible for all parts of the heart, but in intact warm-blooded animals pacemaker activity is normally confined to the S-A node and the A-V node (Fig. 339). Other parts of the Purkinje system may also normally generate impulses, but it is not certain that all portions of the mammalian heart normally can generate impulses. However, it is clear that with even minor departures from normal physiology, extrasystolic (i.e., abnormal) beats may originate at both atrial and ventricular sites. The pacemaker with the highest inherent rhythm will dominate the heart rate, and impulses conducted from it will depolarize slower pacemakers faster than they can generate impulses. Normally, the dominant pacemaker is the S-A node. The A-V node is the pacemaker with the second highest inherent rate; if the S-A node fails or is abnormally slowed, the A-V node will usually control the heart rate.

The process by which the S–A and A–V nodes generate impulses is not known. It is possible that these cells differ from others in being more permeable to sodium when at rest, and therefore at the end of each cycle they may gradually depolarize to the level at which rapid depolarization takes place. (See Chap. 4.)

The spread of activity in the atrium commences in the S-A node and spreads like the wave pattern produced when a stone is dropped into still water. The elliptical shape of the area of initial depolarization probably results from nearly simultaneous pacemaker activity at many points in the S-A node. Plots of atrial excitation by Lewis[21] and those made by Puech[25] agree closely (Fig. 340). From the region of the S-A node, the wave of atrial depolarization proceeds at a velocity of slightly less than 1 m. per second toward the borders of the two atria and of the interatrial septum. No specialized pathway for atrial excitation has been discovered to date; indeed, it seems that no such pathway exists, although some anatomists believe that there is an atrial conduction system.[8] Because of the shape of the atrium and its position in the body, we may think of normal atrial excitation as consisting of three divergent waves moving inferiorly, to

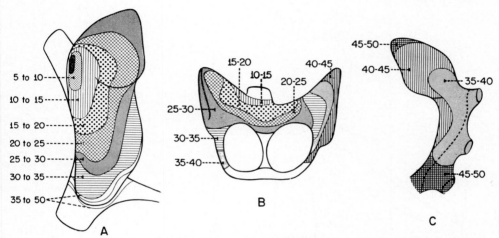

FIG. 340.   Pathway and mode of atrial activation. *A*, Right atrium and right atrial appendage viewed from right. Activity begins in sinus node (*black*) and progresses toward borders of atrium. *B*, Activation of atria viewed from anterior aspect. *C*, Activation of left atrium and appendage. Shading shows areas activated within each 5 millisecond period. Duration of P wave was 50 milliseconds. (After Puech. *L'activité electrique auriculaire.* Paris, Masson et Cie, 1916.)

the right and slightly anteriorly from the S-A node toward the inferior atrial borders. Electrodes placed almost anywhere on the precordium (except near the right shoulder) will thus record a positive potential as the atrium depolarizes. Conversely, lead VR and esophageal leads will record a negative P wave (Fig. 341). The P wave usually has a smooth rounded contour, although it may at times be notched or peaked; it has an average duration of 90 milliseconds in man and an amplitude of less than 0.25 mV.

As has been noted (Chap. 4), the initial phase of depolarization in cardiac cells is followed by a plateau during which the membrane potential changes little. During this period of "electrical systole," all cells are nearly in the same electrical state, and virtually no current flows from one region to another. Consequently, no potential changes are seen in electrocardiographic leads until the rapid phase of repolarization terminates electrical systole and produces a repolarization complex. During the plateau the cells are in an absolutely and relatively refractory state, and cannot be excited by electrical stimulation.

Repolarization of the atrium in the dog and in man normally occurs during the depolarization of the ventricles, and the repolarization potential is concealed by the much larger potentials of the ventricles. There is thus an isoelectric period between the end of atrial depolarization and the beginning of ventricular depolarization, although, as will be discussed, portions of the atrioventricular (A-V) conduction system are depolarizing during this time. Infrequently, the ventricular potentials do not conceal the atrial repolarization potential (referred to as the T_a wave), and it may be seen as a very small mirror image of the P wave. It is probable, although there is no direct evidence to support this contention, that repolarization of the atrium progresses in a direction similar to that followed by depolarization. Since the electrical charges in repolarization are oppositely arranged across the boundaries between resting and active tissue, the resultant potentials have a polarity opposite that seen during depolarization. The small size of the repolarization complex possibly reflects the fact that, during repolarization, activity in some portions of the atrium cancels activity of other portions. Also, the repolarization deflection occurs during the terminal (most rapid) phase of cellular repolarization, and during this phase the time rate of voltage change is much slower than the rate during depolarization.

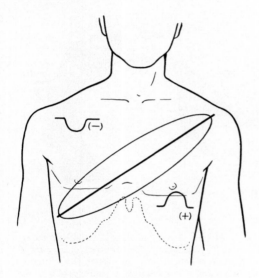

FIG. 341. Diagrams of shapes of P waves which would be recorded at various places at body surface. Since general direction of atrial activation is from right arm toward left leg, electrodes on upper part of body will see a negative potential during atrial activation; those on the lower part will see a positive potential. There will be a plane, as indicated on drawing, where an electrode would record both positive and negative activity.

Passage of the Impulse Through the A-V Node.   The period from the beginning of the P wave to the beginning of the QRS complex is referred to as the P-R interval. It is measured from the first recorded atrial activity to the beginning of ventricular activity, and usually has a duration of 0.12 to 0.2 second (average: 0.16 second) in man and 0.08 second in the dog. The potentials generated by the A-V node and the Purkinje fibers are far too small to influence electrodes at the body surface or to be recorded by extracellular electrodes which are farther than a few millimeters from these tissues. Recently, however, it has become possible to record potentials from the cells in and near the A-V node with both intracellular and extracellular electrodes.

The atrial musculature in the region near the A-V node is depolarized when atrial depolarization is about two-thirds complete. Records made with intracellular electrodes by Cranefield and Hoffman[8] (Fig. 342) indicate that a large part of the time between atrial firing and firing of the common bundle is consumed while the electrical wave passes through cells in the A-V nodal region which differ in their electrical characteristics from either atrial or bundle cells, having instead characteristics quite similar to cells of the sinus node, as the figure indicates. These cells have a diastolic prepotential, a rate of initial depolarization slower than that of other cardiac cells, and a smaller action potential.

An extracellular electrode in the A-V nodal region of a dog[29] records no clear potentials for 5 to 15 milliseconds after the depolarization of atrial cells in the nodal region (Fig. 343). At the end of this period, A-V nodal potentials are recorded. In unipolar records the upper A-V node displays a negative-going potential which develops slowly (over 10 to 15 milliseconds), remains at its maximal negative value for some time, and returns more rapidly toward zero. The potential in the center of the node is positive-negative, and that at the lower end of the node is positive and is terminated by a negative-going common bundle potential. These potentials are found only within the A-V node. Their shapes are similar, but not identical, to those recorded from a propagated wave in a muscle strip (see Chap. 4), and we may conclude that conduction *within* the A-V node qualitatively resembles conduction elsewhere in the heart and involves no chemical transmission like that found at the myoneural junction or at the central synapses.

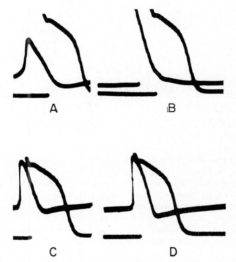

FIG. 342. Intracellular records from sinus node, atrial muscle, A-V nodal region and common bundle. For timing purposes, large potential which has lowest base line is repeated and is taken near common bundle. *A*, Smaller potential which begins earlier is from sinus nodal region. It shows a diastolic prepotential and slow rate of depolarization with lack of overshoot. *B*, Earlier potential, which has a resting potential slightly lower than that of common bundle and which depolarizes to about the same extent, is from ordinary atrial muscle. Atrial potential occurs somewhat later than potential from sinus node. *C*, Earlier potential, from upper A-V node, shows a smaller amplitude and a small diastolic prepotential after rapid repolarization. *D*, A similar potential with a diastolic prepotential is seen occurring somewhat later and closer in time to the depolarization of the common bundle. This potential is from the mid A-V node. (From Cranefield and Hoffman, *Circulation Res.*, 1959, 7:11–18.)

Several disorders of conduction through the A-V node may be observed experimentally. The term "first degree A-V block" designates a condition in which the interval between the P wave and the QRS complex is prolonged. This condition can be produced experimentally by administering drugs (procaine, potassium, digitalis glycosides, acetylcholine) which slow conduction, or by stimulating the atrium at rates higher than three impulses per second. During the latter procedure, the P-R interval increases as shown in Figure 344. This increase in the P-R interval occurs because conduction is slowed in cells which lie *between* the atrial fibers and the upper A-V node. The A-V nodal potential occurs later than normal, but its configuration is not altered. These cells are also the most susceptible to complete A-V block; i.e., the impulse reaches this region but does not proceed into the A-V node proper or into the ventricular Purkinje system.

Because of this susceptibility to incomplete and complete block, the region of the A-V node can be spoken of as having the lowest safety factor found in the atrioventricular

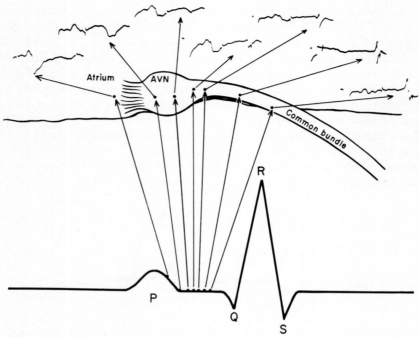

FIG. 343.   Potentials recorded extracellularly at seven sites near A-V nodal and common bundle region. Potential at far left is recorded from atrial muscle upstream from A-V node. As can be seen, it occurs during downstroke of P wave. Second potential from left is from head or upper end of A-V node. It shows an atrial potential followed by a large negative-going A-V nodal potential. Third potential from left is recorded in middle of A-V node. It shows a positive-negative atrial potential followed by a rapid negative-going common bundle potential. Farther downstream, common bundle potentials show more positivity, becoming positive-negative at the far right. As can be seen, a large part of interval between end of P wave and beginning of QRS complex is occupied by events in the A-V nodal region. (From Scher *et al.*, *Circulation Res.*, 1959, *7*, 54–61).

conduction system. The region lying immediately upstream from the A-V node is composed of very fine muscle fibers interspersed with connective tissue. The slow conduction velocity (0.05 m. per second) and the low safety factor here may result from some property of the muscle fibers (their small size) and/or from their geometric relation to the A-V node. It is possible that the fine fibers in this region must excite a volume of tissue much larger than themselves in transmitting activation to the A-V node. When conduction passes from a small volume of fibers into a larger volume, a relatively insufficient depolarizing current may be present. This lack of current can cause "downstream" cells to reach threshold more slowly and thus can produce a low safety factor.

Within the A-V node the conduction velocity (about 0.1 m. per second) is somewhat faster than in the region immediately above the node. Once the A-V node is excited, the impulse passes to the Purkinje fibers of the common bundle and the right and left bundles, and also to the ventricles. First degree conduction block (slowing of conduction) *within* the node is rare and occurs during rapid stimulation only when severe block already exists in the region upstream from the node. The conduction velocity in the Purkinje fibers of the bundles is much higher—up to 2.0 m. per second—and reflects their large size. The conduction system is syncytial and responds in an all-or-none fashion to atrial activation. This fact has been demonstrated by Weidmann[42] and confirmed in studies with extracellular electrodes. Potentials recorded from the conducting bundles under all conditions always have the same configuration during forward,

TABLE 16. UPPER LIMITS OF THE NORMAL P-R INTERVAL*

HEART RATE	BELOW 70	71–90	91–110	111–130	ABOVE 130
Large adults	0.21	0.20	0.19	0.18	0.17
Small adults	0.20	0.19	0.18	0.17	0.16
Children, ages 14 to 17	0.19	0.18	0.17	0.16	0.15
Children, ages 7 to 13	0.18	0.17	0.16	0.15	0.14
Children, ages 1½ to 6	0.17	0.165	0.155	0.145	0.135
Children, ages 0 to 1½	0.16	0.15	0.145	0.135	0.125

* From Ashman, R., and Hull, E.: Essentials of Electrocardiography, 2nd ed., New York, The Macmillan Co., 1945.

i.e., atrioventricular, conduction.[29] Figure 343 indicates the position of the wavefront of activation at various times between atrial and ventricular depolarization.

Over the range of normal heart rates the P-R interval in man (Table 16) varies with rate in a manner opposite to that described above. The P-R interval becomes progressively *shorter* when the heart rate changes over the range from 70 to 130 beats per minute. However, the type of first degree block produced in dogs is also noted in human subjects under abnormally high frequencies. It appears that as the rate increases within the normal range, the A-V conduction system is able to conduct at a slightly faster rate. Presumably this difference between the effects of an increase of rate in the normal range and those of abnormally high rates arises because the cells at first are in a better physiologic state and later become unable to conduct at high rates. The P-R interval is quite short in children, a situation which probably reflects the shorter anatomic pathways and faster heart rates.

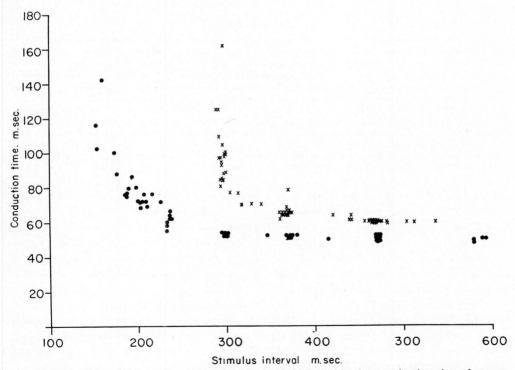

FIG. 344. Stimuli delivered to S-A node at intervals indicated lead to conduction times between S-A and A-V nodes shown by dots. Retrograde conduction is indicated by crosses. When stimuli are delivered to A-V node, conduction time is from A-V to S-A node.

Ventricular Activation.   As in the atrium, the nature of the procedures involved has limited direct determination of ventricular excitation pathways to animal experiments. Ventricular activation has been plotted in detail only in the dog, although some studies have been conducted on the rhesus monkey heart, but much evidence suggests that data obtained from the canine heart are applicable to the human.[38, 43]

The classic experiments concerning ventricular activation were performed by Lewis in 1915.[21] Using stimulating and recording electrodes on the surface of the heart, he demonstrated that the general movement of the excitation wave in the wall is from within outward. He noted that the time required for the impulse to travel from a point of stimulation on the ventricular surface to another surface point at some distance was not altered if the epicardial muscle between these points was cut. From this observation, he reasoned that the impulse travels from the point of stimulation to the endocardium,

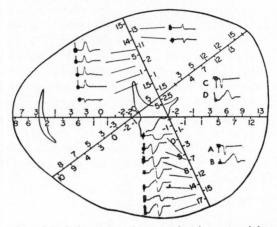

FIG. 345.   Cross-section of dog's heart near its apex showing potentials recorded at various sites. Unipolar records appear below horizontal line and bipolar records above. Unipolar records near cavity show mostly a negative (downward) potential; those near surface of heart show a positive potential followed by a negative potential. Bipolar records are generally upright, indicating that wave of activity moves from inside out in posterior left wall. Instant of activity at a point is indicated by peak of bipolar record. Numbers indicate time of local activity as measured from the bipolar records.

Instant of local activity can be *approximated* by finding an inflection point in unipolar record. Such an inflection point marks time when over-all activity shifts from approaching to receding. Time reference potential *A* and electrocardiogram *B* were taken simultaneously with unipolar records; *C* and *D* were simultaneous with bipolar records. Last points to be activated in wall are near epicardium; first points near endocardium. Latest point in section shown is in center of septum along horizontal electrode. (From Scher and Young. *Circulation Res.*, 1956, 4:461–469.)

moves rapidly over the endocardial surface, and then travels from the inside to the outside at the recording point. In actuality the wave travels through the wall at a slow speed and over the endocardium more rapidly, and the wavefront therefore will at times be at an angle to both endocardial and epicardial surfaces. In addition, Lewis calculated propagation velocities for endocardial and mural depolarization that agree well with those directly measured. Finally, he plotted the times of arrival of activation waves over the ventricular surface.

Lewis' plots of activation of the ventricular surface did not make it possible to describe the pathway of excitation *within* the walls, although this pathway was deductively approximated.[22] Within the last decade, the course of ventricular depolarization in the dog has been plotted by the use of extracellular electrode assemblies consisting of several recording terminals along a central shaft.[11, 22, 24, 30]

A 15 terminal electrode assembly has been used in conjunction with multichannel oscilloscope recording apparatus.[30] The terminals are usually placed 1 mm. apart along a central shaft. If this electrode is inserted perpendicular to the ventricular wall, activity in the entire thickness of muscle can be recorded without moving the electrode. Two types of records are taken. In one, the potential difference is recorded between each terminal and an "indifferent" (i.e., distant) point, usually at the body surface (Fig. 345). In such a "unipolar" record, the potential will be positive if the net sum of all electrical activity within the heart is approaching the recording point. If the activity is receding from that point, the potential will be negative. Thus, the shapes of the potentials can indicate the movement of the boundaries between resting and active muscle. In the other type of record, termed "bipolar," the voltage difference between two adjacent terminals on the electrode is recorded. Such a record is not influenced by activity at a distance, but accurately indicates the instant of activity between the two terminals (Fig. 345). The multichannel recording technique makes it possible to determine the time activity at many points—as many as 900 in a single experiment—by inserting a large number of electrodes at different locations in the ventricles. The time of activity is determined with reference to some fixed point in the ventricles, and it is then possible to construct a map which indicates in three dimensions the pathway followed by the wave of depolarization (Fig. 347).

The spread of activity in a coronal section of a dog heart illustrates some salient features of the process. Although the section shown in Figure 346 did not contain the first and last points activated in the ventricles, it can be seen that the general direction

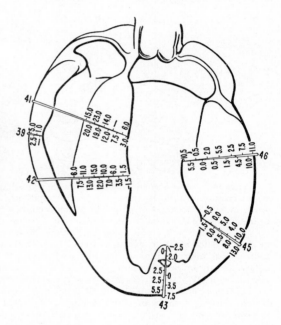

FIG. 346. Coronal section of dog's heart showing time of activation at many points along six electrodes. In wall, activity generally moves from inside out. There are, however, several reversals of directions. Under papillary muscle along electrode 46, wave of activity moved toward endocardium and toward epicardium. Septum is excited by waves moving centrally from both septal surfaces. Latest points activated are in middle of basal septum.

of excitation in the right and left walls is from within out. It can also be seen that the process is not entirely uniform; the direction of activation may reverse, particularly in the regions near the endocardium and under the papillary muscles and trabeculations. The major portion of the septum is excited from both endocardial surfaces by waves moving toward its center; however, the activation of the basal septum is predominantly from the left.

The average velocity of conduction through the ventricular muscle is about 0.3 m. per second. Calculation of this velocity requires use of a three dimensional plot of activity and measurement of the time and distance between two successive positions of the wavefront. If velocity is calculated in a direction other than that followed by the activating wave, the value obtained will be too high. The velocity of the activation wave on the endocardial surface appears to be several meters per second, but this is an apparent velocity resulting from the activation of many points on the endocardium nearly simultaneously. If endocardial velocity is ascertained by stimulating an endocardial point and recording the resultant spread of activity, the velocity is about 1 m. per second.[31]

These general aspects of ventricular excitation are widely accepted, although there are disagreements about the extent to which direction reverses in the left wall, and about the excitation of the septum.[11, 22]

ACTIVATION OF MURAL MYOCARDIUM.   The spread of activity near the endocardium has been difficult to establish. Some claim that most of the wall thickness is excited simultaneously[24] and this has been cited as evidence that most of the mural muscle, particularly that bordering the epicardium, is "electrically silent." Other investigators find that only a small fraction of the wall is excited at one time. Although excitation in some places in the wall does not spread directly from the inside to the outside, the general movement in the walls is from within out. In the right wall, activity always moves from the inside to the outside.

SEPTAL ACTIVATION.   Sodi-Pallares and his coworkers[22] have concluded that the septum is excited almost entirely from the left and that a "region of delay" in the septum

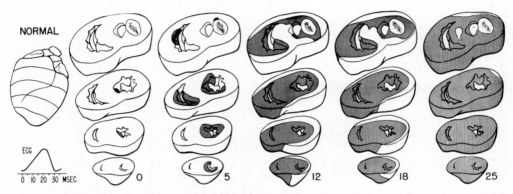

FIG. 347.   Pathway of normal ventricular excitation in dog as discerned by noting extent of depolarization at 0, 5, 12, 18 and 25 milliseconds after beginning of QRS complex. Small drawing of heart indicates positions of planes in which records were taken. Lead II electrocardiogram is labeled to indicate total duration of electrical activity.

At 0 millisecond, small amount of muscle bordering left cavity is active. Apparently this volume of muscle is too small to give a deflection in peripheral electrocardiogram at this amplification. At 5 milliseconds after beginning of QRS, an incomplete and irregular cone of activity surrounds left cavity, mostly on septal aspect, and a smaller cone surrounds right cavity. By 12 milliseconds after beginning of QRS, these two cones have united in lower three sections and have joined slightly in upper section. Heart now contains a cone of depolarized muscle within an incomplete cone of muscle which is still in resting state. Notice breakthrough of electrical activity anteriorly on right. This leaves activity in posterior and leftward portion of ventricles unopposed. This pattern of excitation continues during next 6 milliseconds. Picture at 18 milliseconds is generally unchanged, although amount of muscle depolarized is, of course, larger; fraction of posterior and left portions in resting state has become smaller. At 25 milliseconds after beginning of QRS complex, only a small amount of muscle in posterior and lateral portion of left wall and of basal septum remains to be excited.

lies at the junction of those portions which are activated from the right and from the left. Sodi-Pallares' "region of delay," however, appears to result from some experimental artefact. Because there are more Purkinje fibers on the left septal border near the base of the heart, the basal region of the septum is excited almost entirely from left to right. Also there is, as stated, a preponderance of left-to-right activity early in QRS.

DETAILS OF VENTRICULAR ACTIVATION (Fig. 347).[30, 32]   Activity is usually initiated a few milliseconds earlier on the left than on the right. Activity on the left commences in two separate areas which are supplied by the anterior and posterior terminations of the left bundle, respectively. The earliest activity on the right occurs at the septal termination of the right bundle in the region of the anterior papillary muscle of the right ventricle. Even when activity does not begin earlier on the left, more tissue on that side is activated early in ventricular depolarization. The early activity on the left is directed from left to right, and the smaller and usually later activity on the right is directed from right to left. The resultant of these opposing forces is directed to the right.

Immediately after the regions near the septal terminations of the bundles are activated, the impulse spreads very rapidly over a large portion of the endocardium near the apex of the heart and in the central region on both sides. This rapid activation is possible because the conduction system ramifies extensively along the endocardium on both sides. We may liken the intraventricular conduction to a tree, with the impulses starting near the trunk. Although the speed of propagation is only 1 m. per second, the impulse reaches the peripheral branches and excites the subendocardial myocardium at many places almost simultaneously. Within a short period, most of the central and apical endocardium on both sides is activated, and the impulse can then proceed in only one general direction, from endocardium to epicardium.

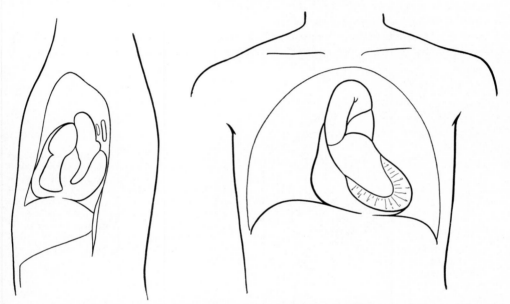

FIG. 348.   Position of heart with respect to body surface in man. Right ventricle is anterior and left ventricle is posterior when viewed from left side. When viewed from front, left ventricle is tilted to left and upward.

The rapid excitation of the endocardium produces, on both sides, incomplete cones of depolarized muscle which extend through both walls and the septum. At 5 milliseconds, as at 10, after the beginning of the QRS complex, these cones are growing by movement of the advancing wave outward in the walls and toward the center of the septum. Electrocardiographically, a consequence of the double invasion of the septum is that the septal forces tend to cancel one another. At 12 milliseconds after the start of the QRS, the cones have united in the septum and have broken through to the surface of the thinner right ventricle. As a consequence of the breakthrough to the anterior right epicardial surface, there is no longer a boundary between active and resting tissue in this region, and the boundary on the left and posterior parts of the heart is now unopposed. At 18 milliseconds after QRS has begun, invasion of the left and right central ventricular surface is complete. At this time, a thin slice of tissue extending from base to apex in the lateral and posterior left wall remains in the resting state, as does a portion of the basal septum. At the end of 25 milliseconds, a small region in the posterior left wall and another in the basal septum remain unexcited. Activity in these regions, directed from apex to base, continues until the end of the QRS complex. A search for the regions which are depolarized last indicated that these lie in the basal septum bordering the atrium.

Ventricular Activation and the QRS Complex. The shape of the ventricular complex recorded at the body surface is determined by the pattern of ventricular activation, the particular ECG lead, and the position of the heart within the chest. The heart of a normal person may be oriented horizontally or vertically, or its axis may lie between these two extremes. The direction of the activation wave will therefore vary with respect to recording points on the body surface according to the position of the heart; also the activation process undoubtedly varies from normal individual to normal individual with such anatomic features as wall thickness, distribution of Purkinje tissues, etc.

The dog heart is often placed quite vertically in the chest in experiments on the pattern of activation. The human heart has a very different orientation. The right ventricle lies anteriorly and the left posteriorly. The septum is tilted slightly forward apically, and the base-to-apex axis of the heart is often quite parallel to the diaphragm (Figs. 338, 348). The human ventricular electrocardiogram can, however, be closely approximated if we transpose the dog's activation pattern to the human thorax.

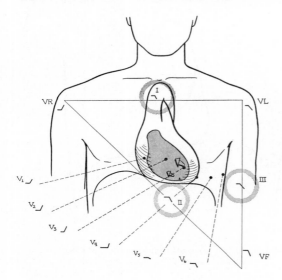

FIG. 349. Mean direction of activity during earliest portion of QRS transposed from canine to human heart. First activity goes from left to right in septum. Because of position of septum in human chest, this results in negative deflection in all bipolar limb leads, positive deflection in VR and in leads on right side of precordium (V_1 through V_4), and negative deflection in V_5, V_6, VL and VF.

As indicated, the initial phase of ventricular activity is usually directed from left to right in the septum and results from earlier and/or greater initial left-to-right activity. This activity, transposed to the human heart (Fig. 349), would produce a wave directed to the right, toward the head (since the left side of the septum lies caudally), and possibly slightly anteriorly. This wave will produce an initial negative deflection in leads I, II and III, which accounts for the Q wave. For the leads on the precordium, the picture is also clear. The leads on the right side of the chest (V_1 and V_2) face the positive side of the wavefront and record an upward deflection, while those on the far left (V_5 and V_6) record a negative deflection.

Immediately after invasion of the septum begins (Fig. 350), rapid conduction through the Purkinje system results in an irregular pattern of inside-out spread in the walls; the transition from the first phase of activity to this second and major phase of ventricular activity is smooth. Within the septum, left-to-right activity predominates slightly. Arrows drawn perpendicular to the advancing wavefront depict the instantaneous vector of depolarization. At 5 milliseconds after the beginning of QRS in the dog (by extrapolation 12 milliseconds after the beginning of QRS in man), the average

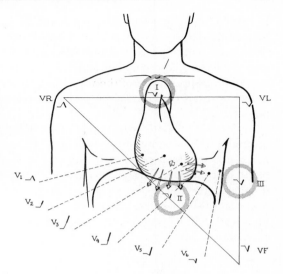

FIG. 350. When about one-quarter of QRS interval has passed, activity is proceeding from left to right in septum, and activity from inside out in wall has begun. Total activity is such that potentials are near zero in all limb leads, both bipolar and unipolar, and in V_1 and V_6. Other leads on chest are positive because activity proceeds toward the apex and free left wall.

direction of these arrows indicates a pattern of activity directed slightly forward to the right and from base to apex. Such a pattern will result in negative deflections in leads II and III and little or no deflection in lead I, which may be positive or negative at this time. The potentials in the leads on the anterior chest surface will differ slightly from those occurring during the earlier phase, since the leads on the right will not "see"* both approaching (left to right) and receding (base to apex) activity. The approaching activity will be in the right wall and on the left septal surface, the receding activity in the left wall and on the septal surface. At this time, there may be little or no potential in these leads and a positive deflection in V_3.

At 15 milliseconds after the onset of QRS in the dog (Fig. 351), union of the two separate masses of activated tissue around the ventricle has produced strong forces directed posteriorly, to the left and inferiorly. The breakthrough of activity to the anterior right wall has greatly reduced the left-to-right component, and over-all activity

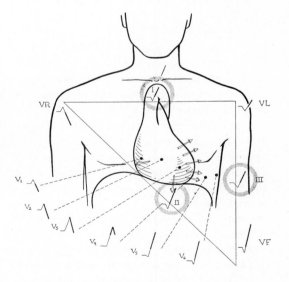

FIG. 351. At about middle of QRS interval, breakthrough of activity to anterior right ventricle has left forces moving to left posteriorly relatively unopposed. The result is a negative deflection in lead VR and positive deflections in all other limb leads. The leads on far right of chest (V_1 and V_2) now see negative activity; potential at V_3 is near zero, and potentials at V_4, V_5 and V_6 are positive.

* What is meant by an electrode "seeing" is explained in Chapter 3

is directed apically, posteriorly and to the left in the apical, lateral and anterior left wall. Some opposing inside-out activity persists in the basal right wall. At this time, positive deflections will appear in all standard limb leads, and the leads on the left side of the chest will "see" approaching activity. The continuation of this pattern results in the eventual disappearance of the wavefront anteriorly, on the right and in the central and apical portions of the heart. Overlying precordial leads will therefore record negative potentials.

The over-all pattern of activity immediately following the above, i.e., about midway through QRS, is a continuation of the movement toward the thin slice of lateral posterior left ventricle which remains in the resting state and a smaller movement toward the basal septum. Depolarization reaches the apex of the heart on the right, but some muscle in the apical region of the left ventricle remains to be depolarized. The net result is a wave moving posteriorly, leftward and slightly toward the apex. Again, the limb leads will be positive. The chest leads except V_5 and V_6 (on the far left) will, however, show negativity.

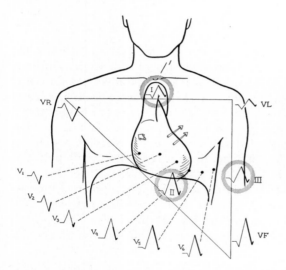

FIG. 352. During terminal portion of QRS complex, activity is directed to left and posteriorly in basal left ventricle and basally in upper septum. This condition results in potentials which are small in all leads. Deflection in VR is positive, deflections in all other limb leads are negative. Potentials are now returned to zero from negative peak in V_1 and V_2 and from positive peak in V_4, V_5 and V_6. This activity results in slight negative potentials in V_3, V_4, V_5 and V_6.

Finally, after depolarization of the apical regions is complete (25 milliseconds), i.e., for the last quarter of the QRS complex, a wave moves forward to the base of the left ventricle, particularly posteriorly and from apex to base in the septum. This wave is relatively ineffective in causing potentials in lead I, although leads II and III should show a negative potential; the potentials in the chest leads will be small but generally negative (Fig. 352).

In Figure 347 it can be seen that the process exhibits a great amount of symmetry around the longitudinal axis of the heart. At various instants, activity is proceeding in opposite directions in the lateral walls and/or in the septum. This symmetry of depolarization leads to "cancellation" of much of the cardiac electrical activity as recorded from the body surface. It has been estimated that the recorded potentials are 5 to 10 per cent of what might be expected if there were no cancellation.[28] Any condition which alters the sequence of ventricular depolarization in a manner to reduce this cancellation will, of course, produce an increase in the magnitude of the potentials recorded in one or more leads. This is true of bundle branch block and of many types of infarction, and also of cases where the impulse arises in abnormal sites.

To summarize, we may divide ventricular activation into three phases, remembering that they succeed one another smoothly and are not separate. The first of these phases is from left to right and anteriorly in the septum. The second, consisting of inside-out activity in the wall plus double invasion of the septum, produces very strong forces directed from base to apex, somewhat posteriorly and to the left. The final phase is the activity—directed from apex-to-base, leftward, and posteriorly—resulting from activation of the basal posterior left wall and the basal septum. A normal 12-lead electrocardiogram is shown in Figure 353.

Ventricular Repolarization. In most electrocardiographic leads in man the T wave has the same electrical polarity as the QRS complex, i.e., is usually upright (Fig. 353). Since the electrical charges across the cell boundaries are oppositely arranged

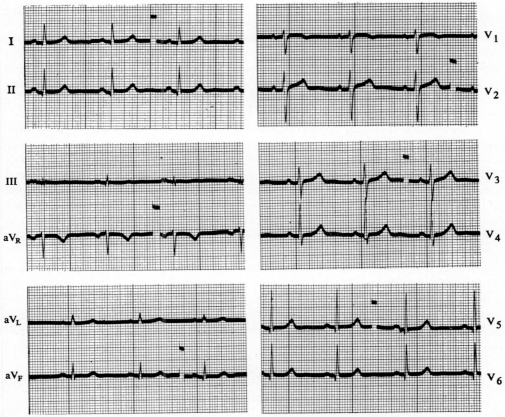

Fig. 353.   A normal 12 lead electrocardiogram. (From Winsor, ed., *Electrocardiographic text book*, New York, American Heart Association, 1956.)

during repolarization and depolarization, the polarity would be opposite if repolarization followed the same pathway as depolarization. Repolarization therefore does not follow the same pathway and, indeed, the pathway tends to be the reverse. It is important in this connection to consider whether repolarization is electrically propagated.

In studies with the intracellular electrode conducted by Cranefield and Hoffman.[8] and by Weidmann,[42] repolarization of a fiber was induced by appropriate stimulation (i.e., by stimuli causing the *inside* of the fiber to become negative) and could propagate through a fiber. In cardiac tissue in low calcium solutions, induced repolarization may propagate through several fibers. It is, however, doubtful that repolarization normally is propagated in the ventricles. Calculations of the density of current flow indicate that the current flowing during repolarization is less than 1 per cent of that flowing during depolarization. Such a small current probably cannot initiate a propagated wave.

If repolarization is not propagated, we may wonder why the configuration of the T wave is consistent under normal conditions. Several factors have been thought to control the sequence of repolarization; among them are temperature and pressure. According to one theory, the pressure differential within the walls favors initiation of repolarization in the outer layers, and repolarization occurs later near the endocardium.[2] Potentials within the right and left cavities of the human heart are negative during repolarization. Sodi-Pallares[22] interpreted these findings as indicating that the T wave normally results from spread of repolarization from the outside to the inside of the left wall. He believed further that electrical forces from other portions of the ventricles cancel one another, and that the right wall and the septum are electrically silent during repolarization, i.e., have no clear-cut direction of repolarization but repolarize at random. Available data do not allow complete acceptance of any theory concerning ventricular repolarization, although the normal "pathway" of repolarization is apparently independent of, although statistically generally opposite to, the pathway of depolarization.

ARRHYTHMIAS

The term "arrhythmia" refers to disturbances of the heart rate, the cardiac rhythm, and the sequence in which the chambers are excited. The arrhythmias have two main causes: disorders of impulse formation and disorders of conduction. In the first of these, the impulse may be generated in the normal site (the S-A node) but at an abnormal rate, or some other portion of the myocardium may function as pacemaker. Origination of the heart beat in the A-V node is abnormal, even though this tissue normally has the ability to generate impulses. Arrhythmias also may result from pacemaker activity in the branches of the conduction system, or even within unspecialized tissues—sites which do not normally generate impulses.

Sinus Rhythm. The term *normal sinus rhythm* indicates that the pacemaker is within the S-A node and that the heart rate is constant and within normal limits. In the condition called *sinus arrhythmia* (Fig. 354), common in children and young adults, the heart rate increases during inspiration and decreases during expiration. Sinus arrhythmia is not pathologic, and is most commonly seen when the individual is resting; it may

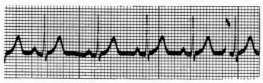

FIG. 354. Sinus arrhythmia; lead II of a child. Intervals between successive QRS complexes from left to right are 17, 15, 15 and 13 mm., or 680, 600, 600 and 520 milliseconds respectively. Heart rates calculated on this basis would be 88, 100, 100 and 115 beats per minute. (From Winsor, ed., *Electrocardiographic text book*, New York, American Heart Association, 1956.)

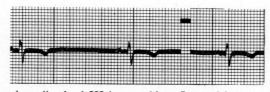

FIG. 355. Sinus bradycardia; lead III in an athlete. Interval between QRS complexes is 1400 milliseconds (34 msec. × 40 msec. per millimeter). Also shows some sinus arrhythmia. Heart rate is 43 beats per minute. (From Winsor, ed., *Electrocardiographic text book*, New York, American Heart Association, 1956.)

disappear when the heart rate increases. The electrocardiographic complexes will, of course, have a normal configuration in the normal heart.

In certain disorders, the impulse originates in the sinus node, but at a rate below or above the normal range. In *sinus bradycardia* (Fig. 355) the rate at which the S-A node is producing impulses is subnormal; the heart rate is below 60 beats a minute, but rarely below 40 beats a minute. Conversely, the heart rate is more than 100 beats a minute in *sinus tachycardia* (Fig. 356) because the sinus node is producing impulses at an

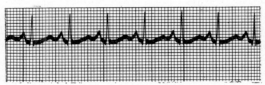

FIG. 356.   Sinus tachycardia in a 13 year old child (lead II). Heart rate is 130 per minute; pacemaker is in sinus node, since each QRS complex is preceded by a P wave at a normal interval. In children of this age, heart rate should not exceed 109 beats per minute. S-T segments are considered to be normal in view of rapid rate. (From Winsor, ed., *Electrocardiographic text book*, New York, American Heart Association, 1956.)

accelerated rate. Aside from the change in rate, the electrocardiographic complex is normal in either of these conditions, and these definitions are somewhat arbitrary. In infants, the normal resting pulse rate is frequently 120 beats per minute or more. When the rate exceeds 160 beats a minute, the condition is usually *atrial tachycardia*, in which case the pacemaker is atrial tissue. In paroxysmal atrial tachycardia the reversion to sinus rhythm is abrupt, and during the paroxysm the rhythm is very regular. Paroxysmal tachycardia of sinus origin is rare; the pacemaker is usually an atrial focus outside the sinus node. As will be discussed, this condition can produce A-V block. The condition is at times controlled by pressure in the carotid sinus or on the eyeballs, procedures activating receptors which can reflexly decrease the heart rate. Ventricular tachycardia will be discussed below. Atrial flutter and fibrillation, two disorders in which the atrial rate is higher than that seen during tachycardia, will be discussed on page 616.

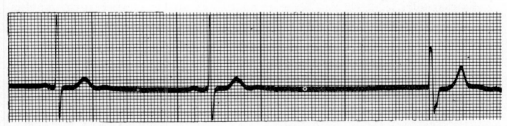

FIG. 357.   Sinus arrest induced by pressure in carotid sinus in a normal individual (Lead V₃). Two normal beats at a slow rate (33 beats per minute, interval 1.8 seconds) followed by a ventricular premature contraction not preceded by a P wave (vagal escape). (From Winsor, ed., *Electrocardiographic text book*, New York, American Heart Association, 1956.)

Sinus arrest (Fig. 357) is a rare condition in which the sinus node does not initiate impulses. It usually results from treatment of heart disease with drugs. Often, the P waves occur less and less frequently and then disappear. A final disorder which may be mentioned is called *wandering pacemaker*. In this condition there are minor changes in the shape of the P wave and changes in the P-R interval, yet the heart rate is not greatly disturbed. It is thought that this condition arises from movement of the pacemaker.

Atrioventricular Nodal Rhythm.   As indicated previously, the A-V node has the second highest rhythmicity of the specialized cardiac tissues. Thus, if activity of the sinus node becomes depressed, or if the rhythmicity of the A-V node is enhanced, the latter may take over the task of initiating impulses and become the cardiac pacemaker. Conduction will progress normally to the ventricular myocardium and often, but less frequently, will also move in a retrograde direction to the atrium.

If Figure 343, illustrating the time of activity along the A-V conduction pathway, is folded so that the crease is at the A-V node, it will be seen that the P wave will occur during the QRS complex when an impulse originating in the A-V node is conducted normally to the ventricle and also backward into the atrium. If the impulse originates in the upper A-V node, the P wave should occur immediately before the QRS complex. In either instance, the P wave in most leads should be inverted, since the general direction of atrial activation is the reverse of normal. In the clinical literature, the terms "upper," "middle" and "lower" A-V nodal rhythm are used, the last describing the situation in which the P wave occurs relatively late with respect to the QRS complex. However, it can be seen from Figure 343 that, if ventricular conduction is normal, the P wave should not occur after the QRS complex unless retrograde conduction is definitely slower. It is possible that certain disorders ascribed to pacemaker activity of the A-V node actually arise from pacemaker activity of the common bundle. As long as ventricular conduction is normal, the QRS complex itself is normal.

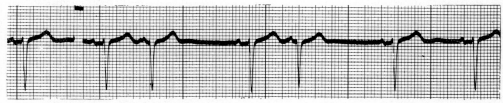

FIG. 358.   Two atrial premature contractions (lead V₁). First two complete complexes are followed by a premature beat, which is followed by a compensatory pause. Fourth complex is followed by a second premature contraction. Fifth beat is again delayed by a compensatory pause; last complex is at a normal interval. Two premature complexes bear a fixed relationship to preceding beats. (From Winsor, ed., *Electrocardiographic text book*, New York, American Heart Association, 1956.)

Extrasystoles.   All cardiac tissue seems to be capable of generating impulses. Slight injury, anoxia, mechanical trauma or friction apparently can increase this tendency, so that a nonspecialized part of the myocardium may become, either continuously or sporadically, a pacemaker for the heart. Such beats are referred to as "ectopic." Abnormal impulses may be formed in the atrium outside the sinus node (atrial premature beats), in the A-V node (nodal premature beats), in the conducting bundles, or in the ventricular musculature (ventricular ectopic beats). A second class of extrasystoles arises in the sinus node as an interpolated premature beat.

ATRIAL PREMATURE CONTRACTIONS (Fig. 358).   Alteration in the site of the atrial pacemaker may result from failure of the sinus node to function normally or from increased excitability of some other locus. If the atrial pacemaker is not within the S-A node, an abnormal P wave will result, but it usually will be followed by normal QRS and T complexes. Should the pacemaker be appreciably closer to or farther from the A-V node than the sinus node, the P-R interval will also be prolonged or shortened. The duration of the P-R interval will be prolonged if an atrial extrasystole arrives at the A-V node during the relatively refractory period of the latter. As has been indicated, the A-V node has a low safety factor and cannot conduct impulses which arrive at a high frequency. If the atrial extrasystole arrives during the absolutely refractory period of the A-V node, the abnormal P wave is not followed by a QRS complex.

NODAL PREMATURE BEATS.   Although the A-V node at times acts as the pacemaker for the heart or for the ventricles, extrasystoles seldom arise within the A-V node.

VENTRICULAR EXTRASYSTOLES (Fig. 359).   An irritable focus within the ventricle may cause regular or irregular ventricular extrasystoles. When the ectopic beat originates within the Purkinje system, the ventricular complex may be normal (origin of beat within the common bundle) or abnormal (origin of beat below the origin of the common bundle). When a beat originates in the ventricular myocardium, the QRS complex will be abnormal in shape and duration. In fact, the origin of an extrasystole can often be deduced from the shape of the QRS complexes recorded from the body surface. For example, if during the extrasystole all chest leads show a marked increase in positivity, the beat must originate in the posterior portion of the heart.

In general, the QRS complex will be prolonged, since conduction over the Purkinje system is not following the normal path. If the analogy between the Purkinje system and a tree is recalled, it will be seen that an impulse originating near a peripheral branch of the tree must be conducted along that branch until it intercepts the normal conduction pathway near the trunk. Even though the ectopic impulse is conducted along the endocardium at normal Purkinje velocity, about 1 meter per second, the time required for depolarization of the ventricles will be increased. With prolongation of the interval between the beginning and the end of ventricular depolarization, those regions which

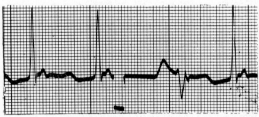

FIG. 359.   Second complex is followed by a ventricular premature beat. Note absence of P wave before this QRS complex, abnormal shape of QRS, altered polarity of T wave. (From Winsor, ed., *Electrocardiographic text book*, New York, American Heart Association, 1956.)

depolarize first tend to repolarize first, and the direction of the T wave will often be opposite that of the QRS complex.

At times, a ventricular extrasystole arises from a single focus which, for unknown reasons, discharges rhythmically to produce a wave with a fixed shape and often with a constant relationship to the normal QRS complex. Such a beat is referred to as a *coupled beat*. It may occur after every normal beat or, often, after every third, fourth, or fifth normal beat. The resulting rhythm is referred to as bigeminy, trigeminy, etc. When an ectopic beat originates below the A-V node, the atria will often beat independently, since the safety factor for retrograde conduction is lower than that for forward conduction. An ectopic beat may be conducted in a retrograde direction and depolarize either the A-V node or, if conducted to the atria, the sinus node. If the S-A node is thus depolarized, it cannot generate a normal impulse until repolarized. Consequently, the interval between the extrasystole and the next normal sinus beat will be abnormally long, and the ventricles will fill to a degree greater than normal. The stroke volume of the beat following the pause will be higher than normal. The combination of the pause and the large stroke volume of the succeeding beat is often perceived by the individual as a "skipped beat" and a definite thump.

Paroxysmal ventricular tachycardia.   At times, an abnormal ventricular focus produces a maintained tachycardia. It frequently leads to ventricular fibrillation (see below), a fatal rhythm.

Conduction Block.   Conduction block may occur almost anywhere between the sinus node and the ventricles, although the most likely site is at the A-V node. S-A block, as previously noted, is rare. An incomplete S-A block may be signaled by irregular dropping of a beat. As mentioned previously, S-A block may also result from prolonged treatment with drugs which depress conduction.

ATRIOVENTRICULAR BLOCK. The A-V node, with its low safety factor, is the structure most susceptible to conduction block. In *first degree block* (Fig. 360), the P-R interval is prolonged; this prolongation is sometimes seen in patients with normal heart rates. The disorder in some of these patients must be analogous to the prolongation of the P-R interval induced in experimental animals by stimulation of the atrium at progres-

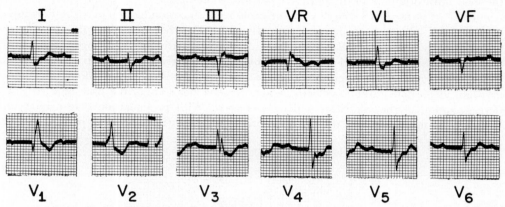

FIG. 360. First degree A-V block in a heart with several other abnormalities. P-R interval, measuring 320 milliseconds, is very much prolonged; at this heart rate, upper normal limit is 200 milliseconds. That this is first degree A-V block is indicated by QRS complex following every P wave. It should be noted further that there are negative S-T segment shifts in leads V_1, V_2 and V_3. Late activity coming toward right in these leads suggests right bundle branch block. This individual shows a first degree A-V block and a right bundle branch block. (From Winsor, ed., *Electrocardiographic text book*, New York, American Heart Association, 1956.)

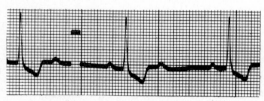

FIG. 361. Two-to-one A-V block. In lead II, record shows three QRS complexes and four P waves; second and fourth P waves are not followed by QRS complexes. Other two P waves are followed by QRS complexes at about a normal interval. Disease is suggested, although by no means proved, by inverted T wave. (From Winsor, ed., *Electrocardiographic text book*, New York, American Heart Association, 1956.)

sively increasing rates. As mentioned earlier, an increase in the heart rate of a normal person results in a decrease in P-R interval as long as the heart rate is not faster than two beats a second. It was postulated that this response of normal man and experimental animals is attributable to improvement in the physiologic condition of the cells as the heart rate increases up to 120 beats per minute. Thus, it would seem that first degree block occurring in man at lower heart rates results from depression of the A-V node by anoxia or some similar factor which makes it impossible for the node to conduct impulses at a normal velocity even though they are arriving at a normal frequency. (In some otherwise normal individuals, A-V block is present from birth.) When, as in paroxysmal tachycardia, impulses arrive at the A-V node at an abnormally high rate, the node may be unable to conduct normally. First degree block or a more serious block may then be seen.

In *second degree block* (Fig. 361), atrial excitation does not always lead to ventricular excitation; i.e., some P waves are not followed by QRS complexes. This condition is an extension of that seen in first degree block, and is observed in the dog when the heart rate is artifically raised above five beats a second. When only alternate P waves are followed by a ventricular complex, the condition is referred to as 2-to-1 block. Other ratios commonly seen are 3:1, 3:2, 4:1, etc.

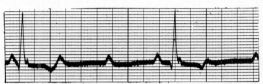

FIG. 362. Complete A-V block. Atria and ventricles are beating independently. Atrial rate is 90 beats per minute; ventricular rate is 29 beats per minute. Atrial pacemaker appears to be in sinus node, and, although it cannot be seen from this record, ventricular pacemaker appears to be near base of ventricles. (This rate is somewhat slower than would be expected were pacemaker in A-V node, and tracings are somewhat prolonged—a finding also indicating that ventricular pacemaker is probably not in A-V node.) (From Winsor, ed., *Electrocardiographic text book*, New York, American Heart Association, 1956.)

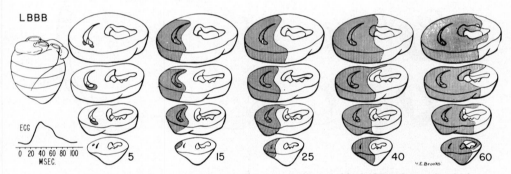

FIG. 363. Ventricular depolarization after left bundle branch block. This figure should be compared with Figure 347, which shows a normal depolarization pattern. Shaded area represents portion of myocardium depolarized up to particular instant indicated at bottom of column, and this is compared with lead II electrocardiogram. Note that activity begins around right cavity, proceeds gradually across septum as depolarization of right free wall is completed, and has reached approximately center of septum at 25 milliseconds after beginning of QRS. Activity continues across septum through 40 milliseconds, and, even at 60 milliseconds after beginning of QRS, lateral left ventricle is not completely excited. Note that both septal activation and activation of left wall are altered by bundle branch block. Increased time required to excite septum and left wall accounts for prolongation of depolarization in complete left bundle branch blocks. This figure, like Figure 347, represents activity in the dog heart, in which the duration of QRS is 40 milliseconds or less. (Becker *et al.*, *Amer. Heart J.*, 1958, *55*:547–556.)

In second degree A-V block, a *Wenckebach phenomenon* may also occur. In this condition the sinus node generates impulses at a constant rate, but the P-R interval grows progressively longer during several beats until there is an atrial complex which is not followed by a ventricular complex. The next atrial complex is followed by a QRS complex and there is a short P-R interval; the interval again grows progressively longer, and the phenomenon is repeated. In experimental animals, the Wenckebach phenomenon can be duplicated with high-frequency stimulation at a rate almost sufficient to cause 2:1 A-V block. Although the exact mechanism is not known, it would appear that the cells between the atrial and the A-V node are functional but close to failure. Consequently, with each successive beat, A-V conduction is slower until, finally, it is completely blocked. When complete block occurs, the cells have a long time in which to recover, so the beat after complete A-V block has a short P-R interval.

Third-degree or *complete A-V block* (Fig. 362) is a condition in which the A-V node is entirely unable to conduct impulses. A pacemaker within the A-V node or in the ventricle controls the ventricular beat, which is independent of and slower than the atrial beat.

BUNDLE BRANCH BLOCK.   Bundle branch block results from failure of transmission in either the right or left conduction bundles or in their terminal ramifications. The usual cause is probably myocardial damage from infarction or fibrosis from long-standing cardiac disease, although right bundle branch block may occur in normal young persons. The term "complete bundle branch block" is an arbitrary designation for beats originating in the A-V node but having a QRS duration of over 120 milliseconds in man. The pattern of ventricular excitation in complete left bundle branch block in the dog is shown in Figure 363; Figure 364 indicates the changes resulting from right bundle branch block. As might be expected, after the main bundle is interrupted, the normal double envelopment of the septum is replaced by one-way activation from the unblocked side, and activation of the free wall begins at the sites first reached by spread of depolari-

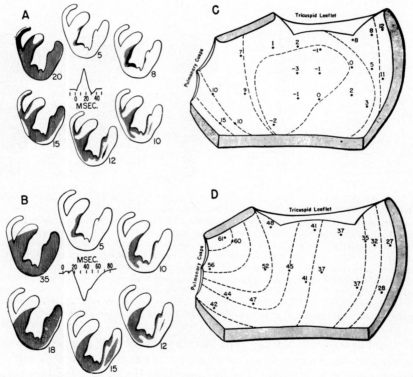

FIG. 364.   Pattern of ventricular depolarization before and after right bundle branch block. *A* and *B*, Sagittal sections through right and left ventricles showing pathway as measured by nine multipolar insertions. Small figures show position in heart of depolarization wave at various stages of depolarization. *A*, Normal depolarization; normal lead II QRS is shown at center. *B*, Pattern of ventricular depolarization during right bundle branch block (same insertion as in *A*). Lead II QRS is typical of canine right bundle branch block.

C and *D*, Pattern of activation of right mural endocardium as viewed from inside right cavity. Shaded areas indicate junction of right wall and septum. Numbers indicate time of depolarization in milliseconds after onset of QRS. Dotted lines approximate wavefront position at 5 millisecond intervals. *C*, Normal depolarization. *D*, Pattern of activation after right bundle branch block. (From Erickson *et al.*, *Circulation Res.*, 1957, 5:5–10.)

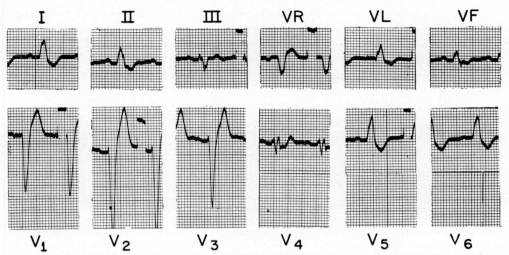

| I | II | III | VR | VL | VF |

| V₁ | V₂ | V₃ | V₄ | V₅ | V₆ |

FIG. 365.   Clinical complete left bundle branch block. QRS complexes are 130 milliseconds long. Sinus rhythm. Leads on right of chest see only receding activity, those on left only approaching activity. (From Winsor, ed., *Electrocardiographic text book*, New York, American Heart Association, 1956.)

zation across the septum. The wave of excitation utilizes the endocardial Purkinje fibers and travels across the endocardium on the blocked side at about 1 m. per second.[4, 14]

Prolongation of the QRS complex in bundle branch block results both from the longer time required to activate the septum and from the longer time required to activate the blocked free wall. The change in the activation of the free wall during right bundle branch block in the dog is shown in Figure 364. Normally, it requires about 18 milliseconds to activate the right mural endocardium, and a large central area is activated within a few milliseconds by the branching Purkinje system. After block, the impulse reaches the wall at the inferior and posterior junctions of the wall and the septum, and spreads anteriorly and superiorly. The smooth progression of the wave is altered as it breaks through the septum superiorly. The total time required to activate the right free wall after block is 35 milliseconds.[14] Similar changes in mural activation are seen in left bundle branch block.

In the dog, complete right bundle branch block doubles the duration of QRS; complete left bundle branch block increases it two and one-half times. Comparable durations of the QRS in man would be 160 and 200 milliseconds for complete right and complete left block, respectively. A clinical diagnosis of complete block is based on far less prolongation of the QRS complex, i.e., 120 milliseconds or more. In complete right bundle branch block we would expect that the right wall would be the last portion of the heart to be activated, a situation which would produce late positive deflections in V₁ and V₂ and aVR. Grant[17] believed that these conditions are met only rarely in clinical examinations and concluded that truly complete right bundle branch block is extremely rare. Complete left bundle branch block (Fig. 365) is more common and is accompanied by clear sights of right-to-left activation of the septum and left ventricle. In bundle branch block, as in ventricular ectopic beats, those portions of the ventricular myocardium which depolarize first tend to repolarize first, and, similarly, the last areas to fire recover latest. Consequently, the T wave tends to become a mirror image of the QRS complex; leads in which the QRS is upright show a downward T wave, etc.

In conditions clinically described as complete bundle branch block, the QRS lasts up to 120 milliseconds. The mechanism of such prolongation is not at all clear. Possibly damage to fine strands of the Purkinje network (arborization block) or even frank myocardial damage might lead to such lengthening of the QRS.

Arrhythmias Involving Greatly Increased Heart Rate; Flutter and Fibrillation. *Paroxysmal tachycardia* (Fig. 366), as has been discussed, is an episode of rapid beating with a sudden onset and termination. At rates of 300 beats a minute or more, the disorder becomes *flutter*. In atrial flutter, the P waves merge, giving a rapid, sawtoothed atrial complex with 2:1 or higher A-V block.

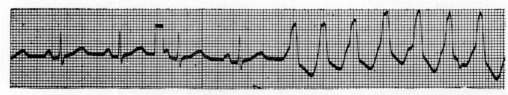

FIG. 366.　Onset of an episode of paroxysmal ventricular tachycardia. In this condition, interval between QRS complexes is somewhat irregular. Individual QRS complexes appear somewhat different, perhaps as a result of superimposition of P waves. Although heart rate (150) is somewhat slow for tachycardia, complexes are typical of this condition, as is inverted T wave. (From Winsor, ed., *Electrocardiographic text book*, New York, American Heart Association, 1956.)

Atrial fibrillation (Fig. 367), which may develop from atrial flutter, is identified by an irregular baseline of fine small oscillations, at rates greater than 500 beats a minute, produced by atrial-electrical activity. The ventricular rate is rapid but irregular, because the A-V node responds irregularly to the atrial impulse. The atrial contraction is ineffective.

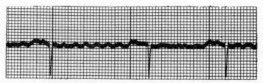

FIG. 367.　Atrial flutter and fibrillation (lead IV). Fine oscillations with duration of 160 milliseconds (4 mm.) are flutter. Periods when baseline is "silent" are probably periods of fibrillation. (From Winsor, ed., *Electrocardiographic text book*, American Heart Association, New York, 1956.)

Ventricular fibrillation is similar to atrial fibrillation (Fig. 367), but, whereas atrial fibrillation may continue for years, fibrillation of the ventricles is generally a terminal event. The chaotic contraction pattern is not adequate for propulsion of the blood into the circulation.

Sir Thomas Lewis[19] thought that atrial fibrillation results from a circus movement of the wave of excitation; i.e., that the conduction process is altered in such a fashion that a wave may "catch its own tail." Models of this condition have been created in animal experiments.[23] If a portion of the tissue around the superior vena cava is damaged by being clamped in a forceps for a few seconds, a low safety factor may result. An impulse started at one side of the damaged region may proceed around the ring, return to the original site, and be conducted slowly through the damaged region and again move around the ring.[26] The term "circus movement" is obviously appropriate. Several alternatives to Lewis's theory have been offered.[34] A rapidly firing focus is considered the cause of arrhythmia in one of these. In another, multiple ectopic foci are thought to discharge constantly and to produce chaotic excitation.

Certain interesting aspects of fibrillation suggested to Lewis that some orderly sequence of events must lead to this condition of complete disorder. In the first place, a certain volume of tissue is necessary for fibrillation to occur. The cat's atrium cannot be made to fibrillate by electrical stimulation, and the cat's ventricle will fibrillate only transiently and recovers spontaneously. The dog's atrium will generally fibrillate transiently and recover spontaneously; whereas, if the dog's ventricle begins to fibrillate, heroic measures are required to end the condition. The critical nature of tissue volume has also been observed in lower animals. The frog's heart usually will not fibrillate, but a large turtle's ventricles may be made to fibrillate by rapid electrical stimulation.

Cooling the heart tends to increase the incidence of fibrillation, and certain ionic changes or addition of hormones and chemicals to bathing solutions increases the tendency to fibrillation. Greatly increasing the extracellular concentration of potassium is effective, as is addition of hormones which increase the tendency toward occurrence of ectopic impulses.

An important relevant point is the clinical observation that the Q-T interval shortens as the heart rate increases. This phenomenon has been extensively investigated by Carmeliet,[6] using the intracellular electrode. If a cardiac cell is stimulated near the end of repolarization, the record during the next beat will show a decreased duration of the action potential and a slightly decreased rate of initial depolarization. If the stimulation is repeated before the end of the shortened complex, the action potential will again shorten and the rate of initial depolarization will again decrease. The decreased slope of initial depolarization leads to slowing of the conduction velocity. At the same time, the length of time that the muscle is depolarized becomes shorter.

In the normal myocardium, the conduction velocities fall between 300 mm. and 800 mm. per second. Purkinje velocity approaches 2 m. per second, and the duration of the action potential is 300 milliseconds. In atrial tissue, which conducts at rates up to 800 mm. per second, about 240 mm. of muscle are in the depolarized state and therefore completely refractory. (This distance is the length of a depolarized segment of a long piece of muscle with the duration of action potential and conduction velocity stated; $L = V \cdot D$.) In ventricular muscle, which conducts at 300 mm. per second, the length of the depolarized segment would be about 90 mm.; in Purkinje tissue, about 600 mm. Since normal ventricular conduction utilizes myocardial and Purkinje tissue, the length of the depolarized segment in either atrium or ventricle is probably greater than that of any pathway normally found in the human heart. If, however, the action potential becomes continuously shorter at the same time that the velocity becomes continuously slower, the length of the depolarized segment will decrease. When this decrease occurs, it is possible for the wave to "catch its own tail." Once this has happened, the process can be repeated. Each successive completion of the circuit can result in a slower conduction velocity, a decreased action potential duration, and a shorter pathway for the circus wave until, finally, it has a very short pathway. At this time, there could be a large number of circus pathways on the myocardium, possibly undergoing continuous change.

In support of this hypothesis it has been reported that, during the early stages of fibrillation in the cooled heart, certain frequencies are repeated on the electrical record and that these finally disappear as fibrillation continues.[1] Records obtained with both intracellular and extracellular electrodes indicate that once fibrillation has been established, the situation is one of complete chaos. It is possible that in such a situation multiple ectopic foci cause the waves.

Ventricular fibrillation is a common cause of sudden death. Its occurrence is one of the hazards of cardiac surgery, particularly of operations conducted under hypothermia. It should be noted that fibrillation can often be terminated by stimulation of the myocardium; 110 V., 60 cycles per second seems ideal, and large electrodes should be used. Fibrillation also, at times, can be terminated by solutions of unphysiologic ionic composition.

Myocardial Injury; Ischemia and Infarction. PHASE I. If a region of myocardium is partially deprived of oxygen, the first change observed electrocardiographically is an alteration of the T wave. Apparently the region of ischemia cannot repolarize normally. Possibly the ischemic region remains depolarized while adjacent regions have returned to the resting state. An overlying electrode will therefore record a negative T wave that is usually larger than normal. A similar change in the T wave is seen during recovery from an infarction. It should be noted that the T wave is a most labile portion of the electrocardiogram and less reliable for diagnostic purposes than other portions of the ventricular complex. Changes similar to those resulting from ischemia arise also from benign causes. If the entire heart is uniformly deprived of oxygen, T wave changes may be widespread.

PHASE II. When a blood vessel supplying the ventricular myocardium is completely occluded by a thrombus or deposition of atheromatous plaques in the vessel wall, and when no collateral circulation exists, the cells previously supplied by this vessel will be completely deprived of oxygen. A complicated series of events will ensue, *all* of them causing the same change in the relationship between the S-T and T-Q segments (Fig. 368).

The first change which takes place is a shortening of the intracellular action potential. This occurs a few seconds after the tying of a ligature in an experimental animal, as has been demonstrated by several investigators.[27, 41] When the action potential is shortened, the injured cells depolarize normally but repolarize more rapidly than do adjacent normal cells. For this reason, during the period of repolarization, i.e., during the S-T segment of the electrocardiogram, current flows from the injured cells to the adjacent normal cells (since, by definition, current flow is from positive to negative). This flow then leads to a change in the S-T segment, which becomes elevated in unipolar leads facing the area of the infarct. This elevation is a primary change in the S-T segment; it is transient, however, and recovery from this phase occurs within a few minutes. While this change is still in effect (and during the period of recovery), a second change takes place: a decrease in the resting potential of the injured cells. Since the resting potential of the injured cells is now lower than that of the adjacent uninjured cells, current flows from the normal cells into the injured ones during electrical diastole. (This current is frequently referred to as the "current of injury.") This condition produces a depression of the T-Q segment of the electrocardiogram in unipolar electrodes facing the area of injury. At first this depression adds to the true S-T segment shift mentioned previously, but it continues after the initial change disappears.

The characteristics of the input capacitors of the electrocardiographic recorder prevent its use to discriminate between a shift in the T-Q segment and a shift in the S-T segment. In the clinical literature, both of these changes are referred to as "S-T segment elevation" in electrodes facing the injury. (Electrodes facing the rear of the injury record the opposite changes.) At present, there seems to be no need to discriminate among these various causes of "S-T segment elevation" during acute and chronic occlusion of the vessels, and such discrimination would present overwhelming technical problems.

A later change, beginning about 30 minutes after occlusion of a vessel, has been described by Durrer.[10] At this time, some cells in or near the "infarcted" region fail to depolarize normally. The injured cells depolarize much later than they normally would. A unipolar electrode facing the area of injury thus sees approaching (positive) activity immediately after the QRS complex. Again, this change produces a true S-T segment elevation, but it has not been demonstrated that conduction time is equal to the S-T interval (200 milliseconds). It is likely that this change and the second change, which is a true T-Q depression, exist together during the period of chronic injury in patients, although there is no direct evidence at present.

PHASE III.   After the initial phases of ischemia and injury have disappeared, the
S-T segment and T wave may return to normal. The diagnosis of such chronic infarcts
is a difficult problem for the practitioner and may be important in determining whether
a patient should be treated or should limit his activity. The major problem exists with
regard to the QRS complex. In many cases, a sizable portion of the myocardium will
have been replaced by scar tissue which is, of course, electrically silent. If the conduction
system has not been impaired by the infarction, the duration of the QRS complex may
be normal; but if a large amount of myocardium is missing, the complex will be changed,
i.e., it will lack the potentials previously contributed by the infarcted region. An electrode which faces the infarcted region and which previously recorded approaching
(positive) activity from that region will record less positivity than normal, or it may
record a negative deflection. If the area of infarction is in a part of the heart which is

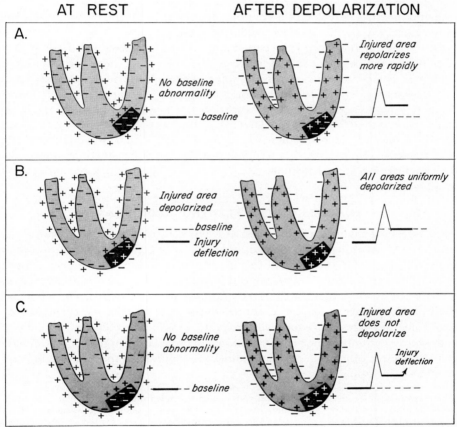

FIG. 368.   Several possible modes of production of S-T segment changes. In *A*, heart is shown as
uniformly depolarized, i.e., there are negative charges on outside and positive charges on inside of all
the membrane—except for muscle, which is in repolarized state (positive charges on outside of membrane), near epicardial surface. Electrode on right will view positive charges; that at left will view
negative charges. This "injury current" occurs *after* QRS complex, and resultant potential is a change
of S-T segment.
    B, Myocardium is uniformly polarized, i.e., at rest, except for a region in center which is injured.
Owing to flow of current into this region from adjoining regions, baseline is depressed at rest. This is
truly a T-Q segment change, and is commonly considered cause of S-T segment changes. Heart is
uniformly depolarized, but depolarizing wave cannot move into a portion of muscle. Wave stays fixed
at this location, so that there is an S-T segment shift. In this instance, however, depolarization does
not become completed. Changes shown in *A* and *B* have been found during acute infarction; change
shown in *C* has not.

normally depolarized easily, this increased negativity may either produce an initial negative deflection or increase the magnitude of a negative deflection which would normally occur in the lead facing the region. An initial negative deflection is referred to as a Q wave, and an *abnormal Q wave* is the most common diagnostic sign of chronic infarction. Q waves are not abnormal *per se:* the abnormality is frequently definable only in terms of magnitude or duration of the wave in a particular lead. Some portions of the body surface normally show Q waves. Although this sign is useful, if it is the sole criterion of infarction, a diagnosis obviously can be made only when the infarction lies in regions which are depolarized early in QRS. Several recent textbooks of electrocardiography have described successful techniques for the detection of an infarction which affects the later portions of the QRS complex.

Some large infarcts may damage the conduction system, thus causing a prolongation of the QRS complex. It may be important to differentiate such prolongation from that seen in bundle branch block, since the latter may be present and innocuous in an otherwise healthy heart. The value of a control electrocardiogram taken before any reason exists to suspect myocardial damage should be apparent.

It is interesting that, during the period after infarction, a fixed relationship between changes in the S-T segment and T wave is often observed: those leads which show elevated S-T segments show a negative T wave. Although the mechanism has not been directly determined, a possible explanation is available by extrapolation from Durrer's[10] and Conrad's[7] observations. Since depolarization is delayed in some cells in the infarcted region, might not these cells also repolarize late? Late depolarization would elevate the S-T segment and late repolarization would cause a negative T wave over the region. That is, the wave of repolarization would approach a lead over the infarction so slowly as to give a large negative deflection. (Remember that approaching repolarization produces a negative potential.)

ANALYSIS OF THE ELECTROCARDIOGRAM

The foregoing discussion is intended as a physiologic consideration and not as an account of electrocardiography. Indeed, a perusal of a complete electrocardiographic textbook will show that only a small fraction of the usual topics have been considered here; and the interpretation of clinical electrocardiograms obviously requires both much more familiarity with pathologic changes and more practical experience. Nevertheless, we shall briefly list here a sequence of procedures to be used in the evaluation of the electrocardiogram. This procedure will probably be sufficient only for the diagnosis of the common arrhythmias which have been listed in this chapter and at times will indicate that other electrocardiographic abnormalities exist although the exact nature of the lesion may not be apparent.

The conventional electrocardiogram will contain the tracings from three unipolar limb leads, the three bipolar limb leads and the six unipolar chest leads. The first procedure is to make sure that these tracings are technically above reproach and to make sure that all the leads have been recorded. At this time the standardization record should be examined to see if a deflection of exactly 1 cm. has been produced by 1 mV. standardization. Each time that the standardization is repeated this accuracy should be checked again. Of course if the amplitude of the standardization is slightly less or more than 1 cm., a correction is easily applied. Rarely, with damaged electronic components, the standardization may exhibit gross overshoot or slurring; if these occur they are a sign that the instrument is in need of repair. Each electrocardiographic lead recorded should contain several beats. The tracing for each lead should have a baseline that does not drift up and down too widely, and there should be no artefact caused by loose electrodes, 60 cycle interference or muscle tremor.

Second, the cardiac rate should be determined by noting the interval between successive beats. At standard speed, each millimeter of the electrocardiographic record equals 40 milliseconds; 25 mm. equal one second. Computation of the heart rate is thus quite simple. Electrocardiographic textbooks contain tables which enable one to measure the interval in millimeters and read off the rate directly; calibrated rulers for this purpose are also available. The ventricular and atrial rates must be determined separately if the chambers depolarize independently. It should be noted whether the rate is regular or irregular; if it is irregular, the number of beats within 10, 20 or 30 seconds must be noted to determine the number of beats per minute. It should next be noted whether the relationships of the P, QRS and T waves are constant or variable. The P-R interval (from the beginning of the P wave to the beginning of QRS) should be measured to see if it is normal, longer than normal or irregular. The duration of QRS and the QT interval (from the beginning of QRS to the end of the T wave) should also be measured. Since these parameters are related to rate and age, tables must be consulted for normal limits.

The next step is to examine the complexes to see whether their shapes and durations are normal. We have previously considered conditions in which the P wave might have an abnormal shape. Several conditions are listed among the arrhythmias in which the QRS complex would be definitely abnormal in shape and/or prolonged. Electrocardiographic diagnosis of ventricular infarction, as can be seen above, rests on alterations in the T wave and/or the S-T segment and/or the QRS complex. It is common practice to determine the electrical axis of the heart (see below), since much diagnosis of electrocardiographic abnormality depends on this determination.

The above procedures should enable even the beginning student to detect many arrhythmias; however, it should be borne in mind that bundle branch block, particularly, cannot be diagnosed on the basis of an analysis of a single tracing. Neither can the origin of many extrasystoles be adequately

MEAN ELECTRICAL AXES

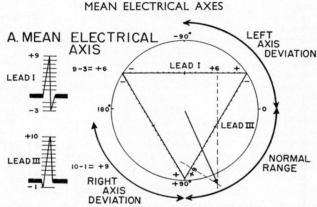

FIG. 369. *A*, The mean electrical axis is computed from two of the three standard limb leads (e.g., leads I and III). The sum of the downward deflections is subtracted from the sum of the upward deflections. For example, the vertical height of the R wave above the baseline is measured in millimeters (+9 mm. in lead I). The total amplitude of the downward deflections (−3 mm. in lead I) is added algebraically to the height of the R wave (+9) and leaves a net value of +6. At a point 6 units toward the plus sign on the lead I line of the triangle, a perpendicular is erected. The net amplitude of upward and downward deflections in lead III is +9 (+10 − 1). A perpendicular erected 9 units toward the plus sign on lead III is extended to intersect the perpendicular from lead I. An arrow drawn from the center of the triangle to the intersection of these two perpendicular lines is the *mean electrical axis*. (From Rushmer, *Cardiac diagnosis*.)

determined in this way. In cases of myocardial infarction, the problem is more complicated, and, although the example given perhaps may seem clear to the student, it nevertheless should be borne in mind that there are many types of infarcts and that there is no substitute for experience in diagnosis.

Calculation of the Electrical Axis. If we consider the limb leads only, it is obvious that at any instant in time, the electromotive force developed by the ventricles will have an average over-all magnitude and direction which we might consider to be closely related to the ventricular activation process. In order to plot accurately such "vector" in the plane of the limb leads, we would need two simultaneous recordings. In practice, a mean vector is plotted according to a procedure developed by Einthoven. For this purpose, it is assumed that (i) the extremities form an equilateral triangle in the frontal plane, (ii) the heart lies at the center of this triangle, and (iii) the mean polarity of a lead (i.e., the net area or mean voltage, either positive or negative, multiplied by time) can be determined from the difference between the positive and negative peaks of the QRS complex.

These assumptions contain certain inaccuracies; nevertheless, the electrical axis has empirical usefulness. The algebraic sum of the positive and negative peaks in a lead is measured in millimeters and is plotted along the proper side of the triangle, as shown in Figure 369. A perpendicular is then drawn at the termination of this line. The procedure is repeated for a second lead. The line joining the center of the triangle and the intersection of the two perpendiculars is the mean electrical axis. In most normal individuals the axis falls between 0° and +90°. If the mean electrical axis lies at an angle greater than +90°, there is said to be *right axis deviation*. If the axis falls in the negative portion of the circle, *left axis deviation* is present. Again, a table of normal and abnormal values should be consulted in borderline cases. A procedure for determining the mean electrical axis by inspection from a *hexaxial* reference system involving unipolar and bipolar limb leads is also often used.

VENTRICULAR GRADIENT. Some electrocardiographers have stressed the "ventricular gradient" as an independent "force" causing the discrepancy in the direction and magnitude of the QRS and T waves. In actual practice the gradient is constructed by ascertaining the difference in the direction and net area between the QRS complex and the T wave. It has been argued by the proponents of the gradient that it is an important parameter since it represents a net difference between over-all directions of depolarization and repolarization. If the heart were composed of structures all having action potentials of identical duration, the depolarization and repolarization would have the same pathway, and the normal ventricular gradient would be zero. Since the directions of the two processes are almost opposite and the ventricular gradient is finite, there may be either some important factor that causes the duration of the action potential to vary in different portions of the heart, or depolarization and repolarization may normally have no causal relationship. The latter conclusion appears most reasonable, and the ventricular gradient seems to have no more than empirical significance; i.e., the QRS complex normally has a shape that is related to the excitation process, which is controlled by the Purkinje fibers, and the T wave has a shape that is unrelated to any factor presently known. Whether directly or not, most systems of electrocardiographic interpretation stress the normal direction of repolarization and its relationship to the direction of depolarization.[10] Certain pathologic changes alter the relationship between the QRS and T waves in a predictable manner, and the ventricular gradient has been used to systematize this relationship.

Vectorcardiography. Much of our present understanding of electrocardiographic recording stems from the pioneering work of Dr. F. N. Wilson and his associates. Wilson developed our present system of recording unipolar chest leads.[43, 45] He also pioneered in the recording of *vectorcardiograms*, which are at present widely considered to be a type of recording which may supplant conventional scalar recordings. The major competition between these systems concerns the recording of the QRS complex.

For purposes of emphasizing the difference between these recording methods, we may regard the conventional scalar recordings as being based on the theory that ventricular depolarization produces some purely "local" potentials on the body surface; that is, each chest lead records predominantly the activity of the immediately underlying myocardium, and adjacent chest leads do *not* merely record different views of the same phenomenon.

Vectorcardiography, on the other hand, is based on the assumption that the heart is electrically so distant from the body surface that the potentials on that surface can be considered to arise from a single fixed-location dipole within the chest. We may consider such a dipole to be a special case of the more general condition when three, and only three, independent current generators are connected to the body. If three such generators deliver voltage to the body, the potential at a given point on the body surface will be a linear function of the instantaneous current of each of these generators. In the case of the cardiac dipole, its X, Y and Z components can each be considered a single instantaneous current generator, and the voltage at a particular body surface point can be considered the resultant of the instantaneous current in the X, Y and Z directions. Actually, at present, no basis exists for differentiating between the dipolar and the more general three-function system. In either case, vectorcardiography is based on the assumption that the voltages recorded on the body surface are indistinguishable from those which would be produced by a dipole within the thorax. Further, the vectorcardiographic technique involves the assumption that all the information that can possibly be derived about ventricular depolarization is contained in three leads which can be recorded from four or more body surface recording points. (Note that a lead in such a case might be recorded from an array of more than two electrodes.) In any event, three leads would contain all the information about the three generators, and recording more than three independent leads may add no new information.

Schmitt[35] and Frank[15] have presented evidence that no "local" voltages occur on the body surface; but localized "Q waves," S-T segment shifts and T wave inversion are often discussed in the electrocardiographic literature. Experiments in the writer's laboratory have been directed at a check of the general three function theory and have involved the use of a mathematical procedure known as factor analysis. This technique, as is implied in its name, is a way of looking at a large amount of related data and extracting the minimal number of variables which will explain them. In our experiments, up to 47 simultaneous electrocardiographic leads are recorded, the potential in each lead is measured at 2 millisecond intervals, and the analysis is performed on an electronic computer. It was found in this analysis that virtually all normal body surface potentials, i.e., over 95 per cent of any lead in a normal adult, can be accounted for by three factors. While not proving the dipole theory, this result does indicate that the voltages at the body surface may be ascribed to three internal generators; it also indicates that multiple chest-lead recording is a redundant procedure.

Unfortunately, even if the evidence that the three-function or vectorcardiographic approach is justified is accepted, the next step is not clear. The vectorcardiographic recording is in some respects more difficult technically than the recording of scalar leads. The fact that only three factors (i.e., three independent voltage changes in time) are involved in ventricular depolarization does not necessarily indicate that these should be recorded vectorially. It is thus possible that recording of three scalar leads will be the method of choice at some future date. The vectorcardiographers themselves do not agree on the recording system to be used. At present, there are at least ten systems of vectorcardiographic recording, each having its proponent. Many electrocardiographers interpret scalar leads in the light of a large number of memorized pathologic patterns, and the vectorcardiographic literature is somewhat less extensive in this regard. Certainly the vast majority of clinical electrocardiograms consist of scalar leads exclusively, although an increasing number of cardiologists utilize the principles of vector analysis to interpret these and attempt to relate the information to normal depolarization pathways. It remains to be seen whether any future system of recording will increase the usefulness of electrocardiography.

REFERENCES

1. ANGELAKOS, E. T. and SHEPHERD, G. M. Circulation Res., 1957, 5:657–658.
2. ASHMAN, R. and HULL, E. Essentials of electrocardiography. New York, Macmillan Co., 1947.
3. BAYLEY, R. H. Ann. N. Y. Acad. Sci., 1957, 65:1110–1126.
4. BECKER, R. A., SCHER, A. M. and ERICKSON, R. V. Amer. Heart J., 1958, 55:547–556.
5. BURGER, H. C. and VAN MILAAN, J. B. Acta med. scand., 1943, 114:584–607.
6. CARMELIET, E. and LACQUET, L. Arch. int. Physiol., 1958, 66:1–21.
7. CONRAD, L. L., CUDDY, T. E. and BAYLEY, R. H. Circulation Res., 1959, 7:555–563.
8. CRANEFIELD, P. F. and HOFFMAN, B. F. Circulation Res., 1959, 7:11–18.
9. CRANEFIELD, P. F. and HOFFMAN, B. F. J. gen. Physiol., 1958, 41:633–649.
10. DURRER, D., v. LIER, A. A. W., v. DAM, R. Th., JONKMAN, E. and DAVID, G. Res.

Comm., Congr. mond. Cardiol., 1958, 3:355–356.
11. DURRER, D. and VAN DER TWEEL, L. H. Ann. N. Y. Acad. Sci., 1957, 65:779–802.
12. EINTHOVEN, W. Ann. Phys., 1903, 12:1059–1071.
13. EINTHOVEN, W. Arch. int. Physiol., 1906, 4:132–164.
14. ERICKSON, R. V., SCHER, A. M. and BECKER, R. A. Circulation Res., 1957, 5:5–10.
15. FRANK, E. Ann. N. Y. Acad. Sci., 1957, 65:980–1002.
16. GARDBERG, M. and ASHMAN, R. Arch. int. Med., 1943, 72:210–230.
17. GRANT, R. P. Clinical electrocardiography. New York, McGraw Hill Co., 1957.
18. HECHT, H. H., BAYLEY, R. H., BROOKS, C., CRANEFIELD, B. F., LEPESCHKIN, E., SCHAEFER, H., SODI-PALLARES, D. and SUCKLING, E. E. Ann. N. Y. Acad. Sci., 1957, 65:932–941.

19. LEWIS, T. *The mechanism and graphic registration of the heart beat*. London, Shaw and Sons, 1925.

20. LEWIS, T., MEAKINS, J. and WHITE, P. D. *Phil. Trans.*, 1914, *B205*:375–420.

21. LEWIS, T. and ROTHSCHILD, M. A. *Phil. Trans.*, 1915, *B206*:181–226.

22. MEDRANO, G. A., BISTENI, A., BRANCATO, R. W., PILEGGI, F. and SODI-PALLARES, D. *Ann. N. Y. Acad. Sci.*, 1957, *65*:804–817.

23. MINES, G. R. *J. Physiol.*, 1913, *46*:349–383.

24. PRINZMETAL, M., SHAW, C. McK. JR., MAX-WELL, M. H., FLAMM, EILEEN J., GOLDMAN, A., KIMURA, N., RAKITA, L., BORDUAS, J. L., ROTHMAN, S. and KENNAMER, R. *Amer. J. Med.*, 1954, *16*:469.

25. PUECH, P. *L'activite electrique auriculaire*. Paris, Masson et Cie, 1916.

26. ROSENBLUETH, A. and GARCIA-RAMOS, J. *Amer. Heart J.*, 1947, *33*:677–684.

27. SAMSON, W. E. and SCHER, A. M. *Fed. Proc.*, 1959, *18*:136.

28. SCHAEFER, H. *N. Y. Acad. Sci.*, 1957, *65*:743–766.

29. SCHER, A. M., RODRIGUEZ, MARIA I., LIIKANE, J. and YOUNG, A. C. *Circulation Res.*, 1959, *7*:54–61.

30. SCHER, A. M. and YOUNG, A. C. *Ann. N. Y. Acad. Sci.*, 1957, *65*:768–778.

31. SCHER, A. M. and YOUNG, A. C. *Circulation Res.*, 1955, *3*:535–542.

32. SCHER, A. M. and YOUNG, A. C. *Circulation Res.*, 1956, *4*:461–469.

33. SCHER, A. M., YOUNG, A. C., MALMGREN, A. L. and PATON, R. R. *Circulation Res.*, 1953, *7*:539–547.

34. SCHERF, D. and SCHMITT, A. *Extrasystoles ana allied arrhythmias*. New York, Grune and Stratton, 1953.

35. SCHMITT, O. H. *Ann. N. Y. Acad. Sci.*, 1957, *65*:1092–1109.

36. SCHWAN, H. P. and KAY, D. F. *Ann. N. Y. Acad. Sci.*, 1957, *65*:1007–1013.

37. SJOSTRAND, F. S., ANDERSSON-CEDERGREN, E. and DEWEY, M. M. *J. Ultrastructure Res.*, 1958, *1*:271–286.

38. SODI-PALLARES, D. *New bases of electrocardiography*. St. Louis, C. V. Mosby Co., 1956.

39. SODI-PALLARES, D., BRANCATO, R. W., PILEGGI, F., MEDRANO, G. A., BISTENI, A. and BARBATO, E. *Amer. Heart J.*, 1957, *54*:498–510.

40. TODD, T. W., Section 29 in *Special cytology*, vol. 2, E. V. COWDRY, ed. New York, Paul B. Hoeber, 1932.

41. TRAUTWEIN, W. and DUDEL, J. *Pflügers Arch. ges. Physiol.*, 1956, *263*:23–32.

42. WEIDMANN, S. *Electrophysiologie der Herzmuskelfaser*. Bern, Hans Huber, 1956.

43. WILSON, F. N., JOHNSTON, F. D., ROSENBAUM, F. F., ERLANGER, H., KOSMANN, C. E., HECHT, H. H., COTRIM, N., MENEZES DE OLIVEIRA, R., SCARSI, R. and BARKER, P. S. *Amer. Heart J.*, 1944, *27*:19–85.

44. WILSON, F. N., MACLEOD, A. G. and BARKER, P. S. *Proc. Soc. exp. Biol. (N. Y.)*, 1932, *29*:1006–1010.

45. WILSON, F. N., ROSENBAUM, F. F. and JOHNSTON, F. D. *Advanc. intern. Med.*, 1947, *2*:1–63.

CHAPTER 28

Nutrition of the Heart*

CARDIAC CIRCULATION

Functional Anatomy. *Arteries.* The arterial blood supply of the heart comes from the two coronary arteries, the right and the left. In about 34 per cent of persons the two arteries may be said to be "balanced," that is, the right coronary artery supplies the right ventricle and the posterior half of the interventricular septum, and the left coronary artery supplies the left ventricle and the anterior half of the interventricular septum. In another 48 per cent the right coronary artery preponderates, and not only supplies the whole of the posterior septal region but contributes to the blood supply of the posterior region of the left ventricle. The remaining 18 per cent fall into the category of left predominance; the circumflex branch of the left coronary artery supplies all of the posterior septum as well as some contiguous portions of the right ventricle. Apparently this last type of coronary architecture is physiologically the least sound, for the incidence of arterial occlusion is unusually high in this group, and infarcts caused by such occlusions generally result in death. In contrast, almost all infarcts found in hearts with a balanced circulation are healed, and two-thirds of those in persons with right coronary artery preponderance are likewise healed.[11]

The distribution of the coronary vessels follows a topographic pattern, i.e., the coronary artery ramifies within the substance of the region to which it runs and supplies the full thickness of the cardiac wall at that point. This view is borne out by (i) the location of the infarcts within the region served by an occluded vessel, (ii) the general course of the finer ramifications of the coronary arteries as visualized by roentgen rays after injection of radiopaque substances, and (iii) the reproduction of certain electro-cardiographic signs of myocardial infarction by experimental injury, such as injection of corrosives, burns and surface application of KCl solutions. In such experiments, the

* Written for the 17th Edition by H. E. Hoff; edited for this edition by Allen M. Scher.

pattern typical of the occlusion of a chosen coronary artery may be duplicated by damage to the region over which the occluded vessel is seen to ramify and which becomes ischemic when the vessel is occluded.

The finer ramifications of the coronary arterial tree are probably physiologic "end arteries" in that they form the sole blood supply to the capillaries into which they ramify. This has been demonstrated by injections of fluids with viscosities approaching that of blood into normal human hearts of any age at normal blood pressures. Little or no mixing of perfusates from the right and left coronary arteries occurs. From studies of this nature reported by Blumgart et al.,[2] it can be concluded that the normal heart contains no anastomoses between arteries with diameters of 40 μ (the size of small terminal arterioles) or more. If a *watery* injection solution is used, the entire heart may be injected from a single artery.

Experimentally, sudden arterial occlusion is followed by infarction in the area supplied by the ligated vessel. If, however, the occlusion is preceded by any preparation which involves opening of the pericardium, ligation of even a large vessel may produce virtually no lasting damage. When a loose knot is placed aseptically under the dog's main left coronary artery and the ends are left under the skin, tightening of the knot several weeks later without opening the chest will produce little or no permanent damage. If the artery is tied at the time of initial exposure or within a day after it, serious damage will result. After the initial surgical procedure, development of collateral circulation and/or hyperemia reduces or abolishes the normal effects of tying the ligature. Likewise, if the occlusion of the vessels takes place slowly, an entire right or left coronary artery may be occluded with minimum necrosis or even with none at all. Injections into such hearts demonstrate an extraordinarily rich network of anastomotic vessels, and all semblance of end arteries is lost. Apparently, the ultimate ramifications of the coronary arterial tree are end arteries only in normal circumstances. An anatomic substrate capable of developing into an effective anastomotic network does exist and often develops when the narrowing and final occlusion of a coronary artery proceeds slowly enough. Absent in a normal heart, this network appears only *when* and *where* it is needed.

Anastomoses between coronary arteries occur not only between branches of the right and left arteries but also between adjacent branches of the same artery; anastomoses between coronary vessels and extracoronary arteries may also occur. These may develop with branches of the aortic vasa vasorum or with branches of vessels in the mediastinum, lungs, parietal pericardium and diaphragm. Surgical methods have been designed to increase the number and effectiveness of these extracardiac anastomoses in attempts to offset the effects of progressive narrowing of the coronary arteries. These procedures include implantation of various vessels into the myocardium and dusting the heart with talc to produce inflammation. It seems unproved that such methods increase survival, except in animal experiments where occlusion is induced after the "protective measures" have been taken and where the protection afforded may be only a result of the opening of the pericardium. It also remains to be established how long such protection persists One recently devised operation consists of tying the internal mammary arteries; this procedure obviously has no effect on coronary blood flow. In instances when occlusion of both coronary arteries at their orifices has been found after death, it may be that the hearts survived because of an effective development of adequate extracardiac anastomoses. Unfortunately, man rarely develops extracoronary anastomoses when the coronary arteries become occluded.

Capillaries. Little is known about the capillaries of cardiac muscle except that the richness of the capillary network surrounding the muscle fibers in all dimensions is not exceeded in any other tissue. There is at least a one-to-one relationship between the capillaries and the muscle fibers. This intimate anatomic relation must contribute significantly to the ability of the fiber to obtain oxygen when the oxygen saturation of the blood is considerably diminished.

Cardiac veins and thebesian vessels. The usual arrangement whereby capillaries drain into venules which in turn drain into even larger veins is found in the heart. The veins follow roughly the distribution of the major arteries, joining finally into a single trunk which empties into the right atrium via the coronary sinus. There is in addition, however, an accessory channel for venous drainage, the thebesian vessels.* These vessels pass directly from the capillaries and veins to the lumina of the ventricle; they are most numerous in the right ventricular side of the interventricular septum. Two other structures should also be mentioned, the arterioluminal and the arteriosinusoidal vessels which form direct communications between the arteries or arterioles and the chamber of the heart. The arterioluminal vessels remain arteriolar to the very end of their course, but the arteriosinusoidal vessels break up shortly into sinusoids which lie between the muscle bundles. These vessels resemble capillaries in possessing thin walls composed only of endothelium; they differ from capillaries in having a larger diameter, from 50 to 250 μ.

The function of the thebesian vessels is still obscure. In the dead heart, ready communication exists between the ventricular cavities and the coronary veins via these channels, and the older supposition was that the thebesian vessels constituted an alternative route for venous drainage. Early work indicated that approximately 60 per cent of the total canine coronary flow passed through the coronary sinus, the other 40 per cent, by implication, entering the ventricular cavities via the thebesian vessels. More recently it has been discovered that the partition between various pathways is by no means constant—that a much smaller proportion of blood, if any, is drained by the thebesian vessels and that other venous channels are of great importance.

Gregg *et al.*[8] painstakingly cannulated most of the numerous anterior cardiac veins that pass to the base of the right ventricle and empty directly into the atrium and found that the blood collected from them was almost sufficient to account for all the coronary outflow not collected from the coronary sinus.

Mechanical Factors Influencing Coronary Blood Flow. *Interference during systole.* Circulation in the frog's heart is apparently a simple in-and-out motion of blood, which enters the sinusoids of the heart during diastole and is squeezed out during systole. A somewhat similar view has been held regarding the mammalian heart. According to this view, the contraction of the ventricles raises intramural pressure enough to stop or reduce arterial flow during part of systole and to increase venous flow by squeezing blood from the capillaries and small veins into the larger veins and into the right atrium. Other views that have prevailed at one time or another for the most part have been reflections of the technical difficulties attending the measurement of flow in the coronary arteries throughout a single cardiac cycle. It must be remembered that the intramural pressure during systole will be higher in the left ventricle than in the right, and will thus hinder inflow on the left to a much larger extent.

Present evidence suggests that the following sequence of events most probably occurs during a normal cardiac cycle in the dog's left coronary artery (Fig. 370).[6] At the end of diastole the velocity of flow is approximately 70 per cent of maximum. During isometric contraction flow into the left coronary arteries stops completely, and there may even be some backflow at a rate approaching 20 per cent of the maximum forward speed. During the period of ejection forward flow recommences and soon reaches its maximum rate at the height of the pressure curve. By the end of systole the velocity has again

---

* After Adam Christian Thebesius, who first described them in his *Dissertatio medica de circulo-sanguinis in corde*, Leyden, 1708 (2nd ed., 1716).

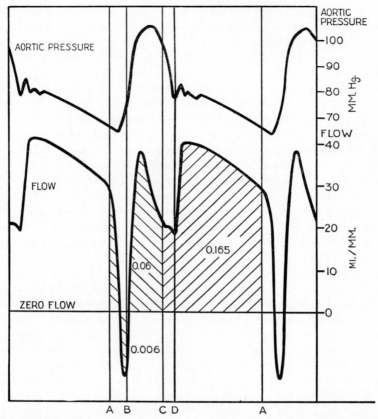

FIG. 370. Blood flow in anterior descending branch of left coronary artery, synchronized with aortic pressure curve. At end of diastole, A, blood is flowing into coronary artery at a rate of 28 ml. per minute. At onset of isometric contraction, A, rate of flow abruptly diminishes and backflow is established momentarily. With beginning of ejection, B, flow recommences and reaches a maximum of 40 ml. per minute shortly before peak of aortic pressure curve. It then declines somewhat in parallel with fall of aortic pressure, only to increase again after closure of aortic valves, D. It finally declines with declining diastolic pressure until next systole begins. Total blood flow during each phase can be calculated from area enclosed by each curve (rate × time). Net flow in systole equals 0.06 minus 0.006 or 0.054 ml.; that during diastole is 0.165 ml. Since heart rate was 131 per minute, total flow is 29 ml. per minute. (From Gregg and Green, *Amer. J. Physiol.*, 1940, *130*:114–125.)

fallen to 50 per cent of its maximum which, however, is soon reached again during isometric relaxation. Throughout diastole the rate of flow falls progressively to about 70 per cent of maximum by the beginning of the next systole. Recently records of coronary flow in dogs have been obtained with electromagnetic flowmeters which do not require cannulation of the vessel (Fig. 371).

In the right coronary artery the inflection points are the same as those on the left, but the changes in flow occurring in the cardiac cycle are far smaller; the flow is never reduced to zero and no backflow occurs (Fig. 372). These results are difficult to extrapolate to humans, since the partition in flow between right and left is different. There is undoubtedly an increased venous outflow from the coronary sinus and the anterior cardiac veins during systole. It also appears that coronary flow increases when asystole is induced by vagal stimulation. This increase may reflect the cessation of a mechanical hindrance to flow during systole, other vagal effects, or both.

When, instead of rate of flow, the volume of flow is calculated—as can be done by measuring the area inclosed by the graph of rate changes—it is seen that a very consider-

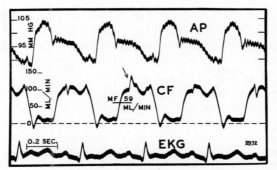

FIG. 371. *Top curve*, Aortic pressure (*AP*), *middle curve*, coronary flow (*CF*) measured with a non-cannulating electromagnetic flowmeter; *bottom curve*, an electrocardiogram. These results are qualitatively similar to those in Figure 372. As can be seen, coronary flow falls during diastole, rises during early systole (before aortic pressure rises), and then falls markedly during ejection phase. Coronary flow again rises to a peak during diastole, and cycle is repeated. Small irregularities on flow curve, indicated by arrow, are electrocardiographic voltages. (Courtesy of Drs. Merrill Spenser and Harold D. Green.)

able net forward flow occurs during systole, even though flow may cease entirely during a brief part of systole. The ratio of total flow during systole to total flow during diastole ranges from 1:1.75 to 1:7.4, with an average of 1:2.4.

Effects of heart rate. The effects of heart rate on coronary flow are difficult to separate from other alterations accompanying rate changes. On purely mechanical grounds, flow might be expected to vary inversely with rate, since increased rate decreases diastole preferentially. Some evidence both for and against this relation can be found in the heart-lung preparation. However, other factors, such as the amount of work performed and the available oxygen, appear to be far more important than rate. Experimental results have also varied widely depending on whether the heart was studied *in situ* or in the heart-lung preparation.

FIG. 372. *Top curve*, Systemic arterial pressure; *middle curve*, flow in right coronary artery; *bottom curve*, approximate right intraventricular pressure. Right coronary flow falls during diastole, rises markedly during early systole, and then, like left coronary flow, falls suddenly with an isometric contraction. Fall in inflow continues during most of ejection phase. Flow rises to a near maximum again in early diastole, then continues to fall. (Courtesy of Drs. Harold D. Green and Donald E. Gregg.)

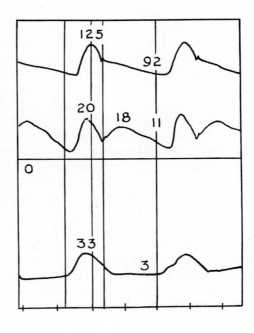

Aortic pressure. "It is *a priori* evident that the aortic blood pressure must constitute the main factor in the control of the coronary circulation."[1] In the heart-lung preparation increases up to fivefold occur when aortic blood pressure is raised from 40 to 60 mm. Hg. to 130 to 140 mm. Hg. A fall in perfusion pressure caused a reduction in coronary inflow from 67 ml. per minute to 19 ml. per minute in an experiment on an isolated heart preparation. In experiments on the heart *in situ* in the anesthetized animal, much the same results are obtained, but they are complicated by alterations in cardiac metabolism and in the vigor of cardiac contraction. In some experiments reported by Gregg,[7] the coronary resistance to flow changed in such a fashion as to be virtually independent of the reflex changes in aortic pressure. Other variables thus appear to override effects of aortic pressure.

Neural Control of Coronary Vessels.   The nerve supply to the coronary arteries is so abundant that anatomists were once led to believe that the myocardium received no nerves and that the so-called cardiac nerves innervated only the coronary arteries. Although this extreme view was in the course of time proved to be incorrect, it serves to emphasize a richness of innervation that, according to Anrep,[1] is unsurpassed in any other artery in the body. Both sympathetic and parasympathetic fibers are present in approximately equal proportions in the larger vessels, but there is a preponderance of parasympathetic fibers in the finer arterioles.

The central regulation and peripheral influence of the two subdivisions of the autonomic nervous system are still unclear. The cause for this lack of knowledge lies in the difficulty of measuring coronary blood flow. Flow in the isolated heart can be measured quite accurately, but the applicability of such results to the intact animal is naturally questionable. On the other hand, the methods, such as Rein's thermostromuhr, which have been used in intact unanesthetized animals have been criticized as inaccurate. Newer flowmeters are being devised to meet the double requirements of accuracy and applicability to normal conditions, and these should add much to the fundamental knowledge of this subject. It has also been difficult to separate with certainty the direct effect of stimulation or section of a nerve from indirect influences arising from alterations in the rate and force of the heart beat and in the aortic blood pressure. Finally and most important, the neurohumors released at various nerve endings within the heart can often have indirect effects which completely mask or reverse their effects on the blood vessels.

Stimulation of the stellate ganglion produces an increase in coronary flow even with minimal changes in heart rate. Inferentially, this demonstrates the existence of sympathetic dilator fibers. However, as Gregg[7] stated, such stimulation is accompanied by an increase in the vigor of contraction and hence in the work and/or metabolism. Evidence for sympathetic vasoconstrictor activity has been obtained in the fibrillating heart, where stellate stimulation usually decreased coronary flow and stellate section increased it. Some investigators have observed decreased coronary flow in the intact heart when they stimulated the vagus and increased flow when they sectioned this nerve. Other investigators report no change or the opposite effects. It appears that further study with better control of all parameters is necessary before definite statements can be made regarding the function of either the sympathetic or the parasympathetic innervation.

Reflex regulation of coronary flow.   No definite evidence exists that any receptors, either within the heart or elsewhere, can reflexly affect coronary flow, although many papers report changes in coronary flow after afferent nerve stimulation, distention of portions of the gastrointestinal tract, pain, increase in cerebral or carotid sinus pressure, etc. However, in none of these studies were other variables affecting coronary flow sufficiently controlled to demonstrate reflex control unequivocally.

Chemical Control. *Oxygen, carbon dioxide and other metabolites.* Much more pronounced than the influence of heart rate, cardiac output, neural factors and autonomic hormones is the action of anoxemia (Fig. 373). An increase in blood flow to as much as five times the control value has been observed during anoxemia. Injection of cyanide reproduces the effects of general anoxia, but an increase in the carbon dioxide content of the inspired air or injection of lactic acid has a much smaller effect. Increased flow with increased carbon dioxide production by the heart appears to be an indirect effect of the decreased oxygen tension of the blood. It is not apparent whether the increased coronary blood flow in anoxia is caused by anoxia *per se* or by metabolites liberated as the result of oxygen lack. However, the increase is independent of neural activity and the heart rate and relatively independent of mean aortic pressure. The view that the increased coronary flow is a direct effect of anoxia is supported by Hilton and Eichholtz'[9] observations of vasodilation produced by anoxemia without a reduction in oxygen consumption (Fig. 374). In such a case, no oxygen debt and no abnormal production of

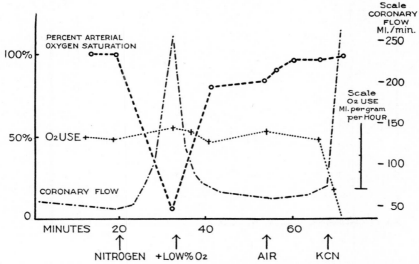

FIG. 373. Graph showing great increase in coronary blood flow in heart-lung preparation when ventilated with nitrogen or when KCN was administered. Oxygen consumption remains constant. (From Hilton and Eichholtz, *J. Physiol.*, 1924–25, *59:*413–425.)

metabolites would occur. It should be noted that the normal resting heart extracts 10 to 12 volumes per cent of oxygen from each 100 ml. of blood and has virtually no oxygen reserve.

The rapidity with which oxygen lack operates has impressed many observers. Green and his coworkers[4] noticed that local ischemia caused by temporary ligation of a coronary artery would produce a marked vasodilatation in the ramifications of the artery occluded. Occlusion of an artery for as short a time as 3 to 5 seconds was followed by an increase as great as 200 to 250 per cent, although no influence on blood pressure or the vigor of myocardial contractions could be detected. Maximal dilatation, producing an increase in flow as great as 500 per cent, was obtained before myocardial contractions began to fail, whereas the increased coronary circulation was maintained for as long as 1.5 minutes after the force of contraction fully recovered in experiments where occlusion was maintained to the point of failure. The hydrogen ion appears to be a mild vasodilator, as does histamine, which is produced in increased quantities by the hypoxic heart.

Autonomic hormones. Determination of the influence of epinephrine, norepinephrine and acetylcholine on the coronary vessels is made difficult by the additional indirect influences exerted on heart rate, aortic blood pressure, vigor of myocardial contraction, cellular metabolism and oxygen consumption. The consensus seems to be, however, that epinephrine excites a moderate dilating influence on the coronary arteries. This effect, it now appears, results largely from the vasodilating action of metabolic products liberated by the increased metabolism induced by the drug. It has been suggested that the angina produced by injection of epinephrine in susceptible subjects occurs because the increase in metabolism and the consequent demand for oxygen far outstrip the increase in flow made possible by any direct vasodilating action of the epinephrine. The effect of norepinephrine is similar but less marked.

As far as acetylcholine is concerned, most workers find that the drug dilates the coronary vessels—quite contrary to what might be expected from the vasoconstriction

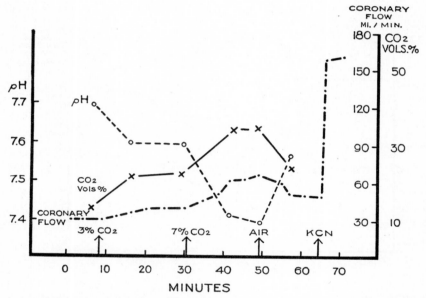

FIG. 374. Illustration of influence of CO_2 on coronary flow. Comparison with Fig. 373 indicates that CO_2 is much less effective as a vasodilator than O_2 lack. (From Hilton and Eichholtz, *J. Physiol.*, 1924–25, *59*:413–425.)

that follows vagal stimulation. The latter effect, when found, may reflect changes in aortic pressure, heart rate, availability of oxygen, or other parameters which can mask the dilator effect of the drug.

There is complete agreement that Pitressin reduces coronary flow, with more or less proportional reduction throughout the cardiac cycle. This reduction, which is sufficient to bring about well marked electrocardiographic signs of myocardial ischemia, is antagonized by epinephrine. Green *et al.*,[5] in confirmation of the original observation by Melville and Stehle, found in experiments on dogs that 0.1 ml. of a 1:1000 solution of epinephrine promptly restored the coronary flow and the vigor of cardiac contraction which had been depressed by 1 to 2 units of Pitressin. Amyl nitrite, nitroglycerin, aminophylline, histamine, acetyl-beta-methylcholine, papaverine, pyridine-beta-carbonic acid, diethylamide (Coramine) and atropine have been noted to increase coronary blood flow. Coronary vasodilatation has been recognized as responsible, at least in part, for the phenomenon.

METABOLISM AND NUTRITION OF THE HEART

Oxygen Metabolism. *Oxygen requirement and cardiac efficiency.* Oxygen requirements in heart-lung preparations are of the order of magnitude of at least 2 to 5 ml. of oxygen per gram of heart per hour when average cardiac outputs are maintained at mean aortic blood pressures close to 100 mm. Hg. With the energy equivalent of oxygen (2 kg. per m. per ml.), the efficiency of the heart can be estimated by calculating the work output by means of a formula which includes the two major ways in which the heart performs work: creating pressure and imparting a kinetic energy to the flowing blood. One such formula is: $W = VP + (MV^2/2\,g)$, where W is the work in kilogrammeters, V is the minute volume in liters, P is the mean aortic pressure in meters of blood, M is the weight of blood, V^2 is the square of mean velocity, and g is the acceleration due to gravity. Assessment of the total work of the heart requires such a computation for both ventricles. The kinetic factor constitutes but a small proportion of the total work

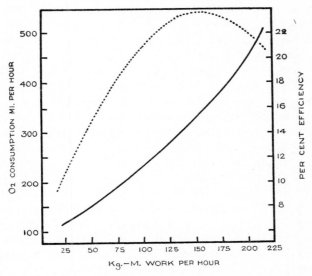

FIG. 375. Graph showing rise in efficiency (*dotted line*) when increased output is mediated by enlargement of stroke volume, without change in rate or mean arterial pressure. Efficiency finally begins to fail as the limits of diastolic distensibility are approached. Continuous line represents oxygen consumption. (From Evans, *J. Physiol.*, 1918–19, *52*:6–14.)

under most conditions and is usually neglected. In these circumstances the efficiency of the heart is usually about 3 to 7 per cent.

Increase in the work of the heart demands additional oxygen but not necessarily a directly proportioned increment, since the efficiency of contraction may change. Augmentation of the work load required by increase in arterial resistance lowers efficiency by approximately 20 per cent, so that a greater than proportional rise in oxygen consumption must occur. Efficiency is lowered when the heart rate increases. Even when the output is unaltered, the oxygen consumption varies almost linearly with heart rate in a fashion which can be expressed mathematically in the following formula: O_2 (ml. per gram per hour) $= 0.0187R$ (rate per min.) $+ 2.23$. This increase in oxygen requirements without alteration in output entails, of course, a reduction in efficiency that may be a critical factor in a failing heart. On the other hand, the increase in work load imposed by greater diastolic filling and consequent greater stroke volume, without change in heart rate or mean arterial pressure, is attended by a marked increase (almost 30 per cent) in efficiency of contractions (Fig. 375). The opinion of some workers is that the output is abnormally low in heart-lung preparations operating at efficiencies of 3 to 10 per cent, and that the efficiency of the human heart in the basal state may be in the neighborhood of 12 to 20 per cent. Calculations based on these figures suggest that the oxygen utilization in the human heart may constitute 4 to 5 per cent of the total consumption.

The conclusions to be drawn from these studies are: (i) the efficiency of the heart is lowered when the demand for increased output is met by an increased heart rate, but is raised when the stroke volume is increased without change in rate; (ii) because of these two opposing tendencies it is not possible to predict the net change in efficiency that might occur in strenuous exercise, but since the trained individual performs the same work at a lower heart rate than does the untrained person, it follows that the trained person is operating at a higher level of cardiac efficiency; (iii) increase in arterial resistance forces the heart to work at a lessened efficiency, unless the heart rate is slowed (Marey's law) to accommodate the same output with a more efficient contraction.

Despite even the most favorable changes in efficiency, the consumption of oxygen in the heart increases markedly in strenuous physical exertion, and values as high as 200 to 250 ml. of oxygen per minute have been suggested as the requirements of the human heart during exhausting physical exertion. In meeting this demand, the heart has access to a number of mechanisms already described, including extensive vasodilatation in the coronary tree and an increase in the mean aortic pressure. In addition, the heart has the ability to increase its oxygen utilization coefficient to an even more marked degree than skeletal muscles. Thus in Figure 373 it can be seen that oxygen consumption may be maintained at a constant level despite a most drastic reduction in the oxygenation of the coronary blood supply. The time may nevertheless come when the demand for oxygen exceeds the supply; the heart then becomes anoxemic, either as it participates in *general* anoxemia affecting the whole body or as it suffers from *localized* anoxemia affecting only part of the heart. To each condition characteristic reactions take place.

General anoxemia. The progressive development of generalized anoxemia involves the heart directly and indirectly. In the early stages of anoxemia or hypoxia the general response is one of stimulation, with increased blood pressure, heart rate and cardiac output. The duration of systole is shortened (Fig. 376), the minute volume of respiration increases, and a relative alkalosis develops because the loss of carbon dioxide by hyperventilation is excessive. This stage, in which it is clear that the heart is operating with normal or even increased efficiency, is terminated classically in a cardiovascular-respiratory crisis; the blood pressure falls abruptly, respiration becomes slower and stops altogether, while the heart slows markedly and shows signs of an A-V block of varying degree. If adequate oxygen is not rapidly made available and artificial respiration is not instituted, death will soon follow. Cardiac changes at this time reflect failure of the cells themselves.

In man and experimental animals this sequence has been followed electrocardiographically to the very moment of collapse. Two findings are almost universally noted: (i) a progressive diminution in the height of the T wave in all leads, beginning at oxygen concentrations of around 14 per cent; and (ii) a moderate depression of the S-T segment, rarely exceeding 1 mm. The S-T segment changes suggest injury of muscle bordering the endocardium. The R wave has also been reported to suffer a progressive diminution. This change and the changes in the T wave probably result from a progressive increase in chest volume resulting from the gradual augmentation in inspiratory tone as anoxemia develops. At the crisis, atrioventricular dissociation may appear in man as well as in the dog. As indicated before, the A-V node has a low safety factor. Once the crisis has appeared, the T wave rapidly reverses to the upright. The amplitude of the T wave continues to grow and may exceed that of R in the QRS complex. The mechanism of these T wave changes is not known, nor is it known whether the mechanism is cellular (i.e., whether the intracellular action potential changes), although the large efflux of potassium from myocardial and other cells undoubtedly plays a role. Indeed, similar changes are seen in hyperkalemia. Arrest may occur at this stage, or the ventricles may continue to beat until widespread intraventricular block develops. All these events occur after the arrest of respiration and may therefore be considered terminal. They undoubtedly reflect the direct effect of anoxemia upon the myocardium as well as the aforementioned outpouring of potassium from anoxemia tissues throughout the body.

The changes in the electrocardiogram preceding the crisis indicate the presence of myocardial anoxemia and resemble the T wave changes following acute myocardial infarction. The ability of the heart to recover from rather long exposure to low oxygen tensions (up to 30 minutes) has been of fundamental importance in the development of open heart and other cardiac surgery.

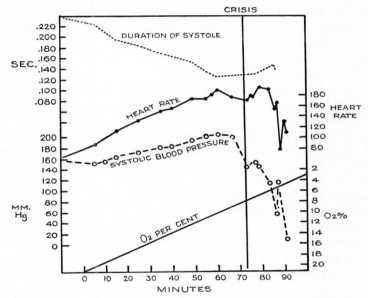

FIG. 376.   Duration of systole (*dots*), heart rate (*solid line with solid circles*), systolic pressure (*dashes with open circles*), and oxygen content of respired air (*solid line*) in dog during progressive anoxia. Until crisis at approximately 8 per cent O_2, all cardiovascular functions are stimulated. Crisis appears to be precipitated by fall in blood pressure. A respiratory crisis occurs at the same time. (From Sands and DeGraff, *Amer. J. Physiol.*, 1925, 74:416–435.)

Localized anoxemia.   If a coronary artery becomes occluded or narrows so abruptly that an adequate collateral circulation cannot develop in time to nourish the myocardial area normally supplied by the artery, a local oxygen deficiency develops. At the center of this region, the deprivation is almost complete; there is a surrounding zone of progressively greater oxygenation, bounded by normal myocardium. Within the zone of oxygen deficiency certain physiologic processes are altered. For example, the configuration of the intracellular action potential changes (Chap. 27). This change is manifest in decreased conduction velocity and altered excitability (threshold, rate of repolarization, rhythm). Also, the force of contraction decreases. Many of the alterations produce changes in the electrocardiogram by which the course of events may be followed.

Diminution of *contractility* is perhaps the most significant alteration. Partial deficiency in oxygen supply, when carried beyond the compensatory ability of the myocardium, is soon followed by weakening of contraction and by dilatation; complete deprivation of oxygen is followed within 30 seconds by cessation of contractions. The most common cause of death in acute coronary occlusion is probably failure of muscular force, and progressive congestive heart failure is the most important complication in patients who recover from the acute attack but whose functional myocardium is insufficient to maintain an adequate cardiac output. Often patients recover from the initial insult of infarction only to die, within two weeks, of cardiac standstill or, more rarely, ventricular fibrillation. The very act of occlusion favors the establishment of collateral circulation, but a myocardium that is totally deprived of oxygen for more than 30 minutes rarely recovers (except in surgery where a pump-oxygenator may support the heart during the initial stages of recovery). Occlusion produces an *infarct*, which is later replaced by noncontractile tissue.

The disturbances of *conduction* accompanying anoxia are important when the anoxic area includes specialized conductile tissue such as the A-V node, the bundle of His, or one of the bundle branches. In the first of these circumstances a burden in addition to the direct loss of contractility may be placed on the heart, since the ventricular rate may be slowed to levels where cardiac output falls. With block of the conduction system distal to the A-V node, the distribution of the impulse within the ventricles may be so delayed that summation of the contributions of the individual muscular elements can no longer yield a vigorous contraction.

Changes in irritability of paramount importance develop in partially anoxemic areas, particularly soon after the anoxemia begins. As has been seen, generalized anoxia stimulates the heart during the precrisis stages—as much via the sympathetic nervous system as by direct action on the myocardium. Other irritable tissues are equally hyperexcitable at certain stages of oxygen want. In heart muscle, this stage of hyperirritability expresses itself in an increased tendency to spontaneous discharge and a shortened refractory period; it also serves as the physiologic background for the ectopic beats that almost invariably arise after occlusion of a coronary artery. These range all the way from isolated extrasystoles arising within the anoxemic area to runs of tachycardia which may ultimately lead to ventricular fibrillation and death. Even when they do not terminate in fibrillation, such tachycardias are clinically important because they may reduce cardiac output.

The *electrocardiogram* reflects certain of these changes in the following sequence: (i) the period of stimulation which all the myocardium passes through as it becomes anoxemic and which persists in the outlying zone for some time; (ii) the current of injury that develops when anoxemia proceeds to such a degree that the integrity of the surface membrane can no longer be maintained (see above); (iii) the more lasting changes which persist in that part of the myocardium which survives but which has an insufficient blood supply; and (iv) the lasting changes in distribution of the cardiac impulse brought about by the permanent loss of myocardial elements.

Inorganic Ions.   The eponym *Ringer's solution* serves as an enduring reminder of Sidney Ringer's contributions to our understanding of the mineral requirements of the heart.[10] Perfusing the frog's heart with artificially constituted fluids of differing compositions, Ringer came to the following conclusions:

(i) "Saline is incapable of sustaining the contractions of the heart, for when blood mixture is replaced by saline, the contractions speedily grow weaker, and in some cases contractility ceases altogether, for no contraction can be excited by even a strong break induction shock."

(ii) "Calcium bicarbonate, or calcium chloride in physiological doses, or even in smaller quantities than are present in the blood, restore good contractions, even when contractility has been lost for seven or eight minutes, and the ventricle no longer responds to strong induction shocks . . . I conclude therefore that a lime salt is necessary for the maintenance of muscular contractility.

(iii) "But whilst calcium salts are necessary for the proper contraction of the heart, yet if unantagonized by potassium salts the beats would become so broad and diastolic dilatation so prolonged that much fusion of the beats would occur and the ventricle would be thrown into a state of tetanus . . .

(iv) "If these two salts are not present in the correct proportions then the trace becomes abnormal. If too little potassium is present the contractions become broader &c. and there results fusion of the beats. If too much potassium is present, or too little lime salts, then the contraction of the ventricle is imperfect, and by increasing the quantity of potassium salt the beat becomes weaker till it stops."

(v) "A small quantity of calcium bicarbonate or calcium chloride (of chloride 1 in 19,500 parts), added to saline solution [0.75 per cent] with 1 part of potassium chloride in 10,000 parts, makes a good artificial circulating fluid and the ventricle will continue beating perfectly for more than four hours, with calcium bicarbonate."

These simple relationships are naturally modified in mammals, where a great many accessory factors must be considered. It is therefore advisable to review the action of these ions in the dog and cat and, as far as possible, in man.

Sodium. Sodium is the ion which is most important for the maintenance of the resting potential of cardiac cells. Since the "sodium pump" produces the ionic gradients across the cell wall, however, wide variations in plasma sodium are well tolerated. The normal plasma level is 140 mEq. per liter. The maximum level compatible with life is approximately 200 mEq. per liter in dogs made hypertonic by withdrawal of drinking water or by intravenous or intraperitoneal injections of 5 per cent saline. In such animals the peripheral pulse is slow and vigorous until the very end; and in both acutely and chronically hypertonic animals nonprotein nitrogen does not rise and urine excretion continues, testifying to the adequate maintenance of circulatory efficiency. The electrocardiogram deviates insignificantly during the rise in serum sodium and is essentially normal immediately before death. Death is invariably caused by respiratory failure while the heart is still beating. Reduction in serum sodium below 100 mEq. per liter, on the other hand, is followed by development of marked signs of cardiovascular inefficiency—rapid weak pulse, low cardiac output, and falling blood pressure—resulting in cardiovascular collapse. Some of these effects occur because the myocardial cells lose their ability to depolarize.

Potassium. In the mammalian heart potassium acts much as it does in the frog. The concentration difference across the cell wall determines the resting potential. If the inside-out concentration is raised, the resting potential will be greater than usual and the cells may not easily depolarize. If the plasma level is excessively high, the cells may not be able to repolarize normally. Increased plasma potassium alters the sequence of recovery in the heart—the amplitude of the T wave is conspicuously altered—and produces widespread, progressive intracardiac block noticeable first in the atrium, then at the A-V node and finally in the ventricle. These effects result from cellular changes. In man as well as in experimental animals, blood pressure is well maintained, falling only when intraventricular block becomes pronounced. On the other hand, an impairment of electrical activity is clearly seen in circumstances in which the serum concentration is lowered (Figs. 377, 378). This impaired conduction will, in turn, impair contractility.

Responsiveness of the heart to acetylcholine is markedly augmented by increments in serum potassium which are well within limits of spontaneous variability. Both of these substances will act to depolarize the cells.

Calcium. The action of calcium can be described, but the mechanism of its action is not clear. Presence of calcium is essential to normal electrical excitability. This ion appears to act at the cell membrane and to be important in the as yet unelucidated sequence of events linking excitation with contraction. In small doses, calcium increases excitability.

In the dog, three phases of calcium activity are found as the serum concentration rises progressively (Figs. 379, 380): (i) initial vagal bradycardia occurring when the serum calcium level is 13 to 35 mg. per cent; (ii) tachycardia and ectopic beats when the level is 30 to 60 mg. per cent; in approximately half of the animals this phase terminates

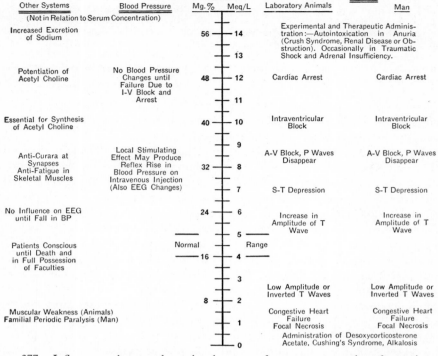

Other Systems (Not in Relation to Serum Concentration)	Blood Pressure	Potassium Mg.%	Meq/L	HEART Laboratory Animals	Man
Increased Excretion of Sodium		56	14	Experimental and Therapeutic Administration:—Autointoxication in Anuria (Crush Syndrome, Renal Disease or Obstruction). Occasionally in Traumatic Shock and Adrenal Insufficiency.	
			13		
Potentiation of Acetyl Choline	No Blood Pressure Changes until Failure Due to I-V Block and Arrest	48	12	Cardiac Arrest	Cardiac Arrest
			11		
Essential for Synthesis of Acetyl Choline		40	10	Intraventricular Block	Intraventricular Block
			9		
Anti-Curara at Synapses Anti-Fatigue in Skeletal Muscles	Local Stimulating Effect May Produce Reflex Rise in Blood Pressure on Intravenous Injection (Also EEG Changes)	32	8	A-V Block, P Waves Disappear	A-V Block, P Waves Disappear
			7	S-T Depression	S-T Depression
No Influence on EEG until Fall in BP		24	6	Increase in Amplitude of T Wave	Increase in Amplitude of T Wave
			5		
Patients Conscious until Death and in Full Possession of Faculties	Normal	16	Range 4		
			3		
		8	2	Low Amplitude or Inverted T Waves	Low Amplitude or Inverted T Waves
Muscular Weakness (Animals) Familial Periodic Paralysis (Man)			1	Congestive Heart Failure Focal Necrosis	Congestive Heart Failure Focal Necrosis
			0	Administration of Desoxycorticosterone Acetate, Cushing's Syndrome, Alkalosis	

FIG. 377. Influence on heart and associated systems of serum concentration of potassium.

in fatal ventricular fibrillation; and (iii) bradycardia not of vagal origin when the concentration is greater than 60 mg. per cent. Applied to man, these findings indicate that spontaneous elevation of serum calcium never reaches levels at which the heart is placed in jeopardy, as can and does occur with potassium. The main consideration must therefore be given to the therapeutic use of calcium salts injected intravenously. The usual therapeutic dose injected at one time is 1 gram (of calcium chloride), which can hardly produce a serum concentration exceeding 20 mg. per cent unless given extremely rapidly; therefore, only the first two stages—the early bradycardia and the stage of rapid ectopic beats—need be considered.

An interesting example of the first phase is, in all probability, the long period of arrest (with syncope) seen in some patients who have received injections of very small

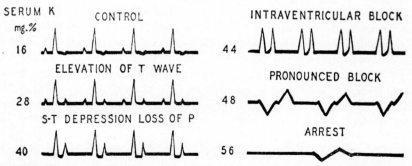

FIG. 378. Diagram showing the progressive changes that occur in electrocardiogram of dog (lead II) as an isotonic solution of potassium chloride is injected at a slow rate. At left is given average level of serum potassium at which the various changes occur. P wave diminishes in amplitude and widens progressively; just before it disappears (not shown here), various stages of A-V block may be seen. (From Winkler *et al., Yale J. Biol. Med.*, 1940, *13*:123–132.)

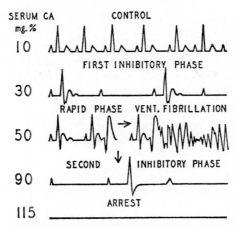

FIG. 379. Diagram illustrating changes in electrocardiogram (lead II) of dog produced by slow infusion of isotonic calcium chloride, with the average concentrations at which the several events occur. First inhibitory stage is of vagal origin, and may be very pronounced. Second phase of acceleration is nearly always marked by ventricular extrasystoles and tachycardia, and may end in fatal ventricular fibrillation. Final phase of slowing and arrest is, of course, found only in animals surviving rapid phase, and is not of vagal origin. (From Winkler *et al.*, *Yale J. Biol. Med.*, 1940, *13*:123–132.)

amounts of calcium. It is unlikely that this vagal effect can ever be intense enough to cause death; therefore the probable cause of fatalities following therapeutic injections in man is ventricular fibrillation. The lowest concentration at which this was observed in dogs was 30 mg. per cent, a concentration considerably greater than that obtained in man with the customary therapeutic dose of calcium salts. Presumably fibrillation may occur very occasionally at a lower level, or a rapid injection may temporarily

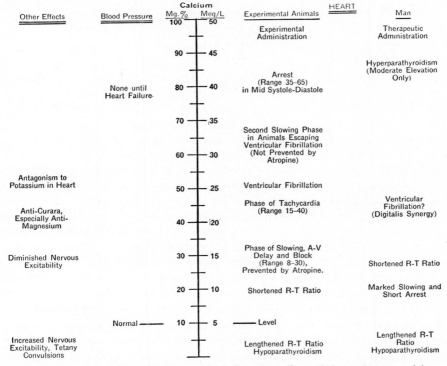

FIG. 380. Summary of important systemic and cardiac effects of elevated serum calcium.

elevate the concentration in arterial blood to toxic levels. The danger of ventricular fibrillation seems to be somewhat greater in digitalized patients, either because of some unconfirmed digitalis synergism or because of the underlying disease in these patients.

Magnesium. Within limits consistent with life, alteration in the concentration of magnesium in the serum has very little effect upon the heart beyond a moderate prolongation of the P-R interval and a variable influence on the heart rate, depending upon the balance between a directly effected slowing of the heart and a reflex increase in rate due to a fall in blood pressure (Fig. 381). It has been claimed that magnesium salts reduce the excitability of the ventricle and thus serve to suppress ventricular ectopic beats.

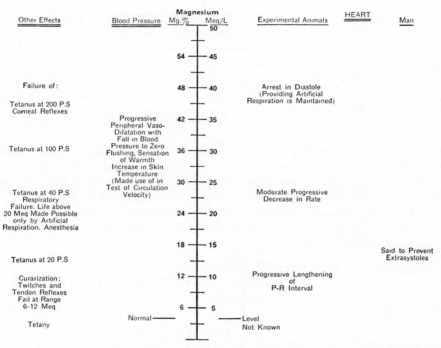

FIG. 381.   Influence on cardiovascular and other systems of serum concentration of magnesium.

The main cardiovascular effect of magnesium salts is to dilate arterioles, thus reducing the systemic blood pressure. This property of magnesium salts may contribute, at least in part, to their therapeutic effectiveness in nephritis and eclampsia in that cerebral circulation is improved. Magnesium may also dilate the veins in much the same way as the nitrites do; it produces syncope related to reduced venous return resulting from excessive pooling of blood in relaxed venous reservoirs. Beyond this, magnesium blocks myoneural junctional transmission much as does curare, and respiration will ultimately stop because the respiratory muscles are paralyzed. This effect occurs when the serum level is below those significantly affecting the heart; thus arrest of the heart cannot occur unless respiration is maintained by artificial respiration. Finally, magnesium acts as an anesthetic, but only at levels very close to those which also produce myoneural block, so it is at times difficult to distinguish between the two effects.

Acid-base equilibrium. The frog heart is rather remarkably resistant to changes in the acid-base composition of its perfusate, and beats have been reported to persist with perfusates as acid as *p*H 5.5 and as alkaline as *p*H 10. Investigation of this problem by intravenous injection of a variety of acids in the intact anesthetized dog reveals: (i) The lethal pH level is very close to 6.0 (range 6.6 to 5.5) and is independent of the acid employed (lactic, HCl). (ii) Changes in atrioventricular or intraventricular conduction are practically nonexistent; there is a slight progressive P-R delay, reaching a maximum of no more than 0.15 seconds (in the dog), and a 1:1 atrioventricular rhythm is maintained to the point of death. (iii) The rate is well maintained, with only moderate slowing, to the very end; arrest comes suddenly as the terminal event. (iv) The amplitude of the T waves increases progressively, and just preterminally there is a marked progressive drop in the S-T segment in all leads, which can be interpreted as due to right ventricular failure. Blood pressure falls precipitously and respiration fails. The heart is arrested in extreme diastole.

It can therefore be concluded that the primary effect of low pH is sudden abolition of the contractility of the heart before any serious changes have occurred in the rate, rhythm or conduction of the cardiac impulse, but that the rapidity with which this event is followed by arrest of the heart and respiratory failure suggests that these systems were overtaxed. Difficulties in conduction are not a significant part of the picture of acid intoxication in the mammalian heart *in situ*. If changes in perfusing fluid are made slowly, greater modifications are possible.

Carbohydrate Metabolism. *Lactic acid.* Although the carbohydrate metabolism of the heart takes the same general course as does that of skeletal muscle, there are at least quantitative differences. The most significant difference is perhaps the importance of the oxidation of lactic acid in the heart. Various investigators have emphasized this importance in a number of ways. (i) Whereas in skeletal muscle the lactic acid concentration is higher in venous than in arterial blood, coronary sinus blood has a lower lactic acid content than arterial blood. This difference indicates that, whereas skeletal muscle liberates lactic acid, well oxygenated cardiac muscle removes lactic acid from the blood. (ii) In perfusion experiments in which the lungs are replaced by an artificial oxygenating device to preclude the glycolysis that can occur in the lungs, the utilization of lactic acid, when present in normal or slightly higher concentrations, can be greater than the utilization of glucose (200 mg. of lactic acid against 70 mg. of glucose per 100 grams of heart per hour). (iii) The diabetic heart can utilize lactate, although its ability to consume glucose is drastically curtailed. Similarly, the well-oxygenated heart can oxidize lactic acid after poisoning with iodoacetic acid.

This concept of lactic acid as an important normal fuel of the heart replaced an older view that lactic acid was harmful to the heart and that the myocardium was less able to withstand its toxic effects than was skeletal muscle. It does not however appear that the heart muscle has a single or even a favored pathway for carbohydrate oxidation. Evidence obtained by catheterization of the coronary sinus[3] indicates that an excess of pyruvate, lactate or glucose leads to increased utilization of the substance. Lactic acid injected intravenously in the dog may have a striking lack of influence apart from its effect on blood pH.

Glycogen and glucose. In anoxemia, especially when the oxygen saturation falls below 25 per cent, utilization of lactic acid fails, and it is produced by the heart rather than absorbed by it. The production of lactic acid is associated with disappearance of myocardial glycogen and ceases when the glycogen stores have been exhausted. The process is presumed to be the chief source of energy available to the anaerobic heart. However this may be, the anaerobic energy supplies of the heart are extremely limited, and the heart is capable of accumulating an oxygen debt of but small proportions and little significance. The heart is instead adapted to function on an aerobic basis, and in anatomic arrangement and physiologic properties it is designed to receive and use a large uninterrupted oxygen supply.

The heart can and does utilize glucose directly, in proportion to its concentration in the blood over a threshold of 54 mg. per cent and in inverse proportion to the quantity of available lactic acid. When the utilization of glucose is increased by addition of glucose to the blood, utilization of lactic acid declines, as it also does when the consumption of glucose is increased by administration of insulin to the diabetic heart. While, therefore, glucose and lactic acid are in a measure interchangeable in supplying the carbohydrate requirements, they are not completely so. Lactic acid appears to be of greater benefit in the hypodynamic heart and is fully utilizable in the iodoacetic acid–poisoned heart. Contrariwise, glucose is indispensable in the synthesis of glycogen. When the heart-artificial lung preparation is forced to work at a high level and given 0.3 mg. of epinephrine per hour, the heart performs well for approximately two hours and then suddenly fails as its glycogen becomes fully depleted. If administration of epinephrine is stopped and the work load is reduced just before failure, the heart can survive in a hypodynamic state for some time. Lactic acid can improve the condition of the hypodynamic heart, but will not restore its glycogen; this can, however, be restored by glucose. It has been suggested on the basis of this and similar experiments that glycogen serves mainly as an emergency substance available when supplies of other carbohydrates are low or when they cannot be utilized.

Cardiac muscle contains a large variety of metabolic enzymes which are important in carbohydrate and fat metabolism, but it contains fewer proteolytic enzymes than do other tissues. For this reason, much basic research in biochemistry is carried out on extracts of heart muscle.

Fat Metabolism. The ability of the heart to utilize fat is shown by: (i) its ability to survive for considerable periods without glucose, lactic acid or glycogen; (ii) the lower respiratory quotient at times observed, particularly in the diabetic heart; and (iii) direct observation of utilization of beta-hydroxybutyric acid. During starvation, the respiratory quotient of the myocardium falls to 0.70, an indication that fat is probably the major metabolite.[3]

REFERENCES

1. ANREP, G. V. and SEGALL, H. N. *Heart*, 1926, *13:*239–260.
2. BLUMGART, H. L., SCHLESINGER, M. J. and DAVIS, E. *Amer. Heart J.*, 1940, *13:*1–91.
3. GOODALE, W. T. and HACKEL, D. B. *Circulation Res.*, 1953, *1:*509–517.
4. GREEN, H. D. and WEGRIA, R. *Amer. J. Physiol.*, 1942, *135:*271–280.
5. GREEN, H. D., WEGRIA, R. and BOYER, N. H. *J. Pharmacol.*, 1942, *76:*378–391.
6. GREGG, D. E. and GREEN, H. D. *Amer. J. Physiol.*, 1940, *130:*114–125.
7. GREGG, D. E. and SHIPLEY, R. E. *Amer. J. Physiol.*, 1942, *141:*382–389.
8. GREGG, D. E., SHIPLEY, R. E. and BIDDER, T. G. *Amer. J. Physiol.*, 1943, *139:*732–741.
9. HILTON, R. and EICHHOLTZ, F. *J. Physiol.*, 1924–25, *59:*413–425.
10. RINGER, S. *J. Physiol.*, 1883–84, *4:*29–42.
11. SCHLESINGER, M. J. *Arch. Path.*, 1940, *30:*403–415.

CHAPTER 29

Hemodynamics and the Physics of the Circulation

By ALAN C. BURTON

Why Hemodynamics?   The heart is a pump, and blood is a fluid forced by the arterial pressure through the blood vessels. Thus, an understanding of the circulation must be based on knowledge of the physical laws governing the behavior of fluids at rest and in motion. Poiseuille,[*] a French physician (1799–1869), wanted to know the relation between the "force of the heart" and the "amount of the circulation," so he investigated the steady flow of water in rigid tubes. His pioneer work, accurate to three or four figures, laid the foundation of the science of rheology, the study of the flow of viscous fluids. While he is honored in every physics textbook, he was as much a physiologist as a physicist.

It is true that in applying these physical laws to the circulation in the living animal we must deal with many complications. Blood is not like water; it is a complex heterogeneous fluid with some abnormal properties of viscosity. The blood vessels are not rigid tubes but are quite distensible, so that their size depends on the blood pressure within them as well as upon the contraction of the smooth muscle in the vessel walls. Also, the flow is not steady but pulsatile in most parts of the vascular bed. These complexities must not deter us from resting the whole structure of our thinking in hemodynamics upon fundamental physics, even if we cannot yet hope to reach the goal of completely understanding the dynamics of the circulation.

Fluids.   A fluid is a substance that cannot *permanently* withstand even the slightest *shearing force*, i.e., a force which tends to change the shape of the substance and to cause one layer of it to slide over an adjacent layer (like the blades of a pair of shears). Gases as well as liquids are fluids; gases, however, differ from liquids in their resistance to

* Pronounced not as "poise-eel" but as "pwaz-œ-ye."

changes in volume but not in resistance to changes in shape. Further, gases are compressible, whereas liquids are almost completely incompressible.

Unlike fluids, solids can resist changes (i.e., deformations) in both shape and volume by virtue of their *elasticity*, which is measured by the magnitude of the resisting force that they develop to a standard deformation. Since the walls of the blood vessels have many properties of solids as well as some properties of liquids, in hemodynamics we must deal with elasticity as well as with *viscosity*, which may be regarded as a kind of fugitive or transitory elasticity.

Pressure in Fluids; Hydrostatics.   Pascal (1623–1662), a French philosopher and mathematician, gave us the laws of fluids at rest, i.e., hydrostatics. He recognized the importance of *fluid pressure*, the force per unit area (dynes per cm.²) exerted by the fluid along any plane at right angles to this plane. His three laws are:

(i) *Fluid pressure is equal in all directions*. The plane over which we estimate the force may lie in any direction, and the fluid "pushes" sideways, upward or downward on any barrier at a given point with the same pressure. This law must have been difficult to understand in Pascal's day. Now that we have the concept provided by the kinetic theory of gases and liquids, with molecules moving rapidly in all directions at random, this first law is easy to grasp. The pressure results from the bombardment by molecules in their thermal agitation of any plane barrier placed in the fluid.

(ii) *Pressures at points lying in the same horizontal plane in a fluid are equal*. The free surface of the fluid is a special case; there the pressures are everywhere atmospheric. This property follows from the definition of a fluid, for if the pressures were not equal, there would be shear forces which would cause movement of fluid until the pressures became equal.

(iii) *The pressure increases with depth under the free surface*. In a fluid at rest under gravity, pressure increases uniformly with the depth. The increase is equal to ρgh dynes per cm.², where ρ is the density of the fluid (grams per ml.), g is the acceleration of gravity (980 cm. per sec. per sec.), and h is the depth (cm.). (Proof of this equation appears in elementary textbooks of physics.) This law underlies the use of the U-tube and the reservoir type of manometer (Chap. 30) in which the pressure is measured as the difference in the levels of two columns of water, saline or mercury supported by the pressure. Indeed this type of manometer provides the only way of measuring *absolute* pressures and all other manometers, such as electromanometers, must be calibrated by comparison with a fluid-column manometer. The absolute pressure, in dynes per square centimeter, is obtained by means of the above formula. For example, if a mercury column with the density of 13.6 is used, the pressure corresponding to 1 mm. Hg is:

$$\rho gh = 13.6 \times 980 \times 0.1 = 1,330 \text{ dynes per cm.}^2$$

Alternatively we might use a column of water or physiologic saline (density 1.04) in the manometer. The pressure corresponding to 1 cm. of saline is:

$$\rho gh = 1.04 \times 980 \times 1 = 1,019 \text{ dynes per cm.}^2$$

To transform a value from millimeters of mercury to centimeters of saline we must multiply by the fraction 13.6/1.04, so that 1 mm. Hg pressure = 13.1 mm. = 1.31 cm. of saline pressure.

The density of blood is about 1.055, and a pressure of 1 mm. Hg corresponds to the pressure of 12.9 cm. of blood. The pressure in the arteries at heart level is pulsatile with a mean value of about 100 mm. Hg. This pressure will support a column of blood 100 × 13.6/1.05 mm. or 129 cm. high, as the Reverend Stephen Hales found in his famous experiment in which he cannulated the carotid artery of a horse with a long vertical tube (described in his book *Haemostaticks** in 1733).

The important point is that the hydrostatic factor, ρgh, applies to the vascular system, as it must. As we shall see later, the resistance to flow in the large arteries (and veins) is very small; therefore, the flow of blood introduces only very small pressure drops in these vessels. If the body is horizontal, the mean arterial pressures in the brain and feet are approximately the same (Fig. 382*A*). When the body is erect, however, the hydrostatic factor reduces the arterial pressure in the brain and increases that in the feet (Fig. 382*B*).

The factor ρgh is considerable. Suppose that the artery in the head is 50 cm. above the heart level: the mean pressure there is now not 100 mm. Hg but $100 - 500/13$, or only about 62 mm. Hg. Similarly, the arterial pressure in the feet (130 cm. below the

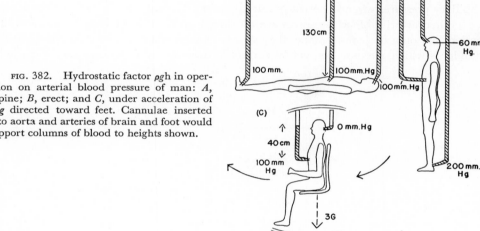

FIG. 382.   Hydrostatic factor ρgh in operation on arterial blood pressure of man: *A*, supine; *B*, erect; and *C*, under acceleration of 3 *g* directed toward feet. Cannulae inserted into aorta and arteries of brain and foot would support columns of blood to heights shown.

heart) may be $100 + 1300/13$, or 200 mm. Hg. It is obvious that very active cardiovascular reflexes are required to deal with the changes in pressure in the distensible vessels.

One interesting direct application of this principle is to aviation physiology in connection with accelerations experienced in high-speed aircraft in acrobatics (Fig. 382*C*). At the bottom of a "loop," the centripetal acceleration may amount to many times *g*. At that instant, the blood effectively has a density correspondingly greater than normal; in other words, we substitute the centripetal acceleration, toward the feet in this case, instead of *g* in the formula ρgh. Suppose that this acceleration is three times gravity (usually written as 3 *g*). The factor ρgh to the head arteries is now $3 \times 500/13$, or 114 mm. Hg. Subtracting this value from the mean pressure of 100 mm. Hg at the heart results in a pressure actually less than atmospheric pressure in the cerebral arteries; i.e., there is no pressure to keep the arteries open so that they can pass the necessary blood to the brain. On this basis we would predict that the limit of human tolerance to acceleration ("positive *g*") without *blackout* resulting from brain anoxia must be close to 3 *g*. Actually, the tolerance of fit young pilots is not much greater, although cardiovascular reflexes can raise the blood pressure during the maneuver to produce a slightly greater tolerance.

If the acceleration force is opposite to that of gravity (this occurs at the start of a power dive) and exactly equal in magnitude, we may have the condition of "weightlessness," of great interest in space medicine since it occurs in the "free motion" of a space satellite. In this condition the *g* of the hydrostatic factor is effectively zero, and pressures in the circulatory system will be independent of the posture and presumably the same as when the man lies in a horizontal plane. Serious effects of weight-

* This book did not enjoy the popularity of his next publication (1734) entitled *Friendly admonition to the Drinkers of Brandy, etc.*, which ran through six editions.

lessness on the circulation are not to be expected. When the opposite acceleration force exceeds the force of gravity, the blood pressure in the brain is above normal. Congestion with blood in the retina results in a visual disturbance known as *red-out*.

The same hydrostatic factor applies to the venous system, although it is modified by the action of the valves in the peripheral dependent veins. If a vein in the foot is cannulated and connected to a long vertical tube of saline, the top of the saline will rise approximately to the level of the heart when the subject is standing absolutely motionless. However, as soon as the leg muscles are contracted rhythmically, the blood in the veins is massaged upward through the valves and cannot return (the "muscle pump"). The venous pressure in the foot then falls markedly. The high venous pressure in the dependent vessels during motionless standing or sitting will increase the capillary pressure and lead to a shift of fluid from the blood stream to the tissues (dependent edema). Who has not discovered that his feet were so swollen that he could not put on his shoes after motionless sleep in a sitting position on a train or plane? Again, very active vasomotor reflexes are required to counteract the effects of the hydrostatic factor on the venous and capillary pressures when the erect posture is assumed.

When arterial blood pressures are measured in the arm or leg or elsewhere in a patient not on a horizontal plane, they *must be corrected to heart level* for comparison with standards which are based on values correct at heart level. This correction is made by

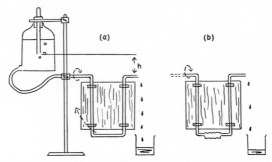

FIG. 383.   Simple apparatus to demonstrate principle of syphon as it operates (*a*) in system of non-distensible tubes and (*b*) where vessels are distensible.

subtracting the factor ρgh if the site of measurement is below the heart, or by adding this factor if the site is above. An approximate value in millimeters of mercury is obtained by dividing the difference in level, in centimeters, by 13 (i.e., 13.6/1.055). The clinical indirect measurement of blood pressure is usually made on the forearm of a seated subject. In this case the level is close enough to that of the heart to require no correction.

APPLICATION OF THE SYPHON.   Archimedes (287–212 B.C.) discovered the principle of the *syphon*. This principle is that the flow of a fluid from point A to point B depends on the difference between the pressures or levels at these points, and not at all upon the levels of the pipe between them, provided that the fluid column is not broken.

Figure 383 shows a simple demonstration of how this principle applies during changes in posture. In *a*, the water from the reservoir flows through a U of rigid glass tubing. The rate of flow shown by the drops emerging is not altered at all, even temporarily, if the plane of the U-tube is swung from horizontal to vertical below or above the bottle, since the pressure head of ρgh is unchanged. If the blood vessels were rigid (indistensible), changing the posture from lying to standing would have no effect at all on the circulation. However, the vessels, especially the veins, are very distensible; therefore, when a man stands up the dependent veins tend to dilate passively. To imitate this condition, a segment of distensible rubber tubing is inserted in the U-tube (Fig. 382B). Now when the U is turned from the horizontal to the vertical plane, there is a transient stoppage of flow as the water entering the rubber tube fills its increased volume (resulting from the increased pressure) instead of flowing on. However, as soon as the steady state is reached and the rubber tube is full, the flow is resumed at the original rate.

Thus temporarily, and *temporarily only*, the blood entering the dependent veins will remain in them to fill the increased volume there, rather than flowing on to the heart. However, once the veins are full under the increased pressure (due to ρgh) the venous return will be restored. There is, of course, a persistent effect on the circulation because the blood volume has shifted to fill the dependent vessels. This shift may cause circulatory collapse (fainting) if the "muscle pump" does not relieve the condition. However, this persistent effect does not depend on the venous return being "uphill." In fact, owing to the applicability of the principle of the syphon, it is a "howler" in fundamental physics to state that the venous return to the heart is made more difficult in the erect posture because such a return is uphill.

Fluids in Motion (Hydrodynamics); Viscosity. A key word in the definition of fluids given at the beginning of this chapter is "permanently," for all fluids can resist a shearing force temporarily. Their resistance to shear depends on the rate of change of deformation (i.e., rate of shear), not upon the amount of deformation or shear that has occurred. Thus shear deformation can be slowed by fluids but cannot be permanently prevented. This property of fluids, the ability to slow changes in their shape, is called

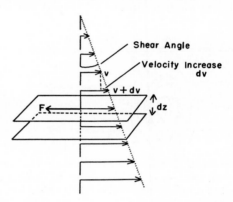

FIG. 384. Diagram of velocity gradien in a flowing viscous fluid and tangential force (*F*) between laminae. (After Edser, *General physics.* London, Macmillan, 1926.)

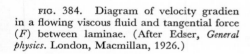

viscosity. Blood is a fluid with a considerable viscosity. The best description of what we mean by "viscosity" is still that given by Sir Isaac Newton, who said it is "*a lack of slipperiness between adjacent layers of fluid.*"

Figure 384 attempts to illustrate the fact that in a viscous fluid in motion, adjacent layers or laminae slide over each other with different velocities, given by the *velocity gradient*, which is also the rate of shear. Then, because there is a "lack of slipperiness" between adjacent layers, the slower layer or lamina tends to retard the faster one, and vice versa. This effect results in a *tangential force* (*F* in Fig. 384) on the interface between the two layers. Newton made the simplest assumption possible, that the tangential force per unit area, i.e., the shear stress, is proportional to the rate of shear.

$$\text{Tangential Force/Area} = \eta \times dv/dz \tag{1}$$

where η is the coefficient of viscosity in poise and dv/dz is the velocity gradient (which is the same as the "rate of shear"), z being the direction at right angles to the stream. The unit, the poise, is of course named in honor of Poiseuille. In words we may define the absolute viscosity, η, as the tangential force per unit area (dynes per cm.²) when the velocity gradient is unity, i.e., 1 cm. per second per cm. Viscosity therefore has the dimensions of mass over the product of length times time ($M \cdot L^{-1} \cdot T^{-1}$).

By a fortunate accident, the viscosity of water at about room temperature, i.e., at 20.2° C., is 0.010000 poise (at 37° C. it is 0.0069 poise). It is thus convenient to use the *centipoise* (0.01 poise) as a practical unit, and to remember that water at room temperature has a viscosity of about 1 centipoise. The viscosity of blood is considerably greater than that of water—three or four times as great for the normal hematocrit value of 50 per cent, mainly because red cells are present. (Details of the viscosity of blood are given in a later section.) A fluid which obeys Newton's equation is said to be "Newtonian." Water and most simple fluids are quite accurately Newtonian. Blood is only approximately so, and is said to have an "anomalous" viscosity.

FLOW OF A VISCOUS FLUID IN A TUBE; POISEUILLE'S LAW. It is sometimes erroneously said that force is required to move blood through the blood vessels because there is "friction between the blood and the walls of the vessels." This statement is completely incorrect. There is a cohesive force between liquids and the solids which they wet, partially or completely. This force prevents movement of the layer of fluid immediately at the wall. Thus an infinitely thin layer of blood in contact with the wall of the blood vessels has a zero velocity of flow. The next layer, a little closer to the axis, has a small velocity; the layer inside the second has a greater velocity; and so on until the axis is

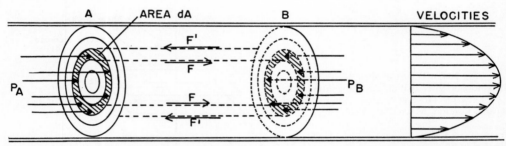

FIG. 385. Diagram of flow of viscous fluid through a tube in concentric cylindrical laminae, showing parabolic distribution of velocities. Pressure force $(P_A - P_B)dA$ is balanced by difference between shear forces, F and F'. F' is greater than F because velocity gradient is increased closer to wall.

reached. There the velocity is maximal. Thus the resistance to flow of blood in the circulation results from the inner friction—the viscosity—of the blood, not at all from friction with the wall. Even the roughness of the wall plays very little part, except at high rates of flow greater than those usually found in the normal circulation. (At these very high rates the flow is quite different from the streamline flow we are describing and becomes turbulent.)

Figure 385 shows how the velocity of an element of fluid in a tube depends on the distance from the axis. The driving force that causes flow through the tube from cross section A to cross section B is a difference of pressure (force per unit area) from A to B. Pressure in a fluid acts at right angles to any cross section and must be the same at all points in a given cross section; if this were not so, there would be a component of flow at right angles to the axis of the tube. By definition this situation is not present in streamline flow. In such flow each lamina of fluid, here a coaxial cylinder, slips over adjacent laminae without any movement from one lamina to another.

Consider the equilibrium of one of the annular cylindrical laminae of fluid in Figure 385. At A the cylinder is being pushed by a force $P_A \times dA$ (force = pressure × cross-sectional area) and at B by a force $P_B \times dA$ exerted in the opposite direction. The net force is $(P_A - P_B) \times dA$.

If the flow is steady, i.e., if there is no acceleration or retardation, Newton's first two laws of motion tell us that the net force must be zero; there must be an opposite force balancing the force $(P_A - P_B)dA$. This balancing force is provided by the tangential forces due to the viscosity of the adjacent layers and described by Newton's equation given above. This viscous force depends on the velocity gradient at each of the two interfaces. By this line of reasoning, Hagen used the methods of calculus to determine the velocity gradient, and therefore the velocities across the tube, for a fluid that has normal viscosity—one which obeys Newton's equation. The calculation is very easy and is given in elementary textbooks of physics. The results are:

(i) The velocity profile (Fig. 385) is a parabola with the maximum flow on the axis of the tube. The velocity at any radius (r) from the axis is given by:

$$V_r = V_m \left(1 - \frac{r^2}{R^2} \right) \tag{2}$$

where V_m is the maximum velocity along the axis and R is the radius of the tube. The velocity at the wall (r = R) is zero. The value of V_m in terms of the viscosity coefficient and the pressure gradient (P) down the tube, i.e., the drop of pressure per unit length of tube, is:

$$V_m = \frac{P \cdot R^2}{4\eta}$$

where R is the radius of the tube.

(ii) The velocity gradient, in contrast, is greatest at the wall and zero on the axis. Most of the viscous force is therefore near the wall, where the gradient of velocity is highest. *The fluid near the wall is much more important in determining the total viscous resistance than is that near the axis.*

Hagen proceeded to calculate the total flow of fluid by adding up (integrating) the contribution to flow of each concentric annular space (Fig. 385). The result is the famous Poiseuille-Hagen formula for the flow, F.

$$F = (P_A - P_B) \times \left(\frac{\pi}{8} \right) \times \left(\frac{1}{\eta} \right) \times \left(\frac{R^4}{1} \right) \tag{3}$$

If P_A and P_B are in c.g.s. units (dynes per cm.^{2}), if η is in poises, and if the dimensions of the tube, its radius (R) and length (l), are in centimeters, the flow (F) will be in milliliters per second.

Poiseuille's formula has been written above in four terms to make obvious how simple it is to remember and understand. Most of it is common sense. We would expect the flow to be proportional to the driving force, the pressure difference $(P_A - P_B)$ across the ends of the tube. There follows a numerical term $(\pi/8)$. The π is there because we are dealing with a cylindrical tube; the 8 arose in the process of Hagen's integration. The next term $(1/\eta)$ is the viscosity term. Again, we would expect the flow to be inverse to the viscosity, since the more viscous the fluid the harder it will be to push it through the tube. Finally we have the geometrical term (R^4/l) depending on the dimensions of the tube. Here we would expect the length to be the denominator. The only unexpected feature is that the radius of the tube appears to the fourth power; we might have expected the cross-sectional area to be the factor concerned and the radius to be squared (R^2).

The dependence on the fourth power of the radius has a most important physiologic consequence. The distribution of the blood to different parts of the body is controlled mainly by means of special bands of smooth muscle in the walls of the arterioles. By the contraction of this smooth muscle under the influence of the nerves or circulating hormones, the blood vessel constricts, i.e., the radius of its lumen is decreased. Other things (the driving pressure and the viscosity) being equal, a decrease to half the radius will actually decrease the flow to a sixteenth of the original value. A decrease of only 16 per cent in radius will halve the flow. There is thus an exquisitely sensitive and effective control of the flow by the arterioles.

VISCOSITY OF BLOOD. *Dependence on hematocrit value.* The viscosity of blood measured in the usual viscometer* very greatly increases as the percentage of the volume of whole blood occupied by erythrocytes (hematocrit value) increases (Fig. 386, *upper curve*).[25] The curve rises more and more steeply, as does an exponential curve; indeed, when the hematocrit value exceeds 70 per cent, blood can hardly be regarded as a fluid any longer. The discoid cells are then tightly packed, and flow must involve their deformation. The accelerated rate of increase in viscosity as the hematocrit value increases is probably a very serious factor in polycythemia (excess of erythrocytes in blood), increasing the work the heart must perform to maintain the circulation. Conversely, during chronic anemia when the hematocrit value is abnormally low, the reduced viscosity may also embarrass the circulation and the heart. Thus, in anemia, if the arterial blood pressure is maintained at normal values (important cardiovascular reflexes tend to ensure this), the total blood flow through the peripheral tissues will be abnormally great and, consequently, cardiac output will be increased.

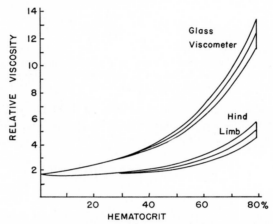

FIG. 386. Relative viscosity of blood versus hematocrit value. *Upper curve,* Values obtained with glass viscometer with a capillary tube radius of 1 mm. *Lower curve,* Values with vessels of dog's hindleg as viscometer. (From Whittaker and Winton. *J. Physiol.*, 1933, 78:339–369.)

Dependence on temperature; relative viscosity. Decrease of temperature greatly increases the viscosity of blood, as it does of all aqueous fluids. The viscosity is about two and one-half times as great at 0° C. as at 37° C. The relative change with temperature is very nearly the same as that in water.[2] Thus the *relative viscosity* of blood, which is defined as the ratio of the viscosity of blood at any temperature to the viscosity of water at the same temperature, is practically constant. The increase in viscosity of the blood in the extremities exposed to cold must be an important factor in reducing the circulation of these parts, as in frostbite or "immersion foot."

Viscosity of blood in very small tubes; Fahraeus-Lindqvist effect. Viscosity is usually measured by using a length of narrow-bore glass tubing as a viscometer and employing Poiseuille's formula to calculate the absolute viscosity; or the relative viscosity may be determined by comparing the flow of water and the test fluid under the same pressure gradient. This comparison was used by Whittaker and Winton[25] to obtain the upper curves of Figure 374. When they compared the rates at which water and blood flowed through the isolated hindlimb of a dog (*lower curve*, Fig. 374), the relative viscosity appeared to be only about half as great for each hematocrit value. The difference between the curves lies in the diameters of the tubes employed as viscometers. The glass

* Usually an instrument which measures the volume of fluid that flows per unit time at a given driving pressure through a tube of known dimensions.

tube used by Whittaker and Winton was about 1 mm. in diameter, but the diameter of the arterioles, which offer the greater resistance, is less than 0.1 mm. Fahraeus and Lindqvist[9] found that with water the size of the tube did not alter the calculated viscosity, but that with blood this value *fell* markedly if the diameter of the tube was less than 1 mm. (Fig. 387). On the basis of their curve, the resistance vessels of the leg of the dog in Whittaker and Winton's experiments had an equivalent diameter of 55 μ, which would correspond to the diameter of arterioles.

There has been much confusion regarding the reason for the Fahraeus-Lindqvist phenomenon. It was thought to have something to do with the axial accumulation of cells (p. 652). It turns out that the phenomenon could be explained as what is called

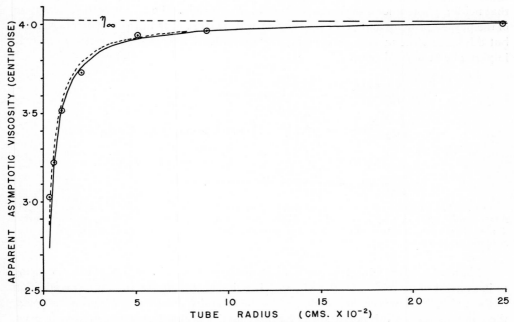

FIG. 387. Fahraeus-Lindqvist effect of size of tube on viscosity. Values calculated on sigma theory for red cell diameters of 6.0 μ (*solid line*) and 6.6 μ (*dotted line*). (Data from Kumin; calculations from Haynes. *The rheology of blood*. Ph.D. Thesis, University of Western Ontario, 1957.)

a *sigma effect*, by which Dix and Scott-Blair[8] explained similar phenomena in colloidal suspensions. Suppose the vessel is so narrow that there is room for only five red cells abreast; we cannot integrate for a series of infinitely thin laminae in deriving Poiseuille's formula. Instead we should sum (sigma is the Greek symbol used by mathematics for a sum of terms) the five terms. This means that the total flow should depend on the sum of the cubes of the natural numbers ($1^3 + 2^3 + 3^3 + 4^3 + 5^3 = 225$)* instead of the integral of r^3 (corresponding to $r^4/4 = 5^4/4 = 156$). On this basis, the effective viscosity in a tube of radius R (R) is related to that in a tube of infinite radius (η_∞) by the formula[1]

$$\eta_R = \eta_\infty/(1 + d/R)^2 \qquad (4)$$

where d is the diameter of the particle and R is the radius of the tube. Figure 387 (*broken line curve*) shows how well the experimental curve for blood can be fitted by this formula if the value chosen for d is 6 μ, which is the diameter of the ox erythrocytes used.

* The sum of the cubes of the natural numbers from 1 to n is equal to $\dfrac{n^2(n + 1)^2}{4}$.

The sigma effect is a very satisfactory explanation of the Fahraeus-Lindqvist phenomenon. The physiologic result is that the work by the heart to force blood through the narrow small vessels of the circulation is less than would be required if the flow there were in laminae of infinitesimal thickness. Axial accumulation (see below) may also play a part.

Dependence of viscosity of blood on rate of flow; anomalous viscosity. A complicated fluid such as blood could hardly be expected to be Newtonian in its viscosity. The proteins of the plasma are not spherical and will be oriented as the rate of flow increases; therefore, viscosity will change. Blood has been said to have the properties of a plastic fluid, which shows no flow at all until the shearing force exceeds a critical value. However, the work of Bingham,[2] after whom plastic fluids are called "Bingham bodies," has shown that neither plasma nor blood is to be thought of as plastic. The effects of the orientation of the plasma proteins and of the discoid red cells by streaming have been demonstrated, but this takes place at such exceedingly low velocities of flow as to be of no physiologic importance at normal rates.

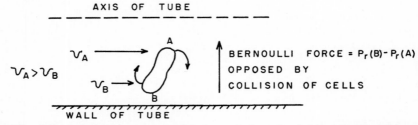

FIG. 388.   Diagram of force causing axial accumulation of red cells in a flowing stream. Cells rotate continuously in a velocity gradient. This rotation leads to a difference in side pressure between *A* and *B* (Bernouilli effect). This effect is eventually balanced by collisions between cells as they accumulate near axis.

Plasma (measured in glass viscometers) has a relative viscosity of about 1.8 owing to its content of proteins, and this viscosity is quite accurately Newtonian. The addition of the red cells, however, definitely makes the viscosity of blood anomalous, although the consequences of this condition in hemodynamics probably have been greatly overemphasized. The anomaly is almost entirely due to the redistribution of red cells in the stream when the blood is caused to flow, as discussed below.

Axial accumulation of red cells.   It has long been known—even since Poiseuille's day—that the red cells in flowing blood tend to accumulate in the axis of the blood vessel and to leave a zone near the wall that is relatively free from cells ("plasma skimming"). This situation can be clearly seen in motion pictures of the circulation in small vessels. The physiologic consequences of axial accumulation may be very important; for instance, small side branches of a blood vessel may draw off blood containing a proportional volume of blood cells considerably less than that for the whole circulation. It is well known that the hematocrit value for blood samples drawn from the capillaries (by needle prick of the skin) is about 25 per cent less than that for whole body blood from the same patient.[10] Plasma skimming may play an important role in the function of the kidney.[15]

In the attempts to explain the established fact of axial accumulation there has been great confusion and controversy. Bayliss,[1] in a review, stated that there are no known physical forces to move the cells toward the axis. More extensive reading of the literature of hydrodynamics (which depends on advanced mathematics) and Starkey's work[21, 22, 23] have elucidated the matter. A particle, even if spherical, in a stream where there is a velocity gradient across the tube will rotate in a complicated way (the Magnus effect). As a result, the path of the particle will be modified by a *Bernouilli force* (like that on a spinning tennis ball), which will cause the particle to swerve (Fig. 388). Moreover, Starkey has demonstrated that a stream of colloidal particles introduced near the wall of a tube carrying a streamline flow is deflected toward the axis. Müller,[13] using a large model in which rubber disks in flowing glycerine solutions imitated red cells, found that the disks, which rotate continuously as predicted, are obviously accumulated at the axis when the rate of flow is increased. A relatively disk-poor zone is left near the wall.

It is easy to see in which direction the effective viscosity will be affected by axial accumulation. The hematocrit value of laminae near the wall of a blood vessel will be reduced; the value at the "core" will be increased. Since the velocity gradient is so much larger near the wall than at the core, the effect of the reduction in viscosity at the periphery greatly outweighs the effect of the increase in viscosity near the axis. As a consequence, the effective viscosity of blood is less than it would be if no axial accumulation took place.

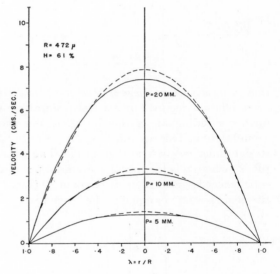

FIG. 389. Velocity profile of blood (hematocrit value, 61 per cent) flowing in a tube (radius 472 μ) at three different values of pressure gradient (P). Broken line is parabole that would apply if there were no axial accumulation. (From Haynes. *The rheology of blood.* Ph.D. Thesis, University of Western Ontario, 1957.)

Axial accumulation will also change the velocity profile from the parabolic curve of a Newtonian fluid to one that is flatter at the axis. The alteration is not great, however (Fig. 389). The solution of the difficult problem of measuring the concentration of cells across the tube was made possible by a recently discovered method[12] of deducing the velocity gradient across the stream from the shape of the pressure-flow curve in a rigid tube. This method is applicable even when the fluid is non-Newtonian.

However, the point at issue has been whether the effective viscosity of blood depends upon the velocity with which it flows. The faster it flows, the greater the force causing axial accumulation. Theoretically, then, the viscosity would depend upon the rate of flow (be reduced for higher rates of flow), and in the Poiseuille equation for flow η would not be a constant but a function of flow. In these circumstances the pressure-flow curves, even in rigid glass tubes, would not be straight but would curve up toward the flow axis (i.e., there would be more flow than expected at high driving pressures). It was thought that this factor of anomalous viscosity might explain the marked nonlinearity of pressure-flow curves of blood in certain vascular beds.

More complete investigation of the pressure-flow curves of blood in glass tubes with different diameters, and the interpretation of these curves by Haynes,[12] have shown

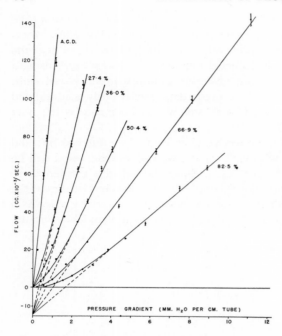

FIG. 390. Empirical flow-pressure curves for suspensions of red cells with different hematocrit values in acid-citrate-dextrose solution in a glass tube with radius of 185 μ; data from Haynes. All curves soon become straight lines with curious property of pointing to common nodal point (*broken lines*). Vertical lines about points represent standard deviations of the means.

that *in the physiologic range of blood flow, blood behaves as if it were a Newtonian fluid*. Axial accumulation occurs, but reaches a saturation value at a very low velocity of flow; i.e., further speeding up of the flow does not accomplish any appreciably greater axial accumulation. This accounts for the pressure-flow curves in glass tubes (Fig. 390) being straight lines except near their origin. The saturation value is reached when the quantity pR/2 (where p is the pressure gradient per unit length of tube and R the radius of the tube) exceeds a critical value of about 20 (Fig. 391). (The quantity pR/2 is an important rheologic parameter equal to the tangential stress at the wall.) Since the normal average

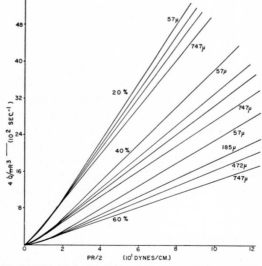

FIG. 391. Rheologic plot bringing together results with glass tubes of different radii (*ordinate*) and at various velocities of flow and hematocrit values. *Abscissa*, Pressure times radius of tube divided by 2. Separation in bundle for each hematocrit value results from Fahraeus-Lindqvist effect. Curves would be straight lines for Newtonian fluids. It is seen that when PR/2 is greater than 20 dynes per cm., the non-Newtonian blood acts as a Newtonian fluid would.

physiologic velocities of flow and the diameters of the various blood vessels—the aorta, arteries, arterioles, capillaries and veins—are known, pR/2 can be estimated for each. It turns out that the lowest value is 60, which is found in the veins. The lowest value for the arterioles—where anomalous viscosity would have the greatest effect since these vessels offer the major part of the total resistance to flow—is about 200. These are well above the critical point (pR/2 = 20) below which blood behaves in a non-Newtonian fashion.

Thus we can conclude that, while axial accumulation takes place and constitutes an important difference between still and flowing blood, in normal physiology we deal nearly always with blood in which axial accumulation is complete. We may thus consider the viscosity as Newtonian within the physiologic range of flow.

Summary.   To summarize the discussion of the viscosity of blood, we must consider the following:

(i) The great dependence on the percentage volume of red cells (the hematocrit value).

(ii) The dependence on the size of the tube, the Fahraeus-Lindqvist effect, which has a simple explanation as a sigma effect. It is of importance in the vascular bed, where the resistance vessels are very small.

(iii) The dependence on velocity of flow, complicated by axial accumulation of cells, a factor which does not play a significant role in the physiologic range of blood flow. In this range the effective viscosity in the blood vessels is a constant, like that of a Newtonian fluid, although this constant is less than it would be if there were no axial accumulation.

Streamline Flow and Turbulence.   When Poiseuille's experiments on fluids flowing through rigid tubes are extended to very high rates of flow, the relation between the driving pressure and the resulting flow changes suddenly (Fig. 392). The first part of the relation is linear, as predictable from Poiseuille's law; but, when a *critical velocity* of flow is reached, the slope of the curve changes, and thereafter the velocity does not increase. An English engineer, Osborne Reynolds,[16] in 1883 showed that at this point of transition the flow changes from streamline, where each lamina slips over adjacent laminae and there is no mixing or interchange of fluid between laminae, to *turbulent flow*. During turbulence, the tube is filled with eddies or whirlpools that are generated and break off from the stream in a rhythmic manner (Fig. 392). In streamline flow a dye injected from a small needle into a given lamina will remain in that lamina and will not mix with the rest of the stream. * In turbulence, the dye immediately appears throughout

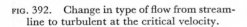
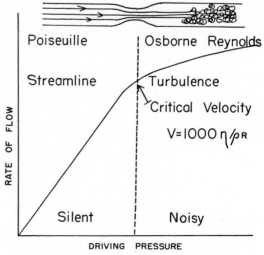

FIG. 392.   Change in type of flow from streamline to turbulent at the critical velocity.

Poiseuille | Osborne Reynolds

Streamline | Turbulence

Critical Velocity

$V = 1000 \, \eta / \rho R$

RATE OF FLOW

Silent | Noisy

DRIVING PRESSURE

* This makes it very difficult to obtain a really representative *mixed* sample of venous blood in studies of cardiac output (Chap. 32).

the tube. In streamline flow, the energy produced by the driving pressure is dissipated against the viscosity of the fluid; in turbulent flow the driving energy is used largely to create the kinetic energy of the eddies, and a new law replaces Poiseuille's law. The resistance to flow now depends on the density of the fluid rather than on its viscosity (since kinetic energy $= \frac{1}{2}\rho V^2$).

Osborne Reynolds showed that the critical velocity at which turbulence appears depends on the viscosity of the fluid, its density and the radius of the cylindrical tube by the relation

$$V_C = \frac{K\eta}{\rho R} \tag{5}$$

where V_C is the critical velocity (in cm. per sec.), η is the viscosity (in poises), ρ the density (in grams per ml.), and R is the radius of the tube (in cm.). K is a constant called *Reynold's number*. It is close to 1000 for many fluids including blood.[7]

The velocity of the blood stream is greatest in the aorta at the height of systole (ejection of blood from the heart). Let us see if the critical velocity is reached here. When the values $\eta = .04$ poise for blood, $\rho = 1$ and R $= 1$ cm. for the aorta are placed in equation 5, the critical velocity is $(1000 \times .004)/(1 \times 1) = 40$ cm. per second. Now, for a man at rest, the cardiac output (i.e., the rate of volume flow in the aorta) is about 5 liters per minute, or 83 ml. per second. The human aorta has a cross-sectional area of about 4 cm.^{2}, so the *mean* velocity throughout the cardiac cycle is about 20 cm. per second (83/4), only half the critical value for turbulence. The velocity during the *ejection period* at the start of systole, however, will exceed the critical velocity. In heavy exercise, where the cardiac output may be four or five times the resting value, there will be turbulence in the aorta during a longer portion of systole. Nowhere else in the normal circulation, except near the heart valves when their opening and closing create sudden high local velocities of flow, will there be turbulence.

SOUNDS OF THE CIRCULATION. Understanding that turbulence depends on a critical velocity of flow is extremely important in connection with the *sounds* in the circulation. Streamline flow is necessarily silent. Nothing about it is vibratory or pulsatile; the laminae of fluid just slip quietly over each other. Turbulence, in contrast, is oscillatory, pulsatile or vibratory; the eddies of turbulence throb and vibrate. Thus noise is created. This is the explanation of the *heart sounds*. They are associated with turbulence in the blood when the valves open or close. It is a matter of controversy whether the sounds heard are generated mostly by the eddies in the blood itself or by vibration of the walls of the vessels or the leaflets of the valves. In any case the existence of a sound depends on the reaching of a critical velocity of flow.

When abnormal sounds are heard in the circulation, an abnormally high velocity exceeding the critical velocity has been reached somewhere. In arteriovenous aneurysm, a direct "shunt" between an artery and a vein has been created by trauma or congenital malformation. Blood rushing through this shunt may greatly exceed the critical velocity, and the vibration, called a "thrill," can be felt over the shunt. Another abnormality which may lead to turbulence is the narrowing of a cardiac valve, as in mitral stenosis. The blood flowing through the valve from atrium to ventricle would normally not be turbulent, but when the orifice is narrowed the flow may become so. The systolic murmurs heard in children during heavy exercise are due to the very greatly increased cardiac output and may be quite innocent. The medical student will do well to remember the advice of the doggerel verse:

Streamline flow is silent.	So when your stethoscope picks up
Remember that, my boys,	A bruit, murmur, sigh,
But when the flow is turbulent	Remember that it's turbulence
There's sure to be a noise.	And you must figure why.

Korotkow's sounds, heard during the indirect measurement of blood pressure (Chap. 30), are an example of the creation of turbulence by the method of measurement. A cuff is wrapped around the upper arm, and the bell of a stethoscope is applied over the brachial artery at the elbow below the edge of the cuff. It is important to realize that if the cuff is not inflated, nothing can be heard from the artery, since the flow in it is streamline. When the cuff is inflated to a pressure above the systolic pressure, the artery is closed by compression and again nothing is heard. As the pressure is allowed to fall below systolic pressure, the artery opens, briefly and slightly, at the height of systole. The jet of blood passing through this narrowed opening exceeds the critical velocity; turbulence results, and a tapping sound signals the event (the systolic criterion). As the pressure in the bag falls below diastolic pressure, the artery will remain open enough throughout the cardiac cycle that the critical velocity for turbulence is no longer reached. All sounds will then cease (the point of "disappearance of sound"). If it is realized that this disappearance of sound corresponds to the velocity falling below the critical value, an event which logically has nothing to do with the diastolic pressure, the mistake will not be made of relying on this point as a criterion for diastolic pressure.[18] (In a normal subject at rest the point of disappearance may accidentally correspond with the true criterion, muffling of the sound—but only accidentally.) Compression of an artery by finger pressure over the superficial tissues will often cause sufficient turbulence beyond the pressure point to allow sounds to be heard with a stethoscope.

In contrast, there is good logic to support a relation between diastolic pressure and the "muffling" of the sound, i.e., a change in its nature, which precedes its disappearance. If the pressure in the cuff is still above the diastolic pressure, there will be a period in each cardiac cycle at the end of diastole during which the artery is closed by the cuff pressure. The sound is thus interrupted by a brief period of silence between each cycle and becomes "staccato." As soon as the cuff pressure falls below the diastolic pressure, the artery presumably will remain open throughout the cardiac cycle, and the periodic interruption of the sounds will disappear. The sounds then become continuous instead of staccato. Comparison of arterial pressures measured by direct catheterization and manometers with those obtained by the indirect cuff method[18] has verified this theoretical prediction that muffling rather than disappearance of sound is the best criterion of diastolic pressure.

Kinetic Energy of Flow; Side and End Pressures. A fluid in motion possesses kinetic energy. Reckoned per unit volume (milliliter) of fluid, kinetic energy is very easily calculated as $1/2 \times$ density $\times$ velocity squared. If the velocity is in centimeters per second, this calculation will give the kinetic energy in ergs per cubic centimeter, which is the same as dynes per square centimeter. Thus the value for kinetic energy has the dimensions of a pressure.

The kinetic energy in a fluid is created from the potential energy, which is the pressure. The principle of Bernouilli, enunciated by this great mathematician in 1726, states that where the velocity of a fluid is greatest, the lateral pressure against the walls is least. A simple demonstration of this is shown in Figure 393. The velocity of the fluid in a tube is greatly increased in the narrow portion, where the cross-sectional area is reduced and where the level of the fluid in the vertical tube (lateral or side pressure) is reduced.

Physiologists, in recording the arterial blood pressure of an animal during an acute experiment, usually sacrifice an artery by cutting across it and tying into it a straight cannula connected to a manometer (Fig. 406). The velocity of blood flow is thus eliminated in the cannula and the kinetic energy of flow is reconverted into pressure. This is an *end pressure*. Alternatively, a T-cannula can be inserted in the artery so that the arterial flow continues and the pressure is measured from the side tube of the T. In this arrangement, the pressure is a *side* or *lateral pressure*, and it will be less than the end pressure in the same artery by an amount equivalent to the kinetic energy of flow, since Bernouilli's principle states that the total energy, i.e., pressure energy plus kinetic energy, must remain a constant.

It is easy to estimate the importance of the kinetic energy factor in the normal circulation. The mean velocity in the aorta for a resting cardiac output (5 liters per minute) is about 20 cm. per second. The kinetic energy per milliliter of blood will then be $1/2 \times 20^2$, or 200 ergs perml., or dynes per cm.[2]. For the usual pulse curve of velocity, the mean kinetic energy (the time mean based on the square of the velocity, rather than on the velocity itself as was the mean above) may then be twice this value, i.e., 400 dynes per cm.[2]. Since 1330 dynes per cm.[2] equals a pressure of 1 mm. Hg (see p. 644), this is a very small value indeed, being only about 0.3 mm. Hg for the mean difference between the side pressure and the end pressure in the aorta. However, in the ejection period of systole, the velocity may be three times the mean, and the kinetic energy will be nine times as great, i.e., about 3 mm. Hg. This value agrees with the experimentally

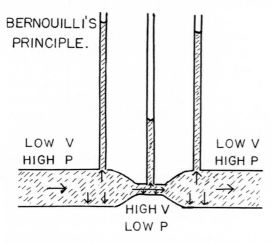

BERNOUILLI'S
PRINCIPLE.

LOW V
HIGH P

LOW V
HIGH P

HIGH V
LOW P

FIG. 393.   Principle of Bernouilli. Velocity (V) is increased in narrow portion of tube, and side pressure (P) is correspondingly reduced.

measured difference between the pressure in the right ventricle (where there is no appreciable kinetic energy) and that at the same instant in the aorta (where kinetic energy is present and must have been created at the expense of pressure.)

It is concluded, then, that in the "resting" subject the kinetic energy factor in the total work of the heart (the difference between the side and end pressures in the aorta) is not very great (3 per cent). However, during heavy exercise, when the cardiac output may be five times the resting level and the velocity in the aorta correspondingly greater, the kinetic energy factor would be 25 times (5^2) this value, i.e., as great as 75 mm. Hg. In these circumstances the kinetic energy created becomes an important part of the total work of the heart, possibly as much as 30 per cent.

In arteries other than the aorta, and in the smaller vessels, the velocity of flow is much less and the kinetic energy factor is completely negligible in normal physiology. For example, the velocity in the capillaries is of the order of 1 mm. per second. The kinetic energy of capillary flow is then $1/2 \times 1 \times 0.1^2$ dynes per cm.[2], which is equivalent to about .0004 mm. Hg, and certainly of no significance at all.

In diseased arteries, however, Bernouilli's principle and the difference between the side and end pressures may become very important. If an atherosclerotic plaque narrows the lumen of, say, a coronary artery (stenosis), the velocity of flow will correspondingly increase through the narrowed portion. The velocity of flow in a main coronary artery is such that the kinetic energy is equivalent to only 0.1 mm. Hg pressure. If, however, the diameter of the lumen is only one-fifth of normal, the cross-sectional area will be 25 times smaller; and if the total resistance to flow in the coronary circuit is still not seriously increased, the velocity of flow will be increased 25 times. Since kinetic energy depends on the square of the velocity, this energy will be increased by a factor of 25^2, or 625 times. Thus the kinetic energy of flow through the stenotic vessel will amount to 62.5 mm. Hg, and the side pressure will be 62.5 mm. less than the end pressure.

The side pressure available to resist further stenosis is greatly reduced, in accordance with Bernouilli's principle, as the lumen narrows. Thus there is an instability in arteries so that narrowing of their lumina tends to persist. If the cross-sectional area is reduced sufficiently, the side pressure may be reduced below zero (atmospheric pressure), as in the laboratory "filter pump," so there is nothing to prevent complete closure of the lumen. However, closure will reduce the flow to zero. The side pressure will then rise to equal the end pressure, and the vessel will open once more.

This sequence of events is the basis of *flutter* in a distensible tube through which a fluid is driven rapidly. Flutter is the basis of the noise produced in all reed instruments, such as the oboe, and in instruments depending on vibrations of the lips, for example, the bugle. The most familiar demonstration of the principle of Bernouilli is perhaps the "sucking in" of the shower curtains when the water is fully turned on.

SUMMARY. The kinetic energy of the flow of blood is not of great importance in the work of the heart with a "resting" cardiac output, except at the height of systole. Kinetic energy becomes important when the cardiac output and work are increased by heavy exercise. The importance of the kinetic energy of blood is slight in normal distributing arteries and quite negligible in smaller vessels. However, kinetic energy becomes exceedingly important when local narrowing of arteries occurs, as in atherosclerosis, since it tends to make such narrowing persist by lowering the side pressure.

Pressure-Flow Relations in Vascular Beds; Distensibility of Blood Vessels. The Poiseuille-Hagen law (see p. 649) for flow of a Newtonian fluid through rigid tubes predicts that flow is proportional to the driving pressure. Accordingly a plot of flow versus driving pressure is linear. If the geometric factor is reduced (radius decreased or length increased), the slope of the straight line on the graph is correspondingly less. Because of this linearity, it is convenient to define *resistance to flow* as the ratio of the driving force to the flow that results. Thus from Poiseuille's equation comes:

$$\text{Res} = \frac{P_A - P_B}{F} \times \left(\frac{8}{\pi}\right) \times \eta \times \left(\frac{1}{R^4}\right) \tag{6}$$

For Newtonian fluids in rigid tubes the resistance is constant at a given temperature because the viscosity factor in the equation is independent of the pressure or the rate of flow. Likewise, in rigid tubes the geometric factor is independent of pressure or flow.

When we turn to actual flow-pressure curves, experimentally determined in an isolated vascular bed, they often are very far from linear. For example, Girling[11] (Fig. 394) measured the flow-pressure curves in the ears and legs of rabbits when their sympathetic vasoconstrictor nerves were stimulated electrically at different frequencies to cause different degrees of constriction of the arterioles. At zero level of stimulation, the vessels were dilated, and the flow-pressure relation was almost a straight line; when the constriction was moderate, the curves were sigmoid. When the constriction was very great, the flow fell rapidly as pressure was reduced and became zero, even though there was still a considerable driving pressure. This point at which there is no flow has been called the *zero flow pressure* or the *critical closing pressure*, the latter term being used because at this point the small vessels have closed completely (i.e., the resistance is infinite). A feature of the curves is that at sufficiently high pressures, considerably greater than the

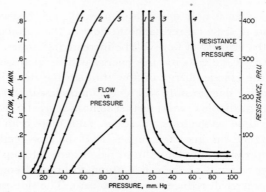

FIG. 394. Flow-pressure curves in rabbit ear (*left*) and resistance-pressure curves deduced from them (*right*). For a Newtonian fluid in rigid tubes, flow-pressure curves would be straight lines through origin and resistance-pressure curves horizontal lines. Curves *1* to *4* represent increasing vasomotor tone produced by electrical stimulation of sympathetic nerves at increasing frequencies from 0.5 to 20 impulses per second.

critical closing pressure, the flow tends to become proportional to the driving pressure; i.e., the resistance reaches a constant value (Fig. 394). All the data on flow-pressure curves obtained by various investigators yield relations between resistance to flow and pressure similar to those shown in Figure 394, although for reasons which need not be given the resistance often does not become infinite.

REASONS FOR SHAPE OF ACTUAL FLOW-PRESSURE CURVES IN VASCULAR BEDS. There has been much controversy over the explanation of the peculiar shape of the flow-pressure curves for vascular beds. Some have attributed it entirely to the anomalous, non-Newtonian, viscous behavior of blood; others entirely to the fact that blood vessels are distensible, causing the geometric factor of Poiseuille's law (R^4/l) to change with the pressure. It is important to note that it is not primarily the driving pressure (arterial pressure minus venous pressure) that determines the size of the distensible vessels but rather the *transmural pressure*, the difference between the intravascular pressure in a given vessel and the pressure outside its wall (tissue pressure, etc.). It now appears quite certain[3] that, although anomalous viscosity of blood plays a role at very low rates of flow, the factor of overwhelming importance is the distensibility of the blood vessels. Two facts attest to this:

(i) If the anomalous viscosity of blood were responsible, blood flow in rigid tubes should show similar nonlinear curves. In fact, the nonlinearity is very slight and only at very low flows (Fig. 390); there is no trace of zero flow or critical closing pressure in these circumstances.

(ii) Again, if anomalous viscosity were responsible, we would expect the flow-pressure curves for vascular beds perfused with Ringer's solution (which is a Newtonian fluid) to be linear. In fact, the shapes of the curves for blood and saline are very similar (Fig. 394), although the absolute viscosity of Ringer's solution is much less and flows are greater.

The zero flow pressure cannot be attributed to "slip," as seen with some plastic fluids, since blood exhibits no sign of such behavior. The explanation, not only of the critical closing pressure but also of the peculiar shape of the curves, is to be found in an analysis of the *equilibrium of the forces acting on the walls of the distensible blood vessels*.

EQUILIBRIUM OF THE BLOOD VESSEL WALL. The key to this analysis,[3] and to an understanding of tension and pressure in hollow organs in general, is the *Law of Laplace*.* The distinction and relations between pressure and tension are often poorly understood,

* This law was first stated by the Marquis de Laplace, French mathematician and physicist, in his *Mécanique céleste* about 1820.

and the words are used interchangeably. In some instances, as in bladder physiology, this habit has greatly retarded the advance of knowledge.

The law of Laplace will be familiar as applying to soap bubbles. In a curved membrane like the cylindrical wall of a blood vessel, the tension (T) can be thought of as the dynes per centimeter of the length of an imaginary slit in the membrane. The pressure inside the membrane must exceed the pressure outside by an amount that depends on this tension and on the shape of the membrane. The shape is characterized for each point on the membrane by two *principal radii of curvature*, R_1 and R_2, in centimeters. The law of Laplace is that this difference of pressure (P), which is best called the *transmural pressure*, is given by the equation:

$$P = T(1/R_1 + 1/R_2) \tag{7}$$

For a cylindrical membrane, as in blood vessels, one radius of curvature (that is in the longitudinal plane) is zero and the other is the radius of the cylinder; the formula thus becomes (see Fig. 395):

$$P = T/R \tag{8}$$

For a sphere, $R_1 = R_2$ and $P = 2T/R$, the formula used for soap bubbles. Equation 8 enables us to calculate the total tension in the walls of different categories of blood vessels from the physiologic mean values of the pressures in them and their histologically determined radii (Table 17).

The tension varies from 200,000 dynes per cm. (about 200 grams per cm.) for the aorta to only 14 dynes per cm. (14 mg. per cm.) for the capillaries. We see that the very thin walled capillary is able to withstand the capillary blood pressure because its radius of curvature is so very small. (A single layer of facial tissue paper will withstand about 50 grams per cm. before tearing, 3000 times as great a force as the capillary is called upon to withstand.) As the radius increases from capillaries to veins, the total tension in the wall increases, even though the blood pressure is reduced. This explains the presence and amount of elastic tissue in the walls of the various vessels. This elastic tissue maintains, without any expenditure of energy, a tension in the wall to balance

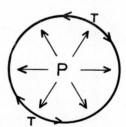

FIG. 395. Diagram of forces operating in equilibrium of wall of cylindrical vessel. Tension (*T*) is in dynes per cm. of length of vessel, pressure (*P*) in dynes per cm.², and radius (*R*) in cm.

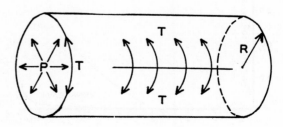

TABLE 17. APPLICATION TO BLOOD VESSELS OF PRESSURE-CURVATURE-TENSION RELATION (T = PR)

TYPE OF VESSEL	MEAN INTERNAL PRESSURE (mm.Hg)	(dynes per cm.²)	RADIUS (R)	TENSION (T) IN WALL (dynes per cm.)	AMOUNT OF ELASTIC TISSUE
Aorta and large arteries	100	1.3×10^5	1.3 cm. or less	170,000	Very elastic, two coats
Small distrib-uting arteries	90	1.2×10^5	0.5 cm.	60,000	Much elastic tissue but more muscular
Arterioles	60	8×10^4	0.15 mm. -62μ	1200–500	Thin elastic intima only
Capillaries	30	4×10^4	4μ	16	None
Venules	20	2.6×10^4	10μ	26	None except in largest
Veins	15	2×10^4	200μ or more	400	Elastic fibers reappear
Vena cava	10	1.3×10^4	1.6 cm.	21,000	Very elastic, fibers increasing in size

the distending force of the blood pressure. The contraction of the smooth muscle of the wall, to control the flow, requires a continuous expenditure of energy.

The law of Laplace enables us to transform data on the distensibility of blood vessels into *tension-length diagrams* for the wall (Fig. 396). For arteries and veins, and for arterioles as deduced from resistance-pressure curves, such elastic diagrams of all blood vessels have a common feature, which was noted long ago by Roy.[19] *As the wall is stretched it resists, not proportionately to each stretch but more and more strongly at each additional stretch.* This feature is absent in such simple elastic systems as a rubber band or a steel wire. These obey Hooke's law; i.e., they give a straight line in the tension-length diagram until, at high degrees of stretch, they yield and the curve is downward, not upward as in Figure 396*B*.

The peculiar elastic behavior of blood vessels has recently been shown to result from the combination of elastin and collagen fibers in the wall. The elastin fibers are

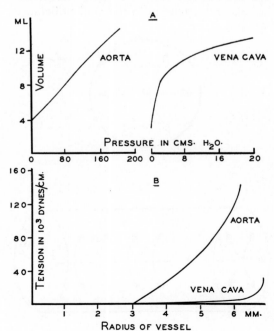

FIG. 396. *A*, Volume-pressure curves for human aorta and vena cava (after Green). *B*, Tension-length diagram derived from curves in *A* by use of law of Laplace.

brought into action by a very slight stretching of the wall, and the much less extensible collagen fibers do not reach their unstretched length until the vessel is considerably distended.[4, 17] The collagen fibers form a protective limiting "jacket." A similar structure of rubber with a canvas jacket is used in garden hose.

Figure 397 shows how, from such a tension-length diagram for the wall of a blood vessel, we can predict the size of the lumen for different transmural pressures when only elastic tension is present. The value for the size must be at the intersection (A) of the straight line representing the Laplacian law ($T = PR$) and a curve for the elastic tension of the typical shape for blood vessels. If the pressure is reduced, the Laplacian line has

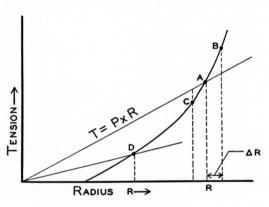

FIG. 397. Diagram to show that radius of a vessel under a given transmural pressure can be deduced from tension-length diagram. (From Burton. *Amer. J. Physiol.*, 1951, *164:* 319–329.)

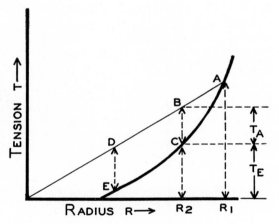

FIG. 398. Same as Figure 397 with active tension from contraction of smooth muscle added. (From Burton. *Amer. J. Physiol.*, 1951, *164:*319–329.)

a reduced slope and the point of intersection moves to a smaller radius, corresponding to point D. Thus the equilibrium, under *pressure* and *elastic tension alone*, is completely stable. If the vessel should increase in radius from A to B, the elastic tension would exceed that required for equilibrium of external and internal pressure and would return the radius to its original value. Similarly, if the vessel grew smaller, the forces would return it to equilibrium.

We now suppose that the contraction of the smooth muscle in the wall has added an *active tension* to the elastic tension produced by the stretch (Fig. 398) and that, as a result, the radius of the vessel has decreased (R_1 to R_2). The total tension BR_2 must be given by the Laplacian line for this new radius. The elastic tension has decreased to CR_2. The active tension must then have been equal to the remainder ($B - C$). Thus we can see how much active tension is required to reduce the radius of the vessel by different amounts. Inspection of the diagram and a little thought will lead to the conclusion that a certain active tension is required to reduce the vessel to near the unstretched condition (DE) and, paradoxically, that no more (actually even less) is required to reduce the radius to zero and cause a complete closure of the vessel, unless new forces prevent this.

Thus there is a fundamental instability in the equilibrium of a cylindrical blood vessel in which the smooth muscle supplies an active tension, i.e., a tension which persists even though the elastic fibers are no longer stretched. Elastic fibers have the important function of making possible a limited stability, but when the vessel wall is unstretched, complete instability appears once more. Blood vessels such as the glomus bodies of arteriovenous anastomoses, which are without elastic tissue, and other structures which have very little, such as the sphincters of the gastrointestinal tract, must be unstable. Typically, such structures are either open or closed and cannot maintain an intermediate size of lumen. The elastic tissue in the wall of a blood vessel is necessary for the stability of its equilibrium under vasomotor tone.

Such reasoning led to an explanation of *critical closing pressure*. For a given degree of vasomotor tone, produced by vasomotor nerves or by pressor drugs, the arterioles in some vascular beds close if their transmural pressure falls below a critical value. Experimentally, critical closing pressures in vascular beds have been found to vary from a minimum of a few millimeters of mercury to a maximum which, in "spasm" of the blood vessels, may greatly exceed the available blood pressure.[6, 10, 14] The same physical analysis, based on the typical shape (Fig. 396) of the tension-length diagram for blood vessel walls, can explain the variety of shapes of flow-pressure curves found in vascular beds. Only a very small degree of distensibility of the resistance vessels (i.e., the arterioles and capillaries) is required to explain the marked nonlinearity of these curves.

There is no doubt regarding the existence of this fundamental limitation of the stability of cylindrical blood vessels under vasomotor tone. Many factors may obscure "critical closure" in vascular beds. While many arterioles may close completely if the transmural pressure is sufficiently reduced, as long as some channels remain open the total blood flow will not be reduced to zero. In many vascular beds, like those in muscle, local mechanisms (reactive hyperemia) lead to vasodilatation if the supply of blood and oxygen is reduced, so that the tendency to close is reduced or absent as the pressure is lowered. Enzymes in the walls of vessels (e.g., amine oxidase) destroy some physiologic pressor agents like norepinephrine. As the flow is reduced, destruction catches up with the supply of the hormone and, again, critical closure will not be achieved. It is astonishing that, in spite of all these factors, actual zero flow pressures have been found in several vascular beds. The importance of the theory lies in its explanation of the rapid rise of resistance if the blood pressure is reduced, so that flow-pressure curves are very nonlinear. A consequence is, as Girling[11] pointed out, that the maintenance of the normal levels of blood pressure is given a new importance. For example, a given degree of vasomotor tone, i.e., a certain number of nerve impulses per minute in sympathetic vasoconstrictor nerves has a much more drastic effect in reducing peripheral blood flow when the blood pressure is low (as in hypotensive shock) than when it is normal.

THE TWO "HEMODYNAMIC PRESSURES." In summary it should be emphasized that *in hemodynamics there are two important pressures.* The first is the *driving pressure*, the difference between the arterial and venous pressures across any part of a vascular bed. The driving pressure primarily governs flow. The second is the *transmural pressure*, particularly of those vessels that supply the major resistance to flow, such as the arterioles. Since the vessels are distensible, the transmural pressure will affect the geometric factor in Poiseuille's law and change the resistance to flow.

Thus, strictly speaking, we cannot think of a single relation between flow and pressure in any vascular bed, but must recognize a whole family of such curves according to the level of the transmural pressures. For instance, if the arterial and venous pressures are raised equally so that their difference (the driving pressure) is the same, the flow will increase because the raised transmural pressure will, owing to the stretching of elastic tissue, "passively" increase the lumina of the small vessels. Similarly if, as is usual in perfusion experiments or in the body, the arterial pressure is increased while the venous pressure remains constant, the transmural pressure in the arterioles, which will be approximately halfway between that in the artery and that in the veins, will be altered. The nonlinear nature of the flow-pressure curves we obtain is mainly due to this change in the transmural pressure (and hence the size) of the arterioles as the arterial pressure is altered.

Use of Resistance to Flow. The several complications have made physiologists reluctant to use the concept of resistance to flow to its full advantage. However, once it is recognized that, universally, the distensibility of the vessels always results in a passive decrease in resistance when transmural pressure falls, and vice versa, interpretation of changes in resistance is usually possible. Suppose that measurements of the driving pressure and flow in, say, a limb show increased resistance. Is this increase indicative of active vasoconstriction (an increase in vasomotor tone), or is the mechanism passive (a result of the distensibility of the vessels)? Usually in such cases (as with a pressor drug) the pressure has either risen or remained constant. An increase in transmural pressure would "passively" tend to increase the luminal diameter of the vessels and so decrease the

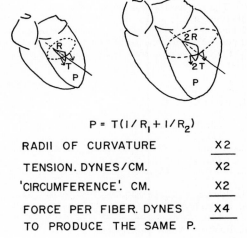

FIG. 399.   Application of law of Laplace to heart showing that, if linear dimensions of heart are doubled, ventricular muscle must produce a tension four times greater to secure same systolic pressure. (From Burton. *Amer. Heart J.*, 1957, *54*:801–810.)

$$P = T(1/R_1 + 1/R_2)$$

RADII OF CURVATURE	X2
TENSION. DYNES/CM.	X2
'CIRCUMFERENCE'. CM.	X2
FORCE PER FIBER. DYNES TO PRODUCE THE SAME P.	X4

resistance. The actual increase in resistance must have been, therefore, "active" vasoconstriction. If, however, the pressure has fallen, an interpretation could not be made without detailed knowledge of the curve of resistance versus transmural pressure for that particular vascular bed (e.g., as in Fig. 394). More often than not, there is no uncertainty in the interpretation.

Laplace's Law and the Heart.   In 1892, Woods,[26] a throat surgeon of the Dublin Children's Hospital, demonstrated that the law of Laplace applied to the heart: that the pressure produced in the ventricles depends not only on the tension developed by the cardiac ventricular muscle in contraction, but also on the size and shape of the heart (i.e., the principal radii of curvature). It is now realized that the load on the heart, which governs its requirement for oxygen, depends mainly on the tension that must be developed in the ventricular muscle and the time this tension is maintained,[5] and very little upon the external work of pumping by the heart. Thus if the heart is dilated, as in heart failure, the heart muscle is at a mechanical disadvantage. If the diameter of the heart is doubled, the radii of curvature are doubled, and the tension per unit length of ventricular wall must be twice as great to produce the same systolic blood pressure (Fig. 399). In effect, the total tension of the muscle is quadrupled. Thus *any increase in the size of the heart increases the load of the heart.* Similarly *increases in heart rate* increase the tension-time integral of the heart muscle, since the time of each contraction is not correspondingly shortened and the speeding up is at the expense of diastole. Also, *increases in blood pressure* impose a great load on the heart since, by the law of Laplace, the tension required is proportional to the pressure. Thus the classic law of Laplace is very important in cardiac management, for it predicts that excitement, which raises the heart rate and blood pressure, may impose a much greater strain on the heart than does mild exercise. A round of golf may be far less dangerous to a cardiac patient than an angry argument with his wife.

EXTERNAL WORK AND EFFICIENCY OF THE HEART. Work done is force times distance moved. For a fluid propelled by pressure, this formula becomes pressure times volume moved. As the pressure in the ventricle changes greatly throughout the ejection period of the cardiac cycle, we must integrate. The work done is $\int P_v \cdot do$, the integral of the pressure with respect to the output. This integral can be evaluated directly if we have a plot of ventricular pressure versus ventricular volume, as Rushmer determines these.[20] However, physiologists more often use the aortic pressure (P_A) than the ventricular pressure (P_v). In this case the kinetic energy factor, $1/2\rho V^2$, must be added; i.e., work $= \int (P_A + 1/2\rho V^2)do$. It has become the practice to use a mean pressure times the output instead of the true integral, but the mean should be a mean with respect to the output, not the usual mean with respect to time. Such approximate calculation of the work of the heart can be very inaccurate, and since the external work has little physiologic importance in the total load on the heart, they would seem hardly worth the effort.

The mechanical efficiency of the heart is defined as the external work done divided by the total energy exchange, which is the sum of the external work and the tension-time integral. Measurements of the efficiency of the heart in heart-lung preparations have shown that it is very low, usually less than 10 per cent. This reflects the fact that of the two terms the tension-time integral is by far the greater. For the same reason, the efficiency increases markedly as the amount of external work is increased.

REFERENCES

1. BAYLISS, L. E. Chap. 6 in *Deformation and flow in biological systems*, A. FREY-WYSSLING, ed. Amsterdam, North Holland Publishing Co., 1952.
2. BINGHAM, E. G. and ROEPKE, R. R. *J. gen. Physiol.*, 1944, *28*:79–83.
3. BURTON, A. C. *Amer. J. Physiol.*, 1951, *164*: 319–329.
4. BURTON, A. C. *Physiol. Rev.*, 1954, *34*:619–642.
5. BURTON, A. C. *Amer. Heart J.*, 1957, *54*:801–810.
6. BURTON, A. C. and YAMADA, S. I. *J. appl. Physiol.*, 1951, *4*:329–339.
7. COULTER, N. A., JR. and PAPPENHEIMER, J. R. *Amer. J. Physiol.*, 1949, *159*:401–408.
8. DIX, F. J. and SCOTT-BLAIR, G. W. *J. appl. Phys.*, 1940, *11*:574–581.
9. FAHRAEUS, R. and LINDQVIST, T. *Amer. J. Physiol.*, 1931, *96*:562–568.
10. GIBSON, J. C., SELIGMAN, A. M., PEACOCK, W. C., AUB, J. C., FINE, J. and EVANS, R. D. *J. clin. Invest.*, 1946, *25*:848–857.
11. GIRLING, F. *Amer. J. Physiol.*, 1952, *170*:131–135.
12. HAYNES, R. H. *The rheology of blood*. Ph.D. Thesis, University of Western Ontario, 1957. See also, HAYNES, R. H. and BURTON, A. C. *Proc. 1st nat. Biophys. Conf.*, 1959, p. 452; *Amer. J. Physiol.*, 1959, *197*:943–950.
13. MÜLLER, A. *Arch. Kreislaufforsch.*, 1941, *8*: 245–282.
14. NICHOL, J., GIRLING, F., CLAXTON, E. B. and BURTON, A. C. *Amer. J. Physiol.*, 1951, *164*:330–344.
15. PAPPENHEIMER, J. R. and KINTER, W. B. *Amer. J. Physiol.*, 1956, *185*:377–390.
16. REYNOLDS, O. *Phil. Trans.*, 1883, *174*:935–982.
17. ROACH, M. R. and BURTON, A. C. *Canad. J. Biochem. Physiol.*, 1957, *35*:681–690.
18. ROBERTS, L. N., SMILEY, J. R. and MANNING, G. W. *Circulation*, 1953, *8*:232–242.
19. ROY, C. S. *J. Physiol.*, 1880–1882, *3*:125–159.
20. RUSHMER, R. F. *Cardiac diagnosis, a physiologic approach.* Philadelphia, W. B. Saunders Co., 1955, viii, 447 pp.
21. STARKEY, T. V. *Brit. J. appl. Phys.*, 1955, *6*:34–37.
22. STARKEY, T. V. *Brit. J. appl. Phys.*, 1956, *7*:52–55.
23. STARKEY, T. V. *Brit. J. appl. Phys.*, 1956, *7*:448–449.
24. THOMA, R. *Abderhalden's Handb. biol. Arbeitsmeth.*, Abt. 5, 1928, *4*(2):1103–1258.
25. WHITTAKER, S. R. F. and WINTON, F. R. *J. Physiol.*, 1933, *78*:339–369.
26. WOODS, R. H. *J. Anat. (Lond.)*, 1892, *26*: 362–370.

CHAPTER 30

The Pressure Gradient and Pulse in the Vascular System

By DONALD H. BARRON

ESTABLISHMENT OF PRESSURE GRADIENT

THE movement of the blood through the capillaries of the systemic and pulmonary circuits is a consequence of a fluid pressure gradient established by the pumping action of the heart. In transferring blood from the venous to the arterial ends of these two circuits the heart functions to reduce the pressure in the veins and to increase it in the arteries, thus maintaining the circulation. The pressure at the venous ends of the two circuits is about zero; at the arterial end of the systemic circuit in man at rest the pressure varies between about 80 mm. Hg at the end of diastole to 120 mm. in systole. The corresponding pressures in the pulmonary artery are much lower, i.e., about 10 and 27 mm. Hg, respectively.

With each contraction the heart projects the contents of its ventricles into the connected vessels, which—together with their larger tributaries—may be regarded as elastic reservoirs or "pressure tanks" guarded at their central ends by the semilunar valves and restricted peripherally by the arterioles (Fig. 400). The arterioles control, by their diameter and by the number of them patent, the rate at which blood escapes from the "pressure tank" into the capillaries. Normally, the volume of blood in the reservoir, be it the aortic or the pulmonary, exceeds its capacity in the relaxed state; that is to say, the walls are normally distended by the enclosed blood. Since the walls are rich in elastic tissue which tends to recoil when stretched, the blood is constantly under pressure. A comparison of the elasticity of different arteries from the same animal demonstrates that the volume of blood in the pulmonary or the systemic reservoir must exceed its capacity in the relaxed state before a head of pressure can be established. Any increase beyond that volume (or a decrease in the capacity of the reservoir) will result in a rise in pressure due to the elastic recoil of the walls (Figs. 401 and 402). This rise in pressure will be a function

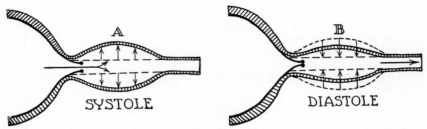

SYSTOLE   DIASTOLE

FIG. 400.   Diagram to illustrate role of elastic walls of aorta in maintenance of circulation. *A*, Walls are distended as ventricular contents enter aorta. *B*, Following closure of aortic valves, elastic recoil of walls drives blood peripherally. Elastic walls serve to store energy during systole and to release it during diastole. (After Rein.)

of the extensibility of the system—the elasticity of its walls. For example, the pressure rise for the same increase in content will be much less in the pulmonary reservoir than in the systemic.

Given the requisite initial content for the establishment of a head of pressure, the volume of blood in the arterial reservoir and the pressure on it will depend upon two variables: (i) the rate at which blood is driven into the reservoir by the ventricle and (ii) the rate at which blood escapes through the arterioles. The rate at which blood enters varies during each cardiac cycle, rising during the early part of systole to decline in the late part and to cease in diastole. Over a longer period, the rate of filling will be determined by the stroke volume and the heart rate.

In contrast with the intermittent manner in which blood enters the arterial reservoir, its escape continues during the whole of the cardiac cycle. This conversion of intermittent to continuous flow is a result of the recoil of the elastic arteries. The walls store and release energy liberated by the ventricle. During diastole they release this energy as the blood is squeezed through the arterioles by the force of their recoil. The volume of blood leaving the reservoir per unit time depends upon the relative magnitude of two factors: (i) the force of the recoil of the walls of the reservoir, tending to drive the blood toward the periphery, and (ii) the resistance offered by the arterioles to the viscous blood. When

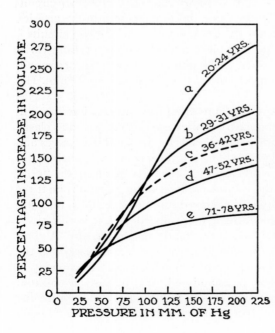

FIG. 401.   Effect of age on percentage increase in volume of isolated human thoracic aortas, obtained at autopsy, for varying pressure. Note that elasticity decreases as age advances but is fairly constant in physiologic pressure range. Curves pass through almost the same elasticity point in this region. (After Hallock and Benson, *J. clin. Invest.*, 1937, *16*:595–602.)

the ventricle, arteries and arterioles are functioning in dynamic equilibrium, the cardiac output and the rate of escape will vary about a mean in each cardiac cycle, as will the volume of blood in the reservoir and the pressure on it.

Soon after the isometric phase of ventricular contraction, the stroke or pulse volume is injected into the arterial reservoir. As the walls of the reservoir are already distended with blood under pressure—the diastolic pressure—before the ventricular ejection begins, the added blood can be accommodated either by the movement of an equivalent volume (in the same interval) peripherad through the arterioles, or by an increase in the content of the reservoir and a concomitant rise in the pressure within it. The proportions of blood accommodated by storage and displacement depend respectively upon the relative force required to overcome the resistance of the arterioles and that required to increase the capacity of the reservoir. The greater the degree of arterial rigidity—be it the consequence of an increased volume of blood in the reservoir or of changes associated with advancing age—the smaller is the volume of blood that can be accommodated and the greater the proportion of the energy of ventricular contraction utilized directly in imparting velocity to the blood. In normal circumstances this proportion may be less than 1 per cent of the total energy of ventricular contraction, although it may be as high as 9 per cent and, in quite abnormal circumstances, as much as 30 per cent.

During the maximum ejection phase of ventricular contraction, blood enters the reservoir more rapidly than it escapes through the arterioles. As a consequence, the volume of blood in the reservoir increases, potential energy is stored in its walls, and the blood pressure rises to a maximum—the systolic pressure. At this point in the cardiac cycle the rate at which blood enters the reservoir is equal to the rate of escape. During the second portion of the ejection phase, the rate of arteriolar drainage exceeds that at which blood enters the reservoir. The volume of blood in the reservoir and the pressure on it continue to fall to reach a minimum—the diastolic pressure—preceding the opening of the semilunar valves in the succeeding cardiac cycle.

This series of events is repeated with each cardiac cycle, and in a system in functional

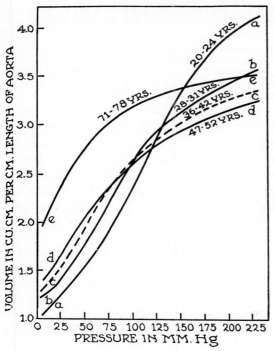

FIG. 402. Effect of increased volume of aorta with advancing age on capacity of aorta to store blood between heart beats in order to convert pulsatile pressure into steady pressure. In physiologic pressure range, increasing aortic rigidity caused by age (Fig. 401) is offset to a considerable extent by concomitant dilatation. (After Hallock and Benson, *J. clin Invest.*, 1937, *16*:595–602.)

equilibrium the peripheral resistance, the volume of blood in the reservoir and the cardiac output are so related that a quantity of blood equal to the stroke volume escapes into the capillaries in each cycle. Any alteration in the peripheral resistance, the stroke volume or the heart rate temporarily disturbs this balance between the input and output and, as a consequence, the volume of blood and the pressure in the reservoir are shifted from their mean values. Attention may now be directed to the circumstances by which the balance between input and output following such an alteration is re-established.

Consider the changes in blood volume and pressure in the reservoir of a system in equilibrium having a heart rate of 75 beats per minute and a stroke volume of 60 ml. The rate of escape into the capillaries is assumed to be constant during the entire cycle, i.e., 15 ml. escapes during systole and 45 ml. during diastole. If now the peripheral

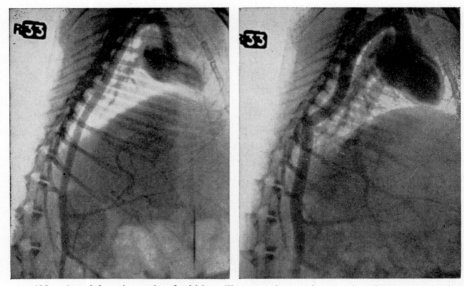

FIG. 403. Arterial angiographs of rabbit to illustrate changes in capacity of great arteries (arterial reservoir) resulting from a great increase in peripheral resistance. Constriction of arterioles resulted from intravenous injection of large dose of epinephrine. Circumstances are exaggerated, not "normal." Second film, made 4 seconds after first, shows dilatation of heart and increase in length and caliber of thoracic and upper abdominal segments of aorta. (From Trueta *et al.*, *Studies of the renal circulation.* Oxford, Blackwell Scientific Publications; Springfield, Ill., Charles C Thomas, 1947.)

resistance is suddenly increased while all other factors remain the same, the rate of out-flow will be diminished. At the end of the succeeding cycle (Fig. 403) less blood will have escaped from the reservoir than entered it, and the diastolic pressure and arterial volumes will be correspondingly elevated. Blood will continue to accumulate in the arteries in diminishing amounts with each succeeding cardiac cycle until their walls are stretched to such a degree that the force of the recoil is sufficient to offset the increased peripheral resistance to blood flow and the system is again in pressure-volume equilibrium at a new but higher level.

In this equilibrium the distensibility of the walls of the arteries for equal pressure increments is diminished. Hence, greater force is required to stretch their walls during systole to accommodate the ventricular contents. As a consequence, more of the energy of ventricular contraction is utilized directly in moving the column of blood in the reservoir peripherad, i.e., in kinetic energy of fluid flow. Accordingly, the velocity of flow is increased and a greater volume of blood leaves the arteries for the capillaries during systole—20 ml. as compared with 15 ml. in the illustrations given. Furthermore, less blood is released during diastole; 40 ml. as compared with 45 ml. are squeezed through arterioles by the elastic tissue during diastole. In short, an increase in peripheral resistance has been balanced by an increase in the mean volume of blood in the reservoir, a concomitant rise in diastolic pressure and arterial rigidity, and a smaller rise in systolic pressure.

Similarly, an increase in heart rate and stroke volume—other factors remaining the same—results in an elevation in the mean volume of blood in the reservoir with a concomitant rise of diastolic and systolic pressures. The increase in the volume of blood in the reservoir is, in this circumstance, a consequence of the decrease in the length of the cardiac cycle and the reduction in the period of diastolic drainage. Blood accumulates in the reservoir in diminishing increments with each beat after the rate increase until, as in the example above, the walls of the reservoir are so distended that their mean resistance to further distention is such that the blood entering during ventricular systole initiates an elastic recoil of the walls which drives the accumulated volume into the capillaries during the shortened diastolic period. Thus the increase in cardiac output is balanced by an elevation of the diastolic volume and pressure, a lesser rise in systolic pressure, and an increase in the velocity of the blood flow. These changes combine to augment the rate of blood flow into the capillaries.

An increase in stroke volume from 60 ml. to, say, about 70 ml., other circumstances remaining the same, also results in an accumulation of blood in the arterial reservoir in decreasing increments with each beat following the change, for the rate of inflow temporarily exceeds the rate of escape into the capillaries. If, however, the initial diastolic volume and pressure are low and the reservoir walls possess the normal elasticity, the increases in diastolic volume and pressure due to the augmented stroke volume will be small. With the relatively low diastolic volume, the force required to distend the walls to accommodate the pulse volume is less than that required to overcome the peripheral resistance. As a consequence very little of the energy of ventricular contraction is utilized directly in moving blood peripherad; the remainder serves to distend the reservoir walls and is liberated in diastole. Accordingly, although the rate of outflow from the reservoir is increased during systole from 15 ml. to 17 or 18 ml., the marked increase is in diastole— from 45 ml. to 52 or 53 ml.

Given circumstances in which the elasticity of the arterial walls is reduced through an increase in the diastolic volume or through changes associated with advancing age, the balance between input and output, disturbed initially by an increase in stroke volume, will be restored by another chain of events. As the force required to distend the reservoir rises further, more and more of the energy of contraction will be utilized to increase the velocity of flow. As a consequence, less energy will be stored in the arterial walls and the pulse pressure will be reduced accordingly.

The role of the aorta and its major branches as an elastic reservoir of relatively high pressure is further illustrated by studies of the flow patterns in its several parts at successive stages in the cardiac cycle. In the portion of the rabbit's aorta distal to the renal arteries blood moves distally during the development of systole, at a velocity that increases rapidly to reach a peak of about 60 cm. per second before the maximum systolic pressure is attained. Owing to the inertia of the blood and the elasticity of the aorta, the increase in total flow lags slightly behind the rise in pressure. With the onset of diastole, the movement of the blood in the distal abdominal aorta is reversed; the flow toward the heart may reach a velocity of 25 cm. per second and the total centripetal flow may equal a third of the centrifugal. The period of centripetal flow is followed by a period in which little or no movement is directed distally.

The velocity and magnitude of the centrifugal blood flow during systole, as might be expected, are reduced with increased peripheral resistance; the reverse flow is correspondingly increased. Lowering the peripheral resistance increases the length of the period of centrifugal flow and reduces the period of centripetal flow. The retrograde flow in the distal aorta appears to be associated with the rate of drainage into the celiac, mesenteric and renal arteries, for in the circumstances of the study the blood moved centrifugally in these vessels throughout diastole. Accordingly, the pattern of flow in the distal aorta in any cardiac cycle will reflect the resistance offered by the femoral and visceral vessels, respectively. In other words, during the cardiac cycle the pattern of flow in the several segments of the aorta varies with the magnitude of the resistance offered by each of its major branches and with their angle of origin, as might be expected in an elastic reservoir of small capacity.

Arterioles and Peripheral Resistance. In contrast to the walls of the aortic reservoir, which are elastic and respond passively to internal forces acting on them, the walls of the arterioles are muscular and active. Changes in the length of transversely oriented muscle fibers in the tunica media rapidly and markedly modify the calibers of

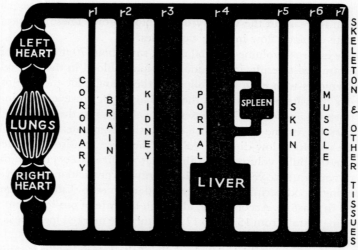

FIG. 404.   Diagram illustrating principal channels (r^1 to r^7) joining arterial and venous sides of systemic system.

these vessels, which join the arterial reservoir and the capillaries. Thus, by acting as variable resistances arranged in parallel between the reservoir and the tissue capillaries, the arterioles regulate the rate at which blood escapes from the great arteries and therefore the volume of blood in them and the pressure on it. On the other side they control the distribution of blood to the tissues and the slope of the pressure gradient between the arteries and the capillaries.

The muscle fibers in the arteriolar walls possess an inherent or basic level of tone that is thought to be determined by blood-borne materials. These fibers are often considered to be the antagonists of the left ventricle, since the ventricle forces blood into the arteries and the arterioles limit its rate of escape. Moreover, the neural control over the heart and certain arterioles exhibits the phenomenon of reciprocal innervation; as these arterioles constrict and the pressure in the aorta rises, the heart rate decreases and the force of the beat lessens. Conversely, arteriolar dilatation and a fall in aortic pressure lead to an increase in heart rate. In addition, the response to neural action and the tone of the arteriolar musculature (and so the caliber of the vessel it invests) are modified by locally produced metabolites and circulating hormones. The details of these regulations are dealt with in Chapter 31.

Another important aspect of the organization of the systemic circuit is its arrangement as a series of parallel channels joining the arterial and venous sides. There are major circuits through the individual organs and regions of the body (Fig. 404) and lesser ones through the tissues themselves; the latter are in turn paralleled by shunts or short circuits, i.e., arteriovenous capillaries and arteriovenous anastomoses. When open, arteriovenous capillaries permit blood to bypass portions of the capillary bed (see Chap. 34), and arteriovenous anastomoses provide an alternative shorter path of low resistance between the arterial and venous sides of the systemic circuit. Thus alterations in the pattern of blood flow may be wrought by changes in the diameter and length of the conducting channels.

The peripheral resistance—the resistance to blood flow in the vascular system—has been defined as the ratio of the driving force or pressure difference between two points in the system and the volume of blood transferred between them per unit time; and the analogy to the resistance in an electrical circuit as described by Ohm's law has been

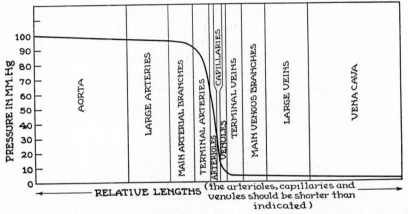

FIG. 405.   Pressure at different anatomic divisions of vascular system in relation to their relative lengths. Notice that most of fall in pressure is arteriolar. (Modified from Green, p. 221, in Glasser, *Medical physics*. Chicago, Year Book Publishers, 1944.)

pointed out. That the larger fraction of this resistance is provided by the smaller vessels, the arterioles and the capillaries, may be inferred from the observation that the pressure on the blood drops very little between the root of the aorta and the points along the great arteries or their smaller branches and, further, that the fall is but slight between the smaller veins and the right atrium. By exclusion the larger portion of the pressure drop must occur across the arterioles and capillaries. As the flow across these small vessels is in the aggregate equal to the cardiac output in the equilibrium state and the pressure drop is large, the resistance must be high. The pressure drop associated with the aggregate of each anatomic unit in the systemic system—the arteries, arterioles, capillaries and veins—is schematically represented in Figure 405.

Actual measurements of the pressure drop along the small vessels—arterioles and capillaries—for technical reasons have been made in only a few parts of the systemic circuit, i.e., in the mesenteric vessels and those of the skin; but the results clearly demonstrate that the greatest drop in pressure along that circuit occurs in its small vessels. In the smaller mesenteric arteries adjacent to the gut the mean pressure on the blood may be only 3 to 4 mm. Hg below that of the aorta. The pressure falls sharply in the mesenteric arterioles—ranging between 25 and 35 mm. Hg at the arteriolar end of the capillaries— and more gradually in the capillary itself. At the venous end the pressure ranges from 10 to 15 mm.; that is to say, something like 55 per cent of the pressure drop occurs in the arterioles and 25 per cent in the capillaries. The remaining 20 per cent of the drop may be assigned to the larger arteries and to the vessels of the portal system and the liver. In the vascular bed of the extremities, between 80 and 85 per cent of the pressure drop between the aorta and the right heart takes place in the arterioles and capillaries.

These proportions and the pressures in the arterioles and capillaries as given are mean values; there are variations along individual circuits owing to the changing state of the small vessels. These variations are of prime importance in the regulation of the pressure head in the aortic reservoir and in the adjustment of the local capillary flow to the metabolic load of the associated tissues. Small changes in the length of the smooth muscle fibers of the arterioles produce quite large variations in the level of the resistance; a reduction of 10 per cent in the length of the individual muscle fibers about an arteriole serves to increase the resistance to flow through it by about 18.5 per cent and reduces the volume of blood escaping into the associated capillaries by approximately one-third. Conversely, dilatation of the arterioles decreases the resistance in that segment and elevates the pressure at the arteriolar end of the capillary; with concomitant capillary dilatation the pressure at the venous end of the capillaries may also rise, but frequently to a lesser degree. That is to say, the total pressure drop across the arterioles, capillaries and venules may remain fairly constant despite variations in the gradient along individual channels, for the factors that regulate the caliber and resistance in each of these segments operate with a degree of independence, and in some circumstances the changes may actually be in opposite directions. For example epinephrine may produce dilatation of capillaries but constriction of arterioles. The importance of variations in the gradient along the capillary in determining the transfer of water between the vascular and extravascular compartments is discussed in Chapter 34.

Local variations in the resistance and flow along individual channels can and do occur without any change in the total peripheral resistance. In such a system of parallel circuits the local variation, if limited in magnitude, can be balanced by oppositely directed changes in other circuits. For the relationship between the total peripheral resistance and that offered by the several individual circuits, see Chapter 29. Compensatory changes in the resistance take place in the circuits through the skin and the viscera; with cooling of the external environment, the flow through the skin may decrease as a compensatory increase occurs in the splanchnic bed. Similarly, a small increase in flow to the skeletal muscle may be accompanied by a decrease in the flow through the splanchnic region without any concomitant change in the cardiac output or mean arterial pressure.

Increased demands such as those associated with heavier muscular exercise may result in a fivefold fall in the total peripheral resistance as the arterioles of the muscles dilate. In these circumstances the pressure head providing the increased blood flow from the arterial reservoir is sustained by an increased cardiac output as well as by a rise in the resistance offered by the parallel circuits leading to organs whose functional needs may be reduced or temporarily suspended.

Thus, through the activity of their circular muscles, the arterioles serve two functions: (i) to change the level of the peripheral resistance and so the blood pressure, and (ii) to regulate the flow of blood to individual organs by local alterations in the resistance along the vessels leading to their capillaries. The manner in which the activities of the arterioles throughout the body are integrated in the performance of these two functions is treated in detail in Chapter 31.

ARTERIAL PRESSURE

Estimated in the resting or preferably the basal state, the pressure on the blood in the great arteries is one of the most instructive indices of the dynamics of the circulation.

As such, this pressure is determined routinely as a part of any complete physical examination and is usually recorded in laboratory experiments on the cardiovascular system. The reasoning relative to the clinical estimation of blood pressure is as follows. Since the prevailing pressure in the right atrium may be taken as zero, the pressure-flow relations in the systemic circuit may be expressed by the equation $P = F \times R$, where P is the pressure in the blood on the arterial reservoir, F is the cardiac output, and R is the peripheral resistance. In the resting or basal state F—since it is determined by the metabolic rate—is minimal. Accordingly, the physician estimates the pressure on the blood in the arterial reservoir as an index of the resistance offered by the arterioles to the blood flow needed to meet the basal metabolic needs of the tissues. In other words, he obtains an index of the heart work necessary to provide that minimal blood flow.

DIRECT METHOD FOR ESTIMATING ARTERIAL BLOOD PRESSURE. The pressure on the blood in the aorta of laboratory animals under experimental conditions is usually meas-

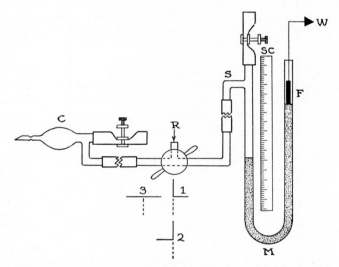

FIG. 406. Recording mercury manometer and its connections. M, Manometer with float (F) and writing point (W). Levels of mercury are read off scale (SC). S, Side tube of manometer, connected by rubber tubing to three-way stopcock at R. R, Reservoir of citrate solution, about 6 feet above level of manometer. Three positions of stopcock are shown: 1, for raising pressure in manometer; 2, for flushing out cannula; and 3, for recording. C, Cannula, connected to stopcock with rubber tubing.

ured directly, i.e., by means of a mercury filled manometer connected through a cannula with the lumen of an artery, carotid or femoral (Fig. 406). The connecting tube leads to a three-way stopcock and thence to the cannula, which is so constructed that small clots can be washed out easily. The tube connecting the arterial cannula with one limb of the U-shaped manometer is filled with an anticoagulant, sodium citrate or bicarbonate. The other limb, open to the air, carries a writing point. The pressure on the blood in the artery tends to displace the mercury in the one limb of the manometer and is opposed by the pressure of the atmosphere on the other. The net displacement, the excess of the arterial pressure over the atmospheric, is indicated by the difference between the heights of the two mercury columns and serves as a measure of the blood pressure in millimeters of mercury. The difference can be read either directly from a scale or from the permanent kymographic record (Fig. 407). To find the height of the column of blood which would be supported by any blood pressure, the pressures recorded in millimeters of mercury must be multiplied by 12.8 since mercury is 12.8 times heavier than blood.

If the manometer is connected with the artery by a T cannula so that the flow in the vessel is not interrupted, the mercury column will be supported by the lateral pressure

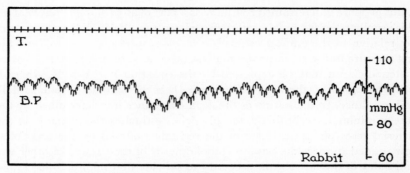

FIG. 407. Typical blood pressure record obtained with mercury manometer. *T*, Time scale; vertical lines are 1 second apart. *B.P.*, Recorded pressure; actual arterial pressure is distance from baseline—line of zero pressure—to trace, multiplied by two. Values for this experiment are given at right. Three influences on blood pressure are indicated. Brief notches, effects of heart beat; longer peaks, effects of respiration; prolonged gradual waves, effects of vasomotor changes. The relative heights of peaks caused by heartbeat and respiration are the reverse of actual relative increases in pressure; owing to inertia, mercury cannot follow completely rapid changes during systole.

on the blood at that point. On the other hand, if the manometer is connected to the artery so that the vessel is occluded, the pressure supporting the mercury column is the "end pressure"—the lateral pressure plus the pressure due to the deceleration of the blood and the transformation of its kinetic energy into potential energy. For the significance of end and lateral pressures, see Chapter 29.

The blood pressure record (Fig. 407) obtained with the mercury manometer connected directly with the arterial lumen usually reveals fluctuations of two patterns: small waves associated with the contraction of the heart and larger variations associated with the respiratory cycle. Because of the inertia of the heavy column of liquid, the waves in records obtained with mercury-filled manometers do not accurately portray the small, rapid variations in blood pressure. Usually the maximum is too low and the minimum is too high; a slowing of the heart may increase the size of each pulse excursion for purely physical reasons. The larger pressure variations are, however, accurately recorded. In fact, the record is usually a good approximation of mean blood pressure (see below). Hence mercury manometers are most useful for recording the considerable variations associated with changes in the rate at which blood leaves the arterial reservoir, i.e., with vasoconstriction and dilatation. Mercury manometers have a number of practical defects (the inconvenience of smoked paper recording, poor portability, entrance of anticoagulants into the blood stream, etc.). For research and teaching purposes, such manometers are being supplanted by penwriters which are activated electrically by strain gauges or other electromechanical transducers.

In circumstances which require accurate records of the rapid fluctuations in pressure associated with the cardiac cycle—the pulse pressure—it is essential to employ manometers with a small moment of inertia. In their essentials manometers of this type consist of a tube, one end of which can be inserted into the artery; the other end is closed by a flexible membrane bearing a mirror. The pressure changes in the vessel deform the membrane, moving the mirror so that it deflects a light beam to a degree which is proportional to the changes in pressure. Permanent records of the deflections may be made by allowing the light beam to fall on a moving strip of photosensitive paper.

INDIRECT OR CLINICAL METHOD FOR ESTIMATING ARTERIAL BLOOD PRESSURE. In this method, the weight of a column of mercury—or other force—required to suppress the pulsations in an artery is employed as a measure of the pressure on the blood. The instrument universally used for the purpose is called a sphygmomanometer (*sphygmos* = pulse), of which there are many different models. Essentially, the instrument (Fig. 408) consists of an inflatable cloth-covered rubber bag (*c*), which fits snugly around the upper arm and is held in position by wrapping an extension of the cloth covering over the bag and about the arm like a bandage. The bag communicates with a mercury manometer (*m*) and can be inflated by a pressure bulb (*b*). On the tube leading from the bulb to the bag there is a needle valve (*v*), which can be opened gradually to allow air to escape and the pressure in the bag to fall.

To estimate the blood pressure by the auscultatory method, the bag is secured in position on the upper arm and the bag pressure is raised to a point well above the systolic blood pressure. The lumen of the vessel is thus completely obliterated. A stethoscope is now applied over the brachial artery just below the lower edge of the bag, and the needle valve is slowly opened to let the pressure in the bag fall. At the moment the pressure in the bag falls to a point at which a pulse wave can break through the compressed artery, a distinct tapping sound is heard through the stethoscope at each pulse beat. The level of the mercury manometer at this moment indicates the systolic pressure. As the pressure in the bag falls, the nature and intensity of the sounds heard in the stethoscope change. The physical reasons for these sounds have already been given (Chapter 29).

In the normal individual, the changes in the sounds heard as the pressure in the manometer falls occur in four phases, known as the *sounds of Korotkow*, after the physician who first described them in 1905. The sounds in the successive phases are described as follows:

Phase 1. Sudden appearance of a clear, sharp, tapping sound, which becomes louder during the first 10 mm. fall in pressure. The reading on the scale at the time of its first appearance corresponds with the *systolic* pressure.

Phase 2. The sound becomes softer, like a murmur, during the next 15 mm. fall in pressure.

Phase 3. The sound becomes louder again during the next 15 mm. fall in pressure.

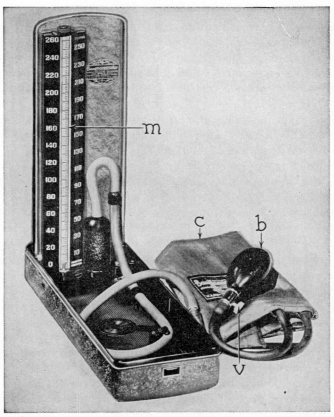

FIG. 408.   Details of modern sphygmomanometer: *m*, mercury column and scale; *b*, pressure bulb; *v*, needle valve; *c*, cuff. (Photograph through courtesy of W. A. Baum Co., Inc., New York.)

Phase 4. The sound suddenly becomes reduced in intensity and develops a muffled quality. The reading on the scale at this time corresponds with the *diastolic* pressure.

If the pressure in the bag is lowered still further, the sounds disappear altogether. There has been considerable discussion as to whether the true diastolic pressure corresponds to the abrupt drop in intensity of the sound in the fourth phase, or to its complete disappearance. The sudden muffling and the complete disappearance may occur at two quite different pressures, in which case the diastolic pressure corresponds to the sudden muffling rather than to the disappearance. It may be remarked that there is little practical value in trying to record the pressures at which each auscultatory phase passes into the next. It is usually sufficient to ascertain the systolic and the diastolic pressures, and these only. The systolic and diastolic pressures are conventionally written as 120/70, 130/90, and so on, the systolic pressure being the first number.

In the palpatory method, the pressure cuff is secured around the upper arm as before, and the bag pressure raised until the radial pulse, as felt at the wrist, is obliterated. The pressure is then slowly lowered by opening the needle valve, and the point at which the radial pulse reappears is taken as the systolic pressure. The method is not exact, and the true systolic pressure is usually 5 to 10 mm. higher than that at which the pulse reappears. Further, the diastolic pressure cannot be measured by the palpatory method. It is standard practice, however, first to find the systolic pressure roughly by the palpatory method, and then to use the stethoscope to determine the systolic and the diastolic pressures.

Pressure on Arterial Blood in Man. The pressure on the blood in the great arteries appears to be maintained at a level that insures a blood flow appropriate to the metabolic demands of the tissues of the body. Thus in essential hypertension, a condition characterized by an abnormally high arterial pressure in persons free from inflammatory kidney disease, urinary obstruction and other known causes of high arterial pressure, neither the oxygen requirements of the body nor the cardiac output changes markedly, although the systolic pressure may rise to 200–300 mm. Hg and the diastolic to 140. In other words, blood flow appears to be determined by tissue requirements, and the pressure head is adjusted to provide that flow even though the peripheral resistance may reach abnormal limits. The pressure head in the aorta is accordingly an index of the heart work required to provide the minimal essential flow. As many circumstances— age, sex, race, heredity, excitement, activity, sleep and disease—modify the tissue demands, and hence the dynamics of the heart and arterioles, it is not surprising that the limits of the range of variation considered to be normal for man have not been sharply defined. There are, however, data that indicate the more common values associated with normal body function.

At birth the arterial pressure ranges between 20 and 60 mm. Hg. By the end of the first month it has risen to between 70 and 80 mm. Hg, and it increases steadily thereafter to about 120 mm. systolic and 80 mm. diastolic in young adult males at rest. The influence of age on the systolic, diastolic and pulse pressures is illustrated in Figure 409, based on data from Hunter's observations of average values in healthy Americans. The graph illustrates the sharp increase which occurs in the systolic pressure about the time of puberty. After the age of 20, both systolic and diastolic pressure rise steadily with advancing years. In girls the increase in systolic pressure at puberty is less marked and is often followed by a decrease until about the 18th year. From then on, the increase is steady as age advances, although the absolute values are about 10 mm. less than in men. Following the menopause, the systolic pressure tends to be a little higher than in men.

In emotional states, i.e., fear, excitement, and worry, the arterial pressure is increased, the systolic more than the diastolic. The rise is due to an increase in the cardiac output, to arteriolar constriction, or to both; and both may be accounted for in part by an increased output of epinephrine by the adrenal glands (see Chap. 34). During restful sleep, on the other hand, the systolic pressure falls 10 to 30 mm.

In exercise both the systolic and the diastolic pressure increase, but more particularly the former. To some extent, the increase is of the same nature as that which occurs as a result of excitement, for it may begin as soon as the individual even thinks of exerting himself. The maximum increase in pressure is roughly proportional to the severity of the exercise, the cardiac output being roughly proportional to the individual's oxygen consumption during the period of exertion. When the exercise ceases, there is a sudden drop in the systolic pressure, probably due to the relaxation of the abdominal muscles. This drop is followed by a secondary rise, roughly proportional to the exertion, which continues for several minutes. The increases in arterial pressure are accompanied by a general increase in the flood flow and in the supply of oxygen to the active and recovering tissues.

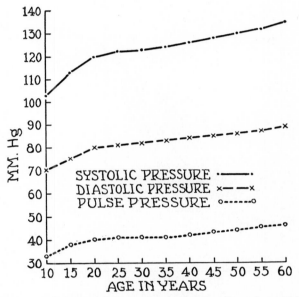

FIG. 409.   Graph illustrating changes with advancing age in diastolic and systolic pressures in arteries.

GRAVITATIONAL EFFECTS ON ARTERIAL PRESSURE.   The arterial blood pressure in man is usually measured in the brachial artery. Although this artery is selected for convenience, it also happens to be situated at the level of the heart when the arm is hanging by the side. At any level below that of the heart, the weight of the column of blood in the vessel acts in the same direction as the arterial blood pressure. If the level is above the heart, the weight of the column opposes the arterial pressure. For example, when a person is standing, the pressure is greater in the femoral artery than in the brachial artery, and the difference (50 to 60 mm. Hg) is the same as the pressure of an imaginary column of blood extending from the one artery to the other. When the individual reclines, the difference disappears.

In the arteries above heart level, the expected difference in pressure due to gravity is not usually observed; the activity of the mechanisms maintaining the pressure on the blood in the arteries is so regulated (Chap. 31) that the pressure in the sinus region—the root of the internal carotid artery—is sufficient to provide an adequate circulation through the brain. Accordingly, the brachial or carotid pressures when a person is erect equal or exceed those when he is lying down.

ARTERIAL PULSE

When the ventricles contract, forcing a volume of blood into the aorta, two quite different things happen in the systemic circulation. One event is the flow of a long column of blood along the arterial tree so that any one particle flows at a velocity of 0.20 to 0.60 m. per second in the arteries and much more slowly in smaller vessels. The second event is an expansion of the vessel wall, occurring first in the proximal segment of the aorta and traveling along the peripheral blood vessels as a result a pressure wave transmitted in the blood. This wave is called the *pulse wave* and is detected at any given point along the arterial tree as the pulse.

The velocity of the pulse wave may be in the range of 4 to 5 m. per second, roughly ten times the velocity of the blood flow. The pulse pressure wave is like the "wave"

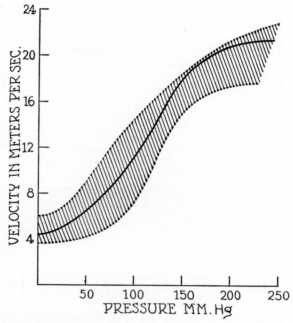

FIG. 410. Graph illustrating relation between internal pressure in segments of isolated "normal" human carotid artery and velocity of pulse wave. Cross-hatched region represents range of variation in 8 normal subjects; continuous line represents results from one subject. (Based on data from Bramwell *et al.*, *Heart*, 1923, *10*:289–300.)

passing through a metal rod which is tapped, or like the chain reaction when the first of a row of billiard balls is struck. The "wave of clicks" travels rapidly through the row of balls, which move only very slightly. From this description, it follows that the pulse can be measured either as an expansion of arteries or as a pressure. For experimental and clinical purposes, pressure rather than expansion is measured, although the clinical practice of feeling the radial (or other) pulse with the fingertips detects the expansion of the artery with each heart beat. If the vessels are normal, the expansion and the pressure wave are clinically related.

Registration of Pressure. When optical manometers were used, great skill and ingenuity were required to measure the rapid pressure changes involved in the pulse. The best of these instruments employed a very stiff membrane and other features to reduce the distance through which the blood mass had to be moved. A mirror on this membrane recorded its movements optically, making possible further reduction of the mass, which distorts the pressure record. All of these problems became less pressing with the introduction of electronic amplifying and recording devices. Strain gauges and capacity transducers are now extensively used.

Characteristics of Pulse Wave. Velocity. When two devices for the recording of surface pulsation are placed at different points on an artery, the speed at which the pulse wave travels toward the periphery can be measured. This velocity varies between 5 and 9 m. per second in normal man. It is determined primarily by the elasticity of the arteries—the more rigid the arterial walls, the greater the velocity. The rigidity of the arterial wall increases as the internal pressure rises. Accordingly, Bramwell et al.[3] found that with an increase in the internal pressure in arterial segments from 100 mm. to 150 mm. Hg the velocity of the pulse wave rose from a mean of about 9 m. to about 16 m. per second (Fig. 410). It is obvious, therefore, that the diastolic pressure has an important

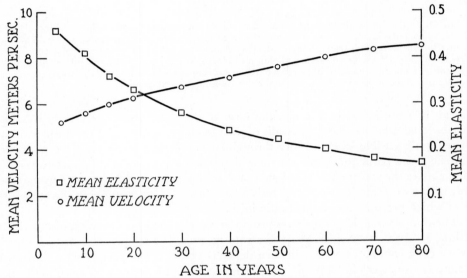

FIG. 411. Graph illustrating changes in velocity of pulse wave and mean elasticity of arteries with advancing age. (Based on data from Bramwell et al., *Heart*, 1923, *10*:233–256.)

influence on the velocity of the pulse. Furthermore, the increased rigidity of the arterial walls which occurs with age concomitantly increases the speed of the pulse wave. In a series of measurements of individuals of different ages, the mean velocity was only 5.2 m. per second in a five year old child but had increased to 8.55 m. per second in a person aged 80 (Fig. 411)[4].

Form of pulse wave. The pressure pulse wave is divided into a systolic and a diastolic portion by a small notch—the incisura—that marks the closure of the semilunar valves between the left ventricle and the aorta (Fig. 412). With the onset of the isometric phase of ventricular relaxation, the blood moves toward the heart and the semilunar valves are distended; concomitantly the pressure falls suddenly, creating the incisura and setting up aftervibrations of the aortic valves and the column of blood. The aftervibration, merging with a reflected wave (see below), gives rise to the dicrotic notch or wave.

The form of the systolic portion of the pressure pulse is determined by three variables: (i) the rate and volume of the ventricular discharge, (ii) the velocity of the pulse wave (i.e., the rigidity of the walls of the arterial system), and (iii) the rate at which blood moves from the arterial reservoir into the capillaries (i.e., the state of the arterioles)

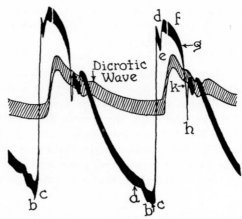

FIG. 412.   Tracing of photographic record of subclavian (central) and radial (peripheral) pulse. On subclavian pulse, *a, b* represent wave due to atrial systole; *b, c,* small wave due to rise in pressure in ventricle before opening of semilunar valves; *c, d* mark beginning of ejection of blood into aorta; *d, e* represent a wave due to vibration of column of blood. At *g* pressure falls suddenly at beginning of diastole or relaxation of ventricle, giving rise to the negative wave or incisura *h; k,* vibrations corresponding to closure of semilunar valves and second heart sound. (After Wiggers.)

With an increase in stroke volume, the form of the pulse wave (previously rounded) either becomes plateau-like if the walls of the vessels are quite rigid, or, if the walls are sufficiently distensible, rises steadily throughout systole. An increase in the peripheral resistance and a reduction in the rate at which blood leaves the arterial system result in an increase in the steepness of the slope of the pressure rise during systole. On the other hand, with a decrease in peripheral resistance—other factors remaining the same—the rate at which pressure rises tends to diminish.

The diastolic portion of the pressure pulse wave follows the cessation of ventricular ejection. Its form is determined by the rate at which blood moves from the arterial system to the capillaries, which in turn depends upon (i) the peripheral resistance or the state of the arterioles and (ii) the elastic recoil of the arteries. Usually the form is that of a smooth curve which declines rapidly at first and then move slowly as the pressure falls.

Distortion of pulse wave in transit.   As the pulse wave passes along the great arteries, its form changes as shown in Figure 413. The systolic pressure reaches progressively higher peaks of shorter duration as the wave passes down the arteries. This phenome-

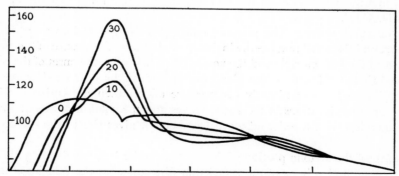

FIG. 413.   Contour of arterial pressure pulse in various parts of aorta. Curve 0, pulse near root of aorta; Curves 10, 20 and 30, pulse at 10, 20 and 30 cm. farther down aorta.

non has been ascribed to reflection of the pulse waves back from the periphery. This second wave is reflected again from the closed semilunar valves. In this way a highly complex system of reflected or standing waves is generated with each pulse beat.

The most important standing-wave system is that in the aorta. In the dog the same system extends peripherally as far as the saphenous artery. In man, however, the leg arteries have a standing-wave system which is separate from that in the aorta, and considerable emphasis has been placed on the differences between the *central pulse*, as recorded in the aorta and other arteries near the heart, and the *peripheral pulse*, as recorded in an artery such as the radial.[8] The peripheral pulse has the same fundamental form as the aortic pulse at the point of origin of the branch artery. Superimposed upon this fundamental form are standing waves resulting from the reflection of the pulse wave by the terminal arterioles of the artery in question. The transmission time over the carotid artery is relatively short; that over the brachial artery is somewhat longer, and that over the leg system of man longer still. In each, the natural period of the standing wave is approximately twice the transmission time.

Nature of Pulse in Health and Disease.   By palpating the pulse the physician may easily determine the heart rate (by simple counting) and whether the rhythm is regular or irregular. He may also learn whether the pulse is large or small, whether the wave rises and falls rapidly (the "water-hammer" pulse of aortic insufficiency), or if one phase or another is unduly prolonged. An experienced observer develops great skill in recognizing changes in the form of the pulse wave by mere palpation. By pressing on the artery he can quickly estimate whether the blood pressure is high or low. Instrumental recording provides additional information, but such procedures are usually not used clinically.

Variations and abnormalities of the pattern of ventricular ejection and its impact upon the root of the aorta are readily detected in records of the central pulse pressure (Fig. 414). When the heart is discharging a normal volume against an increased aortic resistance resulting from vasoconstriction, the initial steep rise in the contour of the pressure pulse is followed by a more gentle incline that terminates with the incisura. The discharge of a normal ventricular volume against the lower aortic resistance associated with vasodilatation develops an initial sharp rise in pressure that continues to a peak and reflects the momentum of the blood as it enters the easily distended arterial system. In these circumstances the outflow during the systolic period is large, and the pressure drop to the incisura is precipitous. With decreased stroke volume, the pressure

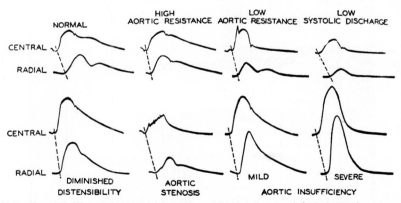

FIG. 414.   Records illustrating contour and amplitude of central (subclavian) and radial pulses in differing circumstances. (From Wiggers, *Circulatory dynamics, physiologic studies,* New York, Grune & Stratton, 1952.)

change during systole describes a gentle arc, for the rate of discharge exceeds but slightly the drainage rate from the arterial reservoir. The flattened curve following the incisura indicates a slow movement of blood from the arterial system into the capillaries. In aortic stenosis the slope of the initial pressure rise during systole reflects the lowered rate at which the ventricular contents enter the aorta, and the delayed peak is further evidence of the longer period of sustained ventricular discharge. Finally, an abrupt rise and fall of the pressure contour associated with the peripheral "water-hammer" pulse indicates incompetence of the aortic valves.

The need for a practical method of quantifying the stroke-by-stroke output of the heart for use in clinical and laboratory studies has led to a great deal of exploration of the possibility that the contour of the centrally recorded pressure pulse may provide the basis for a cardiac stroke index. Although the results obtained thus far are not wholly satisfactory, further refinements may make the method applicable.[1, 9, 11, 12, 13, 14]

VENOUS PRESSURE

Movement of Blood Through Systemic Veins to the Heart.   As the blood leaves the capillaries it enters the veins, a system of converging vessels serving both as a conduit and as a low pressure reservoir of large capacity. From this reservoir the blood is fed to the right heart. The distensibility of that organ represents the resistance to the flow from the venous reservoir, and the rate at which blood leaves the reservoir to enter the right heart determines the cardiac output.

The walls of the veins are suited to this storage function at low pressure. They are thin, elastic and, except for the portal system, sparsely clothed with muscle fibers. The thin, flaccid walls of an empty vein are flattened and approximated, but they yield to very small increments of internal pressure. A rise of a few millimeters of water may increase the capacity of the lumen threefold; a rise of 130 mm. H_2O may increase the capacity about sixfold. Beyond this level the increment of increase in capacity per unit rise in pressure falls off rapidly. The variations in capacity resulting from low pressure fluctuations are opposed by the muscular elements in the walls; these elements respond to nervous, hormonal and chemical stimuli. The force developed by the smooth muscle is very limited. Except for those regions in which the hydrostatic forces are pronounced, the resistance offered to their action is small, because the capacity of the right ventricle

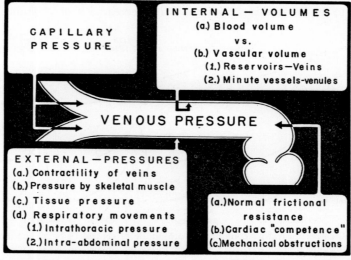

FIG. 415.   Schematic representation of factors concerned in maintenance of venous pressure. (After Landis and Hortenstein, *Physiol. Rev.*, 1950, *30*:1–32.)

increases passively with very small increments of pressure. The increased return to that cavity, resulting from the decrease in the capacity of the venous reservoir, is transferred to the pulmonary circulation by an increase in the stroke volume and rate. Thus the changing capacity of the principal components of the venous reservoir—the portal system with its appendage, the spleen, and the venous plexus in the skin—serves to regulate the cardiac output by controlling the volume of blood that reaches the right heart per unit of time.

When the systemic system is in equilibrium, blood is returned to the right heart from the venous reservoir at the same rate at which it enters from the capillaries, and the volume of blood in each segment of the vascular net—the aorta, the arteries, the capillaries and the veins—is relatively constant.

A rise in the capacity of the capillary bed through an increase in the number of patent capillaries in an active tissue may be balanced by a decrease in the capacity of the venous reservoir. Conversely a decrease in the capacity of the capillary segment of the systemic circuit can be balanced by an increase in the volume of blood held in the veins. That is to say, the veins play an important role in regulating the distribution of the blood and act reciprocally with the arteries and the capillaries.

In man at rest, whether recumbent, sitting or standing, the blood from the venules is returned to the right side of the heart by the pressure head in the arterial reservoir, although the pressure gradient between venules and right atrium and the flow can be modified by a number of accessory factors, i.e., action of the muscles of respiration, elasticity of the lungs, the force of gravity, the action of skeletal and visceral muscles, the valves of the veins, and, finally, the action of the right heart (see Fig. 415). In the recumbent individual, as relaxed as possible, the pressure caused by left ventricular action is of the order of 80 to 245 mm. H_2O (average about 150 mm. H_2O, or 11 mm. Hg) in the venous ends of the capillaries and 5 mm. H_2O in the great veins at their entrance to the right atrium. This pressure gradient is adequate to promote the flow of blood back to the heart, but can be steepened (i) by arteriolar dilatation accompanied by venoconstriction or in the absence of marked venodilatation, thus elevating the pressure in the venous capillaries and venules, and (ii) by an increase in the rate at which the right heart transfers the blood from the great veins into the pulmonary system. Cardio-acceleration serves to reduce the pressure in the great veins; moreover, a rise in venous pressure serves to increase the heart rate through receptors associated with vagal afferents. Conversely, a reduction in cardiac output resulting from vagal inhibition is followed by an increase in the central venous pressure that may amount to 60 to 70 mm. H_2O.

This pressure gradient maintained by the heart between the venous capillaries and the right atrium is further increased by the negative intrathoracic pressure which is established through the recoil of the elastic tissue of the lungs. In the natural state, the pressure in the thorax at any instant is less than atmospheric by the amount of tension required to overcome the elasticity of the lungs and expand them to the size of the thoracic cavity. The recoil of this elastic tissue, exerted upon the thoracic wall, the diaphragm and the layers of the mediastinum, reduces the pressure on the structures in the mediastinum by about 80 to 120 mm. H_2O in quiet expiration and inspiration, respectively, and by 400 to 640 mm. H_2O during deepest inspiration. That is to say, the pressure gradient established by the heart between the venous capillaries and the right atrium (150 − 5, or 145 mm. H_2O) is further increased in the recumbent, relaxed person to about 225 mm. H_2O (145 + 80) through the recoil of the elastic tissue of the lungs.

The pressure on the intrathoracic veins can be further diminished or increased voluntarily and reflexly when the respiratory and abdominal muscles act to alter the capacity of the thorax with the glottis closed, as during the expiratory effort in lifting a heavy weight or straining at stool. Accordingly, the intrathoracic pressure rises, the negative pressure due to elastic recoil of the lungs is offset, the heart decreases in size, and the venous return is impaired. Conversely, a normal inspiratory effort or one made with the glottis closed increases the venous return via the superior vena cava by further decreasing the intrathoracic pressure. This effect on the venous return from the inferior vena cava is variable, however, for accessory factors—increased intra-abdominal pressure, narrowing of the caval opening in the diaphragm—that tend to offset the reduction in intrathoracic pressure come into play. (See Franklin[7] for a detailed discussion of these factors.)

Thus far only the principal factors influencing the venous return in recumbent and relaxed individuals have been discussed. Consider now the manner in which the venous return is affected when the individual stands up. In a system of tubes with rigid walls and filled with fluid, pressure is everywhere the same when the system is horizontal. When the system is placed vertically, it remains filled with fluid throughout, but the

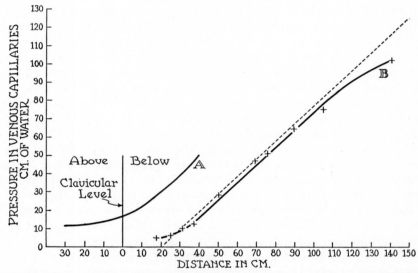

FIG. 416. Graph illustrating variation in pressure in venous capillaries of (A) hand, (B) foot, measured at positions relative to clavicle. (Based on data of Landis[10] and of Carrier and Rehberg.[6])

pressure is greater in the bottom than in the top by an amount equal to the length of the vertical column of fluid multiplied by its density. When an elastic distensible system of tubes, similarly filled, is shifted from the horizontal to the vertical position, the fluid accumulates in the dependent parts—other factors remaining the same—under the influence of the hydrostatic and atmospheric pressures.

The vascular bed is such a system of elastic tubes. Accordingly, when an individual moves from a recumbent to a vertical position, blood tends to accumulate in the dependent and most distensible portions, i.e., the veins and the capillaries. Thus the return of blood from the regions below the atrium, although promoted by the force of ventricular contraction and the negative pressure in the thorax as in the recumbent position, is opposed by the force of gravity. Hence one might expect the pressure in the venous capillaries of any dependent part to equal the weight of a column of blood of the same length as the vertical distance between the venous point and the level of the atrium or, in the case of the arm, the level of the subclavian vein.

Observations on the capillary pressures in the hand at the level of the clavicle demonstrate that this expectation is fulfilled[6, 10] (see Fig. 416). As the hand is lowered below the reference point—the clavicle—the pressure in the capillaries increases regularly with the increase in vertical distance, although the pressure tends to be somewhat less than expected at the lowest level. The constancy of the capillary pressure in the hand at levels above the right atrium (approximately 7 cm. below the clavicle) appears to be due to the negative pressure in the chest and the flaccidity of the veins. As the hand is raised and the blood momentarily flows more rapidly toward the heart, the veins begin to collapse and in doing so increase their resistance to blood flow. The flaccid veins yield to the slightest external pressure; as a consequence, the negative pressure which would develop in a rigid tube raised above the level of its entrance into the chest is offset by the increase in the functional resistance of the veins, since they flatten more and more as the hand is raised.

Similarly, the pressure on the blood in the veins of the dorsum of the foot of a man at rest is equal to the pressure exerted by a column of blood extending from the vein to the level of the right atrium (Fig. 416). This pressure is of the order of 90 mm. Hg or 115 cm. of blood. During exercise—walking—the pressure is reduced to about 22 mm. Hg (range 11 to 31) by the action of the so-called muscle pump. Each venous segment, guarded at its ends by valves or the capillary resistance, is pressed upon by the contracting muscle,

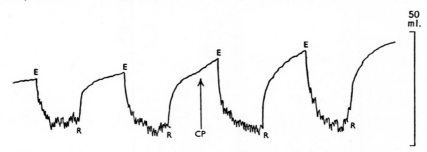

FIG. 417.   Recorded changes in volume of calf of leg illustrating action of muscle pump during rhythmic exercise. Decrease in volume is signaled by downward movement of writing point. At *E*, calf muscles contracted once per second for 10 seconds. *R*, 10 seconds rest. At *CP*, cuff above knee inflated to 90 mm. Hg until end of record. (From Barcroft and Swan, *Sympathetic control of human blood vessels*, London, E. Arnold & Co., 1953.)

driving the blood toward the heart and filling the adjacent headward segments. As the muscles relax their pressure, the venous valves prevent regurgitation, and the empty venous segments are filled from the periphery as a result of the propelling force of the left ventricle. The action of the pump is readily demonstrated by means of the plethysmograph arranged to measure calf volume. Figure 417 shows a record of the changes in calf volume during alternate periods of rest and exercise. With exercise, the calf volume is decreased as the blood accumulated during the rest period is pumped out of the veins toward the heart. The record further illustrates the pressure developed by the "muscle pump." At *CP* a cuff above the knee was inflated to 90 mm. Hg, yet the pump reduced the volume of blood in the calf veins against that resistance; blood was forced out under the cuff. A similar pumplike action is said to be exercised on the blood in the splanchnic bed by the rhythmic contractions of the stomach and the intestine.

In some otherwise normal persons the compensatory changes in the capacity of the splanchnic bed are less readily evoked than usual. These people are very sensitive to the sudden assumption or the prolonged maintenance of the vertical position. They feel giddy and faint as a result of the fall in blood pressure, which may amount to 25 to 30 mm. Hg, and they may even experience momentary unconsciousness. Patients who have been confined to bed for long periods may experience the same symptoms when they first try to walk.

Measurement of Pressure in Systemic Veins. The simplest clinical method for the estimation of the pressure in the right atrium in the resting individual is that of Gaertner. The arm is allowed to hang by the side until the veins fill with blood; then it is slowly raised until the veins in the back of the hand just begin to collapse. The height above the heart level at which this collapse occurs indicates the venous pressure in millimeters of blood in the right atrium, since the arm vein is essentially a manometer tube ending in the right atrium. ("Heart level" for the recumbent individual is midway between the dorsal aspect of the thorax and the xiphoid process; when one is sitting up, the reference level is a plane passing horizontally through the fourth intercostal space at its junction with the sternum.) Another convenient index of the venous pressure at the right atrium of a recumbent individual with his head raised on a pillow is the height above the clavicle to which the external jugular vein is visibly distended.

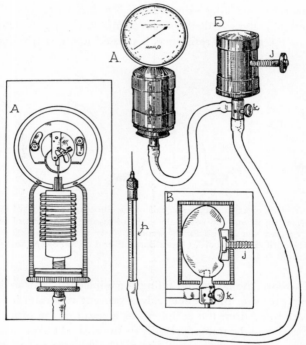

FIG. 418. Diagram of phlebomanometer: *A*, aneroid manometer; *B*, pressure chamber with screw, *j*, for varying pressure; *k*, needle valve; *n*, glass adapter holding hypodermic needle. (Through courtesy of Dr. G. E. Burch, School of Medicine, Tulane University.)

The pressures in peripheral veins can be measured with a small glass chamber sealed to the skin overlying a vein and connected to a pressure bulb and a water manometer. The pressure in the air-tight chamber is raised until the vein collapses; the pressure registered by the water manometer then equals the venous pressure. More satisfactory results can be obtained by inserting a hypodermic needle, connected to a water manometer, directly into the vein. An apparatus such as a phlebomanometer (Fig. 418) can then be used to measure the pressure in various superficial veins, both large and small. In this phlebomanometer[5] a very sensitive aneroid barometer is used to measure the pressure. A rubber tube leads to a glass adapter which holds the hypodermic needle, and the tube also communicates with a small pressure chamber in which the pressure can be varied by turning a screw. The pressure in the chamber is reduced to draw a little sodium citrate solution into the needle to form a meniscus in a glass adapter. When the needle is inserted into the vein, the pressure causes blood to enter the needle and move the meniscus farther along the glass adapter. The pressure in the chamber is increased until the meniscus assumes its original position; the pressure as registered on the barometer measures the venous pressure.

To eliminate the gravitational difference, venous pressure usually is measured with the subject reclining. The result is corrected to the heart level by determining the vertical distance between the point of measurement and the level of the heart. This distance is added to or subtracted from the venous pressure as measured in centimeters of water.

Normal Variations in Venous Pressures.   Measurements of venous pressure in man in a basal condition, i.e., after he has been lying down for at least 15 minutes, demonstrate considerable variations in different individuals. The pressure in the median basilic vein, for example, varies between 40 and 100 mm. H_2O after correction for differences from the reference plane of the heart. Conditions under which the blood flow is increased cause only a temporary rise in venous pressure, for the heart normally meets the greater demand by increasing its rate and stroke volume. These increases enable the heart to transfer a greater amount of blood from the venous to the arterial side of the circulation per unit time. A sustained elevation of the pressure in the roots of the great veins clearly points to a myocardial insufficiency.

VENOUS PRESSURE IN HEART FAILURE.   When the cardiac muscle is unable to transfer the usual amount of blood from the venous side of the circulation to the arterial side, there result (i) a deficit of blood on the arterial side and (ii) an accumulation of blood on the venous side. In some circumstances ("forward failure," as in fainting or other forms of syncope) it is the deficit on the arterial side which gives rise to symptoms (low blood pressure, unconsciousness and, sometimes, sudden death). More frequently, symptoms result from the accumulation of blood on the venous side; the condition is then known as "backward failure," or *congestive heart failure.*

Suppose that this failure begins at the left ventricle, which becomes unable to transfer the usual amount of blood from the pulmonary veins to the aorta and the systemic circulation. Blood then accumulates in the veins and capillaries of the lungs, and this gives rise to *dyspnea,* or shortness of breath, due to impulses which pass up to the medulla through the afferent vagi and stimulate the respiratory center. Along with the dyspnea go a diminution in *vital capacity,* because the accumulated blood prevents the filling of the lungs with air, and *cyanosis,* because oxygen cannot diffuse sufficiently rapidly to oxygenate the blood in the congested lung capillaries. Sometimes the venous pressure in the pulmonary capillaries becomes so great that the dyspnea passes into *pulmonary edema,* in which the alveoli of the lungs are filled with edema fluid. If the congestion and pressure in the pulmonary circuit are so high that the right ventricle cannot adequately transfer blood from the venous side of the circulation to the pulmonary vessels, a new set of symptoms—all due to the accumulation of blood in the systemic veins— make their appearance. These are congestion of the veins of the neck and of the liver and spleen; *peripheral edema,* due to an increase in the venous pressure and therefore of the filtration pressure in the capillaries, in dependent parts such as the ankles; scanty urine, because so much of the body water is immobilized in the form of edema fluid; and sometimes the extreme forms of edema, *ascites* (accumulation of fluid in the peritoneal cavity) and *hydrothorax* (accumulation of fluid in the pleural cavities).

VENOUS PULSE

Usually the arterial pulse wave disappears in the arterioles, although as a result of arteriolar dilatation it may spread through the capillaries and appear in the veins. The term *venous pulse,* however, is generally applied to a quite different phenomenon—a pulse observed in the large veins (jugular) near the heart. This pulse results not from a pressure transmitted through the capillaries but from positive and negative pressure changes occurring in the heart or neighboring arteries and transmitted to the great veins. The records are usually taken from the external or internal jugular vein, where the venous pulse is quite large. In certain pathologic conditions it is also plainly discernible at greater distances from the heart and may even cause a noticeable pulsation of the liver ("liver pulse"). The curve of the venous pulse is a means of determining the contraction rate of the atria, just as the arterial pulse curve permits counting of ventricular contractions. For this reason venous pulse records are important in the interpretation of various irregularities of the heart beat.

Tracings of the typical venous pulse in the jugular veins show three positive main waves, labeled *a, c* and *v* in the same manner as the waves in the atrial pressure curve are labeled, and three negative waves, *x, x'* and *y* (Fig. 418*a*). Many tracings, however, are far from typical. Frequently successive waves are merged together, and subsidiary waves sometimes appear. In disease it may be impossible to identify the waves unless one has a simultaneous record of the arterial pulse from which he can determine the beginning of ventricular systole.

In the venous pulse the positive wave immediately preceding ventricular contraction is the *a*

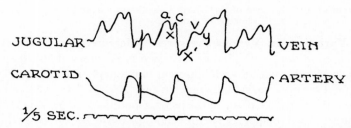

FIG. 418a. Upper tracing records pulse of jugular vein; lower tracing is from carotid artery. (After Best and Taylor, *The physiological basis of medical practice*, 1st ed., Baltimore, W. Wood & Co., 1937.)

wave caused by atrial contraction. Following this is the first negative wave, *x*, which marks the beginning of atrial relaxation. Next comes the positive *c* wave, resulting primarily from a rise in atrial pressure synchronous with ventricular contraction; transmission of the pulse from the neighboring carotid artery may also contribute to the *c* wave. It is followed by the negative wave, *x'*, which is attributed to the shortening of the ventricle from base to apex so that the septum is drawn down and the atrioventricular valves are closed. The next wave is the positive *v* wave, which reflects the rise in atrial pressure as the chamber is filled. The last negative wave, *y*, reflects the fall in atrial pressure when the atrioventricular valves open and the blood is emptied into the ventricle. The *y* wave passes into the positive *a* wave, and the cycle is repeated.

REFERENCES

1. ALEXANDER, R. S. *Fed. Proc.*, 1952, *11*:738–749.
2. BARCROFT, H. and SWAN, H. J. C. *Sympathetic control of human blood vessels*. London, E. Arnold & Co., 1953.
3. BRAMWELL, J. C., DOWNING, A. C., and HILL, A. V. *Heart*, 1923, *10*:289–300.
4. BRAMWELL, J. C., HILL, A. V. and McSWINEY, B. A. *Heart*, 1923, *10*:233–256.
5. BURCH, G. E. and WINSOR, T. *J. Amer. med. Ass.*, 1943, *123*:91–92.
6. CARRIER, E. B. and REHBERG, P. B. *Skand. Arch. Physiol.*, 1923, *44*:20–31.
7. FRANKLIN, K. J. *A monograph on veins*. Springfield, Ill., Charles C Thomas, 1937.
8. HAMILTON, W. F. *Amer. J. Physiol.*, 1944, *141*:235–241.
9. HUGGINS, R. A. and SMITH, E. L. *Fed. Proc.*, 1952, *11*:767–773.
10. LANDIS, E. M. *Heart*, 1930, *15*:209–228.
11. OPDYKE, D. F. *Fed. Proc.*, 1952, *11*:733–737.
12. PETERSON, L. H. *Fed. Proc.*, 1952, *11*:762–766.
13. REMINGTON, J. W. *Fed. Proc.*, 1952, *11*:750–761.
14. REMINGTON, J. W., NOBACK, C. R., HAMILTON, W. F. and GOLD, J. J. *Amer. J. Physiol.*, 1948, *153*:298–308.
15. WIGGERS, C. J. *The pressure pulses in the cardiovascular system*. New York, Longmans, Green & Co., 1928.
16. WIGGERS, C. J. *Circulatory dynamics, physiologic studies*. New York, Grune & Stratton, 1952.

CHAPTER 31

Vasomotor Regulation

By DONALD H. BARRON

THE volume and pattern of blood flow in the vascular system are so regulated that the composition and temperature of the extracellular fluid remain fairly constant despite wide variations in the metabolic levels of the tissues and organs. This constancy is achieved by appropriate balance between the flow through tissues (muscle, for example) which remove from the blood materials used as energy sources and for tissue repair and the flow through organs (lungs, kidney, liver and skin) which restore the composition of blood by replacing materials previously removed or by subtracting the byproducts of metabolism. The balance in flow is the result of the integrated activity of the heart and the smooth muscle in the walls of the muscular arteries, the arterioles and the veins.

The smooth muscle on the arterial side of the circulation modifies the caliber of muscular arteries and arterioles and so the rate at which blood flows from the aortic reservoir to the tissues; that is to say, arterial smooth muscle functions in the regulation of (i) the volume of blood in the arterial reservoir and the pressure in the aorta and (ii) the rate at which blood reaches an organ for the exchanges with the interstitial fluid. On the venous side the smooth muscle serves to alter the capacity of the individual segments—to vary the amount of blood in the veins and to determine the rate at which blood leaves the venous reservoir for the right heart. Thus, by modifying resistance on the arterial side and capacity on the venous side, the smooth muscle of the vascular bed determines the distribution of the blood in the systemic circuit.

The activity of the musculature of the vascular bed is modified and integrated directly and indirectly by changes in the composition of the extracellular fluid. Local variations in the concentration of metabolites alter directly the tone of the smooth muscles in the arterioles of the area and form the fundamental link between the metabolic rate of a tissue and the blood flow through it.

691

The indirect control is exercised via the nervous system. Specialized sensory endings of peripheral afferents and cells within the integrative centers of the central nervous system meter with varying degrees of sensitivity the oxygen and carbon dioxide tensions, the hydrogen ion concentration and the temperature of the blood and extracellular fluid. Efferent neurons activated by these meters modify in an integrated fashion the heart rate, the resistance offered by arterioles and the capacity of the veins.

The local (direct) and the neural (indirect) control mechanisms act synergistically to satisfy the metabolic demands of the peripheral tissues. At the same time they maintain relatively unchanged the composition and temperature of the arterial blood. Through a further group of endings which meter the degree of distention of the walls of the vessels at the arterial and venous ends of the systemic circulation, the pressure gradient between them is maintained within fairly narrow limits despite wide variations in peripheral blood flow in response to local tissue demands. Accordingly, each regulatory change in the vascular system, of necessity, is not confined to a single segment, for a change in one is accompanied by compensatory reactions elsewhere that stabilize the composition of the blood.

The vasomotor system normally functions as an integrated unit, and this fact should not be lost to sight even though our present-day investigative techniques enable us to follow changes in only limited regions of it. Regulation of the peripheral part of the cardiovascular system is the main topic of this chapter. The next chapter will complete the picture with a consideration of the heart's role, which is alteration of its output.

Methods Used to Study Vasomotor Activity. The ideal method for the study of the vasomotor system would be one that allowed the observer to follow simultaneously changes in the activity of the heart, the arterial pressure, the state of the arterioles in the organs, and, finally, variations in the capacity of the segments of the venous system. The nearest approach to this type of recording achieved thus far was made by Rein, who used multiple thermostromuhrs for following changes in the pattern of blood flow from the arterial reservoir at the same time he recorded the arterial pressure.[34] For the most part, studies of vasomotor regulation have been restricted to analysis of the concomitant activities in two and sometimes three of its anatomic units. Methods for the study of changes in cardiac activity and in the dynamics of the arterial reservoir are introduced in Chapters 32 and 30, respectively. The changing state of the veins has been followed principally by recording the blood flow through specific isolated venous segments at constant pressure and by measurements of the pressures in the right atrium and portal vein. Of the peripheral structures, however, the arterioles have been the principal focus of attention.

If an organ can be visualized, blanching will be the observed manifestation of arteriolar constriction, and flushing and congestion the manifestations of vasodilatation. Changes in arteriolar resistance may be inferred from a change in the slope of the pressure decrement in the arterial tree; a rise in arterial pressure and a fall in venous pressure, other things being equal, denote arteriolar constriction. If the area involved is large enough, the increased resistance will produce a perceptible difference in pressure in the aorta as well as in the affected organ; there will be a general rise in diastolic blood pressure. Conversely, if the arterial pressure decreases and the venous pressure increases, arteriolar dilatation has occurred. If the method is applied to a definite organ—the brain, for example—the evidence that vasomotor changes are taking place is decisive when the simultaneously observed pressures in the artery and the vein of the organ vary in opposite directions.

Other conditions remaining the same, vasoconstriction in an organ is accompanied by a diminution in its volume; vasodilatation, by an increase. The method of studying the volume of organs is called plethysmography (Fig. 419). Plethysmographs have been designed for special organs, and some of these instruments have been given special names. Thus the plethysmograph used upon the kidney and the spleen has been termed an oncometer; that for the heart a cardiometer. The precise form and structure of a plethysmograph varies, of course, with the organ studied, but the principle involved is the same in all cases. The organ is enclosed in a container with rigid walls which have but one opening. Through this opening the container is connected by pressure tubing with a device which will record the changes in volume. The connections between the recorder and the plethysmograph, and the space in the interior of the latter not occupied by the organ, may be filled with air or, as is more often the case, with *water*.

Arteriolar dilatation in the skin, muscle, gland or brain, and the resultant increased blood flow, other circumstances remaining the same, are accompanied by a rise in temperature; conversely, vasoconstriction is followed by a fall in the temperature of the affected organ. These changes in temperature, as recorded by means of thermocouples applied to or embedded in the tissue, afford a ready means for following the

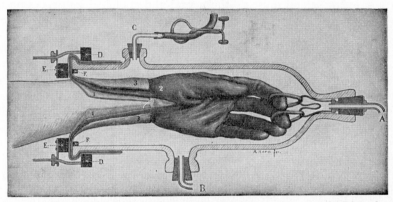

FIG. 419.   Detailed drawing of glass plethysmograph with arrangement of rubber glove to prevent leaking without compressing veins: *2*, glove with its gauntlet reflected over end of glass cylinder; *1* and *3*, supporting pieces of stout rubber tubing; *D* and *E*, sections of outer and inner rings of hard rubber to fasten reflected rubber tubing and reduce opening for arm.

variations in the state of the arterioles. Finally, appropriate use of any of the methods for measuring the volume of blood flow in the artery supplying an organ (see Chap. 33) serves to indicate the variations in the resistance to flow offered by the arterioles and the capillaries.

Through the application of these methods it has been shown that the smooth muscle of the vascular bed, like smooth muscle in other organs, possesses an inherent tone; i.e., a tendency to shorten or to resist elongation is typical of the resting or basal state. This tendency, as indicated above, can be modified by changes in the local environment or via the nervous system, but it does not depend on that system for its genesis. It is maintained in the arterioles or "resistance vessels" in opposition to the distending force exerted through the blood at each beat by the heart and by the action of internal secretions such as angiotonin and epinephrine.

The level of the inherent tone of the smooth muscle of the vessels apparently is not the same in all segments of the vascular bed. Comparisons of vessels in the basal state indicate that tone is high in some arterioles and low in others, e.g., high in those of a cat's skeletal muscle but low in the arteriovenous shunts of its paw. The functional significance of these differences in basal tone is not entirely clear at present, but they may be related to the role of the particular organ in body function.

Further, these methods have demonstrated that rapid alterations in the tone of the arterioles are wrought by two distinct mechanisms, nervous and chemical (including metabolites and hormones). The degree to which each of these mechanisms modifies arteriolar tone differs in the vascular net from region to region. The tone of the intrinsic arterioles of the heart and nervous system is modified primarily by variations in the concentrations of metabolites acting locally and directly on the muscle; the changes evoked by neural action are supportive and secondary. The tone of other arterioles, e.g., those in the arteriovenous anastomoses of the skin that function in the regulation of heat loss from the body, is controlled almost exclusively by the nervous system. Again the significance of the difference to which the tone of the smooth muscle of the vascular bed is altered through local chemical changes or by neural mechanism appears to be associated with the relative roles of the segment in: (i) the nutrition of an organ; (ii) the maintenance of the uniform composition of the blood; and (iii) the maintenance of the circulation itself, i.e., the pressure on the blood in the arterial reservoir. The nutritive vessels are chiefly under local chemical control, whereas the others are subject to neural regulation. When a bed serves two functions—e.g., local nutrition and maintenance of the circulation, as in skeletal muscle—the neural and chemical influences on the arterioles may operate in opposing directions, the final result being the algebraic sum of the two actions.

REGULATION BY THE NERVOUS SYSTEM

Innervation of the Arterioles. Neural control over the tone of the arterioles is exercised through two functionally distinct sets of nerve fibers: (i) the vasoconstrictor fibers, which act to increase the tone of the smooth muscle of the arterioles and cause a diminution in the size of the vessels, and (ii) the vasodilator fibers, which act to relax (inhibit) the tonic contraction of the muscular coats of the arteries and thus increase the diameter of the lumen.[16]

Claude Bernard first discovered the existence of vasoconstrictor nerve fibers to the blood vessels in 1851, when he observed that if the sympathetic nerve in the neck of the rabbit was cut the blood vessels in the ear on the same side became very much dilated. He and other observers later showed that if the peripheral end of the severed nerve is stimulated electrically the ear becomes blanched, owing to a vasoconstriction of the blood vessels. Bernard was doubly fortunate in being the first to demonstrate the existence of a second class of nerve fibers, which, when stimulated, cause a dilatation of the blood vessels and are therefore called vasodilators. This discovery was made during study of the chorda tympani, which sends secretory fibers to the submaxillary gland. When this nerve is cut and its peripheral end is stimulated, a secretion of saliva results. At the same time, as Bernard showed, the blood vessels of the gland dilate; the flow of blood is greatly increased in the efferent vein and may even show a pulse.

The activities of these two groups of fibers, with the apparent exception of the vasodilators of the somatic nervous system (see below), are regulated by medullary and spinal neurons which are in turn controlled by the local concentrations of metabolites in the extracellular fluid and by impulses arriving from (i) the special afferents to the blood vessels and the chemoceptors—the carotid sinus, depressor, and vagus nerves; (ii) general somatic and visceral afferents; and (iii) the higher centers of the brain, particularly the hypothalamus and the cerebral cortex.

GENERAL DISTRIBUTION AND COURSE OF THE VASOCONSTRICTOR AND VASODILATOR FIBERS. The vasoconstrictor fibers have been described in Chapter 9. The nature and course of vasodilator fibers, however, require additional description.

The distribution pattern of the neurons and axons which dilate the arterioles lacks the simplicity and uniformity that mark the organization of the vasoconstrictors. Whereas all the vasoconstrictor neurons belong to the sympathetic division of the autonomic nervous system, vasodilator neurons are not, as might have been expected, confined to the parasympathetic system. In addition to the parasympathetic vasodilators, there is a second group of fibers which leave the spinal cord in the thoracolumbar region, commingled with the preganglionic vasoconstrictor fibers.[5] A third group of neurons in the somatic division of the nervous system, the activity of which is followed by vasodilatation, has been described. The neurons of the first two groups—the vasodilators in the sympathetic and parasympathetic outflows—are efferents, whereas the cells of the somatic system which evoke vasodilatation are generally agreed to be afferent neurons, with their cell bodies in the spinal ganglia, though the question cannot be regarded as settled.

The demonstration of the existence of vasodilator fibers in mixed nerves has been difficult, for the stimulation of a nerve containing both constrictors and dilators may give only a constrictor effect. Several methods have been used to avoid this masking of vasodilatation by vasoconstrictors. Pharmacologic agents such as ergotoxine, which paralyzes the endings of the vasoconstrictor fibers without inhibiting the action of the vasodilators, have been employed. Advantage has also been taken of the fact that vasoconstrictor fibers degenerate much more rapidly after separation from their cell body than do vasodilators; the vasodilators retain their excitability for some six to ten days after division, whereas the vasoconstrictor fibers lose their excitability on the third or fourth day. Further, in some nerves cooling paralyzes vasoconstrictor fibers before the vasodilators. By selective paralysis of nerve fibers and the employment of the recording devices described above, vasodilator nerves have been traced to the blood vessels by the following routes.

Via parasympathetic outflow. Vasodilator fibers to the vessels of the sublingual and submaxillary glands are found in the chorda tympani branch of the facial nerve; the glossopharyngeal nerve contains the vasodilator fibers to the vessels of parotid gland, the posterior third of the tongue, the tonsils and the pharynx. The vagus is said to contain vasodilator fibers to the coronary arteries.[23] The sacral portion of the parasympathetic outflow contributes, through the second, third, and fourth sacral nerves, the dilator fibers which go to the vessels of the clitoris or the penis. These fibers join the hypogastric plexus at the nervi erigentes. All parasympathetic vasodilator fibers are of the cholinergic variety.

Via sympathetic system. Vasodilator fibers to the vessels in mucous membrane of the mouth (lips, gums and palate), the nostrils, and the skin of the cheeks may be activated by stimulation of the cervical sympathetic. The fibers are distributed to the individual vessels via branches of the trigeminal nerve. In the dog, at least, vasodilators to the coronary arteries appear to be included in the branches of the stellate ganglion; the vessels of the skeletal muscles of the limbs receive vasodilator fibers from the thoracolumbar outflow via the branches of the brachial and lumbar plexus; and the sympathetic vasodilators to the abdominal viscera, intestine, spleen and kidneys are components of the splanchnics. The fibers of this group, like those of the parasympathetic vasodilators, are cholinergic.

Via somatic nervous system. The existence of vasodilators among the *afferents* of somatic nerves has been debated since Stricker first demonstrated in 1876 that stimulation of the *peripheral* ends of severed dorsal roots contributing to the sciatic resulted in a rise in temperature and a marked reddening of the foot. His observations were confirmed by Bayliss,[3] who demonstrated that the cell bodies for the fibers responsible for the vasodilatation are in the dorsal root ganglia. As these fibers, in both their structure and course, resembled ordinary sensory fibers, Bayliss concluded that they were identical and inferred that the vasodilatation of the skin vessels was brought about by impulses passing centrifugally or antidromically in them.

The hypothesis advanced to explain the peripheral action of the antidromically conducted impulses is as follows. At the periphery some sensory fibers are branched and one or more of these branches of a single fiber end near or on arterioles of the vascular bed of the skin. Thus local stimulation, such as the application of an irritant to the skin, sets up an axon reflex that acts on the arterioles, as well as the centrally conducted train of sensory impulses. Similarly, stimulation of the sensory fiber at its passage in the dorsal root or anywhere along its more proximal parts would set up impulses reaching the arterioles via the same collateral and also cause vasodilatation. Hinsey and Gasser[19] have shown that the sensory fibers concerned belong to the small medullated group (3 to 5 μ). These investigators suggested that the action of the collateral on the arteriole resulted from the liberation of acetylcholine at its terminal. Experiments by Holton and Perry[22] support the view that the action of the nerve upon the arteriole is chemically mediated and indicate that the dorsal root vasodilator substance may be closely related to, or identical with, adenosine triphosphate.

That vasodilatation does follow antidromic stimulation of the dorsal roots appears to be fairly generally accepted at present. The point debated is: Are such antidromic impulses normally set up in the central ends of the dorsal roots as a part of the integrated neural control of the blood vessels of the skin? Experimental evidence indicating an affirmative answer to this question has been offered by Bayliss,[3] but its validity has been challenged by Folkow and his associates,[13] who have studied the question carefully with negative results.

Innervation of the Veins.   Although the muscular coat of the venules and veins is less well developed than is that of the arteries, and although the internal pressure against which this coat contracts is normally less, the force of contraction appears to be considerable. During venoconstriction the veins of the forearm can develop pressure increases of the order of 40 to 50 mm. Hg in closed segments. On the basis of their control by neural mechanisms the veins of the body may be divided into three groups: (i) the superficial veins that return the blood from the skin, (ii) the mesenteric veins, and (iii) the veins of the muscles and the vena cava.[10] Those of the first group are innervated via the sympathetic outflow; the veins in the skin of the hindlimb of the dog, for example, are controlled by fibers that leave the cord via the ventral roots of segments L_{2-4}. The fibers controlling the veins of the skin of the forelimb leave the cord via the ventral roots of segments T_{6-8} to relay in the stellate ganglion. The central origin of the sympathetic control of the mesenteric veins is represented in T_{3-11}; the postganglionic fibers arise from cells in the celiac and mesenteric ganglia. The fibers to the veins of these two groups bring about venoconstriction. Apparently, there are no dilator fibers to the veins; venodilatation appears to result from a decrease in the activity of venoconstrictor fibers. Finally, there is no conclusive evidence that, in the dog at least, the veins of the third group possess a motor innervation.

The evidence available indicates that the nerve fibers to the veins are adrenergic. A venoconstrictor response initiated reflexly is not abolished by atropinization, and it is generally agreed that epinephrine constricts veins.[14]

Spinal Vasomotor Center.   The vasomotor neurons which lie within the cord may be termed elements of the spinal vasomotor center. This designation is justified, for a certain amount of integration occurs at spinal levels—integration which may be observed in segmental vasomotor reflexes. Reflexes of this type were first described by Lovén, who saw them in the ear and in the hindleg of the rabbit, and they are named for him. Since then, similar reflexes have been demonstrated in a variety of organs, so their occurrence may be fairly regarded as general.

For example warming the skin of the spinal animal results in a vasodilatation in the intestine, whereas cooling the skin—or its exposure to noxious stimuli—provokes a vasoconstriction in the intestine. Conversely, in spinal man cutaneous vasoconstriction has been elicited by stimulation of visceral pain fibers. The vasomotor neurons of the spinal cord, in addition to their response to spinal afferents, appear to exercise a tonic effect on the smooth muscle of the blood vessels that is modified by, but does not owe its genesis to, the higher centers.

Immediately after the spinal cord is sectioned in the lower thoracic region, the portion of the spinal vasomotor center caudal to the cut is paralyzed, the paralysis being manifested by vasodilatation in the caudal extremities. If the animal is kept alive for some time, the spinal centers and the vessels gradually recover their tone, although they are not connected with the vasomotor centers in the brain. This return of the tone may be attributed to activity of the vasomotor neurons of the lower thoracic and upper lumbar segments, since vascular paralysis is again produced when this portion of the cord is destroyed or the splanchnic nerves are sectioned. The time required for the restoration of vasomotor tone by the autonomous action of the spinal centers varies from one species to another. The loss of tone and its recovery are a part of a larger phenomenon, spinal shock (see Chap. 7).

Medullary Vasomotor Center. The vasodilatation which follows transection of the spinal cord in the thoracic region demonstrates that the vasoconstrictor neurons at the spinal level are normally activated continually by impulses reaching them from the higher centers. If the cord is transected at any point between the level of the first and eighth cervical segments, this tonic influence is removed from all the vasoconstrictors of the body and the arterial pressure falls as blood pools in the veins. That this tonic influence originates in cells in the medulla is shown by the observation that transection of the brain stem at the upper border of the pons leaves the vasoconstrictor tone and the blood pressure unaffected, whereas transection between that level and the first cervical segment of the cord lowers the arterial pressure more and more as section is made more caudally in the medulla. The further observation that the basic reflex control of the distribution of the blood in the vascular system is destroyed by section at the level of the first cervical segment but spared by one through the upper border of the pons demonstrates that the principal control of the circulation, the musculature of the heart, arterioles, veins, etc., is exercised from the medulla. The medullary components involved are frequently referred to as "the vasomotor center" without further qualification. (The term "center," as used here, implies a functional rather than an anatomic unit—one in which impulses from a variety of sources are integrated and their effects expressed in coordinate action by a group of muscles to attain an objective which serves to offset or balance the effects of the initial stress or environmental change.)

The functional organization of the medullary vasomotor center has been tested by a variety of techniques, i.e., the effects of the destruction of small regions, the injection of acetycholine into its substance and electrical stimulation of selected loci by means of the Horsley-Clarke stereotaxic apparatus (Chap. 10). The results, which are in general agreement, have defined more precisely the region concerned with cardiovascular regulation and have demonstrated that there is a degree of localization of function within that region. The loci from which the control of the vascular system can be modified are situated in the tegmentum caudal to the midpoint of the pons and cranial to the obex or the upper limit of the spinal cord. (See Figure 420 for the gross anatomic landmarks.)

Within the tegmentum the loci from which vasoconstriction and cardioacceleration* can be evoked—collectively called the "pressor center"—are distributed through the lateral reticular formation of the rostral two-thirds of the medulla (Fig. 421). Loci from which a decrease in vasoconstrictor activity and a fall in heart rate can be evoked, "the depressor center," are found principally in the reticular formation of the caudal half of the medulla. (To date no evidence has been obtained to indicate that vasodilator fibers *per se* can be activated by stimulation of the medullary tegmentum.) Each of these centers is a reflex center. Destruction of the "pressor center" abolishes the effects of activation of peripheral afferents that normally produce vasoconstriction, but does not alter the "depressor" reflexes. These remain so long as the "depressor center" is intact. Similarly, destruction of the "depressor center" leaves the pressor reflex mechanisms unaltered. The details of the functional interaction of these two centers, as well as their

---

* In many such studies changes in blood pressure are the criterion of effective medullary stimulation or destruction. Such pressure changes reflect both vascular and cardiac changes. Additional information on cardiac control is given in Chapter 32.

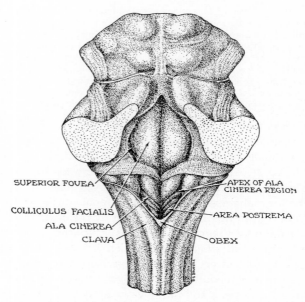

FIG. 420.   Landmarks in floor of fourth ventricle of human brain.

relations with other structures in the tegmentum, remain to be worked out. Both extend axons to vasoconstrictor neurons of the cord, and the activity of the final common path appears to represent the algebraic sum of their control. (Reference is commonly made to other functional subdivisions of the medullary vasomotor center, i.e., the cardio-acceleratory, cardioinhibitory and venomotor centers; however, these are terms of convenience rather than anatomic entities.)

The tonic activity of the neurons of the "pressor center"—and there is some evidence that neurons in the depressor center are similarly active—appears to be endogenous. That is to say, the neurons continue to discharge rhythmically after all neural control by peripheral afferents and higher centers has been removed, so long as their chemical environment is maintained within normal limits. Thus their activity appears to be fundamentally related to the chemical composition of the interstitial fluid which bathes them, although this activity is modified by nerve impulses that reach the neurons.

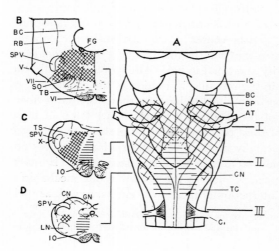

FIG. 421.   Location of "pressor" (*diagonal cross hatch*) and "depressor" (*horizontal hatch*) centers in medulla of cat. A, Diagram of brain stem; B, C and D, cross sections of brain stem at levels I, II and III in A. AT, Auditory tubercle; BC, brachium conjunctiva; BP, brachium ponti; C_1, first cervical nerve; CN, cuneate nucleus; FG, facial genu; GN, gracile nucleus; IC, inferior colliculus; IO, inferior olivary nucleus; LN, lateral reticular nucleus; RB, restiform body; SO, superior olivary nucleus; SPV, spinal trigeminal tract; TB, trapezoid body; TC, tuberculum cinereum; TS, tractus solitarius; V, VI, VII, X, corresponding cranial nerves; I, II, III, levels of transection. (From Alexander, *J. Neurophysiol.*, 1946, 9:205–217.)

Records of nerve impulses in the vasoconstrictor fibers to the arterioles indicate that, under experimental conditions and with the animal anesthetized or decerebrate, the "pressor center" discharges continuously and somewhat rhythmically. The rhythm of the impulse groups is often associated with the respiratory rhythm; at other times it is related to the heart rate, although not infrequently it bears no relationship to any other observable cyclic phenomenon in the body. Under certain unusual conditions the "centers" may exhibit other rhythmic variations in activity which are visible in a periodic waxing and waning of the general arterial pressure (Fig. 422); the waves are much longer than those associated with respiratory movements. These periodic variations in the blood pressure are occasionally observed experimentally, but their ultimate cause is not understood. They are usually designated as Traube-Hering waves, although this term, strictly speaking, should be reserved for the waves synchronous with the respiratory movements which Traube observed in animals with the thorax open and the diaphragm paralyzed. These waves, too, result from rhythmic variations in the activity of the vasoconstrictor center. During sleep, certain much longer wavelike variations also occur. These are doubtless due to a rhythmic change of tone in the vasomotor centers.

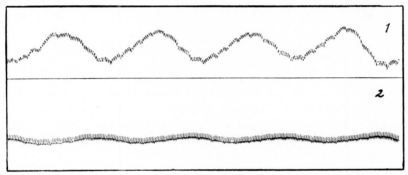

FIG. 422.   Rhythmic vasomotor waves of blood pressure in dog (Traube-Hering waves). Upper tracing (1) is blood pressure record taken with mercury manometer; lower tracing (2) is taken with Hürthle manometer. Seven distinct respiratory waves of blood pressure may be recognized on each large wave. (Dawson.)

NEURAL CONTROL OF MEDULLARY VASOMOTOR CENTER.   For purposes of description the sensory fibers which act on the spinal and medullary vasomotor centers may be classified as "depressor" and "pressor" afferents according to the pattern of the cardiovascular response that follows an increase in their activity.

Depressor afferents.   The adventitia and media of the arch of the aorta, the root of the innominate and the proximal portions of the internal carotid arteries are supplied with nerve endings similar to Golgi tendon organs by the aortic branches of the vagi and the sinus branches of the glossopharyngeal nerves, respectively (Fig. 423). These endings are normally stimulated by the increase in the capacity of the invested vessels—an increase that results from an elevation in the pressure on the blood within them; these sensory fibers are the proprioceptors of the cardiovascular system (Fig. 424A). The greater the internal pressure, the more rapidly the individual endings fire and the larger is the number of endings excited. At all pressures found in the normal rabbit some endings are discharging, and the rise in the pressure that results from the systolic discharge is accompanied by an increase in the number of impulses per second in the fibers active at the end of diastole and by an increase in the number of active fibers during systole. When the pressure on the blood in the arterial reservoir falls below the normal, impulse discharges from these receptors in the great arteries progressively decrease. Because the receptors are continuously discharging "depressor" impulses at normal levels of blood

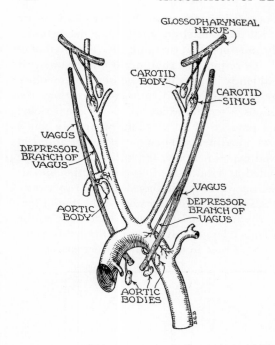

FIG. 423. Diagram illustrating position and nerve supply of carotid sinuses and aortic arch, together with carotid and aortic bodies.

pressure, the system can regulate against a fall as well as against a rise in pressure. For this reason these afferents from the great arteries are frequently referred to as "buffer" nerves, the analogy being drawn with a solution which minimizes changes in pH.

The central effects of impulse discharges from these receptors in the walls of the arteries can be illustrated by electrical stimulation of the sinus branch of the glosso-pharyngeal, or the separate vagal component—depressor nerve—from the aorta in the rabbit, when the compensatory action of the others has been removed by section or paralysis. The heart rate and the force of the beat are diminished; the peripheral resist-

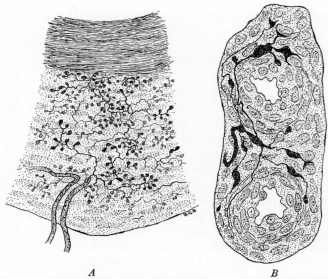

A   B

FIG. 424. Diagram showing characteristics of afferent endings in (A) carotid sinus and (B) carotid body. (After de Castro.)

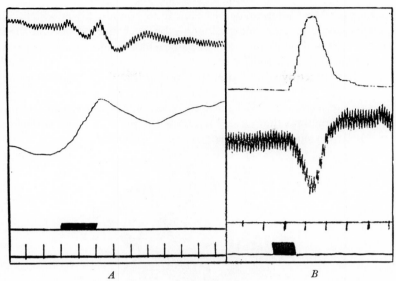

A   *B*

FIG. 425.   *A*, Excitation of vasodilators as illustrated by increase in volume of ear (*middle curve*) during stimulation of depressor fibers of vagus. *Upper curve*, Blood pressure. Cervical sympathetic cut. Time in 10 sec. intervals. *B*, Intestinal volume (*upper curve*) increases during stimulation of central end of vagus (depressor) owing to inhibition of vasoconstrictors as blood pressure (*lower curve*) falls. Time in 10 sec. intervals. (From Bayliss, *Proc. Roy. Soc.*, 1908, *80B:*339–375; and Bayliss, *The vaso-motor system*, New York, Longmans, Green & Co., 1923.)

ance is decreased by a vasodilatation in the splanchnic bed, skin, salivary glands and skeletal muscles, the amount depending upon the intensity and duration of the stimulation. Concomitantly the tone of the veins of the splanchnic bed decreases because the venoconstrictors are inhibited, and blood tends to pool within the splanchnic bed and the spleen. As a consequence the venous return to the heart is decreased and the cardiac output and blood pressure fall (Fig. 425*B*). The mean volume of blood in the arterial reservoir is decreased, and the amount in the venous side of the systemic circuit is increased. (The cardiac effects will be discussed further in the next chapter.) Similar effects can be produced by a compression of the internal carotid artery to increase the pressure in the sinus, by electrical stimulation of the walls of the sinus, or by artifically increasing the pressure within the vessel.

Conversely, a *reduction* in the number of impulses reaching the medullary vasomotor center from the aortic and sinus endings can be accomplished naturally by a reduction in the pressure in the arteries or experimentally by transection of the buffer nerves. In both cases the result is a rise in systemic blood pressure as a consequence of (i) an increase in the peripheral resistance (primarily through vasoconstriction in the splanchnic bed, although the arterioles of other regions may be involved to a lesser degree); and (ii) an increase in cardiac output as the spleen and splanchnic veins diminish in size to increase the blood flow to the heart.[21]

There appear to be similar pressure sensitive areas in the organs and structures supplied by the celiac and mesenteric vessels. Vasoconstriction in limb vessels and a diminution in the volume of the spleen follow a fall in blood pressure in an animal deprived of its four buffer nerves and the medullary vasomotor center. With an increase in blood pressure, the changes in the spleen and limb vessels are oppositely directed.

Evidence is slowly accumulating that fibers intermingled in other nerves to blood vessels of the skin and viscera—the peritoneum, the anus, the vagina and spermatic cord—can also effect a fall in blood pressure by inducing vasodilatation in the splanchnic region. Thus, stimulation of the sciatic and other mixed nerves may produce vasodilatation if the nerves are (i) cooled, (ii) stimulated at a particular stage in regeneration, or (iii) activated by weak stimuli or mechanically. These depressor fibers in the spinal nerves connect centrally with internuncial neurons to end in the medulla.

Pressor afferents. Most afferent nerves appear to contain fibers which, if excited, provoke a rise in arterial pressure independent of both cardiac effects and the secretion of epinephrine. The impulses pursue a spinal path, which suggests that the pressor fibers are pain fibers. Whatever their source and route to the vasomotor centers, the impulses appear to work their effect by stimulating the "pressor" and inhibiting the "depressor" centers.

The walls of the intrapericardial portions of the venae cavae and the pulmonary veins contain sensory endings that closely resemble the pressure receptors of the carotid sinus (Fig. 426). These endings, supplied by vagal fibers, are thought to be tension

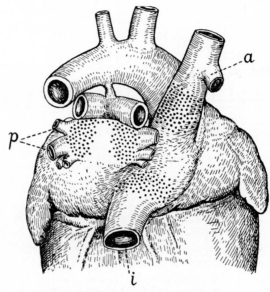

FIG. 426. The heart of a kitten as viewed from the back. Dots on roots of veins indicate distribution of subendothelial receptors. *a*, Azygos veins; *i*, inferior vena cava; *p*, pulmonary veins. (From Nonidez, *Amer. J. Anat.*, 1937, *61*:203–232.)

receptors that signal an increase in the volume of blood in the associated cavities, and by their activity induce cardioacceleration (Bainbridge reflex). Experimental expansion of the roots of the great veins results in a cardioacceleration that is abolished by vagal section. The reflex mechanism served by these receptors appears to provide for a more rapid transfer of blood from the venous to the systemic side of the heart; and this mechanism is thought to be associated with the quickening of the heart during muscular exercise. An associated increase in the peripheral resistance due to vasoconstriction is said to accompany the cardioacceleration of the Bainbridge reflex. This aspect of the reflex would oppose the action of the sinus and aortic nerves and may, for example, permit a rise of pressure which would be of value in increasing blood flow during exercise.

Gammon and Bronk[15] recorded discharges from the peripheral end of the splanchnic nerve and found that impulses are set up in its afferent fibers by distention of the vessels. The impulses arise from Pacinian corpuscles of the mesenteries as a result of their mechanical deformation by the distention of neighboring as well as intrinsic vessels. Increasing the distention of the vessels increases the frequency of impulse discharge, and vice versa. The reflex effects of these discharges have not been finally determined, but some evidence indicates that they activate the vasoconstrictor fibers to the gut.

Control by higher centers. It has already been pointed out that stimulation of cells located in the posterior and lateral hypothalamic nuclei results in a rise in blood pressure. The rise is due in the main to vasoconstriction, but there may be an undiscovered decrease in vasodilator tone at the same time. The relations of the cerebral cortex to the vasomotor centers remain to be worked out. Although cortical stimulation has been observed to increase blood pressure, plethysmographic studies in man demonstrate clearly that the centers are affected in a pressor or depressor manner by psychic states and activities. Mental work, especially mental interest, is followed by a constriction of the blood vessels of the skin—a pressor effect (Fig. 427). On the other hand, feelings of

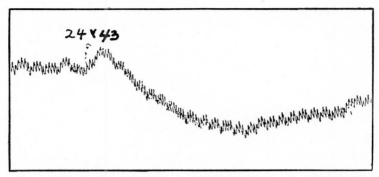

FIG. 427.   Plethysmographic curve of forearm. Volume of arm was recorded by means of a counter-weighted tambour; record shows pulse waves. A problem in mental arithmetic—the product of 24 by 43—caused marked constriction of arm.

embarrassment or shame are often associated with a depressor effect—a dilatation in the vessels of the skin manifested, for example, in the act of blushing. In each event it must be assumed that impulses in intracentral paths between the cortex, the hypothalamus and the medulla alter the levels of vasoconstrictor and dilator tone.

CHEMICAL REGULATION

Chemical Regulation of Medullary Vasomotor Center. VIA CAROTID AND AORTIC BODIES.   Within these bodies, afferent fibers passing via the glossopharyngeal nerves from the carotid bodies and via the vagi from the aortic and preganglionic bodies arborize about the intrinsic epithelial cells to end in reticulated swellings (Fig. 424B). These reticulated endings appear to be excited by constituents of the fluid bathing them and to be tonically active at normal carbon dioxide and oxygen pressures of the arterial blood. A rise in the carbon dioxide tension in the blood perfusing the carotid sinus region and body results in an increase in the frequency of the impulse discharge in individual nerve fibers as well as an increase in the number of active fibers. A similar effect follows a fall in the oxygen pressure. Conversely, if the carbon dioxide tension falls, or if the oxygen tension rises, the neural activity falls below that occurring at normal concentrations.

The effects of impulses from the carotid body on the medullary vasomotor center have been demonstrated by isolating the carotid region from the rest of the circulation, but leaving its nerve intact, and then perfusing the region. Perfusion of the sinus region with an acid fluid augments reflexly the arterial pressure through an increase in the heart rate and a rise in the peripheral resistance; conversely, when the perfusate is alkaline, the pressure falls as a result of a bradycardia caused by an increase in the activity of the cardioinhibitory center and a fall in peripheral resistance through arteriolar dilatation. Similarly, an increase in the carbon dioxide tension in the blood, without alteration of the pH, increases the activity of the cardioaccelerator and vasoconstrictor centers to increase the arterial pressure; whereas lowering the carbon dioxide pressure produces the opposite effect. Further, when the carotid sinus region of one animal is perfused as a part of the circulation of a second animal breathing a gas mixture poor in oxygen, the arterial pressure is similarly increased through vasoconstriction and cardioacceleration. The effects of alterations in the level of activity of chemoreceptors on venomotor tone or on cardiac output have not been studied. However, it seems quite unlikely that these receptors influence only the arteriolar musculature, although available evidence indicates that the sole different segment of their reflex pathway is the thoracolumbar sympathetic outflow. In Chapter 37 it will be shown that these chemoreceptors modify breathing in order that an adequate oxygen supply to the tissues may be maintained.

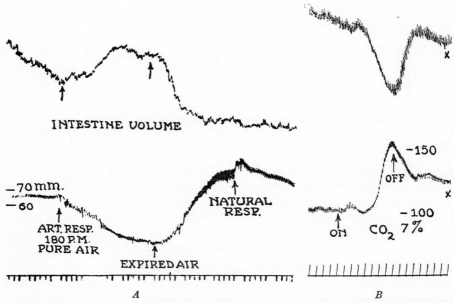

FIG. 428.   Kymograph records illustrating (*A*) fall in systemic blood pressure which accompanies hyperventilation (Dale and Evans) and (*B*) rise in blood pressure (*lower curve*) and fall in intestinal volume (*upper curve*) when 7 per cent of CO_2 is added to inspired air (Mathison). (From Dale and Evans, *J. Physiol.*, 1922, *56*:125–145; and Mathison, *ibid.*, 1911, *42*:283–300.)

DIRECT ACTION ON VASOMOTOR CENTERS.   In addition to the influence of the peripheral chemoreceptors, the activities of the vasomotor centers are modified directly by changes in the composition of their blood supply. Thus, when the lungs of an animal are overventilated and the carbon dioxide pressure in the blood is decreased, the blood pressure falls, owing in part to a vasodilatation in the splanchnic region (Fig. 428*A*). When normal lung ventilation is reinstated and the carbon dioxide pressure in the blood increases, the blood pressure rises and the intestinal volume decreases.[8] Conversely, an artificial increase in the carbon dioxide content of the alveolar air and of the blood results in a vasoconstriction in the splanchnic area accompanied by a rise in blood pressure. With the fall in the carbon dioxide pressure, the volume of the intestine increases, indicating a vasodilatation; at the same time the blood pressure returns toward normal.

The changes in arterial pressure caused by altering the hydrogen ion concentration and the carbon dioxide pressure in the blood are similar, but are not the same. For example, Dale and Evans[8] found that wide variations produced by adding fixed acid or base to the blood produced surprisingly little effect upon the circulation. A reduction in the oxygen pressure in the inspired air, such as may be brought about by giving a decerebrate preparation nitrogen to breathe, is accompanied by a vasoconstriction in the splanchnic region and a rise in blood pressure.

Direct Action on the Arterioles. The chemical substances which bring about arteriolar constriction and relaxation by direct action upon these vessels may be divided into two groups, the metabolites and the hormones. The first group includes carbon dioxide, oxygen, hydrogen and hydroxyl ions; the second, epinephrine, sympathin E and I (see below), vasopressin (Pitressin) and renin. The metabolites exercise a local effect on the arterioles; the hormones a general effect.

METABOLITES. Experiments in which portions of the vascular system were perfused with Ringer's solution or blood have demonstrated that a rise in the hydrogen ion concentration, an increase in the carbon dioxide pressure, or a reduction in the oxygen pressure of the perfusing fluid tends to relax the arterioles by direct action. Conversely, a rise in the concentration of the hydroxyl ion or an increase in the oxygen pressure has a constricting effect. Under normal conditions the hydrogen ion concentration tends to rise in an active tissue, owing to the increased production and local accumulation of carbon dioxide or lactic acid; simultaneously, the oxygen pressure in the tissue diminishes. Both circumstances favor arteriolar dilatation and a compensatory increase in blood flow. Thus the local effects of a rise in the carbon dioxide pressure and the fall in oxygen are the opposite of those which are exercised through the carotid and aortic bodies or, in the case of carbon dioxide, directly on vasomotor centers. Nevertheless, the two actions are complementary; the action via the nervous system, general arteriolar constriction, by raising the blood pressure increases the rate of flow through the locally dilated arterioles.

HORMONES. Addition of small amounts of the secretion of the adrenal medulla to the circulating blood, either by intravenous injection or by increased activity of the gland, affects the arterioles of a given tissue, just as stimulation of the tissue's sympathetic supply does. The arterioles of the skin, the mucous membranes and the splanchnic bed constrict; the arterioles in skeletal muscle, however, dilate.

This difference in effect appears to be explained by the fact that the secretory discharge from the adrenal medulla is not a single substance but a mixture containing norepinephrine and epinephrine. The norepinephrine component exercises the constrictor effect on the arterioles of the splanchnic bed, skin and mucous membranes to parallel and reinforce the action of the transmitter liberated by the intrinsic sympathetic efferents. Recent studies suggest that the transmitter designated sympathin E by Cannon and his coworkers is norepinephrine; the synergic action of the secretion of the adrenal medulla and the local efferent fibers is thus readily explicable. On the other hand, the epinephrine released by the adrenal medulla acts in conjunction with those sympathetic efferents that inhibit or dilate the arterioles of skeletal muscles—effects mediated by sympathin I according to Cannon but now thought to be transmitted by locally produced epinephrine. The materials liberated by the effectors of the sympathetic system are not rapidly destroyed; like the secretions of the adrenal medulla they circulate in the blood and may act at some distance from the site of their production.

Although any participation by the pituitary gland in the normal control of the arterioles remains to be discovered, extracts of the posterior lobe (the pars nervosa) yield a substance, vasopressin, which produces vasoconstriction in the systemic arterioles and the coronary and pulmonary vessels. This constriction is of shorter duration than is that produced by epinephrine, and a second injection soon after the first is usually followed by vasodilatation.

The female sex hormones progesterone and estrogen markedly affect the smooth muscle of the walls of the vessels supplying the ovary and the uterus; these hormones may affect the venomotor tone in some regions as well. The hormonal effects on the vessels develop more slowly than do those evoked by neural action or by metabolites. Vasodilatation in the uterine blood vessels is first observed some 20 to 30 minutes after intravenous injection of estrogenic hormone. There is evidence as well that some unidentified hormone released by the fetus induces dilatation of uterine vessels. The role of these hormones in the regulation of the blood flow to the uterus may be more important than that of either metabolites or the neural mechanisms.[26, 35]

OTHER SUBSTANCES.   In addition to the metabolites and hormones, some other substances which affect the arterioles directly merit consideration. Histamine (beta-imidazolylethylamine), derived from the acid histidine, is present in all mammalian tissues in a bound and inactive form. It produces arteriolar dilatation in man, the monkey and the dog, and it has been suggested that the release of histamine in excessive amounts when tissues are multilated may account for the fall in blood pressure and the marked capillary dilatation observed in traumatic shock. Adenylic acid, which is one of the substances (phosphate is the other) formed when adenyl-pyrophosphate breaks down during muscular activity, has been found in extracts of cardiac and skeletal muscles, the spleen, the kidney and the brain. When injected intravenously, it produces general dilatation of the arterioles and a slowing of the heart. The importance of adenylic acid, like that of histamine, rests on the possibility that it may be released into the circulation as a result of tissue damage.

Yet another substance of interest because of its action on the arterioles is angiotonin. An extract that may be obtained from the kidney, renin, acts as an enzyme on a substrate associated with the pseudoglobulin fraction of the blood to produce a pressor substance, angiotonin. The principal action of this substance appears to be to increase the peripheral resistance by vasoconstriction through a direct action on arteriolar muscles. In normal individuals angiotonin is quickly inactivated and does not appear to have any role in the maintenance of normal blood pressure. In contrast, angiotonin remains active in the circulation of patients with hypertension for longer periods and may play a considerable part in the maintenance of a high peripheral resistance, thus keeping the blood pressure at hypertensive levels.

REFERENCES

1. ALEXANDER, R. S. *J. Neurophysiol.*, 1946, *9:* 205–217.
2. BAINBRIDGE, F. A. *J. Physiol.*, 1915, *50:*65–84.
3. BAYLISS, W. M. *The vaso-motor system.* New York, Longmans, Green & Co., 1923.
4. BRONK, D. W. and STELLA, G. *J. cell. comp. Physiol.*, 1932, *1:*113–130.
5. BURN, J. H. *Physiol. Rev.*, 1938, *18:*137–153.
6. COMROE, J. H. *Amer. J. Physiol.*, 1939, *127:* 176.
7. DALE, H. H. *J. Physiol.*, 1906, *34:*163–206.
8. DALE, H. H. and EVANS, C. L. *J. Physiol.*, 1922, *56:*125–145.
9. DICKINSON, C. J. *J. Physiol.*, 1950, *111:*399–407.
10. DONEGAN, J. F. *J. Physiol.*, 1921, *55:*226–245.
11. DUGGAN, J. J., LOGAN LOVE, V. and LYONS, R. H. *Circulation*, 1953, 7:869–873.
12. FLEISCH, A. *Pflüg. Arch. ges. Physiol.*, 1931, *226:*393–410.
13. FOLKOW, B., STROM, G. and UVNAS, B. *Acta physiol. scand.*, 1950, *21:*145–158.
14. FRANKLIN, K. J. *A monograph on veins.* Springfield, Ill., Charles C Thomas, 1937.
15. GAMMON, G. D. and BRONK, D. W. *Amer. J. Physiol.*, 1935, *114:*77–84.

16. GASKELL, W. H. *The involuntary nervous system.* New York, Longmans, Green & Co., 1916.
17. HEYMANS, C. and BOUCKAERT, J. J. *Ergebn. Physiol.*, 1939, *41:*28–55.
18. HEYMANS, C. and NEIL, E. *Reflexogenic areas of the cardiovascular system.* London, J. & A. Churchill Ltd., 1958.
19. HINSEY, J. and GASSER, H. S. *Amer. J. Physiol.*, 1928, *87:*368–380.
20. HOLLINSHEAD, W. H. *Amer. J. Physiol.*, 1947, *147:*654–660.
21. HOLT, J. P., RASHKIND, W. J., BERNSTEIN, R. and GREISEN, J. C. *Amer. J. Physiol.*, 1946, *146:*410–420.
22. HOLTON, P. and PERRY, W. L. M. *J. Physiol.*, 1951, *114:*240–251.
23. KATZ, L. N. and JOCHIM, K. *Amer. J. Physiol.*, 1939, *126:*395–401.
24. LANDGREN, S. and NEIL, E. *Acta phsyiol. scand.*, 1951, *23:*158–167.
25. LINDGREN, P. and UVNAS, B. *Amer. J. Physiol.*, 1954, *176:*68–76.
26. MARKEE, J. E. *Amer. J. Physiol.*, 1932, *100:* 32–39.
27. McDOWALL, R. J. S. *The control of the circu-*

lation of the blood. New York, Longmans, Green & Co., 1938.

28. McDowall, R. J. S. *The control of the circulation of the blood. Supplemental volume.* London, W. A. Dawson and Sons Ltd., 1956.

29. Mathison, G. C. *J. Physiol.*, 1910, *41:*416–449.

30. Mathison, G. C. *J. Physiol.*, 1911, *42:*283–300.

31. Nonidez, J. *Amer. J. Anat.*, 1935, *57:*259–301

32. Nonidez, J. *Amer. J. Anat.*, 1937, *61:*203–232.

33. Ranson, S. W. and Billingsley, P. R. *Amer. J. Physiol.*, 1916, *41:*85–90.

34. Rein, H. *Ergebn. Physiol.*, 1931, *32:*28–72.

35. Reynolds, S. R. M. *Amer. J. Obstet. Gynec.*, 1938, *36:*437–440.

36. Sassa, K. and Miyazaki, H. *J. Physiol.*, 1920, *54:*203–212.

CHAPTER 32

Control of Cardiac Output

By ROBERT F. RUSHMER

THE tissues and organs of the body subserve a wide variety of functions, many of which are dependent upon the blood flow through the vascular network in the tissue. For example, blood flow through the skin increases during dissipation of heat; perfusion of the gastrointestinal tract increases during digestion of food; and exercising skeletal muscle requires a greatly accelerated blood flow to supply oxygen and remove waste products. Factors affecting blood flow through various tissues and organs are discussed in Chapter 33. The distribution of blood to various vascular beds is controlled by complex local and central vasomotor mechanisms which are discussed in Chapter 31. Most adjustments of blood flow also involve a simultaneous adjustment of the total quantity of blood flowing through the vascular system and a corresponding increase in the quantity of blood pumped by the heart. This chapter is devoted to the role of the heart in the overall circulatory adjustment.

The term *cardiac output* indicates the quantity of blood ejected each minute by either the right *or* the left ventricle, not the combined output of both ventricles. This definition is based on the concept that the systemic and pulmonary circulations are connected in series so that no blood passes directly from one circuit to the other. Normally, this condition obtains except that part of the bronchial circulation drains into the pulmonary veins. In general, the flow through the systemic circuit and that through the pulmonary circuit are regarded as precisely equal. Similarly, the average outputs of the right and left ventricles are considered identical, and the output computed for one ventricle is applied to the other. Dividing the mean cardiac output (in milliliters per minute) by the heart rate per minute gives the mean volume ejected per stroke, the *stroke volume*.

A sudden increase in blood flow through a large vascular bed (e.g., in exercising muscle) exceeding the compensatory restriction of blood flow in other vascular beds must be accompanied by a corresponding increase in cardiac output to prevent drastic changes in the arterial blood pressure. Consider a simple hydraulic system consisting of a mechanical pump and adjustable valves (Fig. 429). If any valve opens suddenly, outflow will increase and perfusion pressure will fall abruptly unless the output from the pump is correspondingly augmented by an increase in the rate or stroke of the piston. Similarly, unless accompanied by correspondingly increased cardiac output, an abrupt vasodilation produces a fall in arterial pressure. Clearly, the mechanisms for control of cardiac output must be intimately connected to vasomotor control to insure continuous coordination of the circulation.

The flow through the hydraulic system illustrated in Figure 429 increases when the output of the pump increases as a result of either a greater stroke volume or an accelerated rate of pumping. Similarly, the quantity of blood pumped through the systemic circulation each minute depends upon the heart rate (strokes per minute) and the stroke volume

SCHEMATIC MODEL OF CARDIOVASCULAR CONTROL

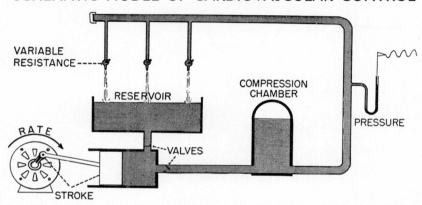

FIG. 429. In a simple hydraulic system, the pressure maintained is determined by the relation between the resistance outflow through the valves and the output of the pump (stroke volume × stroke rate). Any change in outflow resistance (e.g., opening of valves) must be followed by a prompt increase in pump output, or the pressure head will fall. In the same way, control of the heart and of peripheral blood vessels are intimately related. (From Rushmer, *Cardiac diagnosis, a physiologic approach.*)

of the left ventricle. Although coordinated cardiovascular responses involve *simultaneous* adaptations in both heart rate and stroke volume, it is convenient to introduce these two mechanisms separately.

CONTROL OF HEART RATE

Normally, the heart rate is established by the periodic discharge of excitatory impulses by the sino-atrial (S-A) node. The pacemaker activity of the S-A node is discussed in Chapter 27. The heart rate is continuously influenced by sympathetic and parasympathetic nerves which are profusely distributed to the region of the S-A node. An increased sympathetic discharge produces acceleration of the heart rate, whereas vagal discharge causes slowing of the heart. If both the vagal and the sympathetic nerves to the heart are cut, the heart rate is faster than normal, a condition which suggests that the vagal effects predominate at rest.

Changes in the heart rate during normal activity involve adjustment of the balance between the effects of the two sets of autonomic nerves. If stimulating electrodes are placed on the vagal and sympathetic nerves leading to the heart, the heart rate can be altered to any desired level at will merely by adjusting the frequency of stimulation applied to one or both nerves (Fig. 430). In the same way, normal adjustments in the heart rate can be effected through the reciprocal innervation in the central nervous system, since the heart rate can be accelerated by a reduction in the vagal discharge frequency, by an increase in sympathetic activity, or both.

AUTONOMIC BALANCE IN HEART RATE CONTROL

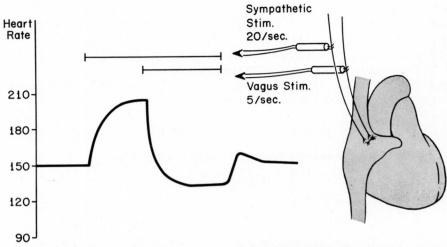

FIG. 430. Autonomic nerves distributed to the sino-atrial node directly influence heart rate. For example, stimulation of the sympathetic nerves at 20 c.p.s. accelerates the heart. Simultaneous stimulation of the vagus overbalances this effect and reduces heart rate below control level. Thus, heart rate is determined by the balance of the autonomic controls at the pacemaker.

CONTROL OF STROKE VOLUME

Before the turn of the century, both heart rate and stroke volume were thought to be under neural control. At that time, techniques were developed by which a beating mammalian heart, isolated from the body, could be artificially maintained by appropriate perfusion. Starling and his associates[7, 8] developed an improved heart-lung preparation affording experimental control over the pressure and the flow of blood into the right ventricle, the resistance to flow out of the left ventricle, and the heart rate. Changes in combined ventricular volume were recorded by means of a cardiometer (Fig. 431A).

Under these experimental conditions, increased inflow into the right ventricle resulted in progressive ventricular distention as the stroke volume increased. The diastolic and systolic volumes of the ventricles also increased when the outflow pressure was increased by elevating the resistance to outflow. In other words, the ventricles distended to greater diastolic volumes in response to either a greater inflow or an increased pressure load. Otto Frank had previously demonstrated that the frog ventricle responds as does isolated skeletal muscle in that, within limits, both develop progressively greater contractile tension as they contract at greater degrees of elongation (see Fig. 431B). In Starling's Linacre lecture[16] in 1915 he enunciated his "law of the heart" to the effect that "the energy of contraction is a function of the length of the muscle fiber." He concluded:

"The adaptation of the heart to variations in demands upon it occurs equally well after total destruction of the nerves connecting the heart with the central nervous system. So we must conclude that the governor mechanism, in virtue of which the heart is able to do more or less work according to the amount of blood which has to be sent on and the resistance to the flow presented by the arterial pressure, must be situated in the walls of the heart itself and presumably in the muscle fibers of which these are composed."

Most investigators interpreted such statements literally, taking them to mean that the principal mechanisms regulating energy release and the stroke volume of the ventricles depend upon the degree of diastolic distention, i.e., on the length of myocardial fibers. The observations on the function of the isolated heart described by Starling were confirmed repeatedly by many investigators, and the "law of the heart" became so universally accepted that a great deal of contradictory evidence was overlooked or ignored.

The Starling concept has generally been interpreted as implying that the normal ventricle tends to empty itself almost completely at rest and to increase in diastolic volume as the stroke volume increases. Roentgenographic evidence from dogs[9] and man[14] shows that increased stroke volume is not always accompanied by diastolic distention. In fact, greater stroke volume is *commonly attained by more complete systolic ejection.* Stead and Warren[17] presented data from patients in whom changes in cardiac output were not necessarily associated with corresponding changes in right ventricular diastolic

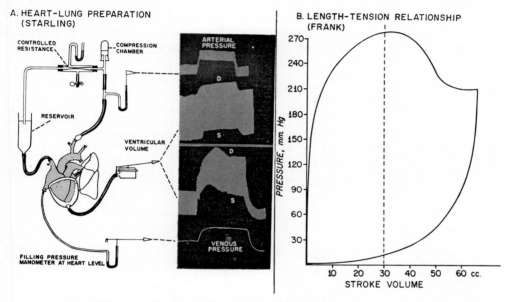

FIG. 431. *A,* The ventricles in the heart-lung preparation respond to an increased work load (either higher arterial pressure or increased inflow) by greater diastolic distention. These observations suggest that the energy released by the myocardium was determined by the length of the myocardial fibers (end-diastolic volume).

B, The length-tension diagram derived from frog myocardium by Otto Frank was used to illustrate Starling's concept that greater contractile tension developed as the myocardium was progressively stretched within limits. The pressure and volume scales represent Starling's estimate of values for man. (From Rushmer, *Cardiac diagnosis, a physiologic approach.*)

pressures. Since the diastolic volume was not measured directly, these data were largely discounted by investigators who regarded Starling's law as the dominant mechanism. In general, evidence derived from isolated or exposed hearts tended to confirm Starling's concept, while observations on intact animals and men were not consistent with this view. In the past few years, evidence has been accumulating that neural control mechanisms are potent enough to obscure the Starling mechanism under most normal conditions. Current emphasis on neural control of the heart represents a reversion to views contained in the first of the 18 editions of this textbook (Howell's *American Textbook of Physiology,* 1896). In many respects, a beginning student of cardiac physiology would be better prepared by reading this venerable text than by reading most modern textbooks on the subject.

The volume ejected by a contracting ventricle is the difference between the diastolic volume and the systolic volume. For many years ventricular ejection was believed to be essentially complete, and it was thought that only insignificant quantities of blood remained in the ventricular chambers at the end of systole. During experiments conducted on hearts which have been isolated or exposed, the ventricles function at abnormally small dimensions. In contrast, studies on intact dogs and on man indicate that the ventricles function at or near their maximal dimensions when the subject is at rest in the supine position (Fig. 432). When the individual stands or sits the ventricles diminish in size so that they are neither fully distended during diastole nor completely emptied during systole. Stroke volume can then be increased by greater diastolic distention or by more complete systolic ejection. For this reason, the factors which influence both diastolic and systolic volumes must be considered.

Factors Affecting Diastolic Volume. Ventricular filling cannot be regarded as a simple process in which elastic walls are distended by incoming fluid until the effective filling pressure becomes balanced by resistance to further distention. In general, the *rate* of ventricular filling depends upon the pressure gradient which propels the blood from atrium to ventricle. The *degree* of filling is affected by the effective filling pressure

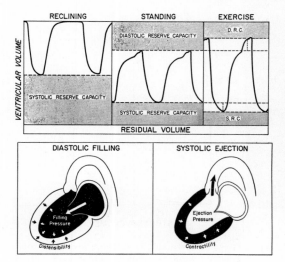

FIG. 432. The diastolic dimensions of the ventricles are maximal in canine and human subjects relaxed in reclining positions. When subject stands, the diastolic, systolic and stroke dimensions all diminish. Under these conditions, stroke volume can theoretically be increased by greater diastolic distention, more complete systolic ejection, or both. However, stroke volume does not increase very much during exercise (see Figs. 434 and 437). Diastolic filling is influenced by the relation between effective filling pressure and ventricular "distensibility." The degree of systolic ejection is determined by the arterial pressure and the myocardial "contractility." (From Rushmer, *Mod. Conc. cardiov. Dis.*, 1958, *27:* 473–477.)

and by the resistance to distention offered by the ventricular walls. However, the resistance to ventricular filling varies during the diastolic interval. When the heart beats at a slow rate, ventricular filling occurs in three phases (see Chap. 26). (i) During early diastole (rapid filling phase), the ventricles distend at a rate which is even more rapid than that at which systolic ejection emptied them (Fig. 432); this rapid filling phase terminates rather abruptly. (ii) Ventricular volume then increases gradually (slow filling phase) or remains constant (diastasis). (iii) Atrial contraction adds an increment of blood to the ventricular volume just before the next ventricular systole begins.

Rapid ventricular filling phase. At the onset of diastole, the atria and the great veins are distended with blood which has accumulated during the preceding systolic interval. As the atrioventricular valves swing open, blood gushes into the spontaneously expanding ventricle. The relaxing ventricular walls tend to spring open toward their diastolic dimensions and offer extremely slight resistance to filling (see "interfascicular tension" below). The ventricular pressure reaches its lowest level during this period; in fact, a slight ventricular suction during this phase of filling can be demonstrated experimentally.[1] Under these conditions, the *rate* of filling is determined primarily by the pressure gradient from the atria to the ventricles. The phase of rapid filling ends rather abruptly at different levels of ventricular distention, which are determined to a large extent by posture (Fig. 432). When the ventricle is functioning at or near its maximal dimensions (e.g., in the reclining position), ventricular filling may cease abruptly at the end of the rapid filling phase. Under other conditions, the rapid filling phase undergoes an abrupt transition into a slow filling phase, which may persist until the next atrial contraction.

Slow filling phase. This phase represents the time during which effective ventricular filling pressure produces progressive ventricular distention only by overcoming the resistance offered by the ventricular wall. The slope of the slow filling curve indicates the rate of filling (Fig. 432). The quantity of blood entering the ventricle during this interval is determined by its duration and by the rate of filling. The duration of the slow filling phase is greatly influenced by the heart rate. Acceleration of the heart reduces the duration of each cardiac cycle. Although the systolic interval is somewhat reduced, the diastolic interval decreases even more, largely at the expense of the slow filling phase. Since the slow filling phase contributes the least to ventricular distention, diastolic filling is restricted least by curtailment of this phase of diastole.

Apparently, the resistance to distention (distensibility) varies under different conditions. The slow filling phase reflects the relationship between the ventricular distensibility and the effective filling pressure. The effective ventricular filling pressure may be defined as the difference between the pressures inside and outside the ventricular walls (intraventricular pressure minus intrathoracic pressure). The intrathoracic pressure is subatmospheric as a result of the elastic recoil of the lungs (see Chap. 35) and varies with respiratory activity. The intraventricular pressure is influenced by many factors including: the heart rate, the position of the body, the total blood volume and the capacity of the venous reservoir system—and by others too numerous and too complicated to be considered here.

Atrial contraction. A final increment of blood is forced into the ventricle by atrial contraction, which normally begins at a brief but appropriate interval before the onset of ventricular systole (see Chap. 26). This contribution to ventricular filling varies from some 40 per cent of the total diastolic filling to essentially zero when the ventricles are at or near their maximal dimensions. The effectiveness of atrial contraction in filling the ventricles is partially determined by the vigor with which the atrial myocardium contracts. Myocardial contractibility is powerfully influenced by sympathetic nerves distributed to both the atrial and the ventricular walls.

Factors Which Influence Ventricular Systolic Ejection. The ventricles eject blood into the arterial system only so long as the intraventricular pressures exceed the pressures in the roots of the corresponding arterial trunks (Fig. 432). Theoretically, the degree of systolic ejection can be increased by reduction in the arterial pressures, but this is not a common physiologic control mechanism. Thus, the volume ejected during systole is determined primarily by the amount of shortening accomplished by the various layers of myocardial fibers before their contractile tension drops to levels below the systemic arterial pressure. The tension developed by myocardial fibers during isometric contraction is affected by their initial length (i.e., by the degree of diastolic distention). This factor is described by the familiar length-tension diagram, which indicates that isometric contractile tension increases with the progressive stretch of muscles within limits (see Fig. 431*B*). By definition, isometric contraction will not produce ejection of blood; for this reason, it is necessary to consider numerous factors which might affect the degree of myocardial shortening during systole.

During isometric contraction, myocardial fibers rapidly develop high tension, which is well sustained during the period of contraction. In contrast, if the muscle shortens rapidly after the peak of isometric contraction has been reached, the tension falls off abruptly even though contraction continues.[5] The fall in contractile tension increases as the rate and extent of shortening become greater, so that, with extremely fast shortening, contractile tension approaches resting tension. If other factors remain constant, the stroke volume will be limited by the rate and extent of myocardial shortening.

Interfascicular tension. Some of the contractile tension developed by myocardial fibers is manifest as tension in the connections between the layers of fibers comprising the ventricular walls.[9, 13] Obviously, the degree of shortening is not the same in different myocardial layers. The layers along the internal circumference of the left ventricle shorten the most, the outer layers of circularly arranged fibers shorten less, and the superficial spiral muscles on the external surface shorten the least of all. The various layers are entwined and interconnected, and the innermost layers of myocardium are compressed and distorted by the action of the outer layers. Since the layers contract in different directions and by different amounts, tension develops in the connections between layers. This interfascicular tension represents the energy of contraction, which is built up and stored during systole and then released as the myocardial fibers relax. The release of interfascicular tension is responsible for the very slight resistance to ventricular distention during the early rapid filling phase, and would account for the development of a ventricular suction during this interval.[1]

The loss of myocardial tension resulting from myocardial shortening and from interfascicular tension could be minimized by conditions which promote maximal stroke volume with minimal myocardial shortening. The amount of myocardial shortening required to eject a specific quantity of blood is much reduced by increased diastolic distention. Consider a sphere with a radius of 5 cm. (circumference: 31.4 cm.) containing 523 ml. Doubling the circumference increases the contained volume to 4186 ml. For the same reason, a very slight reduction in the circumference of a large sphere may eject a much greater volume than the same reduction in the circumference of a small sphere. Although the ventricles are not strictly spherical or cylindrical, this principle applies. Only slight shortening of the myocardial fibers during ventricular systole would be advantageous because, in these circumstances, contractile tension would be better maintained during ejection, and the energy losses in the form of friction and tensions developed within the heart wall would be diminished. Also, since the rate of myocardial shortening could be less, the losses of energy resulting from viscosity effects would be reduced. For these reasons, the volume ejected, the amount of energy released, and the efficiency of contraction would all tend to be increased by greater diastolic distention in accordance with Starling's law of the heart. On the other hand, the total myocardial tension required to increase ventricular pressure becomes greater as ventricular filling increases.

Law of Laplace. If the left ventricle is regarded as a cylinder surrounded by circularly oriented fibers, then the physical law governing tension in the walls of a distensible cylinder may be applied to cardiac function.* According to this law, the tension in the myocardial fibers necessary to sustain a particular level of intraventricular pressure is greater when the ventricle is distended than when it is more completely emptied.

The extent of systolic ejection depends upon the contractile tension developed and sustained by the myocardial fibers as the ventricles eject blood. Myocardial tension becomes progressively more effective in maintaining intraventricular pressures as the radius of the chamber is diminished (law of Laplace). This beneficial effect is countered by the loss of tension involved in myocardial shortening and development of interfascicular tension. There are undoubtedly other factors, but it is clear that systolic ejection ceases when the various opposing forces become balanced. This balance occurs at different levels of systolic ejection, primarily because the contractile properties or *contractility* of the myocardium is influenced by the action of sympathetic nerves distributed to the ventricular myocardium.

*For a discussion of this law (pressure equals tension divided by the radius) see Chapter 29 and Rushmer.[9]

Changes in myocardial contractility caused by sympathetic activity. Stimulation of the sympathetic nerves to the heart profoundly affects ventricular function. The systolic pressure within the ventricles rises much faster and reaches higher levels. These observations signify that the contracting myocardial fibers developed higher tension more rapidly. The duration of systole is shortened, and the rate at which ventricular pressure falls is more abrupt. Diastolic filling is somewhat reduced, partly because filling time is reduced by the faster heart rate. Systolic emptying is more complete, so the ventricles function at smaller systolic and diastolic volumes. These changes in the contractile properties of the ventricular myocardium are generally described by the term *increased contractility.* The mean effective ventricular filling pressure is usually unchanged, but the early diastolic pressure is often diminished (increased distensibility?) and the pressure increment during atrial contraction is usually greater (increased contractility). These effects are induced by the release of epinephrine-like substances at the sympathetic nerve endings, but the exact mechanisms by which these hormones can produce such dramatic effects are not known. These effects are so potent that they can completely override and obscure Starling's postulated relation between diastolic distention and release of energy by the myocardium.

Neural Control Mechanisms. The heart rate is determined primarily by the balance between the effects of transmitter hormones (acetylcholine and epinephrine-like substances) at the vagal and sympathetic nerve endings at the pacemaker (S-A node). The distribution and course of the autonomic nerve fibers to the heart were outlined in Chapter 9. The preganglionic parasympathetic fibers originate in the dorsal motor nucleus of the vagus in the medulla oblongata. This nucleus discharges impulses which slow the heart and serves as one of the cardioregulatory centers in the medulla oblongata, the cardioinhibitory center. Nearby is a poorly defined area thought to be the cardioaccelerator center. Impulses resulting from stimulation within this area descend through the spinal cord to the outflow of the sympathetic fibers distributed to the heart; these impulses produce acceleration of the heart rate. These cardioregulatory centers are reciprocally linked: stimulation of one is associated with inhibition of the other. They are also closely related to the medullary vasomotor centers (Fig. 421) and are bombarded by the same types of afferent inflow (see Chap. 10).

These medullary centers play an important role in the regulation of systemic arterial blood pressure (Fig. 433). The systemic arterial blood pressure is monitored by sensory nerve endings in the wall of the aorta and in the carotid sinus. These pressoreceptor endings respond to an elevation of arterial blood pressure by increasing their frequency of discharge. Their impulses reach the medullary centers by way of cranial nerves IX and X, and act to inhibit the cardioaccelerator and vasodilator centers and to increase the activity of the cardioinhibitory and vasoconstrictor centers. By this mechanism, a drop in systemic arterial pressure reduces the discharge from the pressoreceptor nerve endings in the arterial walls. The activity of the motor nucleus of the vagus is then inhibited, and, reciprocally, activity in the sympathetic nerves to the heart and the peripheral vessels increases to restore the arterial blood pressure to normal levels. Thus, an increase in systemic arterial pressure induces prompt compensatory adjustments which restore blood pressure to "normal levels." However, the "normal" blood pressure varies under different conditions (e.g., rest versus exercise) and in different individuals.

The mechanism which "sets" the level of blood pressure toward which the pressoreceptor mechanisms act is unknown. The pressoreceptor mechanism serves to stabilize the cardiovascular system by initiating compensatory reactions whenever arterial pressure changes. Such a mechanism cannot initiate cardiovascular adjustments of the sort which should accompany changes in level of activity (e.g., exercise). In addition to the pressure regulating mechanisms, a bewildering array of sensory nerve fibers from the chemoreceptor nerve endings, from the walls of the atria, from the ventricles, from the great vessels and from the lungs and other viscera enter the central nervous system and induce reflex cardiovascular and respiratory responses. Impulses traversing these nerve pathways probably induce compensatory reactions when circulatory conditions are altered in these diverse regions.

Circulatory adjustments generally are initiated primarily from the brain above the level of the medullary centers. Many common experiences indicate that the brain induces cardiovascular responses to such circumstances as excitement, apprehension, pain or anticipation of physical activity. Pathways passing from the cerebral cortex and hypo-

A. ARTERIAL PRESSURE REGULATION   B. INITIATION OF EXERCISE RESPONSE

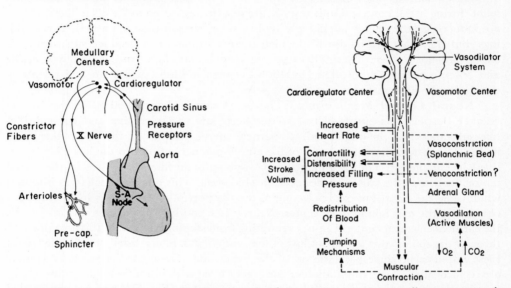

FIG. 433. *A*, Regulation of arterial pressure involves pressoreceptors responding to pressure in the carotid sinus and aortic arch. The impulses play upon the medullary centers of cardiovascular control, which in turn adjust peripheral vascular resistance and cardiac output to compensate for changes in arterial pressure.

B, Cardiovascular adjustments to exertion are apparently initiated by higher centers of nervous system, acting through autonomic pathways directly to produce vasodilatation in skeletal muscles, vasoconstriction in inactive tissues, tachycardia and increased myocardial contractility and distensibility. These changes would be augmented by peripheral factors such as metabolites, muscular and respiratory pumping action, etc.

thalamus to the heart and blood vessels by way of the autonomic nerves (Fig. 433*B*) were mentioned in Chapter 10. In addition, profound changes in cardiovascular function can be produced by electrical stimulation of the brain. It is now possible to show that these levels of the brain do prepare the cardiovascular system for increased bodily activity. For example, a wide variety of changes in cardiac function can be achieved by stimulating various sites in the hypothalamus. Applied in carefully selected areas, hypothalamic stimulation may induce changes in left ventricular performance which closely simulate the changes occurring during spontaneous exercise by the same dog (see Fig. 435). The hypothalamus, through which fibers from many different areas of the brain converge, appears to be an integrating center for such autonomic responses.

COORDINATED CARDIOVASCULAR RESPONSE

Neural pathways from many parts of the brain pass through the hypothalamus to the sympathetic outflow, the linkage being such that an appropriate autonomic response can be induced at the moment when changes in behavior are initiated in the brain.

Thus, a decision to increase physical activity may also result in an acceleration of the heart rate and an increase in contractility induced by sympathetic outflow to the heart, while other impulses pass down through a special sympathetic vasodilator system to produce vasodilation in the contracting skeletal muscle. By integrated neural control mechanisms, visceral function can be adjusted promptly to changes in the functional state of the organism.

Cardiac Control in Intact Animals. The foregoing discussion outlined some factors which might be important in normal regulation of cardiac output. Determination

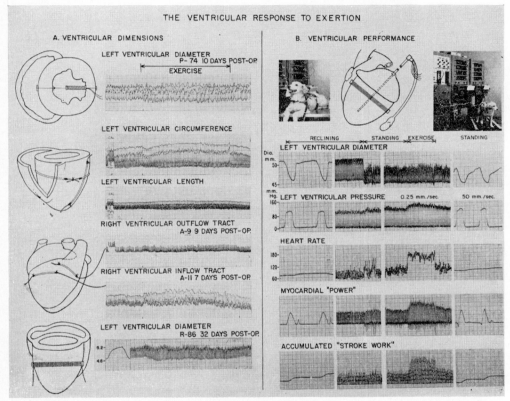

FIG. 434. *A*, The ventricular response to exertion by intact dogs involves very little change in the several ventricular dimensions which were measured directly. A slight increase in systolic excursion was produced by increased diastolic distention, more complete systolic ejection, or both (see Fig. 432).

B, In resting recumbent dogs, the left ventricular dimensions are maximal; they diminish when the animal stands (see also Fig. 432). Exercise results in slight changes in dimensions, increased systolic ventricular pressure, little change in mean ventricular diastolic pressure, pronounced tachycardia, increased power output by the myocardium, and greater work per stroke and work per unit time. (From Rushmer and Smith, *Physiol. Rev.*, 1959, *39*:41–68.)

of which of these mechanisms are being utilized requires direct measurement of ventricular performance in terms of certain critical variables, such as pressure, volume and flow of blood. These measurements can be accomplished quite readily in isolated or exposed hearts by means of the heart-lung preparation illustrated in Figure 431, but such experimental preparations lack essential control mechanisms, particularly those of the central nervous system acting through the autonomic nerves. Establishing the role of various mechanisms in normal cardiovascular control ultimately involves measurement of the critical variables in intact, unanesthetized animals and men whose full complement of control mechanisms are functioning normally.

Such studies on human subjects pose serious problems, but techniques have been developed recently which permit continuous analysis of left ventricular performance in intact dogs during spontaneous activity (Fig. 434). For example, the changes in heart rate, left ventricular diameter, effective left ventricular pressure, and stroke work during spontaneous changes in a dog's position are illustrated in Figure 434B. While the animal was reclining, the left ventricular diameter reached a maximal value at the end of the early diastolic filling period. When the animal stood up, the diastolic and systolic diam-

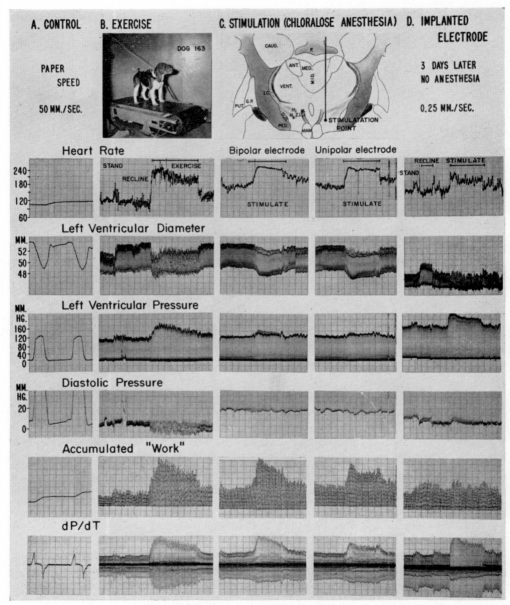

FIG. 435. A, Control records on a dog taken at paper speed of 50 mm. per second. B, Left ventricular response to running on a treadmill at 3 m.p.h. at a 5 per cent grade. C, Later the same day; dog was anesthetized, and a highly localized stimulus near the H₂ field of Forel produced a marked ventricular response. The electrode was sealed in place. D, Three days later, the hypothalamic region was stimulated through implanted electrode. Left ventricular response accurately mimicked that previously seen during exercise, but was not accompanied by movement of the animal. (From Rushmer and Smith, *Physiol. Rev.*, 1959, *39*:41–68.)

eters diminished promptly. The stroke change in diameter and the stroke work both diminished as the diastolic filling diminished. Thus, the energy release (stroke work) during each successive cardiac cycle diminished as the diastolic filling was reduced, in accordance with Starling's law of the heart. These changes in left ventricular performance are consistently observed under these particular conditions. In normal men, the heart has been reported to function at maximal dimensions when the subject is at rest in the supine position and to diminish in size when he stands.[15] The stroke volume and the stroke work are also reduced when the individual assumes an erect position.

The changes in dimension of the right and left ventricles of intact dogs during exercise on a treadmill at 3 m.p.h. on a 5 per cent grade are also illustrated in Figure 434B. In general, the diastolic and systolic dimensions were not greatly altered during exercise, and the stroke was but slightly increased or was unchanged. These responses bear no obvious relation to the changes induced experimentally in the heart-lung preparation shown in Figure 431.

Stimulation of selected areas in the hypothalamus profoundly changes left ventricular function, various cardiac responses being induced by stimulation of different regions. Changes in left ventricular performance very similar to those observed during spontaneous exercise can be produced, particularly by stimulation in the periventricular gray matter and near the H_2 field of Forel (Fig. 435). These changes are not necessarily accompanied by any evidence of muscular movement. This observation demonstrates that the left ventricular response during exercise can result from impulses in the central nervous system without any muscular exertion, and it might explain the anticipatory cardiac response that sometimes occurs in dogs well trained in experimental exercise. When left ventricular performance is analyzed continuously in intact dogs by means of electronic gauges and computers, increased stroke output and stroke work during exercise are observed to be accomplished primarily by an increase in heart rate with little contribution by an increase in stroke volume. Available evidence indicates that a similar cardiac response occurs in normal human subjects during physical exertion (see Fig. 437).

METHODS FOR MEASURING CARDIAC PERFORMANCE IN MAN

Procedures for direct and continuous measurement of the critical parameters of cardiac function (e.g., Fig. 434B) are not yet available for use on human subjects. In the past ten years, techniques have been developed which involve the threading of long, slender tubes (catheters) into systemic veins to pass into the right atrium, the right ventricle and the pulmonary artery, or directly into the left atrium and ventricle, or into a systemic artery. With suitable recording equipment, pressure can thus be ascertained in all portions of the cardiovascular system into which a small catheter can be introduced.

The size of the heart can be visualized by means of roentgenograms, and its volume computed by application of empirical formulas.[4] This procedure has been rendered more accurate by the development of simultaneous roentgenograms which portray the heart in two planes 90 degrees apart (biplane roentgenography). The size and configuration of the individual cardiac chambers can be visualized by intravenous injection of radiopaque substances which cast a heavy shadow on an x-ray plate while they are moving through the heart and the blood vessels. By rapid film advancement, sequences of bipolar roentgenograms can be exposed at rates of four to six a second. If a motion picture camera is used to record fluoroscopic images, the changes in the size and shape of the heart can be visualized at normal speeds or even in slow motion. Although the stroke volume ejected by the ventricles can be estimated from x-ray pictures, blood flow is usually computed by means of the Fick Principle or the Stewart Principle.

Fick Principle. If the quantity of a substance in the blood either increases or decreases while passing through an organ, the blood flow through the organ can be computed from three values: (i) the quantity of the substance in the blood entering the organ, (ii) the quantity of the substance in the blood leaving the organ, and (iii) the total quantity of the substance exchanged per unit time. Since all the blood passes through the lungs during a single complete circulation, the cardiac output can be determined by estimating the blood flow through the lungs per minute. In this application, the volume of blood which must flow through the lungs to transport the oxygen taken up from the alveoli per unit time is computed. For convenience, the following formula is employed:

$$\frac{\text{Cardiac Output}}{\text{(pulmonary blood flow)}} = \frac{\text{Oxygen Consumed Per Minute}}{\text{Arteriovenous Oxygen Difference in ml. per liter}}$$

The oxygen consumption can be readily determined from analysis of the inspired and expired air (Fig. 436). For purposes of determining the arteriovenous difference, the oxygen content of pulmonary venous blood is the same as that in any systemic artery from which samples can be drawn. Since blood returning from tissues with different oxygen requirements contains widely varying quantities of oxygen, samples representing a complete mixture of blood from various systemic veins must be used to compute the pulmonary blood flow.

In past years, a number of ingenious methods were employed to estimate the oxygen content of mixed venous blood, but all these were indirect. With the development of techniques for inserting catheters by way of peripheral veins into the right ventricle and the pulmonary artery, samples of "mixed venous blood" can be withdrawn directly from the pulmonary artery.[2] Thus, the true arteriovenous oxygen difference can be learned by determining the difference between the measured oxygen content of blood in the

CARDIAC OUTPUT DETERMINED BY THE FICK PRINCIPLE

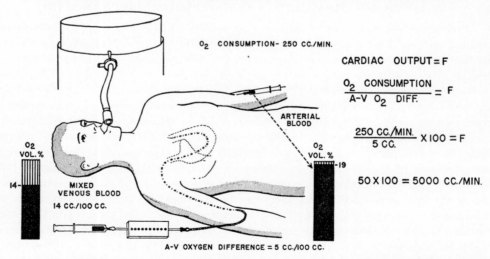

FIG. 436. Cardiac output can be computed in accordance with the Fick principle by simultaneously measuring the oxygen content of samples of systemic arterial blood and mixed venous blood. To obtain adequate mixing of venous blood from various tissues, the sample is best drawn from the pulmonary artery. The oxygen consumption divided by the arteriovenous oxygen differences, times 100, gives the cardiac output in cc. per minute. (From Rushmer, *Cardiac diagnosis, a physiologic approach.*)

pulmonary artery and in a systemic artery. Combination of these measurements with simultaneous measurement of oxygen consumption permits computation of cardiac output entirely from directly obtained values. This procedure is termed the "direct Fick method" (see Fig. 436).

Stewart Principle. The volume of fluid in a container can be calculated by adding a known quantity of dye and measuring its concentration after it has become evenly dispersed throughout the fluid medium. The volume is computed according to the formula $V = Q/C$, where V is the volume, Q is the quantity of dye added and C is the concentration of dye. Similarly, the volume of fluid passing through a simple tubular system can be determined by measuring the average concentration of a known quantity of dye and the time during which the sampling occurred. These values are combined according to the formula $F = Q/Ct$, where F is flow, Q is the quantity of dye injected, C is the average concentration of the dye, and t is the duration of sampling. This method is theoretically accurate so long as all of the dye passes the sampling point before recirculation begins. In practice, recirculation generally occurs during sampling, but techniques have been devised to correct for this complication.[3]

Cardiac Reserve. Most cardiovascular adjustments involve only slight changes in cardiac output. Normally, the capacity of the heart is not taxed except by intense physical exertion. The maximum physical work which can be accomplished is limited by the delivery of oxygen to the exercising muscle. In fact, the extent of physical exertion is limited by the total oxygen consumption of the body.

The total quantity of oxygen delivered to the tissues depends principally upon two factors: (i) the arteriovenous oxygen difference and (ii) the cardiac output. Studies with indirect Fick procedures indicated that the arteriovenous oxygen difference increased only slightly or remained constant as the level of exercise increased. The cardiac output was reported to increase in direct proportion to the oxygen consumption. Stroke volume was computed by dividing the cardiac output by the heart rate. These studies formed the basis for the widespread notion that the increased cardiac output during exercise was attained by increasing both stroke volume and heart rate to about the same extent. Now, of course, the *indirect* procedures used in these studies have been largely abandoned in favor of the direct Fick and Stewart Principles, which are decidedly more reliable.

Ten studies of the responses by normal human subjects during various levels of physical exercise, when supine and when erect, are summarized[12] in Figure 437. Measurements of cardiac output according to the direct Fick or Stewart-Hamilton techniques revealed that the stroke volume during exercise was either slightly elevated or was not significantly increased over the values obtained at rest in the horizontal position.[10] Control values for stroke volume of erect subjects were significantly less than the values in recumbent subjects. For this reason, the stroke volume in exercising erect subjects was generally somewhat greater than the erect control values. At peak levels of exercise, oxygen consumption reaches a maximum that is not exceeded even with greater physical work.[6] Under these conditions, the stroke volume may increase above the recumbent control values.

The heart rate increased progressively with greater work loads until it reached a maximum of about 180 beats per minute (Fig. 437B). This level is generally regarded as the maximum effective heart rate beyond which further acceleration causes a reduction in stroke volume and no net gain in cardiac output. Clearly, the increased cardiac output during exertion was attained primarily by tachycardia in these subjects.

The extraction of oxygen from the blood during its circulation through the systemic capillaries is indicated by the arteriovenous oxygen difference. In the studies illustrated in Figure 437, the arteriovenous oxygen difference increased progressively as work loads increased, and was still increasing at the maximum level of oxygen consumption which could be sustained even for only brief periods (e.g., $2\frac{1}{2}$ minutes).

Of the three mechanisms for increasing delivery of oxygen to the tissues, oxygen extraction from the blood (arteriovenous oxygen difference) contributes most; the heart rate increases somewhat more than twofold and then levels off; stroke volume is not consistently elevated over recumbent control values even at maximal levels of exercise (Fig. 437D). However, it is worth noting that if the heart rate is accelerated by means of

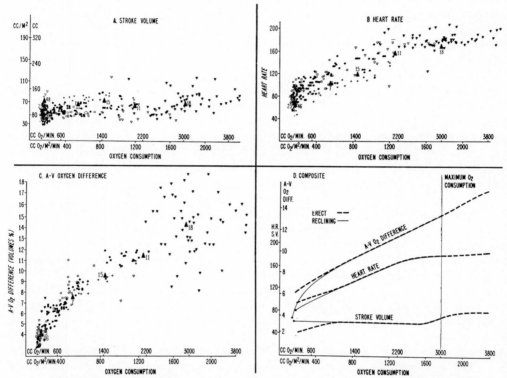

FIG. 437. Data compiled from ten studies with the Fick or Stewart principle on normal human subjects. A, Stroke volume tends to remain at approximately the recumbent control level during exertion sufficient to increase total oxygen consumption more than tenfold. B, Heart rate increases progressively with greater physical exertion until rate is about 180 beats per minute; it then levels off. C, Oxygen extraction from the blood, indicated by arteriovenous oxygen differences, appears to increase with exertion until oxygen consumption has attained maximal values. D, Control values in erect subjects are characterized by smaller stroke volume, faster heart rate and higher arteriovenous oxygen difference than those in recumbent subjects. During exertion, stroke volume increases somewhat above erect control values.

an artificial pacemaker, the size of the heart and the stroke volume diminish progressively.[10, 11] Thus, the factors that tend to maintain a constant stroke volume in the presence of fast heart rates during exercise are presumably the same factors that formerly were invoked to explain an increase in stroke volume (i.e., greater myocardial contractility, greater ventricular distensibility, more rapid ventricular filling, diastolic distention, Starling's law of the heart, etc.). Furthermore, stroke volume apparently does increase at extreme levels of physical exertion by untrained persons and in trained athletes, who typically have a slower heart rate at any given level of exercise. Stroke volume also increases in certain disease states which involve a long-continued increase in cardiac output; included among these are anemia, patent ductus arteriosus and Paget's disease. These diseases correspond to enforced "training" so far as the heart is concerned.

REFERENCES

1. BRECHER, G. A., MIXTER, G., JR. and SHARE, L. *Amer. J. Physiol.*, 1952, *171:*194–203.
2. COURNAND, A., RILEY, R. L., BREED, E. S., BALDWIN, E. DE F. and RICHARDS, D. W., JR. *J. clin. Invest.*, 1945, *24:*106–116.
3. HAMILTON, W. F. Pp. 191–194 in *Medical physics*, vol. 2, GLASSER, O., ed. Chicago, Year Book Publishers, 1950.
4. KJELLBERG, S. R., LÖNROTH, H. and RUDHE, U. *Acta radiol. (Stockh.)*, 1951, *35:*413–427.
5. LUNDIN, G. *Acta physiol. scand.*, 1944, 7 (Suppl. 20):1–86.
6. MITCHELL, J. H., SPROULE, B. J. and CHAPMAN, C. B. *J. clin. Invest.*, 1958, *37:*538–547.
7. PATTERSON, S. W., PIPER, H. and STARLING, E. H. *J. Physiol.*, 1914, *48:*465–513.
8. PATTERSON, S. W. and STARLING, E. H. *J. Physiol.*, 1914, *48:*357–379.
9. RUSHMER, R. F. *Cardiac diagnosis: a physiologic approach.* Philadelphia, W. B. Saunders, 1955, viii, 447 pp.
10. RUSHMER, R. F. *Circulation*, 1959, *20:*897–905.
11. RUSHMER, R. F. *Amer. J. Physiol.*, 1959, *196:*745–750.
12. RUSHMER, R. F. and SMITH, O. A., JR. *Physiol. Rev.*, 1959, *39:*41–68.
13. RUSHMER, R. F. and THAL, N. *Amer. J. Physiol.*, 1952, *168:*509–521.
14. SJÖSTRAND, T. *Physiol. Rev.*, 1953, *33:*202–228.
15. SJÖSTRAND, T. *Minn. Med.*, 1954, *37:*10–15, 29.
16. STARLING, E. H. *The Linacre lecture on the law of the heart, given at Cambridge, 1915.* London, Longmans, Green, 1918, 28 pp.
17. STEAD, E. A., JR. and WARREN, J. V. *Arch. intern. Med.*, 1947, *80:*237–248.

Circulation Through Special Regions*

THE organization and operation of the vasomotor mechanisms regulating the pressure gradient and the distribution of blood in the system having been discussed in Chapters 31 and 32, the regulation of blood flow through individual organs may now be considered. Such circulation is regulated in accordance with the role of the organs in the body economy; and the pulmonary circulation—the link between the right and left sides of the heart and thus between the venous and arterial sides of the systemic circulation—completes the circuit.

Methods for Estimation of Volume of Blood Flow. The simplest stromuhr or flowmeter is that devised by Ludwig in 1867. It was a great improvement over the previous practice of merely opening an artery and measuring the flow from it. The lack of peripheral resistance and the exsanguination of the animal, inherent in the earlier method, were avoided by inserting into the circulation the device shown in Figure 438. This stromuhr allowed the blood to flow from one end of a cut vessel into it and to return to the circulation through the other end of the vessel. In this way no blood was lost, and the flow, from vessel to stromuhr and from stromuhr to vessel again, encountered the full peripheral resistance offered by the vascular bed.

Other kinds of stromuhr. Several stromuhrs based on the same principle as Ludwig's, some of them driven electrically, have been devised. In addition, there are several kinds which depend on quite different principles.

One of the simplest is the *bubble flowmeter*,[26, 69] in which a small bubble is introduced into one end of a tube of known capacity that joins the two ends of a severed vessel. The length of time required for the bubble to be carried the length of the tube by the blood is measured with a stopwatch. An air trap at the distal end of the tube collects the bubbles and prevents their escape into the general circulation.

In *Rein's thermostromuhr*,[63] which is applied to the outside of the unopened vessel, a small diathermy unit heats the blood lying between two heating electrodes (*H* in Fig. 439). Two thermojunctions, one placed upstream and the other downstream, record the temperatures at L_1 and L_2 through a recording

---

* Originally written for the 15th edition by William F. Hamilton; revised for subsequent editions by D. H. Barron and T. C. Ruch.

galvanometer. The difference in temperature is a function of the velocity of blood flow and becomes smaller as the rate of flow increases. An improved form of the instrument, designed for use with unanesthetized animals and for continuous observation, has been described by Baldes et al.[3]

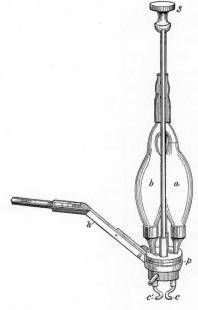

FIG. 438. Diagram of Ludwig's stromuhr: a and b, glass bulbs; c and c', cannulae inserted into cut ends of vessel; p, movable plate upon which stromuhr is turned by twisting screw s; h, holder.

The *electromagnetic flowmeter*,[49] developed independently by Kolin and by Wetterer, depends on the principle that when an electrical conductor, in this case the column of blood in the vessel, moves across the lines of force of a magnetic field, a potential difference is developed in the conductor. Under certain conditions, which can be fulfilled in practice, this potential difference is proportional to the rate of blood flow. A uniform magnetic field is applied to the outside of the unopened vessel by either an electromagnet or a permanent magnet, and the potential developed is drawn off from the walls of the vessel through nonpolarizable electrodes. As the potential is small, it must be amplified before being recorded with a galvanometer or oscillograph.

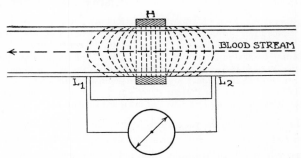

FIG. 439. Diagram of Rein's thermostromuhr: H, heating electrodes applied to outside of vessel; L_1 and L_2, the two thermojunctions leading to galvanometer.

The preferable methods for measurement of blood flow are those which least disturb the circulation, i.e., plethysmography[4] and those in which some material is lost to or removed from the blood by the tissue under study. The amount of any substance X removed from the blood by an organ per unit time is equal to the total amount of the substance brought to that organ by the arterial blood less the amount removed via the veins in the same interval, i.e.,

$$\text{cm.}^3 \text{ X in organ} = \text{cm.}^3 \text{ X brought by arteries} - \text{cm.}^3 \text{ X removed by veins.}$$

As $\quad$ cm.^{3} X brought by arteries $= [X]_a \times$ blood flow

and $\quad$ cm.^{3} X removed via veins $= [X]_v \times$ blood flow

then $\quad$ cm.^{3} X in organ $=$ blood flow $[X]_a - [X]_v$

or $\quad$ blood flow $= \dfrac{\text{cm.}^3 \text{ X in organ}}{[X]_a - [X]_v}$

when $[X]_a$ and $[X]_v$ equal the concentrations of X per cm.[3] of blood in the artery and vein, respectively. Bromsulphalein has been so used in the estimation of liver blood flow,[14, 59] and nitrous oxide in studies of flow through the brain[48] and through the uterus in pregnant patients.[2]

BLOOD FLOW THROUGH THE LUNGS

The pulmonary circulation has two functions: (i) to transfer the blood from the right side of the heart to the left and (ii) to expose the blood to the pulmonary epithelium, where gases are exchanged between the plasma and the alveolar air. The second function is achieved very rapidly. Within two or three seconds blood previously in the right ventricle is exposed in a layer about 10 μ thick with an area of over 100 square feet.[75] A few seconds later, it is collected in the left ventricle. During the brief time the blood is in the lung capillaries, complete equilibrium between the carbon dioxide in the alveolar air and that in the plasma is established. At the same time the blood becomes almost completely oxygenated. The composition of the alveolar air is regulated by the respiratory system so that normal gas pressures in the arterial blood are maintained despite wide variations in the volume of blood flowing through the lungs per unit time.

Over a period of time the right and left ventricles, contracting synchronously, eject equivalent amounts of blood. The blood from the right ventricle raises the pressure in the pulmonary arterial tree from a diastolic level of 7 to 12 mm. Hg (average 10 mm.) to a systolic level of 25 to 28 mm. Hg (average 27 mm.);[47] an equivalent volume of blood raises the pressure in the aorta to 40 mm. Hg. This difference arises because the pulmonary arterial tree, in contrast to the systemic, is more distensible and less elastic and offers less resistance. The pulse wave velocity is much lower in the pulmonary tree, and the mean pressure in the pulmonary artery is only 20 mm. Hg. The resistance in the arterioles of the lungs is only about one-fifth of that in the longer systemic arteries.

The resistance of the systemic circulation serves to maintain a pressure gradient which is so regulated that blood is distributed to different organs in accordance with their needs. Since all parts of the lungs are functionally similar, it appears to be immaterial whether blood is sent to one normal lobe or another. Shunting of blood away from diseased tissue sometimes occurs, but this can be explained without postulating the existence of vasomotor mechanisms like those regulating the systemic arterioles.

In pioneer experiments in which the lungs were artificially perfused or were part of a heart-lung preparation, similar procedures produced similar changes in systemic and pulmonary peripheral resistance—findings that seemed to indicate neural and chemical control of peripheral resistance in the lung. These experimental conditions, however, were quite abnormal in that the pulmonary vessels were forcibly constricted.[18, 31, 40, 74] Normal perfusion pressures produced a blood flow which was only one-tenth or one-twentieth of that in intact animals. In these circumstances, nerve stimulation or the injection of drugs might well cause an increased resistance in the pulmonary bed and a decreased blood flow through the lungs not at all indicative of normal function.

When the blood pressure is recorded from the pulmonary artery of an intact unanesthetized animal, only very slight changes in response to experimental procedures are observed. Thus, when the pulmonary blood flow is increased as a result of exercise[27] or as a result of the administration of drugs which produce systemic vasodilatation, there is only a very small increase in the pulmonary arterial pressure. If the resistance remained the same, doubling the blood flow would double the difference between pressure in the arteries and veins. Actually the pressure difference between the pulmonary arteries and veins increases very little, indicating that the increase in blood flow is accompanied by a decrease in resistance. This apparent decrease in resistance can be easily explained if one assumes that the blood normally flows through partially collapsed vessels which open passively, offering little or no resistance to flow as the stream increases.[40, 44, 47]

Large variations of pressure do occur in the pulmonary artery. Aside from passive changes which result from variations in intrathoracic pressure and do not distend the lung vessels, there are those which result from the backing up of blood into the lungs when the left ventricle is functioning inadequately. These variations occur clinically in congestive failure of the circulation[41] and can be produced experimentally by injection of overwhelming doses of epinephrine that bring about a constriction in the systemic arterioles and a rise in blood pressure against which the left side of the heart cannot discharge.[39] The rise in pulmonary arterial pressure is then equalled by a rise in pulmonary venous pressure, and the pressure gradient between the artery and vein is either unchanged or lessened. A rise in the pressure gradient from the pulmonary artery to the pulmonary vein can be regarded as a clear indication of an increase in the resistance of the pulmonary bed only when there is no increase in pulmonary blood flow. Such a clear indication of increased resistance is not seen following such normal stimuli as exercise,[27] acetylcholine, epinephrine,[40, 44, 47] angiotonin and renin,[50, 55] but only after toxic doses of various substances.[76]

It is well recognized that the oxygen tension of systemic arterial blood does not decrease during pneumonia as much as would be expected on the basis of the proportion of lung tissue which is not ventilated.[70, 71] Also, if a collapsed and a normal lung received blood at equal rates and in equal quantities, the resulting mixture of aerated and non-aerated blood should have an oxygen saturation less than normal by an amount proportional to the amount of unventilated lung tissue. In an animal with one lung collapsed, however, the oxygen saturation of the systemic arterial blood is nearly normal. Hence, in these circumstances, blood must be shunted away from the collapsed area. Such redistribution appears to be achieved by the following means.

The peripheral resistance of the collapsed lung is 5 to 7 mm. Hg higher than that of the normal lung, because the collapsed lung is under atmospheric pressure and the normal lung is under intrathoracic pressure. Since a much smaller change in the pressure gradient between the pulmonary artery and the left atrium results in increased blood flow through the lungs, the 5 to 7 mm. Hg rise is probably sufficient to divert blood from the collapsed lung into the normal one. A similar increase in resistance to blood flow probably occurs when the alveoli are filled with exudate (pneumonia) and when single lobes and lobules are collapsed (atelectasis). However, this mechanism for diverting blood from the collapsed lung is not as effective when the pulmonary vascular pressures are high and the lungs are congested as a result of left ventricular failure; pneumonia leads to anoxia much more readily in patients with congestive failure than in those with a normal circulation.

Although apparently not involved in the regulation of peripheral resistance, a rich supply of vasomotor nerves does serve the pulmonary arteries and arterioles.[53] It alters the capacity of the pulmonary tree and thus the size of the pulmonary blood reservoir.

The amount of blood contained in the lungs varies concomitantly with the pulmonary venous pressure.[31] As in the systemic venous reservoir, pulmonary venous pressure is lowered by cardioacceleration and increased by left ventricular failure. These changes in the pulmonary venous pressure produce passive changes in the filling of the pulmonary blood reservoir. When the amount of blood in the lungs increases, it encroaches upon the space available in the chest for air,[25] as indicated by a reduction in vital capacity in congestive heart failure. A marked decrease in vital capacity occurs in the normal person when he lies down.[24, 41, 46] This decrease is related to changes in the circulation because the diminution in vital capacity is much less when the venous return is hindered by tourniquets placed about the bases of the arms and legs before the subject reclines. Because the tourniquets trap blood in the vascular bed of the extremities, any increase in return for storage in the lungs is subnormal. As a consequence, the normal postural pulmonary congestion is reduced so that the subject's vital capacity is nearer that which he possessed when standing.

Changes in intrathoracic pressure affect blood flow and blood pressure both directly and indirectly. Pressure rises simultaneously and equally in the thorax, abdomen and cerebrospinal canal as a result of expiratory efforts such as coughing and straining.[42] During inspiratory efforts such as gasping, the abdominal pressure may increase, while the thoracic pressure decreases and cerebrospinal pressure maintains an intermediate level.

During an expiratory effort there is no change in the pressure gradient which transfers either venous or arterial blood from one part of the three great cavities to another, but the rise in pressure in the thorax, cerebrospinal canal and abdomen is transmitted directly to the heart and blood vessels, producing a rise in the pressure of the incompressible blood these vessels contain. This pressure rise, which may, in a vigorous cough, amount to 100 to 150 mm. Hg, puts no strain on the walls of the vessels within the three great cavities. It is transmitted along the arterial tree to the head and the extremities, where it produces a rise in the effective arterial pressure. During a coughing spell the peripheral arterial pressure may fluctuate over a range two or three times the normal.[42, 43]

If the high intrathoracic pressure is maintained for more than a few seconds (as in straining at stool), it interferes with the venous return (Fig. 440). This reduces the width

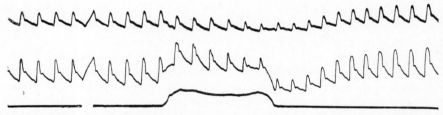

FIG. 440. Effect of increased intrathoracic pressure upon blood pressure in man. From below upward: intrathoracic pressure, arterial pressure, arterial pressure minus intrathoracic pressure as recorded by a differential manometer.

of the pulse pressure and the mean height of the arterial pressure, so that the intrathoracic blood vessels are less distended than normal, although the vessels outside the three great cavities may contain blood at a pressure that is above normal.

When the straining suddenly ceases, the high intrathoracic pressure no longer supports the arterial pressure, and the pressure in the extrathoracic vessels suddenly falls by the same amount as the decrease in straining pressure. The pressure distending the intrathoracic vessels, however, does not change. This phase of the response to strain (Valsalva's experiment) is short-lived, because the blood which had been dammed back in the great veins by the high intrathoracic pressure surges back to the heart. There results a great increase in the mean arterial pressure and in the pulse pressure, and often a reflex cardiac slowing. During the strain, the thoracic pressure is transmitted to the great arteries in the chest and out over the arterial tree. The arterial pressure is therefore the sum of the intrathoracic pressure and the pressure actually produced by the heart beat. Only pressure of cardiac origin distends the vessels of the thorax, abdomen and brain, but the pressure produced by contraction of the thoracic and abdominal walls distends also the peripheral vessels.

Arterial pressure changes which result from changes in intrathoracic pressure are, therefore, of two kinds: those which result from simple propagation of thoracic pressure and those which result from changes in cardiac output produced by changes which the variations in intrathoracic pressure make in cardiac filling. In normal life, the venous pressure is such that the heart is equally well filled in all phases of the respiratory cycle;

but if for any reason the venous pressure is low or the intrathoracic pressure changes are large, fluctuations in blood flow produce pressure changes which are added to those produced by simple propagation of intrathoracic pressure. Changes in blood pressure produced by changes in blood flow, in relation to the phases of the respiratory cycle, are delayed by the length of time it takes to flush blood through the heart and lungs.

BLOOD FLOW THROUGH THE LIVER

The blood for the liver is supplied through two separate channels, one bringing arterial and the other venous blood. The arterialized blood enters via the hepatic artery to be distributed to the walls of the biliary channels, the portal blood vessels, Glisson's capsule and the investing connective tissue. From these structures the blood drains into the hepatic veins. The venous blood from the splanchnic bed is distributed to the parenchyma of the liver through branches of the portal vein that run from the hilum or central region toward the surface of the organ in courses more or less parallel to those

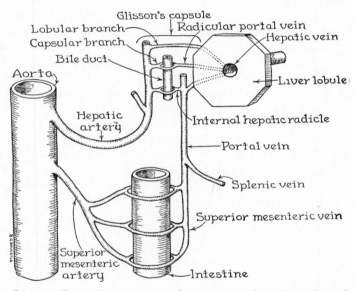

FIG. 441.   Diagram illustrating anastomoses between systemic and portal vessels in liver.

of the hepatic veins which convey blood from the sinusoids toward the inferior vena cava (Fig. 441). Throughout the liver substance, the branches of these two vascular trees—intrahepatic portal and hepatic venous—run in close approximation, although conducting in opposite directions. They are separated from each other by a relatively thin layer of parenchyma. The sinusoids of this parenchyma, together with other small afferent and efferent vessels distributed along the length of the two systems, provide channels through which blood can move from a portal to an adjacent hepatic vein at all levels from the hilum to the periphery of the liver. Radiographic studies indicate there are no shunts as such in the vascular bed of the liver, although blood sometimes perfuses more rapidly through the central channels and more slowly, or not at all, through the more peripheral.[20, 21] That is to say, the deeper or more central parts of the liver may be perfused to the exclusion of the more distal or peripheral parts. These radiographic studies are in accord with earlier observations suggesting that the intra-hepatic circulation may be intermittent,[3] and, further, that as much as 75 per cent of the hepatic circulation may be inactive during conditions in which the musculature of the liver vessels is neither excited nor inhibited.

In the resting man[15, 59] the combined blood flow to the liver from the hepatic artery and the portal vein, as estimated by the clearance of bromsulphalein, is about 1400 ml. per minute (circa 800 ml. per square meter of body surface), a figure that is of the same order as that obtained in unanesthetized dogs,[66] i.e., 82 ml. per minute per 100 grams of liver. In man this flow represents about 20 per cent of the cardiac output. If the circumstances governing hepatic blood flow in the human are comparable to those in the dog,[13, 68] 10 to 30 per cent of the blood enters the liver via the hepatic artery and 70 to 90 per cent via the portal vein. In conditions other than rest, the wide variations in flow through one vessel are reflected in compensatory changes in the other. However, the combined inflow via the hepatic artery[16] and portal vein may briefly exceed or fall below the outflow in the hepatic veins as blood is stored or released from the liver sinusoids, sometimes in a rhythmic fashion.

Variations in blood flow through the liver primarily result from intrahepatic vasomotor changes.[38] Vasomotor fibers to intrahepatic branches of the portal vein leave the cord from the third to the 11th thoracic spinal segment in the dog, the main concentration being centered in T_{5-9}. Stimulation of these fibers results in constriction of the intrahepatic vessels of the portal venous tree, a marked rise in the pressure in the portal vein, a decrease in the liver volume and an acceleration of the transhepatic circulation. Essentially similar changes follow the intraportal injection of epinephrine. Vasoconstrictor fibers are contributed via the splanchnics and the hepatic plexus to the arterioles of the branches of the hepatic artery. Vasodilatation of these arterioles occurs as a part of the reflex adjustments of the vasomotor system, but the existence of vasodilator fibers leading to them has not been demonstrated; the response appears to be a passive one.

Although the hepatic veins of the dog possess a muscular coat that serves to constrict them in a sphincter-like fashion under the influence of histamine, this arrangement appears to be a species peculiarity and not a general feature among mammals. There is at the moment no satisfactory evidence for the existence of such sphincters in man, nor is there any clear indication that the hepatic veins, except in the carnivora, modify the blood flow from the liver to the inferior vena cava.

Through the operations of these mechanisms, acting directly or reflexly, the volume of the liver is decreased in response to an increase in the carbon dioxide content of the inspired air, to oxygen want, and to a decrease in blood volume—all stresses that evoke a pressor response in the vasomotor system. Conversely, liver volume increases as a part of depressor adjustments. That is to say, the liver acts as a blood store. For example, in response to epinephrine injected into the portal vein, the liver of the dog can deliver into the inferior vena cava a volume of blood equal to 26 to 59 per cent of the hepatic weight.[34, 56, 66] This blood is said to have been stored in the liver, not because it is in a cul-de-sac, but because the blood can be directed to other portions of the vascular system.[6] The transfer is accomplished by the conversion of a fairly large bed with a slowly moving stream into a smaller one in which the flow is faster. Decreasing the rate of flow through the liver conversely increases the volume of blood in it. At the moment there is no evidence to indicate that in cardiac insufficiency the liver blood flow is decreased in relation to that of other parts of the circulation, but under such conditions in man the liver may contain 1.5 liters of blood. The storage of blood by the liver reduces the venous return and so the load on the heart.

The vascular bed of the liver exercises a further regulation over the circulating blood volume through its relationship with the portal system.[52] Because of their position between two variable resistances provided by the arterioles of the gut at one end and the intrahepatic vessels on the other, the portal vein and its tributaries function as a blood depot. An increase in the resistance offered by the mesenteric arterioles, such as occurs reflexly when the demands of the extrasplanchnic areas are high, decreases the inflow to the portal system; through concomitant constriction of the portal vessels the blood is driven, at a pressure adequate to overcome their low resistance, through the intrahepatic portal branches and the sinusoids into the hepatic veins and the inferior vena cava.[9, 10] Conversely, dilatation of the arterioles leading to the portal system is followed by an increase in its content of blood; simultaneous dilatation of the capillaries and vessels of the splanchnic bed permits a large increase in the capacity of the system, and the associated dilatation of the larger portal vessels results in a fall in the pressure on the blood and a diminished flow through the intrahepatic vessels.[10]

This regulatory capacity is indicated by data of two varieties. Infusion of small amounts of fluid is said to dilate segments of mesenteric veins with their nerve supply intact but separated from the circulation. Conversely, withdrawal of blood from the circulation is followed by constriction. Further, infusion of large volumes of fluid result in a sharp rise in the volume of blood in the portal system and in the pressure on it, in the absence of any change in the pressure in the inferior vena cava. The rise in pressure in the portal system is thought to indicate an increase in the resistance to flow through the liver that serves to trap and retain the added volume of fluid in the portal system. The resistance offered by the intrahepatic vessels that serves to pool blood in the portal system may be said to be neural in origin, for denervation of the liver destroys this capacity and removes a principal part of the regulatory control through which the hepatic portal system modifies the venous return and the cardiac output.

BLOOD FLOW THROUGH THE SPLEEN

As the blood flow through an active organ is increased over that occurring during the inactive state, so also is the volume of blood which is present in its vascular bed. Thus in exercise, when a large number of muscles are simultaneously active and the minute volume rises to four or five times the resting value, the volume of circulating blood increases and the pressure rises slightly. A similar increase in the volume of circulating blood occurs during regulation against heat, when the blood flow through the skin is increased and the minute volume may be doubled or more. In these and like circumstances, the volume of circulating blood is increased by the withdrawals of blood from stores or depots into the active circulation. These depots include the aorta, the great veins, the portal system, the venous plexus of the skin, the liver sinusoids, the spleen and the lungs.

Although the volume of the aorta and its larger branches does change in certain circumstances,[32] these vessels do not give up appreciable quantities of blood during activity, because the arterial pressure equals or exceeds that in the resting state; and the aorta, as a consequence, is almost as widely distended during exercise as it is at rest. The reservoirs or blood depots are, therefore, to be thought of as appendages to the venous system, providing a means, by emptying and filling, for the regulation of the venous return. From these depots sufficient blood may be withdrawn during severe exercise to increase the volume of circulating blood between 25 and 30 per cent. Of this quantity an estimated 200 to 250 ml. can be contributed by the spleen; the remainder is probably provided by the portal circulation, the skin, the liver and the lungs. Blood may be withdrawn from these depots—as pointed out in the discussions of the circulation through the liver, the lungs and the skin—by the reduction in venous pressure which results from cardioacceleration; also it may be forced out by the active contraction of the walls of these reservoirs evoked through the action of the sympathetic nervous system. The spleen empties actively; the other depots empty both passively and actively.[28]

The smooth muscle of the capsule and trabeculae of the spleen is provided with efferent fibers by the sympathetic outflow via the splanchnics and along the splenic artery. Upon activation of these efferent nerves the spleen contracts, producing a pressure which in some animals (if the vein is occluded) may reach 100 mm. Hg, and expels its store of blood into the splenic vein. The variety of circumstances in which these fibers are active and the splenic blood is returned to the active circulation has been admirably demonstrated by Barcroft[7] on dogs with exteriorized spleens, in which the volume changes could be measured or followed visually. The acute circumstances—in addition to exercise and exposure to raised external temperature—in which the volume of the spleen decreases include hemorrhage, emotional conditions, anoxia and the administration of certain anesthetics such as chloroform and ether; the subacute circumstances include estrus, pregnancy and lactation. Acute or subacute, these are circumstances in which there is an increase in either blood flow or metabolism to be balanced by an increase in blood volume or a rise in oxygen-carrying power of the blood. The balance is achieved through two mechanisms: (i) a fall in systemic blood pressure working via the carotid sinus and depressor nerves, and (ii) anoxia signaled by the carotid bodies, leading in each circumstance to a reflex contraction of the spleen.

The evidence that the blood which is forced from the spleen in these conditions of stress was stored there and kept out of the general circulation was also provided by Barcroft. When rats were made to breathe mixtures containing 0.6 to 0.7 per cent carbon monoxide in air, there was a lag of about 30 minutes before the concentration of CO-hemoglobin in the red blood cells of the spleen became equal to that of the red cells in the circulating blood. Conversely, CO-hemoglobin was lost from the spleen pulp less readily than from the general circulation when animals were given air to breathe in place of the gas mixture. These observations have been confirmed and extended to other animal species by a number of investigators.

Dilator fibers to the spleen have not been demonstrated, although a rise in pressure in the carotid sinus or stimulation of the depressor nerve in the rabbit leads to reflex dilatation of the spleen. Dilatation is, therefore, a passive process and appears to be produced by the exposure of the spleen to arterial pressure as a result of the relaxation of the arterioles and/or by constriction of the splenic vein by the action of the venomotor fibers which end in its musculature. Destruction of these fibers, which in the dog reach the splenic vein via the left phrenic nerve, abolishes reflex dilatation of the spleen.

The nervous control of the flow through the splenic vein appears to be important in another connection, i.e., the concentration of the blood in the spleen. In those animals whose spleens have a well developed muscular capsule, the rhythmic splenic contractions, by increasing the internal pressure, and the splenic vein, by preventing the escape of splenic blood, serve to filter and to squeeze out the fluid which is returned to the general circulation via the lymph. The blood coming from the spleen in these animals—the horse, the dog and the cat—is rich in corpuscles. Cruikshank found, for example, that the blood expelled from the cat's spleen by splanchnic stimulation was equal to 2.6 to 5.6 per cent of the total circulating blood volume and possessed an average hemoglobin value of 115 per cent, although that of some samples reached 140 per cent.

BLOOD FLOW THROUGH THE KIDNEY

The primary role of the kidney in the over-all economy of the body is the regulation of the composition of the blood; accordingly, the blood flow through the kidney is related more intimately to the general body metabolism and the composition of the blood than to local metabolic requirements. The total kidney blood flow in an individual in the postabsorptive state is of the order of 1.3 liters per minute, or about one-fourth of the cardiac output, and, like it, is proportional to the body surface and metabolic rate.

The blood reaching the kidney via the renal artery may reach the renal vein via either of two routes.[72] One leads from the afferent arterioles of the interlobular arteries through the cortical glomeruli into the interlobular capillary net that drains into the interlobular veins. The second route is via the afferent arterioles of the juxtamedullary glomeruli, through the vasa recta, to the interlobular veins. In some circumstances perfusion through the cortical route may be interrupted and blood diverted to the second; it has been suggested that, conversely, the flow may be concurrently increased through the cortex and diminished through medullary routes.

Nervous Control. The existence of both vasoconstrictor and vasodilator fibers to the intrarenal vessels of the kidney has been recognized since Bradford's classic studies in 1899.[14] In the dog, vasoconstrictor fibers to the kidney leave the cord in the anterior roots of segments T_{6-12}, being most concentrated in T_{10-13}; vasodilator fibers, concentrated in the anterior roots of T_{11-13} enter the splanchnic nerve to relay in the inferior mesenteric ganglia, from whence postganglionic fibers enter the hilum of the kidney. Stimulation of the fibers of the renal plexus results in a decrease in kidney volume,[14] a blanching of the cortex,[29] and a cessation of the flow through the cortical glomeruli.[19] Accordingly, vasoconstrictor fibers must reach the interlobular arteries, and the fact that vessels in only one sector of the cortex may be affected indicates that the fibers in the renal plexus are selectively distributed to the periphery. There is evidence, too, that vasoconstrictor fibers reach the vessels of the medulla, because stimulation of the renal plexus reduces the medullary flow as estimated with a thermocouple flowmeter.[65] The intrarenal distribution of the vasodilator fibers identified by Bradford has not been determined.

In man, there appears to be no increase in renal flow when the action of the vasomotor centers on the kidney vessels is paralyzed by spinal anesthesia. This fact argues against the existence of any persistent vasoconstrictor tone of neurogenic origin in the basal state. Moreover, the vascular bed of the kidney, as judged from plethysmographic records of the whole organ, takes a very minor part in pressure adjustments when the dynamics of the cardiovascular system are altered by stimulation of the depressor nerve or the central end of the sciatic; the adjustments that do occur in the inter-renal system during these "pressor" and "depressor" responses appear to be directed to the maintenance of constant flow despite the changing pressures.[14] Further, the kidney flow is little altered during the vasomotor adjustments associated with warming and cooling the whole animal.[63] On the other hand, blood is diverted from the kidney as a part of a pressor response to electrical stimulation of foci in the anterior sigmoid gyri in cats, an effect that is abolished by renal denervation.[45] Moreover, the inhalation of ether and cyclopropane is associated with a pronounced increase in the resistance of the vascular net of the kidney that is of neural origin.[60] The role of these responses to cortical stimulation and to inhaled anesthetics in the general economy of the body is far from clear; equally obscure is the significance of the renal ischemia of neural origin that occurs in response to anoxia (8 per cent oxygen in nitrogen) and hypercapnia (9 to 25 per cent carbon dioxide in oxygen).[29] These responses illustrate the mechanism but they offer little clue to its purpose.

Chemical Control. As a consequence of the abundant flow, the kidney receives a blood supply in excess of its metabolic needs, and the arteriovenous oxygen difference is low. It is not surprising, therefore, that no relationship between the metabolic needs of the kidney and the blood flow has been established beyond the fact that the oxygen consumption increases in proportion to blood flow, although it is not related to urine flow. There is some evidence, however, that a change in urea clearance may be effected by increasing the protein content of the diet, and that this change in clearance is accompanied by an increase in the blood flow through the kidney; but the data do not permit a statement on the extent to which the increase in flow is a result of local changes in the kidney or of an increase in the general circulation.

BLOOD FLOW THROUGH THE UTERUS

The role of the uterus in the female reproductive cycle largely determines its blood flow. In the barren uterus the flow waxes and wanes during the menstrual cycle; in the gravid uterus the blood flow increases to provide for the growing fetus and its membranes. Finally, at parturition the flow is modified by the contractions of the uterine musculature, and after the expulsion of the fetus it returns to the level typical of the barren uterus. The factors which regulate the blood flow through the uterine vascular bed in each one of these three stages have not been finally determined.

The vasomotor fibers with which the uterine and vaginal vessels are supplied appear to belong entirely to the sympathetic system. Their activation is followed by vasoconstriction which is not abolished by atropine; when their tonic control is removed (for example, by transection of the spinal cord), the uterine vascular bed becomes dilated and congested for a time. Despite these indications, the nervous control of the uterine vessels must be accessory rather than essential, for sympathectomized females can conceive and give birth to normal young.

The dominant control over the vessels of the uterus appears to be exercised by hormones. For example, under the influence of estrin the uterus becomes hyperemic before its metabolic activity is increased; hence, estrin appears to have a direct effect upon the vessels themselves. The blood leaving the uterus under these circumstances is arterial in color, for the increase in the volume of the circulation exceeds the oxygen requirements of the tissues. However, fluid is lost and the perfused tissue becomes swollen and edematous as a result of an increased capillary filtration.

In the early stages of gestation the same relationships continue. The blood flow through the uterus is quite in excess of the oxygen requirements of the tissues it supplies, as is indicated by the high oxygen content of the blood in the uterine veins. In the period that follows, the minute volume of blood appears to increase in parallel with the growth of placenta, reaching a maximum near the end of the first two-thirds of the gestation period. Thereafter, the blood flow remains relatively constant, although the metabolic requirements of the uterine contents continue to increase, with the result that the blood leaving the uterus contains progressively less oxygen. Since the blood flow appears to be correlated with the size of the placenta and not with the oxygen requirements of the tissues supplied, the evidence favors the view that the placental hormones are prominent

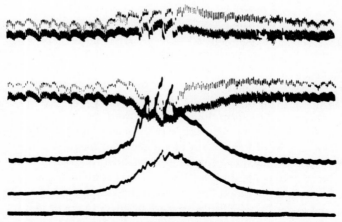

FIG. 442.   Pressure relations during labor. From above downward: arterial pressure, arterial pressure minus uterine pressure, uterine pressure, uterine pressure minus gastric pressure.

in the control of the uterine circulation. This possibility receives some support from studies on the hypertension which often disturbs the later months of pregnancy. Hypertension with eclamptic-like convulsions has been produced by restricting the blood flow through the uterine arteries[61] as well as by mechanically preventing the increase in renal blood flow normally associated with pregnancy.[23] The hypertension is relieved either with the termination of pregnancy or with the removal of the restriction on the renal or uterine blood flow.

During parturition, the circulation through the uterus and the placenta is modified by the high intrauterine pressure which develops during labor pains;[77] the arterial pressure rises and the pulse pressure increases (Fig. 442), since the uterine contraction forces the venous blood from the placenta and thereby increases the venous return. In spite of this rise in blood pressure, there is a fall in the head of pressure irrigating the placenta, because the intrauterine pressure rises more than the blood pressure.

The pressure within the uterus can be measured by leading an air column from a balloon in the uterus to a manometer. By comparison with a record of the blood pressure taken simultaneously, the amount by which the latter exceeds the former can be estimated. This excess pressure, or effective head of pressure, can also be recorded by means of the differential manometer (Fig. 443).

Increases in intrauterine pressure are produced not only by the contraction of the uterine musculature but also by the contraction of the abdominal walls, which raises the pressure within the abdomen and uterus equally. An increase in intrauterine pressure brought about in this manner does not impair the uterine circulation, for it is transmitted directly to the abdominal and thoracic blood vessels and hence is balanced by a simultaneous increase in arterial pressure. There is, therefore, no net change in the pressure

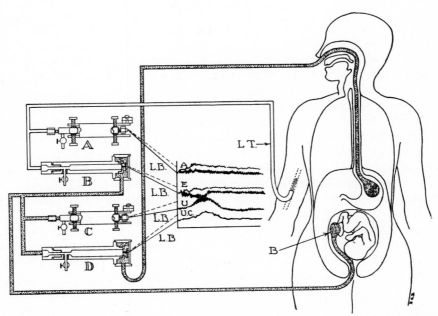

FIG. 443. Diagram showing simultaneous recording of arterial pressure (A), of head of pressure irrigating placenta (E), of intrauterine pressure (U), and of force which uterine wall contributes to intrauterine pressure. E is obtained by leading arterial pressure to optical manometer, membrane of which is enclosed in chamber to which intrauterine pressure is led. Contribution of uterine wall to intrauterine pressure is measured by a similar differential manometer which subtracts intragastric pressure from uterine pressure.

which irrigates the uterus unless straining is prolonged for ten or 15 seconds and interferes with the venous return to the heart. The reflex bearing down efforts last such a short time that this factor plays no role. Voluntary bearing down is often prolonged at the urging of the obstetrician, so that the circulation may fail for want of venous return.

Careful measurements indicate that during the course of normal labor the blood flow through the placenta is insured by the natural relationship between intrauterine and arterial pressure. Unfortunately this is not true when drugs (ergot and Pituitrin) are administered to hasten the course of labor (Fig. 444). Administration of these drugs results in an abnormally high intrauterine pressure which is maintained for a long time. This high intrauterine pressure prevents blood from reaching the placenta for a length of time sufficient to produce serious signs of fetal asphyxia (cardiac slowing, weak fetal heart sounds or even cessation of heartbeat).

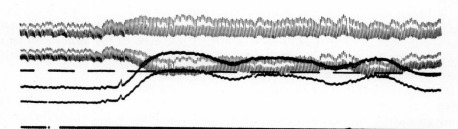

FIG. 444.   Effect of pituitary extract upon uterine and blood pressures. From above downward: arterial pressure, arterial pressure minus uterine pressure, uterine pressure, uterine pressure minus gastric pressure.

BLOOD FLOW TO THE SKIN

The vascular bed of the skin—in addition to providing for the metabolic needs of its tissues—plays a prominent role in the regulation of the body temperature. The changes in blood flow associated with the metabolic needs are governed predominantly by local mechanisms; those associated with the regulation of heat loss are under the control of centers in the hypothalamus.

Control of Circulation.   CHEMICAL MECHANISMS.   Of the local mechanisms which maintain the blood flow in accordance with metabolic needs of the skin, the action of locally formed metabolites directly upon the arteriolar wall is the simplest because it is an independent affector;[64] that is to say, the dilatation produced by metabolites does not depend upon the integrity of any nervous connection.[57]

The most striking illustration of the action of local metabolites is *reactive hyperemia*. When, for example, the blood flow to the arm is arrested, the arterioles gradually dilate. As a result, when blood is again permitted to flow, the skin becomes flushed and hot and begins to throb. Plethysmographic evidence indicates that a blood flow greater than that prior to the arrest is manifest with the first pulse beat after the release of the occlusion; hence, the arterioles appear to have dilated during the period of ischemia. The degree of dilatation is proportional to the duration of the ischemia. When pure oxygen is allowed to diffuse through the skin while the circulation is arrested, reactive hyperemia no longer follows ischemia.[33] Presumably, reactive hyperemia is caused by accumulation of a metabolite of anoxic cells during the ischemia. This metabolite has not yet been identified.

After sympathectomy, the flow of blood through the paw of the cat is determined by the metabolic rate of the cutaneous tissues. Specifically, when the metabolic rate is varied by changing the temperature of the paw, the blood flow is regulated so that the arteriovenous oxygen difference is constant over wide ranges of oxygen consumption and blood flow.[30]

NERVOUS MECHANISMS. The blood flow through the skin is also regulated locally by means of the axon reflex. The vascular reactions which follow injury serve to illustrate its function.[54] If a drop of weak histamine solution is laid on the skin and the underlying region is pricked with a needle, the subcutaneous tissues are injured by the chemical. A similar injury is produced by pricking alone in a sensitive (urticarial) skin. A local redness due to capillary dilatation appears in the injury area and is followed by a swelling which obscures the color of the dilated capillaries, producing a pale wheal. A red flare, which is due to arteriolar dilatation, surrounds the wheal. If the skin has been anesthetized, the red flare is absent. A nervous element is therefore necessary for the response. If, however, the cutaneous nerve trunk is narcotized or has only recently been cut, the flare is present. The response is, therefore, not mediated by a reflex through the central nervous system, although the peripheral nerve fiber is necessary because the red flare is no longer seen if the cutaneous nerve has been cut long enough before to have degenerated.

The hypothesis usually accepted to account for the above facts is that the afferent fiber from the receptor in the skin gives off a collateral to the blood vessel; activation of this collateral causes dilatation of the arterioles responsible for the red flare. The anatomic background for such a mechanism was worked out by Woollard in 1926.[78] Further evidence that collaterals from sensory nerves have a vasomotor function has been provided by plethysmographic studies which indicate that, when the peripheral end of a severed dorsal root is stimulated, the vessels in the corresponding skin area dilate; and there is some evidence to indicate that this path plays a role in the reflex adjustment of cutaneous blood flow.[8]

The importance of the axon reflex and the direct responses of arterioles in the regulation of the circulation can be illustrated by the fact that peripheral blood vessels deprived of their connection with the central nervous system by sympathectomy,[8, 17] by spinal anesthesia,[67] or even by the complete destruction of the spinal cord[55] can still respond by dilating and constricting as the occasion demands. Furthermore, the finer adjustments of the circulation which result in the local regulation of temperature are said to depend on local cutaneous mechanisms and short reflexes, whereas the center for temperature regulation in the hypothalamus serves to prevent gross changes in the temperature of the blood.[11]

Stimulation of the afferent end of the auricular nerve brings about a dilatation of the ear vessels. This and similar reflex responses in which a dilatation is produced in a field localized about the site of the stimulus are commonly spoken of as "Lovén reflexes."[7] The same stimulus which evokes a Lovén reflex is followed by axonal and general reflexes as well. The general reflexes may be considered as responses to superficial pain, for they give rise to a generalized vasoconstriction which is part of the emergency mechanism, and consequently to a rise in blood pressure. Thus two effects from painful stimulation can be recognized—a local dilatation which may be aimed toward local repair of injury, and a generalized constriction which is a part of the response to emergency and which fits the whole organism for combat or flight.

HORMONAL MECHANISMS. Two hormonal mechanisms can be clearly distinguished in control of the circulation to the skin and elsewhere: (i) angiotonin which is elaborated in response to the secretion of renin by the kidney and which serves to regulate the myogenic tone of all of the arterioles in the body; and (ii) the sympathetic hormone epinephrine, which, together with sympathin, mimics the action of sympathetic endings and produces specific and adaptive constrictions in response to emergency situations. Acetylcholine, secreted by parasympathetic and other nerve endings, has little systemic effect.

Role in Temperature Regulation. It was pointed out in Chapter 10 that peripheral vasoconstriction and vasodilatation are among the mechanisms utilized by the hypothalamus in the regulation of heat loss and conservation. Cutaneous vasodilatation in response to a rise in body temperature is a prepotent reflex. Blood will flow through the skin of an overheated individual even when his circulation fails to meet the demands of the body's activity. This failure precipitates a fall in blood pressure which, in cool environments, would give rise to cutaneous vasoconstriction. In the overheated individual the constriction is not achieved, with the result that the fall in blood pressure in heat exhaustion is often shocklike in its intensity.[22] If the environmental temperature increases to a moderate degree, generalized cutaneous vasodilatation is not accompanied by a fall in blood pressure. The widened vascular bed is filled by a movement of tissue fluids into the vascular space, with a resulting increase in the blood volume of from 10 to 20 per cent.[6, 12]

Storage Function. The vascular bed of the skin—in particular the subpapillary venous plexus—is thought to serve as a blood store. A dog may be infused with a volume of blood equal to its own circulating volume without raising its arterial or venous pressures beyond physiologic limits.[58] Microscopic examination of the skin of a dog so infused reveals that the subpapillary venous plexus is much engorged. The implication is, of course, that a fraction of the infused blood has been stored in the plexus. This blood in the venous plexus can be returned to the active circulation by a reduction of the venous pressure through cardiac acceleration and perhaps by an active contraction of the venous walls.

BLOOD SUPPLY TO THE SKELETAL MUSCLES

The method of plethysmography has been applied with conspicuous success to an analysis of the factors that modify the blood flow through the muscles of the forearm and calf. In these limbs the muscles form such a substantial part of the tissue enclosed by the plethysmograph—about 85 per cent in the case of the forearm—that any material variation from the resting flow can be attributed to a change in the circulation through them. The increase in flow resulting from hyperemia in the skin on the enclosed portion of the extremity has been shown to be but 1.0 to 2.2 ml. per 100 cm.³ of limb.

The results obtained from such studies on man corroborate and extend the results of earlier experiments made on animals[51] in which the flow and its changes were followed in the vessels leading to or from a muscle or muscle group. At rest, the blood flow through the forearm muscles that act on the wrist is of the order of 2 to 7 ml. per 100 cm.³ of muscle per minute, a rate that is at the lower end of the range obtained in studies on animals, i.e., 4 to 44 ml. per 100 cm.³ per minute; but it is one that would appear to be more truly representative of the flow in the muscles of the normal limb. In strong rhythmic exercise, the rate of flow may increase during the phases of relaxation to about 40 ml. per minute for each 100 cm.³ of tissue enclosed.

When a skeletal muscle contracts as a result of direct stimulation of its motor nerve or voluntary or reflex action, the movement of the blood through its muscles is altered (i) by changes in the intrinsic state of the vessels and (ii) by the mechanical action of the contracting fibers as they compress the associated vessels. Each of these effects tends to increase with the increase in the force of the contraction; the pattern of blood flow is the resultant of their interaction and the pressure head in the aorta. The initial effect on the movement of blood in the vascular net of the muscles appears to be a mechanical one. As the muscle contracts, the flow from the associated veins increases sharply as the blood contained within them during the resting stage is pressed out and driven toward the right heart. Simultaneously, if the force of the contraction is sufficient, the flow in the intramuscular arteries may actually be reversed. This period, during which the intramuscular vessels on either side of the capillaries are emptied and the venous outflow is increased, is followed by one in which the outflow is decreased—an interval in which the intramuscular vessels are refilled. If the contraction of the muscle is such that the tension developed is, say, 10 per cent of the possible maximum above the resting level, a hyperemia may develop. The period of diminished flow is followed by one in which the volume of flow rises to a plateau where it persists as the tension is maintained; the increased flow is due to the active dilatation of the intramuscular vessels. With the relaxation of the tension and the external pressure on the vessels, there may be an additional sharp increase in the flow rate, after which it falls slowly toward the resting level. The degree of postcontraction hyperemia and its duration are, of course, functions of the energy released by the muscle. Evidence derived from flow rate studies on the gastrocnemius-soleus complex in man indicates that, during a tension 20 per cent of maximal,

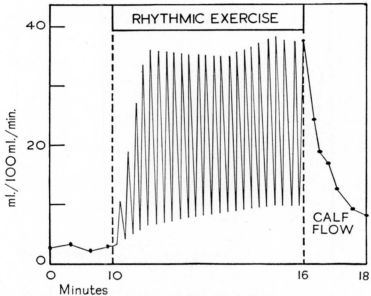

FIG. 445. Schematic representation of changes in blood flow through muscles of calf during strong rhythmic contraction. (From Barcroft and Swan, *Sympathetic control of human blood vessels*. London, E. Arnold, 1953.)

the mechanical action of the muscles may prevent the development of the hyperemia that is seen during weaker contractions and reduce the flow to insignificant amounts— that is to say, in the calf muscles of man the flow appears to be very free and relatively unaffected by the mechanical action of contractions that are 10 per cent of maximal, whereas it is nearly or quite obstructed when the force of contraction exceeds a critical level just above that range. Similar effects doubtless occur in other contracting muscles, although the relationship between the degree of limitation of the flow and the fraction of maximal tension developed may vary. Certainly, the mechanical effect of the contracting muscles can be considerable, for forceful contraction of the forearm muscles may obliterate the radial pulse, and contraction of the leg muscles can drive blood from a segment in which the venous pressure is elevated to 90 to 100 mm. Hg by means of a proximally placed inflated cuff.

In rhythmically contracting muscles, the alterations in the pattern of blood flow follow much the same sequence with each contraction. As release follows contraction, the flow through the muscles increases sharply, and each ensuing contraction drives the larger volume of blood in the expanded bed forward toward the heart. The variations in flow as they occur in the calf muscles during strong rhythmic contraction are schematically represented in Figure 445.

Vasoconstrictor fibers appear to be distributed to vessels of skeletal muscle in all mammals, for it is generally agreed that cutting a motor nerve increases the flow through the associated muscle, and in man procaine block of the sympathetic fibers to the forearm muscles, sparing those to the skin, serves to increase the blood flow to about twice its resting level. Conversely, intense stimulation of the motor nerve of a curarized muscle is followed by a vasoconstriction that can be abolished by ergotoxine. Vasodilator fibers serve the skeletal muscles of the extremities in man and the dog, but appear to be absent from the muscles of some other animals, e.g., the rabbit and the monkey. The activity of

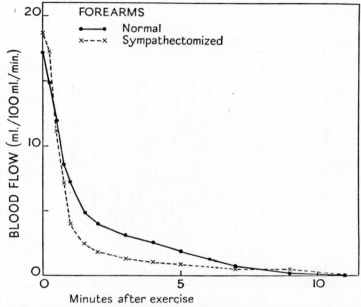

FIG. 446. Graph illustrating initial magnitude and decline of blood flow in normal and sympathectomized forearm muscles after exercise. Similarity of the two curves is evidence that the arterioles that dilate during exercise are not under control of sympathetic nervous system. (From Grant, *Clin. Sci.*, 1938, *3*:157–174.)

the vasomotor fibers to skeletal muscle might be expected to be linked with the increased blood flow occurring during exercise, but that is clearly not the case, for Grant[35, 36] and more recently H. Barcroft and his collaborators[4] have shown that the hyperemia which follows standard exercise is essentially the same in normal and sympathectomized muscle (Fig. 446). Similarly, releasing the sympathetic vasoconstrictor tone to a muscle by heating the limb before the exercise, although it serves to increase the rate of flow through the vessels in the muscle during the ensuing activity, does not alter the "blood debt" acquired. This "debt" is repaid in the postexercise period. The inference is that, in the main, the vasodilatation that occurs in exercise is caused by the action of metabolites. If that inference is correctly drawn, there would appear to be two more or less independent vascular nets in skeletal muscle: one that serves its metabolic needs and is regulated by the concentrations of local metabolites, and a second that is under the control of the sympathetic system.

Of these two nets, only the latter appears to be influenced by epinephrine. Injected intra-arterially, epinephrine produces a transient vasodilatation that appears to be due to direct local action, for it occurs in the sympathectomized limb; injected intravenously, however, epinephrine produces the same transient vasodilatation, but it is followed by a sustained dilatation of a lesser magnitude. This action of intravenous epinephrine is thought to result from the action of a hormone which is released during the passage of the epinephrine from the venous to the arterial side of the circulation—one that works its effect only when the sympathetic innervation is intact or has recently been so. In any event, this sustained period of increased blood flow, like that due to warming, does not alter the extent or duration of the hyperemia of the postexercise period. The vessels affected are apparently not those influenced by the locally produced metabolites. Norepinephrine, thought to be the mediator of excitatory sympathetic nerve impulses, when infused into either a vein or the associated artery in very small doses (2.5 μg. per min.), causes an arteriolar constriction and diminished blood flow in muscle without any vasodilatation. Similar changes in muscle blood flow appear to be produced in the cat by these two substances, epinephrine and norepinephrine.

What is the wider function of these vascular channels that are under the control of the nervous system? To this question no final answer can be given, but the channels may provide a mechanism for the redistribution of blood in the vascular net. The contraction of one muscle of a limb evokes vasodilatation in the resting muscles of the same and in those of the opposite limb. And there appears to be an even higher level of integration of these vessels in skeletal muscle supplied with vasomotor fibers, for Green and Hoff[37] have shown that the volume of the muscles represented in a portion of the motor cortex increases as a result of vasodilatation induced by previous stimulation of the cortical region. The vasodilatation, evoked reflexly or by cortical stimulation, was assumed in the past to provide an increased blood flow in anticipation of activity, but the evidence now available appears to contradict that view.

CIRCULATION THROUGH THE BRAIN

By JOHN L. PATTERSON, JR.*

THE brain is one of the most actively metabolizing organs of the body. This metabolism depends for its ultimate energy supply primarily upon the aerobic combustion of glucose. Since there is little storage of glucose and oxygen, even brief interference with the cerebral circulation can bring about profound disturbances of neurologic and mental functions. Duration of consciousness, for example, is less than 10 seconds following complete cessation of circulation through the brain. These conditions necessitate a large and continuously sustained cerebral circulation.

METHODS FOR MEASUREMENT OF BLOOD FLOW. The cerebral blood flow in man can now be measured with reasonable accuracy by techniques employing inert gases and based on the Fick principle. Of these, the nitrous oxide method of Kety and Schmidt[37] is the most important. Their technique is made possible by virtue of the almost complete separation of the intracranial and extracranial circulations in man. The subject breathes a low, subanesthetic concentration of nitrous oxide and the concentration of the gas is determined in serial samples of arterial and internal jugular venous blood. Since the initial concentration of this gas in the blood and brain is zero, its uptake per unit weight of brain can be learned from the amount of gas in a unit volume of jugular venous blood when the latter is in equilibrium with the concentration in the brain. Ten to 14 minutes of inhalation is required for the establishment of this equilibrium. The mean cerebral blood flow per unit weight of brain is obtained when the uptake value is divided by the mean difference between the arterial and internal jugular venous concentrations.

A method for examining the regional circulation of the brain in animals has recently

* Incorporating material written for the 17th edition by Dr. E. C. Hoff

been developed by Kety and his colleagues.[85] This technique involves the administration of a relatively inert radioactive gas. Its arterial concentration is monitored continuously, and the concentrations in specific regions are determined from radioautographs of sections of the brain after quick freezing. These data permit the estimation of blood flow in a given region—an important consideration, since large regional differences exist.

Total blood flow, as opposed to flow per unit weight of brain, can be determined by continuous or discontinuous injections of an indicator, such as Evans blue dye (T-1824), into one internal carotid artery. The concentration of the dye in the internal jugular venous blood is then determined (method of Gibbs). The technical problem of injection of the indicator has limited the usefulness of the method.

Useful information can be obtained by older methods of studying the cerebral circulation. The pial circulation has been directly visualized through a cranial window. Qualitative information regarding flow can be obtained by measuring with a thermocouple the rate at which the blood cools a warm wire inserted into the brain substance or into a vessel. Ingenious flowmeters have been interposed into the inflow or outflow systems. The arteriovenous oxygen difference of the brain can be used to measure continuously change in blood flow under conditions of constancy of the cerebral oxygen consumption, since, under these conditions, blood flow and the reciprocal of $(A-V)_{O_2}$ vary proportionally.[92]

In a recumbent person the normal blood flow averages about 54 ml. per 100 grams of brain tissue per minute, or about 750 ml. per minute for the whole brain. The corresponding oxygen consumption in conscious, alert individuals is 3.3 ml. per 100 grams of brain tissue, or about 45 ml. per minute for the entire brain. Thus the brain, representing only 2 per cent of the body weight, ordinarily receives about 16 per cent of the cardiac output and consumes nearly 20 per cent of the oxygen used by the entire body in the basal state. Nutritive requirements vary in different cerebral regions and within the same region under different states of activity. For example, in conscious cats the gray matter may have six times as much blood flow as white matter. In these animals stimulation of the retina by flashes of light increases the flow in the areas of the brain involved in visual function.[85]

A unique feature of the cerebral circulation is that it takes place within a relatively rigid container, the cranium. The spinal dural tube is somewhat less rigid, and, since its contents are continuous with those of the cranium, the volume of the system as a whole can actually be altered to a small extent. Since the brain is nearly incompressible, it follows that the combined volume of the brain tissue, cerebrospinal fluid and intracranial blood must be nearly constant, and that the volume of any one of these components can be increased only at the expense of one or both of the others. An early formulation of this concept, known as the "Monro-Kellie doctrine" or hypothesis, states, in essence, that the quantity of blood within the cranium must be approximately constant at all times, in health or disease. Obvious exceptions to this generalization are the cranium of a young child prior to union of the bony sutures and that of an adult with a cranial defect. It should be emphasized that the Monro-Kellie doctrine refers to quantity of blood, not to blood flow.

VASCULAR ARCHITECTURE AND INNERVATION.[94, 99, 100]   The human brain is supplied with blood entirely by the internal carotid and vertebral arteries. At the base of the hemispheres these arteries are united by the circle of Willis and its six large branches, thus forming a manifold for distribution of blood. From these trunks, branches project into the cortical and subcortical tissues. In general, the internal carotid arteries supply blood to the arterior and middle portions of the brain on each side, whereas the basilar artery, formed by union of the two vertebral arteries, supplies the occipital lobes and the structures within the posterior fossa. Normally there is little exchange of blood between the right and left halves of the circle of Willis, probably because of an equality of blood pressure. Indeed, the communicating arteries of the circle of Willis form an inadequate anastomosis, so that blood flow to the brain following unilateral carotid ligation may be seriously disturbed, especially in elderly patients.

Two groups of cerebral veins, the external or superficial and the internal or deep, connected by anastomoses, open into the venous sinuses. These larger spaces are contained between folds of the dura mater or between the dura mater and the bone. The openings of the larger cerebral veins into these sinuses have no valves, but are kept patent and protected from closure by the structure of the dura mater around the orifices. Blood may leave the brain by the internal jugular veins (the most important outflow), by anastomoses with the orbital and pterygoid plexuses of veins, by way of emissary

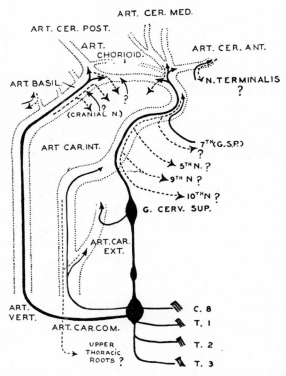

FIG. 447. Innervation of cerebral blood vessels—possible anatomic pathways. Efferent nerves are drawn in solid lines and afferent nerves in broken lines. (From McNaughton, *Res. Publ. Ass. nerv. ment Dis.*, 1938, *18*:190.)

vessels through the cranium, and by channels which join the vertebral plexus of veins. This last channel operates normally in some individuals and is capable of taking over venous drainage after occlusion of the jugular veins and even of the superior vena cava. Considerable mixing of venous blood from the two halves of the brain occurs. It has been estimated that approximately one-third of the blood in the internal jugular vein on one side normally derives from the opposite half of the brain.

The histologic appearance of the blood vessels of the brain is essentially that of vessels elsewhere in the body, although there are minor differences. It has been claimed by some that the arteries in the substance of the brain possess a thinner muscular layer than do arteries of comparable size elsewhere. The elastic fibers are possibly more numerous in cerebral arteries than in the vessels of other parts of the body and have a different arrangement. The veins have extremely thin walls composed largely of connective tissue.

The tributaries of the veins are received at a much more obtuse angle than that at which the arterial branches are given off. Both arteries and veins are accompanied by myelinated and unmyelinated nerve fibers. The unmyelinated fibers are believed to carry vasomotor impulses; the myelinated fibers are thought to be sensory afferents. Sympathetic innervation to the internal carotid and vertebral arteries is derived from the stellate and superior cervical ganglia. Parasympathetic fibers to the pericarotid plexus pass from the facial nerve through the geniculate ganglion, and from there travel via the great superficial petrosal nerve. The degree of functional activity of these vasoconstrictor (sympathetic) and vasodilator (parasympathetic) fibers in man is uncertain. The meningeal vessels are supplied with fibers from the Vth, VIIth, IXth, Xth and XIIth cranial nerves (Fig. 447).

End-arteries of brain. On the theory that infarcts occur only where there is no anastomosis between arteries, Cohnheim in 1872 inferred that the vessels of the brain are terminal or end-arteries. Following from the observations by Pfeiffer, and more recently by Scharrer,[95] it has been agreed that the vast majority of arteries in the brains of opossiums, cats, rats, rabbits and monkeys are end-arteries, but that no end-arteries are present in the human brain. Precapillary anastomoses within the brain of rats, cats, rabbits, monkeys and man have been observed. However, such precapillary anastomosis is insufficient to maintain adequate circulation if an artery to a given area of the cerebrum is occluded. It is probable that minute vessels of the order of precapillaries anastomose with precapillaries, but that only rarely do cerebral arteries *per se* anastomose with each other. Everywhere, gray matter has a far richer, denser vascular supply than does the white matter, a finding consistent with the higher rate of metabolism of the gray matter. Within the gray matter itself the vascularity varies in different cellular layers of the cortex and in different subcortical ganglia. This relative vascularity of various parts of the brain and the peculiarities of capillary structure and arrangement[102] may be factors in the localization of disease in various parts of the nervous system.

Regulation of the Cerebral Circulation. The general principle that regional blood flow is regulated to serve the metabolic needs of the tissues holds true for the brain. The over-all metabolism of the brain, as indicated by its oxygen consumption, is remarkably uniform, although the metabolic needs of local areas undoubtedly do vary. Contrary to expectation, recent studies have shown that the cerebral oxygen consumption is the same during such extremes of the conscious state as severe intellectual activity and sleep.[91, 102] This situation necessitates a system of regulation which will insure a nearly constant level of blood flow through the brain rather than a system adaptable to widely fluctuating metabolic and, therefore, circulatory needs. Symptoms of serious cerebral ischemia develop when the blood flow is reduced to about 60 per cent of its value in the resting recumbent state,[79e] emphasizing the relatively narrow range of permissible variation in the blood flow through the brain.

The rate of blood flow through the brain is determined by (i) the effective perfusion pressure, which is the difference between the arterial and venous pressures at brain level and (ii) the cerebral vascular resistance, which is the hindrance imposed on the flow of blood through the cerebral vessels. Perfusion pressure is largely determined by the mean arterial blood pressure, but changes in cerebral blood flow do not, as was once believed, passively follow changes in this pressure. When the numerous mechanisms which control peripheral vascular tone and the rate and force of contraction of the heart fail to maintain normal arterial blood pressure, intrinsic mechanisms are brought into play to alter cerebral vascular resistance. This resistance actually represents the resultant of all factors which impede blood flow through the cerebral vessels and includes (i) those factors which affect the caliber of the lumen of the blood vessels—the muscular tone and elastic state of the vascular wall, the external pressure on the vessels (i.e., intracranial pressure), and structural changes secondary to disease; and (ii) blood viscosity. These major determinants of cerebral blood flow are schematically represented in Figure 448.

EFFECTIVE PERFUSION PRESSURE. The major component of the net or effective cerebral perfusion pressure is the arterial pressure at brain level. The pressure in the internal jugular veins in a subject in the recumbent position is less than 10 mm. Hg in health and, since mean arterial pressure is 90 to 95 mm. Hg, hinders only slightly the outflow of blood from the brain. Change in venous pressure with change in body position, to be discussed later, assumes some importance in the maintenance of cerebral blood flow when the subject stands. The multiple nervous, humoral and mechanical mechanisms which insure a normal systemic arterial blood pressure are considered in detail in Chapters 31 and 32. That moderate variation in arterial pressure occurs in health during

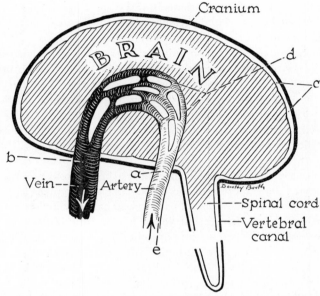

FIG. 448. Schematic representation of major determinants of cerebral blood flow: *a*, arterial pressure at brain level; *b*, venous pressure at brain level; *c*, intracranial pressure; *d*, state of the vascular bed; *e*, viscosity of the blood.

the stresses of normal daily activity—and that still greater variation occurs in disease states—necessitates active mechanisms for effecting adjustments in the vascular bed of the brain. Examples of such pressure variations are the fall in arterial pressure at brain level when the upright posture is assumed, the rise in pressure associated with anxiety, and the fall in pressure which occurs when an area of heart muscle is suddenly deprived of its blood supply.

CEREBRAL VASCULAR RESISTANCE. Active changes in the caliber of the cerebral vessels reduce the fluctuations in blood flow which are secondary to changes in arterial pressure, so that the variations in flow are smaller than the variations in pressure. The effects of abnormal arterial oxygen and carbon dioxide tensions on the functions of the brain are also offset in some degree by active adjustments in cerebral vascular resistance. The common method of obtaining a figure for the cerebral vascular resistance has been to divide the mean arterial pressure (or, more accurately, the effective perfusion pressure) at brain level by the cerebral blood flow.

Intracranial pressure is one of the influences which regulate the cerebral circulation, although its role is a secondary one. This term is applied to the pressure in the space between the skull and the brain, and, therefore, the pressure on the subarachnoidal fluid and presumably also in the ventricles of the brain, since the two spaces are in communication. Intracranial pressure is approximately the same as or very slightly higher than the pressure in the venous sinuses. The intracranial pressure is affected by both the arterial and the intracranial venous pressure, but particularly the venous pressure, which it tends to parallel. Changes in intracranial pressure with shifts in body position approximately balance the changes in intracranial venous pressure (presumably also in capillary pressure) and in this way exert a stabilizing effect on the vascular bed of the brain.

As long as the intracranial pressure remains well below that of the arteries supplying the brain, the circulation in this region is not critically affected, and there may be little change in systemic blood pressure, pulse rate or respiration. In man the intracranial pressure must be 450 mm. of water (33 mm. Hg) or higher before mean cerebral blood flow is significantly reduced.[89] The patients in this study showed an excellent correlation between the level of the intracranial pressure and both the calculated cerebral vascular resistance and the mean arterial blood pressure. Such correlation with arterial pressure was observed in acute experiments on animals in Cushing's classic studies. Under conditions of high intracranial pressure, the reduction in blood flow through the medulla stimulates the cardioinhibitory center, causing a slower heart beat; at the same time it also stimulates the vasomotor center, producing a general vasoconstriction in the rest of the body. The effects of this vasoconstriction are a rise in the arterial pressure and an increase in cranial circulation. It is obvious that, if intracranial pressure were raised to the level of systolic arterial pressure and maintained there, cerebral blood flow would cease.

CHEMICAL CONTROL.   The major mechanism of intrinsic control of the cerebral circulation resides in the responses of the blood vessels to changes in blood gas tension. The effects of alteration in the tension of oxygen and carbon dioxide in the arterial blood have been extensively studied in recent years. Under conditions of stable oxygen consumption and carbon dioxide production, any change in blood flow will result in changes in the oxygen and carbon dioxide tensions in the capillaries, venules and veins. The most important adjustment which the cerebral vessels are called upon to make is the dilator response to a fall in arterial pressure and the resulting fall in blood flow. With diminished blood flow and constant metabolism, each unit of flowing blood will have a greater amount of oxygen extracted from it and a greater amount of carbon dioxide added. Oxygen tension will therefore fall in the intracerebral blood and also in brain tissue, and the carbon dioxide tension will rise. Both of these changes in gas tension are stimuli to vasodilatation. Conversely, a rise in arterial pressure with an increase in blood flow will produce an increase in oxygen tension and a decrease in carbon dioxide tension, both of these changes being vasoconstrictor stimuli. The effect of the increased oxygen tension is, however, probably so small as to be of no significance. The relation to cerebral vascular control of the changes in blood pH associated with these changes in gas tension is unclear at present.

The results of a number of investigations[88, 98, 103] on the effects of alteration in arterial carbon dioxide tension are presented in composite form in Figure 449. The right side of the curve shows the increase in cerebral blood flow which occurs in response to an elevation in arterial carbon dioxide tension above the normal mean of 40 to 41 mm. Hg. There is little or no change in flow until the carbon dioxide tension has increased by about 4 mm. Hg, but beyond this point there is a rapid and progressive increase in blood flow with additional increases in carbon dioxide tension. An increase of 16 mm. Hg in carbon dioxide tension will, on the average, double the cerebral blood flow and an increase of 38 mm. Hg will triple the flow. The intense dyspnea experienced by the subject makes study beyond this point difficult. Most of the increase in blood flow can be attributed to active cerebral vasodilatation, with a rise in arterial blood pressure making a small contribution. For example, an increase of 14 mm. Hg in carbon dioxide tension was associated with a 14 mm. Hg rise in mean arterial blood pressure. The left side of the curve in Figure 449 shows the strikingly different response of the cerebral circulation to a reduction in the arterial carbon dioxide tension. Although the threshold of the mean response cannot be identified with complete precision, it is probable that a very small (about 2 mm. Hg) reduction in the arterial carbon dioxide tension initiates vasoconstriction. The reduction in blood flow per unit change in carbon dioxide tension is far smaller than the increase in flow when the tension is raised. Most of the change in flow is attributable to vasoconstriction, since an appreciable fall in arterial blood pressure occurs only when the carbon dioxide tension is markedly reduced. A decrease in carbon dioxide tension of 25 mm. Hg is associated with a decrease in blood flow of about 35 per cent, and extrapolation of the curve suggests that the maximum reduction in flow obtainable will not exceed 40 per cent. This is fortunate, since serious cerebral hypoxia would result if the vasoconstriction were more intense.

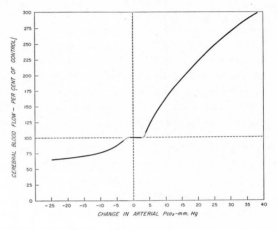

FIG. 449. The full range of response of the cerebral blood flow to elevation and to reduction in arterial CO₂ tension. (Composite curve from data of Kety and colleagues and Patterson and colleagues.)

Blood pH falls as the blood carbon dioxide tension increases and rises as the tension decreases, when the changes in carbon dioxide are primary. It has been thought that alterations in blood pH produce effects which parallel those of changes in carbon dioxide tension, but recent observations on induced acidosis and alkalosis in man have cast doubt on this view.[98] It is probable that an increase in pH produces moderate cerebral vasodilatation, but the effect of a reduction in pH is unclear. Present evidence favors the conclusion that alterations in blood pH play a minor role in the control of the circulation in the brain.

The oxygen tension in the blood vessels of the brain is the second major factor in chemical control of the cerebral circulation. The full range of the response has been investigated in less detail than has the response to carbon dioxide. The reduction in arterial oxygen tension resulting from inhalation of a 10 per cent oxygen mixture produces a relatively marked vasodilatation, with an increase in blood flow amounting to 35 per cent.[88] It is probable that the reduced arterial oxygen tension would have produced a greater increase in blood flow if the associated increase in pulmonary ventilation had not caused a simultaneous 4 mm. Hg fall in arterial carbon dioxide tension. When 85 to 100 per cent oxygen is inhaled, the cerebral blood flow is reduced 13 per cent, but inhalation of 50 per cent oxygen causes minimal vasoconstriction.[88] The vasoconstrictor effect of a high arterial oxygen tension raises questions regarding possible contraindications to the use of oxygen. It is probable that even 100 per cent oxygen produces insufficient slowing of the cerebral circulation to constitute a strong contraindication except in patients with far advanced cerebral vascular disease. The effect of 100 per cent oxygen in depressing pulmonary ventilation in states of arterial hypoxia is another matter, however.

It is reasonable to ask how these data on the effects of altered arterial blood gas tensions relate to normal control of the cerebral circulation. It is probable that these changes in blood gas tension, and perhaps also the associated changes in tissue gas tension, act directly upon the smooth muscle of the vascular wall, although local perivascular nervous pathways conceivably could be involved. As previously discussed, changes in gas tension in the blood in the capillaries, venules and veins occur secondarily to changes in blood flow. It is not known if these secondary changes in carbon dioxide and oxygen tension produce quantitatively the same responses as those produced by primary alterations in the arterial gas tensions, but the directional effects are the same and it is likely that the responses are of similar magnitude. Apparently the gas tension changes in capillary and venous blood cause vasomotor reactions in the arterioles "upstream," but the mechanism for this retrograde effect is not known. It can be calculated that a 25 to 30 per cent fall in cerebral blood flow is required to raise end-capillary and venous carbon dioxide tension to the approximate vasodilator threshold, but this calculation does not take into account the simultaneous effect of the fall in oxygen tension, which almost certainly advances the vasodilator response. It is not known whether the effects of alterations in the carbon dioxide and oxygen tensions are additive or synergistic.

When the changes in arterial gas tension are primary, as for example in hyperventilation with resulting reduction in arterial carbon dioxide tension, competitive effects can be introduced. The vasoconstriction resulting from the lowering of carbon dioxide tension in turn results in a decrease in blood flow. Since hyperventilation adds very little oxygen to normal arterial blood, the effect of the reduction in cerebral blood flow will be a fall in capillary and venous oxygen tension. These changes in oxygen tension are vasodilator stimuli which will oppose the constrictor effect of the fall in arterial carbon dioxide tension. Furthermore, it can be seen that the fall in capillary and venous carbon dioxide tension will be smaller than the fall in arterial carbon dioxide tension since more carbon dioxide from the brain will be added to each unit of flowing blood. One effect of this mechanism is the prevention of extreme reduction in tissue carbon dioxide tension. The rise in arterial pH associated with hyperventilation may also help limit the magnitude of the vasoconstriction produced by a fall in arterial carbon dioxide tension. In contrast, the forces opposing vasodilatation when arterial carbon dioxide tension is raised are relatively weak.

A number of disease states are associated with changes in the tensions of the arterial blood gases, and these in turn affect the cerebral circulation. In patients whose abnormalities are of long standing, the changes in the circulation in the brain may be quantitatively smaller than those changes which would occur in health in response to brief changes in gas tension. Blood vessels which have undergone structural changes, e.g., atherosclerosis, may be less responsive than normal vessels to either acute or chronic abnormality of the blood gases.

VASCULAR REACTIONS TO PRESSURE. There is some evidence[80, 81, 84] that arteries and arterioles actually "feel" the distending pressure in the lumen and react by constricting in response to pressure elevation and by dilating in response to pressure reduction. This response of vascular smooth muscle apparently is not mediated through nervous pathways. Such an active mechanism would protect the brain during extreme fluctuations in systemic arterial pressure. It is to be distinguished from the passive changes in the caliber of capillaries and veins that occur with changes in transmural pressure.

NEUROGENIC CONTROL. The innervation of the blood vessels of the brain has been described earlier. The participation of this innervation in the control of the cerebral circulation has not been fully clarified, despite many investigations of the problem. The studies have, of necessity, been carried out mainly on animals, since both direct stimulation and the cutting of nerves are often required.

In man, according to Forbes,[82] no positive evidence of vasomotor nerves in the brain has been obtained, although both myelinated and unmyelinated nerves may be histologically demonstrated on intracranial blood vessels. Reduction in sympathetic inflow by local anesthetic block of the stellate ganglion does not alter the cerebral blood flow in man.[96]

The function of sympathetic fibers has been demonstrated by Forbes in animals.[83] A slight but definite constriction of the pial arteries followed electrical stimulation of the cervical sympathetic nerve. Stimulation of the stellate ganglion was without effect.

The evidence on neurogenic control, drawn from numerous sources, may be briefly summarized as follows: A degree of neurogenic control of the cerebral vascular bed probably exists, but this control is weak. It may participate in fine adjustments but does not effect major changes in cerebral vascular resistance. Perivascular nerves may have a role in local vascular control within the brain, but the nature of this role is speculative at present.

Cerebral Circulation in Certain Physiologic States. AGING. Conflicting findings have been reported on the effect of the aging process, perhaps because it is difficult to include only "normal" individuals in the older age groups. A slight decrease in blood flow and oxygen uptake per unit weight of brain in older persons without overt evidence of vascular disease has been reported.[86] No significant change in either variable was found in a more recent study in which a group with a mean age of 72 years was carefully selected to exclude persons with even slight evidence of vascular disease.[79] Significantly, in this same study a group of elderly individuals with asymptomatic arteriosclerosis had a slight reduction in cerebral blood flow and oxygen consumption. It thus appears that. chronologic age *per se* is not responsible for any reduction in blood flow and metabolism.

STANDING. When a person stands up, the cerebral blood flow decreases 21 per cent, but cerebral oxygen consumption does not change.[96] The decrease in blood flow results from a fall in mean arterial pressure at brain level, averaging 29 mm. Hg in one study[97] and 19 mm. Hg in another.[93] An important factor in the postural adjustment is a 7 mm. Hg average fall in jugular venous pressure which offsets about one-third of the decline in arterial pressure.[93] At the same time, the cerebrospinal fluid pressure at brain level falls to the same degree as the venous pressure, thus assisting in the maintenance of the normal caliber of the cerebral veins and probably of the capillaries. Changes in gas tensions in the cerebral capillaries and veins, secondary to a decrease in blood flow as previously described, may make a small contribution to the circulatory adjustment. In some individuals an increase in pulmonary ventilation in the upright position is sufficient to reduce the arterial carbon dioxide tension by several millimeters of mercury and therefore to offset the intrinsic adjustment.

REFERENCES

1. ADAMS, W. R. and VEITH, I., eds. *Pulmonary circulation. An international symposium, 1958.* New York, Grune & Stratton, 1959, xv, 316 pp.
2. ASSALI, N. S. *Amer. J. Obstet. Gynec.,* 1953, *66:*3–10.
3. BALDES, E. J., HERRICK, J. F. and ESSEX, H. E. *Proc. Soc. exp. Biol. (N. Y.),* 1933, *30:*1109–1111.
4. BARCROFT, H. and SWAN, H. J. C. *Sympathetic control of human blood vessels.* London, E. Arnold, 1953.
5. BARCROFT, J. *The respiratory function of the blood.* Cambridge, Cambridge University Press, 1914.
6. BARCROFT, J., MEAKINS, J. C., DAVIES, H. W., SCOTT, J. M. D. and FETTER, W. J. *Philos. Trans.,* 1923, *B211:*351–464.
7. BARCROFT, J. and STEPHENS, J. G. *J. Physi.,* 1927, *64:*1–22.

8. BAYLISS, W. M. *The vaso-motor system.* New York, Longmans, Green & Co., 1923.
9. BAYLISS, W. M. and STARLING, E. H. *J. Physiol.*, 1894, *16*:159–202.
10. BAYLISS, W. M. and STARLING, E. H. *J. Physiol.*, 1895, *17*:120–128.
11. BAZETT, H. C. *Physiol. Rev.*, 1927, 7:531–599.
12. BAZETT, H. C., SUNDERMAN, F. W., DOUPE, J. and SCOTT, J. C. *Amer. J. Physiol.*, 1940, *129*:69–83.
13. BLALOCK, A. and MASON, M. F. *Amer. J. Physiol.*, 1936, *117*:328–334.
14. BRADFORD, J. R. *J. Physiol.*, 1889, *10*:358–407.
15. BRADLEY, S. E., INGELFINGER, F. J., BRADLEY, G. P. and CURRY, J. J. *J. clin. Invest.*, 1945, *24*:890–897.
16. BURTON-OPITZ, R. *Quart. J. exp. Physiol.*, 1910, *3*:297–314.
17. CANNON, W. B., NEWTON, H. F., BRIGHT, E. M., MENKIN, V. and MOORE, R. M. *Amer. J. Physiol.*, 1929, *89*:84–107.
18. DALY, I. DeB. *Physiol. Rev.*, 1933, *13*:149–184.
19. DANIEL, P. M., PEABODY, C. N. and PRICHARD, M. M. L. *Quart. J. exp. Physiol.*, 1952, *37*:11–18.
20. DANIEL, P. M. and PRICHARD, M. M. L. *J. Physiol.*, 1951, *114*:521–537.
21. DANIEL, P. M. and PRICHARD, M. M. L. *J. Physiol.*, 1951, *114*:538–548.
22. DILL, D. B. *Life, heat and altitude.* Cambridge, Harvard University Press, 1938.
23. DILL, L. V. and ERICKSON, C. C. *Proc. Soc. exp. Biol.* (*N. Y.*), 1938, *39*:362–367.
24. DOW, P. *Amer. J. Physiol.*, 1939, *127*:793–795.
25. DRINKER, C. K., CHURCHILL, E. D. and FERRY, R. M. *Amer. J. Physiol.*, 1926, *77*:590–624.
26. DUMKE, P. R. and SCHMIDT, C. F. *Amer. J. Physiol.*, 1943, *138*:421–431.
27. DUNN, J. S. *J. Physiol.*, 1919, *53*:iii–iv.
28. FRANKLIN, K. J. *A monograph on veins.* Springfield, Ill., Charles C Thomas, 1937.
29. FRANKLIN, K. J., McGEE, L. E. and ULLMANN, E. A. *J. Physiol.*, 1951, *112*:43–53.
30. FREEMAN, N. E. and ZELLER, J. W. *Amer. J. Physiol.*, 1937, *120*:475–485.
31. FUHNER, H. and STARLING, E. H. *J. Physiol.*, 1913, *47*:286–304.
32. GIANTURCO, C. and STEGGERDA, F. R. *Amer. J. Roentgenol.*, 1937, *37*:175–179.
33. GOLDSCHMIDT, S. and McGLONE, B. *Amer. J. Physiol.*, 1934, *109*:42.
34. GRAB, W., JANSEN, S. and REIN, H. *Z. Biol.*, 1929, *89*:324.
35. GRANT, R. T. *Clin. Sci.*, 1938, *3*:157–174.
36. GRANT, R. T. and PEARSON, R. S. B. *Clin. Sci.*, 1938, *3*:119–140.
37. GREEN, H. D. and HOFF, E. C. *Amer. J. Physiol.*, 1937, *118*:641–658.
38. GRIFFITH, F. R., JR. and EMERY, F. E. *Amer. J. Physiol.*, 1930, *95*:20–34.
39. HAMILTON, W. F. *Amer. J. Physiol.*, 1932, *102*:551–558.
40. HAMILTON, W. F. Pp. 324–331 in: *Publ. no. 13, Amer. Ass. Adv. Sci.*, 1940.
41. HAMILTON, W. F., MOORE, J. W., KINSMAN, J. M. and SPURLING, R. G. *Amer. J. Physiol.*, 1932, *99*:534–551.
42. HAMILTON, W. F., WOODBURY, R. A. and HARPER, H. T., JR. *J. Amer. med. Ass.*, 1936, *107*:853–856.
43. HAMILTON, W. F., WOODBURY, R. A. and HARPER, H. T., JR. *Amer. J. Physiol.*, 1944, *141*:42–50.
44. HAMILTON, W. F., WOODBURY, R. A. and VOGT, E. *Amer. J. Physiol.*, 1939, *125*:130–141.
45. HOFF, E. C., KELL, J. F., JR., HASTINGS, N., SHOLES, D. M. and GRAY, E. H. *J. Neurophysiol.*, 1951, *14*:317–332.
46. HUTCHINSON, J. *Encyclopedia of anatomy and physiology.* London, 1849–1852.
47. JOHNSON, V., HAMILTON, W. F., KATZ, L. N. and WEINSTEIN, W. *Amer. J. Physiol.*, 1937, *120*:624–634.
48. KETY, S. S. and SCHMIDT, C. F. *J. clin. Invest.*, 1948, *27*:476–483.
49. KOLIN, A. *Proc. Soc. exp. Biol.* (*N. Y.*), 1936, *35*:53–56.
50. KOLIN, A. *Proc. Soc. exp. Biol.* (*N. Y.*), 1941, *46*:233–239.
51. KRAMER, K. and QUENSEL, W. *Pflüg. Arch. ges. Physiol.*, 1938, *239*:620–643.
52. KROGH, A. *Skand. Arch. Physiol.*, 1912, *27*:227–248.
53. LARSELL, O. *J. comp. Neurol.*, 1921, *33*:105–131.
54. LEWIS, T. *The blood vessels of the human skin and their responses.* London, Shaw and Sons, 1927.
55. LUCIANI, L. *Human physiology III. Muscular and nervous systems.* London, Macmillan Co., 1915.
56. McMICHAEL, J. *J. Physiol.*, 1932, *75*:241–263.
57. MARTIN, E. G., WOOLLEY, E. C. and MILLER, M. *Amer. J. Physiol.*, 1932, *100*:407–416.
58. MEEK, W. J. and EYSTER, J. A. E. *Amer. J. Physiol.*, 1922, *61*:186–202.
59. MEYERS, J. D. *J. clin. Invest.*, 1947, *62*:1130–1137.
60 MILES, B. E. and DE WARDENER, H. E. *J. Physiol.*, 1952, *118*:140–144.
61. PAGE, E. W. *Amer. J. Obstet. Gynec.*, 1939, *37*:291–293.
62. PARKER, G. H. *The elementary nervous system.* (*Monographs on experimental biology.*) Philadelphia, J. B. Lippincott Co., 1919.
63. REIN, H. *Z. Biol.*, 1928, *87*:394–418.
64. REIN, H. *Ergebn. Physiol.*, 1931, *23*:28–72.
65. SCHER, A. M. *Amer. J. Physiol.*, 1951, *167*:539–545.
66. SCHWIEGK, H. *Arch. exp. Path. Pharmak.*, 1932, *168*:693–714.
67. SMITH, H. W., ROVENSTINE, E. A., GOLDRING, W., CHASIS, H. and RANGES, H. A. *J. clin. Invest.*, 1939, *18*:319–341.
68. SOSKIN, S., ESSEX, H. E., HERNICK, J. F. and MANN, F. C. *Amer. J. Physiol.*, 1938, *124*:558–567.
69. SOSKIN, S., PRIEST, W. S. and SCHUTZ, W. J. *Amer. J. Physiol.*, 1934, *108*:107–117.

70. STADIE, W. C. *J. exp. Med.*, 1919, *30*:215–240.

71. TORNING, K. *Acta tuberc. scand.*, 1933, *7*:233–284; *8*:1–77.

72. TRUETA, J., BARCLAY, A. E., FRANKLIN, K. J., DANIEL, P. M. and PRICHARD, M. M. L. *Studies of the renal circulation.* Springfield, Ill., Charles C Thomas, 1947.

73. WAKIM, K. G. and MANN, F. C. *Anat. Rec.*, 1942, *82*:233–254.

74. WIGGERS, C. J. *Physiol. Rev.*, 1921, *1*:239–268.

75. WILSON, H. G. *Amer. J. Anat.*, 1922, *30*:267–295.

76. WOODBURY, R. A. and HAMILTON, W. F. *J. Pharmacol.*, 1941, *71*:293–300.

77. WOODBURY, R. A., HAMILTON, W. F. and TORPIN, R. *Amer. J. Physiol.*, 1938, *121*:640–649.

78. WOOLLARD, H. H. *Heart*, 1926, *13*:319–336.

CIRCULATION THROUGH THE BRAIN

79. DASTUR, D. K., LANE, M. H., HANSEN, D. B., KETY, S. S., BUTLER, R. N., PERLIN, S. and SOKOLOFF, L. *Effects of aging on cerebral circulation and metabolism in man.* National Institutes of Health Monograph. In press.

79a. FINNERTY, F. A., WITKIN, L. and FAZEKAS, J. F. *J. clin. Invest.*, 1954, *33*:1227–1232.

80. FOG, M. *J. Neurol. Psychiat.*, 1938, *1*:187–197.

81. FOLKOW, B. *Acta physiol. scand.*, 1953, *27*:99–117.

82. FORBES, H. S. *Arch. Neurol. Psychiat. (Chicago)*, 1940, *43*:804–814.

83. FORBES, H. S. and COBB, S. S. *Brain*, 1938, *61*:221–233.

84. FORBES, H. S., NASON, G. I. and WORTMAN, R. C. *Arch. Neurol. Psychiat. (Chicago)*, 1937, *37*:334–350.

85. FREYGANG, W. H., JR. and SOKOLOFF, L. *Advanc. biol. med. Phys.*, 1958, *6*:263–279.

86. HEYMAN, A., PATTERSON, J. L., JR., DUKE, T. W. and BATTEY, L. L. *New Engl. J. Med.*, 1953, *249*:223–229.

87. KETY, S. S. and SCHMIDT, C. F. *J. clin. Invest.*, 1948, *27*:476–483.

88. KETY, S. S. and SCHMIDT, C. F. *J. clin. Invest.*, 1948, *27*:484–492.

89. KETY, S. S., SHENKIN, H. A. and SCHMIDT, C. F. *J. clin. Invest.*, 1948, *27*:493–499.

90. LASSEN, N. A. *Physiol. Rev.*, 1959, *39*:183–238.

91. MANGOLD, R., SOKOLOFF, L., CONNER, E., KLEINERMAN, J., THERMAN, P. G. and KETY, S. S. *J. clin. Invest.*, 1955, *34*:1092–1100.

92. PATTERSON, J. L., JR., HEYMAN, A. and BATTEY, L. L. *J. clin. Invest.*, 1955, *34*:1857–1864.

93. PATTERSON, J. L., JR. and WARREN, J. V. *J. clin. Invest.*, 1952, *31*:653.

94. Research Publications, Association for Research in Nervous and Mental Diseases, 1938, *18*:979 pp.

95. SCHARRER, E. *Quart. Rev. Biol.*, 1944, *19*:308–318.

96. SCHEINBERG, P. and JAYNE, H. W. *Circulation*, 1952, *5*:225–236.

97. SCHEINBERG, P. and STEAD, E. A. *J. clin. Invest.*, 1949, *28*:1163–1171.

98. SCHIEVE, J. F. and WILSON, W. P. *J. clin. Invest.*, 1953, *32*:33–38.

99. SCHMIDT, C. F. *The cerebral circulation in health and disease.* Springfield, Ill., Charles C Thomas Co., 1950.

100. SHENKIN, H. A., HARMEL, M. H. and KETY, S. S. *Arch. Neurol. Psychiat. (Chicago)*, 1948, *60*:240–252.

101. SOKOLOFF, L. *Pharmacol. Rev.*, 1959, *11*:1–85.

102. SOKOLOFF, L., MANGOLD, R., WECHSLER, R. L., KENNEDY, C. and KETY, S. S. *J. clin. Invest.*, 1955, *34*:1101–1108.

103. WASSERMAN, A. J. and PATTERSON, J. L., JR. In manuscript.

The Capillaries and Lymphatics*

WE have seen that the functions of the cardiovascular system appear to be integrated and directed toward the maintenance of the constant composition and temperature of the fluid environment of the tissue spaces. This objective is achieved by means of the circulating blood, which replaces the materials utilized by the tissues and removes certain by-products of metabolism. The exchange of these constituents between the blood and tissue fluid takes place across the semipermeable membrane provided by the walls of the capillaries. Exchange is facilitated by the slow movement of the blood and by the appropriate fluid pressure gradient along the capillary, and also by a proper adjustment between the surface area of the blood exposed to the tissue fluids by the capillaries and the activity of the associated tissues. The composition of the blood so altered by the additions and withdrawals that take place in its passage through one set of capillaries is restored by perfusion through others—i.e., those in the lungs, the kidneys, etc.

The exchanges in the capillaries are the focal point for the integrated activity of the several parts of the circulatory system—the heart, the arteries, the arterioles and the veins. This activity and the number of patent capillaries are modified by the concentration of metabolites in (i) the extracellular fluid and (ii) the aterial blood. An increase in the activity of the tissues serves to alter the composition of the extracellular fluid locally; this alteration in turn results in a local compensatory increase in blood flow effected by a decrease in the resistance offered by the arterioles and capillaries. The increase in flow is maintained through the action of the several parts of the cardiovascular system, integrated by neural and hormonal control; finally, the activities of the nervous system are in turn modified primarily by the composition of the arterial blood in the associated capillaries. Thus, the exchanges across the capillaries form the *raison d'être* of the cardiovascular system.

* Revised from chapter written for the 17th edition by Eric Ponder.

CIRCULATION THROUGH THE CAPILLARIES

The circulation in the capillaries can easily be observed by examining the web or mesentery of the frog or the mesentery of the mouse under moderate powers of the microscope. The small arterioles will be seen to terminate, by quite a rapid transition in structure, in the capillaries. The endothelium becomes thinner, the muscular and fibrous walls disappear, and there remains only the delicate capillary wall, anchored in place by connective tissue fibers, which here and there may produce sharp kinks in the vessels.

The most striking feature of the capillary bed is that not all capillaries are open at one and the same time. In resting tissue, the number along which blood can flow is much smaller than the number which open as the tissue becomes active. Krogh's observations[4] on the capillaries of living muscle show that, under resting conditions, only a few capillaries are open and that these are often so constricted that red cells can make their way through them only after considerable distortion. In stimulated muscle, on the other hand, large numbers of previously invisible capillaries open, with the result that the rate of blood flow through the tissue, and therefore its oxygen supply, is greatly increased. By injecting India ink into the circulation and stimulating the muscle, Krogh counted 190 capillaries per mm.^{2}, as compared with five capillaries per mm.^{2} in a resting muscle used as a control. In some resting tissues, accordingly, it is not uncommon to find that only 1/20 to 1/50 of the total capillary bed is open to the circulation. In other tissues, e.g., brain tissue, however, the number of capillaries open is about the same whether the blood flow is great or small.

These changes in the amount of the capillary bed which is occupied by actively circulating blood result, in part, from the peculiar anatomic arrangement of the capillaries into two types of vessel: the a-v capillaries and the true capillaries. The a-v capillaries are direct continuations of small arterioles and can be traced through to the venous circulation. These direct circuits are always open, even when the tissue is resting. The proximal portion of an a-v capillary has a distinct, although not extensively developed, muscular coat. The true capillaries arise as branches of the arterioles, metarterioles and the a-v capillaries, and anastomose with each other to form the bulk of the capillary network. The true capillaries rejoin the a-v capillaries near their venous ends (Fig. 450). There is always a vigorous circulation through the a-v capillaries because they are a direct pathway from the arterioles to the venules and offer little resistance to the flow of blood. The true capillaries, on the other hand, are abrupt offshoots of the arterioles, and are readily cut off from the rapid circulation through the a-v trunk by a contraction of the musculature of the metarterioles ("precapillary sphincters"). This arrangement allows of the utilization of the two types of vessel at different times according to the level of activity of the tissue.[9]

The length of capillaries averages 0.4 mm. to 0.7 mm.; the diameters may vary from 15 or 20 μ to 5 μ or even less. In these narrow vessels there is no rapidly moving axial stream such as is seen in arterioles, in which the red cells are hurried along in the middle of the vessel while the white cells remain in the more slowly moving fluid near the walls. The narrower capillaries, indeed, can scarcely accommodate the red and white cells which flow through them. The cells must get through as best they can, often being temporarily stopped and also being squeezed out of shape. The red cells thus come into very close contact with the capillary endothelium.

It has been estimated that the total area of the capillary walls in human voluntary muscle is about 6000 m.^{2} and that each milliliter of blood which passes through them comes into contact with about 6000 cm.^{2} of capillary surface. Such a situation is very

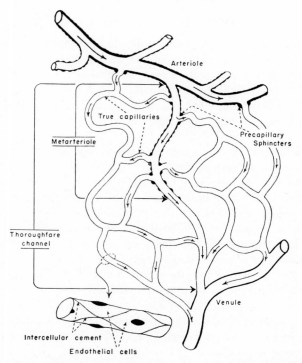

FIG. 450.   Schematic diagram of ideal capillary bed according to Chambers and Zweifach. Distribution of muscle is indicated by the heavier wall thickness. Note limited distribution along thoroughfare channel and precapillary sphincters. Insert is a highly magnified portion of true capillary wall. There is reason to believe that most exchange of solutes takes place through the small area of intercellular cement rather than through the endothelial cells. (Sketch by Thomas E. Nelson, Jr.)

favorable to the rapid diffusion of gases and other substances from the blood in the capillaries to the tissues which lie beyond their walls.

The Capillary Wall.   The wall of the typical capillary is composed of endothelial cells held together by an "intercellular cement substance." The endothelial cells are thin, flat plates with a homogeneous cytoplasm and a long, granular nucleus. When the capillaries are collapsed the cells may be wrinkled into folds; the folds disappear when the capillary is dilated, and greater dilatation must result in a stretching of the capillary walls which may produce an increase in their permeability. While these endothelial cells have been credited with contractility, it is very doubtful that they are responsible for any changes in the caliber of the capillary. Most observers have concluded that active contractility occurs only in a-v capillaries and metarterioles, which possess a musculature. The true capillaries, however, can be said to have a sluggishly operating capillary tone, which is a reflection of a state of elasticity inherent in the living endothelium.

Larger cells with long cytoplasmic processes are arranged in a saddle-like manner along the endothelial tube in some regions (Fig. 451). These are called Rouget cells;

FIG. 451.   Structure of a capillary.

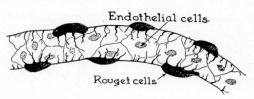

special histologic methods are required to demonstrate their presence. Some observers have considered them the homologues of plain muscle fibers, and it was once thought that they were responsible for the contraction of capillaries. Other observers have identified Rouget cells as wandering cells of the tissues that have adapted themselves to the shape of the capillary wall. This identification is the more plausible and Rouget cells are no longer looked upon as essential contractile elements. These cells are absent from the otherwise typical capillaries in the bat's wing. The subject of the contractility of capillaries has been reviewed by Zweifach,[8] and the idea of "vasomotion," or spontaneous irregular contraction and relaxation of the metarterioles and precapillary sphincters, is now well established.

The fact that red cells, white cells and inanimate particles such as India ink can escape from apparently uninjured capillaries into the surrounding tissue spaces has directed attention to the spaces between the endothelial cells and to the properties of the intercellular cement substance which normally fills them. Not only red cells but even larger objects can pass through the capillary wall without damaging it; microfilariae 5 μ in breadth pass from the blood to the lymph. Actual holes or stomata between the endothelial plates were once postulated. Chambers and Zweifach,[2] however, have emphasized that the substance between the endothelial plates is the most likely point of passage of both large and small particles.

In experiments in which frog capillaries were perfused with Ringer-gelatin solutions, Chambers and Zweifach[2] arrived at conclusions which are best given in their own words:

"I. *The inter-endothelial cell cement during normal blood circulation.*

"1. The endothelial lines can be stained, under viable conditions, by spraying 10% $AgNO_3$ on the outer surface of the capillaries with a micropipette. The blackened substance of the cement is gradually washed away by the blood stream and replaced by fresh cement.

"2. Carbon, suspended in the blood stream, adheres to the sticky cement without adhering to the exposed surfaces of the endothelial cells. In this way the carbon-deposit outlines the endothelial cells.

"3. When the capillary is prodded with a microneedle, there occurs an immediate flattening of red cells against the irritated wall and a local accumulation of carbon. This indicates an excessive leakage of fluid through that region of the capillary.

"II. *The effect of perfusion of physiological salt solutions containing ash-free gelatin (0.5%) on the inter-endothelial cell cement.*

"A. By varying the calcium content of the perfusate.

"4. The capillary bed can be perfused with a normal Ringer-gelatin solution for over 100 minutes with no visible abnormalities.

"5. With solutions lacking calcium, a softening of the cement is indicated by its increased stickiness and its being washed away.

"6. With solutions containing double the amount of calcium, the stickiness of the endothelial lines becomes intensified and later the entire inner surface of the endothelial wall becomes sticky.

"B. By varying the *p*H.

"7. An increase in acidity of the medium induces early and intense stickiness followed by pronounced leakiness of the capillary wall.

"III. *The relation between the induced changes in the endothelial cement and the extrusion of particulate matter and the appearance of edema.*

"8. The lack of calcium and increase in acidity soften the cement (evidenced by increased stickiness to carbon) and enhance its dissipation. These conditions favor the extrusion of formed elements of the perfusate (e.g., carbon, leucocytes, red cells) and accelerate the outward diffusion of the perfusate."

Zweifach[9] has further shown that the rate at which edema appears in the frog mesentery when the *p*H is varied also depends on the calcium content of the perfusion fluid, and summarizes the experimental evidence by saying,

"The physical state of the capillary wall depends upon the calcium content of the perfusate. The conditions produced are reversible, and appear closely analogous to those of epithelial membranes in which the intercellular cement reacts to inorganic salts as if it were itself a salt. The absence of calcium from the medium serves to increase the instability of the cement substance through the replacement of the relatively stable but reversible calcium salt by the soluble sodium or potassium salt. Increased acidity acts to increase the ionization of the cement and thereby enhanced its dissipation. An important role of the endothelial cell would appear to be the continual secretion of an intercellular cement, the chemical stability of which controls the permeability of the blood capillary."

The possibility that capillary permeability depends on the nature and integrity of the intercellular cement substance rather than on the permeability of the membranes of the endothelial cells themselves is an important concept in capillary physiology.

Capillary Reactions. It is now recognized that some vessels of the capillary network, in addition to the metarterioles, have the inherent ability to contract and dilate, and that these changes are not mere passive accompaniments of pressure changes in the arterioles, as was once believed. Although the adjustment of the capillary circulation to the requirements of tissue metabolism apparently depends to a far greater extent on chemical than on nervous stimuli, the capillaries are to some extent under nervous control, and both vasoconstrictors and vasodilators have been described.

Most of the changes in capillary diameter which occur when a tissue passes from a resting to an active state are caused by lack of oxygen and the accumulation of metabolites. Investigations as early as those of Gaskell in 1877 and of Roy and Graham Brown in 1879 led to the following conclusion: "There is a local mechanism, independent of centers in the medulla and spinal cord, by which the degree of dilatation of the vessels (capillaries) is varied in accordance with the requirements of the tissues." This view has been confirmed by many observers. Bayliss first showed that carbon dioxide has a local vasodilator effect, and subsequently Ebbecke, Barcroft and Kato, Gesell, and many others found capillary dilatation to be dependent on anoxia or the presence of metabolic products of tissue activity. Krogh and Rethberg, for example, placed rabbits in respirators from which the carbon dioxide could be absorbed with soda lime and in which the oxygen content could be controlled. As the oxygen tension in the animal's blood fell, cyanosis developed and was accompanied by capillary dilatation, which might be due either to the low oxygen content of the blood or to the accumulation of metabolites such as lactic acid. Further determinations showed that the pH changes in the blood were themselves insufficient to produce the capillary dilatation, which was finally attributed to the anoxemia itself. This experiment is typical of many.

Although the results of experiments like this are not at all in question, there is a tendency, initiated by Lewis,[6] to look upon the changes in capillary diameter as results of the action of a *specific substance* rather than as direct results of diminished oxygen tension, increased carbon dioxide tension, accumulation of lactic acid and so on. Lewis's view is that the agent causing the capillary dilatation when the tissue passes from the resting to the active state ("functional hyperemia") is histamine-like, is a normal metabolite of cells which release it in proportion to their activity, and is the substance ("H-substance") which tissue cells release when they are injured mechanically. Anrep[1] reviewed the subject insofar as it relates to the regulation of the circulation in muscle, and presented evidence both for the effects of a specific histamine-like substance and for the effects of accumulated acid metabolites and anoxemia.

Although capillary dilatation is controlled by local conditions and by substances produced locally, there is evidence that the tone of the capillaries, in the amphibia at least, is maintained by the action of a hormone derived from the pituitary. Rethberg first observed that the capillaries of the frog become dilated after removal of the pituitary, and this aspect of capillary control has been extensively investigated by Krogh. Assuming for the moment that the results obtained in the amphibia are not peculiar to that vertebrate class, we arrive at a hypothesis of this kind: The capillaries of resting tissue are maintained in a state of contraction by the action of a pituitary hormone. When the tissue becomes active, the cells consume oxygen and produce metabolites (H-substance and others); these tend to bring about capillary dilatation. As the capillaries dilate, fresh blood flows through the tissue, removing the metabolites and bringing a new supply of the pituitary hormone; the capillaries then contract until another accumulation of metabolites produces dilatation, and the cycle of events is repeated again and again in proportion to the activity of the tissue. This hypothesis is valuable in enabling us to understand how the blood supply of a tissue is adapted to its needs; too much insistence, however, should not be placed on the role of the pituitary hormone, for which the evidence is not nearly as convincing in the mammal as it is in the amphibian.

Vascular reactions in the skin (the "triple response"). The study of the vascular reactions of the skin is important for an understanding of capillary responses and the mechanisms underlying them. The observations can easily be made on the skin on the front of the forearm.

If the skin is lightly stroked with a blunt instrument, a line of pallor appears in about 15 to 20 seconds along the path of the instrument. The pallor increases in intensity for about 30 to 60 seconds and then gradually fades (three to five minutes). This *"white reaction"* is due to capillary contraction following direct stimulation, and, at the height of the pallor, the capillaries will remain closed against a pressure of as much as 100 mm. Hg.

If the instrument is drawn over the skin more firmly, a red instead of a white line appears after a shorter latent period (three to 15 seconds) and may last for several minutes or even half an hour. This *"red reaction"* is dependent in duration and intensity on the degree of stimulus provided by the blunt instrument, and is due to capillary dilatation. It occurs with full intensity even when the circulation to the skin area is cut off with a tourniquet, and even when all nerves to the skin area have degenerated. The reaction is accordingly an active process, not dependent on either pressure in the arterioles or nervous mechanisms.

If the stimulus is still stronger or repeated sufficiently often, a bright red flush or flare spreads outward from the border of the red line, usually within 15 to 30 seconds after the first appearance of the red reaction. This *"red flare"* reaction does not occur if the circulation to the part is cut off, and is due to a dilatation of the arteriole. It occurs when the nerves to the skin area are cut, but not when they have degenerated, and so is due to a local axon reflex mechanism.

If the stimulus is still more intense, the local red reaction grows paler and begins to become raised above the surface of the surrounding skin. This *local edema* or *wheal formation* reflects the escape from the injured capillaries of a fluid similar in composition to blood plasma. In some sensitive skins the wheal formation occurs unusually readily, so that letters and words, lightly traced on the skin with a blunt point, appear written on the skin as wheals which may persist for half an hour or more. This is known as *dermographism*. After a variable length of time the wheals lose their sharpness by becoming wider and less raised, and finally they disappear altogether.

The succession of events, red reaction, flare and wheal formation, is called the *triple response*, and it is believed that these three reactions are brought about by the diffusion of a substance liberated by the cells of the skin along the path traced by the instrument. The hypothetical diffusible substance closely resembles histamine in its effects (production of capillary dilatation by direct action, of arteriole dilatation by means of an axon reflex, and of the wheal by increasing capillary permeability); this is Lewis's "H-substance" (see above), but it may actually be histamine itself. Although the reactions which constitute the triple response are most easily studied in the skin, they can also be demonstrated in the viscera (liver, spleen and kidney).

VASCULAR REACTIONS IN INFLAMMATION. The vascular changes which occur in an inflamed area involve reactions similar to those of the triple response, and like them are independent of all except local innervation. Injury by direct trauma or by bacterial toxins causes a liberation of a histamine-like substance from the tissue cells. The diffusion of this substance is followed by capillary dilatation and an increase in capillary permeability.[7] As in the triple response, there is an increased transudation of fluid from the dilated and highly permeable capillaries, the walls of which now permit not only water and solutes, but also proteins, to pass readily into the extracellular spaces. In this way the inflamed tissue becomes filled with a protein-rich edema fluid. The process is aided by two additional factors: the dilatation of nearby arterioles, brought about by axon reflexes and resulting in a still greater blood flow into the dilated capillaries, and an obstruction, probably by clots of fibrin, of the lymphatics draining the area. As a result of the increased blood flow, the inflamed area becomes red and warm; as a result of the transudation of edema fluid, it becomes turgid; and as a result of the turgor, there is pain. These constitute the classic signs of inflammation.

The leukocytes in the dilated capillaries of inflamed tissue tend to adhere to the endothelial walls and then to pass through them into the extracellular spaces surrounding the tissue cells. Red cells may accompany the white, and within a few hours the white cell count in the edema fluid of an inflamed area (e.g., the fluid of a blister) may be as high as 30,000 per ml. This tendency for leukocytes (principally polymorphs) to collect in regions of inflammation is called leukotaxis. Menkin has brought forward evidence that it is due to a nitrogenous substance, which he calls leukotaxine and which has properties quite different from those of histamine.

Capillary Permeability. The rate of passage of a substance across the capillary wall is measured in terms of the increment of the substance dS which passes through in time dt. The rate is directly proportional to the area A of the wall, the driving force between the inside and the outside of the capillary, and the diffusion constant for the substance, and is inversely proportional to the thickness of the capillary wall. If the thickness is considered as being constant, its value may be incorporated into the diffusion constant to give a permeability constant (k) so that the rate of penetration becomes

$$\frac{dS}{dt} = kA(C_i - C_o),$$

where C_i is the total pressure (mechanical and osmotic) inside the capillary and C_o the total pressure outside (see below). In the case of the permeability to water, the amount which penetrates is measured as the volume in μ^3 which filters across each μ^2 of membrane per second under a pressure difference of 1 atmosphere. To determine this rate, we require an experiment in which capillary pressure, capillary diameter (and hence area), and transudation of fluid from the capillary are all measured simultaneously. Such experiments were carried out by Landis.[5] A fine tube, connected to a manometer, was inserted into a capillary of the mesentery of the frog and perfused with a weak solution of toluidine blue in Ringer. The amount of fluid passing through the capillary wall in known times under known pressures was then measured. The figure which Landis obtained for the rate of penetration of water was about 60 μ^3 per μ^2 per second per atmosphere of pressure, which is so much greater than the value obtained for any other type of cell as to lead to the conclusion that the water passes through fairly large pores in the capillary wall. Possibly most of its passage takes place through the intercellular junctions and the cement substance.

Starling's hypothesis. Little is known about the permeability of the capillaries to the electrolytes and nonelectrolytes of plasma, although such substances apparently penetrate in the order water > urea > glucose > sucrose. Even if substances such as these were to diffuse freely, their diffusion rates would differ because of differences in their molecular size. In the absence of precise information, it is usually assumed that all the constituents of plasma except the proteins can pass across the capillary wall without difficulty. This simplification of the situation led Starling (1895) to make his classic statement about the conditions in the capillary which regulate the transfer of water. The force of capillary pressure, which tends to drive water outward, was supposed to be balanced by the osmotic pressure of the plasma proteins, which draws water inward from the extracellular fluid outside the capillary. If this hypothesis is put into symbols, what is required by Starling's theory is that at equilibrium there shall be a balance between the "effective" blood pressure within the capillary (CP) and the "effective" osmotic pressure of the plasma. The effective osmotic pressure of the plasma is the difference between the osmotic pressure of the plasma inside the capillary (OP_{plasma}) and the osmotic pressure of the extracellular fluid ($OP_{e.f.}$) outside the capillary. It must also be borne in mind that the capillary pressure is to some extent offset by the pressure in the tissues outside the extracellular space, or by the "tissue turgor pressure" (TP). Collecting these various quantities, we must have, at equilibrium,

$$CP - TP = OP_{plasma} - OP_{e.f.}$$

If the left hand side of the equation is greater than the right, water will move out of the capillary until the balance is attained. If the right hand side is the greater, water will move into the capillary. All the pressures, mechanical and osmotic, must be measured in the same units, usually atmospheres (1 atmosphere = 760 mm. Hg).

One simplification which was introduced into the original statement of Starling's theory is that the difference between the osmotic pressure of the plasma and that of the extracellular fluid is the same as the osmotic pressure produced by the plasma proteins. This would be true if the typical capillary wall were completely impermeable to protein, but it is now recognized that it is not. Some leakage of protein is the rule, and the cases of the glomerular membrane and the walls of the capillaries of the chorioid plexuses, which protein normally does not cross, are the exceptions. Fibrinogen, albumin and globulin are all able to pass through most capillary walls, their rate of diffusion being sufficient to reduce their osmotic effect to 70 to 90 per cent of what it would be if the capillary wall were altogether impermeable to them. Because the diffusion of the very large molecules of antisera is slow and incomplete, the concentration of antiserum in the lymph is quite small. Antisera are accordingly not very effective when given intravenously, and lymph is a fluid of low bactericidal power. Since bacteria can leave the capillaries just as many inanimate particles do, they may flourish in the lymph without being agglutinated or lysed by it.

Only in a very few cases has the permeability of the capillary wall been analyzed in terms of the area and of the total pressures, mechanical and osmotic, on the inside and the outside of the vessel. It is usually impossible to obtain the necessary data with sufficient accuracy, and even Starling's theory does not rest on a basis of unimpeachable experiment. The theory, however, allows us to make predictions which can be approximately verified by the limited experimental methods at our disposal. It should be kept in mind in this connection that experiments on capillary permeability in the intact animal are semiquantitative at best. Part of the reason for this is that theory speaks of "permeability" and "effective capillary pressure," whereas experiment shows that both the permeability and the capillary pressure are not only extremely variable in themselves, but are variable from point to point along the vessel. This variability makes it very difficult to be sure that the terms of the theoretical concepts correspond to the results of the experiments.

Capillary pressure. The pressure in the typical capillary is sometimes above and sometimes below the effective osmotic pressure of the plasma proteins. It may be measured directly by inserting a micropipette connected with a manometer into the lumen of a capillary of the animal (frog, mouse, dog: the mesenteric capillaries are usually used)[5] or indirectly by observing the pressure necessary to cause the collapse of the capillaries of the skin. This is done by placing a cover glass of known area on the surface of the skin and adding weights until the skin begins to blanch, or by placing a small glass-roofed chamber connected to a manometer over an area of skin and raising the pressure until blanching occurs. Alternatively, pressure may be applied in the region of the nail bed and the collapse of individual capillaries observed with the low powers of the microscope.

TABLE 18. CAPILLARY PRESSURE

INVESTIGATOR	ANIMAL	VESSEL OBSERVED	CAPILLARY PRESSURE CM. OF H_2O
Landis	Frog	Mesentery:	
		Average arteriolar capillary	14.5
		Average venous capillary	10
	Rat	Mesentery	13–49
	Man	Skin of hand:	
		Arteriolar limb	28–65
		Top of loop	20–43
		Venous limb	8–24
	Guinea pig	Mesentery	13–49
Königes and Otto	Cat	Intestinal villus:	
		Capillary	42

All the indirect methods, although suitable for use in man, give results which are difficult to interpret; indeed, they probably measure the pressure in the venous plexuses of the skin rather than the capillary pressure.

The results of attempts to measure capillary pressure vary within wide limits, and values from 0.5 to 54 mm. Hg have been recorded. A few of the findings are shown in Table 18. All these were obtained by the direct cannulation of a vessel, and are expressed in cm. of H_2O. The values obtained by indirect methods are still more variable.

In general, constriction of the arterioles causes the pressure in the capillaries fed by them to fall, and dilatation of the arterioles causes capillary pressure to rise. In addition to these passive effects increases or decreases in capillary pressure may be results of the ability of metarterioles and precapillaries to contract independently or of changes in capillary tone. An increase in venous pressure, however, has the constant effect of increasing capillary pressure, and so of increasing the rate at which fluid filters from the capillary into the extracellular spaces. Hemorrhage, on the other hand, decreases capillary pressure, thus increasing the passage of fluid *from* the extracellular spaces into the capillary bed, as Starling's theory requires.

Table 18 shows that the pressure at the arterial end of a capillary tends to be higher than that at the venous end, and it is generally agreed that there is a gradient of decreasing pressure from one end of a capillary to the other. This gradient has important implications from the standpoint of Starling's theory, for if the pressure at the arterial end is higher than the effective osmotic pressure of the plasma, and if the pressure at the venous end is lower than the effective osmotic pressure of the plasma, fluid will pass out of the capillary at its arterial end and be reabsorbed into the capillary at its venous end. In this way, a circulation of fluid, from the capillary to the extracellular spaces and back again is set up, but its magnitude and significance are far from clear. The briskness of this circulation, moreover, will depend on the difference in pressure between the arterial end and the venous end, and any factor which tends to abolish this difference will tend to abolish the movement of fluid. Thus an increase in venous pressure raises the mean capillary pressure, increasing passage of fluid out of the capillary; and at the same time it raises the pressure at the venous end of the capillary and so decreases reabsorption. There is accordingly a double reason for the accumulation of fluid in the tissue spaces (edema) when the venous return from some area of the body is obstructed.

Gradient of capillary permeability. Rous, McMaster and their associates have studied the permeability of capillaries to a series of dyes of increasing molecular size and have found a continuous gradient of permeability which increases as one goes from the arterial to the venous end of the vessel. This gradient does not depend on capillary pressure; indeed, the permeability is greatest at the venous end where the pressure is smallest. Zweifach confirmed the observations and found that the extent of the gradient varies with the length of the vessel. As a result, considerable differences in the rate of diffusion of dyes and in the molecular size of the dyes which diffuse are observed only in long capillaries. If the flow in the capillary is reversed, as can be done by compressing the proper side channels and venules with microdissection needles, the gradient of permeability is reversed also, permeability now being greatest near the arterial end. This finding led Zweifach to attribute the existence of the gradient to some factor which is present in the blood of the venous end of the vessel rather than to permanent structural differences in the endothelial wall.

The principal facts relating to the permeability of various kinds of capillaries to dyes are excellently summarized in Figure 452. Because there is a permeability gradient

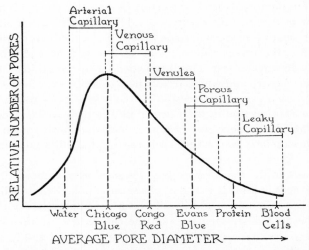

FIG. 452. Diagram to illustrate approximate porosity of different capillary subdivisions and o abnormal capillaries. Curve shows distribution of different sizes of pores. (From Zweifach, *Cold Spr. Harb. Symp. quant. Biol.*, 1940, 8:216–223.)

for dyes, it does not follow, of course, that the same gradient exists for water and dissolved substances. There may be one gradient for large molecules and another for water and crystalloids.

Variations in capillary permeability. Knowledge of the variations in capillary permeability in the intact animal is largely derived from experiments in which an increase in lymph flow or an accumulation of edema fluid has been taken as evidence of an increase in the rate of filtration through the capillary walls of the part affected.

The least doubtful of the effects are those produced by the *lack of oxygen*, but the experimental production of anoxemia and tissue anoxia is so largely accompanied by changes in the carbon dioxide tension, the accumulation of other metabolites, changes in pH, and alterations in capillary pressure that the effects of these factors cannot be disentangled at present. In experiments by Landis, the rate of filtration in the individual capillaries of the frog was increased three or four times by a short period of oxygen deprivation. Prolonged oxygen lack rendered the capillary wall so permeable that even protein molecules passed through with ease. Restoration of the oxygen tension was followed by a return of the permeability to something near its original value, provided that the period of anoxia was not so long that irreversible changes occurred. Compared with the effects of oxygen lack, those of accumulation of carbon dioxide and the accompanying pH changes are relatively small. Saslow showed that the web of the frog can be perfused four hours provided the perfusion fluid contains red cells to carry oxygen for the use of the tissue. In the absence of the red cells, the relative anoxia renders the capillary wall more permeable, and the web becomes edematous.

In the dog, Maurer has shown that the lymph flow from the cardiac lymphatic trunk begins to increase when the oxygen saturation falls to about 75 per cent, reaching a maximum when the saturation is about 50 per cent of normal. When the carbon dioxide content of the blood was approximately doubled, the lymph flow was also doubled. Such experiments as have been done in man, however, have not shown that either a decrease in oxygen tension or an increase in carbon dioxide tension has much effect on capillary permeability. The rate of swelling of a human arm constricted by a sphygmomanometer cuff and enclosed in a plethysmograph is not appreciably altered by the oxygen content or the carbon dioxide content of the inspired air, even though both are varied considerably. It may reasonably be asked whether this failure to observe effects of changes of oxygen and carbon dioxide tensions in the intact animal is not largely due to the relative crudeness of the experimental methods employed.

During activity, the tissues require more oxygen, glucose and other substances in solution than they do when at rest. This is provided for by the capillary dilatation which accompanies tissue activity and which results in a great increase in the area of the wall through which diffusion can take place (p. 753). There is no evidence that the greater supply results from an increase in the permeability of the capillary endothelium itself. Histamine and the H-substance, for example, have not been shown to increase the permeability of the capillary wall except insofar as capillary dilatation increases the area of the wall and the pressure on it.

Since variations in the *ionic composition of the environment* so markedly affect the permeability of many cells, it is likely that the cells of the capillary endothelium are similarly affected. The work of Chambers and Zweifach on the importance of the pH and ionic composition of the fluid circulating through the capillaries has already been cited (p. 753). In addition to the changes produced by variations in pH and in calcium content, Zweifach has described an effect of the plasma proteins which occurs because they clog the pores in the intercellular cement and make it less permeable. Colloidal perfusion fluids are known to be greatly superior to fluids such as Ringer's solution, and it is possible to continue the perfusion of a tissue for hours without edema developing if one uses Ringer-gelatin or Ringer to which serum proteins have been added, instead of Ringer's solution alone. This is explained in part by the osmotic pressure of the colloid producing reabsorption of water at the venous ends of the capillaries (Starling's theory, p. 758), but part of the explanation is that fluids such as Ringer's solution wash the cement substance away from the endothelial junctions and render the capillaries more permeable. This washing-away is prevented by the addition of colloids such as acacia, gelatin or the serum proteins, which are absorbed as a colloidal layer inside the capillary wall.

It is very doubtful whether any variations which occur in the ionic constitution of the blood of the intact animal are great enough to produce changes in capillary permeability. In severe malnutrition the plasma protein concentration may fall to levels (4.5 to 5.5 grams per 100 ml.) at which generalized edema occurs, but Starling's theory would account for this on the basis of diminished reabsorption of fluid by the capillaries.

Changes in *temperature*, either an increase to 45° C. or a decrease to 5° C., cause an increase in the lymph flow from the nasopharynx. An increase in temperature from 14° C. to 45° C. results in a doubling of the filtration from the capillaries of the arm (Landis and Gibbon). Because higher temperature affects filtration through the skin capillaries, swelling of the feet and hands and an increase in any pre-existing edema are commonly observed when a person moves from a temperate to a tropical climate.

Because whole blood, or even a fluid containing red cells or some plasma protein, is so much better a perfusion fluid than any saline solution, it has been supposed that blood may normally contain *specific chemical substances* which keep the capillary wall from becoming unduly permeable, just as the hormone of the pituitary may maintain capillary tone. Variations in the amount of such substances, were they shown to exist, might then be responsible for variations in capillary permeability. Experiments designed to demonstrate the existence of these specific substances have failed to do so except perhaps in a single instance. In observations on the edema which occurs in the skin around the genitals and anus of monkeys in relation to the menstrual cycle, Arkroyd and Zuckerman found that the administration of estrone increases the amount of extracellular fluid in the tissues, giving rise to a local edema. This result may be due to a local change in capillary permeability, but the demonstration is as yet incomplete.

Capillary Poisons. Although the presence of specific chemical substances which control capillary permeability has not been demonstrated, we know that a large number of drugs and druglike substances profoundly affect the integrity of the capillary wall. Some of these effects are *direct*, e.g., if solutions of saponin or of the bile salts are perfused through a limb, the cells of the capillary endothelium are subjected to a direct cytolytic action, and the perfusion fluid leaks out of the capillaries in proportion to the amount of injury to their walls. The active principles of the venoms of poisonous snakes and spiders, of bees and of certain marine animals probably act in the same general way.[7] If these substances gain access to the blood stream in sufficient concentration, they produce widespread injury which results in edema and hemorrhages. If the escape of edema fluid is great enough, the blood may become so concentrated and viscous that the heart cannot force it through the vessels; the blood pressure then falls, and death results. Mercuric chloride, gold chloride, arsenicals and the salts of many heavy metals may have similar direct effects on the capillary wall.

Other effects may be *indirect*, and it is often very difficult to distinguish between these and the direct effects. A substance such as histamine, for example, probably has no effect on capillary permeability per se, but it produces capillary dilatation, which leads in turn to stasis of the blood in the capillary, anoxemia, anoxia of the cells of the endothelial wall, and, finally, to an increase in capillary permeability as a result of the anoxia.

Pathology furnishes many instances of deterioration of the capillary wall as a result of the action of various kinds of toxins. Hemorrhages of varying size take place at the points of injury or deterioration, and appear as purplish spots in the skin (purpura). If they do not appear spontaneously, they can be made to occur by raising the pressure in the capillaries of the arm by applying a tourniquet or the cuff of a sphygmomanometer in which the pressure is raised to midway between the systolic and diastolic pressures. The pressure is maintained for eight minutes, and the petechial hemorrhages which occur within 15 minutes in a 5 cm. circle on the skin of the front of the forearm are counted. In a normal adult the number is ten or less. Alternatively, a small suction cup can be applied to the skin of the forearm, and the negative pressure required to produce petechial hemorrhages determined. Tests such as these are referred to as *capillary fragility* tests.

EXEMIA IN WOUND SHOCK. Extensive tissue injury is frequently followed by a concentration of the blood (hemoconcentration), the red cells occupying as much as 80 per cent of the total volume instead of the normal 40 to 45 per cent. This hemoconcentration results from loss of fluid from the blood vessels (*exemia*), the red cells, for the most part, being left behind. Whether the loss of plasma occurs because of a local or a general increase in capillary permeability has been much discussed. Those who believe that the increase in permeability is general have attempted to isolate or identify a substance, produced at the point of injury, which can be held responsible. Histamine-like substances and substances derived from the breakdown of proteins were at one time considered as possibilities. The evidence now points to the loss of fluid as being primarily local. When such an injury as a fracture of a femur occurs, for example, as much as 1500 ml. of fluid may be lost into the tissues of the thigh as edema develops; since this amount is about half the plasma in circulation, the resultant hemoconcentration is very great (volume occupied by red cells = 70 per cent, instead of 40 per cent). The possibility of an additional general effect has been revived; it has been suggested that the "general factor" in wound shock is toxin produced by anaerobic organisms infecting the wound. These toxins enter the circulation and are responsible for many of the "general" effects observed, but whether they act as capillary poisons and produce increases in capillary permeability in parts remote from the wound has not been decided. Adenosine triphosphate and related compounds have also been suggested as the "general factor."

In this connection, it should be observed that inhalation anesthetics tend to increase the permeability of capillaries. During long-continued anesthesia with ether, for example, the increased rate of filtration is sufficient to give rise to an appreciable increase in hemoconcentration. Possible effects of the anesthetic must always be considered in experiments on capillary permeability and lymph flow which involve the use of anesthetized animals.

About 75 years ago Heidenhain and other investigators found that various substances (extracts of crayfish muscle, extracts of leech heads, extracts of strawberries, histamine, peptone and many different proteins) produce an increase in both the rate of flow and the solid content of lymph from the thoracic ducts of dogs. Heidenhain called these substances "lymphagogues of the first class." He thought that they acted on the endothelial cells of the lymphatics, which he believed to have true secretory properties. We now recognize that all the substances included under the term "lymphagogues of the first class" are capillary poisons, and that the increased flow of lymph is due to an increased filtration and loss of proteins through the damaged capillary walls.

Atypical Capillaries.   The capillaries of the *liver sinusoids* are atypical in that their wall is reduced to an endothelial sheet so thin, and so closely applied to the surface of the liver cells, that there has been doubt regarding its very existence. At intervals along the wall there appear the highly phagocytic Kupffer cells, which are stellate cells with processes that extend around, and even across, the liver sinusoids, in which the pressure is very low. The permeability of the walls of the liver sinusoids is very high, and proteins are able to pass across them easily. This results in the protein content of the lymph from the liver being almost as high as that of plasma itself.

The capillaries of the *spleen* resemble those of the liver sinusoids in being very permeable to all the components of plasma. The permeability is so great that at one time it was thought that the walls of the splenic capillaries were fenestrated, i.e., interrupted at intervals by holes.

The capillaries of the *chorioid plexuses*, of the *ciliary body* and of the *glomerulus* of the kidney are atypical in that they are normally completely impermeable to protein. The urine contains no protein (in man), and the cerebrospinal fluid contains only traces. The glomerular capillaries are reinforced by the epithelial cells of Bowman's capsule, and those of the chorioid plexuses are similarly reinforced by an epithelial layer. Fluid leaving these capillaries has thus to pass through two layers of cells.

THE LYMPHATICS

Arrangement and Structure of the Lymphatics.   Just as the extracellular space surrounding the tissue cells is supplied with water and dissolved substances through the walls of the capillary network, so is it drained by a network of lymphatics (Fig. 453). The lymphatic network is about as extensive as the capillary network, and begins as a series of blind, closed tubes which converge on one another to form first a series of lymphatic plexuses, and then smaller, and finally larger, lymphatic vessels and trunks. In the skin, for example, there are two such plexuses. The more superficial of the two, in which the lymph can move in all directions, connects with the deeper, which has valves so that the lymph moves in one direction only. Valves are present in all the larger lymphatic trunks, which have smooth muscle in their walls, and which are contractile (unlike the smaller lymphatics, which are not). In particular anatomic situations the course of the larger lymphatics is interrupted by lymph glands or nodes, a number of lymphatics converging on the periphery of the node and breaking up into lymphoid sinuses, separated by masses of lymphoid tissue and supporting trabeculae. The sinuses lead into one or more efferent lymphatics, by which the lymph leaves the node. Ultimately, all the lymphatics converge on the lymph duct and the thoracic duct, which empty their contents into the right and left subclavian veins respectively. In the limbs at least, it seems to be a rule that lymph never reaches the blood without passing through at least one lymph node, one of the principal functions of which is to act as a filter for microorganisms.

Some structures, e.g., the bone marrow, the alveoli of the lung and the pulp of the spleen, have no lymphatics. The lymphatic drainage of voluntary muscle is probably confined to the fascial planes between groups of fibers, and it is very doubtful if the central nervous system is provided with lymphatics at all.

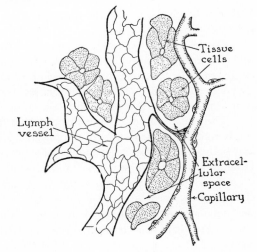

FIG. 453.   A capillary and an adjacent lymph vessel.

The walls of the lymphatic capillaries are composed of very thin endothelial cells, held together by an intercellular cement substance similar to that of the blood capillaries. Except in the case of the lacteals and of the larger lymph trunks, the lymph vessels lack the power of contractility. As a result they are unaffected by the many drugs which cause constriction and dilatation of the blood capillaries. The cells of the lymph vessel walls have little, if any, phagocytic activity, and particles as large as bacteria can pass through or between them, just as in the case of the blood capillary wall.

Formation of Lymph.   The old idea that the cells of the lymph capillary have secretory properties has been completely abandoned, and we now regard the formation of lymph as an entirely passive process. As we have seen, the pressure in the blood capillaries causes filtration of water, solutes and a small amount of protein into the extracellular space surrounded by the tissue cells—but only so long as the outwardly directed capillary pressure is just balanced by the effective osmotic pressure of the plasma proteins plus the tissue turgor pressure (Starling's theory; p. 759). Since the lymphatic system provides the extracellular spaces with a series of drainage channels, its function is to relieve the tissue pressure consequent to filtration from the capillaries. In ordinary circumstances, indeed, the amount of lymph drainage from an area is equal to the amount filtered from the capillaries at their arterial ends minus the amount reabsorbed at their venous ends, and the tissue turgor pressure remains substantially constant. If the lymph vessels draining an area are obstructed, however, the capillary filtration results in the accumulation of fluid in the extracellular space (edema), and the tissue turgor pressure rises. It might be supposed that the lymphatics in such edematous tissue would collapse as a result of the increased tissue turgor pressure, but their connective tissue attachments apparently support them and keep them open.

McMaster has shown that—in small localized areas of skin—the passage of fluid from the extra-cellular spaces into the blood vessels is not continuous but intermittent. It is likely that the conditions of fluid exchange are constantly changing in the skin, and perhaps elsewhere as well, and that the passage of fluid from and to the blood stream is periodic. These periodic phenomena probably occur because the flow in the blood vessels themselves is intermittent.

Most studies on the composition of lymph and on lymph flow are based on experiments in which cannulae are placed in the larger lymphatic trunks. These are the thoracic duct, the right lymph duct, the cervical lymph ducts and the larger lymph trunks draining the limbs. By cannulating individual lymphatics from the heart, lungs, liver, etc., one can obtain lymph from these organs.

The *total volume of the lymph* in the body is not known. The attempts to estimate it indicate that it is not greater than the total volume of the blood and is probably considerably smaller.

Composition of lymph. From the manner of its formation we would expect lymph to have approximately the same composition as the fluid which filters through the capillary walls, i.e., to contain water and most solutes in about the same proportions as they exist in plasma, but considerably less protein. Table 19 shows the average composition of the cervical lymph of the dog, compared with that of plasma.

The principal conclusion to be drawn from these data is that the ionic pattern of the lymph is similar to that of the plasma, all the differences being in a direction which can be accounted for by the lower protein content of the lymph and the existence of a Donnan equilibrium between lymph and plasma.

The lymph contains a number of enzymes (amylase, maltase, diastase, lipase, cholesterinase, protease and catalase, among others). These may be derived either from the blood stream or from the tissue cells. Although lymph coagulates, very little is known about the clotting mechanism. Presumably it is similar to that in blood, for fibrinogen, calcium and thromboplastin are all present. The protein content of the lymph derived from different regions varies considerably. Lymph from the liver has the highest protein content (about 5 per cent), as one would expect from the fact that the capillaries of the

TABLE 19. COMPARISON OF AVERAGE COMPOSITION OF CERVICAL LYMPH
AND BLOOD PLASMA OF DOG

	PROTEIN GM./ 100 ML.	SUGAR MG./ 100 ML.	N.P.N. MG./ 100 ML.	UREA MG./ 100 ML.	CREATININE MG./ 100 ML.	Cl AS NaCl MG./ 100 ML.
Plasma	6.18	123	32.6	21.7	1.37	441
Lymph	3.12	132	34.8	23.5	1.40	431

	URIC ACID MG./ 100 ML.	AMINO ACIDS MG./ 100 ML.	PHOSPHORUS MG./100 ML. Total	PHOSPHORUS MG./100 ML. Inorg.	CALCIUM MG./ 100 ML.	pH
Plasma	Trace	4.90	22.0	5.6	11.7	7.34
Lymph	Trace	4.84	11.8	5.9	9.8	7.41

(From Heim, *Amer. J. Physiol.*, 1933, *103*:553–558.)

liver sinusoids are very freely permeable to protein. Next in order comes the lymph from the thoracic duct (about 4 per cent); then the lymph from the heart, kidney and intestine; then that from the lungs and from the cervical region; and, finally, that from the skin and subcutaneous tissues (1 to 2 per cent). These differences no doubt correspond to differences in capillary permeability to proteins. The amounts of other substances present in the lymph do not vary greatly, except that the lymphatics draining the intestine (lacteals) may contain large amounts of fat after meals. The lacteals are believed to be completely permeable to fat, and it is the suspended fat droplets which give the intestinal lymph (chyle) its milky appearance. When they reach the blood stream these small fat droplets are called chylomicrons.

Flow of lymph. Since the lymphatics are, for the most part, noncontractile, the movement of lymph in the mammal must depend on forces outside the lymphatic system. These are of two kinds: (i) contraction of the muscles of the region and (ii) the pressure generated by filtration of fluid from the capillaries. By injecting small amounts of dye into the skin of the human forearm, McMaster and Hudack demonstrated a flow of lymph even in quiescent regions, for the dye appeared as far as 15 cm. from the point of injection within five minutes. The amount of lymph which can be collected from a lymph duct draining a limb, however, is very small when the limb is at rest. If the limb is actively moving, or if it is moved passively or even massaged, the lymph flow is greatly increased and tends to become constant with continued activity. This can be shown by cannulating a lymph duct in the leg of the dog, and observing the rate of flow during various phases of activity.[3] The contractions of the limb muscles squeeze the lymph along the lymphatics, and the effect of passive motion and of massage are about the same.

Similar squeezing of lymph along the lymphatics results from the contractions of the heart muscle and from the peristaltic movements of the smooth muscle in the visceral walls. As might be expected, the lymph flow from the heart varies, in a general sort of way, with the rate and amplitude of the contractions, i.e., with the work done by the heart. The flow of lymph from the intestines can be greatly increased by injecting pilocarpine, muscarine or Pituitrin, all of which increase the contraction of smooth muscle. The movement of the lymph in the lacteals is also aided by their rhythmic contractions and by contractions of the intestinal villi from which the lymph originates.

Anything which increases the rate of filtration of fluid from the capillaries tends to increase the flow of lymph. Raising the venous pressure, and with it the mean pressure in the capillaries, is particularly effective. If the inferior vena cava, for example, is obstructed above the entry of the hepatic veins, the flow of lymph in the thoracic duct increases greatly as a result of the increase in pressure in the hepatic capillaries. Similarly, ligation of the portal vein, which causes an increase in the pressure in the capillaries of the intestine, results in a four- to fivefold increase in the flow of lymph from the intestine. Increases in the arterial pressure are much less effective, but any considerable decrease in arterial pressure is followed by a diminution in lymph flow or even by its cessation. Both increases (to 45° C.) and decreases (to 5° C.) in temperature result in an increased filtration from the capillaries and therefore in an increased lymph flow. Again, the flow of lymph from the heart rises to a maximum when the oxygen tension of the blood is reduced to about 70 per cent of saturation (Maurer's experiments, p. 762), and the effects of changes in oxygen and carbon dioxide tension on the rate of capillary filtration are in general closely paralleled by their effect on lymph flow.

The question of whether an increased flow of lymph results from increased tissue activity has been the subject of many classic experiments. Most of these support the conclusion that lymph flow begins to increase shortly after the tissue (gland, muscle) responds to stimulation and that maximum flow coincides with the period of greatest tissue metabolism. The increased formation of lymph is attributed to the production of metabolites which diffuse out of the active tissue into the extracellular space. This diffusion results in an increase in osmotic pressure of solutes in the extracellular fluid; fluid from the blood stream then moves through the capillary walls to restore the equilibrium. The entry of this fluid into the extracellular space is followed by an increased flow of lymph. The metabolites may also increase the permeability of the capillary endothelium, and so make the lymph flow all the greater. In active tissues there are more open capillaries, and consequently a greater area of capillary wall across which fluid transfers can take place. This increase in area permits very rapid movements of fluid. In muscle, the increased amount of lymph produced is squeezed along the smaller lymphatics by the muscular contractions, and this pumping also increases the flow of lymph. In a stimulated gland, e.g., the submaxillary, the cells empty their secretion into the ducts and then draw on the surrounding extracellular fluid for water with which to restore their volume; this produces a concentration of the extracellular fluid, an increase in its osmotic pressure, and a transfer of fluid from the blood stream through the capillary wall to restore the equilibrium. These movements of water result in an increased formation of lymph and in an increased lymph flow.

It must be admitted, however, that the results of the classic experiments have not been wholly confirmed by subsequent investigations, and some of the explanations which seemed to be reasonable at the time are not so convincing now. Drinker and Yoffey[3] reviewed a number of experiments on the lymph flow from the liver, pancreas, salivary glands and kidneys during activity as compared with rest. In all of these the results were negative, inconclusive or disputed.

The action of "lymphagogues of the first class" has already been discussed (p. 764). These are essentially capillary poisons which act by increasing the permeability of the capillary endothelial wall. Heidenhain also described "lymphagogues of the second class," of which hypertonic sodium chloride and hypertonic glucose (50 per cent) are examples. When injected into the blood stream these substances pass rapidly across the capillary wall into the extracellular space and raise its osmotic pressure; water then leaves the cells of the tissues (intracellular space) to restore equilibrium, and in doing so increases the volume of fluid in the extracellular space. Since this space is drained by the lymphatics, an increased flow of lymph results. The effect is to redistribute water, which moves from the intracellular space into the extracellular space, the tissues becoming relatively dehydrated. The water which is transferred to the extracellular space eventually reaches the blood stream *via* the lymph, and is excreted. The lymph flow, meanwhile, is greatly increased.

CLINICAL CORRELATIONS. *Edema.* When the flow of lymph drains the extracellular space inadequately, an excessive amount of fluid collects in the tissue spaces and becomes visible as edema. Edema can arise in many ways, an enumeration of which would virtually constitute a review of the material of this chapter.

1. When the mean capillary pressure is increased, the filtration of fluid from the capillaries is increased, and the balance between filtration at the arterial end of the capillary and absorption at the venous end is upset in the favor of filtration into the extracellular space. If the lymphatic drainage is unable to cope with the increased transudation from the capillaries, fluid collects in the extracellular space and gives rise to edema. Since the most usual cause of an increase in mean capillary pressure is an increase in venous pressure, while the most common cause of an increased venous pressure is a failing power of the heart muscle, *cardiac edema* is associated with heart failure. Aided by gravity, fluid collects in the extracellular spaces of dependent parts, such as the ankles when the individual is upright and the back and sacrum when he is in bed. Accumulations of fluid may also be found in the peritoneal cavity (ascites), the pleural cavities, etc.

Any mechanical obstruction of the veins leading from a part, as by tumors or by the formation of clots in the lumen of a vein (thrombosis), raises the venous pressure and produces local edema in just the same way. Obstruction of the portal vein draining the intestines may produce large accumulations of fluid in the peritoneal cavity.

2. A reduction in the concentration of plasma proteins below a certain critical value (4.5 to 5.5 grams per 100 ml.) results in edema because the absorbing power of the capillaries at their venous ends,

which depends on the effective osmotic pressure of the plasma proteins, is reduced. Filtration then exceeds absorption, and edema tends to develop, particularly in dependent parts. The principal causes of a reduction in the concentration of plasma proteins are malnutrition, in which sufficient protein either is not supplied or is not synthesized in the body, and conditions in which protein is lost from the body through abnormal paths, usually by hemorrhage or through damaged kidneys.

3. Any factor which increases capillary permeability tends to produce edema. Both heat ("tropical edema") and cold (as in frostbite) act in this way. A number of capillary poisons, such as the salts of heavy metals, the toxins of certain bacteria and the histamine-like substances liberated in inflammatory conditions and in anaphylactic responses, tend to produce edema by increasing local, and even general, capillary permeability. It is believed that the edema of malnutrition ("prison camp edema") is contributed to by vitamin deficiencies and a resulting deterioration of the capillary wall.

4. Obstruction of the lymphatics results in edema, although the intercommunication between the lymphatic plexuses is so free in the mammal that it is very difficult to produce complete obstruction. This may occur, however, when the lymphatic trunks are blocked with tumor cells or with organisms such as filariae, and some lymphatic obstruction always occurs in local inflammatory processes. While the turgor of the inflamed part is due essentially to increased filtration through dilated and injured capillaries, it is aggravated by the local lymphatic obstruction.

5. Ingestion of sodium chloride tends to produce a generalized edema, or at least water retention, because each gram of sodium chloride requires 100 ml. of water to dissolve it in isotonic solution. This retention is particularly likely to occur in conditions in which the kidney excretes poorly.

Rate of lymph flow. The quantity of lymph in circulation and the rate of flow are not large in the mammal under ordinary physiologic conditions. In the dog, the lymph flow from the heart is only 0.005 to 0.025 ml. per minute. There is no correlation between the rate of lymph flow and either the weight of the animal or the weight of its heart. The lymph flow in the leg lymphatics is about 0.06 ml. per minute when a dog walks; when the animal is at rest, it is very difficult to obtain lymph at all. The flow in the thoracic duct is about 0.6 ml. per minute in the dog, and 1.0 to 1.5 ml. per minute in man (fasting).

The pressure which can be recorded by inserting a cannula in lymphatic vessels is extremely variable. It amounts to some 2 to 4 cm. of water in the lymphatics of the skin, 15 cm. of water in the thoracic duct and in the lymphatics of the beating heart, and as much as 40 cm. of water in the lymphatics of the intestinal villi. It is clear from these figures that the circulation of lymph in the mammal is not very brisk. In the amphibian, flow is much less sluggish, because the lymphatic system possesses lymph hearts which drive the lymph along the larger lymphatics.

Cell Content of Lymph. The number of cells found per cubic millimeter of lymph depends very largely on the number of lymph nodes the lymph has passed through. Lymph draining the extracellular space in peripheral regions and not having passed through any nodes has a cell count of about 500 cells per mm.³, whereas the lymph of the thoracic duct and right lymph duct, having traversed many nodes, contains about 40,000 cells per mm.³, and sometimes three or four times as many.

Nearly all the cells are lymphocytes, although there are occasional eosinophils and still more occasional monocytes. A few red cells are found even in peripheral lymph, especially during activity; apparently they make their way across the capillary wall into the extracellular space, and from there through the lymph vessel wall into the small lymphatics. The lymphocytes are derived from the lymph nodes and other lymphoid tissue (e.g., Peyer's patches in the intestine), and probably all the lymphocytes of the blood stream are delivered to it through the lymphatics. After ligation of the thoracic duct and the right lymph duct, the number of lymphocytes in the blood stream falls to virtually zero. About 200 million lymphocytes enter the blood of the dog each hour through these great lymphatic ducts. Most of the lymphocytes remain in the blood stream for less than a day, their fate being either disintegration or extrusion through the mucous membranes of the alimentary canal; a few, however, pass through the capillary walls into the extracellular space and thence into the lymph again.

The controversial question of "digestion leukocytosis," about which a large literature has accumulated, is closely related to the subject of the cell content of lymph. The evidence points, somewhat uncertainly, to there being a mechanical "flushing out" of the lymphoid tissue of the intestine during a meal, particularly if the meal is rich in protein. This, together with the increased flow in the lymph channels leading from the alimentary tract, results in a pouring of a larger number of lymphocytes than usual into the blood stream and in a "digestion leukocytosis" in the course of which the white cell count in the blood may increase several fold. Although the consensus is that no such increase occurs after a meal in man, there is evidence for its occurrence in the dog and other mammals.

Lymphoid Tissue. In the mammal, lymphoid tissue exists as masses of cells, principally lymphocytes, held together in a supporting framework of reticulum cells, fibrous and elastic tissue, and sometimes plain muscle fibers. Anatomically speaking, it can be divided into the lymphoid tissue of the lymph nodes, that in the mucous membranes, particularly of the alimentary canal (tonsils, Peyer's patches, etc.), and that of the spleen. By dissection and weighing of all the recognizable masses of lymphoid tissue, it has been estimated that they constitute about 1 per cent of the body weight.

The lymph enters the typical lymph node through a number of afferent lymphatics which converge near the hilum. As in passing through the node, the lymph must traverse a meshwork of sinusoids, lined by phagocytic cells and divided by a reticulum. This meshwork acts as a mechanical barrier to the passage of particles, as well as being phagocytic. The primary function of the node is thus that of acting as a filter of bacteria. While this function is exercised principally when the lymph is infected, there is some disputed evidence that a state of "subinfection" exists even in health, and that the lymph nodes filter out bacteria which have entered the lymph stream through minute "physiologic defects" in the skin and mucous membranes.

A number of other functions of the lymphoid tissue during health have been suggested, and it is understandable that some function other than that of defense against invading bacteria should be sought for a tissue which makes up so large a proportion of the body weight. Among the additional functions which have been considered are (i) the metabolism and transport of fat and protein, (ii) the storage of vitamins, (iii) the production of hormones and antihormones, and (iv) the destruction of, and sometimes the production of, red cells. The one function about which there is no doubt is the production of lymphocytes, and White and Dougherty have established the presence in lymphocytes of a protein identical with the gamma globulin of serum. Antibodies (modified globulins) have also been demonstrated in the lymphocytes obtained from immunized animals. The rate of release of the normal and modified globulins from the lymphocytes is influenced by the hormones of the adrenal cortex, the action of which is dependent on a stimulation of the adrenal cortex by pituitary adrenotrophic hormone. The adrenal hormones produce an increase in the rate of dissolution of the cytoplasm of the cells of the lymphoid tissue, and also a destruction of large numbers of circulating lymphocytes.

REFERENCES

1. ANREP, G. V. *Studies on cardiovascular regulation.* Stanford, Stanford University Press, 1936.
2. CHAMBERS, R. and ZWEIFACH, B. W. *J. cell. comp. Physiol.,* 1940, *15*:255–272.
3. DRINKER, C. K. and YOFFEY, J. M. *Lymphatics, lymph, and lymphoid tissue.* Cambridge, Harvard University Press, 1941.
4. KROGH, A. *The anatomy and physiology of capillaries,* revised ed. New Haven, Yale University Press, 1929.
5. LANDIS, E. M. *Physiol. Rev.,* 1934, *14*:404–482.
6. LEWIS, T. Chap. 5 in his: *The blood vessels of the human skin and their responses.* London, Shaw & Sons, Ltd., 1927.
7. MOON, V. H. *Shock and related capillary phenomena.* New York, Toronto, and London, Oxford University Press, 1938.
8. ZWEIFACH, B. W. *Amer. J. Anat.,* 1936–1937, *60*:473–514.
9. ZWEIFACH, B. W. *Cold Spr. Harb. Symp. quant. Biol.,* 1940, *8*:216–223.

SECTION VIII

Respiration

CHAPTER 35

Anatomy and Physics of Respiration

By LOREN D. CARLSON

THE term "respiration" refers to the exchange of gas between an organism and its environment. The true object of respiration was demonstrated by Lavoisier (1777) after carbon dioxide in expired air had been discovered by J. Black (1757) and after the properties of oxygen had been discovered and investigated by J. Priestley (1774). In a single cell, gases may be exchanged by diffusion, but in the complex human organism two elaborate systems—the respiratory system and the gas transportation system—are needed to supply sufficient oxygen and to remove carbon dioxide from the cells as it is produced. The transportation system within the body is discussed in Chapter 36.

The respiratory system exchanges air with the environment. A necessary consequence of this exchange is the loss of water by evaporation and of heat. The respiratory system in the resting state is capable of supplying oxygen at the rate of 200 ml. per minute, but may increase the supply to 2000 ml. per minute or more under conditions of heavy exercise. Respiration in man may be considered in terms of the functional subdivisions of the system, and clinical tests of function are designed to determine the extent to which each subdivision malfunctions during disease. These subdivisions are (i) the mechanical properties of the lungs and the thoracic cage, and (ii) the mechanisms of mixing and diffusion of gases in the lungs and perfusion of the lungs by blood.

Mechanically, the lung is a system composed of an elastic tissue connected to the exterior by the respiratory passages. The lungs share the closed chest cavity with the heart and the great vessels, and are held firmly to the pleural surfaces by surface tension. The elasticity of the lungs gives rise to a negative pressure in the intrathoracic space. Although it is frequently convenient to discuss the lung as though it were a balloon or bellows, the size and structure of the distributing tubes—the trachea, bronchi and bronchioles—and the intricacies of the terminal alveoli must also be considered in any accurate description of pulmonary function (Fig. 454).

A change in the volume of air in the lung is brought about by a change in the volume of the chest or thorax. This change may be effected in part by the muscular diaphragm, which is attached posteriorly to the lumbar vertebrae and ribs, and extends

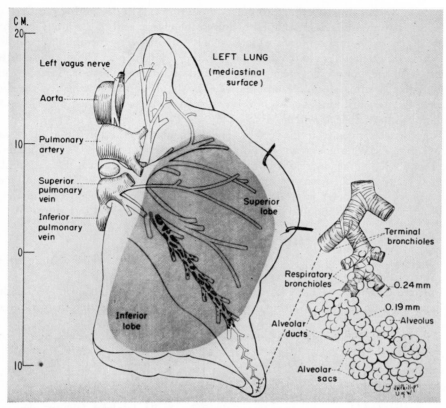

FIG. 454. Drawing of left lung reflected to show mediastinal surface and position of heart (*shaded area*). Scale at left gives approximate distances from heart level. One branching bronchus is shaded to show cartilage. Enlargement at right shows structure of alveolus and dimensions of smaller units. (Dr. A. Boyden kindly aided with preparation of sketch.)

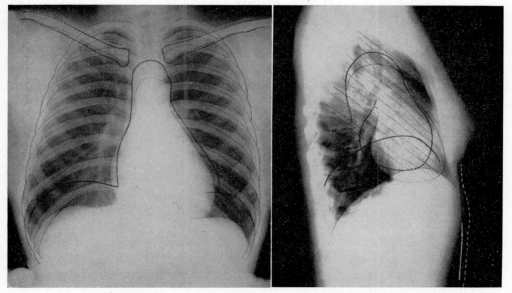

FIG. 455. *Left*, Posteroanterior radiograph of chest at full inspiration and full expiration, superimposed. Note change in diaphragm position, rib position, width of intercostal spaces and outline of heart. The darkness of the lung fields indicates amount of air. *Right*, Lateral radiograph. Heart outline is below anterior level of diaphragm; the liver rises into this region. (Radiographs by M. Figley, M.D.)

anteriorly and ventrally, as a sheet, to the xyphoid process. In the resting position of the thorax, the diaphragm is dome-shaped owing to the elastic pull of the lungs and/or the pressure of the abdominal contents, which are held in position by the abdominal muscles. Thus, these latter muscles contribute to respiratory movements. The diaphragm tends to flatten with age, but it is not clear whether this flattening results from a loss of elasticity or from a decrease in abdominal muscle tone. The diaphragm is attached by the central tendon to the pericardium, thus establishing a relationship to the mediastinal contents. It cannot be contracted at will.[4]

The ribs are connected to the vertebrae in such a manner that, in the adult, elevation increases thoracic volume and the reverse process decreases volume. The circumference of the costal (rib) arches increases in the first to the sixth pair of ribs. Elevation of ribs one to five increases the anteroposterior dimension; ribs six to ten contribute an increase in the transverse diameter as well. The relative contributions of the ribs and the diaphragm at a full inspiration and at a full expiration are illustrated in Figure 455.

MECHANICAL FUNCTION

The mechanical properties of this system are studied by measuring volume displacement, rate of flow of gas, and pressure change.

Volume Changes.   Changes in volume are measured with a spirometer, as shown in principle in Figure 456. In normal respiration, inspiration starting from the resting

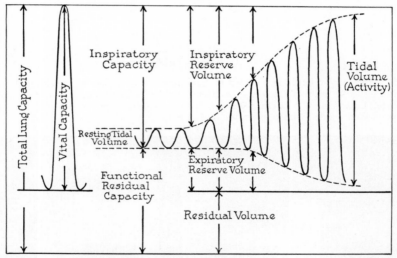

FIG. 456.   Relationships between various subdivisions of lung air. Note that tidal volume is only a small fraction of total lung capacity. (After *Fed. Proc.*, 1950, *9:*602–605.)

position of the chest is an active process, which is followed by passive relaxation. The volume exchanged is the *tidal volume*. The tidal volume increases during muscular activity and certain emotional states. If a normal person or a patient is asked to inspire maximally, the volume taken into the lungs is the *inspiratory capacity*. The difference between the tidal volume and the maximum inspiratory volume is the *inspiratory reserve volume*. Similarly, a maximum amount that can be expired after a tidal expiration is the *expiratory reserve capacity*. During activity the tidal volume increases mainly by encroaching on the inspiratory reserve volume. The sum of the inspiratory and expiratory reserve capacities comprises the *vital capacity*. Maximum expiratory effort does not completely empty the lungs. There is a *residual volume*, which may be measured by methods to be described

TABLE 20.   LUNG VOLUMES (BTPS)*

Inspiratory capacity	3600 ml.
Expiratory reserve volume	1200 ml.
Vital capacity	4800 ml.
Residual volume (RV)	1200 ml.
Functional residual capacity	2400 ml.
Total lung capacity (TLC)	6000 ml.
RV/TLC × 100	20%

* From Comroe et al., *The lung. Clinical physiology and pulmonary function tests.* Chicago, Yearbook Publishers, 1955.

below. The expiratory reserve capacity and the residual volume comprise the *functional reserve capacity* (Fig. 456).

The volume of the lungs varies according to body size and sex. The values may be expressed by formulas or in tabular form (Table 20; see also Table 21). The *minute volume* is the product of the tidal volume and the respiratory rate.

Static lung volumes give indices of *available* function, but description of pressure changes and rates of flow add materially to the description of lung mechanics.

Velocity of Flow.   Instantaneous rates of flow of air in and out of the lungs are measured with a variety of flowmeters and are also assessed from the volume expired in a unit time or from the slope of the inspiratory and expiratory curves. The principle of all flowmeters is essentially the same, although many designs exist. The respired air passes through a resistance which varies with flow, preferably linearly. This resistance can be provided by a large number of small orifices, as in a 400-mesh Monel screen; by a series of capillary tubes; or by a set of concentric cylinders. The resistance to flow must be small; less than 1 inch at 100 liters per minute is desirable. Flowmeters of the orifice type are poor because the resistance is not linear with flow but increases rapidly at high flow rates.

In normal inspiration or expiration, the velocity of flow increases from zero to a maximum that can be roughly estimated in liters per minute by multiplying the minute volume by 2.5. Impairment of flow increases the work of breathing and reduces the tidal volume. Impairment of velocity results from an increase in resistance or a weakening of the respiratory muscles. Velocity may be influenced by a restricted chest volume if the test requires inspiration or expiration of a large volume. Increased resistance is usually manifest during expiration.

High velocities are used to clear the lung passages, as in a cough. These velocities may be as high as 500 liters per minute.

Pressure.   In considering the pressure changes during respiration, one must keep in mind the distinction between the pressure outside the lungs and the pressure within the lungs. The pressure in the thoracic cavity outside the lungs is designated as the *intrathoracic pressure.* It is the pressure exerted upon the heart, the great blood vessels, the thoracic duct, the esophagus and the intrapleural lymph.[24] The pressure within the lungs and the air passages is termed the *intrapulmonic pressure.* This pressure is always greater than the intrathoracic pressure by an amount equal to the elastic force of the lungs.

Intrapulmonic pressure.   The air passages and alveoli of the lungs are in free communication with the external air; consequently, in every position of rest, whether at the end of inspiration or of expiration, the pressure in these cavities is equal to the atmospheric pressure. During the act of inspiration—i.e., during the inflow of air—the intrapulmonic pressure temporarily falls below that of the atmosphere. The extent of this decrease depends, naturally, upon the rapidity and amplitude of the inspiratory movement and upon the size of the opening to the interior. If the air passages are abnormally constricted, the fall of pressure during inspiration will be correspondingly magnified in the parts below the constriction, as happens during bronchial asthma, edema of the glottis or a cold in the head. Under normal conditions the fall in intrapulmonic pressure during a quiet inspiration is not large, only 2 to 3 mm. Hg.

At the end of inspiration, the pressure rises again to atmospheric. During expiration the elastic recoil of the chest wall is rapid enough to compress the air somewhat during its escape. The result is a slight but temporary rise in pressure to about 3 mm. Hg above atmospheric pressure. Changes in intrapulmonic pressure much greater than these can be obtained if the glottis is firmly closed during attempted inspiration and expiration. Vigorous inspiratory movements under such conditions may lower the pressure to 30 to 80 mm. Hg below atmospheric, whereas strong expiratory movements similarly may raise the pressure to 60 to 100 mm. Hg above atmospheric.

The smaller bronchi possess a distinct muscular layer, and contraction of these muscles can greatly modify the resistance to the movement of air. Their exact function in the normal respiratory cycle is unknown.[21] They are controlled by the autonomic nervous system and may relax rhythmically with inspiration, affording easier entrance of air to the ultimate air sacs. It is thought that these muscles are strongly contracted during asthmatic attacks, and the pressure changes in the alveolar air must then be much greater than normal. Epinephrine is useful in attacks of asthma since it may cause the bronchiolar musculature to relax so that the alveoli can be more easily ventilated.

Intrathoracic pressure. In the fetus the lungs are solid and completely fill all of the thoracic cavity that is not occupied by other organs. Inspiratory movements of the diaphragm at birth increase the volume of the thorax slightly, and air enters the lungs; careful measurements by Hermann[19] show that at this time only slightly subatmospheric pressures exist in the thorax. The subatmospheric pressure of 4 mm. Hg or so found in the adult[7] evidently develops gradually and must arise because the thorax increases in size more rapidly and to a greater extent than the lungs do. In order to fill the cavity, the lungs stretch more and more. The lungs are continually pulling away from the thoracic cage with a force which varies with inspiratory movements.[5] The intrapleural lymph is under tension and, like all liquids, has considerable tensile strength (intermolecular attractive forces); it is fully capable of holding the lungs expanded, even during the greatest stresses possible physiologically. Seemingly the expanded lung is protected in normal circumstances from any danger of returning to a fetal state of consolidation. At the end of a forced expiration the lungs are still somewhat extended, and a considerable, though reduced, tension still exists in the intrapleural space.

The relations between the atmospheric, intrapulmonic and intrathoracic pressures during a normal respiratory cycle are illustrated in Figure 457. The difference between the intrapulmonic and the intrathoracic pressure is a measure not only of the elastic force of the lungs but also of the tension exerted by the intrapleural lymph. Large variations in intrathoracic pressure can markedly affect the heart and circulation. The great veins and the right side of the heart are thin-walled structures, and, since they lie in the mediastinal space, they are subjected to all variations of the intrathoracic pressure. The venous return cannot remain constant during the respiratory cycle, and the heart rate and the blood pressure must change accordingly. The extent of the fluctuations in rate and pressure is largely determined by the sensitivity of an individual's cardiovascular reflex control mechanisms.

These interrelations of the respiration and cardiovascular systems form the rationale for a simple procedure, the Flack test,[11] which has been used as a fitness test. The subject blows as long as possible into a mercury manometer with a force equal to 40 mm. Hg. The test determines both his breath-holding capacity and the ability of his vascular system to maintain an adequate venous return under conditions of high intrathoracic

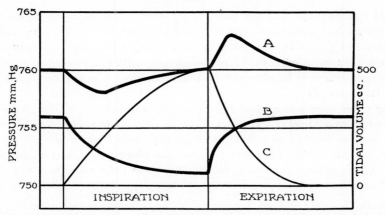

FIG. 457. Diagram to illustrate relationships between intrapulmonic pressure (*A*), intrathoracic pressure (*B*), and tidal air volume (*C*). At end of inspiration and expiration intrapulmonic pressure is equal to external atmospheric pressure (760 mm. Hg in this instance). The difference between intrapulmonic and intrathoracic pressure is a measure of elastic force of the lungs and also the tension exerted by the intrapleural lymph.

pressure. Considerable knowledge of the subject's physical and psychologic state can be obtained by carefully noting the pulse rate, the pressure fluctuations and the behavior of the respiration after the pressure is released.

Pneumothorax. When the pleural cavity is opened by any means, air enters and causes shrinkage of the corresponding lung. This condition is called *pneumothorax*.[17] Air may enter the pleural space through a gunshot or stab wound of the chest or through a defect in the pleural investment of the lung, as after rupture of a tubercle in pulmonary tuberculosis. In the latter case, of course, air enters from the alveoli of the lungs. From the considerations of the mechanics of lung inflation discussed above, it is evident that an expandable volume of air in the pleura can interfere greatly with normal ventilation of the lungs. If a large external opening to the pleural space is permitted to persist, the lungs may collapse completely. If the wound is closed, the amount of interference with ventilation depends upon the volume of the air pocket.[8] With any degree of pneumothorax the intrathoracic pressure rises, and, since the mediastinum is not rigid, it is displaced away from the region of the trapped air.

In the vicinity of the pneumothorax, a more or less extensive region of the lung may collapse, and the small amount of air remaining in the affected alveoli will be rapidly absorbed by the circulating blood, the final result being a condition of local consolidation or incomplete expansion known as *atelectasis*. (The same condition of local consolidation may also arise if, for any reason, the alveolar ducts or the bronchioles are blocked for any length of time.) In man, pneumothorax occurs most frequently when the visceral pleura becomes so eroded by disease that openings appear.

Pneumothorax is used therapeutically to reduce the extent of the respiratory movements of a diseased lung. Measured quantities of air are introduced into the pleura so that the infected lung is partially collapsed. Healing is generally promoted by placing the lung at rest. The injected air in the closed pneumothorax is slowly absorbed by the circulating blood, and the lung again expands as the absorption takes place. To maintain the pneumothorax for any length of time, air must be injected every few days.

Pressure-Volume Relationships. Knowledge of the pressure-volume relations in the human lung gives a better understanding of the mechanics of breathing. Some of these relationships are shown in Figure 458, which presents results from two experiments. In the first of these, the extent of inflation of the lungs was measured in a spirometer and expressed as a percentage of the vital capacity; full inspiration represents 100 per cent of the vital capacity and full expiration 0 per cent. Then, at various degrees of lung inflation, the subject was asked to relax completely with his glottis open, while his nose was clamped and his mouth was connected to a tube attached to a mercury manometer. The pressure thus recorded is the relaxation pressure, P_r. (The maximal inspiratory and expiration pressures may be obtained by maximal effort.) As will be shown later, P_r is related to lung compliance.

In the other experiment yielding data shown in Figure 458, the subject breathed normally while in a Drinker resuscitator (see p. 787). The pressure in the resuscitator was set at varying levels, and at each pressure the subject performed the vital capacity maneuver (see Fig. 456). The tidal volume was plotted as a percentage of the vital capacity. It is significant that these values depart from P_r, since they indicate involvement of the respiratory muscles when the tendency is to inflate or deflate the lungs.

In addition, Figure 458 illustrates how the various lung volumes change during pressure breathing, a therapeutic procedure useful in resuscitation and in alleviation of the respiratory distress of asthmatics. From the tidal volume curves and the relaxation pressure curve, it is possible to estimate the work of breathing. The area $GHVr$ represents the elastic work required for inhalation of 500 ml. of air if inspira-

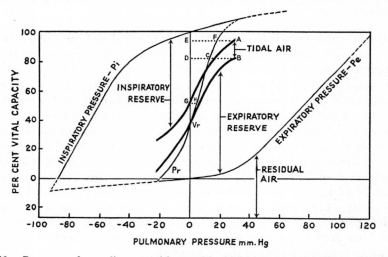

FIG. 458. Pressure-volume diagram of lung with tidal air and relaxation pressure (P_r) curves added. Areas $GHVr$ and $FABC$ represent elastic work of breathing at normal and 30 mm. Hg positive pressure, respectively. Vr is relaxation volume or volume at rest position of thorax. (From Rahn *et al.*, *Amer. J. Physiol.*, 1946, *146*:161–178.)

tion is begun from the midposition or relaxation volume (V_r). This work is accomplished by the inspiratory muscles and amounts to 1.8 kg. per cm. If positive pressure breathing at 30 cm. H_2O is employed, the elastic work is done by the expiratory muscles and is much greater—approximately 10 kg. per cm. It is interesting that, when half the work is inspiratory and half is expiratory, the minimum work for normal respiration is accomplished at a positive pressure of some 3.5 mm. Hg, although the gain over more normal conditions is very slight.

Clinical Tests. Determination of pulmonary function includes the measurement of static lung volume in the manner described. Attention to the nature of the curves, as well as observation of the subject during the test, will add information concerning function. Figure 459 shows curves obtained for a normal subject and for patients with fibrosis of the lungs, asthma and emphysema; the paper of the recording spirometer moved sufficiently fast to indicate differences in the rate of flow, as well as in volume, by changes in the slope of the volume line. Compare particularly the velocity during full expiration and full inspiration. In the patient with fibrosis the impairment of volume was not accompanied by impairment of the flow rate. In the patient with emphysema, impairment of flow rate was particularly noticeable during expiration.

The tendency for impairment of flow rate, reflecting unusual resistance, to affect expiration has been the basis of two pulmonary function tests. One, the *timed vital capacity*, in practice measures the volume expired in one-half or one second; this method was devised and tested by Gaensler.[12] A second method involves measurement of the *maximum instantaneous flow;* i.e., the rate at which expired air passes through a flowmeter is recorded from instant to instant throughout an expiration.[15]

A pulmonary function test which has gained considerable favor is termed the *maximum breathing capacity.* This test combines the parameters of flow and volume in a measurement of the maximum volume that can be breathed in 15 seconds. The patient is instructed to breath as deeply and rapidly as possible. Normal values for this test have have been set up in tables and as equations (Table 21). Figure 459 shows schematically

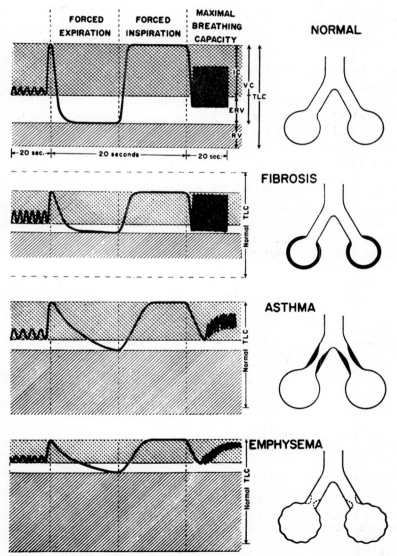

FIG. 459.   Schematic diagrams of lung volumes and capacities with normal compared to restrictive (fibrosis) and obstructive impairment (asthma and emphysema). Note position of tidal volume in respect to vital capacity, the maximum expiratory flow, and the form and position of the maximum breathing capacity maneuver. (From Comroe *et al., The lung. Clinical physiology and pulmonary function tests.* Chicago, Yearbook Publishers, 1955.)

TABLE 21.   FORMULAS USED TO CALCULATE NORMAL VALUES
FOR TESTS OF PULMONARY FUNCTION

TEST	SUBJECT	FORMULA
Vital capacity (in liters, BTPS)	Adult male	$[27.63 - (0.112 \times age)] \times$ height in cm. $\times 10^{-3}$
	Adult female	$[21.73 - (0.101 \times age)] \times$ height in cm. $\times 10^{-3}$
Total lung capacity (in liters, BTPS)	16–34 years male or female	(Vital capacity in liters)/0.8
	35–49 years male or female	(Vital capacity in liters)/0.766
	50–69 years male or female	(Vital capacity in liters)/0.692
Maximal breathing capacity (in liters, BTPS)	Adult male	$[86.5 - (0.522 \times age)] \times$ body surface area in m.^{2}
	Adult female	$[71.3 - (0.474 \times age)] \times$ body surface area in m.^{2}

the influence of restrictive and obstructive impairment on expiratory flow and maximum breathing capacity.

The above tests provide measurements adequate to discern gross malfunction; but, when the disorder is subtle, their results are sometimes equivocal. The tests may be affected by motivation and by the varying manner in which they are given—e.g., with the patient reclining, sitting or standing. Care must also be taken to express the different units in comparable terms.

WORK OF BREATHING

A review of the mechanical properties presented schematically in Figure 460 will emphasize the principles with which we have dealt and will permit a discussion of the work of breathing. The volume in the lung changes as the intrathoracic pressure changes. The extent to which the intrathoracic pressure changes with a change in volume is

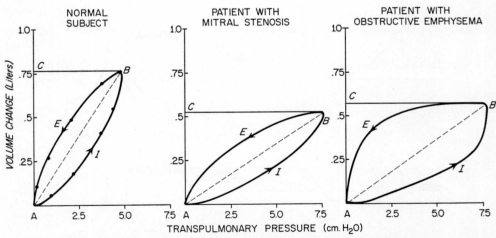

FIG. 460.   Volume-pressure diagrams to illustrate concepts involved in work of breathing. Dotted line *AB* represents pulmonary compliance. Area of triangle *ABC* represents work. Heavy line traces pressure change with a single breath over path *I* for inspiration and path *E* for expiration. Actual work is represented by area $A \to I \to BC$. A simple formation of work against elastance (1/compliance) in the normal is 0.5 (0.75 liters $\times$ 5 cm.). For total work, the factor 0.5 is changed to 0.7 to get an approximate value, and maximum transpulmonary pressure is used. Changes in compliance and resistance to air flow are illustrated in diagrams for patients with mitral stenosis and obstructive emphysema. (After *Cardiopulmon. Facts*, 1959, 2(2):1–3.)

termed *compliance*. The normal value is 0.1 liter per cm. H_2O for the lung. The extent to which changes in pulmonary volume follow changes in intrapleural pressure is then measured when no air is flowing into the lungs, or when the intrapulmonary pressure is equal to the atmospheric pressure. Flow into the lungs occurs when there is a pressure difference, and measurement of the rate of flow and the pressure difference quantitates the resistance to flow. In Figure 460, the normal mechanical properties of the lungs are compared with those in a pulmonary system in which resistance to flow is increased and with those in a system in which compliance is increased. The data shown in Figure 460 are also illustrative of changes measured in clinical patients.

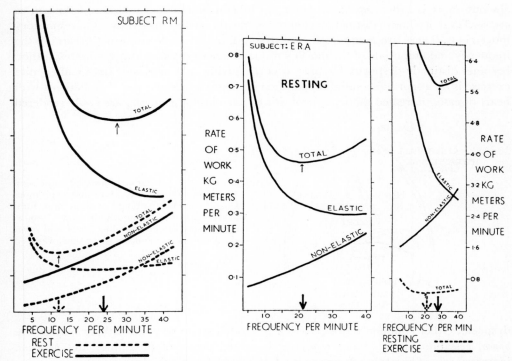

FIG. 461.   Diagrams of work of ventilating the lungs at rest and during exercise in normal subject (*left*) and patient with mitral stenosis (*right pair*). Light arrows on curves of total work indicate frequency at which least respiratory work is required. Heavy arrows at bottom of diagrams indicate actual frequency of respiration.* (From Christie, *Proc. R. Soc. Med.*, 1953, *46*:381–386.)

The work of breathing is normally determined by three factors—elastic forces, air viscosity and air turbulence[25]—but may be approached in an elementary fashion by considering the simple statement that work equals force times distance, or pressure times volume. Thus, in the diagram in Figure 460, the work required to inhale a single breath of 750 ml. in the normal system is 0.750 liter times 4.75 cm. H_2O, divided by 2, or about 1.8 kg.-cm. In the second example, the increase in work is mostly required to overcome resistance. In the third, additional work is needed to overcome decreased compliance. The kinds of interference set up by each of these two factors have been termed *obstructive impairment* and *restrictive impairment*, respectively. Figure 461 shows the work of breathing related to respiratory rate and demonstrates that the adjustment of tidal volume and respiratory rate seems to depend on the work of breathing.

* Work against elastic resistance equals 0.5 $P_{el}V$. For total work of resistance and elastance the maximum pressure is reached during flow. An approximation of the work may be obtained by using the numerical factor 0.7 in place of 0.5 when P_{max}/P_{el} is greater than 0.75 and the factor 0.8 when P_{max}/P_{el} is less than 0.75. (McIlroy and Eldridge, *Clin. Sci.*, 1956, *15*:329–335.)

Breathing Movements.   The frequency and amplitude of the respiratory movements vary greatly. Rates of inspiration as low as three times a minute reportedly have
been seen in healthy human beings. However, the normal rate in a resting individual
is considered to be 16 times a minute. During forced or labored breathing, the rate may
increase greatly. The volume of air inhaled in a single breath, the tidal volume, also
varies widely, the average in resting man being about 500 ml. Excellent quantitative
records of breathing movements can be obtained with a clinical basal metabolism
machine, a spirometer. The record, a graph of volume as a function of time, is called
a *spirogram*.

Ordinarily, we are unaware of the respiratory act, and such breathing made without
obvious effort is called *eupnea*. In contrast, difficult or labored breathing is known as
dyspnea.[27] A sharp line of distinction cannot be drawn between the two types of respiratory
movements. There are many degrees of dyspnea, and doubtless in quiet breathing the
frequency and amplitude of the movement may increase considerably before respiration
becomes distinctly dyspneic. Dyspnea occurring while a person is at rest or after mild
exercise is an abnormal condition and often indicates a diseased state.[6, 23] Patients with
heart disease, untreated diabetes, nephritis or anemia, for example, are easily rendered

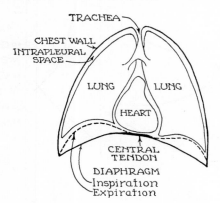

FIG. 462.   Relative position of diaphragm
at end of normal inspiration and expiration.
During quiet breathing, position of central
tendon changes but slightly; in forced inspiration it may descend, pulling heart and other
viscera of the mediastinal space downward.

dyspneic. Other common terms referring to modifications of the breathing pattern are
apnea, cessation of breathing; *hyperpnea*, increased depth of breathing; and *polypnea*,
increased rate of breathing. Dyspnea is related to the fraction of the maximum breathing
capacity used[2] and to the work of breathing.[22]

Inspiration.   The volume of the thorax can be increased in two ways. The diaphragm can contract and effectively increase the cephalocaudal dimensions of the
thorax, a method of breathing called *abdominal* because movements of the abdominal
walls are necessary concomitants. Or the ribs can be elevated to increase the cross-
sectional area of the chest, a method appropriately called *costal*. Either method is adequate to meet the respiratory demands of eupnea and mild exercise. However, in normal
man both methods are operative at all times and are effectively coordinated to meet
the increased respiratory demands of strenuous exercise. Throughout life the diaphragm
is probably the main muscle of inspiration, and dimensional changes resulting from its
movements account for the greater part of the total volume of air inspired during
eupnea.

Contraction of the diaphragm.   In the relaxed state the right and left sides of the diaphragm are elevated above the central tendon by the pressure of the abdominal contents;
in the contracted state these arches are flattened (Fig. 462) and the displaced abdominal
viscera are accommodated by simultaneous relaxation of the abdominal musculature
and protrusion of the abdominal walls. In eupnea there is little movement of the central

tendon, but in forced inspiration the heart may be pulled downward and the lower ribs may be pulled inward to some extent. The movement of the lower ribs is counteracted in part by the rise in abdominal pressure and in part by contraction of the quadratus lumborum and the serratus posterior inferior. The motion of the diaphragm as a whole, because of the plane of its attachments, is almost as much forward as downward, and it is most effective in ventilation of the lower lobes of the lungs. The diaphragm is innervated on each side by a phrenic nerve, and transection of a phrenic nerve paralyzes the half of the diaphragm on the same side.

Elevation of the ribs. In eupnea the first rib and the manubrium sterni are fixed; in dyspnea they are elevated by contraction of the sternocleidomastoid, scaleni and pectoralis minor. The other ribs are moved toward the first rib during inspiration by contraction of the external intercostal muscles, which extend from the lower edge of one rib to the upper edge of the rib below. When these muscles contract, the ribs are elevated and more nearly at right angles to the spine (Fig. 463). Bronk and Ferguson[3] established

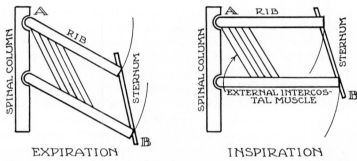

EXPIRATION   INSPIRATION

FIG. 463. Schema to indicate manner in which first five ribs function to increase anteroposterior diameter of chest during inspiration. The successive costal arches increase in length, and, as ribs rise, anteroposterior diameter of chest is effectively extended. Note that points *A* and *B* are closer together when ribs are elevated. The attachments of external intercostal muscles are such that they tend to shorten distance *A–B* when they contract.

the inspiratory function of the external intercostal and intercartilaginous portion of the internal intercostal muscles by observing the electrical activity of the motor nerves going to them. Action currents in the respective nerves occurred synchronously with contraction of the diaphragm. Other muscles also act to elevate the ribs and are thus classed as inspiratory.[13, 14] These are the levatores costarum and the serratus posterior superior, which run downward from the vertebral column to the ribs.

Expiration. The volume of the thorax can be decreased in various ways. The chest may return passively from its expanded state by virtue of the elastic forces of the lungs and the thorax; the transversus thoracis and interosseous portion of the internal intercostals may contract and depress the ribs;[1] or the muscles of the abdominal wall may contract and force the diaphragm up into the thorax. During eupnea, expiration is largely passive, and it is only during vigorous breathing that the expiratory muscles are called into action. The main muscles of expiration are the internal and external oblique, the rectus and the transversus muscles of the abdominal wall. When these contract, the pressure in the abdominal cavity is raised. If the glottis is kept open, the increased abdominal pressure forces the diaphragm into the thorax, and air is expelled from the lungs. If the glottis is firmly closed, no air can escape and the increased abdominal pressure affects mainly the pelvic organs, an effect which is obtained during micturition, defecation and parturition. The participation of the expiratory muscles during vigorous breathing makes possible increases in both the amplitude and the frequency of the respiratory movements. Forced expiration not only speeds up the expiratory phase, but also reduces the thoracic volume below normal so that a greater quantity of air per breath is expelled from the lungs. There is some evidence that the inspiratory muscles contract during expiration to slow the rate of passive relaxation of the lungs and check the movement of the rib cage.

Accessory Respiratory Movements.   In addition to the muscles whose action directly enlarges or diminishes the capacity of the thorax, certain others connected with the air passages contract rhythmically with inspiration, and may be properly designated as accessory muscles of respiration. The muscles especially concerned are those controlling the size of the glottis and the opening of the external nares. The glottis is dilated at each inspiration by contraction of the posterior crico-arytenoid muscles, and the elevators of the wings of the nares come into play. These movements occur during normal breathing by some persons and also in many animals, such as the rabbit and the horse. They are invariably present in dyspneic breathing. The useful result of these movements is a reduction in the resistance to an inflow of air.

Breathing Movements of Lungs.   It is evident from a consideration of the chest wall that the lungs cannot inflate by simple expansion from a central point. The apical, posterior and mediastinal surfaces of the lungs are in contact with regions of the thorax which move very little, and the portion of the lungs adjacent to these surfaces can be said to expand indirectly. The sternocostal and diaphragmatic regions of the lungs have the greatest motion and are said to expand directly.

Not all parts of the lungs are equally elastic. Keith[20] distinguished three zones of varying degrees of expansibility: (i) the root zone, which has the least distensibility, containing the bronchi, the arteries, the veins and fibrous tissue; (ii) the intermediate zone, which contain the smaller ramifications of the bronchi, arteries and veins that radiate toward the outer surface of the lungs and also the pulmonary tissue distributed between the rays; and (iii) the outer zone, in which the largest volume changes take place, containing principally pulmonary elastic tissue and air sacs. During inspiration all the air passages appear to elongate, and the pulmonary tissues expand to fill the new space created by the lengthening of the radiating bronchioles. The root of the lung moves forward and downward, creating the space which the indirectly expanded regions of the lung occupy at full inspiration.

It is probable that during normal quiet breathing not all lung alveoli share equally in effecting gas exchange with the blood. The relatively smaller ventilation of the apex of the lung and other indirectly expanded regions may explain why these regions are more often the site of primary pathologic lesions such as those of tuberculosis.

MIXTURE OF GASES IN THE LUNGS

The discussion thus far has dealt with the mechanics of air exchange. This mechanical function is, however, merely a means to the end of bringing air into contact with blood perfusing the lung. Before this event occurs, there is an intervening step, the mixture of gases in the lungs. The introduction to the discussion of lung volumes indicated the existence of an expiratory capacity which is not fully used and a residual volume which cannot be expired. As mentioned above, the expiratory capacity and the residual volume make up the functional reserve capacity. Thus, even in deepest breathing, the air in the lung is not replaced. Rather, the tidal air, ranging from 500 ml. in quiet breathing to 2000 ml. in deep breathing, is intermixed with 1500 ml. of functional reserve air. The size of the latter is a factor in the mixing of gases in the lungs.

The functional reserve capacity is measured by a simple gas method in which either the nitrogen in the lungs or a foreign gas such as helium may be the diluent. If the subject breathes into and out of a spirometer with the volume V_S from his lungs (V_L) when the spirometer contains no nitrogen and the lung volume is 80 per cent nitrogen, then at equilibrium $0.8 V_L = X(V_L + V_S)$, where X is the new and smaller fraction of nitrogen. (This must be true, since nitrogen is not lost—it is merely redistributed.) Since X as a fraction of nitrogen can be measured and V_S is known, $V_L = XV_S/(0.8 - X)$.

One method of determining the degree of mixing in the lung is to measure the time that passes before all the nitrogen is removed from the lungs when the subject is breathing oxygen. Conversely, the fraction of nitrogen remaining after a given period of oxygen breathing may be measured. *Pulmonary emptying time* is such a test and involves seven minutes of breathing oxygen.[9] At the end of this time, the expired air of a normal person will be about 2 per cent nitrogen, whereas the value may approach 20 per cent in persons with poor mixing.

New analytic methods, particularly with the nitrogen analyzer, provide more rapid measures. Figure 464 is a tracing from such a test, and careful study of it will give an insight into the mixing problem. This method has been extended to measurements in

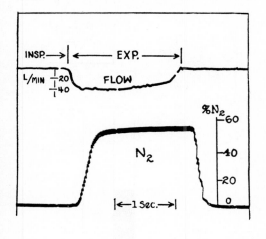
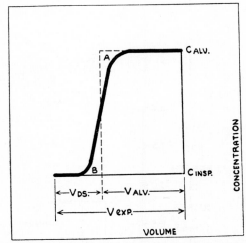

FIG. 464. *Left*, Record of instantaneous expiration flow in liters per minute (*upper trace*) with the expiratory N_2 analysis following a single breath of N_2. Ascending limb of N_2 curve is analyzed further at *right* to present geometrically Bohr's formula. If area *A* equals area *B*, flow to left of perpendicular forming these is from dead space. Nature of alveolar portion of N_2 curve is determined by the mixing in the lungs. (From Fowler, *Amer. J. Physiol.*, 1948, *154*:405–416.)

each lung (bronchospirometry) or in separate lobes (lobar spirometry). Thereby a tuberculous or neoplastic disease affecting only one lobe and not detectable in a loss of vital capacity can be diagnosed and localized.

Dead Space. Figure 464 indicates a further problem relating to pulmonary mixing—the dead space. Not all of the tidal inflow is atmospheric air; at the end of expiration the air passages are filled with alveolar air. During inspiration this air is driven back into the depths of the lung by the incoming air. Thus, in round numbers, perhaps only 150 ml. of the 500 ml. of tidal air is available for diluting the carbon dioxide and elevating the oxygen content of the functional reserve air. Undoubtedly the respiratory passages contribute heavily to the dead space as measured. Other factors have led to the differentiation of anatomic and physiologic dead space.

Anatomic dead space is the internal volume from the nose and mouth down to the alveoli. It is called dead space because no direct exchange of oxygen and carbon dioxide occurs within it. *Physiologic dead space* includes the anatomic dead space, the inspired gas ventilating alveoli with no blood flow, and the inspired gas ventilating some alveoli in excess of the amount required to convert the gas content of surrounding capillary blood to that of arterial blood. Measurement of the anatomic dead space is based on Bohr's formula (see Chap. 36). Calculation of the dead space in the upper tracing of Figure 464 will give a volume of approximately 150 ml.

Measured values for dead space vary in a minor manner with the gas used, but are related to lung volume, chest position and time of breath holding. Dead space increases during exercise.[28]

ARTIFICIAL RESPIRATION

In laboratory experiments on animals, artificial respiration is frequently employed after the use of curare, after cessation of respiration from overdoses of anesthetics, when it is necessary to open the chest, etc. The method usually used involves expansion of the lungs by pressure. A bellows or blast worked by hand or machinery is connected with the trachea, and the lungs are dilated rhythmically. Provision is made for the

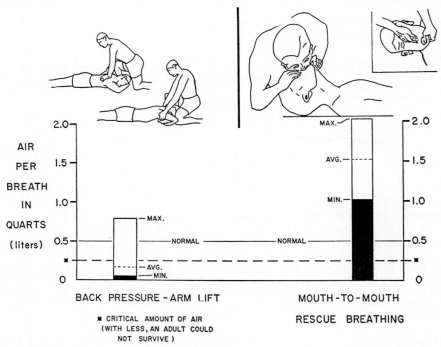

FIG. 465. Amount of ventilation received in two methods of resuscitation as determined by laboratory studies on anesthetized, paralyzed subjects. Sketches above show technique of applying each method. Inset, manipulation of subject's nose and mouth for mouth to mouth resuscitation. (From *Bull. med. Soc. Co. Erie*, 1958, *35* (3).)

escape of expired air by the use of valves, or by a small hole in the tracheal cannula. Numerous forms of respiration pumps have been devised for this purpose.

In man, when respiration is suspended as a result of drowning, electrical shock, pressure upon the medulla, etc., artificial respiration must be used in order to restore normal breathing. Bellows ordinarily cannot be used in such cases. Some method must be employed to expand and contract the chest alternately, and many different procedures have been suggested. Up to recent years the most favored method was that known as the Schafer[26] prone pressure method. A newer method, the Holger Nielsen back pressure-arm lift technique,[16a] has distinct advantages, as demonstrated by actual ventilation accomplished. In this method (Fig. 465) the subject is placed in the prone position with one cheek resting on his hands. Obstructions are removed from his mouth, and his tongue is pulled forward. The operator kneels in front of the subject and places his hands (with thumbs almost touching and fingers spread out) on the subject's back just below the shoulder blades. The operator rocks forward and, keeping his elbows straight, presses slowly and evenly on the subject's back. The operator rocks backward and releases the pressure slowly, then grasps the subject's arms just above the elbows. The subject's arms are now drawn forward and upward until slight resistance is felt; the arms are then dropped. This procedure gives good ventilation to the lungs of unconscious subjects and should be repeated ten to 12 times a minute. After natural breathing returns the subject should be watched and artificial respiration begun again if any sign of failure is noted. A half hour or more may be required before normal breathing movements start. Mouth to mouth resuscitation has gained new favor,[16] and appears to give more ventilation than pressure methods (Fig. 465).

Special instruments (pulmotors, lungmotors, resuscitators) have been devised, but some training is required to operate them properly, and they are not as a rule available for instant use. In resuscitation, the important matter is to apply artificial respiration promptly. Individuals who have ceased to breathe from accident or from other cause are in need of artificial respiration and should be given immediate treatment by the mouth to mouth or some other method. The delay incident to removal to a hospital may be fatal and is justifiable only when there is no one at hand to give artificial respiration. If complications which necessitate hospital treatment exist or arise, artificial respiration should be maintained in transit and after the arrival at the hospital until spontaneous respiration begins. Henderson and Haggard[18] have shown that, in cases of feeble or suspended respiration, the activity of the respiratory center may be stimulated by adding a small amount (5 per cent) of carbon dioxide to the respired air. It is often advisable to use a mixture of oxygen and 5 per cent carbon dioxide for resuscitation if the mixture is available, irrespective of the method of artificial respiration employed. For resuscitation of subjects exposed to carbon monoxide gas, the carbon dioxide mixture is particularly valuable.[18] When long-continued artificial respiration is required, the manual method may be replaced advantageously by the Drinker[10] respirator, which makes use of a subatmospheric pressure applied to the outside of the chest to obtain an expansion of the lungs. The body, with the exception of the head, is placed in a chamber in which the pressure is reduced rhythmically by a pump. The thorax and the lungs are expanded by the pressure differential created between the lungs and the exterior of the chest, and in this way respiration may be kept up indefinitely with no danger of injury to the lungs.

REFERENCES

1. ANDERSON, F. M. and LINDSLEY, D. B. *J. Lab. clin. Med.*, 1935, *20*:623–628.
2. BLOOMER, W. E. *Yale J. Biol. Med.*, 1947, *20*:135–166.
3. BRONK, D. W. and FERGUSON, L. K. *Amer. J. Physiol.*, 1935, *110*:700–714.
4. CAMPBELL, E. J. MORAN. *The respiratory muscles and the mechanics of breathing.* Chicago, Yearbook Publishers, 1958.
5. CHRISTIE, R. V. *J. clin. Invest.*, 1934, *13*:295–321.
6. CHRISTIE, R. V. *Quart. J. Med.*, 1938, 7:421–454.
7. CHRISTIE, R. V. and McINTOSH, C. A. *J. clin. Invest.*, 1934, *13*:279–294.
8. CHRISTIE, R. V. and McINTOSH, C. A. *Quart. J. Med.*, 1936, *5*:445–454.
9. COURNAND, A., BALDWIN, E. DE F., DARLING, R. C. and RUCHARDS, D. W., JR. *J. clin. Invest.*, 1941, *20*:681–689.
10. DRINKER, P. and McKHANN, C. F. *J. Amer. med. Ass.*, 1929, *92*:1658–1660.
11. FLACK, M. *Lancet*, 1919, *96*:210–212.
12. GAENSLER, E. A. *Amer. Rev. Tuberc.*, 1951, *64*:256–278.
13. GESELL, R. *Amer. J. Physiol.*, 1936, *115*:168–180.
14. GESELL, R. *Amer. J. Physiol.*, 1936, *116*:228–238.
15. GOLDSMITH, J. R. and YOUNG, A. C. *J. appl. Physiol.*, 1956, 8:562–564.
16. GORDON, A. S., FRYE, C. W., GITTELSON, L., SADOVE, M. S. and BEATTIE, E. J., JR. *J. Amer. med. Ass.*, 1958, *167*:320–328.
16a. GORDON, A. S., SADOVE, M. S., RAYMON, F. and IVY, A. C. *J. Amer. med. Ass.*, 1951, *147*:1444–1453. See also: *Ibid.* 1454–1455.
17. GRAHAM, E. A. and BELL, R. D. *Amer. J. med. Sci.*, 1918, *156*:839–871.

18. HENDERSON, Y. and HAGGARD, H. W. *J. Amer. med. Ass.*, 1922, *79*:1137–1145.
19. HERMANN, L. *Pflüg. Arch. ges. Physiol.*, 1883, *30*:276–287.
20. KEITH, A. Pp. 182–207 in: HILL, L., ed. *The mechanism of respiration in man: Further advances in physiology.* London, E. Arnold & Co., 1909.
21. MACKLIN, C. C. *Physiol. Rev.*, 1929, *9*:1–60.
22. MARSHALL, R., McILROY, M. B. and CHRISTIE, R. V. *Clin. Sci.*, 1954, *13*:135–146.
23. MEAKINS, J. C. *J. Amer. med. Ass.*, 1934, *103*:1442–1445.
24. MELTZER, S. J. *J. Physiol.*, 1892, *13*:218–238.
25. OTIS, A. B., FENN, W. O. and RAHN, H. *J. appl. Physiol.*, 1950, *2*:592–607.
26. SCHAFER, E. A. *Med.-chir. Trans. (Lond.),* 1903–04, *87*:609–623.
27. WIGGERS, C. J. *J. Amer. med. Ass.*, 1931, *96*:603–610.
28. YOUNG, A. C. *J. appl. Physiol.*, 1955, *8*:91–94

CHAPTER 36

Gas Exchange and Transportation*

By LOREN D. CARLSON

PROPERTIES OF GASES AND LIQUIDS

The behavior of the respiratory gases in the body cannot be understood unless the student is thoroughly familiar with the simple properties of gases and liquids. The following paragraphs present an elementary view of the kinetic concept of fluids. Fluids are thought to be composed of particles (molecules) in incessant motion. The molecules continually collide with each other and with the containing vessel, and the pressure exerted by a fluid is simply the summated impacts of the molecules on a confining wall. Diffusion in a mixture of substances is also a consequence of this motion, for the continual movement of the individual particles will more or less rapidly equalize local differences in concentration produced when the mixture is made. In the gas state the individual particles are so far apart that their attraction for each other is negligibly small, and a

---

* Including material prepared for the 17th edition by L. F. Nims.

gas, because of the incessant motion of its individual particles, will completely fill all of the available volume. Gases therefore can exert only pressure. In the liquid state the molecules still have freedom of motion, but they are so close together that they are subject to strong intermolecular attractive forces. Liquids have a volume independent of the container, and can exert both pressure and tension effects in a closed space, as the intra-pleural fluid does in the thorax.

The behavior of gases can be summarized by simple laws and principles. *Boyle's law* states that the pressure of a gas is inversely proportional to its volume, temperature remaining constant. This law is explained by the kinetic theory, for decreasing the volume of a gas increases the number of particles per unit volume and increases the number of impacts upon the walls of the container. *Charles' law* states that the pressure of a gas is directly proportional to its absolute temperature, volume remaining constant. This law is also explained by the kinetic theory, for increasing the temperature of a gas increases the velocity of the molecular motions and the force of the summated impacts. *Avogadro's principle* states that different gases which have the same volume at the same temperature and pressure contain an equal number of molecules, and is the basis of the volumetric method of determining the composition of gaseous mixtures. This principle, together with the laws of Boyle and Charles, can be combined in a simple mathematical expression, the *ideal gas law*,

$$PV = nRT$$

In this expression, P is the pressure exerted by the gas, V is the volume of the gas, n is the number of mols of the gas, T is the absolute temperature ($0°$ C. $= 273°$ A), and R is a constant whose value depends upon the units in which the variables are expressed. When the pressure is expressed in atmospheres, the volume in liters, and the temperature in centigrade degrees absolute, R has the value of 0.082 liter atmospheres per mol per degree. Real gases deviate slightly from this ideal expression, but the deviations are so small at ordinary temperatures that the gas law in the form given can be used with confidence to calculate the compositions or the pressures of the respiratory gases.

Partial Pressures.   Each gas in a mixture of gases behaves as if it alone occupied the total volume and exerts a pressure, its partial pressure,* independently of the other gases present (*Dalton's law* of partial pressure). The sum of the partial pressures of the individual gases is equal to the total pressure. The partial pressure of a gas in a mixture is easily calculated from the composition of the mixture. Dalton's law in conjunction with the perfect gas law allows one to state that the partial pressure of a gas in a mixture is equal to the product of the mol fraction and the total pressure. The partial pressures of oxygen, nitrogen and carbon dioxide in dry air in millimeters of mercury when the total pressure is one atmosphere (760 mm. Hg) are therefore: $O_2 = 0.21 \times 760$, or 160 mm. Hg; $N_2 = 0.79 \times 760$, or 600 mm. Hg; $CO_2 = 0.0004 \times 760$, or 0.30 mm. Hg. In physiology it is customary to speak of the compositions of gases in terms of volumes per cent. Avogadro's principle makes it evident that volumes per cent and mols per cent are numerically equal for gas mixtures.

Vapor Pressures.   The air of the lungs contains water vapor in addition to the other gases present. The water vapor obeys Dalton's law and exerts a pressure independently of the other gases present. Gases in contact with water receive water molecules by evaporation until the number of molecules leaving the liquid phase is equal to the number of molecules returning from the gas phase. Since the number leaving the liquid phase is proportional to the temperature of the liquid, the partial pressure of water in

---

* By convention, partial pressure is denoted by "p" followed by the chemical symbol for the gas, as pO_2, pCO_2, etc.

the gas phase is also proportional to the temperature. The temperature of the air in the lungs is 37° C., and the air of the lungs is thought to be in equilibrium with respect to water so that the partial pressure of water in the alveolar air is 47 mm. Hg. The composition of respired air is usually expressed as though it were dry, and to calculate the partial pressures from the composition it is necessary to subtract the partial pressure of water vapor from the total pressure before determining the partial pressures of other gases. For example, 5.6 per cent of a sample of dry alveolar air was CO_2. The partial pressure of CO_2 in the alveolar air at atmospheric pressure was $0.056 \times (760 - 47)$, or 40 mm. Hg.

Solubility and Partial Pressures of Gases in Liquids. The quantity of gas physically dissolved in a liquid at constant temperature is directly proportional to the partial pressure of the gas in the gas phase (*Henry's law* of solubility of gases). At equilibrium the number of gas molecules leaving the liquid per unit time is equal to the number entering the liquid, and any change in the partial pressure of the gas produces a corresponding change in the equilibrium. The gas in the liquid phase also has a partial pressure, and under equilibrium conditions the partial pressures of the gas in the gas phase and in the liquid phase are said to be equal. To determine the partial pressure of a gas in a liquid it is necessary to determine the composition and pressures of the gas in an equilibrated gas phase.

The amount of gas dissolved in physical solution must be carefully distinguished from the pressure of the gas in solution. At the partial pressures equivalent to those found in the alveoli, blood contains 0.25 ml. of O_2, 2.69 ml. of CO_2 and 1.04 ml. of N_2 in physical solution per 100 ml. of blood. The amounts of O_2 and CO_2 present in circulating blood are of course much greater than the amounts of the gases that are physically dissolved because the blood carries O_2 and CO_2 largely in chemical combination. The chemically combined gas no longer contributes to partial pressure of the physically dissolved gas.

Determination of the amounts of O_2 and CO_2 in a particular blood sample is a procedure involving a high degree of chemical skill and has been well described in laboratory textbooks.[37] The gases from a sample of blood are extracted completely and in a condition for quantitative analysis by some form of a vacuum pump and then reabsorbed one by one in suitable chemical reagents. The volume, temperature and pressure are noted at each stage of the analysis, and the number of mols of each gas can then be calculated by substitution of the known quantities into the perfect gas equation. To determine the partial pressures of the gases in the blood, the blood is equilibrated with a volume of gas so small that no essential changes take place in the blood as equilibrium is approached. Chemical analysis of the gas phase will then allow a calculation of the partial pressures of the fluid phase. A method for measuring pO_2 in the tissues and blood of living animals depends on the fact that dissolved O_2 will react electrochemically at the cathode of an electrolysis cell and give rise to a current which is, under standardized conditions, proportional to the amount of O_2 present.[13]

PROPERTIES OF RESPIRED AIR

Composition. The constituents of atmospheric air important to human respiration are O_2, N_2 and H_2O. The rare gases (argon, krypton, etc.) have not been shown to be biologically significant, and in physiologic gas analysis their quantities or concentrations are determined and included with the values reported for N_2. With respect to O_2, N_2 and CO_2, the air we breathe has a remarkably uniform composition. Samples of dry air taken at many sites, from sea level to the highest attainable altitudes, have contained these constituents in the same proportions. Man and other air-breathing animals do not have a method of storing significant amounts of O_2, but are dependent upon a continuous gas exchange with the air surrounding them. Interruption of this exchange results in death in a few moments.

The essential facts of external respiration are to be found in a knowledge of the compositions of inspired, expired and alveolar air. Respired air loses O_2 and gains CO_2; conversely, the blood absorbs O_2 and loses CO_2 according to the body needs. The composition of the expired air varies, of course, with the depth and frequency of breathing movements and during any one breath, but the respiratory mechanisms are so controlled (Chap. 35) that the alveolar air is maintained with but slight changes in its

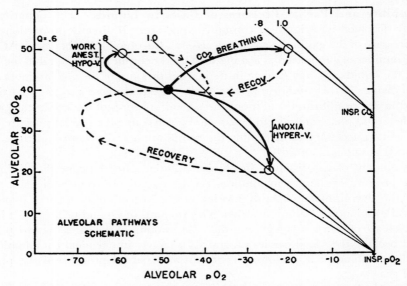

FIG. 466.   Principal pathways that have been observed during hyperpnea, anoxia, hypoventilation, exercise and CO_2 breathing as well as the pathways of recovery. Heavy lines indicate the path to a new steady state, which occurs in three to four minutes. (From Rahn and Otis, *J. appl. Physiol.*, 1949, *1*:717–724.)

composition despite wide fluctuations in the demands for O_2. Figure 466 illustrates changes in partial pressure and percentage of O_2 and CO_2 in various conditions, and representative values including those for N_2 are given in Table 23.

The amount of O_2 absorbed is somewhat greater than the amount of CO_2 given off. This apparent discrepancy is explained by the general fact that O_2 is used to oxidize not only the carbon but also the hydrogen of ingested food; consequently, although most of the O_2 is eliminated in the expired air as CO_2, some is excreted as H_2O. The ratio of the amount of CO_2 expired to the amount of O_2 absorbed is called the *respiratory exchange ratio* (R) or, previously, the *respiratory quotient* (R.Q.). Knowledge of the R is helpful

TABLE 23.   *COMPOSITION OF DRY INSPIRED, EXPIRED AND ALVEOLAR AIR IN MAN AT REST, AT SEA LEVEL, IN MOLS PER CENT OR VOLUMES PER CENT*

	N_2 MOLS %	O_2 MOLS %	CO_2 MOLS %
Inspired air	79.02	20.94	0.04
Expired air	79.2	16.3	4.5
Alveolar air	80.4	14.0	5.6

in interpeting data on O_2 consumption[15] and is necessary if the caloric value of a given amount of consumed O_2 is to be estimated (Chap. 48).

Physiologic Significance of Nitrogen. The difference in concentration of N_2 in inspired and expired air recorded in Table 23 is not brought about by production of gaseous N_2 in the body, but is a reflection of the inequality in the amounts of O_2 and CO_2 exchanged. No known metabolic reaction of the human body involves molecular N_2. In ordinary circumstances, N_2 is merely a diluent of the O_2 in the air breathed.

DECOMPRESSION SICKNESS. The N_2 in the body is in simple physical solution and exists in all the tissues and the blood at a pressure equal to its average partial pressure in the alveolar air. The solubility of N_2 is greatest in fat. Caisson workers and deep-sea divers, of necessity, breathe air under greatly increased pressure, and the amount of N_2 dissolved in their tissues at equilibrium increases in direct proportion to the increased partial pressure of this gas in their alveolar air. When these workers return to normal pressure, their tissues are supersaturated with N_2. If they are too rapidly decompressed, this gas is released from solution as small bubbles, which are distributed in many tissues and in the blood stream.[21, 22] By mechanical distention of the tissues and by formation of aero-emboli, these gas bubbles can produce a variety of clinical symptoms,[25] manifest chiefly by pain and collectively termed *decompression sickness*, or "the bends." The aviator who flies above 25,000 feet may also experience decompression sickness, for his tissues are supersaturated with N_2 at the prevailing low pressures. Decompression sickness can be avoided by means of slow decompression or by elimination of a large part of the N_2 from the body before ascent.[17] Under atmospheric pressure the average man has about 1.5 liters of N_2 dissolved in his body tissues.[6, 7]

Temperature. Expired air is warmed to the body temperature, or nearly, and is saturated with water vapor. Since inhaled air is usually much cooler than the body and is far from being saturated with water vapor, the act of breathing evidently entails a considerable loss of body heat. Breathing is, in fact, one means by which body temperature can be regulated, although this is a subsidiary means in man. In the dog, on the other hand, panting is a very important aid to the control of body temperature. Heat is lost in respiration not only by warming of the air in the air passages, but also by evaporation of water in the alveoli. The conversion of water from its liquid to its gaseous form is attended by the absorption of heat; the lungs account for about 10 per cent of the heat exchange of the body (see Chap. 49).

Partial Pressure and Gas Exchange. Although the partial pressure of gases is not the same in all alveoli, it is generally considered to be. Martin and Young[33] have demonstrated the existence of differences between the upper and lower lobes of the lung. Measurements of the pO_2 in air, the alveoli, the arterial blood and the tissues demonstrate that the pO_2 decreases as the cells are approached. O_2 flows down a pressure gradient, i.e., from a region where the partial pressure is higher to one where the partial pressure is lower. At no place in the respiratory system is it necessary to assume active transport, a movement against the partial pressure gradient, to explain the exchange of

TABLE 24. *PARTIAL PRESSURES OF RESPIRATORY GASES AT VARIOUS SITES IN RESPIRATORY CIRCUIT OF MAN AT REST AT SEA LEVEL*

SAMPLE	GAS PARTIAL PRESSURE				
	O_2 mm. Hg	CO_2 mm. Hg	N_2 mm. Hg	H_2O mm. Hg	Total mm. Hg
Inspired air	158	0.3	596	5.7	760
Expired air	116	32	565	47	760
Alveolar air	100	40	573	47	760
Arterial blood	100	40	573	47	760
Venous blood	40	46	573	47	706
Tissues	30 or less	50 or more	573	47	700

O_2. CO_2 is produced in the cells and exists there at the highest partial pressure, whereas the pCO_2 in the external air is very low. CO_2, like O_2, diffuses down a pressure gradient. The pO_2 and pCO_2 in the alveolar air, the blood and the tissues determine the quantities of these gases held in physical solution, the rapidity with which they are transferred across limiting membranes, and the degree of completion of certain reversible chemical reactions important for the transportation of respiratory gases in the blood. In Table 24 are listed representative values for the partial pressures of various respiratory gases at selected sites in the respiratory circuit.

GAS EXCHANGE IN THE LUNGS

The exchange of respiratory gases across the capillary and alveolar endothelium takes place very rapidly. Venous blood enters the lung capillaries with a pO_2 below and a pCO_2 above those of the alveolar air (Table 24), and within the 0.7 second or so before the blood leaves[40] it comes to practical equilibrium with the alveolar air.[14] Several factors govern the rates at which the gases are exchanged across the alveolar

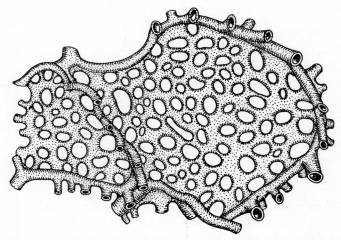

FIG. 467. Capillary network in lungs. Note extensive absorption surface presented by capillaries. (Redrawn from Miller, *The Lung*, 1937.)

surface: (i) the partial pressure of the respiratory gases in the alveoli and in the capillary blood perfusing them—gas turnover by individual alveoli (alveolar turnover ratio) or by different sections of the lung may vary; (ii) the permeability of the limiting membranes to O_2 and CO_2 (diffusing capacity of pulmonary capillary membrane); (iii) the rates at which the respective gases react with the blood constituents; (iv) the area of the absorbing surface; (v) the time that the blood is in contact with the breathing surface; and (vi) the volume of blood exposed to the alveolar air at any one time. The extreme efficiency of the mechanisms of external respiration is apparent, for even under conditions of greatest O_2 uptake during strenuous exercise the arterial blood leaves the lungs with a full complement of O_2.

Alveolar Function. The alveoli form an effective mechanism for gas exchange. They consist of an extensive network of capillaries (Fig. 467), held together by alveolar endothelium—probably the richest capillary network in the entire body.[34] These capillaries are almost entirely surrounded by alveolar air, and O_2 has only to diffuse through two thin layers of cells—the pulmonary and the capillary endothelium—a distance of 1 to 2 μ in order to reach the blood.[29] Some observers think that the alveolar lining is discontinuous and that only the capillary endothelium separates the blood from the pulmonary air;[28] however, electronmicrographs show two separate membranes.[31] The total respiratory surface of the lungs has been variously estimated as 50 to 100 m.², 25 to 50 times the surface area of the body.[18, 48] The amount of blood in the alveolar capillaries is 60 ml. in the resting subject. The total volume of blood they can contain varies with body position, but may be 1.0 to 1.5 liters.

During exercise, when the demands for O_2 are increased, ventilation also increases. More O_2 is taken into the lungs and more is carried away by the arterial blood. Two factors are largely responsible for bringing about the increased removal of O_2 from the lungs. First, the cardiac output is raised and more blood flows through the lungs, an adjustment that can account for a sevenfold or eightfold increase in the amount of O_2 absorbed. Second, the venous blood contains less O_2, having lost more to the tissues; consequently, it can pick up more O_2 per unit volume while in the lungs. This arrangement can greatly increase the amount of O_2 absorbed.

The lungs themselves are not entirely passive when the requirements of exercise are to be met. Wearn et al.[47] have observed spontaneous variations in the blood supply to the air sacs (Fig. 468). Such a mechanism would serve the useful function of adjusting

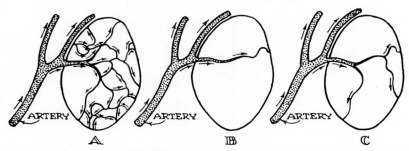

ARTERY   ARTERY   ARTERY

A   B   C

FIG. 468.   Spontaneous changes in blood flow through pulmonary air sac. The changes indicated would have physiologic effect of adjusting area of breathing surface to O_2 needs of animal. (From Wearn et al., Amer. J. Physiol., 1934, 109:236–256.)

the area of the breathing surface to the needs of the moment. Roughton's investigations[40] indicate that the changes in alveolar capillary circulation are probably not as great as might be inferred from Figure 468. He found that the amount of blood increased from 60 to 95 ml. in the alveolar capillaries while the subject was working hard.

Alveolar Air.   The air in the lungs which is important physiologically is that portion which is in gaseous equilibrium with the arterial blood, the *alveolar air*. Strictly speaking, this is the air in direct contact with the alveolar surface. It is difficult to obtain samples of this air for chemical examination, but in the past it was assumed that the air obtained at the end of a maximal expiration is representative of alveolar air. Comroe and Dripps[11] found that end expiratory air samples from normal men contained O_2 at a partial pressure of 97.4 mm. Hg. The average pO_2 in the arterial blood of these subjects was 97.1 mm. Hg. The close agreement between the two sets of data suggests that, over all, arterial blood is in nearly perfect gaseous equilibrium with the alveolar air. Actually, as shown in Figure 469, the pCO_2 and pO_2 of alveolar air are constantly changing. Also, the relation between the partial pressures in the blood and the air in a particular region is dependent on the ventilation of the air sacs.

The manner in which new air reaches the alveolar surface is still somewhat uncertain. With the increase in volume and the drop in pressure in these regions, air rushes in. The currents set up by the incoming air and the process of gaseous diffusion serve to mix the air in the alveolar sacs[12] and rapidly bring this gas to a uniform composition. However, more poorly ventilated alveoli will tend to approach gaseous equilibrium with the venous blood, and the blood passing through these alveoli will not be arterialized. In contrast, air in overventilated alveoli will not approach gaseous equilibrium with arterial blood.

Diffusion of Gases Through Body Tissues. The volume of gas in milliliters that is transferred per minute across the pulmonary membranes when the difference between the partial pressure of gas in the alveolar air and in the capillary blood is 1 mm. Hg has been called by Krogh[30] the *diffusion constant* of the lungs. She found the diffusion constant of O_2 to vary from a minimum of 20 during resting conditions to a maximum of 60 during exercise.

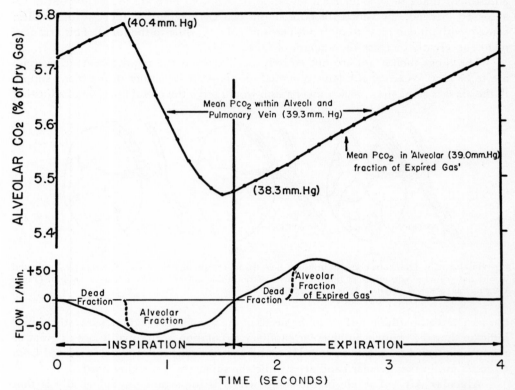

FIG. 469. Fluctuations in alveolar P_{CO_2} computed for a normal respiratory cycle. There is a damping effect owing to variation of blood flow and capacity of tissue for CO_2. The best time for an expired sample of mean alveolar gas for CO_2 determination is shortly after midexpiration. If most of the alveolar gas expired comes out early in expiration, the CO_2 therein will have a lower tension than that of mean arterial blood. (From DuBois *et al.*, *J. appl. Physiol.*, 1952, 4:535–548.)

The average pressure gradient across the alveolar membrane is difficult to determine. If it is assumed that the average alveolar-arterial pressure gradient is only one-third of the maximal obtainable (i.e., one-third of 60 mm. Hg), then 20 mm. Hg × 20 ml. per mm. Hg = 400 ml. of O_2 that would be delivered to the blood each minute, a value well above the resting requirement of 250 ml. a minute. Thus, the maximal gas exchange (3500 ml. of O_2 or more) during exercise can also be accounted for by diffusion. The product of the diffusion constant and the average pressure gradient exceeds the amount of O_2 transferred. Only during severe exercise or in disease conditions does the blood fail to approach gaseous equilibrium with alveolar air as closely as it does in the resting state.

The intrinsic rate of diffusion of any substance is a function of its solubility, its molecular weight and the permeability of the medium. Although a larger molecule than O_2, CO_2 is so highly soluble in the body fluids that it diffuses through the tissue 20 to 30 times as rapidly as O_2 does. There is no difficulty, therefore, in accounting for the exchange of CO_2 in the lungs, even though it is driven out of them by a pressure difference much smaller than that propelling the O_2.

TRANSPORT OF O_2 AND CO_2

As explained in Chapter 24, blood can absorb more O_2 and CO_2 than can be carried in physical solution. Hemoglobin (HHb)* has the chemical property of combining reversibly with both O_2 and CO_2. The physical chemistry of this consideration has been discussed, but not its physiology. If the blood contained no HHb, a circulating blood volume 75 times larger than the normal would be needed to satisfy the requirements for O_2. The affinity of HHb for O_2 is so nicely adjusted that the blood leaves the lungs fully oxygenated, yet all of the O_2 can be released in the tissues. The combination

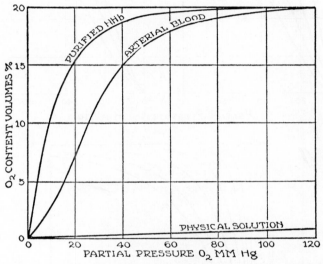

FIG. 470. O_2 contents of arterial blood and plasma (physical solution) and a dilute solution of purified HHb at various partial pressures of O_2. Note difference in shape of absorption curves of purified HHb and arterial blood and small amount of O_2 carried in physical solution. (After Barcroft.)

of HHb with O_2, $HHb + O_2 \rightleftharpoons HHbO_2$ (oxyhemoglobin), is regulated by the pO_2. In the lungs, at a partial pressure of 100 mm. Hg, the reaction is 97 per cent complete. In the tissues, 60 per cent of the O_2 in the blood is released at a pressure greater than 20 mm. Hg.

Blood contains somewhat less than 15 grams of HHb per 100 ml. Each gram of HHb can combine with 1.36 ml. of O_2 so that fully oxygenated blood contains 20 ml. of O_2 per 100 ml. of blood (the O_2 capacity of the blood). Since HHb does not become completely saturated with O_2 until the pO_2 is 150 mm. Hg, arterial blood leaving the lungs is only 98 per cent saturated.[14] The amount of O_2 per 100 ml. of blood in a particular sample is designated as the O_2 content of the blood.

Oxygen Dissociation Curve. When samples of blood are equilibrated with air containing O_2 at various partial pressures, the amount of O_2 in the blood is not directly proportional to the partial pressures. A plot of the observed O_2 content of each sample against the partial pressures of O_2 is distinctly S-shaped (Fig. 470). The dissociation

* "HHb" is used to denote nonionized hemoglobin and also the fact that hemoglobin acts as an acid.

curve of purified HHbO$_2$ is hyperbolic. This is the expected result if O$_2$ combines with HHb according to the reaction HHb $+$ O$_2$ $\rightleftharpoons$ HHbO$_2$. Studies of purified HHb solutions[5] have shown that the oxygenation reaction of HHb is affected by the CO$_2$ content, the acidity, the ionic concentration, and the temperature of the medium in which the HHb is dissolved. The concentration of HHb itself is not without effect. Concentrated solutions of purified HHbO$_2$ give a distinctly S-shaped curve, but the S-shaped dissociation of whole blood most likely results from a summation of the various factors enumer-

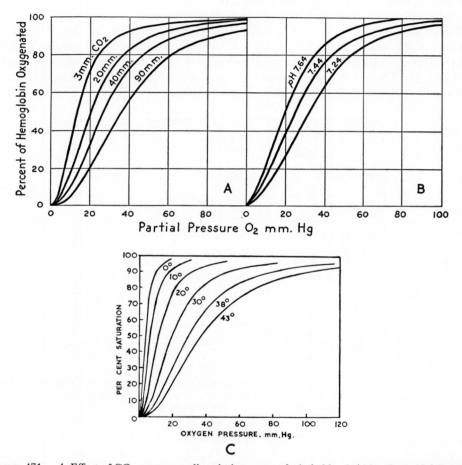

FIG. 471.   *A*, Effect of CO$_2$ on oxygen dissociation curve of whole blood. (After Barcroft.) *B*, Effect of acidity on oxygen dissociation curve of blood. (After Peters and Van Slyke.) *C*, Effect of temperature on oxygen dissociation curve of blood. (From Roughton, Chap. 5 in *Handbook of respiratory physiology*, W. M. Boothby, ed. Randolph Air Force Base, Texas, Air University, USAF School of Aviation Medicine, 1954.)

ated, the more important being the salt composition of blood and the highly concentrated form of HHb in the interior of the erythrocyte.

The shape of the O$_2$ dissociation curve of blood is of definite physiologic significance. That the curve is flat above a pressure of 80 mm. Hg insures a practically constant composition of arterial blood despite wide variations in the alveolar O$_2$ pressure. The steep portion between 20 and 60 mm. Hg insures delivery of a large amount of the blood O$_2$ to the tissues with a reasonable head of pressure.

Effect of temperature on O$_2$ dissociation curve (Fig. 471C).   An increase in temperature will shift the O$_2$ dissociation curve to the right. Less O$_2$ is held by the HHb at a given

pO_2. The temperature effect is of some aid in the release of O_2 to the tissues, for the temperature is somewhat higher in the vicinity of actively metabolizing cells than near resting tissues, and somewhat more O_2 is given up. It should be remembered that all tissues are not at 37° C. The temperature of the hand or foot may drop to 10° C. or lower, with a consequent temperature gradient along the arm or leg. Less O_2 will be given up for an equal tissue O_2 pressure. This effect of temperature on the release of O_2 is an important consideration in the extremities exposed to low temperatures, since the hemoglobin then resembles myoglobin.

Effect of CO_2 and pH on O_2 dissociation curve. An increase in either the CO_2 pressure or the acidity of blood[9] will also favor the dissociation of the acid $HHbO_2$ (Fig. 471). The effect of CO_2 is particularly important physiologically, since the production of CO_2 by the tissues automatically favors the transfer of O_2. In fact, the amount of O_2 (or CO_2) the blood will hold is inversely proportional to the pCO_2 (or pO_2) in the blood. The action of CO_2 in releasing O_2 from the blood is twofold. CO_2 increases the acidity of blood (lowers the *pH*) and forms carbamino compounds ($HHbCO_2$) with the hemo-

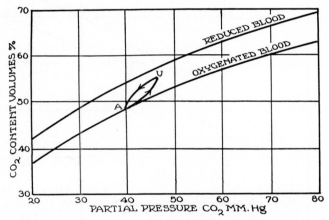

FIG. 472. CO_2 titration curve of whole blood. Note that oxygenated blood contains less CO_2 at a given pressure of CO_2 than reduced blood. Blood goes through a cycle, as indicated by *A* (arterial blood) and *V* (venous blood), in the capillaries of tissues and lungs. (After Peters and Van Slyke.)

globin. $HHbCO_2$ has much less affinity for O_2 than HHb has.[39] These reactions result in a lowering of the amount of O_2 which the blood will hold at a given O_2 pressure and therefore more O_2 is made available to the tissues.

Condition of CO_2 in Blood. The blood contains little CO_2 in physical solution; the major portion is carried in chemical combination. The forms of combined CO_2 now recognized are carbonic acid (H_2CO_3) and bicarbonate ion (HCO_3^-), present in both cells and plasma, and carbamino hemoglobin ($HHbCO_2$). All the forms of CO_2 are in chemical equilibrium with one another. A further complication is that the red cell is relatively impermeable to cations; at equilibrium the concentration of HCO_3^- in the cell differs from that in the plasma. A dissociation curve of CO_2 in blood can be obtained in the same way as one is obtained for O_2. Blood is equilibrated with gases containing CO_2 at various partial pressures, and the CO_2 content of the equilibrated blood is determined by blood gas analysis. The form of the CO_2 absorption curves for oxygenated and reduced blood is given in Figure 472. These curves demonstrate that the dissociation of CO_2 is affected by pO_2 in a fashion similar to that in which the O_2 dissociation curve is affected by CO_2 pressure. The absorption of O_2 aids in the unloading of CO_2 in the lungs, and the absorption of CO_2 aids in the unloading of O_2 in the tissues.

In a vacuum a $NaHCO_3$ solution gives off only half of its CO_2. $2NaHCO_3 \rightleftharpoons Na_2CO_3 + CO_2 + H_2O$. Plasma behaves like a simple bicarbonate solution. More of its bicarbonate is extracted in a vacuum, however, because acid phosphates and other weak acids which aid in driving off its CO_2 are present. Whole blood, on the other hand, will release all of its CO_2 to a vacuum. The difference in behavior between whole blood and plasma or bicarbonate solutions is due to the acid properties of hemoglobin. Both HHb and $HHbO_2$ can furnish sufficient H^+ to carry the reaction $H^+ + HCO_3^- \rightleftharpoons H_2CO_3 \rightleftharpoons H_2O + CO_2$ to completion. $HHbO_2$ is a stronger acid than HHb. In the lungs, the following series of reversible chemical reactions take place as O_2 enters the blood:

$$O_2 + HHb \rightleftharpoons HHbO_2 \rightleftharpoons HbO_2^- + H^+$$
$$H^+ + HCO_3^- \rightleftharpoons H_2CO_3 \rightleftharpoons H_2O + CO_2$$

The $HHbO_2$ releases H^+ to combine with HCO_3^-. Since the reactions are reversible, an increase of either O_2 or CO_2 in the blood will, in accordance with the law of mass action, drive the reaction in the appropriate direction. The actual titration curves of $HHbO_2$ and HHb with NaOH are given in Figure 473. From this figure it is apparent that the oxygenation of HHb can furnish 0.7 mol of H^+ per mol of O_2 absorbed to combine with HCO_3^-.

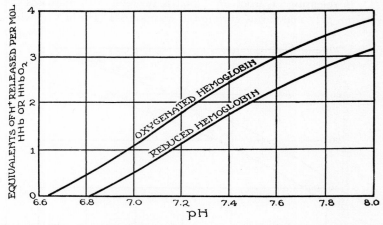

FIG. 473. Acid-base titration curves of oxygenated and reduced HHb. As O_2 is released from HbO_2, the weaker base Hb^- can combine with H^+ to form HHb. For each mol of O_2 given up to tissues, 0.7 mol of H^+ from the ionization of H_2CO_3 can be neutralized by the Hb without change in pH (isohydric cycle). (After Peters and Van Slyke.)

$HHbCO_2$. Approximately one-fifth of the total CO_2 in the blood is carried[43] as $HHbCO_2$ in which, as first suggested by Henriques,[24] the CO_2 is combined directly with amino groups of the HHb molecules,

$$HHbNH_2 + CO_2 \rightleftharpoons HHbNHCOOH$$

Other protein molecules in the blood besides the HHb molecules can probably carry CO_2 in the same manner. The product formed by the combination of CO_2 with HHb is physiologically the more important of the carbamino compounds because it enters into a reversible reaction with O_2,

$$O_2 + HHbCO_2 \rightleftharpoons HHbO_2 + CO_2$$

This is an important reaction in the respiratory exchange, since it provides a rapid method[39] by which CO_2 can be taken up or released without marked changes in pH.

Velocity of the Reactions. The complex series of chemical reactions occurring in the blood as it gains or loses O_2 and CO_2 is apparently completed while the blood is passing through the capillaries (0.7 sec.). Roughton[39] and others have investigated the velocities of the various reactions and found that all but one are rapid enough to accomplish this end. The single exception is the reaction which comprises the hydration of

CO_2 ($H_2O + CO_3 \overset{slow}{\rightarrow} H_2CO_3$). In a search for an explanation of the apparent speed with which this reaction is accomplished in the body, an enzyme, carbonic anhydrase, was discovered. This enzyme is not present in the plasma, but is found, like hemoglobin, in the red cells. Carbonic anhydrase speeds up the hydration of CO_2 and the dehydration of H_2CO_3 so that these reactions are also completed by the time the blood has left the capillaries.

GAS EXCHANGE IN THE TISSUES

The chemical reactions that take place in the blood, as O_2 is delivered to the tissues can now be summarized. Figure 474 contains in outline form the important steps in this sequence of events. The series of reactions is reversed in the lungs. CO_2, being continually produced in the tissue cells, exists there at the highest partial pressures.

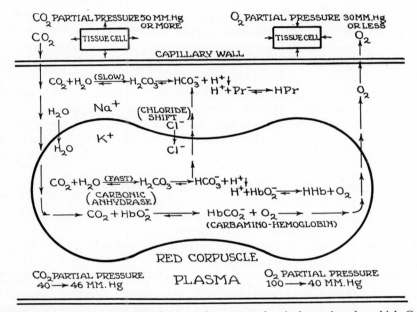

FIG. 474. Schema to summarize the more important chemical reactions by which O_2 is made available to tissues. Forces initiating and controlling exchange of gases are gradients in partial pressure of CO_2 and of O_2 between capillary blood and tissue cells.

CO_2 diffuses from the cells, through the interstitial fluid and the capillary walls, and into the plasma. Some of the CO_2 reacts slowly with H_2O in the plasma to form H_2CO_3 which in turn ionizes and liberates H^+. A considerable part of the H^+ immediately combines with the plasma proteins which tend to buffer the plasma (see Chap. 24). The major portion of the CO_2 diffuses into the red corpuscles, where it can carry out two reactions. The CO_2 can combine with water exactly as it did in the plasma; however, the reaction is rapid, since here it is catalyzed by carbonic anhydrase. The H^+ that is eventually released is taken up by HbO_2^- to form HHb and O_2, and the resultant O_2 diffuses out of the cell to supply the largest fraction of the O_2 gained by the tissues from the blood. This series of chemical reactions in the erythrocyte has been termed the *isohydric* cycle because the uptake of CO_2 and the release of O_2 is accomplished without the production of an excess of H^+. The buffering power of HbO_2^- allows a large amount of CO_2 to be absorbed and O_2 to be released without marked change in acidity. The excess HCO_3^- diffuses out of the cell into the plasma. This diffusion, if uncompensated, would leave an excess of positive ions in the cell. To keep the positive and negative ions in balance, Cl^- ions simultaneously move into the cell. The balance cannot be restored by movement of K^+ ions because the red cell membranes are relatively impermeable to positive ions. This exchange has been called the *chloride shift* and serves the useful purpose of allowing a great deal of HCO_3^- to be carried in the plasma. Some of the CO_2 combines with the various forms of HHb, the most important reaction being with HbO_2, for this combination releases O_2 without involving a change in pH. The interrelations of O_2 and CO_2 in the red cell are only an example of the general mutual dependence of O_2 and CO_2 during the whole process of O_2 utilization.

Supply of O_2 to the Tissues.   The tissues absorb what O_2 they need from the blood and leave the rest. The amount absorbed per unit time is a function of the blood flow through the tissue and the pressure of O_2 in the tissue.

The *coefficient of O_2 utilization* is defined as the arteriovenous difference in O_2 concentration divided by the concentration of O_2 in the arterial blood. The brain has a coefficient of $6.7/19.6 = 34$ per cent. Active muscle can remove all O_2 from the blood and thus have a coefficient of O_2 utilization approaching 100 per cent. When the activity of tissues and their need for O_2 increase, additional O_2 can be supplied only from an increased flow of blood through the tissues, since the O_2 content of the blood cannot be increased. The pressure gradient between the capillaries and the active cells increases both because the blood supply has increased and because the cells are using O_2 at a faster rate. The venous blood returning from these cells contains less O_2 than normal, and the coefficient of O_2 utilization is increased. The threefold or greater increase in blood perfusion rate plus the threefold or greater increase in the coefficient of O_2 utilization can mean a ninefold or greater increase in the rate at which O_2 is supplied to vigorously active tissues.

Respiration and Acid-Base Balance.   The body has many defenses against an alteration of its acid-base balance (see Chap. 24). We have seen how O_2 and CO_2 are carried and exchanged in the blood without much change in pH. The blood becomes only slightly more acid as it passes through the tissues.

The body as a whole is buffered by a physiologic mechanism.[23] Respiration is so controlled (Chap. 38) that the partial pressure of CO_2 in the arterial blood normally does not deviate greatly from 40 mm. Hg. If the CO_2 production in the body rises slightly, ventilation increases and the elimination of CO_2 is rapidly adjusted to preserve the optimal acid-base condition of the body. In a sense, respiration represents the first line of defense of the body against acid-base changes.

Summary.   The events in one respiratory cycle (one breath) may be visualized with the aid of Figure 469. At the end of expiration, the air in the anatomic dead space is that expelled last from the alveoli. During the interval before inspiration, O_2 continues to be removed and CO_2 to be added in the alveoli at rates determined by the blood flow and the partial pressures. On inspiration, the gas in the dead space enters the alveoli, and air or inspired gas enters the lung, diluting the gas already present by mixing with it. The size of the alveoli is such that diffusion is not a limiting factor. Some of these events can be measured with instantaneous gas analyzers, as shown in Figure 469.

GAS EXCHANGE EQUATIONS

An understanding of the relation between O_2 and CO_2, which is helpful in the daily solution of respiratory problems, can be obtained by careful study of the O_2-CO_2 diagram in Figure 475. Like any chart faced in its entirety, Figure 475 appears forbidding at first glance, but its meaning becomes clearer when it is examined closely. The basic elements are the values for pCO_2 on the abscissa and for pO_2 on the ordinate. The horizontal lines are reference lines for the total volume of CO_2 present, and the vertical lines are reference values for volumes per cent of oxyhemoglobin. At any respiratory exchange ratio a specific point may be found on the lines representing that R value. Only two R lines are shown; others can readily be conrstucted from the gas equations given below. The value of pO_2 and pCO_2 will be influenced by the alveolar ventilation ($\dot{V}_A$). If $\dot{V}_A$ is expressed as liters per minute (BTPS) per 100 ml. of O_2 taken up, then the value for two or five would appear as given along the vertical lines of the diagram. A final factor is related to perfusion by the blood ($\dot{Q}_B$). For a given composition of

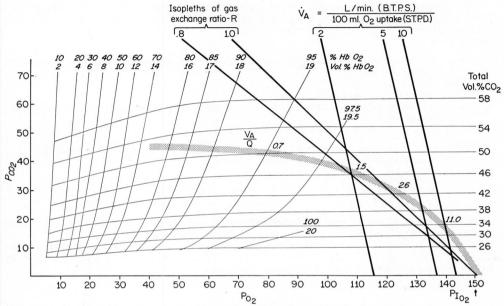

FIG. 475. Coordinates represent pO_2 and pCO_2. Horizontal heavy lines are reference lines for whole blood CO_2 in volumes per cent. Curved vertical lines represent volumes per cent O_2 in whole blood with a normal hemoglobin; these can also be represented as percentage saturation. Originating at a P_{IO_2} of 150 mm. are two R lines, 1.0 and 0.8. Slanting vertical lines represent alveolar ventilation per 100 cm.³ O_2 uptake. Curved stippled line originates at left with mixed venous blood—no ventilation of alveoli—and passes through ratios of $\dot{V}_A/Q$ as shown, reaching infinity at the moistened inspired gas point. If the inspired oxygen is at 150 mm. Hg and the alveolar pO_2 is 100, at R of 0.8, pCO_2 would be 40 mm. Hg, and about 48 volumes per cent CO_2 would be in the blood; with a normal hemoglobin, about 19.5 volumes per cent of O_2 would be carried. To maintain this value, an alveolar ventilation of about 1.7 liters per 100 cm.³ O_2 uptake would be required. (After Rahn and Fenn, *The oxygen-carbon dioxide diagram*, Wright Air Development Center, 1953.)

venous blood and inspired air, the alveolar or arterial gas tensions are determined by this ratio. This factor can be entered on the diagram as $\dot{V}_A/\dot{Q}_B$, where this ratio is equal to

$$\frac{\dot{V}_A}{\dot{Q}_B} = \frac{0.864 \, (\text{arterial} - \text{venous})_{O_2}R}{P_{A_{CO_2}}}$$

The constant 0.864 is used to convert the values to the proper gas volumes. The line passes through the ratios that are labeled 0.7, 1.5, 2.6 and 11.0. An infinite volume would intersect at an air value for O_2 and CO_2. The pCO_2 and pO_2 in alveolar gas and alveolar blood will differ if there is a diffusion gradient. Thus, a different R line would be drawn for blood.[38]

The volume and composition of various portions of the expired gases may be determined under a variety of experimental conditions. From the results of such analyses it is possible to compute many important physiologic quantities relating to O_2 consumption, CO_2 production, metabolic respiratory quotient, O_2 saturation of arterial blood, the efficiency of pulmonary ventilation, and acid-base equilibria. In the past it has been customary to treat each of these factors separately and to perform detailed computations especially derived for each portion of exhaled gas and for each variable under immediate consideration. It is now recognized that all such calculations are but special cases of general equations which may be applied to any portion of the exhaled gases and which include, implicitly, all of the related variables. For example, the detailed computations used in the clinical determination of the respiratory quotient by the Tissot Method are but a special case of general equations which also describe the composition of alveolar gas or the percentage of oxygen needed in aircraft at different altitudes.

DEFINITION AND USE OF SYMBOLS

Many different sets of symbols have been used to denote respiratory variables. In 1950, a group of clinical and research physiologists interested in respiration met to standardize the definitions and symbols used here.[1]

Principal variables.

V — gas volume in general. Pressure, temperature and percentage saturation with water vapor must be stated.

P — gas pressure in general.

F — fractional concentration in *dry* gas.

R — respiratory exchange ratio in general (or respiratory quotient, R.Q.); volume CO_2 per volume O_2.

f — respiratory frequency in breaths per unit time.

Localization in the gas phase is represented by small capital letters immediately following the principal variable. For example, V_E denotes the volume of expired gas.

I — inspired gas	T — tidal gas
E — expired gas	D — dead space gas
A — alveolar gas	B — barometric (ambient atmosphere)

Molecular species is denoted by the full chemical symbol, to be in small capital letters immediately following the principal variable. Thus, V_{O_2} represents volume of oxygen.

When *both* location and molecular species are required, the first modifying letter will be used for location and the second for species. Thus, the pressure of oxygen in alveolar gas is represented by $P_{A_{O_2}}$. In this case the chemical symbol appears as a subscript.

Special Symbols and Abbreviations.

$\dot{X}$ — a dot above any symbol represents a rate. Thus, $\dot{V}_{O_2}$ represents volume of oxygen per unit time.

s — subscript to denote the steady state.

STPD — standard temperature, pressure, dry (0° C., 760 mm. Hg).

BTPS — body temperature, pressure, saturated with water vapor.

ATPS — ambient temperature, pressure, saturated with water vapor.

RESPIRATORY GAS EQUATIONS AND THEIR APPLICATIONS

All forms of the respiratory gas equations derive from three obvious equalities or equations. Consider the volume (measured at STPD) of any aliquot portion of gas which has undergone respiratory exchange. For convenience, let us consider the total volume of gas expired in a given time (V_E), although exactly the same relationships will apply to an aliquot of alveolar gas (V_A) or to any other part of the exhaled gases.

EQUALITY 1. The volume of expired gas equals the volume of inspired gas minus the oxygen consumed plus the carbon dioxide produced. Thus

$$V_E = V_I - V_{O_2} + V_{CO_2} \tag{i}$$

EQUALITY 2. The volume of oxygen consumed from the inspired gas equals the volume of oxygen inspired in V_I minus the volume of oxygen expired in V_E. Thus

$$V_{O_2} = F_{I_{O_2}} \cdot V_I - F_{E_{O_2}} \cdot V_E \tag{ii}$$

EQUALITY 3. The volume of carbon dioxide produced in expired gas equals the volume of carbon dioxide in V_E minus the volume of carbon dioxide in V_I. Thus

$$V_{CO_2} = F_{E_{CO_2}} \cdot V_E - F_{I_{CO_2}} \cdot V_I \tag{iii}$$

For most practical applications the fraction of CO_2 in inspired gas is negligible, and for this case

$$V_{CO_2} = F_{E_{CO_2}} \cdot V_E \tag{iii'}$$

These three statements of equality contain implicitly all the variables which are commonly of interest in calculations relating to the composition of respiratory gases. From them, by means of elementary algebra, are derived the following applications.

Application 1. To calculate the rate of oxygen consumption ($\dot{V}_{O_2}$) from the volume of expired gas and the composition of expired and inspired gas, assume $F_{I_{CO_2}} = 0$.

In this case let $\dot{V}_E$ be the volume (STPD) expired per minute. Substituting ii and iii' in i we have

$$\dot{V}_E = \dot{V}_I \cdot (F_{I_{O_2}} \cdot \dot{V}_I - F_{E_{O_2}} \cdot \dot{V}_E) + F_{E_{CO_2}} \cdot \dot{V}_E$$

whence

$$\dot{V}_I = \dot{V}_E(1 - F_{E_{O_2}} - F_{E_{CO_2}}) \div (1 - F_{I_{O_2}})$$

Substituting this value of $\dot{V}_I$ in ii we have

$$\dot{V}_{O_2} = \frac{\dot{V}_E}{(1 - F_{I_{O_2}})} \times (F_{I_{O_2}} - F_{I_{O_2}} \cdot F_{E_{CO_2}} - F_{E_{O_2}}) \tag{1}$$

It should be emphasized that $\dot{V}_E$, which is usually measured in a spirometer at ATPS, must be corrected to STPD. When CO_2 is present in the inspired gas, the solution of the three equalities is more elaborate and Equation 1 becomes

$$\dot{V}_{O_2} = \dot{V}_E \frac{[F_{I_{O_2}}(1 - F_{E_{CO_2}}) - F_{E_{O_2}}(1 - F_{I_{CO_2}})]}{(1 - F_{I_{O_2}} - F_{I_{CO_2}})} \tag{1'}$$

Application 2. To calculate the rate of CO_2 production ($\dot{V}_{CO_2}$) from the volume of expired gas and the composition of expired and inspired gas.

Provided that the CO_2 in the inspired gas is negligible, this application is obtained directly from iii', where V_E refers to the total gas volume expired per minute (STPD).

$$\dot{V}_{CO_2} = F_{E_{CO_2}} \cdot \dot{V}_E \tag{2}$$

When CO_2 is present in the inspired gas, the solution of the three equalities is again more elaborate, and we have

$$\dot{V}_{CO_2} = \dot{V}_E \frac{[F_{E_{CO_2}}(1 - F_{I_{O_2}}) - F_{I_{CO_2}}(1 - F_{E_{O_2}})]}{(1 - F_{I_{O_2}} - F_{I_{CO_2}})} \tag{2'}$$

Application 3. To calculate the respiratory gas exchange ratio, $R = \dot{V}_{CO_2}/\dot{V}_{O_2}$. Provided that $F_{I_{CO_2}}$ is negligible, we can substitute Equation 2 $\div$ Equation 1 whence,

$$R = \frac{F_{E_{CO_2}}(1 - F_{I_{O_2}})}{F_{I_{O_2}} - F_{I_{O_2}} \cdot F_{E_{CO_2}} - F_{E_{O_2}}} \tag{3}$$

Note that R is independent of V_E and includes only the fractions of O_2 and CO_2 in inspired and expired gas. Since the equalities from which R is derived apply to any portion of exhaled gas, the equation may be applied to an "alveolar" sample or to any other portion of gas which has undergone the respiratory exchange. Thus, in the case of alveolar gas,

$$R_A = \frac{F_{A_{CO_2}}(1 - F_{I_{O_2}})}{F_{I_{O_2}} - F_{I_{O_2}} \cdot F_{A_{CO_2}} - F_{A_{O_2}}} \tag{3'}$$

Application 4. To calculate the pressures of oxygen and carbon dioxide in alveolar gas.

For applications relating to acid-base equilibria, diffusion of oxygen in the lungs, or the arterial oxygen saturation, it is frequently convenient to express gas fractions in terms of the partial pressures as they exist in the lungs or the blood. For this purpose it is necessary to introduce the definitions

$$F_{A_{O_2}} = \frac{P_{A_{O_2}}}{P_B - 47} \text{ and } F_{A_{CO_2}} = \frac{P_{A_{CO_2}}}{P_B - 47}$$

where $P_{A_{O_2}}$ and $P_{A_{CO_2}}$ are the partial pressures exerted by these gases in the alveolar phase and $P_B - 47$ is the total (barometric) pressure of all the dry gases. (Vapor pressure of water = 47 mm. Hg at body temperature.) Introducing these definitions into Equation 3, we have

$$R = \frac{\dfrac{P_{A_{CO_2}}}{(P_B - 47)}(1 - F_{I_{O_2}})}{F_{I_{O_2}} - F_{I_{O_2}}\dfrac{R_{A_{CO_2}}}{(P_B - 47)} - \dfrac{P_{A_{O_2}}}{(P_B - 47)}} = \frac{P_{A_{CO_2}}(1 - F_{I_{O_2}})}{F_{I_{O_2}}(P_B - 47 - P_{A_{CO_2}}) - P_{A_{O_2}}}$$

Solving this equation for $P_{A_{O_2}}$ we have,

$$P_{A_{O_2}} = F_{I_{O_2}}(P_B - 47) - P_{A_{CO_2}}\left[F_{I_{O_2}} + \frac{(1 - F_{I_{O_2}})}{R_A}\right] \tag{4}$$

This equation (4) is of great practical importance in aviation and is now the basis of oxygen specifications for aircraft. Note that in persons with normal alveolar CO_2 (39 mm. Hg) and a normal respiratory exchange ratio ($R_A = 0.82$) the only remaining factors which determine the alveolar oxygen pressure (and hence the oxygen saturation of the blood) are the barometric pressure (altitude) and the fraction of oxygen in inspired gas. Thus, it is possible, with the aid of Equation 4 to specify the fraction of oxygen required at any altitude in order to maintain a given alveolar oxygen pressure. This form of the equation is also obviously important in the therapeutic use of oxygen, for it defines the fraction of oxygen in inspired gas which must be employed to achieve any desired alveolar oxygen pressure.

P_{AO_2} can be expressed as a function of oxygen uptake

$$P_{AO_2} = P_{IO_2} - \frac{0.864 \, \dot{V}_{O_2}(1 - F_{IO_2})}{\dot{V}_A} - F_{IO_2}P_{ACO_2}$$

$$\dot{V}_A = \frac{0.864 \, \dot{V}_{O_2}R}{P_{ACO_2}}$$

By the Fick principle, $\dot{V}_{O_2} = Q(Ca_{O_2} - Cv_{O_2})$

$$\dot{V}_A = \frac{0.864 \, Q(Ca_{O_2} - Cv_{O_2}) \, R}{P_{ACO_2}}$$

where Q is the blood flow, Ca_{O_2} is the arterial oxygen content, Cv_{O_2} the venous oxygen content and 0.864 is a numerical factor to correct $\dot{V}_A$ (BTPS) to STPD since $\dot{V}_{O_2}$ is normally expressed STPD. This equation leads to the relationship in Figure 475.

RELATIONS BETWEEN ALVEOLAR AND EXPIRED GASES; RESPIRATORY DEAD SPACE

The total exhaled gas differs in composition from alveolar gas only as a result of the physiologic dead space. The alveolar gas remaining in the respiratory tree, the "dead space" gas (V_D), is drawn back into the alveoli at the onset of the subsequent tidal inspiration (V_T). Thus the volume of new gas from the atmosphere which actually reaches the alveoli is $V_T - V_D$. In contrast to the total respiratory minute volume ($V_E = V_T \cdot f$), the *effective* minute volume or *alveolar ventilation* is only $V_A = (V_T - V_D)f$.

BOHR FORMULA FOR RESPIRATORY DEAD SPACE. We have seen that the volume of dead space in a normal individual engaged in light activity is from one-fourth to one-third of the tidal volume; in patients with pulmonary disease it may be substantially greater. The dead space is therefore an exceedingly important quantity to consider. It is ordinarily estimated by the Bohr formula, which may be derived as follows: Let V_X represent the volume of O_2, CO_2 or foreign gas voided to the atmosphere in a single tidal respiration.

$$V_X = V_D \cdot F_{IX} + (V_T - V_D) \cdot F_{AX} = V_T F_{EX}$$

Eliminating V_X and solving for V_D we have,

$$V_D = V_T \cdot \frac{(F_{EX} - F_{AX})}{(F_{IX} - F_{AX})} \tag{5}$$

If the dead space is known from other measurements, then Equation 5 allows the calculation of alveolar gas composition from the composition of expired gas and the tidal volume. Thus, rearrangement of Equation 5 yields

$$F_{AX} = \frac{V_T \cdot F_{EX} - V_D \cdot F_{IX}}{V_T - V_D} \tag{5'}$$

It is wise to specify the molecular species employed, e.g., V_{DCO_2} or V_{DO_2}, because the dead space (as determined from the Bohr formula) is not necessarily identical for all gases. Also the dead space as determined by conventional methods (Equation 5) has the curious property of increasing in proportion to the tidal volume. The significance of these variations of physiologic dead space has never been satisfactorily explained, and great caution must be exercised in their interpretation. They may be associated with differences in the definition of "alveolar" gas. Very probably the usual methods for taking "alveolar" gas samples lead to spurious values for F_{AX}, particularly at large tidal volumes.

RELATIONS BETWEEN VENTILATION AND METABOLISM

It is an everyday observation that when an individual exercises he consumes oxygen at a greater rate and also breathes more deeply and frequently. The relationship between metabolic oxygen consumption and the effective alveolar ventilation is, however, no haphazard affair; it may be analyzed quantitatively as follows:

$$\dot{V}_{CO_2} = F_{ACO_2} \cdot \dot{V}_A \qquad \text{where } \dot{V}_A = \text{volume per minute, STPD.}$$

But $\dot{V}_{CO_2} = R \cdot \dot{V}_{O_2}$ whence,

$$\dot{V}_A = \frac{R}{F_{ACO_2}} \cdot \dot{V}_{O_2} = \frac{R(P_B - 47)}{P_{ACO_2}} \cdot \dot{V}_{O_2} \tag{6}$$

Equation 6 forms the basis for interpretation of experimental data obtained during exercise. A consideration of this relationship shows the following fundamental points.

(a) For any given rate of oxygen consumption in the steady state of respiratory exchange ($R = Rs$), the alveolar CO_2 pressure is reciprocally related to the effective ventilation. A doubling of an alveolar ventilation will exactly halve the alveolar CO_2 pressure. The pressure of CO_2 in the alveoli (and hence in the arterial blood) is uniquely determined by the ratio of metabolic oxygen consumption to ventilation. $P_B = 760$ mm. Hg and $R = Rs = 0.90$, we have:

(b) Conversely, if the CO_2 pressure remains constant, then the ventilation must increase in precise proportion to the oxygen consumption. Under normal conditions, where $P_{ACO_2} = 39$ mm. Hg, $P_B = 760$ mm. Hg and $R = Rs = 0.90$, we have:

$$\dot{V}_A = \frac{0.9 \times (760 - 47)}{39} \cdot \dot{V}_{O_2} = 16 \times \dot{V}_{O_2}$$

We may therefore state that in order to maintain a normal alveolar CO_2 (and hence a normal arterial blood CO_2), the ventilation must be 16 times as large as the oxygen consumption at all levels of activity. Any deviation from this simple relation signifies an alteration of alveolar CO_2.

SUMMARY OF RESPIRATORY EQUATIONS

RESPIRATORY QUANTITY	EQUATION
1. The rate of oxygen consumption. Expressed as vol./min., STPD. F_{ICO_2} assumed to be 0.	$\dot{V}_{O_2} = \dfrac{\dot{V}_E}{(1 - F_{IO_2})}(F_{IO_2} - F_{IO_2} \cdot F_{ECO_2} - F_{EO_2})$
2. The rate of CO_2 production. Expressed as vol./min., STPD. F_{ICO_2} assumed to be 0.	$\dot{V}_{CO_2} = \dot{V}_E \times F_{ECO_2}$
3. The respiratory exchange ratio. The expired gas fractions may refer to alveolar, total expired, or any other portion of exhaled gas. $F_{ICO_2} = 0$	$R = \dfrac{F_{ECO_2}(1 - F_{IO_2})}{F_{IO_2} - F_{IO_2} \cdot F_{ECO_2} - F_{EO_2}}$
4. The pressure of oxygen in alveolar gas. F_{ICO_2} assumed to be 0.	$P_{AO_2} = F_{IO_2}(P_B - 47) - P_{ACO_2}\left(F_{IO_2} + \dfrac{(1 - F_{IO_2})}{R}\right)$
5. The respiratory dead space to any gas, x. (Bohr formula.)	$V_{DX} = V_T \dfrac{(F_{EX} - F_{AX})}{(F_{IX} - F_{AX})}$
6. The relation between ventilation and metabolism.	$\dot{V}_A = \dfrac{R(P_B - 47)}{P_{ACO_2}} \times \dot{V}_{O_2}$

CLINICAL CORRELATIONS

Whenever the cells of the body cannot use sufficient O_2 to support normal function, they are said to be suffering from *anoxia*. If they do not receive an adequate supply from the blood, the condition is called *anoxemia*. Lack of O_2 represents a condition of extreme hazard to the integrity of the body. In the words of Haldane,[20] "anoxemia" not only causes "stoppage of a machine, it is also the total ruin of the supposed machinery." Ordinarily, the body has effective means of preventing anoxia, but in unusual conditions even mild anoxia leads to a vicious circle which, if not broken, results in rapid deterioration and death.

It is possible to differentiate four general types of anoxia. Delineation of these types is based on the physiologic factors described above and provides a rational classification of the clinical anoxias.* (i) *Stagnant anoxia* arises when the flow of blood through a tissue is reduced. (ii) *Anoxic anoxia* results from interference with the exchange of O_2 across the lungs or some preceding step in respiration. (iii) *Anemic anoxia* follows reduction of the O_2 carrying capacity of the blood. (iv) *Histotoxic anoxia*, occurs when the tissue cells cannot use efficiently the O_2 available to them. Figure 476 illustrates how a knowledge of the O_2 content and the percentage saturation of arterial and venous blood makes it possible to distinguish the various types of anoxia. The O_2 content of the arterial blood

* The first three forms were originally described by Barcroft;[3] the fourth by Peters and Van Slyke.[36]

is normal in stagnant and histotoxic anoxia, and is reduced in anoxic and anemic anoxia. The venous blood contains less O_2 than normal if the anoxia is stagnant, anoxic or anemic; in histotoxic anoxia the O_2 content of the venous blood is above normal.

Stagnant anoxia.   When the blood flow is reduced, stagnant anoxia develops. The reduction in flow may occur locally as a result of interference with the peripheral circulation, as in arterial spasm, Raynaud's disease, embolism and other diseases of the blood vessels. Reduced flow may also occur generally, as it does in shock, cardiac insufficiency and vasomotor collapse. During certain maneuvers of an airplane, an aviator may experience short periods of stagnant anoxia in his retinas and brain, resulting in a loss of vision followed by unconsciousness—"blacking out." The heart cannot pump blood against the high centrifugal forces developed during rapid turns, and the brain is deprived of blood. Occlusion of the blood supply to the brain leads to unconsciousness

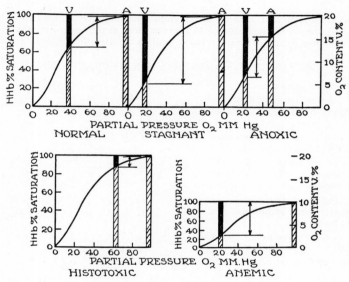

FIG. 476.   Composition of arterial (*A*) and venous (*V*) blood found in various types of anoxia and their relation to O_2 absorption curve of hemoglobin. Hatched areas indicate amount of $HHbO_2$ present in blood. Amount of O_2 removed from blood as it passes through tissues is expressed as difference in O_2 content of arterial and venous blood. (After Means.)

within 6 seconds (syncope or fainting). The O_2 content of the arterial blood is normal in stagnant anoxia, but the percentage saturation of the venous blood is low. The blood flows through the tissues more slowly than usual, and more O_2 per unit volume of blood is removed by the tissues.

Anoxic anoxia.   Reduction of the pO_2 in the arterial blood causes anoxic anoxia. Its effects are general, and it may be produced by any condition reducing the amount of O_2 available for formation of oxyhemoglobin or interfering with the transfer of O_2 from air to blood in the lungs. Anoxic anoxia is encountered in pneumonia, drowning and paralysis of the respiratory muscles; it also results from breathing gases deficient in O_2. The threat of anoxic anoxia limits the altitudes men can attain by climbing or air travel. Paul Bert[8] demonstrated in 1870 that the deleterious effects of reduced barometric pressures are actually effects of the lowered pO_2. Modern high altitude flights in airplanes would be impossible without equipment supplying O_2 at partial pressures approximating 150 mm. Hg. Anoxic anoxia is indicated by a low percentage saturation of arterial blood with O_2. The pO_2 of venous blood is also lowered because the tissues extract their needs from the low oxygen content of the arterial blood.

Histotoxic anoxia. When the tissue cells are unable to utilize O_2, histotoxic anoxia ensues. Alcohol, narcotics and such poisons as cyanide interfere with the ability of the cells to use the O_2 available to them, even though the supply is entirely normal. In histotoxic anoxia, the venous O_2 saturation is higher than normal. The blood passing through the tissue does not lose its O_2, since the oxidative system of the cells cannot accept it. The anoxia produced may be either general or local, the site depending upon the distribution of the disturbing substances.

Anemic anoxia. If the O_2 carrying capacity of the blood is reduced, the result is anemic anoxia. This capacity may decrease because there is insufficient HHb in the blood or because some HHb has been modified so that it can no longer transport O_2. The effects are general. A primary loss of HHb occurs in anemia and after hemorrhage. Nitrites, chlorates and many other substances can change HHb into methemoglobin, a modification of HHb which cannot combine reversibly with O_2. Carbon monoxide produces anemic anoxia by blocking the reactive groups of HHb with which O_2 combines. During anemic anoxia the O_2 content of the arterial blood is reduced and that of the venous blood is correspondingly reduced to supply the needed amounts of O_2.

Effects of Oxygen Lack. In general, the symptoms associated with anoxia depend more upon the rapidity with which the anoxic state develops, and upon the degree of anoxia reached, than upon the type of anoxia present. This relation is understandable, since the signs and symptoms are the expression of the malfunction of the anoxic cells; the type of anoxia becomes important only when treatment is considered. The small differences that do exist between the types of anoxia (except for histotoxic anoxia) are explained by the differences in the partial pressures at which a given amount of O_2 can be delivered. In histotoxic anoxia the consequences of selectively blocking a particular chemical reaction in the oxidative chain can differ greatly from the effects of failing to provide adequate O_2 for the final steps. The symptoms of acute, rapidly developing anoxia are like those of alcoholic intoxication, which is a form of histotoxic anoxia; the symptoms of chronic anoxia, on the other hand, are like fatigue.[3] All cells and tissues in the body are affected in some degree by anoxia.[46]

Fulminating anoxia. The O_2 content of blood falls rapidly when atmospheres deficient in O_2 are breathed, when cardiac arrest occurs, or when the breathing movements cease. Aviators at high altitudes who suddenly lose their O_2 supply, miners who walk into pockets of methane or of N_2 and CO_2, and patients who breathe nitrous oxide undiluted with O_2 can collapse and become unconscious in a minute or less. Death may follow in a very short time unless proper treatment is immediately given. Recovery is equally rapid if the O_2 supply of the tissues is restored promptly and is quite complete if the anoxic state has been of short duration. While the anoxic state is developing, the individual can become unconscious without ever being aware that he is in any danger; and he may, on being restored to a conscious state, deny the lapse of consciousness. During the induction of the anoxic state the respiratory and the cardiovascular systems can be greatly stimulated. Hyperpnea, tachycardia and an elevated blood pressure may occur. As the anoxic state becomes profound, the respiration slows, becomes gasping and finally ceases. The blood pressure falls, and eventually the heart fails, usually a short time after the last breath has been taken.

Acute anoxia. If the anoxia develops more slowly, a variety of symptoms are produced. The symptoms of a mild anoxia, whether produced by alcohol, carbon monoxide or an ascent to high altitudes, are indicative of malfunction of the central nervous system. At first there is a feeling of well-being, a feeling of increased satisfaction and power. As the anoxia becomes progressively greater, a period characterized by unstable emotions and loss of judgment supervenes. The individual loses his critical capacity and is unaware of or cannot properly evaluate his deficiencies. Muscular incoordination.

deterioration of vision and memory loss may be pronounced. Fixity of ideas may be predominant and the individual will persist in doing foolish things even at extreme hazard to his own welfare. He may be unable to accomplish a simple procedure that will insure his safety. Hyperpnea may be pronounced, or a feeling of lassitude and extreme weakness may set in. Nausea and vomiting frequently occur and the individual may suddenly collapse. Unconsciousness is often preceded by profound convulsions or may set in with cardiac syncope. The changes produced in respiration, in the heart rate and in the blood pressure are extremely variable,[41] but a not uncommon finding is an increased ventilation and heart rate and an elevated blood pressure.

Chronic anoxia. If the anoxia develops so slowly that the compensating mechanisms of the body keep pace, the anoxia may be symptomless, or relatively so. Such anoxia is produced by living at high altitudes or by a leaky gas fixture. The main effect is a loss of physiologic reserve resulting in a limitation of the individual's physical activities. Such a person is easily fatigued, and as the chronic anoxia becomes more profound, he may become listless and constantly suffer from a feeling of extreme tiredness. Slight exertion will produce air hunger and dyspnea. Dwellers at high altitudes, even though acclimatized, may suffer at times from "mountain sickness." The symptoms are head-ache, weakness, nausea, loss of appetite and, occasionally, stupor and coma.[27] Rapid deterioration may set in without warning, and unless the chronic anoxia is relieved the individual may die in a cardiac crisis.

The compensatory mechanisms of the body are stimulated by anoxia. In mild anoxia the adjustment is complete and the individual becomes so perfectly adapted to his new internal and external environment that he can be ostensibly in perfect health under conditions that would be extremely hazardous if he had encountered them suddenly. A person acclimatized to an elevation of 15,000 feet has an increased vital capacity and an increased minute volume of breathing.[45] The amount of hemoglobin in the blood increases considerably, an adaptation achieved over several weeks.[42] In fact, the O_2 capacity of the blood may be greater than normal, even though the pO_2 in the alveoli and in the arterial blood is much reduced (65 mm. Hg). The blood is distinctly more alkaline and contains less CO_2 at a slightly lower pressure. The acclimatization is not achieved without loss of physiologic reserve. At 14,000 feet, the amount of exercise required to increase the pulse rate is about 60 per cent of that needed at sea level.[4]

Cyanosis. In "cyanosis," the skin or mucous membranes appear bluish, and the color disappears if blood is pressed from the superficial capillaries. Cyanosis occurs only if these *capillaries contain more than 5 grams of HHb (unsaturated hemoglobin) per 100 ml. of blood.*[32] The abnormal color appears because reduced HHb is purplish, whereas $HHbO_2$ is bright red; the color of the skin depends upon the absolute amount of reduced HHb. Cyanosis may be a prominent feature of anoxias other than histotoxic anoxia and some forms of anemic anoxia. In histotoxic anemia, the HHb is, of course, properly oxygenated, and the blood is bright red. In anemia, less than 5 grams of HHb per 100 ml. of blood may be present.

The clinical appearance of cyanosis is dependent upon the state of the capillaries, the pigmentation and the thickness of the patient's skin. Since these factors vary from individual to individual, cyanosis is a poor indicator of the degree of anoxia. In the presence of polycythemia, or after adaptation to high altitudes, cyanosis is much en-hanced and may appear when anoxia is relatively slight. In the anoxia produced by carbon monoxide, cyanosis does not occur, since the HHbCO compound is a bright cherry red. Methemoglobin is dark and, when present in large amounts, leads to appre-ciable cyanosis.

Cyanosis also occurs in normal individuals who develop anoxic or stagnant anoxia. In the first instance, arterial blood does not become fully saturated in the lung; in the second, the blood is abnormally deoxygenated in the tissues. In addition to respiratory causes, intermixture of arterial and venous blood, as in congenital heart defects, may result in cyanosis—a condition giving rise to the phrase "blue babies."

Hyperpnea. All of the manifestations of anoxia cannot be ascribed to O_2 lack. A prominent feature of acute anoxic anoxia is hyperpnea with an attendant loss of CO_2. When exposed to lowered barometric pressure, an animal increases its ventilation; CO_2 is washed out of the arterial blood, and the blood rapidly becomes alkaline.[10] If the degree of anoxia is not too great (O_2 saturation of arterial blood above 60 per cent), the change in acid-base balance is typical of a respiratory alkalosis, the uncompensated loss of CO_2 (see Chap. 24). Mosso[35] was among the first to recognize that a loss of CO_2 occurs and to insist upon the importance of *acapnia* in the production of the symptoms of acute anoxic anoxia. In many patients, the sequence of signs and symptoms during the development of anoxic anoxia is similar to the sequence brought on by voluntary hyperventilation of normal air.[26]

Addition of CO_2 to a breathing mixture deficient in O_2 can lessen or prevent some of the changes thought to be typical of anoxic anoxia.[19] At present, the mutual interaction of O_2 and CO_2 cannot be explained, but evidence is increasing that CO_2 does more than play a physicochemical role in the adjustment of acid-base balance. CO_2 is utilized by animal tissues[16] and may, in some manner as yet only dimly understood, regulate the rate at which the physiologic oxidations are carried on by the body.

Hyperventilation syndrome. Certain persons appear to react to sensory stimulation or to life stresses by a hyperpnea which is not caused by anoxia. This response may be manifested by disturbances of cerebral function like those resulting from anoxia, by tetany, or even by unconsciousness and convulsions, especially in epileptic patients.

Therapeutic Use of Oxygen. When O_2 transfer across the lungs is impeded, as in pneumonia or pulmonary edema, dramatic relief can be provided by having the patient breathe an atmosphere enriched with O_2. The increased pO_2 in the alveolar air increases the rate at which O_2 diffuses through the air spaces and the alveolar membranes of the lungs, and the blood leaves the lungs with a greater load of O_2. If, however, the arterial blood is already fully saturated when it leaves the lung, little benefit is derived from breathing O_2 under an enhanced partial pressure, because only the small amount that can be carried as a result of the increased physical solubility is added to the blood. Some observers believe that this relief is of some benefit.[2]

The extensive use of O_2 to treat carbon monoxide anoxia is predicated upon a different principle. Increasing the pO_2 in the arterial blood aids in the dissociation of HHbCO, and the carbon monoxide is more easily eliminated. The objective in the treatment of carbon monoxide anoxia is to restore the O_2 carrying capacity of the blood as quickly as possible.

Some care must be taken in administering O_2. Comfortable masks and oxygen tents have been developed in which the atmosphere the patient breathes is easily controlled. It is common practice to maintain the O_2 concentration in the tent above 50 per cent or more, providing a partial pressure of 300 to 400 mm. Hg.

O_2 toxicity. Paul Bert[8] was the first to observe that O_2 at high partial pressures is not tolerated well by warm-blooded animals. When exposed to a pO_2 of three atmospheres or more, such animals show signs of profound disturbance of the central nervous system. They may collapse and die in violent convulsions. If O_2 at a partial pressure of one atmosphere is breathed for a long time, edema of the lungs may ensue, with the paradoxical result that the animal dies of anoxia. These effects limit the therapeutic use of O_2, for, even though it is theoretically possible to increase the pO_2 to such an extent that the metabolic demands of the tissues could be met by the physically dissolved O_2, the tissues would die. A high pO_2 apparently blocks the oxidative chains of reactions by actually destroying some important enzymes.[44] The reasons for the inflammatory changes

in the lungs with partial pressures of O_2 above 0.8 atmosphere is not clearly understood, but, if O_2 is to be administered for long periods, it is best to keep the pO_2 somewhat below 0.8 atmosphere.

It has recently been shown that an alarming increase in blindness (retrolental fibroplasia) in premature infants was caused by increasing the O_2 concentration in incubators to excessive levels. Diving with aqualung equipment, which makes the diver independent of a surface supply of O_2, also carries a hazard. The air must be delivered at a high pressure to permit inspiratory excursions against the pressure of the atmosphere and water. In sensitive persons, serious symptoms may appear after prolonged immersion combined with exercise at depths as little as 33 feet.

REFERENCES

1. ANON. Fed. Proc., 1950, 9:602–605.
2. BARACH, A. L. Principles and practices of inhalational therapy. Philadelphia, J. B. Lippincott, 1944.
3. BARCROFT, J. Lancet, 1920, 99:485–489.
4. BARCROFT, J. The respiratory function of the blood. Part I. Lessons from high altitude. Cambridge, Cambridge University Press, 1925.
5. BARCROFT, J. The respiratory function of the blood. Part 2. Haemoglobin. Cambridge, Cambridge University Press, 1928.
6. BEHNKE, A. R. Harvey Lect., 1942, 37:198–226.
7. BEHNKE, A. R., THOMSON, R. M. and SHAW, L. A. Amer. J. Physiol., 1936, 114:137–146.
8. BERT, P. Researches in experimental physiology. HITCHCOCK, M. A. and HITCHCOCK, F. A., trans. Columbus, Ohio, College Book Co., 1943.
9. BOHR, C., HASSELBALCH, K. and KROGH, A. Skand. Arch. Physiol., 1904, 16:402–412.
10. CLARKE, R. W., MARSHALL, C. and NIMS, L. F. Amer. J. Physiol., 1944, 142:483–486.
11. COMROE, J. H., JR. and DRIPPS, R. D., JR. Amer. J. Physiol., 1944, 142:700–707.
12. DARLING, R. C., COURNAND, A. and RICHARDS, D. W., JR. J. clin. Invest., 1944, 23:55–67.
13. DAVIES, P. W. and BRINK, F., JR. Rev. sci. Instrum., 1942, 13:524–533.
14. DRABKIN, D. L. and SCHMIDT, C. F. J. biol. Chem., 1945, 157:69–83.
15. DU BOIS, E. F. Basal metabolism in health and disease. Philadelphia, Lea & Febiger, 1936.
16. EVANS, E. A., JR. Science, 1942, 96:25–29.
17. FULTON, J. F., ed. Decompression sickness. Philadelphia, W. B. Saunders Co., 1951.
18. GERTZ, H. Z. Biol., 1928, 88:172–182.
19. GIBBS, F. A., GIBBS, E. L., LENNOX, W. G. and NIMS, L. F. J. Aviat. Med., 1943, 14:250–261.
20. HALDANE, J. S. Brit. med. J., 1919, 2:65–71.
21. HARVEY, E. N., BARNES, D. K., McELROY, W. D., WHITELEY, A. H., PEASE, D. C. and COOPER, K. W. J. cell. comp. Physiol., 1944, 24:1–22.
22. HARVEY, E. N., WHITELEY, A. H., McELROY, W. D., PEASE, D. C. and BARNES, D. K. J. cell. comp. Physiol., 1944, 24:23–34.
23. HENDERSON, Y. Physiol. Rev., 1925, 5:131–160.
24. HENRIQUES, O. M. Biochem. Z., 1928, 200: 10–17.

25. HILL, L. Caisson sickness and the physiology of work in compressed air. London, Edward Arnold, 1912.
26. HINSHAW, H. C., RUSHMER, R. F. and BOOTHBY, W. M. J. Aviat. Med., 1943, 14:100–104.
27. HURTADO, A. J. Amer. med. Ass., 1942, 120: 1278–1282.
28. JOSSELYN, L. E. Anat. Rec., 1935, 62:147–171.
29. KROGH, A. The anatomy and physiology of the capillaries, Rev. & enl. ed. New Haven, Yale University Press, 1929.
30. KROGH, M. J. Physiol., 1915, 49:271–300.
31. LOW, F. N. Anat. Rec., 1953, 117:241–264.
32. LUNDSGAARD, C. and VAN SLYKE, D. D. Medicine, Baltimore, 1923, 2:1–76.
33. MARTIN, C. J. and YOUNG, A. C. J. appl. Physiol., 1957, 11:371–476.
34. MILLER, W. S. The lung. Springfield, Ill., Charles C Thomas, 1937.
35. MOSSO, A. and MARRO, G. Arch. ital. Biol., 1903, 39:387–394.
36. PETERS, J. P. and VAN SLYKE, D. D. Chap. 12 in their: Quantitative clinical chemistry. I. Interpretations. Baltimore, Williams & Wilkins Co., 1931.
37. PETERS, J. P. and VAN SLYKE, D. D. Quantitative clinical chemistry. Vol. II. Methods. Baltimore, Williams & Wilkins Co., 1931.
38. RILEY, R. L. Amer. J. Med., 1951, 10:210–220.
39. ROUGHTON, F. J. W. Physiol. Rev., 1935, 15:241–296.
40. ROUGHTON, F. J. W. Amer. J. Physiol., 1945, 143:621–633.
41. SCHNEIDER, E. C. Physiol. Rev., 1921, 1:631–659.
42. SCHNEIDER, E. C. and HAVENS, L. C. Amer. J. Physiol., 1915, 36:380–397.
43. STADIE, W. C. and O'BRIEN, H. J. biol. Chem., 1937, 117:439–470.
44. STADIE, W. C., RIGGS, B. C. and HAUGAARD, N. Amer. J. med. Sci., 1944, 207:84–114.
45. TALBOTT, J. H. and DILL, D. B. Amer. J. med. Sci., 1936, 192:626–639.
46. VAN LIERE, E. J. Anoxia, its effects on the body. Chicago, University of Chicago Press, 1942.
47. WEARN, J. T., ERNSTENE, A. C., BROMER, A. W., BARR, J. S., GERMAN, W. J. and ZSCHIESCHE, L. J. Amer. J. Physiol., 1934, 109:236–256.
48. WILLSON, H. G. Amer. J. Anat., 1922, 30: 267–287.

CHAPTER 37

Neural Control of Respiration

By ALLAN C. YOUNG

WHILE the main functions of the respiratory system are to provide O_2, eliminate CO_2 and maintain a constant pH of the blood, this system participates in many other functions. The chest, lungs and upper respiratory tract provide controlled movement of air for sniffing, coughing, sneezing and vomiting; for such expressions of emotion as laughing and sobbing; and for a variety of highly skilled voluntary movements such as speaking, singing and blowing a wind instrument. It is interesting that, as Campbell[8] has emphasized, both the relative and total extent to which various muscle groups are active may be very different in voluntary and involuntary breathing movements.

PERIPHERAL NEURAL MECHANISMS

Efferent Discharge. The phrenic nerves, originating in C_2, C_3 and C_4, provide the innervation for the diaphragm. The intercostal muscles receive their innervation from T_{1-6} via the intercostal nerves; the abdominal muscles receive theirs from L_1 and T_{7-12}. The scaleni are innervated from C_{4-8}, and the innervation of the sternomastoids is derived from C_2 and the spinal accessory nerve. It is reasonable to speculate that the respiratory act is integrated in the brain stem rather than in the spinal cord, because so many segmental levels are involved in the innervation of respiratory muscle.

The periodic respiratory enlargement and contraction of the thoracic space are superimposed upon an underlying postural tone. Tidal exhalations do not leave the thorax in full expiration, but in a state of partial inspiration, which is not far from the midposition of the thorax. This state is maintained by a tetanus in a smaller or larger proportion of the inspiratory motor units, each unit firing at rather slow rates (five to 20 impulses per second). The diaphragm as well as the intercostal muscles is involved.[6, 17, 18] Undoubtedly the source of this activity is in general postural, and it represents participation of the inspiratory mechanism in the maintenance of the upright posture. There is, however, a definite respiratory component, inasmuch as the degree of inspiratory tone is regulated, via the carotid and aortic bodies, by the O_2 and CO_2 content of the blood.[15]

The expiratory muscles also exhibit a basic tonic activity, since certain of them, like the inspiratory muscles, oppose by contraction the force of gravity and participate therefore in the maintenance of upright posture. Thus the muscles of the abdomen, while functioning in respiration as expiratory muscles, are also important postural muscles serving to retain the abdominal contents.

The act of inspiration begins against a background of tonic innervation of both inspiratory and expiratory muscles. Simultaneously two events centrally coordinated occur: (i) those units supplying inspiratory muscles which are in tonic contraction increase their rate of firing (Fig. 477), and (ii) the tonic firing of expiratory units is

FIG. 477. Discharge from single motor unit of external intercostal muscle. Unit fired continuously throughout inspiration and expiration, but rate increased during inspiration. Middle line is pneumograph (inspiration down) and lower line is graph of impulse frequency. (From Bronk and Ferguson, *Amer. J. Physiol.*, 1935, *110*:700–707.)

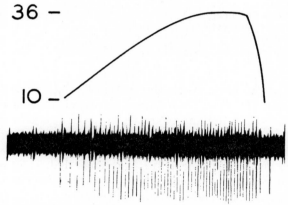

FIG. 478. Characteristic slowly augmenting inspiratory discharge of single motor fiber of phrenic nerve of dog. This record was obtained during complete motor paralysis produced by intravenous injection of curare. Vagus nerves are sectioned. Frequency of firing is plotted on ordinates above original electrogram. (From Gesell *et al.*, *Amer. J. Physiol.*, 1940, *128*:629–634.)

reciprocally inhibited. As the size of the thorax increases, and the diaphragm descends, the expiratory apparatus gives way in equal degree to accommodate for this movement. In addition, as inspiration proceeds, new units are added, or "recruited," so that the inspiratory act gains force as it proceeds (Fig. 478). The firing of individual units accelerates in rate, resulting in a progressive increment in the strength of contraction of each unit. By increase in the number of active units, and by augmentation in the strength of each unit's contraction through its increasing rate of discharge, inspiration grows to a peak determined by the various factors that control the depth of respiration. The whole accelerating tempo is then abruptly terminated. Other inspiratory units cease firing more slowly.[8] Units participating in the maintenance of inspiratory tone return to their former slow steady tetanus, which is maintained throughout expiration. The tonic expiratory discharge recommences.

In normal quiet breathing, this is at times the whole of the respiratory act, but often some traces of active expiration develop, reciprocating with inspiration (Fig. 479).

Virtually nothing is known of the size and numbers of the motor units of the respiratory system. Much more is known about the rates of discharge in single phrenic and intercostal motor units, which have been studied repeatedly. Basically the rates are slow, particularly at the onset of inspiration, at the end of expiration and during the tonic phases, and may amount to no more than five to ten discharges per second. Accelerating as respiration progresses, the rates reach the neighborhood of 30 to 40 impulses per second at the end of normal inspiration. Even with an extreme respiratory drive producing a maximum hyperpnea, rates above 100 per second are rarely seen; this rate is close to the upper limit of motoneuron discharge to skeletal muscle in normal circumstances.

Afferent Pathways. The respiratory system is affected by stimuli, especially noxious stimuli, from many parts of the body; it is also affected to some extent by proprioceptors of the limb and possibly by other muscles. These proprioceptors may be of some importance in the control of breathing (Chap. 38). The afferent nerve fibers which are most effective in controlling and modifying respiration are contained in the glossopharyngeal (IXth) and vagus (Xth) nerves. These nerves carry impulses from the carotid and aortic bodies or glomera (Chap. 9), which contain chemoreceptors responsive to increased pCO_2 and lowered pO_2 in the arterial blood.[11, 12] The Xth nerve carries impulses from many types of receptor, but mainly from (i) chemoreceptors of

FIG. 479. Simultaneous records of motor nerve impulses to internal intercostal muscle (*upper record*) in expiration, and to external intercostal muscle (*lower record*) in inspiration; vagi and carotid sinus nerves cut, animal completely immobilized with curare. *Bottom line*, time—0.2 sec. intervals. (From Bronk and Ferguson, *Amer. J. Physiol.*, 1935, *110*:700–707.)

the aortic glomus, (ii) stretch receptors in the large veins,[2] (iii) nociceptors subserving the cough reflex, and (iv) stretch receptors[16] located in the lungs—the most important type insofar as respiration is concerned.

Receptors which fire when the lungs are inflated were first studied by Adrian.[1] Two types are distinguished on the basis of threshold and rate of adaptation (Fig. 480).[22, 23] Slowly adapting receptors fire with relatively slight degrees of lung distention and reflexly decrease activity of phrenic motoneurons. Rapidly adapting receptors respond only to forcible distention of the lungs, i.e., lung volumes exceeding eupneic tidal volumes, and elicit a brief increase in phrenic motoneuron discharge. Widdicombe[50] localized these receptors in the tracheobronchial tree and believed they are identical with the mechanoreceptors of the cough reflex. Lung stretch receptors are supplied by the larger vagal afferents having conduction velocities ranging from 14 to 59 m. per second. Deflation of the lungs elicits a marked increase in phrenic motoneuron discharge.[23] Knowlton and Larrabee[22] noted that inflation-sensitive receptors often fired also on lung deflation. However, Paintal[32] has identified units which respond to deflation but not to inflation. It is likely that these receptors are responsible for the increased inspiratory discharge when the lungs are deflated.

HERING-BREUER REFLEXES. In 1865, Hering and Breuer[16] discovered that the stretch receptors detect inflation and deflation of the lungs and that the afferent discharge into the brain stem alters the respiratory cycle. Their findings were elaborated by Head in 1880. These investigators found that inflation of the lungs tends to terminate inspiration and that collapse of the lungs tends to initiate it. (The inflation-terminating receptor is the slowly adapting one mentioned above.) It was natural to conclude that these reflexes provide a self-regulatory mechanism or, in modern language, a regulatory feedback. The inspiratory-terminating reflex is supposedly operative in the range of eupneic breathing. However, the end organs for the inspiration excitatory reflex respond only to extreme deflation (either passive or active) or in deep respiration. Recent studies described below raise the possibility that these afferents do not control respiration cycle by cycle but rather provide a background of respiratory drive.

COUGH REFLEX.[49, 50]   Coughing results from mechanical or chemical irritation of endings in the respiratory passages. Discharge in mechanoreceptors elicited by introducing a tube into the trachea inhibits phrenic motoneuron discharge and causes expiratory efforts and bronchiolar constriction. Mechanoreceptors may also be excited by abrupt volume changes in the isolated tracheobronchial system. The receptive zone most sensitive to mechanical stimuli is the inner surface of the larynx. The tracheal bifurcation and the lower half of the trachea are also sensitive, but the main bronchi are relatively insensitive.

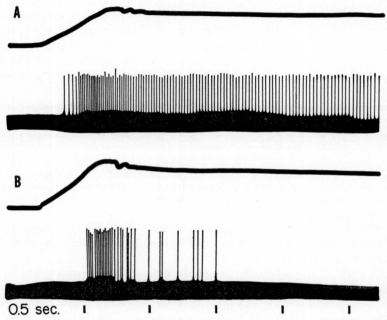

FIG. 480.   Responses of two types of afferent vagal fibers to inflation of lungs (chest wall removed). Upper trace in both records, intratracheal pressure; respiration pump stopped in expiration just before start of both records. Fibers responding as shown in *A* adapt slowly. Fibers responding as shown in *B* adapt rapidly. (After Knowlton and Larrabee, *Amer. J. Physiol.*, 1946, *147*:100–114.)

Chemically induced coughing follows inhalation of sulfur dioxide. This gas is effective when introduced through an endobronchial catheter so that the gas comes into contact with only the lungs and smaller bronchi. A weaker cough is produced by perfusing sulfur dioxide through the isolated tracheobronchial system. The individuality of the mechanosensitive and chemosensitive cough reflex afferents has been established by single unit recording. The former adapt rapidly to volume changes and are found in greatest concentration near the larynx and carina. They respond readily to mechanical stimulation or inhalation of powders, but are relatively insensitive to sulfur dioxide. The chemosensitive receptors adapt more slowly to volume changes, are widely distributed in the tracheobronchial system, and respond readily to sulfur dioxide. Both mechanically and chemically induced coughing are decreased by vagotomy, but both vagotomy and sympathectomy are required to abolish the reflex.

CENTRAL NEURAL MECHANISMS

As has been mentioned above, respiration is affected by a wide variety of afferent stimuli, is subject to voluntary control, and takes part in a variety of emotional expressions. It is not too surprising, then, to find that respiratory responses follow electrical stimulation of several levels of the central nervous system and several regions of the cerebral cortex.

Cerebral Cortex. Spencer[39] was the first to call attention to respiratory responses to stimulation of the presylvian area. Two general areas within this region have been mapped. (i) An *accelerator area* lies on the anterior sigmoid gyrus and immediately adjacent cortex of the medial surface of the hemisphere in the dog and cat; a comparable area in the monkey lies just rostral to the superior precentral gyrus. Portions of this area are rostral to the motor representation of the face, tongue, glottis, etc.; and stimulation of them gives rise to rhythmic licking, chewing and swallowing movements with salivation. Croaking, grunting and other forms of vocalization occur. (ii) An *inhibitory area* definable in the dog and cat is relatively large, including the gyrus compositus anterior and most of the cortex of the sylvian and ectosylvian gyri; in the cat the gyrus proreus is also included. In the monkey an inhibitory field is located just caudal to the lower end of the inferior precentral sulcus. Mastication is also obtained by stimulating this area. A second area producing acceleration of respiration coincides closely with motor area II. Respiratory movements appear therefore to be localized in both cortical representations of the body musculature.

More recently, attention has been focused upon the respiratory effects of stimulating the *limbic* area of the cortex, i.e., the region forming the hilus of the hemispheres and embracing the medial and orbital surfaces of the frontal lobe (Chap. 22). Mapping of responsive zones reveals that the cortex of the posterior orbital surface, the cingulate gyrus, the tip of the temporal pole, the anterior temporal operculum, and the anterior insula form a continuous strip of cortex giving rise to respiratory responses. The larger part of the "insular-orbital" area is inhibitory, as is the larger part of the cingulate gyrus. These findings have been confirmed in man by stimulation at the time of operation for prefrontal leukotomy.

Since alteration of autonomic activity may also be elicited by stimulation of the same general regions, they appear to subserve the autonomic and respiratory correlates of certain types of behavior. The close association with the olfactory area naturally recalls that sniffing and breathing are necessary for olfaction, and the nearness of the respiratory area on the convexity of the cortex to Broca's area suggests the integration of speech and breathing at a cortical level. The association of masticatory and swallowing movements with respiratory change on stimulation of area 6 points to a cortical integration of the various components of food-taking. If, as has been suggested, the orbital and other limbic areas are concerned with emotional behavior, it is logical that breathing, which is a component of emotional expression, should be altered by stimulation of these areas.

According to conventional neurology, one would expect to find respiratory representation in cortical area 4, the motor area from which the pyramidal tracts arise, because respiration is subject to voluntary acceleration or inhibition. This does not appear to be so. Although the trunk and thoracic musculature is represented in this area, there is no evidence of coordinated employment of these muscles in acts suggestive of respiration when their cortical representation is stimulated, and pyramidal section in the cat does not influence the respiratory responses to cortical stimulation. It might therefore be concluded that respiration does not have a pyramidal control and that the voluntary regulation of respiration is mediated by extrapyramidal pathways.

Pons and Medulla. ELECTRICAL STIMULATION. The respiratory responses to stimulation of the pons and medulla are greater and more discrete than are the responses to cortical stimulation. When specific small regions are stimulated, the patterns of breathing change in a manner dependent upon the site of the stimulus. Changes in rate, inspiratory apnea (apneusis), apnea at normal end expiration, and expiratory apnea are elicited by stimulation in different pontine and medullary areas.[31] Figure 481 shows the more or less discrete localization of the regions from which each of these effects may be produced. Earlier, less detailed work[7, 34] had yielded essentially similar results except for the localization of the regions causing expiratory apnea. It should be noted that stimulation of one side of the pons and medulla affects equally the respiratory muscles on both sides of the body. This finding, together with evidence from lesions,[36, 37] indicates extensive cross connections between the two sides of the brain stem and/or descent of impulses from one-half of the pons and medulla to musculature on both sides of the body.

SECTION AND ABLATION. The results of transection at various levels in the pons and medulla (Fig. 482) are quite different when the vagi are intact and when they are sectioned.

Transection with vagi intact. In an animal with the standard midcollicular decerebration, breathing is essentially indistinguishable from that in the intact animal. Thus, the

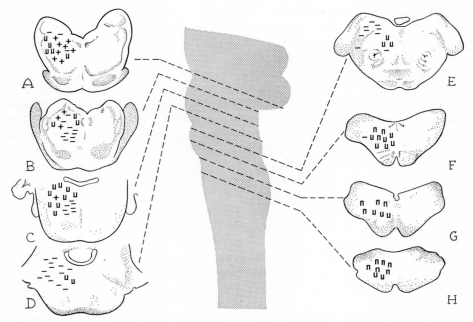

U = Inspiratory spasm   Π = Active expiration   — = Expiratory standstill
                         + = Expiratory acceleration

FIG. 481. Summary diagram showing the types of respiratory responses elicited by stimulating brain stem at various levels between the isthmus of the pons (*A*) and 2 mm. caudal to the obex (*H*). (After Ngai and Wang, *Amer. J. Physiol.*, 1957, *190*:343–349.)

influences on respiration of the cortical areas discussed above and of the temperature regulation centers in the hypothalamus (see Chap. 10) are not necessary for normal respiration. Transections in the pons do not markedly affect the pattern of breathing, although the rate is usually slowed. Transection in the rostral medulla,* however, may lead to marked changes in the breathing pattern,[4, 5, 19, 20, 48] which may be eupneic but is usually of a gasping type and may resemble Biot's breathing (brief periods of rapid breathing followed by pauses in expiration). Transection below a plane 2 mm. caudal to the rostral border of the medulla causes cessation of respiration.

Transection after section of vagi. When the above series of sections is made in an animal with both vagi cut or blocked, the effect of the pontine transections is very different. [4, 5, 19, 20, 24–28, 33–35, 40, 41] Although transection at the rostral border of the pons

* The medullopontine junction is defined here (after Wang) as a plane running from the acoustic stria dorsally to the caudal border of the trapezoid body on the ventral surface.

again produces little effect, transection slightly below this level causes dramatic changes. Initially rhythmic respiration gives way to sustained inspiration, or apneusis, which may last for minutes. This inspiratory spasm is usually followed by *apneustic* breathing. In this type of breathing, the inspiratory effort is strong and sustained, lasting for seconds or even minutes, and expiration consists only of a brief relaxation of the sustained inspiration. More caudal transections in the pons usually decrease the duration of the inspiratory phase and increase the duration of the expiratory phase. The effect on the inspiratory phase is the greater, so the net result is an increase in the mean respiratory rate. Thus the more caudal the lesion, the more nearly normal the rate and the duration of the inspiratory and expiratory phases.

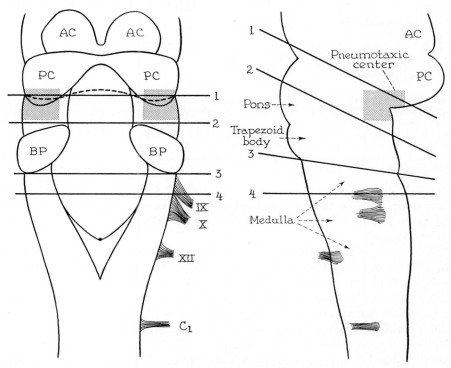

FIG. 482.   Diagram showing location of pneumotaxic center and critical levels of transection. *1*, Lower midbrain section; *2*, high pontine section; *3*, section at medullo-pontine junction as defined by Wang *et al.*; *4*, section 2 mm. caudal to rostral border. *AC*, Anterior colliculus; *PC*, posterior colliculus; *BP*, brachium pontis. (After Wang *et al.*, *Amer. J. Physiol.*, 1957, *190*:333-342.)

The results of transection through the rostral medulla are not appreciably different when the vagi are cut and when the vagi are intact, even though the Xth cranial nerve enters the medulla below the level of section.

Respiratory centers.   As a result of experiments depending on transection and other surgical techniques, a series of centers (actually subcenters) have been defined. The region in the anterior pons, destruction of which in combination with vagotomy leads to apneusis and apneustic respiration, is called the *pneumotaxic center*. From the transection experiments described above, this center clearly lies in the extreme rostral pons. Tang[44] has shown that bilateral ablation of a few cubic millimeters in the dorsolateral tegmentum of the pons leads to apneusis followed by apneustic breathing (Fig. 483). Unilateral lesions are ineffective. Subsequent workers[48] have found that somewhat larger bilateral lesions, placed slightly more medially, will also cause apneusis. All workers agree that midline lesions are ineffective. These differences in localization are very slight, a matter

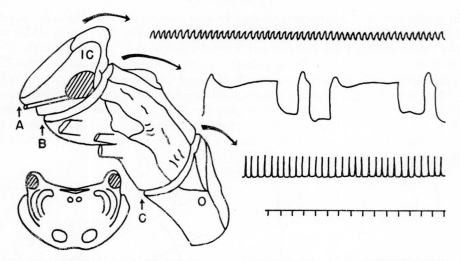

FIG. 483.   Diagram showing respiratory patterns of vagotomized cats after brain stem lesions. *A*, Midcollicular transection results in rhythmic breathing resembling normal pattern. *B*, Transection caudal to inferior colliculi results in hypertonic breathing pattern (apneustic breathing). Same pattern can be obtained by bilateral lesions of hatched area. Lower left diagram shows a cross section through critical hatched area ("pneumotaxic" center or area). *C*, Transection 3 to 5 mm. above obex results in atonic breathing pattern (gasping). *IC*, Inferior colliculus; *O*, obex. Time in 10 sec. intervals. (From Tang, *Amer. J. Physiol.*, 1953, *172*:645–652.)

of 1 or 2 mm., and may be only apparent owing to damage beyond the visible sites of the lesions; or it may be necessary to remove only a portion of each pneumotaxic center to produce apneusis.

The *apneustic center* is defined as those regions of the caudal two-thirds of the pons which, subsequent to section of the vagi and ablation of the pneumotaxic center, *support* apneusis and apneustic breathing. This center, as its name implies, provides an inspiratory drive. As more and more of it is eliminated, the inspiratory phase becomes shorter and shorter, or less apneustic. The apneustic center has not been localized to any particular pontine structure but apparently is part of the reticular facilitatory area.

The *medullary respiratory center* is often in error called simply "the respiratory center." Its exact localization and whether it is divided into an inspiratory and an expiratory center are matters of continuing investigation (see below).

ELECTRICAL RECORDING.   The techniques of stimulation and ablation have certain limitations. With ablation it is difficult to know the exact limits of the destruction of nervous tissue; the question whether the effects are those of destruction of the cell bodies or of interruption of nerve pathways passing through the area is also a problem. With electrical stimulation, it is difficult to know whether the elements being stimulated are a "center" or fibers passing to or issuing from it; with unipolar electrodes, the spread of current is an additional problem. Also, it is not possible to know to what degree the response is abnormal, owing to the nearly synchronous volleys excited by electrical stimulation.

By recording with microelectrodes, one can determine the activity of cells or fibers subjected to only minimal damage (Chap. 1). The respiratory system is particularly suitable for study by this technique, since the firing of at least some cells involved in respiratory movements is periodic at the respiratory rate. However, considerable care is required to minimize the false periodic firing which is related to brain movements induced by breathing and which may cause the electrode to move with respect to the neurons. This source of confusion was not always recognized in early experiments. The criterion most useful in eliminating such an artefact is the constancy of spike amplitude during the respiratory cycle.

Electrical activity of the pons.   Whether periodically firing cells exist in the pons has been a subject of controversy. However, at least in the decerebrate cat, it seems that there are pontine cells which fire trains of impulses with the same periodicity as respiration, although usually not in phase with either inspiration or expiration.[10, 43] Periodic firing in the pneumotaxic center isolated from incoming impulses has not been found,[9] and therefore this center does not seem to be the site of the rhythmic neural activity responsible for the respiratory rhythm in the absence of the vagus.

Electrical activity of the medulla.   The electrical activity related to respiration recorded from the medulla of decerebrate animals is more striking than that recorded from the pons.[13] Although a few active units may be found in other places, most of the activity is confined to the region near the level of the obex.[1, 14, 30, 47] As shown in Figure 484, potentials believed to be from cell bodies which fire during inspiration are recorded for the most part slightly rostral to the obex, whereas potentials from cell bodies firing during

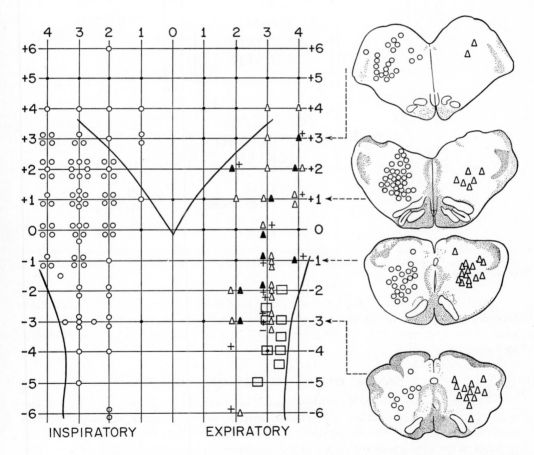

FIG. 484.   Points in medulla and cervical cord of cat which are active during respiration. *Left*, Points plotted along stereotaxic coordinates, in millimeters, rostral (+) and caudal (−) to obex; although separated here for clarity, inspiratory and expiratory points are present on both sides of midline. o, Inspiratory points; ▲, early expiratory points; △, late expiratory; + expiratory of undefined timing; □, sites of activity appearing to be from fibers. (After Haber *et al., Amer. J. Physiol.,* 1957, *190:*350–355, and Nelson, *J. Neurophysiol.,* 1959, *22:*590–598.)

Right, Sections at levels indicated by arrows to stereotaxic grid. o, Inspiratory points; △, expiratory points. (After Haber *et al., Amer. J. Physiol.,* 1957, *190:*350–355.)

expiration tend to occur slightly caudal to the obex. These neurons are not afferents of vagal origin, since the activity persists when the vagal inputs are blocked. As will be seen by comparing Figures 484 and 482, the extent and location of the areas yielding electrical activity differ distinctly from those of areas yielding respiratory responses to stimulation. Impulses periodic with respiration which disappear when the vagi are blocked are also found in the medulla. These impulses are recorded mainly in the same general region as the inspiratory neurons, i.e., somewhat rostral to the obex. This activity appears to originate in the region of the tractus solitarius. Periodic neuronal activity has also been recorded in the isolated medulla. This activity presumably reflects the inherent rhythmic ability of the medullary respiratory center.

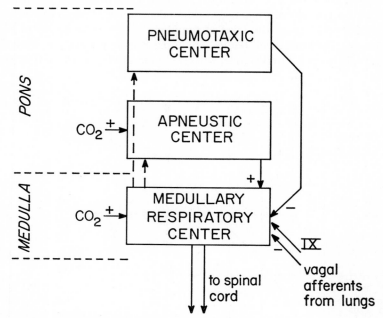

FIG. 485.   Schematic diagram of the central respiratory centers showing possible interconnections and the points at which CO_2 and impulses from the lungs impinge; + augmentative and − inhibitory to inspiratory discharge.

Activity of fibers from the inspiratory and expiratory cells has been traced from the medulla to the level of the second cervical segment.[28] The information from ablation, stimulation and recording can be incorporated in a schematic organization, as shown in Figure 485.

GENESIS OF THE RESPIRATORY RHYTHM

The experiments described above establish that the medullary portion of the respiratory center is capable of rhythmic activity which roughly resembles normal respiration. Section of the vagus nerve has little effect on this rhythm, which, in fact, endures in the absence of any neural input whatsoever (isolated medullary center). The initiation and maintenance of a rhythm can therefore be centrogenic; a model employing only two neurons will be described later.

Just above the medullary level is the apneustic center, which acts in conjunction with the medullary centers but which can exert an inspiratory drive that obscures rhythmic medullary activity in the absence of higher pontine centers and the vagal input. If the vagi are intact, rhythmic breathing is maintained. It may be inferred that the vagi operate through this apneustic center, although they enter the medulla farther down. As we shall see, at least two interpretations of the relation between the vagi and the apneustic center are possible: (i) At each breath the vagal impulses periodic with inspiration inhibit the inspiratory drive of the apneustic center; and (ii) the vagal impulses balance the inspiratory drive of the apneustic center at the medullary respiratory center, and the periodic nature of the vagal input is of secondary importance.

That the effect of vagal impulses is not solely a function of a waxing and waning of their bombardment of the respiratory centers is shown by the following experiment. Apneusis following anterior pontine section may be interrupted and a normal type of rhythmic respiration reinstated by steady stimulation of the vagus.[21, 45] This is done

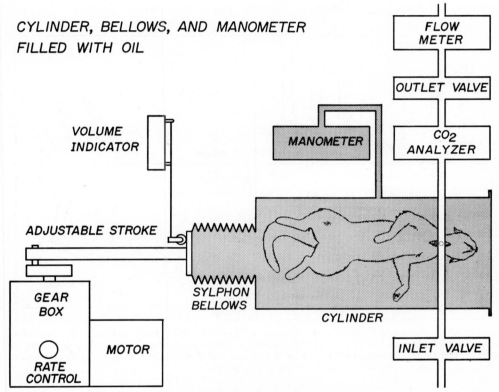

FIG. 486. An apparatus to measure pressure-volume relationships (impedance) of the respiratory system. (From A. C. Young, unpublished experiments.)

most physiologically by holding the lungs distended in the apparatus shown in Figure 486, thus evoking a continuous discharge from the stretch receptors in the lungs. Pressure measurements in the oil bath surrounding the animal reveal periodic respiratory efforts which are reasonably normal in rate and nature. When this vagal discharge is terminated by holding the lung at the end expiratory position, apneusis ensues. In passing it may be noted that chemical respiratory drives are also involved as a continuous and antagonistic respiratory drive. The amount of vagal discharge necessary to interrupt apneusis is determined by the pCO_2 of the blood; the higher the pCO_2, the greater the continuous vagal discharge necessary to reinstate rhythmic respiration.

The pneumotaxic center, like the vagus, opposes the apneustic center, since, in the absence of vagal input, the pneumotaxic center maintains the normal respiration of the decerebrate preparation. The ability of this center to promote rhythmic respiration is therefore clearly not due to periodic vagal impulses. Lumsden,[24, 25] as his choice of the term "pneumotaxic center" indicates, ascribed the rhythmicity of breathing to this pontine area. Pitts *et al.*[33, 34, 35] went further and ascribed respiratory rhythm to a breath-by-breath discharge of the pneumotaxic center. This was visualized as follows. As the "inspiratory center" discharged caudally to the respiratory muscles, it also discharged rostrally to the pneumotaxic center, which in turn discharged caudally to curb the inspiratory center discharge. Even within the reticular substance it is difficult to account for the time lapse in this hypothetical circuit. Moreover, Hoff and Breckenridge[4, 5, 19, 20] showed that the respiratory rhythm could be maintained by the medullary respiratory center separated from both the vagi and the pneumotaxic center.

Increasingly, the tendency is to think that respiratory rhythm is derived from the interplay of descending impulses and from the interaction between neurons. This view

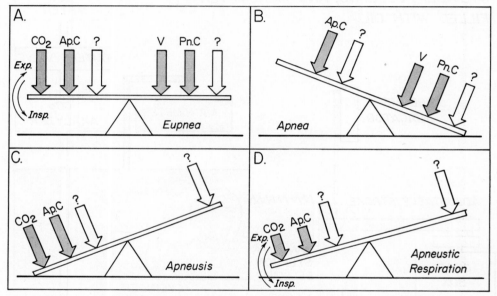

FIG. 487. Summary diagram of the summation of neural and chemical influences on respiration. *Ap.C* and *Pn.C*, Apneustic and pneumotaxic centers, respectively; *V*, vagal afferent impulses from the lungs. Forces to left of fulcrum tend to cause inspiration and those to right tend to inhibit respiration. Balance is the condition for oscillation (rhythmic breathing).

can be explained on two levels: (i) by appeal to simple analogy and (ii) by appeal to a knowledge of the factors which make for oscillation in electronic or other control systems.* An oversimplified model of a system which has some of the properties of the respiratory system is the familiar seesaw. Figure 487 illustrates this. As long as the "forces" exerted on the two ends of the seesaw are approximately balanced, a minimum amount of energy will keep the system oscillating. When, however, the "force" on one side is appreciably greater than that on the other, the amount of energy required to keep the system oscil-

---

* Analogies to the respiratory system can be found in spinal reflex action, although the neural levels are different.[38] The divided spinal cord tends to yield alternate flexion and extension (stepping), and a favorable condition for bilateral stepping is the concurrent and equal stimulation of homologous nerves on both sides of the body. When the spinal cord is connected with the brain stem, oscillatory phenomena disappear and the system is biased toward extension (decerebrate rigidity). When still higher levels (upper midbrain and hypothalamus) are included in the system, flexor and extensor reflex excitability are again more nearly balanced, and oscillating phenomena occur (e.g., effective walking occurs). The principles derived from a study of control systems have applicability beyond the respiratory system, and these applications are just commencing to be realized.

lating will be increased. Either the resulting movement will stop, or the swings will be centered at the heavy end.

Respiration Viewed as an Oscillatory System. The central neural mechanism controlling respiratory movements belongs to a class of systems, including many mechanical and electrical systems, capable of oscillation. It is helpful in understanding the respiratory system to consider rather generally the properties of a system which lead to a rhythmic output, i.e., to oscillation. Since neural systems must be mechanistic, there *must* be a broad similarity between them and non-neural oscillatory systems. Mathematicians and control systems engineers conceive of oscillating systems as falling into the following three classes.[29, 42, 46]

Type I. Linear systems. Consider a system with an input and an output. The system could be of any reasonable type—electrical, mechanical, chemical—or it could be a mixture of types. For example, the input could be mols of O_2 used per minute in an electrochemical reaction, and the output could be amperes of current flowing as a result of the chemical reaction. The system might be one in which the input and the output were of the same type, like the input and output voltage in an amplifier; or, the number of impulses per second in an afferent neural volley could be the input and the number of impulses per second in the resulting efferent discharge the output. If, in any of these systems, the output is directly proportional to the input, that system is called "linear." A large number of physical and chemical systems are linear or nearly so, and their properties have been very thoroughly studied and applied. For our purpose, a few properties of linear systems will be considered.

(i) Sinusoidal inputs always lead to sinusoidal outputs. In general, the outputs are not the same shape as the inputs for other shapes of waves.

(ii) To make an oscillator of a linear system it is necessary to "connect" the output (i.e., feed it back) to the input. The conditions for oscillation are: (a) the phase shift from input to output must be exactly zero or exactly an integral number of cycles and (b) the output must be greater than the input. If there is a frequency at which these conditions can be met, the system will oscillate with the sinusoidal wave at this frequency. Oscillators of this type are used to generate sinusoidal waves for radio and television audio frequency oscillators.

(iii) If the response of a linear system is known for all frequencies of the input, the properties of the system are completely known, and the output for any form of input can be calculated.

Type II. Nearly linear systems. The theory of linear systems may be extended to account for the properties of systems which are nearly linear. In these, the output may contain frequencies which are harmonics of the input signal; however, such harmonics become negligible as the input and output amplitudes of the system are reduced. An example of this kind of system is the standard phonograph amplifier.

Type III. Nonlinear systems. A third type of system is currently being studied extensively by mathematicians and engineers. It is "nonlinear" because its output is not proportional to its input. Systems of this third type may have properties which cannot be approximated by linear and nearly linear systems. In general, nonlinear systems do not produce sinusoidal waves when used as oscillators, and the oscillations do not become sinusoidal as amplitude is reduced. Nonlinear systems may also produce subharmonics or fractional-order subharmonics; that is, if an input is of a particular frequency, the output may be at a frequency of one-third, one-half, two-thirds, etc., of the input frequency. Further, the properties of nonlinear systems cannot be completely determined from knowledge of their response to any one kind of input. There is no unique general method of studying these systems; each must be approached with a variety of analytic and experimental techniques. Some nonlinear systems do have properties which cannot be obtained in linear or nearly linear systems with the same number of elements. Nonlinear systems are used in counting and scaling circuits, in sweep circuits in oscilloscopes and television sets, and in pulse generators and coincidence counters.

System Analysis of Breathing. In the above terms, the type of system involved in the neural control of breathing can be determined with experimental techniques already familar (Fig. 486). The volume of the lungs may be controlled in any desired manner in order to control vagal input to the respiratory centers in the brain stem. The output may be measured as changes in the pressure produced in the oil tank by the respiratory muscles. Alternatively, nerve impulses in the phrenic nerves can be recorded electrically. With the input from the vagus held constant, the chemical input may be controlled by varying the CO_2 level in the blood. Neural drive and chemical effects can thus be measured separately or in combination.

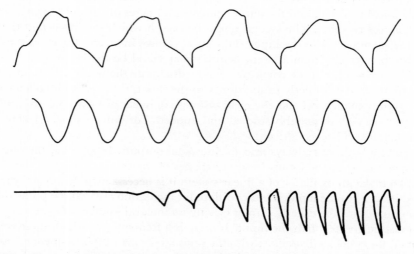

FIG. 488. Patterns of pressure changes produced in oil bath (see Fig. 486) by inspiratory activity of respiratory muscles. *Top,* Changes during imposed lung volume. *Center,* Sine wave for comparison with pressure curve above; note that it does not become sinusoidal even at low amplitude. (From A. C. Young, unpublished experiments.) *Bottom,* changes during recovery from apnea while lung volume was fixed.

When the animal is rendered apneic by hyperventilation, the output drops to zero, and the system does not oscillate until the CO_2 concentration increases. The pressure changes produced during recovery from apnea are shown in Figure 488. It is clear that the output is not sinusoidal even at the lowest amplitudes, and it thus appears that the respiratory system is nonlinear. A further check is obtained when the lung volume is changed sinusoidally and the resulting pressure output is recorded. The output, depending on the input frequency, may be either harmonically or subharmonically related to the input frequency; Figure 488 shows an example that is subharmonically related. We may therefore conclude that the respiratory system is nonlinear, having at least two nonoscillating positions, apnea and apneusis, and an oscillatory range between these limits in which normal eupneic breathing occurs.

NONLINEAR NEURAL MODEL. A possible neural model of a system which would oscillate is shown in Figure 489. This model is much oversimplified in that it shows only two neurons; the actual system would be composed of many connected neurons. The neurons in Figure 489 must have three properties. The first is similar to adaptation in sense organs. Thus, with a continuous bombardment by afferent impulses, the number of impulses from the neurons must at first be high and then gradually decline. Secondly,

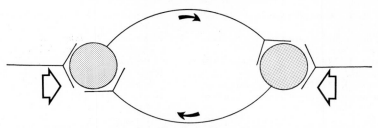

FIG. 489. Diagram of a simple two-neuron, oscillatory system giving properties described in text.

the number of efferent impulses per second at first must be actually higher than the number in the afferent volley (gain greater than unity). The third essential property is that at least one of the neurons must have a nonlinear relation between its output frequency and the frequency of the input to it. Both the first and second properties—"adaptation" and a gain greater than one—have been observed in interneurons in the spinal cord. The third condition is commonly encountered in the nervous system. When neurons with these properties are connected as shown in Figure 489, the system will give bursts of impulses, the interval of the bursts being determined by the "time constant" of the adaptation-like process and, to some extent, by the nonlinear properties of the cells. This situation can be simulated by an electric analogue and is, in fact, the well known multivibrator.

In such a system, if additional afferents synapse with the cells, a sufficiently strong continuous discharge will stop the oscillation of the system, in which case one of the cells will discharge continuously while the other cell is nearly quiescent. In the analogue, the corresponding effect is observable if the individual tubes in the multivibrator are biased with an impressed voltage. In general, systems of this nature have two or more stable positions and an intervening region of continuous oscillation. They also have the general properties listed in the discussion of nonlinear systems. These oscillating pairs of neurons could be in the medullary respiratory area and conform to the cells that fire during inspiration and expiration.

A more complete model would, of course, have to take into account interconnections between individual pairs of cells. Such interconnections are required to lock the oscillator together in order to gain a synchronous discharge like that occurring in breathing. The more complete model would also have to take into account additional interconnections between the neurons via pathways in the pons (apneustic and pneumotaxic center). These centers may act primarily as biases; there is evidence to the contrary, however, since electrical activity corresponding to the respiration has been recorded.[10, 43]

In relatively complex systems of this nature it is not usually possible to speak of the oscillation as resulting from connections between specific elements, but it may be a property of the interconnections of the relatively large number of cells. For this reason it is rather dangerous to think of the rhythmicity of such a system as residing in a particular region of the brain stem merely because this part is capable of oscillation when isolated from other parts. It is possible that a large number of other groups of cells would also oscillate if they could be isolated surgically.

REFERENCES

1. ADRIAN, E. D. *J. Physiol.*, 1933, *79:*322–358.
2. AVIADO, D. M., JR., LI, T. H., KALOW, W., SCHMIDT, C. F., TURNBULL, G. L., PESKIN, G. W., HESS, M. E. and WEISS, A. J. *Amer. J. Physiol.*, 1951, *165:*261–277.
3. VON BAUMGARTEN, R. and KANZOW, E. *Arch. ital. Biol.*, 1958, *96:*361–373.
4. BRECKENRIDGE, C. G. and HOFF, H. E. *Amer. J. Physiol.*, 1950, *160:*385–394.
5. BRECKENRIDGE, C. G., HOFF, H. E. and

SMITH, H. T. *Amer. J. Physiol.*, 1950, *162:* 74–79.

6. BRONK, D. W. and FERGUSON, L. K. *Amer. J. Physiol.*, 1935, *110:*700–707.

7. BROOKHART, J. M. *Amer. J. Physiol.*, 1940, *129:*709–723.

8. CAMPBELL, E. J. M. *The respiratory muscles and the mechanics of breathing*. Chicago, Yearbook Publishers, Inc., 1958, xvi, 131 pp.

9. COHEN, M. I. *Amer. J. Physiol.*, 1959, *195:* 23–27.

10. COHEN, M. K. and WANG, S. C. *J. Neurophysiol.*, 1959, *22:*33–50.

11. COMROE, J. H. *Amer. J. Physiol.*, 1939, *127:* 176–191.

12. COMROE, J. H. and SCHMIDT, C. F. *Amer. J. Physiol.*, 1938, *121:*75–97.

13. GESELL, R., BRICKER, J. and MAGEE, C. *Amer. J. Physiol.*, 1936, *117:*423–452.

14. HABER, E., KOHN, K., NGAI, S. H., HOLODAY, D. A. and WANG, S. C. *Amer. J. Physiol.*, 1957, *190:*350–355.

15. HARRIS, A. S. *Amer. J. Physiol.*, 1945, *143:* 140–147.

16. HERING, E. and BREUER, J. *S. B. Akad. wiss. Wien*, 1868, *57:*672–677; *58:*909–.

17. HESS, W. R. *Pflüg. Arch. ges. Physiol.*, 1936, *237:*24–39.

18. HESS, W. R. and WYSS, O. A. M. *Pflüg. Arch. ges. Physiol.*, 1936, *237:*761–770.

19. HOFF, H. E. and BRECKENRIDGE, C. G. *Amer. J. Physiol.*, 1949, *158:*157–172.

20. HOFF, H. E., BRECKENRIDGE, C. G. and CUNNINGHAM, J. E. *Amer. J. Physiol.*, 1950, *160:*485–489.

21. KERR, D. I. B., DUNLOP, C. W., BEST, E. D. and MULLNER, J. A. *Amer. J. Physiol.*, 1954, *176:*508–512.

22. KNOWLTON, G. C. and LARRABEE, M. G. *Amer. J. Physiol.*, 1946, *147:*100–114.

23. LARRABEE, M. G. and KNOWLTON, G. C. *Amer. J. Physiol.*, 1946, *147:*90–99.

24. LUMSDEN, T. *J. Physiol.*, 1923, *57:*153–160.

25. LUMSDEN, T. *J. Physiol.*, 1923, *57:*354–367.

26. MARCKWALD, M. *Z. Biol.*, 1887, *23:*149–283.

27. MARCKWALD, M. *The movements of respiration and their innervation in the rabbit*. Trans. by HAIG, T. A., London, Blackie & Son, 1888.

28. MARCKWALD, M. and KRONECKER, H. *Arch. Anat. Physiol. wiss. Med.*, 1880, 441–446.

29. MINORSKY, N. *Introduction to non-linear mechanics*. Ann Arbor, Mich., J. W. Edwards, 1947.

30. NELSON, J. R. *J. Neurophysiol.*, 1959, *22:*590–598.

31. NGAI, S. H. and WANG, S. C. *Amer. J. Physiol.*, 1957, *190:*343–349.

32. PAINTAL, A. S. *J. Physiol.*, 1953, *121:*341–359.

33. PITTS, R. F., MAGOUN, H. W. and RANSON, S. W. *Amer. J. Physiol.*, 1939, *126:*673–688.

34. PITTS, R. F., MAGOUN, H. W. and RANSON, S. W. *Amer. J. Physiol.*, 1939, *126:*689–701.

35. PITTS, R. F., MAGOUN, H. W. and RANSON, S. W. *Amer. J. Physiol.*, 1939, *127:*654–670.

36. SCHIFF, J. M. *Lehrbuch der Physiologie des Menschen*. Lahr, Schaufenburg, 1858–59.

37. SCHIFF, J. M. MORITZ SCHIFF'S *Gesammelte Beitrage zur Physiologie*. Lausanne, B. Benda, 1894, 4 vols. (see vol. 1).

38. SHERRINGTON, C. S. *J. Physiol.*, 1913, *47:* 196–214.

39. SPENCER, W. G. *Phil. Trans.*, 1894, *B185:* 609–657.

40. STELLA, G. *J. Physiol.*, 1938, *93:*263–275.

41. STELLA, G. *J. Physiol.*, 1939, *95:*365–372.

42. STOKER, J. J. *Nonlinear vibrations in mechanical and electrical systems*. New York, Interscience Publishers, 1950, xix, 273 pp.

43. TAKAGI, K. and NAKAYAMA, T. *Science*, 1958, *128:*1206.

44. TANG, P. C. *Amer. J. Physiol.*, 1953, *172:* 645–652.

45. TANG, P. C. and YOUNG, A. C. *Fed. Proc.*, 1956, *15:*184.

46. TRUXAL, J. G. *Automatic feedback control system synthesis*. New York, McGraw-Hill, 1955, xiii, 675 pp.

47. WALDRING, S. and DIRKEN, M. N. J. *J. Neurophysiol.*, 1951, *14:*227–242.

48. WANG, S. C., NGAI, S. H. and FRUMIN, M. J. *Amer. J. Physiol.*, 1957, *190:*333–342.

49. WIDDICOMBE, J. G. *J. Physiol.*, 1954, *123:*55–70.

50. WIDDICOMBE, J. G. *J. Physiol.*, 1954, *123:*71–104.

Regulation of Respiration*

To separate the chemical from the neural regulation of respiration is in a very real sense nonphysiologic and artificial. The three factors that most importantly regulate respiration are the chemical composition of the blood, the hierarchy of centers within the nervous system, and the array of afferent impulses which impinge upon these centers. It is a fluctuating control, in which now one and then another factor may be the paramount determinant of the pattern of the moment. Von Euler and Söderberg[19] remark on the relative electrical "silence" of the deafferented medulla, but if the CO_2 content of the air mixture by which the animal is ventilated is raised to 6.5 per cent, typical respiratory potentials appear. In other circumstances, an anoxic medulla may be driven by stimulation of chemoreceptors, in default of which apnea supervenes. The decerebrate dog given morphine breathes because of a supramedullary drive; if the pons is removed, breathing stops.

CHEMICAL REGULATION OF BREATHING

Carbon Dioxide. Recognition of the preponderant role that CO_2 plays in the day-by-day regulation of respiration emerged from the studies of Haldane and his school, whose work still remains a great landmark in the history of the chemical control of ventilation. Haldane[9] reviewed the evidence pointing to these conclusions:

(i) In human respiratory experiments, breathing became noticeably increased when the proportion of CO_2 in the air rose to about 3 per cent and the proportion of O_2 fell to about 17 per cent; breathing was very markedly augmented when CO_2 reached 6 per cent. When the experiment was repeated with the absorption of CO_2 by soda lime there was no noticeable difference in breathing until the O_2 fell below about 14 per cent. When, finally, the CO_2 absorber was removed but O_2 was added so that O_2 content remained abnormally high throughout, hyperpnea developed just as when ordinary air was employed. In other similar studies it was found that the distressed breathing in acute rebreathing trials results almost entirely from the accumulation of CO_2, whereas with low concentrations of O_2 consciousness could be lost suddenly without prodromal respiratory distress.

(ii) The concentration of CO_2 in alveolar air, which within broad limits reflects the concentration of CO_2 in arterial blood, is remarkably constant in any individual over a wide span of time and activity and is maintained so until the O_2 concentration in the inspired air falls to about 12 to 13 per cent and the alveolar O_2 falls to 8 per cent. At such time alveolar CO_2 begins to diminish.

* Written for 17th edition by H. E. Hoff and C. G. Breckenridge; edited by T. C. Ruch.

(iii) When, however, the alveolar CO_2 concentration rises as CO_2 is added to the inspired air, ventilation promptly increases. A minute increase (about 0.25 per cent) in the alveolar CO_2 leads to a 100 per cent increase in breathing.

(iv) Conversely, lowering the alveolar CO_2 content by voluntary hyperventilation produces apnea. The ability to hold the breath is also increased by preliminary hyperventilation and diminished by breathing air to which CO_2 has been added.

(v) The increased production of CO_2 during exercise is associated with an elevation of alveolar CO_2 and an increased ventilation, although with more energetic exercise the CO_2 content begins to fall. (While this is a common reaction, it does not occur in all individuals.)

From these observations, Haldane concluded that the respiratory system seems to be governed more by the necessity for getting rid of CO_2 than by a need for taking in

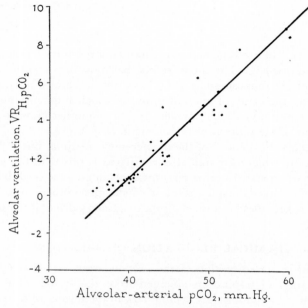

FIG. 490.   Alveolar ventilation in multiples of normal resting value as function of alveolar-arterial pCO_2 in CO_2 inhalation experiments. Plotted points represent average values for 10 subjects in 200 individual determinations. (From Gray, *Pulmonary ventilation and its physiological regulation*. Springfield, Ill., Charles C Thomas, 1949.)

O_2, and that the chemical control of breathing focuses on the homeostasis of alveolar pCO_2. The basic essentials of this relationship are illustrated in Figure 490, in which ventilation, expressed in multiples of the normal value for alveolar ventilation (total ventilation minus dead space ventilation), is plotted against the partial pressure of alveolar (and hence arterial) CO_2. The subscript H,pCO_2 is used to indicate, as will be discussed later, that CO_2 in the blood has both a direct effect on breathing and an indirect effect via its influence on the hydrogen ion concentration.

The increase in ventilation when CO_2 is inhaled is compensatory, tending to mitigate the rise in alveolar pCO_2 that would otherwise occur. Thus, in an experiment Haldane conducted on himself, breathing 3.8 per cent CO_2 increased ventilation 258 per cent while the CO_2 concentration in alveolar air rose only from 5.62 to 5.97 per cent. Breathing 5.28 per cent CO_2 increased ventilation 447 per cent while the alveolar CO_2 rose to 6.55 per cent. Without such an increase in ventilation, arterial pCO_2 would begin to approach levels which have harmful central effects. [An alveolar air concentra-

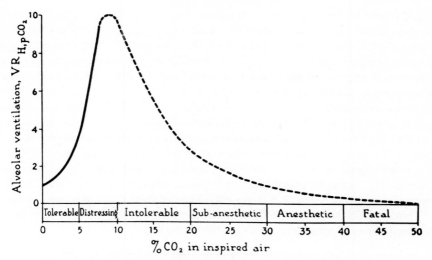

FIG. 491.   Ventilatory response as function of percentage of CO_2 inspired. (From Gray, *Pulmonary ventilation and its physiological regulation*. Springfield, Ill., Charles C Thomas, 1949.)

tion of 5.62 per cent corresponds to a pCO_2 of 43 mm. Hg. In the presence of 3.8 per cent CO_2 (pCO_2 30 mm. Hg) in the inspired air, the alveolar pCO_2 would rise to 43 + 30, or 73 mm. Hg, corresponding to an alveolar CO_2 of over 9 per cent, if ventilation were not increased.] The peak of the hyperpneic response to increased concentrations of CO_2 in the inspired air is reached in acute experiments at close to 9 per cent; after this, central depression begins to reduce the respiratory response (Fig. 491), and higher levels become intolerable—anesthetic and fatal.

In the past it was a common practice to use 5 per cent CO_2 and 95 per cent oxygen in the resuscitation of asphyxiated persons. In most instances the use of CO_2 is unwarranted. Because the patient's arterial and alveolar CO_2 pressures are far above normal owing to the suspension of breathing, the addition of 5 per cent CO_2 to the inspired gas increases the hypercapnia and may cause the arterial CO_2 to increase to depressant, anesthetic or even lethal levels.

Effects of diminished CO_2 pressure.   If the pCO_2 in alveolar air and the arterial blood is reduced slightly below the normal value of 40 mm. Hg by voluntary hyperventilation, apnea of brief duration results when the voluntary effort is suspended. The greater the reduction in pCO_2, the longer the apnea. By breathing as deeply and as rapidly as possible, one can lower the alveolar CO_2 pressure by as much as 20 to 30 mm. Hg to a level causing apnea lasting several minutes. Furthermore, when spontaneous breathing returns, it is frequently periodic, as shown in Figure 492. The periodicity of the succeeding respiration is conventionally attributed to fluctuations in the alveolar pO_2 and pCO_2 during the period of recovery. These fluctuations occur as illustrated in Figure 493. The alveolar pO_2 falls precipitously during the first period of apnea and rises thereafter

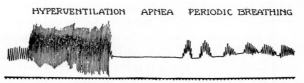

FIG. 492.   Apnea of two minutes' duration following a two-minute period of voluntary hyperventilation. Apnea was succeeded by periodic breathing. (From Douglas and Haldane, *J. Physiol.*, 1909, *38:*401.)

with each period of breathing, only to fall during the apnea. Each period of apnea is supposed to initiate the breathing cycle, which in turn produces apnea by restoring a more normal pO_2 and by lowering the pCO_2. It is apparent that the alveolar gas levels could be the result rather than the cause of periodic breathing. Servocontrol analysis suggests several avenues of approach in determining the cause of the oscillation represented by periodic breathing (Chap. 37).

Variation in sensitivity to CO_2; CO_2 threshold. In studies on two normal subjects exposed to acute hypoxia, Nielson and Smith[16] observed certain most significant alterations in the curve relating ventilation to the alveolar pCO_2 as this was raised by adding CO_2 to the inspired gas mixtures. These changes demonstrated that CO_2 does not act as a respiratory stimulant at all levels, but only when it rises to a threshold level near 30 mm. Hg. Since the pCO_2 in acute hypoxia may fall below this level, it is obvious that hypoxic breathing when CO_2 is not added to the inspired air has no element of CO_2 drive. This explains why sudden flooding of the system with O_2, or other procedures which annul chemoreceptor drive, may result in apnea.

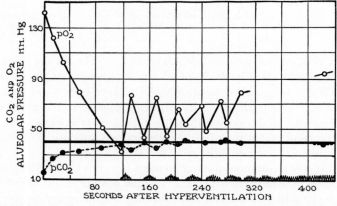

FIG. 493. Variations in alveolar oxygen and carbon dioxide pressures following hyperventilation, which account for the apnea and periodic breathing. Note that alveolar oxygen pressure was high and carbon dioxide pressure low immediately after overbreathing. Carbon dioxide pressure rose, but, before it returned to normal (*heavy horizontal line*), oxygen pressure fell sufficiently to stimulate respiration reflexly. First series of respirations then occurred (see bottom of chart), elevating oxygen pressure and lowering carbon dioxide pressure. (From Douglas and Haldane, *J. Physiol.*, 1909, *38:*401.)

In chronic exposure to atmospheres deficient in O_2, apnea does not occur, and arrest of chemoreceptor drive has little influence on ventilation. The lowered ranges of pCO_2 found in chronic hypoxic breathing do alter ventilation. Obviously the threshold to CO_2 has fallen, so that a pCO_2 which is ineffective in acute hypoxia becomes able to direct breathing in the chronic state. Lowering the pCO_2 by prolonged hyperventilation in a respirator or by prolonged ingestion of ammonium chloride also results in a lowering of threshold to CO_2; further, it demonstrates a general tendency of the respiratory system to adjust in time to reductions in pCO_2 and thus to maintain the effectiveness of the CO_2 regulation of breathing. The respiratory centers may also adjust to chronic effects of abnormally high CO_2 by reducing their responsiveness, but this has not been proved. In pulmonary emphysema the level of CO_2 in the arterial blood is chronically elevated because the pulmonary ventilation is inefficient. The respiratory centers become adjusted to this high pCO_2 so that CO_2 no longer dominates the chemical control of breathing, which is taken over by hypoxic drive via the chemoreceptors.[1] Administration of O_2 designed to alleviate the hypoxia may weaken ventilation by diminishing the hypoxic drive, and thus may lead to an additional increase in CO_2 and to an actual depression of respiration. Artificial respiration can at times break the vicious circle, bring the pCO_2 back to normal ranges, and restore a more normal pattern of respiratory control.

Mode of action of CO_2. There is a growing realization that CO_2 participates in cellular metabolism as a molecular individual and not simply as a regulator of hydrogen ion concentration. It is known that CO_2 can be metabolized by cells. In low concentrations it increases the rate of O_2 consumption in certain tissues and the rate of glycolysis in tissue slices of the medulla. Lorente de Nó emphasized that CO_2 is essential to the normal behavior of nervous tissue: "It can be said that the presence of 5 per cent CO_2 increases the ability of the nerve to perform work, undoubtedly because the enzymatic mechanisms

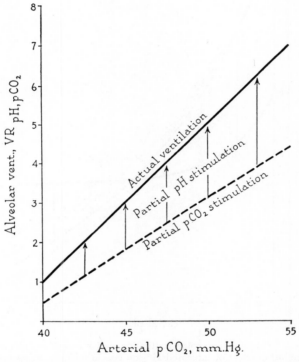

FIG. 494.   Analysis of partial stimulating effects on alveolar ventilation of increased pCO_2 and increased H^+ ion concentration in experiments in which CO_2 was inhaled. (From Gray, *Pulmonary ventilation and its physiological regulation.* Springfield, Ill., Charles C Thomas, 1949.)

of nerve utilize stores of metabolic energy more readily or more effectively in the presence than in the absence of a certain concentration of CO_2." [15]

Hydrogen Ion Concentration.   In a simple buffer system the concentration of H^+ depends upon the relative concentrations of the free acid and its salt, as expressed in the familiar Henderson-Hasselbalch formula: $pH = (BHCO_3/H_2CO_3) + pK$. In such a system increase in pCO_2 would increase the value of H_2CO_3 and thus lower pH. Therefore an increase in alveolar pCO_2 will diminish pH and cause an acidemia; whereas diminution of the alveolar pCO_2, as by voluntary or reflex hyperventilation, will increase the pH and cause alkalemia.

This fact and the observation that injection of acid stimulates respiration raise the question whether CO_2 operates via a change in pH—either in the arterial blood or within the chemosensitive cells of the medulla. When, however, the ventilatory effects of equal increases in acidity produced by CO_2 inhalation and by metabolic acidity are compared, the increase produced by CO_2 far exceeds that evoked by acidity. For this and other reasons Gray[7] takes the pragmatic view that CO_2 and acidity stimulate respiration individually, as separate species, and that their effects are additive algebraically. When treated mathematically, this view gives good predictive value. The response to CO_2 inhalation, for example, represents the addition of two factors—the increased CO_2 and the consequently increased acidity—both of which operate in the direction of increasing ventilation.

Figure 494 illustrates how the increased ventilation (Fig. 491) is the composite of these two factors. In metabolic acidity (Fig. 495, *left*), the factors act oppositely: acidity

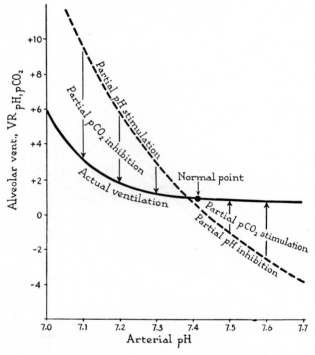

FIG. 495.   Analysis of resultant alveolar ventilation under conditions of metabolic acidosis and alkalosis. Partial stimulating effect of increased H^+ ion concentration and partial inhibiting effect of decreased H^+ ion concentration are incompletely balanced by opposite partial effects of changes in pCO_2. (From Gray, *Pulmonary ventilation and its physiological regulation.* Springfield, Ill., Charles C Thomas, 1949.)

stimulates respiration, pCO_2 diminishes because ventilation increases, and the CO_2 drive is consequently lessened. The net ventilation is thus less than that induced by pH alone. Oppositely (Fig. 495, *right*), in metabolic alkalosis the influence of an increased pH per se would diminish ventilation, but CO_2 accumulates, increases the CO_2 stimulation and maintains ventilation. The hyperpnea produced by a fall in pH is a compensatory device tending to mitigate the rise in pH which occurs because reduction of pCO_2 increases the proportion $BHCO_3/H_2CO_3$ as a result of the reduction in H_2CO_3. The changes that occur in breathing when pH is altered, together with the consequent alteration in pCO_2, which in turn mitigates the primary pH changes, thus serve as an important means of maintaining the homeostasis of pH within the body.

The site of the action of pH as a respiratory stimulant is uncertain. There may be an element of peripheral chemoreceptor stimulation at a high threshold, but the preponderant effect is thought to be central, for it continues after deafferentation of peripheral chemoreceptors.

Oxygen. The almost exclusive interest in the regulation of ventilation by CO_2 was modified when Heymans and his associates demonstrated the respiratory and circulatory reflexes from the region of the carotid sinus. It is now recognized that *chemoreceptors* as well as *pressoreceptors* lie at the bifurcation of the common carotid arteries and also at the arch of the aorta. Both have respiratory effects, but the *chemoreceptors* are particularly significant because they are sensitive to O_2 tension as well as CO_2 tension in the blood perfusing them; they provide, reflexly, for the regulation of respiration by pO_2, a chemical control which the respiratory center lacks.

The carotid and aortic glomera are the chemoreceptor organs. The carotid glomera are small epithelioid bodies attached to the occipital arteries close to their points of

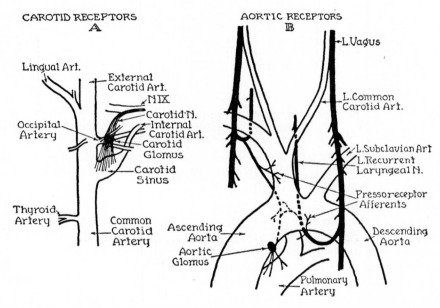

FIG. 496.   Diagrammatic representation of location and neural connections of carotid and aortic chemoreceptors and pressoreceptors (dog). (From Comroe, *Amer. J. Physiol.*, 1939, *127*:176–191; and Comroe and Schmidt, *Amer. J. Physiol.*, 1938, *121*:75–97.)

origin from the external carotid arteries. The aortic glomus is single and lies within the concavity of the arch of the aorta. The relations of the glomera in the dog are shown diagrammatically in Figure 496, taken from the work of Comroe[2] and Comroe and Schmidt.[3] According to DeCastro[6] and Nonidez,[17] the glomera are formed of cords of rounded epithelioid receptor cells separated from the blood stream only by the thin walls of sinusoidal capillaries. Afferent nerve fibers are found on and between the receptor cells. These afferents emerge from the carotid glomera to form the carotid nerves (nerves of Hering) that join the glossopharyngeal nerves which enter the medulla oblongata. The afferents from the single aortic glomus enter both the right and left depressor nerves (nerves of Cyon) which extend centrally in the vagus trunks.

Chemoreceptor Reflexes from Carotid and Aortic Glomera.   Heymans and his associates studied the respiratory reflexes produced by perfusing the carotid glomera with Ringer's solution which had been altered in composition in various ways. The perfusion pressure was kept constant so that pressoreceptor reflexes would not confuse the results. The brain of the animal was adequately supplied with blood through the intact vertebral

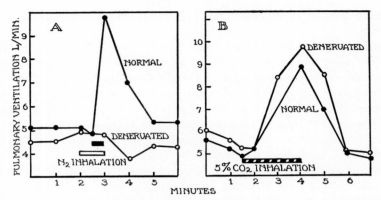

arteries. It was found that a decrease in O_2 pressure, an increase in CO_2 pressure and an increase in the acidity of the perfusion fluid caused marked reflex stimulation of breathing.

Figure 497 illustrates a complementary experiment, comparing the responses of animals to anoxia and hypercapnia before and after denervation of the carotid glomera. After denervation, ventilation actually diminishes in response to hypoxia instead of increasing as expected. This finding supports the view that the stimulation of breathing by anoxia is largely reflex; centrally, anoxia is only depressing. By contrast the response to inspiration of 5 per cent CO_2 is not significantly different in the normal and in the chemoreceptor denervated animal (Fig. 497*B*). Nevertheless there may be an element of peripheral response to pH or pCO_2, as indicated by Figure 498. Since the response to these factors persists after denervation of chemoreceptors, the peripheral response is dispensable because pH and pCO_2 have direct central effects. What quantitative contribution peripheral sensitivity to pCO_2 and pH makes in the ensemble of respiratory regulation has not been determined.

Role of Chemoreceptor Reflexes in Respiratory Regulation. Figure 499 shows that the chemoreceptors of the cat, at least, discharge when the animal is breathing 20 per cent O_2, as in air. If this is also true of other species, it suggests that the respiratory center normally receives a certain amount of chemoreceptor drive. Consistent with this view is the observation that, when normal dogs are given pure O_2 to breathe, a moderate reduction in ventilation occurs, presumably representing the subtraction of the chemo-

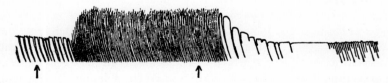

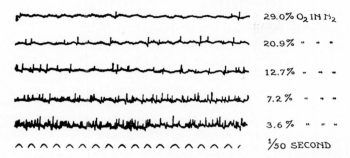

FIG. 499.   Impulses from chemoreceptors of carotid glomus (cat) during artificial overventilation with gas mixtures in which O$_2$ content was progressively reduced. Note that impulses were discharged even when gas contained more O$_2$ (29.0 per cent) than air does and that discharge progressively increased as O$_2$ content was lowered. (From von Euler *et al.*, *Skand. Arch. Physiol.*, 1940, *83:*132–152.)

receptor contribution to respiratory drive. A more marked reduction takes place when newborn and, particularly, premature infants are given 100 per cent O$_2$, and it has been concluded that infants normally have an active chemoreflex drive.[5] Adults, however, do not respond in this manner; if anything, ventilation increases slightly. There seems to be a definite threshold for the appearance of anoxic hyperventilation in both man and dogs at approximately the point where Haldane placed it—the equivalent of 12 to 13 per cent O$_2$.

The increase in pulmonary ventilation caused by *chronic* anoxia is not great. As can be seen in Figure 500, at the limit of tolerance alveolar ventilation is increased only 75 per cent. (Acutely, much higher levels are reached temporarily.) It is apparent that the anoxic drive is quickly counteracted by reduction in the centrogenic drive produced by the reduction in pCO$_2$ and acidity resulting from the anoxic hyperventilation. Gray has been able to calculate a curve (*broken line*, Fig. 501) which represents the influence on ventilation of arterial pO$_2$ alone. With high pO$_2$ (at the right of the curve) there is very little chemoreceptor drive, and breathing is maintained by the presence of CO$_2$ and *p*H drives. At the other end of the curve, ventilation as shown in the solid line is, on the contrary, limited by the reduction of pCO$_2$ and the rise in *p*H. Here the drive is exclusively chemoreceptor. At extreme limits of anoxia breathing is further limited by

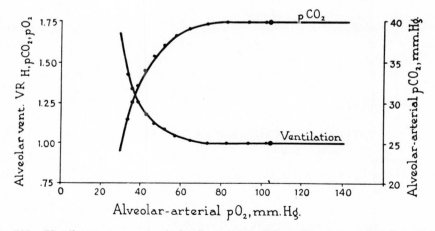

FIG. 500.   Ventilatory response and alveolar-arterial pCO$_2$ as functions of alveolar-arterial pO$_2$ in acute exposure to anoxia of altitude. (From Gray, *Pulmonary ventilation and its physiological regulation.* Springfield, Ill., Charles C Thomas, 1949.)

rapidly progressing anoxic depression of the center; despite the high level of chemoreceptor bombardment, ventilation will ultimately fail.

It has been implicit in the preceding paragraphs that the chemoreceptor response
to anoxia is initiated by a decline in the *partial pressure* of O_2 in arterial blood and not
by its *content*. This means that the protection against anoxia afforded by the peripheral
chemoreceptor mechanism is of use only when the anoxia results from a lowered tension
of O_2 and not when the O_2 carrying power of the blood is lowered without change in
tension. The local needs of the cells of the carotid and aortic glomera can be satisfied
by even the small amount of O_2 carried in simple solution in blood, provided the tension
is normal. A typical example of the latter circumstance is afforded by carbon monoxide
poisoning. The compound of carbon monoxide and hemoglobin can so preoccupy the
O_2 transport system that tissue anoxia threatens because the volume of O_2 supplied to

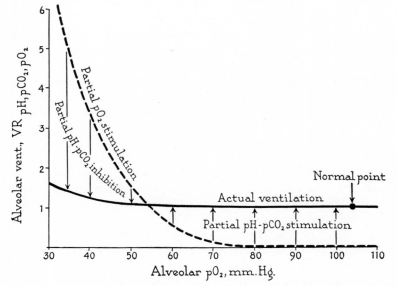

FIG. 501.   Analysis of resultant alveolar ventilation under conditions of anoxia in which a partial
stimulating effect of low pO_2 is incompletely balanced by a partial inhibiting effect of low pCO_2. (From
Gray, *Pulmonary ventilation and its physiological regulation*. Springfield, Ill., Charles C Thomas, 1949.)

the tissues is inadequate. Breathing is not stimulated because the pO_2 does not fall.
Anemia, methemoglobinemia and peripheral circulatory failure are other examples.
In the last-named condition, however, peripheral blood flow through the carotid and
aortic glomera may become so slow that the normal metabolic demands of the chemosensitive receptor cells, small as they are, are no longer adequately supplied, and chemoreceptor firing will begin because of local anoxia.

STIMULATION OF RESPIRATION IN EXERCISE

The hyperpnea of exercise serves as an example of the manner in which many
factors can combine to regulate the ultimate discharge of the medullary respiratory
centers.

"The outstanding feature of the hyperpnea of exercise is its precise adjustment to the metabolic
requirements of the organism. In moderate exercise, ventilation is directly proportional to oxygen
consumption so that a constant ventilatory equivalent (i.e., ventilation/100 cc. of oxygen consumed)
is maintained. In severe exercise with oxygen consumptions above 2.0 to 2.5 l/minute, ventilation
increases more rapidly than metabolism and the ventilatory equivalent rises."[8]

This relation is shown graphically in the right of Figure 502. It will be noted that if the ventilation and the work produced are graphed against the O_2 consumed, parallel lines result over a wide range. Some of the factors which might account for the increased rate and depth of respiration during muscular exercise are shown in the left half of Figure 502.

During exercise requiring up to 1 liter O_2 per minute, the alveolar pCO_2 increases, and this factor by itself can account for much of the increased ventilation during exercise. At this rate, anoxia and the production of acid or other metabolites need not be invoked. Above work rates involving an O_2 consumption of 1 liter per minute, alveolar tension falls steadily. This chemoreceptive drive, far from causing the hyperpnea of exercise,

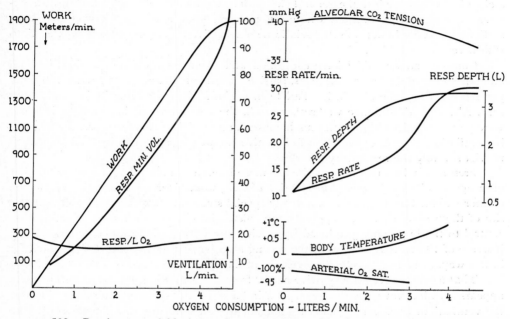

FIG. 502.   Respiratory variables in response to exercise on a bicycle ergometer. All curves obtained from same experiments on normal men and plotted against liters of O_2 consumption per minute. (Data from Christensen, *Arbeitsphysiol.*, 1931–32, *5*:463; after Schmidt in Bard, ed., *Medical physiology*, St. Louis, C. V. Mosby Co., 1956.)

is actually reduced by the increased ventilation caused by some more powerful agent. The fall in O_2 saturation of arterial blood and the increased body temperature are in the right direction, but are quantitatively insufficient to account for the increased ventilation. The hydrogen ion concentration of the blood does not increase in moderate exercise, but such an increase may be a factor in the steep rise in ventilation as work approaches its maximum.

Since the known chemical respiratory drives are quantitatively insufficient to account for the hyperpnea of exercise, specific chemical or neural drives have been sought. Specific stimulating substances from exercising muscles have not been demonstrated; specific neural drives can be visualized as originating in the cerebral cortex, the exercising muscles (and joints), or both. Krogh and Lindhard,[14] as early as 1913, realized that CO_2 production or O_2 lack could not explain the respiratory adjustments to moderate exercise. They concluded that the hyperpnea of exercise represents a facilitation of the respiratory centers by the cerebral cortex as a part of the voluntary movement. Since 1913, neurophysiologists have discovered a variety of cortical influences on respiration which indicate that the requisite neural apparatus exists (see Chap. 37).

While cortically initiated hyperpnea may explain the tendency to overventilate at the onset of exercise, it has not been proved that the cerebral cortex can *quantitatively* control ventilation so that it accurately parallels work or oxygen consumption; subjective estimates of our own pulmonary ventilation are quite inaccurate.

A search for a sensory return from the exercising limb began with the observation by Harrison *et. al.*[10] that movements of the hand are accompanied by an increase in ventilation, even when the circulation is completely cut off by a pressure cuff so that metabolic products from the active muscles cannot reach the respiratory center. These investigators suggested that peripheral receptors are stimulated by movement, initiating impulses that reflexly stimulate breathing. To exclude all possibility of the liberation of a chemical substance into the general circulation, Harrison *et al.* repeated their observations on anesthetized animals whose leg muscles, bone and blood vessels had been sectioned, leaving intact only the sciatic nerve. Passive movement of this isolated limb still increased breathing.

Comroe and Schmidt[4] have confirmed and extended these observations in both animals and man. In humans subjects, passive movement of one leg at the knee 100 times per minute when the circulation had been occluded increased ventilation by 40 per cent. Although this change was rather small, the movements which brought it about were passive and involved small muscle masses and few joints. Furthermore, the increase in ventilation must have caused a fall in alveolar pCO_2 and a rise in pH sufficient to restrict severely the respiratory response.

Presumably in muscular exercise the more intense stimulation of a greater number of receptors, plus the increased production of CO_2, would increase ventilation to a much greater extent. Comroe and Schmidt lay special stress on joint receptors as the major site of these reflexes. Otis,[18] applying the calculations of Gray's theory of respiratory control to the hyperpnea produced by passive movements of the limbs, found that an increase of 100 to 150 per cent of the resting alveolar ventilation can be accounted for in this way, although "passive" movement of the limbs also increases metabolism.

That a sensory respiratory drive comes from the exercising musculoskeletal system appears certain. However, the hyperpnea induced by this drive no more than doubles the ventilation. Such an increase is sufficient to be significant as a factor additive to increased alveolar CO_2 in the ventilatory adjustments to slight exercise; but it has been the consensus of opinion that, even taking into account the small amount of musculature involved in these experimental situations, the increase in ventilation is not great enough to be a significant factor in the hyperpnea of moderate and heavy exercise. Recently, however, experiments in anesthetized dogs depending on direct electrical stimulation of limb muscles have yielded ventilatory changes eight times the resting level. Moreover, the ventilation has been linearly related to O_2 consumption, much as in human experiments.[11, 12, 13] The possibility of cortical and humoral elements in the hyperpnea was ruled out, but nociceptive stimulation as well as muscular contraction might be a factor with this mode of stimulation. Nevertheless, the experiments reopen the question.

REFERENCES

1. BOUTOURLINE-YOUNG, H. J. and WHITTEN-BERGER, J. L. *J. clin. Invest.*, 1951, *30:*838–847.
2. COMROE, J. H. *Amer. J. Physiol.*, 1939, *127:* 176–191.
3. COMROE, J. H. and SCHMIDT, C. F. *Amer. J. Physiol.*, 1938, *121:*75–97.
4. COMROE, J. H. and SCHMIDT, C. F. *Amer. J. Physiol.*, 1943, *138:*536–547.
5. CROSS, K. W. and OPPÉ, T. E. *J. Physiol.*, 1952, *117:*38–55.
6. DECASTRO, F. *Trab. Lab. Invest. biol. Univ. Madr.*, 1926, 24:365–432.
7. GRAY, J. S. *Pulmonary ventilation and its physiological regulation.* Springfield, Ill., Charles C Thomas, 1949.
8. GRODINS, F. S. *Physiol. Rev.*, 1950, *30:*222–329.

9. HALDANE, J. S. *Respiration.* New Haven, Yale University Press, 1922.

10. HARRISON, W. G., JR., CALHOUN, J. A. and HARRISON, T. R. *Amer. J. Physiol.*, 1932, *100*:68–73.

11. KAO, F. F. *Amer. J. Physiol.*, 1956, *185*:145–151.

12. KAO, F. F. and RAY, L. H. *Amer. J. Physiol.*, 1954, *179*:249–254.

13. KAO, F. F., SCHLIG, B. B. and BROOKS, C. McC. *J. appl. Physiol.*, 1955, *10*:379–386.

14. KROGH, A. and LINDHARD, J. *J. Physiol.*, 1913, *47*:112–136.

15. LORENTE DE NÓ, R. *Stud. Rockefeller Inst. med. Res.*, 1947, *131–132*.

16. NIELSON, M. and SMITH, H. *Acta physiol. scand.*, 1951–52, *24*:293–313.

17. NONIDEZ, J. F. *Amer. J. Anat.*, 1935, *57*:259–301.

18. OTIS, A. B. *J. appl. Physiol.*, 1949, *1*:734–751.

19. VON EULER, C. and SÖDERBERG, U. *J. Physiol.*, 1952, *118*:545–554.

SECTION IX

Kidney Function and Body Fluids

CHAPTER 39

The Kidney

By ALAN KOCH

REGULATION of the body fluids is accomplished primarily by the kidneys. These two organs, which together weigh only about 300 grams, directly control the volume and composition of the extracellular fluid, and exert indirect control over the intracellular fluid. This regulatory task is fulfilled so successfully that, over a wide range of water and solute intake, the volume and the composition of the fluids in the body are held remarkably constant. In order to effect this control, a great many different operations are required. The multiplicity of operations and the versatility of each lead to great diversity of renal function. This apparent complexity, however, can be explained by the electrochemistry of fluids, the permeability characteristics of renal structures, and metabolic pumps such as the ones already discussed in Chapter 1.

Properties of Solutions. A *solution* consists of a fluid medium, called the *solvent*, in which are distributed a number of particles, the *solute*. The concentration (C or [S]) of a substance in a solution is defined as the quantity present (Q) in mols, millimols, or micromols, divided by the volume (V) in liters or cubic centimeters through which it is distributed. The concept of concentration is frequently generalized to that of mol fraction. The *mol fraction* of a substance in a solution is defined as the number of molecules of that substance divided by the total number of molecules present in the solution.

As will be remembered from physical chemistry, the mol fraction of a solvent, and therefore of the total solute, can be measured by determination of the colligative properties of the solution. These properties include the lowering of the vapor pressure, elevation of the boiling point, lowering of the freezing point, and osmotic pressure. The changes

844

are all measures of the same thing, the tendency of water molecules to escape from the solution. The physical chemistry of solutions is discussed lucidly by Moore.[19]

The relationship between the quantity present, the volume through which it is distributed, and the resulting concentration is given by:

$$C = \frac{Q}{V}$$

This relationship, which has been developed for a static system, can also be applied to a system, like the kidneys, in which fluids are moving. Only the steady state situation, i.e., the situation in which the concentration in the flowing fluid is not changing with time, will be considered. The *mass flow* is the quantity of solute (Q), in millimols or milligrams, which passes a cross section every minute and is symbolized by $\dot{Q}$.* The *volume flow* is the volume of the solvent which passes a cross section every minute and is symbolized by $\dot{V}$. In a given period, the quantity which passes a cross section is $\dot{Q}\Delta t$, and the volume through which it is distributed is the volume which passes, $\dot{V}\Delta t$. The concentration of material is still Q/V; hence, $C = \dot{Q}\Delta t/\dot{V}\Delta t$, and the equation is

$$C = \frac{\dot{Q}}{\dot{V}}$$

Terminology. Unfortunately, renal terminology arose independently, without reference to physical terminology. Concentrations were considered fundamental quantities, and mass or mass flows were derived from them. In addition, no explicit distinction is customarily made between mass and mass flow or between volume and volume flow. In standard renal notation, the plasma concentration is denoted by P, and a subscript is used to indicate the substance. The urinary concentrations are denoted by U, with a subscript to indicate the substance. The rate of urine flow is denoted by V.

TABLE 25.   CORRELATION OF TERMS DESCRIBING RENAL FUNCTION

STANDARD RENAL NOMENCLATURE	MEANING	NOMENCLATURE USED HERE	UNITS
P_{Na}	Plasma concentration of Na^+	$[Na]_p$	$\mu M./cm.^3$ or mM./liter
U_G	Urinary concentration of glucose	$[G]_u$	$\mu M./cm.^3$, mM./liter, or $\mu M./cm.^3$ or mg.
V	Rate of urine flow	$\dot{V}_u$	$cm.^3$/minute
$U_{Cl}V$	Rate of excretion Cl^-	$\dot{Q}_{Cl_u}$	$\mu M.$/minute
C_{PAH} or RPF	The rate of flow of plasma into the kidney, measured by the clearance of PAH	$\dot{V}_p$	$cm.^3$/minute
C_{in} or GFR	The rate of flow of glomerular filtrate into the nephrons, measured by the clearance of inulin	$\dot{V}_g$	$cm.^3$/minute
L_K or $C_{in} \times P_k$	The filtered load of K^+; i.e., the rate at which K^+ is filtered at the glomerulus	$\dot{Q}_{K_g}$	$\mu M.$/minute
$\dfrac{C_{urea}}{C_{in}}$	The clearance ratio of urea; i.e., the fraction of the filtered urea which is excreted	$\dfrac{\dot{Q}_{urea_u}}{\dot{Q}_{urea_g}}$	no units

* Pronounced "Q dot"; the dot to express rate is a symbol going back to Sir Isaac Newton.

846   KIDNEY FUNCTION AND BODY FLUIDS

In this chapter, a different system of notation is used. The mass of a substance will be denoted by Q, the mass flow will be denoted by $\dot{Q}$, and $\dot{V}$ will indicate volume flow. Square brackets will be used to indicate concentration, and a subscript will tell where the concentration is measured. Table 25 gives the conversions between the two systems.

Functional Anatomy. Gross structure (Fig. 503). The medial side of the kidney contains a deep sinus through which the ureter and all the blood vessels enter or leave the renal parenchyma. Just outside the renal sinus, the ureter expands into the extrarenal pelvis, which continues inside the border of the sinus as the intrarenal pelvis.

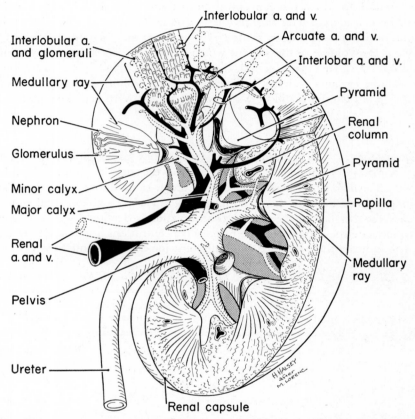

FIG. 503.   Gross structure of the kidney, sagittal section. (After Smith, *Principles of renal physiology.*)

The intrarenal pelvis divides into two major calyces, each of which subdivides into two or three minor calyces. Each minor calyx terminates around the base of one or two papillae. Formed urine is delivered into the collecting duct system in the renal papillae, passes through the papillary duct system into a minor calyx, and thence goes eventually to the bladder.

A medullary and a cortical type of tissue can be distinguished when the kidney is sectioned longitudinally. The triangularly shaped papillae give rise to medullary pyramids which, in turn, give rise to medullary rays; the over-all impression is one of a decrease in the density of medullary substance as the cortex is approached. Cortical substance lines the surface of the organ and, between medullary pyramids, dips in toward the medulla in the renal columns.

Microscopic structure (Fig. 504).[17]   The unit of structure and function in the kidney is the *nephron*. Renal parenchyma is composed of a great many nephrons, each

with its associated blood supply. Urine is formed in the nephrons, and total renal function can be viewed as a summation of the function of about two million extremely similar
but distinct units. A nephron is composed of two major sections, a *glomerulus* and a
tubule. The glomerulus consists of Bowman's capsule, the spherical blind end of the tubule,
and of coiled capillaries. These capillaries lie within an invagination of the capsule,
which is formed of squamous epithelium.

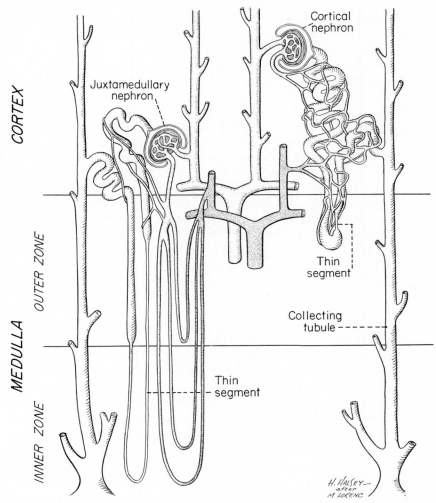

FIG. 504.   Structural differences between cortical and juxtamedullary nephrons. (After Smith, *The
kidney, its structure and function in health and disease.*)

The tubular portion of the nephron begins at the glomerulus and undergoes several
convolutions in this region, traveling generally outward toward the cortex. The tubule
then straightens and descends in a straight line toward the medulla. The convoluted
portion and the first part of the descending portion constitute the *proximal tubule*. Near
the end of the descent the walls of the tubule become exceedingly thin. The thin-walled
portion is termed the *thin segment* of the loop of Henle. After a sharp hairpin turn the
tubule travels back toward its associated glomerulus in the cortex. Along this ascending
limb the walls become thick again. The point of thickening marks the beginning of the
distal tubule. In the region of the glomerulus, the tubule undergoes several more convolutions before emptying into the system of *collecting ducts*. These ducts travel in straight

lines through the medulla; they accept fluid from several nephrons, coalesce, and then enter the renal papillae. Cortical substance is thus composed of glomeruli and the proximal and distal convoluted portions of the tubules; medullary substance of the descending and ascending limbs of the tubules and the collecting duct system.

Short *afferent arterioles*, each feeding a glomerulus, arise from the intralobular arteries. Upon entering the corpuscle, the afferent arteriole arborizes into six to ten glomerular capillaries, which lie close to the invaginated surface of Bowman's capsule. The capillaries then recombine to form the *efferent arteriole*, which leaves the glomerulus and goes to the tubular portion of the nephron. Upon reaching the proximal portion of the tubule, the efferent arteriole arborizes into a second group of capillaries, the *peritubular capillaries*, which wind around the tubule. These capillaries traverse the entire length of the renal tubule, following both its descending course into the medulla and its ascending return. At this point, the capillaries coalesce to form the renal venules.

The kidney is abundantly supplied with nerves, which travel beside the major arteries and apparently innervate the arteriolar vasculature. There is no evidence that these nerves supply the nephron.

All tubules are not quite alike and all vascular supplies are not identical. Nephrons with glomeruli lying in the outer two-thirds of the cortex tend to have very short descending and ascending limbs and only vestigial loops of Henle. The efferent arterioles of these nephrons are very short, and the peritubular ramification occurs immediately and extensively. Nephrons whose glomeruli lie in the deeper third of the cortex have a rather different structure. These nephrons have long descending and ascending limbs, which penetrate deeply into the renal pyramids and possess well developed loops. The efferent arterioles of these nephrons tend to be long and, instead of ramifying extensively into peritubular capillaries, give rise to one or two long straight vessels, the *vasa recti*. These vessels follow the course of the nephron into and out of the medullary pyramids and do not appear to break up into true capillaries.

Precis of Renal Function. The quantity of blood entering the kidneys every minute represents one-fourth to one-fifth of the resting cardiac output. As the blood flows through the glomerular capillaries, about one-fifth of the plasma water passes through the membranes of the capillaries and glomerulus to enter the proximal portion of the renal tubule. The blood remaining in the vascular system enters the efferent arterioles and perfuses the tubules via the peritubular capillaries. The plasma water removed from the blood is termed the *glomerular filtrate;* the process of removal is *glomerular filtration*. Glomerular filtrate is an ultrafiltrate and normally contains no erythrocytes and little or no plasma protein. Other molecules which are sufficiently small to be in true solution pass freely through the glomerular membranes. All major ions, glucose, amino acids and urea appear in the glomerular filtrate at approximately the concentration at which they exist in the plasma.

In the tubule, both solute and water transport take place. Materials are transported across the tubular epithelium from the lumen of the tubule to the interstitial fluid surrounding the nephron and thence to the blood in the peritubular capillaries. This process is called *reabsorption* and results in the return of filtered material to the blood stream. Materials are also transported from the peritubular blood to the interstitial fluid, across the tubular epithelium, and into the lumen. This process is called *secretion* and results in an excretion which is more rapid than would be possible solely through glomerular filtration. The terms reabsorption and secretion denote direction rather than a difference in mechanism. All the glucose that is filtered may return to the circulation and remain in the body as a result of complete reabsorption. Conversely, all the p-amino-hippuric acid (PAH) that enters the kidneys may leave in the urine, even though only one-fifth of the material is filtered. This complete excretion results from the efficient secretory system for PAH.

The proximal tubule reabsorbs physiologically important solute material and secretes organic substances that are destined for excretion. The filtered glucose and amino acids are reabsorbed, as are most filtered Na^+ and Cl^- and some filtered HCO_3^-. As solute particles are removed by active transport processes, the osmotic gradient produced causes reabsorption of water as well. The distal tubule and collecting duct are engaged primarily in the precise regulation of acid-base and K^+ balance. Since much of the filtered solute and water is reabsorbed proximally, both $\dot{V}$ and $\dot{Q}$ are relatively small in the distal tubule. Na^+ is reabsorbed distally as well as proximally, the distal mechanism being an ion exchange in which Na^+ reabsorption is balanced by H^+ or K^+ secretion. Final modification of urinary solute concentration to form a hypertonic urine probably occurs in the collecting ducts.

FLUID DYNAMICS

Two roles are played by the blood that enters the kidney. The first is to supply oxygen and metabolites to enable the kidney to function; this is the role filled by the blood in any organ. In the kidney, however, the blood must also supply the water and solute material which the kidney will process. Because of this latter role, fluid dynamics in the kidney differ from those in any other organ.

The volume of blood flowing into the kidney exceeds by far the amount needed to meet its requirements for oxygen and metabolites. Two corollaries of this high volume flow may be pointed out. First, the extraction of oxygen and metabolites is normally extremely low. Second, in an emergency such as hemorrhage, the reduction of renal blood flow which occurs causes an increase, or lessens a decrease, in the blood flow in

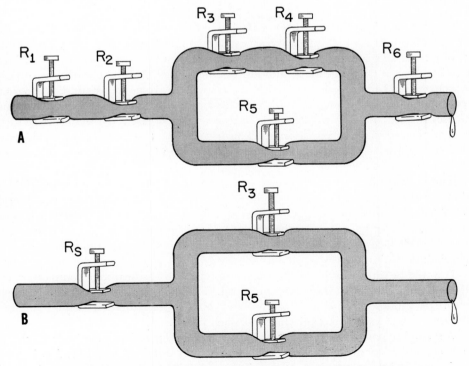

FIG. 505.   A, Analogue of fluid flow in the kidney; B, simplified analogue.

other regions. Normally 1 to 1.5 liters of blood enter the two kidneys each minute. After hemorrhage or severe injury, the flow may be reduced to as little as 250 cm.[3] per minute.

Physiologic Analysis of Blood Flow. The study of renal fluid dynamics is an application of the principle that flow is equal to the quotient of the pressure drop and the vascular resistance (Ohm's law). A highly diagrammatic illustration of renal fluid circulation is given in Figure 505*A*. Each screw clamp corresponds to a resistance, and the degree of constriction is related to the amount of resistance contributed by that element. The resistances represent resistance to flow of blood: R_1 from the renal artery to the afferent arterioles; R_2 in the afferent arterioles; R_3 in the efferent arterioles; R_4 in the peritubular capillaries; R_5 the combined resistance of glomerular filtration and the flow of filtrate through the tubular lumen; and R_6 the resistance of the entire venous bed. Urine flow is ignored, for its rate is negligible in comparison with plasma flow.

Two points are evident from the diagram. If the pressures at each point in the system and all the resistances were known, the total flow and the flow in each limb could be computed. Unfortunately, the resistances are not known; indeed, the flows, as estimated by other means, are used to compute the resistances. The main point is that *the total plasma flow is split at the glomerulus, some fluid being filtered to enter the tubular lumen and some fluid continuing in the vascular system.* The relative size of the two flows is determined by the relative resistances in the two parallel branches. Since most of the tubular fluid is probably reabsorbed early, R_4 can be considered a series resistance, and all the series resistances can be lumped into a single one, R_s (Fig. 505*B*). From the laws of addition of resistances in series and in parallel, the ratio of the rate of glomerular filtration (GFR) to the total rate of plasma flow (RPF) can be expressed as a function of the resistances in the two limbs. This ratio is referred to as the *filtration fraction.*

$$\frac{\dot{V}_g}{\dot{V}_p} = \frac{R_3}{R_3 + R_5} = \frac{GFR}{RPF}$$

Control of Flow Rates; Autoregulation. Both filtration rate and plasma flow may be varied over a wide range by both extrarenal and intrarenal factors. The volume flow of plasma through the kidney depends directly on the arterial pressure. So long as the resistances are constant, the relationship is linear; this is approximately the situation in other organs. In the kidney, however, the resistances are not constant, but are themselves functions of the pressure. With increasing pressure, the total vascular resistance increases so that, although the flow does increase, this increase is *less* than it would have been had the resistance stayed constant. This is one of the two facets of the phenomenon called *autoregulation.* The other facet is that the filtration fraction falls when the plasma flow increases (Fig. 506).

The changes in resistance occurring after renal nerve stimulation, emotional reactions or the administration of sympathomimetic agents are presumably caused by arteriolar vasoconstriction similar to that found in other splanchnic beds. Much of this constriction probably occurs in the afferent arterioles. However, the autoregulatory changes take place in the isolated perfused kidney and hence cannot be caused by extrinsic innervation.

It would be simpler if the two facets of autoregulation arose from a common process, and several mechanisms have been proposed. The oldest invokes intrarenal reflexes. Pressure is supposedly "sensed" within the kidney,[37] but there is neither anatomic evidence nor a physiologic requirement for such reflex arcs.

A second hypothesis suggests that changes in vascular resistance arise from changes in extravascular volume.[13, 29] As blood pressure increases, capillary filtration increases (or absorption into the peritubular capillaries of fluid reabsorbed from nephrons decreases); since the interstitial fluid is elastically constrained, blood vessels are somewhat narrowed and vascular resistance increases. The main evidence for this hypothesis comes from two types of experiments. For a time after a sudden step increase in perfusion pressure, more plasma enters than leaves the kidney. The rise in vascular resistance follows the same time course as does the increase in kidney weight. The implication is that some of the plasma entering the kidney moves into the interstitial fluid and causes the increase in vascular resistance. Perfusion of solutions of varying concentration produced the predicted results; dilute solutions increased vascular resistance (and kidney weight) and concentrated solutions decreased resistance (and kidney weight). The second facet of autoregulation, the failure of the filtration rate to increase proportionately with plasma flow and the resulting decrease in filtration fraction, reflects a change in the relative resistances in the two pathways available to plasma in the glomerular tuft. Most of the increase in total renal resistance appears to be in the tubular path, thereby decreasing the filtration fraction.

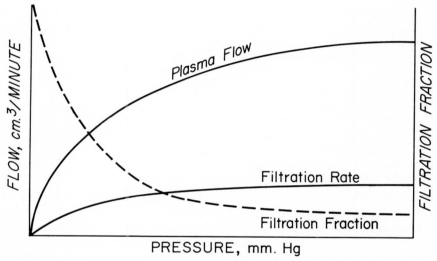

FIG. 506. Pressure dependance of renal plasma flow ($\dot{V}_p$), filtration rate ($\dot{V}_g$), and filtration fraction ($\dot{V}_g/\dot{V}_p$).

Clearance Studies. This method, first used physiologically by Smith, has quantified the study of normal and pathologic renal mechanisms. A clearance value expresses the degree to which a substance is removed from the blood by excretion into urine. This value is expressed not as a percentage but rather as the number of cubic centimeters which would be "cleared" were all of the substances removed. It is therefore the virtual rather than the actual amount of blood cleared. A good way of looking at clearance is that it is the number of cubic centimeters of blood which would have to be presented to the nephron to provide the amount of substance actually found in the urine, in a unit time.

$$\text{Clearance} = \frac{\dot{Q}_u}{C_p} \quad \text{or} \quad \frac{UV}{P} \quad \text{or} \quad \frac{\text{amount of substance in urine per minute}}{\text{concentration of substance in plasma}}$$

The units of clearance are those of volume flow, cubic centimeters per minute.

The clearances of two particular substances are especially important. The clearance of PAH is a measure of renal plasma flow; the clearance of inulin is a measure of the filtration rate. Knowledge of these volume flows allows calculation of some of the important relationships in renal fluid dynamics; it also enables us to know the mass flows of material entering the kidney or being filtered or being presented to the peritubular borders of tubular cells. The mass flow of a substance is the product of the volume flow of solute and the concentration of the material of interest.

CLEARANCE RATIOS. One can determine the clearance of glucose or sodium just as well as the clearance of inulin or of PAH. However, it is only in the latter two cases that any physical meaning can be attached to the term. The clearance of glucose is related in some manner to the excretion of glucose, but this information alone does not tell how the kidney handles glucose. A derived computation, the *clearance ratio*, does give important information about the way a substance is handled by the kidney. The clearance ratio is the ratio of the clearance of a substance to the clearance of inulin. The clearance of inulin gives the amount of glomerular filtration. If the latter amount is multiplied by the plasma concentration of the substance under investigation, the amount of the substance entering the tubule, the *filtered load* is known. If the substance, in addition to being filtered, is also secreted by the tubule, the clearance of the substance will be higher than that of inulin. If the substance is reabsorbed, its clearance will obviously be lower.

These relationships may be developed as follows: The clearance of a substance is $\dot{Q}_u/C_p$ and the clearance of inulin is numerically equal to the filtration rate. Hence the clearance ratio is $\dot{Q}_u/C_p\dot{V}_g$. But $C_p\dot{V}_g$ is the filtered load of the material ($\dot{Q}_g$); therefore,

$$\text{Clearance Ratio} = \frac{\dot{Q}_u}{\dot{Q}_g} = \frac{UV}{P \times GFR} = \frac{\text{concentration in urine} \times \text{urine volume}}{\text{plasma in concentration} \times \text{glomerular filtration}}$$

When the clearance ratio is less than 1, *net* reabsorption occurs, but it cannot be stated whether secretion also takes place. If filtration and reabsorption are the only processes operating, the clearance ratio gives a quantitative measure of the reabsorptive process; if secretion also occurs, a theoretical possibility, this ratio gives a minimum value for the reabsorptive process. When the clearance ratio is greater than 1, *net* secretion occurs. When filtration and secretion are the only processes operating, the clearance ratio gives a quantitative measure of the secretory process. The clearance ratio is 1 for inulin or for any substance which is handled like inulin.

Although the clearance experiment has been the technique most widely used in the study of renal function, other methods are also available. These include experiments in which a glomerulus or tubule is cannulated with a small capillary tube and fluid is collected from a single nephron. This procedure is difficult, as is the analysis of the minute quantity of fluid obtained, but it was by this *tour de force* that Richards and his group established the composition of glomerular fluids and the nature of glomerular function. These investigators showed that glomerular fluid is like plasma in all measurable ways and that it is derived from plasma simply by filtration. Later, Walker et al.[42] showed that the solute concentration remains constant in the proximal tubule, but that glucose and water are reabsorbed. The recent work of Wirz,[46] of Ullrich,[38, 39, 40, 41] and of Gottschalk,[11] which has included not only collection of tubular fluid but also analysis of whole renal slices, can be regarded an extension of Richards' pioneer investigations.

Clearance methods and the other methods discussed to this point are all steady state measurements. Techniques for studying transients have recently been developed. Chinard injects materials into the renal artery "instantaneously" and analyzes the patterns of their appearance in both renal venous blood and urine. He has shown that glucose is transported across renal cells without entering into cellular metabolism. In addition, he has reported many provocative findings pertaining to the handling of electrolytes by the kidney. More recently, another method has been used by Malvin and Wilde and by Pitts and his coworkers. In so-called "stop-flow" experiments, the ureter is blocked for four to eight minutes. It is then opened and the accumulated tubular fluid is collected serially. The first samples are presumed to have come from the most distal portions of the nephron; later samples are presumed to have been "processed" by the more proximal portions. Considerable information on the localization of tubular function has been obtained in this manner. In the remainder of this chapter, information obtained by all these methods will be presented.

MEASUREMENT OF RENAL PLASMA FLOW.   Blood flow could be measured by interrupting the renal artery or vein and inserting a flowmeter. Although this procedure has been followed experimentally, it is obviously not applicable to man, and even in work on animals it is too difficult for routine determinations. Indirect methods are therefore used. The kidney is regarded as a Y tube of the type illustrated in Figure 507*b*. If renal tissue neither creates nor destroys a material, the rate at which the material enters the kidney through the renal artery must equal the rate at which it leaves by the two available routes, the renal vein and the urine. If the arterial and venous concentrations of such a substance and the rate at which it is excreted by the kidney are known, the rate at which plasma must enter the kidney can be calculated. This procedure is already familiar as the Fick principle (Chap. 32). Thus, if the renal arterial plasma concentration of a substance is 3 mg. per liter and the renal venous plasma concentration is 2 mg. per liter, 1 liter of plasma must pass through the kidney each minute in order to furnish

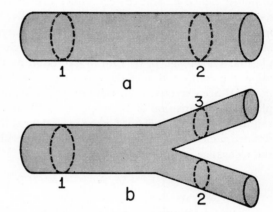

FIG. 507. *a*, Straight tube (Q_1) must equal $\dot{Q}_2$; *b*, tube $\dot{Q}_1$ must equal $\dot{Q}_2 + \dot{Q}_3$

sufficient material to account for an excretion rate of 1 mg. per minute. For substance S, the plasma flow ($\dot{V}_p$) is given by the formula:

$$\dot{V}_p = \frac{\dot{Q}_{su}}{[S]_a - [S]_v} \quad \text{or} \quad RPF = \frac{UV}{P_a - P_v} \quad \text{or} \quad \frac{\text{amount in urine per unit time}}{\text{loss per liter of plasma}}$$

All that is necessary is to collect urine in a given period of time and, sometime during this period, to obtain a sample of arterial plasma (systemic venous plasma will usually have about the same concentration) and a sample of renal venous plasma. The latter sample can be obtained by catheterization of the renal vein.

The method described is simple and applicable to any substance that is neither destroyed nor created in the kidney. Renal venous catheterization is obviously the most difficult procedure, but this can be avoided by selecting a substance which, once it has entered the kidney, is entirely excreted in the urine. The two agents most commonly used are iodopyracet (Diodrast) and para-aminohippuric acid (PAH). The renal venous plasma concentration of either of these agents is zero, and no renal venous plasma sample is needed. The rate at which the material enters the kidney is equal to the rate at which it is excreted, and the flow can be computed from the clearance of PAH:

$$\dot{V}_p = \frac{\dot{Q}_{PAH_u}}{PAH_p} \quad \text{or} \quad RPF = \frac{U_{PAH}V}{P_{PAH}}$$

Any substance which is abstracted completely from renal plasma enters the nephron by two routes: (i) by filtration at the glomerulus; (ii) by transport across the tubular cells of the portion of the substance remaining in the plasma that passes along the peritubular capillaries. Further, the transcellular transport mechanism must be exceedingly active if the last trace of the material is to be removed from the plasma. A class of cyclic organic acids, including the two mentioned above, appears to be handled in the kidney in approximately this manner.

Even at low plasma concentrations of PAH (or other compounds of this group) about 10 per cent of the material is still present in renal venous plasma. Hence, the plasma flow computed from the PAH clearance is about 10 per cent lower than the actual flow. Indirect evidence suggests that the incomplete excretion of PAH results from shunting of blood through connective tissue or from the perfusion of damaged nephrons.[35] The plasma flow computed from PAH is sometimes called the "effective renal plasma flow" and that computed from the extraction, using the complete equation, the "total renal plasma flow."

MEASUREMENT OF GLOMERULAR FILTRATION RATE. Glomerular fluid cannot be sampled except in animal experiments, and even there the procedure is extremely difficult; hence clearance techniques are used. Consider a substance that is neither secreted nor reabsorbed by renal tubular cells (Fig. 507a). In the steady state, as much material leaves the nephron each minute as enters it; $\dot{Q}_g = \dot{Q}_u$. Since the concentration of this material in glomerular fluid is approximately the same as the concentration in plasma, knowledge of its rate of excretion and plasma concentration are sufficient to allow the computation of the rate of glomerular filtration. If 210 mg. of the measuring material are excreted each minute, the same amount has entered the nephrons. If the plasma concentration is 2 mg. per ml., 105 ml. of fluid must enter the glomeruli each minute in order to account for the mass flow of the measuring material. We have already defined a clearance in such terms. The glomerular filtration rate can be calculated from the clearance of inulin.

$$V_g = \frac{\dot{Q}_{In_u}}{[In]_p} = GFR = C_{In} = \frac{U_{In}V}{P_{In}}$$

Several materials are suitable for the estimation of filtration rate. As stated, the substance must be neither created nor destroyed in the nephrons; further, its concentration in the glomerular filtrate should be proportional to the concentration in plasma. Other criteria which must be met are given by Smith.[33] The substance which fulfills these criteria best is *inulin*, a fructose polysaccharide derived from Jerusalem artichokes. In all species in which the inulin clearance has been examined, it appears to be an accurate measure of filtration. Other substances which may be used include ferrocyanide and sucrose in man and the dog and creatinine in the dog.

NORMAL VALUES OF FILTRATION RATE AND PLASMA FLOW. Renal mass and, consequently, the values for the filtration rate and plasma flow correlate fairly well with the body surface area. For this reason, values for the plasma flow and filtration rate in man are generally expressed in terms of surface area and then corrected to the value of a hypothetical man with a surface area of 1.73 m.². In animals, this correction is frequently neglected. In men, plasma flow averages 655 cm.³ per minute, and the filtration rate 127 cm.³ per minute. In women, plasma flow averages 600 cm.³ per minute, and filtration rate 118 cm.³ per minute. Both volume flows decrease with increasing age and fall in an approximately linear fashion from the stated values at the age of about 30 years to approximately half those values by the age of 75. The measured values vary considerably in the absence of clinically detectable illness.

TUBULAR TRANSPORT

The main activity of the kidney is to transport solute materials and water across tubular cells. Such transport is termed *reabsorption* when its direction is from the tubular lumen to the interstitial fluid; it is termed *secretion* when its direction is from the interstitial fluid to the tubular lumen. The two terms denote the direction of the transport and have no implications as to the cellular basis of the transport. Transtubular transport is said to be *passive* when it can be accounted for on the basis of a *passive flux equation* (see below) and *active* when this equation does not account for the observed transport.

Principles of Transport. PASSIVE TRANSPORT. The principles governing transport of solute across membranes, discussed fully in Chapter 1, will be briefly recapitulated here. The passive transport of a component of a solution across a membrane may result from one of two distinct types of motion. Movement of the whole solution through the membrane carries with it all specific components; this is termed *bulk flow*. Movement of the component through the solution lodged in the membrane and thus through the membrane itself is termed *diffusion*. Diffusion will occur regardless of whether the fluid in the membrane is moving or stationary. In general, both kinds of movement may exist, and the total movement of a component through the membrane is the sum of its bulk flow and its diffusion. Two factors are important in the diffusion term of the transport equation, the concentration gradient and the voltage gradient. To decide whether a specific substance is transported passively it is necessary to compare its transport quantitatively with that predicted by the equation derived below.

The bulk flow of a component in a solution is the product of the velocity of the solution with respect to the membrane and the concentration of the component in the solution. The *flux* in mols per cm.² per second due to bulk flow is given by the expression:

$$\mathbf{M}_{\text{bulk flow}} = C\dot{V}$$

This expression is the same as $\dot{Q} = C\dot{V}$, given above. The diffusion term generally includes the gradients of both concentration and voltage; these gradients will produce movement of the component through the solution as a whole. In one dimension, the gradient (grad) of a function may be defined as the rate of change of the function with distance. Movement through the solution is in the direction of the negative of the gradient (see Chap. 1).

Consider two different solutions of glucose separated by a membrane. Grad C is equal to $(C_1 - C_2)/\delta$, where δ is the thickness of the membrane. If the membrane is permeable to glucose, glucose will move from the side of higher concentration to the side of lower concentration, i.e., it will move down its gradient. The flux is given by the expression:

$$\mathbf{M} = D\frac{C_2 - C_1}{\delta} = \frac{D}{\delta}(C_2 - C_1) = P(C_2 - C_1)$$

where D is the diffusion coefficient, and P the permeability. Permeability includes both the diffusivity within the membrane and the membrane thickness. In the same manner, if two identical solutions of NaCl are separated by a membrane which is permeable only to Na⁺, and if a voltage gradient (grad ε) is impressed across the membrane by an external source, Na⁺ will move down the voltage gradient. The flux of Na⁺ will be from the side of higher electric potential to the side of lower electric potential. The magnitude of the flux will be proportional to the charge on the particle, to grad ε, and to the number of particles present which can move. The expression for net flux under these conditions is:

$$\mathbf{M} = -D\frac{ZF}{RT}C\,\text{grad}\,\varepsilon$$

where Z is the charge of the particle, F is the Faraday, R is the universal gas constant and T is the absolute temperature. The diffusion term is the sum of the concentration and electrical terms:

$$\mathbf{M}_{\text{diffusion}} = -D(\text{grad}\,C + \frac{ZF}{RT}C\,\text{grad}\,\varepsilon)$$

The total passive transport of a substance with respect to the membrane is the sum of the bulk flow and the diffusion terms.

$$\mathbf{M} = -D(\text{grad}\,C + \frac{ZF}{RT}C\,\text{grad}\,\varepsilon) + C\dot{V}$$

In the steady state, when the volume flow is zero, this equation gives rise to the Ussing equation for passive transport. For a cation, this is:

$$\frac{\mathbf{M}_{12}}{\mathbf{M}_{21}} = \frac{C_1}{C_2}\exp\frac{ZF}{RT}(\varepsilon_1 - \varepsilon_2)$$

where M_{12} is the one-way flux from compartment 1 to compartment 2, and M_{21} is the reverse flux. At equilibrium, when the volume flow and net flux are both zero, the flux equation can be integrated to give the familiar Nernst equation, which for a cation is:

$$\varepsilon_1 - \varepsilon_2 = \frac{RT}{ZF} \log\frac{C_1}{C_2}$$

ACTIVE TRANSPORT.   Transport is said to be active when, in addition to the passive terms, another term is required to describe it. Detectable active transport thus requires the combination of a pump that will move material across the membrane and relative impermeability that will prevent rapid diffusion of material back to the site from which it came. In the kidney, the transport of most physiologically important solutes is active. Specific examples include the reabsorption of Na^+ and glucose and the secretion of K^+ and PAH.

In some tissues (e.g., nerve, skeletal muscle and erythrocytes), the concentration gradient, the voltage gradient and the net flux can be measured; the experimental results can then be compared with a passive flux equation. However, neither the intracellular nor intraluminal concentrations in the kidney are known with any accuracy, and the measurement of potentials is still in its infancy. The decision that a given substance is actively or passively transported must frequently be based on indirect evidence. Fulfillment of four ancillary criteria provides strong presumptive evidence for active transport. These criteria are the demonstration of (i) a maximum rate of tubular transport, (ii) competition between similar molecular species, (iii) inhibition by metabolic inhibitors, and (iv) in certain cases, failure to vary in the expected manner with such variables as urine flow or pH.

The first two criteria imply a specific combination between the transported substance and the transport system at a limited number of sites. When all sites are occupied, a maximum rate of transport has been attained and further elevation of the plasma concentration of the material will not increase the rate of transport. If some sites are occupied with one molecular species, correspondingly fewer sites are available for transport of a similar compound handled by the same system. The third criterion implies that the transport requires energy derived from cellular metabolism. The fourth criterion is a portion of the definition given above of active transport. Glucose transport, for example, is not changed by wide variations in the rate of urine flow or the pH of urine. Reabsorption of urea, on the other hand, is closely related to the reabsorption of water, a finding that suggests that bulk flow may play a significant role.

Substances Passively Transported by the Kidney.   Tubular transport of ammonia, of a group of organic acids and bases, of most or all of the filtered water, and of at least a portion of the filtered urea fit passive flux equations. In the case of weak acids or bases, the relative concentrations of the ionized and nonionized forms depend on the pH of the tubular fluid and on the dissociation constant of the substance. Each of the two forms must be treated separately, and the measured rate of excretion will be the sum of their individual rates of excretion. Chloride and bicarbonate are also transported passively; their tubular transport is determined by active sodium transport.

Substances Actively Transported by the Kidney.   Substances which are transported actively are also influenced by passive effects, but in renal systems the active mechanisms greatly predominate. Active transport systems in the kidney may be roughly divided into two classes, called for convenience types A and B. Whether the substance exhibits a transport maximum (Tm) is important in the dichotomy between types A and B.

CALCULATION OF Tm.   Tm is the maximum rate of tubular transport; it applies to reabsorption and secretion. By definition, a maximum can be determined only if the tubular cells can be presented with amounts greater than those they can transport. Tm is computed by comparing the amount excreted and the amount filtered during maximum transport, e.g., $\dot{Q}_g - \dot{Q}_u$. Tm is a positive quantity when there is net reabsorption and a negative quantity when there is net secretion. All of a reabsorbed substance, such as glucose, entering the tubule either must be transported or must appear in the urine. If the amount of glomerular filtration is determined from the inulin celarance, and if this amount is multiplied by the plasma concentration of glucose, the *quantity* of the substance entering the tubule per unit time (filtered load) is known. Subtracting from this the amount not transported—the amount appearing in the urine in the same unit time—tells how much passed through the tubular walls.

In conventional clearance, the Tm of glucose is

$$Tm_G = C_{in}P_G - U_GV$$

or more simply

$$Tm_G = \dot{Q}_{gG} - \dot{Q}_{uG} = \dot{V}_g[G]_p - \dot{Q}_{uG}$$

Then, $Tm_G = 350$ mg. per minute.

DEFINITION OF TYPE A AND TYPE B SYSTEMS. Tubular transport in a type A system exhibits a definite Tm and a sharp plateau; transport is relatively complete until the system is presented with more material than it can transport (Tm is exceeded). Type B systems fail to transport material completely, even when the amounts presented to the cells are relatively small, and do not exhibit a sharp Tm within physiologically attainable ranges. Transport of glucose is a classic example of type A reabsorption, and transport of PAH of type A secretion. Na^+ transport is a classic example of type B reabsorption, and K^+ transport of type B secretion. In general, organic substances are processed in type A systems and ionic substances in type B systems. Transport of divalent ions is predominantly type A; transport of amino acids is intermediate.

The reasons for the differences in transport systems are not known. One way of visualizing the process is derived from enzyme kinetics and involves the following assumptions: (i) active transport requires a preliminary reaction between the transported material and some cellular element forming a precursor combination, (ii) a limited number of transport sites and hence a maximum rate of transport exists, (iii) the combination follows the law of mass action at low degrees of saturation of cellular elements, and (iv) the rate of transport is proportional to the amount of precursor formed.

The first and second assumptions imply a dissociation constant (K) for the combination of the cellular element and the transported material. The negative log of K would then be pK. When K is low (pK is high), the combination forms readily, and little material will escape transport until Tm is reached. Thus, when pK/Tm is high, transport will rise rapidly as a function of the amount of material presented to the cells until the filtered load ($\dot{Q}_g = \dot{V}_g \times C_p$) is about equal to Tm, and the plasma concentration will equilibrate in this region. In a system in which the ratio of pK/Tm is low (type B), transport will increase less rapidly as a function of load, and some material will always escape transport. Because of this latter factor, equilibration for a reabsorbed material will occur considerably below the maximum rate of transport in a type B system. Indeed, the maximum rate of transport may be so high as to be physiologically unattainable.

The relationship between the amount of material presented to the tubules per unit time and the amount transported in both type A and B systems is illustrated in Figure 508. Such graphs do not, however, indicate how urinary excretion varies as a function of plasma concentration for various systems. Two methods are commonly used to depict this relationship. The first is to superpose plots of the load presented to the cells, the amount of the material excreted, and the difference between the two, which represents the amount transported. All of these factors are presented as functions of the load. The second method is to plot the fraction of the filtered load excreted ($\dot{Q}_u/\dot{Q}_g$ = clearance ratio) as a function of the filtered load. Both of these plots are presented in Figures 509 and 510.

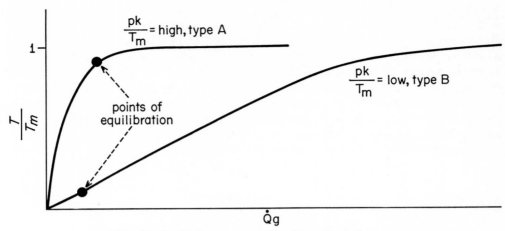

FIG. 508.   Distinction between type A and type B tubular transport.

In a type A reabsorptive system, reabsorption is complete at low filtered loads, and there is no urinary excretion. The clearance ratio is therefore zero. As the load is increased above Tm, the increment in excretion is just equal to the increment in the load. At all plasma concentrations above that which produces a filtered load equal to Tm, the rate of excretion is given by the expression $\dot{Q}_u = \dot{Q}_g - Tm = C_p \times \dot{V}_g - Tm$. The clearance ratio also rises from zero and approaches 1 asymptotically.

Reabsorption in a type B system is never complete; some material is excreted even at the lowest filtered load. As the load is increased, reabsorption increases, but not at the same rate as the load. Thus excretion increases continuously. The clearance ratio starts at some value above zero and increases slowly and continuously toward 1. These relationships are illustrated in Figure 509.

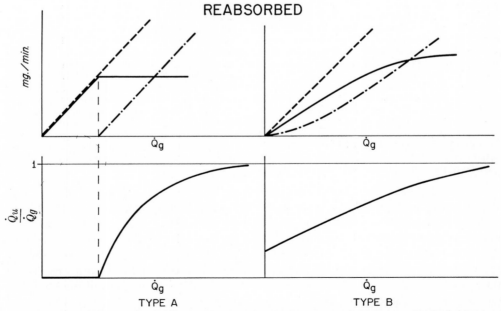

FIG. 509.   Relationships between measures of tubular transport activity for a reabsorbed substance. *Upper graphs*, Dashed line, filtered load; solid line, tubular transport; dot-dashed line, excretion. *Lower graphs*, Clearance ratio as a function of filtered load.

In secretory systems, the material that appears in the urine is composed of two moieties, one which entered the lumen at the glomerulus and one which entered as a result of transtubular transport. The former, which is the filtered load, is always proportional to the plasma concentration (barring peculiarities in protein binding), whereas the latter depends on transport.

When the plasma concentration of a type A secreted material is low, all or a fixed fraction of the material which escapes glomerular filtration is transported. So long as the plasma concentration remains well below that resulting in Tm, the amount of solute contributed to the urine by both filtration and transport increases in proportion to the plasma concentration. In these circumstances, the clearance ratio remains constant and above 1. If the plasma concentration is such that the amount presented to the tubules

SECRETED

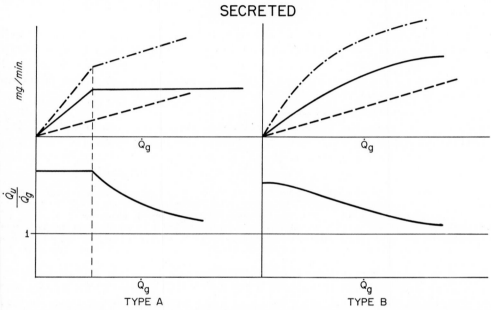

FIG. 510.   Relationships between measures of tubular transport activity for a secreted substance
Symbols as in Fig. 509.

is above Tm,* the amount secreted remains constant. Although the rate of excretion in urine still increases as the plasma concentration increases, the only cause for this greater excretion is the increase in the filtered load. Since the total excretion no longer increases at the same rate as the plasma concentration does, the clearance ratio falls. It declines asymptotically from its initial high value (which is characteristic for the substance) toward 1.

When a type B system is engaged in secretion, there is a continual decrease in the rate at which excretion increases as tubular load increases. The clearance ratio thus falls throughout the whole range of plasma concentrations, approaching 1 as an asymptote. These relationships are illustrated in Figure 510.

Transport of Specific Substances. UREA.[30]   Urea clearance ratios in mammals are always less than 1, indicating net reabsorption. The clearance ratio is a function of the rate of urine flow, being low (but not 0) for low values of flow and approaching 1 at

---

* Remember that the amount presented to the tubules is equal to the amount which enters the kidney each minute, less the amount which is filtered at the glomerulus. The tubular load of PAH $= \dot{V}_p[PAH]_p - \dot{V}_g[PAH]_p = [PAH]_p(\dot{V}_p - \dot{V}_g)$.

very high values. This finding is largely responsible for the classic theory that urea is transported solely by passive diffusion. Reabsorption of luminal fluid elevates the intra-luminal concentration and thus produces a concentration gradient between intraluminal and interstitial fluid. This concentration gradient is presumed to be the driving force for urea reabsorption. It is further presumed that renal epithelium is sparingly permeable to urea and that equilibration is never achieved. The disparity from equilibrium increases with increased urine flow, and thus the clearance ratio is increased as urine flow is elevated.

Although diffusion undoubtedly plays a significant role in the tubular handling of urea, it is likely that active transport is also involved. The findings of Schmidt-Nielson[31] that the relationship between the rate of urine flow and the urea clearance ratio can be modified and that these modifications become manifest after protein deprivation; the demonstration of renal tubular secretion of urea in the bullfrog and other anurans;[8, 33] and the demonstration of active reabsorption in elasmobranchs;[33] all indicate that a weak transport system might be involved.

GLUCOSE. Glucose transport was one of the first renal transport systems to be well delineated; the work was done by Shannon and Fisher.[32] Both stop-flow experiments and micropuncture studies[42, 47] indicate that glucose reabsorption occurs in the proximal tubule and normally proceeds there essentially to completion. Any glucose escaping re-absorption in this region is destined for excretion.

The maximum rate of transport is 375 mg. per minute $\pm$80 mg. in men and slightly lower in women. Endocrine imbalances may alter Tm_G slightly, but, in the main, it is quite constant and depends only on the number of nephrons functioning. For this reason, measurement of Tm_G is sometimes used clinically to estimate the number of functioning nephrons. This measurement is called "tubular reabsorptive capacity."

Several other monosaccharides, including fructose and galactose, are reabsorbed by systems which appear to share some element with glucose reabsorption. Xylose is reabsorbed wholly by the same system. The high xylose clearance ratio, the effective inhibition of xylose clearance by glucose, and the absence of a sharp Tm for xylose are all consistent with the assumption that the dissociation constant between xylose and the transport system is high (pK is low). The system appears to have a low value of pK/Tm for xylose and a high value for glucose. Hence, the system exhibits type A behavior for glucose and type B behavior for xylose.

If Tm_G is 375 mg. per minute and the filtration rate is 120 cm.[3] per minute, one can compute that the plasma concentration at which Tm_G is attained is about 300 mg. per 100 cm.[3] of plasma (160 mg. per 100 cm.[3] whole blood). Since plasma glucose is normally only about 130 mg. per 100 cm.[3], one can predict that normal urine should be glucose-free and that the concentration of glucose in plasma is not normally controlled by the kidney.

In diabetic patients, the tissues may utilize glucose so poorly that the plasma con-centration is largely controlled by the kidney. In such persons, the fasting glucose concentration in plasma is about the maximum rate of glucose transport divided by the filtration rate. This situation, in which the plasma concentration of a solute is maintained at the maximum concentration attainable without urinary loss, is termed *glomerular-tubular balance*.

PARA-AMINOHIPPURIC ACID. PAH is bound to plasma proteins; hence, its concen-tration is not the same in glomerular filtrate and in plasma. Instead, the concentration in the glomerular filtrate is the same as the concentration of unbound PAH in plasma water. In man, this value is taken to be 78 per cent of the total plasma concentration. So avid is the tubular transport system, or so rapid is the binding reaction, that tubular cells remove essentially all of the PAH—both bound and unbound—from the blood perfusing them, so long as the amount presented per minute is less than Tm. This secretory system, like the glucose reabsorptive system, is located in the very first portion of the nephron.[16, 27]

The Tm of PAH is 80 mg. per minute ± 17 mg. in man and somewhat lower in women. The value is quite constant and is the basis for another clinical test of tubular functions that is similar to the use of Tm_G. Tm_{PAH} is considered an estimate of "tubular secretory capacity."

A large number of other compounds are transported by the same system. All are aromatic organic acids, the most important being penicillin. Before supplies of penicillin became plentiful, considerable effort was expended in attempting to inhibit this system. It was found that the transport involves two steps. The first is a specific combination with a "carrier" molecule; the second is transport of the resulting complex. Chemical reactions leading to the decomposition and release of the acid occur at the luminal border. Tubular secretion is competitively inhibited either by a compound which combines well with the carrier but which is transported only slowly, or, better, by a compound which combines well with the carrier but which cannot undergo the biochemical transformation necessary for decomposition. Probenecid (Benemid), which falls in the latter class, was developed as a result of these investigations. Penicillin is now cheaper than probenecid, and the original purpose of the drug is largely forgotten. However, it also inhibits the renal reabsorption of uric acid and is now widely used in the treatment of chronic gout.

SODIUM. Reabsorption of Na^+ is involved with the transport of several other ions, being comprised of reabsorption in association with Cl^- and HCO_3^- and reabsorption in exchange for H^+ and K^+. The preservation of charge neutrality requires the reabsorption of an anion or the secretion of a cation for each Na^+ reabsorbed.* Hence, Na^+ reabsorption is the sum of these ancillary ion transports. The transports of Cl^-, HCO_3^-, H^+ and K^+ are discussed separately here.

Our knowledge of Na^+ transport can be summarized in three statements. (i) Reabsorption of Na^+ undoubtedly results from active transport. (ii) The ancillary ion fluxes, anion reabsorption and cation secretion, are capable of homeostatic modification. (iii) Reabsorption of Na^+ exhibits type B kinetics.

Active transport of Na^+. The conditions under which Na^+ transport occurs indicate that it is active. Most of the filtered Na^+ is reabsorbed in the proximal tubule. This region of the nephron is freely permeable to water. As Na^+ and an associated anion are reabsorbed, water is reabsorbed in osmotically equivalent quantities. The mol fractions of both water and Na^+ in proximal tubular fluid normally remain at the values found in plasma.[42] The inside of the tubular cell is about 70 mV. negative to the interstitial fluid and about 50 mV. negative to the luminal fluid.[9] The high potentials measured across the two cellular membranes render it unlikely that water transport, resulting from either osmotic or hydrostatic pressure gradients, is primary and that Na^+ and anions drift across the tubular cells secondarily. The magnitude of these potentials also indicate that bulk flow is not the predominant term in reabsorption of either Na^+ or the attendant anions.

Since we know the concentrations of Na^+ in the fluids on either side of the tubular cell and the electric potential across the cell, we can compute the passive flux of cations. Normally the concentration gradient is zero and the voltage gradient is the only passive force present. The net passive flux, then, is in the direction of the negative of the gradient, i.e., from a region of high potential to a region of low potential. Were this the only force present, there would be net tubular secretion of cations. Inasmuch as Na^+ is reabsorbed, another force must act upon the ion. This force, which opposes the voltage gradient and produces Na^+ reabsorption, is active Na^+ transport.

Sodium-potassium pump. The details of Na^+ reabsorption are not known, but a hypothetical mechanism explains most of the data. It assumes that a Na^+-K^+ exchange pump, similar to that in nerve cells, is situated in the interstitial border of renal tubular cells. This pump transports Na^+ from the inside of the cell to the interstitial fluid and

---

* The reabsorption of as little as one part in 1000 of the filtered Na^+ without associated anion reabsorption or cation secretion would produce an increase in the potential across the tubular cell of at least 1 V. per minute. This is 30 to 50 times the steady state potential.

K$^+$ in the reverse direction. One K$^+$ is taken up for each Na$^+$ extruded, and the pump is electrically neutral. Active Na$^+$ transport is assumed to be either extremely weak or absent from the luminal membrane.

In the proximal tubule, the interstitial membrane is assumed to be freely permeable to K$^+$ and Cl$^-$, but not to Na$^+$. Na$^+$ is pumped across this membrane. The luminal border is permeable to Na$^+$ and Cl$^-$, but only poorly permeable to K$^+$. Reabsorption of Na$^+$ entails concurrent movement of Cl$^-$. The initial process is the active exchange wherein Na$^+$ is extruded from the cell and K$^+$ is taken up. As a consequence, the intracellular concentration of Na$^+$ is lowered and that of K$^+$ is raised. The concentration gradient of Na$^+$ between the luminal and the cell fluid increases, and Na$^+$ enters the cell from the lumen. As Na$^+$ crosses the luminal membrane, the resulting change in the voltage across the membrane drives Cl$^-$ into the cell. The entering Na$^+$ replaces the Na$^+$ that has been pumped out, while the entering Cl$^-$ elevates cellular Cl$^-$. Now the cellular concentrations of K$^+$ and Cl$^-$ are both higher than they were. Both ions diffuse across the interstitial membrane. The over-all reaction is the reabsorption of one Na$^+$ and one Cl$^-$. No net transport of K$^+$ takes place, this ion simply plays the

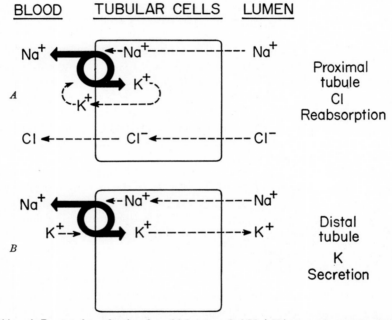

FIG. 511.   *A*, Proposed mechanism by which a coupled Na$^+$-K$^+$ pump in proximal tubular cells causes Na$^+$ reabsorption with associated anion reabsorption. *B*, Proposed mechanism by which a similar pump in the distal tubular cells causes Na$^+$ reabsorption with associated K$^+$ secretion.

role of a catalyst. Since the active transport step is electrically neutral, the membrane voltages arise from differences in the passive permeabilities of the ions involved. Figure 511*A* illustrates this mechanism in the proximal tubule. HCO$_3^-$ could be reabsorbed by this mechanism too, but is not known to be.

In the distal tubule, the permeability of the interstitial membrane to K$^+$ is assumed to be very low. Here, the entry of Na$^+$ into the cell is accompanied by secretion of K$^+$. Since it cannot diffuse back across the interstitial membrane, the K$^+$ that enters the cell in the exchange pump is driven across the luminal membrane into luminal fluid. Figure 511*B* illustrates the action of this mechanism in the distal tubule.

This hypothesis has several corollaries which can be tested experimentally. Digitalis compounds inhibit a coupled Na$^+$-K$^+$ pump. Apparently, they compete with K$^+$ for the transport system. Elevation of the extracellular K$^+$ concentration antagonizes the inhibitory action. If a Na$^+$-K$^+$ pump is the mechanism of Na$^+$ transport in the tubules, administration of a digitalis compound would reduce Na$^+$ reabsorption, and this effect should be antagonized by elevation of the plasma concentration of K$^+$. These predictions have been verified.[14]

It also would be predicted that excretion of K$^+$ should increase if the sodium salt of any nonreabsorbable anion were substituted for Na$^+$ and Cl$^-$ in the tubular lumen. In these conditions, luminal Na$^+$ is still present to drive the exchange reaction; therefore, if no anion can be reabsorbed, some K$^+$ must be secreted proximally. An increased rate of K$^+$ excretion after the administration of such salts is a well known experimental finding. At any rate of Na^+ excretion, the rate of K^+ excretion is higher when the predominant anion in the urine is sulfate, PAH or ferrocyanide than when the anion is Cl^-.

Finally, it would be predicted that agents which inhibit proximal Na^+ reabsorption should also inhibit K^+ secretion. This prediction is true for all mercurial diuretics and is apparently true for xanthine diuretics *in vitro*.[18, 22] Other diuretic agents generally increase the rate at which HCO_3^-, in addition to Cl^-, is excreted. Elevation of HCO_3^- excretion elevates K^+ secretion.

CHLORIDE. Cl^- is reabsorbed in the proximal tubule. No maximum rate of transport has been defined; Cl^- reabsorption is always incomplete, but increases as the filtered load increases. Wesson has described the behavior of Cl^- both during stable conditions and during rapidly changing Cl^- loads.[43, 45] About 80 per cent of the filtered Na^+ is reabsorbed in association with Cl^-.

Homer Smith[33] postulated two distinct processes for Na^+ and Cl^- reabsorption: (i) a proximal process capable of transporting large amounts of solute, but incapable of producing any marked concentration gradients, and (ii) a distal process, of limited capacity, capable of producing and maintaining striking concentration gradients in either direction. The recent stop-flow experiments appear to support this view in that two regions of Na^+ and Cl^- transport have been found.[15, 27] A proximal region is sensitive to diuretic agents but does not lower luminal concentration. A distal region, on the other hand, lowers the concentration markedly but fails to respond to diuretic agents.

BICARBONATE.[10]   Reabsorption of HCO_3^- begins in the early part of the proximal tubule and normally continues in the collecting duct. The reabsorption depends on the filtered load, as in type B systems. The amount of HCO_3^- reabsorbed also varies in proportion to the CO_2 tension of plasma. At a CO_2 tension of 1.25 mEq. per liter of plasma (37 mm. Hg), about 25 mEq. of HCO_3^- are reabsorbed per liter of glomerular filtrate. Prolonged respiratory acidosis enhances the effect of CO_2.[36]

About 20 per cent of the filtered Na^+ is reabsorbed with HCO_3^-. In the collecting duct, any HCO_3^- still present is reabsorbed as the result of H^+ secretion. Luminal HCO_3^- combines with the secreted H^+ to form H_2CO_3, which decomposes to form CO_2 and water. The CO_2 diffuses across the tubular cells to the peritubular blood; the water enters the tubular lumen.* The reaction results in the net reabsorption of Na^+ and HCO_3^-. It is not known how HCO_3^- is reabsorbed proximally Two possibilities may be mentioned. H^+ secretion might extend throughout the proximal tubule, and proximal reabsorption might be secondary to H^+ secretion, just as distal reabsorption is. Alternatively, proximal HCO_3^- reabsorption might occur secondary to Na^+ reabsorption in the same manner as reabsorption of Cl^- does. Although the evidence is inadequate for differentiation of these possibilities, the former hypothesis is generally assumed to be correct.

The CO_2 tension is usually higher in urine than in plasma; but, when plasma HCO_3^- is low, urinary CO_2 tension may be lower than in plasma.[6] Low urinary CO_2 tension probably exists when HCO_3^- reabsorption is completed before the fluid leaves the proximal tubule—a reflection, but probably not a measure, of proximal reabsorption of HCO_3^-. Probably, urinary CO_2 tension is high when the distal H^+ secretory system is involved in HCO_3^- reabsorption. High urinary CO_2 tension reflects, and probably is a crude measure of, distal reabsorption of HCO_3^-.

HYDROGEN.[25]   Pitts and Alexander's demonstration[26] in 1945 that H^+ is secreted into the renal tubule was a milestone for two reasons. First, it provided convincing evidence that physiologically important solutes are secreted by the renal tubule. Previously, secretion of only nonphysiologic organic dyes had been proved. The experiments of Pitts and Alexander indicated that tubular secretion is important in the control of normal body constituents. The second important facet of their experiments is that they indicated a fruitful approach to the analysis of electrolyte excretion (and of type B

---

* The amount of water secreted is minute. If all the filtered HCO_3^- is reabsorbed via H^+ secretion, about 0.04 cm.³ of water will be added to the luminal contents each minute.

excretion in general). It is necessary to compare the quantities excreted and filtered rather than to compare clearances.

H^+ is secreted into the distal portion of the nephron in an exchange in which Na^+ is reabsorbed from the lumen and H^+ is secreted into it. Much of this exchange may take place in the collecting duct,[39] but it may also occur in the proximal tubule. There is no sharply defined maximum rate, since the rate at which the ion exchange proceeds depends on the simultaneous availability of luminal Na^+ and cellular H^+. Thus, the rate of H^+ secretion tends to be increased both by an increase in the rate of Na^+ excretion (i.e., an increase in the rate at which Na^+ is presented to the distal tubular cells) and by an increase in the amount of cellular H^+ available to the transport mechanism.

Secretion of H^+ has three consequences: (i) it causes the reabsorption of filtered HCO_3^-; (ii) it acidifies the urine; and (iii) it is indirectly responsible for the secretion of NH_4^+. In the proximal tubule, H^+ secretion, if present, gives rise only to HCO_3^- reabsorption, as discussed on page 863. Distally, when the reabsorption of HCO_3^- has been completed, additional secretion of H^+ leads to an acid urine. The transport systems appear to work with decreasing efficiency as the gradient of H^+ concentration is increased, and secretion comes to a halt when the ratio of H^+ across the cell membrane is about 400. (The minimum urinary pH is about 4.4. If the pH of the tubular cell is about 7.0, the ratio of H^+ between the two solutions is $10^{2.6} = 400$.) The total amount of titratable acid that can be secreted therefore depends on the buffer capacity of urine. If the urine is highly buffered, large amounts of H^+ can be added to it without producing large changes in urinary pH. Conversely, when the buffer capacity is very low, only small amounts of H^+ can be added before urinary pH falls to such a low level that H^+ transport is reduced.

Ammonia.[23] NH_3 is formed by the deamination of amino acids by the cells of the distal tubule or of the collecting duct. Ullrich et al.[38] have presented evidence that the site is the collecting duct. The luminal membrane is freely permeable to NH_3, and it diffuses into the tubular lumen. Here, the free base ionizes and produces its conjugate acid, NH_4^+. The tubular epithelium is only slightly permeable to NH_4^+, and most of this acid is therefore trapped in the lumen and destined for excretion. The relative concentrations of NH_3 and NH_4^+ in luminal fluid can be determined by solving the equilibrium equation $[NH_3][H^+]/[NH_4^+] = K$, where K has the value of $10^{-9.3}$. Some of the NH_4^+ formed in the tubular lumen subsequently diffuses back into epithelial cells as a result of the concentration gradient of this ion, but the amount of this diffusion is probably small. The rate of ammonia excretion is the product of the urine flow and the concentration of NH_4^+ (the concentration of NH_3 is so low that it can be neglected). The major variables determining this concentration are the urinary pH and the rate at which NH_3 is produced by renal cells. The diffusion of NH_3 into the tubular lumen uses up H^+ and tends to keep the luminal pH from falling as rapidly as it would if NH_3 were not produced. Consequently, the secretion of NH_3 allows H^+ secretion to continue, and the continuance of H^+ secretion allows still more NH_4^+ to be excreted.

The secretion of each H^+ leaves a HCO_3^- within the tubular cell and also brings into the cell a Na^+. The Na^+ is transported out of the cell into the peritubular blood in association with the HCO_3^-. Thus, the secretion of each H^+, whether involved in reabsorption of HCO_3^-, urinary acidification or NH^+ excretion, results in the return of Na^+ and HCO_3^- to peritubular blood. When titratable acid and NH_4^+ are being excreted, renal venous blood contains not only all the HCO_3^- that entered the kidney (for reabsorption of HCO_3^- is complete in this condition), but an additional amount of HCO_3^- equal to the amounts of titratable acid and NH_4^+ that have been excreted. These relationships are illustrated in Figure 512.

POTASSIUM.[4]   The clearance ratio of K^+ is normally less than 1, a fact demonstrating that K^+ is reabsorbed. In 1948, Berliner and Kennedy[1] and Mudge *et al.*[20] simultaneously reported that the clearance ratio of K^+ could exceed 1 and that tubular secretion, as well as tubular reabsorption, takes place. Reabsorption occurs in the proximal and secretion in the distal tubule. Almost all of the filtered K^+ is reabsorbed, and almost all of the K^+ which appears in the urine enters the tubule via the secretory process.[3, 15] The secretory system has the important regulatory role. This system is an ion exchange in which lumen Na^+ is reabsorbed and interstitial K^+ is secreted.[2] The transport system

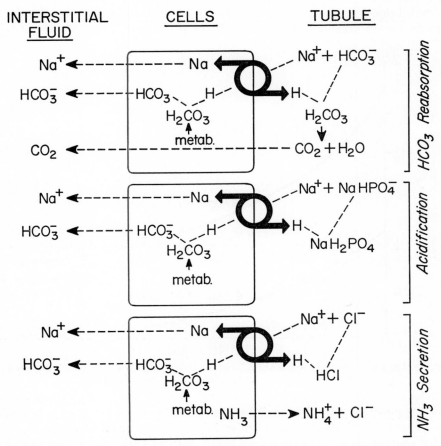

FIG. 512.   Summary of effects of distal hydrogen ion exchange. Broken lines indicate passive transport; solid lines, active transport.

is type B, the rate depending on the availability of both luminal Na^+ and cellular K^+. Although cellular K^+ is important in determining the rate of secretion, the K^+ must eventually come from the blood perfusing the cells. An equal amount of Na^+ is reabsorbed when K^+ is secreted, but this amounts only to about 1 per cent of the filtered Na^+. Thus, secretion of K^+ is important in the regulation of body K^+, but is insignificant in the regulation of body Na^+.

The mechanisms involved in the reabsorption and secretion of K^+ are entirely unknown, but certain clues are available. K^+ secretion is probably active since (i) it is inhibited by metabolic inhibitors,[22] (ii) it is independent of the rate of urine flow,[15] (iii) a maximum rate of transport has been observed in the chicken,[24] and (iv) it is homeostatic in nature. The process is an exchange of luminal Na^+ for cellular or inter-stitial K^+. Since the postulated mechanism for Na^+ involves such an ion exchange, since the agents which decrease Na^+ reabsorption also decrease K^+ secretion (as long as they do not produce a large change in the excretion of HCO_3^-), and since the conditions which favor Na^+ reabsorption while interdicting anion reabsorption also favor K^+ secretion, it seems likely that K^+ secretion in the distal tubule is accomplished by the mechanism which accomplishes the reabsorption of Na^+ in the proximal tubule.

WATER.[11]   Most of the water filtered from the plasma in the glomeruli is reabsorbed in the tubules; only 1 to 2 per cent of the amount filtered is normally excreted in the urine. Both urine flow and the concentration of solute particles in the urine may vary widely; the rate of urine flow may be less than 1 per cent or more than 50 per cent of

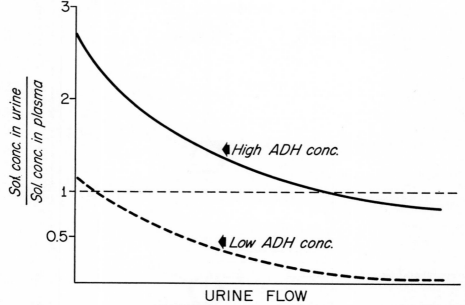

FIG. 513.   Relationship between urine flow ($\dot{V}_u$) and the ratio of urinary to plasma solute concentration (C_u/C_p). *Solid line*, Dehydration; *dashed line*, hydration.

the rate of glomerular filtration, and the concentration of solute may vary from almost zero to three or four times the concentration in the glomerular filtrate.

The concentration of solute in the urine depends both on the concentration of antidiuretic hormone (ADH) in the plasma perfusing the kidney and on the rate of urine flow. ADH synthesis in the hypothalamus, its passage from the hypothalamus to the hypophysis, and its release into the blood stream are discussed in Chapter 52.

When plasma entering the kidney contains a high concentration of ADH, the solute concentration is higher in the urine than in plasma; urine is *hypertonic* to plasma. When little or no ADH enters the kidney, the concentration of solute is much lower in the urine than in plasma; urine is *hypotonic* to plasma. The rate at which ADH is released depends on the solute concentration in circulating plasma. If the concentration is high, the hypophysis releases ADH into the blood. When the hormone reaches the kidney, water reabsorption is promoted and the urine becomes hypertonic. The water returned to the body reduces the concentration of the solute in body fluids. Conversely, if the concentration of solute in plasma is low, ADH is not released. In these circumstances, hypotonic urine is excreted, and large amounts of water are lost from the body. This loss tends to concentrate body fluids.

Within the limits set by the concentration of ADH in the plasma entering the kidney, the concentration of solute in the formed urine depends on the rate of urine flow. At low rates of flow, solute concentration is relatively high; it decreases progressively as urine flow increases. Urinary concentration of solute as a function of both rate of urinary flow and release of ADH is depicted in Figure 513.

In terms of the mechanisms of transport of water, the nephron is apparently divisible into three parts. The proximal tubule is freely permeable to water. The mol fraction of water is the same in cortical interstitial fluid and in plasma. As solute is reabsorbed, the mol fraction of water in the luminal solution becomes higher than the mol fraction of water in the interstitial fluid surrounding the nephron. A gradient of concentration of water is set up between the two phases, and water moves from the tubular lumen to

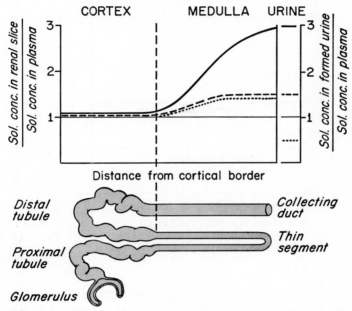

FIG. 514.   Solute concentration in slices of kidney as a function of depth. A juxtamedullary nephron is also shown to indicate structures present at each level. Concentrations are shown for three conditions: low urine flow with adequate ADH (*solid line*), high urine flow with adequate ADH (*dashed line*), and high urine flow with inadequate ADH (*dotted line*). It should be remembered that a renal slice contains both tubular contents and interstitial fluid. (Data from Ullrich and Jarausch. *Pflügers Arch. ges. Physiol.*, 1958, *267*:491–496.)

the interstitial fluid. Since the proximal tubular cells are apparently quite permeable to water, the concentration gradient remains low, and the fluid traversing the proximal tubule remains nearly isotonic to plasma. Urinary concentrations of solute must therefore be modified by processes occurring in Henle's loop, the distal tubule or the collecting duct.

Current explanations of the mechanisms modifying solute concentration derive from four lines of evidence.

(i) Mammals can excrete urine with a solute concentration greater or less than that in plasma. The maximum concentration that can be produced in different animals correlates closely with the length of the thin segments. Only birds and mammals have true thin segments and can elaborate urine which is hypertonic to plasma.

(ii) The mol fraction of solute is lower in slices of kidney taken from the cortex than in slices taken from the medulla. The deeper the site in the medulla from which the sample is derived, the higher the mol fraction of solute.[41] When adequate amounts of ADH are present, the solute concentration of the formed urine approximates that found in the tips of the renal papillae. During water diuresis, when ADH is absent, the solute concentrations of the papillary tips and the formed urine are disparate (Fig. 514).[46]

(iii) Proximal tubular fluid is isotonic to plasma, but fluid collected from the proximal portion of the distal tubule is hypotonic to plasma during the production of either hypertonic or hypotonic urine. When ADH is present, the fluid in the distal portions of the distal tubule is again isotonic to plasma. In the collecting duct, the solute concentration rises still higher to produce a urine which is hypertonic to plasma. In contrast, when ADH is not present, the solute concentration of the already hypotonic fluid decreases during its passage through the distal tubules and collecting duct. The concentration of luminal fluid as a function of distance along the distal tubule is depicted in Figure 515.

(iv) ADH increases the permeability of frog skin to water.[28]

The mol fraction of water is higher in the fluid which enters the distal tubule than in the cortical interstitital fluid. As fluid leaves the distal tubule and passes through the collecting ducts, traveling progressively deeper into the medulla, the surrounding mol fraction of water falls progressively. Hence, at all times after leaving the thin segment,

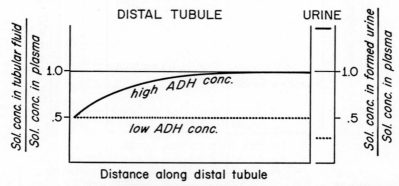

FIG. 515. Solute concentration of tubular fluid as a function of length along the distal tubule, when adequate amounts of ADH are present (*solid line*) and during water diuresis (*dotted line*). (Data from Wirz, *Helv. physiol. acta*, 1956, *14*:353–362, and Gottschalk and Mylle, *Amer. J. Physiol.*, 1959, *196*:927–936.)

tubular fluid flows past interstitial fluid with a mol fraction of water lower than its own. The concentration gradient tends to drive water out of the distal tubule and collecting duct. When ADH is present, the membranes of the distal tubule and collecting duct are highly permeable to water, and the efflux of water from tubular to interstitial fluid is high. Reabsorption of water in the distal tubule reduces the water concentration of luminal fluid from the high value it has when it enters to a value very near that of cortical interstitial fluid (or plasma). Subsequent reabsorption of water in the collecting ducts lowers the water concentration of luminal fluid still further and produces a urine which is hypertonic to plasma. When ADH is absent, the two terminal segments of the nephron are not particularly permeable to water. Despite a high gradient, very little water is reabsorbed, and most of the water that enters the distal tubule is excreted in the urine. Under these conditions, the concentration of water is even higher in the formed urine than in the fluid that enters the distal tubule, owing to the distal reabsorption of HCO_3^-.[12]

The system described above accounts for the production of urine which is hypertonic or hypotonic to plasma. However, two points are still unexplained. First, how is the medullary interstitial fluid rendered and maintained hypertonic to systemic plasma; second, how does the fluid in the ascending limb become hypotonic to plasma?

The luminal fluid enters the descending limb of the thin segment as a solution isotonic to plasma, but emerges from the ascending limb hypotonic to plasma. Either water is added to tubular fluid or solute is removed from it in this segment. Although the available data do not distinguish between these alternatives, Na^+ reabsorption from the ascending limb of Henle's loop is assumed to be the process responsible.[5]

In the steady state, the net amount of water entering the interstitial fluid from the collecting duct and the blood must equal the amount which leaves the duct. If excretion of solute is suddenly elevated, more fluid enters the collecting duct and, for any concentration gradient, more fluid can be reabsorbed into the interstitial fluid. A transient state is produced during which the medulla gains water. Water accumulates in the interstitial fluid until the solute concentration has decreased sufficiently to bring the medulla back into a steady state. The result is that, during osmotic diuresis, the maximum solute concentration attained in the medulla is lower than the concentration attained during low rates of urine flow.

INTEGRATION OF TUBULAR FUNCTIONS

As the glomerular filtrate enters the proximal tubule, transtubular transport of solute and water begins. Reabsorption of glucose and amino acids and the secretion of PAH occur only in this region of the tubule; the amounts of these substances leaving this region of the nephron are the amounts destined for excretion. As a result of the active transport of Na^+, both Cl^- and HCO_3^- are reabsorbed. About 90 per cent of the filtered Na^+ is reabsorbed by active transport in the proximal tubule. This process is responsible for all reabsorption of Cl^- and, usually, for about half the reabsorption of HCO_3^-. Most of the filtered K^+ is reabsorbed. The proximal tubule is freely permeable to water, and, as solute is reabsorbed, water is reabsorbed at an equivalent rate. The solute concentration in the luminal fluid leaving the proximal tubule is the same as that of systemic blood, but the volume flow has been reduced to about 10 per cent of the filtration rate.

The tubular fluid then enters the thin segment, which dips into the medulla. In the ascending limb of the loop of Henle, the tubular fluid is diluted and, concomitantly, medullary interstitial fluid is concentrated.

In the distal tubule and collecting duct, cation exchanges predominate. Luminal Na^+ is reabsorbed in exchange for both H^+ and K^+. Secretion of H^+ here normally accounts for about 9 per cent and secretion of K^+ for about 1 per cent of the total Na^+ reabsorption. Almost all of the K^+ appearing in the urine enters the lumen in the distal tubule via the secretory process. The distal secretion of H^+ brings about additional reabsorption of HCO_3^-. When the amount of HCO_3^- entering the distal tubule from the thin segment is large, the whole H^+ secretory system may be involved in reabsorption of HCO_3^-. When the amount of entering HCO_3^- is small, more H^+ is secreted per minute than is necessary to complete HCO_3^- reabsorption. The secretion of additional H^+ renders the tubular fluid acid. As the pH of luminal fluid falls. NH_3, which is produced in distal tubular cells, diffuses across the cell membrane into the tubular fluid. There, most of the NH_3 is converted into the conjugate acid, NH_4^+. K^+ secretion probably takes place in the distal tubule, whereas H^+ and NH_3 secretion probably occur in the collecting duct.

The distal tubule is permeable to water in the presence of ADH. When this hormone is present, the dilute tubular fluid entering the distal tubule rapidly loses water to the cortical interstitial compartment. Under these conditions, fluid leaving the distal tubule has a solute concentration the same as that of systemic blood. In the absence of ADH, water reabsorption does not occur, and the volume of fluid flowing out of the distal tubule is approximately the same as the volume flowing into it.

Upon leaving the distal tubule, the fluid enters the collecting ducts. These ducts traverse the medulla. When ADH is present, the epithelium of this region is permeable to water, which is abstracted from tubular fluid so that the urine is concentrated. The final concentration is approximately the same as that at the tip of the renal papillae. When ADH is not present, the collecting ducts act only as conduits, and the volume flow that enters is substantially identical to the urinary flow.

DIURESIS

The condition in which there is a high rate of urine flow is called "diuresis." Two general types exist: *water diuresis* and *osmotic diuresis*. A water diuresis occurs when the blood contains inadequate amounts of ADH. Solute transport is affected only minimally, but an abnormally high rate of water excretion is observed. The total solute concentration is very low and may be as low as one-tenth that of plasma. Ingestion of water causes a water diuresis by inhibiting the release of ADH, as does ingestion of alcohol. *Diabetes insipidus* is a state of permanent water diuresis caused by destruction of the posterior pituitary or of the supraventricular nucleus of the hypothalamus. Administration of exogenous ADH reduces a water diuresis.

Osmotic diuresis results from an increase in the rate of solute excretion. Since water excretion varies directly with solute excretion, an increase in the latter will cause an increase in the former. Generally, osmotic diuresis is induced either without change in water balance or in association with mild dehydration. Adequate ADH is present to insure the formation of urine with a solute concentration the same as that at the tips of renal papillae. The sole cause for the increase in urine flow is an increase in solute excretion. Excessive excretion of any solute will produce an osmotic diuresis. Thus, in the diabetic patient, the concentration of glucose in the plasma is high, and the load of glucose filtered at the glomerulus is greater than Tm_G. Large amounts of glucose may be excreted in the urine. In addition, organic acids are incompletely metabolized, and these compounds must also be excreted. The consequent elevation of solute excretion brings about an elevation of urine flow. After large doses of urea have been administered, significant quantities may escape into the urine, producing osmotic diuresis. Inhibition of Na^+ reabsorption by diuretic agents produces an osmotic diuresis in which the high rate of excretion of Na^+ and its attendant anion are responsible for the increase in urine flow.

Regardless of the cause of an osmotic diuresis, if it is sufficiently severe, the rate of Na^+ excretion is increased. Two explanations have been advanced for this phenomenon, which is picturesquely referred to as "sweeping out Na^+." Wesson and Anslow[44] call attention to the fact that the presence of an osmotic diuretic lowers the Na^+ concentration in proximal tubules and that the cells in these tubules must then transport Na^+ against a significant concentration gradient. These workers suggest that when the concentration gradient becomes too large, the system simply is unable to reabsorb more Na^+, and the Na^+ remaining in the lumen escapes into the urine. Mudge *et al.*[21] prefer to think of the "sweeping out" as reflecting a reduced time of contact between the fluid and tubular cells when the rate of urine flow is high. No choice between these hypotheses can now be made.

Clinically useful diuretic agents decrease Na^+ reabsorption and thus lead to an increase in the rate of Na^+ excretion. This increase in the rate of Na^+ excretion is the primary and desired effect, and the increase in urine flow is an automatic consequence.

ENDOCRINE CONTROL OF RENAL FUNCTION

The kidneys are autonomous to a remarkable degree. Solute and water excretion vary widely with the composition of the plasma. This intrinsic regulation of renal function, however, can be modified by hormones. Regulation of renal function is a defense in depth; a mean value for the transport is established by the endocrine milieu, and moment-to-moment variations in transport around this mean result from local variations in the rate at which material is presented to tubular cells. We normally think only of these rapid changes; and, indeed, as long as the external environment is not varied too greatly, the slower hormonally induced changes in renal function may not appear. When severe stress is laid on the animal's regulatory systems, however, hormonal regulation is brought into play. Four different effects may be mentioned. These are those induced by ADH, by parathyroid hormone, by the renotrophic hormones, and by aldosterone. ADH has been discussed above; its effect, unlike that of other hormones, is rapid. The effect of ADH on tubular permeability of water is immediate, and changes in the ADH concentration in the blood lag only ten to 15 minutes behind changes in the solute concentration.

Increases in the concentration of circulating parathyroid hormone increase the rate of phosphate excretion by reducing net tubular reabsorption. The release of parathyroid hormone is regulated by the plasma concentration of calcium; as the calcium concentration falls, the amount of circulating hormone rises. Plasma is nearly a saturated solution of calcium phosphate, and the product of the calcium and the phosphate concentrations is about constant. As more parathyroid hormone is released, more phosphate is excreted. The plasma phosphate concentration then falls, and the plasma calcium concentration rises. This last change reduces the release of the hormone. The kidney and the parathyroid gland work together to control calcium and phosphate balance.

Hormones of the third group modify cellular metabolism throughout the body, and renal cells are only one of their points of action. Somatotropin from the anterior pituitary, corticosterone and cortisol from the adrenal cortex, and thyroid hormone all exhibit a renotrophic action. That is, they increase the total amount of renal tissue, the plasma flow rate, the filtration rate and all renal function. This effect is not regulatory, but is exerted because renal cells, like all other cells, respond to these hormones.

Aldosterone, which is released from the adrenal cortex, has a striking effect on the renal transport of Na^+ and K^+. This effect develops over days or weeks and is of long duration. If excessive aldosterone is present, an excessive amount of Na^+ is retained in the body. K^+ secretion is also hyperactive, and an excessive amount of this ion is lost. Absence of the hormone leads to opposite changes. In adrenal insufficiency, the loss of Na^+ leads to a large loss of extracellular fluid. Circulatory collapse eventually ensues. Striking as the effects of aldosterone on renal ion transport are, this hormone probably is not primarily concerned with the regulation of renal function, for it seems to enhance the rate of active Na^+ extrusion from all cells in the body.[48]

Attention has been directed to the renal action of aldosterone for two reasons. First, the renal effect is the most obvious one in the body. As discussed in Chapter 1, a 5 per cent change in Na^+ pumping is barely detectable in muscle or brain tissue. In the kidney, however, a 5 per cent increase in Na^+ reabsorption results in striking retention of this ion. The situation is simply a reflection of the extremely high flux rates in the kidney and of the fact that Na^+ excretion is always very small in comparison with Na^+ reabsorption. Second, renal ion transport modifies the release of aldosterone itself.

There appear to be two important stimuli for aldosterone secretion: (i) the ratio of K^+ to Na^+ concentration in plasma, and (ii) the blood volume. At high values of the ion concentration ratio, aldosterone is released at a high rate. As a result of this increase in circulating aldosterone, Na^+ reabsorption and K^+ secretion increase so that the ratio is reduced. At low values of the ion concentration ratio, the opposite changes occur, and the ratio is brought back toward normal. Increase in blood volume decreases and depletion of blood volume increases the rate at which aldosterone is released. Since the blood volume varies with the size of the extracellular fluid compartment, Na^+ excretion will vary in such a manner as to tend to keep blood volume constant. The changes in aldosterone secretion just discussed may be hormonally mediated.[7] The kidney and the adrenal cortex therefore constitute a long-term controlling system which maintains the cation composition and volume of the plasma.

REFERENCES

1. BERLINER, R. W. and KENNEDY, T. J. *Proc. Soc. exp. Biol. (N. Y.)*, 1948, *67*:542–545.

2. BERLINER, R. W., KENNEDY, T. J. and HILTON, J. G. *Amer. J. Physiol.*, 1950, *162*:348–367.

3. BERLINER, R. W., KENNEDY, T. J. and ORLOFF, J. *Amer. J. Med*, 1951, *11*:274–282.

4. BERLINER, R. W., KENNEDY, T. J. and ORLOFF, J. *Arch. int. Pharmacodyn.*, 1954, *97*:299–312.

5. BERLINER, R. W., LEVINSKY, N. G., DAVIDSON, D. G. and EDAN, M. *Amer. J. Med.*, 1958, *24*:72–86.

6. BRODSKY, W. A., MILEY, J. F., KAIM, J. T. and NARESCHANDRA, P. S. *Amer. J. Phsyiol.*, 1958, *193*:108–122.

7. FARRELL, G. *Physiol. Rev.*, 1958, *38*:709–728.

8. FORSTER, R. P. *Amer. J. Physiol.*, 1954, *179*:372–377.

9. GIEBISCH, G. *J. cell. comp. Physiol.*, 1958, *51*:221–239.

10. GILMAN, A. and BRAZEAU, P. *Amer. J. Med.*, 1953, *15*:765–770.

11. GOTTSCHALK, C. W. and MYLLE, M. *Amer. J. Physiol.*, 1959, *196*:927–936.

12. HILGER, H. H., KLUMPER, J. D. and ULLRICH, K. J. *Pflüg. Arch. ges. Physiol.*, 1958, *267*:218–237.

13. HINSHAW, L. B., DAY, S. B. and CARLSON, C. H. *Amer. J. Physiol.*, 1959, *197*:309–312.

14. KOCH, A. *Physiologist*, 1958, *1*:42.

15. KOCH, A., BRAZEAU, P. and GILMAN, A. *Amer. J. Physiol.*, 1956, *186*:350–356.

16. MALVIN, R. L., WILDE, W. S. and SULLIVAN, L. P. *Amer. J. Physiol.*, 1958, *194*:135–142.

17. MAXIMOW, A. and BLOOM, W. *Textbook of histology*, 7th ed. Philadelphia, W. B. Saunders, 1957.

18. McBRIDE, W. O., WEINER, I. M. and MUDGE, G. H. *Fed. Proc.*, 1958, *17*:107.

19. MOORE, W. J. *Physical chemistry*, 2nd ed. New York, Prentice-Hall, Inc., 1955.

20. MUDGE, G. H., FOULKS, J. and GILMAN, A. *Proc. Soc. exp. Biol. (N. Y.)*, 1948, *67*:542–545.

21. MUDGE, G. H., FOULKS, J. and GILMAN, A. *Amer. J. Physiol.*, 1949, *158*:218–230.

22. MUDGE, G. H., FOULKS, J. and GILMAN, A. *Amer. J. Physiol.*, 1950, *161*:159–166.

23. ORLOFF, J. and BERLINER, R. W. *J. clin. Invest.*, 1956, *35*:223–235.

24. ORLOFF, J. and DAVIDSON, D. G. *J. clin. Invest.*, 1959, *38*:21–30.

25. PITTS, R. F. *Fed. Proc.*, 1948, *7*:418–426.

26. PITTS, R. F. and ALEXANDER, R. S. *Amer. J Physiol.*, 1945, *144*:239–254.

27. PITTS, R. F., GURD, R. S., KESSLER, R. H. and HIERHOLZER, K. *Amer. J Physiol.*, 1958, *194*:125–134.

28. SAWYER, W. H. Pp. 171–179 in *The neurohypophysis, Symposium of the Colston Research Society*, H. HELLER, ed. New York, Academic Press, 1957.

29. SCHER, A. M. *Nature (Lond.)*, 1959, *184*:1322–1323.

30. SCHMIDT-NIELSEN, B. *Physiol. Rev.*, 1958, *38*:139–168.

31. SCHMIDT-NIELSEN, B. *Amer. J. Physiol.*, 1958, *194*:221–228.

32. SHANNON, J. A. and FISHER, S. *Amer. J. Physiol.*, 1938, *122*:765–774.

33. SMITH, H. W. *The kidney, its structure and function in health and disease*. New York, Oxford University Press, 1951.

34. SMITH, H. W. *Principles of renal physiology*. New York, Oxford University Press, 1956.

35. SMITH, H. W., FINKELSTEIN, N., ALIMINOSA, L., CRAWFORD, B. and GRABER, M. *J. clin. Invest.*, 1945, *24*:388–404.

36. SULLIVAN, W. J. and DORMAN, P. J. *J. clin. Invest.*, 1955, *34*:268–276.

37. THOMPSON, D. D., KAVALER, F., LOZANO, R. and PITTS, R. F. *Amer. J. Physiol.*, 1957, *191*:493–500.

38. ULLRICH, K. J., DRENCKHAHN, F. O. and JARAUSCH, K. H. *Pflüg. Arch. ges. Physiol.*, 1955, *261*:62–77.

39. ULLRICH, K. J. and EIGLER, F. W. *Pflüg. Arch. ges. Physiol.*, 1958, *267*:491–496.

40. ULLRICH, K. J., HILGER, H. H. and KLUMPER, J. D. *Pflüg. Arch. ges. Physiol.*, 1958, *267*:244–250.

41. ULLRICH, K. J. and JARAUSCH, K. H. *Pflüg. Arch. ges. Physiol.*, 1956, *262*:537–550.

42. WALKER, A. M., BOTT, P. A., OLIVER, J. and MacDOWELL, M. C. *Amer. J. Physiol.*, 1941, *134*:580–595.

43. WESSON, L. G., JR. *Amer. J. Physiol.*, 1958, *195*:133–136.

44. WESSON, L. G., JR. and ANSLOW, W. P. *Amer. J. Physiol.*, 1948, *153*:465–474.

45. WESSON, L. G., JR. and ANSLOW, W. P., JR. *Amer. J. Physiol.*, 1955, *180*:237–248.

46. WIRZ, H. *Helv. physiol. acta*, 1956, *14*:353–362.

47. WIRZ, H. and BOTT, P. A. *Proc. Soc. exp. Biol. (N. Y.)*, 1954, *87*:405–407.

48. WOODBURY, D. M. and KOCH, A. *Proc. Soc. exp. Biol. (N. Y.)*, 1957, *94*:720–723.

CHAPTER 40

Physiology of Body Fluids

By RAÚL HERNÁNDEZ-PEÓN

DISTRIBUTION, COMPOSITION AND MEASUREMENT

Distribution and Composition. Total body water constitutes a very high proportion of the body weight in the "average" man. However, comparisons of total body water and total body weight result in an illusory concept of the range of individual variation in body fluids, because fatty tissue, which occurs in various amounts in different persons, contains little water. If one compares individuals on the basis of fat-free tissues only (lean body mass), the relation between total body fluids and tissue weight is remarkably constant[43] (Fig. 516). In the adult this proportion amounts to 72 per cent ± a standard deviation of 3. This figure is higher in the newborn, about 82 per cent.[44, 48] Fluids in the body are distributed in several natural compartments, between which a continuous exchange takes place in addition to the exchange with the external environment. It is logical to consider the total body fluid to be distributed in two main compartments: the fluid contained within cells being *intracellular fluid*, and that outside the cells being *extracellular fluid*. By methods to be described later, it has been possible to estimate the total volume of body water as well as the volumes in the individual compartments. The values obtained by these methods are summarized in Tables 27 and 28.

Extracellular fluid. This portion constitutes the internal environment that surrounds the cells individually and collectively, and is the medium through which exchanges between the cells and their external environment occur. The extracellular fluid itself can be separated into two general subdivisions: the intravascular fluid and the extravascular fluid. The blood plasma constitutes the bulk of the intravascular fluid and contains the major portion of the proteins of the extracellular space. The extravascular fluid includes all extracellular fluid found outside the vascular bed. Extravascular fluid

873

is further compartmentalized according to the different anatomic spaces involved. The largest proportion of the extravascular fluid is the interstitial fluid which fills the intercellular spaces; lymph is considered interstitial, since the lymphatic vessels simply drain fluid from the interstitial spaces. The rest of the extracellular fluid outside the vessels is located in special compartments of the body: cerebrospinal fluid, aqueous humor of the eye, synovial fluid, bile, secretions in glandular lumina, water in the gastrointestinal tract, and fluid to be excreted as urine in the urinary tract. Although a portion of the extravascular fluid in these special compartments is in a strict sense outside of the body, all this fluid is included in the total body water. The fluid contained within membranes having permeability characteristics differing from those of most capillary walls forms a "confined" portion of the extravascular fluid in contrast with most of the interstitial fluid.

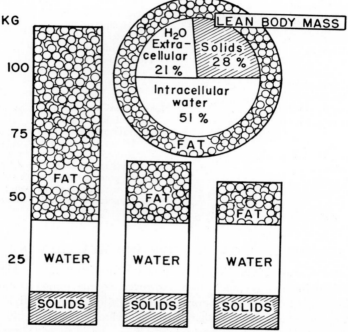

FIG. 516.　Variability of fat content with respect to body weight and percentage of water in lean body mass found in adult.

Extracellular fluid has an ionic composition similar to that of sea water, and the ions are found in approximately the same relative proportions, although the total ionic concentration of sea water is several times that of extracellular fluid. This resemblance suggests that extracellular fluid was originally derived from the ancient oceans, which were more dilute than those of today. Anions in extracellular fluid include chloride, bicarbonate, sulfate, phosphate and small amounts of protein; the cations are sodium, potassium, calcium and magnesium. Among the cations, sodium has the highest concentration and is the predominant electrolyte responsible for the osmotic pressure of this fluid phase of the body. The composition differs in the various divisions of the extracellular fluid; for example, interstitial fluid differs from plasma mainly in protein content. Proteins of the interstitial fluid are found mainly in lymph, especially in lymph draining from the liver. The approximate composition of various extracellular fluids is given in Table 26.

Various parts of the "confined" portion of the extravascular fluid (sweat, saliva, urine in the bladder) have osmotic pressures which differ from that of plasma. However,

*TABLE 26. APPROXIMATE COMPOSITION OF VARIOUS EXTRACELLULAR FLUIDS**

FLUID	Na mM./l.	K mM./l.	Ca mM./l.	Mg mM./l.	Cl mM./l.	HCO₃ mM./l.	PROTEIN gm./l.	WATER* gm./l.
Serum	142	4.3	2.5	1.7	100	25	70	940
Ultrafiltrate of serum	145	3.3	1.6	1.2	111	28		993
Spinal fluid	147	2.8	1.7		125	21		993
Gastric juice	20	8			145			993
Bile	140	8			108	38		990
Pancreatic juice	140	5			40	110		993
Jejunal juice	138	5			110	30		993
Sweat	82	5			85			993

* It must be noted that these values, especially those for plasma, are somewhat lower when expressed per liter of water.

(From Darrow, *New Engl. J. Med.*, 1945, *233*:91–97.)

an osmotic pressure the same as that of plasma is maintained in most fluid which is bathing cells.[39] Although a dynamic osmotic equilibrium appears to prevail between the extracellular and intracellular fluids, the assumption of a uniform osmotic pressure throughout the body has been questioned (see below).[42]

Intracellular fluid. It is important to note that the intracellular fluid volume is more than twice that of extracellular fluid. The main anions of the intracellular fluid are phosphate and protein; however, bicarbonate, sulfate and chloride are also present. The chief intracellular cations are potassium and magnesium, but there is also intracellular sodium. The ionic composition varies in different tissues. The cells of mammalian skeletal muscle, liver, spleen, heart, brain and kidney contain very little, if any, chloride; whereas red blood cells, connective tissue, gastric mucosa, testes and, probably, lung tissue contain significant quantities of chloride.[33] The use of isotopic tracers has permitted estimation in man of the average concentrations of total exchangeable electrolytes in the two major fluid compartments. The concentration of potassium in the intracellular phase has been estimated to vary between 96 and 125 mEq. per liter of intracellular water, with an average of 112 mEq. per liter. Total intracellular sodium averages 37 mEq. per liter of intracellular water (range 31 to 43).[11] It is worth noting that total exchangeable sodium represents only slightly more than one-half of total body sodium; the remainder is found in bone and cartilage, and most of it is presumably present as an insoluble or undissociated compound.[24] Because the volume of intracellular fluid is large, the total amount of intracellular sodium constitutes about one-third of the total exchangeable sodium (excluding bone sodium). The total intracellular chloride in man has been estimated to have an average concentration of 25 mEq. per liter (range 21 to 30) and represents about 30 per cent (range 20 to 40) of the total chloride.[12] It must be re-emphasized that the total values just mentioned are not directly applicable to individual tissues.

Measurement. It is not a simple matter to measure the volume of water in the compartments described above, and indirect methods are necessarily used. The technique commonly used is based on the dilution principle.[14] Originally applied with dyes in humans by Keith, Rowntree and Geraghty in 1915 this same principle applied with radioactive isotopes has recently provided quantitatively more accurate information. It will be recalled that the dilution principle is that the amount of a substance (Q_s)

dissolved in a volume of solution (V) is the product of the concentration of the substance, [S], and the volume, or $Q = [S]V$. The desired volume is $V = Q/[S]$, and both Q and [S] are measurable. In determinations of body fluid the factor of excretion usually must be considered. Thus, if the tracer substance is assumed to be uniformly distributed throughout the physiologic solution, this simple formula can be derived:

$$\text{Volume of distribution} = \frac{\text{Amount injected} - \text{amount excreted}}{\text{Concentration in diluting fluid}}.$$

An ideal substance for measurement of body fluids by the dilution principle would fulfill the following requirements: (i) no toxicity, (ii) no formation or destruction in the body, (iii) no combination with other body constituents, (iv) no excretion during the period of distribution, (v) rapid and uniform distribution throughout the space to be measured, (vi) absolute restraint within the space to be measured, (vii) no influence on body fluid distribution, and (viii) accurate and easy quantitative determination.

Total body water. Estimates of total body water in the living organism have been attempted by dilution with substances that theoretically distribute rapidly throughout the body. Among the materials used, the following may be listed: urea, thiourea, sulfanilamide, antipyrine, deuterium oxide (heavy water) and tritium oxide.* Total body water has also been calculated by estimating the subject's specific gravity (immersion technique); this method has yielded figures of the same order of magnitude as those obtained by heavy water and antipyrine methods. A summary of the values obtained for total body water as a function of age and sex is given in Table 27.

TABLE 27. TOTAL BODY WATER

SUBJECTS	AGE	TOTAL BODY WATER ml./kg.		TOTAL BODY WATER liters/sq. m. body surface	
		Mean	Range	Mean	Range
	Range				
Children	2–28 (days)	767	718–830	12.1	9.8–13.8
	1–9 (months)	626	530–708	12.9	11.3–14.6
	1–9 (years)	589	552–628	14.2	13.1–16.7
Adult Men	YEARS 10.5–15.6	590	518–632	19.2	15.7–24.1
	17–34	611	533–703	23.3	21.2–26.1
	35–52	554	447–641	22.2	20.0–24.6
	57–86	543	478–628	20.8	19.7–22.5
Adult Women	12–15	562	498–595	17.6	16.0–19.4
	20–31	512	456–599	18.0	15.3–20.0
	36–54	482	405–543	17.7	16.2–19.5
	60–82	462	420–534	17.1	16.1–18.2

(Values taken from Edelman *et al.*, *Surg. Gynec. Obstet.*, 1952, *95*:1–12.)

* The latter two contain hydrogen isotopes which exchange with H atoms in body water and with the exchangeable H atoms in organic molecules. However, since these exchangeable H atoms in organic molecules have been estimated to correspond to a water equivalent of only 0.5 to 2.0 per cent of the body weight in man,[41] this factor does not preclude reasonable accuracy in determinations of body water by the use of these tracers.

TABLE 28. DISTRIBUTION OF BODY WATER

FLUID SPACE	ADULT MEN (11–96 years)		ADULT WOMEN (12–94 years)		INFANTS (1–9 months)	
	Values expressed as percentage of body weight					
	Mean	Range	Mean	Range	Mean	Range
Total body water	58 [a]	44.7–70.2	49 [a]	39.3–59.9	61 [b]	52.0–72.5
Extracellular fluid	17.5[c]	14.0–19.7	17.5[d]	15.3–21.0	26.7[b]	21.0–33.0
Plasma	4.3[c]	3.5– 5.7	4.2[c]	2.7– 5.2	5.8[b]	4.9– 6.8
Interstitial fluid	13.2[f]	11.5–14.0	13.3[f]	12.6–15.8	20.2[f]	16.1–26.2
Intracellular fluid	40.6[g]	34.7–48.0	31.5[g]	26.7–44.1	35 [b]	21.1–45.9

a, calculated from literature; b, from Katcher et al., J. clin. Invest., 1953, 32:1013–1024; c, from Deane, J. clin. Invest., 1951, 30:1469–1470; d, from Edelman et al., Science, 1952, 115:447–454; e, from Gibson and Evans, J. clin. Invest., 1937, 16:317–328; f, difference between the preceding values for extracellular fluid and plasma volume. It should be noted that the true value must be somewhat lower because of the confined space not estimated; g, difference between the preceding values for total body water and extracellular fluid.

Extracellular fluid volume.   Measurement of extracellular fluid volume has proved difficult because of the requirement for uniform and exclusively extracellular distribution of the tracer substance employed. No single substance has been found which completely satisfies all the requirements. Chloride, bromide, sodium thiocyanate and the radio-isotopes of chloride, bromide and sodium have proved to be inadequate because all enter some cells.[30] Sodium thiosulfate, radiosulfate and the carbohydrates, sucrose, mannitol and inulin—especially the last—presumably give more accurate indices of the extracellular fluid volume, and the values obtained with these substances are similar. In all probability the volume indicated by these more reliable substances is somewhat less than the true volume of the total extracellular fluid. The values obtained for extracellular fluid volume are given in Table 28. The distribution of body fluids has not been measured as many times in women as in men. From the few values available, it appears that the volume of extracellular fluid in relation to body weight is similar in both sexes. This suggests that, on a fat-free basis, women have a higher volume of extracellular fluid than men. It should be noted that the relative volume of this fluid compartment is higher in the infant than in the adult.

Blood and plasma volume.   As discussed in Chapter 23, a number of methods have been used in attempts to determine total blood volume *in vivo*. The most reliable measurements are obtained from simultaneous direct determinations of both plasma volume and cell volume by the dilution method. In man the average value for the total blood volume measured in this way is about 5.7 liters (range 4.09 to 7.76), which corresponds to an average of 7.7 per cent of body weight.[21] Adult women probably have a lower average blood voume per unit body weight than do adult men, but the paucity of simultaneous determinations of plasma and red cell volume in normal women prevents conclusions as to sex variations of total blood volume. Calculations of total blood volume derived from plasma volume and hematocrit values give lower averages for women than for men because the former have smaller peripheral venous hematocrit values, but the plasma volume per unit body weight is not significantly different in men and women.[20]

The average plasma volume values and ranges for men, women and infants are given in Table 28. The similar averages for adult men and women suggest a higher percentage in the latter on a fat-free basis. Infants have a higher percentage than adults per unit of body weight.

Intracellular fluid volume. The volume of intracellular fluid cannot be determined directly by a dilution method. This value is estimated by calculating the difference between simultaneous measurements of total body water and extracellular water. Therefore, the accuracy of intracellular determinations depends chiefly on the accuracy of extracellular fluid measurement. The figures so calculated and expressed in Table 28 must be somewhat higher than the true volume of intracellular fluid.

DYNAMIC ASPECTS OF BODY FLUIDS

Fluid Intake. The total volume of fluid in the body is maintained by balancing the over-all intake and output of water. The necessity for increasing or decreasing one or the other of these activities is detected by specialized areas of the central nervous system which are responsive to changes in plasma osmotic pressure (Chap. 10). Thirst and its role in the regulation of water intake are discussed in Chapter 16.

Fluid Absorption. The stomach absorbs practically no water; hence, the intestinal mucosa not only absorbs ingested water and electrolytes, but also reabsorbs most of the digestive secretions, the volume of which amounts to more than 6 liters in 24 hours. It can be seen that any interference with this reabsorptive process, as in diarrhea or vomiting, may rapidly lead to a state of dehydration. Studies with radioisotope tracers[3] have shown that both water and electrolytes continuously move in both directions across the intestinal wall, i.e., from intestinal lumen to blood stream and vice versa. Consequently, the net transfer for either fluid component is the algebraic sum of the opposing fluxes across the intestinal epithelium. The rate of water movement from gut to blood (calculated from the rate of disappearance of deuterium oxide) and the net water movement (measured as a volume change) are strongly influenced by the osmotic activity of the fluid in the intestine, whereas the rate of water movement into the gut is not influenced by the osmotic concentration of the intestinal fluid. Thus, a more rapid absorption is observed from dilute than from isotonic solutions, and with strongly hypertonic solutions the net movement of water is into the gut. When solutions of different concentrations of sodium chloride are placed in intestinal loops, a general tendency for the fluid to become isosmotic with plasma is observed. Experiments on rats have shown that ingested water is rapidly absorbed in the upper one-fifth of the small intestine and that intestinal fluid has become isotonic with plasma at about the end of the upper fifth. The influence of hydrostatic factors on intestinal water reabsorption is shown by the finding in the dog that maximal reabsorption of water in the gut occurs at an optimal hydrostatic pressure of about 20 cm. of saline. Circulatory factors also influence intestinal water reabsorption. Moderate congestion in the mesenteric veins and lymphatics results in a decreased rate of reabsorption of isotonic saline in the intestinal loops.

Exchange Between Intravascular and Interstitial Fluids. *Water exchange.* Water is continuously exchanged between the intravascular and interstitial fluids through the walls of the capillaries. This fluid exchange depends upon physical processes (filtration and diffusion), opposed by the colloid osmotic pressure of the blood, without active transport processes. The hydrodynamic factors of filtration were disclosed by Starling and have already been discussed briefly. His fundamental postulate is that net water flow between the plasma and the interstitial fluid is a resultant of the net hydrostatic pressure, which tends to produce an outward filtration of water, and the net osmotic force, which tends to produce an inward filtration (Fig. 517). The net hydrostatic pressure is the capillary blood pressure less the interstitial or tissue pressure. Insofar as proteins appear to be the only plasma solutes not freely diffusible through capillary membranes (although some proteins escape from capillaries, particularly in the viscera), the osmotic transfer of water across the capillary wall is controlled by the colloidal osmotic (oncotic) pressure maintained by the protein constituents of the plasma.

Modern concepts of capillary circulation[5, 15] have resulted in an elaboration of this schema. Although a full account is given in Chapter 34, it must be emphasized here that each capillary bed is formed by a "preferential channel" (metarteriole), coursing from a terminal arteriole to a venule with a rather constant nonpulsatile blood flow and a network of "true capillaries" branching from the metarteriole and draining into the collecting venule. True capillaries have an asynchronous intermittent blood flow because the precapillary sphincters contract rhythmically at their junction with the metarteriole. Hydrostatic pressure in the preferential channel remains relatively high and so favors a constant outward filtration. On the other hand, the hydrostatic pressure in the true capillaries is subject to periodic variations which allow the colloid osmotic pressure

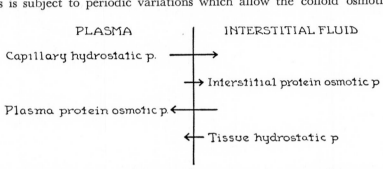

FIG. 517.   Forces which determine the distribution of fluid between plasma and interstitial spaces.

within the capillary to predominate intermittently, thus favoring inward filtration of fluid during these periods. The total surface for inward and outward filtration, then, is regulated by contraction and relaxation of precapillary sphincters according to the functional needs of the tissues. Thus, an increase either in the number of contracted sphincters or in the duration of the contractile period will favor an increased inward filtration. Conversely, a reduction of this rhythmic activity will favor outward filtration (Fig. 518).

Net exchange of water between plasma and interstitial space can be influenced by vasomotor activity of the arterioles, by venous outflow and by interstitial pressure. In general, arteriolar constriction decreases capillary pressure and arteriolar dilatation increases it. It follows that the vasomotor changes of the arterioles can alter the balance between outward and inward filtration without necessarily modifying the filtration area. Similarly, venous blood flow can affect the circulation and pressure in the capillary bed. Interference with free venous outflow, as is seen in some pathologic conditions, will increase capillary pressure, thus favoring outward filtration. Interstitial pressure exerts its effect by opposing outward filtration; the higher the pressure the less the outward filtration, and vice versa. Interstitial pressure is dependent upon the amount of fluid, the volume of space available and the elasticity of the limiting wall; e.g., interstitial pressure is higher in those muscles with tight fascial sheaths and increases significantly when venous congestion distends the veins. Regional differences in interstitial pressure may explain the tendency of edema fluid to accumulate primarily in sites of greater distensibility, as in the subcutaneous tissue of eyelids and scrotum, whereas fluid less frequently accumulates in muscles. Likewise, loss of normal tissue elasticity, as seen after excessive loss of weight, favors accumulation of edema fluid.

Since the colloidal osmotic pressure of plasma largely opposes the effective hydrostatic force, it is conceivable that a lowering of the plasma protein content (hypoproteinemia) may lead to accumulation of interstitial fluid (edema).

Solute exchange. The rapid exchange of plasma solutes through capillary walls appears to take place mainly by diffusion. It has been suggested[37] that the entire area of the capillary wall is available for diffusion of lipid-soluble molecules (O_2 and CO_2), whereas the area for diffusion of water and lipid-insoluble molecules (sodium chloride, urea and glucose) represents only 0.2 per cent of the total surface area of the capillary wall. This area may be limited to intercellular spaces. A concept of restricted diffusion through pores has been developed to account for the fact that the lipid-insoluble molecules diffuse less rapidly than might be expected from free diffusion. The degree of so-called molecular sieving (ratio of the concentration of a solute in the filtrate to the

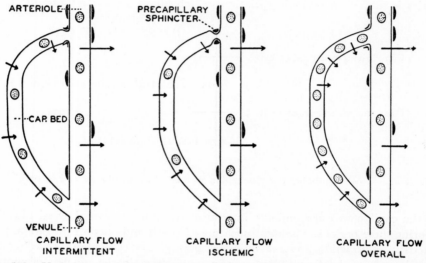

FIG. 518. Variations of fluid exchange in capillary bed produced by changes in contractile activity of precapillary sphincters. (From Zweifach, *Basic mechanisms in peripheral vascular homeostasis.* Trans. Third Conference, New York, Josiah Macy, Jr. Foundation, 1950.)

concentration in the filtrand) appears to depend on the size of the molecule, the size of the pores and, with large molecules, the rate of water filtration. According to this theory, the effective pore size in the capillary wall is big enough to permit the passage of even large molecules like plasma proteins. However, within the physiologic range of filtration rate, a high degree of molecular sieving occurs which would diminish at abnormally low rates of filtration. On the other hand, small molecules like urea are not sieved at the physiologic rates of filtration, but they would be sieved if the filtration rate were sufficiently large.

Exchange Between Intracellular and Extracellular Fluids. *Water transfer.* A continuous water exchange takes place between the extracellular and intracellular compartments. Diffusion, osmotic forces and metabolic activity in certain tissues are the underlying processes which control this water transfer. Analysis of the curves of diffusion of deuterium oxide show that the rate of water exchange between blood and tissues varies in different tissues.[13] The red blood cell exchanges water most rapidly. Internal organs like the brain (cerebral cortex), liver and stomach also exchange water rapidly, whereas supporting structures like skeletal muscle and bone exchange water at a slower rate. The net transfer of water through the cellular membrane is determined by the effective osmotic pressure inside and outside the membrane. An increase in the osmotic pressure of the extracellular fluid will shift water from cells; conversely, a diminution in osmotic pressure of extracellular fluid will shift water into cells. Similarly, an increase or decrease in the osmotic pressure of the intracellular fluid will bring about transfer of water to or from the cell. Since the effective osmotic pressure of the extracellular fluid phase depends almost entirely on its sodium content, the preponderant importance of this ion in the distribution of body fluid becomes apparent.

Although a perfect osmotic equilibrium appears to prevail throughout the body, some evidence indicates deviations from osmotic equality between plasma and some tissues. The freezing point depression method (cryoscopic technique) reveals that red blood cell mass is isosmotic with plasma, and brain and skeletal muscle are only 5 to 10 per cent higher in osmolarity than plasma. On the other hand, secretory organs (liver, pancreas, kidney, stomach and gut) show a high degree of hypertonicity. The osmotic activity of the liver and the kidney, measured by the cryoscopic technique, reached values of 438 mosm. per liter when that of plasma was 295 mosm. per liter.[4] Moreover, solutions of sodium chloride, to be isotonic with parenchymatous cells of liver, must have twice the molar concentration of sodium chloride in the blood serum. Similar differences have been found for pancreatic tissue. Depression of cellular metabolism in these "hypertonic" tissues by toxic agents or oxygen lack diminishes their osmotic activity. On the basis of these findings, Robinson[42] has suggested a continuing process of active extrusion of water from these cells. This active process would require the expenditure of energy derived from cellular metabolism and would maintain a steady dynamic equilibrium between those phases which have different osmotic pressures.

The distribution of water between the extracellular and intracellular spaces is also influenced by the adrenocortical hormones which regulate electrolytes, but it is not certain that these hormones influence water exchange directly. During adrenal insufficiency the volume of the extracellular space decreases and that of the intracellular space increases before there is any decrease in plasma sodium concentration.[19] Conversely, desoxycorticosterone acetate (DOCA) produces a decrease in the intracellular spaces and an increase in the extracellular spaces before plasma sodium rises. Cortisone and adrenocorticotrophic hormone (ACTH) induce a transient shift of water into the extracellular compartment with a simultaneous increase in total extracellular sodium and chloride but no change in plasma sodium concentration.[29] Adrenal cortical extract produces an increase in the intracellular space without modifying the extracellular fluid volume. Despite these significant changes in extracellular fluid volume, plasma volume changes little in mild adrenal insufficiency or during the administration of adrenocortical hormones. This observation indicates that plasma volume is not a sensitive index of changes in extracellular fluid volume.

Transfer of solutes. As previously stated, the concentrations of solutes in intracellular and extracellular fluids are different. Proteins as such do not pass through cell membranes, but the other cellular constituents are continuously exchanging. As discussed in Chapter 1, the general mechanisms are:[46, 47] (i) simple diffusion in which the flux across the membrane is a function of the electrical and/or chemical potentials on each side of the membrane and (ii) active transport which involves energy expenditure and permits transfer of a substance against an electrochemical gradient. Organic solutes of small molecular weight, such as urea, creatinine and organic acids, appear to pass freely through most cellular membranes by simple diffusion and presumably contribute little to the physical exchange of water across cell membranes. Ions, especially sodium and potassium, pass more slowly between intracellular and extracellular compartments than between intravascular and interstitial fluids. Sodium, calcium and magnesium ions are actively extruded from cells with the maintenance of a lower intracellular electrochemical activity, and potassium is transported into cells, at least in nerve, skeletal muscle and cardiac muscle (Chap. 1).

Transfer of ions between intracellular and extracellular fluids and the ionic composition of cellular fluid are importantly linked to acid-base equilibria. The studies of

Darrow[9] and Cooke[7] have shown that, in metabolic disturbances, there is a reciprocal relationship between the changes in intracellular sodium and potassium. Darrow related these changes in muscle sodium and potassium to serum bicarbonate concentration, but Cooke et al.[6] have since demonstrated that intracellular electrolyte composition is better related to extracellular pH. When the pH is altered by respiratory acidosis or alkalosis, changes in serum bicarbonate concentration are just the reverse of those seen during metabolic disturbances, but the changes in intracellular sodium concentration are the same. Calculations by Singer et al.[45] in studies on man agree with those of Cooke et al. on the rat and indicate that respiratory disturbances of pH differ from metabolic disturbances in that intracellular potassium is less affected, if at all. It has been proposed that during the production of alkalosis by potassium deficiency three potassium ions leaving the cell must be exchanged for the two sodium ions and one hydrogen ion that enter the cells. Recovery from this alkalosis after the administration of potassium salts is similarly explained by the ratio exchange of three potassium ions entering the cell for two sodium ions and one hydrogen ion leaving it. Hydrogen, by combining with bicarbonate in extracellular fluid, forms carbon dioxide and water. This would explain the drop in the high concentration of bicarbonate in plasma.

The role of the lungs, kidneys and blood proteins in maintaining blood pH has been recognized for some time, and each is treated in the appropriate chapter. Movements of ions between body compartments are also important in blood buffering.[3] Following intravenous administration of sodium bicarbonate into nephrectomized animals, the totality of the sodium ions remained in the inulin space,* whereas one-third of the bicarbonate ions disappeared and an equivalent quantity of chloride ions entered the inulin space. Likewise, after infusion of hydrochloric acid, a considerable amount of sodium and a smaller amount of potassium were transferred to the inulin space. It has been calculated that approximately one-fourth to one-third of the infused hydrochloric acid was neutralized by the pre-existing bicarbonate in the extracellular fluid, and two-thirds to three-fourths of the acid were neutralized by base entering the inulin space from elsewhere. Although it is not possible to determine in these experiments how much of the transferred ions came from the intracellular space and how much from other body depots, it is evident that homeostatic mechanisms within body compartments operate to defend the constancy of the pH of the internal environment.

Net movements of potassium are also closely related to cellular activity. During glycogenesis, 0.35 mM. of potassium per gram of glycogen enter the cells. Nitrogen storage also seems to demand an increase in intracellular potassium. On the other hand, cellular catabolism releases potassium, and conditions involving anoxia are accompanied by replacement of cellular potassium by sodium. Potassium also moves out of the cell during dehydration. Under the action of adrenocortical extract, adrenocorticotrophic hormone (ACTH) and desoxycorticosterone acetate (DOCA), muscle potassium is diminished. This change in electrolyte metabolism in the tissues occurs even in the absence of the kidney, and reflects an action of the adrenocortical hormones independent of the well known effect of these hormones on renal excretion of electrolytes.[50] A large reduction of the intracellular potassium concentration is associated with dietary magnesium deficit, even with abundant potassium intake.[8]

Fluid Output. Fluid is continuously lost from the body through various pathways—the kidney, the body surface, the pulmonary alveolar membranes and the sweat glands. Most of this fluid loss is "obligated" by renal osmotic forces and by cutaneous, pulmonary and oral evaporation. However, the "variable" or "facultative" loss of fluid depends upon excretion of water through the renal and glandular epithelia. Only the

---

* The fluid volume in the body exclusive of the intracellular fluid.

renal output is directed toward the regulation of body fluids, since glandular secretions subserve other functions.

The kidney helps to maintain the constancy of the osmolarity and volume of body fluids by eliminating or conserving water and sodium. These functions are regulated by two independent neurohormonal systems, the "antidiuretic system" and the "antinatruretic system."

The antidiuretic system regulates the excretion of osmotically free water, the increase or decrease of which are termed "diuresis" and "antidiuresis," respectively. It has already been pointed out that renal excretion of osmotically unobligated water depends upon the action of the antidiuretic hormone (ADH) on the renal tubule to increase its osmotic permeability which favors transfer of water from the glomerular filtrate to the blood (Chaps. 10 and 39). Secretion of ADH is regulated by the supraoptico-hypophysial system, which is sensitive to the osmolarity of extracellular fluid. Hypotonicity of the extracellular fluid reduces the rate of secretion of ADH, thus permitting the excretion of a large volume of "dilute" urine. On the other hand, hypertonicity of the extracellular fluid increases ADH secretion, and this leads to the conservation of water by the excretion of a reduced amount of "concentrated" urine. In this way, by increasing or decreasing the excretion of osmotically free water, the antidiuretic system tends to maintain the osmolarity of body fluids within a narrow range.

It has been proposed that the activity of the supraoptico-hypophysial system depends not only upon plasma osmolarity but also on the volume of body fluids. Isosmotic reduction of extracellular fluid volume increases blood ADH titers, and similar volume expansion decreases ADH titers. Unfortunately, blood ADH assay methods are suspect. Isosmotic reduction of extracellular fluid volume leads to oliguria, and similar expansion leads to diuresis. Whether these changes are dependent on alterations in ADH secretion or on hemodynamic changes resulting in variations of glomerular filtration rate is not entirely clear.

Receptors which might signal the plasma volume have been described by Paintal.[36] They are located in the right atrium and are innervated by vagal afferent fibers; their discharge pattern is synchronized with atrial diastole, when the atrium is stretched as it fills with blood. Artificial distention of the atrium increases the rate of firing. Left atrial distention also results in diuresis, which is abolished by blocking the vagus.[25] The proposed interpretation of such experiments is that atrial receptor discharge, which increases with expansion of the plasma volume, inhibits the hypothalamico-hypophysial system, thus decreasing ADH secretion and inducing diuresis. Reduction of the plasma volume, by diminishing receptor discharge, produces the opposite result.

An interesting phenomenon which attracts attention to the inhibitory processes within the antidiuretic system is the diuresis induced by isotonic saline in prehydrated subjects. Although infusion of 3 liters of saline produced no significant changes in urine flow in subjects who had received no fluid during the preceding 13 to 17 hours, infusion of this amount elicited *maximal diuresis* in subjects who had ingested 2 liters of water eight to 13 hours before the saline infusion.[27] The maximal diuretic effect was observed eight hours after prehydration, i.e., four or five hours after most of the prehydrating water had been excreted. That the diuretic response did not result from persistence of excess water is further supported by the less abundant diuresis obtained when the interval between prehydration and saline infusion was shorter than eight hours. If the infusion was given more than 13 hours after prehydration, no diuresis occurred.

The mechanism of the antinatruretic system is even less well understood. The consensus of opinion at the present time is that reabsorption of sodium is at least partly regulated by the adrenocortical hormone aldosterone (see Chap. 39). Secretion of aldosterone appears to be largely independent of hypophysial regulation, but may be regulated by the neurohumoral agent glomerulotropin (see Chap. 10). Decreased sodium excretion follows a variety of experimental procedures, such as hemorrhage,[22, 31, 35] venous occlusion by pressure cuffs about the limbs,[18, 49] partial occlusion of the vena cava[16] and change from the supine to the erect position.[23, 38] In other experiments, the same maneuvers have been shown to increase plasma levels of aldosterone.[10, 17, 34] Because these procedures have in common the tendency to decrease right atrial diastolic volume and thus to reduce the stimulus to the atrial receptors, it has been postulated that these receptors are part of the afferent limb of a regulatory mechanism inhibiting secretion of aldosterone. More direct experimental distention of the right atrium, by traction on sutures placed in the atrial wall and brought to the exterior of the chest, reduced aldosterone secretion by 50 per cent.[32]

The correlation between plasma volume and aldosterone secretion is not, however, absolute. For example, reduction of plasma volume by dehydration does not alter aldosterone secretion, provided the sodium intake remains normal;[1] but similar contraction of plasma volume in salt-depleted subjects results in the expected increase in aldosterone secretion. For this reason it has been suggested that plasma sodium levels play a part in modulating aldosterone secretion, although the mechanism is obscure.

Insensible water loss. Apart from sweating, water is continuously lost through the skin and lungs by evaporation. Unlike sweating, this loss is not noticed—is "insensible." This evaporation accounts for the dissipation of approximately 25 per cent of the resting metabolic heat production (in an environment of moderate humidity and below 88° F. or 31° C.). This water contains no solutes. Water vapor found in the expired air following the inhalation of dry air indicates a transfer of water from body fluids across the alveolar membranes. Such insensible water loss from the lungs is naturally influenced by changes in pulmonary ventilation. The insensible loss of water from skin is not an active secretory process, as sweating is, but is governed by physical factors, such as vapor pressure of the external and internal environment, air and skin temperatures and air movement. It occurs by diffusion through the keratinized layers of skin, and, under resting conditions at temperatures 88° below F. (31° C.), accounts for nearly all the evaporation from skin. Various studies indicate that water also passes into the body through the skin and lungs.

Sweating. Sweating is an active secretory process concerned mainly with temperature regulation. Thus, although sweating affects both salt and water in body fluids, it is not directly involved in fluid regulation. Most of the sweat glands are activated when the demands for heat loss are increased, as in exercise or in an elevated environmental temperature. Sweating rates as high as 60 to 70 ml. per minute over short periods (30 minutes); 500 to 1500 ml. per hour for several hours have been reported. However, a high rate of sweating is not maintained for a long time, and a decline occurs even though the water which is lost is replaced by drinking.[28] Sweating is reduced when salt in excess of that lost is ingested[26] or injected.[28] Similarly, sweating may be reduced in severe dehydration,[28] although moderate water deficiency does not influence the rate of sweating.

The concentration of solutes in sweat differs from that of the interstitial fluid, and, furthermore, sweat solute concentrations vary greatly in different areas of the body. Sodium chloride is at lower concentrations in sweat than in plasma, whereas potassium concentration is usually higher. The important fact is that despite the mechanism of sodium conservation a hazardous loss of sodium can result from excessive sweating.

Other means of fluid excretion. A small amount of water is excreted with the feces (approximately 100 to 200 ml. per day) and with glandular secretory products, such as salivary, lacrimal and genital secretions. During lactation, water may be lost through the mammary glands.

NORMAL AND ALTERED FLUID BALANCE

Normal Fluid Balance. Despite wide variations in the daily intake and output of water, total body fluid volume remains remarkably constant. In the adult under normal conditions and over extended periods, the total intake must necessarily equal the total output. The several sources of water intake are: (i) water ingested orally; (ii) water in food; (iii) water derived from oxidation of food. In addition, water can be formed by polymerization in metabolic processes. The water content of food contributes a considerable proportion—more than is often realized. Meat contains 70 per cent water, and certain vegetables and fruits are nearly 100 per cent water. Daily average values for the quantities of water taken into the body and excreted by various avenues are given in Table 29.

TABLE 29. AVERAGE DAILY WATER BALANCE

WATER INTAKE (APPROXIMATE)		WATER EXCRETION (APPROXIMATE)	
Drinking water	1200 cc.	Urine	1400 cc.
Food water content	1000 cc.	Insensible water loss	900 cc.
Water of oxidation	300 cc.	Stool	200 cc.
	2500 cc.		2500 cc.

The intake requirement for water generally parallels energy metabolism, and it has been estimated to be approximately 1 ml. of water per calorie. The fluctuations in the total volume of body fluid which occur during water loss and water replacement take place largely in the extracellular fluid. The total turnover of water represents a greater percentage of the volume of extracellular fluid in infants than in adults. Therefore, in infancy any excessive loss of fluid (diarrhea or vomiting) leads more rapidly to serious disturbances than in the adult. Daily changes in the total water content of the body are reflected by changes in body weight. This fact is utilized in the clinical estimation of water balance. The following formula has been derived for measurements of changes in body water through knowledge of the amounts of solids ingested and excreted and of the metabolic characteristics of the diet:[40]

Water balance = weight balance + solids + food burned.

Alterations of Fluid Balance. Disturbances in water and electrolyte metabolism involve alterations in the volume, distribution, and/or composition of body fluids. The causes are multiple but are generally related to failure to maintain a normal ratio between intake and output, failure of the mechanisms which regulate internal distribution, or both. The types of disturbance, the characteristics of each type, and the homeostatic mechanisms which normally tend to restore the lost equilibrium are presented in Figure 519. Primary causes are given in the text.

Hypotonic contraction of volume (Fig. 519a). Diminution of fluid volume associated with decreased tonicity is usually the result of sodium depletion caused by abnormal loss of sodium rather than by deficient intake.[2] This is true because the mechanisms for sodium conservation are most effective when they are normally active. Excessive loss of sodium may occur from the gastrointestinal tract, from the kidney or from sweat glands. Loss of gastrointestinal secretions by vomiting, diarrhea or through an external fistula is the most common clinical cause of sodium depletion. The risk of sodium depletion by this route is serious because the sodium contained in the various gastrointestinal secretions of one day represents about one-third of the total exchangeable sodium of the body. Sodium depletion consequent to excessive urinary excretion results from decreased tubular reabsorption rather than increased glomerular filtration. Sodium depletion is accompanied by water loss, and the volume of extracellular fluid is consequently reduced. The initial fall in sodium concentration in the extracellular fluid decreases the secretion of antidiuretic hormone, which contributes to the increased excretion of water by the kidney. Concurrently, a shift of water to the intracellular fluid compartment further diminishes the volume of extracellular fluid. This reduction of extracellular fluid volume may be associated with a lowered cardiac output and a clinical picture of peripheral circulatory failure. However, the collapse of the circulation does not appear to be related to the fall in plasma volume since the reduction in the cardiac output and blood pressure may occur abruptly before the plasma volume is diminished.[15] In the late stages of this syndrome, significant reduction in extracellular fluid volume results in a reduced excre-

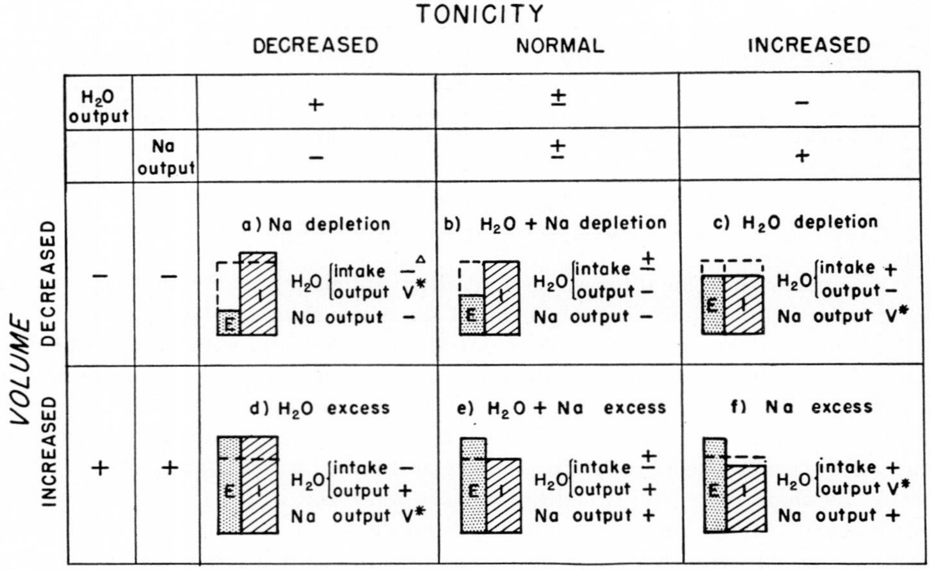

TONICITY

		DECREASED	NORMAL	INCREASED
H_2O output		+	±	−
	Na output	−	±	+
VOLUME DECREASED	− −	**a) Na depletion** $H_2O \begin{cases} \text{intake} & -^\Delta \\ \text{output} & V^* \end{cases}$ Na output −	**b) H_2O + Na depletion** $H_2O \begin{cases} \text{intake} & \pm \\ \text{output} & - \end{cases}$ Na output −	**c) H_2O depletion** $H_2O \begin{cases} \text{intake} & + \\ \text{output} & - \end{cases}$ Na output V^*
VOLUME INCREASED	+ +	**d) H_2O excess** $H_2O \begin{cases} \text{intake} & - \\ \text{output} & + \end{cases}$ Na output V^*	**e) H_2O + Na excess** $H_2O \begin{cases} \text{intake} & \pm \\ \text{output} & + \end{cases}$ Na output +	**f) Na excess** $H_2O \begin{cases} \text{intake} & + \\ \text{output} & V^* \end{cases}$ Na output +

FIG. 519. Primary water and/or electrolyte disturbances associated with alterations of body fluid volume and tonicity found in various clinical and experimental conditions. Changes in water and sodium output which result from either altered tonicity or volume are represented along abscissae and ordinates, respectively. Net effects on water and sodium balances and redistribution of water between extracellular and intracellular compartments in each of illustrated conditions are indicated. Dotted outline represents normal pattern of fluid distribution. Since changes in tonicity are same for both extra- and intracellular compartments, diagrams represent only changes of volume. E refers to extracellular fluid, I to intracellular fluid. Increase and decrease are indicated by signs + and −; ± indicates no change. Δ With persistent hypotonicity H_2O intake may be normal. V^* indicates variability since volume and tonicity changes act in opposite directions on output. In general, decreased volume takes precedence over change in tonicity and change in tonicity takes precedence over increased volume.

tion of water owing to both a fall in glomerular filtration and an activation of the antidiuretic secretory mechanism. As far as excretion of sodium is concerned, both decreased effective osmotic pressure and reduced volume of the extracellular fluid result in a decreased renal excretion of salt when the homeostatic sodium regulatory mechanism is unimpaired.

Isotonic contraction of volume (Fig. 519b). This condition is found whenever water is lost in proportion to sodium, as in hemorrhage or extensive burns. Proportional depletion of salt and water may also be observed in starvation without water deprivation and in mild gastrointestinal fluid loss without excessive intake of water. The reduced extracellular fluid volume stimulates sodium-retaining and water-retaining mechanisms to restore normal volume.

Hypertonic contraction of volume (Fig. 519c). A decreased fluid volume with high tonicity results from an excessive loss of water in relation to sodium. Water deprivation, excessive sweating without drinking, and diabetes insipidus may cause this syndrome. Although the rise in the effective osmotic pressure of the plasma leads to a reduction in urine flow by stimulating the release of ADH, the obligatory loss of water through the kidney, skin and lungs finally results in a diminution of the extracellular fluid. Because sweat is hypotonic, excessive sweating without replacement of water results in a loss of more water than sodium. For the same reason, water balance early in diabetes insipidus is negative, and the patient rarely drinks enough water at any one time to replace the initial water deficit. In all these conditions water is shifted from the intracellular space as a consequence of the rise in the effective osmotic pressure of the extracellular fluid, so that, eventually, fluid is lost proportionately from both compartments. With a loss of intracellular fluid a loss in potassium occurs. The presence of thirst and of relatively good circulatory conditions differentiates this syndrome from that associated with decreased extracellular fluid volume resulting from salt depletion.

Hypotonic expansion of volume (Fig. 519d). Extracellular fluid becomes hypotonic if its volume is increased while the total body sodium remains at normal levels. Normally, water excess practically never occurs in man because any tendency toward hypotonicity inhibits secretion of ADH and the ensuing water diuresis eliminates the excessive water load. However, whenever there is any interference with the processes of water elimination by the kidney, e.g., in patients with oliguira or anuria due to disease or injection of Pitressin, an expansion of body fluids by the forced intake of water can occur without parallel changes of body sodium content. This has been called "water intoxication." The reduced effective osmotic pressure in the extracellular compartment produces a shift of water to the intracellular space. The mechanisms which would normally tend to counteract water excess are: diminished water intake secondary to decreased thirst, and augmented renal excretion of water.

Isotonic expansion of volume (Fig. 519e). Expanded body fluid volume with a normal tonicity is the result of retention of sodium with a proportional retention of water. Clinically this water retention is usually most pronounced in the interstitial portion of the extravascular compartment, and this accumulation of isotonic fluid is referred to as edema. Although a high ingestion of sodium may lead to an excess of sodium in the body, proportional sodium and water retention are usually the consequence of reduced sodium excretion, particularly by the kidneys. The factors regulating renal sodium excretion are discussed in Chapter 39. For our purposes here, it is enough to say that any condition involving a decrease in glomerular filtration rate or an increase in tubular sodium reabsorption may lead to sodium retention.

Hypertonic expansion of volume (Fig. 519f). This condition is primarily due to sodium excess with a smaller increment of water. Sodium excess may result from forced intake of salt or from the administration of hypertonic saline. The elevated osmotic pressure of the extracellular fluid stimulates thirst, augments ADH secretion, and brings about a shift of water from the intracellular space. All of these effects contribute to the expansion of the extracellular fluid volume. Increased renal excretion of sodium tends to restore normal body fluid tonicity and volume.

Obviously, adequate management of these syndromes, as of any pathologic disturbance, is necessarily based on an appreciation of the physiologic mechanisms involved.

REFERENCES

1. BARTER, F. C., LIDDLE, G. W., DUNCAN, L. E., BARBER, J. K. and DeLEA, C. J. clin. Invest., 1956, 35:1306–1315.
2. BLACK, D. A. K. Sodium metabolism in health and disease. Oxford, Blackwell Scientific Publications, Ltd., 1952.
3. BRADLEY, S. E., ed. Renal function. Trans. Fourth Conference, New York, Josiah Macy, Jr. Foundation, 1952.
4. BRODSKY, W. A. J. clin. Invest., 1953, 32:556.
5. CHAMBERS, R. and ZWEIFACH, B. W. Physiol. Rev., 1947, 27:436–463.

6. COOKE, R. E., COUGHLIN, F. R., JR. and SEGAR, W. E. *J. clin. Invest.*, 1952, *31*:1006–1010.

7. COOKE, R. E., SEGAR, W. E., CHEEK, D. B., COVILLE, F. E. and DARROW, D. C. *J. clin. Invest.*, 1952, *31*:798–805.

8. COTLOVE, E., HOLLIDAY, M. A., SCHWARTZ, R. and WALLACE, W. M. *Amer. J. Physiol.*, 1951, *167*:665–675.

9. DARROW, D. C. *New Engl. J. Med.*, 1950, *242*:978–983, 1014–1018.

10. DAVIS, J. O., PECHET, M. M., BALL, W. C. and GOODKIND, M. J. *J. clin. Invest.*, 1957, *36*:689–694.

11. DEANE, N. and SMITH, H. W. *J. clin. Invest.*, 1952, *31*:197–199.

12. DEANE, N., ZIFF, M. and SMITH, H. W. *J. clin. Invest.*, 1952, *31*:200–203.

13. EDELMAN, I. S. *Amer. J. Physiol.*, 1952, *171*:279–296.

14. EDELMAN, I. S., OLNEY, J. M., JAMES, A. H., BROOKS, L. and MOORE, F. D. *Science*, 1952, *115*:447–454.

15. ELKINTON, J. R., DANOWSKI, T. S. and WINKLER, A. W. *J. clin. Invest.*, 1946, *25*:120–129.

16. FARBER, S. J., BECKER, W. H. and EICHNA, L. W. *J. clin. Invest.*, 1953, *32*:1145–1162.

17. FARRELL, G. L., ROSNAGLE, R. S. and RAUSCHKOLB, E. W. *Circulation Res.*, 1956, *4*:606–611.

18. FITZHUGH, F. W., JR., McWHORTER, R. L., JR., ESTES, E. H., JR., WARREN, J. V. and MERRILL, A. J. *J. clin. Invest.*, 1953, *32*:1163–1170.

19. GAUDINO, M. and LEVITT, M. F. *J. clin. Invest.*, 1949, *28*:1487–1497.

20. GIBSON, J. G., 2ND and EVANS, W. A., JR. *J. clin. Invest.*, 1937, *16*:317–328.

21. GIBSON, J. G., 2ND, PEACOCK, W. C., SELIGMAN, A. M. and SACK, T. *J. clin. Invest.*, 1946, *25*:838–847.

22. GOODYER, A. V. N. and JAEGER, C. A. *Amer. J. Physiol.*, 1955, *180*:69–74.

23. GOODYER, A. V. N. and SELDIN, D. W. *J. clin. Invest.*, 1953, *32*:242–250.

24. HARRISON, H. E., DARROW, D. C. and YANNET, H. *J. biol. Chem.*, 1936, *113*:515–529.

25. HENRY, J. P. and PEARCE, J. W. *J. Physiol.*, 1956, *131*:572–585.

26. KUNO, Y. *The physiology of human perspiration.* London, J. and A. Churchill, Ltd., 1934.

27. LADD, M. *J. appl. Physiol.*, 1951, *3*:379–387.

28. LADELL, W. S. S. *Brit. med. Bull.*, 1945, *3*:175–179.

29. LEVITT, M. F. and BADER, M. E. *Amer. J. Med.*, 1951, *11*:715–723.

30. LEVITT, M. F. and GAUDINO, M. *Amer. J. Med.*, 1950, *9*:208–215.

31. LOMBARDO, T. A., EISENBERG, S., OLIVER, B. B., VIAR, W. N., EDDLEMAN, E. E., JR. and HARRISON, T. R. *Circulation*, 1951, *3*:260–270.

32. McCALLY, M., ANDERSON, C. H. and FARRELL, G. L. *Proc. 40th Mtg. Endocrine Soc.*, 1958.

33. MANERY, J. F. and HASTINGS, A. B. *J. biol. Chem.*, 1939, *127*:657–676.

34. MULLER, A. F., MANNING, E. L. and RIONDEL, A. M. *Aldosterone, an international symposium.* London, Churchill, 1958.

35. NETRAVISESH, V. and WHITE, H. L. *Amer. J. Physiol.*, 1950, *161*:442–447.

36. PAINTAL, A. S. *J. Physiol.*, 1953, *120*:596–610.

37. PAPPENHEIMER, J. R. *Physiol. Rev.*, 1953, *33*:387–423.

38. PEARCE, M. L. and NEWMAN, E. V. *J. clin. Invest.*, 1954, *33*:1089–1094.

39. PETERS, J. P. *Physiol. Rev.*, 1944, *24*:491–531.

40. PETERS, J. P. and VAN SLYKE, D. D. *Quantitative clinical chemistry.* Vol. I, *Interpretations,* 2nd ed. Baltimore, Williams & Wilkins Co., 1946.

41. PINSON, E. A. *Physiol. Rev.*, 1952, *32*:123–134.

42. ROBINSON, J. R. *Biol. Rev.*, 1953, *28*:158–194.

43. ROBINSON, J. R. and McCANCE, R. A. *Ann. Rev. Physiol.*, 1952, *14*:115–142.

44. SHOHL, A. T. *Mineral metabolism.* (American Chemical Society, Series 82.) New York, Reinhold Publishing Corporation, 1939.

45. SINGER, R. B., ELKINTON, J. R., BARKER, E. S. and CLARK, J. K. *J. clin. Invest.*, 1953, *32*:604.

46. STEINBACH, H. B. *Ann. Rev. Physiol.*, 1951, *13*:21–40.

47. USSING, H. H. *Physiol. Rev.*, 1949, *29*:127–155.

48. WIDDOWSON, E. M., McCANCE, R. A. and SPRAY, C. M. *Clin. Sci.*, 1951, *10*:113–125.

49. WILKINS, R. W., TINSLEY, C. M., CULBERTSON, J. W., BURROWS, B. A., JUDSON, W. E. and BURNETT, C. H. *J. clin. Invest.*, 1953, *32*:1101–1116.

50. WOODBURY, D. M. *Amer. J. Physiol.*, 1953, *174*:1–19.

51. ZWEIFACH, B. W. *Basic mechanisms in peripheral vascular homeostasis.* Trans. Third Conference, New York, Josiah Macy, Jr. Foundation, 1950.

CHAPTER 41

Cerebrospinal Fluid

By ROBERT B. LIVINGSTON

CEREBROSPINAL fluid (c.s.f.) is a clear, colorless solution found within the cerebral ventricles, the spinal canal, and the subarachnoid spaces. It forms a physically and chemically protective chamber for the brain. Cerebrospinal fluid is derived from the arteries entering the craniospinal compartment and drains into venous channels leaving this region; part escapes into lymphatic vessels by way of meningeal extensions along emergent cranial and spinal nerve roots. The pressure of c.s.f. lies along the downward gradient between the arterial and venous pressures.

Each of the several parts of this hydraulic system communicates with the rest of the c.s.f. pool, and there is evidence of more or less mixing or "circulation" of the liquid from its various sites of origin to the places where it is reabsorbed. The lateral ventricles and the third ventricle are connected by the two foramina of Monro; the aqueduct of Sylvius provides a narrow communication between the third and fourth ventricles (Fig. 520). In the roof of the fourth ventricle there are communications between the internal ventricular chambers and the external cranial and spinal subarachnoid spaces by way of the foramina of Magendie, Luschka and Elze. All four cerebral ventricles contain dense clusters of blood vessels which are supported by infolded extensions of the pia and ependyma. The capillaries are covered by a single layer of modified ependyma possessing many of the structural characteristics of glandular cells: many mitochondria, large Golgi bodies, large nuclei, one or more nucleoli and "secretory" granules and vacuoles. This epithelial layer possesses a brushlike surface, and many of the cells are ciliated. According to Schaltenbrand,[27] "The living cell occasionally extends through the *bordure en brosse* finger-like processes which seem to evacuate their contents into the surrounding fluid." These clusters of vessels, together with their covering epithelium, make up the chorioid plexuses which participate in the elaboration of c.s.f.

Cerebrospinal fluid is not only found within the ventricular chambers and subarachnoid spaces, but it also appears to penetrate the cerebral and spinal parenchyma, mingling with the interstitial fluid bathing the cellular elements of the nervous system. The combined ventricular, subarachnoid and interstitial spaces thus form an intercommunicating compartment. Movements of particles and ions within this system appear to result from some ebb and flow throughout the ventricular and subarachnoid spaces and from diffusion within the extracellular spaces. Exchange between the blood stream and this entire c.s.f. compartment does not take place as freely as does the transfer

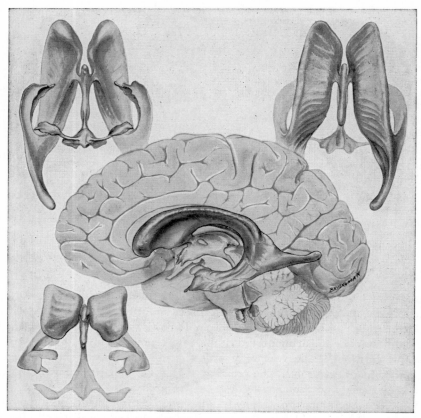

FIG. 520. Drawing of brain and cerebral ventricles illustrating their approximate relationships. Original model in University of California at Los Angeles School of Medicine collection was mounted in plastic by James Kerns and Charles Bridgman and consists of a left ventricular cast of Wood's metal superimposed upon a right cerebral hemisphere. An inferior, a superior and a frontal view of ventricular system, modified from Key and Retzius,[14] are added to this drawing. Large horn-shaped lateral ventricles are joined by foramina of Monro to midline third ventricle. This chamber narrows posteroinferiorly to form the long, narrow aqueduct of Sylvius, which connects with fourth ventricle. Cerebrospinal fluid is not confined to ventricles but finds access to cerebrospinal subarachnoid spaces through certain foramina in roof of fourth ventricle, and also from this ventricle directly into spinal canal. Because the arachnoid bridges over most sulci and indentations on brain surface, there are numerous cerebrospinal channels surrounding the brain, the largest of which are called cisterns.

between plasma and extracellular fluid elsewhere. A consideration of the physiology of cerebrospinal fluid includes (i) its general functions, (ii) the mechanisms of its formation and reabsorption, and (iii) the nature of this "blood-brain barrier."

SUPPORT OF BRAIN BY CEREBROSPINAL FLUID

Coverings of Brain. Several anatomic and physical factors are important to an understanding of the normal stability of the brain *in situ*. The skull conforms only roughly to the outer surface of the brain. Nervous tissue has but feeble rigidity and offers very little resistance to changes in shape; it can easily be retracted by gentle pressure. Alone in the skull, unsupported by the leptomeninges and c.s.f., the brain would be subject to lethal damage under conditions of everyday life and could by no means withstand the punishment of even a minor head injury. Placed on a table, a fresh, unfixed brain proves so soft that it soon suffers distortion and even rupture because of the forces exerted by its own weight.

The dura mater, which is closely applied to the cranial vault and is in some places firmly adherent to the endosteum, somewhat more faithfully encloses the central nervous system. In addition, the dura mater affords two important partitions: the falx and the tentorium. The falx partially compartmentalizes the two cerebral hemispheres. The tentorium forms a fixed and relatively inelastic collar around the brain stem. Like the

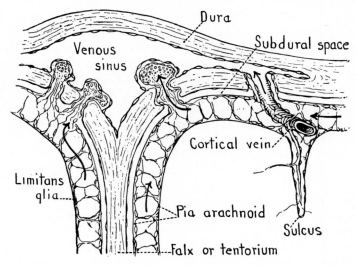

FIG. 521.   Drawing of leptomeninges, illustrating subarachnoid space through which cerebrospinal fluid percolates. Fluid may escape by way of arachnoid villi, thin sacculations which penetrate venous sinus contained within dura, or by way of venules which ultimately drain into same sinus. Arachnoid and pia mater are joined by multitudinous filaments, the pia being closely applied to contours of brain, the arachnoid following the dura, separated from it by potential subdural space. In its course out of brain, the vein is separated from the pia by Virchow-Robin space. (Modified from Weed, *J. med. Res.*, 1914, *31*:57–92.)

bony rim of the foramen magnum this meningeal collar may become an instrument for the destruction of neighboring nervous tissue during compression of the skull at childbirth, during injury associated with violent acceleration of the head, and during elevation of intracranial pressure from any cause.

The arachnoid is applied closely to the dura mater and clings to it by virtue of the surface tension of a thin film of serous fluid. This prevents separation of the two surfaces unless forces sufficient to cause cavitation are applied, or unless air or blood is admitted into the plane of their separation—the potential subdural space. This film of fluid offers little resistance to movement of one surface upon the other, except in the region of the meningeal partitions already mentioned and at the points of entrance and exit of blood vessels, nerve roots, etc. Therefore, the brain is relatively free to slide within the cranial vault, a fact that has been demonstrated by substituting a translucent plastic cranium for the top of the skull.[22]

The arachnoid coat does not intimately follow the contours of individual sulci and fissures of the brain, whereas the pia mater is applied directly to the glia limitans itself (Fig. 521). As a consequence, the subarachnoid space is thin over the convolutions and deeper in the region of indentations of the brain, thus providing in certain regions enlarged spaces known as cisterns, in which a pooling of c.s.f. occurs. Extensions of the subarachnoid space, known as the Virchow-Robin spaces, form perivascular sleeves covering the larger blood vessels during part of their penetration of the brain; the outer walls of these channels are formed by pial investments, and the inner walls are composed of the mesenchymatous coverings of the vessels themselves.[20] These spaces can be seen to accompany both arteries and veins but evidently are obliterated through the loss of both pial and adventitial layers throughout the region of precapillaries, capillaries and venules. Cerebral capillaries thus are separated from nervous tissue only by a continuous basement membrane which they share with the adjacent neuronal and glial elements.

Between the arachnoid and pia, manifold fibrous tissue connections form a forest of delicate stanchions through which c.s.f. percolates. These would appear to be too fine and insubstantial to be of importance in the support of such a heavy organ as the brain if it were not for the fact that the c.s.f. imparts buoyancy to that structure.

Buoyancy of Neuraxis. Buoyancy of any body submerged in fluid is determined by the weight of the fluid displaced. The comparative densities of c.s.f. and nervous tissue are such that a brain and spinal cord weighing about 1500 grams when removed from the craniospinal vault will have a net weight *in situ* of less than 50 grams.* When the virtual light weight of the brain in this situation is taken into account, it is understandable that the minute but manifold fibrous tissue connections between the arachnoid and pia can provide the nervous system with a protective suspension. The nervous system is supported by a combination of: (i) the weight of c.s.f. which it displaces; (ii) the profusion of filamentous connections in the pia-arachnoid; (iii) the surface tension between coapted arachnoid and dura mater; (iv) the dentate ligaments and other ligaments directly stabilizing the neuraxis; (v) compartmentalization by the dura mater, which is supported by the skeleton; and (vi), supplementarily, the blood vessels and nerve roots which enter and leave the central nervous system.

The importance of c.s.f. in giving buoyancy to the brain and spinal cord becomes immediately obvious when an air or oxygen encephalogram is made. In this procedure, as much fluid as possible may be withdrawn and replaced with gas in order to provide an x-ray contrast between nervous tissue and the ventricular and subarachnoid chambers. When this is done, the full weight of the nervous system rests upon delicate meningeal, nervous and vascular structures. Encephalography is usually decidedly painful because of traction upon nerve roots themselves or upon nerve fibers which course along the meninges or accompany blood vessels. If a large amount of fluid is withdrawn, deep sedation is required, and the procedure is followed by a headache which lasts for many hours. During this time the slightest jarring of the head will greatly intensify the pain.

By virtue of its buoyant effect, the c.s.f. substantially reduces the momentum (inertia) of the brain in response to other acceleratory forces besides gravitation. *As a result of the support and protection of the central nervous system by its meningeal and watery envelopes, the feebly rigid brain can withstand stresses inflicted on the head in the course of everyday living.* Nevertheless, during severe head injury, the brain is subject to damage (i) by deformation or invasion of the skull, with direct damage thereby inflicted on the soft structures beneath, and (ii) by sudden angular acceleration which can cause shearing strains that tear or rupture nervous tissue and blood vessels. Holbourn has considered some of these

$$* \text{ Weight of c.n.s. } in\ situ = \text{ weight of c.n.s. in air} \left(1 - \frac{\text{s.g. cerebrospinal fluid}}{\text{s.g. nervous tissue}} \right)$$

$$= 1500 \left(1 - \frac{1.007}{1.040} \right)$$

$$= 49 \text{ gm.}$$

factors relating to the mechanics of head injury and to the herniation of cerebral tissues through confined openings, e.g., the foramen magnum, the tentorial incisura, or bony defects.[11, 12]

HYDRODYNAMICS. The problem of c.s.f. pressure and dynamics can be investigated by puncturing with a fine needle the lumbar subarachnoid space or the cisterna magna at the base of the occiput, or by inserting a needle through a trephine hole into one of the lateral cerebral ventricles. With this communication established, it is a simple matter to attach to the needle a graduated glass cylinder manometer or a mercury or strain gauge manometer which requires less displacement of fluid for pressure determinations. The procedure ordinarily is performed with the subject lying on his side, with the needle in the lumbar subarachnoid space. If he is relaxed and breathing quietly, the c.s.f. pressure is normally found to be about 70 to 160 mm. H_2O.

The cranial vault and spinal column, together with the almost inelastic dura, form a semirigid chamber which is completely filled by the brain and spinal cord, the cerebrospinal vascular bed and the c.s.f. Because this chamber is semirigid and because its tissue and fluid contents are practically incompressible, it offers great resistance to swift movement or change in volume of any single constituent: there must be an almost exactly equal and opposite effect in one or another of the remaining components. These facts have become known as the Monro-Kellie doctrine. Ryder and his associates have explored these mechanisms in detail.[25]

Effects of acceleration. Because of the continuity of the venous column between the craniospinal and thoracic veins, and by virtue of the Monro-Kellie effect, the c.s.f. helps preserve an effective arteriovenous siphon through the brain even during acceleration. Rapid positive angular acceleration (head toward the center of rotation) causes the pressure in arterial and venous channels and in the c.s.f. to fall in direct proportion to the acceleration, so that essentially normal pressure differences are sustained. The relative incompressibility of the skull and its contents prevents collapse of the cerebral veins. There is an almost instantaneous decrease in cerebral vascular resistance, too. This decrease is considered to result from a passive distention of cerebral vessels in replacement of some intracranial c.s.f., which is displaced toward lower levels as a consequence of drainage of spinal venous plexuses into the veins of the abdomen and legs. It is evident that the maintained siphon effect, the patency of vessels and the lowered cerebral vascular resistance all contribute to preserving an effective cerebral blood flow (Fig. 522).[9] Commenting on this, Kety says, "Nature may not have realized that some of her creatures with short necks were going to be subjected to excessive centrifugal forces, but she did have to design a giraffe and I am quite sure that it is this mechanism which preserves whatever cerebral circulation that animal has."[13]

The osseous surroundings of the vertebral column tend to reduce the extent of headward flow of c.s.f. when the body is tilted to the head-down position or during negative angular acceleration (feet toward the center of rotation). The rigidity of the intact skeleton surrounding the neuraxis thus tends to prevent undue displacement of the supportive c.s.f. bath. Both vascular and c.s.f. pressures may vary widely according to the forces involved, but they vary so nearly in parallel that very little strain is imposed on the venous walls. Even in extremely severe conditions, the protective bony and connective tissue coverings of the nervous system greatly reduce shifting of fluid parts and thereby largely prevent the deformation or displacement of nervous structures. When the skull is opened and its contents are exposed to atmospheric pressure, the cranial dura mater which would otherwise have been upheld by the bony vault falls in upon the brain, permitting a collapse of cerebral vessels and a marked displacement of c.s.f. into the dependent regions. In such instances, cerebral blood flow is readily disturbed, and the cisternal and ventricular fluid pressures are above atmospheric.

During less rapidly imposed forces, relatively slow adjustments can occur through altered rates of formation and reabsorption of c.s.f. The brain itself is capable of some change in volume by the gain or loss of interstitial or intracellular fluid. Most of the leeway within the "hard bony box" enclosing the nervous system, however, is that provided by the inflow and escape of blood.

Effects of compression of vessels.   Any interference with the flow of blood along vessels leading to and from the nervous system is accompanied by alterations in the pressure of the c.s.f. and by whatever slight displacement of the fluid is permitted within the enclosed hydraulic system. The c.s.f. pressure thus quickly reflects slight changes in the dimension of the local vascular bed. Since the thoracic and cerebrospinal veins are in direct continuity, respiratory movements, sneezing, coughing or straining are accompanied by changes in intracranial pressure. During inspiration, for example, the reduction of pressure in the superior vena cava and the increase of pressure in the inferior vena

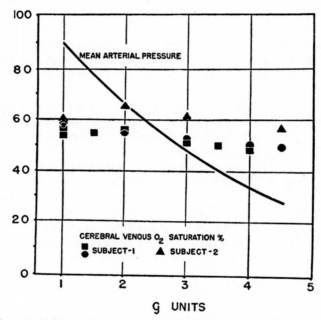

FIG. 522.   Mean arterial pressure at head level plotted against acceleration. Ordinates: pressure in mm. Hg and venous oxygen saturation in per cent. Abscissae: angular acceleration in units of gravity. Note that in spite of induced fall in mean arterial blood pressure cerebral venous oxygen saturation remains essentially constant during prolonged accelerations of 1–2 minutes. See text for explanation of role of intact skull and vertebral column, leptomeninges, and cerebrospinal fluid in preserving cerebral blood flow during this stress. (Graph from Henry *et al.*, *J. clin. Invest.*, 1951, *30:* 292–300.)

cava tend to shift c.s.f. pressures so that there is a slight headward flow of c.s.f. during inspiration and a reverse flow during expiration.

Prolonged hard straining of the thorax as in lifting, blowing or defecating, although causing a marked rise in arterial pressure, causes an equivalent rise in c.s.f. pressure transmitted from the thoracic to the cerebral veins. Thus during straining there is a protection against rupture of cerebral vessels. However, such strains may be followed after their release by increased cardiac output (resulting from the entrance of dammed-up venous blood) on top of intense vasopressor responses (initiated reflexly during the continued thoracic strain)—the classic Valsalva phenomenon. The resulting high arterial pressure is now, after release of the strain, not balanced by an equivalent c.s.f. pressure rise, and any likelihood of rupture of cerebral vessels associated with straining is increased at this moment.

Compression of the jugular veins or pressure applied to the abdomen will yield a prompt rise in c.s.f. pressure. Compression of the jugular veins, however, will not be followed by a rise of fluid pressure in the lumbar subarachnoid space if there is a block anywhere in the spinal subarachnoid space, e.g., as in a spinal cord or meningeal swelling from tumor or inflammation. If there is only partial block, the pressure will rise slowly, and—after jugular compression is discontinued—return to the initial pressure will also be slow. The utilization of these facts is clinically important, and the jugular compression test, known as the Queckenstedt test,[24] has become an important part of c.s.f. examination. However, if the suspected lesion is located at or above the foramen magnum, the Queckenstedt test will contribute no useful information and may be hazardous.

INTRACRANIAL FLUID RELATIONS

Pressure Relations Between Different Parts of C.S.F. Compartment. Since all parts of the c.s.f. pool communicate with each other, pressures determined at different sites are systematically related to each other according to the integrity of the skull and dura mater and to the posture or movement of the individual. When the subject is sitting up, the c.s.f. pressure at the cisterna magna is approximately zero, that in the ventricle is below atmospheric pressure, and that in the lumbar region ranges up to 400 to 500 mm. H_2O. When the subject is horizontal, the pressures at these sites are approximately equal. Since the c.s.f. is apparently in quite free communication with interstitial fluid, it is evident that a measurement of ventricular or subarachnoid pressure closely reflects the pressure acting upon neurons at the same horizontal level.

Pressure Relations Between C.S.F. and Vascular Bed. Considering the relationship between capillaries and interstitial fluid elsewhere in the body, one would predict that at equilibrium—that is, with equal rates of formation and reabsorption of fluid—the c.s.f. pressure would be equal to the average capillary hydrostatic pressure less the capillary osmotic pressure. From Pouiseuille's law the concept is derived that capillary pressure should be directly related to cerebral blood flow multiplied by the resistance to cerebral blood outflow plus the outlet venous pressure.[25]

Induced Changes in C.S.F. Volume. If fluid is added to the c.s.f. chambers, there must be a sharp transient rise in c.s.f. pressure followed by immediate displacement of some of the blood volume contained in the distensible craniospinal vascular bed. A new unstable balance will follow with slightly elevated c.s.f. pressure, tending to increase reabsorption of the fluid and return the system to equilibrium. (Depending upon the degree of distensibility and volume of the cerebral and systemic vascular pools, there may be considerable c.s.f. volume change with relatively small pressure changes.)

The reverse tendency obtains when fluid is withdrawn, seepage occurring in the direction of restoring the initial c.s.f. pressure and volume. When c.s.f. is withdrawn, the vascular circuits temporarily expand until a new pressure relationship at a slightly lower level is achieved. Since the ability of the blood vessels to expand is limited by their structure, the vascular compensation for loss of relatively large amounts of c.s.f. is inadequate, and low intracerebral pressures result. If sufficient spinal fluid is withdrawn, the resting pressure will reach an equilibrium with atmospheric pressure; free drainage will no longer be possible, and only a small additional amount can be withdrawn by application of moderate tension. Any further drainage can be accomplished only by waiting for further accumulation or by replacing the remaining fluid with some other substance. By injecting air or oxygen and withdrawing spinal fluid, and by changing the position of the subject in order to favor drainage of the ventricles, it is possible to obtain up to 200 ml. of the fluid. This amount probably represents the approximate total of fluid normally present.

It has been demonstrated that, although the capacity of the craniospinal chambers is limited, indefinite amounts of c.s.f. can be added or withdrawn by small increments with a repetition of these pressure responses. The necessary conclusion is that the procedure of adding to or subtracting from the c.s.f. volume induces alterations in pressure which result in net seepage in that direction which will restore the initial state.[25]

If the nervous tissue or the meninges are swollen, as by an expanding growth or an abscess, considerably less space is available within the semirigid bony enclosure for either c.s.f. or the local blood volume. In these circumstances, the pressure falls to a greater extent and is less completely compensated after fluid is withdrawn. Conversely, if less of the total volume is occupied by the nervous system or meninges (atrophy or after surgical removal) and there is a relatively large pool of c.s.f., withdrawal of the same amount of fluid will be followed by only a slight reduction in its pressure. In 1923 Ayala, observing these facts, pointed out their usefulness in differentiating between expanding lesions and those featuring abnormally large accumulations of cerebrospinal fluid.[1] Savitsky and Kessler computed an Ayala index as that number which is equal to the ratio of final to initial pressure multiplied by a factor of ten (equal to the number of milliliters of c.s.f. withdrawn for this test). If the index is between 1 and 5, a diagnosis of space-occupying lesions is favored. Between 5 and 6, the index is considered equivocal, but above 6.5, the index is thought to indicate that an expanding lesion is probably not involved.[26]

Increased Intracranial Pressure.   Intracranial pressure may increase relatively abruptly or insidiously. Following a severe head injury associated with bleeding into the ventricles or into the substance of the brain itself, many of the pressure and blood-brain barrier relations (see below) are upset. Extravasations introduce a large quantity of plasma proteins into the normally nearly protein-free c.s.f., thereby tending by increased osmotic force to augment the c.s.f. volume. Cellular elements tend to block some of the c.s.f. reabsorptive mechanisms, thereby compounding the difficulty. In cases of inflammation or neoplasm, tissue expansion may also be quite rapid, so that in a period of a few hours or days blockade of the cerebral aqueduct or tentorial incisura or of the foramen magnum may occur. Cerebrospinal fluid volume and pressure rapidly elevated by any of these means will naturally interfere with cerebral blood flow. It is well known that in such circumstances the arterial blood pressure is reflexly adjusted to successively higher levels until the reflex mechanisms themselves fail (presumably because of anoxia of the brain stem) and death ensues. Surgical intervention to remove the cause of the high intracranial pressure or palliative decompression of the skull by craniotomy may be life saving.

Increased intracranial pressure developing gradually over a period of months, as in slow growing neoplasms, may be associated with such gradual and adequate reflex adjustments of pressure relations that intact cerebral functions may exist with an intracranial pressure elevated three or four times normal. This may be the cause of an otherwise inexplicable and asymptomatic arterial hypertension.

Since the meningeal coverings of the cerebrum course outward along the optic nerve and the dura mater ends by attachment to the sclera, there is formed here a c.s.f. *cul de sac*. Increased intracranial pressure may express itself by expanding this space against the limiting tension of the dura mater. In this way, increased intracranial pressure can embarrass venous and lymphatic return from the retina by obstructing the central vein traveling in the interior of the nerve and the associated lymph channels. Obstruction of the lymph channels is said to give rise to swelling of the nerve head, and obstruction of the vein to dilatation of retinal veins. Considerable circulatory interference may occur before vision is disturbed, but choked disc or papilledema and passive venous congestion can be identified by ophthalmoscopy.

Interstitial Fluid of the Brain.   In the brain, determination of the sodium, chloride or inulin "space"—a technique useful for estimating extracellular volume in other tissues—has not yielded consistent results. The estimated dimensions in the brain do not agree from one species of ion or substance to another but suggest an "interstitial fluid compartment" representing anywhere from 15 to more than 30 per cent of the total brain volume.[6] Electron microscopy, with adequate assurance against artefacts, has shown clearly that the brain is composed of closely packed glia, nerve cells and their processes, and blood vessels, mainly capillaries with their accompanying basement membrane.[17, 28] The cellular components are so closely packed that there are only minute gaps (fairly constant at 200 Å.) between adjacent elements. Taken as a whole, this extracellular space provides an enormous surface wetting the cells, but it occupies little volume. The total interstitial fluid space determined by electron microscopy is no more than 2 to 5 per cent of the total brain volume. This "space" may contain a mucoprotein polysaccharide "ground substance" which might itself affect transfer of substances. As yet, the nature of the interstitial fluid and the nature of the distinctions between it and the cytoplasm of the various glia and nerve cells have not been portrayed chemically. The apparent sodium, chloride and inulin "spaces" must represent mainly *intra*cellular spaces, presumably including some of the glia. Thus, although we know quite a lot about the chemistry of c.s.f., we know almost nothing about that of the interstitial fluid immediately surrounding the neurons and glia, and it is only an assumption to treat c.s.f. as if it were identical with this fluid.[40]

Time lapse photography of tissue cultures of nerve cells and neuroglia portrays the glia, especially, as having spontaneously active, slow, protoplasmic movements and undulations of their abundant membranes.[21] Such undulatory movements sweep systematically along the cell fringes and processes of both oligodendrocytes and astrocytes, and occur with a frequency and regularity that would probably contribute to the local circulation and mixing of extracellular fluid among the interstices of the nerve cells, glia and capillaries. Astrocytes in tissue culture and *in vivo* respond with an abrupt reduction of the resting potential and a subsequent slow recovery following electrical stimulation.[5, 10, 30] Electrical stimulation of glia also initiates slow, long-lasting, contractile movements.[5] Since glia may be affected by the accumulation of local metabolites, and since they also may receive synaptic endings from neurons,[21] local neuronal activity may cause increased glial activity and thereby accentuate the local mechanical circulation of interstitial fluid.

FORMATION AND REABSORPTION OF CEREBROSPINAL FLUID

Fluid Formation by Chorioid Plexus.   It is generally believed that the chorioid plexus plays the most important role in the formation of cerebrospinal fluid (see above). Early in fetal life the glandlike structure of the plexus takes on a histologic appearance of secretory activity coinciding with a change in nature of the fluid from a material of gelatinous consistency to a watery fluid that resembles normal c.s.f. Flexner demonstrated that at this time the chorioid plexus develops an oxidation-reduction potential between epithelium and stroma and that this is accompanied by a functional modification relating to the transport of basic and acidic dyes.[8]

If there is an obstruction at the aqueduct or elsewhere in the ventricular system, internal hydrocephalus develops. One must conclude from this fact that any absorptive mechanisms within the ventricular system are not adequate to match the rate of formation of fluid by the chorioid plexus. This constitutes the evidence that there is a "third circulation," in which fluid may be exchanged in either direction at a great many points along the entire blood-brain barrier, but in which there is a *net flow* of c.s.f. from the chorioid plexus through the ventricular system and into the spinal and cerebral subarachnoid spaces. At these loci the balance is restored by additional venous reabsorption. Presumably, in so-called communicating hydrocephalus in which no interventricular obstruction can be demonstrated, a retardation of reabsorptive processes at the capillary and venous side of the circuit may have developed. This latter has been imitated experimentally by the introduction of particulate matter to clog the absorptive channels. Evidence combines to indicate that c.s.f. can be produced against a hydrostatic gradient and that at least the chorioid plexus is capable of such forced production.

Extraventricular c.s.f. formation.   Schaltenbrand and Putnam injected fluorescein intravenously in the cat while watching the chorioid plexus under the microscope. They observed thick green clouds of fluid billowing out from the region of the plexus. In addition to formation at these sites, however, they noted the rapid appearance of green color leaking out around all vessels of the subarachnoid space.[27] If hypotonic solutions are introduced into the blood stream, the rate of formation of c.s.f. is greatly increased.[36, 37] In these circumstances it is apparent that the fluid can be formed from all cerebrospinal capillaries, even those deep within the parenchyma of the nervous system. Fluid has been shown to escape from these capillaries into the Virchow-Robin spaces and thence into the subarachnoid space. Flexner stated, "Under normal conditions no more than very small amounts of fluid pass into the subarachnoid space from a single perivascular space . . . It may be added, however, that it is not unreasonable to suppose that normally there is a very sluggish, probably irregular or interrupted movement of fluid from the perivascular spaces to the subarachnoid space."[7] More recent experiments using radio-isotopes reinforce the view that c.s.f. is elaborated by the chorioid plexus, the pial vessels, and presumably also by capillaries throughout the nervous tissue itself.[29, 31, 34] These studies also demonstrate that the various individual constituents of the c.s.f. are added to this fluid at different rates. Hence the c.s.f. represents a bringing together from many sources of many relatively independently contributed components.

Sites of Reabsorption.   Injection of hypertonic intravenous solutions is followed by a reversed effect, resulting in a decrease of c.s.f. volume.[36, 37] Observation of the movement of dye particles or radioactive ions during injection of such hypertonic solutions has shown that reabsorption of c.s.f. may occur by way of parenchymal capillaries as well as through arachnoid villi. In fact reabsorption of the fluid appears to take place even through capillaries of the chorioid plexus. When dyes are introduced into the fluid without interference with blood flow or osmotic pressure relationships, it is possible to locate the normal site of reabsorption of c.s.f. Most of the dye is found congregated about the arachnoid villi and Pacchionian bodies which together are taken to be the main portals of fluid escape.[2, 4, 35] The arachnoid villi offer a thin two-cell barrier (endothelium and arachnoid) between the c.s.f. and venous blood and are considered to be the most important routes of reabsorption.

Brierley and Field have demonstrated the importance of communications between the subarachnoid space and various lymphatic channels. They have traced India ink particles from the subarachnoid space along the meningeal extensions accompanying the olfactory tracts, optic nerves and spinal nerve roots; in each instance the particles find their way through the leptomeninges and diffuse across variable distances of connective tissue and fat to be picked up by lymphatic channels.[4] Dye particles, for instance, begin to appear in prevertebral lymph nodes within a matter of minutes after their introduction in replacement of normal c.s.f. at normal pressures. Because most of these smaller lymphatic channels are valveless they may transport particulate matter from abdominal lymph channels in a retrograde direction to dorsal root ganglia, adjacent membranes and the spinal cord itself. This may provide one avenue for the movement of virus and other particles toward the central nervous system.

Influences Inducing Seepage.   It is obvious that, although there may be local discrepancies, normally the over-all formation and reabsorption of c.s.f. must be proceeding at the same rates. Whatever the physiologic mechanisms concerned, they are homeostatic in the sense that if they are disturbed they tend to return to an equilibrium state. Such disturbances can be induced by adding to or withdrawing fluid, modifying cerebral blood flow, changing cerebral blood volume and altering osmotic tension of blood or c.s.f. or both.[25, 27] If initial pressure is elevated such disturbances have a larger effect. This is presumably because elasticity in the blood vessels and leptomeninges is already partially taken up so that any additional changes in volume are accompanied by steeper rises or falls in absolute pressure. Aside from the peculiarities brought about by the hard bony encasement of the brain, these changes appear to take place in accordance with general physiologic principles obtaining across other biologic membranes; i.e., hydrostatic and osmotic forces combine to bring about shifts from one fluid compartment to another.

The processes of formation and reabsorption of c.s.f. take place simultaneously and are capable of considerable independent variation. Information about the over-all rates of accumulation and drainage of c.s.f. has been derived indirectly. Thus, when a large quantity of fluid is withdrawn replacement takes place rapidly, but it is not known if this represents simply acceleration of formation, retardation of reabsorption, or a combination of both. The average rate of formation under normal circumstances has been estimated at 0.3 ml. per minute.[6] This rate is by no means fixed, and, since it is closely related to alterations in the osmotic and hydrostatic pressure of the blood, it must vary considerably among different individuals and from time to time in the same individual.

Aliquorrhea. A curious abnormality of c.s.f. production known as aliquorrhea was first described by Leriche.[15] It is characterized by scanty fluid at abnormally low pressures. Some authors find that 7 per cent of their neurosurgical patients have verified intracranial hypotension associated with a rapid or insidious onset of headache, vomiting, confusion and neurologic defects such as hemiplegia, oculomotor paralysis, seizures and hypothalamic symptoms, e.g., hyperthermia, diabetes insipidus.[23] Sixty-eight per cent of 238 cases of aliquorrhea were secondary to trauma, postoperative complications and various medical and surgical disorders, including severe dehydration. Thirty-two per cent, however, were without assignable cause. According to Page,[19] this condition might arise by way of one or more of three possible mechanisms: excessive loss of fluid, as by leakage from a head wound or needle puncture site; insufficient production of fluid (associated in some cases with an atrophic appearance of the chorioid plexus); or enlargement of the c.s.f. space, as following the removal of a large intracranial mass. Symptoms due to depletion of fluid are promptly relieved following intrathecal injection of sterile saline.

It is evident, therefore, that not only by virtue of its cerebrospinal fluid bath is the brain protected from damaging ballottement within the cranium, but that continuing simultaneous shifts in the rates of formation and reabsorption of the fluid ensure hydraulic homeostasis. This much appears to be straightforward; it now remains to consider the evidence for an even more important biochemical protection afforded the nervous system through the mechanisms of formation and reabsorption of c.s.f.

THE BLOOD-BRAIN BARRIER

Concept of an Ultrafiltrate. In common with the earliest conceptualizations relating to other biologic membranes, the tissue surfaces responsible for the elaboration and reabsorption of c.s.f. were likened to simple filters. In some respects the fluid resembles an ultrafiltrate of plasma: (i) c.s.f. tends toward equilibrium with blood following variations in the concentration of oxygen, sugar, urea, Na^+ and Cl^- ions and many other substances in the blood; (ii) no substance not normally found in blood is normally found in c.s.f.; and (iii) the production and reabsorption of c.s.f. are responsive to shifts in osmotic forces in the blood, and the direction of fluid transport across the membranes of chorioid plexuses and parenchymal capillaries may be reversed. Nevertheless, the idea that c.s.f. is an ultrafiltrate is probably simpler than the reality; physical chemical concepts of an ultrafiltrate or "pure dialysate" are derived from the laboratory use of cellophane or porcelain filters. There is no reason *a priori* for confidence that a biologic membrane will behave in exactly the same manner as a nonliving filter; no biologic membrane has yet been found to have exactly these characteristics. Moreover, the partitions between the blood and c.s.f. appear to be more complex structurally than those separating the blood from the extracellular fluid in most other parts of the body. Finally, since the c.s.f. is manufactured and contained in living tissue, and since it commingles to some extent with the extracellular fluid bathing all neurons, neuroglia, etc., one is not surprised to discover that c.s.f. contains some additions to or subtractions

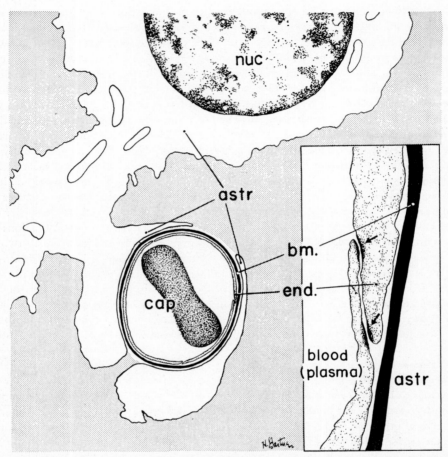

FIG. 523. Drawing based on electron photomicrograph at magnification X 6500; insert based on another electron photomicrograph at magnification X 90,000. The clear space represents a glial cell, including one of its major arms and a pair of perivascular feet almost completely surrounding a capillary. The stippled field represents the remainder of the parenchymal tissue, including nerve fibers, glial processes, etc. The capillary contains an erythrocyte. The capillary endothelium is seen to be surrounded by basement membrane. In the insert is shown the junction of two endothelial cells, the junction being sealed by terminal bar condensations indicated by arrows. The basement membrane is seen to be dense and continuous and is in effect shared by endothelium and the adjacent glial cell. (Drawing adapted from photomicrographs in: Maynard, E. A., Schultz, R. L. and Pease, D. C. *Amer J. Anat.*, 1957, *100:*409–433.)

from the composition of a simple dialysate even if such a dialysate were in fact initially produced.

Anatomy of the Blood-c.s.f. and Blood-brain Barrier. Blood entering the chorioid plexuses is separated from the c.s.f. by an endothelial wall, a layer of loose connective tissue made up of pia-arachnoid, and an ependymal epithelium.[16, 18, 38] The chorioidal capillary endothelium is fenestrated as if to provide a minimal barrier to diffusion. The capillary wall is surrounded by a very thin basement membrane, which represents the only continuous barrier between the blood and the loose subepithelial tissue spaces. The basilar surfaces of the cuboidal epithelial cells are deeply folded, and the walls of neighboring cells are elaborately interdigitated. The ventricular surfaces of the epithelium are specialized into a brush border. Occasionally these cells have two or three cilia. Under the electron microscope, the brush border is seen to be composed of very profuse and deep membranous foldings. Presumably the chorioid plexuses supply the bulk of the c.s.f., although its volume and composition might be considerably affected locally or generally by its other boundary tissues.

Within the parenchyma of the brain, the capillary endothelium appears to be continuous (without fenestrations); the cells overlap and are apparently sealed together by terminal bars[17] (Fig. 523). A dense, continuous basement membrane is shared between these capillaries and the adjacent glia and nerve cells and their processes. This basement membrane is, in turn, nearly completely invested by a sheath of neuroglial processes which cover approximately 85 per cent of the total capillary surface; the remaining "bare" capillary is in direct contact across the basement membrane with nerve cells and fibers[17] (Fig. 523). This sheathing of the capillaries by neuroglial processes may provide an additional or perhaps a sufficient mechanism for the peculiar regulation of transport between blood and brain. These special anatomic features of cerebrospinal blood vessels may be related to the special physiologic relations between the blood stream and the cerebrospinal and interstitial fluids of the nervous system; it may be by these structural means that the c.s.f. takes on its particular chemical design.

Physiologic Evidence of the Blood-c.s.f. and Blood-brain Barrier. The c.s.f. and the brain itself appear to be protected in important biochemical respects and to be maintained in more complete homeostasis than other tissues.[6, 31, 33] Bile pigments, penicillin and many other substances do not cross the normal blood-c.s.f. and blood-brain barrier, although they readily penetrate tissues elsewhere. A pH difference of 0.2 is maintained across the barrier, and OH^- and H^+ are precluded from easy entry. Na^+, K^+, Ca^{++}, Mg^{++}, Cl^- and HPO_4^{--} can enter only after an exaggerated delay three to 30 times that for their transfer elsewhere.* Similarly, many organic acids may be nearly completely restrained from entering. On the other hand, basic or neutral acids can usually penetrate, although slowly. Glucose appears to be actively transported, whereas oxygen and carbon dioxide do not appear to be in any way impeded in crossing the barrier. In pathologic conditions involving anoxia, inflammation or laceration of the brain, the barrier may partially break down and permit a rapid entry of ions, organic acids, etc.

The barrier appears to be lacking in the vascular supply to brain tumors. This provides a basis for localization of brain tumors by radioactive tracer injection into the blood stream and examination with a scintillation counter over the head or at the end of a probe introduced into the brain during surgery. The physiologic barrier appears normally to be lacking in certain specific regions: the pineal body, the pituitary gland, endocrine parts of the hypothalamus, and the area postrema.[39] Neuroendocrine and electrolyte regulation by the central nervous system may require direct access between neurons and the blood stream in these regions. Perhaps they accommodate central receptor systems which are triggered by substances that cannot cross the barrier elsewhere.

The existence of a barrier affecting most of the central nervous system may be thought of as providing protection against inappropriate ionic perturbations. As discussed

---

* The rate of transfer of substances into the c.s.f. from plasma is more difficult to determine than most physiologic experiments suggest, inasmuch as a very large *intra*cellular volume, as well as the c.s.f. and the *inter*cellular volume, is available for accumulation. Thus, any substance that crosses the barrier moderately slowly but enters the cells swiftly may falsely appear to be "blocked" as though it had never reached the c.s.f. In order to determine whether a given natural constituent is undergoing a net transport into c.s.f. across a certain membrane the rate of transfer in both directions across that membrane must be measured under fixed conditions.[29]

in Chapter 2, Na$^+$ and K$^+$ play an important role in the transmission of action currents within the nervous system; Ca^{++}, K$^+$ and Mg^{++} fluctuations introduced directly into the brain produce striking and sometimes disastrous effects on vasomotor and respiratory reflexes; similarly the concentrations of H$^+$ and OH$^-$ may be critical. By having a mechanism for the controlled admission of ions, the nervous system may be shielded against too abrupt changes in its chemical environment. Perhaps the c.s.f. can play a further role in this respect; whatever ions or other substances are discharged from the cell during activity will become diluted insofar as they can mix with the relatively large pool of c.s.f. and will thereby cause less local disturbance.[32] Note that the most active parts (gray matter) of the brain are turned toward the subarachnoid and ventricular (c.s.f.) surfaces. Perhaps the c.s.f. is also a reservoir, holding nearby those substances which are lost during neuronal discharge but which must be replaced again during recovery. Instead of being swept away by the blood stream, they would be husbanded within the c.s.f. from which they might more readily be taken up again.[32] *Altogether the barrier provides mechanisms whereby the cerebrospinal fluid can act as a buffer for the nervous system, not only against complex physical insults but also against intricate chemical perturbations.*

REFERENCES

1. AYALA, G. Z. *Neurol. Psychiat.*, 1923, *84*:42–95.
2. BRIERLEY, J. B. *J. Neurol. Psychiat.*, 1950, *13*:203–215.
3. BRIERLEY, J. B. Pp. 121-135 in: *Metabolism of the nervous system*, RICHTER, D., ed., New York, Pergamon Press, 1957.
4. BRIERLEY, J. B. and FIELD, E. J. *J. Anat.*, Lond., 1948, *82*:153–166.
5. CHANG, J. J. and HILD, W. *J. cell. comp. Physiol.*, 1959, *53*:139–144.
6. DAVSON, H. *Physiology of the ocular and cerebrospinal fluids*. London, Churchill, 1956, viii, 388 pp.
7. FLEXNER, L. B. *Quart. Rev. Biol.*, 1933, *8*:397–422.
8. FLEXNER, L. B. *J. biol. Chem.*, 1938, *126*:619–626.
9. HENRY, J. P., GAUER, O. H., KETY, S. S. and KRAMER, K. *J. clin. Invest.*, 1951, *30*:292–300.
10. HILD, W., CHANG, J. J. and TASAKI, I. *Experientia*, 1958, *14*:220–221.
11. HOLBOURN, A. H. S. *Lancet*, 1943, *245*:438–441.
12. HOLBOURN, A. H. S. *J. Neurosurg.*, 1944, *1*:190–200.
13. KETY, S. S. (Personal communication.)
14. KEY, E. A. H. and RETZIUS, G. *Studien in der Anatomie des Nervenssystems und des Bindegewebes*. Stockholm, Samson och Wallin, 1875–1876.
15. LERICHE, R. *Lyon Chir.*, 1920, *16*:638–651.
16. MAXWELL, D. S. and PEASE, D. C. *J. biophys. biochem. Cytol.*, 1956, *2*:467–474.
17. MAYNARD, E. A., SCHULTZ, R. L. and PEASE, D. C. *Amer. J. Anat.*, 1957, *100*:409–433.
18. MILLEN, J. W. and ROGERS, G. E. *J. biophys. biochem. Cytol.*, 1956, *2*:407–416.
19. PAGE, F. *Lancet*, 1953, *264*:1–5.
20. PATEK, P. R. *Anat. Rec.*, 1944, *88*:1–24.
21. POMERAT, C. M. Pp. 162–175 in: WINDLE, W. F., ed. *Biology of neuroglia*, Springfield, Illinois, Charles C Thomas, 1958.
22. PUDENZ, R. H. and SHELDON, C. H. *J. Neurosurg.*, 1946, *3*:487–505.
23. PUECH, P., GUILLY, P., MORICE, J. and BRUN, M. *Proc. Roy. Soc. Med.*, 1948, *41*:722–775.
24. QUECKENSTEDT, H. *Dtsch. Z. Nervenheilk.*, 1916, *55*:325–333.
25. RYDER, H. W., ESPEY, F. F., KIMBELL, F. D., PENKA, E. J., ROSENAUER, A., POLOLSKY, B. and EVANS, J. P. *J. Lab. clin. Med.*, 1953, *41*:428–435.
26. SAVITSKY, N. and KESSLER, N. M. *Arch. Neurol. Psychiat. (Chicago)*, 1938, *39*:988–1002.
27. SCHALTENBRAND, G. *Lancet*, 1953, *264*:805–808.
28. SCHULTZ, R. L., MAYNARD, E. A. and PEASE, D. C. *Amer. J. Anat.*, 1957, *100*:369–388.
29. SELVERSTONE, B. Pp. 147–167 in: WOLSTENHOLME, G. E. W. and O'CONNOR, C. M., eds. *Ciba Foundation symposium on the cerebrospinal fluid production, circulation and absorption*. London, Churchill, 1958.
30. TASAKI, I. and CHANG, J. J. *Science*, 1958 *128*:1209–1210.
31. TSCHIRGI, R. D. Pp. 34–46 in: *The biology of mental health and disease. Millbank Memorial Fund*. New York, Hoeber, 1952.
32. TSCHIRGI, R. D. (Personal communication.)
33. WALLACE, G. B. and BRODIE, B. B. *J. Pharmacol.*, 1940, *70*:418–427.
34. WANG, J. C. *J. gen. Physiol.*, 1948, *31*:259–268
35. WEED, L. H. *J. med. Res.*, 1914, *31*:57–92.
36. WEED, L. H. and McKIBBEN, P. S. *Amer. J. Physiol.*, 1919, *48*:512–530.
37. WEED, L. H. and McKIBBEN, P. S. *Amer. J. Physiol.*, 1919, *48*:531–558.
38. WISLOCKI, G. B. and LADMAN, A. J. Pp. 55–79 in: *Ciba foundation symposium on the cerebrospinal fluid production, circulation and absorption* WOLSTENHOLME, G. E. W., and O'CONNOR, C. M. eds. London, Churchill, 1958.
39. WISLOCKI, G. B. and LEDUC, E. H. *J. comp Neurol.*, 1952, *96*:371–414.
40. WOLSTENHOLME, G. E. W. and O'CONNOR, C. M., eds. *Ciba foundation symposium on the cerebrospinal fluid production, circulation and absorption*. London, Churchill, 1958, xii 335 pp.

SECTION X

Digestive and Urinary Systems

CHAPTER 42

General Functions of the Digestive System

By PAUL F. FENTON

THE integrity of living organisms can be maintained only if adequate materials are available to supply the energy-yielding oxidative reactions and to furnish the building blocks for repair, growth and reproduction. Structurally simple organisms such as protozoa may acquire nutrients by diffusion or phagocytosis, with digestion occurring intracellularly. In the vertebrates, a highly specialized digestive system reduces ingested foods to chemical entities which are readily transported by the circulatory system. These digestive systems are composed of a great variety of structural elements and are capable of executing a multitude of diverse functions. Structurally and functionally vertebrate digestive systems are highly adapted for the efficient execution of the processes of digestion and absorption. The duplication of function which is encountered frequently is at least partially responsible for the fact that digestion and absorption may be impaired in disease but are seldom totally abolished. The margin of safety thus provided (a form of error control) appears to be a fundamental characteristic of biologic systems.

STRUCTURE AND FUNCTION

In essence, the digestive tract is a tube designed for the task of receiving, digesting, and absorbing the chemical substances which constitute the ingested food. In general, the digestive tube consists of an inner lining, *the mucous membrane*, composed of epithelium and connective tissue (*lamina propria*); the mucous membrane is in turn surrounded by a series of muscular coats. In most parts of the digestive tract the mucous membrane is demarcated by a thin muscular layer, the *muscularis mucosae*. The loose connective tissue which lies beneath the muscularis mucosae (when the latter is present) is called the *submucosa*. This is in turn surrounded by two or three layers of smooth muscle. The entire tube is surrounded by a sheath of connective tissue, the *serosa*. In the small intestine the mucous membrane is highly folded to form the *intestinal villi*, whose chief function appears to be the presentation of a large absorptive area through which digested food materials can be transferred to the circulatory system. It has been estimated that the ratio of mucosal to serosal surface in the dog's small intestine is 8.5:1. Histologically, the stratified squamous epithelium of the oral cavity, pharynx and esophagus gives way to a simple columnar epithelium at the cardia, the entry of the esophagus into the stomach. The latter type of epithelium, which is perhaps best suited for the rapid passage of water and solutes from the lumen into the circulatory system or from the blood stream into the lumen, is found throughout the stomach and the small and large intestines. Stratified squamous epithelium appears again only in the anal region.

Glands. Numerous invaginations of the mucosa form the glands whose cells secrete many of the important digestive and lubricating fluids. Other secretions are formed by large glandular structures which lie outside the digestive tract but are connected with it by ducts which carry their secretions into its lumen. Glands which take stains more or less specific for mucin are termed mucous glands; too often, the glands which do not take mucin stains are indiscriminately called serous glands.

A rough division can be made into three groups according to the type of secretion produced. (i) Glands of the mucous type usually originate the highly viscous secretion rich in mucin (there are some notable exceptions). They act principally to lubricate the contents of the alimentary tract. The mucous glands of the stomach aid in protecting the mucosa against the eroding action of hydrochloric acid. (ii) Serous glands, on the other hand, produce a thin, watery fluid and are found primarily in the oral cavity, stomach and small intestine. The parotid gland and the pancreas are important examples of this type of gland. (iii) Mixed glands contain cells of both a mucous and a serous nature. These are found in many parts of the alimentary tract, but two important examples are the submaxillary and sublingual glands.

By far the greatest density of glands is found in the stomach and small intestine, the two organs which bring about the most extensive mechanical and chemical changes of the ingested foods. In the stomach the glands are of the simple, branched, tubular type containing four main cell types: (i) parietal cells, responsible for the production of hydrochloric acid; (ii) chief cells, secreting pepsinogen; (iii) mucous neck cells, producing mucus; and (iv) argentaffine cells of unknown function. In the pyloric region of the stomach the glands become deeper and more highly branched; they contain cells which resemble the chief and mucous neck cells. A few parietal cells may be present. The absence of any significant number of acid-producing cells permits the pyloric region of the stomach to begin the neutralization of acid chyme in preparation for its entry into the sensitive duodenum. Not very different from the pyloric region in appearance is the area of the duodenum containing Brunner's glands. There is today considerable evidence

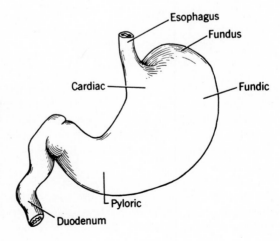

FIG. 524. Subdivisions of human stomach. (From Montagna, *Comparative anatomy.* New York, John Wiley & Sons, 1959.)

that the secretion of the pyloric region of the stomach resembles the secretion of the first part of the duodenum.

Musculature. The musculature of the upper portion of the esophagus consists of striated muscle capable of participating in the voluntary act of swallowing. The middle portion contains some smooth muscle bundles in addition to striated fibers; the lower part contains no striated muscle fibers at all. The smooth muscle bundles of the esophagus are not arranged in the regular pattern of circular and longitudinal layers typical of

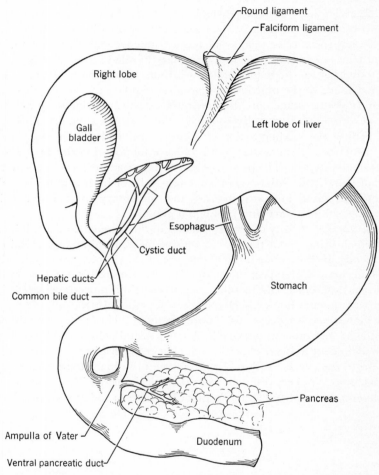

FIG. 525. Liver and gallbladder of man. (From Montagna, *Comparative anatomy.* New York, John Wiley & Sons, 1959.)

the other parts of the alimentary tract, although two distinct layers are recognizable. The outer, longitudinal coat is present throughout the stomach and the small and large intestines, but is rather incomplete in the latter. The circular layer tends to become more pronounced caudad in the alimentary canal. A third muscular coat is apparent, the oblique layer.

The stomach deviates considerably in shape from the other tubular portions of the digestive system (Fig. 524) and has slightly different functions. Although digestion does take place in the stomach, this organ serves the very useful purpose of a reservoir which influences considerably the physical consistency and osmotic pressure of its contents

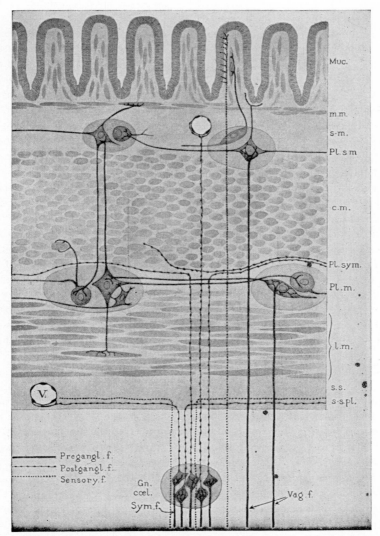

FIG. 526. Diagrammatic representation of relations of the elements of gut plexuses as seen in longitudinal section of gut wall. *Muc.*, mucosa; *m.m.*, muscularis mucosae; *s.m.*, submucosa; *Pl.s.m.*, submucous plexus; *c.m.*, circular muscle; *Pl.sym.*, sympathetic plexus; *Pl.m.*, myenteric plexus; *l.m.*, longitudinal muscle; *s.s.*, subserosa; *s.s.pl.*, subserous plexus; *Gn.coel.*, celial ganglion; *Sym.f.*, sympathetic fibers; *Vag.f.*, vagal fibers; *V.*, vessel. (From Hill, *Philos. Trans.*, 1927, *B215:*375.)

and the rate at which these contents are supplied to the delicate structures of the small intestine.

Sphincters. Much of the earlier interpretation of the movements of chyme from one portion of the alimentary tract to another was based upon the supposed function of the several sphincters: the cardia, the pylorus, the ileocecal sphincter and the internal and external anal sphincters. In man the cardia is frequently indistinct—more of a functional than an anatomic sphincter. On the other hand, the pylorus is formed by a distinct thickening of the circular fibers of the muscularis externa and by the infiltration of connective tissue into the muscular layer, but surgical removal of the pyloric sphincter does not appear to affect the rate of emptying of the stomach or alter in any way the sequence of mechanical events in stomach and intestine. The ileocecal and internal anal sphincters also consist essentially of thickened layers of smooth muscle. However, the external anal sphincter contains largely striated muscle.

Gallbladder. Although bile contains no enzymes of great importance, it nevertheless is a digestive secretion of considerable importance. It contains surface-active agents, the bile salts, which are intimately concerned with the digestion and absorption of lipids and other fat-soluble materials. Secreted by the hepatic parenchymal cells, bile is carried by an intricate network of vessels to the gallbladder, where much of it is stored until required in the digestive process. The surface layer of the gallbladder consists of tall, columnar epithelium suggestive of absorptive or secretory function. There is, indeed, much evidence that the mucosa lining the gallbladder considerably alters the composition of the bile. Beneath the mucosa is a layer of irregularly arranged loose muscle fibers mixed with elastic connective tissue (Fig. 525).

Innervation. Early investigations of the motor activity of the alimentary tract showed that this function could be maintained despite the sectioning of all extrinsic nerve supplies to the tissue in question. The carefully integrated, rhythmic movements of the stomach and intestines can be modified by, but can occur in the absence of, the extrinsic nerve supply. Two intricate networks of nerve cells play important roles in the automatic functioning of the alimentary tract; one is the myenteric plexus of Auerbach, the other the submucous plexus of Meissner. Some writers have called attention to the existence of no less than five discrete plexuses in the wall of the bowel. Preganglionic fibers of the parasympathetic system synapse with cells of the myenteric plexuses, while postganglionic sympathetic fibers directly innervate smooth muscle, glands and blood vessels. The sympathetic fibers may form the intramuscular and submucous plexuses (Fig. 526).

FOODS

The major function of the alimentary tract is the transfer of food material from the gastrointestinal lumen into the circulatory system. Some of the chemical substances involved—carbohydrates, lipids, proteins, minerals, vitamins, water—play roles which, in broad outline at least, are well known. They serve as sources of energy, as structural material, or as regulators of metabolic processes (see Section XI). However, the animal and vegetable tissues consumed by man contain many other chemical entities whose possible role is little understood. Some of these compounds possess the ability to stimulate secretory or motor activity in one or another portion of the alimentary tract. For this reason alone it would be desirable to know more of their chemical nature.

The carbohydrates of the ordinary human diet are derived almost exclusively from plant foods. In terms of quantities consumed, starch and sucrose by far lead the list. Starch is a relatively insoluble polysaccharide which does not readily pass through living membranes. Before it can move from the lumen of the alimentary tract into the circulatory system it must be hydrolyzed to glucose, which is water soluble and readily diffusible. Sucrose, a disaccharide, is usually hydrolyzed to glucose and fructose before absorption takes place. When large quantities of this sugar are ingested, some will be absorbed without prior hydrolysis. Such unchanged sucrose is not utilized by the organism but is excreted unchanged. The celluloses and hemicelluloses of the cell walls of plants constitute another important group of carbohydrates. These substances determine to a large degree the digestibility of plant tissue, since they may so firmly encase the nutritionally useful cell contents that the digestive enzymes do not have ready access to them. Since celluloses and hemicelluloses are little attacked by digestive enzymes or even by intestinal bacteria, these materials constitute the greater part of the "roughage" of the diet. The effect of roughage on several gastrointestinal functions is discussed in a later chapter.

Significant quantities of lipids and proteins are derived from both plant and animal foods. Of the many food substances which may be classed as lipids, the triglycerides of the higher fatty acids are quantitatively the most significant. Phospholipids are also found in appreciable quantities. The proteins are by far the most complex chemical substances found in foods. These compounds of extraordinarily high molecular weight are as a rule insoluble in water and must be digested before they can be efficiently dealt with by the absorbing cells.

The alimentary tract not only is the portal of entry of the essential food substances but is often the first organ system affected by nutritional deficiencies. Such lesions in turn may lead to progressive disturbances of digestion and assimilation.

ENZYMES

Historical note. The hydrolysis of carbohydrate, fat and protein ordinarily proceeds *in vitro* at such a slow rate or requires such extreme conditions as to be completely out of the question as a physiologic mechanism. Among the definitive steps toward our modern concept of enzyme-catalyzed alimentary digestion were the work of Wharton and Silvius, calling attention to the salivary glands as possible agents in the digestion of foods, the work of van Helmont and of Borelli on the stomach as an organ of digestion, and the writings of Spallanzani and Réaumur on the digestive action of gastric juice. Beaumont's observation of the stomach of Alexis St. Martin led directly to Claude Bernard's attempts to prepare gastric fistulae in experimental animals. This approach was used successfully by Heidenhain and Pavlov.

Kirchoff's discovery in 1814 of the digestion of starch by malt amylase was soon followed by a demonstration of the amylolytic properties of saliva. In 1837 Berzelius characterized fermentation as a catalytic process and helped pave the way to the recognition of enzymes as organic catalysts.

Nature of Enzymes. Enzymes are organic catalysts, protein in nature, elaborated by living cells and capable of altering the velocity of a chemical reaction without being destroyed or permanently altered in the process. Some reactions proceed so slowly in the absence of the proper enzyme that the enzyme would appear to be capable of initiating certain chemical reactions. The mechanism by which many, if not all, enzymes act is by combining temporarily with the substrate and reducing the energy of activation. For example, the energy of activation for the decomposition of hydrogen peroxide into water and oxygen is 18,000 cal. per mol. The energy of activation is only 11,700 cal. per mol when the reaction is catalyzed by colloidal platinum, and drops to 5500 in the presence of liver catalase.

Enzymes are usually named according to their substrates or the tasks which they perform, the suffix *-ase* being added. However, it is still common practice to employ the traditional names given some enzymes when they were first discovered. Thus it is suitable to speak of pepsin and trypsin, although ptyalin is more generally referred to now as salivary amylase. Enzymatic reactions are reversible, although the endergonic step may need to be coupled with a suitable exergonic reaction. The ability of a number of digestive enzymes to catalyze a reaction in both directions has been demonstrated. The proteases in particular have been used for study of the synthesis of peptide bonds as possible models for the intracellular net synthesis of proteins.

Enzymes exhibit a high degree of *specificity*, that is, their action is limited to specific types of substrates. The absolute specificity of the digestive enzymes has long been recognized. Thus a proteolytic enzyme will not hydrolyze carbohydrates or lipids. Carbohydrases will not cleave lipids or proteins, nor will lipases act upon carbohydrates or proteins. Specificity extends even further. Maltase acts to a significant degree only upon α-glucosides but not upon β-glucosides. On the other hand, detailed analysis of some relatively complex enzymatic processes has shown clearly that enzymes may carry out more than one function. Thus, proteolytic enzymes may cleave not only peptide bonds but some specific ester linkages. The structural requirements of the substrates have been worked out most extensively in the case of the proteolytic enzymes. Although all members of this category have in common the ability to cleave the peptide bond, they differ widely from one another in their requirements for other structural conditions which determine their ability to break a given peptide bond. So far, three major groups of proteolytic enzymes are recognized. The aminopeptidases are exopeptidases which hydrolyze peptide bonds at the terminal portion of a peptide chain, provided the bonds are located adjacent to a free (terminal) amino group and the carbon atom between the free amino group and the peptide bond possesses a side chain of either the benzyl or p-hydroxybenzyl group. The carboxypeptidases are exopeptidases which split peptide bonds adjacent to a free terminal carboxyl group. The side chain requirements are the same as those of the aminopeptidases. The proteinases are endopeptidases which cleave peptide bonds well removed from the terminal position in the peptide chain. The side chain requirements are as follows: pepsin and chymotrypsin, benzyl or p-hydroxybenzyl; trypsin, aminobutyl or guanidopropyl. The benzyl group side chain is that found in phenylalanine, the p-hydroxybenzyl group is that of tyrosine, the aminobutyl group is found in lysine, and the guanidopropyl group in arginine. Evidence regarding the structural requirements of the substrate together with information on the action of cations[29] in catalysis has led to concepts of the combination of enzyme and substrate at one or more active sites on the enzyme protein molecule. Relatively new techniques for determining the sequence of amino acids in protein molecules has led to some information on the composition of these active sites.

Factors Influencing Enzyme Activity. In general, increasing the concentration of the substrate increases the activity of an enzyme. It is frequently found, however, that increasing the substrate concentration beyond a specific maximum leads to a gradual diminution of enzymatic activity. Increasing the concentration of enzyme in a given system usually leads to an increase in the rate of chemical change. The influence of temperature is interesting. The temperature coefficients (ratio of reaction velocities at intervals of 10° C.) for most enzymes lie between 1.3 and 3.5. Thus, increasing the temperature at which the reaction is carried out increases the reaction velocity. Since the enzymes are proteins, there is a definite upper limit; most enzymes are destroyed if subjected to a temperature of 80° C. or higher. The point of balance between the accelerating effect of increasing temperature and the destructive effect of heat lies usually between 40 and 50° C. but may be lower. It is perhaps more than a fortuitous coincidence that, in the mammalian organisms, enzymes act at a temperature a little less than 40° C. The temperature effect has been carefully analyzed by Sizer.[28] Another critical factor in the environment of the enzyme is the hydrogen ion concentration. For each enzyme there is a certain limited range of hydrogen ion concentration in which the enzyme shows optimal activity. In the case of pepsin this optimal zone lies between pH 1.5 and 2.0, although certain simple peptides are split optimally by pepsin at pH 4.0. Salivary and pancreatic amylases show optimal activity at a pH near neutrality; liver arginase acts most rapidly at pH 9.5 to 9.9.

A number of the digestive enzymes are elaborated in a form which is incapable of catalysis. These are called proenzymes or zymogens. The conversion into the active enzyme is sometimes an autocatalytic reaction but in some instances requires the mediation of a kinase. Most widely studied of these agents is enterokinase, produced by the glands of the small intestine and capable of converting trypsinogen into trypsin. Activators of a somewhat different sort are (i) certain metals, e.g., calcium and the activation of adenosinetriphosphatase, chloride and salivary amylase, (ii) agents which influence the state of the substrate, e.g., bile salts and the action of pancreatic lipase on a triglyceride, and (iii) protective substances, e.g., inert proteins and urease in the presence of a toxic heavy metal. On the other hand, a great variety of agents have the ability to inhibit or abolish enzyme activity. Examples of this are well known: heavy metals, cyanide, fluorides, ultraviolet and infrared light (in some instances, visible light), naturally occurring organic inhibitors (these are frequently cited to explain why the alimentary tract does not ordinarily digest itself and why intestinal parasites manage to survive), and finally specific immune bodies which organisms develop if small doses of an enzyme are repeatedly injected intravenously.[30]

SECRETION AND ABSORPTION[10, 11, 13, 14, 18]

Two of the most important processes occurring in the alimentary tract, secretion of digestive juices and absorption of digested food materials, involve transferring solvents and solutes across semipermeable membranes. Both processes require the mediation of specific chemical reactions and the expenditure of energy. Both processes can function simultaneously—if not in the same region of the digestive tract, at least in closely adjacent areas.

Cellular permeability. A tremendous amount of literature has accumulated on the subject of cellular permeability. Overton's classic study[25] established certain rules of permeability of cells which have, on the whole, been amply confirmed by more modern investigations.[8, 20] The compounds which usually penetrate the cell most rapidly are hydrocarbons, esters, organic acids and bases, and relatively unsubstituted alcohols, aldehydes and ketones. The substitution of additional hydroxyl groups decreases the rate of penetration. Polar compounds such as sugars and amino acids would be expected to penetrate the lipoid layers of the cell membrane only slowly. Yet these metabolically important compounds enter the cell at considerable speeds by processes which apparently are under endocrine control. The active transport of molecules which are only slightly lipoid-soluble requires an energy-yielding device. The appearance of increased amounts of phosphorylated sugars in the intestinal mucosa during sugar absorption has sometimes been interpreted as a device for maintaining a high diffusion gradient across the cell membrane. However, this phenomenon may well reflect an acceleration of energy-yielding reactions in the oxidation of carbohydrate.

Traditionally, the relationship between penetration rate of a substance and its solubility in fats has been interpreted to mean that the cell membrane is essentially lipid in nature. Chemical analysis of the membranes of erythrocytes[26] has shown that two phospholipids, cephalin and lecithin, and cholesterol constitute about 90 per cent of the total lipid fraction. It has also been shown that the red cell membrane contains a measurable quantity of protein. The presence of protein has suggested the very interesting possibility that the interlinked polypeptide chains are responsible for the sievelike behavior of cell membranes under specific conditions.

It has been observed that some very small molecules penetrate faster than their lipid-solubility would cause one to predict. Such observations have led to attempts to formulate a picture of the cell membrane as composed of a lipid layer with adsorbed protein, the lipid layer containing minute pores which permit the extraordinarily rapid passage of very small molecules of low lipid-solubility. Transport across such a membrane may occur by several processes: (i) by solution in the lipid of the membrane, (ii) by passage through the pores, and (iii) by temporary combination with a constituent of the membrane.

Harris[18] has collected evidence for each of these processes. One formulation of the structure of the cell membrane is that by Davson and Danielli.[14] They assumed that there are a very few layers of lipoid material with an adsorbed layer of protein (Fig. 527). The concept of a cell membrane as a mosaic of lipoid and protein areas is also attractive.[19]

Whatever the morphologic and chemical nature of the membrane, permeability may be defined as the degree of resistance offered to the passage of a substance crossing the membrane under the influence of some driving force. The latter appears to be twofold: in some instances the passage may be the result merely of a diffusion gradient (difference in concentration of the specific substance on the two sides of the membrane); in other cases the driving force appears to be some specific chemical reaction or chain of reactions involved in the transport of the substance across the membrane. In the event that penetration occurs without the intervention of the cell itself, the rate of such penetration is governed not only by the concentration gradient but also by lipoid solubility and the molecular volume of the solute. If active transfer is involved, a source of energy is required, and the rate of penetration can be considerably altered by interfering with the oxidative mechanism.

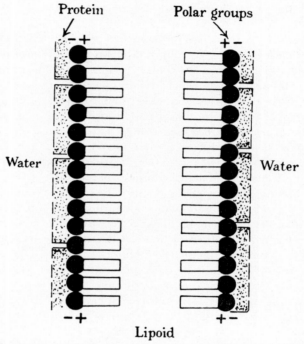

FIG. 527. Suggested molecular arrangement of cell surface. (From Davson and Danielli, *The permeability of natural membranes*, 2d ed. London, Cambridge University Press, 1952.)

Incomplete as our knowledge of cellular permeability may be, we know still less about the permeability of the whole groups of cells that compose the absorptive membrane of the alimentary tract.

Secretion. Although the digestive juices are composed chiefly of water, electrolytes and proteins, they vary widely in their content of these substances.[2] The materials which constitute the digestive secretions are obtained ultimately from the blood stream, and some by-products in the formation of the secretions are returned to the blood.

Secretion is not a simple outflowing of water and dissolved material. It involves the expenditure of energy; it is a form of work. Ludwig showed in 1851 that blocking the duct of the submaxillary gland and stimulating the fibers of the chorda tympani evoked a secretion of saliva despite the fact that the hydrostatic pressure in the duct exceeded the blood pressure. The widely varying composition of the digestive secretions is further proof that the secreting cells actively participate in the formation of the product. Digestive glands show increased oxygen consumption and carbohydrate utilization during the secretory process. The additional energy thus produced presumably is expended in transferring material across the cell membranes and in the resynthesis of the zymogen granules which are typical of cells involved in enzyme secretion. Osterhout[24] has attempted to explain the secretion of water, at least, on the basis of local osmotic pressure changes within the secretory cells. Davies[12] has suggested that in some cases the actively secreting structure is not the cell as a whole but the subcellular mitochondria. The idea is intriguing because the mitrochondria play a vital role in cellular oxidation.

Absorption.   Absorption is defined here quite arbitrarily as the movement of molecules from the lumen of the digestive tract into the circulatory system, blood or lymph. The fundamental problems are the same as those for secretion. There is involved a transfer across a semipermeable membrane, presumably lipid in composition with adsorbed protein and possibly with pores of small size. The transfer may occur in part by simple diffusion or may involve, to a greater or lesser extent, active translocation necessitating the expenditure of energy. Many early investigators made valiant attempts to explain absorption of nutrient materials from the alimentary tract in terms of oversimplified physicochemical principles. With increasing knowledge of active transport in

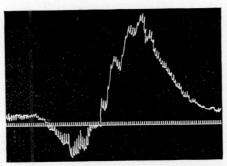

FIG. 528a.   Peristaltic contractions of small intestine (dog). Horizontal line gives time in seconds. Curve was obtained by recording diameter of intestine at a given point. A dilatation (wave of inhibition) preceded strong contraction. Smaller waves due to effect of respiratory movements on recording device.

general, absorption of substances from the gastrointestinal tract is being re-examined. The principles involved in passive and active transport have been fully stated in Chapters 1 and 39.

MOTILITY OF DIGESTIVE TRACT

The movements of the alimentary canal can be divided roughly into two types: those which serve principally to mix the contents of any given part of the tract, and those which primarily move the contents from one locus of activity to another. All this is accomplished by a series of complex contractions of the longitudinal and circular muscle coats. The contractions of the smooth muscle fibers are integrated by the intrinsic plexuses, whose activity, however, is modified by the extrinsic parasympathetic and sympathetic innervation.

Peristalsis.   The classic work of Bayliss and Starling[3] led these workers to formulate the "law of the intestine." They had found that, when the intestinal wall is stimulated, a local contraction of the muscular coats occurs. This contraction passes as a wave down the intestine preceded by a wave of inhibition. These pressure changes (Fig. 528a) have been recorded by many workers with the aid of inflated balloons introduced into the lumen of the intestine. The contraction wave presumably serves to force the contents of the alimentary tract to move caudad; the state of receptive relaxation which precedes the wave has been viewed as an aid to the movement of the column of intestinal contents. Alvarez[1] has vigorously challenged this concept of a "law of the intestine" because it was demonstrated with balloons placed in the denervated bowel of animals which had received castor oil. With the aid of somewhat different techniques, he found that electrical stimulation of the serosal surface of the rabbit resulted in contraction both above and below the point of stimulation. Alvarez concluded that the wave of contraction runs caudad without being preceded by receptive relaxation. In the course of extensive studies on the motility of the pyloric sphincter and adjacent regions Meschan and Quigley[23] found definite evidence of a decrease in intraluminal pressure preceding the contraction wave. The decrease, however, was small and did not occur each time. These workers concluded that the wave of inhibition or receptive relaxation is real but is neither essential nor important. On the basis of later investigations Brody et al.[6] concluded that negative intraluminal pressures (which would accompany a wave of relaxation) rarely precede a wave of contraction. No evidence of a preceding fall in pressure in a duodenal bulb is seen in Figure 528b.

Peristaltic waves differ in the distance they travel caudad. Some disappear after having traversed but a few inches of intestine. At other times, a *peristaltic rush* sweeps over great sections of the alimentary tract; in fact, some may sweep from the cardia to the rectum. A spiral movement of the bolus during its passage through the small intestine has been observed and attributed to activity of the spiral muscular layer in the wall of the gut.[27]

That the wave of contraction is propagated in part by the stimulatory effect of intestinal contents was shown by cutting the intestine and re-establishing continuity with

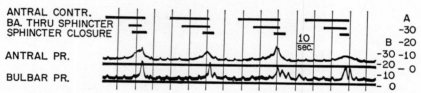

FIG. 528b.   Recordings of pressure relationships in upper digestive tract. (After Werle *et al.*, *Amer. J. Physiol.*, 1941, *131*:606–614.)

a piece of glass tubing. Despite the complete severance of all layers of the gut, a new wave of contraction was set up in the lower portion by the passage of intestinal contents propelled through the glass tube by the contraction wave of the upper segment. Conversely, a contraction wave can be propagated even under conditions which prevent the passage of intestinal contents. Although the existence and nature of peristaltic waves have perhaps been most extensively studied in the small intestine, similar phenomena can be observed in the stomach and large intestine. The human stomach undergoes a succession of rapid changes in shape as the peristaltic wave sweeps over it.

Peristaltic waves may begin anywhere in the digestive tract. A number of them have their origin in the neighborhood of the cardia; these may cease when they reach the incisura. On the other hand, they may, under suitable conditions, continue as peristaltic rushes as far as the colon. Mass peristaltic movements involving the large intestine do occur, but they are usually infrequent; they are concerned largely with the evacuation of feces from the rectum. In addition to the easily demonstrable peristaltic waves small, slowly traveling contraction waves have been described.

Tonus Rhythm.   Slow alterations in the tonus of the musculature have been described for all parts of the digestive tract. At times these contractions serve to adapt the alimentary tract to the volume of its contents; but, since it occurs during fasting, this cannot be its sole function.

Rhythmic Segmentation.   This type of movement is usually superimposed upon the tonus rhythm just described. Cannon[7] has given an excellent description of this type of activity, which is essentially a mixing process. Segmentation occurs at regular intervals for a short time; it then ceases, to reappear in another portion of the intestine. These contractions have been observed to occur more frequently in the duodenum than in the jejunum or ileum. The necessity for mixing intestinal contents with digestive secretions is, of course, greater in the duodenum than in the lower parts of the small intestine where digestion is virtually complete.

Pendular Movements. This type of movement is seen in the small and in the large intestine and consists of rhythmic to-and-fro motion of a segment of gut while the contents apparently remain stationary.

Movements of Muscularis Mucosae. The possible functions of the intestinal villi in the processes of secretion and absorption have attracted considerable attention. Relatively little investigative work has been done on the muscularis mucosae which is responsible for the motility of the villi. King and Robinson[22] found that the muscularis mucosae from the large and small intestine behaved much alike. Since villi are present only in the small intestine, it would seem that the role of this inner muscular layer, in addition to activating the villi, is also that of mixing and transporting the contents of the alimentary tract. In this respect it supplements the movements that have previously been discussed.

Integration and Control of Motility.[16] Smooth muscles possess the ability to initiate spontaneous contractions. Such myogenic contractions can be demonstrated by the use of plexus-free circular muscle, a technique employed by Gasser[17] and others. Properly prepared, such strips of muscle contain few if any nerve cell bodies, although they may contain some fibers. These preparations show spontaneous rhythmic contractions and respond to acetylcholine with increased tone and at times with an increase in the magnitude of the contractions. Both atropine and epinephrine may inhibit contractions. It seems possible that pendular movements and tonus rhythm of the alimentary tract may be ascribed directly to these spontaneous contractions of circular smooth muscle.

On the other hand, the propagated peristaltic waves require the mediation of the enteric plexuses—most likely of Auerbach's plexus located between the circular and longitudinal muscle coats. This plexus is largely of parasympathetic origin, but may transmit some sympathetic fibers. The peristaltic wave has its origin in the myenteric reflex.[5] If the intestinal mucosa is lightly stroked, or if the intestine is stretched longitudinally, a powerful sustained contraction occurs orad to the stimulation. Alternatively, the rhythmic activity is heightened. In either case the myenteric reflex would propel the contents of the intestine toward the rectum.

Iggo[21] has studied the electrophysiologic activity of the unmyelinated C fibers in the vagus. He concluded that distention-sensitive receptors are "in series" with these afferent fibers. Thus smooth muscle tone could be expected to modify the response of the receptors to distention. It was found, for example, that rapid distention of the intestine resulted in higher luminal pressure than did slow distention with identical volumes of saline. This increased smooth muscle tone was accompanied by a higher rate of discharge over the afferent fibers. The signals presumably serve to a limited degree as tension—or volume—indicators. The receptors are located in the smooth musculature of the stomach or intestine.

Thus smooth muscle may itself initiate contractions in response to suitable stimuli but depends for propagation of these disturbances upon the integrity of the intrinsic nerve supply. Integration of activity in widely separated regions of the alimentary tract requires the mediation of the extrinsic nerve supply. In addition, motor activity may be influenced by certain humoral agents, for example, the inhibition of gastric motility by enterogastrone or the stimulation of gallbladder contraction by cholecystokinin.

Metabolism of Gastrointestinal Musculature. Crandall *et al.*[9] have shown that the organs drained by the portal vein utilize glucose and acetone bodies as sources of energy. This was determined by careful chemical analysis of the inflowing and outflowing blood. Drugs such as acetylcholine, muscarine and eserine have been known for some time to cause contractions of longitudinal and circular muscles of the alimentary tract. These agents, however, proved incapable of evoking contractions of the longitudinal muscle coat if glucose was omitted from the medium in which the preparation was suspended.[15] The addition of glucose or pyruvic acid permitted the drugs to exert their usual function. Fructose, galactose and mannose were less effective. The addition of lactate was found to be beneficial primarily to the circular muscle coat.

REFERENCES

1. ALVAREZ, W. C. *An introduction to gastroenterology, being the third edition of the mechanics of the digestive tract.* New York, Paul B. Hoeber, 1940.
2. BABKIN, B. P. *Secretory mechanism of the digestive glands.* New York, Paul B. Hoeber, 1944, xix, 900 pp.
3. BAYLISS, W. M. and STARLING, E. H. *J. Physiol.*, 1899, *24*:99–143.
4. BOZLER, E. *Biol. Symp.*, 1941, *3*:95–110.
5. BOZLER, E. *Amer. J. Physiol.*, 1949, *157*:329–337.
6. BRODY, D. A., WERLE, J. M., MESCHAN, I. and QUIGLEY, J. P. *Amer. J. Physiol.*, 1940, *130*:791–801.
7. CANNON, W. B. *Amer. J. Physiol.*, 1902, *6*:251–277.
8. *Cold Spring Harbor Symposia on Quantitative Biology.* 1940, *8.*
9. CRANDALL, L. A., JR., LIPSCOMB, A. and BARKER, S. B. *Proc. Soc. exp. Biol. (N. Y.),* 1946, *63*:533–536.
10. DANIELLI, J. F. *Symp. Soc. exp. Biol.*, 1952, *6*:1–15.
11. DANIELLI, J. F. *Symp. Soc. exp. Biol.*, 1954, *8*:502–516.
12. DAVIES, R. E. *Symp. Soc. exp. Biol.*, 1954, *8*:453–475.
13. DAVSON, H. *Symp. Soc. exp. Biol.*, 1954, *8*:16–26.
14. DAVSON, H. and DANIELLI, J. F. *The permeability of natural membranes,* 2d ed. Cambridge, Cambridge University Press, 1952, xii, 365 pp.
15. FELDBERG, W. and SOLANDT, O. M. *J. Physiol.*, 1942, *101*:137–171.
16. FISCHER, E. *Physiol. Rev.*, 1944, *24*:467–490.
17. GASSER, H. S. *J. Pharmacol.*, 1926, *27*:395–410.
18. HARRIS, E. J. *Transport and accumulation in biological systems.* London, Butterworths Scientific Publications, 1956, ix, 291 pp.
19. HÖBER, R. *Physical chemistry of cells and tissues.* Philadelphia, The Blakiston Company, 1945, xiii, 676 pp.
20. HÖBER, R. and HÖBER, JOSEPHINE. *J. cell. comp. Physiol.*, 1937, *10*:401–422.
21. IGGO, A. *Quart. J. exp. Physiol.*, 1957, *42:* 130–143.
22. KING, C. E. and ROBINSON, M. H. *Amer. J. Physiol.*, 1945, *143*:325–335.
23. MESCHAN, I. and QUIGLEY, J. P. *Amer. J. Physiol.*, 1938, *121*:350–357.
24. OSTERHOUT, W. J. V. *J. gen. Physiol.*, 1947, *30*:439–447.
25. OVERTON, E. *Pflüg. Arch. ges. Physiol.*, 1902, *92*:115–280.
26. PARPART, A. K. and DZIEMIAN, A. J. *Cold Spr. Harb. Symp. quant. Biol.*, 1940, *8*:17–24.
27. REID, P. E., IVY, A. C. and QUIGLEY, J. P. *Amer. J. Physiol.*, 1934, *109*:483–487.
28. SIZER, I. W. *Advanc. Enzymol.*, 1943, *3*:35–62.
29. SMITH, E. L., DAVIS, N. C., ADAMS, E. and SPACKMAN, D. H. Pp. 291–318 in *A symposium on the mechanism of enzyme action,* W. D. MCELROY and B. GLASS, eds. Baltimore, Johns Hopkins Press, 1954.
30. SUMNER, J. B. and MYRBÄCK, K. *The enzymes. Chemistry and mechanism of action,* vol. 1. New York, Academic Press, 1950.
31. VERZAR, F. and McDOUGALL, E. J. *Absorption from the intestine.* New York, Longmans, Green & Co., 1936.

CHAPTER 43

The Mouth and Esophagus

By PAUL F. FENTON

THE oral cavity, with its associated glandular structures, teeth and tongue, is the site of considerable alteration in the chemical and physical structure of the ingested food. Man's conscious awareness of food is dependent upon sensory stimuli carried to the central nervous system by several pathways, chief among which are those for vision, olfaction and taste. Sensory impulses are also conveyed from the alimentary tract by the afferent fibers of the autonomic nervous system. It is a familiar fact that the sight, smell, and taste of food (even the thought of food) can profoundly influence various parts of the digestive system. This is the first link in a complicated and highly coordinated chain of events which results in the almost complete digestion and absorption of the ingested food.

SALIVARY GLANDS

Control of Secretion.[21]   The early work of Ludwig and Heidenhain established that salivary secretion is more than the filtration of water and electrolytes and that the salivary glands are under the dual control of the sympathetic and parasympathetic nervous systems. Heidenhain noted that the dog's submaxillary gland could be made to secrete saliva of great volume but low concentration of organic matter (mucin, etc.) when the chorda tympani was stimulated. On the other hand, stimulation of the sympathetic fibers to the gland resulted in a scanty secretion with a fairly high concentration of organic matter. The former type of stimulation brought about dilatation of the blood vessels of the gland; the latter caused vasoconstriction. It has been demonstrated repeatedly that stimulation of the parasympathetic or sympathetic nerves to the salivary glands gives rise to two different secretions. The most plausible explanations are: (i) each secretory cell receives fibers from both autonomic divisions and responds in a different manner to each; or (ii) each cell receives fibers from only one division and the composition of the resulting secretion depends upon which group of cells is stimulated. The former concept was formulated by Heidenhain; the latter has been championed by Langley and more recently by Babkin.[1] Heidenhain's relatively simple concept that one division of the autonomic nervous system regulates the output of water and salts while the other controls the liberation of the organic constituents (largely proteins) breaks down when one considers the evidence that the chorda controls not only the secretion of water and salts but also affects the liberation of proteins. For example, it has been

917

shown that the protein content of the submaxillary secretion varies with the strength of the stimulus applied to the chorda tympani. The diminution of protein output upon prolonged chorda stimulation has been attributed to exhaustion of the precursor.[30] Conversely, atropine, acting in a sense antagonistically to the parasympathetic nervous system, has been shown to diminish not only the volume output of the salivary secretion but also the secretion of organic substances.[2] These and other observations show clearly that the chorda influences the outflow of water and protein, but they do not in themselves prove that each cell of the salivary glands receives its innervation from only one division of the autonomic nervous system.

The histologic investigations by Stormont[31] and Rawlinson[26] have greatly strengthened the idea that specific secretory cells of the salivary glands receive their innervation from only one division of the autonomic nervous system. The work of Rawlinson indicates that stimulation of the chorda tympani of the cat gives rise to histologic changes in the mucous cells but not in the demilunes of the submaxillary gland. Conversely, stimulation of the sympathetic fibers produces changes in the demilunes. When the sympathetics are severed and the chorda is stimulated, it is the mucous cells which undergo reduction in size; the demilunes show little change. Stimulation of the severed sympathetic trunk then gives rise to typical changes in the demilunes. Sympathetic stimulation after severance of the chorda also gives rise to changes in the demilune cells. If such histologic alterations may be taken as indices of secretory activity, one might conclude that the chorda tympani controls the secretory processes of the mucous cells while the sympathetic fibers to the submaxillary regulate secretion by the demilunes (serous cells). Such might very well be the case in the cat, in which the saliva secreted after sympathetic stimulation is generally less viscous than that secreted after stimulation of the chorda (in contrast to the results with dogs).

Langenskiöld[20] has studied the potentials developed by salivary glands during the secretory process. On the basis of these studies he concludes that all secretory cells of the submaxillary gland that are innervated by sympathetic fibers also are innervated by the chorda tympani.

Paralytic and Augmented Secretions. After the chorda tympani has been sectioned, a watery secretion flows spontaneously from the submaxillary gland. This flow, termed paralytic secretion, may reflect supersensitivity to epinephrine following denervation.[8, 9] Augmented secretion occurs when stimulation of the sympathetic fibers of the submaxillary glands has been preceded by stimulation of the chorda tympani. The volume produced by such combined stimulation is appreciably greater than that produced by sympathetic stimulation alone. It has been suggested[22] that chorda stimulation sensitizes the gland to subsequent sympathetic stimulation.

Normal Mechanism of Salivary Secretion. The preceding discussion has dealt with the innervation of the salivary glands and the types of secretion elicited experimentally. That the normal mechanism evoking salivary secretion is quite different from that occurring under artificial conditions is shown by the fact that the exhaustion of granular material so typical of electrical stimulation of the efferent nerves is never seen when the glands are reflexly stimulated by placing suitable materials in the mouth. Salivary secretion as the result of thinking of food or in response to the sight and smell of food is familiar to all. These conditioned reflexes involve previous experience, of course. The reflexes initiated when the taste buds are suitably stimulated are somewhat better understood. Afferent impulses are carried to the central nervous system by the VIIth, IXth and Xth cranial nerves. These fiber tracts make intimate connection with the nucleus of the solitary fasciculus, which in turn makes connection with the visceral reflex centers and with the cortical center for taste.[25] Wang[33] has found the salivatory center of the cat in the dorsolateral reticular formation, dorsomedial to the spinal trigeminal nucleus and dorsal to and at the level of the facial nucleus. The rostral portion of this area supplies the submaxillary glands while the caudal part supplies the parotids. Gantt[11, 12] has studied quantitatively the secretion obtained in response to conditioned and unconditioned reflex stimulation. The volume of secretion was found to be related to the quantity of food supplied.

The nature and strength of the stimulus placed in the mouth influences quite considerably the composition of the resulting secretion.[3] Diminishing the strength of the stimulus reduced the volume, the chloride concentration, and the acid-combining power of the secreted saliva. Each stimulus evoked a typical secretion from the parotid gland. This, together with other observations, led Baxter to conclude that each stimulus placed in the mouth acted reflexly upon various parts of the salivatory centers, which in turn evoked secretion by different cell types in the salivary glands. Reflex stimulation of salivary flow is abolished by severing the parasympathetic nerve supply to the several glands, suggesting that the main burden of salivary secretion rests upon the cells innervated by parasympathetic fibers.

Composition of Saliva. No single concise statement of the composition of saliva is possible. The nature and strength of the stimulus, as well as the state of the glands at the moment of stimulation, determine the precise composition. Thus the secretion of the submaxillary gland will contain a higher percentage of solids when the stimulus is bread-and-meat powder than when hydrochloric acid is employed. The difference is due largely to an increase in the concentration of organic matter in the saliva. Increasing the strength of the stimulus will usually result in greater volume of secretion and higher concentration of the inorganic constituents. This increase is due largely to an increase in the concentration of sodium and chloride, the concentration of potassium and calcium ordinarily being little changed. Increasing the strength of stimulation results in a greater concentration of the organic fraction unless the gland is already exhausted from previous stimulation. It has been estimated that an individual may produce between 1 and 1.5 liters of saliva in the course of a day. In addition to the substances already mentioned, the saliva contains many of the constituents of blood plasma. The proteins in saliva have so far been discussed as a single entity or as part of the organic fraction. The chief protein is, of course, mucin. Salivary amylase, or ptyalin, is present in human saliva but not in that of the dog or the cat. Other proteins may also be present.

MASTICATION

Mastication is a voluntary act which accomplishes two functions: mixing the ingested food with the saliva and reducing the food particles to a size convenient for swallowing. Carnivores, on the whole, swallow relatively large food particles, whereas man usually reduces food to somewhat smaller size before permitting it to reach his stomach. Mastication is intimately related to the proper stimulation of the salivary glands. The secretion of saliva in turn brings about the lubrication of the bolus in preparation for deglutition and initiates (in man and some other animals) the digestion of starch. The articulation of the mandible with the skull permits a great variety of movements.

Some faddists have assumed that prolonged chewing of food has great value because they believe it promotes more complete digestion of the food mass. Two considerations may be cited against this view. First, salivary digestion continues in the stomach for about a half hour after the first bolus enters the stomach (Chap. 44). Second, fluids leave the stomach more quickly than does semifluid and relatively solid material. Too prolonged chewing means that only highly fluid material reaches the stomach; since it leaves the viscus sooner, it is possible that there would be some failure of desired gastric digestion. This is illustrated by the observations of Childrey et al.[5] on dogs and those of

Gianturco[13] on cats. Dogs have been observed to digest meat swallowed in large pieces more completely than when the meat is ingested in a finely ground form. In cats fed lumps of meat mixed with barium, Gianturco noticed by an x-ray technique that such lumps were held in the stomach for a considerable period and slowly dissolved away. When ground meat was given, however, it passed quickly from the stomach into the intestine after presumably only slight digestion by the gastric juice.

Some measurements have been made of the force exerted during crushing and chewing. Howell and Manly[15] have determined the biting force in human subjects to be from 11 to 25 kg. for incisors, and from 29 to 90 kg. for molars. According to Triska,[32] dogs when chewing bones exert a pressure as high as 165 kg.

SALIVARY DIGESTION

Although food does not ordinarily remain in the mouth for any length of time, salivary digestion, in the proper sense, accounts for an appreciable part of starch digestion. Much of this process occurs in the stomach, since saliva mixed intimately with the swallowed food remains active for a considerable period after it reaches the stomach. Salivary digestion of starch may be continued in the stomach for 15 to 30 minutes before the hydrochloric acid of gastric juice penetrates the bolus sufficiently to inactivate the salivary amylase. Some 70 per cent of ingested potato starch and 60 per cent of bread starch is converted to maltose prior to the evacuation of chyme from the stomach. According to Bergeim, salivary amylase is not reactivated when it reaches the small intestine. It is generally agreed that cooking effects the splitting of the cellulose coating of starch granules, thus rendering them more accessible to the action of the amylases. The classic description of the chemical aspects of starch digestion pictures the starch molecule as being degraded step-wise through the intermediate stages of erythrodextrin, the achroodextrins and maltose, with maltose being split off at each stage. Glucose formation was thought to be due to the presence of minute quantities of maltase. Newer evidence indicates that human salivary amylase acting *in vitro* is capable of completely digesting starch if a sufficient amount of the enzyme is present. A three-way equilibrium among achroodextrin, glucose and maltose is suggested, with glucose, maltose and dextrin (synthesized by reversal of the hydrolytic process) accumulating as end-products. No evidence could be secured that human saliva is capable of digesting maltose. This would seem to rule out the possibility of the existence of a salivary maltase, a conclusion in agreement with those of several experimenters.

DEGLUTITION[4, 6, 7, 10, 14, 18, 23, 27, 32]

Swallowing is an act which may be initiated voluntarily but which is completed reflexly. Broadly speaking, deglutitional movements, although involving a complex musculature, reduce to (i) movements and inhibition of contraction which open the passage ahead of the bolus and (ii) those which close the passage behind the bolus, sweeping out any remnants of food. The sequential inhibition and contraction of muscles in swallowing is shown in Figure 529. The application of cinéfluorographic[27] and pressure recording techniques[10] has proved more illuminating than fluoroscopic studies of swallowing.

The first stage is the shaping and fashioning of the bolus at the back of the tongue. The bolus is propelled through the pharyngeal gate by an elevation of the tongue against the hard palate, the gate having been opened slightly in advance by an elevation of the soft palate and a relaxation of the faucial pillars. The gate is closed behind the bolus by a reversal of these latter maneuvers and a backward pressure of the tongue. Contraction of the superior and middle constrictors of the pharynx forces the bolus along.

The next stage, in which the bolus passes through the laryngeal pharynx, is an active one involving constriction of the pharyngeal walls, backward bending of the epiglottis, and an upward movement of the larynx, trachea and pharynx observable from the outside as the bobbing of the Adam's apple. Closure of the larynx to prevent entrance of food into the trachea is accomplished not only by the lidlike action of the epiglottis but also by closure of the glottis. (The tip of the epiglottis can be removed without interference with swallowing.) Swallowing ends with contraction of the inferior constrictor (cricopharyngeus) behind the bolus, completing a stripping action by the wave of contraction passing through the pharyngeal musculature. This event may be continued by a peristaltic wave stripping the esophagus; this usually does not occur when swallowing is repeated rapidly. Those interested in the pharyngeal mechanics of the competitive ingestion of large quantities of liquids should study the cinéfluorographic analysis by Ramsey et al.[24]

The peristaltic wave, which may take 5 to 6 seconds to traverse the esophagus, begins as part of the response to sensory stimulation of the receptors in the back of the

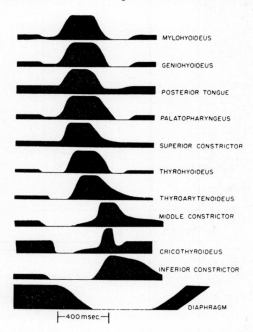

FIG. 529. Schematic summary of electromyographic activity in deglutition for unanesthetized dog medulla. Height of line for each muscle indicates intensity of action observed, ranging from complete silence to maximum occurring in deglutition. In certain muscles, firing more intense than represented here was observed in other synergies. Action of diaphragm is that seen in eupnea. Contours of rise and fall of activity are not considered accurate. (From Doty and Bosma, J. Neurophysiol., 1956, 19:44–60.)

MYLOHYOIDEUS

GENIOHYOIDEUS

POSTERIOR TONGUE

PALATOPHARYNGEUS

SUPERIOR CONSTRICTOR

THYROHYOIDEUS

THYROARYTENOIDEUS

MIDDLE CONSTRICTOR

CRICOTHYROIDEUS

INFERIOR CONSTRICTOR

DIAPHRAGM

|—400 msec.—|

mouth and pharynx. The afferent nerves concerned in this reflex are the sensory fibers to the mucous membrane of the pharynx and esophagus, including branches of the glossopharyngeal nerve, the trigeminal nerve, the vagus and the superior laryngeal division of the vagus. Artificial stimulation of this last nerve produces swallowing movements.

The motor fibers concerned in the reflex comprise the hypoglossal, the trigeminal, the glossopharyngeal, the vagus and the spinal accessory nerves. It has been shown in the cat and dog that the cervical portion of the esophagus is innervated primarily by the pharyngoesophageal nerve, which branches from the vagus above the ganglion nodosum.[17] The lower part of the cervical portion receives innervation also from the recurrent laryngeal nerve. In the lower part of the esophagus, where the muscle fibers are smooth, the wave of peristalsis moves along independently of extrinsic nerves, as is the case in the intestines. The difference between the upper and lower parts is thus related to the difference in types of muscle fibers and their innervation.

In addition to the main reflex, certain secondary reflexes exist and are called forth by stimulation of sensory fibers in the esophageal wall. These stimuli lead to reflex contraction of the musculature above the bolus and thus to liberation of a series of reflex contractions which are sufficient to move the bolus downward. If the primary reflex initiated at the beginning of the swallow succeeds only in forcing the bolus into the upper portion of the esophagus, this secondary or accessory mechanism comes into play and insures the transportation of the bolus to the stomach. In this series of secondary reflexes, as in the more complicated primary reflex, the vagus nerve forms a part of the path, and the reflex center therefore lies in the medulla.

The pressure changes have been analyzed in detail by Fyke and Code,[10] who found under resting conditions a band of elevated pressure in the lower portion of the pharynx

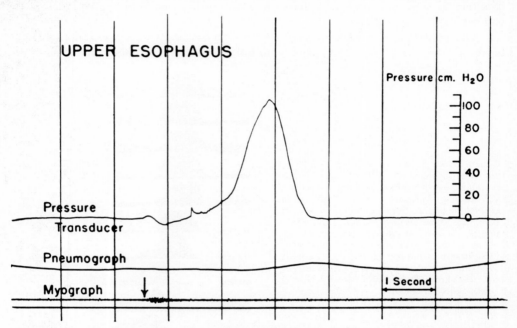

FIG. 530.   Pressure changes in esophagus after swallowing. (From Fyke and Code, *Gastroenterology*, 1955, *29*:24–34.)

at the level of the cricoid cartilage that presumably serves as a sphincter at the beginning of the esophagus. Swallowing initiates high positive pressure in the pharynx, while negative pressure develops at the pharyngoesophageal junction and the esophagus. This creates a pressure gradient of considerable magnitude. The high pressure wave is transmitted as a normal peristaltic wave over the full length of the esophagus (Fig. 530).

THE CARDIA

Although there is no anatomic cardiac sphincter, the muscle at the junction of the esophagus and the stomach does carry out the functions of a sphincter. This region is richly supplied with fibers from the myenteric plexuses. There is fairly general agreement that stimulation of the vagus relaxes the cardia,[19] but it has been claimed that this relaxation is followed by constriction. Section of the sympathetic nerve supply also brings about relaxation of the cardia, and stimulation of the splanchnics to the cardia results in its constriction. Sectioning the vagi at the level of the diaphragm results in spasm of the cardia. Studies in which the vagi were sectioned at various levels have shown that the inhibitory vagal fibers branch off from the main vagal trunks just above the level of the arch of the aorta to take an intrinsic course in the wall of the esophagus.[16]

This helps to explain why stimulation of the vagi at the level of the diaphragm does not relax the cardia whereas stimulation of the vagi at the neck causes inhibition.

Schlegel and Code[29] have studied the pressure at the gastroesophageal junction. They observed a band of resting pressure higher than that in either the esophagus or the fundus of the stomach, a finding which suggests a functional sphincter. When swallowing begins, this pressure drops and then rises to a maximum as the peristaltic wave passes. It then returns to the resting level. This junctional zone therefore acts as a sphincter, relaxing just before the arrival of the peristaltic wave but at other times preventing regurgitation of the stomach contents into the lower esophagus.

Achalasia.   In this condition, there is a narrowing of the terminal segment of the esophagus and a failure to open in the deglutition sequence. The resulting accumulation of liquid and food in the lower esophagus often leads to a gross swelling. Also called "cardiospasm" or "mega-esophagus," achalasia is similar to Hirschsprung's disease or megacolon (see Chap. 46) and is caused by a degeneration of Auerbach's plexus. Vagal section produces a striking achalasia in the monkey, an event suggesting that the vagal discharge into Auerbach's plexus is critical in the opening of the cardia.

REFERENCES

1. BABKIN, B. P. *Secretory mechanism of the digestive glands.* New York, Paul B. Hoeber, 1944, xix, 900 pp.
2. BAXTER, H. *Amer. J. Physiol.,* 1931, *97:*450–458.
3. BAXTER, H. *J. biol. Chem.* 1933, *102:*203–217.
4. BOSMA, J. F. *Physiol. Rev.,* 1957, *37:*275–300.
5. CHILDREY, J. H., ALVAREZ, W. C. and MANN, F. C. *Arch. intern. Med.,* 1930, *46:*361–374.
6. CODE, C. F., CREAMER, B., SCHLEGEL, J. F., OLSEN, A. M., DONOGHUE, F. E. and ANDERSEN, H. A. *An atlas of esophageal motility in health and disease.* Springfield, Ill., Charles C Thomas, 1958.
7. DOTY, R. W. and BOSMA, J. F. *J. Neurophysiol.,* 1956, *19:*44–60.
8. EMMELIN, N. *Physiol. Rev.,* 1952, *32:*21–46.
9. FLEMING, A. J. and MACINTOSH, F. C. *Quart. J. exp. Physiol.,* 1935, *25:*207–212.
10. FYKE, F. E., JR. and CODE, C. F. *Gastroenterology,* 1955, *29:*24–34.
11. GANTT, W. H. *Amer. J. Physiol.,* 1937, *119:* 493–507.
12. GANTT, W. H. *Amer. J. Physiol.,* 1938, *123:*74.
13. GIANTURCO, C. *Amer. J. Roentgenol.,* 1934, *31:*735–744.
14. HIGHTOWER, N. C., JR. *Amer. J. Surg.,* 1957, *93:*154–162.
15. HOWELL, A. H. and MANLY, R. S. *J. dent. Res.,* 1948, *27:*705–712.
16. HWANG, K., ESSEX, H. E. and MANN, F. C. *Amer. J. Physiol.,* 1947, *149:*429–448.
17. HWANG, K., GROSSMAN, M. I. and IVY, A. C.

Amer. J. Physiol., 1948, *154:*343–357.
18. INGELFINGER, F. J. *Physiol. Rev.,* 1958, *38:* 533–584.
19. KNIGHT, G. C. *Brit. J. Surg.,* 1934, *22:*155–168.
20. LANGENSKIÖLD, A. *Acta physiol. scand.,* 1941, 2(Suppl. 6):1–109.
21. LUNDBERG, A. *Physiol. Rev.,* 1958, *38:*21–40.
22. MACINTOSH, F. C. and RAWLINSON, H. E. *Quart. J. exp. Physiol.,* 1935, *25:*199–205.
23. MOSHER, H. P. *Laryngoscope (St. Louis),* 1927, *37:*235–262.
24. RAMSEY, G. H., WATSON, J. S., GROMIAK, R. and WEINBERG, S. A. *Radiology,* 1955, *64:* 498–518.
25. RASMUSSEN, A. T. *The principal nervous pathways.* New York, The Macmillan Co., 1941.
26. RAWLINSON, H. E. *Anat. Rec.,* 1933, *57:*289–301.
27. RUSHMER, R. F. and HENDRON, J. A. *J. appl. Physiol.,* 1951, *3:*622–630.
28. SANCHEZ, G. C., KRAMER, P. and INGELFINGER, F. J. *Gastroenterology,* 1953, *25:*321–332.
29. SCHLEGEL, J. F. and CODE, C. F. *Amer. J. Physiol.,* 1958, *193:*9–14.
30. STAVRAKY, G. W. *Amer. J. Physiol.,* 1940, *129:*539–545.
31. STORMONT, D. L. *Anat. Rec.,* 1926, *32:*242–243.
32. TRISKA, W. *Pflüg. Arch. ges. Physiol.,* 1924, *204:*660–667.
33. WANG, S. C. *J. Neurophysiol.,* 1943, *6:*195–202

CHAPTER 44

The Stomach

By PAUL F. FENTON

IT is often claimed that the stomach is not essential to the vital economy of the human body. While this is true to a limited degree, surgical removal of the stomach alters very considerably the individual's digestive capacities. The stomach acts as a temporary storage place by retaining ingested food until it has been reduced to a form acceptable to the duodenum. Digestion occurs in the stomach, but all the digestive functions of this organ can, as far as is known today, be carried out elsewhere if necessary. The stomach's highly acidic contents exert some bactericidal influence, and its secretion completes the chymification of ingested food begun by the saliva.

SECRETIONS OF THE STOMACH

In some studies of "gastric juice," samples of true secretion have been collected from specific regions of the stomach; in others the gastric contents have been aspirated after a test meal. The test meal, as well as the swallowed saliva, makes the latter type of study quite unreliable except as an indication of gross disturbances of the secretory mechanism. The gastric juice secreted in response to physiologic stimuli is an acidic fluid of low specific gravity more or less colored by bile regurgitated from the duodenum. Hydrochloric acid is present in a concentration of approximately 0.12 N. (The concentration is half this in an aspirated test meal.) Also present are salts of sodium, potassium and calcium. The proteins contained in gastric juice are mucin and, in small concentrations, the enzymes pepsin, rennin and lipase. Less well defined than these three enzymes is the so-called "intrinsic factor" which acts upon the "extrinsic factor" (vitamin B_{12}) in food to form the hematopoietic substance used in the formation of red blood cells. The volume of gastric juice secreted by man in one day may range as high as 2 to 3 liters. Normally nearly all of this fluid and the salts it contains are reabsorbed; yet it is easy to see why such disturbances as vomiting or diarrhea may lead to profound alterations of the body's water and electrolyte balance.

METHODS OF OBTAINING GASTRIC SECRETION. Studies of gastric contents obtained by withdrawing swallowed sponges and digestion studies on encapsulated foods left in the stomach for short periods have provided much valuable information about gastric secretions and their mode of action. Still more interesting are the observations made of human subjects who have suffered accidental fistulae of the stomach, the most famous example being Beaumont's study of Alexis St. Martin in 1833. Since then, several similar subjects have been studied.[2, 48] Such fistulae can also be produced surgically in experimental animals, whose gastric contents can then be removed for examination under rigidly defined conditions.

A great step forward was made when Heidenhain introduced his procedure for resecting specific portions of the stomach and converting them into isolated pouches (or little stomachs) with openings directly through the body wall. The secretion of discrete parts of the stomach could thus be studied without contamination of the secretion by saliva, duodenal fluid or ingested food. The experimental value of such a preparation was limited, however, since the original blood and nerve supply was considerably interrupted. This disadvantage was overcome by Pavlov, who prepared gastric pouches with a nerve and blood supply presumed to be intact.*

A particularly useful preparation in disentangling humoral factors is the transplanted, denervated pouch. A portion of the stomach wall is resected, shaped into a pouch, and transplanted to a region of the body possessing excellent blood supply. Following the establishment of collateral circulation through the new pouch, the pedicle carrying the old blood and nerve supply is completely severed.

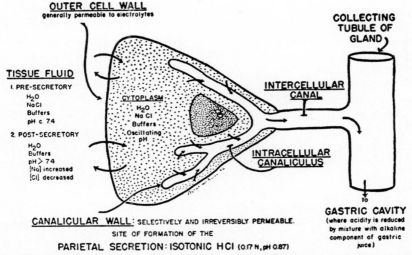

FIG. 531. Schematic representation of process of HCl formation in parietal cell of stomach. Chemical reactions at wall of intracellular canaliculus: $NaCl + H_2O \rightarrow HCl + NaOH$. NaOH reacts with cellular buffers. (From Hollander, *Gastroenterology*, 1943, *1:*427.)

The new pouch thus possesses an adequate blood supply but is essentially denervated and will secrete only in response to direct stimulation by secretagogues placed in the pouch or to agents in the circulating blood.

Another approach which gives important information consists of mounting specific portions of gastric mucosa in special chambers which permit the detection of chemical changes on both sides of the membrane. With sufficiently small animals (frog, mouse) it is possible to study the secretions of the entire stomach (or mucosa) ligated at the cardia and pylorus and incubated in a suitable medium supplying adequate oxygenation.

Secretion of Hydrochloric Acid.

Cytochemical evidence suggests that the parietal cells of the mammalian stomach elaborate hydrochloric acid. While the pH of parietal cell cytoplasm remains nearly neutral, the pH of the canalicular content falls to very low levels during acid secretion (Fig. 531). No other cell type in the gastric mucosa seems at the moment a likely source of hydrochloric acid. (The beaver's stomach contains a "cardiac gland," heavily populated with parietal cells, which yields a profuse secretion of HCl of pH 1.02.[32])

Gastric juice collected from the fundic region of the stomach is highly acid, while the juice from the pyloric area is generally slightly alkaline. Irritation of the gastric

* But see Hollander and Jemerin.[26]

mucosa usually elicits the flow of mucus which may act as a diluting or, to some extent, neutralizing agent. Thus the stomach can produce a variety of secretions, and the juice which is aspirated from the whole stomach is a mixture of several fluids. In addition, the type of stimulus used to evoke the flow of juice will determine to a great extent the type of secretion obtained. The pH of gastric juice as it comes from the canaliculi is less than 1; the fluid is then rendered more alkaline (pH 1.5 to 2.5) by mixture with other gastric secretions.

It has long been known, through analysis of parietal secretion and blood plasma, that the osmotic pressures of the two fluids normally are nearly identical. Gilman and Cowgill[14] showed that alterations in the ionic concentration of blood plasma led to parallel changes in the chloride concentration of the parietal secretion (Fig. 532). Many investigators have confirmed this dependence of parietal chloride concentration upon the ionic constitution of the blood. It is now generally recognized that the parietal secretion, if secured without contamination, contains hydrogen ions in a concentration of approximately 0.16 N, chloride ions 0.166 N, and some fixed base. It has been argued that the primary acidity is difficult to determine owing to rapid neutralization and possible back diffusion of HCl. By bathing the mucosa with glycine buffer to trap the secreted acid, Teorell[44] obtained indirect evidence suggesting that the primary acidity, the initial secretory product, may be much more concentrated than 0.167N

While hydrochloric acid is being secreted, an equivalent amount of bicarbonate ion enters the blood stream. This movement of bicarbonate may be so large after a heavy meal that it manifests itself as the so-called alkaline tide, a transient alkalinization of the urine. Davenport and Fisher[5] demonstrated that the parietal cells of the stomach contained significant quantities of the enzyme carbonic anhydrase, which catalyzes the hydration of carbon dioxide. *In vitro*, the stomach mucosa of small animals can be stimulated to produce acid by the addition of histamine or of parasympathomimetic drugs to the nutrient medium. During the secretory process the oxygen and substrate requirements of the isolated tissue are greatly increased. Bicarbonate leaves the tissue on the serosal side. When the tissue attains a high secretory rate, an external source of carbon dioxide is required to supplement that produced within the cell. If the tissue is deprived of external carbon dioxide, acid secretion may continue at a significant rate, but serious damage is done to the mucosa. This has led Davies[6] to suggest that the primary function of carbonic anhydrase is the hydration of carbon dioxide, the latter

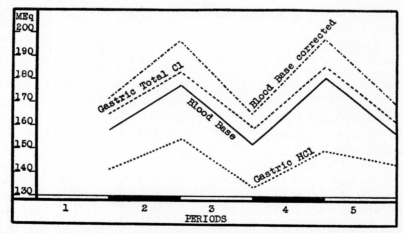

FIG. 532. Parallel changes in gastric acidity and total chloride with changes in blood base concentration. Gastric juice was obtained from Heidenhain or Pavlov pouch in response to histamine. (From Gilman and Cowgill, *Amer. J. Physiol.*, 1931, 99:174.)

serving to neutralize the alkali produced during secretion. Davenport[4] has suggested that lactic acid produced during glycolysis aids significantly in the neutralization of alkali.

The essentiality of carbonic anhydrase in HCl formation has been in doubt since early studies showed that extensive inhibition of the enzyme had little effect on secretion. However, newer and more potent carbonic anhydrase inhibitors do depress HCl formation. Therefore, it seems that the enzyme may play a vital role in gastric secretion.[27] The energy for the active secretion of both hydrogen and chloride ions apparently can come from carbohydrate, pyruvate, lactate or acetoacetate. Cyanide and iodoacetate, which inhibit energy metabolism, also inhibit the secretion of HCl.

Investigations of possible substrates which might furnish the energy for secretion of hydrochloric acid have led Davenport[4] to conclude that stimulation of the secretory epithelium does not necessarily increase the rate of substrate disappearance, although it increases the secretion of acid. He concludes from this that secretory stimulants effect qualitative changes in the metabolism of the substrate. *In vitro*, studies have shown acid production not to exceed four molecules per molecule of oxygen consumed. This is consistent with the widely held view that the hydrogen ion results from intracellular oxidation requiring the transport of one electron for each hydrogen ion produced. Since a molecule of oxygen is capable of accepting four electrons, it could be the ultimate electron acceptor in the formation of four hydrogen ions. Under certain conditions, some additional acid may be formed during the anaerobic breakdown of carbohydrate.

THEORIES OF ACID FORMATION. A satisfactory explanation of HCl formation must account for all known facts. The numerous hypotheses currently being discussed either do not explain all that is known or involve assumptions which are not yet amenable to experimental analysis.[21] Hollander[25] has postulated a process of membrane hydrolysis of NaCl to HCl and NaOH in which the acid is secreted immediately into the canaliculus and the remaining base is neutralized by cellular buffers. A cellular mechanism is presumed to pump acid and water across the membrane. Rehm[39, 40] has concerned himself primarily with the inherent potential differences between the mucosal and serosal sides of the stomach wall. This potential difference originates between the submucosa and the mucosal surface and thus resides largely in the secretory epithelium. When the potential difference is enhanced by an external current, secretion of HCl increases. Reversing the applied current reduces the secretory rate. The electromotive force of the gastric wall supplies only a small part of the total secretion energy. Rehm and others have shown that the potential of the mucosa is such that chloride ion should move toward the serosal side. This has been taken as additional evidence that chloride is actively secreted by the gastric glands. He has raised the possibility that hydrogen ions may be secreted by the surface epithelial cells while the parietal cells contribute chloride.

It has been suggested that acid moves across the cell membrane in combination with a carrier molecule. Davies[6] and others have suggested that the hydrogen ion originates in the cellular oxidative processes in which metabolite hydrogen is known to exist as hydrogen ion in the course of electron transport.

Secretion of Pepsin. The inactive proenzyme pepsinogen is elaborated by the chief cells of the fundus. It is activated on contact with hydrochloric acid, although the activation process may proceed autocatalytically. Pepsin secretion occurs in response to nervous stimulation, particularly by way of the parasympathetic innervation. Suitable stimulation of the sympathetic nerve supply to the stomach may, however, elicit some pepsin output. The secretion of pepsinogen occurs continuously, though at a low level, in man, but is intermittent or absent in some animals.[23] Secretion of pepsinogen may be abolished by atropine but not by vagotomy. The blocking action of atropine interferes only with the secretion of pepsinogen, not with its synthesis. Although histamine does not stimulate pepsinogen secretion in experimental animals, it has a strong secretory effect in man. Administration of the hormone enterogastrone will inhibit the secretion of the enzyme.

Nonparietal Secretion. It has long been known that the secretion of the pyloric region of the stomach is usually slightly alkaline. Presumably this region contributes the bulk of the nonparietal secretion. Gray and Bucher[16] have tentatively calculated the composition of this alkaline nonparietal secretion to be: sodium 0.155 N, potassium 0.007 N, calcium 0.004 N, chloride 0.133 N, and bicarbonate 0.033 N. Flow of the non-parietal juice can be evoked by mild irritation of the mucosa, by contact with hypertonic solutions, by the administration of small doses of histamine, and by many other stimuli. Its function, perhaps, in addition to the partial neutralization of acid prior to its entry into the small intestine, is the dilution of irritating substances present in the gastric lumen.

Secretion of Mucus. Mild mechanical or chemical irritation of the gastric mucosa elicits the secretion of mucus.[24] This clear, viscous fluid adheres strongly to the surface epithelium. The mucous barrier (mucus plus surface epithelium) presumably protects against chemical, mechanical and thermal irritation, particularly against the hydro-chloric acid and pepsin which are almost always present. The neck chief cells of the gastric glands secrete what has been called a mucoid fluid, whereas the surface epithelium secretes a product which is much more jelly-like. The pH of the mucus ranges from 6.8 to 9.2. The chloride concentration of mucus is 0.122 N, and the buffer capacity between the initial pH and pH 3.5 is 0.04 N. It has been shown that the secretion of the neck chief cells is particularly potent as the intrinsic factor in hematopoiesis.[15]

CONTROL OF GASTRIC SECRETION

The very high, constant acidity of the parietal cell secretion has already been discussed. The acidity of the gastric contents is extremely variable and is never as high as that of pure parietal juice. Dilution is of considerable importance. The parietal secretion is not the only one occurring under physiologic conditions. Other digestive juices, together with the fluids of the ingested meal, act to dilute the acid of the parietal secretion. Neutralization by other components of the gastric secretion also has been considered by some to be of importance in the regulation of gastric acidity. Regurgitation of alkaline duodenal contents is significant in the regulation of intragastric acidity.[47]

Acid itself, on reaching the duodenum, can inhibit the secretion of the parietal cells. One may therefore consider the acidity of the gastric contents as a function of the rate of secretion of parietal juice, the latter being determined by the type of stimulus applied to the secretory cells and by the degree of acidity existing in the stomach at any given time. Dilution of the parietal juice by other secretions of the stomach, by the ingested food, and by regurgitation of duodenal contents also plays a role.

Three Phases of Gastric Secretion. Depending upon the origin of the stimuli which signal the secretion of gastric juice, three distinct aspects of secretion have been elucidated: the *cephalic, gastric* and *intestinal*. The *cephalic* phase includes both uncon-ditioned and conditioned reflexes. The taste of food is sufficient to initiate a copious flow of gastric juice. Superimposed upon this are conditioned reflexes, discovered by Pavlov,[34] which involve the senses of sight, smell, etc.

One of Pavlov's great contributions, which made such studies possible, was the preparation of esophagotomized dogs with gastric pouches. The esophagotomy permits the animal to swallow food more or less normally but allows the swallowed bolus to escape through an opening in the neck without ever reaching the stomach.

The *appetite juice*, as the secretion of the cephalic phase is often called, appears to be a composite of all gastric secretions; it is highly acid and contains much pepsin and neutral chloride (from the nonparietal secretion). Sectioning of the vagi just above the stomach completely eliminates the cephalic phase of gastric secretion.

Since the cephalic phase of gastric secretion is of rather short duration, usually no more than 30 minutes, it does little more than initiate gastric digestion. To a considerable extent, however, the secretagogues liberated during this brief interval initiate the second or *gastric* phase of secretion.

Certain foods or digestion products of foods when placed directly in the stomach elicit the secretion of gastric juice (Fig. 533). Beaumont believed that gentle rubbing of the gastric mucosa of his patient, Alexis St. Martin, resulted in the flow of juice. Pavlov challenged this view because the gastric pouches in his animals did not secrete when he placed particles of sand in them. In 1906, Edkins[10] postulated the existence of a gastric hormone, *gastrin*. Extracts of the mucosa of the pyloric antrum, when injected intravenously, elicited the flow of gastric juice. Although many objections were subsequently raised to Edkins' experiments, especially that his extracts contained histamine, the existence of gastrin is now generally accepted. Grossman *et al.*[18] showed that distention

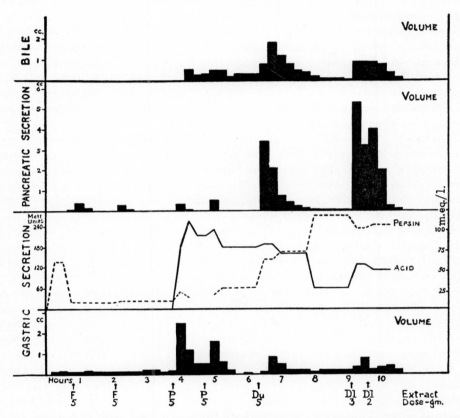

FIG. 533.   Gastric secretion, pancreatic secretion and bile flow in response to extracts from various parts of stomach and duodenum. Extracts of fundus (*F*) were nearly inert, while those of pylorus (*P*) gave copious secretion of acid. Extracts of upper and lower duodenum (*Du, Dl*) elicited production of pepsin. (From Komarov, *Rev. canad. Biol.*, 1942, 1:391.)

of the pyloric portion of the stomach stimulates the secretion of hydrochloric acid by the fundic glands, and this effect still occurs when all nervous connections between the stimulated portion of the stomach and the portion responding with secretion have been interrupted. This interruption was accomplished by subcutaneous transplantation of either the pyloric or the fundic portion. This would seem to constitute conclusive evidence for the existence of a hormone for gastric secretion. Komarov[29, 30] has isolated from the antrum mucosa a protein fraction which possesses all the properties of gastrin but is apparently free from histamine. Like histamine it appears to stimulate primarily the parietal cells; that is, it elicits the flow of a highly acidic fluid low in pepsin. Many gastrin preparations were undoubtedly contaminated with histamine, itself a potent stimulant of the parietal cells. The most recent additional proof of the existence of a gastrin hormone mechanism is seen in the investigations by Dragstedt *et al.*[8, 9] These investigators transplanted the antrum of the stomach into the duodenum or the colon and in addition prepared Pavlov or Heidenhain pouches in the same animals. They concluded: "The antrum is a gland of internal secretion, distinct in function, which produces a specific excitant of gastric secretion when it comes into contact with the usual content of the stomach, duodenum or colon after feeding . . . The data secured in these transplantation experiments provide conclusive support for the validity of Edkins' gastrin hypothesis."[9]

In 1942 Uvnäs proved that vagal discharge from electrical stimulation or from the cephalic phase of gastric secretion produces less secretion from the intact fundus if the pyloric region of the stomach is removed.[45] From his experiments it was concluded that vagal stimulation leads to gastrin secretion. Although denervated fundic pouches do not usually respond to insulin-induced vagal discharge, the fundus apparently does produce gastrin in response to vagal stimulation if the pylorus is protected from acid secretion.[33] This relation might be a neurohumoral effect or an indirect effect of the antral hypermobility. A neural link in the release of gastrin is indicated by recent experiments in which local anesthetics applied to the antrum blocked the release of gastrin in response to distention and to chemical stimuli.[49]

The third or *intestinal* phase of gastric secretion is initiated by some humoral mechanism when certain, though not all, food products or secretagogues come into contact with intestinal mucosa. The duodenum, like the pyloric antrum, seems capable of secreting a gastrin-like substance. The utility of such a mechanism in promoting greater gastric digestion is obvious. However, little attention to this mechanism, first described by Pavlov, has been paid in recent years.

Doig *et al.*[7] have reported significant observations on a "decorticate" man with a gastric fistula. Extensive injury to the cerebral cortex had rendered the patient permanently unconscious. Tracheotomy and gastrostomy were performed to facilitate his care. In this patient, (i) gastric secretion persisted under all conditions; (ii) no change of secretion followed the administration of insulin; (iii) locally applied histamine, atropine and epinephrine had their usual effects; (iv) there were no reactions to stimuli which require interpretation by the individual; and (v) there were also no reactions to stimulation with noxious agents. In this patient, the various stimuli and nervous mechanisms involved in the cephalic phase could not operate.

Vagal impulses stimulate the secretion of acid, pepsin and mucus; atropine has inhibitory effects, and pilocarpine excitatory effects. Vagal discharges are caused by sham feeding (the cephalic phase of digestion) and insulin hypoglycemia, and apparently occur continuously at a low level since vagotomy reduces so-called "interdigestive secretion." In some manner vagotomy also reduces the responsiveness of the parietal glands to histamine and other stimulating substances. Vagotomy, which must be complete, is an effective means of treating peptic ulcer.

Histamine is a powerful stimulant of the parietal cell and is used in place of a test meal to stimulate acid secretion. On the other hand, it has little or no effect on the secretion of pepsin.[13] The gastric mucosa is extremely rich in histamine, and it appears in gastric juice secreted in response to a wide variety of stimuli. In laboratory animals, histaminase, an enzyme destroying histamine, reduces hydrochloric acid secretion not only in response to histamine but also in response to sham feeding or injection of parasympathomimetic drugs.[18] These facts strongly suggest that histamine is a link in the chain of neurohumoral events which stimulate the parietal cell.[11] It is possible that postganglionic vagal fibers release acetylcholine, which in turn releases histamine; it would then be the immediate neurohumor for the parietal cells.

The mechanism by which secretagogues or the distention stimulus evokes the liberation of gastrin has often been investigated. That injection of atropine or topical application of cocaine can abolish the liberation of the hormone suggests very strongly that a local neural mechanism is involved in the process.[17] It has been suggested that histamine is the only chemical agent actually capable of stimulating the parietal cell and that all other known stimulants of acid secretion must first cause the liberation of histamine.

Duodenal Control of Acid Secretion. Many substances when in contact with the mucous membranes of the small intestine *inhibit* the secretion of gastric juice. Among these are fat and hypertonic solutions of carbohydrates, amino acids, and salt when brought in contact with the duodenal mucosa. Although this inhibitory mechanism is partly under nervous control, the existence of a humoral agent, *enterogastrone*, has been demonstrated. Relatively crude preparations of this hormone when administered intravenously will inhibit acid secretion in response to histamine as well as inhibit both acid and pepsin secretion in response to food. A closely related substance, *urogastrone*, has been isolated from normal urine. Many attempts have been made to use these secretory depressants in the prevention and cure of peptic ulcer. Enterogastrone also depresses motility and gastric emptying (see below).

GASTRIC DIGESTION

Pepsin. This enzyme is formed by the chief cells of the fundus, but has also been found in the pyloric region. Pepsin acts preferentially on native proteins at an optimum pH of 2.0, the latter depending to a considerable extent upon other conditions. For example, pepsin can digest certain specific peptides at a pH of 4.0. Continued action of pepsin *in vitro* will result in the cleavage of about 30 per cent of the peptide bonds of the protein molecule, forming proteoses, peptones and some amino acids. Pepsin does not act upon such proteins as the keratins and mucins, nor does it attack protein derivatives of low molecular weight except for some very specific synthetic peptides. With the partial breakdown of the protein components of the ingested foodstuffs comes a liberation of much of the cell contents as well as a considerable disintegration of tissue structure. The resulting dispersion of the cell contents helps to initiate the gastric and intestinal phases of the gastric secretory process. It seems likely also that pepsin plays a significant role in the liberation of vitamins (especially of the B complex) from their combination with proteins.

Rennin. There has been much controversy about the actual existence of a milk-coagulating enzyme. The debate originated largely because pepsin purified in varying degrees clotted milk. However, it has been claimed that rennin preparations totally free of peptic activity can be secured. Furthermore, it is no longer accepted that isolation of a crystalline substance is a guarantee of its purity or homogeneity; a crystalline preparation of pepsin might very well be contaminated with other enzymes such as rennin. Since rennin has a pH optimum very different from the pH usually found in the adult human stomach, it seems unlikely that this enzyme is important in the food economy of the human adult. The infant stomach with its low acid secretion is a much more favorable place for rennitic activity. This obviously meets the needs of the situation, since the infant relies for some time upon milk as its chief source of food. It is often said that the "purpose" of the rennitic substance is to coagulate milk to slow the rate at which it flows from the stomach and thus to permit peptic digestion to take place. The possibility exists that rennin initiates certain as yet unappreciated changes in the casein molecule which render the latter susceptible to the action of other proteases.

Lipase. It is not quite certain that this enzyme is a product of gastric secretion. It may be argued that lipase enters the stomach as the result of regurgitation of duodenal contents. At any rate, the pH of the adult stomach is quite unfavorable for the action

of lipase, although it may play a role in the digestive processes of the infant's gastrointestinal tract.

MOVEMENTS OF THE STOMACH

Grützner's[20] old and widely quoted experiment in which he fed colored foods
seriatim to rats showed that the food arranges itself in the stomach in distinct layers. The
earliest bolus is pushed to the periphery—i.e., toward the greater curvature—while
succeeding morsels are layered in concentric spheres with the most recently swallowed
bolus still near the cardia. The outermost layer of food thus comes in intimate contact
with the enzymes and HCl of the gastric juice and is subjected to its digestive and
solvent action, while salivary digestion can continue at the pH persisting in the innermost portion of the food mass for some time. The peristaltic contractions of the stomach,
superimposed upon its tonic contractions, serve to move the semiliquid chyme along
the periphery of the food mass toward the pylorus. These contractions begin within a

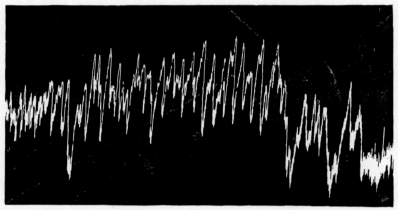

FIG. 534.   Normal hunger contractions from empty stomach of man aged 31, after fast of 25 hours.
(From Patterson, *Ann. N. Y. Acad. Sci.*, 1933, *34*:252.)

few minutes after food enters the stomach. They recur at 20 second intervals and are
initiated by the distention of the musculature resulting from the presence of food.
Peristaltic waves which travel only a short distance and do not reach the pylorus undoubtedly aid in the mixing of at least that portion of the ingested food near the gastric
wall. Together with longer-traveling waves, they aid in moving the chyme toward the
pylorus.

When a balloon is placed in the empty stomach of a normal person, the record
shows four types of waves. One is caused by the arterial pulse, and another by respiratory
movements. The third type of wave has been called the *tonus rhythm* and is caused by
contractions of the fundus; these are not usually interpreted subjectively as hunger
pangs. The fourth type of contraction is most significant and consists of periods of
relatively powerful rhythmic contractions which may alternate with periods of quiescence
(Fig. 534). Each individual contraction of this type lasts for about 30 seconds and may
be superimposed upon the tonus rhythm; it may be subjectively interpreted as "hunger."
These contractions occur usually in series, the number in a period varying from about
20 to as many as 70. The series begins with comparatively feeble contractions with long
intervening pauses. Finally the pauses disappear and the contractions become more
pronounced. In some instances, more often in young individuals, they may finally
become so pronounced that they result in a continued contraction lasting several minutes.
The duration of the entire hunger period can vary from about one-half to one and one-

half hours; the average is from 30 to 45 or 50 minutes. Hunger contractions and their relation to hunger sensation and food intake are discussed in Chapter 16.

Vomiting. The act of vomiting causes an ejection of gastric contents through the esophagus and mouth. The material which is removed from the alimentary tract by this process may consist only of gastric contents, but in severe and prolonged vomiting it may also contain appreciable amounts of intestinal material. Vomiting is usually a reflex act; its stimulus may arise in many parts of the body. Most frequently, vomiting is initiated by irritation of the oropharynx or the gastrointestinal mucosa. Other loci are the semicircular canals (motion sickness) and the genitourinary tract. In some persons any disagreeable emotion or noxious impulse may set the whole process in operation. As described in Chapter 16, central emetic agents act not upon the vomiting center but upon a chemoreceptive trigger zone nearby, in the floor of the fourth ventricle.

No matter what the cause, the familiar pattern of events which follows is the same. Nausea and excessive salivation herald the deep inspirations which are part of the retching movements. Usually the glottis is closed and the nasal passages are protected against the influx of vomitus. The fundus of the stomach, the cardia and the esophagus are relaxed, while the pylorus and the pyloric region of the stomach appear to contract. Forceful descent of the diaphragm and contraction of the abdominal muscles exert enough pressure upon the contents of the stomach to force such material through the relaxed cardia and esophagus. Whether the stomach musculature takes any propulsive part in the act of vomiting is problematic. If the stomach is removed, administration of a suitable emetic will still elicit typical retching movements. Conversely, paralysis of the abdominal musculature prevents vomiting. In addition to nausea and salivation, vomiting is accompanied by weakness, perspiration, pallor, lacrimation and, often, a fall in blood pressure.

Gastric Emptying. The presence of an easily identifiable pyloric sphincter between the stomach and duodenum has led to numerous theories in which the pylorus is viewed as a gate, prohibiting the exit of food from the stomach until some optimal state of the chyme is supposedly achieved. For example, the so-called acid-control theory was very popular at one time. The increasing acidity of the gastric contents in the course of digestion was supposed to cause the sphincter to relax and permit the escape of chyme into the duodenum. The gradually rising acidity of the upper duodenum would then cause closure of the pylorus to permit neutralization of the acidic duodenal contents.

Using multiple balloons to record the passage of tonus and peristaltic waves, Thomas[42] and his associates demonstrated that the pylorus functions as the pyloric antrum and the duodenal bulb do. In place of the bulky balloons, Quigley and his associates[1, 35-38, 46] have employed electronic pressure transducers to indicate gastrointestinal pressure changes. The tubing which leads from the lumen to the transducer has a diameter of 3 mm. at the tip and 0.75 mm. elsewhere. This device creates a minimum of irritation and is far more sensitive than older methods. The evidence indicates that the pylorus has little if any effect upon gastric emptying. The driving force of the emptying process was visualized as the pressure differential between the pyloric antrum and the duodenal bulb, the pressure being the result of increased tonus with superimposed peristalsis. In addition, it was demonstrated in a most convincing fashion that, if the pylorus is held open, the emptying rate of the stomach is in no way affected.[3] It has been shown also that surgical excision of the pylorus does not influence the rate at which specific substances leave the stomach.

From the work of Thomas and of Quigley and their associates a gradual synthesis of ideas has evolved which, in simplified form, may be stated as follows:

1. The pylorus is anatomically and physiologically integrated with its adjoining

structures, the pyloric antrum and the duodenal bulb. Tonus changes involve all three structures in a similar manner, both qualitatively and quantitatively. The three parts respond similarly to the passage of a peristaltic wave; that is, the antral contraction is followed by pyloric and duodenal bulb contractions. Because the pylorus remains contracted somewhat longer than the antrum and bulb, excessive regurgitation of duodenal contents is prevented, since the pylorus usually is still contracted when the duodenal bulb contracts. Bilateral vagotomy has no effect upon this sequence of events, although it does reduce the amplitude of the peristaltic contractions, thus reducing the emptying rate of the stomach.

2. The driving force of the emptying process is the pressure differential between the gastric and the duodenal side of the pylorus. Pressure is built up by tonic contractions and peristaltic waves. These in turn probably are initiated in response to the distention of the smooth muscle coats of the gastric wall by the presence of food in the stomach. The rate of emptying is a linear function of gastric volume until the stomach is nearly empty.

3. The tonus and peristalsis of the stomach—the driving force of the emptying process—are profoundly influenced by the state of the duodenum. Distention of the duodenum, mechanical irritation and the presence of hypertonic or hypotonic solutions and foodstuffs or their breakdown products reduce the motility of the gastric musculature. Thomas[43] lists the latter in the order of their potency when in the concentrations usually encountered as: fats, fatty acids, proteases, peptones, amino acids, sugars and other products of starch digestion, and hydrogen ions (pH 3.5 to 6.0).

4. The mechanism by which the duodenum controls gastric tone and peristalsis, and hence gastric emptying, is twofold: (i) an enterogastric reflex employing the vagus nerve and (ii) a humoral mechanism—enterogastrone. The products of protein digestion, acid and nonspecific irritants work through the reflex mechanism. Fats and carbohydrates work mainly through the humoral mechanism, although a reflex component has been clearly demonstrated.[38]

5. Reflex influences of the stomach and ileum upon each other have been described. Shortly after food enters the stomach the motility of the ileum is increased. Conversely, if the ileum is full, the emptying of chyme from the stomach is delayed. Distention of the colon is known to inhibit gastric motility. The splanchnics presumably are the efferent fibers involved.

6. The insulin-vagus system plays a role in the regulation of gastric emptying. The administration of insulin augments gastric motility if the vagal nerve supply to that organ is intact. Vagotomy, on the other hand, increases the time required for the stomach to empty.

Many interesting observations on the motility and secretion of the digestive system have been made by Abbott, Karr and Miller and their associates and by Shay and his coworkers.[12, 31, 41] Both groups worked largely with human subjects, using the multiple lumen tube which permits isolation of segments of the alimentary tract and facilitates introduction into and removal from such segments of specific solutions. This work has brought out the very important fact that the duodenum has far greater power to dilute hypertonic solutions than has the stomach (although the latter can effect very considerable reductions in concentration). This work also has made it clear that the stomach and the duodenum working as a unit can bring even very concentrated glucose solutions near isotonicity in a relatively short time.

It is therefore evident that the alimentary tract possesses an array of mechanisms which act to protect the delicate duodenal membrane against untoward influences of substances contained in the stomach. The latter in turn is capable of reducing these materials (by digestion or dilution) to a form more readily acceptable to the duodenum.

ABSORPTION FROM THE STOMACH[28]

Many substances have been reported to be absorbed from the stomach. Among these are sugars, proteins or their digestion products, alcohol, carbon dioxide and others. Since a really satisfactory method for the study of absorption from the stomach has never been found, it is difficult to evaluate the merits of the various claims. In the case of glucose, an interesting situation exists. Absorption of this compound from the human stomach has been reported numerous times, but its absorption from the rat stomach usually has not been observed. In the case of the dog, opinion is divided. Studies of this type require the introduction of glucose solutions into the stomach isolated from the small intestine by some convenient measure. At the end of a specified time the remaining glucose is washed out of the stomach and quantitatively determined. It is certainly difficult to assure the complete isolation of the human stomach from the duodenum. This has been attempted by placing a balloon at the pylorus or by instilling oil into the duodenum in the hope that by this measure gastric emptying may be inhibited. It is doubtful whether either procedure can entirely prevent the escape of some glucose solution from the stomach into the intestine. Furthermore, it is difficult to wash all the remaining quantity of glucose from the stomach. Glucose adhering to the folds of the mucosa would be calculated as having been absorbed. In the rat it is a simple matter to place a ligature at the pylorus, thus preventing the escape of glucose during the experiment. One also can take drastic measures to assure the complete washing out of the remaining glucose. Final word on the general problem of gastric absorption evidently must await the development of adequate research techniques. One can say, however, that available evidence supports the view that the absorption of food is not the primary function of the stomach.

REFERENCES

1. BRODY, D. A. and QUIGLEY, J. P. *Gastroenterology*, 1947, *9*:570–575.
2. CARLSON, A. J. *The control of hunger in health and disease.* Chicago, University of Chicago Press, 1916, vii, 319 pp.
3. CRIDER, J. O. and THOMAS, J. E. *Amer. J. dig. Dis.*, 1937, *4*:295–300.
4. DAVENPORT, H. W. *Fed. Proc.*, 1952, *11*:715–721.
5. DAVENPORT, H. W. and FISHER, R. B. *Amer. J. Physiol.*, 1940, *131*:165–175.
6. DAVIES, R. E. *Biol. Rev.*, 1951, *26*:87–120.
7. DOIG, R. K., WOLF, S. and WOLFF, H. G. *Gastroenterology*, 1953, *23*:40–44.
8. DRAGSTEDT, L. R., OBERHELMAN, H. A., JR., WOODWARD, E. R. and SMITH, C. A. *Amer. J. Physiol.*, 1952, *171*:7–16.
9. DRAGSTEDT, L. R., WOODWARD, E. R., OBERHELMAN, H. A., JR., STORER, E. H. and SMITH, C. A. *Amer. J. Physiol.*, 1951, *165*:386–398.
10. EDKINS, J. S. *J. Physiol.*, 1906, *34*:133–144.
11. EMMELIN, N. and KAHLSON, G. S. *Acta physiol. scand.*, 1944, *8*:289–304.
12. GERSHON-COHEN, J. and SHAY, H. *Amer. J. dig. Dis.*, 1937, *4*:637–643.
13. GILMAN, A. and COWGILL, G. R. *Amer. J. Physiol.*, 1931, *97*:124–130.
14. GILMAN, A. and COWGILL, G. R. *Amer. J. Physiol.*, 1931, *99*:172–178.
15. GLASS, G. B. J., BOYD, L. J., RUBINSTEIN, M. A. and SVIGALS, C. S. *Science*, 1952, *115*:101–108.
16. GRAY, J. S. and BUCHER, G. R. *Amer. J. Physiol.*, 1941, *133*:542–550.
17. GROSSMAN, M. I. *Physiol. Rev.*, 1950, *30*:33–90.
18. GROSSMAN, M. I. and ROBERTSON, C. R. *Amer. J. Physiol.*, 1948, *153*:447–453.
19. GROSSMAN, M. I., ROBERTSON, C. R. and IVY, A. C. *Amer. J. Physiol.*, 1948, *153*:1–9.
20. GRÜTZNER, P. *Pflüg. Arch. ges. Physiol.*, 1905, *106*:463–522.
21. HEINZ, E. and ÖBRINK, K. J. *Physiol. Rev.*, 1954, *34*:643–673.
22. HEINZ, E., ÖBRINK, K. J. and ULFENDAHL, H. *Gastroenterology*, 1954, *27*:98–112.
23. HIRSCHOWITZ, B. I. *Physiol. Rev.*, 1957, *37*:475–511.
24. HOLLANDER, F. *Gastroenterology*, 1944, *3*:403–405.
25. HOLLANDER, F. *Science*, 1949, *110*:57–63.
26. HOLLANDER, F. and JEMERIN, E. E. *Proc. Soc. exp. Biol. (N. Y.)*, 1938, *39*:87–90.
27. JANOWITZ, H. D. and HOLLANDER, F. *Gastroenterology*, 1956, *30*:536–537.
28. KAREL, L. *Physiol. Rev.*, 1948, *28*:433–450.
29. KOMAROV, S. A. *Rev. canad. Biol.*, 1942, *1*:191–205.
30. KOMAROV, S. A. *Rev. canad. Biol.*, 1942, *1*:377–401.

31. MILLER, T. G. *Gastroenterology*, 1944, *3:*141–154.
32. NASSET, E. S. *J. Mammal.*, 1953, *34:*204–209.
33. OBERHELMAN, H. A., RIGLER, S. P. and DRAGSTEDT, L. R. *Amer. J. Physiol.*, 1957, *190:*391–395.
34. PAVLOV, I. P. *The work of the digestive glands*, 2d English ed. Trans. by W. H. THOMPSON. London, C. Griffin & Co., 1910, xiv, 266 pp.
35. QUIGLEY, J. P. and BRODY, D. A. *Amer. J. Med.*, 1952, *13:*73–81.
36. QUIGLEY, J. P., WERLE, J. M. and BRODY, D. *Amer. J. dig. Dis.*, 1940, *7:*434–435.
37. QUIGLEY, J. P., WERLE, J., LIGON, E. W., JR., READ, M. R., RADZOW, K. H. and MESCHAN, I. *Amer. J. Physiol.*, 1941, *134:*132–140.
38. QUIGLEY, J. P., ZETTELMAN, H. J. and IVY, A. C. *Amer. J. Physiol.*, 1934, *108:*643–651.
39. REHM, W. S. *Gastroenterology*, 1950, *14:*401–417.
40. REHM, W. S., DENNIS, W. H. and BRODSKY, W. A. *Amer. J. Physiol.*, 1958, *192:*14–22.
41. SHAY, H., GERSHON-COHEN, J. and FELS, S. S. *Amer. J. dig. Dis.*, 1942, *9:*124–128.
42. THOMAS, J. E. *Rev. Gastroent.*, 1935, *2:*32–38.
43. THOMAS, J. E. *Physiol. Rev.*, 1957, *37:*453–474.
44. TEORELL, T. *J. Physiol.*, 1940, *97:*308–315.
45. UVNÄS, B. *Acta physiol. scand.*, 1942, *4*(Suppl. 13):1–86.
46. WERLE, J. M., BRODY, D. A., LIGON, E. W., JR., READ, M. R. and QUIGLEY, J. P. *Amer. J. Physiol.*, 1941, *131:*606–614.
47. WILHELMJ, C. M., FINNEGAN, R. W. and HILL, F. C. *Amer. J. dig. Dis.*, 1937, *4:*547–550.
48. WOLF, S. and WOLFF, H. G. *Human gastric function*. New York, Oxford University Press, 1943, xvi, 262 pp.
49. WOODWARD, E. R. and SHAPIRO, H. *Amer. J. Physiol.*, 1958, *192:*479–481.

CHAPTER 45

The Small Intestine

By PAUL F. FENTON

THE small intestine carries out a variety of digestive processes catalyzed by the enzymes of the pancreatic and intestinal secretions. It can also emulsify ingested lipoid substances, rendering them more susceptible to lipolysis and absorption. Hypertonic solutions are rapidly diluted; hypotonic ones are concentrated. Finally, this portion of the alimentary tract effects the absorption of numerous substances with a remarkable degree of selectivity. Digestion, initiated in the mouth and stomach, is carried to completion so efficiently that only small quantities of unaltered foodstuffs enter the large intestine. The absorption process is in most instances so rapid that only traces of digestion products remain in the intestine. This chapter is concerned, therefore, with the mechanisms controlling the secretion of the pancreatic and intestinal juices, with the formation and expulsion of bile, and with the processes of absorption. The motility of the small intestine has already been discussed in Chapter 42.

EXTERNAL SECRETION OF THE PANCREAS

The composition of the pancreatic juice depends upon the nature of the stimulus applied to the secretory cells, the immediate stimulus being neural or humoral. The facts suggest mechanisms which permit the formation of pancreatic juice suitable in composition for the specific tasks at hand.

Neural Control of Pancreatic Secretion. The acinar cells of the pancreas receive fibers from the vagus. Many workers have shown that stimulation of the vagus results in a secretion which may be no more copious than the resting secretion, and no different in pH, but whose enzyme content is tremendously increased.

The evidence concerning the role of the splanchnics in the control of pancreatic secretion is not at all clear. Babkin et al.[2] found that stimulation of the splanchnics gave rise to the same type of secretion elicited by stimulation of the vagi. Since atropine abolished the response to splanchnic stimulation, it might be concluded that the impulses are carried by cholinergic fibers. Splanchnic stimulation resulted in loss of zymogen granules. More recently, however, Richins[40] extensively investigated the pancreatic innervation. He concluded that the sympathetic fibers terminate about the pancreatic blood vessels. The question is, then, whether the secretion of small volumes of pancreatic juice after stimulation of the splanchnics is caused primarily by vasomotor changes. A potent argument against such a concept seems to be the decided effect of splanchnic stimulation on the zymogen granules of the acinar cells.

Humoral Control of Pancreatic Secretion. Although neural control of the pancreas was established by Pavlov, evidence soon accumulated that other mechanisms are involved. It was shown that the introduction of hydrochloric acid into the duodenum elicits the secretion of pancreatic juice. It was noticed also, and with some surprise, that the denervated pancreas is capable of responding to the presence of acid in the duodenum. It remained for Bayliss and Starling[4] to demonstrate that the effect of hydrochloric acid is mediated by a chemical agent carried by the blood. Acid extracts of the duodenal mucosa, when injected intravenously, gave rise to profuse secretory activity of the pancreas. The active agent, given the name *secretin*, was the first hormone clearly characterized. Most useful in verifying the existence and the mechanism of secretin is

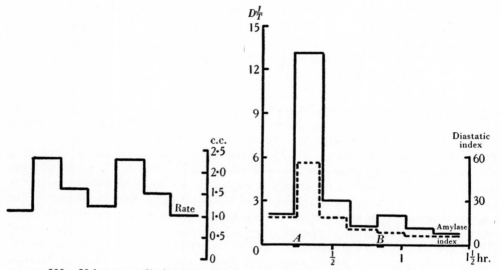

FIG. 535.   Volume rate (*left*) and amylase content of pancreatic juice (*right*) secreted in response to secretin containing pancreozymin at *A* and to secretin alone at *B*. (From Harper and Raper, *J. Physiol.*, 1943, *102*:122.)

the autotransplantation operation of Ivy and Farrell.[28] As with the transplantation of small gastric pouches, it is possible to rule out almost completely the interference of nervous factors in the study of pancreatic secretion.

The pancreatic juice secreted in response to secretin is of low specific gravity, low enzyme content, and of higher pH than the fasting secretion or the juice obtained in response to nervous stimulation. The zymogen granules are little changed. Thomas and Crider[46] carried out a semiquantitative study of the pH threshold of the secretin mechanism. Intraduodenal administration of acid solutions of pH less than 5 resulted in stimulation of pancreatic juice flow. The significance of this observation will be discussed later in the light of the fact that the pH in the duodenum rarely falls below 5.

Although most secretion preparations elicit only weak pancreatic juice, some evoke considerable enzyme production. A second hormone in the intestinal mucosa, pancreozymin, also acts upon the pancreas. This agent, identified by Harper and Raper,[23] increases the enzyme output of the pancreas (Fig. 535), and is effective even after secretin has called forth the flow of low enzyme pancreatic juice.

Wang and Grossman[51] have tested a variety of substances for their ability to cause the liberation of secretin or pancreozymin. The criteria employed were volume response (secretin mechanism) or enzyme output (pancreozymin mechanism) of denervated transplanted pancreatic tissue. Introduction of HCl into the small intestine caused primarily the liberation of secretin, athough some pancreozymin was called forth. Peptones, amino acids, fats and soaps stimulated the secretion of both hormones. Carbohydrates were ineffective.

Functions of Pancreatic Juice. Like gastric secretion, secretion of digestive juice is controlled by the neural and humoral mechanisms so that it is specifically suited to the task at hand. Ordinarily this task is the digestion of foodstuffs entering the small intestine from the stomach. For this purpose the humoral mechanisms alone would be adequate, since pancreozymin causes the secretion of substantial quantities of enzymes. Similarly, the neural mechanism would be adequate, since vagal stimulation results in the flow of a secretion rich in enzymes. Quite conceivable the "purpose" of the secretin mechanism might be to aid in the neutralization of acid chyme in the duodenum. If one can truly consider the pH threshold for secretin production to be between

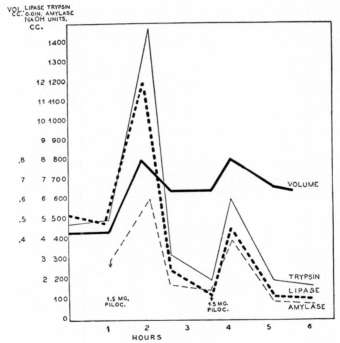

FIG. 536.   Parallel concentrations of pancreatic enzymes. (From Baxter, *Amer. J. dig. Dis.*, 1935 36, 2:109.)

pH 4 and 5, one might well question whether this hormone is very frequently called into play. It might be that only abnormally high concentrations of acid can elicit the production of secretin which in turn stimulates the flow of a pancreatic secretion higher in bicarbonate than that evoked by pancreozymin or vagal stimulation.

Many investigators have pointed out that the principal enzymes of pancreatic juice are secreted in parallel concentrations no matter what stimulus is applied (Fig. 536). However, there is evidence that the previous dietary regimen can influence to some extent the production of certain enzymes. A high carbohydrate diet fed for some time resulted in the formation of a pancreatic juice rich in amylase but low in trypsin. A high protein diet increased the trypsin content of the pancreatic secretion, whereas a high fat diet had little effect on any of the important enzymes.

The diverse array of proteolytic, lipolytic and amylolytic enzymes in pancreatic juice are almost capable of digesting by themselves all of the ingested foodstuffs. Trypsin is secreted by the acinar cells as its inactive precursor, or zymogen, called trypsinogen. Upon entering the alimentary tract by way of the pancreatic duct, the zymogen is acted upon by enterokinase, present in succus entericus, and is converted into the active enzyme. Trypsin itself also converts trypsinogen into trypsin. This enzyme exerts very little digestive action on native proteins, but acts readily on denatured proteins. Therefore it seems significant that the warmth and the acidity of the stomach provide conditions suitable for the denaturation of many ingested native proteins. Trypsin is also capable of acting upon partially digested proteins such as might be formed by brief action of pepsin on food proteins. The optimal pH for the activity of trypsin is 7.8. According to some investigators the reaction of the small intestine does not usually become so alkaline, so trypsin may act with somewhat less than maximal efficiency. Chymotrypsinogen, another proteolytic zymogen, is activated by trypsin. It acts in a manner similar to trypsin, but possesses somewhat greater rennitic power and its proteolytic action is weaker. Pepsin, trypsin and chymotrypsin together are ordinarily capable of reducing nearly all ingested proteins to the polypeptide stage. Pancreatic juice also contains a carboxypolypeptidase capable of digesting certain peptides. (For enzyme specificity see Chap. 42.)

Pancreatic amylase, an enzyme which acts upon starch in a manner similar to that of salivary amylase, is somewhat more active than its counterpart in saliva. Pancreatic amylase shows maximal activity at pH 7.0. It breaks down starch to the various dextrins and eventually to maltose.

Lipase of pancreatic juice has a pH optimum of 8.0, again a value considerably higher than one would expect to encounter in the small intestine. There are many reports that the bile salts exert a specific activating effect on lipase. It seems possible, however, that this effect is largely due to the emulsification of dietary fat and the facilitation of the digestive action through provision of a larger substrate surface. The digestibility of fats appears to depend largely upon their melting points, animal and vegetable fats being digested with equal ease if their melting points are below 46° C.[12] Fats of higher melting points are not well digested, apparently because emulsification is difficult or impossible. It is interesting to note that the pancreas is perhaps the only digestive organ which can form a lipolytic enzyme capable of digestive activity under the conditions prevailing in the adult gastrointestinal tract. This is in distinct contrast to the multitude of enzymes which exist for the digestion of carbohydrates and proteins.

SECRETIONS OF THE SMALL INTESTINE

The secretions of the glands in the wall of the small intestine are not as clearly identified as are those of the salivary glands, stomach and pancreas. Various workers have recognized the presence of amylase, lipase, aminopolypeptidase, enterokinase, maltase, sucrase, lactase, and a variety of other enzymes in the intestinal secretion. The duodenal area that contains Brunner's glands produces an extremely viscous secretion, which is probably enzyme-free. In the rabbit, its pH may be as high as 8.0 to 8.2, but in man the secretion is nearly neutral, or even acid.[33, 41] Brunner's glands in most species studied secrete continuously, their activity increasing upon direct contact with a number of food substances. The principal function of the Brunner's gland secretion can no longer be said to be neutralization of acid chyme. The mucoid nature of the secretion probably protects the mucosa from the proteolytic enzymes.

The glands of Lieberkühn produce a copious secretion that is less viscous than that obtained from Brunner's glands. It contains measurable quantities of the enzymes listed above (Fig. 537).

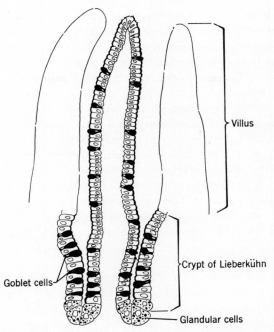

FIG. 537.   Diagram of villus and associated secretory structures. (From Montagna, *Comparative anatomy.*
New York, John Wiley & Sons, 1959.)

Neural Control of Intestinal Secretion.   Vagal stimulation or parasympathomimetic drugs evoke a secretion of mucoid fluid from the Brunner's gland area. Administration of eserine or sectioning of the sympathetic nerve supply gives rise to a similar
secretion.[54] The effect of vagal stimulation upon the part of the small intestine containing
no Brunner's glands is somewhat uncertain.

Humoral Control of Intestinal Secretion.   The existence of a humoral agent
controlling the formation of succus entericus was demonstrated in 1935 by Nasset *et al.*[35]

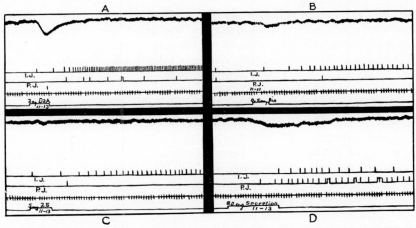

FIG. 538.   Results from injection of best lots of enterocrinin. *I.J.,* Intestinal juice; *P.J.,* Pancreatic
juice. *A,* Intestinal secretion increased 19 drops per min. by dose of 70 γ per kg. *B,* One-fifth response
in intestine from one-quarter above dose; no pancreatic secretion. *C,* Effect of 0.17 mg. per kg. picric
acid precipitate from hog gut extract; vasodilatin and secretin free. *D,* Control injection of secretin.
Upper trace in each record is blood pressure. (From Nasset, *Amer. J. Physiol.,* 1938, *121:*485. After
Babkin, *Secretory mechanism of the digestive glands.* Paul B. Hoeber, Inc., 1944.)

This substance, given the name *enterocrinin*, was found by Nasset[34] to be extractable from the small intestine as well as from the large intestine. A highly active, crystalline product has been prepared which elicits the flow of succus entericus from transplanted, denervated intestinal loops, but which has no effect on pancreatic secretion and is free from vasodilatins. Such findings seem to establish beyond doubt the existence of a distinct humoral agent (Fig. 538).[24]

Enterocrinin activity is augmented by feeding and by interruption of the nerve supply.[41] This hormone, when administered subcutaneously or intravenously, has no effect on intestinal motility; the augmented secretion is therefore not a secondary response to increased motor activity. The fact that enterocrinin augments not only the volume of secretion but also the amount of enzyme produced differentiates it again from gastrin and secretin which affect only the volume of secretion, and from pancreozymin which affects the production of enzymes. There remains, of course, the possibility that enterocrinin is a mixture of two hormones, one affecting the volume of secretion and the other increasing enzyme output. The hormone is probably a protein or protein derivative.[18, 19]

BILE

Bile, a secretion of the liver, is a mucous, greenish-yellow fluid, usually faintly alkaline in reaction. Its chief components are the bile salts, bile pigments, cholesterol, lecithin, fat and various inorganic salts. With the exception of the bile salts, the constituents of bile are excretory products with no important functions to perform in the alimentary tract. The bile salts are, however, intimately concerned in the digestion and absorption of fats and similar materials.

The specific gravity of hepatic bile is usually about 1.01; bladder bile is more concentrated. The gallbladder retrieves for the body the water and strong electrolytes excreted in bile by the liver. The removal of water is so extensive that hepatic bile with 2.5 per cent solids is concentrated to contain 15 per cent or more solids after only a short time in the gallbladder. Under normal conditions it effects a concentration of six- to tenfold. The material destined to enter the intestine is a concentrated solution of bile pigments (an excretory product) and bile salts (a digestive aid).

When the gallbladder contracts, its contents are poured into the duodenum. Bile pigments remain in the intestine and are excreted, imparting to the feces their characteristic color. Bile salts, after aiding in lipid emulsification, are absorbed by the lower intestine and return, via the portal system, to the liver. This so-called enterohepatic circulation is quite efficient; only 10 to 15 per cent of the secreted bile salts are lost from the body and require replacement by synthesis from various steroid precursors. The receipt of bile salts from the portal circulation is the most important single stimulus to *choleresis*, the increased output of bile by the liver. Another choleretic factor is the hormone norsecretin, a specific hormone present in secretin preparations as a contaminant. Proteins (meat, liver) in the alimentary tract stimulate the flow of hepatic bile to a greater extent than does olive oil. Carbohydrates have little effect, although the oral or intravenous administration of 50 per cent glucose tends to inhibit bile flow if the latter is continually drained away from the gut. The feeding of whole bile increases the volume flow of hepatic bile with an increase in the output of cholesterol, bile salts and bile pigments.[42, 43] When bile salts alone are administered, the flow of all bile constituents except pigments increases.

The normal circulation of bile salts between liver and gut may be visualized as follows. During fasting, nearly all the bile salts may be found in bladder bile. Upon the entry of chyme into the duodenum, the gallbladder contracts and empties much of its contents into the intestine. In the meantime, the bladder becomes filled with very dilute bile, which is concentrated by reabsorption of water. As the bile salts are absorbed from the gut, their choleretic action enhances the rate of bile production, and the two factors—increased production of hepatic bile and water reabsorption in the gallbladder—combine to produce again a concentrated solution of bile salts and pigments in the gallbladder. In the interval between meals, the bile stored in the bladder becomes even more concentrated, owing to the absorption of water.

Emptying of Gallbladder. The entry of bile into the intestine may be effected by contraction of the muscular coat of the bladder or by relaxation of the sphincter of Oddi. Although these two mechanisms probably operate synergistically on many occasions, each alone is capable of permitting the flow of bile. Agents which promote the emptying of the gallbladder by either mechanism are called *cholecystagogues;* substances which specifically stimulate contraction of the gallbladder are *cholecystokinetic* agents.[27] The gallbladder contracts when proteins, fats or fatty acids, or hydrochloric acid comes in contact with the duodenal mucosa. Peptides or amino acids are less effective; carbohydrates have no effect whatever.

Although vagal stimulation causes contraction of the gallbladder, the organ responds normally to an egg yolk meal after both vagi have been cut.[6] Some hormonal mechanism is sufficient to evacuate the gallbladder. Ivy and Oldberg[29] showed that an extract of duodenum injected intravenously causes contraction of the gallbladder. The existence of this hormone, termed *cholecystokinin*, has been verified by cross circulation experiments and other procedures. When Hong *et al.*[25] introduced dilute HCl or fat into isolated loops of small intestine, the pressure within the gallbladder rose. Instillation of procaine into the loop abolished the response to acid, but the pressure still rose after ingestion of a meal or injection of a cholecystokinin preparation. Injection of hexamethonium chloride intravenously abolished the pressure rise in response to a meal as well as to HCl in the isolated loop, but cholecystokinin was still effective. It was concluded that substances eliciting gallbladder contraction must act on receptors in the small intestine, and that these are connected to the cholecystokinin-producing cells by nervous pathways which are blocked by hexamethonium chloride.

It seems reasonable to assume that the gallbladder could empty itself most readily if its contractions were accompanied by relaxation of the sphincter of Oddi, which can resist a force of 300 mm. H_2O. Many cholecystokinetic agents are able to cause relaxation of the sphincter of Oddi. Magnesium sulfate, the nitrites and a group of antispasmodic drugs act almost exclusively on the sphincter. Under normal conditions bladder bile passes the sphincter during the passage of a peristaltic wave over the duodenum. This is, however, not an essential condition. The sphincter appears to serve the function of helping to retain bile in the bladder during the interval between meals.

Ivy[26] concluded that the gallbladder has the following functions: (i) storage of bile during the interval between meals; (ii) regulation of pressure within the biliary tract, with the gallbladder acting as a safety valve; (iii) reabsorption of some of the substances excreted by the liver; and (iv) addition of a mucoid secretion to the hepatic bile.

ABSORPTION FROM SMALL INTESTINE

The small intestine is the principal site for the absorption of the digestion products of carbohydrates, fats and proteins. Anatomically the small intestine is well suited to the task of transferring materials from the lumen into the blood stream or lymph because the villi provide an extensive absorption surface unlike anything found elsewhere in the alimentary tract. The completeness of the absorptive process has been demonstrated in experimental animals and in patients with fistulae of the lower ileum. The residue collected from the terminal portion of the ileum contains only some 15 per cent of nitrogenous compounds, mainly derived from sloughed-off cells, gastrointestinal secretions and microorganisms. Carbohydrates and fats are normally nearly completely absorbed. Also absorbed are many substances which would be better left in the intestine and excreted. Conversely, in the absence of bile, after alteration of the intestinal mucosa by disease or nutritional disorders, after interference with pancreatic secretion, in diarrhea, and in a variety of other pathologic conditions, the absorption of various food substances may be seriously handicapped.

Absorption of Carbohydrates. The first suggestion that sugar transport is active came from the work of Cori.[11] He showed that various monosaccharides are absorbed at different rates. If the absorption rate of glucose is arbitrarily taken to be 100, the relative rates of absorption of other sugars are: galactose, 110; fructose, 43; mannose, 19; xylose, 15; arabinose, 9. These results are not the diffusion rates that would be expected if the sugars were penetrating an inert membrane. Absorption of monosaccharides is usually complete and hence, at least in the terminal portion of the gut, must be against a concentration gradient. Bárány and Sperber[3] showed that movement against such a gradient takes place even when water reabsorption (bulk flow) is artificially stopped. In the rat, glucose is completely absorbed by the middle of the small intestine.[39]

The absorption rate following a dose of glucose declines with time despite the presence in the alimentary tract of appreciable amounts of unabsorbed sugar[8, 17, 39] As the concentration of the administered solution is increased, carbohydrate absorbed per unit time is increased.[17] Although sugar is absorbed more rapidly from concentrated solutions than from dilute solutions of equal volume, the feeding of dilute solutions of large volume may speed gastric evacuation sufficiently to permit rapid absorption.[5]

The endocrines affect intestinal absorption. Apparently, the absorption rate is increased by insulin and thyroid hormone; and hypophysectomy, thyroidectomy and possibly pancreatectomy decrease the absorption rate. Marrazzi[31] observed that in the rat the rate of carbohydrate absorption was lowered not only by adrenalectomy but also by a sham operation which left the adrenals undamaged. The adrenalectomized rat supported by salt therapy is apparently capable of absorbing carbohydrates at the normal rate.

As has been pointed out in earlier chapters, the mechanism of active transfer is currently of great interest. Early data on the organic phosphate accumulation during carbohydrate absorption gave rise to the attractive hypothesis that actively absorbed carbohydrates are phosphorylated. This theory, however, is opposed by a substantial array of facts. Phosphorylation of sugars by intestinal mucosal homogenates does not occur at rates proportional to the absorption rates in the intact animal; galactose, a rapidly absorbed sugar, is phosphorylated very slowly.[45] Since phosphorylation would presumably occur at carbons 1 or 6, blocking of these positions should drastically lower the absorption rate. However, in isolated intestinal loops 1-deoxyglucose and 6-deoxyglucose are absorbed at about the rate of glucose itself.[13]

Substantial evidence now exists[1] that glucose passes through the intestinal mucosa essentially unchanged and that this passage is unidirectional. Intestinal and renal glucose absorption appear to be quite similar, both in specificity to the sugar and in inhibition characteristics.

Absorption of Fats. The very early physiologists made the surprising observation that feeding an animal food rich in fat was followed by the appearance in the mesenteries of clearly visible, milky vessels quite distinct from the arteries and veins, which were already well known. This was how the lymphatic vessels were discovered. Later, microscopic examination of blood and chyle revealed the presence of tiny droplets of fat, the *chylomicrons*. The appearance of chylomicrons in blood and lymph led at first to the conclusion that fats are absorbed without prior digestion. Munk collected lymph from a patient with a fistula of the thoracic duct and demonstrated that about 60 per cent of the dietary fat could be recovered from the fistula. The early recognition of bile as an emulsifying agent helped to strengthen the idea that fat was absorbed as finely divided particles. This view was vigorously challenged by Pflüger at the turn of the century, and it was gradually replaced by the idea that lipolysis precedes absorption. Verzár[48] has supported and extended the lipolysis theory, developing the concept of the hydrotropic action of the bile salts. The molecular combination of bile salts with fatty acids renders fatty acids water-soluble, and this was seen as the mechanism which permits transfer of the acids across the intestinal membrane. More recently, Frazer[20] developed a theory of fat absorption which combines the lipolysis theory and the older idea of absorption of emulsified but intact fat. Frazer's investigations shifted attention back to the possibility that fat absorption may occur without prior digestion. He felt that some of the ingested fat is digested and absorbed as the free fatty acids (passing via the portal circulation to the liver), while the remainder is absorbed as neutral fat and passes into the lymphatic vessels (partition theory).

Reiser et al.[38] tested this hypothesis critically by administering fats in which the glycerin was isotopically labeled and esterified with nonmetabolizable fatty acids. Between one-fourth and one-half of the ingested fat was completely hydrolyzed before absorption. All of the remainder was hydrolyzed to a monoglyceride and absorbed in that form. Consequently, chylomicrons do not reflect the absorption of unhydrolyzed fat, as suggested by Frazer, but rather a resynthesis immediately after intestinal absorption.

Cholesterol requires fatty acids and bile salts for maximal absorption and seems to be absorbed even against a concentration gradient.[7, 47]

Absorption of Proteins and Amino Acids. Proteins are normally considered to be absorbed only after hydrolysis of their constituent amino acids. This statement is not entirely accurate, for the occurrence of food allergies implies that immunologically detectable amounts of protein or polypeptide may be absorbed in some people.[22] Further, the polypeptide hormone insulin is absorbed to some extent from Thiry-Vella loops in dogs.[16] Both of these methods of detection are exquisitely sensitive, and, from the standpoint of nutrition, proteins or polypeptides are usually not absorbed. Indeed, were as much as 0.1 per cent of ingested protein absorbed unchanged, the consequent allergic reactions would proscribe eating the same food twice.

It has been shown that, as in the case of glucose, the rate of absorption of amino acids increases when greater amounts are fed. Chase and Lewis[9] found glycine to be absorbed most rapidly of the amino acids. Arranging some of the amino acids in order of decreasing absorption rate gave the following series: glycine, alanine, cystine, glutamic acid, valine, methionine, leucine, tryptophane, isoleucine and norleucine, and isovaline. In 1947, Schofield and Lewis[44] showed that alanine was absorbed more rapidly than β-alanine and serine more rapidly than isoserine. This suggests that, as the amino group is moved away from the carboxyl group, the absorption rate of the substance is decreased. Replacement of a hydrogen atom by a hydroxyl group also decreases the absorbability of the compound, alanine being absorbed more rapidly than serine and β-alanine more rapidly than isoserine. Kratzer[30] has studied amino acid absorption in the chick and concluded that the absorption rate varies inversely with the molal volume of the amino acid. Thus glycine was absorbed most rapidly and tryptophane most slowly. As in the case of glucose, the absorption rates of amino acids decrease with time.[15] Direct evidence for the active transport of amino acids has been obtained by the use of isolated segments of small intestine.[53] It has been suggested that measurable amounts of glutamic and aspartic acids may participate in transamination forming alanine.[36]

Absorption of Water and Electrolytes. From the standpoint of day-to-day comfort or critical health, disturbances of fluid and electrolyte absorption are probably more important than disturbances of nutrient absorption. Ions and water are absorbed from both the small and the large intestine. Visscher et al.[49] clearly showed that sodium chloride can be absorbed against a concentration gradient. This finding implies that either sodium or chloride is transported actively—but it does not say which. More recently, Curran and Solomon[14] and Cooperstein and Hogben[10] have analyzed the relation between ion fluxes and electric potential in the gut. Both groups concluded that sodium must be the ion that is transported actively.

The permeability of the gut wall to sodium is surprisingly great. It is greatest in the duodenum, less in the jejunum, lesser still in the ileum, and least in the colon.[50] Thus, the effects of active sodium transport are minor in the duodenum and jejunum, where sodium leaks back into the lumen as rapidly as it is pumped out. In the ileum, and especially in the colon, more sodium is actively transported than can diffuse back, and effective salt absorption occurs.

Curran and Solomon[14] showed that water transport is entirely passive and is normally secondary to solute movement. However, hypertonic solutions pull water into the gut, and water is rapidly absorbed from hypotonic solutions. Since water absorption is passive, a driving force is needed. As solute absorption occurs, intestinal fluid becomes slightly hypotonic. The resulting concentration gradient of water drives the water across the intestinal epithelium.

A rather special mechanism appears to function in the absorption of iron. In the normal adult this element is but slowly absorbed; if, however, the need for iron arises, the absorption rate can be considerably increased—as, for example, after hemorrhage. The mechanism which carefully regulates the passage of iron across the intestinal membrane has been described by Granick[21] as follows. Ferrous iron of the mucosal cells is in equilibrium with the transport form of iron (its combination with serum globulin) and with ferritin (large molecular weight protein-iron complex) of the intestinal mucosa. Reduction in the amount of circulating iron leads to liberation of the element from the ferritin stores. Iron can then be absorbed from the gut (Fig. 539). Ferritin might thus

$$
\begin{array}{ccc}
\text{Gastrointestinal tract} & \text{Mucosal cell} & \text{Blood stream} \\
Fe^{++} \quad \longrightarrow & Fe^{++} \quad \rightleftarrows & \text{Serum Globulin } Fe^{+++} \\
& \Updownarrow & \\
& \text{Ferritin } (Fe^{+++}) &
\end{array}
$$

FIG. 539.   Role of ferritin in iron absorption. (From Granick, *J. biol. Chem.*, 1946, *164*:745.)

be a storage form as well as a blocking agent which controls the absorption of dietary iron according to metabolic need. Bile does not appear to be directly involved in iron absorption but functions by facilitating the absorption of fatty acids which would otherwise form insoluble iron soaps in the gut and retard iron absorption.

The absorption of calcium, magnesium and phosphorus is not well understood. To some extent the amounts absorbed are determined by the quantities fed. Proteins appear to further the absorption of calcium and magnesium,[32] while lactose exerts a beneficial effect on the absorption of calcium. The presence in the alimentary tract of excessive amounts of fatty acids (as in faulty fat digestion and absorption) may lead to the loss of large amounts of calcium and magnesium from the body as insoluble soaps. It has been shown[52] with the aid of the radioactive isotope that phosphorus absorption begins within five minutes after the element is introduced into the duodenum and that the maximal absorption rate is reached in about half an hour, with absorption still incomplete in four hours.

REFERENCES

1. ATKINSON, R. M., PARSONS, B. J. and SMYTH, D. H. *J. Physiol.*, 1957, *135*:581–589.
2. BABKIN, B. P., HEBB, C. O. and SERGEYEV, M. A. *Amer. J. Physiol.*, 1938, *123*:5–6.
3. BÁRÁNY, E. and SPERBER, E. *Skand. Arch. Physiol.*, 1939, *81*:290–299.
4. BAYLISS, W. M. and STARLING, E. H. *J. Physiol.*, 1902, *28*:323–353.
5. BIRCHALL, E. F., FENTON, P. F. and PIERCE, H. B. *Amer. J. Physiol.*, 1946, *146*:610–612.
6. BOYDEN, E. A. and VAN BUSKIRK, C. *Proc. Soc. exp. Biol. (N. Y.)*, 1943, *53*:174–175.
7. BROGSTRÖM, B., LINDHE, B. and WLODAWER, P. *Proc. Soc. exp. Biol. (N. Y.)*, 1958, *99*:365–368.
8. BURGET, G. E., MOORE, P. and LLOYD, R. *Amer. J. Physiol.*, 1932, *101*:565–569.
9. CHASE, B. W. and LEWIS, H. B. *J. biol. Chem.*, 1934, *106*:315–321.
10. COOPERSTEIN, I. L. and HOGBEN, L. A. M. *J. gen. Physiol.*, 1959, *42*:461–473.
11. CORI, C. F. *J. biol. Chem.*, 1925, *66*:691–715.
12. COWGILL, G. R. *Physiol. Rev.*, 1945, *25*:664–686.
13. CRANE, R. K. and KRANE, S. M. *Biochim. biophys. acta*, 1956, *20*:568–569.
14. CURRAN, P. S. and SOLOMON, A. K. *J. gen. Physiol.*, 1957, *41*:143–168.
15. DOTY, J. R. and EATON, A. G. *J. biol. Chem.*, 1937, *122*:139–146.
16. DRIVER, R. L. and MURLIN, J. R. *Amer. J. Physiol.*, 1941, *132*:281–292.
17. FENTON, P. F. *Amer. J. Physiol.*, 1945, *144*:609–619.
18. FINK, R. M. *Amer. J. Physiol.*, 1943, *139*:633–637.
19. FINK, R. M. and NASSET, E. S. *Amer. J. Physiol.*, 1943, *139*:626–632.
20. FRAZER, A. C. *Physiol. Rev.*, 1940, *20*:561–581.
21. GRANICK, S. *J. biol. Chem.*, 1946, *164*:737–746.
22. GRAY, I. and WALZER, M. *Amer. J. dig. Dis.*, 1938, *5*:345–348.
23. HARPER, A. A. and RAPER, H. S. *J. Physiol.*, 1943, *102*:115–125.
24. HEGGENESS, F. W. and NASSET, E. S. *Amer. J. Physiol.*, 1951, *167*:159–165.
25. HONG, S. S., MAGEE, D. F. and CREWDSON, F. *Gastroenterology*, 1956, *30*:625–630.
26. IVY, A. C. *Physiol. Rev.*, 1934, *14*:1–102.
27. IVY, A. C. *Gastroenterology*, 1944, *3*:54–57.
28. IVY, A. C. and FARRELL, J. I. *Amer. J. Physiol.*, 1926, *77*:474–479.
29. IVY, A. C. and OLDBERG, E. *Amer. J. Physiol.*, 1928, *86*:599–613.
30. KRATZER, F. H. *J. biol. Chem.*, 1944, *153*:237–247.
31. MARRAZZI, R. *Amer. J. Physiol.*, 1940, *131*:36–42.
32. MCCANCE, R. A., WIDDOWSON, E. M. and LEHMANN, H. *Biochem. J.*, 1942, *36*:686–691.
33. MCGEE, L. C. and HASTINGS, A. D. *J. biol. Chem.*, 1942, *142*:893–904.
34. NASSET, E. S. *Amer. J. Physiol.*, 1938, *121*:481–487.
35. NASSET, E. S., PIERCE, H. B. and MURLIN, J. R. *Amer. J. Physiol.*, 1935, *111*:145–158.
36. NEAME, K. D. and WISEMAN, G. *J. Physiol.*, 1957, *135*:442–450.
37. PIERCE, H. B., OSGOOD, H. S. and POLANSKY, J. B. *J. Nutr.*, 1929, *1*:247–270.
38. REISER, R., BRYSON, M. J., CARR, M. J. and KUIKEN, K. A. *J. biol. Chem.*, 1952, *194*:131–138.
39. REYNELL, P. C. and SPRAY, G. H. *J. Physiol.*, 1956, *131*:452–462.
40. RICHINS, C. A. *J. comp. Neurol.*, 1945, *83*:223–236.
41. SCHIFFRIN, M. J. and NASSET, E. S. *Amer. J. Physiol.*, 1939, *128*:70–80.
42. SCHMIDT, C. R., BEAZELL, J. M., ATKINSON, A. J. and IVY, A. C. *Amer. J. dig. Dis.*, 1938, *5*:613–617.
43. SCHMIDT, C. R., BEAZELL, J. M., BERMAN, A. L., IVY, A. C. and ATKINSON, A. J. *Amer. J. Physiol.*, 1939, *126*:120–135.
44. SCHOFIELD, F. A. and LEWIS, H. B. *J. biol. Chem.*, 1947, *168*:439–445.
45. SOLS, A. *Biochim. biophys. acta*, 1956, *19*:144–152.
46. THOMAS, J. E. and CRIDER, J. O. *Amer. J. Physiol.*, 1940, *131*:349–356.
47. VAHOUNY, G. V., WOO, C. H and TREADWELL, C. R. *Amer. J. Physiol.*, 1958, *193*:41–46.
48. VERZÁR, F. and McDOUGALL, E. J. *Absorption from the intestine.* New York, Longmans, Green & Co., 1936.
49. VISSCHER, M. B., FETCHER, E. S., JR., CARR, C. W., GREGOR, H. P., BUSHEY, M. S. and BARKER, D. E. *Amer. J. Physiol.*, 1944, *142*:550–575.
50. VISSCHER, M. B., VARCO, R. H., CARR, C. W., DEAN, R. B., and ERICKSON, D. *Amer. J. Physiol.*, 1944, *141*:488–505.
51. WANG, C. C. and GROSSMAN, M. I. *Amer. J. Physiol.*, 1951, *164*:527–545.
52. WEISSBERGER, L. H. and NASSET, E. S. *Amer. J. Physiol.*, 1942, *138*:149–155.
53. WISEMAN, G. *J. Physiol.*, 1956, *133*:626–630.
54. WRIGHT, R. D., JENNINGS, M. A., FLOREY, H. W. and LIUM, R. *Quart. J. exp. Physiol.*, 1940, *30*:73–120.

CHAPTER 46

The Large Intestine

By PAUL F. FENTON

IN man the functions of the large intestine are relatively few but important. This organ conserves water, acts as a temporary storage place for the waste products of digestion, and to a limited extent it can absorb food materials which may find their way into it. In addition, the colon acts as an incubator for numerous bacteria which, through their ability to synthesize certain nutritional factors, contribute to the over-all nutritional status of the individual.

MOVEMENTS OF THE COLON

The temporary storage function of the colon is documented by its size, distensibility, and periodic and relatively sluggish motility. During its prolonged stay in the colon, water is progressively absorbed, so that the liquid chyme is transformed into semisolid feces; a substantial amount of water is thus conserved. The relative quiescence of the proximal colon may be correlated with the comparatively slight development of the myenteric plexus and its scanty extrinsic innervation, derived from the vagus nerve. In the more distal portions, the excitatory innervation is derived from the pelvic nerve and the myenteric plexus is more abundant.

The movements of the colon may be divided into the autogenic and the exogenic. In the first category are the familiar segmentation movements which divide the colon into sausage-like segments, haustrations. Apparently these haustral contractions progress a short distance, rolling the fecal contents, mixing them, and exposing them to the mucosal surface. Exposure of all the contents to the mucosa is, of course, a greater problem here than in the small intestine, owing to the colon's larger diameter. Peristaltic movements and weak antiperistalsis sometimes occur. The occurrence of antiperistalsis supports the belief that the main function of colonic movement is not propulsion but retention and mixing to prompt absorption.

Propulsive movements which sweep over the colon, effectively translocating the colonic contents, occur several times a day. The strongest propulsive movement is caused by a "mass contraction" of one section of the colon, completely emptying its contents into the next section. These mass contractions originate intrinsically from stretching of the colonic walls, the resulting translocation of contents ending the stimulus. The most powerful propulsive movements moving fecal material into the rectum are the gastro-colic and duodenocolic reflexes. It is common experience that a feeling of a need to detecate often follows eating. This sensation results from a reflex, initiated by the distention of the stomach and duodenum, which causes mass contractions and resulting mass movements of large amounts of the colonic contents from the proximal to the distal colon. "Reflex" is perhaps a misnomer, because the stomach exerts its influence on the colon *mainly* by a wave of excitation passing along the small intestine rather than through the extrinsic innervation and the spinal cord.

Pressure Recording from the Colon in Man. Using improved pressure recording with balloons and electronic transducers, Code *et al.*[5] have restudied colonic motility in man. They employ a system of nomenclature introduced by Templeton and Lawson[11] and applied to man by Adler *et al.*[1] Pressure waves with different characteristics are termed types I, II and III without prejudice in respect to the function served. Type I waves are small (less than 10 cm. H_2O), simple in form, and highly regular. Rates of 13

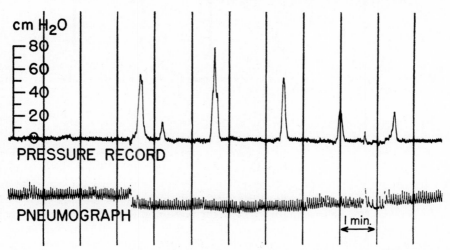

FIG. 540.   Type II waves recorded with an electric pressure transducer from pelvic colon of a normal fasting person. (From Code *et al.*, *Ann. N. Y. Acad. Sci.*, 1954, *58*:317–335.)

per minute in the pelvic colon and six per minute in the descending colon are representative. The function of these waves is unknown.

Type II waves, as seen in Figure 540, are stronger and larger contractions than type I and are the commonest. They last one-half to one-third of a minute and can, as in Figure 540, reach pressures ranging from 60 to 80 cm. H_2O. Type II waves are identified with mixing rather than propulsion (since tandem systems of balloons do not show progression), although they do move short distances as described for haustral contractions.

Type III waves are composed of low (10 cm. H_2O), slow (one or two minute) changes in the baseline pressure upon which type I and type II waves are superimposed, as in Figure 541. Type III waves are infrequent, at least in the pelvic colon where most of the recordings were made. Code and his coworkers suggest that type III waves aid absorption by increasing luminal pressure.

In patients with ulcerative colitis, simple, but very strong (to 100 cm. H_2O), propulsive contractions have been recorded and termed type IV waves (Fig. 542). Tandem balloon recording shows that these contractions are not peristaltic but affect two balloons simultaneously. Type IV waves are equated with mass movements.

It will be noted that none of these four waves is equated with peristalsis, which may not exist in the distal reaches of the colon.

Megacolon.   Peristalsis and mass contraction of the colon are apparently more

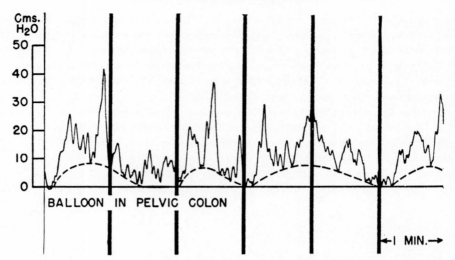

FIG. 541. Type III waves recorded from pelvic colon of a normal person after ingestion of food. Type III wave is indicated by dashed line. Superimposed type I and II waves shown by continuous line. (From Spriggs *et al.*, *Gastroenterology*, 1951, *19:*480–491.)

dependent upon the intrinsic myenteric plexus than upon spinal reflex action. Both mechanisms are set aside by a degeneration of a narrow band of the Auerbach's myenteric plexus. The result is megacolon, comparable to megaesophagus discussed in Chapter 43. The colon reaches a prodigious size. The condition is not, as once thought, caused by (inhibitory) sympathetic overactivity, nor is it relieved by sympathectomy.

Defecation. The desire to defecate is felt only when the feces, propelled by mass peristaltic movement, have actually entered the rectum and produced some distention. The internal and external anal sphincters prevent the escape of the accumulated fecal mass. The internal anal sphincter consists of a thickening of the circular layer of smooth muscle. The tonic contraction of the external sphincter is maintained by the pudendal,

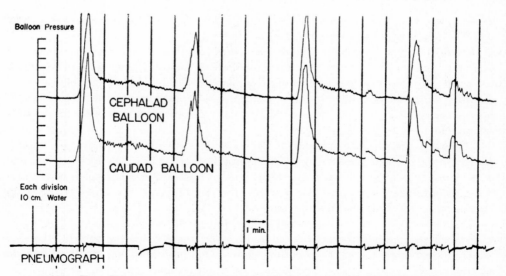

FIG. 542. Type IV waves recorded from tandem balloons placed in transverse colon through a colonic stoma. Note that waves occur simultaneously in both balloons. (From Code *et al.*, *Amer. J. Med.*, 1952, *13:*328–351.)

a somatic nerve.[3] Distention of the colon reflexly opens the sphincter by inhibiting this tone. While there are distinct species differences, in man the lumbar sympathetics are probably excitatory to the internal sphincter; the parasympathetic innervation via the pelvic nerve is inhibitory, as shown in Figure 543. The sympathetic innervation plays no role in defecation;[8] in fact, the act can be executed by patients whose upper sacral segments have been destroyed. These reflex-like contractions are ascribed to a peripheral nerve plexus. However, the integrity of the sacral cord segments and the parasympathetic fibers brings about a stronger and more effective defecatory reflex.

The act of defecation as it occurs normally is partly a voluntary and partly an involuntary act. When distention of the rectum becomes sufficient to constitute an

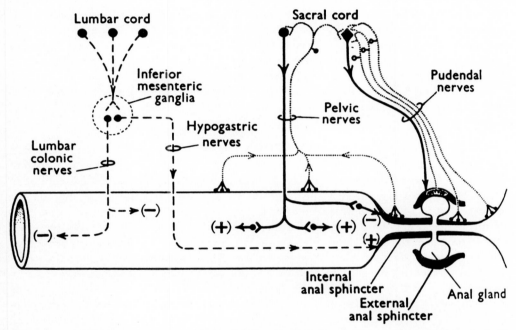

FIG. 543.   Diagram of innervation of anal sphincters and distal colon of cat. (From Bishop et al., J. Physiol., 1956, 134:229-240.)

adequate stimulus, contraction of the colon and relaxation of the anal sphincters leads to evacuation of the fecal mass. The reflexes concerned here involve only the sacral portions of the spinal cord. The voluntary part of the act of defecation involves relaxation of the external sphincter, but may include contractions of the diaphragm and the abdominal muscles.

Laxation.   Food can affect laxation in two ways, (i) by its bulk, upon which the colonic wall may contract, and (ii) by the presence of substances which have a drug-like action on the intestine. Food that contains a significantly larger amount of indigestible material or roughage passes through the intestinal tract quickly. In their studies with wheat bran, Cowgill and collaborators[6] obtained data suggesting that in healthy men an intake of not less than 90 to 100 mg. of crude fiber per kilogram of body weight per day should be associated with satisfactory laxation as determined by amount of material eliminated and the subjective impressions of the individual. Observations of patients suffering from chronic constipation showed that they, as compared with normal subjects, had greater capacity to break down in the alimentary tract (possibly by bacterial action) the crude fiber present in certain fruits and vegetables, with resultant failure to secure satisfactory laxation. It has since been shown[7, 9, 12] that what has been called crude fiber consists chiefly of lignin, cellulose and hemicellulose, these carbohydrates being present in varying amounts. These substances undergo bacterial decomposition in the intestine, lignin being the most resistant and hemicellulose the least.

SECRETION BY THE LARGE INTESTINE

Man's large intestine carries out no important digestive activities. Although the large intestine does not secrete spontaneously, local stimulation of the mucosa elicits the secretion of a thick mucoid fluid of alkaline reaction (pH 8.3 to 8.4). Digestive enzymes in the secretion of the large intestine are simply received with chyme from the small intestine. A dipeptidase and a trace of amylase may be present in the large intestinal secretion. Stimulation of the pelvic nerves evokes the secretion of a mucoid fluid; this response is enhanced by eserine and is blocked by atropine. Stimulation of the central end of the pelvic nerve elicits the typical secretion, presumably by centrifugal impulses over the intact trunk. The sympathetic nerve supply to the large intestine appears to have some inhibitory role in the secretory process.

Colonic mucous secretion is regarded as protective against both mechanical irritation (which is a stimulant to mucous secretion) and the acids produced by bacterial action on food remnants.

COMPOSITION OF FECES

It has been estimated that in man some 400 ml. of liquid matter pass from the ileum into the cecum in the course of a day. Except in water content this fluid is similar to feces. During passage through the large intestine, water is removed, so that on the average 100 to 150 grams of fecal matter is excreted each day. As much as 25 per cent of this material may be composed of dead and living microorganisms of the large intestine. Analysis of the feces shows that about 75 per cent of the total weight is accounted for by the water content. Food residues are therefore a surprisingly small fecal component. The feces always contain at least a small percentage of fat apparently of endogenous origin, that is, secreted into the alimentary tract. A number of nitrogen containing substances are also lost with the feces. These include the protein and nonprotein compounds of the microorganisms, digestive enzymes carried into the large intestine from the small intestine, mucus, epithelial cells sloughed off from the alimentary tract walls, and any nitrogenous food substances which have escaped digestion and absorption. A small amount of nitrogen is also present in various amines, such as tyramine, histamine, cadaverine, and putrescine, formed by the bacterial decarboxylation of their respective amino acids. Similarly, one finds indole and skatole, which impart to the feces their characteristic odor. Contrary to popular belief, the odor of stools is not caused by a "sluggish colon" and putrefaction, but by an overactivity of the intestinal tract sweeping out an excessive amount of indole and skatole.

The color of the feces depends to a considerable extent upon the diet. Stercobilin and stercobilinogen, derivatives of the bile pigments bilirubin and biliverdin, impart to the excreta their normal brown pigmentation. Failure of bile secretion results in chalk colored feces, a point of diagnostic significance. Diets high in meat tend to give rise to a much darker stool; the ingestion of much milk imparts to the feces a very light color. Various plant pigments such as those in beets also modify the color of the stool. The excretion of large amounts of fat in conditions of incomplete fat absorption gives the feces a pale color, especially if the entry of bile pigments into the digestive tract is interfered with. Certain drugs also change the color of the feces. Finally, the presence of blood turns the stool red, dark brown or black, depending on whether the lesion is in the lower or upper part of the digestive system.

It is possible to identify a number of steroids in fecal matter, among them cholesterol and bile salts. Plant steroids may also be present in small amounts. The latter originate in the ingested food and are not absorbed from the alimentary tract. Present also are a number of organic acids originating mainly from the fermentation of carbohydrates. Acetic, lactic and butyric acids, among others, have been identified. Other products of bacterial action are H_2S, CO_2, CH_4, H_2, NH_3, phenols and mercaptans. A considerable number of inorganic salts are excreted in the stool. Important among these are the salts of calcium, magnesium, iron and copper. Salts of sodium and potassium also are present, but these are excreted to a greater extent by the kidneys. Undigested or indigestible food substances contribute a variable number of constituents to the feces.

The pH of the feces is usually given as 7. While this is true on the outside of the fecal mass, the pH in the interior, where bacterial action may be producing substantial quantities of organic acids, may be as low as 5.

Indicative of the endogenous nature of many of the fecal constituents is the fact that even in prolonged fasting a small quantity of fecal matter is formed and excreted. This contains nearly all substances found in the normal stool. Analysis of the feces formed during fasting is often important in metabolic experiments in which retention ratios are to be calculated. In some instances, as in protein balance studies, the basal excretion of nitrogen is determined while the subject of the experiment is receiving a calorically adequate diet as free as possible of nitrogenous compounds.

MICROORGANISMS OF ALIMENTARY TRACT

Among the more numerous microorganisms found in the digestive tract are *Escherichia coli*, *Aerobacter aerogenes*, *Clostridium welchii*, a group of cocci, and various lactobacilli including *Lactobacillus bifidus*. Although these organisms may be found in the small intestine, they are far less numerous there than in the large intestine. Acting upon undigested or unabsorbed carbohydrate residues in the large intestine, these organisms form a number of organic acids, together with such other end-products as carbon dioxide. Under unusual conditions, so much acid may be produced that the mucosa is irritated and diarrhea ensues. Action of microorganisms upon protein and protein derivatives gives rise to various amines which presumably could exert deleterious effects upon the host. Whether this is actually the case has been debated by Alvarez.[2] Since most of the symptoms of intestinal autointoxication can be produced simply by packing the rectum with inert material, it seems reasonable to conclude that the absorption of toxic products of bacterial action plays a rather minor role in the development of the symptoms described as "autointoxication."

Rather than being considered harmful, intestinal bacteria are now believed to play a significant role in the nutrition of man and other animals. Certain of the intestinal organisms have the ability to synthesize vitamins of the B complex and vitamin K from relatively simple and readily available materials. Liberation of these substances from the bacterial cells and subsequent absorption of the released vitamins can contribute materially to the nutrition of the host. Vitamin K, the antihemorrhagic factor, is so produced, and the human neonate is liable to hemorrhage until the intestinal flora produce sufficient vitamin K. One may take as an example two members of the vitamin B complex, biotin and folic acid. It has been impossible to demonstrate under ordinary conditions a requirement for these factors by the rat or the mouse. If, however, an insoluble sulfonamide or streptomycin is administered to the animals, deficiency symptoms may be observed. The presence of the antibiotic in the digestive tract either reduces the number of surviving organisms or alters the metabolic pattern in such a way that synthesis of vitamins is prohibited. In the case of the other members of the B complex, intestinal synthesis does not make the difference between a dietary requirement or no dietary requirement, as is the case with biotin and folic acid. Intestinal synthesis does, however, reduce the amounts of the various nutritional factors which must be included in the diet.

The intestinal flora has been shown to play a role in the bacterial invasion of the blood stream which occurs after moderate exposure to ionizing radiation. The organisms which invade, and often kill, are identical with the ones found in the alimentary tract.[4]

REFERENCES

1. ADLER, H. F., ATKINSON, A. J. and IVY, A. C. Amer. J. dig. Dis., 1941, 8:197–202.
2. ALVAREZ, W. C. An introduction to gastroenterology, being the third edition of The mechanics of the digestive tract. New York, Paul B. Hoeber, Inc., 1940.
3. BISHOP, B., GARRY, R. C., ROBERTS, T. D. M. and TODD, J. K. J. Physiol., 1956, 134: 229–240.
4. BRADNER, W. T., BERNSTEIN, S. E. and McCARTHY, R. E. Proc. Soc. exp. Biol. (N. Y.), 1955, 89:107–111.
5. CODE, C. F., WILKINSON, G. R., JR. and SAUER, W. G. Ann. N. Y. Acad. Sci., 1954, 58:317–335.
6. COWGILL, G. R. and SULLIVAN, A. J. J. Amer. med. Ass., 1933, 100:795–802.
7. CRAMPTON, E. W. and MAYNARD, L. A. J. Nutr., 1938, 15:383–395.
8. DENNY-BROWN, D. and ROBERTSON, E. G. Brain, 1935, 58:256–310.
9. HELLER, V. G. and WALL, R. J. Nutr., 1940, 19:141–149.
10. QUIGLEY, J. P. Ann. N. Y. Acad. Sci., 1954, 58:297–305, 335.
11. TEMPLETON, R. D. and LAWSON, H. Amer. J. Physiol., 1931, 96:667–676.
12. WILLIAMS, R. D. and OLMSTED, W. H. J. Nutr., 1936, 11:433–449.

CHAPTER 47

The Urinary Bladder

By THEODORE C. RUCH

THE function of the bladder is of great concern to urologists and neurologists and of some concern to neurophysiologists. Conflicting concepts, unphysiologic terminology, ignorance of fundamental anatomy and physiology of such structures as the "internal sphincter," and the intermixture of mechanical, pathologic and neural factors—all contribute to making bladder function a complex subject.

Innervation of Bladder. The motor nerve supply to the bladder and its sphincters is derived from both divisions of the autonomic nervous system and from the somatic nervous system (Fig. 544). Afferent and efferent fibers are conducted in the same nerves.

Parasympathetic. The preganglionic fibers supplying the bladder issue from the spinal cord mainly at S_3, although there is a small contribution from S_2, S_4, or both. Heimburger et al.[7] established this outflow in man by root blocks. The sacral outflow accounts for the vulnerability of bladder control in lesions of the conus medullaris or the cauda equina. The preganglionic fibers traverse the *pelvic* nerves (nervi erigentes) and the inferior hypogastric plexus, intermingling with sympathetic fibers, to synapse with postganglionic neurons in the ganglion clumps lodged in the bladder wall. These fibers constitute the efferents for the detrusor muscle and the internal sphincter.

Sympathetic. The preganglionic outflow is from the upper lumbar and lower thoracic segments of the spinal cord. Fibers from the lumbar prevertebral ganglia and the preaortic nerve plexus descend along the abdominal aorta to form, at its bifurcation, the "presacral nerve"—more properly the superior hypogastric plexus—which, in turn, divides into two strands, the hypogastric nerves. The hypogastric nerves, coursing along the anterior surface of the sacrum, join the inferior hypogastric plexus and are distributed to the bladder. The sympathetic fibers appear to play little or no part in micturition; those to the internal sphincter (motor) probably prevent reflux into the bladder during ejaculation.

Somatic. Somatic efferent fibers are confined to the external sphincter and prostatic urethra, which they reach by way of the third and fourth anterior roots and the pudendal nerve.

Afferent. The afferent fibers for the micturition reflex (and for the sense of bladder fullness) traverse the pelvic nerve. Painful impulses from the bladder dome are conducted by the hypogastric nerves; those from the trigone by the pelvic nerve. Sensory impulses from the urethra traverse the pudendal nerve.

Clinical and Laboratory Study of Bladder. The methods commonly used for clinical and laboratory study of the bladder are (i) cystometry, which yields information on detrusor tonus, micturition threshold and power, and sensation; (ii) cystography

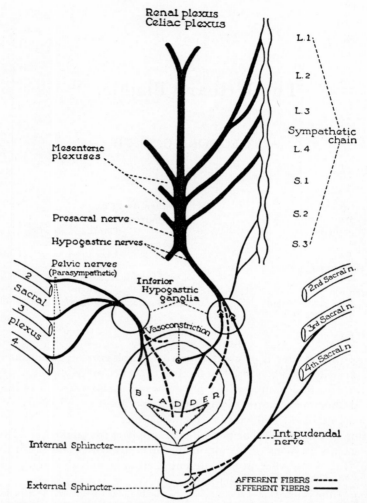

FIG. 544.   Diagram showing efferent and afferent pathways to bladder and sphincters. Postganglionic parasympathetic neurons are omitted. (From McLellan, *The neurogenic bladder*. Springfield, Ill., Charles C Thomas, 1939.)

with x-ray opaque substances; (iii) cystoscopy by which a surprising amount of functional information can be gained; and (iv) the recording of times and volumes of micturition.

   Cystometry.   The cystometer is used to determine a pressure-volume curve of the bladder by means of a fluid reservoir, a manometer, and a catheter connected by a three-way stopcock. A light tambour may be added. The intravesical pressure should be measured while the bladder is connected with the manometer and disconnected from the filling reservoir, and after the fluid has ceased to flow. Fluid is introduced into the bladder either steadily (at a slow rate) or in volume increments spaced a few minutes apart. Pressure is plotted against volume to yield a cystometrogram. Rhythmic tonus waves, the threshold, vigor, and duration of the micturition reflex, and subjective sensations are all important.

   As shown in Figure 545, the cystometrogram or pressure-volume curve typically consists of three parts: (i) an initial rise when the first increment is added (segment I), which is probably due to intra-abdominal pressure;[17, 19, 20] (ii) segment II, a prolonged, nearly flat segment (0 to 10 or 15 cm. H_2O), the steepness of which is held to reflect detrusor "tonus;"* (iii) in a normally innervated bladder a sharp rise of pressure ensues, indicating a micturition reflex contraction of some strength (150 cm). The threshold for micturition is, then, the volume of filling (stretch) just previous to the reflex. When reflex micturition is wanting, the micturition pressure rise is replaced by a slow rise. Segment III, probably represents the passive stretch of elastic connective tissue of the vesical wall. The cystometrogram therefore reflects two functions: (i) the amount of bladder tonus and (ii) the threshold and strength of the micturition contraction of the detrusor. The third problem of micturition is, of course, the control of the sphincters.

Bladder Hypotonus. A normal bladder holds its contents under very low pressure, usually less than 10 cm. H_2O. Moreover, it holds increasing volumes of fluid with little increase in intravesical pressure. (The kidneys are therefore not required to secrete against a high pressure.) In clinical parlance, a steeper than normal curve is termed

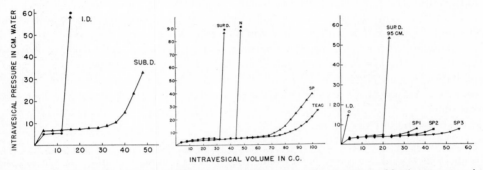

FIG. 545. Cystometrograms obtained in cats after various neural lesions of brain stem or spinal cord and after autonomic blocking agents (*TEAC*). Long arrows represent micturition and point to dot or square giving pressure generated. Threshold is next volume to right of point where arrows originate. Note the three phases of cystometrogram seen when micturition is absent, e.g., *SUB.D.* and *SP. I.D.*, *SUB.D.* and *SUP.D.* mean inter-, sub- and supracollicular decerebration; *SP1*, *SP2* and *SP3*, successive determinations after spinal transection. (After Tang, *Amer. J. Physiol.*, 1955, *187*:249–257.)

"hypertonic," and a flatter than normal curve, "hypotonic." The significance of the slope of the curve, i.e., of bladder tonus, has long been confusing. Many writers,[4, 5, 10, 11] directly or by implication, consider bladder tonus a reflex phenomenon. They liken it to the stretch reflex ("tonus") of skeletal muscle or ascribe it to a "peripheral reflex" served by an intramural plexus of the bladder wall. However, a myotatic reflex yields a steadily increasing reflex contraction to increasing stretch (see Fig. 102, p. 175), whereas the bladder accommodates a new volume *with little persisting increase in pressure.* This superficially resembles a lengthening reaction, but no such inhibitory reflex has been demonstrated. The flatness of the initial limb of the normal cystometrogram is sometimes accounted for by assuming that the stretch reflex arcs are activated at low volumes but are "inhibited" from the brain. These are all "neurogenic" theories of bladder tonus. A second view, the myogenic theory, is that the reaction to stretch and supposed accommodation are largely properties of the smooth muscle and connective tissue of the bladder wall, and are entirely nonreflex and non-neural in origin. These two hypotheses lead to quite different interpretations of the neurogenic disturbances of bladder function. The first emphasizes the overactivity or release of tonic bladder reflexes, spinal or peripheral. The second emphasizes the physical state of the bladder wall as a result of infection and of changes secondary to interferences with the micturition reflex, e.g., stretching or shrinking.

* The term "tonus," recognized by physiologists as a cloak for ignorance, is used here operationally to mean "that which is reflected in the pressure-volume curve of the bladder."

Nesbit et al.,[12, 14] Tang and Ruch,[20] and Carpenter and Root[3] studied the effects of anesthesia, spinal or root section and autonomic blocking agents on segment II of the cystometrogram in human patients and experimental animals. Whereas all abolish micturition, none reduces bladder tonus, which indicates that it is not reflex in nature (Fig. 545). Furthermore, brain stem transections, which greatly augment (release) limb reflex tonus and the excitability of the micturition reflex, also fail to influence bladder tonus.[20] Even death or deep anesthesia is ineffective. The one factor which will alter the initial limb of the cystometrogram is the stretch produced by the accumulation of urine or that involved in a cystometric determination when the bladder is unprotected by the micturition reflex, as after spinal or pelvic nerve section. Successive decreases in bladder tonus occur after each of a series of cystometric determinations (Fig. 545). Changes which might be ascribed to a drug or a sacral nerve section are actually due simply to the stretch involved in the control cystometric determination.

Physical analysis of bladder tone. A physical analysis of bladder tone confirms the above physiologic analysis and reveals a common interpretative error in cystometry.[2, 16, 22] If the response of the bladder to increasing volume is thought of in terms of mural tension rather than intravesical pressure, any need to postulate a reflex or other "vital" explanation for the flatness of segment II of the cystometrogram disappears. Analysis shows that the tension in the bladder walls is steadily mounting as volume increases; stress mounts even more rapidly. The difference between pressure and mural tension derives from the law of Laplace.

Consider the bladder as a perfect sphere composed of two hemispheres as in Figure 546. The pressure in the bladder as recorded in the cystometrogram is acting to force the two hemispheres apart. This total force must be P (force per unit area) times the area of the imaginary circular plane separating the two hemispheres, or $P \cdot 2\pi R^2$. This total force must be just balanced by the forces in the vesical wall at the junction of the two hemispheres. If these forces are of magnitude T per unit length of wall, then T times the circumferences ($T \cdot 2\pi R$) is the total force in the vesical wall holding the hemispheres together. This permits writing the equation of Laplace for a sphere:

$$T \cdot 2\pi R = P\pi R^2 \text{ or } P = 2(T/R)$$

If the pressure within the bladder stays approximately constant, as in segment II of the cystometrogram, the increase in the radius must be approximately equalled by an increase in wall tension. During this phase, the bladder wall approximately follows Hooke's law, i.e., T is proportional to length. This is seen in Figure 546, in which the same cystometrogram is plotted as pressure and as mural tension. It will be seen that the two curves correspond at the larger volumes at which the radius is changing little, so that $T \simeq P$. However, at the lower volumes the tension rises steadily but along a more gradual slope because the radius is changing. To make the tension independent of the changes in the thickness of the bladder wall as it expands, the bladder response can be plotted as stress (calculated with certain assumptions from two knowns, pressure and volume). Here it is quite evident that stress, or tension per unit area, mounts steadily during segment II and increasingly during segment III.

It is clearly more meaningful to plot experimental or clinical cystometrograms in terms of tension instead of pressure. Although the radius is not known, it can be inferred from the volume, if the bladder is assumed to be spherical, and the tension can be calculated from the pressure.

$$P = \frac{2T}{\sqrt[3]{V\frac{3}{4}\pi}} = T = \frac{P}{2} \cdot \sqrt[3]{V\frac{3}{4}\pi}$$

A plot which is related to stress is gained by multiplying pressure times volume. For ease of calculation these values can be obtained from tables relating the radius to the volume of a sphere, or calculated from the formula

$$T = P \cdot \sqrt[3]{V} \cdot 0.312$$

To avoid large numbers, T should be plotted in grams force per centimeter rather than dynes; P is in centimeters of water, and volumes are in cubic centimeters.

It is apparent that the flatness of segment II of the cystometrogram requires no explanation in terms of reflex inhibitory relaxation. At the higher volumes of segment II, the sharply rising tension and stress mean that elastic elements are no longer approximating Hooke's law or, more probably, that some inelastic connective tissue element such as collagen has come into play.

Bladder Hypertonus. Convincing evidence that so-called "hypertonus" is also a physical rather than a reflex or neural phenomenon was given by Veenema et al.[21] In dogs, they prevented urine from entering the bladder by leading the ureters to the

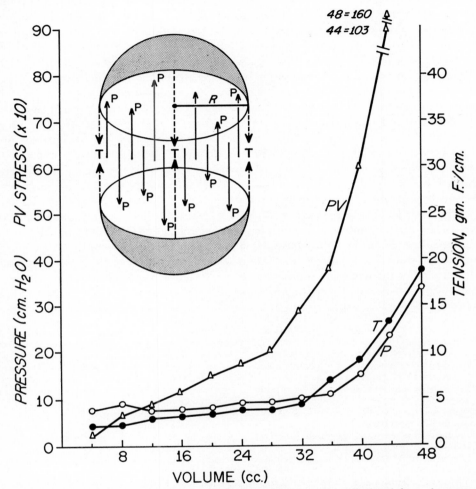

FIG. 546. Press, tension and stress plots of the cystometrogram, calculated from the pressure-volume curve as described in text. Note that as the plot more closely approximates a statement of what is occurring in the walls of the bladder the flat segment II of the cystometrogram disappears. Note that plot for P and T are in absolute units, while that for stress is in relative units. (Data from Tang. J. Neurophysiol., 1955, 18:583–595.)

exterior of the body. Several days later, cystometrograms were obtained under general and spinal anesthesia to abolish the micturition reflex. The result seen in Figure 547 suggests that the "climbing" type of curve is a rapidly developing physical change (five dogs) due to shrinkage of the bladder rather than to any type of neurogenic hypertonus. No histologic or weight change indicative of hypertrophy like that following pelvic nerve section was found. Thus, the two series of studies suggest that abnormalities in the second limb of the cystometrogram are the result of physical changes in the bladder wall, the "flat" type of curve being caused by stretch and the "climbing" type by shrinkage. Neither is a reflex phenomenon.

Micturition.   The act of micturition involves the action of the detrusor reflex and the opening and closing of the sphincters. The basis of the detrusor contraction is a spinal stretch reflex arc subject to inhibition and facilitation from higher centers. (There is some evidence that weak and brief emptying contractions can be integrated through the mural plexus—a "peripheral reflex"?) To study the sphincters, Denny-Brown and Robertson[4] introduced a catheter-within-a-catheter into the urinary tract. The inner catheter served for filling and for recording intravesical pressure. By withdrawing the outer catheter and recording the pressure distal to the internal or the external sphincter, the opening and closing of the sphincters could be studied. Given the right degree of distention, the detrusor activity can, with some difficulty, be initiated voluntarily. Voluntary micturition begins with a relaxation of the perineum and a strong vesical contraction. Opening of the internal sphincter occurs only later and after a variable rise in pressure (18 to 43 cm.). The internal sphincter cannot be voluntarily opened or closed independently of detrusor contraction and relaxation, respectively. Nor can it be forced by straining (intra-abdominal pressure). The external sphincter (M. compressor urethrae) cannot be voluntarily opened independently of detrusor activity, but can be powerfully closed while the detrusor continues to contract. Opening of the external sphincter is accomplished by a reflex inhibition of tonic pudendal nerve discharge from afferents originating in the bladder and urethra.

The internal sphincter opens and closes sequentially, its opening following upon detrusor contraction and its closing upon detrusor relaxation. Since the muscles of the internal sphincter do not form a true anatomic sphincter but are continuations of the longitudinal muscular layers of the bladder wall, the sphincter opening may represent either a part of the detrusor contraction or a coordination effected through the nerve plexus of the body wall. There is no evidence that either the pelvic nerve or the sympathetics relax the musculature around the bladder neck as a part of micturition.

CLINICAL CORRELATIONS: *Tabetic bladder dysfunction.*   The most severe neurogenic disturbance of bladder function is that occurring clinically with tabes dorsalis or experimentally after section of the sacral posterior roots. Progressive enlargement and overflow incontinence commence immediately and persist; the micturition reflex is in complete and enduring abeyance. Voluntary micturition is possible only with great effort. The micturition reflex suffers the same fate as the stretch reflex in deafferented skeletal muscle. The second limb of the pressure-volume curve is lower and flatter than normal, and the third segment shifts to the higher volumes. Without good reason, this is commonly ascribed to loss of a tonic stretch reflex. Actually, the hypotonus simply represents changes in the property of the smooth muscle secondary to prolonged dilatation. The primary difficulty, therefore, is the absence of the micturition reflex which normally protects the bladder muscle from stretching. Exactly the same situation exists during the initial stages of spinal shock following transection (Fig. 547).

Decentralized or autonomous bladder.   Lesions of the conus medullaris, cauda equina or pelvic nerve destroy entirely the efferent as well as the afferent connections of the bladder. The bladder is thus decentralized except for the unimportant sympathetic efferent and afferent connections. The behavior of the bladder is conditioned by the smooth muscle and by whatever neural control is effected through the mural plexus.[5, 9, 10, 11] Initially no active micturition contractions are elicited by effort or in cysto-

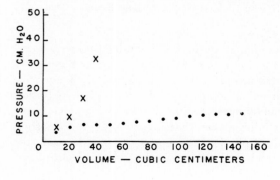

FIG. 547.   Cystometrogram of dog with micturition prevented by general anesthesia and local anesthesia of sacral roots (*dots*). Crosses show pressure-volume relation 39 days after both ureters were transplanted to exterior of body. (From Veenema *et al.*, *J. Urol.*, 1952, *68*:237–241.)

metric examination. There is overflow incontinence. Later, a remarkable change occurs; small, brief waves of contraction occur spontaneously or in reaction to stretch or increased intra-abdominal pressures. The larger waves are accompanied by opening of the sphincters, but are inadequate in tension and duration for effective micturition. This results in escape of only small amounts of fluid, leaving residual urine. Such contractions, and particularly the partially coordinated action of the sphincter and detrusor, are often held to mean that the mural plexus serves a "peripheral" reflex. Several facts are difficult to square with the assumption of an independently active peripheral plexus; e.g., no such activities follow interruption of the spinal reflex arcs for micturition by posterior root section. The bladder wall undergoes great hypertrophy after decentralization, which may alter the initial limb of the cystometrogram.

Automatic bladder of spinal transection. As noted, the initial stage of acute spinal shock following transection of the spinal cord above the sacral region is like that following decentralization. No micturition reflex is elicitable; after a period of retention, overflow incontinence supervenes. The retention apparently represents failure of the sequential detrusor-sphincter action. In favorable cases an automatic or "reflex" bladder is established, sometimes with a large residual urine resulting from the weakness and brevity of the micturition reflex; at other times the micturition reflex seems hyperirritable. The lack of voluntary control and knowledge of the time of micturition can be partly circumvented by using sensory stimulations or bladder pressure to precipitate micturition. Some victims of spinal injury develop what is termed *hypertonic cord bladder*[11] or a *reflex neurogenic bladder*.[10] The initial segment of the cystometrogram rises sharply, quite strong micturition contractions occur with small degrees of filling (100 ml.), and residual urine is small. Smaller, spontaneous, regularly occurring detrusor contractions are also present. These phenomena do not appear to occur in spinal animals, and no clear physiologic interpretation is possible. The possibility of an irritative basis as in cystitis must be taken into account.

Encephalic Control of Micturition. Micturition, a stretch reflex of the bladder, like the stretch reflex of skeletal muscle,[15] is subject to control from several levels of the nervous system. For both reflexes, the basic arc is spinal, and, since they both fail for a period after spinal transection, they both must depend on the brain for facilitation. The origin of the facilitatory impulses for the bladder, as stated by Barrington[1] and others,[6, 9] lies in the anterior pontine region in the location indicated in Figure 548. Section above this level, as in the classic intercollicular decerebration, results in extremely hyperactive micturition reflexes.[18] Cooling[6] or focal lesions at this level or section just below it results in a "spinal" cystometrogram, i.e., complete failure of micturition because a facilitatory area has been destroyed (Fig. 545). The micturition reflex is thus comparable to decerebrate rigidity, although one is phasic and the other postural. The low threshold of the micturition reflex in the intercollicular decerebrate preparation (*I.D.* in Fig. 545) indicates that some area above this level has an inhibitory effect. As shown in Figure 548, *right*, an inhibitory area has been located in the middle of the midbrain. A supracollicular transection passing just above this level results in a threshold not much different from normal (*SUP.D.*, Fig. 545) and, after a section just below it (intercollicular),

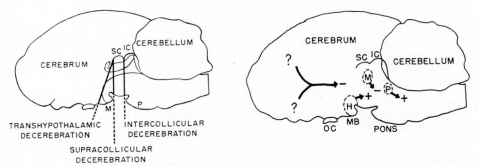

FIG. 548. Schematic sagittal section of cat's brain showing on left transections employed in studying brain stem control of micturition. Diagram at right shows locus of areas (*H*, *M*, *P*), as determined by transections and Horsley-Clarke lesions, which facilitate and inhibit micturition: + means facilitation and − means inhibition of micturition reflex; *SC* and *IC*, superior and inferior colliculi; *M* and *MB*, mammillary bodies; *OC*, optic chiasm. (From Tang, *J. Neurophysiol.*, 1955, *18*:583–595 and Tang and Ruch, *J. comp. Neurol.*, 1956, *106*:213–245.)

there is a sharp decrease in threshold. Thus, the nearly normal threshold of the supra-collicular decerebration apparently indicates a balance between any more rostral inhibitory and excitatory influences and also a balance between an inhibitory and a facilitatory area below it.

Transection through the hypothalamus (Fig. 548) results in a very low micturition threshold, indicating that a strong inhibitory influence originating in the cortex has been removed. The posterior hypothalamic area is facilitatory, since lesions of it or a supracollicular section just below it causes a prompt increase in the threshold.

Stimulation experiments add the information that the cerebellum exerts an effect on the bladder, possibly through one of these regions, and that the cortical bladder regions lie in the cingular gyrus and the orbital surface of the frontal lobe. These are excitatory, and the inhibitory cortical areas have not been demonstrated.

The higher control of the micturition reflex obviously is far more complex than the disinhibition of a spinal reflex described in the clinical literature.[12] At the same time it is more understandable in familiar neurophysiologic terms. In fact, no better illustration of the similarity between the higher control of somatic and autonomic reflexes can be found than that obtained by comparing the micturition reflex with the myotatic reflex of the hind limb following lesions at different levels of the nervous system. However, certain differences must be kept in mind, e.g., neither the spinal cord nor the brain controls bladder tone which is a peripheral non-neural phenomenon, whereas the tone of somatic muscles originates entirely in spinal reflexes and suprasegmental mechanisms. The neural mechanism for efficient storage and expulsion of urine consists of the sacral spinal reflex arcs, the anterior pons, the midbrain, the posterior hypothalamus and the cerebral cortex. The neural mechanism which determines when and where this mechanism will operate, a matter of considerable importance to the individual, is the contribution of the cerebral cortex.

REFERENCES

1. BARRINGTON, F. J. F. Brain, 1921, 44:23–53.
2. BRODY, D. A. and QUIGLEY, J. P. Bull. math. Biophys., 1948, 10:25–30.
3. CARPENTER, F. G. and ROOT, W. S. Amer. J. Physiol., 1951, 166:686–691.
4. DENNY-BROWN, D. and ROBERTSON, E. G. Brain, 1933, 56:149–190.
5. DENNY-BROWN, D. and ROBERTSON, E. G. Brain, 1933, 56:397–463.
6. EAST, N. R. Supraspinal control of bladder reflexes. M.A. Thesis, University of Washington, Seattle, 1948.
7. HEIMBURGER, R. F., FREEMAN, L. W. and WILDE, N. J. J. Neurosurg., 1948, 5:154–164.
8. JACOBSON, C. E. J. Urol., 1945, 53:670–695.
9. LANGWORTHY, O. R., KOLB, L. C. and LEWIS, L. G. Physiology of micturition. Baltimore, Williams & Wilkins, 1940.
10. McLELLAN, F. C. The neurogenic bladder. Springfield, Ill., Charles C Thomas, 1939.
11. MUNRO, D. New Engl. J. Med., 1936, 215:766–777.
12. NESBIT, R. M. and BAUM, W. C. Neurology, 1954, 4:190–199.
13. NESBIT, R. M. and LAPIDES, J. Arch. Surg., 1948, 56:138–144.
14. NESBIT, R. M., LAPIDES, J., VALK, W. W., SUTLER, M., BERRY, R. L., LYONS, R. H., CAMPBELL, K. N. and MOE, G. K. J. Urol., 1947, 57:242–250.
15. SHERRINGTON, C. S. Brain, 1915, 38:191–234.
16. SMITH, R. F. and WATSON, M. R. Unpublished observations.
17. TANG, P. C. Brain stem control of micturition and respiration. Ph.D. Thesis, University of Washington, Seattle, 1953.
18. TANG, P. C. J. Neurophysiol., 1955, 18:583–595.
19. TANG, P. C. and RUCH, T. C. J. comp. Neurol., 1956, 106:213–246.
20. TANG, P. C. and RUCH, T. C. Amer. J. Physiol., 1955, 181:249–257.
21. VEENEMA, R. J., CARPENTER, F. G. and ROOT, W. S. J. Urol., 1952, 68:237–241.
22. WINTON, F. R. and BAYLISS, L. E. Human physiology. Boston, Little, Brown & Co., 1955.

SECTION XI

Metabolism

CHAPTER 48

Energy Exchange

By JOHN R. BROBECK

METABOLISM, meaning "change," is a word used to identify the changes which occur within living organisms in the course of their being alive. It may be used with such a broad meaning that it becomes practically synonymous with the sum total of the chemical and physical reactions necessary for life. Metabolism is also used in a more limited sense to refer to those reactions in which a certain type of foodstuff or its derivatives can be identified, as in carbohydrate metabolism, or it may be still further restricted to discussion of some particular compound, for example, glucose metabolism. The term is used occasionally to refer to a subject like "water metabolism," where a substance enters the body, moves around through its various parts, and leaves through kidneys, skin or some other route, having undergone no real change in the process. Water "exchange" seems to be a preferable term for this type of activity, so that the term water metabolism may be reserved for reactions in which water takes part in a chemical way. These would include H_2O synthesis in oxidations, and also hydrolysis, the formation of anhydrides and similar chemical changes.

Two other words found in discussions of metabolism are anabolism and catabolism; they mean "to build up" and "to throw down," respectively. Anabolism has been applied to synthetic reactions leading to storage of energy in the body; catabolism designates the breakdown of tissue and the utilization of its stored energy. At the time that these two terms were most widely used, the nature of the metabolism of foodstuffs was not as well understood as it is now; and it therefore seemed possible to separate anabolism from catabolism. It is now clear that this separation is sometimes impossible, since many changes earlier regarded as anabolic are necessarily accompanied by those which are catabolic. Synthesis and storage of fat may serve as an example. When fat is formed from carbohydrate and stored in fatty tissues, and anabolism appears to be in progress, a catabolic reaction must take place at the same time to furnish energy for the synthesis. This is true also during protein synthesis, and, in general, anabolic or synthetic reactions may be said to be *coupled* with catabolic reactions as a source of energy. As the

964

chemistry of these reactions becomes better known, the older terms are used less frequently, their place being taken by the names of the reactions involved.

Energy exchange signifies all of the gains and losses of energy between the body and its environment. In animal physiology, four kinds of energy are to be considered—chemical, electrical, mechanical and thermal; the principles describing their interrelationships are identical with those of the thermodynamics of nonliving systems. The peculiar nature of the mechanisms through which cells carry on their metabolism does, however, place limitations upon interconversions among the several types of energy which may not exist in purely physical systems. Animal cells utilize for work the energy from only one source, chemical reactions, especially those reactions in which bonds uniting carbon and hydrogen are converted into bonds between carbon and oxygen (CO_2) or hydrogen and oxygen (H_2O). Work accomplished may be mechanical, electrical, or chemical, i.e., synthetic. In addition to the work, some of the energy always appears as heat; since the total amount of energy in the system does not change, the greater the relative heat production, the smaller the amount of work that can be accomplished. With reference to work potential, the heat is lost to the cell, since it has no mechanism capable of utilizing thermal energy; that is, the body is not a heat engine. The relationship between the quantity of chemical energy released and the amount of heat produced is a measure of the efficiency of the system in that a smaller relative heat production signifies a greater efficiency. Depending upon the circumstances and the type of work, cellular mechanisms isolated from the body may have efficiencies as high as 50 per cent, although under more natural conditions the figure is usually less than 30 per cent. In many instances all of the energy is converted to heat with no measurable work at all.

Energy Sources. The immediate source of energy for any given cellular reaction is "high energy" compounds previously synthesized and stored within the cell. Other stores may exist in other cells—for example in adipose tissue or the liver. In drawing upon these reserves the animal depletes its energy resources to provide work and heat. Eventually this energy must be replenished if the animal is to survive in good health, and thus energy must be obtained from sources outside the body. Sources of energy are included

in food in the form of —C—H bonds capable of being opened at the temperature, pH

and chemical environment created by cellular activities. Not all of the naturally occur-

ring —C—H bonds can be utilized by the body; for example, those of mineral oils and

their derivatives, although useful in engines and motors, are useless in metabolism. To be available to animal cells the carbon and hydrogen must exist in molecules having configurations similar to those of the molecules composing the cells. Cells consist of proteins, carbohydrates and lipids, and foods are limited to these same classes of compounds. In the body the energy of food and of stored substances is utilized through the same reactions. When the products of digestion have entered the body fluids, they mingle with similar compounds derived from tissues of the body as well as from earlier feedings, and together make up a metabolic "pool" supplying cells with energy. From this pool the cells utilize a compound without prejudice as to its origin. The purpose of food, therefore, is to replenish this pool and add to the total amount of energy available to the animal.

Heat. The largest part of the energy released in metabolic reactions is converted to heat. Under resting conditions in a fasting subject, all of the exchange takes the form of heat production, and the over-all exchange can be summarized as the oxidation of energy stores to liberate heat. The heat is not released as in an engine since reactions in the body occur at a nearly constant temperature, well below the temperature necessary for combustion of foods in a flame. Biologic oxidations occur gradually, in stepwise fashion, through transfer of electrons and hydrogen ions from one intermediary compound to another. At intervals during these transfers energy becomes available for work; some of the energy is also liberated as heat, the only function of which appears to be its usefulness in maintaining a favorable temperature within the cell.

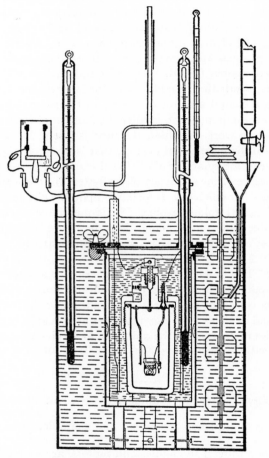

FIG. 549.   Combustion bomb and calorimeter as designed by Richards and Barry, *J. Amer. chem. Soc.*, 1915, *37*:993. (From Clark, *Topics in physical chemistry*, 2nd ed. Baltimore, Williams & Wilkins Co., 1952.)

In metabolic studies heat is measured by its effect upon the temperature of a system. The effect upon the temperature of a known amount of water is used as a standard. The unit employed is the *calorie*, originally defined as the amount of heat necessary to raise the temperature of 1 gram of water from 14.5° to 15.5° C. One *kilocalorie* (kcal., kg. cal., Calorie, or Cal.) is equal to 1000 calories (cal.). The small or gram calorie (15° C.) has a value of 4.185 absolute joules.[5] For most purposes in biology any difference in the third decimal place is insignificant, because measurements cannot be made with enough accuracy to justify its use. Furthermore, the conversion of heat units from calories to joules is uncommon in biology, except in certain specialized areas of biochemistry and biophysics, and is practically unknown in medicine. Some authors, however, believe the use of joules is preferable, and Clark[5] has written, "It is hoped that biochemists and clinicians will do what they can, within limits set by immediate convenience, to aid in the transition" (p. 391).

Although the body is not a heat engine and does not burn foods in a flame, the amount of energy released as heat when a given amount of a substance is oxidized in the body is exactly the same as that released when the material is oxidized through combustion. The intermediary steps are not important in a thermodynamic balance sheet; only the energy content of the reactants and of the products of the reaction needs to be taken into account. When the products are identical—usually carbon dioxide and water, both inside and outside the body—the amount of energy which can be given off as heat must be the same under the two circumstances. This point is important in measuring energy exchange, because the calorific value of the foodstuffs can be determined more easily and more accurately outside the body. The procedure is known as calorimetry, and an apparatus like the bomb calorimeter of Bertholet (Fig. 549) is utilized. The measurement is both complicated and difficult, although simple in principle. A weighed amount of a sample is placed on a platinum wire in an atmosphere of oxygen within a metal chamber or "bomb." The chamber is then tightly closed and suspended in a water bath. An electric current through the platinum wire ignites the specimen, inducing complete combustion with formation of H_2O, CO_2, and, in the case of protein, oxides of nitrogen, sulfur and phosphorus. After correction is made for storage of heat within the several components of the calorimeter, the heat of combustion may be calculated from the weight of the water in the bath and its temperature change. Introducing the proper corrections and establishing the characteristics of the calorimeter are among the more difficult features of the method. Results, in general, are more accurate than is needed for most purposes in biology. Every compound has a characteristic heat of combustion, depending upon its chemical structure. For glucose the value is 3.74; for sucrose, 3.94; for glycogen, 4.19; and for starch, 4.18 kcal. per gm. Fats vary, depending upon their constituent fatty acids; palmitic acid releases 9.28, stearic acid, 9.55, and oleic acid, 9.47 kcal. per gm.; glycerol provides 4.31 kcal. per gm. (Clark,[5] p. 397). Animal fats are said to average 9.3 kcal. per gm. Animal proteins yield about 5.6 kcal. per gm. in a calorimeter, but in the body they liberate only 4.3 kcal. per gm. because they are not completely oxidized; the difference between the two figures represents the calorific value of the end-products of protein metabolism, chiefly urea and ammonia. Most of these figures exceed in accuracy the needs of most measurements in the field of metabolism and nutrition, where average values are often employed. The values 4.1 kcal. per gm. for carbohydrate and protein in the body, and 9.3 kcal. per gm. for fat are frequently used.

Work. The capacity of using chemical energy to do work enables cells to exhibit contraction, conduction, secretion, chemical syntheses and other signs of life. Mechanical work, the product of force × distance, is accomplished when an object is lifted or given an acceleration. It is measured in foot-pounds, kilogram-meters, dyne-centimeters, calories, ergs or joules. Chemical work is done in synthesis of compounds processing stored chemical energy; secretory work brings about a concentration gradient. Several of these processes, including synthesis and secretion, are involved in the phenomenon of conduction of a nerve impulse. Contraction of a muscle cell, with the development of tension or with shortening or both, involves first of all chemical work which may become transposed into physical work. Synthetic work and secretory work are doubtless similar to these others in their mechanisms, although less is known about them. All forms of work appear to require the creation within cells of a certain class of compounds, which includes the pyrophosphates of adenine and acetyl coenzyme A—compounds containing an anhydride bond which upon hydrolysis releases a rather large amount of energy. The bond has been called a "high energy" or "energy rich" bond, and seems to represent a fundamental mechanism for energy storage and utilization in all types of work.[13] Little is known, however, of the processes linking this chemical type with other types of energy.

Later in this chapter the methods used in setting up a balance sheet for energy exchange will be described, and it will become necessary to decide whether work is done at every muscular contraction, in every synthesis, and during all secretion. This is sometimes a difficult question to answer. When a man lifts an object and places it upon a shelf, he does work in proportion to the weight and the height of the lifting; the shelf, however, does no work in supporting the weight. It follows, then, that if the man instead of the shelf holds the weight up he does no further work however long he sustains the effort. The energy expended by his muscles after the original lifting is not recoverable as work; it is all converted into heat within his body.

If a man lifts one object after another and places them upon the shelf, his work accomplishment increases as the weight upon the shelf becomes progressively heavier. If he has only one object which he lifts ten times, his work is no greater than if he lifted it once; yet his total energy expenditure and heat production will reflect the extra liftings. The functioning of the bodily machine can be nearly identical under the two conditions in spite of, and with the exception of, the difference in the amount of true work. Because of this similarity the physiology of working is often studied in laboratories under conditions where a physicist would say there is no work. A physiologist knows that within the limits of accuracy of his measurements it does not matter whether he lifts ten objects to the shelf, or lifts one object ten times; his energy expenditure will be nearly the same in the two experiments. (If he wishes to avoid the error introduced by returning the object to the floor nine times, someone else can do this for him. This refinement, however, will not alter the total amount of physical work done.) In short, physiologists take certain liberties in their calculations of work output, but these liberties are based upon the demonstration that the human machine functions the same in doing work or in merely pretending to do it.

This principle applies likewise in the work of secretion, synthesis and conduction. Work accomplished by the stomach in secretion of hydrochloric acid may be calculated if the total amount of acid secreted is known, together with the concentration gradient set up for hydrogen ions and chloride ions. Yet this work does not appear as such in any balance sheet of energy exchange for the body as a whole, since the acid from the stomach is neutralized by secretions of pancreas and duodenum, the energy of the high concentration of acid appearing as heat during the neutralization. So it is with the work of the heart, often determined as the product of cardiac output and the pressure gradient between the aorta and the right atrium: the heart, considered alone, does work, but the work is converted into heat in overcoming friction as the blood courses through the rest of the circulatory system. Following the passage of a nerve impulse a fiber does work, probably in re-establishing a concentration gradient for sodium and potassium; the maintenance of this gradient during the resting state, however, does not add to the sum total of work done by the fiber, since it is similar to the activity of the man holding up the weight which he lifted sometime earlier. From this it should be apparent that in any measurement of work it is essential to define the system under study. For the remaining pages of this chapter the system is the body as a whole, without reference to intermediary processes or to differences of energy level existing between different organs or tissues.

Storage. As a factor in energy exchange the significance of energy storage varies with the age, sex and metabolic state of the individual, as well as with his state of nutrition, activity and environmental temperature. When a child is growing he is storing energy; an adult in gaining weight is likewise in positive energy balance. The gain of weight occurs through the storage of compounds synthesized within the body from foodstuffs, and therefore represents chemical work. Like mechanical work, this chemical work is more or less inefficient and is accompanied by liberation of energy as heat. The efficiency probably varies from one type of synthesis to another, although data are not available for any detailed comparisons. (The synthesis of protein is said to be accomplished with an efficiency of about 45 per cent.[14]) The body has certain depots, for example, the fat, which provide energy for cells throughout the body; it also has the more specialized types of reserve set aside for the utilization of a single cell. Muscle glycogen, phosphocreatine and adenosine triphosphate are examples of the latter, as are all of the compounds containing energy-rich bonds, mentioned above. Energy must be added to the system to synthesize these bonds initially, and a large part of this energy can be recovered later in the work of the cell.

The first law of thermodynamics, describing the constancy of the total amount of energy within a system, suggests that a simple relationship must exist among the four variables of energy exchange, as follows:

$$\text{Food intake} = \text{heat loss} + \text{work output} + \text{energy storage}$$

where the storage has a negative sign when reserves are being utilized. If intake exceeds heat loss and work, the extra energy is stored within the body; energy is lost from the reserves if food intake is smaller than heat plus work. Since this relationship is now unquestioned, it is well to recall that a little more than 60 years ago there was some uncertainty about this equation and the question of whether living systems might utilize energy differently from other physical and chemical systems. Rubner in 1894 demonstrated that the energy value of the metabolic mixture is equal to the total heat production of a fasting, resting animal, as this equation states.[19] With this equation it is possible to study energy *balance* as well as energy exchange, if three of the four variables in the equation can be measured. Sometimes this is not possible, and it may be more convenient to reduce one or more of the variables to zero and so remove it from the balance sheet. The following section describes experiments where this has been done; it also includes some discussion of the significance of measurements which have been made. A good source of supplementary material on this subject is the monograph on bioenergetics by Brody.[3]

METABOLIC RATE

One of the methods often employed for studying energy balance is to observe the subject of the experiment while he is both resting and fasting. Food and work can then be removed from consideration, leaving heat loss as the only avenue of energy dissipation and negative storage of energy as the only source. To achieve this state, human patients are usually asked to come to the laboratory in the morning after having eaten nothing since dinner the night before; they are then allowed to recline at rest until their metabolic state becomes stabilized, when either their energy loss in the form of heat or the energy equivalent of the tissues utilized to provide this energy may be measured. In clinical practice both of these values are inferred from yet a third measurement, the rate of oxygen consumption, which is converted to a rate of heat production through use of certain constants previously determined in more complete experiments. Each of these determinations—heat production, oxygen consumption and energy drawn from bodily reserves—will now be reviewed briefly.

Direct Calorimetry. The total heat production of a human subject or an experimental animal can be estimated by recording the temperature change of a known weight of water employed to absorb the heat. Results are obtained in calories, as in bomb calorimetry of foodstuffs. In practice, however, this procedure is so difficult and tedious that it is now seldom employed. One must be able to measure or to control every avenue of heat loss—to the environmental air, to other physical objects, and into vaporized water—as well as to detect positive or negative heat storage, i.e., temperature change, in the subject or in the apparatus. For the period of the test the subject is placed at rest within a thermally insulated chamber or box, a calorimeter (Fig. 550). Within the chamber are tubes through which water can be circulated from the outside; a meter measures the rate of circulation, while thermometers or thermocouples indicate the temperature of the water entering and leaving the chamber. Provision is made also for the circulation of air and for measuring its rate of circulation, temperature change, and the amount of water vapor taken up from the skin and respiratory membranes of the subject. This last measurement is important because water absorbs 0.58 kcal. per gram when it passes from the liquid to the vapor state at 33° C. Heat produced by the subject may be transmitted into the circulating water or into the current of air including its water vapor, or the heat may be stored by the contents of the chamber, including the subject; no heat storage will occur, however, if the rate of flow and temperature of the circulating water are properly adjusted to the rate of heat production. The subject's

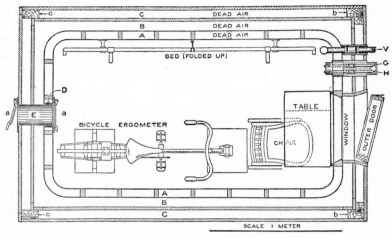

FIG. 550.   Horizontal section of respiration calorimeter. Portions shaded are of wood: A, dead air space between Cu and Zn walls; B, dead air space between Zn wall and inside wooden wall; C, dead air space between inside and outside wooden walls; D, pneumatic packing, air and heat insulated; E, food aperture tube; a, a, airtight ports (glass); G, ingoing water for absorbing heat; H, outcoming water; V, ventilating air current. (From Atwater and Benedict.)

total heat production will then equal his heat loss, which can be calculated from the measurements made upon the currents of water and air. By this method of direct calorimetry, Harris and Benedict found that the total heat production of a fasting, resting male subject is about 1600 kcal. per day.[9] Application of the method is not limited to the fasting, resting state, however, and the total heat production may be estimated under any given set of conditions of feeding, activity and environmental temperature.

More recently, somewhat easier methods have been invented for direct calorimetry with the aid of electrical and electronic techniques. One of them utilizes two identical chambers, one containing the animal to be tested and the other an electrical heater. Thermocouples placed at comparable sites in the walls of both chambers are connected through control circuits so that the amount of current supplied to the heating element is controlled by the temperature gradient between the two chambers. If the one containing the animal becomes cooler than the other, the current is automatically decreased; if the animal unit is warmer, the current is increased. With appropriate controls the amount of heat released in the two chambers may be almost perfectly balanced, with the result that a record of the current flow and voltage across the heating unit becomes a record of the animal's heat production during that interval. (A correction must be made, of course, for storage of heat.)

Another method utilizes thermocouples to measure the temperature gradient between two boxes, one inside the other, with the animal in the center (Fig. 551). Rate of heat transfer from one box to another is equal to the thermal gradient, multiplied by a constant which depends upon the material in the boxes, their distance apart, the substance between them, their size, etc. The constant is determined empirically by burning within the calorimeter a measured quantity of a substance with a known heat of combustion while the resulting thermal gradient is recorded. Once this constant is deter-

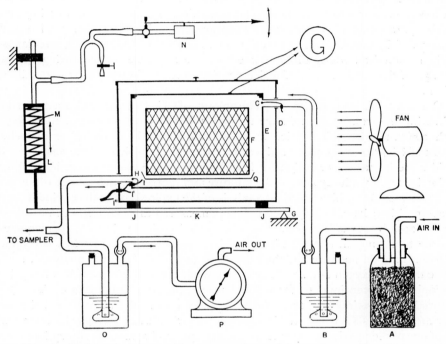

FIG. 551. Radiation calorimeter, with apparatus for studying exchange of respiratory gases and for recording activity. A, Soda lime bottle; B, H_2SO_4 bottle; C, thermocouple in air inlet; D, outer shell of calorimeter; E, inner shell; F, wire cage for animal; G, fulcrum for activity recorder; H, thermocouple in air exit; I, I', I'', thermocouple leads from animal and inner and outer shells, respectively; J, rubber insulators; K, activity platform; L, rubber tubing; M, coil spring; N, tambour for activity recorder; O, H_2SO_4 bottle; P, air flowmeter. (From Prouty et $al.$, $Rev.$ $sci.$ $Instrum.$, 1949, 20:357–363.)

mined it can be utilized to calculate an unknown rate of heat production from the thermal gradient which it creates. Even more convenient is a calorimeter in which a material such as Fiberglas is used as the gradient layer between the two sets of thermocouples. A calorimeter of this type recently designed for use with monkeys or dogs gives accurate estimations of heat production in intervals as short as 15 minutes.[11]

Indirect Calorimetry. Energy released within the body also can be calculated from the rate of elimination of the end-products of the oxidations. Three types of end-products are taken into account, carbon dioxide, water and nitrogen-containing compounds (chiefly urea) derived from protein. The small amount of water produced is difficult to identify, however; a more convenient measurement is therefore used in its place, that of oxygen consumption. The composition and the amount of each type of compound in the metabolic mixture can be determined by measuring intake of oxygen, output of carbon dioxide and excretion of nitrogen.

Nitrogen output is measured by analysis of urine, since practically all nitrogen derived from oxidation of protein is eliminated from the body via the kidneys. Chemical analysis of proteins shows them to be approximately 16 per cent nitrogen; the urinary nitrogen multiplied by 6.25 therefore gives the weight of the protein utilized in the interval represented by the urine specimen. From this quantity, the calories derived from protein are obtained by multiplying by 4.3 kcal. per gm. of protein (a figure a bit higher than that used in dietetics); the quantities of oxygen used and of carbon dioxide formed in protein metabolism are calculated from combining weights, using the empirical formula for a typical protein in an equation where oxidation yields carbon dioxide, water and urea. If the subject was resting and fasting all of the energy from the protein must have been converted into heat. There remains the problem of estimating the rates of carbohydrate and fat metabolism. They are determined from the total respiratory exchanges of O_2 and CO_2, less the calculated amounts of O_2 and CO_2 associated with protein metabolism. Many different methods are available for measuring the rate of exchange of these gases, most of which are reviewed by DuBois,[8] Comroe,[6] Lilly[12] and Carlson.[4]

CARBON DIOXIDE PRODUCTION. The amount of CO_2 given off is frequently estimated by drawing the expired gas mixture through tubes or chambers containing chemicals which combine with this particular gas. "Soda lime" is frequently employed. The amount of CO_2 taken up is determined from the gain in weight of the absorbent if it is a solid material (after correction for loss of water in the reaction) or, if an absorbing solution is used, by adding acid to the mixture and measuring the volume of the evolved gas. Other methods utilize chemical analysis of the expired gas to determine its percentage composition; its volume per unit time is measured after collection in a spirometer or a collapsible (Douglas) bag. The product of (volume/time) $\times$ (percentage/100) gives the total amount of CO_2 eliminated during the collection period. (Oxygen concentration may be measured at the same time the CO_2 content is analyzed, and from the two the total oxygen uptake can be determined, as noted below.) Still other principles are employed in continuous flow methods; here, also, the volume of expiratory gas is measured, but continuously as a rate of flow, by means of an instrument similar to a water meter. The CO_2 concentration may be recorded simultaneously by taking advantage of one of the physical properties of the gas, such as its infrared absorption, electrical conductivity, light refraction or thermal conductivity. In some instances, mass spectroscopy is utilized for this purpose. The instruments needed for these methods are more costly than those used in older techniques, but they may be more accurate, are usually more convenient, and provide a continuous record which cannot be obtained by other means.

OXYGEN CONSUMPTION. Oxygen consumption may be estimated by four techniques, three of which are suitable for use with human subjects. The fourth is reserved for studies on small animals.

(i) Using the Benedict-Roth apparatus or the Krogh apparatus, the subject breathes from and into a system which includes a spirometer ("breathing chamber," Fig. 552). The amount of oxygen used may be calculated either from the changing volume of the spirometer or by measuring the amount of oxygen which must be added to restore the initial volume of the system. As the apparatus is now used, the former measurement is employed; in the Atwater-Rosa-Benedict respiration calorimeter, however, a cylinder of oxygen was weighed before and after the original volume of the system had been restored.

(ii) With a spirometer or a Douglas bag, the oxygen consumption may be estimated simultaneously during the carbon dioxide analysis described above. All exhaled gas is collected for a given period and later analyzed in order to determine its concentration of oxygen, nitrogen and carbon dioxide. Since nitrogen is a passive gas in respiration, the total amount of nitrogen in the bag must equal the nitrogen of the inspired air. From the volume of the exhaled air and its nitrogen content, therefore, the volume of inspired air may be calculated arithmetically. The amount of oxygen in the inspired air may then be calculated by multiplying volume by concentration; subtracting the amount of oxygen in the exhaled air gives the oxygen uptake of the subject.

(iii) The oxygen uptake may be recorded by continuously analyzing expired air and measuring its rate of elimination. Theoretically, both CO_2 and O_2 concentrations should be determined and the calculation of oxygen uptake made as in (ii), above. Accuracy sufficient for most purposes, however, can be obtained from the O_2 analysis

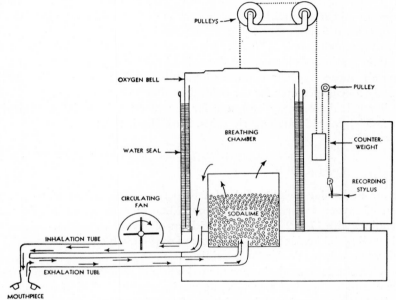

FIG. 552.   Sanborn apparatus (modified Benedict apparatus) for direct estimation of human oxygen consumption.

and the volume measurement, if the subject is breathing room air.[4] The oxygen concentration is usually determined by use of a Pauling meter,[17] which measures the paramagnetic effect of the oxygen as it passes through an analyzer. Students familiar with the principle of operation of a mass spectrometer will realize that it, too, may be used for determination of oxygen concentration or, for that matter, the concentration of any gas in a mixture.

(iv) The oxygen consumption of small animals may be estimated gravimetrically in an apparatus originally designed by Haldane. The animal is placed in a chamber through which a current of dry, carbon dioxide-free air is drawn. As the air leaves the chamber it is passed over chemicals which remove the carbon dioxide and water added to it by the animal. The chamber (containing the animal) and the carbon dioxide and water absorption tubes are weighed at the beginning and again at the end of the experiment. It is evident that the system as a whole can gain weight only by the process of oxygen uptake in the lungs—oxygen which is eventually combined with carbon and hydrogen to form the carbon dioxide and water absorbed from the outgoing air. The oxygen consumption is equal, therefore, to the final weight of the animal plus CO_2 plus H_2O, minus the initial weight of the animal. In this way the oxygen uptake is determined without knowledge of the volume of either the incoming or the outgoing air, provided that no CO_2 or H_2O enters or leaves the system as a whole.

Calorific value of oxygen: respiratory quotient. Oxygen reacts with carbohydrate, protein or fat in certain definite proportions with the formation of a definite quantity of carbon dioxide and water. In the oxidation of glucose, the relationships among the four substances are expressed by this equation:

$$C_6H_{12}O_6 + 6O_2 \rightarrow 6CO_2 + 6H_2O$$

One gram-molecular weight of glucose (180 grams) combines with six times the gram-molecular weight of oxygen (192 grams) to form 264 grams of carbon dioxide and 108 grams of water. The oxygen and carbon dioxide each have a volume of approximately 22.4×6, or 134.4 liters; therefore 1 gram of glucose reacts with $134.4 \div 180$, or 0.75 liter of oxygen to form an equal volume of carbon dioxide. Since the reaction liberates 3.74 kcal. of heat, it follows that 1 liter of oxygen is the equivalent of $3.74 \div 0.75$, or 5 kcal. of heat when glucose is oxidized. One gram of starch or glycogen liberates slightly more heat than 1 gram of glucose, but the oxidation of starch or glycogen also requires proportionately more oxygen; consequently, the calorific value of oxygen remains approximately 5 kcal. per liter for the oxidation of any carbohydrate.

A similar calculation may be made for the reaction in which a typical fat, the glyceride of oleic, palmitic and stearic acids, is oxidized, thus:

$$\begin{matrix} C_{15}H_{31}COO \\ C_{17}H_{35}COO \\ C_{17}H_{33}COO \end{matrix} \Big\rangle C_3H_5 + 78O_2 \longrightarrow 55CO_2 + 52H_2O$$

Here, a gram-molecular weight of the fat (860 grams) combines with 22.4×78, or 1747.2 liters of oxygen to form 22.4×55, or 1232.0 liters of carbon dioxide; therefore, 1 gram combines with $1747.2 \div 860$, or 2.03 liters of oxygen to form 1.43 liters of carbon dioxide, liberating 9.5 kcal. of heat; or 1 liter of oxygen is the equivalent of $9.5 \div 2.03$, or 4.7 kcal. when this particular fat is oxidized.

Although a similar calculation for the oxidation of protein is more difficult because of its more complex chemical structure, approximately 0.97 liter of oxygen is believed to be required per gram of protein, with the formation of 0.78 liter of carbon dioxide and the liberation of 4.3 kcal. of heat; or, 1 liter of oxygen is the equivalent of 4.5 kcal. when protein is oxidized. If one compares the results of the calculations included in the last three paragraphs, one notices that the ratio of carbon dioxide to oxygen differs for the three classes of foodstuffs. This ratio is called the *respiratory quotient*, and may be written thus:

$$\frac{\text{Vol. of } CO_2}{\text{Vol. of } O_2} = \text{R.Q.}$$

For carbohydrate the respiratory quotient is always 1.0, for fat about 0.70, and for protein about 0.80. Table 30 summarizes these data.

TABLE 30

	CARBOHYDRATE	ANIMAL FAT	ANIMAL PROTEIN
Calories per gm.	3.7 –4.3	9.5	4.3
Liters of CO_2 per gm.	0.75–0.83	1.43	0.78
Liters of O_2 per gm.	0.75–0.83	2.03	0.97
Respiratory quotient	1.00	0.70–0.71	0.80–0.82
Calorific value of 1 liter of O_2	5.0 kcal.	4.7 kcal.	4.5 kcal.

Because the respiratory quotient is based solely upon the rate of exchange of the respiratory gases, the R.Q. may be affected by factors other than those already considered (Fig. 553). Thus, an interference with CO_2 transport such as occurs in acidosis or during hyperventilation very quickly obscures the metabolic significance of the R.Q., because the amount of CO_2 given off in the lungs is then determined largely by the severity of the respiratory irregularity rather than by the composition of the metabolic mixture. Interconversions of foodstuffs similarly affect the R.Q., while certain other reactions of the intermediary metabolism, notably ketogenesis, also alter the CO_2/O_2 ratio. In spite of the possibility of its being influenced by any or all of these factors, however, the respiratory quotient is useful in determining the composition of the metabolic mixture if the measurements upon which it is based are made under well controlled conditions.

When the oxygen consumption, carbon dioxide production and nitrogen excretion of the individual are known, the composition of his metabolic mixture can be determined as follows: the nitrogen excretion is multiplied by 6.25 to give the number of grams of

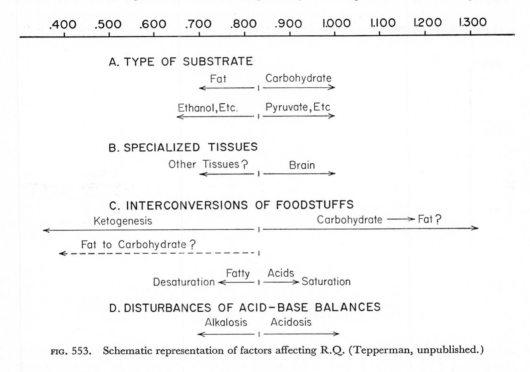

FIG. 553.   Schematic representation of factors affecting R.Q. (Tepperman, unpublished.)

protein oxidized; this in turn is multiplied by 0.97 to give the volume of oxygen, or by 0.78 to give the volume of carbon dioxide involved in protein catabolism. From the total respiratory exchange the oxygen and carbon dioxide of protein metabolism are next subtracted, leaving the amounts of oxygen and carbon dioxide associated with the utilization of carbohydrate and fat. In other words, the total oxygen consumption minus the oxygen utilized in protein oxidation equals the nonprotein oxygen consumption; and the nonprotein carbon dioxide production may be calculated by a similar procedure. From these two there may be obtained the *nonprotein respiratory quotient*, which expresses the relationship between the carbon dioxide and oxygen produced and used, respectively, in the oxidation of fat and carbohydrate. Mathematical analysis of the nonprotein R.Q. will then reveal the amount of fat and of carbohydrate utilized. For example, if the nonprotein R.Q. is near 0.70, it means that only fat has been burned, whereas if the value approaches 1.00, the oxidation of only carbohydrate is suggested. These relationships have been expressed graphically in Figure 554 in such a way that the percentage of oxygen used in carbohydrate catabolism may be read along the abscissa. From this percentage and the total nonprotein oxygen consumption, the volume of oxygen used either in carbohydrate or in fat catabolism may be calculated, and the heat derived from each may be determined by multiplying the volume of oxygen by the calorific value of oxygen for that type of compound. The sum of the two quantities of heat so arrived at, plus the heat derived from the oxidation of protein (see above), is the total heat production as estimated indirectly from the measurement of the respiratory metabolism and nitrogen excretion. The procedure in its entirety is known as *indirect calorimetry*.

Measurement of energy exchange from oxygen consumption. The method of indirect calorimetry was invaluable in proving that living systems are subject to the laws of thermodynamics, and it was useful in assessing the importance of protein as a source of energy. When physicians became interested in the metabolic rate as a test for thyroid dysfunction, however, measurement began to be simplified. DuBois and others found that under standard conditions of resting and fasting the respiratory quotient is approximately 0.82 and the calorific value of oxygen 4.825 kcal. per liter.[8] With these figures the metabolic

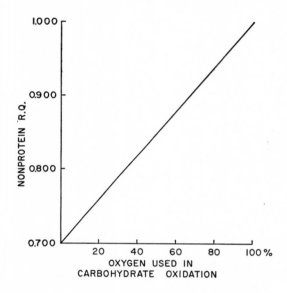

FIG. 554. Linear relationship between nonprotein R. Q. and percentage of the nonprotein oxygen consumption which is used in oxidation of carbohydrate.

rate is now usually calculated from the oxygen consumption alone. In this procedure the energy obtained from protein oxidation is assumed to be approximately one-eighth of the total heat production of a fasting resting subject. Weir[20] has gone a step further in suggesting that the calorific value of the expired air may be used as a constant, with measurement of only its volume. His basis for this suggestion will prove of interest to students interested in quantitative treatment of biologic data.

In summary, the total energy expenditure can be measured by the technique of direct calorimetry, under circumstances where all of the energy is converted to heat because the subject performs no work and accomplishes no energy storage. The amount of energy dissipated as heat can be estimated by the method of indirect calorimetry, in which the amount and the composition of the metabolic mixture are determined from the oxygen consumption, carbon dioxide production, and urinary nitrogen excretion. The results of indirect calorimetry may be expressed in calories because the calorific values of carbohydrate, fat, and protein have been determined experimentally. Interpretation of these results is based upon the chemical theory of combining weights.

Factors Which Affect Metabolic Rate. BODY SIZE. The larger the individual, the greater his energy exchange; large animals eat more and can do more work than small ones, and their heat production is greater even when they are at rest. The increased rate of energy exchange, however, is not directly proportional to their greater body weight, nor to any other single criterion of body size, since the relationship of the two variables is an exponential one.[10] A straight-line relationship can be obtained by plotting the logarithm of weight against the logarithm of heat production (Fig. 555), or by plotting metabolic rate against a power function of body weight, such as the two-thirds or three-fourths power of weight. Investigators usually employ one of these exponents in presenting their data, or else they record both the metabolic rate and the weight of the animal so that the reader can make his own favorite type of correlation.

In medical laboratories the situation is unfortunately complicated by a tradition that the rate of metabolism should be proportional to the surface area. This is an old

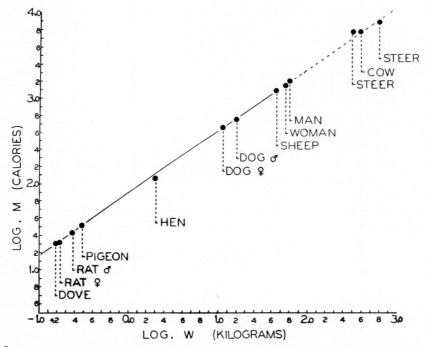

FIG. 555. Log. of metabolism/log. of body weight. (After Kleiber, *Hilgardia*, 1932, 6:315–353.)

idea, based upon the concept that, since warm-blooded animals all have approximately the same body temperature, and since loss of heat occurs mainly at body surfaces, the animals must all produce heat in proportion to the rate of loss, i.e., in proportion to their surface area. One of the first difficulties to arise was the problem of measuring the surface area of an irregularly shaped object such as a human body. DuBois and DuBois[7] eventually solved this problem by covering the surface of the skin with pieces of paper and then measuring the areas of the pieces with a planimeter. They then derived an equation for calculation of area in square meters, from weight in kilograms and height in centimeters, as follows:

$$\text{Area} = \text{weight}^{0.425} \times \text{height}^{0.725} \times 0.007184.$$

The formula is intended to take into account the possibility that the surface area of a tall individual may be no greater—or may even be less—than that of a shorter, stouter person, as well as considering other possible combinations of weight and height. The two measurements necessary are easily secured; from nomograms designed for the purpose the "surface area" is easily derived. Its convenience has led to general use of this method in clinical laboratories in this country.

Meanwhile a vigorous opposition to this clinical habit has arisen among experimental scientists, who have pointed out that the surface where heat is lost is not the same as the surface area of the skin, since the radiating surface is affected by posture and other factors. Further, insulation in the form of hair, wool, feathers or clothing alters the rate of heat loss. For these reasons and others, it now seems desirable to give up the older form of expression and adopt a better one, and the time seems to be approaching when this transition can be made rather easily. Physicians are not utilizing the metabolic rate as much as they did, since more reliable methods are now available for studying the function of the thyroid gland. Eventually they may virtually abandon the procedure, allowing it to revert to the scientists who will then have to agree upon some better form of expression. The search for an acceptable standard of reference has led to attempts to estimate the amount of active tissue in the body, on the inference that most of the variability in weight among adult individuals of a given species is due to accumulation of fat, a relatively inactive tissue in energy exchange. "Lean body mass" is the term given to tissues exclusive of adipose tissues; "active tissue mass" excludes also bone minerals and extracellular fluids. Methods of estimating the size of these fractions of the body are reviewed by Miller.[16] Their usefulness may be summarized somewhat arbitrarily by stating that, when comparison is desired between individuals of different species in a uniform state of energy balance, the exponential function of body weight is a suitable reference standard. If the conditions of energy balance are different, however, especially in comparing individuals within a species where one may be fat and another lean, the lean body mass or the active body mass is more satisfactory. In many instances all of the data should be recorded, including the rate of energy exchange in calories per unit time, the body weight and height, and the percentage composition of the body with reference to fat and protein. Any record that does not include all of these factors may be misleading under certain conditions.

BASAL METABOLIC RATE. The clinical use of data regarding energy exchange is still further complicated by the custom of expressing results, not only in terms of "surface area," but also as a percentage deviation from normal values. As a clinical test the metabolic rate is usually measured in the morning after at least eight hours of sleep, 12 to 14 hours after the most recent meal, with the subject under no stress due to environmental temperature, and under conditions where he has been physically, mentally and emotionally at rest for 30 minutes. The oxygen consumption is measured, and from this the heat production is calculated in kcal. per hour per sq. m. of body surface. The result is subtracted from the standard normal value for patients of that age and sex, divided by the standard value, multiplied by 100, and thus expressed as a percentage above or below the normal level. Standard values were established by Harris and Benedict[9] and by Boothby et al.[2] in their large series of determinations made on normal individuals (Table 31). A basal metabolic rate of +7 signifies a total heat production 7 per cent above the standard average for individuals of that sex and age group. Plus 10 and minus 10 are usually taken as the normal limits since, in a large series, 80 to 90 per cent of the results fall within ±10 per cent of the mean for the group. Expression in percentage may be a convenient procedure, but it sometimes leads to careless thinking because the actual heat production is disregarded once the calculation has been made. In the case of an obese subject, for example, to say that the basal metabolic rate is normal is only to say that heat production has increased in proportion to the increase in "surface area." This tends to obscure the magnitude of the real increase in total heat production—the conversion into heat of perhaps twice as much energy as the normal subject dissipates in this way.

Calories per square meter per hour

AGE	MALES	FEMALES	AGE	MALES	FEMALES
5	(53.0)	(51.6)	20–24	41.0	36.9
6	52.7	50.7	25–29	40.3	36.6
7	52.0	49.3	30–34	39.8	36.2
8	51.2	48.1	35–39	39.2	35.8
9	50.4	46.9	40–44	38.3	35.3
10	49.5	45.8	45–49	37.8	35.0
11	48.6	44.6			
12	47.8	43.4	50–54	37.2	34.5
13	47.1	42.0	55–59	36.6	34.1
14	46.2	41.0			
15	45.3	39.6	60–64	36.0	33.8
16	44.7	38.5	65–69	35.3	33.4
17	43.7	37.4			
18	42.9	37.3	70–74	(34.8)	(32.8)
19	42.1	37.2	75–79	(34.2)	(32.3)

The several factors which influence basal metabolism have been studied extensively.[8] Data published from several different laboratories have shown that basal metabolism is to a certain extent determined by the sex of the individual, in that the fasting, resting energy exchange of women tends to be 6 to 10 per cent lower than that of men of comparable size, but the reason for this difference is not known. The circumstances under which the individual, either male or female, has been living are also important. Basal heat production is lower in subjects who have been maintained on calorically restricted diets than it is in well fed individuals, and acclimatization to either a remarkably cold or a hot environment significantly changes the basal metabolic rate (see below).

Basal metabolism is not the lowest possible energy exchange because during sleep the heat production falls below the "basal" level. The difference, amounting to approximately 10 per cent, is at least partially attributable to a more complete muscular relaxation in sleep. The expression, "basal metabolism," may be applied only to measurements performed when the subject is awake.

GROWTH. Age is another factor to be considered in evaluating the energy exchange of different individuals, since the fasting, resting metabolism increases as the individual grows and matures, and then falls with approaching senility. For his size, the growing youth has a higher metabolic rate than the adult because growth is an energy-expending process (Fig. 556). It is normally accompanied by a hearty "appetite," an increased food consumption or energy intake and, consequently, an elevation of the total metabolism or energy exchange. This elevation is comprised of these three factors: (i) In the form of protoplasm, energy is retained during growth, since every increase in the size and weight of the body represents the laying aside or storage of chemical energy. (ii) Storage takes place in the form of protein, fat and carbohydrates, all of which require for their synthesis the addition of free energy to the system; this energy is ordinarily obtained from oxidative reactions simultaneously carried on in the growing cells. (iii) Free energy liberation and utilization are always accompanied by the loss of a considerable fraction of the energy as heat.

During a short period of fasting like the one required for the measurement of basal metabolic rate, the energy exchange of a growing youth is continued at a high level even though he is losing weight, since the body for a time maintains its usual synthetic reactions at the expense of previously stored materials. An adult does the same but at a lower rate of metabolism. In the growing subject both the anabolism and the catabolism of protein continue at an elevated level during a short fast, so that the stage may be described as one in which the rate of "turnover" of protein and other tissue compounds is higher than in the adult.

FOOD.   Earlier in this chapter the role of food in providing energy for the body was discussed, together with the possibility of storage of energy within the organism. Food also has another important relationship to energy balance, since the resting heat production increases after food is eaten. This means that energy is released less efficiently from

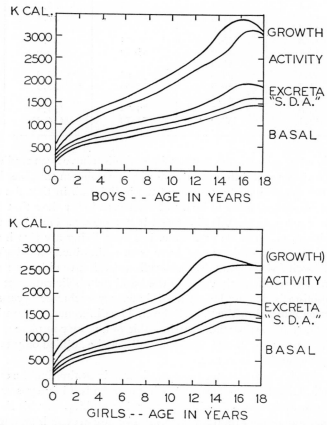

FIG. 556.   Factors contributing to total energy exchange as influenced by age and growth of boys and girls. (From Holt and McIntosh, *Holt's diseases of infancy and childhood*, 11th ed. D. Appleton-Century Co., Inc., 1940.)

foods than from the body's reserves, and that foodstuff energy cannot be substituted calorie for calorie for energy obtained from stored fat, protein or carbohydrate. Rubner in 1885 showed that for each class of foodstuffs a characteristic amount of extra heat is produced; protein food elevates the heat production for a period of some hours by an amount which equals 25 to 30 per cent of the energy value of the protein that was fed, while fat and carbohydrate evoke less marked, but nevertheless appreciable, rises. Suppose that the heat production of a fasting, resting subject is measured and that the subject is then given an amount of protein calorically equal to his total heat production (estimated) for the next four or five hours. If his heat production is recorded while the protein is being catabolized, it will become evident that the protein fails to satisfy his energy requirement because the total energy expenditure rises by about 25 to 30 per cent of the calorific value of the protein. While it is true that the food tends to spare the body's reserves, it is also true that the extra energy spent in the utilization of the food is obtained from those same reserves. And in order completely to prevent the simultaneous oxidation of tissue reserves, the caloric value of protein food must be one-fourth to one-third greater than the basal energy exchange during the time the food will be oxidized. In the case of food made up of carbohydrate or fat, however, a smaller excess will be sufficient.

Unfortunately, there is no general agreement regarding the method of expressing this effect—whether the extra heat in calories should be referred to the caloric value of the food or to some other quantity, such as the resulting extra nitrogen excretion. For this reason there remains some controversy as to whether the magnitude of the effect varies with age, nutritional state, environmental temperature or the conditions of activity of the endocrine glands. The effect of food upon total energy exchange was designated by Rubner as *specific dynamic action*, or S.D.A. Its conciseness recommends the term for general use, especially in the abbreviated form; but the nature of the effect is probably not accurately denoted by these words.

The site of liberation of all of the extra heat cannot be identified, although it has been shown that only an insignificant portion is contributed by the digestive glands and the muscle of the gastrointestinal tract, inasmuch as the specific dynamic action is only slightly diminished when amino acids, for example, are given intravenously rather than orally. Various suggestions have been offered, but experimental results seem to bear out the general theory proposed by Rubner that the excess heat production is the result of intermediary processes of metabolism of the absorbed food. Wilhelmj, Bollman and Mann have shown by experiments on hepatectomized dogs that a large fraction of the heat liberated in the utilization of amino acids is normally produced in the liver, probably in the course of the deamination of the acids and the formation of urea.[21] The heat is so-called free heat, which is not available for the work of the tissues, although it contributes to the heat of the body and may be of some importance in regulation of body temperature.

MUSCULAR EXERCISE.   Another variable of great importance is muscular exercise, which is accompanied by the liberation of energy and heat in muscle cells. Under favorable circumstances the ratio between the heat and the calorific value of the work accomplished may be 4 to 1; or, the efficiency of muscle is about 20 per cent. This compares favorably with the efficiency of a steam engine (10 to 25 per cent) or a gasoline motor (25 per cent). If muscular contractions neither raise an object nor change a momentum, however, their net efficiency may be much less than 20 per cent, and under certain conditions all of the energy ultimately may be dissipated as heat. The energy may then be measured directly in a respiration calorimeter; in this way Benedict[1] showed that the over-all heat production may be increased as much as tenfold during severe muscular exertion (Table 32). In the liberation of this heat or in doing work, an equivalent amount of either foodstuff or reserve chemical energy is utilized by the muscles, and the oxygen consumption and carbon dioxide production rise proportionately. One result of this elevated energy exchange is that a subject who increases his activity requires more food if his energy balance is to be maintained.

ENVIRONMENTAL TEMPERATURE.   Heat produced by muscular activity may or may not be advantageous to the body, depending largely on the environmental temperature at that time. In a warm environment where the body already has all of the heat it needs, muscular exertion presents a serious problem in heat dissipation; but, in the cold, the heat of muscular contraction materially aids in the maintenance of the normal body temperature, and mammals possess a physiologic mechanism—shivering—which operates in cold environments to provide heat by this means. Shivering brings about an

*TABLE 32.   AVERAGE NORMAL OUTPUT OF CARBON DIOXIDE AND
HEAT FROM THE BODY*

CONDITIONS OF MUSCULAR ACTIVITY	AVERAGE QUANTITIES PER HOUR	
	Carbon Dioxide, Gm.	Heat, KCal.
Man at rest, sleeping	25	65
Man at rest, awake, sitting up	35	100
Man at light muscular exercise	55	170
Man at moderately active muscular exercise	100	290
Man at severe muscular exercise	150	450
Man at very severe muscular exercise	210	600

abrupt rise in oxygen consumption, heat production, and over-all energy exchange, but it is not the only reaction through which the metabolic rate is affected by temperature, since, in some animals at least, exposure to cold increases the *basal* oxygen consumption entirely apart from the shivering reaction. This elevation of the basal metabolic rate develops gradually during cold exposure, and is associated with histologic changes in the thyroid gland which indicate that the thyroid is hyperactive, liberating into the blood stream an unusually large amount of its hormone. The hormone in turn acts upon the cells of the body to enhance their rate of heat production.

Magnus-Levy[15] was the first to find that patients with thyroid disease exhibit characteristic alterations in their fasting, resting oxygen consumption, and the basal metabolic rate has been widely used as an aid in making diagnoses of thyroid dysfunction. In hyperthyroidism the basal oxygen consumption may be increased by as much as 75 per cent, whereas hypothyroidism may be accompanied by rates of minus 20 to minus 40. Correction of the thyroid abnormality by appropriate medical or surgical treatment allows the basal metabolic rate to return to a normal level. As one might expect, either type of thyroid abnormality may be accompanied by a deficit of temperature regulation; hyperthyroidism with its high level of heat production makes the patient uncomfortable in the summer; hypothyroidism causes discomfort in cold winter weather.

FEVER.   Many of the pathologic alterations of total energy exchange encountered clinically are related in one way or another to the normal variations already described. Fever, or elevation of body temperature, however, brings into play a factor as yet unmentioned here. In the laboratory it can easily be shown that the speed of a chemical reaction varies with its temperature in such a way that the rate is approximately doubled for each elevation of 10° C. When the body temperature rises above the normal level, an increase in the rate of its basic reactions is therefore to be expected. With the onset of fever there is an increase in heat production in skeletal muscles analogous to shivering— a "shaking chill." This muscular activity is accompanied by a decrease in the rate of heat loss resulting from cutaneous vasoconstriction and suppression of sweating. Together these mechanisms increase the heat content of the body and, hence, the mean body temperature, and thereby enhance still further the over-all rate of heat production.

REFERENCES

1. BENEDICT, F. G. *Science*, 1915, *42*:75–84.
2. BOOTHBY, W. M., BERKSON, J. and DUNN, H. L. *Amer. J. Physiol.*, 1936, *116*:468–484.
3. BRODY, S. *Bioenergetics and growth.* New York, Reinhold Publishing Corporation, 1945.
4. CARLSON, L. D. *Meth. med. Res.*, 1954, *6*:60–73.
5. CLARK, W. M. *Topics in physical chemistry*, 2nd ed. Baltimore, Williams & Wilkins Company, 1952.
6. COMROE, J. H., JR. *Meth. med. Res.*, 1950, *2*:122–131.
7. DUBOIS, D. and DUBOIS, E. F. *Arch. intern. Med.*, 1916, *17*:863–871.

8. DuBois, E. F. *Basal metabolism in health and disease*, 3rd ed. Philadelphia, Lea & Febiger, 1936.

9. Harris, J. A. and Benedict, F. G. *A biometric study of basal metabolism in man.* Washington, Carnegie Institution of Washington, Publ. 279, 1919.

10. Kleiber, M. *Physiol. Rev.*, 1947, 27:511–541.

11. Lawton, R. W., Prouty, L. R. and Hardy, J. D. *Rev. sci. Instrum.*, 1954, 25:370–377.

12. Lilly, J. C. *Meth. med. Res.*, 1950, 2:131–138.

13. Lipmann, F. *Adv. Enzymol.*, 1941, 1:99–162.

14. Long, C. N. H. *Ann. N. Y. Acad. Sci.*, 1943, 43:364–426.

15. Magnus-Levy, A. *Z. klin. Med.*, 1897, 33:269–314.

16. Miller, A. T., Jr. *Meth. med. Res.*, 1954, 6:74–84.

17. Pauling, L., Wood, R. E. and Sturdivant, J. H. *Science*, 1946, 103:338.

18. Rubner, M. *S. B. bayer, Akad. Wiss.*, 1885, 15:452–461.

19. Rubner, M. *Z. biol.*, 1894, 30:73–142.

20. Weir, J. B. de V. *J. Physiol.*, 1949, 109:1–9.

21. Wilhelmj, C. M. *Physiol. Rev.*, 1935, 15:202–220.

CHAPTER 49

Regulation of Energy Exchange

By JOHN R. BROBECK

THE common observation that men and women reach a plateau of body weight when they become young adults suggests some kind of natural balancing of energy gain and energy output which tends to stabilize the size of energy reserves. This stabilization occurs because the body has mechanisms for control of food intake, activity, heat production and heat loss. Such control is spoken of as a regulation, because it tends to preserve a given variable at a constant level under a given set of conditions, and because it alters the variable when changes occur in the environment or within the body.

Perhaps the clearest example of regulation is body temperature, and it is also the best understood. One can easily identify the mechanisms by which heat production is either increased or decreased and those by which heat loss is enhanced or diminished. All of these mechanisms are controlled by the central nervous system. Through the functioning of specialized cells sensitive to heat, the brain is given information about the temperature of the inside and the surface of the body. This information (and related information about other physiologic variables) is integrated by the brain into a control pattern typical of the situation, and heat loss and production are adjusted to achieve a certain mean body temperature. In many circumstances these adjustments are amazingly well suited to the conditions, so that the central body temperature deviates very little.

The mechanisms regulating body temperature are used as a model for study and description of other regulations. The model can also be applied to regulation of food intake and activity, but these two variables are not as constant as body temperature and less is known about the control systems. Nevertheless, food intake is considered first here because it is the only energy source; temperature, activity and energy storage then follow as variables in energy disposition.

REGULATION OF FOOD INTAKE

Sensations of hunger and satiety cannot be studied in laboratory animals because both terms imply a subjective experience or "feeling" which can be verified only in humans. In the laboratory, however, an animal's food intake can be measured directly, experimental conditions can be controlled and altered individually, and by measuring the amount of food ingested per unit time, one may draw conclusions regarding the function of mechanisms which normally impel the animal to eat more or less as circumstances may require. From this type of study, the following relationships have been established: (i) Within certain limits, the common laboratory animals can compensate for periods of food deprivation by increasing their intake when food is again made available. (ii) Animals forced to run eat more than do inactive controls. (iii) Normal, immature animals increase their food intake as growth occurs. (iv) Hypophysectomy depresses food intake and growth. (v) Injection of anterior lobe extracts, which cause nitrogen retention, increases food intake in intact as well as hypophysectomized animals. (vi) Insulin increases food intake when administered before feeding time. (vii) Depancreatized animals with the hyperglycemia and glycosuria of "pancreatic" diabetes eat large amounts of food. (viii) Administration of thyroid preparations enhances food intake; (ix) thyroidectomy depresses feeding by about 20 per cent at the usual room temperatures. (x) Food intake is lower during estrus than during diestrus, and (xi) increases during lactation. (xii) In cold environments food consumption rises; (xiii) in hot environments it falls below normal levels. (xiv) During fever the food intake is spontaneously depressed (in human subjects as well as in experimental animals). (xv) Animals and patients whose stomachs have been denervated or even completely removed eat the same amount of food as normal controls, although their feeding habits may be changed in such a way that they eat smaller amounts but eat more often.

Most of these observations apply to human subjects as truly as to experimental animals, but data obtained in the laboratory are more impressive than clinical results because human "appetite" is influenced by a multitude of factors, including mental or psychic attitudes, which either do not exist or can be fairly well controlled in the lower animals.

With the exception of fever and, possibly, insulin hypoglycemia, all of the experimental conditions enumerated above are alike in that each of them represents a change in the rate of energy expenditure to which the animal responds with an alteration of food intake. During recovery from fasting, during growth or nitrogen retention, lactation, cold exposure, exercise, pancreatic diabetes, experimental hyperthyroidism and, possibly, hyperinsulinism, the energy requirement of the animal is enhanced; *hyperphagia* or increased food intake therefore appears to be a compensatory process. And the decreased food intake of exposure to warm environments or following hypophysectomy or thyroidectomy similarly reflects the diminished energy requirements of the animal in question. The significance of these adjustments in maintaining energy balance does not need further comment. Only during fever is the food intake *decreased* while the total energy expenditure is *increased* above normal levels.

There is another condition characterized by increased food intake, hypothalamic obesity, induced by clinical or experimental lesions in the hypothalamus. In most experimental animals, the appropriate lesions are made surgically, but in mice they can be made by injection of gold thioglucose.[11, 23] These animals eat large quantities of food—as much as two or three times the normal daily intake. Since their rate of energy expenditure is at first not much affected, their hyperphagia upsets the normal equilibrium between intake and output, and the animals are faced with the problem of getting rid of a huge food surplus. They dispose of this by burning some of it and by storing the remainder (the larger portion) as fat, with the result that they eventually become remarkably obese. This condition (Fig. 557) is said to be caused by "hypothalamic hyperphagia." It has been observed in rats, cats, dogs and monkeys, and there is no reason to question its identity with the obesity of human subjects who suffer from tumors, infections or other pathologic processes involving the base of the brain, including the hypothalamus.

The hyperphagia of animals with hypothalamic lesions must be distinguished from all of the other types of hyperphagia enumerated above. In growth, hyperthyroidism and cold exposure, the enhanced food intake is a compensatory response to a condition of altered energy expenditure. Energy equilibrium is not disturbed by the extra food

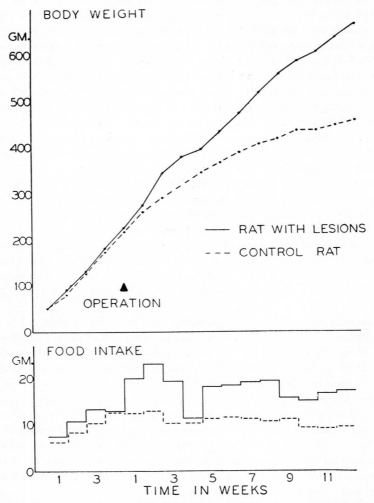

FIG. 557. Effect of appropriate hypothalamic lesions upon food intake and weight gain in the albino rat. (From Brobeck *et al.*, *Yale J. Biol. Med.*, 1943, *15*:831–853.)

but rather is maintained, and the animal's ability to increase its food intake proves that the mechanisms which regulate the energy supply are functioning normally. However, in the animal with hypothalamic lesions, the enhanced food consumption appears to be the result of a basic disturbance in the regulatory mechanisms themselves.

Another kind of feeding disturbance can be induced by injury to the hypothalamus, when the lesions are bilaterally symmetrical and restricted to the lateral hypothalamic area at the level of the median eminence (Fig. 558). Following such injury animals exhibit a complete and prolonged failure of spontaneous feeding, although they have

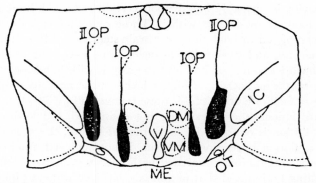

FIG. 558. Transverse section through tuberal region of hypothalamus. Medial lesions (*I OP*) induced hyperphagia and obesity; lateral lesions (*II OP*) abolished feeding. *ME*, Median eminence; *OT*, optic tract; *IC*, internal capsule; *DM*, dorsomedial nucleus; *VM*, ventromedial nucleus; *V*, third ventricle. (From Anand and Brobeck, *Yale J. Biol. Med.*, 1951, *24*:123–140.)

no other obvious abnormalities.[1] They will starve to death with food present in their cages, showing not the slightest interest in the food; yet they may be kept alive and in good condition by intragastric feeding. Electrical stimulation of these regions is followed by a considerable increase in food intake in otherwise normal animals.[9] The lateral hypothalamus evidently contains a mechanism essential for feeding behavior, and it is probably the unopposed activity of this mechanism that causes hyperphagia in animals with lesions in the medial part of the hypothalamus. The medial and lateral mechanisms evidently interact in the normal regulation of feeding.

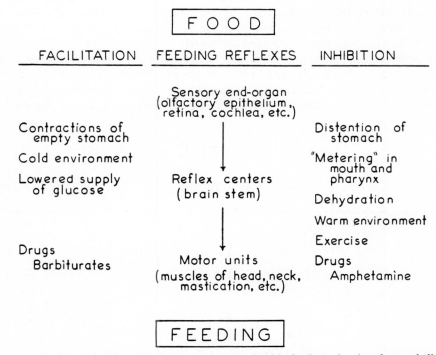

FIG. 559. Diagram of basic reflex pathways concerned with feeding, showing factors believed to facilitate and to inhibit these reflexes.

Feeding behavior is probably based upon certain reflexes initiated by the sight, sound or odor of food, or by contact with it. Those reflexes which do not involve the special senses are completed through the lower brain stem, since Miller and Sherrington[26] observed reflex chewing and swallowing in decerebrate cats. The reflexes causing an animal to move toward a source of food and to grasp it with hands or mouth are more complex, possibly requiring activity of higher levels of the nervous system. The hypothalamus may act to facilitate or to inhibit these reflexes (Fig. 559). If the facilitation is removed by lateral lesions, the reflexes are not completed and feeding is abolished; whereas if the inhibition is removed by more medial lesions, the animals overeat and become obese. Regulation of feeding, however, is not achieved autonomously, but is integrated with other regulations concerned with energy exchange. The hyperactivity preceding the feeding period and that of animals deprived of food (above) seem to be examples of the interaction of these regulations. Other examples will possibly be discovered through further study.

Another topic of some interest is the nature of the changes within the body which are capable of signaling to the brain that feeding has taken place or is necessary. Perhaps one kind of signal increases appetite and diminishes satiety, thereby enhancing food intake. (This same signal may also bring about the increase in generalized or locomotor activity which normally anticipates a feeding period.) Another kind of signal, or the first signal in reverse direction, may indicate that feeding has taken place, that nourishment is on its way to the tissues, and that feeding should cease.

There is no lack of possible reactions in the body that might serve as these signals. Several of the prominent ones are shown in Figure 560. First of all there is the act of eating. Experiments by Janowitz and Grossman[17] have revealed that in chewing and swallowing food a certain degree of satiation is produced, even if the food does not reach the stomach. Filling the stomach is another important reaction that has been studied by several investigators, including Carlson.[7] Mayer's experiments have implied some relationship to blood sugar levels or, better, to the availability of glucose to the nervous system.[25] Other studies have emphasized the correlation between thirst and hunger and also the relationship between feeding and the conditions of temperature regulation. Perhaps the list should be extended to include the products of digestion. The function of the nervous system is to integrate all of these changes—and any others yet unknown— into a common denominator, the activity of neurons responsible for finding food and eating it.

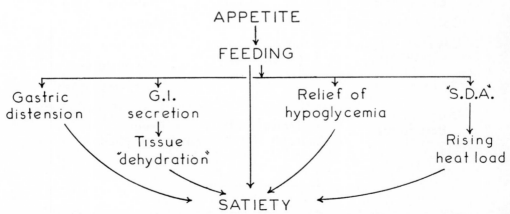

FIG. 560. Outline of factors known to play a part in converting *appetite* into *satiety*. The process of eating, itself, is one such factor; others include the reactions and mechanisms listed on the diagram.

REGULATION OF MOTOR OUTPUT

Measurement of Locomotor Activity.   The measurement of motor output requires the use of apparatus specifically adapted to the type of activity in question.
Experimental animals ordinarily do not accomplish "work" as man does, but they do
use food energy for muscular contractions, especially those contractions by means of
which they move from one place to another. With appropriate apparatus this locomotor
activity can be measured and may be taken, in the words of Slonaker,[33] "as an indicator
of all of the activities of an individual. Numerous observations of the activities of the rat
readily convince one of the fact that though running is only one phase of activity, it goes
hand in hand with and is proportional to the other activities."

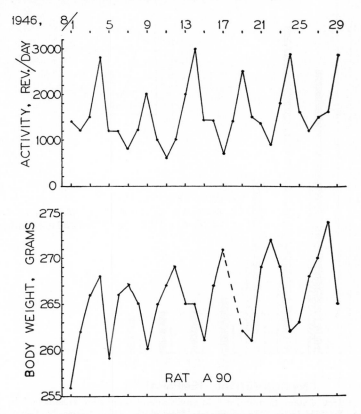

FIG. 561.   Rhythms of activity and body weight. Weight gain occurs during diestrus, weight loss
during estrus. (From Brobeck *et al.*, *Endocrinology*, 1947, *40*:65–72.)

NORMAL ACTIVITY RHYTHMS.   A convenient and widely used device for measuring
locomotion is called the "activity cage"; it consists either of a table or a wide wheel
which rotates freely on a bearing-suspended shaft. A counter records each revolution as
the animal turns the cage on its axis. Beside the "activity" cage there is usually a small
"living" cage in which food and water are provided. With this type of apparatus some
of the factors which influence motor output have been discovered. Wang[35] and Slonaker[34]
have shown that the sex cycle of the female definitely affects spontaneous activity, since,
on the day of estrus, rats run eight or ten times as much as on the intervening days of
their cycle (Fig. 561). Ovariectomy abolishes this estral hyperactivity, and the implantation of ovaries subsequently restores the response. Male rats fail to show a similar

rhythm, although castrated males with implanted ovaries are said to undergo cyclic changes in activity which suggest the female type of behavior. Richter[29] discovered that both male and female rats accomplish most of their running just before they begin to eat and that the ingestion of food is followed by a period of quiescence.

Browman[6] found that still another rhythm of activity is associated with the diurnal cycle of light and dark. Rats are more active in the dark, and by artificial control of the lighting conditions, the rats can be made to run more during the dark daytime periods than during the lighted nighttime hours. Browman found also that temperature variations tend to influence the activity when the effect of light and dark has been abolished by blinding the animals. His blinded rats ran more in cooler than in warmer environments.

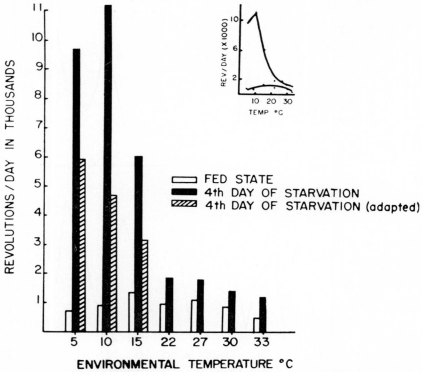

FIG. 562.   Effect of starvation and a cold environment upon spontaneous activity of rats. (From Stevenson, J. A. F., *Cold Injury*, *Third Conference*, New York, Josiah Macy, Jr. Foundation, 1954, pp. 165–168.)

The results of all these experiments can be summarized with the statement that the activity of rats is increased by the dark, in cold environments, during starvation (Fig. 562), just before feeding time and, in the female, during estrus; activity is depressed in the light, in warm environments, after feeding, and during diestrus, pregnancy, pseudopregnancy and lactation. The cause of activity rhythms is not known, and at the present time one cannot say whether each rhythm is unique in its origin or whether all depend upon some common basic mechanism. From a metabolic point of view, their regulation has one distinctive feature, in that at least three of the conditions where hyperactivity occurs are characterized by either an actual or an incipient energy deficit. In cold exposure and during estrus, and in the short interval just before a feeding period, the rat is undergoing a progressive depletion of energy reserves because of either an increased energy output or a limitation of supply. But in the face of this real or threatened deficit, the animal further increases the rate of energy utilization by indulging in the luxury of hyperactivity (Fig. 561). A related phenomenon appears when the food intake is arbitrarily restricted in quantity; on an amount of food which allows a regular gain of body weight by inactive rats, animals free to run in activity cages will exercise enough to bring about a continual weight loss (Fig. 563). Whatever the nature of the mechanisms regulating motor output, it is clear that their function is not directed solely toward the goal of energy balance.

Regulatory Deficits.   In a certain few clinical conditions, one of which is an infectious disease called *encephalitis lethargica*, muscular activity may be reduced even to the point of complete flaccidity of all the voluntary muscles. At autopsy, neurons of the posterior hypothalamus have been found to be damaged or destroyed as the result of the infection, and this observation had led to the opinion that normal activity is maintained in some way by this part of the brain stem. This opinion is supported by studies

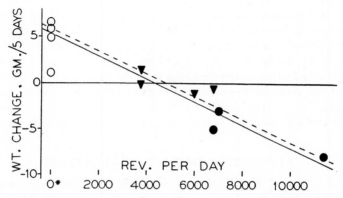

FIG. 563.   Negative correlation between locomotor activity and weight gain in female rats maintained on constant food intake in constant temperature room. *Cages closed to prevent running. (From Brobeck, *Amer. J. Physiol.*, 1945, *143*:1–5.)

on monkeys, cats and rats.[16,27] Animals with experimentally produced discrete lesions of the central and posterior hypothalamus become lethargic and tend to be somnolent; in activity cages the rats may run little or not at all. Ranson suggested that the hypothalamus is a "waking center," and, from his experiments and those of other investigators, one may conclude that this part of the diencephalon participates in some way in the normal regulation of motor output.

Opposed to the lethargy and inactivity of animals with certain hypothalamic lesions is a state of almost continuous locomotion that has been produced in rats, cats and monkeys by the bilateral ablation of portions of the frontal lobes. Animals subjected to this operation move almost constantly about the cage. As Ruch and Shenkin pointed out,[30] the disturbance is not one of generalized irritability and hyperexcitability, because the animals are in other respects docile and quiescent. The operation specifically changes the amount of the animal's locomotion. Ruch and Shenkin produced hyperactivity in monkeys by bilateral lesions in a small area on the orbital surface of the frontal lobes, whereas Davis[3] found hyperactivity only in animals having injury to the tip of the caudate nuclei, which underlie the areas removed by Ruch and Shenkin. These authors further observed that regulation of food intake was normal in their monkeys; in spite of the high level of energy expenditure occasioned by their hyperactivity, the animals lost only a small amount of weight because they ate more food than they had eaten before the operation.

Experimental study suggests, therefore, that at least two levels of the central nervous system participate in the normal regulation of motor output: the hypothalamus and the frontal cortex, especially a specific area on the orbital surface of the frontal lobe. At the present time it is impossible to say whether these two levels function together to bring about the normal rhythms of locomotor activity. It is fairly clear, however, that the energy utilization of normal animals may undergo large quantitative changes because their motor output varies from time to time, and that in certain circumstances these variations may tend to upset rather than preserve energy equilibrium.

In normal man the motor output may vary all the way from the relaxation of deep sleep to the heroic efforts associated with athletic records or deeds of valor. The energy requirements of various types of activity are fairly well known, as are the adjustments in the several functions comprising what is known as the physiology of muscular exercise. Less attention has been given to the regulation of this activity, that is, to the topic which might be called the "willingness" to work. Why are some persons more energetic than others? Why does a team play well one day and poorly another? Under what conditions is the work output the greatest, and what determines the efficiency of the work? All of these questions are of interest, and possibly important, in industry as well as in sports, but few data are available to answer them. A method for conducting research in this field is suggested by the report of Kraut and Muller,[20] who studied the work output of men during the war in Germany when food supplies were limited. Providing extra food increased the work done by the men; but even greater rises in work were induced by offering cigarettes as a reward in place of food. In these men, as in laboratory animals, the regulation of work output was not necessarily directed toward the goal of energy balance.

REGULATION OF BODY TEMPERATURE

Nature of Thermal Equilibrium. Through metabolic reactions every animal produces heat in amounts that depend upon the several factors described in the preceding chapter. Evidence that this heat is lost from the body just about as rapidly as it is produced is found in the relatively constant body temperature of all animals. How the heat is lost, however, differs in the various animals. Birds and mammals are said to be "warm-blooded" or *homothermic* because their body temperature is, within wide limits, independent of environmental temperature. Reptiles, amphibia and fish, on the other hand, are called *poikilothermic* because their abilities to control their body temperature are limited. Their most effective means of protection against thermal stress may be simply to escape from it by burrowing, diving or migration. When environmental temperature is lowered, poikilotherms lose heat and reduce their rate of heat production, since the chemical reactions of the body go slower when body temperature falls. If the environmental temperature is raised, heat is gained by the body and its metabolism is speeded up; the rate is approximately doubled for a rise of 10° C. Birds and mammals, by contrast, actually tend to increase their rate of heat production and decrease their rate of heat loss during cold exposure, whereas in a warm environment their heat production may be minimal while heat loss is enhanced. As will be noted, the activity of skeletal muscle is the principal mechanism for changing heat production; the management of surface temperature (skin temperature in man) is the most important device for adjusting heat loss.

The biochemical reactions responsible for metabolism impose two different requirements upon the mechanisms regulating body temperature. In the first place, most enzymes are sensitive to temperature change, in that a fall of only a few degrees may almost completely inhibit the activity of the enzyme. Unless the body temperature is maintained above a certain minimal level (within a few degrees of 99° F., rectal temperature), metabolism will be so retarded that normal behavior is impossible and death may result. Second, heat is liberated in the course of biologic oxidations, and, unless provision is made for heat dissipation, overheating of the body may occur. This would increase the rate of metabolism and elevate still further the amount of heat formed, thereby laying a heavy work load upon the cells of the cardiovascular and respiratory systems which must distribute foodstuffs and oxygen and remove the products of metabolism. Moreover, at high temperatures (above 106° F.) the cells of the central nervous system cannot function normally, and prostration, coma and even death will ensue as the neurons succumb to the effects of the heat. Tissue proteins in general are heat-sensitive compounds, and the enzymes, in particular, become irreversibly inactivated when subjected to heat. For the continuation of metabolic processes, therefore, the body temperature must be high enough for a certain rate of enzymatic activity and yet not so high as to inactivate the enzymes, including those of the central nervous system.

Since temperature regulation is sometimes a problem of warming and sometimes a question of cooling, one is not surprised to find that there is an environmental temperature at which both of those problems are least difficult to solve. When an unclothed man or a laboratory animal is at rest in the postabsorptive state, a normal body temperature is most easily maintained at a room temperature of about 86° F. (30° C.). The individual is then able to lose to the environment all of the heat formed by his basal metabolic processes, retaining only the amount which comprises normal storage without calling upon any of the reserve mechanisms of heat loss. At this temperature, however, it is not possible to dispose of the extra heat produced during muscular exercise or during the assimilation of food unless some accessory method of heat loss is utilized. For everyday living, man is more comfortable in environments somewhat cooler than 86° F., where he can easily dissipate in his clothed condition the heat he produces in excess of his basal output.

Measurement of Heat Content and Heat Transfer. In speaking of the constancy of body temperature, the adjective "relatively" is used to indicate that this variable is not fixed at a given value. Temperature varies from time to time, and it is not uniform throughout the body. Spontaneous variations are naturally greatest in the more exposed parts of the body, the skin and extremities, and least in the interior. The temperature of the rectum, therefore, is more nearly constant than that of any other part of the body where temperature can be measured conveniently. Within the mouth the temperature is more variable, being affected by eating or drinking hot or cold food or fluid, by mouth breathing, and by air temperature, smoking and other factors. Whereas 98.6° and 99.6° F. are often considered to be the normal oral and rectal temperatures respectively, it is better to speak of normal ranges of temperature—98 to 99° F. for the mouth and 99 to 100° F. for the rectum.

The temperature of the body shows a diurnal rhythm and is affected by the manner of living, time of meals, and the sleeping and waking cycle. In general, one can say that the lowest temperatures are recorded about six or seven o'clock in the morning and the highest levels about 12 hours later; there is then a gradual decrease during the night. The difference between maximum and minimum may amount to a degree or more centigrade. Age is also an important factor, since infants and young children may have normal temperatures as much as a degree higher than those of adults. Because it is the site of heat loss under most environmental conditions, man's skin is somewhat cooler than the interior of his body. At indoor temperatures (70° F., 21° C.), the temperature of the skin of the forehead is about 91.5° F., but varies with air temperature, rate of air movement, nature of the clothing, etc. Skin temperature is different from place to place on the surface of the body, the skin of the extremities being cooler than that of the trunk (Fig. 564). In those portions of the body interposed between the cooler surface and the warmer depths, the temperature is intermediate and variable, changing whenever the gradient between the deep and surface temperature is altered.

Transfer of heat by either conduction or radiation occurs only along a thermal gradient, from a warmer to a cooler object. To estimate the rate of heat loss from the body it is sometimes necessary to measure this gradient by determining the over-all surface temperature. Similarly, to determine the rate of heat exchange between the depths and the surface of the body, both interior and surface temperatures may be required. Although these cannot be measured exactly because of the variability already noted, physiologists have developed conventions and arbitrary definitions that permit them to handle these variables in a quantitative fashion.[14] One of these is the concept of "mean" surface temperature, where each part of the body is assumed to contribute to the surface temperature in proportion to its own surface area. A common method of

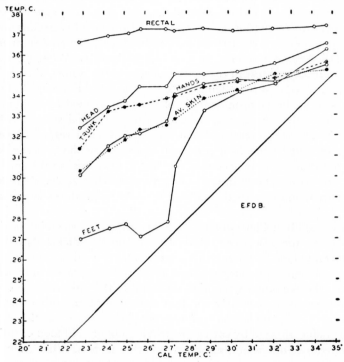

FIG. 564.   Skin and rectal temperatures of a subject during basal experiments at different environmental temperatures. (From DuBois, *Bull. N. Y. Acad. Med.*, 1939, *15*:143–173.)

calculating this mean is to measure the skin temperatures of the head, arms, hands, feet, legs, thighs and trunk. Each temperature is then multiplied by the percentage of skin which it represents, and the resulting values are added; thus:

$$\text{Mean skin temperature} = (.07\ T_{head} + .14\ T_{arms} + .05\ T_{hands} + .07\ T_{feet} + .13\ T_{legs} + .19\ T_{thighs} + .35\ T_{trunk})$$

Knowing the mean skin temperature, one can calculate the mean body temperature if he assumes that the rectal temperature represents the temperature of two-thirds of the body and the skin temperature that of the other third.

$$\text{Mean body temperature} = (0.67 \times \text{rectal temp.}) + (0.33 \times \text{skin temp.})$$

This quantity is useful in deciding whether heat has been stored within the body. The amount of heat gained or lost is equal to the change in mean body temperature multiplied by the specific heat of the body and the body's mass.

$$\text{Heat storage} = \text{temp. change} \times \text{specific heat} \times \text{mass}$$

Two of these terms can be measured with reasonable accuracy—temperature change and mass. Specific heat is more difficult to estimate; but, since it is nearly constant, at least in short experiments, its possible variability is not important. A value of 0.83 gcal. per gm. per degree C. is often used.

With the equation for mean skin temperature it is possible to calculate another variable, heat conductance within the body. This is defined as the coefficient of heat transfer from the depths to the surface of the body, or the rate of heat exchange divided by the difference between the internal temperature and the mean skin temperature, as follows:

$$\text{Conductance} = \frac{\text{rate of heat transfer}}{\text{rectal temp.} - \text{mean skin temp.}}$$

As ordinarily calculated, this has the dimensions of kcal. per hr. per degree C., referring to the whole body conductance. With the body in any given state of thermal equilibrium, neither gaining nor decreasing in net heat content, the rate of heat transfer equals metabolic rate, and can be so measured (see Chap. 48).

Heat Production.   Heat production is lowest during sleep, somewhat higher when the subject is awake but fasting and resting, and shows characteristic elevations after the ingestion of food and during and after muscular exercise (see Chap. 48). Muscular contractions are attended by the liberation of relatively large amounts of heat, and it is a part of everyone's experience that work or some other muscular activity will counteract the effect of outside cold. Stamping the feet, swinging the arms, and slapping the hands are familiar means of warming the extremities on cold days. These procedures increase the blood flow and therefore the temperature of the part in question, but they also elevate the total heat production. Shivering is another reaction which accomplishes the same result, since the basal heat production may be more than doubled by this involuntary activity of skeletal muscles. In normal animals, shivering always tends to maintain temperature equilibrium, and the animal shivers only when hypothermia threatens. Voluntary exercise, on the other hand, may either preserve or disturb the equilibrium, depending upon the environmental conditions at the time the exercise is carried out. On a cold day the heat so produced contributes to the maintenance of body temperature, but on a hot day exercise multiples the problems of adequate heat dissipation.

For many years physiologists have been attempting to prove or disprove the hypothesis that the rate of heat production can be changed by mechanisms which do not involve the contraction of skeletal muscles. Small experimental animals like the rat are evidently able to vary their rate of heat production in the space of a few hours by some mechanism in which the hormones of the thyroid gland, the adrenal cortex and, possibly, the adrenal medulla participate without any obvious change in either voluntary or involuntary muscular activity. The hormones secreted by these glands apparently promote metabolic reactions producing heat when normal animals are exposed to cold. Whether a similar reaction takes place in man is still undecided; man protects himself against cold by clothing and artificial heat, with the result that alterations in the rate of physiologic heat production are less important than they are in the lower animals. Such alterations are known to occur, however, upon prolonged exposure to unusual environmental temperatures; they then are considered to be a part of the reaction pattern known as "acclimatization."

Heat Loss.   PHYSICAL PROCESSES.   Heat is normally lost from the body by three physical processes, radiation, conduction and the vaporization of water, the relative importance of which varies with environmental conditions. DuBois and Hardy estimated that under experimental conditions in the laboratory, with external temperatures of 70 to 80° F., loss by radiation constitutes 60 to 65 per cent of the total and the loss by evaporation about 20 to 30 per cent.[12] These figures change greatly, of course, with variations in external temperature, as indicated in Figure 565, which represents results obtained by DuBois and his coworkers upon a nude subject, in "basal" condition, exposed to varying temperatures while in a respiration calorimeter. At low temperatures, radiation is the main factor in heat dissipation, whereas at temperatures of 34 to 35° C. (93 to 95° F.) radiation and conduction decrease and heat loss is effected only through vaporization. The data of Table 33, compiled by Rubner * from experiments made upon a fasting dog, illustrate the same general phenomena in another species.

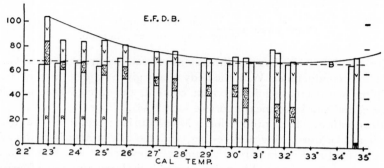

FIG. 565.   Changes in heat production and heat loss in nude male subject, in basal condition, at varying external temperatures. Blank columns to left indicate heat production; columns to right, heat elimination; V, vaporization; C, convection; R, radiation. The figures along the ordinate indicate calories per hour, those along the abscissa the temperature, centigrade. (From DuBois, *Bull. N. Y. Acad. Med.*, 1939, Ser. 2, *15*:143–173.)

Radiation is the transfer of heat from the surface of one object to that of another without physical contact between the two. It can be accomplished only when a temperature gradient exists between the two objects, but when the transfer is in progress the temperature gradient tends to disappear as the warmer object loses and the cooler object gains heat. The body radiates heat to every relatively cool object near it—the furnishings of a room and its floor, walls and ceiling, the ground, pavement, buildings, bodies of water, or any other natural or artificial surface. Radiation may be a hindrance in physiologic temperature regulation because it may transfer heat in a direction disadvantageous to the body. When surrounding objects are able to radiate heat to the body because they are warmer than the surface of the skin, the heat usually is not needed because the basal heat production equals or exceeds the need of the moment; and in a cool environment when the body needs to conserve heat, this heat may be lost to cooler objects in the vicinity. In the experiment of DuBois and his coworkers, for example, at an environmental temperature of 23° C. a large amount of heat which the body could ill afford to lose was lost by radiation, but at a temperature of 34° C. there was virtually

TABLE 33.   HEAT LOSS IN FASTING DOG

TEMPERATURE	CALORIES LOST BY RADIATION AND CONDUCTION	CALORIES LOST BY EVAPORATION	TOTAL CALORIES OF METABOLISM
7° C.	78.5	7.9	86.4
15	55.3	7.7	63.0
20	45.3	10.6	55.9
25	41.0	13.2	54.2
30	33.2	23.0	56.2

* Lusk gave a good account of Rubner's many contributions to the study of metabolism.[21]

no loss by radiation (Fig. 565). There are exceptions to this generalization, it is true; radiant heat from the sun reflected from the surface of the snow enables one to ski in clothing of light weight even when the temperature of the air is fairly low, and the temperature of radiating surfaces can be artificially controlled by means of a heating or cooling system, in order to facilitate rather than to hinder the process of temperature regulation.

Conduction is a less important means of heat loss; it includes the transfer of heat to any substance in contact with the body—the air which covers the skin, the clothing, the tidal air which is warmed in the respiratory passages and the lungs, and the foodstuffs and water taken into the gastrointestinal tract, in addition to other physical objects with which contact is made from time to time. Here again the direction of heat transfer usually tends to oppose the body's need; cool air cools the body further, and hot air intensifies the problem of heat dissipation. By artificially regulating the temperature of the ambient air, the situation can be improved; air conditioning units operate on this principle, providing warm air in the winter and cool air in the summer in order to minimize and to promote heat loss, respectively. (They also cool objects in the environment, and thus make possible a loss by radiation.) Still a third physical process, vaporization of water, removes heat from the surface of the skin and the respiratory tract because 1 gram of water takes up something more than 0.6 kcal. from its surroundings when it passes from the liquid to the vapor state at a temperature of about 33° C. under physiologic conditions.[14] Since the skin and respiratory membranes are always moist, heat is continually lost by this route except when the air around the body is so saturated with water that evaporation cannot occur. When the air is dry, as in a desert, water evaporates almost instantaneously from the skin; prevention of overheating is much easier, therefore, in a hot, dry climate than in a hot, humid one.

PHYSIOLOGIC MECHANISMS. Loss of heat from the body takes place principally at two surfaces, the skin and the epithelium of the respiratory system; the amount of heat lost depends upon the surface area and its wetness, the temperature and relative humidity of the air, and the rate of air flow over the surface. For any given temperature gradient between the body and its environment, the total heat transfer varies directly with the surface area. This is why a large person normally loses more heat than a smaller one and obese patients dissipate more heat than normal subjects (Chap. 48). The area of exposed skin is also affected by the posture of the body. The position of the arms, for example, determines whether heat exchange can occur at the surface of the axillae. In experimental animals exposed to cold, a marked reduction in the area of exposed skin is brought about when the animal assumes a spheroid form by adducting the legs and flexing the spinal column; a corresponding increase accompanies warm exposure as the result of abduction of the extremities and extension of the spine. Similar alterations of the exposed area of respiratory epithelium may likewise occur, especially in those animals which pant in warm environments.

Since the loss of heat both by radiation and conduction is proportional to the temperature gradient between the surface of the body and its environment, the ability of the animal to change each of the temperatures in question is of considerable interest. Man creates environmental temperatures of his own choosing by constructing buildings equipped with artificial heating and cooling systems; in this way he can secure a favorable temperature gradient whatever the natural weather conditions. The lower animals attain the same general result by moving from one environment to another, but their range of choice is obviously more limited than man's. Changes in the temperature of the body surfaces, on the other hand, are brought about in man and the lower animals through the activity of three different physiologic mechanisms. In the first place, surface temperature is determined largely by the ease with which heat is transported from the depths to the surface of the body, that is, by tissue conductance. This transport is partially accomplished by conduction through tissues and tissue fluids, a process which is not easily altered in a quantitative sense; but, more important than this, heat is brought to the surface by the circulating blood. Water, present in blood to the extent of about 80 per cent by volume, has a high heat capacity and therefore can take up relatively large quantities of heat in warmer parts of the body and give up this heat in the cooler regions. In the cutaneous circulation, heat is ordinarily given up by the blood, the temperature of which is thereby lowered while the temperature of the skin rises. The total amount of heat brought to a given area is conditioned by the rate of blood flow through the area. If the arterioles are constricted, the rate of flow is retarded, the total heat transfer from blood to skin tends to be small, and the skin remains cool; but with arteriolar dilatation the rate of flow is brisk, a large quantity of heat may be exchanged, and the skin becomes warm. Eventually the temperature of the skin might equal that of the circulating blood were it not for the intervention of the other mechanisms shortly to be described.

Surface temperature also depends upon the ease with which heat is transferred from the body to the environment and vice versa; if conduction or radiation is retarded by the interposition of some heat-insulating material, surface temperature will undergo a corresponding change. With effective insulation, although the temperature of the skin may remain at a high level under the clothing, the rate of heat loss may be greatly reduced because, as far as heat loss is concerned, the body has replaced its natural surface with an artificial one (the clothing) having a temperature only a few degrees removed from that of the environment. Insulative clothing may be designed to give protection against heat as well as cold, but man ordinarily needs that protection only when he is exposed to unusually high temperatures, i.e., those encountered by fire-fighters where asbestos clothing may enable a man to survive a short exposure to the extreme heat. The skin of the lower animals carries its own insulating material in the form of hair or fur. Through the phenomenon of *horripilation*, erection of the hair, the thickness of the layer of nonconducting air entrapped between the individual hairs can be increased and the temperature gradient between the surface of the hairy coat and a cool environment can be reduced. In a warm environment the hair lies flat, providing only a thin layer of insulation which more easily transfers heat from the skin to the animal's surroundings. Insulating material, either clothing or fur, limits cutaneous heat exchange, therefore, by replacing the temperature gradient between the body of a nude subject and his environment with three such gradients. One of these three exists between the skin and the inner surface of the insulation, another between the outer surface of the insulation and the environment, and the third gradient is found between the inner and outer surfaces of the insulation. The effectiveness of clothing in decreasing heat loss is proportional to the magnitude of this third gradient, which in turn depends upon the nature and thickness of the nonconducting substance.

Finally, the temperature of body surfaces is modified by the humidity of the surface, since approximately 0.6 kcal. of heat is removed by the vaporization of each gram of water from the respiratory membranes or the skin. There is a certain rather small amount of water, amounting in man to about 50 ml. per hour, which is always lost from these two surfaces because they are moist; this is known as the "insensible water loss," to distinguish it from the sweat, the "sensible loss." Because the humidity of the respiratory passages is not subject to wide variation, quantitative changes in the rate of heat loss can be brought about there only by changing the area of the exposed surface. In the process of panting, a large increase in the total quantity of heat lost from the mouth and respiratory tract is effected by exposing to the air a larger surface of the oral and lingual epithelium. The rate of air flow across these surfaces is also a physiologic variable, and, as an integral part of the panting response, the movement of air is tremendously enhanced by the rapid, shallow breathing. In spite of the increased rate of evaporation which is thereby made possible, the epithelium is kept moist by a more generous flow from the salivary glands. Man's rate of heat loss is similarly altered by the vaporization of water, but the excess water is not vaporized from the respiratory membranes but from the surface of the skin (Fig. 566). Dill[10] reported a maximal rate of evaporation of water of over 1.6 liters per hour during work in a hot, dry atmosphere. This is the equivalent of 870 kcal. per hour, or almost 7000 kcal. during an eight-hour day. Most of the water which made this evaporation possible was secreted by the sweat glands.

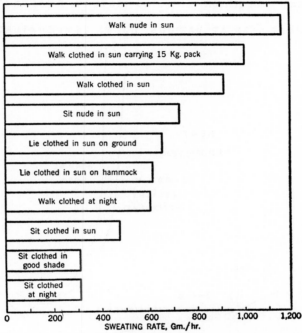

FIG. 566. Sweating rates under 10 conditions of exposure to desert at air temperature of 100° F. dry bulb. (From Gosselin, p. 64, in Adolph *et al.: Physiology of man in the desert.* New York, Interscience Publishers, Inc., 1947.)

Role of the Central Nervous System in Temperature Regulation. All reactions which have been identified with the maintenance of thermal equilibrium are under the control of the central nervous system. This control is exerted through both the somatic and the visceral motor nerves, and possibly via the anterior pituitary and other endocrine glands. The somatic motor fibers activate the respiratory muscles which produce panting, as well as the muscles of the trunk and extremities responsible for posture, for "voluntary" activity, and for shivering. The visceral motor neurons of the autonomic nervous system activate the cutaneous blood vessels, the sweat glands, and the pilo-erector muscles of the hair follicles. Preservation of a relatively constant body temperature may require, therefore, the participation of several different levels of the central nervous system and integration of the activity of those levels. Where this integration is achieved is a problem of some importance.

REGULATION BY THE HYPOTHALAMUS. Integration of the reactions which maintain temperature equilibrium is accomplished in the hypothalamus, the ventral portion of the diencephalon lying behind the optic chiasma, above the hypophysis and rostral to the cerebral peduncles of the midbrain. The hypothalamus functions as a regulator which is able to change the rate of heat production and heat dissipation through its influence upon the somatic and visceral motor neurons of the brain stem and spinal cord.[28] The anterior hypothalamus is usually said to be responsible for protection against hot environments; the posterior hypothalamus confers resistance to cold.

Temperature-sensitive receptors. Through the somatic and visceral motor neurons of the brain and spinal cord, the hypothalamus normally modulates the rate of heat formation and dissipation in such a way that the central or deep temperature of a resting individual is almost constant in spite of fairly wide variations in the temperature of the environment and in the physiologic state of the body (Fig. 567). It is imp rtant to inquire

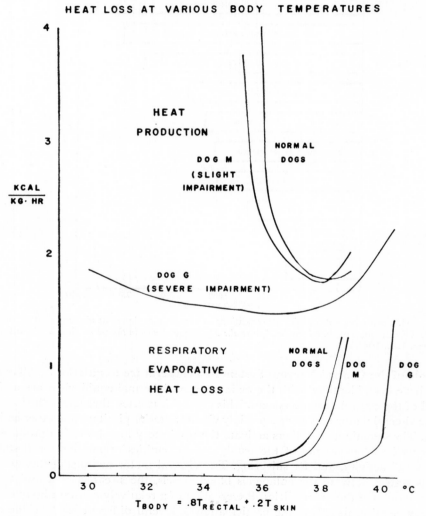

HEAT PRODUCTION AND RESPIRATORY EVAPORATIVE

HEAT LOSS AT VARIOUS BODY TEMPERATURES

FIG. 567. Graphs showing relationship between body temperature (*abscissa*) and metabolic rate (*upper ordinate*) or evaporative heat loss (*lower ordinate*). Normal dogs exhibit increased metabolic rate when body temperature falls below 37° C. and higher evaporative heat loss with body temperature of 38° C. or above. Dogs with hypothalamic lesion (Dogs *M* and *G*) show failure of both heat production in cold and evaporative heat loss in warm environment, the extent of the failure depending upon the size and position of the hypothalamic injury. Dog *G* showed almost no metabolic response in the cold environment. (After Hammel, H. T.; cited from Thompson, R. H., Ph.D. dissertation, University of Pennsylvania, 1959.)

how this part of the diencephalon is called into action and what factors determine whether the mechanisms of heat loss or those of heat conservation are brought into play at any given moment. Two sensitive mechanisms, one central and the other peripheral, appear to interact in this regulation. The central one consists of thermal-sensitive neurons in the anterior hypothalamus; its existence was first demonstrated by Barbour[2] in experiments in which he warmed and cooled this portion of the brain. Magoun and his collaborators[22] were later able to activate selectively certain mechanisms of heat loss (polypnea, panting and sweating) by heating the anterior hypothalamus of cats with high frequency currents (Figs. 568, 569). The most responsive region lay in the suprachiasmatic and preoptic regions, but a zone of lesser sensitivity extended caudally into the dorsal part of the hypothalamus. More recently the experiment has been repeated by Fusco in the laboratory of Hardy and Hammel, using unanesthetized dogs with implanted electrodes (Fig. 570).

If the anterior hypothalamus is purposely injured, fever occurs with recovery from the anesthetic and is followed, if the animal survives, by a permanent deficit of regulation upon exposure to hot environments. All of this evidence suggests that the anterior hypothalamus is sensitive to heat and that it has the function of pro-

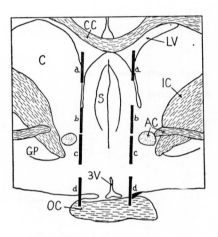

FIG. 568. Transverse section through brain of cat. Positions of two electrodes during heating are shown at *a, b, c* and *d*. *AC*, Anterior commissure; *C*, caudate nucleus; *CC*, corpus callosum; *GP*, globus pallidus; *IC*, internal capsule; *LV*, lateral ventricle; *OC*, optic chiasma; *S*, septum; *3V*, third ventricle. (From Magoun *et al.*, *J. Neurophysiol.*, 1938, *1*:101–114.)

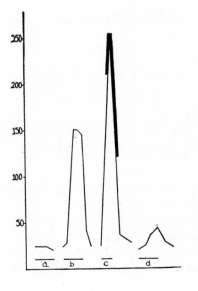

FIG. 569. Chart showing respective respiratory responses obtained from heating at positions *a, b, c* and *d* in Fig. 568. Respiratory rate is shown on the ordinate; panting is shown by a heavy line. Period *a* represents 5 min. Other times all in proportion. (From Magoun *et al.*, *J. Neurophysiol.*, 1938, *1*:101–114.)

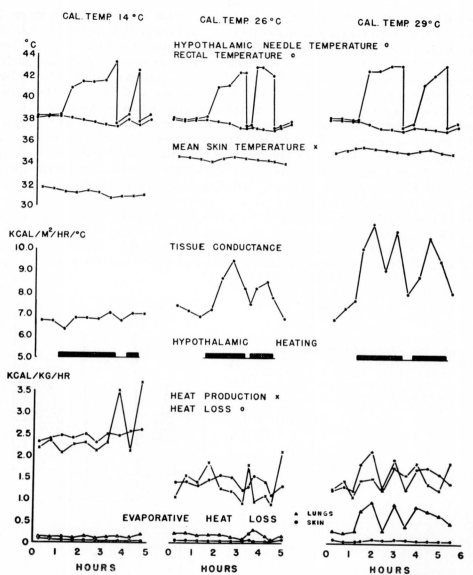

FIG. 570.   Graphs showing responses of unanesthetized dog during local heating of hypothalamus using implanted electrodes. Experiments were conducted at three different environmental temperatures, 14°, 26° and 29° C. From above downward, curves show hypothalamic temperature, rectal temperature and mean skin temperature; tissue conductance and time of hypothalamic heating; heat production and heat loss; evaporative heat loss through lungs and skin. The data demonstrate the sensitivity of the hypothalamic mechanism to local heating and show that the nature of the dog's responses depends upon environmental temperature. For example, at 29° C. the local heating led to an increase in tissue conductance and evaporative heat loss that were not seen at 14° C. (Fusco, Madeline M., Ph.D. dissertation, University of Pennsylvania, 1959.)

tecting the animal against hyperthermia. The caudal part of the hypothalamus, on the other hand, appears to protect the animal against cooling. When large lesions are produced in the caudal hypothalamus, the animal becomes inactive; its posture is not normal, it fails to eat spontaneously, does not shiver or show pilo-erection in cold environments, and, in brief, is almost poikilothermic in the acute stage. With smaller lesions and in the chronic state these animals have a normal rectal temperature when they are kept in a room at the usual environmental temperatures; deficits of regulation, however, can be demonstrated by exposure to either a hot or a cold environment (Fig. 567).

The peripheral mechanism includes the thermal-sensitive endings of skin, mucous membranes, etc., where reflexes begin when the environmental temperature is changed.[3] Under natural conditions all of the motor mechanisms of temperature regulation may be brought into activity with no obvious change in the central temperature of the body, provided that the hypothalamus itself is normal. This suggests that the peripheral mechanism is effective through integrations which occur in the hypothalamus. If the deep temperature has not changed, there can be no stimulus to the sensitive neurons of the hypothalamus, and yet the constancy of the deep temperature is evidence that the hypothalamus is functioning properly. It is clear, therefore, that the hypothalamus has

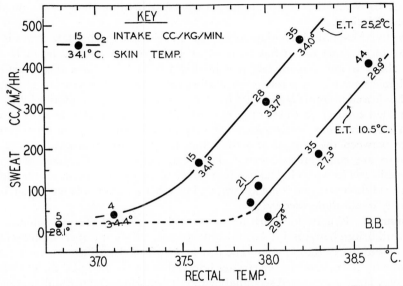

FIG. 571. Relation of rate of sweating to increasing rectal temperature. Increments in rectal temperature were produced by increasing intensities of work as indicated by O_2 intake of subject. Increasing work did not affect skin temperature. (From Robinson, p. 212, in Newburgh: *Physiology of heat regulation and the science of clothing*. Philadelphia, W. B. Saunders Co., 1949.)

two separable functions in this regulation—as an integrator of all of the information available to the nervous system relative to temperature, and as a sensing element capable of supplying a specific type of information, the central or deep body temperature.

The peripheral reflexes rather than the central receptors appear to provide the basis of regulation when a resting, fasting animal is exposed to heat or cold. The central receptors, on the other hand, appear to function when temperature is not the only variable which must be regulated in a given set of circumstances. For example, during exercise the distribution of blood in the body, the rate of pulmonary ventilation, posture, activity of skeletal muscles, etc., cannot be controlled for purposes of temperature regulation exclusively, and the central temperature then varies depending upon the work load and the ambient temperature (Fig. 571). Under these conditions the change in deep temperature is great enough to activate the neurons of the central mechanism, which then becomes more important than the peripheral reflexes.

FEVER. By definition, the word *fever* refers to any condition in which the temperature of the body is above the normal range of 98° to 99° F. orally and 99° to 100° F. in the rectum. Every such elevation means that the body contains more heat than it did before the fever began; with the onset of fever either the rate of heat dissipation must have decreased or the rate of heat production increased, or both changes may have occurred. In reality, the onset is usually marked by the reactions normally observed when a subject is exposed to cold—shivering (shaking chill), pilo-erection ("gooseflesh"), cutaneous vasoconstriction and the absence of sweat. All of these conspire to augment the total amount of heat contained within the body. The termination of a bout of fever, on the other hand, is characterized by the normal reactions of heat exposure—muscular relaxation, sweating and cutaneous vasodilatation. In this way the extra heat previously stored is rather quickly disposed of, and the body temperature returns to the normal level. Both the onset and termination of fever are effected through the activity of mechanisms normally responsible for thermal equilibrium, and fever is abnormal only in that the mechanisms of heat production and conservation are called into action at a time when their function is apparently not needed because there exists no threat to thermal equilibrium.

If the hypothalamus is considered to be a "physiologic thermostat," fever is a condition in which the thermostat has been set at a higher than normal level. How this is brought about is not known, but it evidently results from some direct action upon hypothalamic neurons. By some as yet undiscovered means the neurons of the anterior hypothalamic and preoptic regions are inhibited and those of the posterior hypothalamus are stimulated to attempt to set up a new equilibrium at a higher level. The response is not an all-or-nothing change, for fever may be established almost anywhere within the range between the normal and the lethal temperature; moreover, fluctuations of temperature are commonly observed. However, despite the frequent occurrence of hyperthermia and its wide clinical use as an index of the course of disease, the physiologic significance of this condition is not known, and whether it hastens recovery from infection, for instance, is still undecided.

Summary. Finally, to return to the general problem of energy exchange and the normal equilibrium between intake and expenditure, the significance of physiologic heat loss may be summarized as follows: The rate at which foodstuffs are converted into heat is made to vary in response to the stresses imposed upon the body by the environmental temperature. Heat is produced seemingly without regard for the over-all energy balance which must be maintained, if at all, through the activity of the mechanisms controlling food intake (see above). In other words, energy balance may be freely sacrificed by the mechanisms which preserve thermal equilibrium. For temperature regulation, however, the body is not dependent solely upon alterations in the rate of heat production, since mechanisms are also available for increasing or decreasing the rate of heat loss per se.

REGULATION OF ENERGY STORAGE

Nature of Energy Reserves. Between the processes of food intake and energy expenditure there is interposed a kind of physiologic "shock absorber," able to cushion the interaction of supply and demand. This "shock absorber" is composed of the reserve chemical energy stored within the cells. It is "elastic," and can expand to conserve surplus energy of the diet or contract to give up its substance in times of emergency or when the diet is insufficient. The process of storage is said to be positive when reserves are being accumulated and negative when they are being used up. Schoenheimer and his colleagues[31] found that a continual interchange takes place between the dietary and cellular proteins, and that similar interchange is always in progress between dietary and depot fat. A molecule stored in a cell is not permanently fixed there but may be taken up again by the blood or lymph while its former place in the cell is assumed by a molecule that may have been absorbed only recently from the animal's food. Schoenheimer has called this the "dynamic state of body constituents." It is evident that the terms positive or negative storage have only a relative significance, because, if a continual interchange is in progress, positive storage can only mean that the rate of deposition for the moment exceeds the rate of reabsorption of the compound in question—that is, the net result is positive in sign. Negative storage occurs when the reserves are being withdrawn more rapidly than they are being replaced.

CARBOHYDRATE RESERVES. The glycogen of the skeletal muscles, heart, and liver constitutes the main carbohydrate reserve of the mammal. In the postabsorptive state the human body is believed to contain 100 to 150 grams of glycogen, which is the equivalent of 400 to 600 kcal. of heat; of this amount, only about one-tenth is found in the liver and the remainder is stored within muscle cells. The ingestion of carbohydrate food leads: (i) to a marked increase in liver glycogen, which may then amount to as much as 75 grams or 5 per cent of the weight of the organ; and (ii) to a less dramatic but nevertheless significant increase in muscle glycogen. Muscular exercise, on the other hand, produces a fall in muscle glycogen. In the normal animal this depletion is only temporary, because the resting level is restored from the glucose of the circulating plasma, which is in turn replenished by the liver, either from its own glycogen or by glyconeogenesis, i.e., the conversion of protein to carbohydrate. Even under the most favorable conditions the total amount of reserve carbohydrate is not large, and glycogen is important, not because of its total quantity, but because of the possibility of a rapid turnover and a transitory storage, both of which tend to adapt the energy supply to the energy expenditure at any given moment. Consequently, a small but adequate amount of carbohydrate is always available for the supply of those cells which use no other foodstuff, for cells which are not able to lay aside their own reserves, and for providing the several intermediaries of the tricarboxylic acid cycle. Because the liver is able to convert certain amino acids to glucose, however, the tissue proteins represent a large potential supply of carbohydrate, far overshadowing the carbohydrate present as such in the body at any one time.

Like many other reversible biologic reactions, carbohydrate storage may be either positive or negative in sign, and the direction of the reaction appears to be determined by carbohydrate levels in body fluids. If liver glycogen is low and blood glucose is relatively high (because sugar is being absorbed from the intestine), the reaction in the liver moves in the direction of glycogen synthesis. But if liver glycogen is relatively abundant and blood glucose is being used rapidly by the tissues, the reaction moves in the direction of glycogen breakdown or glycolysis. A similar relationship exists between blood sugar and muscle glycogen. The direction of the reaction apparently conforms to the law of mass action, and although many intermediary chemical changes are known to be involved in the transformation of glucose to glycogen, or vice versa, it is possible to predict the direction of the whole series of reactions if the relative levels of glucose and glycogen inside and outside the cell are known. Or, more correctly, it is possible to make this prediction from the law of mass action provided the glycogen content of the cell has not already attained a certain maximal level, for there is a limit to the amount of glycogen which can be stored in either liver or muscle. When this limit is reached, glucose is no longer stored as carbohydrate but is converted to fat, in which form an almost unlimited energy reserve can be accumulated, as described below. Experiments upon animals from which the individual endocrine glands have been removed and upon those same animals and also normal animals injected with various hormones have shown that the processes of glycogen synthesis and breakdown are profoundly affected by the organs of internal secretion (see Chap. 52).

PROTEIN RESERVES. The total protein content of the body of a man weighing 70 kg. is about 14 kg., or 20 per cent of the body weight. If the subject of the experiment is a well fed adult, adding protein to his diet fails to induce any significant positive storage of protein, but rather increases the urinary excretion of nitrogen and the storage of fat which is formed from deaminated amino acid residues. But if protein is removed from the diet or if the subject fasts, a negative storage will occur as tissue protein is broken down to furnish energy and heat to the body. When protein or amino acid nitrogen is again made available in the diet in large enough quantities, a positive storage will be observed until a reconstitution of tissue protein has taken place. The body of the normal, well fed adult may be said to contain reserve protein to the extent of 2 or 3 kg., or about 16 per cent of the total protein content. The growth hormone of the anterior lobe of the hypophysis facilitates nitrogen retention and protein synthesis, whereas extracts of the adrenal cortex increase the amount of nitrogen and potassium excreted in the urine. The nature of these reactions is given in the following chapters.

LIPID RESERVES. Like the storage of carbohydrate and protein, lipid storage may be either positive or negative in sign; it is accomplished through chemical reactions which appear to be easily reversible, and a continual interchange normally occurs between substances circulating in the blood and compounds already deposited in the tissues. In one remarkable particular, however, the storage of fat differs from the storage of carbohydrate and protein. Positive storage of carbohydrate and protein occurs only in immature, growing animals or in adults whose reserves have been temporarily depleted, and in every case there is a normal limit above which the body's content of these two types of compounds cannot be elevated. When the depots are full, no more can be added. But in the storage of fat there appears to be almost no limit to the amount which can be deposited and retained by either the growing youth or the adult. Net positive storage evidently can continue for an indefinite period, since the available depots of the subcutaneous tissue, omentum, subperitoneal tissue, epicardium, skeletal muscle and other parts of the body never appear to become full and may contain altogether more than 100 kg. of fat. Since the calorific value of fat is twice that of carbohydrate or protein, a certain economy of bulk is achieved by storing energy in the adipose tissue, especially because fat, unlike the other foodstuffs, is stored almost anhydrously.

Regulation of lipid storage by the central nervous system or by hormones has often been proposed but never established as a factor determining the total fat content of the body. As mentioned earlier in this chapter, the amount of energy stored as fat seems to depend upon the balance between energy intake as food and expenditure as work and heat. For individual tissues and organs, however, recent evidence shows that the rate of lipogenesis is affected by the presence or absence of enzymes and cofactors which might serve as parts of regulating systems (see Siperstein[32]). Mayer's explanation of the development of obesity in obese-hyperglycemic mice is related to this concept, in that he concludes that the animals preferentially convert substrates into fat.[24, 25] In so doing they have limited ability to utilize certain substrates as sources of energy for work and heat, and thus experience a deficiency of heat production in the cold and a low energy output as "spontaneous" activity. Their relative lack of available energy then leads to hyperphagia in partial compensation for their energy need. This type of obesity has been called "metabolic" to specify its origin in some particular defect of intermediary metabolism. The hyperphagia, then, is not a result of a defect in the regulating system, but rather a response of the system to a metabolic "error."

On the other hand, abnormalities of energy storage may be created by disturbances of regulation. The one which has been studied most extensively is hypothalamic obesity, where energy surplus occurs mainly because food intake is enhanced. There may be in addition some decrease in motor output,[16] and Brooks described a small but significant lowering of the basal metabolic rate.[5] The combination of these three changes has been taken as evidence that the hypothalamus regulates energy exchange and establishes the pattern of regulation which the animal follows from time to time. Following this particular type of hypothalamic lesion, a pattern is established for energy accumulation, with excessive intake and reduced expenditure, at least in the early stages of the obesity. Clinical literature contains many references to the possibility that cases of human obesity have their origin in abnormal functioning of the hypothalamus. At the present time this can be neither proved nor disproved, except that it is clear that most fat patients do not have hypothalamic lesions. Perhaps, as Jolliffe has suggested, their regulatory mechanisms are less sensitive and less precise than they should be.[18] Again, since the hypothalamus is related anatomically to other structures of the brain stem and limbic systems, its regulatory functions may be modulated by activities in other parts of the brain. Normally the hypothalamus may balance the several factors of energy exchange, but the exact nature of the balance may be affected to a large measure by what is going on throughout the nervous system.

CONCLUSION

In regulation of the variables of energy exchange, there is a demonstrable "physiologic reserve" or "margin of safety," as there is in other functions of the body. For example, under resting conditions the body is able either to store extra heat or to lose heat through change in mean body temperature. The heat reserve, however, is not large, and maintenance of body temperature depends rather upon reserves of heat production and heat loss. Again, the body is capable of greater activity than it usually shows; this extra capacity for work may be regarded as a reserve, even though at present we do not know much about its regulation. In the third instance, energy storage, the presence of a reserve is obvious under most conditions; the fat of the body constitutes a reserve to be drawn upon when energy intake is low. No doubt this same principle applies also to food intake, regulation of which should be expected to exhibit a reserve or margin of safety. Animals naturally live under conditions where food is sometimes available and sometimes scarce. Between feeding periods there may be intervals when searching, hunting and even migration are necessary. Environmental temperature may be low, with resulting high energy expenditure. Thus, the regulation of food intake should be organized so that, when food is found, the animal can eat more than its immediate needs and thus survive the next starvation and be able to locate its next meal. If this is true, the fat stores of the body are tokens of the reserve in regulation of food consumption. Moreover, if the animal never suffers from starvation, the reserve in food intake will be literally cumulative, leading to persistent gain in body weight. Many animals kept in laboratories where food is always available show such a gain, which many authors believe to be a deteriment to health and longevity. A similar situation is used by farmers in fattening domestic animals; they feed a high caloric diet in practically unlimited amounts to animals restricted in their activity. If the regulation were organized so that animals could eat only what they need, they could not be fattened by this technique. The susceptibility of laboratory mice to this method of fattening varies from strain to strain, and is most obvious when the diet has a high fat content.[13] Many observers have suggested that men and women also exhibit this phenomenon. With food easy to get, and with work output decreasing year by year, energy accumulates as fat. If we are to preserve an "ideal" weight, we cannot do it by relying upon the unconscious regulating mechanisms, but must give the matter our purposeful attention. If we worked harder, or if food were less plentiful, we probably would not have this problem.

One should not overlook the principle stated by Brody[4] that on any given food intake there is a limit to body weight gain. The larger the body, the greater the cost of maintaining it. If environmental temperature and activity are constant, there is only one size the body can attain on a particular food intake, since any increase above that size requires extra energy for maintenance. Any decrease in size brings about an energy surplus which will be used to restore the original body mass. Provided only that the body can remain alive on the food given, the size of the body will come into an equilibrium typical of that specific intake and expenditure. There is no evidence that this involves a "regulation" of body weight *per se*, and, if a constancy of weight follows, it does so for physical and biochemical reasons rather than because of active control. The active regulations concerned with body weight are, rather, regulation of food intake, heat loss and activity, which together determine what the weight will be.

Food intake, however, may be affected by the amount of energy stored in the body. Perhaps the most convincing evidence is the observation that animals forcibly overfed and then given food *ad libitum* will fail to eat until their body weight has returned to the expected normal level. Kennedy[19] and Hervey[15] have used a lipostatic hypothesis to explain the feeding behavior of rats with hypothalamic obesity, suggesting that the animals overeat until they achieve a new, enlarged reserve of fat. They believe that the size of the fat depots is reflected in changing levels of some substance present in body fluids. Certainly, the amount of food eaten is determined to a large extent by what happens to the food. For example, more food is eaten when amino acids are utilized for growth than when they are de-aminated for oxidation or lipid synthesis. How the body detects these variations in metabolism and thereby alters the appropriate regulation remains a mystery and a subject for further experimental study.

REFERENCES

1. ANAND, B. K. and BROBECK, J. R. *Yale J. Biol. Med.*, 1951, 24:123–140.
2. BARBOUR, H. G. *Arch. exp. Path. Pharmak.*, 1912, 70:1–26.
3. BAZETT, H. C. Pp. 109–192 in NEWBURGH, L. H., ed., *Physiology of heat regulation and the science of clothing.* Philadelphia, W. B. Saunders Company, 1949.
4. BRODY, S. *Bioenergetics and growth.* New York, Reinhold, 1945.
5. BROOKS, C. McC. and MARINE, D. N. *Fed. Proc.*, 1946, 5:12.
6. BROWMAN, L. G. *J. exp. Zool.*, 1943, 94:477–489.
7. CARLSON, A. J. *Control of hunger in health and disease.* Chicago, University of Chicago Press, second imp., 1916.
8. DAVIS, G. D. *Locomotor hyperactivity induced by cerebral lesions in the monkey.* Ph.D. thesis, Yale University, 1951.
9. DELGADO, J. M. R. and ANAND, B. K. *Amer. J. Physiol.*, 1953, 172:162–168.
10. DILL, D. B. *Life, heat, and altitude.* Cambridge, Harvard University Press, 1938.
11. DRACHMAN, R. H. and TEPPERMAN, J. *Yale J. Biol. Med.*, 1954, 26:394–409.
12. DUBOIS, E. F. *Bull. N. Y. Acad. Med.*, 1939, Ser. 2, 15:143–173.
13. FENTON, F. F. *Amer. J. Physiol.*, 1956, 184:52–54.
14. HARDY, J. D. Pp. 78–108 in NEWBURGH, L. H., ed., *Physiology of heat regulation and the science of clothing.* Philadelphia, W. B. Saunders Company, 1949.
15. HERVEY, G. R. *J. Physiol.*, 1958, 145:336–352.
16. HETHERINGTON, A. W. and RANSON, S. W. *Amer. J. Physiol.*, 1942, 136:609–617.
17. JANOWITZ, H. D. and GROSSMAN, M. I. *Amer. J. Physiol.*, 1949, 159:143–148.
18. JOLLIFFE, N. *Reduce and stay reduced.* New York, Simon & Schuster, 3rd printing, 1952.
19. KENNEDY, G. C. *Proc. roy. Soc.*, 1953, B140:578–592.
20. KRAUT, H. A. and MULLER, E. A. *Science*, 1946, 104:495–497.
21. LUSK, G. *The elements of the science of nutrition*, 4th ed. Philadelphia, W. B. Saunders Company, 1928.
22. MAGOUN, H. W., HARRISON, F., BROBECK, J. R. and RANSON, S. W. *J. Neurophysiol.*, 1938, 1:101–114.
23. MARSHALL, N. B., BARRNETT, R. J. and MAYER, J. *Proc. Soc. exp. Biol. (N. Y.)*, 1955, 90:240–244.
24. MAYER, J. *Physiol. Rev.*, 1953, 33:472–508.
25. MAYER, J. *Ann. N. Y. Acad. Sci.*, 1955, 63:15–43.
26. MILLER, F. R. and SHERRINGTON, C. S. *Quart. J. exp. Physiol.*, 1916, 9:147–186.
27. RANSON, S. W. *Harvey Lect.*, 1936–37, 32:92–121.
28. RANSON, S. W. *Res. Publ. Ass. nerv. ment. Dis.*, 1940, 20:342–399.
29. RICHTER, C. P. *Quart. Rev. Biol.*, 1927, 2:307–343.
30. RUCH, T. C. and SHENKIN, H. A. *J. Neurophysiol.*, 1943, 6:349–360.
31. SCHOENHEIMER, R. *The dynamic state of body constituents.* Cambridge, Harvard University Press, 1942.
32. SIPERSTEIN, M. D. *Amer. J. Med.*, 1959, 26:685–702.
33. SLONAKER, J. R. *J. Anim. Behav.*, 1912, 2:20–42.
34. SLONAKER, J. R. *Amer. J. Physiol.*, 1925, 73:485–503.
35. WANG, G. H. *Amer. Nat.*, 1924, 58:36–42.

Intermediary Metabolism*

ENERGY exchange of the body as a whole is made up of the metabolic reactions of individual organs and tissues; these latter may be difficult to study by the over-all methods described in Chapter 48. Knowing that carbohydrate is oxidized to carbon

dioxide and water does not describe the release of energy of the $-\overset{|}{\underset{|}{C}}-H$ bonding within

the cells, nor does the formation of urea from protein give a satisfactory account of the course of protein metabolism. More specific research methods especially adapted for studying the component parts of the total metabolism must be applied. In principle, however, these techniques may be related to the procedures for measuring total energy exchange, including both direct and indirect calorimetry. Thus, heat production of a muscle may be measured directly and correlated with the utilization of energy and capacity to do work; or the secretory work of gland cells may be estimated. Or the materials providing energy to a cellular system may be identified, the end-products may be determined, and the amounts of oxygen used and carbon dioxide produced may be measured. The most specific methods developed for this type of study are chemical or physicochemical in nature, suitable for revealing even subtle changes in chemical configurations as a compound is being catabolized. In many instances the chemical reactions can be made to occur outside the body. Many of the intermediary constituents have been discovered through this technique, and the mechanisms of cellular energy exchange are beginning to be revealed.

* Written for the 17th edition by J. R. Brobeck.

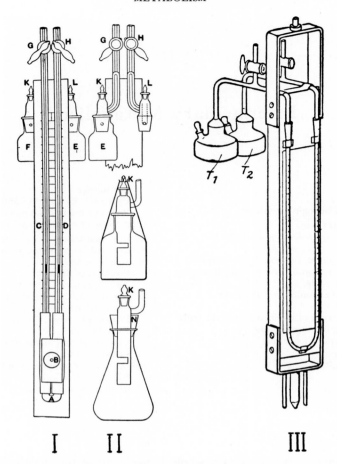

FIG. 572.   Differential manometer of Barcroft:[1] *I* and *II*, as used for blood gas analysis; *III*, as used by Negelein and Warburg[33] for measuring tissue respiration. *C* and *D* are manometers attached to glass vessels, *F* and *E*, containing blood samples. *B* is a leveling device for the manometer. Similarly, T_1 and T_2 are vessels where tissue specimens to be studied are placed.

One of the common instruments for studying biochemical reactions is the Barcroft-Warburg apparatus (Fig. 572). A thin slice of tissue or a suspension of cells is placed in a buffered solution in a closed vessel in contact with a gas mixture of known composition and volume. Cells will survive and carry on metabolic reactions for several hours under these conditions; at the end of the time, the solution, the tissue and the gas mixture are analyzed to learn the nature and the extent of the chemical changes that have taken place. The experimental conditions may be varied by altering the composition of the solution, the gas mixture or the temperature. The effects of biologic variables may be discovered by comparing samples from different species of animals, animals subjected to operations or administration of drugs, or animals in different metabolic states. Compounds containing an uncommon isotope of a particular element may also be used—e.g. deuterium in place of hydrogen, heavy nitrogen (N^{15}) in place of N^{14}, radioactive carbon (C^{14}) and radioactive iodine (I^{131}). The presence of the isotope provides a convenient label or "tag," so that the molecules containing the unusual isotope can be identified in a mixture of molecules. Isotopic methods also may serve to outline a metabolic pathway when the isotope can be followed from one compound to another; the rate of the reactions may be determined by estimating the rate at which the concentration of the isotope is changing in a given compound. In the study of intermediary metabolism the various isotopic methods are probably more widely used than any other one type of experimental technique; their importance cannot be emphasized too strongly. More detailed description of these methods, however, must be obtained in textbooks, monographs and periodicals devoted to chemistry.[11, 35]

Enzymes.   Chemical reactions occur in biologic systems according to the principles and laws of general chemical theory. Their speed is hastened by catalysis, without which the reactions would not provide energy rapidly enough for normal physiologic responses. These catalysts are protein in nature and thus differ from the more common catalysts, e.g., platinum, of inorganic chemistry. Biologic catalysts are known as enzymes. They are synthesized by living cells and may be active after removal from the cell, but their activity is lost when the protein is changed from its native state, as, for example, in denaturation. One of their most striking characteristics is their specificity, and they are usually named for this quality by adding "-ase" to a word designating the structure upon which they act. Many enzymes catalyze only a single chemical reaction and require a particular compound or "substrate" as one of the reactants. Others, certain peptidases, for example, are specific for a certain chemical grouping and will accept as a substrate any compound having that particular grouping. Still other enzymes may appear to have more than one type of activity. Fruton and Simmonds[11] mention as an example the apparent esterase activity of certain peptidases and proteinases. The role of these enzymes and others in the digestion of foodstuffs has been discussed earlier.

Although it has received much attention, the action of enzymes is not well understood because the chemical nature of proteins is still uncertain. The effects of variations in enzyme concentration, substrate concentration, pH or temperature, the presence of metals, and the addition of inhibitors are discussed in the biochemical literature, where one may also read the suggestions and speculations of authors interested in mechanisms of enzymatic catalysis. Of greater usefulness to students, perhaps, are the classifications of enzymes also to be found in textbooks of biochemistry. Since the number of known enzymes is large and the reactions in which they participate are numerous, a logical classification serves a useful purpose (see Tables 34 and 35).

In addition to the protein part of the molecule, many enzymes contain also a non-protein center of activity, known as a "prosthetic group," which may participate in the reaction catalyzed by the enzyme as a kind of cosubstrate, undergoing a reversible chemical change. Green[13] has classified the oxidative enzymes according to the nature of their prosthetic groups as follows: iron porphyrin proteins, pyridinoproteins, flavoproteins, copper proteins, thiaminoproteins, plus a group of unknown structure. In certain instances the prosthetic group may be separated from the enzyme by dialysis; the dialyzable portion is then known as a "coenzyme," and the nondialyzable, protein part as an "apoenzyme," meaning derived from an enzyme. The two parts together may be called a "holoenzyme," that is, an entire or complete enzyme. Coenzymes are heat-stable and of relatively low molecular weight and simple chemical structure; apoenzymes are inactive when the coenzyme is removed and are activated by addition of the coenzyme. They are permanently altered by heating, so that even the presence of the coenzyme will not restore their catalytic activity. This inactivation by heat is related to their structure as proteins, as are their high molecular weight and complex structure. Some enzymes are not known to have prosthetic groups; furthermore, it is not certain that every coenzyme serves as a prosthetic group. This confusion is a natural result of ignorance about the nature of the interaction of enzymes and substrates and of the bonding between coenzymes and apoenzymes. Like other similar problems, these will be clarified when more is learned about the constitution of proteins.[12]

Like the more familiar reactions seen in the inorganic chemistry laboratory, some metabolic reactions are easily reversible and some are not. If the reaction involves only an insignificant change in potential chemical energy, it is usually reversible; but if that change is large, the reaction appears to run only "downhill," i.e., in the direction of a decrease in free energy and an increase in entropy. Both types of reaction are catalyzed by enzymes, but the enzyme, like any other catalyst, does not determine the direction of the reaction (Chap. 42). Thus, the enzyme phosphorylase, which catalyzes the synthesis of glycogen *from* glucose-1-phosphate, also catalyzes the breakdown of glycogen

TABLE 34. SOME TYPE REACTIONS CATALYZED BY ENZYMES

(From Fruton and Simmonds, *General biochemistry*, New York, John Wiley & Sons, Inc., 1953.)

TYPE REACTIONS	ENZYME GROUP
1. Hydrolysis-Condensation or Replacement	
$RCO—NHR' + H_2O \rightleftharpoons RCOOH + R'NH_2$ $RCO—NHR' + R''NH_2 \rightleftharpoons RCO—NHR'' + R'NH_2$ $\Big\}$	Proteinases, Peptidases, and Amidases
$RCO—OR' + H_2O \rightleftharpoons RCOOH + R'OH$ $RCO—OR' + R''OH \rightleftharpoons RCO—OR'' + R'OH$ $\Big\}$	Esterases
$R—PO_3H_2 + H_2O \rightleftharpoons RH + H_3PO_4$ $R—PO_3H_2 + R'OH \rightleftharpoons RH + R'O—PO_3H_2$ $R—PO_3H_2 + R'NH_2 \rightleftharpoons RH + R'NH—PO_3H_2$ $\Big\}$	Phosphatases and Transphosphorylases
$\underset{R'—\vert}{\overset{H}{\underset{\vert}{R—C—O}}} + H_2O \rightleftharpoons RH + \underset{R'—\vert}{\overset{H}{\underset{\vert}{HO—C—O}}}$	Glycosidases*
$\underset{R'—\vert}{\overset{H}{\underset{\vert}{R—C—O}}} + R''H \rightleftharpoons RH + \underset{R'—\vert}{\overset{H}{\underset{\vert}{R''—C—O}}}$	Transglycosidases*
2. Phosphorolysis-Condensation	
$\underset{R'—\vert}{\overset{H}{\underset{\vert}{R—C—O}}} + H_3PO_4 \rightleftharpoons RH + \underset{R'—\vert}{\overset{H}{\underset{\vert}{H_2O_3PO—C—O}}}$	Phosphorylases*
3. Cleavage or Formation of C—C Linkages	
$RCOOH \rightleftharpoons RH + CO_2$	Decarboxylases
$\underset{HO\ \ H}{\overset{H\ OH}{R—C—C—R'}} \rightleftharpoons RCH_2OH + R'CHO$	Aldolases
4. Hydration-Dehydration and Related Processes	
$\underset{HCR_2}{\overset{H}{\underset{\vert}{R—C—OH}}} \rightleftharpoons \underset{CR_2}{\overset{}{R—CH}} + H_2O$	Hydrases and related enzymes (elements of H_2O or NH_3 may be replaced by those of H_2S)
$\underset{HCR_2}{\overset{H}{\underset{\vert}{R—C—NH_2}}} \rightleftharpoons \underset{CR_2}{\overset{}{R—CH}} + NH_3$	
5. Oxidation-Reduction	
$AH_2 + B \rightleftharpoons A + BH_2$	Dehydrogenases
$2Fe^{++} + \frac{1}{2}O_2 + 2H^+ \rightarrow 2Fe^{+++} + H_2O$ $AH_2 + O_2 \rightarrow A + H_2O_2$ $\Big\}$	Oxidases
$AH_2 + H_2O_2 \rightarrow A + 2H_2O$ $2H_2O_2 \rightarrow 2H_2O + O_2$ $\Big\}$	Peroxidases and Catalases

* The type formula $\underset{R'—\vert}{\overset{H}{\underset{\vert}{R—C—O}}}$ denotes a glycoside.

to glucose-1-phosphate. Whether glycogen is built up or broken down is determined by other considerations, of which the most obvious perhaps are the relative concentrations of the reacting substances. Therefore, this and many other similarly *reversible* reactions may be driven almost to completion in one direction if the end-products of the reaction are removed in order to maintain their concentrations at levels low enough to prevent a

TABLE 35. SOME CRYSTALLINE ENZYMES

(From Fruton and Simmonds, *General biochemistry*, New York, John Wiley & Sons, Inc., 1953.)

ENZYME	SOURCE	REFERENCE
Alcohol dehydrogenase	Yeast	E. Negelein and H.-J. Wulff, *Biochem. Z.*, *293*:351 (1937).
Aldolase	Muscle (rabbit, rat)	J. F. Taylor *et al.*, *J. Biol. Chem.*, *173*:591 (1948).
α-Amylase	Barley	S. Schwimmer and A. K. Balls, *J. Biol. Chem.*, *779*:1063 (1949).
	Human saliva	K. H. Meyer *et al.*, *Helv. Chim. Acta*, *31*:2158 (1948).
	Swine pancreas	K. H. Meyer *et al.*, *Helv. Chim. Acta*, *30*:64 (1947).
β-Amylase	Sweet potato	A. K. Balls *et al.*, *J. Biol. Chem.*, *173*:9 (1948).
ATP-1, 3-diphosphoglyceric acid transphosphorylase	Yeast	T. Bücher, *Naturwissenschaften*, *30*:756 (1942).
ATP-phosphopyruvic acid transphosphorylase	Rat muscle	F. Kubowitz and P. Ott, *Biochem. Z.*, *377*:193 (1944).
Carbonic anhydrase	Beef erythrocytes	D. A. Scott and A. M. Fisher, *J. Biol. Chem.*, *144*:371 (1942).
Carboxypeptidase	Beef pancreas	M. L. Anson, *J. Gen. Physiol.*, *20*:663 (1937).
Catalase	Beef liver	J. B. Sumner and A. L. Dounce, *J. Biol. Chem.*, *121*:417 (1937).
	Beef erythrocytes	M. Laskowski and J. B. Sumner, *Science,* *94*:615 (1941).
	Micrococcus lysodeikticus	D. Herbert and A. J. Pinsent, *Biochem. J.*, *43*:193 (1948).
Chymopapain	*Carica papaya*	E. F. Jansen and A. K. Balls, *J. Biol. Chem.*, *137*:459 (1941).
Chymotrypsin	Beef pancreas	M. Kunitz and J. H. Northrop, *J. Gen. Physiol.*, *18*:433 (1935).
Enolase	Yeast	O. Warburg and W. Christian, *Biochem. Z.*, *310*:384 (1942).
Glyceraldehyde phosphate dehydrogenase	Rabbit muscle	G. T. Cori *et al.*, *J. Biol. Chem.*, *173*:605 (1948).
Hexokinase	Yeast	M. Kunitz and M. R. McDonald, *J. Gen. Physiol.*, *29*:393 (1946).
Lactic dehydrogenase	Beef heart	F. B. Straub, *Biochem. J.*, *34*:483 (1940).
Lysozyme	Egg white	G. Alderton and H. L. Fevold, *J. Biol. Chem.*, *164*:1 (1946).
Pepsin	Swine stomach	J. H. Northrop, *J. Gen. Physiol.*, *13*:739 (1930).
	Salmon	E. R. Norris and D. W. Elam, *J. Biol. Chem.*, *134*:443 (1940).
Peroxidase	Horseradish	H. Theorell, *Enzymologia*, *10*:250 (1942).
	Milk	H. Theorell and Å. Akesson, *Arkiv Kemi*, *17B*, no. 7 (1943).
Phosphorylase	Rabbit muscle	A. A. Green and G. T. Cori, *J. Biol. Chem.*, *151*:21 (1943).
Pyrophosphatase	Yeast	M. Kunitz, *J. Gen. Physiol.*, *35*:423 (1952).
Rennin	Calf stomach	N. J. Berridge, *Biochem. J.*, *39*:179 (1945).
Ribonuclease	Beef pancreas	M. Kunitz, *J. Gen. Physiol.*, *24*:15 (1940).
Trypsin	Beef pancreas	J. H. Northrop and M. Kunitz, *J. Gen. Physiol.*, *16*:267 (1932); *19*:991 (1936).
Urease	Jack bean	J. B. Sumner, *J. Biol. Chem.*, *69*:435 (1926).
Yellow enzyme	Yeast	H. Theorell, *Biochem. Z.*, *278*:263 (1935).

reversal of the reaction and the attainment of an equilibrium state. On the other hand, if its free energy change is large, a reaction spontaneously goes so far in the downhill direction that it becomes, in effect, *irreversible*. For example, the interaction of glucose and adenosine triphosphate (ATP) to yield glucose-6-phosphate and adenosine diphosphate always moves in this one direction because of the high energy level of the ATP. Fortunately, living cells possess mechanisms for detouring around such an irreversible reaction and for bringing about the uphill or synthetic reactions which will not occur spontaneously alone. This the cells do by coupling their syntheses with supplementary oxidative or energy-yielding reactions which serve as a source of chemical power. Thus, ADP is recoverted to ATP by an oxidative phosphorylation, while glucose-6-phosphate may be split to glucose and phosphate by another enzyme, phosphatase. It follows, therefore, that whenever an important change in free energy is in question, the breakdown and the synthesis of a given compound may occur by quite different pathways, since the latter must proceed through one or more of these coupled reactions.

Mechanism of Biologic Oxidations.   Certain principles of intermediary metabolism have been established, and the significance of key reactions is understood. Perhaps the most important of these reactions is the series known as the tricarboxylic, the citric,

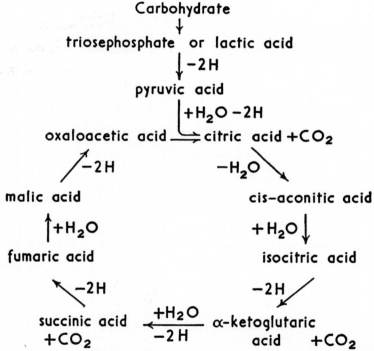

FIG. 573.   Original citric acid cycle, from Krebs and Johnson, 1937. (From Krebs, *Harvey Lect.*, 1950, 44:165–199.)

or the Krebs cycle. Some years ago this cycle was identified as a possible pathway for the utilization of energy from carbohydrate sources in skeletal muscle: later, its presence in other tissues was discovered; and, ultimately, its role in the metabolism of all types of foodstuffs was demonstrated, with the result that this cycle is now known to be a "final common pathway" in the oxidations of carbohydrate, fatty acids, and certain amino acids. [16, 17]

In Figure 573 the cycle is shown with the common names instead of the structural formulas of the participating compounds. The cycle may be said to begin after a two-carbon derivative of carbohydrate, fat or protein has been "activated" by an enzymatic reaction which combines the two-carbon compound ("acetyl") with a substance known as coenzyme A.[19, 21] This coenzyme includes the vitamin known as pantothenic acid as a part of its structure, as other coenzymes include other vitamins. Its specific function is transfer of the two-carbon unit in both oxidative and synthetic reactions (Fig. 574). Acetyl coenzyme A in the presence of oxaloacetic acid and an appropriate enzyme system yields reduce coenzyme A and citric acid, a familiar six-carbon, tricarboxylic acid. With the aid of other enzyme systems there are then formed, in order,

cis-aconitic acid (named from aconite, a poisonous herb),
isocitric acid,
α-keto glutaric acid (named from gluten + tartaric acid),
succinic acid (from Latin word for amber),
fumaric acid (Iceland moss),
malic acid (Latin for apple), and then
oxaloacetic acid.

In passing through this cycle the acetyl yields two molecules of carbon dioxide, while oxidation is occurring with removal of four hydrogen atoms. For the moment it is not essential to memorize the names of all of these acids or their order in the cycle; rather, one should recognize that all foodstuffs are degraded to the two-carbon stage, and that from this stage their oxidation appears to take place through a common pathway. The cycle begins with formation of a six-carbon compound from the two-carbon

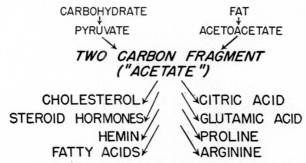

FIG. 574.   Products synthesized from two-carbon fragments or acetyl of acetyl coenzyme A. (From Lipmann, *Harvey Lect.*, 1948, 44:99–123.)

unit and oxaloacetic acid, and results in the liberation of energy, carbon dioxide and hydrogen (which ultimately goes to form water). In the following pages the processes through which the foodstuffs arrive at this two-carbon stage and some of the prominent intermediaries are reviewed.

CARBOHYDRATE METABOLISM

Carbohydrates of Biologic Importance.   Carbohydrate metabolism includes all of the reactions undergone in the body by ingested carbohydrates and by those formed in the body from noncarbohydrate sources. In these two categories are included the following: (i) the polysaccharides—starch and glycogen; (ii) the disaccharides—maltose, sucrose, and lactose; and (iii) the monosaccharides—the hexose sugars (glucose, fructose, and galactose) and certain pentoses (ribose and others). The disaccharides and polysaccharides, except glycogen and lactose, are hydrolyzed to monosaccharides—glucose, fructose or galactose—in the gastrointestinal tract.

The processes of intermediary metabolism, therefore, are concerned primarily with the monosaccharides, the compounds into which they may be converted and the compounds from which they may be formed. Among these compounds are: (i) glycogen, composed of a still undetermined number of glucose units; (ii) pyruvic acid (CH_3—CO—COOH), lactic acid (CH_3—CHOH—COOH) and acetic acid (CH_3—COOH), which are the three most familiar of the series of compounds intermediate between glucose and CO_2 and H_2O; (iii) certain less easily isolated intermediary compounds, such as the phosphoric acid esters of hexose and triose sugars, the four-carbon dicarboxylic acids (succinic, fumaric, malic and oxaloacetic), as well as the five-carbon and six-carbon compounds of the tricarboxylic acid cycle; (iv) neutral fats which may be synthesized from carbohydrate; and (v) glycerol and the amino acids from which glucose may be produced. Of primary importance is the understanding of the over-all pattern of carbo-hydrate metabolism and the roles played by glucose, glycogen, lactic and pyruvic acids ("lactate" and "pyruvate") and the acetate ion in its active form as a part of the acetyl-coenzyme A complex. Once their relationships are thoroughly understood, the positions of the less familiar intermediate compounds are more easily grasped.

Carbohydrate Supply of the Body. BLOOD GLUCOSE AS A DYNAMIC EQUILIBRIUM. The blood glucose (blood sugar) is a well known form of carbohydrate, present in whole blood of mammals in the fasting state in a concentration of about 60 to 80 mg. per 100

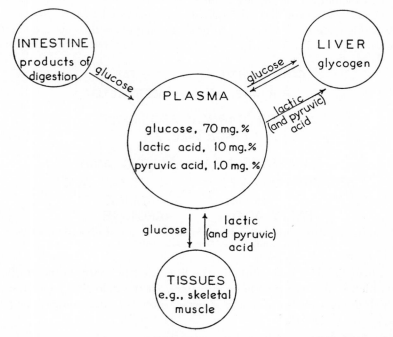

FIG. 575.   Diagram of interchanges of glucose and lactic and pyruvic acids between plasma and the organs which take part in carbohydrate metabolism.

ml., although after a meal rich in carbohydrate the concentration may temporarily rise as high as 130 to 140 mg. per 100 ml. Glucose is a reducing sugar, and the ordinary methods for determining its concentration are based upon this property; but there are other reducing substances of noncarbohydrate nature present in blood, and in testing for glucose care must be taken to exclude, as far as possible, the effects of these other compounds.

The blood glucose is the form in which carbohydrate is transported via the circula-tion from one part of the body to another (Fig. 575). Certain organs (the gut and the liver) may increase the glucose content of the blood perfusing them, whereas other organs (the brain, active muscle and the liver as well, in appropriate circumstances) withdraw glucose from the blood. In view of the diverse influences to which the blood glucose level is subjected, its relative constancy is a truly remarkable phenomenon; it is possible only because while one organ adds glucose to the blood some other part of the body is able to take up the excess almost immediately. Similarly, when the level tends to fall because glucose is being rapidly used, there are reserves which may be drawn upon for replacement. In either of these situations the organ primarily responsible for taking up the surplus or restoring the deficiency is the liver. Mann and his collaborators[24] found that, when the liver has been removed from a dog, the blood glucose falls progressively over a period of hours and the animal dies. If glucose solution is given by infusion or hypodermoclysis, the animal lives until the injected glucose has been utilized, when hypoglycemia again becomes evident. Conversely, since a hepatectomized dog is unable to dispose normally of excess glucose, an extremely high blood sugar level (hyperglycemia) follows glucose administration. The liver owes its commanding position in the control of the blood sugar level to its ability either to synthesize glucose into glycogen and fat, or to convert glycogen and certain amino acids into glucose, as circumstances may require.

If the blood sugar falls below a level of approximately 40 mg. per 100 ml., the subject undergoes a series of reactions initiated by the effects of the hypoglycemia upon neurons of the central nervous system. A sense of weakness and hunger may be noted, and is followed by sweating, cutaneous vasomotor reactions (either vasoconstriction or vasodilatation), salivation, lacrimation, shivering and involuntary urination and defecation. Convulsions, coma and death may ensue if the sequence is not interrupted by the administration of glucose. Hyperglycemia, on the other hand, in itself causes no symptoms. It occurs following ingestion of food (particularly sugars), during anxiety or fear, in diabetes mellitus, and following removal of the pancreas or injury to the islets of Langerhans in experimental animals. If the hyperglycemia is severe enough (above 250 mg. per 100 ml.), glucose is lost from the blood through the kidneys (see Chap. 39). Diabetes mellitus is the condition in which this situation most often occurs.

Both the rate at which glucose is added to the plasma and the rate at which it is removed are regulated in a large part by hormones secreted by the anterior lobe of the hypophysis, the pancreatic islets and the cortices and medullae of the adrenals. When insulin, for example, is given intravenously to a normal animal or human subject, the blood sugar begins to fall within a few minutes; the magnitude of the fall depends to a certain extent upon how much insulin has been injected. If the dose is not large, the insulin will be inactivated in the body within 30 to 60 minutes, and the blood sugar will then begin to be restored. Epinephrine, on the other hand, produces a prompt rise in blood sugar levels.

The normal, physiologic state of the blood sugar represents what may be called a "dynamic equilibrium." This phrase implies that the blood glucose is relatively constant, but it also implies that this constancy is the result not of inactivity, but rather of a variable regulation of the rates at which glucose is added to and withdrawn from the blood. The body's ability to maintain this equilibrium is often tested both experimentally and clinically by temporarily upsetting the equilibrium and measuring the length of time necessary for restoration to occur. Two different types of procedures are used. One, called a test of insulin "sensitivity," consists of measuring the severity and duration of the hypoglycemia evoked by a known quantity of insulin (Sec. XII) to test the mechanisms responsible for the addition of glucose to the circulating blood. The other procedure, known as a test of glucose "tolerance," consists of measuring the magnitude and duration of the hyperglycemia produced by the administration of a known quantity of glucose or glucose solution. (Intravenous injection gives somewhat more uniform results than oral administration because of the influence of the rate of intestinal absorption. In hypothyroidism, absorption is delayed.) By this means the integrity of the mechanisms through which glucose is utilized and stored may be determined (Fig. 576).

LIVER GLYCOGEN AND CARBOHYDRATE STORAGE. The possibility that liver glycogen represents a stored form of glucose was first proposed by the great French physiologist,

Claude Bernard,[26] who recognized that the liver can either remove or add glucose as blood passes through it. Both types of response depend upon the liver's ability to effect a series of reversible reactions in which the complex polysaccharide glycogen is synthesized from hexose units with the removal of water. This relationship is expressed empirically in the following equation:

$$n[C_6H_{12}O_6] \rightleftharpoons (C_6H_{10}O_5)_nH_2O + (n - 1)\ H_2O$$

The liver of a well fed dog may contain as much as 3 to 5 per cent glycogen—a reservoir from which glucose may be supplied to the tissues using it. If the human liver stores an equivalent amount, in the fed state there are available possibly 75 grams or slightly more than 300 kcal. If, on the other hand, an animal is fasted before its liver is removed for analysis, the glycogen content is quite low—a few tenths of 1 per cent—which signifies that the once generous store has been converted to glucose and used by the body.

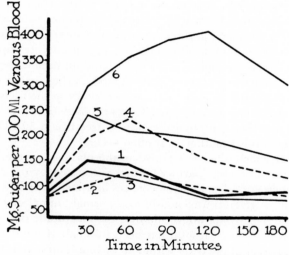

FIG. 576. Glucose tolerance curves. 1, Normal; 2, a case of hypothyroidism; 3, a case of renal diabetes; 4, a case of hyperthyroidism; 5, a case of mild diabetes; 6, a case of severe diabetes. (Data collected in the Hospital Laboratories of the Research and Educational Hospitals, Chicago, Ill. From Levinson and MacFate, *Clinical laboratory diagnosis*, 2nd ed. Philadelphia, Lea & Febiger, 1943.)

Approximately 100 years after Claude Bernard's important experiments upon liver glycogen, the chemical reactions interposed between glucose and glycogen were identified, and the enzymes responsible for each step were isolated.[6] The first step, beginning with glucose, is a phosphorylation, which is catalyzed by hexokinase and yields glucose-6-phosphate, with adenosine triphosphate (ATP) serving as a phosphate donor. Under the influence of another enzyme, phosphoglucomutase, an intramolecular rearrangement then occurs which yields glucose-1-phosphate (the so-called Cori ester); this compound is in turn acted upon by a third enzyme, phosphorylase, which removes the phosphate and synthesizes glycogen. The entire series of reactions can be carried out in a test tube in the presence of appropriate amounts of each of these substances and certain metallic ions. It should be noted, however, that no glycogen will be formed unless a small amount of preformed glycogen is already present in the reacting mixture. This is said to "prime" the reaction, possibly by furnishing a skeleton to which glucose units may be added. In test tube experiments, inorganic phosphate accumulates as glycogen is formed and soon inhibits the reaction unless some provision is made for chemically disposing of the phosphate. This effect is apparently of negligible importance in the liver cell because other enzyme systems take up the phosphate and ultimately return it to the adenine phosphates to resynthesize ATP. These reactions have been summarized in the following equations:

$$\text{Glucose} + \text{ATP} \xrightarrow{\textit{hexokinase}} \text{Glucose-6-phosphate} + \text{ADP}$$

$$\text{Glucose-6-phosphate} \underset{\textit{phosphoglucomutase}}{\rightleftharpoons} \text{Glucose-1-phosphate}$$

$$\text{Glucose-1-phosphate} \underset{\textit{phosphorylase}}{\rightleftharpoons} \text{Glycogen} + \text{PO}_4$$

Fructose may also serve as a source of glycogen by way of this same series of reactions, since there is present in the liver an enzyme identified as an *isomerase* because it is able to convert fructose-6-phosphate into glucose-6-phosphate.

Glycogen breakdown (glycogenolysis or glucogenesis) occurs through the reversal of this same series of reactions, except that the hexokinase reaction which would form ATP is not reversible (see above). Instead, free glucose is formed by the action of another widely distributed enzyme—phosphatase—which splits glucose-6-phosphate to glucose and inorganic phosphate. The glucose thus liberated diffuses out of the hepatic cell into the blood in the liver sinusoids, provided the glucose concentration of that blood is below the glucose concentration of the intracellular fluid.

GLUCONEOGENESIS. The liver also supplies the blood with glucose derived from other sources, certain amino acids and the glycerol portion of fat molecules. The reactions by which this is accomplished are designated by the term "gluconeogenesis," which suggests the noncarbohydrate origin of the material from which the glucose is produced. The details of the reactions are discussed later in this chapter in the section on protein metabolism. The glucose formed from these sources is indistinguishable by ordinary tests from that derived from starch, glycogen or the disaccharides, and its fate in the body does not need to be considered separately.

Peripheral Utilization of Carbohydrate. IN SKELETAL MUSCLE. The circulatory system distributes to the cells of the body the carbohydrate, primarily glucose, supplied by digestive tract and liver (Fig. 575). In the cells the chemical energy of the glucose is liberated as heat or work, or storage takes place, depending upon the nature of the individual cell. Not all of the reactions involved in glucose utilization have been discovered, but enough has been learned about the metabolism of one particular tissue— skeletal muscle—to yield a valuable insight into the nature of intracellular processes in general. One of the interesting characteristics of skeletal muscle is its ability to synthesize and retain glycogen. By setting aside a carbohydrate reserve (from 0.5 to 1.0 per cent of the weight of the muscle) the cell acquires the capacity to work when the supply of blood glucose is not immediately adequate. The reactions through which muscle glycogen is synthesized from glucose appear to be identical with those which occur in the liver. Moreover, the breakdown or hydrolysis of muscle glycogen evidently begins by way of reactions similar to those described above for liver glycogen. But in the muscle the phosphate radical is not split off at the hexose stage, as it may be in the liver, but is retained until there has been accomplished a series of reactions which ultimately yield the three-carbon compounds, pyruvic or lactic acid. Two general pathways of utilization, designated as aerobic and anaerobic to indicate their respective dependence and independence of molecular oxygen, are known to exist. Of the two, anaerobic glycolysis has been the more widely studied, but lack of knowledge of the other should not obscure its position as quantitatively the more important under normal conditions. *Aerobic* metabo-

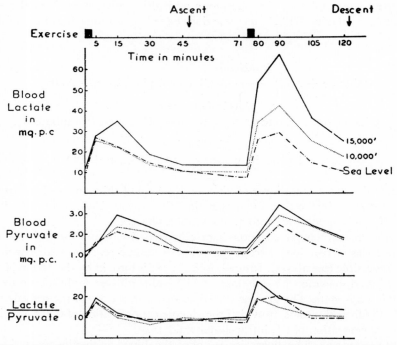

FIG. 577.   Elevation of blood lactic and pyruvic acid levels following exercise on a bicycle ergometer. The graphs include three different control periods of exercise at sea level, each of which is followed by another exercise period either at sea level or at a simulated altitude of 10,000 or 15,000 feet. (From Tepperman and Tepperman, *J. clin. Invest.*, 1948, *27*:176–186.)

lism derives from a carbohydrate molecule all of its energy, since the carbon and hydrogen are completely oxidized. *Anaerobic* glycolysis of a molecule of glucose, on the other hand, yields two molecules of lactic acid, the energy content of which is approximately nine-tenths that of the original glucose. It is obvious that, unless lactate can be utilized in some way, the body will lose an important source of energy whenever the muscle cell is obliged to carry on anaerobic metabolism. There appear to be two pathways by which lactate may be reclaimed. In the presence of oxygen, lactate may be oxidized back to pyruvic acid in the muscle cell, where it may then re-enter the usual catabolic channels or may be resynthesized to glycogen; or, because of its high diffusibility, the lactate may actually leave the muscle, diffuse into the blood and lymph, and thus be carried to the liver where its utilization or synthesis into glycogen and a subsequent conversion to blood glucose may be accomplished. The latter method of disposal is sometimes referred to as the "Cori cycle" because Cori first outlined the scheme—muscle glycogen → lactic acid → liver glycogen → blood glucose → (muscle glycogen).

Significance of lactic and pyruvic acids.   Most of the intermediary products of muscle metabolism are present in muscle in low concentration at any given time, and they are relatively nondiffusible; consequently they do not appear in blood from muscles in significant amounts. Lactic and pyruvic acids, however, are like carbon dioxide and water in that they do leave the muscles via the blood, especially when anaerobic utilization of carbohydrate is in progress. This may occur during vigorous exercise, or during less strenuous exercise when the subject is breathing air having a reduced oxygen tension, as at high altitudes (Fig. 577). The magnitude of the rise in blood levels is an index of the extent of anaerobic glycolysis. Following the exercise the lactate and pyruvate are no longer produced in large quantities, the liver removes the acids circulating in the blood, and the blood levels again return to resting values.

UTILIZATION IN OTHER ORGANS.   Skeletal muscle is only one of the many sites in which carbohydrate is broken down to yield energy and heat, but it happens to be the one site in which the intermediary reactions have been intensively studied. For the present it must serve, therefore, as a model of the lines along which description of metabolic reactions in their entirety will be ultimately completed. Eventually one must distinguish the processes through which energy is made available for mechanical work from the processes associated with organic syntheses and from those responsible for other phenomena, such as secretion, conduction, etc. It now appears that these processes are all alike in that the energy is made available by way of high-energy chemical bonds. An analysis of the energy available for work in certain of these phosphorylations has revealed that a pyrophosphate such as adenosine triphosphate, when converted to the diphosphate, yields approximately 10.5 kcal. per mol—a yield five times greater than that of hydrolysis of an ester such as glucose-1-phosphate, which yields only about 2.0 kcal. per mol. The energy required in the first place to form these high-energy bonds is obtained from cyclic oxidative reactions in which hydrogen atoms and electrons are transferred to progressively lower energy levels with release of energy and heat. Most of the energy obtained from carbohydrate is released by oxidation of pyruvate via the tricarboxylic or citric acid cycle (Krebs).

Interconversions of Foodstuffs.   Pyruvic acid (CH_3—CO—COOH) and its derivative, "acetyl" or active acetate, are important intermediaries in carbohydrate metabolism. Pyruvate may be a somewhat less familiar substance than glucose and glycogen, since it is a compound seldom encountered outside this specialized field, yet it is a key substance in glycolysis, in the formation of carbohydrate from certain amino acids, and in carbohydrate oxidation. "Acetyl" is produced from pyruvic acid by decarboxylation

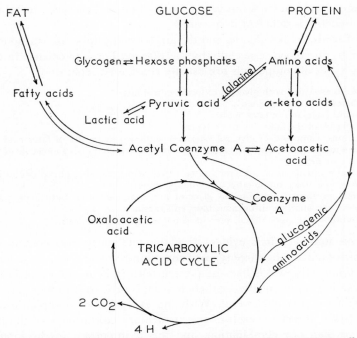

FIG. 578.   Diagram to illustrate interconversions among the three classes of foodstuffs. Many of the interconversions occur in liver; oxidations take place in all tissues.

and combination of the two-carbon residue with coenzyme A; this reaction is oxidative in nature and may be considered to be irreversible. It is the step leading from the three-carbon stage into the citric acid cycle, where oxidation is completed and most of the energy obtained by oxidations is released and utilized. This formation of acetyl coenzyme A occurs in liver as well as in muscle, and in the liver the active acetate may take part in a number of reactions in addition to the possibility of oxidation through the tricarboxylic acid cycle. Condensation of two acetate molecules may occur with formation of acetoacetate, from which β-hydroxy-butyric acid may be derived; or the acetate may be utilized in synthesis of fatty acids or cholesterol, etc. (Fig. 578). Through active acetate the pathways of carbohydrate, protein and lipid metabolism come together, since acetate is formed in oxidations of all three, in conversion of protein to carbohydrate, and of carbohydrate to fat.

LIPID METABOLISM

Nutritive Value of Lipids. The lipids of food are absorbed into the lacteals chiefly as neutral fats which enter the blood either directly or by way of the chyle of the great thoracic duct. This fat remains in the circulation for an appreciable time, being slowly taken up by tissues which participate in lipid metabolism. Speaking generally, the essential nutritive value of foodstuff fats is that they furnish energy to the body; for this they are well suited because they contain more energy, weight for weight, than the proteins or the carbohydrates. When food is eaten in excess of the actual metabolic activity of the body, the excess is stored mainly in the adipose tissue as fat, to be drawn upon in case of need, as, for instance, during partial or complete starvation. A starving animal, after its relatively small supply of preformed glycogen is exhausted, lives entirely upon body proteins and fats; the larger the supply of fat, the more effectively the protein tissues will be conserved and the longer the individual can survive complete food deprivation. Lipids are continually being oxidized for energy and heat, however, not only during complete abstention from food, but in the course of normal everyday metabolism, as well as when food energy is deficient in amount.

Plasma Lipids. Like glucose and the amino acids, lipids are transported throughout the body by the blood, especially by the plasma. For convenience in classification the following types of compounds are usually considered separately:

1. Fatty acids esterified with glycerol to form neutral fat;
2. Free cholesterol (not esterified);
3. Cholesterol esters of the fatty acids;
4. Phospholipids of the following three types:
   a. Lecithins, composed of glycerol esterified with two molecules of fatty acid and combined with a molecule of phosphoric acid, which in turn is united with a molecule of the nitrogenous base, choline;
   b. Cephalins, made up of glycerol and two fatty acid molecules, plus phosphoric acid and the nitrogenous base, amino-ethyl alcohol (colamine);
   c. Sphingomyelins, containing no glycerol but composed of a fatty acid, phosphoric acid, choline and another nitrogenous base, sphingosine;
5. Compounds as yet unidentified, present in relatively small amounts.

From this summary it is evident that the total fatty acid content of plasma is normally distributed among three types of compounds: neutral fat, cholesterol esters and the phospholipids. Glycerol is likewise present both in neutral fat and in the phospholipids, lecithin and cephalin; the total cholesterol is divided into free (28 per cent) and esterified (72 per cent) cholesterol. With the exception of phosphoric acid and the nitrogenous bases, therefore, each of the elementary constituents of the plasma lipids exists in more than one combination, and this is important in the interpretation of changes in the concentration of the individual lipid fractions.

Many attempts have been made to establish normal values and to discover the factors that determine the plasma lipid concentrations. Beyond the facts that hyperlipemia occurs during absorption of fat from the gut and that prolonged starvation evokes a significant rise in cholesterol and phospholipid,[14] however, little is known of the mechanisms of their normal regulation. The values vary somewhat from one individual to another and even from day to day in any one individual, but, in spite of this variability, normal levels have been determined. By the methods of Peters and Man[27] the total fatty acid content of human serum ranges from 5.6 to 19.0 mEq. per liter; cholesterol varies from 123 to 274 mg. per 100 ml.; lipid phosphorus, from 6.4 to 12.0 mg. per 100 ml.; and neutral fat (expressed as fatty acid), from 0.1 to 6.1 mEq. per liter.

Two interesting problems concerning lipid transport remain to be solved. The first is how lipids, which are naturally immiscible with water, are so readily distributed throughout the watery fluids of the body, and the second is to explain the ability of lipid molecules to penetrate freely certain cellular membranes and their apparent inability to penetrate others. The phospholipids, lecithin and cephalin, are believed to be important intermediaries in fatty acid transport. These phospholipids are thought to be capable of serving this function, since they are miscible with water and can diffuse through membranes similar to those of blood capillaries;[4] neither this hypothesis nor others proposed to account for the same phenomena have yet been proved conclusively.

Lipid Utilization. FAT STORAGE. Lipids absorbed from the intestine are carried by the plasma to three possible fates, one of which is storage in the adipose tissue of the body. By far the largest part of this storage occurs in the subcutaneous tissue, the omentum, pericardium, and retroperitoneal tissue, and between the fibers of skeletal muscles. In these locations lipids are deposited mainly in the form of neutral fat—that is, glycerol esters of the fatty acids. Views upon the origin of body fat have undergone a number of changes in the last hundred years, illustrating how development of experimental methods leads often at first to half-truths which are corrected later by more extensive work. Dumas and others held to the natural view that the fat of the body originates directly from the fat of the food. Liebig,[18] applying his more exact methods, demonstrated that this source is sometimes insufficient to account for all the fat. The amount of fat yielded by the milk of a cow, for instance, may be greater than the amount in the food. He also pointed out that the fat of each species of animal is more or less peculiar, the fat of the sheep having a higher melting point than pork fat, and both differing in composition from the fat taken as food. He thought that the chief source of body fat was carbohydrate food, and this belief agreed well with the experience of agriculturists in using such foods to fatten animals for market. The modern point of view is that the fat of the body originates partly from the lipids of the food and partly from carbohydrate and protein through interconversions discussed below (Fig. 578).

The first proof that food fats may be deposited as such in the adipose tissues of the body was obtained by feeding foreign fats to dogs (linseed oil, grapeseed oil and mutton fat) and demonstrating that those fats can afterward be recognized in their tissues. Other feeding experiments suggest that the normal fat of the food undergoes a similar fate. Thus, Hofmann used a dog weighing 26 kg. and allowed it to starve until its weight was reduced to 16 kg. It was then fed for five days on a little meat and large quantities of fat. At the end of that time the animal was sacrificed and analyzed. Its body contained 1353 grams of fat, of which only 131 grams could have come from the protein used, assuming that this material can serve as a fat former. Much of the fat found, therefore, was probably derived from the ingested fat. Later Schoenheimer[28] and his colleagues labeled individual fatty acid molecules with isotopic hydrogen (deuterium) and found that, of the total number of labeled molecules fed to the animal, a large proportion was deposited in the adipose tissues unchanged. Moreover, they found a continual interchange of fatty acids between lipids of the diet and those of the animal's depots, and clearly demonstrated that, even when the individual's caloric intake equals or exceeds his expenditure, a significant amount of depot fat is continuously being replaced by dietary fatty acids. Two separate processes may be presumed to be involved in this reaction—one, a process of deposition, the other a process of removal from the depots. If the animal is in energy balance, the rates at which the two proceed must be equal; but when balance is disturbed, the rate of one may exceed the rate of the other, and the depots may either increase or decrease. The regulation of the rates of these reactions is discussed in Chapters 49 and 51.

PATHWAYS OF OXIDATION AND SYNTHESIS. Lipids not stored in the adipose tissue and lipids withdrawn from it may be oxidized within the cells of the body with the liberation of heat and energy. Two general pathways appear to be involved. When oxidation occurs via one of them, so-called "direct utilization," intermediary compounds do not accumulate in body fluids in significant concentration; during utilization via

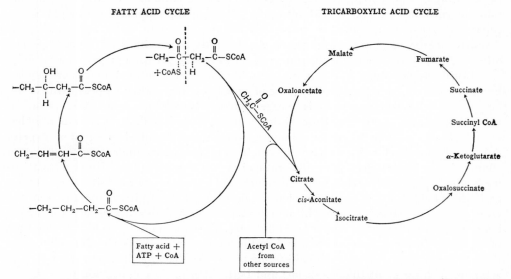

FIG. 579. Relationship of fatty acid degeneration cycle to the tricarboxylic acid cycle. (From White et al., Principles of biochemistry, 2d ed. New York, McGraw-Hill, 1959.)

the other pathway, however, intermediary compounds known as ketone bodies—beta-hydroxy-butyric acid, acetoacetic acid and acetone—do tend to accumulate, and their concentrations may rise to levels high enough to disturb seriously the normal acid-base equilibrium of body fluids.

The most important mechanism of fatty acid oxidation, beta-oxidation, was described by Knoop[15] more than half a century ago. He arrived at this theory from a study of the oxidation products of the phenyl compounds of fatty acids. He found that phenyl propionic acid, $C_6H_5CH_2CH_2COOH$, on oxidation yields benzoic acid, C_6H_5-COOH, without the intermediate formation of phenyl acetic acid, $C_6H_5CH_2COOH$, as might have been expected if the oxidation had taken place at the alpha carbon. By oxidation at the beta carbon the two end carbons were oxidized off with the production of benzoic acid. When the longer fatty acid chains—butyric, valerianic, caproic, etc.— were combined with the phenyl radical and oxidized, the acids with an even number of carbon atoms gave phenyl acetic as an end-product, whereas those with an odd number gave benzoic acid. From this and other evidence Knoop stated what is now firmly established, that the long carbon chain of the fatty acid is oxidized at the beta carbon atom (the second carbon from the carboxyl group). The two end carbons are split off as acetyl CoA, as shown in Figure 579, and a fatty acid containing two fewer carbon atoms remains.

The first stage in fatty acid utilization yields a combination of the acid and co-enzyme A through the carboxyl group of the former and the sulfhydryl group of the coenzyme, with loss of H_2O. This new compound is represented as —CO—S—CoA in Figure 579. The reaction requires energy, provided in animal tissues through combination and conversion of ATP, fatty acid and coenzyme A. Following this activation, the fatty acid enters a cycle of reactions, the fatty acid cycle of Lynen (Fig. 579), where oxidations occur and a two-carbon fragment is removed from the chain in the form of acetyl coenzyme A, which enters the tricarboxylic acid cycle of Krebs. Passage through the former cycle a second time will remove a second two-carbon portion from the fatty acid, and so on until beta-oxidation is completed to the four-carbon state.

The fatty acid cycle is a mechanism of widespread distribution in biologic systems—for synthesis of fatty acids as well as for their oxidation. All of its stages are reversible; when fat is being synthesized from carbohydrate these reactions are the reductions that are reflected in the high R.Q. of this condition (Chap. 48).

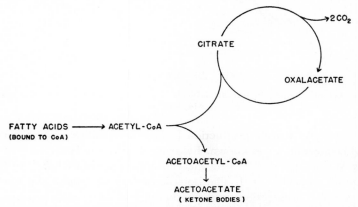

FIG. 580. Diagram of oxidation of fatty acids via tricarboxylic acid cycle. (From Lynen, *Harvey Lect.*, 1954, *48*:210–244.)

The bond formed by removal of water from the carboxyl and sulfhydryl groups is said to be a "high-energy" bond, since its hydrolysis yields approximately 12.4 kcal. per mol.

A second pathway for lipid utilization begins with the activation of fatty acids as in direct utilization; the products of the fatty acid cycle, however, instead of combining with oxaloacetate and entering the Krebs cycle, condense to form acetoacetyl coenzyme A, from which acetoacetic acid is formed by an irreversible hydrolysis catalyzed by a de-acylase (Fig. 580). The presence of this enzyme assures the movement of the over-all reaction in the direction of acetoacetate production, since it removes from the reversible parts of the system the acetoacetyl coenzyme A which would otherwise inhibit further progress in this direction. Discovery of these mechanisms explains several otherwise puzzling observations about ketone formation. For example, a molecule of fatty acid is known to produce as many as four molecules of ketone bodies, which would not be possible if only the four-carbon remainder of the oxidation process could be converted to acetoacetic acid. Caproic acid (hexanoic, C_6) yields more ketones than butyric acid, while certain branched-chain acids yield ketones in amounts which require condensation of two-carbon compounds. MacKay and his associates[22] proposed this beta-oxidation-

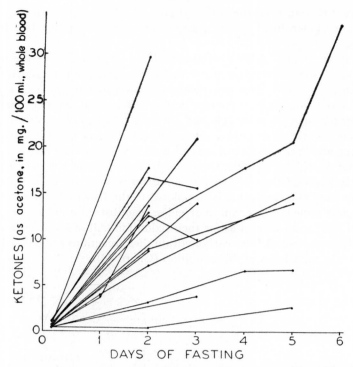

FIG. 581.   Blood ketone changes in human subjects during starvation. (From Kartin *et al.*, *J. clin. Invest.*, 1944, *23:*824–835.)

condensation theory of ketone production before the significance of the reactions involving acetyl coenzyme A was known. Evidence for the condensation was obtained in liver slices by Weinhouse *et al.*,[34] who incorporated isotopic carbon into the carboxyl group of octanoic (caprylic) acid. The isotopic carbon was eventually found in aceto-acetic acid in equal concentrations in the carbonyl (—CO—) and carboxyl (—COOH) groups, suggesting that a significant amount of the ketone must have been formed by condensation of two of the terminal carboxyl groups from the original octanoic acid.

Ketones are normal intermediaries in the course of the oxidation of fatty acids. Both in the intact animal and in tissue slices, ketones are readily formed in the liver, but they appear to be utilized there only slightly. In the intact animal their concentration in liver rises high enough to cause them to diffuse into the blood of the hepatic sinusoids and thus to evoke a generalized ketonemia. Carried throughout the body by the plasma, they are then taken up by cells where their oxidation to carbon dioxide and water is completed. Ketonemia is most intense when the body is deriving the greater part of its energy and heat from lipid catabolism, as, for example, during starvation (Fig. 581) or in diabetes mellitus. Ketonemia can be reduced during starvation by administering carbohydrate, which provides another type of substrate and reduces the need for lipid oxidation. Similarly, in diabetes mellitus where available carbohydrate is not utilized because adequate amounts of insulin are not present, administration of insulin promotes glucose utilization, relieves the individual's dependence upon fat catabolism, and causes diminution of the ketosis. The ability to achieve this response is very important in the management of clinical diabetes mellitus because, although the keto acids are valuable sources of energy, they are also fairly strong organic acids, and as such they disturb the mechanisms of acid-base regulation in body fluids and may even bring about fatal acidosis if severe, uncontrolled ketonemia is allowed to persist.

The liver is the only organ capable of adding ketones to the blood with which it is perfused, and it supplies them to the periphery as it supplies blood glucose. The amount supplied depends upon the extent of the animal's utilization of lipids for heat and energy. Attempts have been made to determine in quantitative terms the importance of hepatic ketogenesis as a pathway of fat utilization. Thus, Stadie[29] and others have suggested that, whereas the peripheral utilization of ketones theoretically could occur rapidly enough to account for four to six times the animal's basal heat production, experimental data indicate that only about 30 per cent of the total amount of fat catabolized is first converted to ketones in the liver, even in animals with uncontrolled pancreatic diabetes with its attendant severe ketosis. Direct utilization in liver and muscle, therefore, appears to be the most important pathway for releasing energy from fatty acids.

ROLE OF LIVER IN LIPID METABOLISM. Through its ability to carry on β-oxidation, to synthesize fatty acids from carbohydrate and protein, and also to provide the rest of the body with ketones, the liver plays a dominant role in lipid as well as in carbohydrate and protein metabolism. As a consequence of its activity in lipid utilization the liver normally contains an appreciable, yet variable, amount of fat. Certain diseases result in the accumulation of excessive amounts of fat in the liver cells; this condition is sometimes called a "degeneration," and sometimes is known as fatty infiltration. The condition is not a disease in itself, but is, rather, a sign of the presence of some derangement of metabolism (Table 36). Fatty liver is to lipid metabolism what hyperglycemia is to carbohydrate metabolism—a rather common condition which need cause concern only when it reaches levels above the rather wide normal range. Most of the experimental work has been done on rats or depancreatized dogs. In rats, a diet relatively high in cholesterol leads to the deposition of cholesterol esters in the liver; diets high in neutral fat or low in choline bring about a deposition of glycerol esters of the fatty acids, as does

TABLE 36.   FATTY LIVERS AND LIPOTROPIC AGENTS
(From West and Todd, *Textbook of biochemistry*, New York, Macmillan Company, 1952.)

CAUSE	LIPOTROPIC AGENT
Deficiencies	
A. Essential fatty acids. Interferes with phospholipid synthesis.	Essential fatty acids.
B. Choline. Interferes with phospholipid synthesis.	Choline, methionine, betaine.
C. Pyridoxine. Increases demand for inositol and choline.	Inositol. Choline and methionine less effective.
D. Pantothenic acid. Effect unknown.	Choline? methionine?
E. Thyroid hormone. Lowered metabolism.	
Excesses	
A. Cystine. Stimulates appetite and metabolism. Diverts methionine.	Choline, methionine.
B. Cholesterol. Competes for fatty acids essential in phospholipid synthesis.	Choline, methionine.
C. Guanidoacetic acid. Takes up methyl groups to form creatine, interferes with choline synthesis.	Choline, methionine.
D. Thiamine. Increases appetite and metabolism. Diverts methionine from choline synthesis.	Choline, methionine.
E. Biotin. Increases demand for inositol.	Inositol, lipocaic.
F. Riboflavin. Increases appetite and metabolism.	Choline, methionine.
G. Niacin. Causes choline deficiency by taking choline methyl groups.	Choline, methionine.
H. Anterior pituitary hormone. Effects possibly due to fat mobilizing factor, adipokinin.	
I. Adrenal cortical hormones. Increase mobilization of fat to liver.	
J. Female sex hormones. Mechanism of action uncertain.	
Liver Poisons. CCl₄, P, etc., cause tissue injury and lowered capacity to metabolize lipids brought to liver.	Choline. Aids in recovery, does not prevent.

TABLE 37. LIPOTROPIC FACTORS

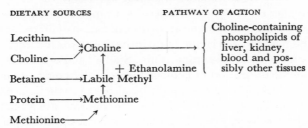

Many tissues fed to animals or patients provide the lipotropic factors. Pancreas, in addition to supplying protein and lecithin, also contributes enzymes which make available methionine and possibly choline from dietary protein and phospholipid. Some protein and choline-containing phospholipid is, of course, provided in the ingested pancreas. (From Best, *Diabetes and insulin and the lipotropic factors*, Springfield, Ill., Charles C Thomas, 1948.)

starvation of the animal; and certain members of the vitamin B complex—especially thiamine and biotin—promote the accumulation of fat in the liver when they are added to the diet of the rat. Depancreatized dogs whose diabetes is controlled with insulin also exhibit remarkably fatty livers. Since the concentration of fats within the organ depends upon the rates at which fat enters and leaves the hepatic cells, an alteration in either of these factors may evoke fatty infiltration. Thus, on a high-fat diet or during starvation, where the animal is catabolizing large quantities of fatty acids, the rate of their transport into the liver cells is probably increased, and the lipoidosis is a manifestation of the increased turnover of liver lipids under these conditions. In pancreatectomized dogs and in rats fed biotin, on the other hand, the fats are thought to accumulate because the hepatic cells cannot dispose of an amount of fat which they usually handle without difficulty. This deficiency may be the result of an inability to synthesize phospholipids (Table 37), since the accumulation of fat can be prevented by adding to the diet compounds known to be components of phospholipid molecules.[7]

Substances which prevent hepatic lipoidosis are said to have a "lipotropic" action. Three types of lipotropic factors have now been distinguished, of which the most generally effective is choline, one of the constituents of the lecithins and sphingomyelins. (Methionine, an amino acid which promotes choline synthesis in the body, may be used in place of choline.) Inositol, also present in phospholipids, is particularly effective against biotin fatty livers. And finally, lipocaic, a substance of as yet unknown chemical composition which can be extracted from the pancreas, prevents the development of fatty infiltration in depancreatized dogs (Table 36). In spite of the relatively extensive experimental study of these various factors, the relationships between the experimentally produced and the clinically observed conditions are not at all obvious.

Conversion of Carbohydrate to Fat. That body fat may originate from carbohydrate was first demonstrated by feeding experiments. Thus, Rubner fed a dog (5.85 kg.) for two days on a diet of sugar, starch, and fat with a total carbon content equal to 176.6 grams. During this period the animal excreted 87.1 grams of carbon. There were retained in the body, therefore, 89.5 grams of carbon. The fat fed, 4.7 grams, contained (4.7 × 0.77) 3.6 grams of carbon. The total nitrogen excreted during this period was 2.55 grams, which indicated a metabolism, therefore, of 16 grams (2.55 × 6.25) of body protein. With the improbable assumption that all of the carbon of this protein was retained in the body, this would account for 8.32 grams of carbon (16 × 0.52); so that 3.6 plus 8.32 or 12 grams of carbon might have originated from sources other than the carbohydrate of the food, leaving, therefore, 89.5 minus 12, or 77.5 grams of carbon, which could have arisen only from the carbohydrate. This quantity of carbon could have been retained only as glycogen or fat. Allowing for the greatest possible storage of glycogen, 78 grams, or 34.6 grams of carbon, there would still remain 42.9 grams of carbon which could have been retained only as fat. In numerous other fattening experiments of different kinds the fat laid on by the animal could not be accounted for by the fat of the food, nor by the assumption that it originated from protein.

In describing the pathways of fatty acid utilization and synthesis in the fatty acid cycle, the reductive reactions necessary for synthesis of fat from carbohydrate were mentioned. In Figure 579 these reductions are marked by the addition of 2H at each of two different stages in the synthetic cycle. In other words, the oxygen content of fatty acids is only about 11 per cent, while oxygen constitutes about 53 per cent of the glucose molecule; compared with the hydrogen and carbon atoms of fatty acids, the hydrogen and carbon of glucose are already partially oxidized. Stated in another way, fat has

$$\text{proportionally more } -\overset{\displaystyle |}{\underset{\displaystyle |}{C}}-\text{H bonds than carbohydrate. Transfer of carbon and hydro-}$$

gen from the glucose to the fatty acid level of less nearly complete oxidation requires the addition of energy to the system—an amount of energy equal to the difference in potential chemical energy between the two types of compounds, plus the energy lost as heat in the reaction as a whole. The transformation is catabolic, therefore, since it is accompanied by an expenditure of energy—an expenditure which may contribute to the "specific dynamic action" of carbohydrate food. Under appropriate conditions, the conversion of any significant amount of glucose to fat can be detected by its effect upon the over-all respiratory quotient of the animal (Chap. 48). The quantity of CO_2 produced in the conversion is greater than the O_2 uptake, and the elimination of the extra CO_2 by the lungs naturally alters the respiratory CO_2/O_2 ratio. Since the numerator is thereby increased, the R.Q. rises proportionately. This change can be observed in isolated tissues, such as liver slices, as well as in the intact animal. When large quantities of fat are being synthesized from carbohydrate, the over-all R.Q. may rise well above unity (at least as high as 1.22).

PROTEIN METABOLISM

Amino Acids as Protein Constituents. Protein utilization proceeds in two stages. The first is accomplished in the gastrointestinal tract where the proteolytic enzymes secreted by digestive glands reduce the large, complex molecules of protein foodstuffs to their constituent parts, the amino acids, or to relatively simple chains of amino acids, the peptides. In molecular weight the proteins range from 13,000 to several millions, but the amino acids vary only from 75 (glycine) to 240 (cystine), which is well within the range of the dimensions of the simple carbohydrates. (The molecular weight of glucose is 180.) Because of their smaller size, relative simplicity and limited number, the amino acids can be studied with relative ease both inside and outside the body, whereas the physiology of the proteins can now be investigated only to a limited extent.

Sources of Amino Acids. PRODUCTS OF DIGESTION. From the intestine the products of protein digestion are absorbed into the portal blood stream and into the lymph, which soon joins the venous blood in the left innominate vein. The addition of these peptides and amino acids to the plasma naturally tends to raise the level of plasma amino nitrogen. Van Slyke[31] found, however, that the rise is much greater in the blood of the portal vein than in that of the systemic circulation, and this observation suggested to him that the liver removes amino acids and simple peptides from the blood perfusing it. When their concentration in the portal blood rises, the liver removes them rapidly enough to minimize their effect upon the composition of the blood of the systemic circulation, but the peripheral tissues also take up and temporarily store a significant quantity. The relative constancy of the blood amino acid level, therefore, results from

TABLE 38.   WEIGHT LOSS DURING STARVATION IN THE CAT (FROM VOIT)

	SUPPOSED WEIGHT OF ORGANS BEFORE STARVATION IN GM.	ACTUAL LOSS OF ORGANS IN GM.	LOSS TO EACH 100 GM. OF FRESH ORGAN (PERCENTAGE LOSS)
Bone	393.4	54.7	13.9
Muscle	1408.4	429.4	30.5
Liver	91.9	49.4	53.7
Kidney	25.1	6.5	25.9
Spleen	8.7	5.8	66.7
Pancreas	6.5	1.1	17.0
Testes	2.5	1.0	40.0
Lungs	15.8	2.8	17.7
Heart	11.5	0.3	2.6
Intestines	118.0	20.9	18.0
Brain and cord	40.7	1.3	3.2
Skin and hair	432.8	89.3	20.6
Fat	275.4	267.2	97.0
Blood	138.5	37.3	27.0
Remainder	136.0	50.0	36.8

a well regulated balance between the rates at which these compounds are added to and removed from the blood. The expression, "dynamic equilibrium," applies as well to the state of the blood amino acids as it does to that of the blood sugar.

TISSUE PROTEINS.   Although the gastrointestinal tract contributes a large quantity of amino acids to the portal blood during the digestion of protein food, the gut is by no means the only source of these compounds. Schoenheimer[28] has shown that amino acids are continually interchanged between the plasma and the protein constituents of organs like the liver, kidney, spleen and skeletal muscle, as well as the plasma proteins. During fasting or starvation, the tissue proteins yield to the blood more amino acids than they withdraw, and thus certain organs, principally the liver and skeletal muscle, clearly become sources of blood amino acid nitrogen. This accounts in a large part for the weight loss of starvation, and explains why certain organs lose more weight than others (Table 38).

PARENTERAL ADMINISTRATION.   Since all of the protein used by the body is reduced to or almost to amino acids in the course of its digestion and absorption, the organism should be able to substitute for its dietary protein requirement an equivalent amount of a proper mixture of amino acids. The first experiments of this kind were made by Loewi, who fed dogs a diet consisting of a certain amount of carbohydrate and fat together with protein which had been previously submitted to a prolonged pancreatic digestion until it was completely hydrolyzed. On this diet the animals were able to synthesize protein. As a matter of fact, animals will live and thrive on a similar diet without the addition of fats or carbohydrates; moreover, the amino acid mixture need not be administered via the gastrointestinal tract but may be injected intravenously.[9] Administration intravenously is useful in the treatment of patients unable to take or to retain proteins given orally, and makes possible better nourishment of patients who would otherwise suffer from protein starvation. Naturally enough, the so-called "essential" amino acids are just as important when given intravenously as when they are given orally, and the "nonessential" acids retain their dispensable character by either route of administration.

Amino Acid Utilization.   PROTEIN SYNTHESIS.   The fate of the amino acids taken up by the liver is highly variable, but it may be predicted from a knowledge of the physiologic state of the individual, including his age, nutritional status, activity and the environmental temperature. For a short time, at least, the liver stores a small amount of amino acid nitrogen,[32] but the greater part of the amino acids is (i) synthesized into protein; (ii) oxidized to carbon dioxide, water and urea; (iii) converted to carbohydrate or fat; or (iv) used in the formation of certain amino acid derivatives, such as glutathione, epinephrine, creatine, etc.

Little is known of the chemical reactions responsible for protein synthesis because the structure of protein molecules has not been clearly revealed. There is, however, no doubt that the amino acids present in the blood and interstitial fluids are precursors of tissue protein or that synthesis of the latter is, in its end-result, the antithesis of the hydrolytic reactions through which proteins are degraded by the organic chemist to yield amino acids. According to the now universally accepted theory of protein structure based upon Emil Fischer's[10] classic studies proteins consist of amino acids united by what is known as the "peptide linkage" in which the amino group of one acid unites with the carboxyl group of another, thus:

$$\underset{\substack{|\\H}}{\overset{\substack{R\\|}}{H_2N-C-COOH}} + \underset{\substack{|\\H}}{\overset{\substack{R\\|}}{H_2N-C-COOH}} \rightleftharpoons \underset{\substack{|\\H}}{\overset{\substack{R\\|}}{H_2N-C-CO}} - NH - \underset{\substack{|\\H}}{\overset{\substack{R\\|}}{C-COOH}} + H_2O$$

By reactions of this type, simple peptides and even polypeptides have been prepared from amino acids in the laboratory, and Bergmann and Fruton[2] have shown that compounds so prepared will serve as substrates for the familiar proteolytic enzymes, trypsin, chymotrypsin, pepsin, cathepsin and others. Since enzymes are highly specific toward their substrates, the obvious conclusion is that the synthetic compounds closely resemble the naturally occurring substrates of the individual enzymes. The peptide bonds prepared *in vitro*, therefore, are probably quite like the bonds formed when protein synthesis takes place within living cells. The various proteins synthesized by the body evidently differ from one another in both the relative and the absolute amounts of the several amino acids present in the molecule, and also in the order of pattern into which the amino acids become organized. The number of possible patterns into which 22 or more amino acids might be arranged to yield compounds with molecular weights up to several millions is beyond comprehension. How the cells of the body are able to arrange such complex patterns properly and how a given cell is able consistently to produce its own characteristic proteins are fascinating problems still awaiting solution.

That protein synthesis enhances the individual's energy exchange was noted in connection with the high basal metabolic rate of growing subjects (Chap. 48). When the opposite reaction occurs—protein breakdown or the hydrolysis of a peptide linkage—energy is liberated as heat, and the amount of energy so liberated is large enough to be a limiting factor in determining the direction of the reaction. That is, in the presence of the appropriate enzyme (or a strong acid or alkali) peptides are spontaneously hydrolyzed with the evolution of heat; but a peptide cannot be synthesized from a mixture of amino acids, even in the presence of the appropriate enzyme, unless energy is supplied to the mixture from some other reaction. The source of this extra energy within a living cell is unknown; ultimately, however, the energy must come from the oxidation of a foodstuff—hence the high basal metabolism associated with active growth.

Although only limited data are available concerning rates of reaction and the quantities of compounds involved in intermediary protein metabolism, the well conceived experiments of Schoenheimer have clearly outlined the over-all picture of these reactions. Schoenheimer and his colleagues[28] labeled or tagged amino acid molecules or portions of molecules by incorporating into them known amounts of the isotopic atoms, heavy nitrogen (N^{15}) and deuterium (heavy hydrogen). Weighed amounts of the labeled amino acids were then fed to mature animals in nitrogen equilibrium (p. 1037). When the carcasses of the rats were analyzed three days later, it was found that the animals had retained each amino acid in the form of protein to the extent of about half of the total

TABLE 39. FATE OF AMINO NITROGEN IN NORMAL ADULT RATS

(Isotopic amino acids—corresponding to 25 mg. N per day for 3 days—were added to normal stock diet)

MATERIAL ANALYZED	PER CENT OF ADMINISTERED N[15] RECOVERED	
	After Feeding $l(-)$-Leucine	After Feeding Glycine
	Per Cent	Per Cent
Excreta		
Feces	2.2	2.6
Urine	27.4	40.8
Animal Body		
Nonprotein N	8.2	11.1
Protein N	56.5	44.3
Total	94.3	98.8

(From Schoenheimer, *The dynamic state of body constituents.* Cambridge, Mass., Harvard University Press, 1942.)

amount which had been fed (Table 39). The various parts of the body retained different amounts: plasma proteins retained the largest relative quantity, while the skeletal muscles retained the largest absolute amount (Table 40). Much of the isotopic nitrogen had been transferred from the amino acid fed in the diet into certain other amino acids of the tissue proteins. Thus, there was not only an exchange of whole amino acids between the diet and the tissue proteins, but also an exchange of amino nitrogen between the amino acids of the diet and those of the tissues. The mechanisms of these exchanges are unknown, but, to a certain extent at least, they must involve an exchange of amino groups as such. When Schoenheimer fed the animals isotopic nitrogen in the form of ammonium citrate, the nitrogen (N^{15}) of the NH_4^+ quickly became incorporated into tissue proteins. The exchange is probably enzymatic in nature, and the name "transaminase" has been given to the type of enzyme responsible for the reaction. The only transaminases thus far isolated from tissues, however, can effect exchange of amino groups among only a very few of the relatively large number of compounds which normally must participate in these reactions (see Ref. 25).

Schoenheimer and his colleagues noted interesting and provocative differences be-

TABLE 40. N^{15} CONTENT OF PROTEIN NITROGEN OBTAINED FROM DIFFERENT ORGANS AFTER FEEDING $l(-)$-LEUCINE AND GLYCINE (25 MG. N PER DAY)

(Calculated for 100 atom per cent N^{15} in compound administered)

ORGAN	AFTER FEEDING $l(-)$-LEUCINE	AFTER FEEDING GLYCINE
Serum	1.67	1.78
Hemoglobin	0.29	0.46
Liver	0.94	1.40
Intestinal wall	1.49	0.98
Kidney	1.38	....
Heart	0.89	....
Spleen	1.10	....
Testes	0.77	....
Skin	0.18	....
Muscle	0.31	0.29

(From Schoenheimer, *The dynamic state of body constituents.* Cambridge, Mass., Harvard University Press, 1942.)

tween various amino acids in their rates of reaction and in the types of reactions in which they participate. With regard to protein synthesis in general, his study may be summarized as follows: Even in the adult animal, protein synthesis occurs at a surprisingly rapid rate (which presumably equals the rate of protein breakdown, since nitrogen balance is maintained). This synthesis involves portions of the molecules of tissue proteins and represents a rapid splitting and resynthesis of peptide bonds whereby amino acids present in body fluids are introduced into the proteins. In this synthesis the cells use even fractions of amino acid molecules with the result that an amino group may be utilized apart from the carbon chain with which it was originally associated. In a younger individual who is actively retaining nitrogen, the rate of protein synthesis exceeds the rate of its breakdown, and this disproportion between the two opposing reactions brings about an absolute increase in tissue proteins, which is one of the essential features of the growth process.

Proteins into which amino acids are synthesized render to the organism a multitude of different services. Most important of all are the enzymes which carry on the energy exchanges that make possible all physiologic and biologic phenomena. Moreover, the transmission of hereditary characters is determined largely by nucleoproteins—the genes—present in the ovum and spermatozoon from which the individual develops. Fibrous proteins of connective tissue, bone, skin, etc., support and protect the organism, while other proteins maintain the typical organization of each cell and every tissue. Plasma proteins have already been discussed (Chap. 23). Through their inability to penetrate capillary membranes easily they play a decisive role in the regulation of body water distribution, and they are believed to represent one form in which protein is transported throughout the body.[23] They include, also, the fibrinogen, which takes part in blood clotting, and the antibodies which confer resistance or immunity to disease. Some of the hormones, e.g., those of the anterior lobe of the hypophysis, the thyroid, parathyroid and pancreatic islets, evidently circulate with the plasma protein. All of these compounds and many others related to them must be acquired by the individual through synthetic reactions which commence with amino acids or with simple peptides. Beginning with the relatively minute quantity present in the fertilized ovum, the individual finally attains adulthood by manufacturing and retaining the proteins necessary for his own characteristic structure and his particular types of energy exchange.

DEAMINATION. Amino acids which are not withdrawn from body fluids in the course of protein synthesis may be oxidized directly or may be converted to carbohydrate or fat. In either case, the characteristic amino group is removed, leaving a carbon-hydrogen-oxygen-containing chain closely related to the three- and four-carbon compounds which serve as intermediaries in the oxidation of carbohydrate and fat and which are indistinguishable by ordinary chemical tests from similar compounds derived from other sources. At this stage of utilization, an arbitrary division into protein, carbohydrate and fat metabolism is scarcely possible, since the past history of the molecule is of little significance to the cell using the intermediary compound. The keto acids formed by oxidative deaminations enter the metabolic pool, where they may become involved in enzymatic reactions which oxidize them to carbon dioxide and water, thus liberating energy and heat. On the other hand, the deaminated residues from certain amino acids may be withdrawn from the "pool" and used in the synthesis of protein again, or of glucose, glycogen, fatty acids, or neutral fat. Thus they may again be identified and classified as one or another of the three basic foodstuffs.

CONVERSION TO GLUCOSE OR GLYCOGEN. The conversion of protein to carbohydrate was first suggested by the experiments of Claude Bernard,[26] who found that after an animal's liver glycogen had been depleted by fasting it could be replenished by feeding protein but not by feeding fat. His observations were confirmed by later investigations which showed that, whenever carbohydrate reserves are depleted in a normal animal, a large fraction of any protein or of amino acid mixtures fed to it can be quantitatively accounted for as glycogen, glucose or their derivatives. Lusk[20] and his colleagues were able to study the carbohydrate-forming potentialities of individual amino acids in dogs given phlorhizin, a drug which selectively inhibits glucose reabsorption in the kidney. Under the influence of phlorhizin glucose is excreted in the urine, the blood sugar falls to low levels, and the animal suffers from a generalized carbohydrate deficiency which is only temporarily relieved by glucose administration. When protein is fed to such an animal, the glucose and the urea nitrogen in the urine rise proportionately (Fig. 582), suggesting that some of the protein has been deaminated and converted to glucose. How much of the protein has been so utilized may be calculated by multiplying the weight of the additional urinary nitrogen by 6.25, since nitrogen is present in protein to the extent of 1 part in 6.25. Lusk found that the ratio of urinary glucose to nitrogen, the D:N or G:N ratio, amounted to as much as 3.65 grams of glucose to every gram of nitrogen.

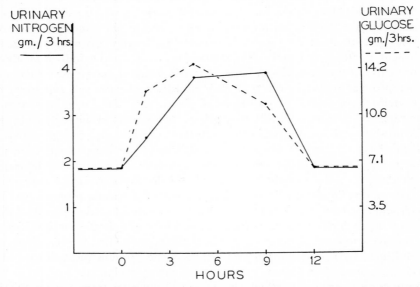

FIG. 582. Curve showing urinary excretion of glucose and nitrogen by phlorhizinized dog fed 500 grams of meat. (From Lusk, *The elements of the science of nutrition*, 4th ed., to conform to earlier practice, 1928.)

In other words, 6.25 grams of protein yielded 3.65 grams of glucose in the phlorhizinized dog, or 58 per cent of the protein was converted to glucose. Drury[8] later suggested that, if account is also taken of glucose which is not excreted because it is catabolized before it reaches the kidneys, the true D:N ratio may be as high as 5 or 6, which suggests that protein may be converted to carbohydrate in a ratio of 1:1. To interpret these results properly, one must remember that the experiments were carried out on adult dogs when the formation of glucose from every possible source was proceeding at a maximal rate owing to the extreme glucose deficiency occasioned by the enormous glucose loss in the urine.

Although the glycogenic property of certain amino acids is most easily measured in animals under the influence of phlorhizin, this same conversion also proceeds under more nearly normal conditions. Some protein is always being changed to carbohydrate, just as some carbohydrate is always being used in amino acid synthesis. The ability to effect gluconeogenesis is particularly important if dietary supplies of carbohydrate are limited as they are when an animal is living on a meat diet or is fasting or starving. A few cells in the body, including those of the central nervous system, obtain most of their energy through oxidation of carbohydrate, and these cells cannot survive even a brief fast if the liver cannot supply them with glucose derived from tissue protein. More than half of the amino acids have been shown to form glucose in the rat or in the dog. The chemical reactions responsible for the conversion have not been discovered, but there is reason to believe that the amino group is removed by an oxidative reaction which yields a keto acid. Thus, deamination of alanine yields pyruvic acid, which is readily converted to glycogen or glycose by the liver.

$$CH_2CH(NH_2)COOH \rightleftarrows CH_3COCOOH \rightleftarrows glycogen \rightleftarrows glucose$$
$$\text{alanine} \qquad\qquad \text{pyruvic acid}$$

CONVERSION TO FAT. Because deamination of the glycogenic amino acids yields compounds identical with certain of the intermediaries of carbohydrate metabolism, the formation of fat from protein and from carbohydrate may occur via the same series of reactions—that is, by way of pyruvate and acetic acid or "acetyl." In addition, certain amino acids are directly diverted into the pathways of fat metabolism through oxidative deaminations which yield ketone bodies (Table 41), but, since only a limited number

TABLE 41.   RELATION OF AMINO ACIDS TO THE TRICARBOXYLIC ACID CYCLE

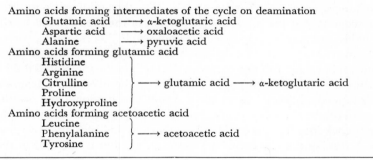

(From Krebs, *Harvey Lectures*, 1950, *44*:165–199.)

of amino acids has been shown to undergo this type of conversion, the significance of this ketogenesis is not clear. Whatever may be the intermediate chemical reactions, it is evident that by converting protein to fat the individual accumulates an energy reserve and conserves most of the potential energy of whatever surplus dietary protein is not utilized in the synthesis of tissue proteins.

Synthesis and Excretion of Urea.   Amino groups removed from the amino acids which are oxidized directly or converted to carbohydrate or fat are eventually excreted by the kidneys as urea, a compound which is synthesized in the liver.* Bollman *et al.*[5] discovered that, after the liver has been removed from a dog, amino acids tend to accumulate in the body fluids and urea formation ceases. Gluconeogenesis from protein is no longer possible, and the animal soon dies because its extrahepatic carbohydrate reserves are exhausted. Synthesis of urea is an endothermic process, requiring the addition of energy from a source outside the reaction. This energy ultimately comes from oxidative reactions, and the extra energy expenditure associated with protein catabolism, i.e, the "specific dynamic action" (Chap. 48) is at least partially explicable on this basis. Deamination seems to be mainly an oxidative process in which ammonia and a keto acid are formed as indicated above. From the ammonia, urea is then synthesized. Krebs and Henseleit[17] have shown that this synthesis can occur by way of a cyclic reaction in which

* Deamination occurs also in the kidney where the amino groups thus split off are subsequently excreted as ammonium ions. This reaction is an important mechanism of acid-base regulation, but has not been established as a notable process in the elimination of the end-products of protein catabolism in general.

the amino acid, arginine, is enzymatically split to urea and ornithine, thus:

$$\underset{H_2N}{\overset{HN}{\diagdown}}C-NHCH_2CH_2CH_2CHNH_2COOH + H_2O \xrightarrow{\;arginase\;}$$
(arginine)

$$\underset{H_2N}{\overset{H_2N}{\diagdown}}C=O + NH_2CH_2CH_2CH_2CHNH_2COOH$$
(urea)   (ornithine)

Ornithine in turn combines with carbon dioxide and with two molecules of the ammonia liberated by the deamination of additional molecules of amino acids; the product of the combination is arginine, and the cycle is thereby completed:

$$2(NH_3) + CO_2 + NH_2CH_2CH_2CH_2CHNH_2COOH \longrightarrow$$
(ornithine)

$$\underset{H_2N}{\overset{HN}{\diagdown}}C-NHCH_2CH_2CH_2CHNH_2COOH + 2H_2O$$
(arginine)

In his work with isotopic nitrogen, Schoenheimer[28] learned that amino groups are indeed rapidly exchanged among the various amino acids, the amidine group of arginine, and urea. This suggests that perhaps a major portion of the urea formed by the liver of an intact animal is produced through the "ornithine cycle." Presumably, tissue protein may be broken down or hydrolyzed to amino acids or simple peptides in any organ of the body. These amino acids and peptides then diffuse into the interstitial fluid of that organ and reach the blood, by which they are carried to the liver. Here deamination occurs, ammonia is formed, arginine is synthesized from CO_2, ammonia and ornithine, and in a reaction catalyzed by the enzyme arginase, urea and ornithine are then produced. The urea diffuses back into the blood of the hepatic sinusoids and, after traversing the heart and lungs, it reaches the kidney, where a certain amount is excreted in the urine (Fig. 583).

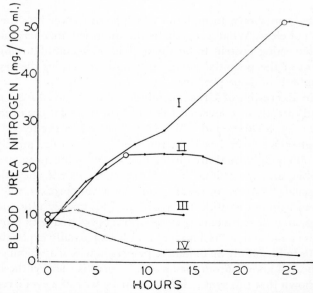

FIG. 583.   Effects of removal of liver on blood urea nitrogen at different levels. Curve *I*, effect of removal of liver at O, 24 hours after removal of both kidneys; curve *II*, effect of removal of liver at O, 8 hours after removal of both kidneys; curve *III*, effect of simultaneous removal of liver and both kidneys; curve *IV*, effect of removal of liver, urinary secretion being maintained. (From Bollman *et al.*, *Amer. J. Physiol.*, 1924, *69*:382.)

NITROGEN EQUILIBRIUM.   This urea contains most of the nitrogen that is taken as a measure of protein catabolism when energy exchange is investigated by the method of indirect calorimetry (Chap. 48). About 16 per cent of the protein molecule is composed of nitrogen which is excreted as urea when protein is oxidized or converted to fat or carbohydrate, so that multiplication of the weight of the nitrogen by 6.25 gives the weight of protein from which it is derived. If the nitrogen content of the food eaten during the period of urine collection is estimated, a balance may be struck which will determine whether the body is gaining or losing nitrogen. If the balance is even, the body is in nitrogen equilibrium—that is, it is receiving in the food as much protein nitrogen as it is metabolizing and eliminating in the excreta. If there is a plus balance in favor of the food, the body must be storing protein; if the balance is minus, the body

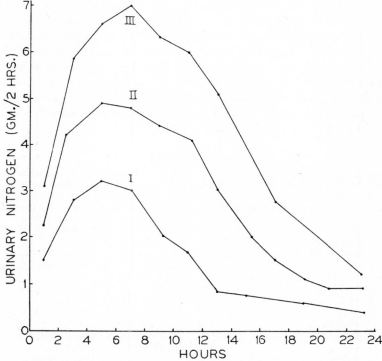

FIG. 584.   Excretion of urinary nitrogen by dog—*I*, after 500 grams meat + 50 grams fat + 350 ml. water; *II*, after 1000 grams meat + 200 ml. water; *III*, after 1500 grams meat + 500 ml. water. On each of these days animal was in nitrogen equilibrium. (From Lusk, *The elements of the science of nutrition*, 4th ed., 1928.)

must be losing protein. During the period of growth, in convalescence, etc., the body does store protein, and under these conditions the balance is in favor of food nitrogen. But throughout adult life, under normal conditions, nitrogen excretion is so regulated that an equilibrium is maintained through long periods. It is important also to bear in mind that nitrogen or protein equilibrium may be established at different levels (Fig. 584). If, for instance, a man in nitrogen equilibrium on a diet containing 10 grams of nitrogen per day is given 20 grams, the extra protein is metabolized and nitrogen equilibrium becomes established at a higher level. Whereas under the first condition 10 grams of nitrogen entered the body in the form of protein and 10 grams left in the nitrogenous excreta, under the second condition 20 grams are furnished each day and 20 grams are lost by excretion. Experimentally there has been found to be a certain low limit of protein which just suffices to maintain nitrogen equibilrium, and, between this level and the capacity of the body to digest and absorb protein food, nitrogen equilibrium may be maintained upon any given amount of protein.

An animal may be brought into nitrogen equilibrium on protein food alone, the amount of protein required being relatively large. If nonprotein foodstuffs are added to the diet, the amount of protein necessary to maintain nitrogen equilibrium may be reduced correspondingly. With reference to the consumption of protein in the body the nonprotein foods are all *protein-sparers;* that is, when only protein food is available, the body uses it for processes which can be carried on with carbohydrate or fat if these foods are available. As has been indicated above, the reactions in which the three classes of foodstuffs may be used interchangeably are those which yield energy and heat.

Other Protein Derivatives. Within the past 50 years much has been learned about the metabolism of the amino acids, especially with reference to the body's handling of the characteristic chemical groupings of the different acids and to the specific reactions in which they participate. There is also beginning to be built up an important body of knowledge about the metabolism of certain protein derivatives such as choline, creatine and creatinine, glutathione and taurine as well as what are called "substituted" proteins, i.e., nucleoproteins, glycoproteins, lipoproteins and phosphoproteins. Study of the metabolism of these compounds promises to yield data of inestimable value regarding protein metabolism in particular and the mechanisms of physiologic energy exchange in general. For the present, however, these subjects remain more directly the concern of the biochemist than of the physiologist.

REFERENCES

1. BARCROFT, J. *J. Physiol.*, 1908, *37*:12–24.
2. BERGMANN, M. and FRUTON, J. S. *Ann. N. Y. Acad. Sci.*, 1944, *45*:409–423.
3. BEST, C. H., LUCAS, C. C. and RIDOUT, J. H. *Ann. N. Y. Acad. Sci.*, 1954, *57*:646–653.
4. BLOOR, W. R. *Biochemistry of the fatty acids.* (American Chemical Society Monograph Series.) New York, Reinhold Publishing Corp., 1943.
5. BOLLMAN, J. L., MANN, F. C. and MAGATH, T. B. *Amer. J. Physiol.*, 1924, *69*:371–392.
6. CORI, C. F. *Biol. Symp.*, 1941, *5*:131–140.
7. CORNATZER, W. E. *Ann. N. Y. Acad. Sci.*, 1954, *57*:919–924.
8. DRURY, D. R. *J. clin. Invest.*, 1942, *21*:153–159.
9. ELMAN, R. *Physiol. Rev.*, 1944, *24*:372–389.
10. FISCHER, E. *Untersuchungen über Aminosäuren, Polypeptide und Proteine.* Berlin, J. Springer, 1906.
11. FRUTON, J. S. and SIMMONDS, S. *General biochemistry.* New York, John Wiley & Sons, Inc., 1953.
12. GLASS, B. Pp. 740–805 in: McELROY, W. D. and GLASS, B. *A symposium on the mechanism of the enzyme action.* Baltimore, Johns Hopkins Press, 1954.
13. GREEN, D. E. *Mechanisms of biological oxidations.* Cambridge, University Press, 1940.
14. KARTIN, B. L., MAN, E. B., WINKLER, A. W. and PETERS, J. P. *J. clin. Invest.*, 1944, *23*:824–835.
15. KNOOP, F. *Beitr. chem. Physiol. Path.*, 1905, *6*:150–162.
16. KREBS, H. A. *Harvey Lect.*, 1950, *44*:165–199.
17. KREBS, H. A. and HENSELEIT, K. *Hoppe-Seyl. Z.*, 1932, *210*:33–66.
18. VON LIEBIG, J. *Die organische Chemie in ihrer Anwendung auf Physiologie und Pathologie,* Braunschweig, F. Vieweg und Sohn, 1842.
19. LIPMANN, F. *Harvey Lect.*, 1948, *44*:99–123.
20. LUSK, G. *The elements of the science of nutrition,* 4th ed. Philadelphia, W. B. Saunders Co., 1928.
21. LYNEN, F. *Harvey Lect.*, 1954, *48*:210–244.
22. MACKAY, E. M. *J. clin. Endocrinol.*, 1943, *3*:101–110.
23. MADDEN, S. C. and WHIPPLE, G. H. *Physiol. Rev.*, 1940, *20*:194–217.
24. MANN, F. C. *Medicine (Baltimore)*, 1927, *6*:419–511.
25. MEISTER, A. *Science*, 1954, *120*:43–50.
26. OLMSTED, J. M. D. *Claude Bernard, physiologist,* New York, Harper & Bros., 1938.
27. PETERS, J. P. and MAN, E. B. *J. Clin. Invest.*, 1943, *22*:707–714.
28. SCHOENHEIMER, R. *The dynamic state of body constituents.* Cambridge, Harvard University Press, 1942.
29. STADIE, W. C. *J. clin. Invest.*, 1940, *19*:843–861.
30. TEPPERMAN, J. and TEPPERMAN, H. M. *J. clin. Invest.*, 1948, *27*:176–186.
31. VAN SLYKE, D. D. *Arch. intern. Med.*, 1917, *19*:56–78.
32. VAN SLYKE, D. D. *Science*, 1942, *95*:259–263.
33. WARBURG, O. *The metabolism of the tumors.* Dickens, F., transl. London, Constable & Co., Ltd., 1930.
34. WEINHOUSE, S., MEDES, G. and FLOYD, N. F. *J. biol. Chem.*, 1944, *155*:143–151.
35. WEST, E. S. and TODD, W. R. *Textbook of biochemistry.* New York, Macmillan Company, 1952.

SECTION XII

Endocrine System

CHAPTER 51

The Hormones

By JANE A. RUSSELL

THE several endocrine glands and their secretions, the hormones, constitute a system for regulating the rates of growth, development and function of certain tissues and the rates of many of the metabolic processes within the body.[1, 3, 4, 5] The endocrine glands are considered as a system and not solely as separate organs, for the hormones seldom act independently of one another or of metabolic events within the body. Moreover, the endocrine system is closely linked, both developmentally and functionally, to the nervous system. In a general sense, the hormones have been considered by some to be a primitive type of integrative device which in higher forms has been superseded in part by the nervous system. Acting more or less independently of nervous regulation in some respects, in others the endocrine system is so related to the nervous system that in effect it serves functionally as an extension of it. This intimate connection between the nervous and endocrine systems allows psychic influences to modify hormonal activities. Numerous clinical and experimental observations attest this relationship.

The hormones may be defined as specific substances secreted by particular organs into the general circulation, which carries these substances to their sites of action elsewhere in the body. Here they *regulate the rates* of specific processes, without contributing significant amounts of energy or matter to the tissues.* Because of the regulatory nature of their roles, either a deficiency or an excess in the circulating levels of the hormones may lead to disorders in the normal development and function of the body.

Hormones of various sorts appear to occur throughout the animal kingdom. Those which are best known, and which will be considered here, are those peculiar to the vertebrates. With respect to most parts of the endocrine system, homologous glandular structures and often identical secretions are found in all vertebrate classes. The relatively little known invertebrate hormones appear to be different substances only rather distantly analogous in their actions to those of the higher animals.

Historical Survey. Despite centuries of observations of the effects of castration in man and animals and of clinical disorders now known to relate to the endocrine system, a clear concept of the general nature of the physiologic role of the endocrine glands did not develop until about 60 years ago. Knowledge of the specific functions of these organs has been accumulated still more recently, and is, we may assume, still relatively scant. The idea of endocrine function is often attributed to Claude Bernard,

---

* Substances which have many of the properties of hormones according to this definition, but which differ in that they are produced by all or many tissues, rather than by a specific organ, have been called parahormones. An example of this class is carbon dioxide, which acts through nervous mechanisms to regulate the respiratory rate.

who in 1855 first described "internal secretion" by an organ of the body; but, as he used the term, it referred to the liberation of metabolites from the liver (this in itself was a revolutionary view at the time) and did not include the concept of the hormone as it is known today. Shortly before, in 1849, Berthold had shown that atrophy of a capon's comb could be prevented by grafting testicular tissue elsewhere in the body of the bird, but this observation remained unnoticed until much later. Apparently without knowledge of Berthold's work, Brown-Séquard and others some 25 years later attempted similar experiments with testicular extracts and grafts in other species, with results which were controversial rather than enlightening.

The eventual stimulus to sound experimental study of the ductless glands came from clinical observation. Association of diseased states of the thyroid and of the adrenal with certain clinical syndromes had been made earlier—toxic or exophthalmic goiter was described by Graves in 1835 and by Basedow in 1840, and a peculiar syndrome accompanied by destruction of the adrenal glands was described by Addison in 1855. To this list was later added myxedema, described first by Gull in 1873 and observed after thyroidectomy in 1883 by the Reverdins and Kocher. These clinical findings suggested to Semon that cretinism, adult myxedema and the post-thyroidectomy syndrome must all be due to failure of thyroid function, and this was confirmed experimentally by Horsley in 1888. Soon thereafter, thyroidectomized animals and myxedematous patients were treated successfully by substitution of fresh or dried thyroid tissue given by mouth.

Up to this date, the nature of endocrine function was unknown. From the time of Addison it had been considered probable that the normal function of the adrenal and other ductless glands must be to remove hypothetical noxious substances from the blood. The "detoxification" theory was applied also to the thyroid gland, and then to the pancreas after Minkowski first produced experimental diabetes mellitus in 1890, and to the parathyroid glands a few years later. It was only after the demonstration of substitution therapy in hypothyroid states, mentioned above, that the modern concept of endocrine function began to be evident. This view—that some organs may regularly liberate into the blood stream substances which are necessary for the normal development and function of other parts of the body—appears to have been first clearly stated by Brown-Séquard and D'Arsonval in 1891. The older idea of detoxification was only slowly relinquished, however, and indeed it still recurs from time to time.

The concept that excess of an endocrine secretion could also produce disease, although it now appears to be a natural corollary of the earlier observations on deficiency of hormones, was only rather gradually developed. Several observations of hyperthyroidism induced by the taking of excessive amounts of thyroid substance, the demonstration of hyperplasia of the thyroid in Graves' disease, and the adenomatous changes seen in the pituitary body in acromegaly and gigantism led finally to the general acceptance of this view in the early years of this century.

The final stage in the development of the modern view of endocrine function was its linkage to Claude Bernard's concept, discussed in previous chapters, that the internal environment is maintained relatively constant. This principle was fully appreciated only long after Bernard's time. The secretion of a hormone in response to a specific stimulus, and thus the intermediation of a hormone in a physiologic response, was first observed by Bayliss and Starling in 1902 in their work on the intestinal hormone, secretin. That hormonal mechanisms might regularly take part in the reactive systems which help to maintain the constancy of the internal environment was apparently first suggested by Starling in 1923, when he called them examples of the "wisdom of the body." Cannon,[1] amplifying this view, included the secretions of certain endocrine organs as integral parts of homeostatic regulation by the autonomic nervous system. Since that time, most of the hormones have come to be considered parts of a larger and more general system, which—like the nervous system—has as its function the integration of the activities of the various parts of the body into those of a coordinated unit.

The name "hormone," from the Greek word meaning arousing or setting in motion, was proposed by Starling in 1905, and although it is hardly applicable in the strict sense to all the endocrine secretions now known, it has been universally adopted as the general term for such secretions.

Functions of Hormones.　The actions of the hormones may usually be included in one of the following categories: (i) morphogenesis, e.g., control of the development and maturation of the gonads and secondary sex organs, of metamorphosis in lower forms, and of the growth of the bones; (ii) integration of autonomic function and of "instinctual" behavior patterns, such as extension of sympathetic system responses and control of sex and maternal behavior; and (iii) maintenance of the internal environment: regulation of the disposition of foodstuffs, electrolytes and water in the body.

The mode of action of the hormones is always regulatory. That is, the hormones do not initiate processes completely *de novo*, but must always have present the normal tissues and enzyme systems upon which to work. A trophic hormone cannot, of course, induce growth of the target organ unless the gland is present in a potentially functional state. Conversely, many processes which are affected by the hormones may display also a considerable degree of autonomy. For example, metabolic reactions which are greatly accelerated *in vivo* by certain hormones may be observed to proceed at measurable rates even in the complete absence of the hormones, either *in vivo* or *in vitro*. The mechanisms by which the hormones bring about their effects are unknown. Although several of these agents produce characteristic effects in surviving tissue slices or minces, convincing evidence that these effects can occur in the absence of intact cells has been obtained only in one or two instances, and in no case has it yet been possible to explain the physiologic activity of the hormone completely on the basis of its actions in a cell-free system. In all probability, the hormones do act by influencing the effectiveness of some specific enzyme systems, but this may be done not in the usual catalytic sense but rather by alteration in the physical or chemical organization of enzyme systems within the cells or in the transport of substrates for enzyme action through cell membranes or into certain parts of the cell.

The endocrine glands obviously may be affected by physiologic mechanisms common to the rest of the organism. The metabolic or nutritional state of the body may influence not only glandular function but also the responsiveness of the organs or tissues affected by the hormones. Moreover, secretion by the endocrine organs can also be affected by the presence of other hormones, by nervous stimuli in many instances, and by other specific environmental factors such as the blood sugar level. Each hormone, then, is not only a regulator itself; its output and effective function may in turn be modified by other factors. Probably no changes occur in, or are forced upon, one part of the endocrine system without inducing some degree of alteration in the function of other parts. In consequence, interpretation of experimental and clinical observation of the effects of deficiency or of excess of a particular hormone has often been difficult. Only with greater knowledge concerning the integration of the endocrine system have some general principles of its operation become clear.

From present evidence, it seems probable that each endocrine organ has normally, when the organism is in a resting state, a fairly constant characteristic rate of secretion of its hormone or hormones, and that this rate is then played upon by changing concentrations of humoral factors or by nervous mechanisms which act as stimuli peculiar to that organ. In general, the response of the endocrine organ to the stimulus is one which tends by various devices to restore the organism to its original state, as it was before the introduction of the change which was the stimulus. Examples of this regulatory role are numerous. Elevation of the blood sugar level is a stimulus to the secretion of insulin, which hastens the removal of sugar from the blood; hypoglycemia is a specific stimulus to the secretion of epinephrine which in turn enhances the release of sugar from the liver. The regulation of the rate of secretion of the trophic hormones of the pituitary body by the circulating level of the secretions of their target organs also is an example of homeostasis. Deficiency of the gonadal, thyroid, or adrenocortical hormones brings about an increase in the rate of secretion of the pituitary hormones controlling these organs, thereby tending to increase the rate of release of the former and to restore the normal hormonal balance. Similarly, the administration of an excess of gonadal, thyroid, or adrenocortical hormones appears to depress the secretion of the respective trophic hormones. This principle—that the endocrine system acts generally in a homeostatic fashion—has provided a framework for many otherwise uncorrelated observations, and, although it may not hold true for every aspect of hormonal activity, it has become a most useful concept.

Methods of Study. The existence of a great many different hormonal factors has been postulated at one time or another, but in many instances the observations on which these theories were based were not critical in nature. For convincing evidence of the presence of a new hormone, or for new functions of known hormones, at least two types of observations are required: the production of a specific syndrome in the absence of the hormone in question and specific physiologic responses to the exogenous administration of the hormone by grafting or implantation of glandular tissue or by infusion of an extract of the tissue. The latter demonstration should include both successful replacement therapy in subjects lacking the hormone and further exaggeration of characteristic effects of the hormone in intact individuals. Confirmatory evidence of hormonal function may sometimes be obtained from the demonstration of histologic or chemical changes in the secreting organ in various physiologic and pathologic states in which the activity of the gland is known to be altered.

Further investigations then concern chemical characterization of the hormone, its mode of action, and factors regulating its secretion. The isolation and identification of the active principle is often exceedingly difficult, requiring the combined efforts of physiologists, biochemists, and pharmacologists. The chemical nature of the known hormones is various; most of them are unstable, and many of them are proteins or peptides difficult to separate from other cellular materials. The hormones are found in the secreting organs only in minute amounts. In most cases the only guide to their presence is their physiologic activity. In each case, suitable methods of bio-assay must, therefore, be developed for use both in preparing the hormone and for estimating the concentrations of the hormone in body tissues and fluids in physiologic and clinical studies.

BIO-ASSAY METHODS. These procedures have become essential tools in modern research in endocrine physiology, but the principles used have not been as widely appreciated as they should be. In such methods, a characteristic physiologic effect of the hormone is made the basis of a quantitative assessment of the amount of the active principle present in a given preparation. The effects of a hormone are often of a qualitative rather than a quantitative nature, or, if they can be measured, are related to the amount of active substance used in the test over only a narrow range of responses. The degree of response—or, if the observations are qualitative, the proportion of positive reactions—is very rarely directly proportional to the amount of active principle given. Instead, the response is related to dosage in one of a variety of complex ways, such as to a function of the logarithm of the dose. Finally, both biologic variation in response (which may be large) and errors inherent in the method of observation may enter into the measurements. It is thus apparent that bio-assay methods at best can never be as precise as chemical measurements. In order to make the tests in any way quantitative, certain principles must be followed strictly.[2]

The first principle in modern bio-assay methods is that the effects of an unknown preparation must be compared with those of a standard preparation containing the same active principle and no others that may interfere with the test. This procedure allows the expression of the activity of the unknown relative to a fixed standard rather than to a variable test object. To render this comparison as accurate as possible, a number of experimental designs have been evolved. If the effects of the standard can be shown to be sufficiently reproducible, comparison of the response of the unknown with a standard dose-response curve is feasible; but usually it is better to test simultaneously two or more doses of both the unknown and the standard. In any case, an essential feature of all comparisons is arrangement of the dosages so that the responses to standard and to unknown are of approximately the same magnitude. Thereby, errors deriving from the complex dose-response relationship are minimized and the major factor relating the unknown and standard potencies is the ratio of the amounts used in the test, which can be measured accurately.

To allow for biologic variation in response to the hormone, a number of observations must be made at each dose level. Obviously, if more than one test animal is used, the subjects must be as uniform as possible in past history and present condition. The numbers of observations required for any particular degree of precision will, of course, vary with the particular test and the conditions in which it is used, and can be determined only by experiment. If the assay has been properly designed, the degree of confidence which can be placed in the figures obtained may be evaluated by statistical methods. It has been found that even in the best bio-assay methods, when all possible precautions are taken, the error is still rather large, the 95 per cent confidence limits (the range of values within which 95 per cent of the observations may be expected to fall) being in these instances of the order of ± 15 to 20 per cent of the true values. For the majority of the methods now in use, the possible error is much greater still. Consequently, it is to be expected that only relatively large changes in the hormone content of the body tissues and fluids in experimental or pathologic conditions may be detected by biologic methods.

In experimental work on the hormones, a large variety of animal species have been used. Although there is general similarity in the endocrine physiology even of quite different species, appreciable quantitative variations have been noted, and sometimes—with respect to finer details of hormone activity—there are qualitative differences as well. Many discrepancies between the results and occasionally between the views of different investigators have been due to differences between the species and strains of experimental animals used. These differences are not altogether disadvantageous, for variety in experimental approach may be facilitated by species differences, and often also the comparative physiology is informative. Nevertheless, generalizations from observations made only in one species may be at times misleading, and for the complete understanding of the physiology and pathology of the endocrine glands in man, careful clinical observation and experiment remain essential.

REFERENCES

1. CANNON, W. B. *The wisdom of the body*, 2nd ed. New York, W. W. Norton & Co., Inc., 1939.
2. EMMENS, C. W., ed. *Hormone assay*. New York, Academic Press, Inc. 1950.
3. PASCHKIS, K. E., RAKOFF, E. and CANTAROW, A. *Clinical Endocrinology*, 2nd Ed., New York, Hoeber-Harper, 1958.
4. PINCUS, G. and THIMANN, K. V., eds. *The hormones; physiology, chemistry, and applications.* New York, Academic Press, Inc., Vol. 1, 1948; Vol. 2, 1950; Vol. 3, 1955.
5. TURNER, C. D. *General endocrinology*. Philadelphia, W. B. Saunders Co., 1960.

CHAPTER 52

The Hypophysis

By JANE A. RUSSELL

THE hypophysis is perhaps the most important single endocrine organ, for its several hormones dominate the activities of the gonads, adrenal cortex and thyroid gland, and, in addition, exert important independent effects. This gland, earlier called the pituitary in reference to a supposed association with the secretion of phlegm, is now also named the hypophysis cerebri, or hypophysis, in reference to its location beneath the brain. Two types of tissue enter into the formation of the hypophysis in embryo. The anterior or glandular portion arises from Rathke's pouch, an evagination of epithelial tissue from what will become the roof of the mouth, and the posterior or neural portion originates as a process of neural ectoderm from the tissue which will form the floor of the third ventricle. The glandular lobe becomes sealed off from the oral epithelium and is eventually separated from it completely by the sphenoid bone, but the neural lobe remains intimately connected with the hypothalamic areas through numerous nerve fibers and some glandular elements which constitute the pituitary stalk. In most species the hypophysis rests in a depression in the sphenoid called the sella turcica. It may be separated from the brain by the diaphragma sella, a membrane of dural origin which is penetrated by the stalk.

Several subdivisions of the hypophysis may be distinguished anatomically. (i) The *adenohypophysis* includes (a) the large *pars distalis* (or anterior lobe proper); (b) the *pars tuberalis*, a much smaller segment which extends some distance up along the stalk; and (c) the *pars intermedia*, a section which varies widely in size in different species and which is often but not invariably separated by a cleft from the rest of the glandular lobe. (ii) The *neurohypophysis* consists of (a) the neural lobe proper, or infundibular process, and (b) the infundibulum, which includes the stalk and the median eminence of the tuber cinereum. The glandular and neural portions of the hypophysis are commonly but not always accurately referred to as the anterior and posterior lobes, respectively. A diagrammatic section of the hypophysis is shown in Figure 585.

The glandular portion (adenohypophysis) consists of large polyhedral cells arranged in irregular cords or nests separated by sinusoids. Three principal types of cells can be identified: chromophobe (with poorly staining cytoplasm), eosinophil (acidophil) or α cells, and basophil or β cells. The latter two types contain numerous granules which stain characteristically. Several forms of both the α and β types of chromophil cell have been distinguished in the rat pituitary in varying physiologic conditions. The chromophobe cells are believed to be inactive forms (immature or exhausted) of the secretory α and β cells. The blood supplied to these portions of the pituitary arises from branches of the internal carotid artery and drains into the surrounding dural sinuses. In most species, relatively very few nerve endings can be demonstrated in the adenohypophysis.

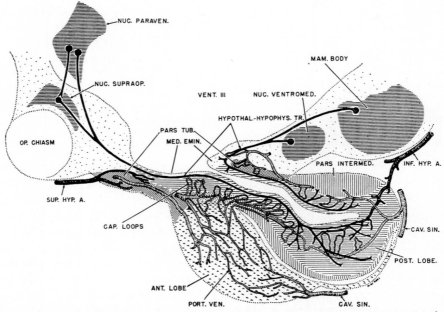

FIG. 585. Principal neural and vascular connections of hypophysis of the cat, in schematic longitudinal section. (Drawn by H. W. Ades.)

The posterior lobe, on the other hand, is distinguished by its rich nerve supply, a large part of the tissue consisting of branching unmyelinated nerve fibers. Formerly it was thought that these fibers innervated some peculiar cells, called pituicytes, which then secreted the hormones of this gland. However, the pituicytes may in fact be glial cells. According to Bodian,[11] the nerve endings may be seen as fine rodlike structures arranged in palisades which abut on capillaries lying in the septa between lobules of the gland. The nerve cell bodies and fibers supplying the posterior lobe contain granules which appear to be secretory in nature, and material staining in the same fashion is seen in the neural lobe, varying in amount with the secretory level of the gland.[66] It has been suggested, therefore, that the nerve cells themselves are the source of the hormone. In any event, since the nerve fibers all arise in certain hypothalamic nuclei, these areas together with the neurohypophysis constitute a continuous functional unit. The blood supply to the neural lobe proper enters posteriorly and is distinct from that to the glandular lobe.

Physiologically, it has been possible for the most part to distinguish only the two main divisions of the hypophysis, the glandular and neural lobes behaving in effect like two independent organs without connection or common control. The glandular lobe is not entirely autonomous in function, however, for many physiologic and clinical observations indicate that nervous mechanisms can affect the actions of this part of gland as well as those of the neurohypophysis. For instance, the occurrence of ovulation after coitus in certain species and the effects of light on gonadal function in birds can be explained only in this way. Until recent years it has not been understood how the central nervous system might exert such control over the glandular lobe, for convincing anatomic evidence of direct neural or vascular connections between the higher centers and the anterior pituitary is lacking. There is, however, another way in which such effects may be brought about. Some years ago Wislocki[79] and later Green and Harris[28] described in several species what is now called the pituitary portal system (Fig. 585). This is a rich capillary plexus formed from branches of the internal carotid artery and lying between the pars tuberalis and the median eminence. From this plexus arise sinusoidal capillary loops which enter the infundibulum, where they appear to be invested by nerve fibers from the hypothalamus, and which then return to the plexus. The blood from these capillaries then drains via the portal venules into the sinuses of the glandular lobe, supplying much of the circulation to this part of the hypophysis. In view of these anatomic relationships, a neurohumoral junction between some of the hypothalamic nuclei and the adenohypophysis at this point has been postulated.[32] Nervous impulses reaching the infundibulum may initiate the secretion of a chemical mediator, or the nerves themselves may secrete such a substance. This humoral agent is then carried through the portal capillaries just described to serve as a stimulator of adenohypophysial activity. The postulated neurosecretory substance or substances have not been isolated or identified with certainty, nor have the hypothalamic nuclei concerned with control of the adenohypophysis been localized satisfactorily; but numerous recent investigations appear to support this general hypothesis.[30, 33, 56, 80] Some aspects of this work will be discussed in connection with the control of secretion of certain individual trophic hormones.

THE ADENOHYPOPHYSIS

Effects of Hypophysectomy. Early attempts at determining the effects of hypophysectomy resulted ambiguously, for the animals usually died from attendant injury to the brain or from infection, or, if they survived, some of the effects observed often were due to damage in the hypothalamic area. Removal of the pituitary body by a transsphenoidal route, which in part avoids these difficulties, was first performed in the dog by Aschner in 1910–1912.[4] A similar operation was devised for the rat by P. E. Smith in 1926, and the relative ease with which this procedure may be performed in this species has greatly facilitated experimental work upon the physiology of the hypophysis.[70] Animals of many other species have since been operated upon in this manner.

The most striking effects of excising either the whole hypophysis or the adenohypophysis alone may be outlined in brief: (i) Atrophy of the gonads and accessory sex organs in the adult, or, in the young, failure of these organs to mature, with resulting complete sterility. (ii) Atrophy of the adrenal cortex, with consequent metabolic derangements. (There is not, however, complete lack of adrenal cortical function.) (iii) Atrophy of the thyroid, low metabolic rate, and other sequelae of thyroid deficiency. (iv) Failure of lactation (hypophysectomy performed late in pregnancy or postpartum). (v) Cessation of growth in the young, some loss of body tissue in the adult, reversion of the hair coat, etc., to the juvenile form. (vi) Alterations in the metabolism of carbohydrate, fat and protein, including hypersensitivity to insulin, a tendency toward hypoglycemia and rapid loss of glycogen stores in fasting, diminished fat catabolism, amelioration of diabetes mellitus or phlorhizin diabetes, and loss of nitrogen from the body. (vii) In amphibia and fish, blanching of the pigment cells of the skin (chromatophores) and failure of the usual adaptive changes in these cells.

Complete operative removal of the pituitary usually is not fatal in itself, in spite of the numerous derangements which it engenders. Hypophysectomized animals tend to have a subnormal life span, however, for they are very sensitive to such deleterious agencies as infections and cold. Also, hypoglycemia may develop if the appetite fails for any reason or if food is withheld for any length of time, and in some species this is a common cause of early death.

The clinical counterpart of hypophysectomy in the adult—usually the result of infarction or tumor of the pituitary—is known as Simmonds' disease. The most prominent symptoms of this disorder are atrophy of the gonads and accessory sex organs, low metabolic rate, a very pale waxy skin, a tendency toward hypoglycemia, insulin sensitivity, liability to shock in surgical procedures or other stressful conditions and, sometimes, signs of adrenal insufficiency. Emaciation, cachexia and premature senility have been considered also to be symptomatic; but in fact marked loss of body substance is not an invariable consequence of hypophysial insufficiency, and when it occurs it may be in large part the result of inanition.[14, 68] Insufficiency of the adenohypophysis in young individuals causes dwarfism; this may be accompanied by other signs of pituitary dysfunction, depending on the degree and type of abnormality in the hypophysis.

Removal of only the neural lobe of the pituitary has much less serious consequences than complete hypophysectomy or removal of the anterior lobe alone. In some species, as in the dog, it is difficult to remove all the secreting posterior lobe tissue, for some is found extending into the tuber cinereum; in these species, simple postlobectomy may then have few sequelae. Even with complete removal of the neurohypophysis, the only marked physiologic effect in mammals is the development of permanent polyuria or diabetes insipidus. After complete hypophysectomy, on the other hand, polyuria of any severity is seen only temporarily. The disappearance of the diabetes insipidus otherwise seen in the absence of the posterior lobe may be due in part to atrophy of the adrenal and thyroid glands; for adrenalectomy or particularly thyroidectomy have an ameliorating effect on diabetes insipidus, possibly by diminishing the solute load on the renal tubules. Also, some degree of reorganization may occur eventually in the severed ends of the hypothalamic-hypophysial nerve tracts, with partial resumption of secretory function at this site.[39]

Hormones of Adenohypophysis. The anterior lobe of the pituitary is the source of at least six distinct hormones: four trophic hormones—the two *gonadotrophins, adrenotrophin* and *thyrotrophin*—which have the unique property of controlling in more or less complete degree the functional integrity of other major endocrine glands; the *lactogenic* or *luteotrophic* hormone, which may be similarly classed in some respects; and the *growth* or *somatotrophic* hormone. In addition to these six hormones, yet another distinct substance with endocrine activity is found in the pituitaries of animals from all vertebrate classes. This is the *melanocyte-stimulating* hormone, which in amphibia and some other lower orders produces changes in the color of the skin when the animal is placed in the dark. From evidence obtained in amphibia, this substance seems to have its origin in the intermediate lobe of the hypophysis; but in mammalian species it is found in all parts of the gland and in practice is obtained from the posterior lobe.

Some attributes of crude pituitary extracts, particularly those connected with metabolic effects, have not yet been assigned finally to any one of these known hormones. Present evidence indicates that these probably can be ascribed to the growth and adrenocorticotrophic hormones.

The six hormones mentioned above, plus the melanocyte-stimulating hormone, have all been obtained in highly purified or concentrated forms from the pituitaries of several species, so that there is no doubt about their separability into distinct entities. All are protein or polypeptide in nature. Although homologous hormones obtained from different species are quite similar in biologic effects, several have been found to differ somewhat in their chemical constitutions and properties, and in certain instances a notable degree of species specificity in activity is evident as well.

Which of the three types of cell found in the adenohypophysis secrete the different hormones is not entirely clear. From pathologic evidence it seems probable that the growth hormone is secreted by the α cells. The degranulation and vacuolation of the β cells which occur after gonadectomy or thyroidectomy appear to indicate that the gonadotrophins and thyrotrophin have their origin in these cells; recent evidence indicates that different types of β cell, distinguishable morphologically, may give rise to these two respective hormones. Evidence concerning the source of lactogenic hormone is controversial, and little is known about the site of formation of adrenocorticotrophin.

TROPHIC HORMONES. The results of excess or deficiency of the trophic hormones are of course mediated through their effects on the respective target glands. In all cases the trophic hormones not only are essential for the complete morphologic development and normal function of the organs affected, but also promote actively the formation and secretion of hormones by these glands. When present in excess, they induce first functional and later morphologic hypertrophy. The trophic pituitary hormones appear to be secreted not at constant rates but in amounts varying with the physiologic state of the animal. Thus they act as sensitive regulators of the endocrine functions of the target organs.

The factors which in turn regulate the production of the trophic hormones by the adenohypophysis are not fully understood. At least two devices are known. First, the circulating level of the target organ hormone in most cases controls inversely the secretion of the respective trophic hormone. That is, where the "end-hormone" is high in concentration, the output of the hypophysial hormone is low; or, when the former is low or absent, the output of the trophic hormone is much increased. Several examples of this relationship will be discussed later. These responses are somewhat slow, however, so that it is unlikely that this type of control is responsible for the minute-to-minute regulation of secretion of the trophic hormones.

A second device, neurosecretory regulation via hypothalamic pathways and the pituitary portal system, seems highly probable.[30, 33, 56, 80] When appropriate lesions are placed in the hypothalamus, varying degrees of gonadal atrophy ensue, and the adrenals and thyroid, although they do not necessarily become completely atrophic, may fail to respond to stimuli which are ordinarily effective. In some cases, notably in connection with adrenotrophin, a very rapid increase in secretion of the trophic hormone has been demonstrated after purely neurogenic stimuli when the hypothalamus is intact, but not when the hypothalamus has been damaged or when certain centers have been depressed by drugs such as morphine. In addition to these two general mechanisms, it is possible also that either certain hypothalamic centers or the hypophysis itself can respond specifically to changes in other metabolic or humoral agents, such as the level of blood glucose, local temperature or the like; but the evidence for these types of control is as yet only suggestive.

Gonadotrophins. In the early work of Aschner[4] on the effects of hypophysectomy in dogs, atrophy of the genital organs was seen. Enlargement of the ovaries and formation of numerous corpora lutea in normal rats treated with pituitary extract were demonstrated by Evans and his collaborators in 1922, and later these investigators indicated the chemical distinction of the gonadotrophic from the growth-promoting factor in the extracts.[23] In the course of further efforts by several groups of investigators to purify the gonadotrophic fraction, it was found that this material also could be separated into two parts. When given separately in small amounts, these factors had relatively little effect on the ovaries of hypophysectomized rats, but when recombined the factors produced marked enlargement of these organs. The two pituitary gonadotrophins have since been obtained in highly purified and concentrated forms, but they have not yet been entirely characterized chemically. One, called the follicle-stimulating hormone (FSH), has as its chief function in the female the development of the ovarian follicles up to the point of ovulation; in the male its function is the development of the seminiferous tubules and maintenance of spermatogenesis. The other pituitary gonadotrophin is called either the luteinizing hormone (LH) or the interstitial cell-stimulating hormone (ICSH). The two descriptive names arose because factors effective in the female and male, respectively, now known to be identical, were at one time thought to be distinct. In the female, the luteinizing hormone cooperates with the follicle-stimulating factor in the final stages of follicular development and ovulation, and probably in the secretion of estrogen; it then alone induces development of lutein tissue. In the male, this hormone induces development of the interstitial tissues of the testis (Leydig tissue) and the secretion of androgen. The follicle-stimulating hormone is usually detected biologically by the development of numerous follicles and enlargement of the ovaries in the immature or hypophysectomized rat. The test is more sensitive when the action of FSH is augmented by a constant amount of LH or of human chorionic gonadotrophin. The luteinizing hormone is assayed by the degree of enlargement it produces in the accessory sex organs, such as the seminal vesicles, in the immature or hypophysectomized male rat.

Gonadotrophins are secreted also by the placenta. These substances, often called chorionic gonadotrophins or anterior pituitary-like hormones (APL), are found in large amounts in the urine and blood of pregnant women, the blood of pregnant mares, and the tissues and urine of patients with certain genital tumors (chorionepithelioma and hydatidiform mole). They have been shown to be produced in cultures of placental tissue *in vitro*, and to be excreted after ovariectomy by pregnant women and mares. In biologic effects, human chorionic gonadotrophin (HCG) resembles LH (ICSH), whereas the hormone obtained from the pregnant mare behaves like a mixture of the two pituitary gonadotrophins. The chorionic hormones differ chemically from the hypophysial hormones but are also protein in nature.

Lactogenic hormone (prolactin, luteotrophin). The existence of a pituitary hormone affecting lactation was first shown by Stricker and Greuter in 1928. Later, Riddle and others found that a similar factor controls proliferation of the crop gland and secretion of crop milk in pigeons, and a convenient method of testing for the hormone based on this effect led to the early isolation of the lactogenic substance in highly purified form. In mammals, the hormone appears to be responsible for the initiation and maintenance of lactation in the prepared mammary gland (previously brought to a responsive stage by the action of ovarian hormones). More recent work indicates that the lactogenic hormone also directly affects the ovary, aiding in the maintenance of the corpora lutea once they are formed and allowing the continued secretion of progesterone. This "luteotrophic" effect can be detected by the inducement of deciduoma formation in response to a foreign body (a characteristic effect of progesterone) in the uterus of the hypophysectomized rat.

Thyrotrophin. Depression of the metabolic rate and involution of the thyroid epithelium in hypophysectomized dogs were first noted by Aschner; and shortly thereafter Smith and Allen independently observed that the pituitary body was necessary for thyroid development in the tadpole and that it could be replaced by implantation of anterior pituitary tissue. Since that time thyrotrophic function of the anterior pituitary has been indicated in a large number of species in the various vertebrate classes. Hyperplasia of the thyroid gland in normal animals following the administration of pituitary extracts was first observed in the guinea pig by Loeb and Bassett in 1928. The thyrotrophic hormone has now been separated from other known pituitary hormones and obtained in highly active form, but it has not yet been purified. It has been assayed by its effects on the size or iodine content of the thyroid gland of young chicks or guinea pigs, on the height of the thyroid epithelium in a variety of species, or on the uptake into or the discharge of radioiodide from the thyroid.

Adrenotrophin. Atrophy of the adrenal cortex after removal of the pituitary body and its repair following the implantation of fresh pituitary tissue were first observed in the rat by P. E. Smith in 1926.[70] At about the same time, pituitary extracts which were growth-promoting were noted by Evans and collaborators to induce also hypertrophy of the adrenal cortices of normal animals. In 1943, the adrenocorticotrophic hormone (ACTH) was obtained from sheep and from swine pituitaries as an apparently pure protein. In 1951–1952, however, several groups of investigators showed that ACTH could be prepared as a much smaller molecule, a polypeptide which was many times more active on a weight basis than the protein ACTH. Such substances have now been obtained in highly purified form from sheep and hog pituitaries, and their structures have been determined.[47] The hormones from both species contain 39 amino acids in a single chain, with molecular weights of about 4500; they are 100 to 200 times as active as the standard protein hormone. The sequence of amino acids (starting from the N-terminal end) in the peptide ACTH from sheep is as follows:

Ser-Tyr-Ser-Met-Glu-His-Phe-Arg-Try-Gly-Lys-Pro-Val-Gly-Lys-Lys-Arg-Arg-Pro-Val-
 1   2   3   4   5   6   7   8   9   10 11 12 13 14 15 16 17 18 19 20

Lys-Val-Tyr-Pro-Ala-Gly-Glu-Asp-Asp-Glu-Ala-Ser-Glu-Ala-Phe-Pro-Leu-Glu-Phe.
 21 22 23 24 25 26 27 28 29 30 31 32 33 34 35 36 37 38 39

The sequence in the hormone from pig pituitaries differs slightly from this in a few positions only. In both species, still smaller molecules having ACTH activity can be prepared by limited digestion with pepsin or with acid; the last 11 amino acid residues (#29 to 39 inclusive) are not necessary for complete activity. The peptide hormone is rapidly absorbed and destroyed when it is injected into animals, so that for maximal effects it must be given either very frequently or in a "depot" form, from which it is slowly released. It is supposed that in the pituitary the peptide hormone must be either adsorbed on or combined with cellular proteins, but it is not known how or in what form the material is actually secreted.

Highly purified peptide ACTH preparations have been shown not only to control the activity and development of the adrenal cortex, but also, independently of their effects on cortical secretion, to have some degree of melanocyte-stimulating activity and to have certain metabolic effects similar to those exhibited by growth hormone. The physiologic significance of these activities is not known.

The hormone has usually been detected by its ability to effect repair or maintenance of cortical tissue in hypophysectomized animals when the material is given over a period of several days. Another specific and extremely sensitive method developed by Sayers *et al.*[65] makes use of the disappearance of ascorbic acid from the adrenal glands within an hour after the hormone is given to hypophysectomized rats.

MELANOCYTE-STIMULATING HORMONE. The secretion by the hypophysis of amphibia of a hormone which controlled pigmentation in the skin and the responses of this pigmentation to light was shown many years ago by Smith, Allen and others. The principal effect of the hormone is to cause immediate dispersion of the pigment granules in the chromatophores (melanocytes) of the skin and so to cause an apparent "expansion" of these cells and an increase in light absorption and in intensity of color in the skin. The same effects are produced on the skin of amphibia by extracts from the pituitaries of animals of all classes, including man. The active principle has been given many names, among them the chromatophore-exciting or -expanding hormone, the melanocyte-stimulating hormone (MSH), melanotrophin, and intermedin. The latter term has been suggested because, in amphibia at least, the substance appears to arise in the pars intermedia of the hypophysis. The hormone can be assayed by its effects on the skin color in intact frogs or toads, or better, by the increase in light absorption induced in the isolated skin of the frog.

The hormone became of particular interest to mammalian physiologists rather recently when it appeared that MSH was related to or might even be identical with ACTH. This suggestion was based on the observations that crude peptide ACTH preparations displayed appreciable MSH activity and that certain changes in the pigmentation of the skin and nevi in man seemed to be related to changes in the secretion of ACTH. It has now been found that the two substances are in fact quite distinct. MSH has been obtained in two different pure forms from the pituitaries (posterior lobes) of swine and cattle, and the structures of these have been determined.[25, 34, 48] The form first characterized (called β MSH) contains 18 amino acids, and as obtained from the pig has the following sequence:

Asp-Glu-Gly-Pro-Tyr-Lys-Met-Glu-His-Phe-Arg-Try-Gly-Ser-Pro-Pro-Lys-Asp.
 1   2   3   4   5   6   7   8   9   10   11   12   13   14   15   16   17   18

A similar form of β MSH obtained from bovine pituitaries differs from this only in containing serine instead of glutamic acid at the 2 position. The form of α MSH from the pig has recently been shown to be:

(Acetyl-N) Ser-Tyr-Ser-Met-Glu-His-Phe-Arg-Try-Gly-Lys-Pro-Val (NH₂)
            1   2   3   4   5   6   7   8   9   10   11   12   13

The potency of these substances as MSH is about 100 times that of pure ACTH, but they have no ACTH activity or other known biologic effects. Highly purified ACTH preparations, on the other hand, do exhibit significant MSH activity. This is undoubtedly a consequence of the fact that the two hormones have extensive sequences of amino acid in common. The entire sequence in α MSH, except for its terminal modifications, is identical with the first 13 amino acids in ACTH, and in β MSH the amino acids at positions 5, 7–13 and 15 are identical with the sequence 2, 4–10 and 12 in ACTH and in α MSH. Thus, ACTH and MSH "overlap" to a large degree in structure and also to some extent in biologic activity as well.

Preparations of MSH bring about changes in the color of the skin and nevi in man; the excretion of MSH-like material is increased in pregnancy and in adrenocortical deficiency, both conditions in which pigmentation is often increased; and cortical hormones suppress the excretion of the MSH-like substance.[45] However, it is not yet certain whether MSH itself is regularly secreted in higher animals, or whether the active factor in these species is in fact ACTH.

GROWTH HORMONE. A relationship between the pituitary gland and growth of the body was first indicated by the pathologic changes seen in the pituitary gland in acromegaly. This rather rare disorder, first described by P. Marie in 1886, is characterized by progressive enlargement of the ends of the long bones, thickening of the skull, lengthening of the jaw, overgrowth of the skin, and enlargement of the viscera. Gigantism was later seen to be a juvenile form of the same disease. After Aschner first showed that hypophysectomy in young animals resulted in dwarfism, it was recognized that the pituitary gland must be the source of an endocrine secretion which enhances body growth. The first successful attempt to influence growth by hormone treatment was that of Long and Evans, who in 1921 produced giant rats by the long-continued daily injection of an extract of ox pituitaries. Similar results have since been obtained in several species.

The growth-promoting hormone, or somatotrophin, from the anterior pituitary has since been obtained from ox pituitaries in virtually pure form,[47, 49, 71, 78] and its chemical and biologic properties have been extensively investigated.[71] It is a globulin with molecular weight about 45,000 and isoelectric point about pH 6.8. Some progress has been made in the elucidation of the structure of the hormone, and it has been reported that the hormone remains active after limited proteolytic digestion, but the form responsible for its biologic activity has not yet been defined. Crude alkaline or saline extracts of ox pituitaries are usually rich in growth hormone, and many of the original observations on the biologic properties of the substance, such as those described below, were made with these extracts or with only partially purified materials. Most of these effects have since been obtained also with the highly purified substance.[63, 71]

Since crude preparations of growth hormone from other species, such as the sheep or pig, have been effective in the rat, dog and cat, it has been supposed until recently that somatotrophins from various mammalian species would be closely similar if not identical substances. However, the hormone has now been prepared in relatively purified forms from a variety of species (pig, sheep, horse, monkey, man, whale and certain fishes), and these have been found to differ considerably in some of their chemical properties (molecular weight, amino acid composition, isoelectric point, etc.) and in biologic specificity. All of these hormones, except those from the fish, are active in the rat. On the other hand, extensive trials in human subjects and in monkeys with bovine and porcine hormones have yielded only equivocal or, more often, entirely negative results. It has now been found that somatotrophin obtained from the monkey is extremely effective in promoting nitrogen retention and bone growth in the monkey, and that hormones from both simian and human sources induce nitrogen retention in both the monkey and man.[42, 43, 57] Apparently, then, the biologic specificity of the growth hormones is such that they are able to act "downward" in the evolutionary line but not "upward." These observations make it seem unlikely that growth hormone preparations can be obtained in sufficient quantities for wide clinical use in man; but it is still possible either that the purified hormone from some other species may be found to resemble human growth hormone sufficiently to be effective when given in large doses, or that an active "core" will be found common to the several forms of hormone and thus will allow the preparation of material active in man from the hormone of some subprimate species.

Hormonal Regulation of Growth. In order to study the actions of a factor controlling growth, such as the pituitary growth hormone, it is necessary to define what is meant by the term "growth" and to consider the criteria to be used in measuring it. Gain in weight is the most usual measure, but without other data gain in weight alone is not sufficiently specific; obviously retention of water would not constitute growth, nor would deposition of fat alone. For true growth, there must be accretion of tissue which has a constitution fairly similar to that of the original body. When the gain in weight is sufficiently great, there may be no doubt that gross increments in the amounts of tissue and size of the supporting structures have occurred. More precise and sensitive indications of growth in animals are changes in the amount of protein in the body, or in the amount of nitrogen retained, and in the size or structure of the bones. By these criteria, the pituitary growth hormone does effect true growth, both in young and in adult animals.

EFFECTS ON BONE GROWTH. In animals whose long bone epiphyses have not yet closed, continued treatment with anterior pituitary extracts will accelerate the growth of both bones and tissues, inducing nearly symmetrical enlargement of all features. The rat, in which the major epiphyses remain open until very late in life, may be made to double its normal size. In adult individuals whose epiphyses are closed, growth-promoting extracts produce a picture identical with that seen clinically in acromegaly; wherever endochondral bone exists, or some remnants of cartilage persist, both chondrogenesis and osteogenesis are initiated, producing the large and characteristically misshapen bones. Where an excess of growth hormone is present during both the juvenile and adult stages, features of both gigantism and acromegaly may be induced. Figure 586 shows the effects of continued treatment with pituitary extract in the dachshund. Overgrowth of the skeletal system and skin is obvious, and visceral enlargement is also present. It will be noted that the achondroplasia normal in this breed of dog has not been affected by the treatment.

When the young animal is hypophysectomized, growth ceases. Both chondrogenesis and osteogenesis come to a standstill, leaving the epiphyses not completely closed but remaining as thin cartilaginous plates. These quiescent zones may be reactivated by growth hormone administered at any later time, even into senescence, to give the

FIG. 586. Effect of chronic treatment with anterior pituitary extract in young dog. *Lower*, Male dachshund given daily intraperitoneal injections of pituitary extract containing growth hormone, from 6th to 32nd week of life. *Upper*, Littermate male, untreated. (From Evans *et al.*, *Growth and gonaastimulating hormone of the anterior hypophysis.* Berkeley, University of California Press, 1933.)

appearance of young, growing bone.[7, 69, 71] Chondrogenesis seems primarily affected, followed by ossification. The effects of the growth hormone upon bone, then, appear to be to induce the persistence of the normal juvenile growth pattern. A sensitive method of assaying growth hormone is based upon the widening of the proximal tibial epiphysial cartilage in young hypophysectomized rats, as seen in Figure 587.

EFFECTS ON SOFT TISSUES. With regular administration of growth hormone, enlargement of the whole body occurs. All or nearly all organs and tissues seem to take part in the response, but they do not all necessarily show the same degree of effect.[29] The functional efficiency of organs enlarged under the influence of the hormone may vary. In the muscles of adult rats treated with growth hormone, the maximal tension developed on stimulation was not increased above normal, so that the tension per unit cross-sectional area was low. On the other hand, the kidney is quite responsive to growth hormone not only in size but also in certain functional respects. The renal plasma flow, glomerular filtration rate, and functions dependent on these factors are particularly affected.[71] Organs whose growth and development is controlled primarily by other hormones, such as the adrenal cortex or the secondary sex organs, may respond to growth hormone also, although usually the effect is not more than in proportion to changes in body weight. It has been observed recently, however, that the presence of somatotrophin may in some cases greatly augment the effectiveness of the respective trophic hormone. Such "synergism" between growth hormone and other hormones has been shown clearly in respect to the action of ACTH on the adrenal cortex and to that of androgens on the preputial glands, and may well be found to occur elsewhere as well.

BODY COMPOSITION AND NITROGEN METABOLISM. That the gain in body weight induced by growth hormone is due to an increment of tissue and not to the accumulation of fat or water alone is shown by analysis of the whole bodies of the treated animals. Some data of this type obtained by Young[82] are shown in Table 42. Three series of

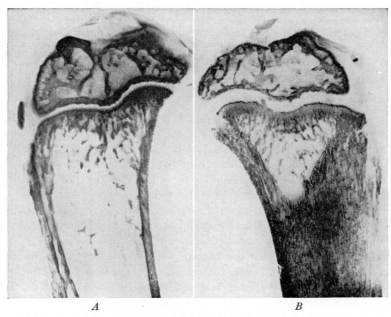

A   B

FIG. 587.   Effect of growth hormone on proximal tibial epiphysis of rat (tibia split longitudinally and stained with silver nitrate). A, Tibia from untreated hypophysectomized rat. B, Tibia from hypophysectomized rat treated with growth hormone for 4 days. (Both animals 34 days of age, 16 days postoperative.) Note increase in width of cartilage (unstained band). (From Evans et al., Endocrinology, 1943, 32:14.)

analyses were performed, one of treated rats given food ad libitum, one of treated animals restricted in their food intake to the same amount given to control rats, and one of untreated animals. Both groups of rats given growth hormone (crude anterior pituitary extract) gained weight, while the untreated animals did not. The animals which were unrestricted in their food intake showed a marked increase in appetite* and gained the most, but even when the food intake was restricted, a considerable gain in weight occurred, amounting to 34 per cent of the initial weight in two months' time. This gain was confined wholly to protein, water, and salts, and was accompanied by a loss of fat. Results similar to these have been obtained also with highly purified growth hormone preparations given to either normal or hypophysectomized animals.

An increase in the amount of body tissue over that of the controls with the same food intake may seem to require a reduction in the proportion of this food used for

* Animals given crude anterior pituitary extract tend to increase their food intake. This effect requires adequate control of food intake in all experiments upon the nature of growth hormone action.

*TABLE 42. COMPOSITION OF MATERIAL ADDED TO THE BODIES OF RATS AS
THE RESULT OF PITUITARY TREATMENTS**

GROUP	AMOUNTS ADDED OF						
	Total Body Weight gm.	Protein gm.	Fat gm.	Ash gm.	Water gm.	Energy Cal.	Body Length mm.
1. Constant diet (52 Cal./day)	+ 80.3	+19.2	−12.3	+4.6	+ 69.8	−39	+ 9.4
2. Unlimited diet (74 Cal./day)	+132.8	+25.6	− 2.0	+1.9	+105.7	+78	+16.2

* Alkaline extract of ox pituitaries equivalent to 125 mg. fresh anterior lobe tissue was given to each rat daily for 9 weeks. Untreated control rats fed 52 Cal. per day gained an average of only 1 gram during this time and did not increase in body length. The figures are averages of data from 10 rats in each group.
(From Young, *Biochem. J.*, 1945, *39*:515–536.)

supplying energy. But neither a diminution in metabolic rate or in activity, nor any remarkable gain in efficiency of utilization of the food ingested, has ever been observed in animals given pituitary extracts. The data in Table 42 show that in this experiment body fat had been metabolized in place of the food calories which were stored as tissue protein. Since the added tissue containing these calories weighed more than the fat from which the energy came, a net gain in dry weight was possible.

The effects of growth hormone on the deposition of body protein can be observed not only when the hormone is given regularly, as in the experiments just described, but also when the nitrogen balance is measured over periods of a few days.[71] Although some of this nitrogen will be lost when the hormone is discontinued, a permanent net gain in body protein usually results. Further, some effects of the hormone on nitrogen metabolism are demonstrable under appropriate conditions within a few hours. The concentration of free amino acids in the blood and tissues falls, and at the same time the rate of urea production is diminished sharply. The latter effect is best seen when a standard amount of protein hydrolysate is given intravenously.[62, 63, 71] The increase in the effectiveness of the hormone when increased amounts of nitrogen are made available suggests that the hormone affects primarily the synthesis of protein, rather than any phase of its catabolism.

*TABLE 43. COMPOSITION OF THE BODIES OF HYPOPHYSECTOMIZED AND
NORMAL RATS PAIR-FED DURING 33 DAYS FOLLOWING OPERATION**

GROUP †	COMPOSITION IN GM. PER 100 GM. INITIAL BODY WEIGHT			
	Total Wt.	Protein	Fat	Water
Initial	100.0	17.8	13.1	64.0
Final				
Controls	81.2	18.2	5.3	54.0
Hypophysectomized	74.0	14.3	9.3	45.7

* The food intake was that amount eaten voluntarily by the hypophysectomized animals.
† 16 rats in each group.
(From Lee and Ayres, *Endocrinology*, 1936, *20*:489.)

After the removal of the hypophysis, mature rats at first tend to lose weight—perhaps as much as 10 to 15 per cent of the body weight—in the weeks following the operation, and then they may remain stable or lose ground only very slowly for a considerable time. Part of this loss of weight is due to diminished appetite, but if the hypophysectomized rats are compared with normal animals given the same amount of food, they still lose more weight than the controls.[44] Analysis of the bodies of such animals, as seen in Table 43, shows that the hypophysectomized animals lose more protein (in this case the controls lost none) and water, and much less fat than the normal rats. Even more dramatic evidence of the effect of the loss of growth hormone is seen when the nitrogen excretion is measured in the first few days after hypophysectomy (Fig. 588). In these experiments, in which the diet would just allow some growth in the un-

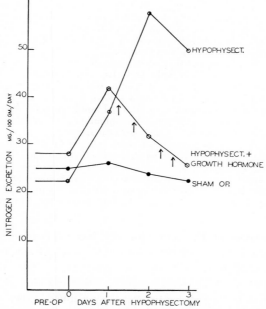

FIG. 588. Nitrogen excretion immediately after hypophysectomy in rats. Growth hormone, 0.25 mg. per 100 grams, was given on the second and third days after operation. The diet, containing 6 per cent casein, was fed for four days before and three days after operation. The average food intake was similar for all groups. (Six to eight observations per group, standard error 1 to 3 mg. per 100 grams.)

operated group, the hypophysectomized rats excreted twice as much nitrogen as the control animals. When growth hormone was given during the postoperative period, this nitrogen loss was abolished. It is evident that somatotrophin is required for normal retention of body protein, not only in young animals but in adult or nongrowing animals as well.

The stabilization of body weight and nitrogen balance of hypophysectomized animals some time later after operation probably is due to the atrophy of the thyroid and adrenal glands which occurs by that time, for the rate of catabolism of endogenous protein is known to be diminished in animals lacking the secretion of either of these organs.

RELATIONSHIP OF GROWTH HORMONE TO OTHER HORMONES. Growth of animals may be influenced by many factors—genetic, nutritional, hormonal and metabolic. It is not to be expected, therefore, that maximal effects of the growth hormone can be obtained if any other requisite of normal growth is deficient. For example, Gordan et al.[27] showed that the amount of growth and nitrogen retention induced in normal adult rats by treatment with growth hormone is strictly dependent on the amount and quality of protein fed. Similarly, adrenalectomized animals do not grow or respond to growth hormone unless the hemodynamic state is fully maintained by adequate substitution therapy.

The relationship of the thyroid hormone to the growth hormone is more complicated. Thyroidectomized animals grow very little; they can be made to grow by administration of either thyroid or pituitary extracts. Hypophysectomized animals, however, will not grow in response to thyroxin. If hypophysectomized-thyroidectomized rats are given growth hormone, they will grow fairly well, but greater growth is obtained when a normal complement of thyroxin is given in addition. Apparently thyroid hormone is required not only for maximal activity of either endogenous or exogenous growth hormone, but also for the normal secretion of this hormone by the pituitary gland.[21, 69] It should be noted that although the presence of some hormone from the thyroid and the adrenal glands is necessary for maximal response to the growth hormone, such effects are not dependent on *increased* secretion by these glands. The thyrotrophic and adrenotrophic hormones are not essential to growth hormone activity.

Available evidence indicates that insulin may be required for the usual effects of growth hormone on nitrogen metabolism. Depancreatized dogs treated with pituitary extract do not retain nitrogen unless insulin is also given. It has been suggested that not only the normal amount of insulin is required for this effect, but that extra insulin also may have to be secreted to allow the growth hormone to act.[54]

The converse question is whether any other hormonal factors can induce protein synthesis and body growth in the absence of the hypophysis. As noted above, the thyroid hormone does not do so. The androgens have been reported to bring about some degree of nitrogen retention after hypophysectomy; but much of the nitrogen increase was found in the accessory sex organs, and was not distributed among other organs as it is when growth hormone is given.[67] It is doubtful, therefore, whether the androgen was inducing much true growth in this case.

Recently, Salter and Best[64] reported that when large amounts of insulin were given together with the large amounts of food required to prevent hypoglycemia, hypophysectomized rats increased in weight and retained appreciable amounts of nitrogen as well as a great deal of fat. They suggested, therefore, that insulin could be considered to be a growth hormone. However, it had been shown earlier that, when hypophysectomized rats were force-fed ample amounts of food during the first few weeks after operation, they lost very little nitrogen as compared to animals fed *ad libitum*. More recently, Wagner and Scow,[77] force-feeding rats over longer periods after hypophysectomy, observed an increase in body weight due mainly to fat deposition but partly to protein retention similar to that seen by Salter and Best; but there was no difference between force-fed animals given insulin and those not given the hormone. Similarly, hypophysectomized rats in which gross hyperphagia was induced by the placement of lesions in the hypothalamus also retained some nitrogen and much fat, regardless of whether insulin was given.[40] It is likely, therefore, that overfeeding by itself can induce some deposition of protein in the absence of the hypophysis, as it does in its presence, but that excess insulin is not required for this effect.

Metabolic Functions of the Anterior Pituitary Gland. Both removal of the anterior pituitary gland and the administration of whole extracts made from the gland have been shown to affect profoundly several phases of the metabolism of carbohydrate and fat, as well as protein metabolism.[5, 8, 16, 35, 36, 61] The many effects of the pituitary extracts have given rise to various names for the responsible factor or factors—among them the diabetogenic, glycotropic, glycostatic and ketogenic "hormones"—according to the effect observed. None of these factors has been demonstrated to be a distinct entity different from all other known pituitary hormones; and although it may be that such exist, current evidence suggests that all of the many phenomena seen may be attributed to growth hormone, or to adrenotrophin acting through the secretion of the adrenal steroids, or to the combined actions of the two factors. The major observations concerning the role of the pituitary gland in the metabolism of carbohydrate and fat are as follows.

(i) *Blood glucose and tissue glycogen stores.* A tendency to develop hypoglycemia spontaneously has been widely noted in hypophysectomized animals. If such animals are well fed, there are usually no noteworthy changes in the levels of glucose and glycogen in the body, but if they are deprived of food for even short periods, the glycogen stores first tend to diminish more rapidly than normally, and then the blood sugar begins to fall. The rate at which these changes appear during fasting varies considerably with species, being much more evident in smaller animals such as the rat than in large animals like the dog. In fasted adrenalectomized animals, similar changes in blood sugar and liver glycogen may be seen, but muscle glycogen is less rapidly depleted than it is after hypophysectomy. This rapid loss of carbohydrate in fasted hypophysectomized animals may be prevented by adrenocortical hormones, presumably through their property of stimulating gluconeogenesis. However, pituitary extracts will maintain normal muscle glycogen levels during fasting even in the absence of the adrenal glands, and purified growth hormone free of adrenotrophin has also been found active in this respect. Thus the adrenal cortex appears to be in part responsible for the maintenance of normal blood sugar and liver glycogen in fasting, whereas the pituitary gland more directly affects muscle glycogen maintenance.

The concentration of glycogen in the heart, unlike that in other muscles, normally rises during fasting. This paradoxical effect was first noted many years ago in the dog and has since been seen in several species. It has now been found in the rat that the hypophysis is necessary for the increase to occur, and that growth hormone not only permits the cardiac glycogen to increase during fasting in the hypophysectomized animal but also hastens and augments the increase which occurs in the normal.[2] Cortical hormones do not reproduce the effect of growth hormone in this respect, but the presence of a small amount of cortical hormone seems to be required for maximal activity of growth hormone.

(ii) *Utilization of carbohydrate.* Fed carbohydrate tends to disappear more rapidly from the body in hypophysectomized animals than in normal animals. The R.Q. is high both in fasting and in fed animals, probably indicating increased utilization of carbohydrate. This conclusion is supported by the observation that the removal of glucose from the blood is much more rapid in hypophysectomized eviscerated rats and rabbits than in control eviscerate preparations. These changes are not observed to the same extent in adrenalectomized animals. In acute experiments in rats it has been found that either pituitary extract or purified growth hormone lowers the R.Q. and increases the deposition of fed carbohydrate, particularly in muscle.[37, 55] The cooperation of both pituitary and adrenal hormones may be required for this effect.

(iii) *Metabolism of fat.* That pituitary extracts are ketogenic has been known for many years. They also cause accumulation of fat in the liver, this fat coming from the body depots. Both the ketogenic and "adipokinetic" effects have been reproduced with purified growth hormone, and, in addition, the concentration of unesterified fatty acids in the blood also has been observed to increase strikingly after administration of growth hormone. These effects taken together indicate that the utilization of fat is increased by the hormone, an effect which would be expected to be concomitant with diminution in the rate of utilization of carbohydrate. None of these effects is reproduced consistently with cortical hormones; but cortical factors have seemed to have synergistic activity, especially in relation to the accumulation of fat in the liver. A further complication in this relationship is that, although cortical steroids are not ketogenic, highly purified ACTH preparations, both protein and peptide, are quite active in this respect. Engel[22] has shown recently that the ketogenic effect, as well as some other metabolic activities associated with growth hormone, can be obtained by the administration of ACTH peptide after the adrenal cortex has been removed. Thus, there appears to be some degree of overlap in biologic activity between ACTH and either somatotrophin itself or some as yet unidentified factor intimately associated with it.

(iv) *Sensitivity to insulin.* Hypophysectomized animals are extremely sensitive to the hypoglycemic effects of insulin, an observation first made in 1924 by Houssay and since confirmed in a variety of animal species and in clinical cases of hypopituitarism. A considerable part of the increased sensitivity may be the result of adrenal cortical atrophy, for adrenalectomized animals are also very sensitive. Crude pituitary extracts, adrenotrophin or adrenal steroids given a few hours before the insulin will prevent or diminish its usual hypoglycemic effects in both normal and hypophysectomized animals. On the other hand, pituitary extract has also been reported to be effective in this respect in adrenalectomized rabbits, and growth hormone free of adrenocorticotrophin has been seen to oppose the action of insulin.[17, 55] It appears, then, that both independent pituitary factors and the adrenal cortical hormones are able to diminish the usual effects of insulin. The contra-insulin factor or factors are often called glycotropic substances, because it was once thought that they acted by increasing the lability of the liver glycogen.

(v) *Pancreatectomy.* If animals which have been made diabetic by removal of the pancreas (see Chap. 53) are then hypophysectomized, a considerable amelioration of the symptoms of diabetes mellitus is observed. Such doubly operated animals are known as Houssay preparations, after the discoverer of the phenomenon.[35, 36] They survive for long periods without insulin, may have blood sugar levels often in the normal range or below, and show little glycosuria or ketonuria, normal fasting nitrogen excretion rates, improved glucose tolerance, and increased or normal R.Q.'s after carbohydrate. The Houssay animal is, however, an unstable creature, easily thrown into extremes of either diabetes mellitus or hypoglycemia by alterations in its state of nutrition, by infections, or by other extraneous influences. The suggestion is strong that the pancreatic hormone, insulin, and one or more pituitary factors are opposed with respect to their normal effects on carbohydrate metabolism. In the absence of both hormones a relatively normal state ensues, but without their protecting regulation the animal is at the mercy of its environment.

As shown by Long and Lukens, adrenalectomy has a very similar effect on pancreatic diabetes, so that part of the Houssay phenomenon may be the result of adrenal atrophy (see Chap. 54). The diabetic state may easily be restored in the Houssay animal by treatment with pituitary extracts, particularly those rich in growth hormone, but not so readily by ACTH or cortical hormones. Since this effect is obtained in the absence of the pancreas, the antagonism between insulin and the pituitary factors affecting carbohydrate metabolism cannot be the result of direct chemical interaction between the hormones, but must be physiologic in nature.

(vi) *Pituitary diabetes.* When crude anterior pituitary extract is given to adult dogs or cats over a period of several days, a state generally similar to pancreatic diabetes may be temporarily induced.[35, 36, 51, 81] Characteristic observations in this state include elevation of the blood sugar, glycosuria, ketonuria and polyuria. The nitrogen balance is positive during this phase, however, rather than negative as in pancreatic diabetes. In species other than the dog and cat, diabetes is rarely induced when the pancreas of the animal is intact, but if the animal has been partially depancreatized to a point just short of producing diabetes, the pituitary extract will induce a diabetic state comparable to that seen in intact dogs and cats. On the cessation of treatment, the pituitary diabetes disappears within a few days.

In animals which are resistant to the diabetogenic effects of pituitary preparations, hypoglycemia rather than hyperglycemia may be seen, and, on continued treatment, an increase in size and number of the islet cells may occur.[55, 59] A specific pancreatrophic factor in the pituitary gland has been suggested as responsible for these effects, but, since hypophysectomized animals show no signs whatever of deficient pancreatic function, this seems unlikely. It is probable that increased islet activity is indirectly called forth to oppose other metabolic effects of the extracts. If the response is adequate, the animal appears resistant to the diabetogenic factor; if it is not, diabetes ensues.

The nature of the hypophysial diabetogenic factor is not known certainly. Typical pituitary diabetes can be produced in dogs and cats by small amounts of purified growth hormone,[13, 15] and no chemical separation of the growth-promoting and diabetogenic activities has yet been achieved.[59] On the other hand, this diabetes is demonstrable only with difficulty in the absence of the adrenal glands; and, moreover, glycosuria can be induced in intact animals of many species with either ACTH or cortical steroids. Hence, both hypophysial and adrenal factors may be implicated. Current evidence suggests that growth hormone is probably the primary diabetogenic agent found in pituitary extracts, but that ACTH, acting through the adrenal steroids, may play a supporting or synergistic role in eliciting this response.

(vii) *Permanent pituitary diabetes (metahypophysial diabetes).* If diabetes is first induced as described above and then maintained for several weeks by the continued administration of pituitary preparations (with increasing dosage if required), then when treatment is stopped the diabetes mellitus may persist indefinitely.[18, 19, 52] This diabetic state is practically indistinguishable from that induced by pancreatectomy, except that survival without insulin is usually much longer. Examination of the pancreas indicates severe damage to the islet cells which normally secrete insulin, so that to all intents pancreatic diabetes mellitus has been induced by the prolonged treatment.[9, 60] If treatment with insulin is instituted during the early stages of the pituitary diabetes, the development of permanent diabetes may be prevented. It has therefore been suggested that continued exposure to the pituitary factor calls forth such an increase in the production of insulin that the islet cells become exhausted and so undergo the degenerative changes which are later evident in the permanent diabetic phase. Purified growth hormone preparations are capable of inducing permanent diabetes,[12] but neither ACTH nor adrenal hormones have been demonstrated to reproduce this effect.

SUMMARY OF METABOLIC EFFECTS OF ANTERIOR PITUITARY GLAND. It is not yet possible to state the exact role of the hypophysis in the intermediate metabolism of carbohydrate and fat. The tenor of the data is that the pituitary gland, acting both directly and through the adrenal cortex, exerts effects which are opposed to those of insulin. Normal metabolism requires the presence of all three of these factors; in the absence of one of the opposing hormones, exaggeration of the effects of the antagonist is seen, whereas in the absence of both, a relatively normal but very unstable state ensues. The relationship of the hormones of the pituitary to those of the adrenal cortex in these respects is less clear. Part of the action of the hypophysial hormones, notably that on gluconeogenesis, is undoubtedly mediated via the adrenal cortex, but that part affecting the utilization of body carbohydrate and fat seems to be directed by factors acting independently of the adrenal glands. The apparent parallelism between some of the effects of the pituitary factor (growth hormone?) and the cortical steroids, as on the utilization of fed carbohydrate (p. 1059), may be similar end-results produced by different mechanisms, or an expression of synergism between the two types of hormones.

THE NEUROHYPOPHYSIS

Hormonal Activities. Although pharmacologic effects of posterior pituitary extracts had been known for many years, the hormonal nature of neurohypophysial function was not shown conclusively until much later. Three types of activity have been attributed to extracts of the posterior lobe in mammals. In 1895, Oliver and Schaffer noted that pituitary extracts would raise the blood pressure of animals. This pressor effect was later indicated to be due to peripheral arteriolar or capillary constriction. Similar extracts also induce strong contractions of the isolated uterus, an effect first noted by Dale in 1906. Other smooth muscle also constricts, but the uterine musculature is most affected. Hence, the principle responsible for the effect is called oxytocic, from the Greek words meaning rapid birth. Extracts of the posterior pituitary have since been used clinically as pressor agents and also particularly to induce uterine contractions during and after parturition. Later, posterior lobe extracts were found also to suppress water excretion and to control diuresis in cases of diabetes insipidus. When given to normal, fully hydrated individuals, such extracts cause increased reabsorption of water by the kidneys and possibly also increased excretion of salt. The loop of Henle is believed to be the site of this action.[73] The mechanisms by which the antidiuretic factor affects renal function and body water are discussed further in Chapters 39 and 40.

Chemical fractionation of posterior lobe extracts was first achieved by Kamm *et al.* in 1928,[39] when they succeeded in separating two fractions containing principally the oxytocic and vasopressor factors, respectively. The antidiuretic factor accompanied the vasopressor substance in this fractionation. Both substances appeared to be polypeptide in nature. In 1950–1953, Du Vigneaud and coworkers obtained two distinct substances in pure form, one of them with oxytocic activity and the other a vasopressor and anti-diuretic agent. In a brilliant series of investigations, these workers then succeeded not only in determining the structures of these substances but also in synthesizing them from their constituent amino acids.[20] Both are basic peptides containing 8 amino acids in a cyclic disulfide form. Vasopressin from ox pituitaries has the following constitution:

$$CyS—Tyr—Phe—Glu(NH_2)—Asp(NH_2)—CyS—Pro—Arg—Gly—NH_2$$

Vasopressin from the pig differs from this material in the substitution of lysine for arginine. Although the structures of the hormones from other mammalian species have not all been established in detail, there is reason to believe that most of them are identical with that from the ox, given above. Oxytocin from ox pituitaries (and presumably also that from other species) has a very similar structure, differing only in two amino acids:

$$CyS—Tyr—Ileu—Glu(NH_2)—Asp(NH_2)—CyS—Pro—Leu—Gly—NH_2$$

The two hormones overlap to some degree in biologic activity as well.[74] Whereas pure oxytocin has very slight if any pressor or antidiuretic activity, the pure vasopressin-antidiuretic hormone possesses also about one-tenth the oxytocic potency shown by the primary oxytocic substance.

Some additional types of biologic activity have now been attributed to the purified oxytocic hormone.[74] This substance is the milk-ejection or milk "let-down" factor which is secreted during nursing or milking and which induces contraction of the myo-epithelial cells surrounding the alveoli of the mammary gland. The oxytocic factor also may induce a fall in the blood pressure; this effect is marked in avian species and is often used as the basis of assay for this hormone. Vasopressin displays both of these activities about in proportion to its oxytocic activity in other respects. Both vasopressin and oxytocin have been found to reproduce the effects of pituitary extracts in inducing spawning behavior in fish.

In addition to the polypeptides, another substance has also been obtained from posterior lobe tissue, a protein which appears pure by all the usual criteria and which exhibits all three types of posterior lobe activity.[38, 75] The molecular weight of this sub-stance is about 30,000, its isoelectric point 4.8—clearly very different from the properties of the smaller active substances described above. The activities per unit weight are very much less than those of the smaller fractions, but the three types of activity are found in a constant proportion identical with that observed in the native gland and shown by the preparations obtained serially during the purification of the protein. It is not yet known whether this protein is merely a factitious adsorbent of the smaller molecules, or whether it is in fact a normal form of the hormone. If the latter were the case, the complex might be secreted as such, or it could function as a storage aggregate which was cleaved intracellularly before the secretion of one or both of the separable factors.

Control of Secretion by the Neurohypophysis. Experimental work on the hormonal role of the neurohypophysis has been concerned mainly with the antidiuretic factor. The only considerable effect of removal of the posterior pituitary without damage to the hypothalamus is the induction of polyuria. A very large volume of dilute urine is secreted constantly. As a consequence, there is also great thirst and a high intake of water (polydipsia). The clinical counterpart of this condition, diabetes insipidus, has long been recognized, having been distinguished from diabetes mellitus (in which polyuria and glycosuria coexist) by Krank in 1794. The only other disorders which have been attributed to a posterior lobe deficiency in mammals are some difficulty in parturition and in lactation, but these have not been constant findings.

Neurohypophysial function—at least with respect to the secretion of the antidiuretic factor—appears to be completely under nervous control. It will be recalled that certain hypothalamic nuclei are intimately connected with the pars nervosa through the pituitary stalk (Fig. 585). The classic work of Ranson and his colleagues[24] demonstrated that if the pituitary stalk is sectioned or if the supra-optic nuclei are destroyed, the effect on water excretion is as if the neurohypophysis itself had been removed. In these conditions the pars nervosa shows atrophic changes and is apparently completely nonfunctional. Conversely, if the neural lobe is removed, degenerative changes may be seen in the hypothalamic nuclei (supra-optic and paraventricular nuclei) from which come the nerves which end in the posterior pituitary. Evidently the antidiuretic function of the posterior pituitary is controlled through the hypothalamico-hypophysial nerve tracts. A material which stains selectively by Gomori's procedure, and also with reagents which react with disulfides, such as occur in the posterior lobe hormones, is found not only in the posterior hypophysis proper but also throughout the hypothalamico-neurohypophysial tracts and in the attached hypothalamic centers.[1, 6, 46, 66] This material disappears from the neurohypophysis when the animal is subject to dehydration, and it is restored on repletion with water, suggesting that the "neurosecretory" granules are either identical with or intimately related to the antidiuretic hormone. When the hypothalamico-hypophysial tracts are cut or the neurohypophysis is removed, this material then tends to accumulate in the proximal ends of the cut neurons. Further, considerable amounts of ADH-active substance can be extracted from the hypothalamus.[50, 53, 74] These and related observations indicate that the neurohypophysial hormones probably are formed in the neurons of these tracts, rather than in the gland itself. The hormones seem to be stored in the posterior lobe, however, and presumably they are secreted from there.

Further evidence of the endocrine nature of neural lobe function has been obtained through study of factors affecting the secretion of water by the kidney.[41, 72, 73] When normal animals are deprived of water, they secrete only a small volume of concentrated urine. Hypophysectomized animals or those from which the neural lobe only has been removed (or rendered inactive by stalk section or lesions in the hypothalamus) continue to secrete urine at the previous rate, even though great dehydration results. If sodium chloride is administered to normally hydrated animals, water secretion is delayed, but, again, hypophysectomized animals do not respond. Apparently either dehydration or the taking of salt, which results in a relative deprivation of water, brings about an increase in the release of the antidiuretic hormone by the pituitary and, by this means, the conservation of water. A substance having antidiuretic properties has been found in the urine of normal rats but not of hypophysectomized rats under these conditions.[3, 26]

Verney has shown that the urine volume is controlled by changes in the osmotic concentration of the blood.[76] If during water diuresis of normal animals a hypertonic solution of salt, dextrose, or sucrose is injected into the carotid artery, a prompt diminution in the rate of water excretion is seen. In mammals in which the neural lobe is absent or nonfunctional, such a change does not occur. An increase of as little as 2 per cent in the effective osmotic concentration of the plasma suffices to induce a prompt increase in the output of ADH and concomitant reduction in urine flow. When the osmotic concentration is diminished, as by the ingestion of a rather large volume of water, the secretion of ADH is suppressed; but it is difficult to demonstrate the effects of small changes in concentration here because the circulating hormone must have time to die away before evidence of reduction in ADH activity can become evident. Verney has suggested the presence in the hypothalamic nuclei of "osmoreceptors," organs sensitive to differences in osmotic concentration of the intracellular and extracellular fluids, which then transmit stimuli to the neural lobe via the supraoptico-hypophysial tracts.

The secretion of ADH seems to be responsive not only to change in osmotic concentration of the plasma but also to a number of other stimuli which presumably either act directly on the hypothalamic centers or reach these centers through neural pathways. After placing fine electrodes in the neural lobe of the rabbit, Harris was able to stimulate this organ electrically by remote control in the unanesthetized intact animal.[31] In such circumstances weak stimuli caused the inhibition of water diuresis, an increase in chloride excretion, and marked activity of the uterine musculature in the rabbit prepared by estrogen treatment. No change in blood pressure was observed. This was the first convincing evidence for the physiologic secretion of the oxytocic factor by the neural lobe.

The careful studies of Verney have shown that pain or even relatively mild emotional disturbances will cause diminution in urine flow, presumably by stimulating the secretion of ADH.[76] In patients who have fainted from any cause, increased amounts of ADH-active material are found in the urine. Many drugs have similar effects, among them acetylcholine, nicotine, morphine and ether. On the other hand, ethyl alcohol strongly inhibits the secretion of the hormone. This effect no doubt accounts for the well known diuretic action of alcohol.

Indirect evidence suggests rather strongly that the ADH-producing system can respond also to change in the effective blood volume, even when the latter is unaccompanied by change in osmotic concentration. This work has been well summarized by Strauss.[72] Any large or sudden expansion of the extracellular fluid or plasma volume, as by injection of isotonic fluids, is followed by an increase in urine flow which may be due to inhibition of ADH secretion. Conversely, reduction of the blood volume (as by venesection, application of tourniquets about the limbs, or even the assumption of a passive erect posture) tends to decrease the urine flow. The breathing of air at negative pressure has been observed to have the same effect as expansion of the blood volume, and so has distention of the left atrium.[34a] It is supposed, therefore, that the stimulus in these cases is not change in the blood volume itself but alteration in pressure or stretch somewhere in the thoracic vascular system, probably in the heart or pulmonary veins.[34a] Impulses from this region would then affect the activity of the hypothalamic-hypophysial system and inhibit the secretion of ADH.

The well known diuretic response to sudden chilling of the skin may be explicable in the same way, since the peripheral vasoconstriction in response to cold would result in a relative increase in the blood volume in the central vessels.

Whether the neurohypophysis plays any significant physiologic role in the regulation of blood pressure is not known. Since the antidiuretic and vasopressor activities appear to be properties of the same molecule, and since much smaller amounts of the substance are required to affect water excretion than to increase the blood pressure, the vasopressor action may represent a pharmacologic effect of excessive amounts of the antidiuretic factor.

REFERENCES

1. ADAMS, C. W. M. and SLOPER, J. C. *J. Endocr.*, 1956, *13*:221–228.
2. ADROUNY, G. A. and RUSSELL, J. A. *Endocrinology*, 1956, *59*:241–251.
3. AMES, R. G., MOORE, D. H. and VAN DYKE, H. B. *Endocrinology*, 1950, *46*:215–227.
4. ASCHNER, B. *Pflüg. Arch. ges. Physiol.*, 1912, *146*:1–146.
5. ASTWOOD, E. B. *The Hormones*, 1955, *3*:235–308.
6. BARRNETT, R. J. *Endocrinology*, 1954, *55*:484–501.
7. BECK, H., ASLING, C. W., SIMPSON, M. E., EVANS, H. M. and LI, C. H. *Amer. J. Anat.*, 1948, *82*:203–217.
8. BENNETT, L. L. and EVANS, H. M. *The Hormones*, 1955, *3*:235–308.
9. BEST, C. H., CAMPBELL, J., HAIST, R. E. and HAM, A. W. *J. Physiol.*, 1942, *101*:17–26.

10. BILLENSTEIN, D. C. and LEVEQUE, T. F. *Endocrinology*, 1955, *56*:704–717.

11. BODIAN, D. *Johns Hopk. Hosp. Bull.*, 1951, *89*:354–376.

12. CAMPBELL, J., CHAIKOFF, L. and DAVIDSON, I. W. F. *Endocrinology*, 1954, *54*:48–58.

13. CAMPBELL, J., DAVISON, I. W. F., SNAIR, W. D. and LEI, H. P. *Endocrinology*, 1950, *46*: 273–281.

14. COOKE, R. T. and SHEEHAN, H. L. *Brit. med. J.*, 1950, *(1)*:928–931.

15. COTES, P. M., REID, E. and YOUNG, F. G. *Nature (Lond.)*, 1949, *164*:209–211.

16. DEBODO, R. A. and ALTSZULER, N. *Vitam. & Horm.*, 1957, *15*:205–258.

17. DEBODO, R. C., KURTZ, M., ANCOWITZ, A. and KIANG, S. P. *Amer. J. Physiol.*, 1950, *163*:310–318.

18. DOHAN, F. C., CHAMBERS, A. H. and FISH, C. A. *Endocrinology*, 1941, *28*:566–579.

19. DOHAN, F. C., FISH, C. A. and LUKENS, F. D. W. *Endocrinology*, 1941, *28*:341–357.

20. DUVIGNEAUD, V. *Harvey Lect.*, 1954–5, *50*:1–26.

21. EARTLY, H. and LEBLONDE, C. P. *Endocrinology*, 1954, *54*:249–71.

22. ENGEL, F. L. and ENGEL, M. G. *Endocrinology*, 1958, *62*:150–158.

23. EVANS, H. M., MEYER, K. and SIMPSON, M. E. *Growth and gonad-stimulating hormone of the anterior hypophysis*. Berkeley, University of California Press, 1933.

24. FISHER, C., INGRAM, W. P. and RANSON, S. W. *Arch. Neurol. Psychiat. (Chicago)*, 1935, *34*: 124–163.

25. GESCHWIND, I. I., LI, C. H. and BARNALFI, L. *J. Amer. chem. Soc.*, 1957, *79*:620–625, 1003–1004.

26. GILMAN, A. and GOODMAN, L. *J. Physiol.*, 1937, *90*:113–124.

27. GORDAN, G. S., BENNETT, L. L., LI, C. H. and EVANS, H. M. *Endocrinology*, 1948, *42*: 153–160.

28. GREEN, J. D. and HARRIS, G. W. *J. Endocr.*, 1947, *5*:136–146.

29. GREENBAUM, A. L. and YOUNG, F. G. *J. Endocr.*, 1953, *9*:127–135.

30. GREER, M. A. *Recent Progr. Horm. Res.*, 1957, *13*:67–104.

31. HARRIS, G. W. *Phil. Trans.*, 1947, B232:385–441.

32. HARRIS, G. W. *Physiol. Rev.*, 1948, *28*:139–179.

33. HARRIS, G. W. *Neural Control of the Pituitary Gland.* Baltimore, Williams & Wilkins Co., 1955.

34. HARRIS, J. I. and ROOS, P. *Biochem. J.*, 1959, *71*:434–455; HARRIS, J. I. *Ibid.*, 451–459.

34a. HENRY, J. P. and PEARCE, J. W. *J. Physiol.*, 1956, *131*:572–585.

35. HOUSSAY, B. A. *New Engl. J. Med.*, 1936, *214*:961–986.

36. HOUSSAY, B. A. *Endocrinology*, 1942, *30*:884–897.

37. ILLINGWORTH, B. A. and RUSSELL, J. A. *Endocrinology*, 1951, *48*:423–434.

38. IRVING, G. W., JR. and DU VIGNEAUD, V. *Ann. N. Y. Acad. Sci.*, 1943, *43*:273–308.

39. KAMM, O., ALDRICH, T. B., GROTE, I. W., ROWE, L. W. and BUGBEE, E. P. *J. Amer. chem. Soc.*, 1928, *50*:573–601.

40. KENNEDEY, G. C. and PARROTT, B. M. V. *J. Endocr.*, 1958, *17*:161–166.

41. KERRIGAN, G. A., TALBOT, N. B. and CRAWFORD, J. D. *J. clin. Endocr.*, 1955, *15*:265–275.

42. KNOBIL, E. *Recent Progr. Horm. Res.*, 1959, *15*:1–58.

43. KNOBIL, E., MORSE, A., WOLF, R. C. and GREEP, R. O. *Endocrinology*, 1958, *62*:348–354.

44. LEE, M. O. and AYRES, G. B. *Endocrinology*, 1936, *20*:489–495.

45. LERNER, A. B., SHIZUMI, K. and BUNDING, I. *J. clin. Endocr.*, 1954, *14*:1463–1490.

46. LEVEQUE, T. F. and SCHARRER, E. *Endocrinology*, 1953, *52*:436–447.

47. LI, C. H. *Advanc. Protein Chem.*, 1956, *11*:101–190.

48. LI, C. H. *Advanc. Protein Chem.*, 1957, *12*:270–317.

49. LI, C. H., EVANS, H. M. and SIMPSON, M. E. *J. biol. Chem.*, 1945, *159*:353–366.

50. LLOYD, C. W. and PIEROG, S. *Endocrinology*, 1955, *56*:718–726.

51. LUKENS, F. D. W. *Amer. J. med. Sci.*, 1946, *212*:229–240.

52. MARKS, H. P. and YOUNG, F. G. *J. Endocr.*, 1939, *1*:470–510.

53. MELVILLE, E. V. and HARE, K. *Endocrinology*, 1945, *36*:332–339.

54. MILMAN, A. E., DEMOOR, P. and LUKENS, F. D. W. *Amer. J. Physiol.*, 1951, *166*:354–363.

55. MILMAN, A. E. and RUSSELL, J. A. *Endocrinology*, 1950, *47*:114–128.

56. MUNSON, P. L. and BRIGGS, F. N. *Recent Progr. Horm. Res.*, 1955, *11*:83–118.

57. RABEN, M. S. *Recent Progr. Horm. Res.*, 1959, *15*:71–105.

58. REID, E. *J. Endocr.*, 1952, *8*:50–55; 1953, *9*:210–23.

59. RICHARDSON, K. C. and YOUNG, F. G. *J. Physiol.*, 1937, *91*:352–364.

60. RICHARDSON, K. C. and YOUNG, F. G. *Lancet*, 1938, *234*:1098–1101.

61. RUSSELL, J. A. *Physiol. Rev.*, 1938, *18*:1–27.

62. RUSSELL, J. A. *Fed. Proc.*, 1955, *14*:696–705.

63. RUSSELL, J. A. *Amer. J. clin. Nutr.*, 1957, *5*:404–416.

64. SALTER, J. M. and BEST, C. H. *Brit. med. J.*, 1953, *(2)*:353–356; *Canad. J. Biochem. Physiol.*, 1957, *35*:913–922.

65. SAYERS, M. A., SAYERS, G. and WOODBURY, L. A. *Endocrinology*, 1948, *42*:379–393.

66. SCHARRER, E. and SCHARRER, B. *Recent Progr. Horm. Res.*, 1954, *10*:183–239.

67. SCOW, R. O. *Endocrinology*, 1952, *51*:42–51.

68. SHEEHAN, H. L. and SUMMERS, V. K. *Quart. J. Med.*, 1949, N.S. *18*:319–378.

69. SIMPSON, M. E., ASLING, C. W. and EVANS, H. M. *Yale J. Biol. Med.*, 1950, *23*:1–27.

70. SMITH, P. E. *Amer. J. Anat.*, 1930, *45*:205–273.

71. SMITH, R. W., GAEBLER, O. H. and LONG, C. N. N., eds. *The hypophyseal growth hormone, nature and actions*, New York, Blakiston Division, McGraw-Hill Co., 1955.

72. STRAUSS, M. C. *Body water in man.* Boston, Little, Brown and Co., 1957.

73. VAN DYKE, H. B. *Physiology and pharmacology of the pituitary body.* Chicago, University of Chicago Press, 1936, vol. 1; 1939, vol. 2.

74. VAN DYKE, H. B., ADAMSONS, R., JR. and ENGEL, S. L. *Recent Progr. Horm. Res.*, 1955, *11*:1–42.

75. VAN DYKE, H. B., CHOW, B. F., GREEP, R. O. and ROTHEN, A. *J. Pharmacol.*, 1942, *74*: 190–209.

76. VERNEY, E. B. *Proc. roy. Soc.*, 1947, *B135*:25–106.

77. WAGNER, E. M. and SCOW, R. O. *Endocrinology*, 1958, *61*:419–425.

78. WILHELMI, A. E., FISHMAN, J. B. and RUSSELL, J. A. *J. biol. Chem.*, 1948, *176*:735–745.

79. WISLOCKI, G. B. *Anat. Rec.*, 1937, *69*:361–387.

80. WOLSTENHOLME, G. E. W., ed. *Ciba Foundation colloquia in endocrinology. Symposium on control of secretion by the anterior pituitary,* 1952, *4*:87–253.

81. YOUNG, F. G. *Biochem. J.*, 1938, *32*:513–523.

82. YOUNG, F. G. *Biochem. J.*, 1945, *39*:515–536.

The Pancreas

By JANE A. RUSSELL

OF ALL the hormones, insulin, from the pancreas, has been the most extensively studied, both experimentally and clinically. Its exact role in intermediate metabolism is, however, still incompletely known. That the pancreas had other than digestive functions was first indicated by von Mering and Minkowski in 1889, when they discovered that pancreatectomy in the dog was followed by the excretion of sugar in the urine and other metabolic abnormalities resembling those seen in the clinical state, diabetes mellitus. The latter disease—a rather common disorder in man—is characterized by polyuria, glycosuria, ketonuria, marked wasting of the body and early death in a comatose state. Minkowski further showed that ligation of the pancreatic duct alone did not induce diabetes. This fact, together with the later observation that the onset of diabetes in depancreatized animals could be delayed by subcutaneous grafts of pancreatic tissue, first suggested that the pancreas had an internal as well as an external secretion.

The presence in the pancreas of small islets or nests of cells which differed histologically from the acinar tissue had been noted by Langerhans in 1869. These islets were shown not to be connected to the duct system into which the external secretion of the pancreas flows. When it was found that the islets of Langerhans remained normal in appearance after ligation of the pancreatic ducts, whereas the acinar tissue became atrophic, it was considered that the islets must be the source of the internal secretion, and the still hypothetical hormone was given the name insulin.

The pancreatic islets, although small, are numerous; their total volume amounts to approximately 1 to 3 per cent of that of the whole pancreas. The islets are composed of at least two kinds of cells which differ in the staining properties of their granules. One type, the larger but less numerous, are called α cells; the other type, the β cells, are now considered to be the ones which secrete insulin. This was suggested by observations made after subtotal pancreatectomy, when degenerative changes in the remaining β cells and diabetes mellitus were seen to develop coincidentally. This view has been amply confirmed by the development of diabetes following the selective destruction of the β cells by alloxan (p. 1069) and by anterior pituitary extracts (Chap. 52).

INSULIN

Following the indication of the existence of an internal secretion of the pancreas, many attempts were made in the early years of this century to prepare from pancreatic tissue a substance which could be used to treat diabetic patients. All such efforts were unsuccessful, the products being either inactive or toxic, until the work of Banting and Best in 1921.[4] Believing the presence of pancreatic digestive enzymes in the extracts to be the cause of their inactivation, these workers extracted the pancreatic tissue of dogs after atrophy of the acinar tissue had been induced by preliminary duct ligation. The extracts so made were found to lower the blood sugar and to prolong the lives of diabetic dogs. Later, Collip, working with Banting and Best, prepared active extracts from cattle pancreas and developed the method by which insulin is now prepared on a huge scale for clinical use.

The hormone is a protein and has been obtained in highly purified forms, both as crystals containing small amounts of zinc and in the amorphous state. The order of arrangement of all the amino acids in the insulin molecule has now been determined,[55] thus making insulin the first protein to have its constitution so established. The smallest active unit consists of two peptide chains, one (A) of 21 amino acids and the other (B) of 30 amino acids joined by two disulfide bridges of cystine. The form may be sketched as follows:

$$\text{Gly} \underset{1}{\quad} \text{CyS} \underset{6}{\quad} \text{CyS} \underset{7}{\quad} (8,9,10) \underset{11}{\text{CyS}} \quad \underset{20}{\text{CyS}} \text{Asp (NH}_2) \underset{21}{} \qquad \text{(A)}$$

$$\text{Phe} \underset{1}{\quad} \text{CyS} \underset{7}{\quad} \text{CyS} \underset{19}{\quad} \text{Ala} \underset{30}{} \qquad \text{(B)}$$

The hormones from a variety of species have identical structures except for some limited differences in the secondary disulfide ring (positions 8 to 10) in the A chain. The hormone is inactivated when the sulfide bridges are broken. It is also inactivated by the digestive enzymes, and so must always be given parenterally.

When insulin is given to animals, the action is of rather short duration; the characteristic blood sugar lowering effect is manifest within minutes, the blood sugar level

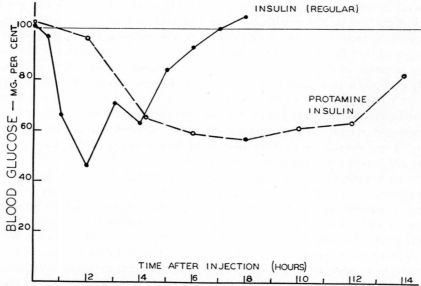

FIG. 589. Effects of soluble insulin and of protamine insulin (both 1 unit per kg.) on blood glucose of normal dog. (After Kerr and Best, *Amer. J. med. Sci.*, 1937, *194*:149.)

reaching a minimum in about one to two hours and then gradually returning to normal. As shown in Figure 589, the rate of absorption from the injection site may be slowed and the period of effective action much prolonged if the insulin is mixed before injection with one of a number of substances which form relatively insoluble complexes with it. Of these, the basic protein derivatives protamine and globin are the most commonly used for the purpose. Such modified insulin preparations make it possible often to treat a diabetic patient adequately with only one injection of insulin per day. The hormone is assayed biologically by its effect on the blood sugar level. In some animals, such as the rabbit, this is measured directly, or in others, e.g., mice, it can be determined by the incidence of convulsions produced under standard conditions.

Alloxan Diabetes.* A new method of inducing pancreatic diabetes was introduced in 1943 with the discovery that alloxan, $\overline{NH \cdot CO \cdot NH \cdot CO \cdot CO \cdot CO}$, exerts a selective specific necrotic action upon the β cells of the islets of Langerhans.[42] After the administration of a single dose of alloxan (on the order of 50 mg. per kg. given intravenously) pathologic changes may be seen in the β cells within a few minutes, and after some days these cells may have disappeared completely. The degree of damage produced by a given dose of alloxan varies considerably, from little or no evident effect to complete destruction, so that the severity of the diabetic state obtained in individual animals may be of any grade. There may also be damage to the liver and kidneys, but if not too severe this damage may be only temporary. The metabolic effects of this destruction of the β cells are similar to those of partial or complete pancreatectomy in almost all respects, except, of course, that the animal does not lack the external secretion of the pancreas. This convenient method of inducing diabetes is now much used in experimental work, particularly in small animals like the rat and rabbit in which the operative removal of the diffuse pancreas is most troublesome.

Effects of Insulin Deficiency. Most of the early studies of experimental diabetes were made in dogs, and the classic description of pancreatic diabetes was derived from this work. Subsequent observations on a number of other species have shown considerable quantitative variations between species and have led to some modification of the earlier views. Although pancreatic diabetes in dogs and cats is almost always fatal within a few weeks at most, goats, sheep, rabbits and monkeys have survived for many months without treatment. The blood sugar of these animals is elevated, particularly when food is given, but in the fasted state normal or even subnormal levels are sometimes seen. Ketonuria, which is usually marked in the pig, cat and man, may be slight or absent in other species. However, even though their diabetes does not appear extremely severe, such depancreatized animals commonly lose weight and succumb eventually to direct or indirect consequences of the lack of insulin. Avian species usually tolerate pancreatectomy with little evident effect, but it has been reported that owls, which are carnivorous, may be made severely diabetic. It may be seen that insulin is not a *sine qua non* of carbohydrate utilization as was once thought, but, instead, like other hormones, it must serve a regulatory function.

The derangements of metabolism which occur in the absence of insulin are evidenced in the following ways:

HYPERGLYCEMIA. An abnormally high blood sugar level is typical of insulin deficiency. The hyperglycemia is greater in the fed state, but usually more or less persistent during fasting as well. Glycosuria is commonly seen (see Chap. 39).

DIURESIS. As discussed in Chapter 39, the urinary volume is usually many times normal; for to accommodate the quantities of glucose excreted a rather large volume of water is required. Large amounts of salt then are also excreted. Thirst, polydipsia and a

* Not to be confused with phlorhizin diabetes.

TABLE 44.   *EXCRETION OF GLUCOSE, NITROGEN AND MINERALS IN*
DIABETES MELLITUS*

	URINE VOL. ml.	GLUCOSE gm.	KETONES gm.	NITROGEN (TOTAL) gm.	MINERALS Na, mEq.	K, mEq.	Cl, mEq.
Case 1							
Controlled with insulin (12 days)	1209	0	0.1	11.8	89	58	83
Without insulin (severe acidosis) (4 days)	2621	150	17.7	18.7	174	152	131
Recovery with insulin (5 days)	1020	0	0.3	11.4	66	8	89
Case 2							
Controlled with insulin (16 days)	1536	0	0.0	14.4	85	67	88
Without insulin (little acidosis) (11 days)	2004	125	0.5	18.3	121	81	108
Recovery with insulin (4 days)	1010	0	0.2	13.5	35	46	32

* Average daily urinary excretion rates in 2 patients in successive periods with and without insulin. Constant amounts of food and water were given daily during the entire period of study: Case 1—125 gm. carbohydrate, 140 gm. fat, 75 gm. protein; Case 2—165 gm. carbohydrate, 155 gm. fat, 87 gm. protein.

(From Atchley *et al., J. clin. Invest.*, 1933, *12*:297.)

tendency toward dehydration result. The data in Table 44, reported by Atchley *et al.*,[2] indicate the magnitudes of the losses of glucose, water and salts seen in diabetic human subjects given constant amounts of fluid and food. Even when no acidosis was present (Case *2*), sodium and chloride were lost in amounts equivalent to about 200 to 300 ml. of extracellular fluid per day. Continued losses of salts of this magnitude must eventually deplete the extracellular fluid volume to a critical degree.

DECREASED UTILIZATION OF EXOGENOUS CARBOHYDRATE.   The rate at which exogenous carbohydrate is utilized must be diminished in diabetes mellitus, for administered glucose is but slowly removed from the blood (Fig. 590), and the equivalent of a considerable part or all of the carbohydrate fed may be excreted in the urine. The defect actually responsible for these effects has been debated extensively. One school of thought has held that utilization of carbohydrate is in fact relatively normal in the diabetic, although taking place at a higher blood sugar level, and that the hyperglycemia is the result only of excessive gluconeogenesis. Glycosuria then occurs simply by overflow.[60] This concept is not in accord with observations on glucose tolerance such as those in Figure 590. These data show that the excess glucose remaining in the blood of diabetic patients is far greater at all blood sugar levels than it is in normal persons. Moreover, the glucose tolerance is reduced in mildly diabetic subjects even when the postabsorptive blood glucose level is normal. Further, it is readily shown that the glucose tolerance of eviscerated animals is greatly reduced and that in such preparations insulin in small doses restores the utilization of blood glucose to normal or above. On the other hand, the reason for the reduction in uptake of exogenous carbohydrate in the absence of insulin has not been clear. As discussed below, the three major routes of disposition of carbohydrate, oxidation, glycogen deposition and fat formation, have all been proposed as the site of the defect.

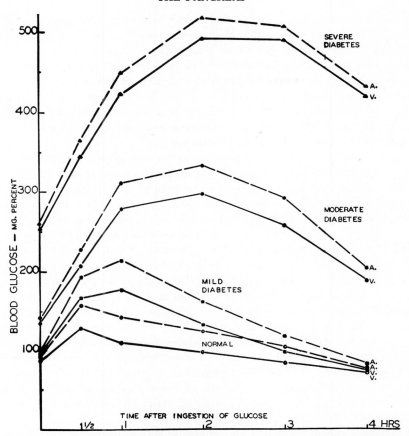

FIG. 590. Arterial and venous glucose tolerance curves in normal and diabetic subjects: composite curves from 44 normal subjects, 48 patients with mild diabetes, 19 with diabetes of medium severity, and 9 with severe diabetes. (From Somogyi, unpublished data, and Somogyi, *J. biol. Chem.*, 1948, *174*:189.)

Although the diabetic animal does not utilize administered carbohydrate in normal fashion, this does not mean that the diabetic is unable to use any carbohydrate. In fact, in hepatectomized depancreatized animals not given glucose, the blood glucose falls nearly as rapidly as it does when the pancreas is present. A substantial part of the glucose thus utilized probably can be accounted for by the metabolism of the brain and nervous tissue, which continue to use carbohydrate as their principal substrate at all times, even in the complete absence of insulin. Another portion may be used by the muscles, including the heart; for during muscle contraction the uptake of sugar from the blood is increased whether insulin is present or not. Thus, the tissues of the diabetic or eviscerated animal must be able to use some carbohydrate in any condition. It should be recalled, however, that in the fasting state the rate of carbohydrate utilization is low also in normal subjects, the output of glucose from the liver and the peripheral utilization accounting for no more than about a quarter of the total metabolic rate.[20, 28] Hence, differences in this respect between normal and diabetic subjects are likely to be minimal in the fasting state. In studies of the mechanism of the defect in diabetes, discussed below, this fact has not always been taken into account.

Carbohydrate oxidation. The only indicator of carbohydrate oxidation readily available until recent years has been the respiratory quotient (R.Q.). This ratio is very low in diabetes (often below 0.7 in the fasting state), and it does rise when glucose is fed as it does normally. However, the R.Q. is a resultant of many processes and—as has often been pointed out—a low value may be due as well to increased ketogenesis or gluconeogenesis or to diminished fat formation as to a reduction in carbohydrate oxidation. The use of radioglucose as a tracer now allows a more direct measure of the rate of oxidation of glucose in diabetes, but the interpretation of data obtained in this way is technically difficult.[3] When tracer amounts of radioglucose were given to diabetic dogs in the postabsorptive state, the production of labeled carbon dioxide appeared to be diminished roughly by half.[3, 22] More marked differences in oxidation rate might be expected under conditions of glucose load, but the fate of larger amounts of isotopic glucose does not seem to have been studied in these circumstances.

Storage of glucose as glycogen. This process has not been sufficiently studied in diabetic animals to make it possible to say whether it is slower in rate than it is in the normal animal. The classic description of both experimental and clinical diabetes mellitus includes the statement that the liver contains little or no glycogen. However, the older data were obtained before certain technical difficulties in the estimation of glycogen in tissues were appreciated, and, furthermore, they were seldom referred to control studies on animals of similar nutritional state. More recently, it has been uniformly observed that alloxan-diabetic rats and rabbits have normal liver glycogen levels when fed and may even have amounts of glycogen in the liver much above those in control animals when fasted.[46, 75] In human subjects with diabetes and in depancreatized dogs and cats under standard conditions, the liver glycogen may be normal or only moderately low, and the muscle glycogen is practically normal.[10, 32, 34, 41] Hence, it appears that insulin is not a critical determinant of the amount of glycogen in the tissues. The *rate* of glycogen synthesis may be subnormal, however. The resynthesis of glycogen in muscle during recovery after induced work has been reported to be somewhat slow in depancreatized animals.[41] Also, after the feeding of glucose, glycogen deposition does not occur in the diaphragm of alloxan diabetic rats, although normally an increase in glycogen content of several fold is seen in this organ.

The glycogen of heart muscle is almost always very much above normal in diabetic animals. This could be the result of increased uptake of glucose by reason of the continuing work of this organ in the presence of high blood glucose levels, or it may conceivably be related to the action of growth hormone on cardiac glycogen (Chap. 52).

Fat formation from carbohydrate. This process, which represents an important pathway in the metabolism of carbohydrate in normal animals, is very slow in the absence of insulin. This is well shown by changes in the uptake of deuterium (isotopic hydrogen,

TABLE 45. *FORMATION OF GLYCOGEN AND FAT IN NORMAL AND IN ALLOXAN DIABETIC RATS FED A HIGH CARBOHYDRATE DIET**

	FINAL D CONCENTRATION [†] (IN PER CENT OF BODY WATER D)				AMOUNTS NEWLY SYNTHESIZED (GM. PER DAY PER ANIMAL)	
	Liver Glycogen	Carcass Glycogen	Liver Fat	Carcass Fat	Glycogen	Fat
Normal rats	23	9	22	10	0.5	1.9
Diabetic rats	43	22	9	9‡	1.4	0.1

* Water containing deuterium (D) was given 56 hours before the tissues were taken for analysis, and the D concentration of the body water maintained constant during the interval.
† Indicates the relative rates of *new* formation of the labeled substances.
‡ The total amount of fat here was very small.
(From Stetten and Boxer, *J. biol. Chem.*, 1944, *156*:271.)

H^2) into the body glycogen and fats of rats given heavy water (Table 45). In these conditions, the concentrations of deuterium in these substances indicate the relative rates of their replacement by material newly formed from smaller molecules,* such as the intermediates in carbohydrate catabolism. Since the animals were fed a diet free of fat, the rate of synthesis of fat (from carbohydrate) is indicated. At the far right of Table 45 the actual amounts of fat and glycogen formed are given as calculated from the rates of replacement and the total amounts of these substances in the body. These data indicate that the diabetic rats synthesized only a small fraction of the fat made by the normal animals under the same conditions. Similar conclusions may be drawn from observations made on liver slices taken from diabetic animals, where the formation of fatty acids from C^{14}-labeled glucose is found to be almost completely abolished.[5, 12, 16] The interpretation of the latter experiments is complicated because oxidation of fat is greatly accelerated in the livers of diabetic animals; in this case, the appearance of isotope in the fat may be reduced because the intermediates between acetyl CoA and fatty acid are "washed out" of the system by the catabolic process, rather than because of any specific defect in the conversion of glucose to fatty acids.

FAT METABOLISM AND KETOGENESIS. The rate of catabolism of fat is much increased in the diabetic animal, for most of its energy must come from this source. Concomitantly, the concentration of ketone bodies (acetoacetic and β-hydroxybutyric acids) in the blood is elevated and these substances are often excreted in the urine in considerable amounts (Table 44). As is now well known, ketogenesis can be considered a normal part of the process of fat metabolism when the latter is proceeding at a high rate; and the ketone bodies, liberated by liver, are used readily as a source of energy by other tissues. In the diabetic, as to a lesser extent in fasting normal individuals, the rate of production of these intermediates may be so great as to exceed their rate of utilization, and so they may accumulate in the blood and be in part excreted.[61, 62]† Other evidence that fat is being used in large amounts is seen in an increase in blood fats, amounting at times to a visible milkiness, and in increased mobilization of fat to the liver. No evidence indicating a direct effect of insulin or of its lack on the catabolism of fat has yet been adduced; rather, it is believed that the increase in fat catabolism seen in diabetes stems indirectly from the reduction in carbohydrate utilization.

The ketone bodies—formed as acids—are immediately neutralized by the buffers of the tissue fluids and blood and are excreted mainly as the sodium and potassium salts. In Table 44 comparison of the data obtained in two diabetic patients indicates the great additional loss of base which occurred when the ketosis was marked. The loss of base, if long continued, leads to latent or actual acidosis. This, together with the depletion of salts and anhydremia resulting from diuresis, may bring about a shocklike state, coma, and death. For the maintenance of life in the diabetic animal, the degree of ketosis induced is the most critical factor.

Since the amount of ketone bodies excreted depends upon the relative rates of their production and utilization, the degree of ketosis observed in the absence of insulin varies widely. This is true even of animals of the same species, for both the formation and the oxidation of ketone bodies may be affected by many factors, such as composition of the diet, nutritional state, the activity of other endocrine organs, or the presence of

* In carbohydrates and fats, the hydrogen atoms attached directly to carbon atoms do not exchange spontaneously with those in the body water. During new formation of glucose and fat from smaller molecules, however, hydrogen atoms taken up from the deuterium-labeled body water become attached to the carbon atoms and remain in the carbohydrate or fat molecules during their life in the body.

† Stadie[61] has calculated from data in the literature that a resting diabetic man may utilize 2.5 gm. of fat per kg. per day (1600 kcal. per day in a 70 kg. man) without ketonuria. With greater rates of fat catabolism, the equivalent of one-third of the excess is excreted as ketone bodies.

infection. The considerable differences between species in survival time without insulin are no doubt partly expressions of differences in susceptibility to ketosis.

LOSS OF NITROGEN. The retention of nitrogen as protein in the tissues appears to be defective in the diabetic. In the fasted depancreatized animal, the rate of nitrogen excretion has been reported to be much increased—at least in the period immediately after operation—and even in the well fed animal a negative nitrogen balance is seen as the supply of insulin is reduced.[14] A further example is seen in the data from the diabetic patients reported in Table 44. During the control periods with insulin, the patients were excreting the same amounts of nitrogen as they ingested; but when insulin therapy was stopped, they began immediately to lose nitrogen. The negative nitrogen balance was in the first case about 8 grams (counting fecal nitrogen), in the other 4 grams per day. A loss of nitrogen from the body of this magnitude, amounting to 25 to 50 grams of protein per day, could not be sustained for many weeks without gravely endangering the proper functioning of the tissue enzyme systems. Whether insulin has a direct role in the sparing of body protein is not known. From the fact that phlorhizinized animals exhibit an increase in protein catabolism at least as great as that seen in depancreatized animals, it has been considered likely that the loss of nitrogen may be an indirect consequence of diminished utilization of carbohydrate. It is possible, however, that insulin may intervene in protein metabolism in some more direct fashion (p. 1077).

GLUCONEOGENESIS. Because glucose may continue to be excreted by diabetic animals even when they are fasted for prolonged periods, it has been considered that the rate of new formation of carbohydrate from noncarbohydrate sources must be increased in the absence of insulin. Gluconeogenesis certainly occurs in diabetic subjects, but whether this occurs at rates much above normal is controversial. Crandall and Lipscomb,[20] who used the angiostomy technique to estimate directly the rate of release of glucose from the liver of the diabetic dog, could find no evidence that gluconeogenesis was increased. On the other hand, a somewhat similar technique applied to diabetic human subjects indicated an increase which was roughly proportional to that of nitrogen catabolism.[9] In alloxan-diabetic and also in phlorhizinized rats infused with C^{14}-glucose Stettin et al.[66, 72] observed a moderate increase in the rate of dilution of the labeled compound with nonisotopic glucose, i.e., with newly formed carbohydrate. From these data it appears that, although the rate of gluconeogenesis may be somewhat greater than normal in the diabetic, it cannot be increased to an extreme degree.

The main source of the carbohydrate excreted in fasting diabetic animals probably is protein. The ratio of the amounts of glucose and nitrogen excreted daily by the fasting diabetic animal is usually about 2 to 3, rarely exceeding 4; these values for the D:N ratio indicate the excretion of glucose containing an equivalent of 25 to 50 per cent of the carbon in the protein metabolized during the period.* From the known content of glycogenic amino acids in most proteins, there is then no reason to look for sources other than protein for the glucose excreted. This consideration is further supported by the classic observation that, when diabetic animals are fed only meat, the urinary glucose to nitrogen ratio is of exactly the same magnitude as that seen in fasting animals. Any increase in the rate of gluconeogenesis is therefore probably the result of increased rates of protein catabolism.

* Most animal proteins contain about 3.3 grams of carbon per gram of nitrogen. If all the carbon in the protein were converted to glucose (or spared equivalent carbon from combustion), then for each gram of nitrogen $3.3 \times 180/72$ or 8.3 grams of glucose could be formed. The classic maximal D:N ratio of 3.5, observed in phlorhizin diabetes, then represents the conversion to glucose of 3.5/8.3 grams or 42 per cent of the carbon in the protein metabolized.

The same D:N ratio also indicates the excretion of glucose equal in weight to 3.5/6.2 or 56 per cent of the protein metabolized. This is frequently taken to mean the conversion of 56 per cent of the protein to carbohydrate; but the conclusion is incorrect, since so much extra oxygen is added to the carbon skeletons in the formation of carbohydrate from amino acids.

SUMMARY. The principal result of insulin deficiency appears to be diminution in the utilization of carbohydrate for oxidative purposes and for fat formation, and possibly also for glycogen deposition. A considerable proportion of the available carbohydrate may then be lost to the body by excretion. As a result of this deficit, body fats and, to some extent, proteins are then utilized in increased amounts, and the substance of part of these also may be lost in the urine as ketones and as glucose.

In these circumstances, the rate of fat catabolism may be very high. It can be calculated from the data of Table 44 that these diabetic subjects, when not given insulin, must have been burning close to 200 grams of fat per day. Of the fat consumed, only a small fraction (5 to 10 per cent) can be accounted for by the excretion of ketone bodies even in severe ketosis; but this narrow margin between production and utilization of ketone bodies is, of course, of the utmost importance in respect to acid-base balance. If the food intake is not considerably increased, body fat must be utilized in place of the glucose excreted, and it will not be replaced at normal rates by synthesis from carbohydrate. Hence, loss of fat from the body is common in severe diabetes; in the two cases here, the deficit must have been at least of the order of 60 to 80 grams per day. With respect to proteins, similarly, the amounts of derived glucose which are lost by excretion can represent but a small proportion of the total energy exchange, but the relative increase in nitrogen catabolism may be very great. In the two cases presented in Table 44, the excretion of nitrogen exceeded the intake by 30 and 50 per cent, respectively. Obviously such losses of fat and protein would in time become extremely serious. In the absence of insulin, the body economy in effect resembles that engendered by chronic starvation. The diabetic animal, even if it avoids acidotic crises, may therefore succumb eventually to the effects of depletion of the body tissues.

Effects of Insulin. The administration of insulin to the diabetic animal reverses all the metabolic alterations otherwise observed. In normal or diabetic animals the most prominent effect of insulin is the induction of an immediate fall in the blood sugar level. This occurs in eviscerated animals at least as readily as in intact ones, so that the primary action of insulin must be mainly on some phase of the removal or utilization of glucose by the peripheral tissues, rather than on the supply of glucose by the liver. The action of insulin on the uptake of glucose is also readily demonstrable in isolated tissues (diaphragm and other muscles and adipose tissue) in vitro.[36, 63] The fate of the glucose removed from the blood under the influence of insulin is various. Much of it is deposited as glycogen in the muscles. This was first shown in eviscerated cats by Best et al. in 1922, and it has been observed consistently in every case in which the amount of glucose available was sufficient to allow an accumulation of glycogen to be seen. Deposition of glycogen also occurs readily in isolated muscle in vitro when insulin is present in the medium. This was demonstrated first by Gemmill et al. in 1941–42 and has since been observed repeatedly by many investigators.[36, 63]

Another considerable part of the glucose must be converted to noncarbohydrate forms, for the disappearance of carbohydrate has been well demonstrated by analysis of the entire bodies of intact mice given insulin.[18, 70] The rise in the R.Q. which occurs when insulin and glucose are given together is consistent with an increase in either the oxidation of glucose or its synthesis into fat. An increase in the output of radio-carbon dioxide from C^{14}-labeled glucose under the influence of insulin has been observed by Feller et al. in diabetic dogs and by Wick et al. in eviscerated rabbits, thus showing that the oxidation of carbohydrate is increased.[22, 73] In normal rabbits given deuterium-labeled water, Stettin and his coworkers demonstrated that insulin greatly accelerated the incorporation of deuterium into both liver and body fats, indicating an increased synthesis of fat from dietary carbohydrate.[65] A marked but temporary increase in the glycogen content of adipose tissue is induced by insulin both in vivo and in vitro; this is interpreted to be the result of increased uptake of glucose preliminary to conversion of the carbohydrate to fat. A considerable hypertrophy of adipose tissue has been reported after the local injection of insulin,[51] and recently an increased rate of fat formation from isotopic glucose has been clearly demonstrated in adipose tissue *in vitro*.[74] Hence, it must be concluded that, directly or indirectly, insulin enhances the removal of glucose by all of its major routes of disposition.

MECHANISM OF ACTION. The exact point at which insulin acts in the metabolism of carbohydrate is still controversial. No evidence has yet been adduced to show that insulin influences directly any of the individual steps of the glycolytic system or of the citric acid cycle. Because insulin undoubtedly does enhance glycogen deposition as well as other routes of transformation of carbohydrate, any unitary concept of insulin action requires that the hormone affect the early stages of carbohydrate metabolism which are common to all pathways. Largely by reason of this rather indirect argument, it has been widely supposed that insulin must act at the first stage of glucose utilization, the phosphorylation of glucose to glucose-6-phosphate by hexokinase and ATP. The only direct evidence favoring this hypothesis was presented in 1947 and 1948 by Cori and his co-workers.[17, 19] Using cell-free extracts of muscle from diabetic rats or extracts of normal brain tissue, these investigators reported that insulin would abolish the usual lag in the action of the hexokinase enzyme system. This effect was attributed not to direct activation of this enzyme by insulin but rather to relief of inhibition by factors from the adrenal cortex and from the anterior pituitary which were also present in the systems. Other investigators have not been able to confirm the existence of this phenomenon.[63, 64]

In recent years, an alternative hypothesis has received much support—that insulin augments the rate of transport or penetration of glucose into the cells before the glucose is phosphorylated.[39, 40, 53] Levine and his coworkers, using eviscerated animals, first showed that insulin greatly increased the volume of distribution in the body of several sugars which were themselves not subject to phosphorylation and which were only slowly metabolized, if at all, in these preparations.[39, 40] The sugars affected were D-galactose, D-xylose and L-arabinose, all having the same configuration in the first three carbon atoms as D-glucose; but the distribution of a variety of other hexoses and pentoses was not influenced. These data indicated that the action of insulin was unrelated to the hexokinase system; instead, insulin acted upon the penetration into the cells of sugars having a specific configuration like that of glucose. Similar effects of insulin have now been demonstrated under a variety of conditions and in several tissues, including diaphragm, skeletal muscle and the isolated heart, but not the liver, brain or erythrocytes.

Glucose itself is so rapidly metabolized that very little free glucose is ever found inside the cells of most organs, and it has been difficult to obtain direct evidence for the action of insulin on the penetration of glucose, as distinct from its further incorporation into hexose-phosphate and other forms. However, Ross[53] has shown that insulin increases the rate of transport of glucose through the ciliary body into the aqueous humor of the eye or into the crystalline lens of the rabbit. Park and coworkers[47, 48, 49] demonstrated accumulation of glucose intracellularly in a variety of tissues when insulin was given, and Fisher and Lindsay[23] also have observed accumulation of glucose in the isolated heart in the presence of insulin. These and the related observations on the action of insulin on nonmetabolizable sugars strongly suggest that the primary site of action of insulin is the cell membrane in some, but not all, tissues and organs. Most of the other effects of insulin would then be supposed to follow as indirect consequences of its enhancement of the rate of entry of glucose into these cells.

OTHER ACTIONS OF INSULIN. In addition to its action on glucose uptake, insulin seems also to have the property of affecting the metabolism of nitrogen.[53] In eviscerated animals the free amino acid content of the blood increases progressively after operation, but when a small amount of insulin is given, this release of amino acids is greatly diminished or even abolished for a time.[8, 35, 44, 54] The effect is independent of the blood glucose level or of the rate of utilization of glucose. Recent evidence obtained in *in vitro* studies suggests that insulin increases the uptake of amino acids into the tissue protein, possibly by enhancing the rate of penetration of the amino acid as it does the penetration of glucose.[37, 43] The latter observations require further elucidation, but are of great interest as suggesting an explanation for the extensive depletion of body protein common in untreated diabetes.

Whether insulin has any direct effect on the metabolism of the liver is uncertain.[38] When insulin is given alone, the liver glycogen always falls in response to the hypoglycemia; or when insulin is given with glucose, less glycogen is deposited in the liver than with glucose alone, apparently because of the preponderant effect of the insulin on the uptake of glucose and deposition of glycogen in muscle. Glucagon, a substance from the pancreas which is present in many insulin preparations, also is glycogenolytic in liver, so that some of the reported effects of insulin in this respect may have been due to the action of this factor; but similar observations have now been obtained with glucagon-free insulin. In isolated liver slices, insulin *in vitro* does not increase the uptake of glucose or deposition of glycogen, nor can any effect of insulin on the distribution of nonmetabolizable sugars be demonstrated in this organ. Some changes in liver metabolism (e.g., reduction in gluconeogenesis, increased uptake of isotopic substrates into fatty acids, decreased ketogenesis) may be seen in liver slices taken from animals given insulin, but only after 12 to 24 hours of pretreatment with the hormone. These effects, then, are very likely indirect results of shifts in metabolism brought about by the action of insulin elsewhere in the animal body.

The only evidence to suggest an immediate action of insulin in the liver comes from two sources. One line of argument comes from changes in the "turnover" of plasma glucose. Wall *et al.*[71] showed that, when tracer amounts of isotopic glucose are infused into an animal at such a rate as to maintain constant specific activity of the plasma glucose, the additional injection of insulin is followed by a small and short-lived *increase* in the specific activity of the plasma glucose. This means that the continuing contribution of unlabeled glucose from the liver must have been reduced during this interval, and therefore that insulin had brought about a net decrease in the output of glucose by the liver. However, this effect was soon overtaken by diminution in specific activity of the plasma glucose resulting from the usual increase in delivery of glucose by the liver in response to hypoglycemia, and the ultimate effect was an increase in plasma glucose turnover. Similarly, as shown by several groups of investigators, when a single dose of isotopic glucose is given, rather than a continuous infusion, the injection of insulin is followed by a temporary abeyance or decrease in the rate of fall of the specific activity of the plasma glucose. Although for technical reasons these experiments are not as reliable quantitatively as those involving the continuous infusion method, they can be interpreted qualitatively in the same way. The other principal line of evidence is given in the recent reports of Haft and Miller,[30] as yet unconfirmed, on the metabolism of isolated perfused rat liver. The addition of very large amounts of insulin to the perfusion medium resulted in some increase in uptake of glucose from the medium and in changes in fat metabolism which could be interpreted as due to changes in glucose uptake or output. Also, Berthet *et al.*[7] have observed some increase in the incorporation of labeled glucose into glycogen in liver both *in vitro* and *in vivo*, but the amounts of insulin employed here were also very large. All of these observations indicate that insulin may act directly on the liver as it does in muscle; but, if so, its effects on this organ are of minor importance quantitatively relative to those so readily elicited in the peripheral tissues.

Hypoglycemia. Hypersecretion of insulin or the administration of excessive amounts of it may lower the blood sugar level to such an extent that serious symptoms ensue.[33] These symptoms of hypoglycemia are referable primarily to the nervous system: weakness, tremor, sweating, dizziness, incoordination and, finally, unconsciousness and generalized tonic-clonic convulsions. The nervous system is largely dependent for its nutrition upon the blood sugar, and, when the concentration of this substance is low, the metabolism of nervous tissues is as effectively limited as if deprived of oxygen. As far as is known, the immediate symptoms of hyperinsulinism are due only to the hypoglycemia induced, for they may be relieved entirely by the administration of sugar. Unless such relief is given promptly, death may occur from spasm of the diaphragm and paralysis of respiration. Following recovery from prolonged hypoglycemia there may be permanent lesions in the brain.

An important consequence of a moderate degree of hypoglycemia (50 to 60 mg. per cent glucose) is general stimulation of the sympathetic system and consequent release of epinephrine—a process which tends to relieve the hypoglycemia (see Chap. 54). Most of the common early signs of hypoglycemia, such as irritability and tremor, are in fact due to the medullary secretion, rather than to the hypoglycemia itself. Many individuals have at some time experienced in small degree the symptoms of reflex sympathetic action during a temporary depression in the blood sugar level. Hypoglycemia of this order has been shown also to initiate secretion of the pituitary corticotrophin and hence presumably to increase the release of cortical steroids. Perhaps to be related to the activity of either or both of the adrenal factors is the observation that the rate of removal of glucose from the blood may be much reduced during and following moderate hypoglycemia.[57, 58] Thus, even relatively mild hypoglycemia may bring about perceptible alterations in physiologic balance.

Control of Insulin Secretion. From the fact that an animal which is dependent on exogenous insulin requires varying amounts of it in different circumstances, it may be inferred that the rate of secretion of insulin is normally not constant. This may be seen particularly well in the diabetic animal or patient given protamine insulin.[52] Here a fairly constant supply of insulin is being made available over many hours, as judged by the uniform normal blood sugar level maintained during fasting. However, this supply of insulin is insufficient to allow a normal glucose tolerance curve, or to prevent hyperglycemia after meals. A normal glucose tolerance curve has been obtained in the depancreatized animal given a constant infusion of insulin;[59, 60] but in this case the amount of insulin used was so large that it would have induced hypoglycemia itself unless glucose had been given along with it. Both of these experiments indicate that, when extra carbohydrate is given to a fasting animal, extra insulin must be supplied by the pancreas in order to allow normal disposition of the sugar.

Further evidence for the secretion of insulin in response to carbohydrate may be seen in the hypoglycemia which frequently follows a carbohydrate tolerance test, an overshooting of the mark, as it were, and in the relative effects of successive doses of glucose. In normal animals the more carbohydrate given, within reasonable limits, the better it is handled, and a second dose of glucose following about one hour after the first produces a much smaller increase in the blood sugar. In the diabetic, the reverse is true. The marked diminution in the insulin content of the pancreas which occurs in animals which are fasted or maintained on low-carbohydrate regimens for several days is consistent with the converse of this effect, the pancreas apparently "resting" in the absence of exogenous carbohydrate.[31]

Factors controlling secretion by the pancreas must be largely or entirely humoral in nature, for, as shown many years ago by Gayet, a pancreas "transplanted" from a normal animal into the circulation of a depancreatized subject first reduces and then maintains the blood sugar level of the recipient with an astonishing degree of precision. More recently, Bennett has shown that the secretion of insulin by such a "transplanted" pancreas must diminish as the blood glucose approaches the normal level. The principal factor in this control of pancreatic secretion appears to be the concentration of glucose in the blood. This was suggested some years ago by the cross-circulation experiments of Zunz and La Barre and was demonstrated recently in more convincing fashion by those of Foà et al.[25] When pancreatic venous blood from one dog was perfused into the jugular or femoral vein of a second, the giving of glucose to the donor dog induced a fall in the blood sugar of the recipient. An increase in the rate of secretion of insulin by the pancreas of the donor in response to elevation of its blood sugar had apparently occurred. Utilizing the adrenodemedullated, alloxan-diabetic, hypophysectomized rat as a sensitive test animal for insulin, Anderson and Long observed that more hypoglycemic material was liberated by the isolated perfused pancreas of the rat when the perfusing fluid was high in glucose than when the glucose concentration was low;[1] and Bornstein, using a similar test animal, presented evidence that the plasma of normal men contained more insulin when the subject was fed than when he was fasting.[11] More exact study of the factors influencing the secretion of insulin awaits the development of yet more sensitive and reliable methods of assaying the extremely small amounts of insulin present in the blood.* However, all current evidence is strong in the indication that the secretion of insulin varies with demand, and hence that the treatment of diabetic patients with insulin entails inevitably a compromise between clinical expedience and the effort to reproduce the normal function of the pancreas.

GLUCAGON (HYPERGLYCEMIC FACTOR, HGF)

Many insulin preparations contain also a substance which raises the blood sugar level temporarily before the hypoglycemic effect of the insulin becomes manifest. This substance, called glucagon or the pancreatic glycogenolytic factor, is quite distinct from insulin and has been obtained as a pure substance with very great biologic activity. It has recently been shown to be a polypeptide, containing 29 amino acids in a single chain.[4a, 13] Its hyperglycemic action, which appears quickly and is of short duration, is due to enhancement of glycogenolysis in the liver.[21, 67, 68] The latter action is readily demonstrable either in vivo or in liver slices in vitro. The mechanism of this effect seems to be identical with that of epinephrine (Chap. 54); that is, it appears to increase the activity of the dephosphophosphorylase kinase, which in turn brings about activation of the enzyme phosphorylase.[50] However, glucagon differs from epinephrine in that it has no detectable effect on the metabolism of muscle, and hence does not cause any increase in the blood lactate, and it has none of the sympathomimetic actions of the latter hormone. It has been difficult to obtain evidence of any cumulative effect of this material, but recently Salter et al.[50] have shown that if the substance is given repeatedly at frequent intervals, chronic (but temporary) hyperglycemia and glycosuria may be induced.

Good circumstantial evidence indicates that glucagon probably has its origin in the α cells of the pancreatic islets.[67, 69] The distribution of glucagon in portions of the pancreas parallels the frequency of the islets, and the material occurs in high concentrations in the pancreas lacking functional acinar tissue, as in the bovine fetal pancreas or in the pancreas of the dog after ligation of the pancreatic duct. It is found in normal amounts in the pancreas in which the β cells of the islets have been destroyed by alloxan, but it is not present in the uncinate process of the dog pancreas, which lacks recognizable

---

* Many attempts have been made to measure the insulin content of plasma by means of its effect on the glucose uptake of the rat diaphragm in vitro. However, the amounts of insulin indicated to be present by this method are much in excess of those which appear in tests for hypoglycemic activity such as those described above. The specificity of the diaphragm tests is therefore doubtful.

α cells.[6] The injection of cobalt chloride in animals of several species is followed by histologic evidence of extensive but temporary damage to the α cells of the pancreas. In this condition glucagon is still present in the pancreas in appreciable amounts, suggesting that the α cells might not be the source of this material;[27] but more recent reports have indicated that the concentration of glucagon can in fact be correlated inversely with the degree of damage evident in the α cells.[5]

Although glucagon is clearly an active agent pharmacologically, its physiologic function is unknown. No convincing evidence of metabolic alterations due to deficient α cell function has yet been adduced. The completely depancreatized animal usually requires less insulin to prevent glycosuria than does an animal made severely diabetic with alloxan. Since the latter presumably has a normal complement of α cells, the lesser severity of diabetes in the depancreatized animal has been supposed to be due to the lack of glucagon. However, as Mirsky has pointed out, the depancreatized animal also lacks the digestive enzymes of the pancreas; absorption of foodstuffs is defective, and so the insulin requirements may be diminished only for this reason. In agreement with this argument, Mirsky found that if alloxan diabetic and depancreatized dogs are compared in the fasting state, the severity of the diabetes is not different.[45] Similarly, the insulin requirements of depancreatized men are little different from those of individuals with spontaneous diabetes if the nutritional status is taken into account.[29] Recently, dogs lacking α cells have been prepared by transplantation of the uncinate process of the pancreas (which contains no α cells) to a subcutaneous site and removal of the rest of the gland. These animals appeared normal at first and then subsequently became diabetic as the grafts degenerated, just as would be expected after subtotal pancreatectomy in which both α and β cells were left. Hence, no changes could be attributed to the absence of the α cells.[6]

Evidence that glucagon may be secreted by the pancreas has been obtained in cross-circulation experiments by Foà et al.[24, 25] If blood from the pancreatic vein of an alloxan-diabetic donor dog is allowed to flow into the circulation of a normal recipient, the blood glucose of the latter rises to a greater extent than can be accounted for by the transfer of blood glucose alone. Further, if the blood glucose of a normal donor animal is reduced by insulin, pancreatic vein blood from this donor is hyperglycemic in the recipient animal. In addition, a substance resembling glucagon in biologic properties has been separated from pancreatic vein blood from the normal dog.[26] However, other hyperglycemic materials besides glucagon may be present in blood from the splanchnic area under some conditions. Therefore, positive identification of the hyperglycemic substance in these cases is required before it may be concluded that glucagon is indeed a second hormone from the pancreas.

REFERENCES

1. ANDERSON, E. and LONG, J. A. *Endocrinology*, 1947. 40:92–97.
2. ATCHLEY, D. W., LOEB, R. L., RICHARDS, D. W., JR., BENEDICT, E. M. and DRISCOLL, M. E. *J. clin. Invest.*, 1933, 12:297–326.
3. BAKER, N., SHREEVE, W. W., SHIPLEY, R. A., INCEFY, G. E. and MILLER, M. *J. biol. Chem.*, 1954, 211:575–592.
4. BANTING, F. G. and BEST, C. H. *J. Lab. clin. Med.*, 1922, 7:251–266; 464–472.
4a. BEHRENS, O. K. and BROMER, W. W. *Vitam. & Horm.*, 1958, 16:264–302.
5. BENCOSME, S. A. and FREI, J. *Proc. Soc. exp. Biol. (N. Y.)*, 1956, 91:589–592.
6. BENCOSME, S. A., MARIZ, S. and FREI, J. *Endocrinology*, 1957, 61:1–11.

7. BERTHET, J., JACQUES, P., HERS, H. G. and DEDUVE, C. *Biochim. biophys. acta*, 1956, 20:190–200.
8. BOLLMAN, J. L., FLOCK, E. V., GRINDLAY, G. H., MANN, F. C. and BLOCK, M. A. *Amer. J. Physiol.*, 1953, 174:467–470.
9. BONDY, P. K., BLOOM, W. L., WHITNER, V. S. and FARRAR, B. W. *J. clin. Invest.*, 1949, 28:1126–1133.
10. BONDY, P. K., SHELDON, W. H. and EVANS, L. D. *J. clin. Invest.*, 1949, 28:1216–1221.
11. BORNSTEIN, J. *Aust. J. exp. Biol. med. Sci.*, 1950, 28:93–97.
12. BRADY, R. O., LUKENS, F. D. W. and GURIN, S. *J. biol. Chem.*, 1951, 193:459–464.
13. BROMER, W. W., SINN, L. G., STRAUB, A.

and Behrens, O. K. *Diabetes*, 1957, *6*:234–238.

14. Chaikoff, I. L. and Forker, L. L. *Endocrinology*, 1950, *46*:319–326.

15. Chernick, S. S. and Chaikoff, I. L. *J. biol. Chem.*, 1951, *188*:389–396.

16. Chernick, S. S., Chaikoff, I. L., Masoro, E. J. and Isaeff, E. *J. biol. Chem.*, 1950, *186*:527–534.

17. Colowick, S. P., Cori, G. T. and Slein, M. W. *J. biol. Chem.*, 1947, *168*:583–596.

18. Cori, C. F. *Physiol. Rev.*, 1931, *11*:143–275.

19. Cori, C. F. *Harvey Lect.*, 1945–46, *41*:253–272.

20. Crandall, L. A., Jr. and Lipscomb, A. *Amer. J. Physiol.*, 1947, *148*:312–318.

21. DeDuve, C. *Lancet*, 1953, (2):99–104.

22. Feller, D. D., Chaikoff, I. L., Strisower, E. H. and Searle, G. L. *J. biol. Chem.*, 1951, *188*:865–880.

23. Fisher, R. B. and Lindsay, D. B. *J. Physiol.*, 1956, *131*:526–541.

24. Foá, P. P., Santamaria, L., Weinstein, H., Berger, S. and Smith, J. A. *Amer. J. Physiol.*, 1952, *171*:32–36.

25. Foá, P. P., Weinstein, H. R. and Smith, J. A. *Amer. J. Physiol.*, 1949, *157*:197–204.

26. Fodden, J. H. and Reed, W. O. *Amer. J. Physiol.*, 1955, *182*:513–517.

27. Goldner, M. G., Volk, B. W. and Lazarus, S. *J. clin. Endocr.*, 1954, *14*:184–192.

28. Greely, P. O. and Drury, D. R. *Amer. J. Physiol.*, 1940, *130*:249–255.

29. Greenfield, J. and Sanders, J. *Surgery*, 1949, *25*:824–838.

30. Haft, D. E. and Miller, L. L. *Amer. J. Physiol.*, 1958, *192*:33–42.

31. Haist, R. E. *Physiol. Rev.*, 1944, *24*:409–444.

32. Hildes, J. A., Sherlock, S. and Walshe, V. *Clin. Sci.*, 1949, *7*:287–295; 297–314.

33. Himwich, H. E. *Amer. J. dig. Dis.*, 1944, *11*:1–8.

34. Houssay, B. S., Biasotti, A. and Dambrosi, R. C. *Rev. Soc. argent. Biol.*, 1936, *12*:185–204.

35. Ingle, D. J., Prestrud, M. C. and Nezamis, J. C. *Amer. J. Physiol.*, 1947, *150*:682–685.

36. Krahl, M. E. *Ann. N. Y. Acad. Sci.*, 1951, *54*:649–670.

37. Krahl, M. E. *Recent Progr. Horm. Res.*, 1956, *12*:199–219.

38. Levine, R. and Fritz, I. B. *Diabetes*, 1956, *5*:209–211.

39. Levine, R. and Goldstein, M. S. *Recent Progr. Horm. Res.*, 1955, *11*:343–375.

40. Levine, R., Goldstein, M., Huddlestun, B. and Klein, S. A. *Amer. J. Physiol.*, 1950, *163*:70–76.

41. Lukens, F. D. W. *Ann. intern. Med.*, 1934, *8*:727–733.

42. Lukens, F. D. W. *Physiol. Rev.*, 1948, *28*:304–330.

43. Manchester, K. L. and Young, F. G. *Biochem. J.*, 1958, *70*:353–358.

44. Mirsky, I. A. *Amer. J. Physiol.*, 1938, *124*:569–575.

45. Mirsky, I. A., Futterman, P., Wachman, J. and Perisutti, G. *Endocrinology*, 1951, *49*:73–81.

46. Morita, Y. and Orten, J. M. *Amer. J. Physiol.*, 1950, *161*:545–549.

47. Park, C. R., Bornstein, J. and Post, R. L. *Amer. J. Physiol.*, 1955, *182*:12–16.

48. Park, C. R. and Johnson, L. H. *Amer. J. Physiol.*, 1955, *182*:17–23.

49. Park, C. R., Johnson, L. H., Wright, J. H. and Batail, H. *Amer. J. Physiol.*, 1957, *191*:13–18.

50. Rall, T. W., Sutherland, E. W. and Berthet, J. *J. biol. Chem.*, 1957, *224*:463–475.

51. Renold, A. E., Marble, A. and Fawcett, D. W. *Endocrinology*, 1950, *46*:55–66.

52. Ricketts, H. T. *J. clin. Invest.*, 1938, *17*:795–801.

53. Ross, E. J. *Medicine*, 1956, *35*:355–388.

54. Russell, J. A. and Cappiello, M. *Endocrinology*, 1949, *44*:127–133.

55. Ryle, A. P., Sanger, F., Smith, L. F. and Kitai, R. *Biochem. J.*, 1955, *60*:541–546.

56. Salter, J. M., Davidson, I. W. F. and Best, C. H. *Diabetes*, 1957, *6*:248–252.

57. Somogyi, M. *Endocrinology*, 1950, *47*:436–442.

58. Somogyi, M. *J. biol. Chem.*, 1951, *193*:859–871.

59. Soskin, S., Allweiss, M. D. and Cohn, D. J. *Amer. J. Physiol.*, 1934, *109*:155–165.

60. Soskin, S. and Levine, R. *Carbohydrate metabolism.* Chicago, University of Chicago Press, rev. ed., 1952.

61. Stadie, W. C. *J. clin. Invest.*, 1940, *19*:843–862.

62. Stadie, W. C. *Physiol. Rev.*, 1945, *25*:395–441.

63. Stadie, W. C. *Physiol. Rev.*, 1954, *34*:52–100.

64. Stadie, W. C., Haugaard, N. and Hills, A. G. *J. biol. Chem.*, 1950, *184*:617–626.

65. Stetten, D. W., Jr. *Recent Progr. Horm. Res.*, 1949, *4*:189–213.

66. Stetten, D. W., Jr., Welt, I. D., Ingle, D. J. and Morley, E. H. *J. biol. Chem.*, 1951, *192*:817–830.

67. Sutherland, E. W. *Recent Progr. Horm. Res.*, 1950, *5*:441–459.

68. Sutherland, E. W. and Cori, C. F. *J. biol. Chem.*, 1951, *188*:531–543.

69. Sutherland, E. W. and DeDuve, C. *J. biol. Chem.*, 1948, *175*:663–674.

70. Swensson, A. *Acta physiol. scand.*, 1945, *11* (Suppl. 33):1–158.

71. Wall, J. S., Steele, R., De Bodo, R. C. and Altszuler, N. *Amer. J. Physiol.*, 1957, *189*:43–50.

72. Welt, I. D., Stetten, D. W., Jr., Ingle, D. J. and Morley, E. H. *J. biol. Chem.*, 1952, *197*:57–66.

73. Wick, A. N., Drury, D. R., Bancroft, R. W. and MacKay, E. M. *J. biol. Chem.*, 1951, *188*:241–249.

74. Winegrad, A. I., and Renold, A. E. *J. biol. Chem.*, 1958, *233*:267–272.

75. Winternitz, W. W. and Lattanzi, W. E. *Endocrinology*, 1956, *58*:232–234.

CHAPTER 54

The Adrenals

By JANE A. RUSSELL

THE paired adrenal (or suprarenal) glands, like the hypophysis, are double organs composed of two distinct types of tissue of different origin and function. In mammals and birds the larger, glandular portion, called the cortex, surrounds tissue of neural origin, the medulla. The two portions are quite separate in the elasmobranch fishes, and in other lower forms various transitional stages exist. The adrenal cortex, or corresponding glandular tissue, arises from the mesoderm in the urogenital zone. Small nests of adrenal glandular cells (called accessory cortical tissue, or "cortical rests") may also be found outside the adrenal capsule in the region of the kidneys or gonads. The medullary tissue, on the other hand, develops from the primitive cells of the sympathetic ganglia, originally from the neural crest, and remains intimately connected with the splanchnic sympathetic nerve supply. Tissue similar to that of the adrenal medulla, called chromaffin tissue, is found also in small bodies adjoining the chain of sympathetic ganglia. In some lower vertebrates these bodies alone represent adrenal medullary tissue, the glandular portion being replaced by a single interrenal body. Although it seems unlikely that the close anatomic approximation of the two portions of the adrenal in the higher animals has been purely fortuitous, no physiologic necessity for the relationship is known.

THE ADRENAL CORTEX

Adrenal cortical tissue consists of large granular cells arranged in what appear to be loose cords or nets separated by sinusoids. Recent studies have shown, however, that the rat adrenal cortex is in fact a tunneled continuum, so that the "cords" are more properly considered as cross sections of sheets of cells.[50] Three strata can be distinguished by the structural arrangement of the cells and blood vessels: a thin glomerular layer next to the fibrous capsule, a broad fascicular zone in which the capillaries run radially, and, next to the medulla, the reticular zone in which the blood vessels are dilated and tortuous. The cells are very rich in lipoids, particularly cholesterol and steroids, and also in ascorbic acid. Changes in the amounts of these substances, measured chemically or histologically, afford some measure of the activity of the gland in varying physiologic conditions.

Cortical tissue exhibits remarkable powers of regeneration and hypertrophy: after removal of one gland, the other will enlarge to twice its normal size; after removal of both, cortical rests may enlarge until their volume approaches that of the original glands; or after enucleation (removal of the contents of the capsule, leaving only shreds of the glomeruli attached), the cortical tissue can be completely regenerated. It is believed that in the adrenal cortex new cells regularly form in the periphery and move gradually toward the reticular zone.

That the adrenal cortex is an endocrine organ essential for life, or practically so, was demonstrated by several investigators during the years 1920–1930. Earlier disagreement as to its importance was shown to be due on the one hand to the great susceptibility of adrenalectomized animals to shock and sepsis, which were often immediately fatal, and, on the other, to the frequent hypertrophy of cortical rests which would maintain the animal indefinitely once the critical postoperative period was passed. The removal of the adrenal medullae alone was shown not to endanger life.

Adrenocortical Insufficiency. After removal of the adrenal glands, a variety of metabolic defects become evident.[49, 72] At first, if operative shock has been avoided, the animal appears relatively normal, but later a decline sets in, rather abruptly in some cases, and death occurs in most species within a week or two. The symptoms before death include loss of appetite, vomiting, diarrhea, asthenia, a variable degree of hypoglycemia, hypotension, hemoconcentration, fall in blood pressure and renal failure. In young animals, growth ceases; in older ones, there is usually loss of weight. The adrenalectomized animal is also extremely susceptible to stresses of all types, such as trauma, cold, heat, toxins and infections. The cause of death varies. Vascular collapse, with hemoconcentration and renal failure, is probably the most common cause, but in some species, such as the rat, hypoglycemia may be fatal before the full course of the other defects is run. Death from intercurrent infection or other stress is common in all species.

In man, chronic adrenal insufficiency, known as Addison's disease, has similar consequences. Usually there is gradual development of weakness, digestive disturbances and hypotension, punctuated by more acute crises resembling the terminal stages after adrenalectomy. Eventually, death occurs in such a crisis. There is also in man a peculiar pigmentation of the skin and mucous membranes which is not seen in animals.

The biochemical changes associated with adrenal cortical insufficiency—as yet incompletely understood—concern the concentrations of electrolytes and water, and the metabolism of carbohydrates and proteins. Low concentrations of sodium and chloride in the plasma and prolongation of life by the administration of salt were first observed by Baumann in 1927.[4, 46] Some years later Loeb[40] observed similar changes in patients with Addison's disease, and also found that restricting the amount of salt in the diet would precipitate the crisis of adrenal insufficiency. Since that time it has been well established that in the absence of the adrenals there is excessive excretion of sodium and chloride by the kidney and diminished clearance of potassium (Fig. 591).[29, 30, 49, 72] In consequence, the plasma sodium falls and the plasma potassium rises. These changes are accompanied by movement of water and potassium into the cells (Table 46) and diminution in the extracellular fluid volume.[28] The blood pressure then begins to fall, the blood becomes more concentrated, and as a result the renal glomerular filtration rate is progressively diminished. The elevation of the blood nonprotein nitrogen which is often seen is probably a consequence of this renal insufficiency.[39]

The excretion of extra water is also much delayed, and an excess of water may be toxic. This is believed to be the result in part of accumulation of water intracellularly and in part of increased resorption of water by the kidney.[22] Measurement of the ability to excrete water and to retain salt is often helpful in the diagnosis of adrenal insufficiency (Addison's disease or hypopituitarism) in man. A rather large amount of water is given by mouth (20 ml. per kg.) and the excretion of water and of sodium or chloride is determined hourly for the next several hours. In the absence of adrenal cortical function, the volume of urine is very low, but sodium chloride continues to be excreted.

If sufficient amounts of sodium chloride with water are given to adrenalectomized animals, the downward course may be slowed or prevented entirely.[29, 72] The salt which continues to be lost in the urine is replaced by this treatment, and in addition the resulting diuresis helps to wash out the potassium which otherwise tends to accumulate. Normal blood pressure, circulation and kidney function (other than with respect to salt excretion) are all maintained (Table 47), and the appetite and digestion are improved.

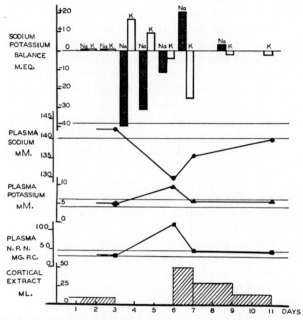

FIG. 591. Effects of withdrawal and replacement of adrenal cortical extract in an adrenalectomized dog. Constant amounts of food and water were given during period of observation. Fine lines indicate approximate range of values seen in normal animals. Note large loss of sodium and retention of potassium on withdrawal of hormone, and reversal of changes on readministration of extract. (After Harrop et al., J. exp. Med., 1936, 64:233.)

Young rats given 1 per cent salt in their drinking water will grow at almost normal rates. The balance of dietary sodium and potassium—as well as the amount of sodium—is important, for a high intake of potassium is deleterious, and in some species reduction in potassium intake as well as increase in sodium is required for complete maintenance. Since adrenalectomized animals may be kept alive for indefinite periods by controlling the amounts of salts ingested, the adrenal cortex to this extent cannot be said to be absolutely essential for life. However, the salt-treated adrenalectomized animal is by no means restored entirely to normal, and some of the remaining defects often endanger life.

The partial success of salt treatment in adrenal insufficiency allows a distinction to be drawn between what may be called the direct and the indirect effects of lack of the adrenal cortex. By "direct" effect is meant one which can be prevented or repaired only by treatment with cortical extract or derived substances, whereas by "indirect" is meant an effect which can be prevented by means other than hormonal substitution. For example, since rats with adrenal insufficiency absorb carbohydrate from the gastro-

TABLE 46. *PLASMA AND TISSUE ELECTROLYTES IN ADRENALECTOMIZED RATS**

	SERUM				MUSCLE (PER KG.) OF FAT-FREE TISSUE	
	Na mM.	K mM.	Cl mM.	N.P.N. mg.%	Na mEq.	K mEq.
Normal	144	5.2	105	35	23.6	109
Adrenalectomized, untreated	136†	7.4	97	96	18.8	117
Adrenalectomized, given sodium salts	143	5.7	102	28	23.6	109
Adrenalectomized, given cortical extract for 48 hrs.	143	5.5	101	22	21.0	106

* All the adrenalectomized rats were allowed to become insufficient before treatment was started with sodium salts (chloride and bicarbonate) or extract. The figures are averages from groups of 8 to 20 rats.

† The drop in serum sodium in species other than the rat is often even more extreme. Harrison and Darrow[28] report an average value of 126 mM. in an untreated adrenalectomized dog.

(From data of Harrison and Darrow, *J. clin. Invest.*, 1938, *17*:77.)

intestinal tract at a slower rate than normal, it has been supposed by some that the adrenal hormones must be concerned generally with the phosphorylation and absorption of glucose. But it has been shown that in normal rats a degree of inanition such as is usual in untreated adrenalectomized rats may alone result in low gastrointestinal absorption rates. Moreover, adrenalectomized rats whose appetite and food intake have been well maintained by adequate salt treatment can absorb glucose at perfectly normal rates. Evidently the cortical hormones need have no direct effect on glucose absorption; the absence of the adrenals influences only indirectly this process through decreasing the food intake. Other indirect effects of adrenal insufficiency include hemoconcentration, renal failure and loss of body weight and depot fat.

The direct effects of adrenal insufficiency—which are incompletely reparable, if at all, by the administration of salt or other such measures—include the following:[49, 72]

(i) Renal function with respect to sodium and potassium remains defective, only the consequences of these derangements being prevented by salt therapy. The susceptibility to water intoxication also is not alleviated.

TABLE 47. *KIDNEY FUNCTION IN THE ADRENALECTOMIZED DOG**

	URINE:PLASMA RATIO OF K	PLASMA N.P.N. mg.%	CLEARANCES OF	
			Urea ml./min.	Creatinine ml./min.
Normal	28	16	33	58
Adrenalectomized, untreated	10	72	8	21
Adrenalectomized, given sodium salts	6	32	25	37
Adrenalectomized, given cortical extract with salts	29	15	30	45

* All estimations were made on the same animal; each figure is the average of five determinations.
(From data of Harrison and Darrow, *Amer. J. Physiol.*, 1939, *125*:631.)

(ii) Sensitivity to stress, e.g., to cold or trauma, and liability to shock persist. The vascular system of an animal lacking adrenocortical function appears to be unable to maintain responsiveness to constrictor agents, or to continue for very long the adjustments which are necessary to maintain the blood pressure and the normal distribution of body fluids when the system is taxed in any manner.[20, 51]

(iii) The work capacity of muscles of adrenalectomized animals, as judged by their ability to respond to prolonged repeated stimulation, is greatly diminished.[33, 34] This effect appears not to be due to any great extent to hypoglycemia or to intrinsic defects within the muscle; but, since it is associated with hemodynamic collapse, it may result mainly from the inability of the animal to maintain its cardiovascular responses to the demands imposed by continued work.

(iv) The thymus and lymph nodes tend to be enlarged and the blood lymphocyte counts to be high. The involutional changes which ordinarily take place in these tissues when an animal is subjected to fasting, trauma or other stresses do not occur in the absence of cortical function.[13]

(v) Alterations in the metabolism of carbohydrate and of protein are demonstrable in appropriate circumstances.[43] As long as salt-maintained animals are well fed and kept in good condition, there may be no important changes in the carbohydrate levels of the body; but when these animals fast or fail to eat well for any reason, hypoglycemia becomes prominent and the liver is rapidly depleted of glycogen. The amount of nitrogen lost from the body during fasting is often less than normal. Hence, it has been suggested that the adrenalectomized animal is unable to draw upon body protein to the normal extent to maintain its blood sugar and liver glycogen during fasting.

The idea that the adrenalectomized animal suffers mainly from a defect in the rate of withdrawal of body protein for catabolism is supported by a variety of observations. No important changes in the catabolism of carbohydrate or of exogenous protein have ever been shown. In the eviscerated preparation, however, the rate of release of amino acids from the tissues is significantly reduced in the absence of cortical steroids and is restored in their presence.[5] In fasting diabetic or phlorhizinized animals, the amounts of glucose and nitrogen excreted are diminished proportionately after adrenalectomy and also are restored by appropriate therapy with cortical extracts.[41, 44] Finally, adrenalectomy abolishes the usual "nitrogen catabolic response" to "stress" [i.e., the increase in the rate of loss of nitrogen from the body (often but not always accompanied by an increase in liver glycogen) which occurs when an animal is subjected to trauma, such as surgery, to anoxia or to many drugs].[35, 49] Although it is often said that gluconeogenesis is defective in the absence of cortical hormones, in most instances the defect must reside mainly in the accessibility of protein for use in gluconeogenesis, rather than in the latter process itself.

Although most of the alterations in carbohydrate and protein metabolism in adrenal-deficient animals may be explained by the defect in protein withdrawal, it is possible that this is not the only metabolic abnormality. Deposition of liver glycogen from glucose is slow, and ketogenesis in fasting is subnormal. These defects may be due in part at least to the poor hemodynamic state, rather than to intrinsic changes in these processes; for the adrenalectomized subject, even when maintained with salt, is not normal in this respect, and the circulation of blood and lymph through the viscera is undoubtedly subnormal. On the other hand, a number of other observations suggest that loss of cortical steroids may lead, at least in some circumstances, to a relative increase in the utilization of carbohydrate and a decrease in mobilization and use of fat. These changes are similar to those observed after hypophysectomy, but of lesser extent. They are best seen in the depancreatized animal which is then adrenalectomized and maintained with salt or small amounts of cortical hormones.[41, 44] As after hypophysectomy, the diabetes is considerably ameliorated by this procedure. Survival is much prolonged, the blood glucose may be within the normal range, ketonemia is diminished, and the glucose tolerance is improved, although usually still subnormal. The diabetes may be reinstated by the administration of large amounts of cortical hormone, or by anterior pituitary hormones in the presence of smaller amounts of cortical steroids. It is possible that the apparent resumption of carbohydrate utilization and reduction in fat catabolism in these conditions is the result of deficient activity of those anterior pituitary factors which require cortical hormones for their full expression (see Chap. 52).

The varied manifestations of adrenal cortical deficiency do not yet permit the statement of a single unique primary defect. If such a defect does exist, as it well may, the end-results which are seen evidently differ according to the functions of the individual organs or systems affected.

Adrenocortical Hormones. Early attempts to maintain life in adrenalectomized animals with extracts of adrenal cortical tissue, made by methods which had proved suitable for preparing insulin and active pituitary preparations, were disappointing. When, however, the fat-soluble nature of the active principle became apparent in the early 1930's, progress was rapid. In the years 1934 to 1938, not one but several such substances were obtained in pure form and their constitutions determined. All proved to be steroids. By 1942, no less than 28 different steroid compounds had been isolated from the adrenal. Only six of these, however, displayed any type of activity expected of an adrenocortical hormone.[54] The remaining steroids include progesterone (which has since been reported to show a slight degree of cortical hormonal activity) and some of its derivatives, several weakly androgenic substances, and a variety of inactive compounds presumed to be either intermediates in the formation of the active steroids or else degradation products.

In addition to these steroids, an amorphous fraction also was obtained which was quite active in the maintenance of life in the adrenalectomized animal but which differed in its chemical properties from any of the pure active substances then known. The active principle of this fraction was isolated in 1952 and 1953 by Simpson and Tait and their collaborators,[27, 64] and, since it was shown to be extremely potent in promoting the renal retention of salt, it was provisionally called "electrocortin." When the structure of this material was elucidated shortly thereafter, it proved to be unique among the steroids in bearing an aldehyde group on carbon 18 and was then given the name *aldosterone*. The discovery and properties of this substance have been reviewed by Gaunt et al.[23]

The structures of the seven naturally occurring active cortical steroids, including aldosterone, are given in Figure 592. These are all closely similar, differing only in the presence or absence of hydroxyl or ketone groupings at carbon 11 and/or the α-hydroxyl at carbon 17. As indicated below, however, these apparently minor differences, together with the aldehyde of aldosterone, are responsible for large differences in the type and degree of hormonal activity displayed by the compounds.

Since the pure cortical steroids are obtained from natural sources only in very small amounts, extensive physiologic investigation and clinical use of these materials awaited practical methods of synthesis. The first to be so prepared, and for many years the only pure steroid which was widely available, was 11-desoxycorticosterone (DOC), synthesized from plant sterols by Reichstein in 1937. The biologic properties of this steroid were soon found to differ profoundly from those of the 11-oxycorticoids, which are the main components of adrenocortical extracts. For this reason, extracts rather than pure steroids were employed in the majority of the original investigations on the physiologic activities of cortical hormones, such as those described below. The discovery in 1949 of the remarkable pharmacologic and therapeutic influences of the 11-oxycorticoids in certain diseased states then stimulated intensive efforts toward the practical synthesis of these compounds. This was finally achieved in 1952 through 1954 by the combined work of many chemists. The first 11-oxysteroid to be prepared was 17-hydroxy, 11-dehydrocorticosterone (Kendall's compound E), which was then given the name *cortisone*. The next was 17-hydroxycorticosterone (Kendall's compound F); this is usually called *hydrocortisone*, since it differs from cortisone only in the hydroxyl replacing the ketone of carbon 11, but it is more properly designated *cortisol*. Further, a number of analogues of the cortical steroids have now been prepared, most of them differing from the parent compounds (usually cortisone or cortisol) in further unsaturation of the A or B rings, in the addition of halogen at carbon 9, or of a methyl group at position 2 or 6, or in combinations of these changes. Many of these substances are much more active than the naturally

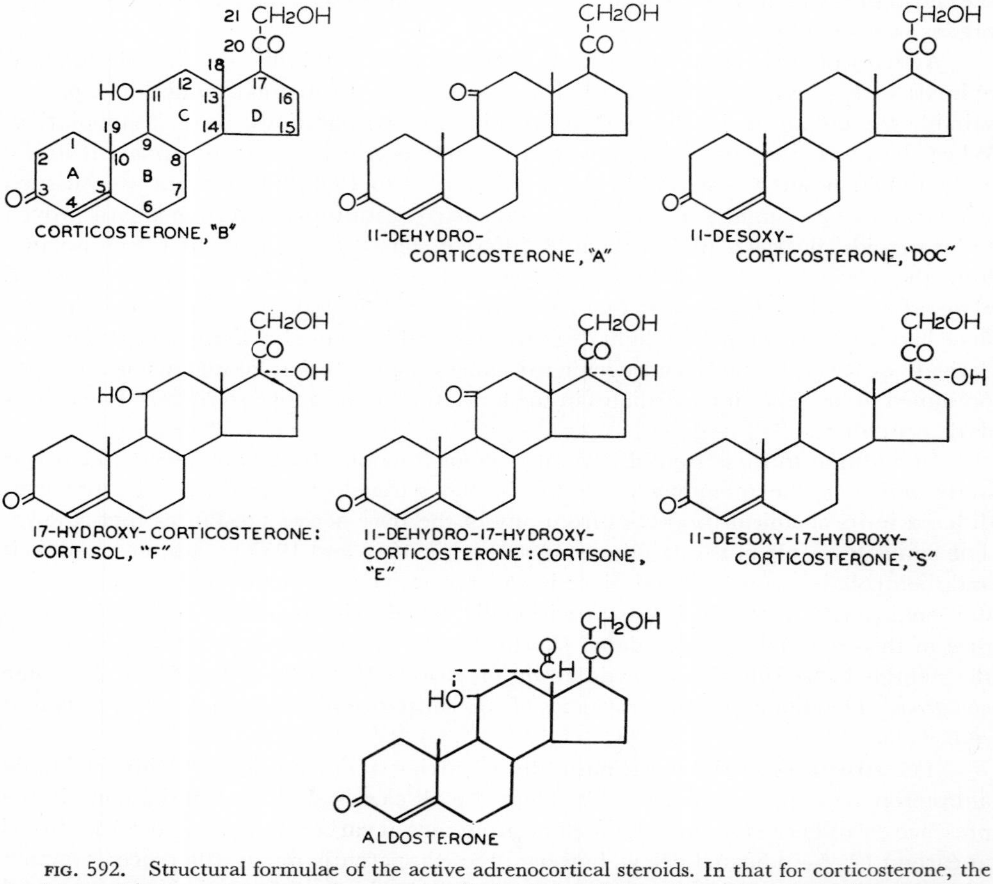

FIG. 592. Structural formulae of the active adrenocortical steroids. In that for corticosterone, the numbers and letters are those used conventionally in designating configuration of steroid compounds. Structures essential for any type of adrenal hormonal activity are the 3-keto, Δ-4 unsaturated grouping in ring A and the two-carbon α-ketol side chain at C-17. An oxygen at C-11 is characteristic of adrenal steroids and is essential for most kinds of activity.

occurring steroids. This greater activity is due partly to the fact that the synthetic compounds may be more slowly destroyed in the body than the corresponding natural substances, but certain of these structural modifications can confer disproportionate activity in certain respects. These synthetic compounds are now being used increasingly for therapeutic purposes.

Secretory products of the adrenal cortex. The nature of the adrenal hormone as secreted by the gland has been elucidated only recently. As indicated above, only small amounts of any of the numerous adrenal steroids can be obtained from glandular tissue. However, as shown a number of years ago, adrenal venous blood from the normal or stimulated gland is extremely active biologically. This indicates that the adrenal steroids are not

TABLE 48. CORTICAL STEROIDS IN ADRENAL VENOUS BLOOD IN THE DOG*

STEROID	NORMAL DOG µg./kg./hr.	HYPOPHYSECTOMIZED DOG µg./kg./hr.
Cortisol	32 (23–46)	2–3
Corticosterone	13	1–2
Desoxycortisol ("S")	4	0.3
Desoxycorticosterone	0.3	0.04
Aldosterone	0.3	0.14

* Averages of eight or more observations (Farrell *et al., Amer. J. Physiol.*, 1955, *182:*269–272.)

stored in the gland in any quantity, but are formed and secreted on demand, as it were. Analysis of adrenal venous effluents has become practicable only with the recent development of suitable chromatographic techniques for the separation and identification of the several steroids. In a survey of a variety of species, Bush[6] has found that in all cases the principal steroids quantitatively are corticosterone and cortisol. The ratio of these two steroids varies widely, however. In man and in the dog, the 17-hydroxy form (cortisol) predominates, whereas the principal compound in the rat and some other species is corticosterone. Smaller amounts of other steroids are secreted also. In Table 48 are shown values obtained for the dog by Farrell and associates.[18, 53] These probably represent maximal rates of secretion, since the blood was obtained during acute laparotomy and cannulation of the adrenal vein. Available evidence indicates a similar relative distribution of forms in man. An idea of the rate of secretion of cortical steroids in man may be obtained from the fact that an Addisonian patient can be well maintained by the daily administration of about 10 mg. of cortisol together with small amounts of desoxycorticosterone or fluorocortisol for salt retention.

Excretion products from adrenal cortex. A very large number of different steroids, some of them of adrenal origin and some from the gonads, have been isolated from human urine. Most of these are excreted either as glucuronides or as sulfates and require hydrolysis before either chemical or biologic estimation. Of the steroids apparently related to the cortical hormones, most are inactive compounds in which one or more of the requisite structural details have been lost or altered in some way. The major metabolites of this type are now thought to be the "tetrahydro" derivatives, i.e., those in which the only change from the original form has been the addition of hydrogen in the A ring to form the saturated hydroxylated derivative in place of the unsaturated ketone. Further reduction may also occur at the C-20 ketone in the side chain.

The active adrenal steroids are secreted unchanged only in minute amounts. As assayed by the glycogen deposition test, the output of the so-called "glucocorticoids" amounts to the equivalent of less than 0.1 mg. per day of cortisone normally and does not exceed a few milligrams per day even in extreme hypercorticalism. A number of chemical methods measuring different groups yield higher values. For example, the "reducing steroids," which contain the α-ketol side chain at C-17 and which therefore will reduce alkaline copper solutions, include all the active adrenal steroids and also many inactive compounds; they are found in normal urine in larger amounts than the glucocorticoids and may be excreted in considerable quantities (up to 20 mg.) in cases of adrenal hyperfunction. Another chemical method now widely employed is based on the triose structure of the side chain of adrenal steroids containing the 17-hydroxyl group. This allows the formation of an osazone with phenylhydrazine which can be measured spectrophometrically (Porter-Silber reaction). This procedure is fairly specific for cortical steroids; but it includes inactive substances such as 17-hydroxy DOC (Reichstein's compound S) as well as derivatives of cortisone and cortisol, and it does not measure corticosterone or its metabolites or steroids reduced at the C-20 oxygen. It is obvious, therefore, that, since no one biologic or chemical method can measure all the compounds of adrenal origin but no others, attempts at providing a specific index of cortical function through measurement of a single type of excretion product can be expected to meet with only limited success.[58]

Another class of compounds found in the urine is also related in part to the adrenal cortex.[47] These are the neutral (i.e., nonphenolic) 17-ketosteroids, substances which bear a single oxygen atom at C-17 rather than a side chain and which are identified by certain color reactions of this group. Included in this class are several of the androgens as well as a number of inactive compounds (but not estrone, which is a phenol as well as a 17-ketosteroid). These substances are excreted by adult men and women in varying amounts, the average for normal men somewhat exceeding that for women or castrate men. In patients with Addison's disease, only very small quantities of the ketosteroids are excreted, whereas in subjects with adrenal hyperplasia or tumors the amounts may be exceedingly large. Thus, the 17-ketosteroids arise in part from the testes but mainly from adrenal tissue. However, these substances are not major metabolic products of normal adrenal steroids, for only small amounts of 17-ketosteroids are excreted after the administration of even quite large doses of cortical hormones. As indicated below, the 17-ketosteroids seem rather to be by-products of cortical activity, or in some cases they may be considered abnormal products.

Biogenesis of the adrenal steroids. The mechanism of formation of the cortical steroids carries important implications for the understanding of the normal physiology of the adrenal gland and of pathologic aberrations in its function. This mechanism has been studied mainly by two methods: first, the characterization and assay of excretion products in conditions of adrenal hyperactivity or following the administration of presumed intermediates in the formation of the hormones, or, second, by study of the reactions carried out by isolated adrenal tissue.[31] By comparing the products obtained in a wide variety of such experiments, it is now possible to prepare an outline of the pathways by which the cortical steroids are synthesized *in vivo*, as summarized briefly in the following scheme:

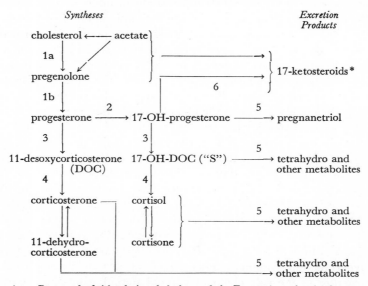

Reactions: 1. a. Removal of side chain of cholesterol. b. Formation of Δ-4,3-keto grouping.
2. 17-hydroxylation.
3. 21-hydroxylation.
4. 11-hydroxylation.
5. Inactivation by reduction of A ring, also 20-keto group.
6. Removal of C-20,21, side chain.

* Includes androgens. Many of these are oxygenated at C-11, as in step 4.

As has long been known, cholesterol occurs normally in the adrenal cortex in very high concentrations and is depleted when the gland is stimulated actively. This suggests that cholesterol may be the principal precursor of the steroid hormones, and this has been confirmed by studies with labeled sterol. However, both cholesterol and the hormones can be formed *de novo* from small molecules such as acetate, and so it is not certain that cholesterol is the only precursor. Present evidence suggests that a minimal rate of steroidogenesis can occur without the formation of cholesterol as an intermediate; however, for rapid formation of hormone (as after stimulation), preformed cholesterol is probably the major source.

Available evidence indicates that the steps between cholesterol and the finished hormones occur in the order shown in the diagram above. The early removal of the long side chain and oxidation of the A ring (step 1) result in the formation of progesterone, which now appears as a key intermediate. The next step (2), hydroxylation at C-17, is not obligatory; but if it occurs it precedes further reactions. This results in the formation of two series of compounds, those with and those without the 17-hydroxyl. As noted above, the relative preponderance of these two series of steroids varies with species. In men, as well as many other species, the 17-hydroxyl series is the more important quantitatively. The next step (3), which occurs with either progesterone or 17-OH-progesterone, is hydroxylation at C-21; finally, at step 4, oxygen is introduced at C-11 to form corticosterone or cortisol. Oxidation of the hydroxyl at C-11, with formation of dehydrocorticosterone (compound A) or cortisone, may occur; but, if so, it is readily reversible. The further metabolism of the steroid hormones, such as the formation of the inactive tetrahydro derivatives, takes place mainly after the hormones have been secreted from the adrenal, in the liver and possibly elsewhere in the body.

The formation of 17-ketosteroids has not been clarified in detail. It is known that the side chains of 17-hydroxy steroids are rather readily cleaved to yield 17-ketosteroids, and 17-hydroxyprogesterone has been shown to give rise to certain of these substances (step 6) as well as to reduction products similar to the tetrahydrocortical steroids (pregnanetriol; step 5). In certain diseases of the adrenal these changes occur together: formation of androgens and the excretion of 17-ketosteroids and of pregnanetriol appear to be increased approximately in parallel. It is therefore supposed that the 17-ketosteroids may arise in part as by-products at this stage of steroidogenesis. Other evidence of a chemical nature suggests, however, that some or all of the ketosteroids may be formed at an earlier stage.

The position of aldosterone in this scheme also is not yet certain. Some indirect evidence suggests that this hormone may be derived from corticosterone.

In certain individuals, one or another of the steps of the synthesis may be defective. This leads to relative or absolute deficiency of the normal adrenal steroids, increased secretion of ACTH in response to this deficiency (p. 1098), and consequent enlargement of the adrenal gland and overproduction of intermediate products and related substances. In most of the cases which have been studied in detail, hydroxylation at C-21 (step 3) seems to be limited, but in others oxygenation at C-11 (step 4) is deficient. Characteristic excretion products include pregnanetriol and related compounds and abnormal quantities of 17-ketosteroids. The condition, which is termed congenital adrenal hyperplasia, has as its principal symptoms virilization or precocious maturity. These are no doubt consequences of the overproduction of androgenic 17-ketosteroids accompanying the compensatory hypertrophy of the adrenals which results from the basic insufficiency.

Hormonal Actions of Adrenal Steroids. Physiologic evaluation of the adrenocortical hormones has faced peculiar difficulties in the variety of effects attributable to cortical activity and in the number of different steroids which have been obtained.

TABLE 49.   RELATIVE POTENCIES OF ADRENOCORTICAL STEROIDS

	COMPARED WITH DESOXYCORTICOSTERONE = 100			COMPARED WITH CORTISOL = 100			
	Maintenance of Adrex. Dogs[a]	Salt Retention[b]	Excretion Ratio Na^{24}/K^{42c}	Liver Glycogen Deposition[d]	Muscle Work (Ingle)[d]	Thymus Involution[e]	Inhibition of Inflammation[b]
Natural steroids							
Cortisol (17-OH corticosterone, hydrocortisone (F))	3–5	±	7	100	100	100	100
Cortisone (17-OH, 11-Dehydrocorticosterone (E))	3–5	±	6	65	62	65	30–75
Corticosterone (B)	15	+	14	35	30	28	30
11-Dehydrocorticosterone (A)	12	+	7	30	20	23	30
17-OH, 11-Desoxycorticosterone (S)	?	3	8	<1	<1	0	0
11-Desoxycorticosterone (DOC)	100	100	100	<1	<1	0	0
Aldosterone	2000–4000	3000–4000	12000	20–30	+	+§	?
Synthetic steroids							
Prednisolone (Δ 1 cortisol)	1	±		300–400		400	300
9 α Fluorocortisol	900	500		1200		900	700–1300

  ± Variable positive or negative effect. + Positive effect, not quantitated.
  § Significant effect on thymus with impure preparations; eosinopenic activity, 25.
  a Swingle, *et al.*[70]
  b Singer and Borman;[66] Lyster, *et al.*;[45] Chen and Wickel;[7] Stafford, *et al.*[67]
  c Simpson and Tait;[63] Grundy, *et al.*[27]
  d Dorfman.[10]
  e Stephenson.[68]

Quantitative assays of extracts or of isolated compounds have been attempted by many methods.[10, 11] The most common procedures have been based on effects in adrenalectomized animals on (i) maintenance of life and normal composition of the body fluids in dogs; (ii) growth and survival in young rats; (iii) protection against some stress, such as cold; (iv) work capacity of muscles during continued stimulation; (v) deposition of glycogen in the liver in fasting rats or mice; (vi) involution of lymphoid tissue such as the thymus; (vii) depletion of circulating lymphocytes or, more often, of blood eosinophils; or (viii) inhibition of certain types of inflammatory reactions. Also, measurements have been made in normal animals of (ix) retention of sodium or radiosodium or of (x) reduction in the ratio of excretion of radiosodium and radiopotassium. A selection of data showing comparative activities of the adrenal steroids by some of these methods is given in Table 49. The physiologic bases of these tests are discussed further below.

On the basis of comparisons like that shown in Table 49, two principal types of cortical steroids have been distinguished: those which are most active in the retention of salt and in the maintenance of life, typified by desoxycorticosterone and often termed "mineralocorticoids;" and those such as cortisone and cortisol which are relatively inactive in these respects but which are most potent in a variety of other activities characteristic of cortical steroids, as in protection against "stress" or in affecting carbohydrate and protein metabolism. The latter group of steroids have usually been termed "11-oxycorticoids," since they have appeared to be distinguishable from the "mineralo-corticoids" on this basis; or, often, they are called "glucocorticoids," in reference to their effects on glycogenesis in the liver. However, data obtained more recently for the "newer" steroids show that this distinction is not complete. Aldosterone, the most active substance known in respect to renal retention of salt, is itself an 11-oxycorticoid and appears to have about the same order of activity as a glucocorticoid as its parent compound corticosterone. Further, the halogenated oxycorticoids, such as fluorocortisol, are also very active in salt-retention but at the same time are several-fold more potent as glucocorticoids than the naturally-occurring parent substances. Although it is still proper to distinguish between steroids which are highly active in mineral metabolism and those which are not, the "glucocorticoid" properties of these substances are not necessarily related inversely to their "mineralocorticoid" activities.

Maintenance of life and sodium retention. All of the naturally-occurring cortical steroids listed in Table 49, like the extracts of adrenal tissue from which they were originally obtained, can maintain life and a semblance of health in adrenalectomized animals. As indicated in the Table, however, the degree of activity of the individual steroids differs considerably. Since their potencies in this respect closely parallel their respective activities in the retention of sodium, it appears that the latter effect is the most critical factor for the maintenance of life. This is in agreement with the fact, mentioned earlier, that the provision of extra sodium salts alone may suffice to support an adrenal-deficient subject. However, the correction by cortical steroids of the critical disturbances in distribution of electrolytes and water does not result simply from amelioration of symptoms, as is the case with salt treatment, but is due instead to specific effects upon the renal tubules.[3, 29, 55] In either normal or adrenalectomized animals, small amounts of the steroids increase the reabsorption of sodium ion in the distal tubule and also usually increase the clearance of potassium ion. The concentrations of electrolytes in the body fluids of the deficient subject are thus restored and normal blood volume and pressure are maintained. As with salt treatment, the indirect effects of cortical insufficiency also are abolished, and renal function, appetite, digestion and growth all may be fully corrected by these steroids.

Although the mechanism of action of the "mineralocorticoids" is different from that of salt therapy, their effects resemble those of salt in that they tend to be limited virtually to the restoration of the hemodynamic state and its attendant phenomena. Desoxycorticosterone has no other actions to speak of and cannot substitute fully for the normal cortical secretion. Aldosterone, the natural hormone for salt retention, does have other properties in addition to its effect on the renal tubule;[23, 64] but this steroid is so enormously potent in salt retention and needs to be secreted or given in such small amounts that in fact its practical effects also are limited to mineral metabolism. The same is true to a lesser extent of the halogenated corticoids; an amount which is optimal for sodium retention is insufficient to replace the normal adrenal secretion in other respects. Thus, although the mineralocorticoids are able to maintain life through their important physiologic effects on renal function, these substances do not provide complete replacement of cortical function.

Before the discovery of aldosterone, the identity of the substance or substances responsible for the salt-retaining activity of the adrenal secretion was unknown. Desoxycorticosterone itself was not known to be secreted in sufficient amounts; but, since all of the active steroids exhibit some degree of activity, it was supposed that some mixture of the known hormones might possibly suffice. Now, however, the very great potency of aldosterone makes it obvious that this steroid is the principal active hormone in this respect. From the figures for secretion of steroids by the dog shown in Table 48, combined with the data for their relative potencies in Table 49, Farrell *et al.*[18] have calculated that aldosterone accounts for about 70 per cent of the salt-retaining activity of adrenal venous blood in the normal animal, corticosterone about 25 to 30 per cent, and desoxycorticosterone only 1 per cent. Available data indicate a similar order in these respects in other species, except that corticosterone may be somewhat more or less important according to the quantity secreted.

"*Oxycorticoid*" *effects.* The adrenal steroids which are oxygenated at C-11, unlike the corresponding desoxy compounds, are able to reverse all of the abnormalities seen in adrenalectomized animals. As shown in Table 49, although the several steroids vary in relative potency, they display closely parallel activities on liver glycogen deposition, on muscle work performance, in involutional action on the thymus and in inhibition of inflammation. From the data available at present, approximately the same relative activities also appear to obtain in respect to nitrogen catabolic effects, to depletion of blood lymphocytes and eosinophils, to the distribution of water in the body and its excretion, and also to the protection of adrenal-deficient subjects against such stresses as surgical trauma, hemorrhage, cold or the administration of certain drugs. It seems likely, therefore, that all of the steroids of this class have much the same actions and functions, differing only in quantitative potency. The two steroids which are now known to comprise the bulk of the normal secretion of the adrenal, cortisol and corticosterone, are entirely typical of this class.

The effects of these steroids are most easily demonstrated in adrenalectomized animals. However, if sufficiently large doses are given, exaggerated or "supranormal" effects can be obtained in intact subjects in most instances. Difficulty in obtaining an exaggerated response may be explained in part by suppression of the animal's own adrenal secretion in the presence of excess hormone (see below); or in some cases other factors than the amount of cortical hormone limit the response. With sufficient dosage of any of the oxycorticoids, the following effects may be induced in normal or adrenal-deficient subjects:

(i) In fasting rats or mice, a marked increase in the liver glycogen is induced within a few hours (Table 50). The blood glucose is increased to a small degree, and the muscle glycogen does not change appreciably. Therefore, the glycogen in the liver must have been newly formed from noncarbohydrate precursors. Since this increase in body carbohydrate is accompanied by a considerable increase in the excretion of nitrogen, it appears that the new carbohydrate is derived from protein broken down under the influence of the hormone.[43] The same conclusions may be drawn from the parallel increases in glucose and nitrogen excretion seen when phlorhizinized adrenalectomized animals are

TABLE 50.   EFFECTS OF ADRENAL CORTICAL EXTRACT ON CARBOHYDRATE STORES AND NITROGEN EXCRETION IN NORMAL FASTING RATS[*][†]

	LIVER GLYCOGEN	MUSCLE GLYCOGEN	BLOOD AND TISSUE FLUID GLUCOSE	TOTAL GLUCOSE	NITROGEN EXCRETED (12 HOURS)
Untreated rats	7	253	37	297	54
Cortical extract given hourly	79	260	54	383	81
Increase	72	(not significant)	17	89‡	27‡

* Fasted 24 hours, with treatment during last 12 hours.

† All values are mg. per 100 gm. body weight.

‡ Note that the ratio of extra glucose to extra nitrogen is 3.3, indicating that the new carbohydrate could all have come from the body protein metabolized during the period.

(From data of Long *et al.*, *Endocrinology*, 1940, *26*:309.)

given the steroids. Excess cortical steroids have little effect on glycogen formation from exogenous amino acids. Therefore, the action of the cortical steroids here does not appear to be upon the process of gluconeogenesis *per se*, but rather upon the provision of amino acids from the body proteins.

(ii) The oxygenated adrenal steroids have been observed in general to have a catabolic effect on protein metabolism. In fasting animals the nitrogen excretion is usually increased, and in fed subjects a negative nitrogen balance is usual; or, with heavy overdosage with the hormones, a profound loss of body substance may be induced. Most of the organs of the body are affected in this circumstance. The lymphoid tissue exhibits the greatest effect, but skin, muscle and many visceral organs also undergo severe depletion of substance.[62] An increase in plasma amino nitrogen has been seen in eviscerated animals given cortical steroids.[5] The liver, on the other hand, usually shows little effect, or may even increase in size. This is understandable, because the amino acids coming from the peripheral tissues must all be funneled through the liver as they are catabolized. Although the enhancement of protein catabolism by cortical hormone is ordinarily one of its most prominent effects, this is not an entirely obligatory action; for it may be modified or even abolished by administration of excess carbohydrate or potassium salts, and by other factors. Small amounts of cortical hormones given alone have relatively little effect on nitrogen loss, but when they are given in conditions which normally tend to induce nitrogen loss (as during fasting, trauma, anoxia or the like), the cortical hormone may hasten or augment the catabolic response.[16, 37] In the adrenalecto-mized subject, in which this response does not otherwise occur, the cortical hormones thus appear to play a "permissive" role in the nitrogen catabolic effect.[15, 34, 35]

(iii) When rather large amounts of the oxygenated adrenal steroids are given to rats, the severity of a pre-existent diabetes may be increased, or, in intact animals force-fed a diet high in carbohydrate, glycosuria may be induced *de novo*.[36, 38] Because under these conditions the nitrogen excretion is not as greatly increased as the glycosuria, it has been considered that the hormones must inhibit the utilization of carbohydrate as well as act to increase its production. In recent work with radioglucose, little evidence of disturbed oxidation of carbohydrate was seen, but massive dilution of the glucose with nonisotopic carbohydrate—that is, a very high rate of gluconeogenesis—was observed in animals given an overdose of cortisone.[75] Apparently, then, increased gluconeogenesis from some source is the principal contributant to the "diabetogenic" effect of cortical hormone; but it is not known whether other hormonal activities, such as those on fat formation, may not also play a part. Glycosuria or diminished glucose tolerance has sometimes been noted in human subjects given large amounts of cortisone or hydrocortisone.

(iv) The distribution of water and salts within the body and the excretion of water can be affected by the active cortical steroids independently of any action they may have on renal excretion of electrolytes. If adrenalectomized animals are allowed to develop renal insufficiency and then without further food, water or salts, are treated with adequate amounts of cortical hormone, the extracellular fluid volume and blood pressure are restored toward normal, hemoconcentration is reduced, and the animal again becomes active and vigorous even though the concentrations of electrolytes in the plasma may remain abnormal.[69, 71] The withdrawal of water from intracellular sites and the apparent increase in circulating electrolytes[21] seem to result from changes in the "permeability" of cells, or, possibly more correctly, from changes in the responsiveness of the capillaries which in turn would affect permeability functions.

Probably related to this phenomenon is the frequent observation of water diuresis following the administration of excess cortical hormones to either normal or adrenal-deficient subjects.[22] This is especially prominent in the presence of a water load. The

17-hydroxycorticoids, such as cortisol, are the most active substances in this respect, as they are in all other aspects of cortical function except salt retention. In consequence, although these steroids can in fact increase renal tubular reabsorption of sodium to some degree, their usual effect is to induce not salt retention but instead a loss of salts with the water excreted.

(v) The adrenal steroids oxygenated at C-11 exhibit striking effects on certain tissues of mesenchymal origin. The number of circulating lymphocytes and eosinophils is markedly diminished within an hour or two after the administration of these compounds,[13, 74] and later the thymus and lymph nodes may undergo drastic involution.[2, 14] Similar effects are seen in conditions of moderately severe "stress" in the intact animal, but not in the absence of the adrenals. It was this observation by Selye which first led to the concept of a generalized "alarm reaction" which included the response of the adrenal cortex to nonspecific stimulation. However, as in the nitrogen catabolic effect, small amounts of cortical steroids which have little effect by themselves may greatly potentiate the actions of other damaging agents. The mechanism of the "thymolytic" effect is not at all understood. It seems to be closely related in its occurrence to the general catabolic action of the steroids, and it may represent another aspect of the same effect exhibited by an especially sensitive type of tissue.

(vi) When the active steroids are given in excess over periods of hours or days, they affect profoundly the inflammatory responses of the tissues in a variety of circumstances: local inflammatory reactions to contact with irritating substances are greatly diminished or delayed, hypersensitivity reactions tend to be suppressed, the healing of wounds and development of fibrous tissue is delayed, and the normal capacity of the tissues to localize certain infectious agents may be considerably diminished.[12, 24, 49, 74] The symptomatic relief of rheumatoid arthritis seen during treatment with cortisone or ACTH, reported by Hench and his coworkers,[32] probably results from suppression of an inflammatory reaction, and the dramatic results of these hormones in serum sickness and other acute hypersensitivity states are certainly due to this effect.[74] Although this alteration in the usual reactions of the tissues is beneficial in many instances, such as those just mentioned, it may in other circumstances be distinctly deleterious, for the inflammatory response is part of the normal mechanism by which infection is combated and healing promoted in the tissues. These actions of the cortical steroids may well be related to the general nitrogen catabolic effects and/or to the lympholytic actions of the hormones; but, again, the fundamental mechanism is unknown.

(vii) The cortical steroids, when given in sufficient amount, are able to restore completely, or nearly so, the resistance of adrenal-deficient subjects to various stresses such as cold, toxic substances and the like.[49] Continued forced exercise, as in the Ingle muscle work test (see p. 1086), probably may be considered as a rather severe generalized type of stress, and the restoration of the ability of the adrenalectomized animals to do prolonged muscle work may be another example of such "resistance." The cortical steroids also restore to normal the constrictor responses of the capillaries to pressor agents.[20, 51] In most of these effects the oxycorticoids are the most effective steroids, but those of the "mineralocorticoid" type also can contribute to the protective effect in some circumstances. There is no convincing evidence that cortical hormones can increase appreciably the resistance of normal individuals to nonspecific stresses. It is probable that at least part of the protective action of cortical steroids against stresses of varied nature is due to redistribution of water and salts, maintenance of pressor responses and like activities, thus allowing proper hemodynamic adaptation to the demands of changing internal and external environments.

As is the case with adrenal deficiency, the manifold actions of the oxysteroids do not yet suggest any single point of activity which can explain all of their effects. If there is a common locus of function, it seems to lie in the functional integrity of the membranes of many types of cells. The actual point of activity might then be either on mechanisms within the cells which support membrane phenomena, or on the permeability of the membranes themselves—or even, as quite a few observations suggest, on properties of the "ground substance" which is the medium of transport into and out of cells.

Hyperfunction of the adrenal cortex occurs rather rarely in man. In its classic form, known as Cushing's syndrome, it is characterized by a distinctive facies with rounding of the face and localized deposition of fat in the shoulders and trunk, by loss of body protein, osteoporosis, fragile skin and poor wound healing, and weakness, by resistance to insulin, and frequently by hypertension.[1] Adrenocortical tumors often secrete an excess of androgenic substances, producing virilism in women and precocious maturity in young individuals.

Relationship of Hypophysis to Adrenal Cortex. The function of the adrenal cortex is controlled almost completely by the adrenotrophic hormone from the adenohypophysis (ACTH). Hypophysectomized animals do not usually die of adrenocortical deficiency, although, except for the critical disturbances in electrolyte metabolism, they show all the other abnormalities of adrenalectomy previously described. From this it has appeared that either the normal cortical steroids continue to be secreted in very small amounts, or, as was proposed by Deane and Greep[8, 9] on the basis of morphologic studies of the adrenal cortex, formation of glucocorticoids ceases but salt-active corticoids continue to be secreted by one part of the cortex (the glomerular zone). It has now been found that the latter is more nearly the case. Analysis of adrenal venous blood in dogs (Table 48) and in rats has shown that, whereas the output (maximal) of most of the corticosteroids falls to low levels within a few hours after hypophysectomy, the output of aldosterone continues at something like half the normal rate.[18, 53, 65] Also, when portions of the adrenal glands of rats are incubated *in vitro*, aldosterone is produced mainly by the section adjacent to the capsule,[25] as predicted by the studies of Deane and Greep.

After hypophysectomy, the secretion rates of all of the steroids—inactive forms as well as major hormones—except aldosterone are reduced about in the same proportion (Table 48). This fact, together with more extensive evidence on the effects of ACTH on the biogenesis of steroids in the adrenal,[31] indicates that the action of the trophic hormone is not on any of the later steps in the synthesis of the active forms (outlined on p. 1091). Instead, the effect must be on the rate of provision of some primary precursor, such as pregnenolone (step 1a or 1b). The formation of aldosterone from corticosterone would then resemble the other transformations in its independence of ACTH. Aldosterone normally constitutes only a minute part of the total steroid secretion (about 1 per cent). Since after hypophysectomy the secretion of steroids is not abolished but reduced only to about 10 per cent of normal, aldosterone still constitutes only a small fraction of the total steroid output, even in the absence of ACTH. Hence, although the rate of formation of the presumed common precursor of all the steroids must be low after hypophysectomy, the output of aldosterone can continue at nearly normal rates regardless of whether the trophic hormone is present. Other factors controlling the secretion of aldosterone are discussed below.

The administration of ACTH to normal or hypophysectomized animals is followed by all the consequences expected from increased secretion of glucocorticoids—nitrogen loss, gluconeogenesis, lympholysis, inhibition of inflammation and the like—and the hypophysectomized animal shows also improved resistance to stress. Some degree of salt retention also is common, probably indicating some increase in the secretion of aldosterone. An increase in the output of 17-ketosteroids usually accompanies the increase in secretion of cortical hormones. As shown by analysis of the adrenal venous effluent, the increase in hormone secretion occurs within minutes after the injection of ACTH.[52]

If the application of ACTH is continued for many hours or days, histologic changes indicating increased activity in the cortex are seen; and, after some days, considerable enlargement of the gland occurs. An early and striking effect of ACTH on the adrenal is reduction in its content of ascorbic acid. This action is the basis of a highly specific and sensitive test for ACTH activity in pituitary preparations and in body fluids when these are given to hypophysectomized animals; in intact animals, it can be used as an indicator of endogenous ACTH secretion.[59, 61]

When an animal is maintained in stressful conditions—as in the cold—for any length of time, the adrenal cortex becomes enlarged; or, if part of the adrenal tissue is removed or damaged, the remainder will hypertrophy. These changes do not occur in the absence of the pituitary. The secretion of ACTH, and hence cortical activity, must then vary with physiologic demand. More detailed studies of adreno-hypophysial relationships have been made possible by observations on changes in excretory products from adrenal hormones, on effects of endogenous cortical steroids on blood lymphocytes and eosinophils, or particularly in experimental animals, on changes in the adrenal ascorbic acid as an indicator of ACTH secretion. By the use of these and related methods in a variety of situations, it has been found that ACTH secretion and consequent cortical activity are increased by almost any change in the internal or external environment.[58] All types of stress—trauma of any kind, cold, heat, pain or fright, infections or inflammation—induce prompt activation of the adrenal cortex. Similarly, ACTH secretion is enhanced by hypoglycemia or by a large number of drugs, including morphine, ether, nicotine and histamine, but not the barbiturates, and it seems also to be increased by moderate exercise. None of these effects is seen in the absence of the hypophysis. Thus, not only does the adrenal cortex secrete its hormones continuously for normal metabolism, but also it must be able to increase its secretion in response to almost any noxious stimulus; and this response is completely controlled by the hypophysial adrenotrophin. These facts, together with the evident necessity for cortical hormones for normal resistance to stress, suggest that responses of the pituitary-adrenal system must play a large part in the regulatory systems which help to protect the animal from environmental hazards.[34, 58]

Control of ACTH Secretion. The mechanisms which bring about the response of the pituitary-adrenal system in exigent circumstances are currently under active investigation. One factor which is known to affect ACTH production is the level of cortical steroids in the body. Chronic cortical insufficiency leads to an increase in the amount of ACTH in the blood and to the hypertrophy of any remaining cortical tissue. Conversely, excess of hormone not only will induce regression of the adrenal cortex by suppressing ACTH secretion, but also, to judge from its effects on the adrenal ascorbic acid, it can prevent the release of ACTH during acute stress. Thus the anterior pituitary and adrenal cortex are in a reciprocal relationship, and any temporary excess or deficiency of either hormone will tend automatically to bring about a restoration of the normal hormonal balance.

These relationships have suggested that nonspecific stress could stimulate the secretion of ACTH by lowering the blood level of the steroids, presumably by somehow inducing increased "utilization" of these materials.[58] However, it is now known that the level of cortical hormone in the blood or tissues is not in fact diminished by stressful stimuli. Moreover, the response of the pituitary to such measures is so very rapid (within minutes or seconds) that it does not seem likely that sufficient destruction of the circulating steroids could possibly occur in time to stimulate the pituitary solely by this means. Finally, Sayers has shown by assay of the ACTH content of the blood of adrenalectomized rats that nonspecific stimuli can bring about increased secretion by the pituitary in the absence of any cortical hormone.[56, 73] It is probable, however, that "reflex" suppression of ACTH secretion by increased cortical hormone levels may be important in limiting the duration of pituitary activity once it has started its response to a stress stimulus.

Another suggested trigger mechanism for the pituitary response is that epinephrine, the secretion of the adrenal medulla, may be a specific stimulant to ACTH secretion.[42] The adrenal medulla is known to be activated via the sympathetic system in all types of stress; the earliest responses of the adrenal cortex to certain stimuli may be reduced or eliminated by surgical interference with the sympathetic-adrenomedullary system; and very small amounts of epinephrine will activate the pituitary-adrenal mechanism even when the pituitary has been transplanted elsewhere in the body. However, since adrenodemedullated or even sympathectomized animals do not appear to suffer from cortical deficiency when faced with stressful stimuli, this cannot be the only mechanism controlling ACTH production.

Finally, and probably most importantly, stimulation of the hypophysis seems to occur by nervous mechanisms via the hypothalamus and the pituitary-portal circulation (Chap. 52). A considerable number of investigators have now shown that if lesions are placed in appropriate areas of the hypothalamus, usually in or near the median eminence, the common responses of the pituitary system to nonspecific stress are lacking.[26, 60] This has been shown after trauma, several drugs, or hypoglycemia, by use of changes in adrenal ascorbic acid, in blood lymphocytes or eosinophils, or in adrenal vein corticoids. The adrenal gland in these cases does not undergo atrophy, indicating that a "basal" level of ACTH secretion continues, but the system is unable to respond to further stimulation. Similarly, pharmacologic blockade of the hypothalamic connections can be induced with certain drugs, a combination of morphine and a barbiturate inhibiting the response of the adrenal to all types of stimuli.[48] It has now been found possible to induce pituitary-adrenal activation in the absence of the hypothalamic link (presence of hypothalamic lesions or blockade) by the administration of suitable extracts of the hypothalamus (median eminence area) or of the posterior pituitary.[57, 60] Also, similar extracts have been shown to induce the release of ACTH by pituitary tissue incubated or cultured *in vitro*, and a substance inducing adrenal activation has been demonstrated in plasma from the pituitary portal vein of the dog. This material, called the "corticotrophin releasing factor" and abbreviated as CRF, has not yet been purified or identified. In its chemical properties it is rather similar to the posterior pituitary peptides, and indeed vasopressin seems to have some degree of CRF activity; but partial chemical separation of the two substances and comparison of their biologic activities show clearly that they are not identical.[57, 60] Thus, there is every indication that much of the regulation of ACTH secretion in response to nonspecific stimuli is mediated via hypothalamic nervous connections and a specific neurohumoral factor acting on the anterior hypophysis.

Control of Aldosterone Secretion. Although the secretion of aldosterone is controlled only to a relatively slight extent by pituitary ACTH, many observations show that aldosterone secretion also is not constant but appears to be regulated by physiologic demand.[17] The principal controlling factor seems to be the intake of sodium salts or some function of the sodium supply, for the secretion of aldosterone is much increased during sodium deprivation in man, the dog and the rat. A number of other regulating mechanisms have also been suggested, but often without sufficient foundation. The most important of these have to do with effects of changes in body fluid volume or some function of the extracellular fluid volume. A marked increase in aldosterone secretion may occur during blood loss or contraction of body water, even when there is no change in the sodium concentration of the plasma, and similar effects are seen during occlusion of the vena cava. Conversely, distention of the right atrium results in a significant reduction of aldosterone secretion. These observations suggest that aldosterone secretion is responsive to "volume receptors" in the right atrium in the same way that antidiuretic hormone is esponsive to volume functions elsewhere. Farrell[17a] presented evidence that these and other factors regulate aldosterone secretion through neurohumoral factors having their source in the midbrain area.

THE ADRENAL MEDULLA

The early discoveries of powerful pharmacologic activity in extracts of adrenal tissue and of secretion of a pressor agent by the adrenal medulla led to the belief, held for many years, that the medulla rather than the cortex was the more important organ. It is now known, of course, that it is the cortex which is essential for life and that removal or denervation of the adrenal medullae without significant damage to the cortices has no obvious ill effects on the health, vigor and reproductive ability of experimental animals.[7, 27, 30] In explanation of this paradox, the emergency theory of epinephrine action (see p. 1107) suggests that removal of the adrenal medullae has appeared to be without effect because its consequences have been observed only in animals leading a sheltered life in the laboratory, and that more demanding environs would reveal greater importance of medullary activity for normal life. In fact, the adrenodemedullated animal does not seem to be particularly sensitive to exigent circumstances, responding in nearly normal fashion to cold, trauma or the like. The only consequences which can be observed regularly are those concerned with carbohydrate metabolism: if hypoglycemia is induced by insulin, recovery of the blood glucose level is rather slower than in the normal subject; and glycogenolysis in muscle (as evidenced by loss of glycogen in the tissue and increase of lactate in the blood) does not occur as it normally does during hypoglycemia or after operative trauma or similar stimuli. These deficiencies do not seem to be of any great functional importance. It is probable that the actions of the sympathetic nervous system, which closely resemble those of the medullary secretion, may suffice for the animal economy in most situations.

The secreting cells of the adrenal medullae are modified ganglion cells, called pheochromocytes because of their distinctive color reactions. They are in intimate connection with preganglionic fibers of the sympathetic nervous system and their secretory activity appears to be controlled completely by stimulation through these nervous pathways. Stimulation through the splanchnics calls forth a marked increase in the amounts of hormone released, whereas section of the splanchnic nerve prevents any secretion.[8] Ganglionic blocking agents also inhibit the secretory activity of the adrenal medulla. The centers which relay stimuli to the gland are located in the posterior hypothalamus.

In addition to the adrenal medullae proper, many small masses of tissue closely resembling the medullae in origin, structure and staining characteristics occur elsewhere. These bodies are found adjacent to the chain of sympathetic ganglia (where they are known as paraganglia), near the bifurcation of the common carotids (here they are called the carotid glands), and in the liver and heart, as well as elsewhere. They contain substances which react chemically like those in the adrenal medullae, and tumors arising from this tissue sometimes produce symptoms identical with those due to excessive medullary secretion. Whether this extramedullary tissue is normally secretory is not known for certain, but there seems to be no reason why it should not be so.

Chemical Nature and Mode of Action of Epinephrine. Oliver and Shäfer in 1895 first observed that extracts of adrenal tissue had a powerful vasopressor action.[41] An active principle was isolated by Aldrich and by Takamine independently in 1901 and was later shown to be a derivative of tyrosine and to have the following constitution:

$$(l)\ HO \bigcirc \overset{\overset{\text{H}}{\text{O}}}{} CH(OH) \cdot CH_2NH \cdot CH_3$$

It is variously called epinephrine, adrenaline or adrenine. (Adrenalin is a proprietary name.) This compound was long considered to be the only hormone of the adrenal medulla. However, it has been found recently that the adrenals contain and secrete yet another active substance.[5, 17, 23, 46] This material, called norepinephrine, noradrenaline or arterenol, differs from epinephrine only in lacking the terminal methyl group. The two compounds are nearly identical in chemical properties, but, although they are generally similar in biologic behavior, they display some differences in nature and degree of activity (see Table 51). Extracts of the adrenal usually contain some two to five times as much epinephrine as norepinephrine, depending on species and age; on sympathetic stimulation, the gland apparently liberates the two substances about in proportion to content. Available evidence indicates that norepinephrine is formed first in all pheochromocytes, and also probably in most sympathetic nerves, and that in the adrenal medullae it is then methylated to form epinephrine.

The epinephrines are quite reactive substances and are readily oxidized to inactive forms, either *in vitro* or *in vivo*. As catechol derivatives, they give distinctive color reactions with ferric and with chromium salts and are responsible for the so-called chromaffin reactions by which adrenomedullary and similar tissues are identified histologically. Oxidation under carefully controlled conditions leads to the formation of adrenochromes, which are derivatives of indole. These substances condense with ethylenediamine to form stable fluorescent compounds, or they may be converted in alkali to the adrenolutines, which are also fluorescent; these procedures form the bases of sensitive and relatively specific chemical procedures for the estimation of the epinephrines in the body fluids. By this means, it has been estimated that the blood of resting normal men contains about 1 μg. per liter of total catechol amines. The hormones are rapidly inactivated in the body, and only minute amounts of the unchanged epinephrines are normally excreted. The major metabolic products seem to be inactive O-methylated derivatives (called the metanephrines) which may be excreted largely as glucuronides.[1, 32] Because these hormones are so quickly destroyed, their action in the body is of very brief duration. When administered intravascularly, their effects are evident almost immediately, but are evanescent. If they are given subcutaneously, however, attendant vasoconstriction in this area slows their absorption, so that maximal effects are seen within 15 to 30 minutes. For prolonged activity, they are also sometimes given in oil intramuscularly.

A large number of synthetic substances chemically related to the epinephrines have been found to have pharmacologic actions similar in one or another respect to the hormones.[33] These substances, together with the epinephrines, are known as sympathomimetic agents.

Because of the similarity between the effects of sympathetic stimulation and of epinephrine, it was long ago suggested that epinephrine might regularly be liberated at the nerve endings and there serve to mediate the impulse from nerve to muscle. As Cannon and Rosenblueth[8] first showed, some sympathomimetic material is indeed liberated from many tissues when the sympathetic innervation is stimulated. The biologic activity of this substance or group of substances was found to be not quite identical with that of epinephrine, and so it was provisionally called sympathin (q.v.). Evidence provided by von Euler[16, 17] and others now indicates that the sympathomimetic substance found in sympathetic nerves and liberated on stimulation is mainly norepinephrine. No purely excitatory or purely inhibitory compounds, corresponding to the hypothetical sympathin E and sympathin I, have been discovered. It is not known whether the sympathins liberated at neuromyal junctions normally diffuse into the blood stream in sufficient amounts to have significant effects elsewhere in the body. If so, their actions would resemble more nearly those of norepinephrine than those of epinephrine.

When the epinephrines act upon smooth muscle and related structures their effects are very similar to those obtained by stimulating the muscle through its sympathetic nerve supply. An intact nerve is not required, however; indeed, most organs are sensitized to these substances by prior denervation. The epinephrines must act therefore not on the nerves or nerve endings but on the effector cells. Since the action of these substances is excitatory in some tissues but inhibitory in others, it seems likely that the site of action is some specialized receptor in the muscle cell which is distinct from the contractile fibers.

Effects of Medullary Hormones. The epinephrines have as their most striking property the ability to affect profoundly the contractility of cardiac and smooth muscle. In addition, epinephrine in particular affects the rate of certain processes in carbohydrate metabolism in striated muscle and liver; and both hormones may affect also the secretory activity of the anterior pituitary, the salivary glands and some other organs.

Actions on smooth muscle. Perhaps because of the well known pressor action of medullary hormones, these substances have usually been considered to be primarily stimulatory in effect. In fact, both epinephrines may act either as excitatory or as inhibitory agents, depending on the organ affected and in some instances on the physiologic state of that organ.[6, 21, 22, 34] Table 51 gives a summary of some of the actions of these substances, together with approximate figures for their relative activities where these are known. As may be seen, with few exceptions the effects of the two substances

TABLE 51. *COMPARATIVE PHYSIOLOGIC ACTIVITIES OF EPINEPHRINE AND NOREPINEPHRINE**

TEST ORGAN OR SYSTEM	EFFECT †	RELATIVE ACTIVITY, E/N †	REMARKS †
Blood pressure	Increase	0.2–0.5	E: systolic mainly
Man, cat, dog			N: both systolic and diastolic
Blood vessels			
Rabbit's ear	Constriction	1–3	
Denervated limb	E: Dilation		
	N: Constriction		
Vasoresistance	E: Decrease		
(man)	N: Increase		
Coronary circulation	Dilation	1 approx.	
Heart			
Frog, perfused	Excitation	20	
Dog, amplitude of	Increase	0.3–1	
contraction			
Eye			
Iris dilators	Excitation	15 approx.	Denervated organs sensitized more
			to N than to E, so activities
Nictitating membrane	Excitation	>10	become approximately equal
Viscera			
Bronchi, histamine	Inhibition	15–20	
contr. in guinea pig			
Uterus, nonpregnant	Inhibition	50–150	Both E and N excitors in rabbit,
(rat, cat)			activity ratio 2–5
Intestine			
rat colon	Inhibition	0.2–1	
ileum, rabbit or	Inhibition	1–3	
guinea pig			

* Data on relative activities mainly from Burn and Hutcheon,[6] Gaddum *et al.*,[22] Lands,[33, 34] and Luduena *et al.*[36]

† E = epinephrine; N = norepinephrine.

are in the same direction. Both tend in general to be stimulatory in the vascular system but to be inhibitory in the viscera. When they are excitatory, the activity of the two compounds is of the same order, with epinephrine usually somewhat the more potent. In inhibitory effects, epinephrine is frequently, but not always, much more active than norepinephrine.

In the vascular system the epinephrines have in general a constrictor effect which is particularly noticeable in the skin and mucosa, the splanchnic bed, the kidneys and the cerebral area. Applied locally to the capillary bed of the mesentery, the hormones constrict the metarterioles and precapillary sphincters and so divert much of the blood from the smaller capillaries through only a few main channels of circulation.[9] The pallor of the skin and mucosa typical of medullary hormone action is probably induced in the same way. The two epinephrines seem to have about the same order of activity on the blood vessels in most areas, with the important exception of those in skeletal muscle. In the latter tissue epinephrine has a transient dilatory effect rather than a constrictor action, and the blood flow through a limb may be increased (Fig. 593).[21, 26]

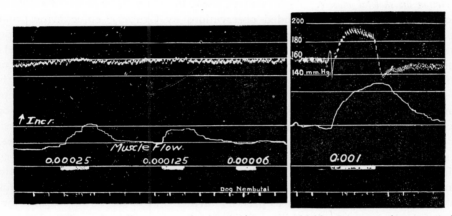

FIG. 593. Effects of small amounts of epinephrine on carotid blood pressure (*upper tracing*) and rate of blood flow through gastrocnemius muscle (*second tracing*) in the dog. Infusion rates in mg. per kg. per min. (*third tracing*); time in minutes (*bottom tracing*). Note that infusion rates just sufficient to increase rate of the blood flow through muscle (by vasodilation) were not adequate to increase blood pressure. (From Cori *et al.*, *Amer. J. Physiol.*, 1935, *114*:53.)

Norepinephrine, on the other hand, has always been reported to diminish the blood flow through skeletal muscle. Such a difference in activity is in accord with observations in man that peripheral vasoresistance is much increased by norepinephrine but is unchanged or may be diminished by epinephrine.[14, 24]

In the heart both the epinephrines are powerful and specific stimulants of the myocardium and conductile tissue, increasing the force, amplitude and frequency of contraction. As a result of their combined actions on the heart and on the blood vessels, these hormones then raise the blood pressure, the pulse rate and, usually, the cardiac output. The two substances differ somewhat in their effects, however; with epinephrine, only the systolic pressure is increased, presumably because its vasodilator activity in the skeletal muscle bed leads to little change in total vasoresistance, whereas with norepinephrine both the systolic and the diastolic pressure are elevated.[2, 14, 24] Hence, norepinephrine usually exhibits a greater total pressor activity than does epinephrine. In intact subjects, the increase in diastolic pressure after norepinephrine commonly results in reflex slowing of the heart, whereas after epinephrine tachycardia is typical. Both substances are inhibitors, i.e., dilators, in the coronary circulation.

In other organs, the effects of the medullary hormones vary. They are constrictor in the iris dilator and in the nictitating membrane, and these effects have been much used as internal indicators of medullary secretion. Here, epinephrine is much more active than norepinephrine, and it was the difference in this respect between administered epinephrine and the effects of splanchnic stimulation which first suggested that another pressor substance in addition to epinephrine might be secreted by the gland.[5] Other sites of excitation by these substances include the sphincters of the gastrointestinal tract and bladder, the splenic capsule and the pilomotor muscles. In the gut, on the other hand, the action is usually to inhibit motility, and the bronchial musculature is relaxed. The uterus of the nonpregnant animal is commonly inhibited also, especially by epinephrine, but the pregnant uterus may be excited by these hormones.

Because of these marked effects on the smooth musculature and on the heart, epinephrine finds important pharmacologic uses as a local vasoconstrictor in surgery, as a bronchodilator in asthma and similar allergic states, and as a heart stimulant in acute emergencies.

Action on skeletal muscle. As was first shown in the pioneer work of Oliver and Shäfer[41] and later in more extended observations by Gruber,[26] epinephrine prolongs the contractile response of muscle during tetanic stimulation and increases the response of the muscle after partial fatigue. This effect was thought for many years to be related to some aspect of neuromuscular transmission; but it has now been shown to occur in isolated tissue whether stimulated directly or indirectly.[4] Cori and Illingworth[13] have suggested recently that this action may possibly be a consequence of the effect of epinephrine on the enzyme phosphorylase. During the early stages of active contraction of muscle, glycogenolysis occurs rapidly, presumably supplying energy for resynthesis of ATP and hence for continued contraction; but the phosphorylase, which catalyzes the first stage of glycogen breakdown and which seems to be limiting in glycogenolysis, is partially inactivated during exercise. As shown by Cori and Illingworth, epinephrine enhances the rate of resynthesis of the active form of phosphorylase in fatigued muscle. This should allow glycogenolysis to proceed further and could be responsible for the action of the hormone on the ability of muscle to continue responding to stimulation.

Action on carbohydrate metabolism. As has long been known, epinephrine is a hyperglycemic agent. Less well appreciated is the fact that it has equally marked effects on muscle glycogen and on the lactic acid content of muscle and blood. The hexose phosphate content of muscle also is much increased.[12] These observations indicate that epinephrine acts at an early stage of glycogenolysis, prior to the formation of glucose-6-phosphate, in both muscle and liver. In liver, glucose is then freed by a phosphatase, but in muscle, which lacks the phosphatase, the glycolytic cycle may go to completion with the formation of lactic acid.[11] The lactic acid formed in muscle may be in part later resynthesized to glycogen in situ, but much of it diffuses into the blood stream from which it is largely removed by the liver and returned into glycogen or glucose. Thus both liver and muscle glycogen—the former directly and the latter indirectly—contribute to the increase in blood sugar brought about by epinephrine.[10] These relationships, known as the Cori cycle, may be schematized in the following manner:

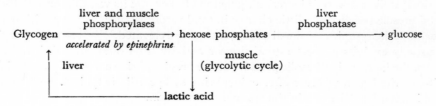

The changes in blood glucose and lactate and in glycogen stores are indicated in Figure 594. It may be noted that the liver glycogen tends to be higher after epinephrine, rather than lower, because of synthesis of glycogen from lactate which has been released from muscle.

The biochemical site of action of epinephrine has been elucidated by Cori, Sutherland, and their coworkers.[42, 45] As they showed some years ago, the limiting reaction in glycogenolysis is phosphorolysis, the formation of glucose-1-phosphate from glycogen, which is catalyzed by the enzyme phosphorylase. When liver slices are incubated with epinephrine, or when the hormone is applied to isolated muscle, the activity of phosphorylase is increased, thus accelerating glycogenolysis. More recently it has been shown that the phosphorylase enzymes of both liver and muscle are found partly in the active state and partly in an inactive form. Further, in both tissues Sutherland and coworkers have shown that specific enzyme systems catalyze the interconversion of one

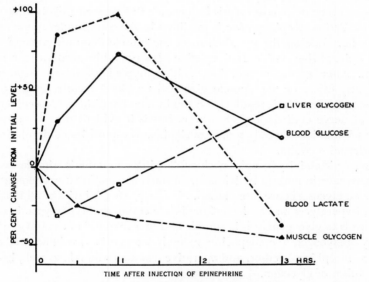

FIG. 594. Effects of epinephrine (0.2 mg./kg. subcutaneously) on tissue glycogen levels, and concentrations of glucose and lactate in blood of normal fed rats. Initial levels (in mg. per cent) were: for muscle glycogen, 570; for liver glycogen, 2400; for blood glucose, 129; for blood lactate, 16. [After Cori *et al.*, *J. biol. Chem.*, 1930, *86*:375 and *Amer. J. Physiol.*, 1930, *94*:557, and unpublished data (Russell).]

form of phosphorylase to another; inactivation occurs on removal of phosphate, and reactivation by the addition of phosphate from ATP by an enzyme which is therefore called dephosphophosphorylase kinase. The effect of epinephrine is to enhance the activity of the latter enzyme system and thus to maintain or increase the amount of phosphorylase in the active state. A conspicuous degree of reactivation of phosphorylase is demonstrable in muscles in which inactivation of the enzyme has occurred during exercise.[13, 35]

Part of the hyperglycemia induced by epinephrine appears to be due to diminution in the rate of glucose utilization by the peripheral tissues. The glucose tolerance is much reduced in eviscerated or normal subjects, and the arteriovenous glucose difference continues to be small even when the arterial blood glucose level is quite high.[10, 20, 31, 43, 44] This may be due to inhibition of hexokinase by accumulated hexose phosphate in muscle.

The increase in blood sugar is brought about by quite small amounts of epinephrine—in some species by less than is required to raise the blood pressure. Norepinephrine, on the other hand, has relatively little effect in this respect. In hyperglycemic activity, norepinephrine has been reported to be from one-fifth to one-twentieth as active as epinephrine.[15] Neither lactacidemia nor glycogenolysis in muscle has been observed with moderate doses of norepinephrine. After very large doses, the blood lactate may rise, but only much later than after epinephrine; this suggests that the tissue anoxia produced by vasoconstriction is the mechanism here rather than a direct effect on glycogenolysis.[3, 37] Norepinephrine also has relatively little effect on phosphorylase activity.

The different effects that epinephrine and norepinephrine have on glycogenolysis may explain some of the differences in their physiologic activities. As has long been known, reduction in *p*H inhibits motility of smooth muscle *in vitro* and produces vasodilation *in vivo*. Lundholm has now presented evidence showing that the vasodilator activity of epinephrine in skeletal muscle is related to the production of lactic acid, and that the inhibitory effects of both epinephrines in several kinds of smooth muscle may be correlated with the degree of glycogenolysis induced.[38, 39, 40] It seems likely that the general vasoconstrictor action of epinephrine is modified in skeletal muscle by the concomitant effects of the hormone on the metabolism of the muscle. The difference in metabolic activities of epinephrine and norepinephrine also probably accounts for yet another phenomenon. After adrenomedullation, neither hypoglycemia nor severe operative trauma has any effect on the muscle glycogen or blood lactate, although in intact animals strong glycogenolysis regularly occurs in such conditions.[3] Norepinephrine may be secreted at nerve endings and elsewhere, but it is evident that even after massive sympathetic stimulation the only source of significant quantities of circulating epinephrine is the adrenal medulla.

Glycogenolytic activity by epinephrine following sympathetic stimulation is a rather common occurrence in normal individuals. In states of emotional excitement, hyperglycemia and even glycosuria are often noted. Similarly, after injuries of all kinds and after many drugs, hyperglycemia and lactacidemia are common. Hypoglycemia of moderate degree also leads to glycogenolysis in muscle and to a rebound of the blood glucose. The susceptibility of glycogen to epinephrine makes it necessary to avoid adrenal-stimulating drugs, such as morphine or ether, and operative trauma or anoxia as well, in any studies of the metabolism of glycogen.

The hyperglycemic effect of epinephrine is in physiologic counterpoise to the action of insulin. When the blood sugar is low (either because of insulin action or from other causes) the secretion of epinephrine is stimulated, and so the return of the blood sugar to normal is hastened. One of the few abnormalities of the adrenodemedullated animal is its slow spontaneous recovery from hypoglycemia. Since increasing the blood sugar calls forth secretion of insulin, it is apparent that these hormones together contribute greatly to the homeostatic regulation of the blood sugar. However, it should be noted that, although epinephrine and insulin are opposed with respect to their effects on the blood sugar, the antagonism does not extend to other aspects of the physiology of either hormone. Epinephrine cannot be classed as a diabetogenic substance.

Other activities. Epinephrine has been shown to increase secretion by the anterior pituitary of adrenotrophin, thyrotrophin and gonadotrophins. Insofar as available data indicate, norepinephrine is relatively feeble in this regard. The physiologic significance of these effects is not known, but some of the actions previously attributed to epinephrine now seem to be more directly those of other hormones. For example, involution of lymphoid tissue—long known to follow the administration of epinephrine—is now known to be brought about by the adrenal cortical steroids secreted in response to adrenocorticotrophin.

The secretory activity of the salivary glands is decreased by epinephrine, but sweating is increased. Both of these effects are readily apparent in man in states of anxiety or fear.

An immediate but short-lived increase in the oxygen consumption follows the administration of epinephrine. The mechanism of this action is not known, but it is thought to be related to the metabolism of the lactic acid released from muscle.

Control of Adrenomedullary Secretion. Factors affecting the secretion of epinephrine were first studied by Cannon and his coworkers,[7] who used the biologic actions of the hormones, such as those on heart rate or on contraction of the nictitating membrane, as internal indicators of medullary activity. By these means, it was soon found that the rate of secretion by this organ varied widely under different circumstances. In basal conditions, as in deep sleep or narcosis, little secretion seemed to be produced; in normal waking conditions, there was just detectable activity; but on stimulation by such procedures as pain, cold or anoxia, by emotional excitement, or by hypoglycemia, secretion of the hormone was greatly increased. These observations have been confirmed more recently by pharmacologic or chemical assays applied to the adrenal gland or adrenal venous blood in animals, or to urinary excretory products in man.[17, 21] Among other stimuli shown to elicit increased medullary activity are exercise (even walking at a moderate pace), anxiety as well as fear or anger, hemorrhage or hypotension, and many drugs, including morphine and ether. The lability of the sympathetic-adrenomedullary system must be recalled in the interpretation or planning of any experimental procedure in man or animals.

All of these stimuli to adrenomedullary secretion are transmitted via hypothalamic nervous centers and the sympathetic innervation of the gland. Direct stimulation of certain centers in the posterior paraventricular area of the hypothalamus may induce a ten-fold increase in the rate of medullary secretion. The secretion of epinephrine and of norepinephrine may be controlled differentially. According to Folkow and von Euler,[19] stimulation of certain areas in the hypothalamus enhances the secretion of epinephrine more than that of norepinephrine, whereas stimulation of other areas nearby has the converse effect. Further, different external stimuli may elicit adrenal secretion in which the proportions of the two hormones differ characteristically. Afferent nerve stimulation or pain seems to increase mainly epinephrine output, whereas asphyxia has little differential effect and carotid occlusion increases norepinephrine secretion to a greater extent. Several workers agree that hypoglycemia stimulates the secretion of epinephrine almost exclusively.[18, 25, 28, 29] Studies in man and other primates seem to indicate that anxiety and related emotional states stimulate mainly norepinephrine secretion. Thus, two semi-distinct systems may exist for the control of adrenomedullary activity.

The function of the adrenomedullary activity has been thought by Cannon and others to be one of adaptation—an emergency mechanism helpful in preparing an animal for "flight or fight" or other activity.[7] The secretion of epinephrine is undoubtedly augmented by noxious stimuli, and many of its effects (such as the increase in heart action and in blood flow through the muscles, or as the "warming up" of the glycogenolytic system) may be considered useful responses to these stimuli. However, it is not clear that the secretion of epinephrines is a necessary or even completely desirable occurrence in higher animals when they are endeavoring to adapt to environmental changes. Some early data purported to show that adrenodemedullated animals could not withstand trauma, cold and the like as well as normal animals; but these observations were made before the importance of the adrenal cortical function was realized, and in many cases damage to the cortices incidental to the removal of the adrenal medullae was responsible for the changes seen. Reinvestigation of some of these points is now required.

As almost anyone knows from personal experience, medullary secretion in response to purely emotional stimuli is not always helpful and may sometimes be almost paralyzing. It is debatable whether this represents a useless physiologic "fault" or whether it is the price one pays for the possession of an autonomic system which is helpful in real, if not fancied, emergencies.

REFERENCES

THE ADRENAL CORTEX

1. ALBRIGHT, F. *Harvey Lect.*, 1942–43, *38*:123–186.
2. BAKER, B. L., INGLE, D. J. and LI, C. H. *Amer. J. Anat.*, 1951, *88*:313–349.
3. BARGER, A. C., BERLIN, R. D. and TULENKO, J. F. *Endocrinology*, 1958, *62*:804–815.
4. BAUMANN, E. J. and KURLAND, S. *J. biol. Chem.*, 1927, *71*:281–302.
5. BONDY, P. K., INGLE, D. J. and MEEKS, R. C. *Endocrinology*, 1954, *55*:355–360.
6. BUSH, I. E. *J. Endocr.*, 1953, *9*:95–100.
7. CHEN, G. and WICKEL, A. *Endocrinology*, 1952, *51*:21–25.
8. DEANE, H. W. and GREEP, R. O. *Endocrinology*, 1949, *45*:42–55.
9. DEANE, H. W., SHAW, J. H. and GREEP, R. O. *Endocrinology*, 1948, *43*:133–153.
10. DORFMAN, R. I. Pp. 325–362 in *Hormone assay*, EMMENS, C. W., ed. New York, Academic Press, 1950.
11. DORFMAN, R. I. *Physiol. Rev.*, 1954, *34*:138–166.
12. DOUGHERTY, T. F. *Recent Progr. Horm. Res.*, 1952, *7*:307–330.
13. DOUGHERTY, T. F. and WHITE, A. *Endocrinology*, 1944, *35*:1–14.
14. DOUGHERTY, T. F. and WHITE, A. *Amer. J. Anat.*, 1945, *77*:81–116.
15. ENGEL, F. L. Pp. 62–78 in *Pituitary-Adrenal Function*, Amer. Assoc. for Advancement of Science, Washington, 1950.
16. ENGEL, F. L. *Endocrinology*, 1952, *50*:462–477.
17. FARRELL, G. *Physiol. Rev.*, 1958, *38*:709–728.
17a. FARRELL, G. *Recent Progr. Horm. Res.*, 1959, *15*:275–298.
18. FARRELL, G. L., RAUSCHKOLB, E. W. and ROYCE, P. C. *Amer. J. Physiol.*, 1955, *182*:269–272.
19. FRIED, J. and BORMAN, A. *Vitam. & Horm.*, 1958, *16*:304–374.
20. FRITZ, I. and LEVINE, R. *Amer. J. Physiol.*, 1951, *165*:457–465.
21. GAUDINO, M. and LEVITT, M. F. *J. clin. Invest.*, 1949, *28*:1487–1497.
22. GAUNT, R., BIRNIE, J. H. and EVERSOLE, W. J. *Physiol. Rev.*, 1949, *29*:281–310.
23. GAUNT, R., RENZI, A. A. and CHART, J. J. *J. clin. Endocr.*, 1955, *15*:621–646.
24. GERMUTH, F. G. *Pharmacol. Rev.*, 1956, *8*:1–24.
25. GIROUD, C. J. P., STACHENKO, J. and VENNING, E. H. *Proc. Soc. exp. Biol.* (*N. Y.*), 1956, *92*:154–158.
26. GREER, M. A. *Recent Progr. Horm. Res.*, 1957, *13*:67–104.
27. GRUNDY, H. M., SIMPSON, S. A., TAIT, J. F. and WOODFORD, M. *Acta endocr.* (*Kbh.*), 1952, *11*:199–220.
28. HARRISON, H. E. and DARROW, D. C. *J. clin. Invest.*, 1938, *17*:77–86.
29. HARRISON, H. E. and DARROW, D. C. *Amer. J. Physiol.*, 1939, *125*:631–643.
30. HARROP, G. A., NICHOLSON, W. M. and STRAUSS, M. *J. exp. Med.*, 1936, *64*:233–251.
31. HECHTER, O. and PINCUS, G. *Physiol. Rev.*, 1954, *34*:459–496.
32. HENCH, P. S., KENDALL, E. C., SLOCUMB, C. H. and POLLEY, H. F. *Arch. intern. Med.*, 1950, *86*:545–666.
33. INGLE, D. J. *Endocrinology*, 1944, *34*:191–202.
34. INGLE, D. J. *J. Endocr.*, 1952, *8*:xxiii–xxxvii.
35. INGLE, D. J. *Acta endocr.* (*Kbh.*), 1954, *17*:172–186.
36. INGLE, D. J. *Diabetes*, 1956, *5*:187–193.
37. INGLE, D. J., MEEKS, R. C. and THOMAS, K. E. *Endocrinology*, 1951, *49*:703–708.
38. INGLE, D. J., SHEPPARD, R., EVANS, J. S. and KUIZENGA, M. H. *Endocrinology*, 1945, *37*:341–356.
39. LOCKET, M. F. *J. Physiol.*, 1949, *109*:250–257.
40. LOEB, R. F. *Harvey Lect.*, 1941–42, *37*:100–128.
41. LONG, C. N. H. *Harvey Lect.*, 1936–37, *32*:194–228; also, *Medicine*, 1937, *16*:215–247.
42. LONG, C. N. H. *Fed. Proc.*, 1947, *6*:461–471.
43. LONG, C. N. H., KATZIN, G. and FRY, E. G. *Endocrinology*, 1940, *26*:309–344.
44. LONG, C. N. H. and LUKENS, F. D. W. *J. exp. Med.*, 1936, *63*:465–490.
45. LYSTER, S. C., BARNES, L. E., LUND, G. H., MEINZINGER, M. M. and BYRNES, W. W. *Proc. Soc. exp. Biol.* (*N. Y.*), 1957, *94*:159–162.
46. MARINE, D. and BAUMANN, E. J. *Amer. J. Physiol.*, 1927, *81*:86–100.
47. MASON, H. L. and ENGSTROM, W. W. *Physiol. Rev.*, 1950, *30*:321–374.
48. MUNSON, P. L. and BRIGGS, F. N. *Recent Progr. Horm. Res.*, 1955, *11*:83–107.
49. NOBLE, R. L. *The Hormones*, 1950, *2*:65–180; *ibid.* 1955, *3*:685–820.
50. PAULY, J. E. *Endocrinology*, 1957, *60*:247–264.
51. RAMEY, E. R., GOLDSTEIN, M. S. and LEVINE, R. *Amer. J. Physiol.*, 1951, *165*:450–455.
52. RAUSCHKOLB, E. W., ROSNAGLE, R. S. and FARRELL, G. L. *Proc. Soc. exp. Biol.* (*N. Y.*), 1954, *86*:785–787.
53. RAUSCHKOLB, E. W., FARRELL, G. L. and KALETSKY, S. *Amer. J. Physiol.*, 1956, *184*:55–58.
54. REICHSTEIN, T. and SHOPPEE, C. W. *Vitam. & Horm.*, 1943, *1*:346–413.
55. ROBERTS, K. E. and PITTS, R. F. *Endocrinology*, 1952, *50*:51–60.

56. ROYCE, P. C. and SAYERS, G. *Endocrinology*, 1958, *63*:794–800.
57. SAFFRAN, M. *Canad. J. Biochem. Physiol.*, 1959, *37*:319–330.
58. SAYERS, G. *Physiol. Rev.*, 1950, *30*:241–320.
59. SAYERS, G. and SAYERS, M. A. *Endocrinology*, 1947, *40*:265–273.
60. SAYERS, G., REDGATE, E. S. and ROYCE, P. C. *Ann. Rev. Physiol.*, 1958, *20*:243–274.
61. SAYERS, G., SAYERS, M. A., LIANG, T. Y. and LONG, C. N. H. *Endocrinology*, 1946, *38*:1–9.
62. SILBER, R. H. and PORTER, C. C. *Endocrinology*, 1953, *52*:518–525.
63. SIMPSON, S. A. and TAIT, J. F. *Endocrinology*, 1952, *50*:150–161.
64. SIMPSON, S. A. and TAIT, J. F. *Recent Progr. Horm. Res.*, 1955, *11*:183–209.
65. SINGER, B. and STACK-DUNNE, M. P. *J. Endocr.*, 1955, *12*:130–145.
66. SINGER, F. M. and BORMAN, A. *Proc. Soc. exp. Biol. (N. Y.)*, 1957, *92*:23–26.
67. STAFFORD, R. O., BARNES, L. E., BORMAN, B. J. and MEINZINGER, M. M. *Proc. Soc.*

68. STEPHENSON, N. R. *Canad. J. Biochem. Physiol.*, 1956, *34*:253–258.
69. SWINGLE, W. W., BRANNICK, L. J., OSBORN, M. and GLENISTER, D. *Proc. Soc. exp. Biol. (N. Y.)*, 1957, *96*:446–452.
70. SWINGLE, W. W., BRANNICK, L. J., PARLOW, A. F. P., BAKER, C. and LeBRIE, S. *Endocrinology*, 1956, *59*:226–232.
71. SWINGLE, W. W., PARKINS, W. M., TAYLOR, A. R. and HAYS, H. W. *Amer. J. Physiol.*, 1936, *116*:438–445.
72. SWINGLE, W. W. and REMINGTON, J. W. *Physiol. Rev.*, 1944, *24*:89–127.
73. SYDNOR, K. L. and SAYERS, G. *Endocrinology*, 1954, *55*:621–636.
74. THORN, G. W., FORSHAM, P. H., FRAWLEY, T. F., HILL, S. R., ROCHE, M., STACHELIN, D. and WILSON, D. L. *New Engl. J. Med.*, 1950, *242*:783–793, 824–834, 865–872.
75. WELT, I. D., STETTIN, D. W., INGLE, D. J. and MORLEY, E. H. *J. biol. Chem.*, 1952, *197*:57–66.

THE ADRENAL MEDULLA

1. AXELROD, J., INSCOE, J. K., SENOH, S. and WITCOP, B. *Biochim. biophys. acta*, 1958, *27*:210–211.
2. BARCROFT, H. and KONZETT, H. *J. Physiol.*, 1949, *110*:194–206.
3. BLOOM, W. R. and RUSSELL, J. A. *Amer. J. Physiol.*, 1955, *183*:356–364.
4. BROWN, G. L., BÜLBRING, E. and BURNS, B. D. *J. Physiol.*, 1948, *107*:115–128.
5. BÜLBRING, E. and BURN, J. H. *Brit. J. Pharmacol.*, 1949, *4*:202–208.
6. BURN, J. H. and HUTCHEON, D. E. *Brit. J. Pharmacol.*, 1949, *4*:373–380.
7. CANNON, W. B. *Bodily changes in pain, hunger, fear, and rage*, 2nd ed., New York, D. Appleton & Co., 1929.
8. CANNON, W. B. and ROSENBLUETH, A. *Autonomic neuroeffector systems*. New York, Macmillan Co., 1937.
9. CHAMBERS, R. and ZWEIFACH, B. W. *Amer. J. Anat.*, 1944, *75*:173–205.
10. CORI, C. F. *Physiol. Rev.*, 1931, *11*:143–275.
11. CORI, C. F. *Endocrinology*, 1940, *26*:285–296.
12. CORI, C. F. and CORI, G. T. *J. biol. Chem.*, 1931, *94*:581–591.
13. CORI, G. T. and ILLINGWORTH, B. *Biochim. biophys. acta*, 1956, *21*:105–110.
14. DiSALVO, R. S., BLOOM, W. L., BRUST, A. A., FERGUSON, R. W. and FERRIS, E. B. *J. clin. Invest.*, 1956, *35*:568–577.
15. ELLIS, S. *Pharmacol. Rev.*, 1956, *8*:485–562.
16. von EULER, U. S. *Pharmacol. Rev.*, 1951, *3*:247–277.
17. von EULER, U. S. *Noradrenaline*. Springfield, Ill., C. C Thomas, 1956.
18. von EULER, U. S. and LUFT, R. *Metabolism*, 1952, *1*:528–532.
19. FOLKOW, B. and von EULER, U. S. *Circulation Res.*, 1954, *2*:191–195.
20. FRITZ, I. B., SHATTON, J., MORTON, J. V. and

LEVINE, R. *Amer. J. Physiol.*, 1957, *189*:57–62.
21. GADDUM, J. H. and HOLTZBAUER, M. *Vitam. & Horm.*, 1957, *15*:151–203.
22. GADDUM, J. H., PEART, W. S. and VOGT, M. *J. Physiol.*, 1949, *108*:467–481.
23. GOLDENBERG, M., FABER, M., ALSTON, E. J. and CHARGAFF, E. C. *Science*, 1949, *109*:534–535.
24. GOLDENBERG, M., PINES, K. L., BALDWIN, E. deF., GREENE, D. G. and ROH, C. E. *Amer. J. Med.*, 1948, *5*:792–806.
25. GOLDFIEN, A., ZILELI, M. S., DESPOINTS, R. H. and BETHUNE, J. E. *Endocrinology*, 1958, *62*:749–757.
26. GRUBER, C. M. *Amer. J. Physiol.*, 1914, *33*:335–355.
27. HARRIS, R. E. and INGLE, D. J. *Amer. J. Physiol.*, 1940, *130*:151–154.
28. HÖKFELT, B. *Endocrinology*, 1953, *53*:536–540.
29. HOLTZBAUER, M. and VOGT, M. *Brit. J. Pharmacol.*, 1954, *9*:249–252.
30. INGLE, D. J., HALES, W. M. and HASELRUD, G. M. *Amer. J. Physiol.*, 1936, *114*:653–656.
31. INGLE, J. D. and NEZAMIS, J. E. *Endocrinology*, 1950, *46*:14–20.
32. KIRSCHNER, N., GOODALL, McC. and ROSEN, L. *Proc. Soc. exp. Biol. (N. Y.)*, 1958, *98*:627–630.
33. LANDS, A. M. *Pharmacol. Rev.*, 1949, *1*:279–309.
34. LANDS, A. M. *Amer. J. Physiol.*, 1952, *169*:11–21.
35. LEONARD, S. L. *Endocrinology*, 1957, *60*:619–624.
36. LUDUENA, F. P., ANANENKO, E., SIEGMUND, O. H. and MILLER, L. C. *J. Pharmacol.*, 1949, *95*:155–170.
37. LUNDHOLM, L. *Acta physiol. scand.*, 1950, *21*:195–204.

38. LUNDHOLM, L. *Acta physiol. scand.*, 1956, *39*(Suppl. 133):1–52.

39. LUNDHOLM, L. and MOHME-LUNDHOLM, E. *Acta physiol. scand.*, 1957, *38*:237–254.

40. MOHME-LUNDHOLM, E. *Acta physiol. scand.*, 1953, *29*(Suppl. 108):1–63.

41. OLIVER, G. and SHÄFER, E. A. *J. Physiol.*, 1895, *18*:230–276.

42. RALL, T. W., SUTHERLAND, E. W. and BERTHET, J. *J. biol. Chem.*, 1957, *224*:463–475.

43. SOMOGYI, M. *J. biol. Chem.*, 1950, *186*:513–526.

44. SOMOGYI, M. *Endocrinology*, 1951, *49*:774–781.

45. SUTHERLAND, E. W. and CORI, C. F. *J. biol. Chem.*, 1951, *188*:531–543.

46. TULLAR, B. F. *Science*, 1949, *109*:536–537.

CHAPTER 55

The Thyroid Gland

By JANE A. RUSSELL

THE thyroid gland, found in the chordates and all higher orders, arises from the anlage of the pharyngeal floor. In most higher forms it consists of two lobes which lie closely on either side of the trachea and are joined by a thin isthmus of thyroid or connective tissue over the anterior surface of the trachea. Aberrant thyroid tissue also may be scattered elsewhere in the neck and upper thoracic regions. The gland is quite variable in size: it is larger in women than in men and enlarges still more during pregnancy; it is relatively larger in young individuals; and its size may also be affected by the iodine content of the diet, the environmental temperature to which the individual is adapted, and other factors.

Microscopically, thyroid tissue is seen to consist entirely of small vesicles or follicles lined with monocellular epithelium and filled with a homogeneous gelatinous substance called the thyroid colloid (Fig. 597). The epithelial cells vary in size and shape from flat through cuboidal to columnar forms, depending on the secretory state of the gland. The amount of colloid may vary widely, usually in roughly inverse proportion to the height of the epithelial cells. Between the follicles, which are spherical and completely closed, is a small amount of loose connective tissue richly invested with capillaries. Postganglionic nerve fibers from the cervical ganglia and vagus enter the thyroid along with the blood vessels and form extensive plexuses in the walls of the smaller arteries within the gland. This innervation is not essential to normal thyroid function, but is believed possibly to affect the rate of thyroid secretion by controlling the rate of blood flow through the organ.

Thyroid Hormone. Following the successful treatment of hypothyroidism with thyroid substance in the early 1890's, the chemistry of thyroid tissue was extensively investigated. An extraordinarily high concentration of iodine in the gland was first observed by Baumann in 1895; about one-fourth of all the iodine in the body is found in this organ, the concentration being of the order of 0.05 per cent of the wet weight, or many hundreds of times that found in any other tissue. It was soon discovered that almost all of the iodine in the thyroid was in organic combination, firmly bound to the protein of the colloid. This colloid protein, first described by Ostwald in 1899, is called thyroglobulin. It is a large molecule (molecular weight approximately 675,000) containing iodine in variable proportions up to 1 per cent by weight. Modern evidence, obtained by radio-autographs, confirms the location in the colloid of most of the thyroid iodine.

After hydrolysis of the thyroid protein, the iodine was still found mainly in organic combination. Kendall in 1915 first succeeded in isolating from the hydrolysate small quantities of a crystalline material, high in iodine, which was active therapeutically in hypothyroid patients.[39] This substance he called *thyroxin*. Its constitution was established by Harington in 1926 to be that of an amino acid related to tyrosine:

$$l-HO \underset{I}{\overset{I}{\bigcirc}} -O- \underset{I}{\overset{I}{\bigcirc}} -CH_2-\underset{\underset{NH_2}{|}}{CH}-COOH$$

It contains 65 per cent of iodine by weight. About one-fourth of the iodine in the normal gland is in the form of thyroxin.

In addition to thyroxin, several other iodine-containing substances have since been found in the thyroid. The principal one of these is 3,5-diiodotyrosine, which accounts for the major part of the remaining iodine in the gland. Monoiodotyrosine also has been reported to be present to the extent of 15 to 20 per cent of the total iodine. Neither of the iodotyrosines displays any hormonal activity. More recently, still another substance has been found: l-3,5,3'-triiodothyronine, which is like thyroxin except that it lacks one iodine in the second ring.[31, 51] This material accounts for only a few hundredths of the iodine in thyroglobulin. In biologic activity it is similar to thyroxin but is frequently even more potent (see p. 1115). A number of synthetic analogues of thyroxin and of triiodothyronine possess similar biologic properties.[5] The most active of these are tetraiodo- and triiodoacetic acids ("tetrac" and "triac"), in which acetate replaces alanine in the side chain.

Nature of the circulating hormone. Because thyroxin is found firmly bound to thyroglobulin, it was considered for many years that iodothyroglobulin, as the complex is called, must be the hormone, rather than thyroxin itself. This view was supported by the finding that the organic iodine of the blood is precipitated with the blood proteins by a number of reagents. More recent evidence indicates, however, that the circulating form of the hormone is thyroxin, not thyroglobulin.[51, 57] Thyroxin is extractable from the plasma proteins by simple treatment with organic solvents such as butyl alcohol, whereas extraction of thyroxin from thyroid tissue requires prior hydrolysis of the proteins with strong alkali. When thyroxin is added to plasma it appears to be mixed immediately with the thyroxin already present (labeled with I^{131}) and thereafter is inseparable from it by repeated recrystallization or distribution between solvents. Finally, thyroxin added to normal purified blood proteins (the albumins and α globulins) combines with them so that it is precipitable by the usual protein-precipitating agents. This evidence shows that the circulating hormone is actually thyroxin, carried in relatively loose combination with plasma proteins. In human plasma, a specific thyroxin-binding protein has recently been identified.[16, 23, 50] This substance, an α globulin (between α_1 and α_2), is in ionic equilibrium with thyroxin and evidently has a very high affinity for the hormone. Triiodothyronine is bound to the same protein but to a much smaller extent.

The concentration of thyroid hormone in the blood, estimated as the protein-bound or as the butanol-extractable iodine, is extremely small. In normal human serum, the values range from 4 to 8 μg. of iodine per 100 ml., or about 10^{-7} molar. In hypothyroid states, values of 0 to 2 μg. per 100 ml. are seen, and in hyperthyroidism the values may be 15 to 20 μg.[8, 47, 44] Most of the blood hormone is in the form of thyroxin, but very small amounts of triiodothyronine also have been detected.[30, 32] The actual amount of free thyroxin, not bound to the carrier protein in plasma, must be very much less than that of the protein-bound thyroxin.

Formation of thyroxin outside the thyroid gland. When elemental iodine (not iodide) is added to casein or other proteins containing tyrosine and the mixture incubated under controlled conditions of pH, temperature, aeration, etc., thyro-active substances are readily formed. Proteins containing as much as 2 to 3 per cent of thyroxin have been obtained in this manner. The process of thyroxin formation under these conditions does not appear to be enzymatic. Chemical evidence indicates that iodination of tyrosine within the protein molecule occurs first, followed by an oxidative coupling of two of the diiodotyrosine residues to form thyroxin. The thyroxin is still attached to the protein and can be freed only after hydrolysis. Thyroxin may be formed *in vivo* in similar fashion.[51] Elemental iodine (injected in oil) may display hormonal activity, apparently because thyroxin is formed at the injection site and diffuses slowly into the rest of the body.[6, 19] Evidently the formation of thyroxin is not specific to the thyroid, but the process must be very greatly facilitated by the enzyme systems in that organ.

Incorporation and Distribution of Iodine in the Thyroid Gland. The thyroid gland of a normal animal has a remarkable capacity for taking up inorganic iodine from the plasma and for fixing it in organic forms. The thyroid contains on the order of 50 mg. per cent of iodine, all but about 1 mg. per cent of it in organic form. In contrast, the iodide concentration of plasma, with average quantities of iodine in the diet, is very low— at most only a few *micrograms* per cent. Iodide administered to animals is very rapidly taken up by the thyroid gland. When tracer amounts of radioiodide* are given to rats or other small animals, detectable quantities appear in the thyroid within a few minutes, and within some hours as much as 60 or 70 per cent of the administered dose may be fixed in the gland (Fig. 596).[12] Most of this is at first in the form of diiodotyrosine; then thyroxin is formed somewhat more slowly. Thus, organic iodination in the thyroid gland appears to follow the same course as in the casein mixtures. With the concentrations of materials found in the thyroid, however, active respiration by the tissue is required to furnish the energy for the oxidation of iodide (to iodine or hypoiodite) and for the oxidative formation of thyroxin.[51, 58, 61]

Normally, the iodide which is taken up is almost as rapidly converted to organic forms. When, however, the formation of organic compounds is blocked (by excessive iodide or by goitrogenic drugs), iodine is still taken up, but most or all of it remains as inorganic iodide (see p. 1117 and Table 53). The concentration of iodide in the gland may then be 200 to 300 times that in the plasma. These observations indicate that thyroid has the ability not only to form organic compounds rapidly but to trap and retain *inorganic* iodide independently of its further transformation.[12] A similar concentrating mechanism for iodide has been described in the salivary glands and in the gastric mucosa. The iodide trap depends upon the continued metabolism of the cells and is evidently the result of an active transport process, but little more is known of the mechanism. Other factors affecting iodine metabolism in the thyroid are discussed further below.

Functions of Thyroid Hormone. Although the presence of functional thyroid tissue is not essential to the life of an animal, a deficiency of the thyroid secretion seriously disturbs its growth, development and well-being.

---

* A tracer dose of isotopic iodine is one which does not appreciably increase the amount of iodine in the body but in effect labels the inorganic iodide of the body fluids.

Deficiency of thyroid hormone. The principal defects induced by lack of thyroxin are the following:

(i) In warm-blooded animals, a low basal metabolic rate is the most characteristic finding, a fact first noted by Magnus-Levy in 1896. In most species, the maximal decrease after thyroidectomy is of the order of 25 to 35 per cent. All the body tissues appear to share in this defect, according to *in vitro* measurements of oxygen utilization by surviving organs. After thyroidectomy or cessation of therapy, the B.M.R. falls gradually at a diminishing rate until it reaches a minimum in about 40 to 60 days in man, or two to three weeks in the rat. This slow decay of the B.M.R. has been thought possibly to be due to a gradual diminution in the concentration of some critical cellular enzymes, but the data on this point are still inconclusive. The pulse rate, cardiac output, and circulation time are all reduced, partly as a consequence of the diminished need for oxygen by the tissues, and probably partly also because the heart muscle shares in the defective metabolism.[56] The body temperature may be low, and there is usually an increased sensitivity to cold.

Obesity, which is popularly supposed to follow from the decrease in metabolic rate, is not a common accompaniment of hypothyroidism in most species, for the appetite is usually diminished as much as or more than the metabolic rate.

Other consequences of thyroid deficiency, like those described below, have been thought probably to be secondary to the decrease in metabolic rate of the organs affected. However, as yet no certain evidence for this relationship exists in most instances. A number of drugs, such as dinitrophenol, are known to elevate the metabolic rate both *in vivo* and *in vitro*, but they are not able to reproduce the effects of the thyroid hormone. Furthermore, thyroidectomy has not been shown to affect the metabolic rate of cold-blooded animals, although it markedly delays somatic development in these forms.

(ii) In thyroid deficiency in young individuals, growth and normal development, particularly of the skeletal and nervous systems, are inhibited.[14, 20, 54] Young thyroidectomized animals grow very slowly for a little time and then remain dwarfed. The development of the centers of ossification of bone is greatly delayed and may never be complete. Treatment of such animals with small amounts of thyroid hormone over weeks or months allows both growth and ossification to proceed normally. However, if the animal is both hypophysectomized and thyroidectomized, the maturation sequence is restored by thyroxin, but general body and skeletal growth does not occur. On the other hand, if pituitary growth hormone is given, growth is resumed but the bones remain immature. Evidently, normal growth and development can be induced only by an appropriate combination of both pituitary and thyroid hormones. This and other evidence indicates that thyroxin controls specifically the rate of development and maturation of the skeleton, but affects general body growth only indirectly by way of the hypophysis. A corollary to this conclusion is that the thyroid also controls pituitary function to a considerable degree (see p. 1121).

When hypothyroidism occurs in the human infant, a condition known as cretinism is induced. This disorder, which in the past has occurred rather frequently in certain areas of the world, is characterized by dwarfism, mental deficiency which may approach idiocy, and a peculiar infantile facies due to poor development of the naso-orbital bones.[37] The abdominal viscera and tongue are often relatively enlarged. Since skeletal development is delayed, the "bone age" of the individual, established by x-ray examination, can be used as an aid in the diagnosis of hypothyroidism and as a guide to therapy in young people.

In lower orders, such as the amphibia, metamorphosis is delayed indefinitely, although growth in size is not much affected.

(iii) In adults as well as in young individuals, reactions of the nervous system and neuromuscular apparatus tend to be slow. A decrease in sensitivity to certain external stimuli has been observed, as has a diminution in the frequency of the α waves of the brain. The tendon reflexes show a delay in contraction and particularly in relaxation time.[41] In man, some degree of mental sluggishness is common, and symptoms ranging from the neurotic to the psychotic or imbecilic may be seen.

(iv) Few specific alterations in intermediate metabolism are recognizable. The fasting nitrogen excretion is diminished about in proportion to the decrease in metabolic rate, as is also the nitrogen excretion in phlorhizin or pancreatic diabetes. The serum cholesterol is high, apparently because the rate of catabolism of cholesterol is diminished to a greater extent than that of its formation.[52] The rate of absorption of carbohydrate and fatty acids from the gastrointestinal tract is diminished; the flat glucose tolerance curve often reported is probably mainly the result of this circumstance. Anemia is quite common.

(v) Myxedema.* In human subjects, but to a lesser extent—if at all—in most animal species, severe thyroid deficiency may be accompanied by a peculiar thickening and puffiness of the skin and subcutaneous tissues, particularly of the face and extremities. The individual may look to be somewhat fat (but usually is not), the skin is dry and coarse on the surface, and there is a characteristic expressionless or mask-like facies. The condition is known as myxedema, from the earlier belief that it is due to an accumulation of mucus in the tissues. Considerable amounts of water, nitrogenous material, and salts are held in the interstitial spaces of the skin,[11] and there may be also some degree of edema of internal organs, particularly of the heart. Little is known of the chemical pathology of this condition. The accumulated material contains mucin (mucoproteins or mucopolysaccharides), which stains characteristically.[9, 24] Since these substances are highly ionized and are rather active osmotically, it is likely that they are responsible for the retention of water and salts interstitially. It is possible that the accumulated material represents an overabundance of the normal "ground substance" resulting from its relatively slow catabolism.

Actions of thyroid hormone. As with the development of thyroid deficiency, the effects of replacement therapy take some time to become evident (Fig. 595). If a single large dose of thyroxin is given, the first detectable change in the metabolic rate may be seen in two to three days and the maximum effect in seven to nine days; with smaller doses given daily, the maximum cumulative effect is reached in several weeks. Triiodothyronine acts more rapidly than does thyroxin, the first changes in B.M.R. becoming evident in 12 to 24 hours and a maximum effect being reached in two to three days after a single dose.[5, 7] The maximal effect of a given dose of triiodothyronine is considerably greater than that of thyroxin, but since the B.M.R. also falls more rapidly after triiodothyronine, the total effects of single doses of the two substances, as summated over many days, may not be greatly different. With chronic dosage, triiodothyronine is usually some three to five times as potent as thyroxin.[32, 51]

In view of the greater activity of triiodothyronine, Gross and Pitt-Rivers and others have suggested that thyroxin is converted to triiodothyronine in the tissues where it acts, and that the latter substance may be the actual active form of the hormone. However, although thyroxin can be deiodinated to triiodothyronine *in vivo* to some degree, the conversion is evidently rather slow in most tissues and it does not seem to be an obligatory process in thyroxin metabolism. An alternative explanation for the greater and more rapid activity of triiodothyronine is that it is less firmly bound to the plasma protein than is thyroxin, and hence that the tissue sites, which must also bind the active

* The word myxedema is often used to mean any hypothyroid state developing in the adult; but the terms are not in fact synonymous since myxedema is only one of the symptoms of thyroid deficiency.

hormones, are able to compete much more effectively for triiodothyronine than for thyroxin.[50, 51] In agreement with this view is the fact that, whereas administered thyroxin raises the protein-bound iodine to normal levels or above, triiodothyronine does not do so but instead is taken out of the blood quite rapidly.[16, 51, 53]

Administration of thyroxin or thyroid substance to hypothyroid individuals can induce remission of all symptoms. In the adult, deficiencies even of long standing may in time be completely remedied. In children with congenital hypothyroidism, if treatment is not begun at a very early stage the defective development of the nervous system may not be completely reparable.

The administration of excessive quantities of thyroid hormone will induce a characteristic train of symptoms both in man and in experimental animals. The metabolic rate is elevated, sometimes even doubled. There is loss of weight (including loss of body protein as well as of fat), diuresis, depletion of liver glycogen and an elevated glucose

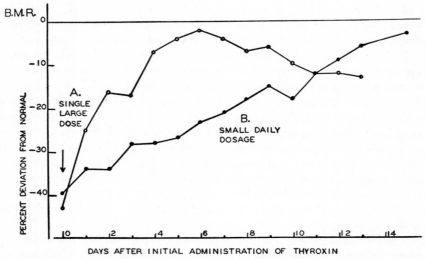

FIG. 595. Effect of thyroxin (polypeptide) on basal metabolic rate of hypothyroid subjects: A, single large dose containing 6.5 mg. of iodine (average figures from 3 cases); B, daily administration of smaller dose containing 0.5 mg. iodine (average of 5 cases). Note slow rate at which hormone affects metabolic rate. Cumulative action of small doses is also evident; in this instance maximum effect of chronic dosage is not yet seen. (After Salter et al., J. clin. Invest., 1933, 12:327.)

tolerance curve. The latter is mainly the result of rapid absorption of glucose from the gastrointestinal tract. Perhaps the most marked effects of hyperthyroidism are on the nervous system. Reflex sensitivity, and particularly the reactivity of the autonomic nervous system, are increased. Sweating, flushing, rapid respiration, palpitations, increased gastrointestinal activity, and fine tremors of the muscles are seen. The heart seems particularly affected; tachycardia may become very marked, and the cardiac output is increased. Emotional disturbances and nervousness are usual in man. The effects of the thyroid hormone on the nervous system are not well understood. They seem not to be closely related to the metabolic rate, for they develop early in the course of the administration of the hormone, before any marked increase in the metabolic rate is seen, and they are not reproduced by other means of increasing the metabolic rate.

The mechanism of action of the thyroid hormone is unknown. Alterations in the concentration or activity of a number of enzyme systems in the tissues have been reported, but as yet no specific point in the metabolic sequence can be singled out as the site of action of the hormone. Several years ago Lardy and others presented evidence suggesting that the action of thyroxin might resemble that of dinitrophenol, which "uncouples" the generation of high-energy phosphate bonds from the supporting oxidative system, thus allowing the latter to function more rapidly but less effectively.[42] However, the concentration of thyroxin required to produce these effects either *in vitro* or *in vivo* was several orders of magnitude greater than that normally present *in vivo*, and recent evidence has indicated that the effects seen may have been artifacts of this unphysiologic concentration.[43] It does not seem likely that the hormone can act as a catalyst *per se*, but it is possible that it may effect the release or manufacture of some cofactor or enzyme which is critical in energy transfer.[4]

Spontaneous hyperthyroidism (Graves' or Basedow's disease) is a rather common condition in man. It may be associated with an adenoma of the thyroid, or more often with a diffuse hyperplasia of the gland. The cause of the latter condition is unknown; it has been postulated that excessive secretion of the thyrotrophic hormone may be responsible. Exophthalmos, which often accompanies the so-called toxic goiter (diffuse hyperplasia), has been reproduced in animals, not by the administration of thyroxin, but by the injection of anterior pituitary extracts.[17, 18]

Use of Radioiodide in the Study of Thyroid Function.   Since highly active radioisotopes of iodine became available about 20 years ago, they have been widely used as biologic "tracers" of iodine.[38, 39] In consequence, more is known of the physiology of the thyroid gland than of any other endocrine organ. As mentioned earlier, when the inorganic iodide of the body is labeled by isotopic iodine,* the active iodine is rapidly incorporated into organic forms in the thyroid. The amount of isotope can then be measured readily with suitable counters either *in vitro* or *in vivo*. The ease with which this can be done has tended, however, to obscure the considerable complexities of interpretation of the information so obtained. The difficulties arise because all the iodide in plasma is not taken up into the thyroid, and because both the plasma iodide and the iodine in the thyroid are subject to "turnover"—that is, are continually being replaced by normal iodine coming into the body in food and water. An outline of iodine metabolism can be sketched as follows:

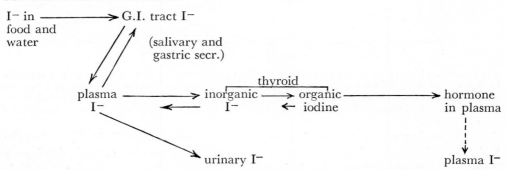

Fate of iodine.[49]   When the plasma iodide is labeled, the iodide is found to go initially in three directions: into the gastrointestinal tract by active secretion of iodide by the salivary glands and stomach, into the thyroid, or into the urine via renal excretion. The three routes are approximately equal in order of magnitude. The iodide in the gastrointestinal tract is largely reabsorbed fairly soon, but of course excreted iodine is lost. Hence, the thyroid and the kidney are in effect in continuous competition for labeled iodide. In normal men, about two-thirds of the labeled material is excreted, and the maximal uptake of I* into the thyroid is only about one-third of the dose injected.[18, 49] In consequence of this relationship, anything which affects renal function and the excretion of iodide will also alter the uptake of I* into the thyroid, but of course in inverse fashion.

* Usually I^{131}, hereafter designated I*.

The concentration of iodide in the plasma is normally very low (at most, a few micrograms per cent), but it can vary considerably, depending on the amounts of iodide coming in with food and water. In theory, higher concentrations of iodide in plasma would dilute a given dose of I*, so that normal iodide would carry less I* with it as it moved into the thyroid or was excreted. However, over a rather wide "normal" range of concentrations of iodide, the rates of thyroid uptake and of iodide excretion seem to be proportional to this concentration.[13, 49, 55] An increase in rate thus tends to counter-balance the dilution of I*, and so the tracer is not much affected by normal variations in plasma iodide. On the other hand, when the plasma iodide is increased much above normal, other factors operate. In this case, the excretion of iodide continues to increase about in proportion to concentration (the renal clearance of iodide is nearly constant over a wide range of iodide concentrations); but the uptake of iodide into the thyroid

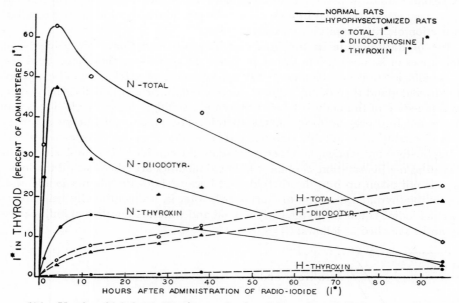

FIG. 596.   Uptake of labeled iodide (tracer dose) and formation of diiodotyrosine and thyroxin in thyroids of normal and hypophysectomized rats. Rates of incorporation of iodide into organic forms, conversion of diiodotyrosine to thyroxin, and release of organic iodine from gland are all much slower in absence of hypophysial thyrotrophin. (From data of Morton *et al.*, *Endocrinology*, 1942, *30*:495.)

does not keep up with concentration because there seems to be a limit of how fast the iodide-trapping mechanism can operate. Consequently, when the plasma iodide is very high, the fraction of I* excreted is increased, and that taken up into the thyroid is low.[13, 55] In man, 1 mg. of sodium iodide given with the tracer reduces the thyroid uptake of I* by about 50 per cent. Similarly, other iodine-containing drugs which can release iodide over long periods also may prevent the normal incorporation of I* by the thyroid.

Another factor which affects the movement of plasma I* is the rate at which the plasma iodide is replaced by normal iodide in food and water. After I* is given, the amount of I* in the plasma ordinarily falls continuously because of this replacement; and in about 24 hours all the I* is removed from the plasma. Therefore, the maximum uptake of I* into the thyroid must be reached at or before this time. If, however, the ratio of replacement rate to amount of plasma iodide (i.e., the relative turnover) is altered, this time scale also will change. With a rapid turnover, the maximum uptake of I* will occur early; with a slow turnover (as when the plasma iodide is high and the intake or the excretion of iodide is low), the maximum may not occur for several days.

Turnover of thyroid iodine. The iodine in inorganic form or organic combination in the thyroid also is always being replaced as the hormone is formed and secreted. This means that I* is first taken up and then put out; when I* is given, the amount of I* in the gland will always reach a maximum and then decrease gradually, ultimately disappearing. In the thyroid of normal men, the secretion rate is small compared to the amount of iodine present in the gland, so that scarcely any I* leaves the gland during the first 24 hours. At this time, when no more I* is coming in from the plasma and little has left the gland, the I* uptake should be maximal and should be an accurate measure of thyroid function. However, if the turnover of iodine in the thyroid is more rapid than this, as in hyperthyroidism in man or as is usual in small animals like the rat, the I* in the gland reaches a peak much earlier (Fig. 596). Since uptake and discharge of

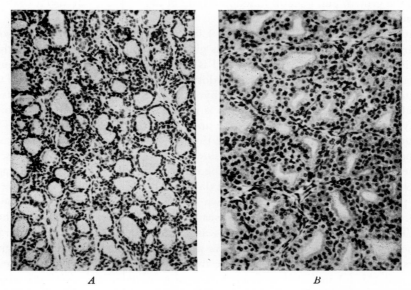

A   *B*

FIG. 597. Sections from thyroids of hypophysectomized rats: *A*, untreated; *B*, given thyrotrophic hormone. Note increased height of epithelial cells, loss of colloid, and increase in size of many of the vesicles under influence of the hormone. (From Evans, p. 315, in: *Science in progress, fifth series,* New Haven, Yale University Press, 1947.)

I* "overlap," a precise measure of thyroid function is difficult to calculate in this case. Probably the best procedure in such conditions is to observe the *rate of fall of the thyroid iodine* when no more I* is being taken up (after the plasma I* has fallen to zero).

Regulation of Thyroid Function by Thyrotrophic Hormone (TSH). In the absence of the hypophysis, the thyroid is diminished in size or fails to develop normally, the cells of the thyroid epithelium become very thin and flat, and the follicular spaces fill with colloid (Fig. 597). Although the thyroid is probably not completely inactive, it must be virtually so, for most of the usual sequelae of thyroidectomy are seen equally after hypophysectomy. The B.M.R. is low, the skeleton does not mature and, in lower forms, metamorphosis does not occur. Also, physiologic hypertrophy of the thyroid, such as that which occurs when an animal is exposed to cold for any length of time, is absent when the pituitary has been removed. Thus, both the growth and the function of the thyroid are dependent almost completely on the presence of thyrotrophic hormone.

When thyrotrophin is given, on the other hand, the epithelial cells become heightened, assuming cuboidal or columnar forms, and much of the colloid disappears. Such changes are spoken of as hyperplasia. Later, new cells and follicles may be formed and the gland becomes much enlarged. These alterations normally are associated with an augmented secretion of thyroxin, as evidenced by increased amounts of protein-bound iodine in the plasma and by physiologic effects such as elevation of the B.M.R.

The point of action of thyrotrophin has been studied by means of its effects on the iodine content of the thyroid and on the rate of incorporation or discharge of radio-iodide by the gland.[12, 38, 59] After removal of the pituitary, the total iodine content of the thyroid remains normal; but administration of thyroid stimulating hormone (TSH) causes prompt discharge of the iodine, mainly as thyroxin. If the thyroid iodine is labeled by prior administration of I*, the rate of decrease in I* in the thyroid can then be followed as a measure of the rate of secretion of hormone. The loss of I* is greatly accelerated by TSH, and this procedure affords one of the most sensitive and precise methods of estimating the activity of the trophic hormone. Evidently, TSH not only controls the growth and general functional level of the thyroid, but also it must actively stimulate secretion of thyroid hormone.

Thyrotrophin also affects the rate of formation of hormone by the thyroid. As shown in Figure 596, when radioiodide is given to hypophysectomized rats the initial rate of incorporation of I* in the thyroid is greatly diminished. The small amount of iodine taken up is converted in part to diiodotyrosine, but only small amounts of thyroxin are formed. In contrast to the normal thyroid, which begins to discharge its labeled iodine after the maximum concentration is reached in a few hours, the thyroid of the hypophysectomized rat continues to take up I* very slowly for several days. Thus, the total rate of replacement of iodine in the thyroid—i.e., the uptake of iodine as well as its discharge as hormone—must be very slow in the absence of the hypophysis.

The opposite effects are seen when the rates of incorporation of I* by hyperplastic thyroids are studied. Some representative data obtained by Chaikoff and coworkers[12] in guinea pigs given thyrotrophin are shown in Table 52. The thyroids of the treated animals were nearly doubled in size, as was also the concentration of plasma hormonal iodine. The iodine content of the glands was much reduced because of discharge of the hormone during treatment. Sixteen hours after tracer amounts of I* were given, the amounts of I* found in the thyroids were trebled as compared to those in the normal glands, and this I* included a much larger proportion of thyroxin; the amounts of labeled thyroxin present in the thyroid and in the plasma were both increased sevenfold

TABLE 52. EFFECT OF THYROTROPHIN ON PLASMA AND THYROID IODINE*

	PLASMA PROTEIN-BOUND I		WT. OF THYROID	THYROID I				
	Total I	I*†		Total I	I* as Per Cent of Amount Given			
					Total	Inorganic Iodide	Diiodo-tyrosine	Thyroxin
	γ/100 ml.		mg.	mg./100 gm.				
Group								
Normal	2.1	12	68	45.2	10.5	0.1	9.5	0.9
Thyrotrophin-treated	5.9	85	122	11.1	33.0	1.0	25.0	7.0

* Guinea pigs (4 or 5 animals per group) were treated with thyrotrophin for 4 days. Then tracer amounts of I* were given and analyses made 16 hours later.
† Per cent of total plasma I*.
(From Chaikoff and Taurog, Ann. N. Y. Acad. Sci., 1948, 50:377.)

over those seen in the controls. There may also have been some increase in the ability to concentrate inorganic iodide. It is apparent that both the formation and the release of thyroxin were accelerated by prior treatment of the animals with thyrotrophin.

A further effect of TSH is seen when the inorganic iodine of the gland is examined. As mentioned earlier, when the incorporation of iodine into organic forms is blocked by certain drugs, I* accumulates in the gland as inorganic iodide. The ratio of the concentration of I* in the thyroid to that in the serum, called the T/S iodide ratio, then becomes much higher than in the normal gland. Under appropriate conditions, this ratio is an indicator of the ability of the gland to concentrate or "trap" inorganic iodide. In hypophysectomized animals, the T/S iodide ratio in the presence of a blocking drug is much lower than it is in a normal animal similarly treated, and this is restored to or even increased above normal by prior treatment with TSH.[34, 35, 59, 62] Changes in the T/S ratio also afford a sensitive indication of TSH activity, appearing with much smaller doses of hormone than are required to affect the size or histologic appearance of the gland. Since the thyroid iodide trapping mechanism limits the rate of organic iodination in the gland, it is possible that the action of TSH on the uptake of I* is on the trapping mechanism, rather than on the formation of thyroid hormones themselves.

Thyrotrophic hormone thus appears to control all the major phases of activity of the thyroid gland: the iodide-concentrating mechanism, the formation of iodotyrosines and iodothyronines, and the secretion of thyroid hormones.

Thyroid Hormone and the Hypophysis. Not only is the thyroid under the control of thyrotrophin, but also, as indicated by both cytologic and physiologic evidence, the thyroid hormone affects the pituitary. In thyroidectomized animals, the number of basophils in the anterior hypophysis is much increased and some of these cells become quite large and vacuolated. Treatment with thyroxin prevents these changes or may even induce some degree of involution in some of the basophil cells.[29] These and related observations have been taken to mean that a certain type of basophil[33, 47, 48] is the source of thyrotrophin and that the secretory activity of this cell is inhibited by thyroxin and enhanced in its absence. In accord with this hypothesis are numerous observations on the effects of thyroxin on thyroid function. For instance, in intact animals as well as in human subjects, treatment with thyroxin inhibits both the uptake of administered I* by the thyroid and its later discharge.[21, 38, 55] Also, following a period of thyroid administration the hormonal iodine content of the serum may temporarily be much lower than normal. Evidently thyroid activity is diminished in the presence of excess thyroid hormone, and this effect is best explained as due to inhibition of thyrotrophin production by the subject's own pituitary. This relationship between the thyroid hormone and the hypophysis is thus entirely parallel to that between adrenocortical hormones or estrogens and the hypophysis in the secretion of the respective trophic factors.

At the same time that the secretion of thyrotrophic hormone is augmented by thyroid deficiency, other changes also are seen in the pituitary. The acidophils lose their granules, and may become completely depleted if no thyroxin at all—either exogenous or endogenous—is available.[29] These cells are very sensitive to thyroxin, and this effect has been used experimentally as an indication of the completeness of thyroid destruction. It is possible that the disappearance of the acidophil granules is to be correlated with the apparent absence of growth hormone production by the pituitary in thyroid deficiency (p. 1114).[20, 54]

Goiter. Visible enlargement of the thyroid gland occurs frequently in man and in domestic animals. Such an enlarged thyroid is called a goiter. The most common type, unaccompanied by any obvious signs of hypofunction or hyperfunction of the gland, is called a simple goiter. This condition has been endemic for centuries in many areas of the world, particularly in inland regions. Although the cause of the formation of such goiters is not known in all cases, it now appears certain that one important contributing factor is a relative or absolute lack of iodine in the diet or drinking water. Many observations have been made relating the geographic distribution of iodine in the soil and in foodstuffs to the prevalence of goiter. A convincing demonstration of the preventive action of iodine was reported by Marine and Kimball in 1920.[45] Among school girls in Akron, Ohio, the incidence of goiter (in individuals previously having normal thyroids) was reduced from 27 per cent in the untreated group to 0.2 per cent in those given extra iodide over periods of a year or two. A more recent survey in Michigan showed a similar reduction in the incidence of goiter following the widespread introduction of iodized salt.[10] In experimental animals maintained on diets very low in iodine, enlargement of the thyroid up to several times the normal size occurs regularly, and this is prevented completely by the administration of small amounts of iodine.

For prevention of goiter, the dietary intake of iodine recommended for normal human subjects is about 0.1 mg. per day, with additional allowances during pregnancy. Since foods grown in soils deficient in iodine may not contain this amount, the use of iodized table salt (containing, for instance, 1 part of iodide per 100,000) is widely practiced, and, indeed, has for many years been required by law in some European countries.

A simple goiter, if it is not large, may carry no particular threat to the health of the individual. It may, however, be indicative of mild or borderline deficiency in thyroid hormone. Overt hypothyroidism is said to develop more frequently in individuals with goiter, and both myxedema and cretinsim have been more common in goitrous regions than elsewhere. In the light of present knowledge of thyroid physiology, it seems likely that enlargement of the thyroid in iodine deficiency is a sign of some increase in the output of pituitary thyrotrophin, which in turn may be the result of at least marginally low levels of circulating thyroid hormone. The enlargement of the gland appears to be functional, in that it enables the organism to make the best use of whatever small amounts of iodine are available.

Thyroid-Inhibiting and Goitrogenic Agents. A large number of substances have been found to have the property of inhibiting thyroid function and in most instances also of inducing the formation of goiters in experimental animals.[1, 3, 67] Some of these agents are now extensively used in studies of thyroid physiology and in the clinical treatment of hyperthyroidism. The active drugs belong to several classes of compounds. The principal types are: (i) anions of certain configuration, represented by thiocyanate but also including such groups as perchlorate or nitrate; (ii) some sulfonamides; and (iii) substituted thioureas and related compounds in which sulfur replaces oxygen. Excess of iodide may be similarly classed in some respects. The most active of these thyroid-

TABLE 53.   EFFECT OF PROPYLTHIOURACIL ON THE THYROID GLAND*

Group	WT. OF THYROID mg.	IODINE IN THYROID MG. PER 100 GM.		I* (PER CENT OF AMOUNT GIVEN, AFTER 6 HOURS)		
		Organic	Inorganic	Total	Organic	Inorganic
Normal	20	48.0	1.2	26	25.0	1.0
Propylthiouracil-treated	58	0.6	0.5	6	0.5	5.5

* Rats were given propylthiouracil for 16 days (0.15 per cent in the diet) and then tracer amount of I*.

(From Taurog et al., J. biol. Chem., 1947, 771:189.)

inhibiting agents are the thiouracils and mercaptoimidazoles. The one most commonly employed in experimental work is propylthiouracil, which is goitrogenic in rats when fed in the amount of 0.1 mg. per 100 grams per day.

Thyroid-inhibiting agents also have been found to occur in nature. It has been known for many years that certain plant foods, notably those of the cabbage and turnip families, can induce goiter in animals when fed in large quantities over a period of time.[27] More recently, acute inhibition of iodine uptake by the thyroid has been demonstrated in normal men after the ingestion of a meal consisting of some of these foods.[28] The active agent occurring in seeds of the brassica family has been identified as vinylthiooxazolidone, a compound related in structure to the thiourea derivatives.[2] It is possible that in some instances the development of goiter in human subjects may be due to the excessive ingestion of foods containing naturally occurring goitrogens of similar type.

Mechanism of action of thyroid inhibitors.[3, 9, 46, 51] When agents of the type described above are given to animals over suitable periods, the thyroid gland becomes very much enlarged, often to several times the normal size. Histologically the gland appears to be hyperplastic, as if thyrotrophin had been given. However, the symptoms exhibited by the animal are those of reduced thyroid function, rather than of excess; the concentration of thyroid hormone in the blood is low, and very little thyroxin is found in the gland. Evidently, then, the effect of the goitrogen is to restrict or prevent the production of thyroxin. The enlargement of the gland requires the presence of the anterior pituitary, and it can be prevented by the administration of thyroxin or triiodothyronine. Hence, the formation of the goiter appears to depend on the action of thyrotrophic hormone: when the formation of thyroxin is blocked by the drug, the blood level of the hormone falls; this stimulates the pituitary to secrete more thyrotrophin—in an effort, it may be imagined, to increase thyroxin production—and the gland becomes ineffectually enlarged.

In accordance with this interpretation of their effects, all of the antithyroid or goitrogenic agents inhibit the uptake of I* by the thyroid gland. The iodine which was present in the gland originally is soon lost because of continued secretion of the hormone without replacement. The mechanisms by which the iodine uptake is inhibited, although similar in end-effects in all cases, differ as between some of the classes of compounds mentioned above. When the thioureas or thiouracils are given, either *in vivo* or *in vitro*, iodination of tyrosine by the thyroid tissue is prevented; on the administration of I* neither diiodotyrosine nor thyroxin is formed, although inorganic iodide is accumulated (Table 53). The sulfonamides are believed to act similarly to the thioureas. Thiocyanate and other large anions, on the other hand, inhibit the concentration of inorganic iodide by the thyroid.[36, 61] This action is seen particularly well in animals previously given thiouracil and then radioiodide.[61] In this case there is first found a high concentration of I* as inorganic iodide because the further incorporation of I* is blocked by thiouracils, but no I* is bound organically. Then, on the administration of thiocyanate, the inorganic iodide is discharged within minutes. The action of thiocyanate and similar anions appears to be that of competition with iodide for the "trapping" mechanism.[66] The loss of iodide then follows by diffusion outward from the area of high concentration of iodide within the gland. The effect of the anion is evident only as long as its concentration in the plasma is high, so that it must be given at frequent intervals in order to suppress thyroid function effectively.

The goitrogenic effects of most of the drugs are considerably affected by the iodine content of the diet—exaggerated when little iodine is present and reduced when the diet contains average amounts of iodine. In the case of thiocyanate, the inhibition of the thyroid function and consequent goiter formation may be overcome completely by the administration of a moderate excess of iodide.

Iodide ion itself, when given in large amounts, has what has been considered a paradoxical action—that of tending to inhibit thyroid function. This effect has been used for many years in the clinical treatment of hyperthyroidism. The dosage of iodine required for suppression of the thyroid is far in excess of that used prophylactically for simple goiter—in men about 10 to 100 mg. per day, as compared with the usual normal daily allowance of 0.1 mg. In rats it has been found that when the level of iodide in the plasma is brought to about 30 μg. per 100 ml. or above, the uptake of I^* in organic forms is almost completely suppressed,[63, 64] and, in man, as little as 5 to 10 μg. per cent of iodide in the plasma may have perceptible effect on thyroid function.[55] In vitro studies suggest that excess iodide inhibits both the iodination of tyrosine and the coupling to form thyroxin. For reasons which are not understood, the inhibiting action of excess iodide is only transient, disappearing after a few days even though high iodide levels are maintained.[65] Hence, enlargement of the thyroid is seldom seen after administration of iodide alone.

Thyroid-inhibiting drugs have been employed in attempts to measure the relative requirements for the thyroid hormone in varying physiologic conditions. If thyroxin is given along with the goitrogen, the thyroid will not enlarge; it is therefore inferred that no stimulus to the pituitary exists and that the exogenous thyroid hormone is supplying the needs of the animal. In rats given constant large amounts of thiouracil, Dempsey and Astwood[15] found that the amount of thyroxin necessary to prevent hypertrophy of the thyroid varied inversely with the environmental temperature to which the animals were exposed. At 25° C. the average requirement of thyroxin was 5.2 γ per day; at 35° C., 1.7 γ; and at 1° C., 9.5 γ. From these data it appears not only that the need for thyroxin is greater in the cold, but that normally cold must act as a stimulus to the pituitary to secrete thyrotrophin and so increase the supply of the hormone.

Control of Secretion of Thyrotrophic Hormone. As has long been known, the thyroid gland varies in size and in apparent activity in different circumstances. Exposure to cold for a period of time is a common stimulus to thyroid activity. The gland is enlarged at puberty, and it is at this time that simple goiter develops most frequently. Other evidence of regulation of thyroid function in accordance with "need" is seen in the enlargement of the thyroid which occurs in pregnancy and in the seasonal variations of thyroid activity in birds and other lower forms. Another very important factor affecting the thyroid gland is the supply of thyroid hormone: as indicated above, the gland is much enlarged when formation of its hormone is prevented, and it is restored to a normal size when the thyroid hormone is replaced. In all of these cases, changes in the secretion of thyrotrophic hormone must be the primary factor controlling the target organ.

The mechanism of regulation of TSH secretion has been investigated in much the same way as that of the control of the output of ACTH. Some years ago, Uotila[60] showed that section of the pituitary stalk prevented hypertrophy of the thyroid in animals exposed to cold. More recently it has been found by several investigators that lesions in certain areas of the hypothalamus will prevent enlargement of the thyroid in response to the administration of goitrogens.[22, 25] The site of lesions effective in this regard is in the anterior part of the median eminence and is distinct from those which affect adrenal and gonadal function. In an animal with an appropriate lesion of this type, the thyroid gland may appear relatively normal in size and in histologic appearance, but it is subnormal in function. The uptake of I^*, disappearance of I^* from the gland, and the T/S ratio are all depressed, and some signs of deficiency of thyroid hormone may be seen. Similarly, when the pituitary is transplanted elsewhere in the body thyroid function is still evident but is distinctly limited.[21] Apparently, then, the secretion of TSH may be to some degree autonomous; but for completely normal secretion under "basal" conditions, or particularly for increased activity in response to need, stimulation of the hypophysis through hypothalamic centers is required.

Since hypothalamic lesions prevent thyroid enlargement after goitrogens, it appears that the site of action of thyroid deficiency in augmenting TSH production must be either in the hypothalamus or somewhere "proximal" to this region. Of interest in this connection is the fact that some other substances in addition to thyroxin can inhibit the secretion of TSH. Dinitrophenol, a drug which raises the metabolic rate but does not otherwise duplicate the actions of the thyroxin, also prevents thyroid enlargement after goitrogens and may even produce a degree of atrophy of the intact thyroid.[26] Also, other means of elevating the body temperature, as by administration of pyrogenic materials or by application of external heat, have similar effects. It appears, then, that it is not the thyroid hormone itself which regulates the hypothalamic-hypophysial system, but rather some function of the metabolic rate. It is possible that other factors which influence TSH production, such as exposure to cold, may operate in part by the same mechanism.

REFERENCES

1. Astwood, E. B., Bissell, A. and Hughes, A. M. *Endocrinology*, 1945, *37*:456–481.
2. Astwood, E. B., Greer, M. A. and Ettlinger, M. G. *J. biol. Chem.*, 1949, *181*:121–130.
3. Astwood, E. B., Sullivan, J., Bissell, A. and Tyslowitz, R. *Endocrinology*, 1943, *32*:210–225.
4. Barker, S. B. *Physiol. Rev.*, 1951, *31*:205–243.
5. Barker, S. B. *Endocrinology*, 1956, *59*:548–554.
6. Barker, S. B. and Lipner, H. J. *Endocrinology*, 1949, *45*:485–490.
7. Blackburn, C. M., McConahey, W. M., Keating, F. R., Jr. and Albert, A. *J. clin. Invest.*, 1954, *33*:819–824.
8. Blackburn, C. M. and Power, M. H. *J. clin. Endocr.*, 1955, *15*:1379–1392.
9. Brewer, D. B. *J. Path. Bact.*, 1951, *63*:503–512.
10. Brush, B. E. and Altland, J. K. *J. clin. Endocr.*, 1952, *12*:1380–1388.
11. Byrom, F. B. *Clin. Sci.*, 1934, *1*:273–285.
12. Chaikoff, I. L. and Taurog, A. *Ann. N. Y. Acad. Sci.*, 1948, *50*:377–402.
13. Childs, D. S., Keating, F. R., Jr., Rall, J. E., Williams, M. M. D. and Power, M. H. *J. clin. Invest.*, 1950, *29*:726–738.
14. Contopoulos, A. N., Simpson, M. E. and Koneff, A. A. *Endocrinology*, 1958, *63*:642–653.
15. Dempsey, E. W. and Astwood, E. B. *Endocrinology*, 1943, *32*:509–518.
16. Dingledine, W. S., Pitt-Rivers, R., and Stanbury, J. B. *J. clin. Endocr.*, 1955, *15*:724–731.
17. Dobyns, B. M. *J. clin. Endocr.*, 1950, *10*:1202–1230.
18. Dobyns, B. M. and Steelman, S. L. *Endocrinology*, 1953, *52*:705–711.
19. Dvoskin, S. *Endocrinology*, 1947, *40*:334–351; *41*:331–333.
20. Eartly, H. and LeBlond, C. P. *Endocrinology*, 1954, *54*:249–271.
21. von Euler, C. and Holmgren, B. *J. Physiol.*, 1956, *131*:125–136; 137–146.
22. Florsheim, W. H. *Endocrinology*, 1958, *62*:783–789.
23. Freinkel, N., Ingbar, S. H. and Dowling, J. T. *J. clin. Invest.*, 1957, *36*:25–37.
24. Gabrilove, G. L. and Ludwig, A. W. *J. clin. Endocr.*, 1957, *17*:925–932.
25. Ganong, W. F., Frederickson, D. S. and Hume, D. M. *Endocrinology*, 1955, *57*:355–362.
26. Goldberg, R. C., Wolff, J. and Greep, R. O. *Endocrinology*, 1955, *56*:560–566; *ibid.*, *60*:38–52.
27. Greer, M. A. *Physiol. Rev.*, 1950, *30*:513–548.
28. Greer, M. A. and Astwood, E. B. *Endocrinology*, 1948, *43*:105–119.
29. Griesbach, W. E. and Purves, H. D. *Brit. J. exp. Path.*, 1943, *24*:174–184; *ibid.*, *26*:13–17.
30. Gross, J. and Pitt-Rivers, R. *Lancet*, 1951, *261*:766–767; *ibid.*, *262*:439–441.
31. Gross, J. and Pitt-Rivers, R. *Biochem. J.*, 1953, *53*:645–652; 652–657.
32. Gross, J. and Pitt-Rivers, R. *Recent Progr. Horm. Res.*, 1954, *10*:109–128.
33. Halmi, N. S. *Endocrinology*, 1950, *47*:289–299; *ibid.*, *50*:140–142.
34. Halmi, N. S. *Endocrinology*, 1954, *54*:97–103; 216–224.
35. Halmi, N. S., Spirtos, B. N., Bogdanove, E. M. and Lipner, H. J. *Endocrinology*, 1953, *52*:19–32.
36. Halmi, N. S., Stuelke, R. G. and Schnell, M. D. *Endocrinology*, 1956, *58*:634–650.
37. Hurxthal, L. M. and Musulin, N. *Amer. J. Med.*, 1946, *1*:56–80.
38. Kelsey, M. P., Haines, S. F. and Keating, F. R. *J. clin. Endocr.*, 1949, *9*:171–210.
39. Kendall, E. C. *Trans. Ass. Amer. Phycns*, 1915, *30*:420–449; *ibid.*, *31*:134–135.
40. Kydd, D. M., Man, E. B. and Peters, J. P. *J. clin. Invest.*, 1950, *29*:1033–1040.
41. Lambert, E. H., Underdahl, L. O., Beck-

ETT, S. and MEDEROS, L. O. *J. clin. Endocr.*, 1951, *11*:1186–1205.

42. LARDY, H. A., and MALEY, G. F. *Recent Progr. Horm. Res.*, 1954, *10*:129–155.

43. LEHNINGER, A. L. P. 217 in *Enzymes: Units of Biological Structure and Function*, GAEBLER, O. H., ed. Academic Press, New York, 1956.

44. MAN, E. B. and BONDY, P. K. *J. clin. Endocr.*, 1957, *17*:1373–1382.

45. MARINE, D. and KIMBALL, O. P. *Arch. intern. Med.*, 1920, *25*:661–672.

46. PITT-RIVERS, R. *Physiol. Rev.*, 1950, *30*:194–205.

47. PURVES, H. D. and GRIESBACH, W. E. *Endocrinology*, 1951, *49*:244–264; 427–428.

48. PURVES, H. D. and GRIESBACH, W. E. *J. Endocr.*, 1956, *13*:365–375.

49. RIGGS, D. S. *Pharmacol. Rev.*, 1952, *4*:284–370.

50. ROBBINS, J. and RALL, J. E. *Recent Progr. Horm. Res.*, 1957, *13*:161–208.

51. ROCHE, J. and MICHEL, R. *Physiol. Rev.*, 1955, *35*:583–610.

52. ROSENMAN, R. H., BYERS, S. O. and FRIEDMAN, M. *J. clin. Endocr.*, 1952, *12*:1287–1299.

53. SELENKOW, H. A. and ASPER, J. P., JR. *J. clin. Endocr.*, 1955, *15*:285–296.

54. SIMPSON, M. E., ASLING, C. W. and EVANS, H. M. *Yale J. Biol. Med.*, 1950, *23*:1–27.

55. STANLEY, M. M. *J. clin. Endocr.*, 1949, *9*:941–954.

56. STEWART, H. J., DEITRICK, J. E. and CRANE, N. F. *J. clin. Invest.*, 1938, *17*:237–248.

57. TAUROG, A. and CHAIKOFF, I. L. *J. biol. Chem.*, 1948, *176*:639–656.

58. TAUROG, A., CHAIKOFF, I. L. and FELLER, D. D. *J. biol. Chem.*, 1947, *171*:189–201.

59. TAUROG, A., TONG, W. and CHAIKOFF, I. L. *Endocrinology*, 1958, *62*:646–663; 664–676.

60. UOTILA, U. U. *Endocrinology*, 1939, *25*:605–614; *ibid.*, *26*:129–135.

61. VANDERLAAN, J. E. and VANDERLAAN, W. P. *Endocrinology*, 1947, *40*:403–416.

62. VANDERLAAN, W. P. and GREER, M. A. *Endocrinology*, 1950, *47*:36–47.

63. WOLFF, J. and CHAIKOFF, I. L. *Endocrinology*, 1948, *42*:468–471; *ibid.*, *43*:174–179.

64. WOLFF, J. and CHAIKOFF, I. L. *J. biol. Chem.*, 1948, *174*:555–564.

65. WOLFF, J., CHAIKOFF, I. L., GOLDBERG, R. C. and MEIER, J. R. *Endocrinology*, 1949, *45*:504–513.

66. WOLLMAN, S. H. *Amer. J. Physiol.*, 1956, *186*:453–459.

67. WYNGAARDEN, J. B., WRIGHT, B. M. and WAYS, P. *Endocrinology*, 1952, *50*:537–549.

CHAPTER 56

The Parathyroid Glands

By JANE A. RUSSELL

INTRODUCTION
HYPOPARATHYROIDISM
  Therapy in hypoparathyroidism

EFFECTS OF PARATHYROID HORMONE
REGULATION OF PARATHYROID ACTIVITY

THE parathyroid glands, which develop from the entoderm of the branchial clefts, are found as small paired bodies in the region of the thyroid gland. The number and position of these glands varies widely even between individuals of the same species. From one to four pairs (most commonly two) are seen. One pair, the superior or "internal" parathyroids, may be imbedded entirely in the thyroid; others, the inferior or "external" glands, are usually found near the dorsolateral surface of the thyroid, but accessory tissue may develop in widely scattered positions in the neck and upper thoracic region. The total weight of the parathyroid tissue in man is about 0.1 gram, and in the rat about 0.0003 gram. In histologic appearance, parathyroid tissue is somewhat like hyperplastic thyroid tissue, without colloid—a resemblance which led early investigators to consider the parathyroid to be accessory or embryonic thyroid tissue.

The external parathyroids were first described anatomically by Sandström in 1880, and then rediscovered by Gley in 1891. It had been noted earlier that removal of the thyroid gland from dogs or cats usually led to convulsive states and often death. Gley found that, although the removal alone of either the thyroid or the external parathyroid tissue had little effect, the removal of both (or complete thyroidectomy, as he called it) would induce tetany. Later, after the discovery of the internal parathyroid tissue, Vessale and Generali in 1896 showed that the nervous manifestations were in fact not the result of thyroid deficiency but could be induced by complete removal of the parathyroid glands alone. The first insight into the nature of the functional changes induced by parathyroidectomy was provided by MacCallum and Voegtlin in 1909,[18] when they showed that the tetany observed in this condition was associated with low levels of calcium in the blood, and that it could be relieved by giving calcium salts. A further relationship of the parathyroids to calcium metabolism was indicated when certain diseases of the bone were found to be associated with tumors of this organ. The endocrine nature of parathyroid function was established conclusively in 1925, when Collip prepared from parathyroid tissue potent extracts which not only would relieve the tetany of parathyroid deficiency but would raise the blood calcium in normal animals.[7, 8] Since that time, the hormone (commonly called *parathormone*) has been further purified and concentrated, but it has not yet been obtained in homogeneous form. Earlier thought to be a protein, it now appears to be a large polypeptide with a molecular weight of 5000 to 10,000.[22] Since it is destroyed by proteolytic enzymes in the digestive tract, the hormone must be given parenterally. Commercial preparations of parathormone available at present are quite crude and are not suitable for maintenance therapy, owing to the early development of resistance to their effects.

The hormone is assayed usually by its effects on the serum calcium concentration. The standard method is based on the increase in serum calcium induced in intact dogs over a period of a day or more, but a much more sensitive and precise procedure utilizes the prevention of the fall in serum calcium which follows within a few hours after parathyroidectomy in rats.[21] Diminution in the serum phosphate or increase in phosphate excretion can also be used in certain circumstances.[12, 15] Although it has been suggested that the hypercalcemic and phosphaturic principles might be separable,[21, 25] the best preparations of parathormone so far obtained have been reported to be equally effective in assays based on serum calcium or on serum phosphate.[22]

The principal actions of the parathyroid hormone concern the metabolism of calcium and phosphorus by the body. The phenomena attending deficiency or excess of the hormone may be better understood if it is recalled that calcium and phosphorus exist in the body mainly as the very insoluble calcium phosphate, and hence that only quite small amounts of either calcium or phosphate ions can be in solution in the blood or tissue fluids. Since the product of the concentrations of the ions is a constant, there is in pure solution a strict reciprocal relationship between them. In body fluids, because proteins and other salts are present, the solubility product is somewhat greater than in pure solution, and the relationship between the concentrations of calcium and phosphate ions is not so clear-cut. Nevertheless, changes in the concentrations of one of these ions are usually followed by inverse changes in the other, and deposition or solution of the salt in bone or other tissues must occur in response to these changes.

The total amounts of calcium and phosphate in the body are large, calcium constituting nearly 2 per cent of the weight of an animal and phosphates about 3 per cent. Nearly all of the calcium is in the bones, mainly as phosphate and carbonates, and the phosphorus, too, is found mainly in the skeleton; the concentrations of calcium and phosphorus in bone are about 10 and 5 per cent, respectively. The soft tissues, although they contain little calcium, contain fairly large amounts of phosphate (up to 0.3 per cent in muscle and nerve). Most of this is in the form of labile organic combinations, as nucleotides, phospholipids, phosphocreatine, and phosphorylated intermediates of carbohydrate metabolism. In the *plasma*, on the other hand, the concentrations of calcium and phosphate are very low. The calcium level is normally about 10 mg. per cent, of which about half is in a freely diffusible state, the rest bound to protein, and the level of inorganic phosphate is 4 to 6 mg. per cent. In comparison with the concentrations of calcium and phosphate ions in plasma, there is then in the body an enormous reserve of both substances from which the ions may be withdrawn (or to which they may return) as the plasma concentrations vary.

The amounts of calcium and phosphate which can be absorbed from the gastrointestinal tract are limited also by the solubility of the salts; the absorption of these substances is then influenced readily by the ratio of calcium and phosphate in the diet, as well as by other factors such as the amount of carbohydrate, vitamins, etc., present. Calcium is excreted for the most part through the gut, with only a fraction of the amount ingested appearing in the urine. The phosphates are excreted to a greater extent by the kidneys, where they play a major part in the maintenance of the acid-base balance of the body.

Hypoparathyroidism. When the parathyroid glands are removed, the severity of the symptoms which may develop varies widely with the species, with the age of the animal, and with the calcium and phosphate contents of the diet.[11, 12] The effects are more pronounced in carnivores, such as the dog and cat; this may result partially from dietary habit, rather than entirely from a difference in metabolism. Younger animals are much more susceptible to parathyroid deficiency than older ones, perhaps because the metabolism of calcium and phosphorus is so much more vigorous in young than in grown animals. In man, hypoparathyroidism occurs very rarely as a result of spontaneous defects, but is seen rather frequently after operative removal of the thyroid gland, when external parathyroid tissue must have been removed as well.

In hypoparathyroidism, the most prominent symptom is hyperirritability of the nervous system, with latent or frank tetany. Carpopedal spasm is an early indication of this state, as is also twitching of the face in response to tapping of the facial nerve (Chvostek's sign). The nervous symptoms tend to increase gradually in severity over periods of days or weeks, until, finally, generalized convulsions develop, with intermittent tonic spasms of all the muscles. Respiratory paralysis may then be fatal. In some species, acute convulsive seizures may occur only when induced by some sudden stimulus, or when the biochemical changes are aggravated by other factors, such as low calcium diets, pregnancy, fasting or alkalosis.

The nervous manifestations are the consequence of low levels of calcium ion in the plasma and tissue fluids. In acute tetany, the concentration of calcium in the serum is of the order of 5 to 7 mg. per cent total calcium (0 to 2 mg. per cent diffusible calcium); and all symptoms may be relieved by the administration of calcium ions. When the blood level of calcium is low, practically no calcium is excreted in the urine (Fig. 598),

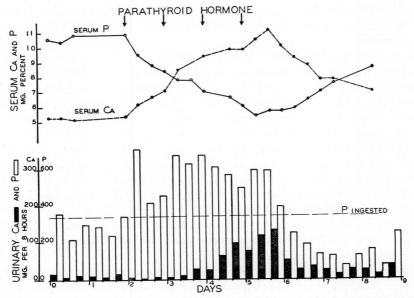

FIG. 598. Effects of parathyroid hormone (50 units per day) in patient with idiopathic hypoparathyroidism. Food constant in amount and composition was given during each 8 hour period. Note immediate increase in excretion of phosphate (negative balance) accompanied by reversals of the high serum phosphate and low serum calcium levels, and much later increase in urinary calcium (as serum calcium rose above 8 mg. per cent). (After Albright and Ellsworth, *J. clin. Invest.*, 1929, 7:183–202.)

so it is obvious that the hypocalcemia is not caused by loss of calcium by this route. When the serum calcium is low, the inorganic phosphate concentration tends to be high. However, urinary phosphate excretion is not increased, as might be expected, but instead it too is usually much diminished. There then tends to be a net retention of both calcium and phosphate in the body. Some of these salts may be excreted through the bowel, but much may be deposited in the bones if the calcium content of the diet is sufficiently high.

The cardinal biochemical changes observed in hypoparathyroidism are, then, low serum calcium levels, high serum phosphate concentrations, and diminished urinary excretion of both calcium and phosphate.[3] As pointed out below (p. 1131), it has been debated whether these changes are referable primarily to increased deposition of bone salts, or to diminution in the excretion of phosphate by the kidney. If the latter, the failure to excrete phosphate would lead to rising phosphate concentrations in the serum, a consequent fall in the serum calcium, and the deposition of calcium phosphate. The principal arguments for this view are based on the converse sequence of effects of administered parathyroid hormone. In disagreement with this concept, Munson[21] and others have found, after parathyroidectomy in rats, that the serum calcium falls to tetanic levels *before* any significant increase occurs in the serum phosphate. Some recent observations have been made on the effects of parathyroidectomy in nephrectomized rats in which the "excretion" of calcium and other ions was maintained by peritoneal lavage. When tracer amounts of isotopic calcium ions (Ca^{45}) were given to such animals, the removal of the parathyroid glands was followed quickly by reduction in the calcium content of the peritoneal fluid, but an increase in the specific activity of calcium. This means that after parathyroidectomy less calcium was released from unlabeled sources, presumably from the bones, than was the case in nephrectomized control animals.[10] These lines of evidence show that changes in phosphate excretion cannot be the primary event after removal of the parathyroid glands. On the other hand, in chronic parathyroid deficiency renal excretion of phosphate is low even when the serum phosphate is high. Hence, although alteration in renal function is not the initiating defect, it must contribute substantially to the biochemical changes which occur in the absence of parathyroid hormone.

Therapy in hypoparathyroidism. The symptoms of chronic hypoparathyroidism can be prevented to a considerable extent by adjustment of the calcium and phosphate contents of the diet.[23] In some species, as the rat, the simple expedient of allowing the animal to drink 1 per cent calcium gluconate or lactate instead of water will maintain the blood calcium at asymptomatic levels. A reduction of the phosphate content of the diet, as well as an increase in the calcium ingested, may be helpful also, and in mild degrees of parathyroid insufficiency in man, a high-calcium, low-phosphate diet may be adequate therapy. In these cases the extra calcium will be partly excreted through the bowel and partly deposited in the bones. On the other hand, low-calcium, high-phosphate diets will greatly aggravate the symptoms of hypoparathyroidism in all species, and the intravenous administration of neutral or alkaline phosphates will induce tetany in symptom-free animals.[11] It is apparent that although parathyroid function is most important in the maintenance of normal mineral metabolism, it is necessary for life and health only in a relative sense.

It has also been found possible to treat hypoparathyroidism successfully with another type of agent, vitamin D (D_2, calciferol) or a related substance, dihydrotachysterol (also known as A.T.10), which, like calciferol, is obtained by irradiation of ergosterol. Although the antitetanic (hypercalcemic) property of the tachysterol was for a time believed unique, it has been demonstrated several times that when calciferol is given in comparable quantities it also will elevate the calcium level of the blood. The amounts of vitamin D required to treat clinical hypoparathyroidism are far in excess of those needed to prevent or to treat rickets—5 to 10 mg. or 200,000 to 400,000 units per day, as compared with 1000 to 2000 units recommended in rickets or osteomalacia. From the high dosage required, and from the fact that dihydrotachysterol is not antirachitic but is at least as effective as calciferol in hypoparathyroidism, it may be concluded that vitamin D activity in the usual sense is not essential to the therapeutic effect in hypoparathyroidism. Albright *et al.*[2] reported that not only would large amounts of either vitamin D or A.T.10 increase the absorption of calcium from the gastrointestinal tract, but that, in addition, each was able to increase the excretion of phosphate in the urine. The effect of A.T.10 on phosphate excretion is said to be more marked than is that of vitamin D. These actions resemble the toxic manifestations of overdosage with vitamin D, when solution of bone from the shafts is seen, accompanied by negative calcium and phosphorus balances.[23] Both calciferol and dihydrotachysterol are much slower in affecting the serum and urinary phosphate than is parathyroid hormone; the maximum effect on continued dosage is seen in about ten days with calciferol and in three to five days with A.T.10, and after cessation of treatment their actions appear to continue for similar lengths of time. Despite the fact that the pharmacologic actions of vitamin D and its relatives may be employed successfully in the treatment of hypoparathyroidism, no direct physiologic connection between these substances and the parathyroid gland is known. Parathyroid hormone is without effect in Vitamin D deficency.

Effects of Parathyroid Hormone. As illustrated in Figure 598, the acute administration of parathyroid extract evokes biochemical changes which are the converse of those seen in parathyroid deficiency. The first effect is an abrupt and marked increase in the rate of phosphate excretion; this may be observed within an hour of the administration of the hormone.[1] Following closely on this phenomenon the serum phosphate starts to fall. The blood calcium begins to rise somewhat more slowly, reaching a maximum in 12 to 18 hours when a single dose is given. The urinary calcium is also increased, but not until a much later time; in the hypoparathyroid patient depicted in Figure 598, whose serum calcium was very slow to start with, calcium excretion did not begin until the serum calcium had reached a level of about 8 mg. per cent.

From the time relationships of these phenomena, Albright et al.[1, 4] suggested that the primary effect of parathyroid hormone is to increase the excretion of phosphate and that the fall in serum inorganic phosphate and the increase in serum calcium and its excretion are secondary consequences of this effect. More recent work leaves little doubt that parathyroid extract has a specific effect upon the excretion of phosphate. The maximum reabsorption of phosphate by the renal tubules is diminished by the hormone,[5, 9, 14, 16, 17] and on the administration of radioactive phosphate, the proportion of the labeled group excreted in the urine is very much increased.[29, 30] In man, the presence of parathyroid adenomata has been associated with defective phosphate resorption (increased clearance), and the removal of the tumors has been associated with reduction in the phosphate clearance toward normal and considerable elevation of the maximal resorption rate.[24]

Acute overdosage with the hormone by repeated administration over a day or so not only raises the serum calcium to great heights, but may bring about a shocklike state.[7, 8] This effect is believed to stem in part from the phosphaturia mentioned above, for large amounts of water and salts are carried with the phosphate. The blood volume falls, blood pressure is reduced, kidney failure ensues, and death may occur from circulatory collapse. These phenomena can be reproduced exactly by the administration of excessive amounts of calcium salts.

On the continued administration of the hormone (in less massive doses but over longer periods), a net negative balance of calcium and phosphate develops; obviously the calcium and phosphate lost must come from the bones. The chronic effects of hyperparathyroidism are evidenced in the form of depletion of minerals of the bone, an increase in the apparent activity of the osteoclasts, the formation of fibrous cysts in the skeletal tissue, and spontaneous fractures and bending of the long bones.* The serum phosphatase is increased in this condition. The high level of calcium in the body fluids may lead to the formation of kidney stones and the metastatic calcification of other soft tissues; this is a common early sign of hyperparathyroidism in man.[4, 19]

The increased osteoclastic activity and demineralization in the skeleton accompanying hyperparathyroidism led originally to the conclusion that the parathyroid hormone was concerned primarily with the metabolism of bone. More recently, it has been debated whether this is the case, or, as indicated above, whether the changes seen in bone may be secondary to the loss of minerals resulting from continued phosphaturia.[12] In order

---

* Hyperparathyroidism leading to a similar condition in man (usually the result of a secreting parathyroid adenoma) is known as osteitis fibrosa cystica or von Recklinghausen's disease.

to decide this point, many attempts have been made to find out whether administered parathyroid hormone can act in the absence of the kidneys. These experiments are complicated because when the kidneys are removed the blood phosphate rises continuously, hyperplasia of the parathyroids may be induced, and histologic changes resembling those of hyperparathyroidism may sometimes be seen in the bones. Most investigators are agreed that parathyroid extracts do not elevate the serum calcium in the absence of the kidneys; but this would not be expected in the face of the rising serum phosphate concentrations. On the other hand, the serum calcium falls in nephrectomized-parathyroidectomized animals as it does in those from which only the parathyroid glands have been removed. Furthermore, the development of hypocalcemia under these conditions may be prevented or diminished by the administration of parathyroid extract.[13, 20, 26, 28] Similarly, when the serum calcium is reduced by oxalate injections, recovery is very slow in the absence of the parathyroids but may be hastened by treatment with extract; these phenomena, too, may be observed in nephrectomized animals.[25]

Finally, Grollman[13] has shown that if the serum phosphate of nephrectomized dogs is maintained at near normal levels by peritoneal lavage, parathormone elicits the usual hypercalcemia. These observations leave no doubt that either endogenous or exogenous parathormone can regulate the serum calcium level in the absence of the kidneys. It thus appears that the hormone has more than one site of action in respect to calcium metabolism: that on the resorption of phosphate by the kidney, which affects the serum calcium indirectly, and one which allows the mobilization of calcium by extrarenal mechanisms, presumably by solution from bone. The relative importance of these two processes, as well as their intimate mechanisms, remain to be determined.

Regulation of Parathyroid Activity. Since the parathyroid glands exhibit a relative degree of hyperplasia in various physiologic and pathologic states, attempts have been made to demonstrate the nature of systems which may regulate the activity of this organ. At present, nervous control of any sort seems minimal, and there is no convincing evidence for a postulated parathyrotrophic hormone from the pituitary gland. The principal regulatory factor governing the secretion of the parathyroid glands has appeared to be the calcium level of the blood. A variety of conditions having in common a tendency to lower the serum calcium levels have also been shown to induce some degree of hyperplasia of the parathyroid glands. These conditions include low calcium diets, lack of vitamin D (rickets), pregnancy, parenteral administration of phosphates or of oxalates or other substances which form insoluble salts with calcium, or kidney diseases in which phosphate is retained. So-called renal rickets (bone changes seen in chronic kidney disease) may be difficult to distinguish from primary hyperparathyroidism on this account.

A more detailed study of the relationships of the calcium and phosphate of the diet to the serum calcium level and to the size of the parathyroid glands in rats is illustrated in Figure 599. As first shown by Stoerk and Carnes,[27] it is the ratio of calcium to phosphorus in the diet which is important in this connection rather than the absolute level of either: a wide range of concentrations in the diet was employed, but as long as the ratios were within the usual limits (0.8 to 2) the serum calcium and the volume of parathyroid tissue were unaffected. A low proportion of calcium with normal phosphorus in the diet led to low serum concentrations of calcium and hyperplasia of the gland, whereas the feeding of little phosphorus with normal amounts of calcium allowed high calcium concentrations and a relative involution of the parathyroid tissue. The level of blood inorganic phosphate in these experiments was rather variable and not so closely related to the diet or to the size of the parathyroids as was the serum calcium, so that the serum phosphate was thought not to be the controlling factor. In further observations of similar nature, Crawford et al. found that, although normal rats showed little change in serum

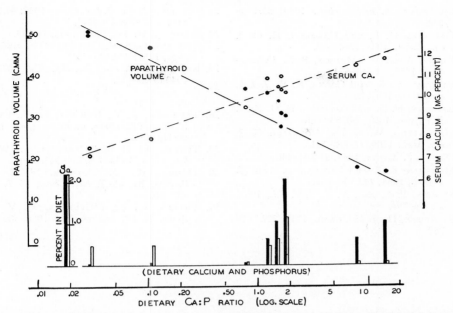

FIG. 599. Relationship of dietary calcium and phosphate to size of parathyroid glands and to serum calcium in rats. (Data from groups of 5 to 10 animals maintained on experimental diets for 4 weeks.) Inverse relationship between serum calcium and size of parathyroids probably indicates increased activity of gland in response to need for maintenance of serum calcium level. This need appears to be conditioned primarily by the ratio of calcium to phosphate in the diet, rather than to the absolute amounts of either substance. (After Stoerk and Carnes, *J. Nutr.*, 1945, *29:*43–50.)

phosphate when the phosphate intake was much increased (decreased Ca:P ratio), parathyroidectomized rats were unable to prevent elevation of the serum phosphate in these conditions and died in hypocalcemia. From this and from correlated changes in tubular reabsorption of phosphate, it was concluded that the parathyroid secretion was increased in response to the increase in phosphate intake or in serum phosphate.[9] Since the serum calcium level would have been expected to vary inversely with that of phosphate, however, it is still not possible to say whether the calcium or phosphate ion concentration may be the more important factor affecting secretory activity of the parathyroids. The hypertrophy of the parathyroid tissue in response to low-calcium diets and the maintenance of normal calcium and phosphate levels in the serum in the face of this restriction are not dependent on the presence of the anterior pituitary.[6] An independent homeostatic relationship between the levels of calcium and phosphate in the blood and the activity of the parathyroid glands is clearly indicated.

REFERENCES

1. ALBRIGHT, F., BAUER, W., ROPES, M. and AUB, J. C. *J. clin. Invest.*, 1929, 7:139–179.
2. ALBRIGHT, F., BLOOMBERG, E., DRAKE, T. and SULKOWITCH, H. W. *J. clin. Invest.*, 1938, 17:317–329.
3. ALBRIGHT, F. and ELLSWORTH, R. *J. clin. Invest.*, 1929, 7:183–202.
4. ALBRIGHT, F. and REIFENSTEIN, E. C., JR. *The parathyroid glands and metabolic bone disease.* Baltimore, Williams & Wilkins, 1948.
5. BARTTER, F. C. *J. clin. Endocr.*, 1954, 14:826.
6. CARNES, W. H., OSEBOLD, J. and STOERK, H. C. *Amer. J. Physiol.*, 1943, 139:188–192.
7. COLLIP, J. B. *J. biol. Chem.*, 1925, 63:395–438.
8. COLLIP, J. B., CLARKE, E. P. and SCOTT, J. W. *J. biol. Chem.*, 1925, 63:439–460.
9. CRAWFORD, J. D., OSBORNE, M. M., JR., TALBOT, N. B., TERRY, M. L. and MORRILL, M. F. *J. clin. Invest.*, 1950, 29:1448–1461.
10. ELLIOTT, J. R. and TALMADGE, R. V. *Endocrinology*, 1958, 62:709–716.
11. GREEP, R. O. *The hormones*, 1948, 1:255–300.
12. GREEP, R. O. and KENNY, A. D. *The hormones*, 1955, 3:153–174.

13. GROLLMAN, A. *Endocrinology*, 1954, *55*:166–172.
14. HARRISON, H. E. and HARRISON, H. C. *J. clin. Invest.*, 1941, *20*:47–55.
15. KENNY, A. D. and MUNSON, P. L. *Endocrinology*, 1959, *64*:513–521.
16. KLEEMAN, C. R. and COOKE, R. E. *J. Lab. clin. Med.*, 1951, *38*:112–127.
17. LEVINSKY, N. G. and DAVIDSON, D. G. *Amer. J. Physiol.*, 1957, *191*:530–536.
18. MACCALLUM, W. G. and VOEGTLIN, C. *J. exp. Med.*, 1909, *11*:118–151.
19. MANDL, F. *Surgery*, 1947, *21*:394–440.
20. MONAHAN, E. P. and FREEMAN, S. *Amer. J. Physiol.*, 1944, *142*:104–106.
21. MUNSON, P. L. *Ann. N. Y. Acad. Sci.*, 1955, *60*:776–794.
22. RASMUSSEN, H. *J. biol. Chem.*, 1957, *229*:781–787.
23. SHELLING, D. H. *J. biol. Chem.*, 1932, *96*:195–214; 215–228; 229–243.
24. SIROTA, J. H. *Fed. Proc.*, 1953, *12*:133.
25. STEWART, G. S. and BOWEN, H. F. *Endocrinology*, 1951, *48*:568–575.
26. STOERK, H. C. *Proc. Soc. exp. Biol.* (*N. Y.*), 1943, *54*:50–53.
27. STOERK, H. C. and CARNES, W. C. *J. Nutr.*, 1945, *29*:43–50.
28. TALMADGE, R. V., KRAINTZ, F. W., FROST, R. C. and KRAINTZ, L. *Endocrinology*, 1953, *52*:318–323.
29. TWEEDY, W. R. and CAMPBELL, W. W. *J. biol. Chem.*, 1944, *154*:339–347.
30. TWEEDY, W. R., CHILCOTE, M. E. and PATRAS, M. C. *J. biol. Chem.*, 1947, *168*:597–610.
31. TWEEDY, W. R., L'HEUREUX, M. V. and ZORN, E. M. *Endocrinology*, 1950, *47*:219–227.

Reproduction

CHAPTER 57

Physiology of Reproduction in the Female

By THOMAS R. FORBES

INTRODUCTION

The most characteristic feature differentiating the animate from the inanimate is the capacity of the former to reproduce itself. It might be considered that all life is directed toward the maintenance of the species and therefore that all vital processes constitute essential phases in the physiology of reproduction. Such a broad aspect of reproduction will not be considered here. However, since reproduction is a fundamental phenomenon, it is at times difficult to distinguish sharply between those physiologic processes directly concerned with reproduction and those indirectly concerned.

Most physiologic processes form complete units within one living body; integrating or coordinating mechanisms do not have to span the space between two organisms. Reproduction in higher animals, however, requires a physiologic adjustment between two separate units. The maintenance of the species is not entrusted to one individual; the contributions of two are essential. Also, the immature organism of mammalian complexity cannot instantaneously adapt itself to an independent existence. After the period of intrauterine residence of the developing embryo and fetus, provision must be made for its extrauterine life, again a process demanding a physiologic coordination between two organisms.

With reproduction, sex must also be considered, and yet "there is no such biologic entity as sex." By "sex," reference is made to the total morphologic and functional difference within the species that can be associated with the production of either sperm or ova. It is impossible to define sex without allusion to sexes, without comparing or contrasting morphologic differences in the gametes, the somatic proportions or modifications of the body, or even in temperament or psychologic qualities.

The early studies on reproduction were concerned mainly with the elucidation to the morphologic differences or homologies of the male and female. After discovery of the microscope and its application to biologic material, attention was directed to studies of sperm, and finally, in 1827, the first mammalian ova were described. Later studies were concerned with the cytologic aspect of the marriage of the sperm and the ovum to produce a single cell capable of multiplication and differentiation and finally of becoming another individual of the species. At the same time the somatic differentiation of the developing organism was studied, and, in the maturing body, a sequence of morphologic alterations was associated with the production of new generations of gametes and with the protection and nourishment of the fertilized ovum, embryo, fetus, and newborn animal or infant.

In 1672, a young Dutch physician, Regnier de Graaf, first described the ovarian follicle (Graafian follicle). He, however, mistook the follicles for eggs, undoubtedly influenced by observations on the ovaries of birds. He considered that "all men and animals take their origin from an egg—existing before coitus in the female testicles." * The ova were not discovered until 1827, when Karl Ernst von Baer first observed the barely macroscopic globules in the ovarian follicles of a dog. Although sperm are much smaller than ova, their discovery followed that of the large Graafian follicles by only a few years, probably because the independent existence of sperm in a fluid medium facilitated their microscopic observation. Antony von Leeuwenhoek first illustrated mammalian sperm in 1678.

The nervous system was first studied in great detail as a system facilitating internal coordination of body function. Early observations indicated, however, that some other mechanisms regulate at least certain aspects of reproductive phenomena. The relation of the gonads to certain sexual manifestations was known from ancient times. After the postulation of internal secretions or hormones as regulators of body functions it was assumed that the gonads might function also as endocrine glands. Experiments involving gonadal ablation and transplantation confirmed these assumptions. Subsequently extracts of the gonads, and finally chemical substances isolated from the gonads, were found to be active in substituting for some gonadal functions. Almost simultaneously, the pituitary gland was shown to regulate the functions of the gonads, and, more recently, the function of the mammary glands. Many specific hormones, several of which have been isolated as chemical entities, enter into the physiologic aspects of reproduction. Even so, the mechanisms regulating some aspects of the phenomena are not yet known, and the probable interrelations of the known hormones are understood incompletely.

THE OVARY AND ITS HORMONES

During the period of active sexual life, the ovaries undergo profound rhythmic, structural and functional changes which are associated with modifications in the structure and function of other tissues, glands or organs, and even in the behavioral characteristics of the mammalian organism. The maturation of the ova in mammals is not a continuous process but an interrupted one: one follicle or group of follicles in the adult ovary grows, matures and ovulates at one time, and others do so at more or less regular, successive intervals. The intervals determined by the cyclic ovarian changes are designated *estrous cycles* in the many nonprimate mammalian species and *menstrual cycles* in man and other primates. These two cycles are similar in that they both reflect the activity of the ovaries, but they are quite different in detail.

The term *estrus* (*oestrus* is preferred by the British) was first used by Walter Heape in 1901 to denote the periods of sexual excitement or "heat" occurring in many animals. (The adjectival form is *estrous*.) Animals of many species have periods of sexual activity restricted to but a few weeks or months during one or two seasons of the year, and are known as seasonal breeders. In some of these species the females are continually receptive to the male ("in estrus") for a period of weeks or months provided copulation does not occur. Other species show a series of estrous cycles, and in the absence of copulation eventually become anestrous at the beginning of the nonbreeding season.

* For an excellent account of de Graaf's studies, with full bibliographic description of his works and translations of the more important passages, see Catchpole, H. R., *Bull. Hist. Med.*, 1940, 8:1261–1300.

Evidence of ovarian endocrine function was first obtained by observations on animals after ovariectomy. The genital tissues retained their infantile characteristics if the animals were young when ovariectomized, or the uteri, mammary glands and vaginal mucosa atrophied if sexually mature animals were ovariectomized. Successful transplants or grafts of ovaries made at various sites largely restored the atrophic genital tissues. *

The early experiments did not clearly reveal whether the follicles or the corpora lutea that formed after ovulation were the source of the endocrine secretion. Histologic examination of the ovarian tissues indicated that the corpora lutea were more obviously glandular than the granulosa cells and surrounding theca of the follicles. In rabbits the corpora lutea were first noted to be essential for the growth of the endometria to a condition permitting implantation of fertilized ova. Pregnancy terminated in rabbits and in animals of several other species when the corpora lutea were removed.[16]

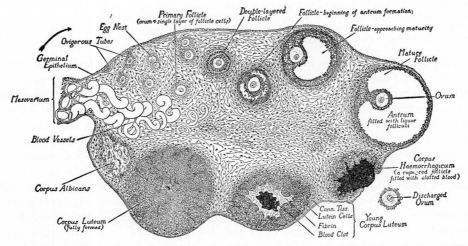

FIG. 600. Schematic diagram of mammalian ovary showing sequence of events in origin, growth and rupture of ovarian follicle and formation and retrogression of a corpus luteum. (By permission from *Embryology of the pig*, 2nd ed., by Patten. Copyright 1944. McGraw-Hill Book Co., Inc.)

The ovary is surrounded, except at the hilus, by a layer of cuboidal epithelial cells which constitute the germinal epithelium (Fig. 600). In some species new ova may arise from this layer and migrate into the ovary even during adult life, but it is doubtful if new ova arise after birth in man. The ovaries at birth contain several hundred thousand ova—a number which progressively diminishes throughout life. The ova develop within follicles which have an inner layer or layers of granulosa cells and outer layers of cells contributed by the ovarian stroma, the theca. A mature follicle contains a cavity filled with liquor folliculi, surrounded by a syncytial mass of granulosa cells. In one clump of these cells, the cumulus oophorus, the ovum is embedded. Surrounding the basement membrane upon which the outermost granulosa cells rest are two layers of ovarian stroma forming a vascular theca interna, which may contain cells with cytoplasmic secretory granules, and a more fibrous theca externa. At ovulation the mature ovum (in man about 120 μ in diameter) escapes. The granulosa cells transform into the luteal cells of a corpus luteum. The vascular ovarian stroma consists of fibroblast-like cells in animals of most species. The stromal cells, however, change in appearance under some conditions.

Most of the ova do not attain maturity. During an average human life span only 400 to 450 may be released. The remainder and by far the greater number of the ova and their follicles regress at different stages in their development.

The endocrine function of the testis was first made clear in 1849 by Arnold Berthold. He was so impressed by the secondary sexual characters of cockerels that he used them in his experiments. Cas-

* Successful transplantations of gonads in mammals have been made from the normal to an abnormal site in one individual (autotransplantation), or from one individual to a closely related individual within the same species (homotransplantation). Grafts of ovaries of one species into another (heterotransplantation) or even between unrelated animals of the same species are seldom if ever successful. Grafts of gonads can be most successfully made in gonadectomized hosts, an observation that at one time led investigators to assume a gonadal antagonism or a competition between the intact and transplanted gonads for some vital substance, designated X-substance by Heape.

trated cockerels (capons) acquired a normal cock's appearance and attitude when testes were transplanted into their abdominal cavities. Although Leydig (1857) described the glandular interstitial cells, now called Leydig cells, in the intertubular areas of the testis, they have only recently been shown to be the source of male hormones. The endocrine activity of the ovaries was first shown convincingly when Emil Knauer (1896) noted that autotransplantation of ovaries prevented the atrophy of the uterus subsequent to ovariectomy and that neural connections between the uteri and ovaries, if they did exist, were not essential.

In 1917, Stockard and Papanicolaou discovered that the types of cells obtained in smears of the vaginal epithelia of guinea pigs could be correlated with the development of follicles in the ovary. When large follicles formed and ovulated, the epithelial cells were cornified. Similarly, in rats and mice the vaginal mucosa cast off cornified epithelial cells which were detectable in smears at those times during the cycle when large or ovulating follicles were present. The morphologic changes in the vaginal smear indicative of estrus appeared in some animals in which ovulation and the formation of corpora lutea did not occur, indicating that the follicles alone could elicit cyclic activity. Liquor folliculi from large follicles or lipoid-soluble extracts of this liquor contained a substance which would induce vaginal cornification in castrated mice, i.e., which would replace the endocrine function of the ovaries with their large follicles. Allen and Doisy,[3] who in 1923 first demonstrated the active substance in cell-free preparations, called it the ovarian follicular hormone or the primary ovarian hormone. Although the granulosa cells were first thought to secrete follicular hormone, later histologic and histochemical studies indicate that the theca interna is probably its source.[20]

The "primary ovarian hormone" was detected also in corpora lutea, blood, other body tissues and urine; in fact, the urine of pregnant women contains large amounts of the estrogenic substance. Two active chemical compounds were identified in pregnancy urines, one called *estrone* and one called *estriol*. Later a third and very active chemical was extracted from pigs' ovaries and was identified as a partially reduced derivative of estrone called *estradiol*. All these compounds produce vaginal cornification and other changes in the genital tissues.[22] Collectively they are called *estrogens* (adjective, *estrogenic*). Estrogens are produced also by the testes of stallions, by adrenal glands and by placentae.[21]

A number of synthetic chemicals which do not possess a cyclopentenophenanthrene nucleus also possess estrogenic activity. The most active of these compounds, 4,4'-dihydroxy-α, β-diethylstilbene, or, as it is commonly called, *stilbestrol*, is almost five times as active as estrone.[21] Many combinations of alkyl groups have been substituted for the ethyl groups. During absorption by the gastrointestinal tract, stilbestrol is less readily destroyed than the normally occurring estrogens, and hence is more suitable for oral administration.

Estrogen is assayed biologically in castrated rats or mice by determining the minimal amount required to produce vaginal cornification from 48 to 56 hours after the first of a series of injections. The International Unit (I.U.) is 0.1 μg. of estrone, or approximately one Mouse Unit (M.U.). In other biologic tests now available for detecting much smaller amounts of hormone, the response to local application of the hormone in the rat's vagina or the immature rat's uterus is determined. Physicochemical methods are also available for the estimation of the estrogens.

The corpora lutea which develop from the ruptured follicles were first associated with uterine changes which facilitate implantation of the ovum, with mammary development, and with the maintenance of pregnancy. It was not until 1929 that Corner and Allen obtained extracts of corpora lutea which would maintain pregnancy in ovariectomized rabbits and induce an endometrium suitable for implantation of a fertilized ovum. The active chemical isolated from these extracts was called *progesterone*. It has also been found in human adrenal cortex, placenta, fat and blood, and in animal tissues. Several apparent metabolites of progesterone are known. Two which are biologically active are Δ^4-3-ketopregnene-20α-ol and Δ^4-3-ketopregnene-20β-ol; these differ from progesterone only in that a hydroxy group replaces the ketone group at the C-20 position. Inactive, closely related compounds isolated from the urine of pregnant women include preg-

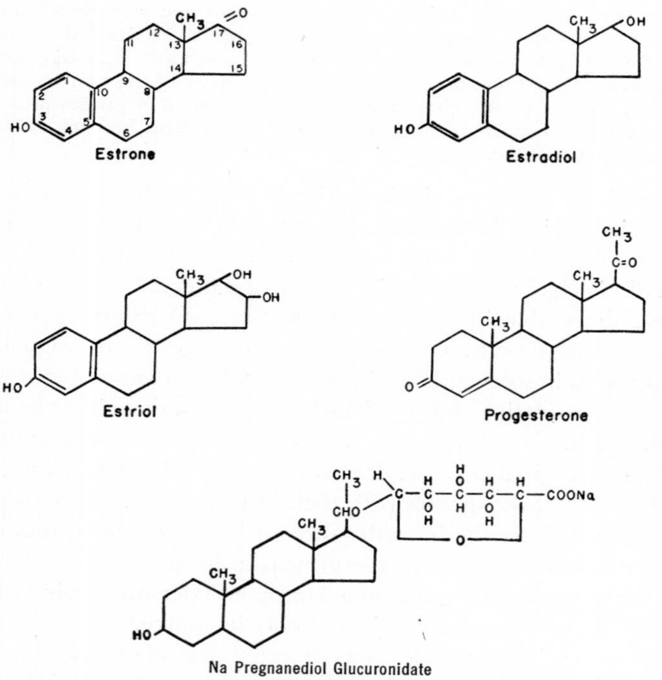

FIG. 601. Structural formulae of three normally occurring estrogens, of progesterone and of sodium pregnanediol glucuronidate.

nanolone, pregnanediol (excreted as sodium pregnanediol glucuronidate; see Fig. 601), pregnanetriol, etc. Progestationally active compounds are called *progestins*.

Progestins may be determined biologically by their capacity to induce formation of a progestational endometrium in young adult rabbits. One mg. of progesterone, for example, equals 1 International Unit (I.U.), the amount of hormone which, when injected during a period of five days, will elicit a well developed progestational reaction by the sixth day (a Corner-Allen unit). Much smaller amounts are effective when applied directly to the endometrium. Solutions containing as little as 0.25 μg. progesterone per 1 ml. will induce a positive response if 0.00075 ml. is injected directly into a ligated segment of the uterus of an ovariectomized mouse of the CHI strain.[46] Biologic tests assay progestins collectively. Physicochemical techniques assay each progestin separately.

THE MENSTRUAL CYCLE

A menstrual cycle is the interval which in the normal nonpregnant primate extends from the onset of one period of uterine bleeding to the onset of the following period. The most frequent length of the cycle in women is 28 days, although it may range from 20 days to about 35 days in apparently normal individuals and even in the same individual.[37] It has been well stated that the one regularity of the menstrual cycle is its irregularity. This variability is not unexpected since so many factors influence the cycle.

The menstrual cycle is divided into several phases, determined largely by the histology of the endometrium (Fig. 602). The first part of the cycle, the period of *menstruation*, or the *menses*, most frequently lasts five days, although again the length of the period may vary. During menstruation hemorrhage occurs in the endometrial stroma, which degenerates and, together with the unclotted interstitial blood, is sloughed into the uterine lumen to attain exit through the vagina as the menstrual discharge. The second period of the cycle is called the *preovulatory stage* (proliferative stage) and lasts for approximately seven to ten days.[4] Epithelium grows out from the remnants of glands in the lamina basalis to repair the uterine mucosa, and the entire endometrium increases in thickness. The straight uterine glands which develop at this time are lined by columnar epithelium. The third period of the cycle is called the *progestational stage* (secretory stage). This period extends over approximately the last 12 to 24 days of the cycle. The endometrium during this period is modified progressively until the stroma becomes loose and edematous and the actively secreting glands become extremely folded and tortuous. Such an endometrium is ready for the implantation of a fertilized ovum. If a fertile ovum is not available, however, the uterine mucosa again degenerates. The changes in the developing endometrial structure are not rapid; they blend into one another. Actually, different areas of the uterine lining of the same individual may be at different stages at any one time.[9]

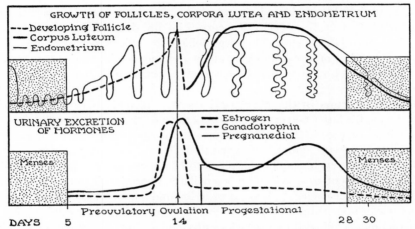

FIG. 602. Diagrammatic presentation of increased thickness of endometrium and changes in shape of endometrial glands in relation to size of ovarian follicles and corpora lutea and urinary excretion of sex hormones and gonadotrophins during a menstrual cycle.

The first menstrual period at puberty is called the *menarche*. The absence of menses subsequent to menarche is designated as *amenorrhea*. Certain premonitory symptoms frequently precede the onset of menstruation, such as pains in the back or head or a general feeling of discomfort. When these symptoms are unusually painful and protracted, the condition is called *dysmenorrhea*. Approximately 35 ml. of blood is usually lost during menses, although the amount may range from 10 to 200 ml. The discharged blood characteristically does not clot during normal menses.

Some authors include two other stages: a stage of repair following menstruation and an "interval" stage during the middle of the cycle. These stages are not included in the preceding classification because the period of repair occurs during menstruation as well as subsequent to it. The "interval" implies a period of rest or absence of change which does not necessarily exist. It should be remembered that, although the existence of definite stages is implied, the endometrial changes are progressive rather than steplike. A progestational or secretory stage does not appear in those cycles in which ovulation does not take place. In such cycles the term "premenstrual" phase would be more satisfactory. The morphologic condition of the endometrium at different stages of ovarian development was first associated and described by Hitschmann and Adler.[45]

Relation Between the Ovaries and the Menstrual Cycle. Just before the onset of menstruation the corpus luteum begins to regress. The secretion of progesterone by the corpus luteum sharply diminishes or stops. The endometrium which developed under the influence of this hormone cannot be maintained. The resulting rapid endometrial degeneration is accompanied by sloughing and hemorrhage. During and after menstruation one or more follicles of moderate size begin to grow more rapidly than other similar follicles. As the rapidly growing follicles attain large sizes, the endometrium increases in thickness. By approximately the midpoint of the menstrual cycle one follicle attains maturity and ovulates. The other larger follicles usually regress—become *atretic*. After ovulation the follicle collapses; the granulosa cells are transformed into luteal cells and become well vascularized to form a corpus luteum. During this period the progestational endometrium develops under the influence of the hormones produced by the corpus luteum.[45]

The preovulatory type of endometrium is attained during the period of follicular growth and the progestational type during the period of luteal development. The rhythmicity of the uterus is maintained by the rhythmic changes in the ovaries. During some cycles ovulation may not occur and corpora lutea may fail to form.[67] Such a cycle would be sterile and might be considered abnormal. An *anovulatory* cycle is superficially indistinguishable from an *ovulatory* cycle. If a corpus luteum does not form, a progestational endometrium does not develop. The large follicle or follicles persist about two weeks beyond the usual time of ovulation and, as they undergo atresia, uterine hemorrhage and slough occur. In such circumstances menstruation occurs from a preovulatory type of endometrium.

Endocrine Factors in the Menstrual Cycle. Women, when ovariectomized at any time during the latter two or three weeks of the menstrual cycle, usually show uterine bleeding within two to six days after the operation. Also, menstruation usually follows section or damage to the spinal cord when these lesions occur during the latter part of the cycle. The entire cycle may be shortened to 12 days or more in such cases. Monkeys menstruate subsequent to ovariectomy even if the operation is performed as early as the seventh day of the cycle.[2, 80] Also, (i) experimental section of the ventral roots of the lower thoracic or upper lumbar spinal nerves, (ii) hemisection of the cord, or (iii) section of the splanchnics is followed by precocious uterine bleeding. Subsequent cycles in these animals occur at intervals similar to those observed preoperatively, an indication that the neural lesions probably produce only transitory trophic deficiencies in the ovaries, deficiencies which are reflected by uterine regression and bleeding.

Estrogens administered to ovariectomized primates in adequate amounts for 10 days or more induce endometrial hypertrophy; if the stimulus is adequate, a preovulatory or proliferative type of endometrium develops.[4] Uterine bleeding occurs within 6 to 10 days after the discontinuance of the injections, the so-called *estrogen-withdrawal bleeding* or menstruation from a proliferative endometrium (Fig. 603). If estrogens are given daily in large amounts, menstruation may be prevented for very long periods; if the dosage is small, periodic bleeding may occur in spite of continuous treatment, the uterus periodically becoming refractory to the levels of hormone administered.

When estrogens are given to intact monkeys or women, menstruation is inhibited if the administration is started during the first part of the cycle but not if it is started during the latter part of the cycle. Approximately two days after the removal of a functional corpus luteum, menstruation occurs and cannot be prevented even if estrogens are injected.[85] The simultaneous administration of estrogen and progesterone induces a progestational (secretory, or premenstrual) endometrium which bleeds within two to three days if injections of both hormones are discontinued or if progesterone alone is withheld, demonstrating again that estrogens will not prevent bleeding from a progestational endometrium that develops in the normal cycle or is induced experimentally (see Fig. 603).

Menstruation cannot be considered to be an actively induced process.[17] It occurs upon cessation of stimulation of the endometrium, and from either a preovulatory or a progestational endometrium; it accompanies uterine involution or regression. Although the uteri of all mammals regress cyclically, marked hemorrhage or menstruation is limited to the noncornuate uteri of primates.

The factors associated with menstruation have been studied in great detail in monkeys by direct observation of the uterine mucosa subsequent to transplantation into the anterior chamber of the eye.[51] The endometrial transplants undergo cyclic changes similar to those of the intact uteri. One to five days before the onset of bleeding, the endometrial circulation is impaired, apparently by an unusual resistance to flow through the coiled arteries in the deeper layers of the endometrium. During this period, the endometrium regresses and becomes thinner. Four to 24 hours before menstruation the coiled arteries constrict for periods of several hours, further reducing the blood supply to the peripheral tissues. At intervals, first one and then another artery dilates, and hemorrhage occurs from the distal arterioles or capillaries into the superficial parts of

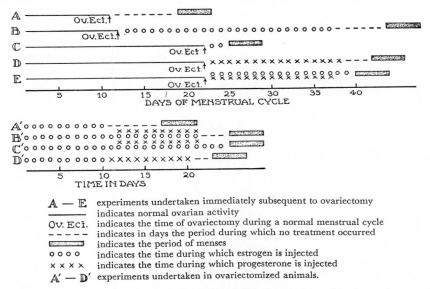

FIG. 603. Diagram of experimental procedures undertaken on women or female monkeys to elucidate the problem of menstruation

the endometrium, forming small hematomas. After a short period (30 seconds to a few minutes) of hemorrhage, the arteries again contract and bleeding ceases. Other coiled endometrial arteries likewise dilate, bleed and constrict, although not simultaneously. Each artery bleeds only once during each cycle; successive series of arteries bleed at different intervals throughout the menstrual period, so one small area of endometrium may hemorrhage, slough and be repaired before another area has sloughed.

Induction of menstrual bleeding by drugs or means which will effect ischemia or hyperemia or alter vascular permeation by fluids has often been attempted, but the results have not contributed significantly to the explanation of periodic hemorrhage.

Bio-assay reveals progestins in human peripheral blood at or shortly before the time of ovulation. They attain a peak equivalent in activity to that of 2 to 5 μg. progesterone per 1 ml. plasma, and then diminish, although they do not necessarily disappear before menstruation begins.[28] Physicochemical assays of plasma samples obtained during the menstrual cycle, on the other hand, detected little or no progesterone and neither isomer of Δ^4-3-ketopregnene-20-ol.[88] The discrepancy in results suggests that there may be still other, unrecognized, progestins or other compounds acting synergistically which contribute activity to the bio-assays and which are not presently detected by physicochemical assay. The latter method has, however, demonstrated both progesterone and Δ^4-3-ketopregnene-20-ol in human corpora lutea of the 15th to 32nd day of the menstrual cycle.[88] In most, but not all, women the body temperature on awakening in the morning is 0.6 to 0.8° F. higher during the luteal phase than during the follicular phase; this elevation is apparently caused by progesterone and may be produced in postmenopausal women by the injection of the hormone.

Physicochemical assays have shown that minute amounts (less than 1 μg. per ml. plasma) of estrone and estriol, but seldom of estradiol-17β, may be present in human peripheral blood throughout most of the menstrual cycle.

Hormones may possibly be consumed in eliciting response in the end-organs upon which they act, may be transformed to inactive compounds at sites removed from the end-organ, or may be excreted in the urine. The amounts of estrogen, progesterone or gonadotrophin produced may be estimated very roughly by determining the amounts of exogenous hormone necessary to restore the function of genital tissues after ovariectomy. The rates at which some of these hormones are excreted may indicate the time

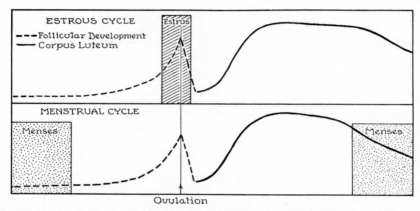

FIG. 604.   Diagrammatic presentation of homology of ovarian changes in estrous and menstrual cycles. Cycles are dated from their most obvious events, estrus and menstruation.

and possibly the rate of their production. Estrogen is excreted in the urine in detectable amounts throughout the menstrual cycle, but in the greatest quantity at the middle of the cycle.[61, 73, 84] Some women may show a second period of increased elimination of estrogens during the latter third of the cycle, but the rate of excretion is always greater during the progestational stage than during the preovulatory phase (Fig. 602). Estriol, but not estrone or estradiol, is usually found in peripheral blood during the human menstrual cycle.[63]

In ovariectomized women, approximately 0.40 mg. is the minimal amount of estrone which must be injected daily to produce an endometrium which will undergo menstrual hemorrhage subsequent to discontinuance of the injections.[83] About 10 mg. of estrone is required per cycle. Because only an amount equivalent in activity to that of about 1 mg. of estrone is excreted per cycle, it might be concluded that only about one-tenth of the total amount that is produced is eliminated. Such a percentage is comparable to that excreted after injection of known doses. The pregnanediol (as sodium pregnanediol glucuronidate) content of the urine during six to 12 days of the latter part of the cycle can be determined gravimetrically.[81] This excretory product of progesterone usually first appears in the urine in detectable amounts about two days after ovulation and is not excreted in appreciable amounts during the two days before menstruation. Pregnanediol is excreted during the periods when active corpora lutea are present in the ovaries and therefore is not found during anovulatory cycles. About 200 mg. of progesterone must be injected over a ten day period into a castrate woman in order to achieve excretion of pregnanediol equal to that occurring in the normal menstrual cycle (20 to 60 mg. of pregnanediol glucuronidate).[57, 82]

Blood levels of progestin and urinary excretion of the estrogenic hormones and pregnanediol correlate rather closely with the sequence of ovarian changes on the one hand, and with the functional changes in the endometrium on the other. Estrogens apparently are produced also by the corpora lutea; estrogenic activity in extracts of these glands has been demonstrated. The increased elimination of estrogens during the latter part of the cycle adds further evidence for the duality of the endocrine activity of the corpora lutea.

Comparison of Menstrual and Estrous Cycles. Among most subhuman or subprimate species the most obvious manifestation of sexual activity in the females occurs during the period of receptivity to the male (estrus). The cycles are dated from the onset of one period of estrus to the onset of the next, and are called estrous cycles (Fig. 604). Some species, such as the rat and mouse, have cycles of four to five days; the guinea pig's cycle lasts about 16 days. Many modifications of the estrous cycle occur in animals of different species. In rabbits, prolonged periods of estrus terminate only with copulation which results in pregnancy, or, if the matings are sterile, in pseudopregnancy. In the absence of mating, a prolonged anestrum follows the protracted estrus.

Ovulation occurs during estrus so that the ovum may be available for fertilization by the sperm. During the menstrual cycle ovulation occurs at the intermenstruum. If ovulation, however, were taken as the point of reference to start the cycles, they would be comparable insofar as the sequence of ovarian changes is concerned.

Estrous behavior or sexual receptivity of laboratory animals may be induced subsequent to ovariectomy by the injection of large amounts of estrogens. The administration of small amounts of estrogens when followed by small doses of progesterone will also induce estrous behavior in ovariectomized rats and guinea pigs. Probably the injected hormones reproduce the conditions eliciting estrus during the normal cycle. This finding probably indicates that progesterone is produced by the large preovulatory follicles. Sexual receptivity in subhuman primates is greatest during the intermenstrual period. In man the periods of greatest sexual receptivity have been less definitely determined.

OVULATION

In man ovulation normally occurs spontaneously, that is, without the imposition of extrinsic stimuli. The limited and not too well controlled endocrine studies on the induction of ovulation in women have contributed little information. A rapid growth of the follicles must occur during a few hours preceding rupture, or at least such is true for all experimental animals. The actual rupture of the follicle has been said to result (i) from increased intrafollicular pressure accompanying an augmented secretion of liquor folliculi, (ii) from ischemia and loss of tissue viability secondary to the increased follicular pressure, and (iii) from enzymes which digest the follicular wall. If any of these theories is correct (none will account for the formation of cystic follicles), the increased follicular pressures or enzymes or other factors antedating ovulation nevertheless must result from gonadotrophic stimulation.

Ovulation normally occurs subsequent to copulation in rabbits, ferrets, cats and in some other species. The inciting stimulus in these animals is in part neural; the semen does not contain an ovulation-provoking factor. The neural stimulation attending mating does not involve the ovaries directly, because transplanted ovaries deprived of their normal innervation or ovaries of sympathectomized animals will ovulate; also, direct stimulation of the ovarian innervation will not provoke ovulation. Intravenous injection of gonadotrophins does, however, induce ovulation. The stimulus of copulation acts upon the hypophysis to release an ovulation-stimulating hormone. If a rabbit's pituitary is removed more than one hour subsequent to mating, ovulation will occur; whereas, if hypophysectomy is performed immediately after copulation, follicular maturation and rupture do not result. The release of gonadotrophin following copulation has been shown also by changes in the cellular structure and by decrease of hormone content of the pituitary gland.

The pathways of transmission of the ovulatory stimuli have been investigated extensively. Section of the sacral cord and abdominal sympathectomy, or removal of the superior cervical ganglia and thoracolumbar sympathectomy, did not prevent postcoital ovulation in rabbits. The sympathetic system has little to do in the regulation of gonadotrophic hormones. Faradic stimulation of the brain, pituitary or tuber cinereum resulted in ovulation. Rabbits with sectioned hypophysial stalks did not ovulate after mating. On the other hand, rats in which the pituitary has been removed and retransplanted into the sella turcica may show complete cycles, and section of the stalk does not prevent ovulation, demonstrating a species difference. It is quite possible that the restoration of normal pituitary secretion of gonadotrophins after stalk section is dependent upon the re-establishment of an adequate hypothalamico-hypophysial vascular connection. Evidence is accumulating from animal experiments that the hypothalamus controls the adenohypophysis through a humoral agent which may be transported to the hypophysis via its portal vessels.[38, 56, 58, 76] The hypothalamus does not appear to regulate the secretion of prolactin. It should be recalled that in rats, as in primates, follicular rupture occurs spontaneously, i.e., without the added stimulus of copulation. In these species another mechanism intrinsic to the animal must be active in periodically inciting the excretion of gonadotrophin.[38, 44] The application of acetylcholine to the pituitary gland of rats has resulted in pseudopregnancy, and the injection of epinephrine into the pituitary gland of the estrous rabbit has induced ovulation. Furthermore, the injection of drugs that inhibit adrenergic activity inhibited ovulation in rabbits subsequent to mating.

Neural lesions may modify sexual behavior as well as other reproductive functions.[76] Hypothalamic lesions in guinea pigs may prevent either estrous behavior or ovarian development; in fact, it has been indicated that the hypothalamus may regulate gonadotrophic function in this species. More work must be done before much can be said about the neural factors in the physiology of reproduction in other than a few species of animals. Lesions of the central nervous system undoubtedly disturb reproduction in man. Hypothalamic lesions may lead to menstrual irregularities or hypofunction. On the other hand, hypothalamic injury may cause precocious sexual maturity. The genital abnormalities in these cases are usually associated with other evidences of pituitary dysfunction.

Time of Ovulation. Many attempts have been made to estimate the time of ovulation in man. Direct methods such as recovery of ova from the uterine tubes, identification of recent corpora lutea, recovery of young embryos, and observations on pregnancies subsequent to restricted intercourse have been used. Attempts to associate ovulation with basal body temperatures, types of cells in the vaginal smears, endometrial structure, excretion of pregnanediol and of gonadotrophin, intermenstrual hemorrhage and pain, and fluctuation in electric potentials have been used as indirect methods of estimating the time of ovulation.[19, 39, 67, 69] In rhesus monkeys, Hartman has been able to determine the time of ovulation by digital palpation of the ovaries through the rectal walls and has checked his observations further by controlled matings. In a large series of animals ovulations occurred between the eighth and 23rd days of the 28 day cycles, with the greater number occurring between the tenth and the 13th days. In man, ovulation apparently takes place usually at comparable times of the cycle, essentially in the middle of the cycle.[39, 48] In abnormally long or short cycles the preovulatory portions show the greater variation and the postovulatory periods tend to be the most nearly uniform, usually 14 to 16 days.[81] It is difficult to ignore some reports that ovulation and fertilization may occur at unusual times of the cycle, even during menstruation.

Regulation of Ovarian Function During the Menstrual Cycle. The rhythmic estrous or menstrual cycles are the result of humoral interreactions between the ovaries and the pituitary. The relation between the ovaries and the pituitary gland was first realized when disturbances in genital development and function were noted in patients with hypophysial tumors of certain types. When techniques were devised whereby pituitaries could be removed from experimental animals, the interpretations made from the earlier observations became established facts. The pituitary became known as the director of ovarian function.[74, 75] The ovarian-stimulating activity of the pituitary—it also stimulates the testes—is referred to as gonadotrophic activity. The gonad-stimulating substances are called gonadotrophins. The rhythmic nature of ovarian activity could not be explained on the basis of hypophysial dominance alone; the pituitary in turn is influenced by the ovaries. This reciprocal relationship between the pituitary and the ovaries was demonstrated, the interreaction between these endocrine glands providing a basis upon which the female sexual cycles may be explained.

Almost simultaneously Aschheim and Zondek[8] and Smith and Engle[75] observed that urine of pregnant women and pituitary glands from animals of several species contain substances which will incite precocious sexual maturity by direct stimulation of the gonads of immature animals. Furthermore, the ovaries of animals from which the pituitary glands were removed remained small, and the follicles failed to grow to a large size. The gonadal deficiencies following pituitary ablation and their restoration by replacement therapy definitely established the pituitary as a gland concerned in reproduction.

Among at least some species of animals the pituitary glands of adult males and females are known to differ, and this difference is determined by the gonads. Ovaries transplanted into intact or castrated adult male rats fail to show cyclic changes of the usual type. The ovarian follicles grow but fail to ovulate and corpora lutea do not form. It is known that male rats' hypophyses contain more gonadotrophin than those of the females but will not establish a rhythmic relationship with the transplanted ovaries, whereas ovaries transplanted into ovariectomized adult female rats show the usual cyclic changes.

If, within one day after birth, testes are transplanted into litter-mate female rats, the pituitary glands of the hosts will be physiologically similar to those of males.[60] Even if the graft is removed after sexual maturity the former host remains in constant estrus and fails to show estrous cycles. The testes transplanted into the immature animal induce an irreversible change in the female host's pituitary. More recently it has been shown that the ovarian cycles may be similarly modified in rats treated with certain androgens during their early postnatal life. The sex difference in the hypophysis is apparently determined by the gonad.[76]

Extracts or implants of pituitary glands induce precocious growth of the ovarian follicles in immature experimental animals. In rats and mice these stimulated follicles may ovulate and form corpora lutea. The injection of some relatively purified pituitary extracts produced growth mainly of the ovarian follicles; others induced ovulation and the formation of corpora lutea as well. These observations led to the impression that at least two pituitary gonadotrophic hormones exist, an assumption that has since been demonstrated to be a fact.[26] One hormone, called follicle-stimulating hormone (FSH), induces ovarian follicular growth in immature or in hypophysectomized female rats. A second pituitary hormone when given by itself has little or no effect on the size of the ovaries, but when administered with a small dose of FSH induces follicular maturation, ovulation and the formation of corpora lutea. It is called luteinizing hormone (LH), or interstitial cell-stimulating hormone (ICSH) because it also acts on the interstitial cells of both ovaries and testes.[32, 49] A small amount of LH greatly augments the response to a small dose of FSH (synergistic effect). Before extensive follicular growth and maturation will occur in hypophysectomized rodents, both gonadotrophic hormones must be injected. A third pituitary hormone, the lactogenic hormone, may be essential for the functional development of the corpora lutea (Fig. 605). FSH and LH are mucoproteins. In the rat they are produced by two specific cell types located in the peripheral (FSH) and central (LH) regions of the pars distalis. Lactogenic hormone is an unconjugated protein of large molecular size.[15]

The manner in which the two ovarian hormones and the two or three gonadotrophic hormones reciprocally and jointly act to establish the estrous or menstrual cycles is not definitely known. The estrous cycles in rats have been explained as follows: The pituitary hormone FSH, especially when a little LH is present (synergistic effect), stimulates follicular growth and the production of estrogen. The estrogen acts upon the pituitary to stimulate the formation of increased amounts of LH (this has been demonstrated) and to cause a decrease in the amount of FSH. Under such conditions, ovulation and the formation of corpora lutea occur. When the corpora lutea begin to regress, the

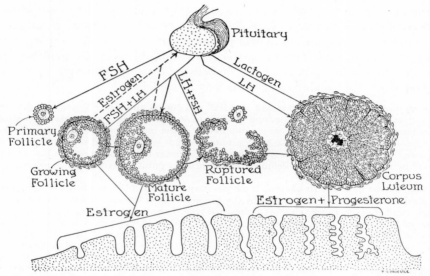

FIG. 605.   Ovarian and pituitary interrelationships in mammalian cycle. FSH (follicle-stimulating hormone) is responsible for follicular growth. FSH and a small amount of LH (luteinizing hormone) stimulate further follicular growth and estrogen production, which in turn increases amount of LH produced. Large amounts of LH and probably small amounts of FSH induce ovulation. Corpora lutea develop under the influence of LH and become functionally active in presence of lactogen.

amounts of ovarian hormones are reduced, with the result that the pituitary again produces FSH to repeat the cycle, a very probable sequence since the amount of FSH increases after castration or ovarian insufficiency. Cyclic changes in the amount of LH have been demonstrated in the pituitaries of rats, the greatest amount being found at estrus.

Similar reciprocal gonad-hypophysial relationships probably exist during the menstrual cycle in man, but they have not been so thoroughly demonstrated. It is believed that FSH is secreted in quantity during the week and a half after menstruation, stimulating the follicle to complete its development. Estrogen is also secreted during this time. Then ovulation occurs, and release of LH supervenes as that of FSH diminishes.[76] Cyclic variations occur in the levels of excretion of urinary gonadotrophin, the greatest amount appearing during the midcycle, usually just before or about the time of the peak of estrogen excretion. Very small amounts of hormone appear in the early part of the cycle (see Fig. 602).

The corpora lutea formed during the normal four to five day estrous cycles of rats or mice were considered for many years to be nonfunctional. More recently the appearance of endometrial stromal cells with large, rounded vesicular nuclei has been attributed specifically to the action of progesterone, and such cells have been observed in the uteri of mice during postestrus.

If mating occurs, even sterile mating in some species, the corpora lutea attain larger size, and more pronounced evidence of their activity is demonstrated. Estrus is prevented for a longer period, progesterone-like material is found in the blood for a longer period, and more advanced endometrial changes occur. Following sterile mating the estrous cycle is inhibited for approximately 12 days in rats and mice, and *pseudopregnancy* is said to occur (normal pregnancy is 19 to 21 days). Animals of many species have prolonged periods of anestrus after ovulation associated with sterile mating or other suitable stimulation, electrical or physical, as with a glass rod. During these periods large corpora lutea are found in the ovaries, progestational changes occur, and deciduomata form in properly stimulated uteri. The injection of gonadotrophin also produces pseudopregnancy in normal rats. Hypophysectomized rats do not form functional corpora lutea when FSH and LH are injected; uterine deciduomata do not develop in the adequately traumatized uteri. If lactogenic hormone is administered, however, the corpora lutea produce progesterone which will facilitate the formation of deciduomata.[25] These experiments demonstrate that at least in this species the final development and functional activity of the corpora lutea depend upon a distinct hormone, the lactogenic hormone, which is also called lactogen. mammotrophin, prolactin, or galactin. Evidence for the luteotrophic action of this hormone in other species is unconvincing.

It was thought that the gonadotrophin excreted in the urine of women during pregnancy produced primarily LH effects in laboratory animals and had an inhibiting effect upon human ovaries. Observations indicate that the progestational stage of the human menstrual cycle is prolonged when large amounts of this gonadotrophin are injected daily; the corpora lutea are maintained in a functional state for longer periods, and pregnanediol is excreted in the urine during this time. The daily injection of 5000 to 10,000 I.U. has a luteotrophic effect. Ovulation has not been induced consistently in man under experimental conditions. Apparently a delicate balance between the amount of FSH and LH must be maintained for follicular growth, and this balance must be readjusted at a proper time to induce ovulation. Follicles may be stimulated to a point beyond which they can be induced to ovulate and thus may become cystic. After much research on the most desirable balances between FSH and LH and on the duration and total doses of the gonadotrophic treatment, it has become possible to induce ovulation rather consistently in monkeys.[41] The experiments in which gonadotrophins have been used to induce ovulation in women have not been convincing.

LIFE CYCLE OF THE OVARY

At birth the ovaries exhibit little evidence of endocrine function; they consist largely of groups of ova and primary follicles in a vascular stroma, and are surrounded by a germinal epithelium except at the hilus. Interstitial cells of a secretory nature have been observed in the ovaries of the newborn in some species but disappear shortly after birth. In man, extensive follicular growth does not occur until the onset of puberty at the age of 10 to 14 years. At this time the *secondary sexual characters* begin to develop; pubic and axillary hair begin to grow and the adult types of body contour appear. Also the *accessory reproductive organs*, the uterus, vagina and mammary glands, start to develop at this time. Hypogonadal individuals or individuals ovariectomized before sexual maturity do not show the usual development of the secondary sexual characters or of the accessory reproductive organs.

Puberty. Puberty is that period of life during which the accessory reproductive organs and secondary sexual characters develop. It terminates at menarche, the first menstrual period. The age at which the first indication of puberty occurs and the rate of the development of the accessory reproductive organs preceding menarche differ from individual to individual. The menstrual periods usually begin in individuals between 13 and 15 years of age, although the age at menarche may range from 10 to 18 years. The early cycles are usually irregular; several months of amenorrhea (absence of menses) may separate the menses. Many early cycles may occur in the absence of ovulation—be *anovulatory*. After irregular cycles extending over intervals of different lengths, more or less regular and normal ovulatory menstrual cycles supervene.

During the prepubertal stage, gonadotrophic hormone is produced in barely detectable amounts; very little of it can be detected in the urine. At puberty the amount of gonadotrophic hormone in the urine increases to approach that excreted in the adult. That puberty must be initiated by the pituitary is indicated by the fact that the ovaries of immature animals can be stimulated with gonadotrophic hormones. What regulates the initiation of gonad stimulation by the pituitary is unknown. It is interesting that at the time of puberty one of the most usual concomitant phenomena is an accentuation of the rate of body growth. If accentuated growth occurs at an early age the menstrual cycles start at a correspondingly early date, and a delayed accentuation of somatic growth is usually associated with a late menarche.[72] The year of the greatest increment of growth is usually the year of menarche. This relation between the growth-stimulating and gonadotrophic functions of the pituitary affords material for increasing conjecture.

Albright *et al.*[1] have described the association of hypo-ovarian states in patients of less than normal stature. Such individuals produce gonadotrophic hormone but little sex hormone and presumably are also deficient in growth hormones. On the other hand, precocious sexual maturity due to gonadal tumors, to adrenal cortical tumors of some types, or to some intracranial neoplasia with resulting hypergonadism may be associated with small stature; growth of these individuals is usually augmented during the early stages of the disease but stops precociously after the brief, abnormally early, accentuated phase. As a result such individuals are usually dwarfed as well as sexually precocious.

Menopause. After 30 to 40 years of menstrual cycles the number of follicles in the ovaries is depleted.[71] The menses may become profuse (*menorrhagia*) and painful (*dysmenorrhea*), or the cycles may become short and irregular, eventually ceasing entirely. The cyclic production of ovarian hormones ceases, the mammary glands atrophy, and the uterus and vagina show variable amounts of regression. This period of gradual subsidence of ovarian function is called the *climacteric* and culminates in the complete cessation of cyclic ovarian activity, the *menopause*.[72] Urinary excretion of estrogen declines and that of pregnanediol ceases, but the excretion of gonadotrophic hormone is augmented. The gonadotrophic hormone in the urine of postmenopausal women contains relatively large amounts of a substance that stimulates ovarian follicles and small amounts of the agent that incites the formation of corpora lutea; in this respect the urinary hormone resembles the follicle-stimulating hormone (FSH) of the pituitary gland. Augmented excretion of gonadotrophic hormone also occurs in artificial menopause induced by surgical removal of the ovaries or x-ray sterilization during the period of sexual maturity. The hormone in the urines of menopausal women is apparently of hypophysial origin and may decrease when estrogens are injected.[68] The conclusion must be that the menopause results from senile changes in the ovary. In the absence of the inhibiting or regulatory effect of ovarian hormones upon the hypophysis, the gland produces an excessive amount of gonadotrophic hormone. The changes in the pituitary at puberty which result in the onset of gonadotrophic activity are not reversed at the menopause; the pituitary, once it starts to stimulate ovarian function, attempts to continue even after the ovary no longer responds.

In addition to the morphologic regression in the accessory genital organs, vasomotor and personality changes frequently accompany the menopause. Vasomotor changes (hot flashes) result from a vascular dilatation in the skin of the head, neck and upper trunk, with flushing, increased sweating and a sensation of suffocation. The hot flashes may be stopped by injecting estrogens, even in amounts inadequate to decrease the amount of urinary gonadotrophin (prolan A). The treatment of menopausal *symptoms* is one of the most common clinical uses of estrogens. The ovarian deficiency after the menopause may not be sufficient to permit complete atrophy of the vaginal mucosa or to result in the disappearance of ovarian hormones from the blood or urine; subthreshold cycles may even occur.

PREGNANCY

An ovum must be fertilized within a few hours after it leaves the follicle at ovulation; at least such conclusions have been drawn from extensive observations upon laboratory animals.[10] If guinea pigs are inseminated artificially from 12 to 18 hours after ovulation, there is a high incidence of pregnancies terminating in abortion and of failure of pregnancy to occur. Artificial insemination during estrus, and therefore within three or four hours either before or after ovulation, institutes normal pregnancies. The period of fertilizability of the ovum must be brief. The ovum is fertilized in the uterine tube. While migrating to the uterus through the uterine tubes, the fertilized ovum divides to form a mass of cells (*morula*), still surrounded by the zona pellucida. Unfertilized ova usually reach the uterus before dissolution.

As the number of cells increases, the cell mass acquires a central cavity. The mass is now called a *blastocyst*. It develops in the uterus within a few days after ovulation and at a time when the endometrium is showing early progestational development. The blastocyst remains free in the uterus for a few days before implantation, during which time the zona pellucida is dissolved. In some mammalian species the blastocysts may remain in this stage for weeks or months before implanting and continuing their growth. The earliest intrauterine human and monkey blastocysts that have been observed have been about seven days old, and may still have been free in the uterus; at least one human morula has been seen. The process of attachment (implantation) is instigated by the blastocyst. From it the extraembryonic trophoblast grows and invades the endometrium. Cells from the developing blastocyst and from the uterine decidua contribute to the placenta. In some animals the mechanical stimulus of a foreign body other than an ovum, or irritation of the lining of the uterus, may elicit a response of the progestational endometrium with the result that deciduomata (the maternal components of the placenta) form. Similar observations have not been made in man; here the maternal part of the placenta has formed only in contact with the developing trophoblast.

The implanted embryo has a definite effect upon the maternal organism. The corpus luteum extends its period of endocrine activity to about one month. The uterine lining fails to undergo the usual menstrual regression. Estrogen is produced in larger amounts subsequent to implantation, and gonadotrophin is excreted in such large amounts that, by the time the expected menstrual period is missed, enough gonadotrophin is excreted to give a positive test for pregnancy.[24, 36]

Aschheim and Zondek[8] discovered large amounts of gonadotrophic hormone in the urines of pregnant women (anterior pituitary-like hormone, APL; pregnancy urine hormone, PU; or prolan) and suggested that its detection constitutes a test for pregnancy. In this test 2 ml. of urine or an alcoholic precipitate of urine are injected into immature mice (or rats). The animals are killed four days (100 hours) after the first of six injections, which are given during the first two days, and their ovaries are examined. An increase in the weight of the ovaries with the formation of large follicles and corpora lutea, some of which may show hemorrhagic spots (blood points), constitutes a positive response. Later Friedman discovered that a single intravenous injection of pregnancy urine induces ovulation in young or isolated female rabbits.[33] Ruptured follicles can be detected within 24 hours after the injection. It is necessary that the rabbits be isolated, as they ovulate upon copulation or even upon copulatory movements in the presence of other females. Ovulation occurs within about ten hours after copulation or after the injection of gonadotrophin or PU in this species. The Aschheim-Zondek and Friedman tests have become routine diagnostic procedures. False positive responses are given with urine of patients with certain genital tumors, among them chorioepitheliomas, which contain tissue similar to that which produces gonadotrophin in the normal placenta. False negative reactions rarely or never occur. Another type of pregnancy test is based on the ability of the gonadotrophin in the urine of a pregnant subject, when injected into male frogs or toads, to induce the release of sperm, which can then be detected in urine taken from the cloaca of the test animal. If pregnancy urine is injected intravenously into the adult female rat, the ovaries will show a distinct hyperemia in two hours.

After the first month of pregnancy the ovaries may be removed and the pregnancy continues to a successful termination in man and in monkeys.[40, 54] The placenta takes over the endocrine function of the ovaries. The pituitary glands have been removed from animals of some species during the latter part of the first half of gestation and pregnancy has continued in a normal manner.

Large amounts of estrogen, pregnanediol, and gonadotrophin are excreted during pregnancy (Fig. 606). The peak of gonadotrophin excretion occurs at about the 45th to 50th day or about one month after the first missed menses; over 100,000 Rat Units may be excreted daily.[24] Pregnanediol and estrogens are excreted in progressively larger amounts as pregnancy progresses, tending to be maximal a few days before parturition.[73] In one study, plasma levels in late human pregnancy were 2.6 to 10.3 μg. per 100 ml. for estrone, 1.2 to 2.9 μg. per 100 ml. for estradiol-17β, and 4.3 to 17.5 μg. per 100 ml. for

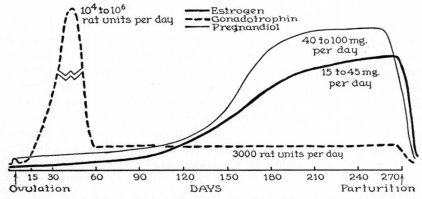

FIG. 606.   Diagrammatic presentation of urinary excretion of estrogen, pregnanediol, and gonadotrophins during pregnancy. At peak of gonadotrophin excretion over 100,000 Rat Units are eliminated daily; 60 to 100 mg. of pregnanediol and 15 to 45 mg. of estrogens are also excreted daily at period of maximal output. The greatest part of the estrogen is estriol, which is much less active biologically than estrone or estradiol, so that bio-assay technique will not reveal such large amounts. Of total, as much as 1 to 3 mg. may be estrone.

estriol.[62] Blood levels of progesterone and other progestins are relatively low during pregnancy in women and monkeys;[29, 87, 88] since pregnanediol is a metabolite of progesterone and since the excretion of pregnanediol increases steadily during pregnancy, it seems likely that the secretion of progesterone also increases during this time but that most of the hormone is promptly metabolized into inactive compounds. However, very few measurements have ever been made of the rate of secretion of steroid sex hormones. The large amounts of gonadotrophin apparently have a stimulating effect upon the ovary; some evidence exists that the gonadotrophin may assist in maintaining function of the corpora lutea during early pregnancy (p. 1147). The rate of gonadotrophin excretion varies among different individuals.

During pregnancy, follicular growth and ovulation are inhibited. The uterus increases in size to accommodate the embryo and fetus; both the number and size of the smooth muscle cells increase. Distention and the endocrine environment both stimulate myometrial growth.[64]

Physiology of the Placenta.   The placenta serves two primary functions: first, it is an organ of exchange between the mother and embryo or fetus; second, it is an endocrine gland producing internal secretions to maintain a compatible environment for the two closely related organisms. At the time of fertilization the mammalian ovum contains a small amount of nutriment in its cytoplasm, an amount which will support only a very limited growth. The uterine secretions may maintain embryonic growth for a brief period—certainly this must occur in the opossum in which the ova never become implanted—but the greater amount of nutriment is received in man by the direct contact of the fetal portion of the placenta with the maternal blood. The exchange of gases through the placenta is not considered here.

As an endocrine gland the placenta produces estrogens, progestins and gonadotrophin.[88] These hormones have all been obtained by extraction of placental tissue; they are more abundant in the fetal part, the chorionic trophoblast, than in the decidua. Probably the syncytial (peripheral) layers of the trophoblast are concerned with production of the steroid hormones and the cytotrophoblast (deepest layers) produces the gonadotrophins.[86] Histochemical studies suggest the presence of steroids in the protoplasm of the syncytium (syntrophoblast). Human placental tissues grown in cultures will produce gonadotrophin that can be bio-assayed in immature mice; the cultures contain largely the Langhans cells of the cytotrophoblast.[47] Also the amount of gonadotrophin produced by the intact placenta tends to parallel the amount of cytotrophoblast, which is maximal early in pregnancy and decreases later in pregnancy. Some experiments have indicated that the placenta also produces lactogenic hormone and growth hormone.

The placenta seems to have a definite life span. If monkey or mouse fetuses are destroyed *in utero* without detaching the placentas, the latter will persist, to be delivered at the time of normal parturition. Under such conditions the placentas continue to produce hormones in much the same manner as during normal pregnancy, insofar as revealed by the weight of the host, the development of the mammary glands and the structure of the vaginal epithelium.

Influence of Maternal Hormones Upon Embryo and Fetus. The large amounts of circulating gonadotrophic and steroid hormones are not without effect on the intrauterine young of some species. The ovaries may be somewhat stimulated; in man the uterus, vagina, prostate and sometimes the mammary glands of the newborn are hypertrophied or stimulated, presumably by the high levels of estrogen. Rapid involution follows birth.[31] Menstruation is sometimes observed within a few days after birth and is attributed to cessation of exposure to maternal hormones. Large amounts of estrogen, when injected into pregnant rodents, have produced anomalous development of the accessory genital organs of the fetuses, although androgens have provoked more striking genital changes when similarly administered, not only to pregnant rodents, but to monkeys. It is possible that high levels of estrogens during pregnancy may influence male embryos so that male pseudohermaphrodites, which are not rare in the human population, result.[12]

Mechanism of Parturition. Pregnancy lasts approximately nine months, or ten lunar months, in man. Each species has a characteristic period of gestation, although slight variations in duration are not uncommon. It has been suggested that the period of gestation is a multiple of the estrous or menstrual cycle—for example, in man it is equal to ten menstrual cycles. The cause of the termination of a normal pregnancy is unknown, although some experiments have been undertaken to clarify the problem. In many species the removal of the corpora lutea terminates pregnancy; however, this is not true in man. The administration of progesterone, or the experimental production of a new group of functional corpora lutea by the injection of gonadotrophins during the latter part of gestation, may prevent or delay parturition in laboratory animals.[42] Under such conditions the young continue to grow and may attain sufficient size to rupture the uterus or may die *in utero* several days after the expected parturition. The onset of parturition in some laboratory animals may result from a decline in the circulating level of progesterone, but this is apparently not the case in man, where the hormone is reported to be absent or to be present in very low concentrations during pregnancy.[13, 29, 88]

Estrogen as well as pregnanediol excretion tends to be maximal during a period of 8 to 10 days before parturition and decreases thereafter, but the wide day-to-day fluctuations and variations in different individuals prevent any evaluation of the proximity of delivery from such data. Some investigators observed an increase in the urinary excretion of free estrogens, in contrast to conjugated estrogens, just preceding parturition, and assumed that the presence of the more active free estrogen might account for the increase of spontaneous irritability of the pregnant uterus and hence terminate gestation. More recent experiments have shown, however, that enormous doses of estrogen may be administered without altering the course of pregnancy in monkeys and in man.[66]

The effect of the oxytocic substance of the posterior lobe of the hypophysis upon the contractions of the uterus has suggested that an increased secretion of this hormone might cause parturition, and observations indicate that there may be an unusual liberation of oxytocic material toward the end of pregnancy. Parturition has occurred in animals of several species after the pituitary gland, including the posterior lobe, has been removed. At the present time convincing evidence of the participation of the hormones of the posterior lobe of the pituitary in parturition is lacking.[76]

Parturition occurs in consequence of more or less periodic contraction of the uterine muscles. The independence of uterine muscular activity from extrinsic innervation has been shown by observations of parturition in animals with bisected spinal cords or complete removal of the sympathetic chains.[64] Extrinsic innervation may act upon the uterus in man, however, since emotional disturbances may provoke premature parturition. The stimulus of suckling is presumed to increase the contraction of the postpartum uterus.

MECHANISM OF SPERM TRANSPORT

The sperm are deposited in the vagina at copulation and must move or be transported through the uterine cervix, the fundus and the tubes to approach and fertilize an ovum. Sperm in some species appear in the uterus immediately after copulation, but the means of their rapid movement through the cervix is not understood. The quality of the mucus secreted by the cervical glands changes during the menstrual cycle, the mucus being much thinner close to the time of ovulation. The less viscous cervical secretions probably make sperm transport through the cervical canal less difficult. The transport of sperm through the uterus is facilitated by uterine contractions. Transport through the uterine tubes perhaps is provided by paths of upward beating cilia (the greater number of cilia beat toward the uterus to assist in the downward transport of the ovum, however), by antiperistaltic tubal contractions, or by a tendency of sperm to swim against a current created by the downward beating cilia, and hence to orient themselves up the tubes and be largely or entirely self-propelled. When sperm from two species or sperm and some nonmotile substance are placed simultaneously in the vagina, uterine cervix or uterus, they do not attain the same levels of the genital tract at the same time, indicating that both the intrinsic motility of the sperm and uterine factors are involved in sperm transport. In addition to permitting the passage of sperm, the cervical mucus must prevent the passage of the vaginal bacterial flora into the usually aseptic uterus.

SOME ADDITIONAL ACTIONS OF FEMALE SEX HORMONES

Many experiments have been undertaken to determine whether the estrogens which provoke normal growth and development of the genital tissues may also instigate unrestricted or malignant growth.[34] Mice given estrogens may acquire mammary, uterine cervical, hypophysial, testicular, or lymphoid tumors. Special inherited susceptibilities or influences transmitted from mother to offspring are required in addition to the endocrine influences before tumors of some organs will develop; estrogens will not incite mammary tumors in mice of any strain. Some nonmalignant overgrowths such as uterine fibroids or cystic endometrial hyperplasias are associated with evidence of hormonal disturbances in man and may be induced in some experimental animals by estrogens. The carcinogenic or tumorigenic action of the different estrogens is proportional to their estrogenic activity, the more active estrogens being more effective than those requiring larger doses for minimal responses.

Serum calcium and lipid levels increase in birds when eggs are being formed. Similar changes occur in birds when estrogens are injected; very high levels of serum calcium and lipids may result. In addition, osseous trabeculae grow into the marrow, increasing the amount of bone. Extreme endosteal ossification occurs in the bones of estrogen-treated mice and the breaking strength of their femurs is increased. The negative calcium balances in some women with postmenopausal osteoporosis become positive when estrogens are administered, and the symptoms are alleviated.

Estrogens cause a dissolution of the pubes at the symphyses in animals of some species, in this way increasing the size of the birth canal. In guinea pigs a relaxation of the pubes precedes parturition and can be reproduced in nonparous animals by estrogen and a distinct hormone, *relaxin*. The loosening of the sacro-iliac joints and pubic symphyses during pregnancy in some women probably results from the action of ovarian hormones.[4]

INACTIVATION OF SEX HORMONES

When estrogens are injected into man only a small portion of the original hormone may be recovered in the urine. The greater part of the hormone is destroyed or inactivated within the body. The liver is an active site of destruction of hormones. In experimental animals estrogens are usually more effective when injected subcutaneously than when placed in the peritoneal cavity or spleen; hormones in the abdominal sites are absorbed and carried by the portal venous system to the liver. The incubation *in vitro* of estrogens with minced or finely sliced liver of some animals results in the rapid destruction of the hormone. Men or women with severe liver disease may show hyperestrogenic responses, apparently elicited by the endogenous hormones which are not destroyed rapidly enough to prevent their accumulation above threshold levels. It has been assumed that an "estrinase" may be present in hepatic and other estrogen-destroying tissues. Tyrosinase will also inactivate estrogens *in vitro*—as will unidentified enzymes in the blood of some species. The end-products of these reactions are not known. The activity of estradiol and estrone is reduced under some conditions by transformation into the somewhat less active estriol, which is excreted as a water-soluble conjugated estrogen. The current idea of hormonal interconversion is: estradiol $\rightleftharpoons$ estrone $\rightharpoonup$ estriol. Estrogens may be transformed into less active or inactive isomers or metabolites. The inactivation may involve conjugation.[21, 61] Incubation of estrogens with kidney slices and perfusion of kidneys *in vitro* with estrogens result in inactivation of some of the hormone.

The progestin content of blood in the renal veins of rabbits and monkeys, as determined by bioassay, is less than that of their renal arterial blood.[30] Progesterone is changed in part into the inactive pregnanediol, excreted in the urine as sodium pregnanediol glucuronidate. Other metabolites are pregnanolone, also inactive, and the active Δ^4-3-ketopregnene-20α-ol and Δ^4-3-ketopregnene-20β-ol. The equivalent of somewhat less than one-half of the progesterone injected is usually recovered as metabolites under the best conditions. The liver may inactivate progesterone by linking it in some manner to protein.

Whether hormones are utilized in the reactions they incite or whether they act as catalysts has been considered. There is no evidence that hormones are utilized in the responses they elicit. The estrogens might well be considered as stimulators of growth of the genital tissues *in vivo* at all stages from at least late fetal life until death. They have not been effective in stimulating the growth of tissues *in vitro*. Progesterone, although it will also stimulate the growth of some genital tissues when given in large amounts, is more intimately concerned with the differentiation of tissues, their stimulation to secretory activity as revealed in the progestational endometrium, and the accumulation of glycogen in the vaginal mucosa. These generalizations are not true in all instances, however; for example, the growth of the maternal placenta is dependent upon progesterone.

PHYSIOLOGY OF THE MYOMETRIUM

The uterine musculature (myometrium) of adult sexually active mammals undergoes spontaneous rhythmic contractions. Many observations have been made upon the intact uteri or isolated uterine muscle preparations of experimental animals, especially of rabbits. In most species the spontaneous contractions are strongest and most frequent when the uteri are under the influence of estrogens; during the progestational stage the myometria are relatively quiescent. Pituitrin, an active principle obtained from the

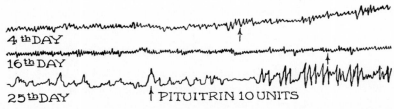

FIG. 607.   Recordings of uterine contractions of a 25 year old woman obtained by use of an intrauterine balloon. At points designated by arrows ten units of Pituitrin were injected. Pregnanediol did not appear in urine of patient until about 18th day of cycle, so first two recordings were taken during preovulatory stages. Biopsies taken on 28th day of cycle showed a progestational endometrium. (After Henry and Browne, *Amer. J. Obstet. Gynec.*, 1943, *45*:927–949.)

posterior pituitary, increases the tonus and height of contractions of the uterine muscle of rabbits subjected to estrogens, but lacks this effect when progesterone is acting upon the uterus. In animals of most other species Pituitrin will incite contractions at all stages of the cycle. The extrinsic innervation of the uterus does not alter the humoral modifications of spontaneous irritability; transplanted denervated uteri respond as do intact uteri to humoral agents.[64] On the other hand, stimulation of the presacral nerve alone also causes contraction of the intact, nonpregnant human uterus.[14]

Variations in the spontaneous contractility of the human myometrium also occur at different phases of the menstrual cycle. Some difference of opinion exists among the numerous investigators who have studied this problem. During the preovulatory stage the uterus undergoes rhythmic small contractions at a relatively rapid rate; in the progestational stage the contractions are more irregular, of greater amplitude, and usually occur at a much slower frequency. Unmistakable changes of the pattern of contractility within 48 hours after ovulation have been described. At all stages of the cycle Pituitrin usually increases uterine tone and the amplitude of contractions, although the changes may be slight. Pituitrin had its greatest effect on the uteri of women in the late premenstrual stage. Throughout anovulatory cycles the myometrial contractions are of the preovulatory type, as would be expected in the absence of a functional corpus luteum.[43] The uteri of castrated females have little or no spontaneous motility (Fig. 607). *In vitro*, rabbit muscle strips show the "stair case" contraction phenomenon; estrogen and progesterone have major but opposing effects on the phenomenon.[18]

Premenstrual pains or dysmenorrhea may be caused by uterine ischemia associated with marked myometrial contractions. Progesterone, when administered to patients with painful postpartum uterine contractions, alleviates the pain, although without inhibiting the contractions. Emotional stress may increase myometrial activity during the premenstrual phase. The human pregnant uterus has a basic pattern of rhythmic contractions; during labor, their frequency and intensity increase, as does the tonus of the uterus. Pain is not experienced until distention of the cervix occurs.[5]

Uterine contractions in man are usually determined by inserting a small thin-walled balloon through the cervix into the uterine lumen and then filling the balloon and the tube connecting it to an adequate recording apparatus with water at a pressure of 10 to 40 mm. Hg. The volume of the uterine lumen varies with the stage of the cycle, tending to be greatest during the progestational stage. If the amount of fluid in the balloon is large, as it might well be in the isotonically distended uterus during the progestational stage in contrast to the preovulatory stage, a small contraction might displace a larger amount of fluid and be recorded as a stronger contraction. Technical irregularities have been used to explain some of the differences in observation in the hands of different investigators.

The uterine contractions of experimental animals may be studied by a similar technique, by the direct observation of the uteri at laparotomy, or through "abdominal windows," or by *in vitro* studies on uteri or uterine muscle strips.

More recently, the contractions of the human pregnant uterus have been studied by passing a fine, nondistensible catheter through the anterior abdominal wall and into the amniotic sac. Increases in amniotic fluid pressure during uterine contractions were then recorded. Similarly, several very small, water-filled balloons on the tips of catheters were implanted at various sites within the uterine muscle and the local contractions at these sites were measured. Throughout pregnancy, slow, slight, local contractions occur rhythmically and without a regular sequence. The pregnant woman is not aware of them. They facilitate the return of venous blood. Stronger, definitely noticeable contractions involving the entire uterus also occur but are infrequent until the end of pregnancy, when they become common (Braxton-Hicks contractions). Finally the major contractions of true labor begin, replacing the earlier localized movements. Labor contractions usually start at the top of the uterus and rapidly spread toward the cervix. Uterine contractions are initiated by two "pacemakers," one near each uterotubal junction.[6, 7]

The blood supply to the uterus increases during pregnancy. In women this organ receives maternal blood at the rate of 750 ml. a minute in the final month of pregnancy; four-fifths of this amount pass through the placenta.[11]

PHYSIOLOGY OF THE VAGINA

The profound and rapid transformation of the vaginal epithelium in rats and mice was mentioned with reference to the bioassay of estrogens. In these species the rapid proliferation of the deeper cells may result in a complete replacement of the entire vaginal epithelium within three days. Administration of estrogen may transform a vaginal epithelium only two or three cell layers thick in a castrated mouse or rat into a thick, stratified squamous structure, the outer layers of which consist of cornified cells. At the same time the large numbers of polymorphonuclear leukocytes characteristic of the diestrous vaginal wall and contents disappear.[4]

In man, marked changes also occur in the vaginal structure. At birth the vaginal epithelium is thick, a response to the high estrogen content of the intrauterine environment.[31] Within a few days the vaginal epithelium is again thin and remains so until puberty. Periodic changes in the epithelium occur during the menstrual cycles and may be detected by the examination of smears of the vaginal contents. The changes are not so easily discerned or in many cases so definite as in rodents. During the mid-intermenstruum the smears contain few leukocytes and many isolated cornified or partially cornified cells with very small pyknotic nuclei; the vaginal pH is low, and the glycogen content of the cells is high. During the progestational stage the partially cornified cells appear in clumps, noncornified epithelial cells increase in number, and leukocytes and bacteria are abundant. Some investigators consider the human vaginal smears sufficiently definitive to permit an estimation of adequate therapy. Estrogen administered to the postmenopausal patient will induce a type of vaginal mucosa characteristic of the mid-intermenstrual period. The addition of progesterone will transform the cornified epithelium into one similar to that seen during the normal premenstrual stage.[59]

The presence of glycogen in the vaginal epithelial cells is apparently attributable to the action of both estrogen and progesterone. The function of the intracellular glycogen is unknown, although the suggestion has been made that it is responsible for the high acidity of the vaginal secretions. The glycogen content is highest in the premenstrual period, and the pH is lowest during the midcycle; the alkaline cervical secretions may reduce the acidity during the latter part of the cycle.

DEVELOPMENT AND FUNCTION OF MAMMARY GLANDS

Milk is necessary for the postpartum nutrition of the young of most species during the period of adaptation to extrauterine life. The mechanisms regulating and synchronizing mammary development and function with sexual and reproductive functions are distinctly mammalian and might be considered a comparatively recent phylogenetic acquisition. It is not unexpected, therefore, that the physiologic regulatory mechanisms of mammary growth and function differ from those of the other female accessory organs.

Normal Development. The breasts are modified skin glands which are first formed during embryonic life and which frequently undergo considerable development during the late fetal stage, presumably under the influence of circulating hormones produced in the placenta. The intrauterine influences, removed at birth, may be responsible for the cystic distention of the breast with a serous fluid called witch's milk. Subsequent to birth, or to the early postnatal hypertrophy, the breasts become very small and persist in this stage until the onset of puberty. With the assumption of ovarian activity, the breasts hypertrophy, and both the stroma and the parenchyma increase in amount. After menarche further mammary growth occurs, probably in cycles paralleling the menstrual cycles. Cyclic mammary growth occurs during the estrous cycles of young mammals of some species.[79]

The prepubertal glands consist of rudimentary ducts extending but a short distance below the flattened nipple areas. During puberty and adolescence the ducts grow by apical proliferation and the number of branching ducts increases until a complex compound tubular gland is formed. It is probable that some alveoli also develop during the menstrual cycles. The greater number of mammary alveoli, however, develop during pregnancy, probably during the first part of pregnancy, transforming the breast to a compound tubulo-alveolar gland. Although the gland may be morphologically complete for some time during the latter part of gestation, lactation usually does not begin until after parturition. If the breasts are suckled and the accumulated colostrum and milk are removed, the gland may function for some time—in some instances for periods of several years. Eventually the glands regress and the alveoli are largely reabsorbed, leaving again essentially a compound tubular mammary structure. After the menopause only the larger ducts may persist in an abundant fibrofatty stroma.

Lactation except following pregnancy is rare in man. Acidophilic cell tumors of the pituitary are associated with acromegaly; during the early stages of this disease spontaneous lactation frequently occurs.

Experimental Studies. Comparatively few observations have been made on the influence of hormones on the human breast. Hypogonadal or postmenopausal women have some breast hypertrophy following topical or systemic applications of estrogens. A feeling of fullness and tenderness of the breasts may occur at the same time. It is assumed that a growth of the parenchymal tissues occurs under such conditions.

Administration of estrogen is followed by varying degrees of mammary development in different species. In immature castrate monkeys and guinea pigs, for example, estrogen induces complete development of the mammary glands at a rate approaching that seen in pregnancy.[35] In the dog, on the other hand, estrogen alone induces little or no mammary growth.[77] Progesterone alone induces either duct or alveolar growth in several species; usually, more rapid and extensive growth occurs after administration of both hormones than after administration of either one singly. Mammary development normally goes to completion only during pregnancy and pseudopregnancy, periods when both estrogen and progesterone are being secreted.

Hypophysectomy appears largely to inhibit or prevent the mammary growth response to estrogen and progesterone (except in mice). Lactogenic hormone and other protein preparations of the pituitary provide at least partial replacement therapy.[50, 55] Administration of preparations of cattle anterior pituitary is followed by mammary growth in castrated and intact male mice, even though no other hormone is given.[78] Some pituitary factor seems to be necessary for mammary growth; in this respect the breasts differ from other accessory genital tissues such as the vagina and uterus, which respond to the ovarian steroids in the absence of the hypophysis. The mechanism of mammary development is further complicated when an explanation is sought for the unilateral proliferation of the subjacent breast tissue that follows cutaneous application of estrogens in amounts too small to elicit systemic effects. If estrogens act indirectly through the pituitary upon the mammary glands, such reactions would not be expected; all the glands should be stimulated. Estrogen can act directly upon the subjacent mammary tissue in intact but not in hypophysectomized animals, however. Further work must be done on more species before the endocrine stimulation of mammary growth is understood. A specific hypophysial hormone may be required or, possibly, the general debility of hypophysectomized animals may be responsible for the restriction of mammary growth.

Lactation.   Although the breasts grow when estrogens are administered to intact animals, a pituitary hormone is necessary to stimulate mammary secretion. The lactogenic hormone induces lactation when injected into animals with completely developed mammary glands. The cuboidal or low columnar cells of the alveoli and the smallest ducts increase in height and elaborate and excrete milk which distends the glands. Normal lactation ceases immediately when the hypophysis is removed, but is maintained if lactogen and adrenotrophic hormone or lactogen and adrenal cortical extracts are given. The maintenance of approximately normal adrenal function or an adequate supply of exogenous adrenal cortical hormone is necessary before lactation can be maintained in hypophysectomized animals. In most species studied, both the onset and the maintenance of lactation require lactogen. The amount of milk secreted during the peak of lactation cannot be increased by lactogen, but, during the declining phase of milk secretion, milk production may be increased in goats and cows. Lactogen has been used clinically in attempts to increase the milk yield in nursing women, but the results have not been convincing. It is probable that deficiencies in milk production are usually caused by factors other than inadequate lactogen.

The lactogenic activity of pituitary extracts was first shown by Stricker and Grüter in 1928 and was confirmed by many other investigators. Riddle[65] noted that the pituitary hormone which induced growth of the pigeon's crop gland (for the production of "pigeon's milk") was the same as the one stimulating lactation. The stimulation of the growth of the pigeon's crop gland is the basis for a bioassay for lactogen. The bioassay facilitated the chemical isolation of lactogen by White et al., who prepared the first pituitary hormone to be obtained in a pure state. One International Unit equals 0.1 mg. of the International Standard Lactogenic Hormone.[52]

Normally lactation begins about the time of parturition or shortly thereafter.[53] The synchronization of the onset of lactation with parturition has been explained by assuming that estrogen or progesterone produced during pregnancy inhibits the liberation of lactogen by the pituitary and that withdrawal of these hormones, as occurs at parturition, permits lactogen production and the onset of lactation. Clinically, for reasons that are not clear, estrogen may either inhibit or stimulate lactation. Estrogen does not prevent the action of lactogen when these hormones are given together, a finding indicating that the steroid hormone acts upon the pituitary and not upon the mammary glands directly. Monkeys given estrogens for long periods begin to lactate.[35] Similarly, young virgin goats or heifers subjected to prolonged treatment with the synthetic estrogen stilbestrol begin to lactate and may produce large quantities of milk. Estrogen increases the lactogen content of the pituitary glands of nonparous or male rats; this action is prevented by simultaneous administration of progesterone. In cows the amount of milk produced is increased up to 30 per cent, and the amount of solids in the milk may be increased by administering thyroxin or thyroglobulin. During lactation the amount of thyrotrophic hormone produced is increased. Lactation may occur in thyroidectomized animals, but the amount of milk is below normal.

Evidence regarding endocrine factors in the initiation and maintenance of lactation is contradictory. Species differences are important. Although hypotheses have been developed in an attempt to reconcile all the findings,[27] further work is required.

Extracts of the posterior hypophysis (Pituitrin) incite the removal of milk from the breast by causing a contraction of the muscle or contractile elements of the alveoli and ducts. The active material is probably the oxytocic factor. Glands from which as much milk has been removed as can be obtained by usual means yield additional quantities when Pituitrin is given. The increased intramammary pressure subsequent to administration of Pituitrin can be readily demonstrated by cannulating the primary ducts.

Suckling in lactating rats stimulates the production of milk in nonsuckled glands for a longer period than when suckling is not permitted, indicating some neural mechanism in the regulation of lactation. Denervated glands lactate if suckling is permitted on some innervated nipples, but lactation fails when only the denervated nipples are suckled. The stimuli provoked by suckling in rats apparently pass along the dorsal roots of the spinal cord and ipsilaterally toward the brain via the ventral portion of the lateral funiculus.[23, 70] How much of a role the stimulus of nursing plays in lactation in animals of other species is less certain.[70]

REFERENCES

1. ALBRIGHT, F., SMITH, P. H. and FRASER, R. *Amer. J. med. Sci.*, 1942, 204:625–648.
2. ALLEN, E. *Contr. Embryol. Carneg. Instn.*, 1927, 19:1–44, 13 pls.
3. ALLEN, E. and DOISY, E. A. *J. Amer. med. Ass.*, 1923, 81:819–821.
4. ALLEN, E., HISAW, F. L. and GARDNER, W. U. Pp. 452–629 in *Sex and internal secretions; a survey of recent research*, 2d ed., E. ALLEN, ed. Baltimore, Williams & Wilkins, 1939, xxxvi, 1346 pp.
5. ALVAREZ, H. and CALDEYRO, R. *Surg. Gynec. Obstet.*, 1950, 97:1–13.
6. ALVAREZ, H. and CALDEYRO-BARCIA, R. *Proc. first World Cong. Fert. Ster.*, 1953, 217–237.
7. ALVAREZ, H. and CALDEYRO-BARCIA, R. *Gynaecologia*, 1954, 138:190–212.
8. ASCHHEIM, S. and ZONDEK, B. *Klin. Wschr.*, 1928, 7:1404–1411.
9. BARTELMEZ, G. W. *Amer. J. Obstet. Gynec.*, 1931, 21:623–643.
10. BLANDAU, R. J. and YOUNG, W. C. *Amer. J. Anat.*, 1939, 64:303–329.
11. BROWNE, J. C. M. *Cold Spr. Harb. Symp. quant. Biol.*, 1954, 19:60–68.
12. BURROWS, H. *Biological actions of sex hormones*, 2d ed. Cambridge, Cambridge University Press, 1949, xiii, 615 pp.
13. BUTT, W. R., MORRIS, PEGGY, MORRIS, C. J. O. R. and WILLIAMS, D. C. *Biochem. J.*, 1951, 49:434–438.
14. CALDEYRO-BARCIA, R. and ALVAREZ, H. *J. appl. Physiol.*, 1954, 6:556–558.
15. COHEN, H. Chap. 4 in *The endocrinology of reproduction*, J. T. VELARDO, ed. New York, Oxford University Press, 1958, viii, 340 pp.
16. CORNER, G. W. *Amer. J. Physiol.*, 1928, 86:74–81.
17. CORNER, G. W. *Harvey Lect.*, 1932–1933, 28:67–89.
18. CSAPO, A. I. and CORNER, G. W. *Endocrinology*, 1952, 51:378–385.
19. D'AMOUR, F. E. *J. clin. Endocr.*, 1943, 3:41–48.
20. DEMPSEY, E. W. and BASSETT, D. L. *Endocrinology*, 1943, 33:384–401.
21. DODDS, E. C., GOLDBERG, L., LAWSON, W. and ROBINSON, R. *Nature (Lond.)*, 1938, 142:34.
22. DOISY, E. A. *Biol. Symp.*, 1942, 9:21–40.
23. EAYRS, J. T. and BADDELEY, R. M. *J. Anat (Lond.)*, 1956, 90:161–171.

24. EVANS, H. M., KOHLS, CLARA L. and WON-
DER, D. H. *J. Amer. med. Ass.*, 1937, *108:*
287–289.
25. EVANS, H. M., SIMPSON, MIRIAM E., LYONS,
W. and TURPEINEN, KAISA. *Endocrinology,*
1941, *28:*933–945.
26. FEVOLD, H. L. Pp. 966–1002 in *Sex and internal
secretions; a survey of recent research,* 2d ed.,
E. ALLEN, ed. Baltimore, Williams & Wilkins, 1939, xxxvi, 1346 pp.
27. FOLLEY, S. J. *The physiology and biochemistry
of lactation.* Springfield, Ill., Charles C
Thomas, 1956, vii, 153 pp.
28. FORBES, T. R. *Amer. J. Obstet. Gynec.,* 1950,
*60:*180–186.
29. FORBES, T. R. *Endocrinology,* 1951, *49:*218–
224.
30. FORBES, T. R., HOOKER, C. W. and PFEIFFER,
C. A. *Endocrinology,* 1950, *47:*83–88.
31. FRAENKEL, L. and PAPANICOLAOU, G. N.
Amer. J. Anat., 1938, *62:*427–451.
32. FRAENKEL-CONRAT, H., LI, C. H., SIMPSON,
MIRIAM, E. and EVANS, H. M. *Endocrinology,* 1940, *27:*793–817.
33. FRIEDMAN, M. H. *Amer. J. Physiol.,* 1929,
*90:*617–622.
34. GARDNER, W. U. *Surgery,* 1944, *16:*8–32.
35. GARDNER, W. U. and VAN WAGENEN, GER-
TRUDE. *Endocrinology,* 1938, *22:*164–172.
36. HAIN, A. M. *J. Endocr.,* 1940, *2:*104–140.
37. HAMAN, J. O. *Amer. J. Obstet. Gynec.,* 1942,
*43:*870–873.
38. HARRIS, G. W. *Neural control of the pituitary
gland.* London, Edward Arnold, 1955,
298 pp.
39. HARTMAN, C. G. *Time of ovulation in women;
a study on the fertile period in the menstrual
cycle.* Baltimore, Williams & Wilkins, 1936,
x, 226 pp.
40. HARTMAN, C. G. *Proc. Soc. exp. Biol. (N. Y.),*
1941, *48:*221–223.
41. HARTMAN, C. G. *Contr. Embryol. Carneg. Instn.,*
1942, *30:*111–126, 2 pls.
42. HECKEL, G. P. and ALLEN, W. M. *Amer. J.
Obstet. Gynec.,* 1938, *35:*131–137.
43. HENRY, J. S. and BROWNE, J. S. L. *Amer. J.
Obstet. Gynec.,* 1943, *45:*927–949.
44. HINSEY, J. C. *Cold Spr. Harb. Symp. quant.
Biol.,* 1937, *5:*269–276.
45. HITSCHMANN, F. and ADLER, L. *Mschr.
Geburtsh. Gynäk.,* 1908, *27:*1–82.
46. HOOKER, C. W. and FORBES, T. R. *Endocrinology,* 1947, *47:*158–169.
47. JONES, G. E. S., GEY, G. O. and GEY, M. K.
Johns Hopk. Hosp. Bull., 1943, *72:*26–
38.
48. KNAUS, H. *Periodic fertility and sterility in woman,
a natural method of birth control,* trans. by
D. H. KITCHIN and KATHLEEN KITCHIN.
Vienna, W. Maudrich, 1934, vi, 162 pp.
49. LI, C. H. and EVANS, H. M. Pp. 631–693 in
The Hormones, vol. 1, G. PINCUS, and K. V.
THIMANN, eds. New York, Academic Press,
1948, 886 pp.
50. LYONS, W. R. Pp. 315–329 in *Essays in biology
in honor of Herbert M. Evans.* Berkeley, University of California Press, 1943, xxxi,
687 pp.
51. MARKEE, J. E. *Contr. Embryol. Carneg. Instn.,*
1940, *28:*219–308, 7 pls.
52. MEITES, J., BERGMAN, A. J. and TURNER,
C. W. *Endocrinology,* 1941, *28:*707–709.
53. MEITES, J. and TURNER, C. W. *Endocrinology,*
1942, *30:*726–733.
54. MELINKOFF, E. *Amer. J. Obstet. Gynec.,* 1950,
*60:*437–439.
55. MIXNER, J. P., BERGMAN, A. J. and TURNER,
C. W. *Endocrinology,* 1942, *31:*461–466.
56. NIKITOVITCH-WINER, M. and EVERETT, J. W.
Endocrinology, 1958, *63:*916–930.
57. OBER, K. G. and WEBER, M. *Klin. Wschr.,*
1951, *29:*53–55.
58. PALAY, S. L. *Amer. J. Anat.,* 1953, *93:*107–
141.
59. PAPANICOLAOU, G. N. and SHORR, E. *Amer.
J. Obstet. Gynec.,* 1936, *31:*806–831.
60. PFEIFFER, C. A. *Amer. J. Anat.,* 1936, *58:*
195–225.
61. PINCUS, G. and PEARLMAN, W. H. *Vitam. &
Horm.,* 1943, *1:*293–343.
62. PREEDY, J. R. K. and AITKEN, ELSIE H.
Lancet, 1957, *272:*191–192.
63. PUCK, A. *Klin. Wschr.,* 1957, *35:*808–812.
64. REYNOLDS, S. R. M. *Physiology of the uterus,*
2d ed. New York, Paul B. Hoeber, 1949,
xxii, 611 pp.
65. RIDDLE, O. and BATES, R. W. Pp. 1088–1117
in *Sex and internal secretions; a survey of recent
research,* 2d ed., E. ALLEN, ed. Baltimore,
Williams & Wilkins, 1939, xxxvi, 1346 pp.
66. ROBINSON, A. L., DATNOW, M. M. and JEFF-
COATE, T. N. A. *Brit. med. J.,* 1935, *1:*
749–753.
67. ROCK, J. and BARTLETT, M. K. *J. Amer. med
Ass.,* 1937, *108:*2022–2028.
68. ROWLANDS, I. W. and SHARPEY-SCHAFER,
E. P. *Brit. med. J.,* 1940, *1:*205–207.
69. RUBENSTEIN, B. B. *Amer. J. Physiol.,* 1937,
*119:*635–641.
70. SELYE, H., COLLIP, J. B. and THOMSON, D. L.
Endocrinology, 1934, *18:*237–248.
71. SHORR, E. *Bull. N. Y. Acad. Med.,* 1940, *16:*
453–474.
72. SIMMONS, KATHERINE and GREULICH, W. W.
J. Pediat., 1943, *22:*518–548.
73. SMITH, G. S., SMITH, O. W. and PINCUS, G.
Amer. J. Physiol., 1938, *121:*98–106.
74. SMITH, P. E. *Amer. J. Anat.,* 1930, *45:*205–
273.
75. SMITH, P. E. and ENGLE, E. T. *Amer. J. Anat.,*
1927, *40:*159–217.
76. SOMMERS, S. C. Chap. 5 in *The endocrinology
of reproduction,* J. T. VELARDO, ed. New
York, Oxford University Press, 1958, viii,
340 pp.
77. TRENTIN, J. J., DEVITA, J. and GARDNER,
W. U. *Anat. Rec.,* 1952, *113:*163–177.
78. TRENTIN, J. J., LEWIS, A. A., BERGMAN, A. J.
and TURNER, C. W. *Endocrinology,* 1943,
*33:*67–74.
79. TURNER, C. W. Pp. 740–803 in *Sex and internal
secretions; a survey of recent research,* 2d ed.,
E. ALLEN, ed. Baltimore, Williams &
Wilkins, 1939, xxxvi, 1346 pp.
80. VAN WAGENEN, GERTRUDE and ZUCKERMAN,
S. *Amer J. Physiol.,* 1933, *106:*416–422.

81. VENNING, ELEANOR H. and BROWNE, J. S. L. *Endocrinology*, 1937, *21*:711–721.
82. VENNING, ELEANOR H. and BROWNE, J. S. L. *Endocrinology*, 1940, *27*:707–720.
83. WERNER, A. A. and COLLIER, W. D. *J. Amer. med. Ass.*, 1933, *101*:1466–1472.
84. WERNER, S. C. *J. clin. Invest.*, 1941, *20*:21–30.
85. WIESBADER, H., ENGLE, E. T. and SMITH, P. E. *Amer. J. Obstet. Gynec.*, 1936, *32*: 1039–1043.
86. WISLOCKI, G. B. and BENNETT, H. S. *Amer. J. Anat.*, 1943, *73*:335–449.
87. ZANDER, J. *Klin. Wschr.*, 1955, *33*:697–701.
88. ZANDER, J., FORBES, T. R., VON MÜNSTERMANN, A. M. and NEHER, R. *J. clin. Endocr.*, 1958, *18*:337–353.

CHAPTER 58

Reproduction in the Male

By CHARLES W. HOOKER

THE part played by the male in reproduction is the production of spermatozoa and their delivery in suitable condition for fertilization of the ovum produced and housed in the female. The elaboration of spermatozoa occurs in the testes; the remainder of the genital system (Fig. 608) consists of excurrent ducts that store and convey the spermatozoa to the exterior and of a series of glands whose secretions are added to the fluid containing the outgoing spermatozoa. In addition to producing spermatozoa, the testes are responsible for the functional maintenance of the rest of the genital system and for the development and maintenance of many of the somatic traits that are considered masculine. The latter functions of the testes are mediated by their internal secretions, and the testes, in turn, are governed primarily by the hypophysis and its gonadotrophic hormones.

Spermatogenesis and Spermatozoa.[11] The mature spermatozoon is a unique and highly differentiated cell which, to accomplish its mission, must be motile, must be capable of entering the ovum, must be capable of initiating the development of the ovum, and must furnish the genetic contribution of the male to the potential offspring. The morphologic development of spermatozoa occurs in the seminiferous tubules of the testis (Fig. 609). The seminiferous tubules make up the bulk of the testis and are tortuously coiled tubules containing two categories of cells: spermatozoa and their antecedent cells, and the cells of Sertoli. Spermatozoa are produced in prodigious numbers; for example, the ram produces upward of four billions daily. The numbers involved in fertilization, however, are by no means as great. Although the number in one ejaculation may be several millions, the number reaching the site of fertilization may be as few as 100 in the rat,[5] and only one fertilizes the ovum.

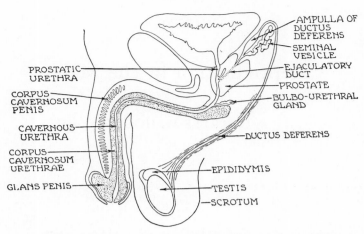

FIG. 608.   Diagram of male genital system. (Modified from Eberth.)

Motility is an obvious attribute of viability of spermatozoa, but movement may be exhibited by spermatozoa that are incapable of fertilizing ova. This circumstance is well illustrated by the observation in the guinea pig that motility may be shown by epididymal spermatozoa for approximately 60 days after separation of the epididymis from the testis, whereas fertilizing capacity persists only 20 to 30 days.[59] Moreover, it is said that the fertilizing capacity of spermatozoa in successive ejaculates declines, and that lowered fertility may result from prolonged sexual rest. In the former instance physiologically immature spermatozoa may be present, and in the latter circumstance the spermatozoa may be senile. In any case, these possibilities are taken into account in the practice of artificial insemination in domestic animals. In most mammals the duration of viability of spermatozoa is much briefer in the genital tract of the female than in that of the male. In the female guinea pig, for example, motility was observed for 41 hours after mating or artificial insemination and fertilizing capacity apparently persisted

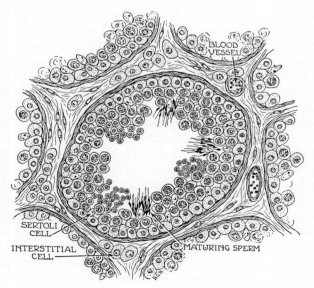

FIG. 609.   Small area of human testis, showing one tubule and portions of several others in cross section, and intertubular tissue.

no more than 22 hours[54]—in contrast to many days' persistence of viability in the genital tract of the male guinea pig.

The speed of independent movement of spermatozoa *in vitro* is roughly 1 to 3 mm. per minute. In some species of animals this rate of migration is sufficient to account for the time observed in transportation of spermatozoa from the vagina to the uterine tube. In other species the rapidity of transportation cannot be accounted for by independent movements of the spermatozoa; contractions of the uterus and tube and ciliary currents in the tube are possible factors. In the human being it has been reported that spermatozoa pass through the uterus in 27 minutes and through the tubes in 42 minutes.[7] It is an interesting circumstance that in many animals the spermatozoa reach the site of fertilization before the ova are released by the ovary. As an example, the rat ovulates approximately ten hours after the onset of sexual receptivity at estrus, and sperm transport from the vagina to the site of fertilization in the tube requires 30 minutes.[4] Accordingly, it is possible for spermatozoa to have to wait more than nine hours for the arrival of the ova. It need hardly be remarked that, although a comparable circumstance may obtain in human reproduction, it does not obviously follow that human spermatozoa must always be so patient.

The unique structure of spermatozoa and their great activity pose for them problems in nutrition and metabolism. The mature sperm cell is essentially a bare nucleus with a flagellum-like tail, and it has no cytoplasm for storing nutritive material. Within the testis it is possible that nutrients are transferred to sperm cells from the cells of Sertoli with which the spermatozoa are connected during their development.[17] After leaving the testis, spermatozoa probably receive their nutrients from the components of the seminal fluid.

Genital Tract. The testes arise in the abdominal region of the embryo and typically descend into the scrotum late in fetal life. The cause and mechanism of the descent are not understood, but not infrequently one and occasionally both testes fail to descend, the condition being known as cryptorchidism. Spermatogenesis is disturbed in the undescended testis, sometimes to the point of complete arrest. The adverse effect of cryptorchidism appears to be largely the result of the higher temperatures to which the testes are subjected.[44] The temperature of the scrotum is slightly lower than that of the abdominal cavity. Experimental procedures and many febrile diseases that raise the temperature of scrotal testes also suppress spermatogenesis, sometimes to the extent of causing sterility. Another serious aspect of failure of descent is the greater liability of the undescended testis to becoming cancerous.[9] After leaving the testis, spermatozoa pass successively through the ductuli efferentes, the ductus epididymis, the ductus deferens, the ejaculatory duct and the urethra. The epididymis and the ampulla of the ductus deferens also serve as depots for the storage of spermatozoa.

The principal glands associated with the genital tract are the seminal vesicles, the prostate and the bulbo-urethral glands, and the greater part of the volume of the seminal fluid is furnished by these glands. Generally speaking, the fluid secreted by each gland has its own characteristic components,[41] and certain of these compounds are believed to be important factors in supporting the highly active movements of ejaculated spermatozoa. Compounds that are secreted by one of these glands in one species may be secreted by another of these glands in a different species. This circumstance is not inconsistent with the fact that in some species one gland may be either lacking or quite small relative to another of the accessory glands of reproduction.

In man the characteristic constituent of the fluid of the seminal vesicles is fructose. The concentration of this unusual sugar in semen exceeds that of glucose in the blood, but fluctuates with the level of blood glucose. Mann has proposed that in the gland glucose is converted into fructose, with glycogen and phosphohexoses serving as intermediary compounds. Fructose serves as a chief source of energy for ejaculated spermatozoa. Another constituent of fresh semen is phosphorylcholine. This substance liberates choline; the presence of choline is the basis for one of the older tests for semen in legal medicine. The observation that the greater part of the phosphorus content of semen is furnished by the seminal vesicles has led to the suggestion that phosphoryl-choline is derived from the seminal vesicles. The physiologic significance of the compound seems to be unknown. It is now recognized that the seminal vesicle does not store spermatozoa, either living or dead. Similarly, the old notion that the intensity of the sex drive may be related to the degree of distention of the seminal vesicles may not be correct.[2]

The constituents of semen, derived primarily or solely from the prostate,[29] are acid phosphatase, citric acid, calcium and a fibrinolysin. The phosphatase is present in semen in very large quantities, and seems to be contributed solely by the prostate. The physiologic significance of this enzyme is not known, and, despite its high concentration in prostatic tissue, it does not enter the blood stream except when malignant growth occurs in the prostate. This fact has been of clinical significance. The functions of prostatic citric acid are not known, but it has been suggested that it may benefit spermatozoan motility; that it may exert a protective action against antinvasin, thereby facilitating the action of hyaluronidase; that it may be related to coagulation and liquefaction of semen; and that it may be involved in the calcium binding of semen. The fibrinolysin of prostatic fluid is primarily responsible for the liquefaction of coagulated semen.

In many rodents ejaculated semen coagulates in the vagina and cervix, forming the so-called copulation or vaginal plug. The plug consists of fluid of the seminal vesicles coagulated by an enzyme secreted in one of the pairs of lobes of the prostatic complex. The function of the copulation plug is not known, but it has often been suggested that it prevents escape of semen from the genital tract of the female. Semen in certain primates coagulates, and in the monkey a specific area of the prostate contains the coagulating enzyme.[56] Whether a similar functional localization obtains in the human prostate has not been determined. The function served by coagulation of the ejaculum in primates is not known. It is interesting, however, that coagulation of semen is in some respects like the coagulation of blood; upon standing the coagulum liquefies.

It seems clear that the secretions of the prostate and seminal vesicles are not essential in the fertilization of the ovum, as shown by successful artificial inseminations with spermatozoa taken from the epididymis. It seems equally clear that in more usual circumstances these secretions contribute to fertilization for the reasons suggested above. In the rat removal of either prostate or seminal vesicles does not abolish conception. Ligation of both glands, however, does prevent conception.[3] The specific defection has not been fully identified.

A group of modified sebaceous glands, the preputial glands, are situated in the prepuce in the region of the corona and discharge their secretion onto the glans penis. Smegma is largely the accumulated secretion of these glands.

Erection.   Erection is primarily a vascular phenomenon and is dependent upon the morphologic pattern of the penis. This organ consists of three cylindrical masses of erectile tissue, two corpora cavernosa penis which lie side by side and above a third cord of erectile tissue, the corpus cavernosum urethrae, which transmits the urethra. The expanded distal end of the corpus cavernosum urethrae forms the glans. Each corpus cavernosum is surrounded by a dense fibrous coat, the tunica albuginea, and all three are enclosed by a layer of fairly dense fascia. At the root of the penis the corpora cavernosa penis diverge laterally as the crura to attach to the pubic arch, and each is covered by a sheet of skeletal muscle, the ischiocavernosus muscle. The expanded corpus cavernosum

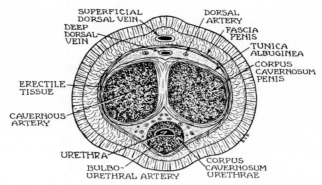

FIG. 610.   Cross section of shaft of penis. (Redrawn from Callander.)

urethrae extends in the midline to the point of entry of the prostatic urethra and is also covered by a sheet of skeletal muscle, the bulbocavernosus.

The erectile tissue receives arterial blood by way of terminal branches of the internal pudendal arteries. These are (Fig. 610) a pair of dorsal arteries that lie on the dorsal surface of the tunica albuginea, a cavernous artery running longitudinally in each corpus cavernosum penis, and a pair of bulbourethral arteries that enter the corpus cavernosum urethrae at the bulb and course longitudinally forward. Branches of these arteries open into the cavernous spaces. Venous blood leaves the penis by way of two veins, the superficial dorsal vein, which drains the glans and the corpus cavernosum urethrae, and the deep dorsal vein, which lies between the dorsal arteries and receives tributaries from the corpora cavernosa penis.

The erectile tissue of the corpora cavernosa is a spongelike system of irregular vascular spaces that are interspersed between the arteries and veins. In the flaccid state these spaces are more or less collapsed and contain little blood; during erection they are quite large cavities distended with blood. This is the immediate mechanism of erection.

The intima of the arteries of the penis has longitudinal ridges that serve to occlude the arteries partially and to restrict the quantity of blood entering the cavernous sinuses.[35] Upon dilatation of these arteries the flow of blood into the penis is tremendously increased and the sinuses are filled. The larger veins of the penis are said to possess funnel-like valves that impede the return of blood from the penis.[35] Moreover, distention of the vascular spaces is thought to press the veins of the cavernous bodies against the tunica albuginea and to restrict escape of blood from the spaces through these veins. Thus the principal event appears to be arterial dilatation; restriction of venous return appears to be largely passive. The pressure in the cavernous spaces during erection approximates that in the carotid artery.[26] It has frequently been suggested that contractions of the ischiocavernosus muscles assist in erection by constricting the veins. Such action is now considered to be of a minor nature.[26, 35] Return of the penis to the flaccid state is initiated by constriction of the arteries. A gradual escape of blood from the cavernous spaces would lower the pressure in the vascular spaces and presumably would result in a reduction of the passive constriction of the veins, and hence a progressively more rapid return of flaccidity.

Dilatation of the penile arteries and erection are induced by stimulation of the pelvic splanchnic nerves, whence their name *nervi erigentes* (Fig. 611). Stimulation of the sympathetic nerve supply results in constriction of the arteries of the penis and subsidence of erection. A center for reflex erection apparently exists in the sacral spinal cord, as shown by stimulation of the glans eliciting erection only when the pudendal nerve is intact.

Psychic stimulation will produce erection after destruction of the sacral cord but not after destruction of the lumbar cord.

Ejaculation. As used commonly, this term covers two distinct actions.[52] The first, emission, is the sudden contraction of the smooth muscle of the internal genital organs that delivers semen into the urethra. The second, or ejaculation in the restricted sense, is the expulsion of seminal fluid from the urethra by contraction of the bulbocavernosus muscle (a skeletal muscle). The process is basically a reflex phenomenon (Fig. 611). The afferent impulses arise chiefly in the sense organs of the glans and are transmitted by the internal pudendal nerves to the spinal cord. Efferent impulses leave the upper lumbar segments of the spinal cord, travel over the lumbar rami communicantes and hypogastric

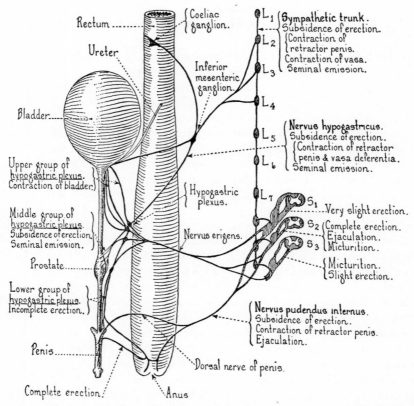

FIG. 611.   Diagram summarizing functional innervation of genital organs of male cat. (From Semans and Langworthy, *J. Urol.*, 1938, *40:*836–846.)

nerves through the hypogastric plexus and evoke emission. The impulses that provoke ejaculation are parasympathetic and travel over the internal pudendal nerves. It is generally thought that an ejaculatory center in the lumbosacral spinal cord integrates the reflexes. The neural control of emission and ejaculation as described here was worked out in the cat by Semans and Langworthy,[52] but the same pattern of control appears to obtain in man.

For many years it was suspected that the several glands discharge their secretions in an orderly sequence during emission. By chemical study of "split ejaculates" Huggins and McDonald[30] have shown that the prostate discharges its secretion before discharge of the seminal vesicles.

The several sensations associated with ejaculation constitute the orgasm. The origin, with respect to both mechanism and location, of these sensations is not fully known. Afferent impulses presumably reach the cerebral cortex, much like impulses giving rise to other visceral sensations. Inasmuch as sexual sensations are of a primitive nature, it is usually assumed that many of the afferent impulses do not ascend higher than the thalamus. The impulses apparently spread through much of the autonomic nervous system and elicit reactions in other viscera.

Sterility and Fertility. In recent years the problem of sterility has received much attention, and one of the significant consequences of this study is the recognition that in barren marriages the husband is the sterile individual at least as often as is the wife. It will be evident that the circumstances of human reproduction make the factors in fertility quite difficult to assess. An ovum is available but once a month, if that often, and its viability is apparently so brief that conception might be considered fortuitous under the most favorable circumstances.

The *sine qua non* for male fertility is adequate numbers of viable spermatozoa in the ejaculum, and much attention has been devoted to defining adequate numbers and adequate viability.[39] The average number of spermatozoa in each milliliter of ejaculated semen of fertile men is probably approximately 100 millions, but the variation is great. It is often said that fewer than 60 million sperm in a milliliter of semen is an indication of probable sterility. Sperm counts as low as 20 million per ml. have, however, been found in men of proved fertility. The total number of spermatozoa in an ejaculation depends upon the volume of the ejaculum, the average in fertile men being approximately 3 ml. The volume of the ejaculum has been examined with reference to fertility and sterility, but a satisfactory correlation seems not to have been made. Quite low volumes may be seen in sterile men with no spermatozoa, but this condition may be associated with hypogonadism.

Abnormal spermatozoa, with two heads or two tails for example, are fairly common, and several authors have suggested that when they amount to 20 per cent of the total count sterility is probably present. A low general level of spermatozoan motility has been associated with sterility, and it has been emphasized that mere movement cannot be considered adequate motility.

The chief constituents of semen have been discussed earlier. It will be apparent that defects in the secretion of certain of these compounds might be expected to impair fertility. The possibility here seems not to have been sufficiently studied to permit generalizations.

Why millions of spermatozoa must be introduced into the female genital tract to insure fertilization of one ovum by a single spermatozoon is still an unanswered question. For a time the finding that semen and sperm suspensions contain high titers of the mucolytic enzyme, hyaluronidase, seemed to offer an answer. This enzyme was found capable of liquefying *in vitro* the gel that surrounds newly ovulated ova of rats and rabbits. The possibility that millions of spermatozoa are necessary to furnish enough hyaluronidase to denude the ovum and thus to permit its penetration by one successful spermatozoon suggested the use of the enzyme in management of sterility. Most of the clinical trials were unsuccessful, and several laboratory observations suggest that hyaluronidase may not function precisely in the manner assumed earlier.[10] Most workers agree, however, that hyaluronidase may facilitate penetration of the ovum and its adnexa by the sperm. Another action of hyaluronidase may lie in its enabling spermatozoa to burrow through the plug of mucus in the cervical canal.[37]

Effects of Castration—Transplantation of Testes. Excision of the testes produces permanent sterility by removing the site of production of spermatozoa. This operation

FIG. 612.   Head of White Leghorn cockerel (left) and of capon (right), showing effects of castration upon comb, wattles, and ear lobes.

in adults of all higher animals and man also results in atrophy of the genital tract and in regression of many masculine characters. If the castration is done prior to the attainment of sexual maturity, the genital organs remain infantile, and many masculine traits fail to manifest themselves. The effects of castration are dramatic in many animals, as is obvious in comparing the physique and temperament of the bull and the ox or of the stallion and the gelding. In the fowl, castration results in a regression of the florid head furnishings (comb, wattles, ear lobes) of the cockerel to the pallid, modest structures of the capon (Fig. 612). The striking growth of the antlers in some male deer or of the horns in certain rams is prevented by castration. Other structures normally developed only in the male, such as the spurs of the cockerel, are not influenced by castration.

The effects of castration are perhaps less conspicuous in man than in the animals mentioned, but they are no less profound.[24, 57] If a child is castrated, the pubertal changes do not occur. The high pitch of the voice is retained; the beard and body hair develop poorly; the body proportions do not become masculine; the genital organs, both internal and external, remain infantile in size and structure; masculine aggressiveness is deficient or absent. If the operation is performed after puberty, the effects are similar but often less striking, and some of them may require a long period to become apparent.

As with other endocrine glands, the first attempts at replacement therapy after castration consisted of the transplantation of testes. Testicular transplants have been made with various degrees of success in many species of animals.[44] If the graft takes, it is usually capable of substituting for the somatic actions of the host's testes. In the 1920's testicular transplants ("goat glands" or "monkey glands") to man received wide popular attention, and many therapeutic claims were made for them. Of course, in the establishment of a testicular graft many of the factors operate that influence any other transplantation. Of these, one of the most significant is the taxonomic or chemical kinship of host and donor species or individuals. Suffice it to say, the practice with respect to human hosts has apparently been largely abandoned.

Androgens—Chemistry and Metabolism.   Although Brown-Séquard's report in 1898 of rejuvenation after injections of aqueous extracts of testicular tissue into himself created much interest, it is generally agreed that the first active testicular extract was prepared in 1927 by McGee, who employed fat solvents. Similar extracts were soon found capable of correcting the recognized changes produced in a variety of animals by castration. Masculinizing activity was also found in extracts of urine, blood, cerebrospinal fluid and bile; the epididymis is apparently the only organ besides the testes, however, whose extracts contain significant levels.

Several pure male hormone compounds (androgens) have been obtained from natural sources or synthesized.[36] Androsterone was prepared from human urine in 1931 by Butenandt and synthesized in 1934 by Ruzicka. Testosterone was obtained from testicular tissue of bulls in 1935 by David, and synthesized in the same year by Ruzicka and by Butenandt. These are the most active of the androgens, one International Unit of biologic activity being present in 100 μg. of androsterone and in 13 to 16 μg. of testosterone. Several compounds related to androsterone and known collectively as 17-ketosteroids have been isolated from human urine. Some of these substances are active biologically as androgens; others are not.

It is generally assumed that the male sex hormone secreted by human testes and circulated in the blood is testosterone. This compound has been identified thus far, however, only in testicular tissue from bulls and horses, although extracts of the testes

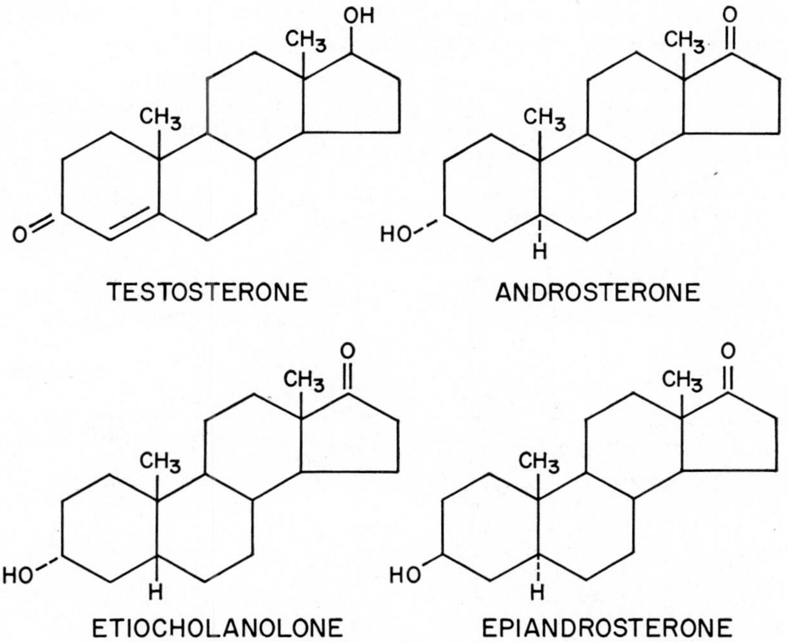

FIG. 613. Testosterone and three urinary 17-ketosteroids that are considered to be its metabolites.

of several species of mammals have shown androgenic activity upon biologic assay. The identity of the androgenic substance in systemic blood seems not to be known, although testosterone has been identified in blood from the spermatic vein.[38] The identification of increased amounts of androsterone[13] and certain other 17-ketosteroids in urine after administration of large amounts of testosterone to men is evidence that these substances are metabolites of testosterone (Fig. 613).

The level of urinary 17-ketosteroids is subject to wide variation that depends on many considerations, and much of the 17-ketosteroid in the urine is derived from adrenal rather than testicular precursors.

As is the situation with other steroid hormones, testosterone disappears rapidly from the animal given this substance. West[58] reported that at least 90 per cent of testosterone disappeared from the blood within ten minutes after intravenous administration. The largest quantity entered fat depots, but disappeared from this site within three hours. Testosterone labeled with radioactive carbon was also rapidly lost in mice and rats, the major portion of the radioactivity being found in urine and feces.[1]

Thus far, the liver and the kidney are the identified sites of inactivation of testosterone. The liver of the rat has been studied most in this respect, and the ability to inactivate testosterone *in vivo* persists even after the liver is subjected to poisoning and to dietary stress.[19] Liver from rats fed a diet deficient in niacin and tryptophane, however, had a diminished capacity to inactivate testosterone *in vitro*.[8] Inactivation of testosterone by rats' liver *in vitro* is an oxidative process, and certain of the enzyme systems involved have been studied. Bile from human subjects given large amounts of testosterone has been found to show no increase in 17-ketosteroids or androgens, although urinary 17-ketosteroids were much increased.[49] Human plasma has recently been found to contain 17-ketosteroids in amounts paralleling urinary titers in different individuals.[18]

Estrogenic as well as androgenic substances have been extracted from testicular tissue. The urine of normal men contains estrogenic material, and the urine of the stallion is the richest known natural source of estrogens. After castration in both man and the stallion, the urinary excretion of estrogens is greatly decreased. The function of testicular estrogen has not been determined.

ASSAY OF ANDROGENS. The original extraction and later purification and synthesis of androgenic compounds depended upon having at hand means of recognizing the active substance. Since the chemical nature of these substances was unknown, biologic responses to them were necessarily employed.

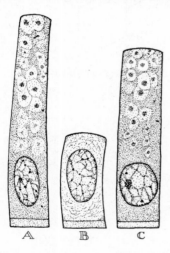

FIG. 614. Cells from epithelium of seminal vesicle of rat to show effect of castration and restitution by injected androgen: *A*, from normal animal; *B*, 20 days after castration; *C*, from a 20 day castrate treated with androgen. (Redrawn from Moore *et al.*, *Amer. J. Anat.*, 1930, *45:*109–136.)

These biologic tests are still valuable in the assay of the androgen, rather than the 17-ketosteroid, content of various tissues and fluids. The basis of the tests is the prevention or correction of changes produced by castration in certain animals. Probably the most widely employed reaction is growth of the comb of the capon (see Fig. 612), and it is upon this reaction that the International Unit (I.U.) of androgenic activity is based. The International Unit is activity equal to that of 100 µg. of pure androsterone. The standard test involves the daily intramuscular or subcutaneous injection of the unknown material into a group of Leghorn capons over a period of five days. At the end of this period the change in the size of the comb in response to 1 I.U. of androgen daily is an increase of 5 mm. in the length plus the height. Another widely used test involves maintenance or restoration of the weight and microscopic structure of the seminal vesicles (Fig. 614) and prostate glands of castrated rats.

The usual procedure in bioassaying androgens has been to administer them systemically, that is, subcutaneously or intramuscularly. It is becoming more common to apply the androgen directly to the structure whose growth is to be induced, for example the comb of the capon. With this method of administration a response is induced by much smaller amounts of androgen; distinct growth of the comb has been caused by a total of 1.2 µg. of androsterone, whereas the daily dose of this substance is 100 µg. when given systemically. It is interesting that testosterone and androsterone exhibit identical activity when applied directly, although testosterone is roughly seven times as active as androsterone when they are administered systemically.

Chemical methods are available for the determination of 17-ketosteroids, and have been used chiefly upon urinary material. Perhaps the most widely used of these reactions is the colorimetric method originated by Zimmermann. This test depends upon the development of a color when *m*-dinitrobenzene reacts with ketones in alkaline solution. Such methods are in effect tests for certain chemical groups and may give positive tests when no biologically active androgens are present.

Actions and Functions of Androgens. The actions of the androgenic hormones involve many parts of the body and many physiologic functions not obviously related to reproduction.[24, 57] The list of functions or actions of androgenic hormones is impressive, but probably is still incomplete. Their identification has been based upon study of the effects of castration or of testicular insufficiency, the repair of these changes by administration of androgens, the effects of excessive amounts of administered androgens, and the correlation of levels of excreted 17-ketosteroids with different bodily states.

Genital system. Each of the several portions of the genital tract (see Fig. 608) is under the controlling influence of the testicular hormone. In the absence of adequate androgen, in the boy or in the eunuch for example, the scrotum is small and its proximal end tends to be wider than the distal end. After puberty the scrotum is much larger, with the distal portion expanded and the proximal portion relatively narrower.[22] To some extent, the size and conformation of the scrotum depend upon the weight and degree of distention exerted by the testes; but in the absence of testes the scrotum may approach normal size and configuration when adequate androgen is supplied artificially. The full development of the penis likewise is contingent upon stimulation by androgen; it remains infantile when insufficient androgen is available and grows when androgen is administered.[23, 57] The several excurrent ducts are also dependent upon androgen for the establishment and maintenance of mature size and structure. The attainment and maintenance of adult size and secretory function in the accessory glands of reproduction—seminal vesicles, prostate, bulbo-urethral glands—also require adequate stimulation by androgen. The effects of androgen are shown most conspicuously by the epithelium of these glands (Fig. 614); indeed, the height of the epithelium is often, within limits, proportional to the level of stimulating androgen.[44] A beginning has been made in studying biochemically the response of these glands to androgen.[43, 50]

The control of the structure and function of the normal prostate gland by androgen suggests that benign hypertrophy of the prostate may perhaps be related to some aberration in the action or production of androgens. This prostatic change is common in men in the later decades of life, and consists of enlargement of one or more portions of the prostate and concomitant difficulty in voiding urine. On the basis of prostatic control at earlier ages, hypertrophy would appear to demand a greatly increased level of stimulation by androgen; yet it occurs at ages when the production of androgen has presumably declined. Some authors have reported the condition developing many years after castration; others have observed regression of the enlarged prostate and a relief of the urinary distress upon castration. Still other investigators have reported relief of the urinary difficulties after administration of androgen without any effect upon the prostate itself; the symptomatic relief is attributed to a strengthening of the bladder musculature sufficiently to overcome the urethral obstruction. Finally, the level of excretion of 17-ketosteroids by patients with prostatic hypertrophy is reported to be not significantly different from that by men of the same age without prostatic disease. The observations are too inconsistent and conflicting to permit a decision as to whether androgens are an important factor in this disease. Estrogens have also received consideration as possible etiologic agents, largely because they modify the prostate glands in mice and rats—the most striking effect being a squamous metaplasia—and cause urinary retention. No convincing evidence for the involvement of estrogens in the disease has been advanced, and the possibility is apparently losing favor.

In contrast, carcinoma of the prostate may be strikingly affected by androgen,[32] and castration has become a widely employed therapeutic measure. The operation apparently does not always influence the primary tumor nor does it prolong the life of the patient, but it may cause a dramatic regression of the metastatic growths and an almost immediate diminution in the pain that characteristically accompanies this tumor.

The administration of estrogens has the same general effects, presumably by producing a physiologic castration through inhibition of the hypophysis.

HAIR. Hair is a conspicuous secondary sex characteristic, with the type, pattern and degree of growth differing in the two sexes and influenced by androgen. The extent of the influence of the androgen evidently depends upon the genetic constitution of the individual, and every generalization apparently has its exceptions in virile men. Growth of hair over the trunk and the extremities is heavier in the presence of androgens. Hair in the axillary and pubic regions depends upon androgen for its full development; it does not appear until puberty, and is sparse in castrates and in eunuchoid men.[24, 57] After castration pubic hair is less luxuriant, and the upward extension of the superior border often disappears. The pattern of head hair is different in the two sexes and is apparently determined by androgen.[22] In immature boys and in girls and women the hairline on the forehead is in the form of a continuous bow-like curve (Fig. 615). In mature men the hairline is usually marked by a recession (calvity) over the lateral frontal region on each side. Calvities are poorly developed or absent in some unquestionably virile men, but apparently they are always absent in hypogonadal or prepubertally castrated men, and can usually be induced in the latter by administration of androgen. This sexual difference in growth of head hair is probably related to common baldness, which is traditionally found only in the male, begins only after puberty, is absent in prepubertally castrated men, and frequently appears after masculinization of women. Moreover, the condition may be induced in many castrated men by administration of therapeutic levels of androgen. Baldness appears to be an hereditary trait that requires a physiologic level of androgen for its development; that is, no amount of androgen can induce baldness in an individual not carrying the hereditary factors for the condition.[25]

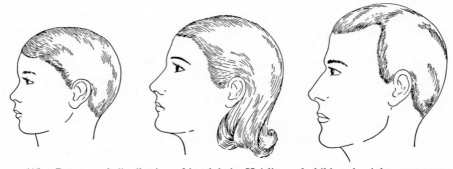

FIG. 615. Patterns of distribution of head hair. Hairlines of child and adult woman are alike, while that of adult man usually shows an indentation in lateral frontal region. (From Greulich et al., Monogr. Soc. Res. Child Dev., 1942, 7:1–85.)

SEBACEOUS GLANDS. The sebaceous glands of the skin are also influenced by androgens. Acne vulgaris, an inflammation of the sebaceous glands, does not appear until puberty, but during adolescence is present in the majority of both males and females. Inasmuch as the disorder does not develop in castrates, but may be induced by administered androgens, androgen appears to be a prerequisite and incitant of acne, although a variety of other factors may also be involved.[23] The high incidence of acne in females does not argue against the primacy of androgen in causing the disorder, inasmuch as androgens are normally present in fairly high levels in the female. A basis for the acnegenic action of the androgens may lie in their enhancing secretory activity of the sebaceous glands as revealed by oiliness of the skin in normal subjects beginning at puberty and in hypogonadal patients upon treatment with androgen.

COLOR OF SKIN. The color of the skin is also influenced by androgens. In castrates and eunuchoids the skin is furrowed or finely wrinkled, soft, and sallow. After administration of androgens and in normal men the skin is firmer and ruddier, and has a darker color.[24, 57] Castrates have little or no ability to tan, but the skin may tan many months after exposure to sunlight upon administration of androgen.[24] In a spectrophotometric study[16] it was found that, as compared with normal men, castrates have a lower quantity of hemoglobin in the skin and that a higher proportion is reduced hemoglobin; carotene is present in greater amounts in the skin; melanin levels are slightly subnormal. Administration of androgen brought the levels of all of these substances within the normal range.

SUBCUTANEOUS FAT. In many instances the pattern of distribution of subcutaneous fat appears to be influenced by androgens.[24, 57] In normal adults abdominal fat usually accumulates above the umbilicus in the male and below the umbilicus in the female. In castrates, fat frequently accumulates in the mammary region, over the trochanters, and in the mons pubis, although these fatty depots may be absent in other castrates of long standing. The ability of administered androgens to modify fat distribution has not been forcibly demonstrated.

VOICE. One of the most readily recognized actions of androgens is upon the depth of the voice.[24, 57] The eunuchoid and prepubertal castrate retain the voice of the immature boy. Administration of androgens results in a lowering of the voice which may, however, take the form merely of hoarseness. These vocal changes may not be accompanied by any special enlargement of the laryngeal cartilages. Androgens affect the voice of women in much the same way, causing hoarseness and deepening. Castration after puberty frequently has no effect upon the depth of the voice.

SKELETON.   There are many indications that the androgens affect skeletal growth, but the relationship appears beset with inconsistencies. The pubertal spurt in somatic growth suggests that androgen may be the stimulus, On the other hand, the prepubertal castrate and the eunuchoid are frequently quite tall and characterized by a disproportionately great length of the bones of the extremities. The administration of androgens is reported to accelerate the closure of the epiphyses and to lead to the termination of growth in tall eunuchoid boys.[33] Contrariwise, the same dose levels of androgens are reported to provoke growth in stunted, eunuchoid boys.[47] The effects on animals are equally confusing. Administration of large amounts of androgens retards growth in rats; but when large amounts of androgens are given along with large amounts of estrogen, somatic growth is less inhibited than when estrogens are given alone.

MUSCLE.   The usually greater muscularity of the male appears to be at least partially attributable to androgen. Muscular growth and increased strength are pubertal traits, and a relative muscular weakness usually characterizes castrated and eunuchoid men.[57] A striking generalized muscular hypertrophy may be induced in guinea pigs by administration of androgens.[46] Increased muscular strength and endurance have also been induced in castrated and hypogonadal men by administration of androgens.[53] To what extent these effects are the result of increased well-being and metabolic improvement has not been fully determined.

VASCULAR SYSTEM.   A testicular deficiency arising before puberty is characteristically accompanied by paleness. Occasionally postpubertal deficiency precipitates hot flashes and flushing of the skin similar to those of the menopausal female.[24, 57] In analyzing the apparent relationship of the cardiovascular system and androgens it has been found that the cutaneous vascular bed of castrates is smaller than in normal men and has less blood flowing through it, and that cutaneous areas with large venous beds contain more reduced hemoglobin, suggesting a venous dilatation in these areas. These changes were reversed by administration of testosterone propionate, and in more "arterial" regions of the skin the volume of blood was increased and it contained more oxyhemoglobin.[16] The small blood vessels of the skin are characterized by fluctuations in excitability in castrated men, and their excitability is reduced by administration of testosterone.[48] The effects of androgens upon blood vessels have led to their use as therapeutic agents in vascular disease.

METABOLISM.   Androgens cause retention of nitrogen, sodium, potassium, inorganic phosphorus and chlorides, with the effect being less in intact than in castrated or eunuchoid men.[34] Creatine is excreted in quite small amounts in normal men, although prepubertal boys, castrates and eunuchoids ordinarily exhibit a creatinuria. This difference in creatine metabolism and excretion is partially to be attributed to androgens inasmuch as these substances usually reduce creatinuria and increase creatine tolerance. The basal metabolism may increase 5 to 15 per cent during treatment with androgen without any change in respiratory quotient, this despite a gain in body weight that may, however, be partially the result of retention of electrolytes and water. As might be expected in the light of their effects upon metabolism, treatment with androgens is also reported to produce significant increases in red cell count, hemoglobin, and hematocrit values.[42] These changes in the blood are considered comparable to those occurring during normal adolescence.

In addition to the numerous actions of androgens in the male, these substances have important effects in the female that have prompted their clinical employment in a variety of gynecologic disorders.

Androgens in Different Periods of Life.   A plausible interpretation of *embryonic sexual differentiation* is the genetic determination of the differentiation of the morphologically indifferent gonad into a testis or ovary. The newly differentiated testis could conceivably secrete an androgen which would provoke growth and differentiation in the male components of the morphologically bipotential genital tract, and either provoke or allow regression of the female components. The results of experiments involving administration of sex hormones to embryos of many species have apparently lent support to the concept of a directional influence of these hormones. In general, androgens have stimulated the male homologues and estrogens the female homologues.[20] Although these effects have not been entirely uniform, the evidence, including the consequences of castration of the embryo, increasingly indicates that the embryonic gonad, especially the testis, has a directional influence in embryonic sex differentiation. Once embryonic sexual differentiation is completed, the sex hormones may cause abnormal development of the genital system in the fetus and be important factors in such malformations as pseudohermaphroditism.[20]

Puberty.   During childhood there is normally little evidence of the activity or presence of the testicular hormone.[22] Small amounts of 17-ketosteroids are present in the urine, but these substances may be adrenal in origin. At puberty, however, a dramatic change occurs. In the short span of a few years the child is transformed into a man. The genital system undergoes rapid growth and maturation, and secondary sex characters, such as the beard, body hair and deeper voice, appear.[22] These changes are clearly dependent upon androgens, as shown by their absence in the castrate and by their evocation by administered androgens. This fact, plus the observation that the changes are preceded and accompanied by accelerated growth of the testes, supports the almost universal belief that pubertal changes result from an abrupt and conspicuous increase in the production of androgen by the testes. This entirely plausible explanation, however, is not supported by the few studies the problem has received. Most investigators have reported a steady increase in the excretion of androgen or 17-ketosteroids with increased age during puberty and adolescence, with no conspicuous increase to coincide

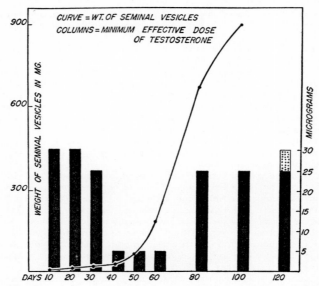

FIG. 616. Chart showing dose level of testosterone required at different ages to elicit response in seminal vesicles of rats castrated at birth. Curve shows growth of seminal vesicles of normal rats. (From Hooker, *Endocrinology*, 1942, *30*:77–84.)

with the onset of puberty.[22] It has been pointed out, however, that variation among individuals of the same age is great with respect to degree of sexual maturation and that comparisons should be made not with age but with development. In the bull, the rise in testicular androgen with increased age was found to be uniform in the young animal, and no conspicuous alteration in level accompanied pubertal changes.[28] The little evidence available accordingly suggests that pubertal changes are not the result of a greatly increased production of androgen. Work in laboratory animals[27] indicates that a major factor responsible for pubertal changes is a tremendous increase at this age in the responsiveness of the tissues to androgen (Fig. 616).

Sexual maturity. During sexual maturity androgens are responsible for the maintenance of most sex characteristics, as shown by the effects of castration. The absence of evident fluctuations in masculinity possibly indicates a steady state of production and action of androgen. Some tendency toward cyclic patterns has been suggested, but has not been established.

Old age. It is popularly supposed that the decline in vigor in advanced age is the result of decline in testicular activity. The level of urinary androgen and 17-ketosteroids in man is somewhat lower, and in the bull the level of testicular androgen is diminished,[28] but whether these levels are sufficiently decreased to account for senile changes is not established. Many clinical endocrinologists recognize a male climacteric occurring at about the same age as the menopause in women. It is characterized by decline in vigor and by vascular instability and other phenomena not unlike those of the menopause, and can frequently be alleviated by the administration of androgens.[24, 57]

Site of Production of Testicular Androgen. The tubules of the testis are situated in a meshwork of intertubular connective tissue, which contains, among other cellular entities, numbers of epithelioid cells resembling gland cells, the interstitial cells of Leydig (Fig. 609). Androgen secreted by the testis obviously must be elaborated in either or both the tubules and the intertubular tissue. That the tubules are not the primary source of the androgen is shown by the usual absence of castration phenomena after atrophy or damage of the tubules, provided the intertubular tissue remains essentially normal. Moreover, tubular growth is not accompanied by an increase in the androgen content of the testes.[28] If the tubules are not the source of the androgen, obviously the intertubular tissue must perform this function. Stimulation of the testis by gonadotrophins results in evident production of androgen only if the Leydig cells are visibly affected.[21] Large quantities of androgen are apparently secreted by experimental tumors of the Leydig cells in mice and by spontaneous interstitial cell tumors in boys. Finally, changes in level of testicular androgen in the bull are paralleled by appropriate cytologic changes in the Leydig cells.[28] It is almost certain that the Leydig cells are the site of production of testicular androgen.

Evidence is accumulating that testicular estrogen is secreted by the tubules, probably by the cells of Sertoli,[31] although the Leydig cells may also participate in this function.

Regulation of Testis by Hypophysis. The testis is under the control of the hypophysis, as shown by atrophy of the testes and the appearance of castration changes after hypophysectomy, and by the restoration of full testicular function upon the administration of suitable gonadotrophic substances. Of the two hypophysial gonadotrophins, follicle-stimulating hormone (FSH) and luteinizing hormone (LH) or interstitial cell-stimulating hormone (ICSH), FSH apparently has no influence upon the production of androgen when given alone. Purified ICSH, however, is capable of provoking the production of sufficient androgen to restore the reproductive system to an essentially normal condition. When the two purified gonadotrophins are given simultaneously the effect upon production of androgen is greater than when ICSH is given alone.[21] These studies have been carried out chiefly upon the rat, and it is not known whether the general principles apply also to man. Other gonadotrophic preparations, such as that from pregnancy urine, and other hypophysial fractions, such as extracts of lactogenic hormone, have been reported to incite the production of androgen in the testes, but the analysis here is incomplete.

The testes, in turn, affect the production of gonadotrophins by the hypophysis. Castration produces cytologic changes in the hypophysis, and results in an increase in the gonadotrophin content of the hypophysis, blood and urine. The administration of androgen to the castrate restores the normal cellular composition of the hypophysis and returns the several gonadotrophin levels to normal. In the intact individual the administration of androgen depresses the gonadotrophin level. Thus there exists a mutual regulation of gonadotrophin and androgen production.

Like the production of androgen, the production of spermatozoa is under the control of the hypophysis. Hypofunction of the hypophysis results in defective spermatogenesis, and extirpation of the hypophysis is followed by cessation of spermatogenesis. Certain gonadotrophic preparations are capable of inducing spermatogenesis precociously in immature animals and of restoring spermatogenesis in hypophysectomized animals. The hypophysial gonadotrophin specifically affecting spermatogenesis is follicle-stimulating hormone (FSH); the other gonadotrophin, ICSH (or LH), is without direct effect upon this process.[21] These generalizations appear well established for the rat; but the situation in man has not been fully analyzed, perhaps largely because it does not lend itself to controlled experiments of this nature. Failure of spermatogenesis in man is not consistently corrected by administration of gonadotrophins.[12] Indeed, damage to the seminiferous tubules after administration of chorionic gonadotrophin has been reported.[40]

Although the fact seems paradoxical, injections of testosterone sustain spermatogenesis in hypophysectomized animals;[45] even more striking is the fact that testosterone will restore spermatogenesis after atrophy of the tubules has become pronounced as a result of hypophysectomy. These observations have been made in a number of laboratory animals, including the monkey. The means by which testosterone exerts its gametogenic action is not known. The observation that intratesticular pellets of testosterone maintain spermatogenesis in neighboring tubules better than in tubules further from the pellet suggests that the action in this circumstance is direct.[14] That the gametogenic action of testosterone is not the result of its androgenicity is suggested by the fact that certain other steroid compounds have a similar action.[45] Notable among these substances is pregnenolone which has no other obvious biologic actions.[15]

Extratesticular Androgen. In addition to being produced by the testes, androgenic substances are also elaborated in other sites, notably the adrenal glands and the ovaries, and especially by tumors of these organs. Certain tumors of the adrenal cortex in boys may induce precocious puberty, and in women these tumors may be masculinizing to the extent of provoking growth of a beard, a generalized hypertrichosis, lowering of the voice, and even baldness. After removal of the tumor the masculine traits regress, showing the tumor to be the source of the androgen. An increase in urinary 17-ketosteroids usually accompanies these tumors.[55] Indeed, such a rise may be pathognomonic for certain adrenal tumors.

A number of experiments in animals have shown that androgen may be produced by the normal adrenal gland. In the prepubertal rat the presence of androgen is indicated by the cytology of the prostate upon which castration has no effect at this age, although adrenalectomy promptly results in typical castration atrophy of this organ. The administration of adrenotrophic preparations has been reported to evoke the production of androgen in castrated but not in adrenalectomized rats. The adrenal androgen may be androstenedione, inasmuch as this androgenic substance has been identified in human adrenal venous blood after administration of ACTH and in perfusates of beef adrenals.[6]

Certain ovarian tumors in women are also virilizing, inducing masculinization comparable to that in the presence of virilizing tumors of the adrenals. In several species of laboratory animals the ovaries may exert masculinizing actions under various experimental conditions, many of which involve an alteration of gonadotrophic stimulation of the ovaries. In some animals the androgen is apparently secreted by the interstitial cells of the ovary, whereas in other species the cells of the theca interna are thought to have this function.

REFERENCES

1. BARRY, M. C., EIDINOFF, M. L., DOBRINER, K. and GALLAGHER, T. F. *Endocrinology*, 1952, *50*:587–599.
2. BEACH, F. A. *Hormones and behavior*. New York, Hoeber, 1948.
3. BLANDAU, R. J. *Amer. J. Anat.*, 1945, 77:253–272.
4. BLANDAU, R. J. and MONEY, W. L. *Anat. Rec.*, 1944, *90*:255–260.
5. BLANDAU, R. J. and ODOR, D. L. *Anat. Rec.*, 1949, *103*:93–110.
6. BLOCH, E., DORFMAN, R. I. and PINCUS, G. *Proc. Soc. exp. Biol.* (*N. Y.*), 1954, *85*:106–110.

7. BROWN, R. L. *Amer. J. Obstet. Gynec.*, 1944, *47:*407–411.
8. BRYSON, M. J., SAMUELS, L. T. and GOLDTHORPE, H. C. *Endocrinology*, 1950, *47:*89–96.
9. CAMPBELL, H. E. *Arch. Surg.*, 1942, *44:*353–369.
10. CHANG, M. C. *Ann. N. Y. Acad. Sci.*, 1950, *52:*1192–1195.
11. CHANG, M. C. and PINCUS, G. *Physiol. Rev.*, 1951, *31:*1–26.
12. DAVIS, C. D., PULLEN, R. L., MADDEN, J. H. M. and HAMBLEN, E. C. *J. clin. Endocr.*, 1943, *3:*268–273.
13. DORFMAN, R. I., COOK, J. W. and HAMILTON, J. B. *J. biol. Chem.*, 1939, *130:*285–295.
14. DVOSKIN, S. *Amer. J. Anat.*, 1944, *75:*289–327.
15. DVOSKIN, S. *Endocrinology*, 1949, *45:*370–374.
16. EDWARDS, E. A., HAMILTON, J. B., DUNTLEY, S. Q. and HUBERT, G. *Endocrinology*, 1941, *28:*119–128.
17. ELFTMAN, H. *Anat. Rec.*, 1950, *106:*381–393.
18. GARDNER, L. I. *J. clin. Endocr.*, 1953, *13:*941–947.
19. GRAYHACK, J. T. and SCOTT, W. W. *Endocrinology*, 1951, *48:*453–461.
20. GREEN, R. R. *J. clin. Endocr.*, 1944, *4:*335–348.
21. GREEP, R. O., VAN DYKE, H. B. and CHOW, B. F. *Endocrinology*, 1942, *30:*635–649.
22. GREULICH, W. W., DORFMAN, R. I., CATCHPOLE, H. R., SOLOMON, C. I. and CULOTTA, C. S. *Monogr. Soc. Res. Child Dev.*, 1942, *7:*1–85.
23. HAMILTON, J. B. *J. clin. Endocr.*, 1941, *1:*570–592.
24. HAMILTON, J. B. Chap. 17, in AMERICAN MEDICAL ASSOCIATION: *Glandular physiology and therapy*, 2d ed., 1942.
25. HAMILTON, J. B. *Amer. J. Anat.*, 1942, *71:*451–480.
26. HENDERSON, V. E. and ROEPKE, M. H. *Amer. J. Physiol.*, 1933, *106:*441–448.
27. HOOKER, C. W. *Endocrinology*, 1942, *30:*77–84.
28. HOOKER, C. W. *Amer. J. Anat.*, 1944, *74:*1–37.
29. HUGGINS, C. *Physiol. Rev.*, 1945, *25:*281–295.
30. HUGGINS, C. and McDONALD, D. F. *J. clin. Endocr.*, 1945, *5:*226–231.
31. HUGGINS, C. and MOULDER, P. V. *Cancer Res.*, 1945, *5:*510–514.
32. HUGGINS, C., STEVENS, R. E., JR. and HODGES, C. V. *Arch. Surg.*, 1941, *43:*209–223.
33. HURXTHAL, L. M. *J. clin. Endocr.*, 1943, *3:*12–19.
34. KENYON, A. T., KNOWLTON, K., SANDIFORD, I., KOCH, F. C. and LOTWIN, G. *Endocrinology*, 1940, *26:*26–45.
35. KISS, F. *Z. Anat. EntwGesch.*, 1921, *61:*455–521.
36. KOCH, F. C. *Physiol. Rev.*, 1937, *17:*153–238.
37. KURZROK, R. and MILLER, E. G., JR. *Amer. J. Obstet. Gynec.*, 1928, *15:*56–72.
38. LUCAS, W. M., WHITMORE, W. F. and WEST, C. D. *J. clin. Endocr.*, 1957, *17:*465.
39. MACLEOD, J. Pp. 61–93, in ENGLE, E. T., ed.: *Studies on testis and ovary; eggs and sperm.* Springfield, Charles C Thomas, 1952.
40. MADDOCK, W. O. and NELSON, W. O. *J. clin. Endocr.*, 1952, *12:*985–1014.
41. MANN, T. and LUTWAK-MANN, C. *Physiol. Rev.*, 1951, *31:*27–55.
42. McCULLAGH, E. P. and JONES, R. *J. clin. Endocr.*, 1942, *2:*243–251.
43. MELAMPY, R. M. and CAVAZOS, L. F. *Endocrinology*, 1953, *52:*173–187.
44. MOORE, C. R. Pp. 353–451, in ALLEN, E., ed.: *Sex and internal secretions*, 2d ed. Baltimore, Williams & Wilkins, 1939.
45. NELSON, W. O. *Cold Spr. Harb. Symp. quant. Biol.*, 1937, *5:*123–135.
46. PAPANICOLAOU, G. N. and FALK, E. A. *Science*, 1938, *87:*238–239.
47. RAPFOGEL, I. *Endocrinology*, 1940, *27:*179–184.
48. REYNOLDS, S. R. M., HAMILTON, J. B., DiPALMA, J. R., HUBERT, G. R. and FOSTER, F. I. *J. clin. Endocr.*, 1942, *2:*228–236.
49. RUBIN, B. L., DORFMAN, R. I. and MILLER, M. *Endocrinology*, 1952, *51:*463–468.
50. RUDOLPH, G. G. and SAMUELS, L. T. *Endocrinology*, 1949, *44:*190–196.
51. SAMUELS, L. T., McCAULAY, C. and SELLERS, D. M. *J. biol. Chem.*, 1947, *168:*477–483.
52. SEMANS, J. H. and LANGWORTHY, O. R. *J. Urol.*, 1938, *40:*836–846.
53. SIMONSON, E., KEARNS, W. M. and ENGER, N. *Endocrinology*, 1941, *28:*506–512.
54. SODERWALL, A. L. and YOUNG, W. C. *Anat. Rec.*, 1940, *78:*19–29.
55. TALBOT, N. B., BUTLER, A. M. and BERMAN, R. A. *J. clin. Invest.*, 1942, *21:*559–570.
56. VAN WAGENEN, G. *Anat. Rec.*, 1936, *66:*411–421.
57. VEST, S. A. and BARELARE, B., JR. *Clinics*, 1943, *1:*1216–1265.
58. WEST, C. D. *Endocrinology*, 1951, *49:*467–473.
59. YOUNG, W. C. *J. Morph.*, 1929, *48:*475–491

Index

Page numbers in *italics* refer to illustrations and tables.